Transas NAVI-Sailor Electronic Charting S...

NOW in a choice of three systems including the outstanding
TSUNAMIS

Fully coded to operate within Windows 95

NAVI... a stor... commerci... of the priva... launch of th... ...viIS system, you can not only ... ...sas electronic navigation in the familiar and efficient environment of Windows 95 but also interface the system with your log, sounder, autopilot, radar and more.

The factor that sets NAVI-Sailor apart is the superlative quality of its charts. Transas charts are not scanned like ARCS or NOAA electronic charts, but *vectorised*. This process entails each chart being individually redrawn by skilled programmers to established quality-control standards, using British Admiralty charts for source data whenever possible. So while scanned charts only permit two or three levels of zoom, Transas charts permit up to 50 layers of detail, each displayed in perfect scale and clarity.

Fully VECTORISED data from Admiralty charts and other official sources ALL ROYALTIES PAID

Backed by the world's largest portfolio of vectorised charts, this affordable NAVI-Sailor system is available to leisure users only from Softwave. The software is optionally offered on a CD-ROM which contains the full Transas chart portfolio. Further charts can be 'released' from the CD at any time by inputting a unique code obtainable by telephone.

Ready-to-run software from £200 to £20,000

- *Plan and navigate voyages with maximum ease and accuracy*
- *Link to a GPS to see your vessel moving in real-time on vectorised Admiralty-derived charts*
- *Turn your PC into a multi-functional electronic navigation station*
- *Move 'seamlessly' from map to map with multi-chart loading*

For more information, phone or fax on the numbers below or visit the Softwave website on www.softwave.co.uk.

CALL 0181-549 0650   FAX 0181-546 1090
or write to Softwave, 4 Aranmoor House, Kingston Hill, Surrey KT2 7LY

Softwave

Which London Docklands marina will suit you best?

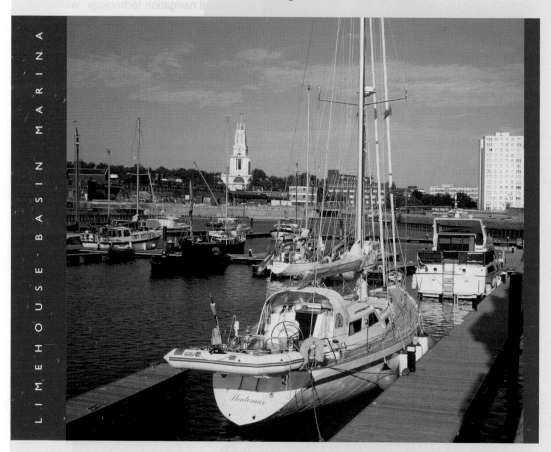

LIMEHOUSE-BASIN MARINA

London Docklands has a rich sea-faring history and that tradition is still kept alive with a superb range of marina facilities within a unique urban landscape.

There's Limehouse Basin Marina. 1¹/₂ miles downstream from Tower Bridge on the north side of the Thames, this offers access to Britain's canal network through the Regent's Canal. The headquarters of the Cruising Association is here, which could be handy.

2¹/₂ miles downstream from Tower Bridge, and on the south side of the Thames, is South Dock Marina. This is our biggest marina. It offers 350 berths, boasts a 20 ton crane and is manned 24 hours (all the others can serve you at night by arrangement). One of Europe's largest shopping centres is within easy walking distance. Historic Greenwich is close by.

Furthest downstream is Galleons Point Marina, our newest anchorage. It offers the widest tidal window, and makes a great base for yachtsmen. Access to London is by Docklands Light Railway or bus, or by car on the new Royal Docks highways. London City Airport, Europe's fastest growing airport, is in the Royal Docks.

At West India Quay we can also accommodate large vessels in still non-tidal waters 9m in depth.

For more information on our marinas, just call the Harbourmaster's Office, London Docklands Development Corporation on 0171 515 1046. We look forward to having you alongside.

London Docklands

THE
MACMILLAN
NAUTICAL ALMANAC
INCORPORATING REED'S

1998

EDITORS
Wing Commander B. D'Oliveira OBE, FRIN
Commander N.L. Featherstone RN

CONSULTANT EDITORS
Commander R.L. Hewitt LVO, RN MIMechE, MRINA, FRIN

IMPROVEMENTS IN THE 1998 EDITION

IMPROVEMENTS IN CHAPTERS ONE TO NINE

CHAPTER TWO
GENERAL INFORMATION

UK Public holidays, Phases of the Moon, Eclipse notes and Standard Times for 1998 have been transferred to Chapter 2.

CHAPTER FOUR
RADIO AIDS

North-West European Loran C chain information and map updated to reflect delay in bringing the Irish transmitter on line.

CHAPTER FIVE
RISE AND SET TABLES

New tables of Sunrise/Sunset/Moonrise/Moonset and Twilight times are now included.

CHAPTER SIX
COMMUNICATIONS

A new map of Navtex areas covering from Norway to Gibraltar has been included. The type size of all tables listing communications stations has been increased slightly to facilitate easier readability and use.

CHAPTER SEVEN
WEATHER

New maps of Marinecall and MetFAX marine have been provided.

CHAPTER EIGHT
SAFETY

All Tables listing HM Coastguard MRCCs, MRSCs and French CROSS stations have been updated to include the latest information available on GMDSS implementation.

❑ **New ports and anchorages:** Once again Macmillan introduces the latest in marina and port developments or enhances chartlets of existing entries, as shown below by geographic areas:

England, South coast: Dartmouth: newly modernised Dart marina.

Channel Islands: Beaucette marina, St Helier's new marina.

France, Channel coast: Diélette, latest developments.

England, East coast: Comprehensive cover and new chartlets of five marinas on the tidal River Thames from Woolwich to Chelsea; Tide Mill Yacht Harbour (R Deben), Hartlepool, Seaham and Sunderland.

Scotland, West coast: Kinlochbervie, Plockton, Kyle Akin, Campbeltown.

England, West coast and Wales: Ramsey (IoM), Conwy, Cardiff, Ilfracombe.

Ireland: Kilmore Quay, Baltimore, Fenit Harbour.

France, Atlantic coast: Port Tudy, Lorient, Piriac, Joinville.

❑ **Chartlet digitisation:** A three year programme to digitise all harbour chartlets offers greater accuracy and speedier corrections.

❑ **Tidal curve graphs:** All have now been moved to the top of the page to make it easier to write in data.

❑ **Area Maps:** 14 Area Maps have been fully digitised to improve presentation and faster correcton. The information blocks on all 21 Area Maps have been extensively revised to a new slimmer style to help reduce clutter, and improve presentation and layout.

1998 ASTRO SUPPLEMENT

A forty-eight page Astro Supplement contains all the information required for Astro-navigation using the Sun, Moon, Aries and Stars. This can be obtained on request by filling in the enclosed order form and enclosing a cheque for £4.00.

The symbol of the **CHART AND NAUTICAL INSTRUMENT TRADE ASSOCIATION**, founded in 1918. With the full support of the Hydrographer of the Navy and leading manufacturers of nautical instruments, members. of the Association are able to place their experience and service at the disposal of the shipping industry and all navigators.

CHART SUPPLY AND CORRECTION SERVICES

The CNITA counts among its members many of the leading Admiralty Chart Agents who can supply your requirements from a single chart or publication to a worldwide outfit and special folio requirements from comprehensive stocks in all the major ports. Carefully trained chart correctors are available to examine and correct all Admiralty charts.

THE CNITA TRACING SERVICE

Although tracings have been in use by the Royal Navy and Admiralty Chart Agents for many years, it was the Chart Committee of the Chart Nautical Instrument Trade Association that successfully negotiated with the Hydrographer of the Navy for them to become available to the merchant navigator and private user.

The CNITA tracing overlay correction service is available from all Admiralty Chart Agents who are members of the Association, and is now supplied to more than 5,000 vessels each week. Each tracing wallet contains the weekly "Notices to Mariners" and the tracings printed with much of the relevant details of the area surrounding the correction, making the correction of each chart a simpler operation. All that the user has to do is match the tracing to the chart, pierce through the small circle showing the exact position of the correction, in conjunction with the "Notices to Mariners", and then transfer the information onto the chart. Navigating Officers welcome the tracings systems for its accuracy and speed. Onboard chart correction time can be cut by up to 80% and Masters can now rest assured that their charts can be kept continually up to date. Reasonably priced, these tracings are an economical and invaluable contribution to safety at sea.

COMPASS ADJUSTING AND NAUTICAL INSTRUMENTS

The CNITA insists that its Compass Adjusters are thoroughly trained to its own high standards, and independently examined by the Department of Trade. For yacht or super tanker our compass adjusters can advise you on the type of compass you need, its siting, and any adjustments needed. CNITA Compass Adjusters are based in all the major ports and are available day and night to "swing" ships.

Members of the CNITA, many with a life long experience in this field, can advise you when purchasing all your nautical instruments. Most suppliers provide an instrument repair service combining traditional craftsmanship with modern methods to ensure that instruments are serviced and tested to a high standard.

ARE YOU COMPLYING WITH THE LATEST INTERNATIONAL REGULATIONS?

Chart and Nautical Instrument Trade Association members established in most UK ports and overseas are able to advise you. For full details of the Association, its activities and its services to the Navigator, write to:

The Secretaries,
CHART AND NAUTICAL INSTRUMENT TRADE ASSOCIATION,
Dalmore House, 310 Vincent Street, GLASGOW G2 5QR.

PORTS WHERE SHIPS' COMPASSES ARE ADJUSTED

Names of member firms. Those marked * have DoT Certified Compass Adjusters available for Adjustment of Compasses, day or night.

Port or District	Name and Address	Telephone
ABERDEEN	*Thomas Gunn Navigation Services, Anchor House, 62 Regents Quay, Aberdeen AB11 5AR.	01224 595045
AVONMOUTH	*Severnside Consultants, Deco Court, South View Business Park, Staple Hill, Bristol BS16 5PJ.	0117-956 8844
BANGOR (N Ireland)	Todd Chart Agency Ltd., 4 Seacliff Road, The Harbour, Bangor, N Ireland BT20 5EY.	01247 466640
BRISTOL	*W F Price & Co Ltd., Northpoint House, Wapping Wharf, Bristol BS1 6UD.	0117-929 2229
FALMOUTH	*Marine Instruments, The Bosun's Locker, Upton Slip, Falmouth TR11 3DQ.	01326 312414
GLASGOW	Brown, Son & Ferguson, Ltd., 4-10 Darnley Street, Glasgow G41 2SD.	0141-429 1234
HULL	*B Cooke & Son, Ltd., Kingston Observatory, 58-59 Market Place, Hull HU1 1RH.	01482 223454
KENT	*SIRS Navigation Ltd., 186a Milton Road, Swanscombe, Kent DA10 0LX.	01322 383672
LIVERPOOL	Dubois-Phillips & McCallum Ltd. Oriel Chambers, Covent Garden, Liverpool L2 8UD.	0151-236 2776
LONDON	*Kelvin Hughes Charts and Maritime Supplies New North Road, Hainault, Ilford, Essex IG6 2UR.	0181-500 6166
	A M Smith (Marine) Ltd., 33 Epping Way, Chingford, London E4 7PB.	0181-529 6988
LOWESTOFT	*Seath Instruments (1992) Ltd., Unit 30, Colville Road Works, Colville Road, Lowestoft NR33 9QS.	01502 573811

Port or District	Name and Address	Telephone
NORTH SHIELDS (Newcastle)	*John Lilley & Gillie Ltd., Clive Street, North Shields, Tyne & Wear NE29 6LF.	0191-257 2217
SOUTHAMPTON	*R J Muir, 22 Seymour Close, Chandlers Ford, Eastleigh, Southampton SO5 2JE.	01703 261042
	Wessex Marine Equipment Ltd., Logistics House, 2nd Avenue Business Park, Millbrook Road East, Southampton SO1 0LP.	01703 510570

OVERSEAS MEMBERS

Port or District	Name and Address
ANTWERP	Bogerd Navtec NV, Oude Leenwnrui 37 Antwerp 2000.
	*Martin & Co. Oude Leewnrui 37, Antwerp 2000.
COPENHAGEN	Iver C Weilbach & Co. A/S, 35 Toldbodgade, Postbox 1560, DK-1253 Copenhagen K.
GOTHENBURG	A B Ramantenn, Knipplagatan 12 S-414 74, Gothenburg.
HONG KONG	George Falconer (Nautical) Ltd., The Hong Kong Jewellery Building, 178-180 Queen's Road, Central Hong Kong.
	Hong Kong Ship's Supplies Co. Room 1614, Melbourne Plaza, 33 Queen's Road, Central Hong Kong.
LISBON	J Garraio & Co. Ltd., Avenida 24 de Julho, 2-1°, D-1200, Lisbon.
ROTTERDAM	*Kelvin Hughes Observator B.V., Nieuwe Langeweg 41, 3194 DC, Hoogvliet (Rt), The Netherlands.
SINGAPORE	Motion Smith, 78 Shenton Way #01-03, Singapore 0207.
SKYTTA	A/S Navicharts, Masteveien 3, N-1483 Skytta, Norway.
URUGUAY	Captain Stephan Nedelchev Soc. Col. Port of Montevideo, Florida 1562, 11100 Montevideo.
VARNA	Captain Lyudmil N. Jordanov, 13A Han Omurtag Str. 9000 Bulgaria.

 1918 - 1998 80 YEARS OF SERVING THE MARINER

Contents

First published 1980
This edition published 1997 by Macmillan
an imprint of Macmillan Publishers Limited
25 Eccleston Place, London SW1W 9NF
and Basingstoke

Associated companies throughout the world

ISBN 0-333-670965

9 8 7 6 5 4 3 2 1

A CIP catalogue record for this book is available from the British
Library

IMPORTANT NOTE
Whilst every care has been taken in compiling the information
contained in this Almanac, the Publishers and Editors accept no
responsibility for any errors or omissions, or for any accidents or
mishaps which may arise from its use

CORRESPONDENCE
Letters on nautical matters should be addressed to:

The Editor, The Macmillan Nautical Almanac
Macmillan General Books, 25 Eccleston Place,
London SW1W 9NF

or The Editor, The Macmillan Nautical Almanac
Edington House, Trent, Sherborne, Dorset DT9 4SR

See also Chapter 1 paragraph 1.2.1

Enquiries about despatch, invoicing or commercial matters
should be addressed to:

Customer Services Department
Macmillan Press Ltd, Houndmills, Basingstoke,
Hampshire RG21 2XS

Enquiries about advertising space should be addressed to:

Communications Management International
Chiltern House, 120 Eskdale Avenue, Chesham,
Buckinghamshire HP5 3BD

Chapters 1-9   Page preparation by
                Wyvern 21 Limited, Bristol

Chapter 10   Cartography and page preparation by
                Lovell Johns Ltd, Oxford

Colour artwork by Dick Vine

Printed and bound in Great Britain by Bath Press
Colourbooks, Glasgow

Sailing HOLIDAYS IN IRELAND - Only the Best

John Stack

THE PINK PAGE SECTION

Marine Supplies & Services Guide
Coastal & Waterways Services
Directory - area by area

This section provides readers with a quick reference to harbours, marinas, companies and organisations currently delivering services - including emergency services, equipment and supplies to boat owners and the boating industry. Each entry carries concise information for guidance.

Pages I-XXXIII lists by types of service and products and XXXIV-LVIII by coastal location.

ACTIVITY HOLIDAYS

STAYSAIL
The Old Rectory, Rectory Road,
Llangwen, Haverfordwest,
Pembrokeshire SA62 4JA.
Tel (01437) 890078 Fax (01437) 899309
Holidays for dinghy/cruiser sailors, or space
and comfort for their non-sailing partners.
Use our dinghies/cruisers or bring your
own. Paint, draw, relax, walk and sightsee.
En-suite rooms overlooking breathtaking
estuary. Scrumptious cooking.

AIR CONDITIONING

CRUISAIR UK LTD
26 Old Wareham Road, Poole,
Dorset BH12 4QR.
Tel (01202) 716469 Fax (01202) 716478
Marine air conditioning.

ANCHORS & CHAINS

GRIFF CHAINS LTD
Quarry Road, Dudley Wood,
Dudley, West Midlands DY2 0ED.
Tel (01384) 569415 Fax (01384) 410580
Manufacturers of mooring systems and
equipment. For over 150 years Griff Chains
has been synonymous with chain, anchor
and chain component development for
marine applications. Quality chains to meet
all markets.

ANEMOMETERS & AUTOPILOTS

THOMAS WALKER GROUP LTD
37-41 Bissell Street,
Birmingham B5 7HR.
Tel 0121-622 4475 Fax 0121-622 4478
Manufacturer of marine instruments
including, Neco Autopilots, Walker Logs
and Towing Logs, Walker Anemometers,
Chernikeeff Logs.

*PLEASE MENTION
THE MACMILLAN NAUTICAL
ALMANAC
WHEN MAKING ENQUIRIES*

BERTHS & MOORINGS

ALBERT DOCK
Albert Dock Co., 7 The Colonnades,
Albert Dock, Liverpool L3 4AA.
Tel 0151-708 7334 Fax 0151-708 0929
The world-famous Albert Dock welcomes
vessels for short or long-term visits.
Maximum length 55m. Concessionary rates
(details on application). Access by prior
agreement.

ARDENTINNY HOTEL
Ardentinny, Loch Long, By Dunoon,
Argyll PA23 8TR.
Tel (01369) 810209 Fax (01369) 810241
A warm Scottish welcome awaits you at the
Ardentinny. Delightful dinners to a very
high standard are prepared by our chef
complemented by a choice of over 50
selections of French and New World wines.
Excellent casual lunches served in the
garden or buttery. Friendly bar, frequented
by yachtsmen, with a good selection of
beer. Seven moorings available.

**BALTIC WHARF
WATER LEISURE CENTRE**
Bristol Harbour, Underfall Yard,
Bristol BS1 6XG.
*Tel 0117-929 7608 Fax 0117-929 4454
Tuition: 0117-952 5202*
Sailing school and centre, with qualified
instruction in most watersports. Also
moorings available throughout the Bristol
harbour for all types of leisurecraft.

W BATES & SON BOATBUILDERS LTD
Bridge Wharf, Chertsey,
Surrey KT16 8LG.
Tel (01932) 562255 Fax (01932) 571161
110-berth marina in quiet picturesque area
and additional riverside moorings. Full
facilities including electricity to most berths,
toilets and showers. 12-ton crane and hard
standing for winter storage. Always a
welcome to visitors from our friendly staff.
Sales office open seven days a week.

BURGH CASTLE MARINA
Butt Lane, Burgh Castle, Norfolk,
Norwich NR31 9PZ.
Tel (01493) 780331
100 serviced pontoons and quay moorings
accessible at all tides. Secure car and boat
parking. Adjoining boatyard services, access
to holiday park showers, laundry and heated
pool. Riverside pub and shop. Complex
open all year.

CARRICKFERGUS MARINA
Rodger's Quay,
Carrickfergus, Co Antrim,
Northern Ireland BT38 8BE.
Tel (01960) 366666 Fax (01960) 350505
300 fully serviced pontoon berths with full
on-shore facilities (half a mile from town
centre). Steeped in a wealth of historical
legend, Carrickfergus has excellent
restaurants, hotels, pubs, shops and a host
of recreational leisure facilities.

CHALLENGE MARINE
Freeman's Wharf,
Falmouth Road, Penryn,
Cornwall TR10 8AS.
Tel (01326) 377222 Fax (01326) 377800
Marine engineers, chandlery, boatyard.
Main Volvo Penta dealer, marina berths,
brokerage and Bombard inflatables' dealer.

CHELSEA HARBOUR LTD
108 The Chambers,
Chelsea Harbour,
London SW10 0XF.
Tel 0171-351 4433 Fax 0171-352 7868
A tranquil and intimate marina of 55 berths
close to the heart of the west end of London.
5-Star hotel, restaurants and bars. Overnight
pontoon and amenities. 24-hour security
patrols and CCTV.

CRINAN BOATS LTD
Crinan, Lochgilphead,
Argyll PA31 8SP.
Tel (01546) 830232 Fax (01546) 830281
Boatbuilders, chandlers, engineers,
slipping, repairs, charts, electricians,
pontoon, moorings, showers, laundry and
basic stores.

DART MARINA
Sandquay, Dartmouth,
Devon TQ6 9PH.
Tel (01803) 833351 Fax (01803) 832307
High quality 110-berth marina on the
fabulous river Dart, opposite the Dart Marina
hotel. A superb situation with all amenities,
24-hour security, hotel and restaurant,
showers, baths and laundry, fuel berth and
a warm welcome to all visitors.

**DEAN & REDDYHOFF LTD
- HASLAR MARINA**
Haslar Road, Gosport,
Hampshire PO12 1NU.
Tel (01705) 601201 Fax (01705) 602201
Haslar Marina is just inside the entrance of
Portsmouth harbour on the Gosport side.
Included in the 600 berths is a visitors' area
which is adjacent to a converted lightship
with bar facilities and excellent toilets and
showers.

**DEAN & REDDYHOFF LTD
- WEYMOUTH MARINA**
70 Commercial Road, Wymouth,
Dorset DT4 8NA.
Tel (01305) 767576 Fax (01305) 767575
This new marina in the inner harbour of
Weymouth provides facilities for visitors
which are proving very popular. The marina
is right next to Weymouth's high street, and
the area has a multitude of pubs and
restaurants.

DUCHY OF CORNWALL
Harbour Office, St Mary's, Isles of Scilly,
Cornwall TR21 0HU.
Tel/Fax (01720) 422768
Port of St Mary's, Isles of Scilly - 38 visitor moorings. New visitor centre, hot showers, toilets, launching facilities, winter storage, security lockers, fuel and fresh water. 5 minutes from town centre. Ferry terminal and airport close by. Contact Harbour Master for more information.

ELKINS BOATYARD
Tidesreach, 18 Convent Meadow,
The Quay, Christchurch,
Dorset BH23 1BD.
Tel (01202) 483141
All boatyard facilities. Moorings alongside, water and electricity, storage ashore, repairs. Boats up to 45', 10 tons maximum, haul-out.

FIDDLERS FERRY YACHT HAVEN
Off Station Road, Penketh, Warrington,
Cheshire WA5 2UJ.
Tel (01925) 727519
Sheltered moorings up to 6'6" draught, 50' long. Access through lock from river Mersey 1½ hours either side of high tide. Signed from A652. Boatyard and lift-out facilities. Annual rate per foot £8.25.

GIGHA HOTEL
Isle of Gigha, Argyll PA41 7AA.
Tel (01583) 505254 Fax (01583) 505244
Beautiful island, good food, lots of booze and friendly folk. Ideal to pick up or leave your family when sailing around the Mull of Kintyre. Moorings, water, fuel, showers and laundry facilities. Self-catering cottages also available. Achamore Gardens and 9-hole golf course.

HAFAN PWLLHELI
Glan Don, Pwllheli, Gwynedd LL53 5YT.
Tel (01758) 701219 Fax (01758) 701443
Hafan Pwllheli has over 400 pontoon berths and offers access at virtually all states of the tide. Ashore, its modern purpose-built facilities include luxury toilets, showers, landerette, a secure boat park for winter storage, 40-ton travel hoist, mobile crane and plenty of space for car parking. Open 24-hours a day, 7 days a week.

HALCON MARINE LTD
The Point, Canvey Island, Essex SS8 7TL.
Tel (01268) 511611 Fax (01268) 510044
Marine engineers, repairs and full boatyard services in this quiet and picturesque area. Berths, moorings, slipping facilities. Summer and winter storage. Dry dock (70t max), diesel 1 or 2 hours ±HW. Water, electric, toilets and showers. A friendly welcome awaits you.

THE HAVEN ARMS PUB & RESTAURANT
Kilrush, Co Clare, Ireland.
Tel +353 65 51267 Fax +353 65 51213
'The Haven Arms' - Kilrush - *Sail* into this pub and restaurant which has become a landmark to generations of local people and visitor alike. The 'Ship' restaurant offers appetising meals complemented by good service from our friendly staff. 'MOORINGS ARE FREE'.

HIGHWAY MARINE LTD
Pillory Gate Wharf, Strand Street,
Sandwich, Kent CT13 9EU.
Tel (01304) 613925 Fax (01304) 614814
Pontoon moorings available in town of Sandwich. Lift-out facilities and hard standing, water, electricity. OMC main dealer with full service centre. New engine sales. Brokerage and boat sales, chandlery.

ISLE OF ANGLESEY COUNTY COUNCIL
Highways & Technical Services
Department, Council Offices, Llangefni,
Anglesey LL77 7TW
Tel (01248) 752331 Fax (01248) 724839
Berths and moorings available at Menai bridge, Amlwch harbour and north east Menai Straits (Beaumaris). Winter storage at competitive rates available at Beaumaris and Amlwch. Contact Maritime Officer 01248 752331 for details.

JERSEY HARBOURS
Harbour Office,
Weighbridge, St Helier,
Jersey JE4 9XF.
Tel (01534) 885588 Fax (01534) 885599
A warm welcome to visiting yachtsmen! Elizabeth Marina opens in April 1998. Berths available on lease - £184.86 per metre. St Helier marina continues to cater for visitng yachts. Both marinas offer excellent facilities.

KAMES HOTEL
Kames, By Tighnabruaich,
Argyll PA21 2AF.
Tel (01700) 811489 Fax (01700) 811 283
On the Kyles of Bute with 15 free moorings. Good food, real ales, fine malts. Showers available for visitors. 10 en-suite bedrooms. Regular music nights. Fresh local seafood in season.

KINSALE YACHT CLUB MARINA
Kinsale, Co Cork, Ireland.
Tel +353 21 772196 Fax +353 21 774426
Mobile +353 87 449471
Magnificent deep water yacht club marina offering Kinsale hospitality to visiting yachtsmen. Full facilities include berths up to 20 metres, fresh water, electricity, diesel on pier. Club bar and wealth of pubs and restaurants in Kinsale. Enter Kinsale harbour - lit at night - no restrictions.

LANGSTONE HARBOUR BOARD
Ferry Road, Hayling Island,
Hampshire PO11 0DG.
Tel (01705) 463419 Fax (01705) 467144
All boatyard facilities. Deep water and tidal moorings available. Water, electricity and diesel. Summer and winter storage. Public slipways. 6-ton crane. Landrover vessel and trailer recovery services.

MARINE ACTIVITIES CENTRE
North Dock Marina,
Sunderland SR6 0PW.
Tel 0191-514 4721 Fax 0191-514 1847
New in 1996 with 85 fully serviced pontoon berths and 108 chain moorings accessible on all tides. Diesel fuel, 24-hour security and close circuit TV surviellance. New marina activities centre with excellent toilets and shower facilities.

THE MAYFLOWER
INTERNATIONAL MARINA
Ocean Quay, Richmond Walk,
Plymouth, Devon PL1 4LS.
Tel (01752) 556633 Fax (01752) 606896
Plymouth's only Five-Gold Anchor marina. Known for its extensive facilities, courtesy and security. Owned by berth holders and run to a very high standard.

NOSS-ON-DART MARINA
Noss Quay, Dartmouth,
Devon TQ6 0EA.
Tel (01803) 833351 Fax (01803) 832307
Peacefully located on the east shore of the river Dart, this relaxing marina is the perfect base for cruising yachtsmen. Extensive parking, chandlery, repair and lift-out facilities, easy access from London and the Midlands. Boat taxi to Dartmouth.

THE OYSTERCATCHER RESTAURANT
Otter Ferry,
Argyll PA21 2DH.
Tel (01700) 821229 Fax (01700) 821300
Situated on Loch Fyne, just north of the Otter Spit, about one hour's sailing from the Crinan canal. Moorings (insured to 12t) free to patrons. French chef and superb food, seafood our speciality. 1996 Tourist Board winner 'BEST PLACE TO EAT'. Children's play area.

THE PANDORA INN
Restronguet Creek,
Mylor Bridge, Falmouth,
Cornwall TR11 5ST.
Tel/Fax (01326) 372678
Thatched creek-side inn with floating pontoon. Morning coffee, delicious bar meals, cream teas and fine dining in the superb Andrew Miller restaurant (entitles yachtsmen to free mooring). Telephone, showers and water available. Open all day in the summer.

PARKSTONE YACHT CLUB
Pearce Avenue, Parkstone, Poole,
Dorset BH14 8EH.
Tel (01202) 743610 Fax (01202) 716394
Deep water club haven facilities in Poole harbour. Access at all states of the tide. Berths for yachts up to 15 metres. Facilities include electricity, fresh water, toilets and showers. Visitors welcome by appointment. Club bar and restaurant.

PORT OF TRURO
Harbour Office,
Town Quay, Truro, Cornwall.
Tel (01872) 72130 Fax (01872) 225346
Facilities for the yachtsman include visitor pontoons located at Turnaware Bar, Ruan Creek and Boscawen Park. Visitor moorings at Woodbury. Quay facilities at Truro with free showers and toilets. Chemical toilet disposal, fresh water and garbage disposal.

RAMSGATE ROYAL HARBOUR MARINA
Harbour Office, Military Road,
Ramsgate, Kent CT11 9LQ.
Tel (01843) 592277 Fax (01843) 590941
Ramsgate Royal Harbour is situated on the south east coast, making an ideal base for crossing to the Continent. 24-hour access

to finger pontoons. Comprehensive security systems. **Amenities:** Launderette, repairs, slipways, boatpark. Competitive rates for permanent berths and discount for visitors' group bookings.

RHU MARINA LTD
Helensburgh,
Dunbartonshire G84 8LN.
Tel (01436) 820238 Fax (01436) 821039
Berths accessible at all times and moorings available situated in an area of outstanding natural beauty, by the Garsloch and 10 minutes from Loch Lomond. Hotels, shops, yacht clubs all adjacent.

RUDDERS BOATYARD & MOORINGS
Church Road, Burton,
Milford Haven,
Pembrokeshire SA73 1NU.
Tel (01646) 600288
Moorings, pontoon, storage. All repairs.

SWANSEA MARINA
Lockside, Maritime Quarter, Swansea,
West Glamorgan SA1 1WG.
Tel (01792) 470310 Fax (01792) 463948
Access all states of the tide except LWST. City centre marina, restaurants, theatres etc. Call us on Channels 18 or 80 to check locking times. Visitors always welcome - a good destination for your annual trip.

TARQUIN YACHT HARBOUR LTD
Thorney Road, Emsworth,
Hampshire PO10 8BP.
Tel (01243) 377727 Fax (01243) 373432
Friendly marina in Chichester harbour. Water, electricity, diesel, Calor gas, 25-tonne mobile crane, slipways, hard-standing and storage areas. Showers and toilets, car parking, chandlery, engineers and boat repairs.

TOWN QUAY MARINA
Town Quay, The Waterfront,
Southampton, Hampshire.
Tel (01703) 234397
Town Quay is a growing development of bars and restaurants on an attractive waterfront environment just minutes away from the city centre.

WEIR QUAY BOATYARD
Heron's Reach, Bere Alston,
Devon PL20 7BT.
Tel (01822) 840474 Fax (01822) 840948
Deepwater swinging moorings, shore storage, full boatyard facilities and services, cranage to 12 tons, repairs, maintenance, slipway. A traditional boatyard at affordable rates 'in a superb setting' on the Tamar, with excellent security.

WORCESTER YACHT CHANDLERS LTD
Unit 7, 75 Waterworks Road,
Barbourne,
Worcester WR1 3EZ.
Tel (01905) 22522 & 27949
Chandlery, paints, ropes, cables, chain, clothing, footwear, shackles, books, bottled gas, anti-foul, fastenings, oakam, fenders. Hard storage, crane, haulage, engine service, oils, navigation aids, buoyancy aids, life jackets, distress flares, **small boat hire.**

BOAT BUILDERS & REPAIRS

AILSA-TROON LTD
Harbour Road, Troon,
Ayrshire KA10 6DN.
Tel (01292) 311311 Fax (01292) 317613
Boatyard with full repair and maintenance facilities for GRP, steel, aluminium, timber and inflatable craft. Ship repair, fabrication and new building work also undertaken in Ailsa's extensive 15 acre covered facilities.

ARDFERN YACHT CENTRE
Ardfern By Lochgilphead,
Argyll PA31 8QN.
Tel (01852) 500247/636
Fax (01852) 500624
Boatyard with full repair and maintenance facilities. Timber and GRP repairs, painting and engineering. Sheltered moorings and pontoon berthing. Winter storage, chandlery, showers, fuel, Calor, brokerage, 20-ton boat hoist, rigging. Hotel, bars and restaurant.

BOATWORKS + LTD
Castle Emplacement,
St Peter Port, Guernsey,
Channel Islands GY1 1AU.
Tel (01481) 726071 Fax (01481) 714224
Boatworks+ provides a comprehensive range of services including boatbuilding and repairs, chandlery, clothing and fuel supplies.

CRINAN BOATS LTD
Crinan, Lochgilphead,
Argyll PA31 8SP.
Tel (01546) 830232 Fax (01546) 830281
Boatbuilders, chandlers, engineers, slipping, repairs, charts, electricians, pontoon, moorings, showers, laundry and basic stores.

D G M BOAT REPAIRS
57 Imber Avenue,
Boscombe Down,
Salisbury, Wiltshire SP4 7JT.
Tel (01980) 624852
GRP specialist repairs.

DARTHAVEN MARINA LTD
Brixham Road, Kingswear,
Dartmouth, Devon TQ6 0SG.
Tel (01803) 752242 Fax (01803) 752722
Marina Office: (01803) 752545
Chandlery: (01803) 752733
Fax: (01803) 752790
All types of repair facilities available. Fully trained staff. 30-ton mobile hoist available all states of tide. Extensive chandlery open 7 days a week. Agents for Autohelm/Raytheon, Cetrek, B&G, Simrad Stowe, Navico, Simpson Lawrence, Sowester, International Paint, Webasto, Yanmar Main Agents, Volvo Penta ASW and Vetus sales and service. Visitors welcome. 24-hour engineering call-out service mobile numbers: 0860 873553 and 0467 250787 for electronics.

ELKINS BOATYARD
Tidesreach, 18 Convent Meadow,
The Quay,
Christchurch,
Dorset BH23 1BD.
Tel (01202) 483141
All boatyard facilities. Moorings alongside, water and electricity, storage ashore, repairs. Boats up to 45', 10 tons maximum, haul-out.

F J HARRIS BSc MRINA CENG
Naval Architect,
Surveyor & Boat Builder
'Gulls Target', 24 Roa Island,
Barrow in Furness, Cumbria LA13 0QL.
Tel (01229) 826084
Surveys of yachts and small craft for condition, insurance and repair. Design of yachts and small craft in traditional and modern materials. Work for MSA codes undertaken.

GWEEK QUAY BOATYARD
Gweek Quay
(Helford River),
Helston, Cornwall TR12 6UF.
Tel (01326) 221657 Fax (01326) 221685
Head of the Helford river. Yacht repair yard, 30-ton crane, chandlery, brokerage, coffee shop, toilets and showers. Boat storage and all boat repair and service facilities. Access approximately 2 hours either side of highwater.

HULL MARINA LTD
Warehouse 13,
Kingston Street,
Hull HU1 2DQ.
Tel (01482) 613451 Fax (01482) 224148
Four-Anchor marina. Situated 5 minutes from the centre of Hull and all national and international transport systems. First class leisure, boatyard and brokerage facilities. 4-Star hotel and quayside restaurants. Professional and caring staff. Competitive rates.

LANGNEY MARINE SERVICES LTD - LMS
Sovereign Harbour Marina,
Pevensey Bay Road, Eastbourne,
East Sussex BN23 6JH.
Tel (01323) 470244 Fax (01323) 470255
We offer a complete service to the boat owner offering repairs on all types of engines, GRP, steel, wood, electronics, rigging, cleaning, etc. We are also contractors to the RNLI.

N W SEAWAYS
Port Dinorwic Marina, Y Felinheli,
Gwynedd, North Wales LL56 4JN.
Tel (01248) 670620 Fax (01248) 671213
Mobile 0468 794361
Condition and pre-purchase surveys and insurance valuations, damage and repair reports, underwater dive inspections. Repair and dry dock facilities available. Call in or phone your requirement for prompt, professional service at competitive rates.

RICE & COLE LTD
Sea End Boathouse,
Burnham-on-Crouch, Essex CM0 8AN.
Tel/Fax (01621) 782063
Boatyard with full repair and shipwright services. Osmosis treatment, painting and spraying, GRP repairs, standing and running rigging, brokerage and chandlery. Visitors welcome to this family-run business on the river Crouch.

ROSDEN GLASS FIBRE
La Rue Durell, La Collette, St Helier,
Jersey JE2 3NB.
Tel (01534) 625418 Fax (01534) 625419
Specialists in all types of glass fibre marine works, structural repairs, alterations, reflow coating, GEL coat work, Blakes Osmosis Treatment Centre. Manufacturers of fuel tanks, bathing platforms and boat builders. General refurbishment and polishing. A division of Precision Plastics (Jersey) Ltd.

SEA-KING BOAT BUILDERS LTD
8A High Street, Leigh-on-Sea,
Essex SS9 2EN.
Tel (01702) 73612
Wooden boatbuilders, dinghies 12', cruisers up to 32' clinker construction, repairs to wooden vessels, iron work to your pattern undertaken. Mast and spars made in wood.

SLEAT MARINE SERVICES
Ardvasar, Isle of Skye IV45 8RU.
Tel (01471) 844216/844387
Yacht charter (bareboat and skippered) from Armadale Bay, Isle of Skye. Six yachts 34' to 40' LOA. All medium to heavy displacement blue water cruisers. Fuel, water and emergency services for passing yachts with problems.

SOUTHDOWN MARINA
Southdown Quay, Millbrook,
Cornwall PL10 1HG.
Tel/Fax (01752) 823084
32-berth marina on edge of river Tamar in quiet location behind Rame Peninsula. Plymouth is just across the river. Quayside berths available for large vessels. Winter storage. 24-hour security. DIY facilities available.

WINTERS MARINE LTD
(Lincombe Boatyard)
Lincombe, Salcombe,
Devon TQ8 8NQ.
Tel (01548) 843580
Deep water pontoon moorings. Winter storage for 150 boats. All maintenance and repair facilities. Slipway capacity 30 tonnes. Inflatable craft sales and service. Lifecraft surveys and repairs. Short and long-term lifecraft hire.

WET & WILD GRAPHICS
7 Firefly Road, Hamble Point Marina,
Hamble, Southampton,
Hampshire SO31 4NB.
Tel (01703) 458332 Fax (01703) 456830
Supply and application of vinyl graphics, signboards, banners and flags. Specialist materials for sails and spinnakers. Brochure available for mail order boat names. Deadlines never a problem!!!

W BATES & SON BOATBUILDERS LTD
Bridge Wharf,
Chertsey, Surrey KT16 8LG.
Tel (01932) 562255 Fax (01932) 571161
110-berth marina in quiet, picturesque area and additional riverside moorings. Full facilities including electricity to most berths, toilets and showers. 12-ton crane and hard standing for winter storage. Always a welcome to visitors from our friendly staff. Sales office open seven days a week.

CALEY MARINA
Canal Road,
Inverness IV3 6NF.
Tel (01463) 236539 Fax (01463) 238323
Open 08.30 - 17.30. Berths: 50 Pontoons (visitors available). Facilities: Fuel, water, pump-out facilities, provisions (nearby shops), repair, cranage, secure storage afloat and ashore. Comprehensive chandlery, showers, workshop. Situated at eastern end of Caledonian canal above Muirtown locks. Access via sea locks 4 hours either side of high water.

DUCHY OF CORNWALL
Harbour Office, St Mary's, Isles of Scilly,
Cornwall TR21 0HU.
Tel/Fax (01720) 422768
Port of St Mary's, Isles of Scilly - 38 visitor moorings. New visitor centre, hot showers, toilets, launching facilities, winter storage, security lockers, fuel and fresh water. 5 minutes from town centre. Ferry terminal and airport close by. Contact Harbour Master for more information.

ELKINS BOATYARD
Tidesreach, 18 Convent Meadow,
The Quay, Christchurch,
Dorset BH23 1BD.
Tel (01202) 483141
All boatyard facilities. Moorings alongside, water and electricity, storage ashore, repairs. Boats up to 45', 10 tons maximum, haul-out.

HALCON MARINE LTD
The Point, Canvey Island, Essex SS8 7TL.
Tel (01268) 511611 Fax (01268) 510044
Marine engineers, repairs and full boatyard services in this quiet and picturesque area. Berths, moorings, slipping facilities. Summer and winter storage. Dry dock (70t max), diesel. 1 or 2 hours ±HW. Water, electric, toilets and showers. A friendly welcome awaits you.

ISLE OF ANGLESEY COUNTY COUNCIL
Highways & Technical Services
Department, Council Offices,
Llangefni, Anglesey LL77 7TW
Tel (01248) 752331 Fax (01248) 724839
Berths and moorings available at Menai bridge, Amlwch harbour and north east Menai Straits (Beaumaris). Winter storage at competitive rates available at Beaumaris and Amlwch. Contact Maritime Officer 01248 752331 for details.

NELSON MARINE TRANSPORT
Trafalgar Garage, Ashleigh Road,
Arnside, Carnforth, Lancashire LA5 0HE.
Tel/Fax (01524) 761481
Nelson Marine Transport and Storage. Specialist haulage nationwide. Competitive rates handled with a friendly, caring respect for boats.

PORT FLAIR LTD
Bradwell Marina, Waterside,
Bradwell-on-Sea, Essex CM0 7RB.
Tel (01621) 776235/776391
300 pontoon berths with water and electricity, petrol and diesel, chandlery, marine slip/hoistage to 20 tons. Repairs, winter lay-ups, licensed club, yacht brokerage.

SOUTHDOWN MARINA
Southdown Quay, Millbrook,
Cornwall PL10 1HG.
Tel/Fax (01752) 823084
32-berth marina on edge of river Tamar in quiet location behind Rame Peninsula. Plymouth is just across the river. Quayside berths available for large vessels. Winter storage. 24-hour security. DIY facilities available.

SPARKES YACHT HARBOUR LTD
38 Wittering Road, Hayling Island,
Hampshire PO11 9SR.
Tel (01705) 463572 Fax (01705) 465741
Sparkes Marina - a small friendly, family run business offering all the facilities you require including access at all states of the tide to a depth of 2 metres at lowest low water springs. In addition to marina berths, accessible through a security gate, we also offer dry boat sailing, moorings, storage ashore plus full maintenance facilities, new boat sales and brokerage, chandlery and restaurant.

TARQUIN YACHT HARBOUR LTD
Thorney Road, Emsworth,
Hampshire PO10 8BP.
Tel (01243) 377727 Fax (01243) 373432
Friendly marina in Chichester harbour. Water, electricity, diesel, Calor gas, 25-tonne mobile crane, slipways, hard-standing and storage areas. Showers and toilets, car parking, chandlery, engineers and boat repairs.

BOATYARD SERVICES & SUPPLIES

ARDORAN MARINE
Lerags, Oban, Argyll PA34 4SE.
Tel (01631) 566123 Fax (01631) 566611
All marine services.

BIRDHAM SHIPYARD LTD
Birdham Pool, Chichester,
West Sussex PO20 7BG.
Tel (01243) 512310 Fax (01243) 513163
Quiet, picturesque marina in Chichester harbour. Moorings available for boats up to 55' overall and 5'6" draught. Chandlery and all boatyard sevices available. Visitors welcome.

BRIGHTON MARINA
Brighton Marina Village, Brighton,
East Sussex BN2 5UF.
Tel (01273) 819919 Fax (01273) 675082
Britain's largest marina (1600 pontoon berths) with marina village under development. TYHA Five-Gold Anchors. Full boatyard and shore facilities. Brokerage and boat sales. Club racing throughout the year. Group visits, rallies welcome.

BURGH CASTLE MARINA
Butt Lane, Burgh Castle, Norfolk,
Norwich NR31 9PZ.
Tel (01493) 780331
100 serviced pontoons and quay moorings accessible at all tides. Secure car and boat parking. Adjoining boatyard services, access to holiday park showers, laundry and heated pool. Riverside pub and shop. Complex open all year.

CHALLENGE MARINE
Freeman's Wharf, Falmouth Road,
Penryn, Cornwall TR10 8AS.
Tel (01326) 377222 Fax (01326) 377800
Marine engineers, chandlery, boatyard. Main Volvo Penta dealer, marina berths, brokerage and Bombard inflatables' dealer.

CRAOBH MARINA
By Lochgilphead, Argyll PA31 8UD.
Tel (01852) 500222 Fax (01852) 500252
250-berth marina on Loch Shuna. Water, electricity, diesel and gas. Full boatyard services. Chandlery. Brokerage. Insurance. Shops, bar. 24-hour access. VHF Ch37 and 80 (M).

DALE SAILING CO LTD
Brunel Quay, Neyland Marina, Neyland,
Pembrokeshirre SA73 1PY.
Tel (01646) 601636 Fax (01646) 601061
Comprehensive chandlery. Hull and engine repair and service.

DART MARINA
Sandquay, Dartmouth, Devon TQ6 9PH.
Tel (01803) 833351 Fax (01803) 832307
High quality 110-berth marina on the fabulous river Dart, opposite the Dart Marina hotel. A superb situation with all amenities, 24-hour security, hotel and restaurant, showers, baths and laundry, fuel berth and a warm welcome to all visitors.

DEACONS BOATYARD LTD
Bursledon Bridge, Southampton,
Hampshire SO3 8AZ.
Tel (01703) 402253 Fax (01703) 405665
This yard provides a comprehensive range of services including moorings, laying-up of boats, boat repairs, marine engineering, rigging, sail making and repairs and brokerage etc.

FIDDLERS FERRY YACHT HAVEN
Off Station Road, Penketh, Warrington,
Cheshire WA5 2UJ.
Tel (01925) 727519
Sheltered moorings upto 6'6" draught, 50' long. Access through lock from river Mersey 1½ hours either side of high tide. Signed from A652. Boatyard and lift-out facilities. Annual rate per foot £8.25.

HALCON MARINE LTD
The Point, Canvey Island, Essex SS8 7TL.
Tel (01268) 511611 Fax (01268) 510044
Marine engineers, repairs and full boatyard services in this quiet and picturesque area. Berths, moorings, slipping facilities. Summer and winter storage. Dry dock (70t max), diesel. 1 or 2 hours ±HW. Water, electric, toilets and showers. A friendly welcome awaits you.

JACKSON YACHT SERVICES
Le Boulevard, St Aubin, Jersey,
Channel Islands JE3 8AB.
Tel (01534) 43819 Fax (01534) 45952
Boatyard and chandler. Sailoft and liferaft service station.

KIP MARINA
The Yacht Harbour, Inverkip,
Renfrewshire PA16 0AS.
Tel (01475) 521485 Fax (01475) 521298
Marina berths for vessels up to 65' LOA. Full boatyard facilities including travel hoist, crane, on-site engineers, GRP repairs etc. Bar, restaurant, saunas, launderette and chandlery.

LANGSTONE HARBOUR BOARD
Ferry Road, Hayling Island,
Hampshire PO11 0DG.
Tel (01705) 463419 Fax (01705) 467144
All boatyard facilities. Deep water and tidal moorings available. Water, electricity and diesel. Summer and winter storage. Public slipways. 6-ton crane. Landrover vessel and trailer recovery services.

LITTLEHAMPTON MARINA LTD
Ferry Road, Littlehampton,
West Sussex BN17 5DS.
Tel (01903) 713553 Fax (01903) 732264
Only 2 miles upstream of harbour entrance, we have deep water pontoon berths with electricity and lighting. Showers, toilets, changing rooms, cafe, and floating pub.

Petrol, marine diesel, slipway with tractor launch, recovery service, and storage compounds. 30 miles from Isle of Wight, 18 miles from Brighton and 14 miles of navigable river which flows through the historic town of Arundel. Good diving and fishing available.

THE MAYFLOWER INTERNATIONAL MARINA
Ocean Quay,
Richmond Walk,
Plymouth, Devon PL1 4LS.
Tel (01752) 556633 Fax (01752) 606896
Plymouth's only Five-Gold Anchor marina. Known for its facilities, courtesy and security. Owned by berth holders and run to a very high standard.

NOSS-ON-DART MARINA
Noss Quay, Dartmouth,
Devon TQ6 0EA.
Tel (01803) 833351 Fax (01803) 832307
Peacefully located on the east shore of the river Dart, this relaxing marina is the perfect base for cruising yachtsmen. Extensive parking, chandlery, repair and lift-out facilities, easy access from London and the Midlands. Boat taxi to Dartmouth.

PORT FALMOUTH BOATYARD
North Parade, Falmouth,
Cornwall TR11 2TB.
Tel (01326) 313248 Fax (01326) 319395
Full boatyard facilities. Powered hoist, slipway cradle.

RICE & COLE LTD
Sea End Boathouse,
Burnham-on-Crouch, Essex CM0 8AN.
Tel/Fax (01621) 782063
Boatyard with full repair and shipwright services. Osmosis treatment, painting and spraying, GRP repairs, standing and running rigging, brokerage and chandlery. Visitors welcome to this family-run business on the river Crouch.

SHOTLEY MARINA LTD
Shotley Gate, Ipswich,
Suffolk IP9 1QJ.
Tel (01473) 788982 Fax (01473) 788868
Fully equipped yard and repair service. Heated workshop (up to 90' LOA). Experts in wood, GRP and steel fabricated vessels from small repairs to full refits. Registered Blakes osmosis centre. Full marine engineering service. Commissioning of new vessels. Please call for further information or a free quotation.

SPARKES YACHT HARBOUR LTD
38 Wittering Road, Hayling Island,
Hampshire PO11 9SR.
Tel (01705) 463572 Fax (01705) 465741
Sparkes Marina - a small friendly, family run business offering all the facilities you require including access at all states of the tide to a depth of 2 metres at lowest low water springs. In addition to marina berths, accessible through a security gate, we also offer dry boat sailing, moorings, storage ashore plus full maintenance facilities, new boat sales and brokerage, chandlery and restaurant.

Sailing HOLIDAYS IN IRELAND
- Only the Best

Call us

KILRUSH CREEK MARINA
+353-65-52072

DONEGAL

SLIGO

CARLINGFORD MARINA CLUB
+353-42-73492

MALAHIDE MARINA VILLAGE
+353-1-8454129

DUBLIN

FENIT HARBOUR MARINA
+353-66-36231

SALVE MARINE
+353-21-831145

HOWTH MARINA
+353-1-8392777

ROSSLARE

COR

DINGLE MARINA
+353-66-51629

KILMORE QUAY MARINA
+353-53-29955

CASTLEPARK MARINA
+353-21-774959

CROSSHAVEN BOATYARD
+353-21-831161

Sail in Ireland and enjoy the experience of a lifetime

Further information from - Sailing Holidays in Ireland , 67a Upper Georges Street, Dun Laoghaire, Co Dublin. Tel +353-1-284 6819

THE LOCAL AUTHORITY
UP TO DATE LOCAL AREA WEATHER INFORMATION BY PHONE OR FAX

FOR A DETAILED 5 DAY LOCAL FORECAST
PHONE 0891 500 4 + area number

FOR A 2 DAY LOCAL FORECAST AND CHARTS
FAX 0897 300 2 + area number

OFFSHORE AREAS	Telephone 2-5 Day Planner 0891 500 PLUS	Fax 2-5 Day Planner 0897 300 PLUS
English Channel	992	270
Southern North Sea	991	271
Irish Sea	954	273
Biscay	953	274
North West Scotland	955	275
Northern North Sea	985	276
Satellite Image	-	277
Index page to all fax products	-	0891 24 66 80

To obtain fax - simply dial 0897 300 plus area number on your fax machine and press the start button when prompted

FOR CURRENT WEATHER CONDITIONS BY PHONE, UPDATED HOURLY CALL
0891 226 4 + area number

Information Supplied by
The Met. Office

For a free Marinecall card or fax helpdesk call
0171 729 8811

Map areas: 51, 64, 52, 53, 63, 54, 65, 62, 61, 55, 60, 56, 59, 58, 57

Locations: ULLAPOOL, INVERNESS, ABERDEEN, OBAN, LEITH, GLASGOW, SUNDERLAND, BELFAST, IMMINGHAM, LIVERPOOL, HOLYHEAD, LOWESTOFT, BURNHAM, LONDON, DOVER, MILFORD HAVEN, AVONMOUTH, PORTSMOUTH, SOUTHAMPTON, PLYMOUTH

Marinecall is a product of TIS plc, Avalon House, 57-63 Scrutton Street London EC2A 4PJ. 0891 calls are charged at 50p per minute at all times (as at March 1997)
0897 calls are charged at £1.50 per minute at all times. (All fax products - maximum 2 pages - Fax service updated daily each morning. Phone service updated morning and afternoon).

TITCHMARSH MARINA
(WALTON-ON-THE-NAZE)
Coles Lane, Walton-on-the-Naze,
Essex CO14 8SL.
Tel (01255) 672185 Fax (01255) 851901
Friendly service in the peaceful backwater.
Visiting yachtsmen welcome. Sheltered
marina berths. Full marina facilities: travel-
lift, cranage, 16amp electricity, diesel.
Winter storage. Restaurant and bar open
every day. Bar meals available all day.
Weekend barbecues. (See the Harbour
Lights Restaurant)

TOLLESBURY MARINA
The Yacht Harbour, Tollesbury, Maldon,
Essex CM9 8SE.
Tel (01621) 869202 Fax (01621) 868489
Dedicated to customer service, this family-
run marina can offer 240 marina berths
with water and electricity on all pontoons.
Cruising club with bar, restaurant,
swimming pool and tennis courts. Repair
workshop, osmosis treatment centre. Full
brokerage service listing over 200 boats.
VHF Ch37 and 80.

WEIR QUAY BOATYARD
Heron's Reach, Bere Alston,
Devon PL20 7BT.
Tel (01822) 840474 Fax (01822) 840948
Deepwater swinging moorings, shore
storage, full boatyard facilities and services,
cranage to 12 tons, repairs, maintenance,
slipway. A traditional boatyard at affordable
rates 'in a superb setting' on the Tamar,
with excellent security.

BOOKS & CHARTS/ PUBLISHERS

BOGERD NAVTEC NV
Oude Leeuwenrui 37, Antwerp 20000,
Germany.
Books and charts.

BOOK CABIN
Unit 20, Canutes Pavilion, Ocean Village,
Southampton, Hampshire SO14 3JS.
Tel (01703) 211199 Fax (01703) 338488
Nautical and general booksellers.

BROWN SON & FERGUSON LTD
4-10 Darnley Street, Glasgow G41 2SD.
Tel 0141-429 1234
Books and charts.

W & H CHINA
Howley Properties Ltd, PO Box 149,
Warrington WA1 2DW.
Tel (01925) 634621 Fax (01925) 418009
Manufacturer of China chart dividers.

B COOKE & SON LTD
Kingston Observatory, 58-59
Market Place, Hull HU1 1RH.
Tel (01482) 223454
Books and Charts. DTp Certificated.

DUBOIS-PHILLIPS & McCALLUM LTD
Oriel Chambers, Covent Garden,
Liverpool L2 8UD.
Tel 0151-236 2776
Books and charts.

THE HARBOUR BOOKSHOP
12 Fairfax Place,
Dartmouth,
Devon TQ6 9AE.
Tel/Fax (01803) 832448
The general bookstore with a specialised
nautical section: Nautical fiction, pilots and
almanacs, log books and charts, seamanship, and RYA publications. Worlwide
mail order. 10% discount on nautical stock
on production of this voucher/advert.

IVER C WEILBACH & CO., A/S
35 Toldbodgade,
Postbox 1560, DK-1253 Copenhagen K,
Denmark.
Books and charts.

John Lewcock
Maritime Bookseller

*Naval
History
*Yachts and
Sailing

*Naval
Architecture
*Ships and
Shipping

6 CHEWELLS LANE, HADDENHAM,
ELY, CAMBS CB6 3SS.
Telephone/Fax: +44 (0)1353 741152

Catalogues Issued - Books Bought

JOHN LEWCOCK
(Maritime Bookseller)
6 Chewells Lane, Haddenham, Ely,
Cambridgeshire CB6 3SS.
Tel/Fax (01353) 741152
We buy and sell secondhand and antiquarian
books on yachting, naval architecture,
maritime history etc. Catalogues issued
regularly complemented by a regular mail
order service. Please telephone or fax your
order on 01353 741152.

JOHN LILLEY & GILLIE LTD
Clive Street, North Shields,
Tyne & Wear NE29 6LF.
Tel 0191-257 2217
Books and Charts. DTp Certificated.

KELVIN HUGHES
CHARTS & MARITIME SUPPLIES
Royal Crescent Road, Southampton,
Hampshire SO14 3NP.
Tel (01703) 634911 Fax (01703) 330014
Charts, books, chandlery, safety equipment
and clothing. Liferaft hire and sales. Also in
London with worldwide mail order service.

KELVIN HUGHES
CHARTS & MARITIME SUPPLIES
New North Road,
Hainault, Ilford,
Essex IG6 2UR.
Tel 0181-500 6166
Books and charts. DTp Certificated.

KELVIN HUGHES OBSERVATOR
Nieuwe Longoweg 41, 3194 DC Hoogvliet
(Rt), The Netherlands.
Book and charts. DTp Certificated.

MARINE INSTRUMENTS
The Bosun's Locker,
Upton Slip, Falmouth,
Cornwall TR11 3DQ.
Tel (01326) 312414
Books and charts. DTp Certificated.

MARTIN & CO
Oude Leewenrui 37,
Antwerp 2000, Germany.
Books and charts. DTp Certificated.

MERIDIAN CHARTWARE LTD
Maggs House,
78 Queens Road, Clifton,
Bristol BS8 1QX.
Tel 0117-907 3327 Fax 0117-907 7548
e-mail: meridian@dial.pipex.com
http://dspace.dial.pipex.com/meridian/
Designers and suppliers of quality marine
software. Electronic charting systems for
the leisure user to the professional mariner,
using the British Admiralty Raster Chart
Service (ARCS). Dedicated Win96/NT
mariner-friendly systems. Official ARCS
chart agent. Suppliers of complete
hardware/software packages.

R J MUIR
22 Seymour Close, Chandlers Forge,
Eastleigh, Southampton,
Hampshire SO5 2JE.
Tel (01703) 261042
Books and Charts. DTp Certificated.

OCEAN LEISURE LTD
11-14 Northumberland Avenue,
London WC2N 5AQ.
Tel 0171-930 5050 Fax 0171-930 3032
Complete range of sailing clothing, swim
and beachwear stocked all year round.
Chandlery includes marine electronic
equipment, marine antiques, books and
charts. Also canoeing, underwater
photography, diving and waterskiing
specialists. Learn to scuba dive.

W F PRICE & CO LTD
Northpoint House,
Wapping Wharf,
Bristol BS1 6UD.
Tel 0117-929 2229
Books and charts. DTp Certificated.

S I R S NAVIGATION LTD
186a Milton Road, Swanscombe,
Kent DA10 0LX.
Tel (01322) 383672
Books and Charts. DTp Certificated.

THE SEA CHEST
NAUTICAL BOOKS & CHARTS
Queen Anne's Battery Marina,
Plymouth, Devon PL4 0LP.
Tel (01752) 222012 Fax (01752) 252679
Admiralty Chart Agent. Worldwide mail
order service.

SEATH INSTRUMENTS (1992) LTD
Unit 30, Colville Road Works,
Colville Road, Lowestoft NR33 9QS.
Tel (01502) 573811
Books and Charts. DTp Certificated.

SEVERNSIDE CONSULTANTS
Deco Court, South View Business Park,
Staple Hill, Bristol BS16 5PJ.
Tel 0117-956 8844
Books and charts. DTp Certificated.

SIMPSON LAWRENCE LTD
218-228 Edmiston Drive,
Glasgow G51 2YT.
Tel 0141-427 5331 Fax 0141-427 5419
e-mail: info@simpson-lawrence.co.uk
Simpson Lawrence are manufacturers and
the UK's largest wholesale distributor of
quality marine equipment.

A M SMITH (MARINE) LTD
33 Epping Way, Chingford E4 7PB.
Tel 0181-529 6988
Books and charts.

SOFTWAVE
4 Aranmor House, Kingston Hill,
Kingston, Surrey KT2 7LY.
Tel 0181-549 0650 Fax 0181-546 1090
www.softwave.co.uk Specialist supplier of
PC based electronic navigation systems
and high quality vectorized charts drawn
from Admiralty and other official sources.
Also tide computing, simulations, hard
ware and on-board installations. *See
advertisement first right hand page in this
volume.*

THOMAS GUNN NAVIGATION SERVICES
Anchor House, 62 Regents Quay,
Aberdeen AB11 5AR.
Tel (01224) 595045
Books and charts. DTp Certificated.

TODD CHART AGENCY LTD
4 Seacliff Road, The Harbour, Bangor,
Northern Ireland BT20 5EY.
Tel (01247) 466640 Fax (01247) 471070
International Admiralty Chart Agent, chart
correction service and nautical booksellers.
Stockist of navigation and chartroom
instruments, binoculars, clocks etc. Mail
order service available. Visa, Access and
American Express accepted.

WARSASH NAUTICAL BOOKSHOP
6 Dibles Road, Warsash, Southampton,
Hampshire SO31 9HZ.
Tel (01489) 572384 Fax (01489) 885756
e-mail: alan@nauticalbooks.co.uk
http://www.nauticalbooks.co.uk
Nautical bookseller and chart agent. Callers
and mail order. Free new and secondhand
book lists. Credit cards taken. Publishers of
the Bibliography of Nautical books.

WESSEX MARINE EQUIPMENT LTD
Logistics House, 2nd Avenue Business
Park, Millbrook Road East,
Southampton, Hampshire SO1 0LP.
Tel (01703) 510570
Books and charts.

BREAKDOWN

DARTHAVEN MARINA LTD
Brixham Road,
Kingswear, Dartmouth,
Devon TQ6 0SG.
Tel (01803) 752242 Fax (01803) 752722
Marina Office: (01803) 752545
Chandlery: (01803) 752733
Fax: (01803) 752790
All types of repair facilities available. Fully
trained staff. 30-ton mobile hoist available
all states of tide. Extensive chandlery open
7 days a week. Agents for Autohelm/
Raytheon, Cetrek, B&G, Simrad Stowe,
Navico, Simpson Lawrence, Sowester,
International Paint, Webasto, Yanmar Main
Agents, Volvo Penta ASW and Vetus sales
and service. Visitors welcome. 24-hour
engineering call-out service mobile
numbers: 0860 873553 and 0467250787
for electronics.

SEASTART
Unit 13 Hamble Point Marina,
School Lane, Hamble,
Southampton SO31 4JD.
Tel 0800 885500 Fax (01703) 458000
SeaStart is the 24-hour marine breakdown
membership service on both sides of the
English Channel and the Channel Islands.
For membership - join now on 0800 885500
using your credit card.

CHANDLERS

**AQUA-MARINE
MANUFACTURING (UK) LTD**
216 Fair Oak Road, Bishopstoke,
Eastleigh, Hampshire SO50 8NJ.
Tel (01703) 694949 Fax (01703) 601381
Sales Fax (01703) 601188
e-mail: sales@aqua-marine.co.uk
Manufacturer and distributor of chandlery,
including: Engel refrigeration, Dutton-
Lainson winches, Anchor fenders, Rule
pumps, Aquaflow water systems, SeaStar
steering and controls, Skyblazer flares.
Admiralty small craft charts, Aquameter
compasses, RWO and Holt fittings,
Danforth anchors, Aqua-Signal lights,
Techimpex cookers

ARDFERN YACHT CENTRE
Ardfern By Lochgilphead,
Argyll PA31 8QN.
Tel (01852) 500247/636
Fax (01852) 500624
Boatyard with full repair and maintenance
facilities. Timber and GRP repairs, painting
and engineering. Sheltered moorings and
pontoon berthing. Winter storage,
chandlery, showers, fuel, Calor, brokerage,
20-ton boat hoist. Hotel, bars and restaurant.

BOATWORKS + LTD
Castle Emplacement, St Peter Port,
Guernsey, Channel Islands GY1 1AU.
Tel (01481) 726071 Fax (01481) 714224
Boatworks+ provides a comprehensive
range of services including boatbuilding
and repairs, chandlery, clothing and fuel
supplies.

BOSUN'S LOCKER
10 Military Road, Royal Harbour,
Ramsgate, Kent CT11 9LG.
Tel/Fax (01843) 597158
The Bosun's Locker, a friendly, family owned
business, caters for a wide range of boat
owners and is staffed by experienced
yachtsmen. The stock is extensive, including
paint, ropes, quality clothing for foul-
weather and fashion, electronics, inflatables
and charts.

BRIXHAM YACHT SUPPLIES LTD
72 Middle Street, Brixham,
Devon TQ5 8EJ.
Tel (01803) 882290
We stock a complete range of sailing and
leisure clothing. English and Continental
pure wool traditional knitwear. Camping
accessories.

CALEY MARINA
Canal Road, Inverness IV3 6NF.
Tel (01463) 236539 Fax (01463) 238323
Open 08.30 - 17.30. Berths: 50 Pontoons
(visitors available). Facilities: Fuel, water,
pump-out facilities, provisions (nearby
shops), repair, cranage, secure storage
afloat and ashore. Comprehensive
chandlery, showers, workshop. Situated at
eastern end of Caledonian canal above
Muirtown locks. Access via sea locks 4
hours either side of high water.

CHALLENGE MARINE
Freeman's Wharf, Falmouth Road,
Penryn, Cornwall TR10 8AS.
Tel (01326) 377222 Fax (01326) 377800
Marine engineers, chandlery, boatyard.
Main Volvo Penta dealer, marina berths,
brokerage and Bombard inflatables' dealer.

COMPASS POINT CHANDLERY
The Quay, High Street, Hamble,
Hampshire SO31 4HA.
Tel (01703) 452388 Fax (01703) 456942
Compass Point is adjacent to the quay at
Hamble. It stocks an attractive selection of
leisure clothing and foul-weather gear as
well as a wide range of chandlery.

CRAOBH MARINA
By Lochgilphead, Argyll PA31 8UD.
Tel (01852) 500222 Fax (01852) 500252
250-berth marina on Loch Shuna. Water,
electricity, diesel and gas. Full boatyard
services. Chandlery. Brokerage. Insurance.
Shops, bar. 24-hour access. VHF Ch37 and
80 (M).

CRINAN BOATS LTD
Crinan, Lochgilphead, Argyll PA31 8SP.
Tel (01546) 830232 Fax (01546) 830281
Boatbuilders, chandlers, engineers,
slipping, repairs, charts, electricians,
pontoon, moorings, showers, laundry and
basic stores.

DARTHAVEN MARINA LTD
Brixham Road, Kingswear, Dartmouth,
Devon TQ6 0SG.
Tel (01803) 752242 Fax (01803) 752722
Marina Office: (01803) 752545
Chandlery: (01803) 752733
Fax: (01803) 752790
All types of repair facilities available. Fully
trained staff. 30-ton mobile hoist available
all states of tide. Extensive chandlery open
7 days a week. Agents for Autohelm/
Raytheon, Cetrek, B&G, Simrad Stowe,
Navico, Simpson Lawrence, Sowester,
International Paint, Webasto, Yanmar Main
Agents, Volvo Penta ASW and Vetus sales
and service. Visitors welcome. 24-hour
engineering call-out service mobile
numbers: 0860 873553 and 0467250787
for electronics.

DOWN MARINE CO LTD
163 Comber Road, Dundonald, Belfast,
Co Down, Northern Ireland BT16 0BU.
Tel/Fax (01237) 480247
Down Marine is a family owned business
specialising in sailing equipment. We stock
a comprehensive range of navigational
instruments, paint, rope, charts, life jackets,
deck hardware, seacocks, toilets, anchors,
all-weather clothing and inflatables etc.

FOX'S MARINA IPSWICH LTD
The Strand, Wherstead, Ipswich,
Suffolk IP2 8SA.
Tel (01473) 689111 Fax (01473) 601737
The most comprehensive boatyard facility
on the east coast. Extensive chandlery.
Marina access 24-hours. Two travel hoists
to 45 tons, 10 ton crane. Full electronics,
rigging, engineering, stainless steel
services. Specialists in osmosis and spray
painting.

GWEEK QUAY BOATYARD
Gweek Quay (Helford River), Helston,
Cornwall TR12 6UF.
Tel (01326) 221657 Fax (01326) 221685
Head of the Helford river. Yacht repair yard,
30-ton crane, chandlery, brokerage, coffee
shop, toilets and showers. Boat storage
and all boat repair and service facilities.
Access approximately 2 hours either side of
highwater.

JOSEPH P LAMB & SONS
Maritime Building
(opposite Albert Dock),
Wapping, Liverpool L1 8DQ.
Tel 0151-709 4861 Fax 0151-709 2786
Situated in the centre of Liverpool, J P
Lamb have provided a service to world
shipping for over 200 years. All chandlery
supplies, clothing, rope, paint and flags are
available. Full sailmaking and repairs. Kemp
Retail Outlet for spars and rigging. Open
Mon to Fri 8am to 5.30pm - Sat 9am to
12.30pm.

KELVIN HUGHES
CHARTS & MARITIME SUPPLIES
Royal Crescent Road, Southampton,
Hampshire SO14 3NP.
Tel (01703) 634911 Fax (01703) 330014
Charts, books, chandlery, safety equipment
and clothing. Liferaft hire and sales. Also in
London with worldwide mail order service.

LIVERPOOL MARINA
Coburg Dock, Sefton Street,
Liverpool L3 4BP.
Tel 0151-709 0578/(2683 after 5pm)
Fax 0151-709 8731.
300-berth yacht harbour. All serviced
pontoons. Tidal access HW ± 2½ hours
approximately, depending on draught. 60-
ton hoist, workshops, bar and restaurant,
toilets and showers. City centre one mile.
Open all year. Active yacht club and yacht
brokerage.

MANX MARINE
35 North Quay, Douglas,
Isle of Man IM1 4LB.
Tel/Fax (01624) 674842
The Island's leading and most established
yacht chandlery. Stockists of quality foul-
weather clothing and thermal wear. Large
stock holdings of stainless steel fixtures
and fittings and a comprehensive range of
general chandlery including rigging
facilities.

MARQUAND BROS LTD
- YACHT CHANDLERS
North Quay, St Peter Port,
Guernsey, Channel Islands.
Tel (01481) 720962 Fax (01481) 713974
Yacht chandlers, stockists of a compreh-
ensive range of marine products. Guernsey
distributor for International Paint. Extensive
leisure and marine clothing department
including Barbour, Driza-Bone, Dubarry and
Quayside.

THE MAYFLOWER
INTERNATIONAL MARINA
Ocean Quay,
Richmond Walk,
Plymouth, Devon PL1 4LS.
Tel (01752) 556633 Fax (01752) 606896
Plymouth's only Five-Gold Anchor marina.
Known for its facilities, courtesy and
security. Owned by berth holders and run to
a very high standard.

NORTH QUAY MARINE
North Side,
St Sampson's Harbour, Guernsey,
Channel Islands.
Tel (01481) 46561 Fax (01481) 43488
The complete boating centre. Full range of
chandlery, rope, chain, lubricants, paint,
boatwear and shoes. Fishing tackle for onshore and on-board. Inflatables and safety
equipment. Electronics and small outboard
engines.

OCEAN LEISURE LTD
11-14 Northumberland Avenue,
London WC2N 5AQ.
Tel 0171-930 5050 Fax 0171-930 3032
Complete range of sailing clothing, swim
and beachwear stocked all year round.
Chandlery includes marine electronic
equipment, marine antiques, books and
charts. Also canoeing, underwater
photography, diving and waterskiing
specialists. Learn to scuba dive.

OCEAN MARINE INTERNATIONAL - OMI
Mayflower International Marina,
Plymouth, Devon PL1 4LS.
Tel (01752) 500121 Fax (01752) 500221
Queen Anne's Battery Marina, Plymouth,
Devon PL1 0LP
Tel (01752) 222688
OMI offer a full range of chandlery, rope,
paint, safety equipment and electronics. All
major clothing agencies held, including
Henri Lloyd and Musto. A commercial ships
stores division is also available.

SEAQUEST MARINE LTD
13 Fountain Street, St Peter Port,
Guernsey, Channel Islands GY1 1BX.
Tel (01481) 721773 Fax (01481) 716738
Seaquest Marine have a fully stocked
chandlery. Agents for Sowester and
Simpson Lawrence. Sole agents for Avon,
Typhoon, Garmin Electronics and Compass
inflatables. Electronics specialising in GPS.
Inflatable specialists. Official Avon service
station. VAT free. Friendly advice.

SHAMROCK CHANDLERY
Shamrock Quay, William Street,
Northam, Southampton,
Hampshire SO14 5QL.
Tel (01703) 632725 Fax (01703) 225611
Situated on Shamrock Quay, a busy working
yard with a pub, restaurant and boutiques.
Shamrock Chandlery is renowned for
extensive quality stocks and service and is
widely used by both the trade and boat
owners.

UPPER DECK MARINE/OUTRIGGERS
Albert Quay, Fowey, Cornwall PL23 1AQ.
Tel (01726) 832287 Fax (01726) 833265
Chandlery, fastenings, paints, cords,
fenders, anchors, compasses, lifejackets,
Gaz. Leading names in waterproofs and
warm wear.

WEYMOUTH OLD HARBOUR
Weymouth & Portland Borough Council,
Borough Engineers Department,
Municipal Offices, North Quay,
Weymouth, Dorset DT4 8TA.
Tel (01305) 206363/206423
Fax (01305) 206276
e-mail: cflowers@weymouth.gov.uk
http://www.weymouth.gov.uk/
marine.htm
Access at all stages of tide. Visitor berths in
the centre of prime tourist resort with shops,
restaurants and night life all at hand. Diesel
fuelling from pontoon or tanker. Chandlery
and repair facilities available.

WORCESTER YACHT CHANDLERS LTD
Unit 7, 75 Waterworks Road, Barbourne,
Worcester WR1 3EZ.
Tel (01905) 22522 & 27949
Chandlery, paints, ropes, cables, chain,
clothing, footwear, shackles, books, bottled
gas, anti-foul, fastenings, oakam, fenders.
Hard storage, crane, haulage, engine
service, oils, navigation aids, buoyancy aids,
life jackets, distress flares, **small boat hire.**

CLOTHING

BOATWORKS + LTD
Castle Emplacement,
St Peter Port, Guernsey,
Channel Islands GY1 1AU.
Tel (01481) 726071 Fax (01481) 714224
Boatworks+ provides a comprehensive range of services including boatbuilding and repairs, chandlery, clothing and fuel supplies.

OCEAN LEISURE LTD
11-14 Northumberland Avenue,
London WC2N 5AQ.
Tel 0171-930 5050 Fax 0171-930 3032
Complete range of sailing clothing, swim and beachwear stocked all year round. Chandlery includes marine electronic equipment, marine antiques, books and charts. Also canoeing, underwater photography, diving and waterskiing specialists. Learn to scuba dive.

OCEAN WORLD LTD
46 High Street, Cowes,
Isle of Wight PO31 7RR.
Tel (01983) 291744 Fax (01983) 297252
Clothing and embroidery services.

OUTRIGGERS/UPPER DECK MARINE
Albert Quay, Fowey,
Cornwall PL23 1AQ.
Tel (01726) 833233 Fax (01726) 833265
'Outriggers' casual and marine clothing, footwear, nautical gifts, Admiralty chart agent and marine books.

COMMUNICATIONS EQUIPMENT

NORTH QUAY MARINE
North Side, St Sampson's Harbour,
Guernsey, Channel Islands.
Tel (01481) 46561 Fax (01481) 43488
The complete boating centre. Full range of chandlery, rope, chain, lubricants, paint, boatwear and shoes. Fishing tackle for on-shore and on-board. Inflatables and safety equipment. Electronics and small outboard engines.

R T TRAINING
286 Sea Front, Hayling Island,
Hampshire PO11 0AZ.
Tel (01705) 462122 Fax (01705) 462138
Weekend radio courses at Southampton and Port Solent for leisure and professional yachtsmen. SSB - 3-day Long Range Certificate (LRC) - optional Satellite module. Restricted to LRC upgrade course. VHF 1-day course/exam.

RADIO & ELECTRONIC SERVICES LTD
Les Chenes, Rohais,
St Peter Port, Guernsey,
Channel Islands GY1 1FB.
Tel (01481) 728837 Fax (01481) 714379
Chart plotters, GPS, C-Map and Navionics charting, radars, VHF fixed and portable radios, autopilots. We offer full electronic supply and service. Sales and service dealers for Furuno, Icom, Shipmate, Cetrek, Autohelm, Robertson and AP Navigator.

RADIO SCHOOL LTD
33 Island Close,
Hayling Island,
Hampshire PO11 0NJ.
Tel (01705) 466450 Fax (01705) 461449
Regular weekend courses/exams for the VHF and Long Range (SSB/Sat.) Radio-telephone Operator's Certificates in UK's only permanent, fully equipped classroom solely dedicated to training small-boat sailors on a full-time, professional basis. Established 1980.

ROWLANDS MARINE ELECTRONICS LTD
Unit 4 Glandon Industrial Estate,
Pwllheli, Gwynedd LL53 5YT.
Tel/Fax (01758) 613193
> **EXPECTED TO BE SETTLED IN OUR NEW PREMISES AT PWLLHELI MARINA FOR 1998 SEASON**

BEMA and BMIF members, dealer for Autohelm, B&G, Cetrek, ICOM, Kelvin Hughes, Marconi, Nasa, Navico, Navstar, Neco, Seafarer, Shipmate, Stowe, Racal-Decca, V-Tronix, Ampro, Walker. Equipment supplied installed and serviced.

COMPASS ADJUSTERS & MANUFACTURERS

B COOKE & SON LTD
Kingston Observatory, 58-59
Market Place, Hull HU1 1RH.
Tel (01482) 223454
Books and Charts. DTp Certificated.

JOHN LILLEY & GILLIE LTD
Clive Street, North Shields,
Tyne & Wear NE29 6LF.
Tel 0191-257 2217
Books and Charts. DTp Certificated.

KELVIN HUGHES
CHARTS & MARITIME SUPPLIES
New North Road,
Hainault, Ilford,
Essex IG6 2UR.
Tel 0181-500 6166
Books and charts. DTp Certificated.

KELVIN HUGHES OBSERVATOR
Nieuwe Longowed 41, 3199 DC, Hoogliet,
The Netherlands.
Book and charts. DTp Certificated.

MARINE INSTRUMENTS
The Bosun's Locker,
Upton Slip, Falmouth,
Cornwall TR11 3DQ.
Tel (01326) 312414
Books and charts. DTp Certificated.

MARTIN & CO
Oude Leewenrui 37, Antwerp 2000,
Germany.
Books and charts. DTp Certificated.

R J MUIR
22 Seymour Close, Chandlers Ford,
Eastleigh, Southampton SO5 2JE.
Tel (01703) 261042
Books and Charts. DTp Certificated.

W F PRICE & CO LTD
Northpoint House, Wapping Wharf,
Bristol BS1 6UD.
Tel 0117-929 2229
Books and charts. DTp Certificated.

S I R S NAVIGATION LTD
186a Milton Road, Swanscombe,
Kent DA10 0LX.
Tel (01322) 383672
Books and Charts. DTp Certificated.

SEATH INSTRUMENTS (1992) LTD
Unit 30, Colville Road Works,
Colville Road, Lowestoft NR33 9QS.
Tel (01502) 573811
Books and charts. DTp Certificated.

SEVERNSIDE CONSULTANTS
Deco Court, South View Business Park,
Staple Hill, Bristol BS16 5PJ.
Tel 0117-956 8844
Books and charts. DTp Certificated.

THOMAS GUNN NAVIGATION SERVICES
Anchor House, 62 Regents Quay,
Aberdeen AB11 5AR.
Tel (01224) 595045
Books and charts. DTp Certificated.

COMPUTERS & SOFTWARE

DOLPHIN MARITIME SOFTWARE LTD
713 Cameron House, White Cross,
Lancaster LA1 4XQ.
Tel/Fax (01524) 841946
e-mail: 100417.744@compuserve.com
Marine computer programs for IBM PC, Psion and Sharp pocket computers. Specialists in navigation, tidal prediction and other programs for both yachting and commercial uses.

MERIDIAN CHARTWARE LTD
Maggs House, 78 Queens Road,
Clifton, Bristol BS8 1QX.
Tel 0117-907 3327 Fax 0117-907 7548
e-mail: meridian@dial.pipex.com
http://dspace.dial.pipex.com/meridian/
Designers and suppliers of quality marine software. Electronic charting systems for the leisure user to the professional mariner, using the British Admiralty Raster Chart Service (ARCS). Dedicated Win96/NT mariner-friendly systems. Official ARCS chart agent. Suppliers of complete hardware/software packages.

PROSSER SCIENTIFIC INSTRUMENTS LTD
Lady Lane Industrial Estate, Hadleigh,
Ipswich, Suffolk IP7 6BQ.
Tel (01473) 823005 Fax (01473) 824095
Manufacturers of a range of marine instruments, including the WEATHERTREND digital barometer, with full 24-hour history, the unique TIDECLOCK tidal data predictor and tidal software for the PSION 3 series.

SOFTWAVE
4 Aranmor House, Kingston Hill,
Kingston, Surrey KT2 7LY.
Tel 0181-549 0650 Fax 0181-546 1090
www.softwave.co.uk
Specialist supplier of PC based electronic
navigation systems and high quality
vectorized charts drawn from Admiralty
and other official sources. Also tide
computing, simulations, hardware and on-
board installations. *See advertisement first
right hand page in this volume.*

CORPORATE YACHT OWNERSHIP

WILDE MARINE SERVICES LTD
PO Box 112, Pollet House, Lower Pollet,
St Peter Port, Guernsey,
Channel Islands GY1 4EA.
Tel (01481) 725840 Fax (01481) 711156
British yacht registration, corporate yacht
ownership and management, marine
insurance, crew placement and management. Wilde Marine Services (previously
known as International Marine Services)
aims to provide a personal and individual
service to its clients.

CORRESPONDENT COURSES

**NATIONAL MARINE
CORRESPONDENCE SCHOOL**
30 Woodside Business Park, Shore Rd,
Birkenhead, Merseyside L41 1EL
Tel/Fax 0151-647 6777
e-mail: sail@nmcs.u-net.com
www.nmcs.u-net.com
The UK's leading correspondence school
with courses from basic navigation to ocean
cruising including RYA courses Day Skipper,
Coastal Skipper/Yachtmaster and Yachtmaster Ocean. RYA accredited for courses
in power and sail, UK and overseas.

DECK EQUIPMENT

GRIFF CHAINS LTD
Quarry Road, Dudley Wood, Dudley,
West Midlands DY2 0ED.
Tel (01384) 569415 Fax (01384) 410580
Manufacturers of mooring systems and
equipment. For over 150 years Griff Chains
has been synonymous with chain, anchor
and chain component development for
marine applications. Quality chains to meet
all markets.

**HARKEN - DISTRIBUTED BY SIMPSON
LAWRENCE**
218-228 Edmiston Drive,
Glasgow G51 2YT.
Tel 0141-427 5331/8 Fax 0141-427 5419
e-mail: info@simpson-lawrence.co.uk
Distributors of **Harken** deck hardware, ball

bearing blocks in all sizes from micros to
maxis, jib reefing and furling systems, from
dinghies to 150 footers, winches, backstay
tensioners, power sheet jammers and deck
shoes. We also distribute **Head Foil** plastic
luff groove systems, and **Edson** steering
and pump-out systems.

LEWMAR MARINE LTD
Southmoor Lane, Havant,
Hampshire PO9 1JJ.
Tel (01705) 471841 Fax (01705) 476043
Manufacturers of winches, windlasses,
hatches, hardware, hydraulics and marine
thrusters for boats ranging in size from 25'
to 300' LOA.

SEAGLAZE MARINE WINDOWS LTD
Wendover Road, Rackheath, Norwich,
Norfolk NR13 6LH.
Tel (01603) 720745 Fax (01603) 721770
Manufacturers of high quality windows,
doors and hatches for the marine industry.
Exclusive suppliers to the RNLI. We will
supply a one-off window/door or a whole
set for your boat, no matter what shape,
size or colour. We also offer a refurbishment
service.

DIESEL MARINE FUEL ADDITIVES

CHICK'S MARINE LTD/VOLVO PENTA
Collings Road, St Peter Port, Guernsey,
Channel Islands GY1 1FL.
Tel (01481) 723716 Fax (01481) 713632
Distributor of diesel fuel biocide used to
treat and protect contamination in fuel tanks
where an algae (bug) is present. Most
owners do not realise what the problem is,
loss of power, blocked fuel filter, exhaust
smoking, resulting in expensive repairs to
injectors - fuel pump - or complete engine
overhaul. Marine engineers, engines,
spares, service - VAT free. Honda outboards,
pumps and generators. Volvo Penta
specialists.

DIVING TUITION

OCEAN LEISURE LTD
11-14 Northumberland Avenue,
London WC2N 5AQ.
Tel 0171-930 5050 Fax 0171-930 3032
Complete range of sailing clothing, swim
and beachwear stocked all year round.
Chandlery includes marine electronic
equipment, marine antiques, books and
charts. Also canoeing, underwater
photography, diving and waterskiing
specialists. Learn to scuba dive.

ELECTRICAL & ELECTRONIC ENGINEERS/REPAIRS

LANGNEY MARINE SERVICES LTD - LMS
Sovereign Harbour Marina,
Pevensey Bay Road, Eastbourne,
East Sussex BN23 6JH.
Tel (01323) 470244 Fax (01323) 470255
We offer a complete service to the boat
owner offering repairs on all types of eng-
ines, GRP, steel, wood, electronics, rigging,
cleaning, etc. We are also contractors to the
RNLI.

MARINE RADIO SERVICES LTD
3 Brook Lane Business Centre,
Brook Lane North, Brentford,
Middlesex TW8 0QY.
Tel/Fax 0181-568 6884
Service and repair of marine radio, radar
and electronic equipment.

OCEAN MARINE INTERNATIONAL - OMI
Mayflower International Marina,
Plymouth, Devon PL1 4LS.
Tel (01752) 500121 Fax (01752) 500221
*Queen Anne's Battery Marina, Plymouth,
Devon PL1 0LP*
Tel (01752) 222688
Sales, service, supply and installation of
marine electronic equipment. South west
agents for Autohelm, Raytheon, Cetrek,
Garmin and other leading manufacturers.

REGIS ELECTRONICS LTD
Regis House, Quay Hill, Lymington,
Hampshire SO41 3AR.
Tel (01590) 679251/679176
Fax (01590) 679910
(also at Cowes, Southampton and
Chichester). Sales, service and installation
of marine electronic equipment. Leading
south coast agents for AUTOHELM,
FURUNO, RAYTHEON, CETREK, STOWE,
ROBERTSON, A.P. NAVIGATOR, GARMIN,
KELVIN HUGHES and other manufacturers
of quality marine electronic equipment.
Competitively priced quotations (including
owner familiarisation and sea trials)
forwarded by return of post.

ROWLANDS MARINE ELECTRONICS LTD
Unit 4 Glandon Industrial Estate,
Pwllheli, Gwynedd LL53 5YT.
Tel/Fax (01758) 613193
**EXPECTED TO BE SETTLED IN OUR
NEW PREMISES AT PWLLHELI
MARINA FOR 1998 SEASON**
BEMA and BMIF members, dealer for
Autohelm, B&G, Cetrek, ICOM, Kelvin
Hughes, Marconi, Nasa, Navico, Navstar,
Neco, Seafarer, Shipmate, Stowe, Racal-
Decca, V-Tronix, Ampro, Walker. Equipment
supplied installed and serviced.

SWALE MARINE (ELECTRICAL)
The Old Stable, North Road,
Queenborough, Kent ME11 5EH.
Tel (01795) 580930 Fax (01795) 667280
For all your electrical and electronic needs.
Authorised agents for: Furuno, Autohelm,
Raytheon and most major manufacturers.
Fight crime with Harbourguard monitored
security: Medway and Swale coverage -
Boatmark registration centre.

USE THESE PAGES ⚓ FOR ALL YOUR MARINE SERVICES AND SUPPLIES

VOLVO PENTA LTD
Otterspool Way, Watford,
Hertfordshire WD2 8HW.
Tel (01923) 28544
Volvo Penta's leading marine power-petrol
and diesel for leisurecraft and workboats -
is supported by an extensive network of
parts and service dealers.

FABRICATIONS & REPAIRS

AILSA-TROON LTD
Harbour Road, Troon,
Ayrshire KA10 6DN.
Tel (01292) 311311 Fax (01292) 317613
Boatyard with full repair and maintenance
facilities for GRP, steel, aluminium, timber
and inflatable craft. Ship repair, fabrication
and new building work also undertaken in
Ailsa's extensive 15 acre covered facilities.

FELTON MARINE ENGINEERING
The Boatyard,
Brighton Marina,
East Sussex BN2 5UF.
Tel (01273) 601779 Fax (01273) 673258
Main Volvo Penta marine dealer. New
engines, sales and service. Genuine Volvo
Penta parts and accessories. Stainless steel
fabrication workshop. Eberspacher heaters,
sales and service centre.

FIRST AID

HOYLAKE SAILING SCHOOL
43a Market Street, Hoylake,
Wirral L47 2BG.
Tel 0151-632 4664 Fax 0151-632 4776
RYA recognised shorebased teaching
establishment offering a wide range of
courses including Day Skipper to
Yachtmaster Ocean, VHF and First Aid. Day,
evening or intensive classes. Pratical
courses by arrangement. Books, charts and
gifts available.

RESCUE EMERGENCY CARE
Hyfrydle, Capel Curig,
Betws-y-Coed,
Gwynedd LL24 0EU.
Tel/Fax (01690) 720400
Our courses meet the requirements for
organisations which require an individual
to hold an H and SE First Aid Certificate,
and our instructors can provide the full REC
training programme for first aid at sea. If
you would like to learn how to handle
emergency situations, we have a programme to suit your needs. On-site or off-
site courses available.

START POINT SAILING
Cover House, 113 Bewdley Road,
Kidderminster,
Worcestershire DY11 6RX.
Tel (01562) 748635 Fax (01562) 746089
Small craft training and tuition - RYA
practical courses, competent crew, day
skipper, yachtmaster, shorebased navi-
gation and pilotage, diesel engine, sea
survival, VHF first aid courses. Competitive
yacht charter from Dartmouth and
Plymouth. Beginners and families welcome.

FLAGS, FLAGSTAFFS & PENNANTS

A 1 PLYMOL FLAGSTAFF COMPANY
Carr Lane Industrial Estate, Hoylake,
Wirral, Merseyside L47 4AY.
Tel 0151-632 1354 Fax 0151-632 4912
Plymol manufacture a range of fibreglass
flagstaffs from 3m to 18m. They can be
supplied complete with fittings for ground
or wall mounting. Plymol also supply all
National flags, house flags, pvc display
banners and bunting.

JOSEPH P LAMB & SONS
Maritime Building
(opposite Albert Dock),
Wapping, Liverpool L1 8DQ.
Tel 0151-709 4861 Fax 0151-709 2786
Situated in the centre of Liverpool, J P
Lamb have provided a service to world
shipping for over 200 years. All chandlery
supplies, clothing, rope, paint and flags are
available. Full sailmaking and repairs. Kemp
Retail Outlet for spars and rigging. Open
Mon to Fri 8am to 5.30pm - Sat 9am to
12.30pm.

SARNIA FLAGS
8 Belmont Road, St Peter Port,
Guernsey, Channel Islands GY1 1PY.
Tel (01481) 725995
Flags and pennants made to order. National
flags, house, club and battle flags, and
burgees made to order. Any size, shape or
design. Prices on request.

GENERAL MAINTENANCE & REPAIR

PETER DE JERSEY
La Contree de Saint, Saints Road,
St Martin, Guernsey,
Channel Islands GY4 6JA.
Tel (01481) 36858
Boat maintenance and repairs. 24-hour
service 01481 36858.

GENERAL MARINE EQUIPMENT

A B MARINE LTD
Castle Walk, St Peter Port,
Guernsey, Channel Islands GY1 1AU.
Tel (01481) 722378 (Fax 01481) 711080
We specialise in safety and survival
equipment and are a DoT approved service
station for liferafts including R.F.D.,
Beaufort/Dunlop, Zodiac, Plastimo and
Lifeguard. We also carry a full range of new
liferafts, dinghies and lifejackets, and are
agents for Bukh marine engines.

AQUA-MARINE
MANUFACTURING (UK) LTD
216 Fair Oak Road, Bishopstoke,
Eastleigh, Hampshire SO50 8NJ.
Tel (01703) 694949 Fax (01703) 601381
Sales Fax (01703) 601188
e-mail: sales@aqua-marine.co.uk.
Manufacturer and distributor of chandlery,
including: Engel refrigeration, Dutton-
Lainson winches, Anchor fenders, Rule
pumps, Aquaflow water systems, SeaStar

steering and controls, Skyblazer flares.
Admiralty small craft charts, Aquameter
compasses, RWO and Holt fittings,
Danforth anchors, Aqua-Signal lights,
Techimpex cookers

C T PLATON LTD
Jays Close, Viables,
Basingstoke,
Hampshire RG22 4BS.
Tel (01256) 358258 Fax (01256) 355015
Manufacturers of Harwood water separators
and filters to remove harmful water from
diesel fuel. Also a range of cold starting aids
for diesel engines and RO Watermakers.
Contact: M Barcy

LEWMAR MARINE LTD
Southmoor Lane, Havant,
Hampshire PO9 1JJ.
Tel (01705) 471841 Fax (01705) 476043
Manufacturers of winches, windlasses,
hatches, hardware, hydraulics and marine
thrusters for boats ranging in size from 25'
to 300' LOA.

SAIL NORTHWEST
45 Ingrow Lane,
Keighley,
West Yorkshire BD22 7BU.
Tel/Fax (01535) 602133
Sail Northwest offers yacht charter,
skippered charter, and management from
Maryport's marina, north Cumbria (40
minutes from M62, Lake District). We also
manufacture customised fused switch
panels, and refurbishment, including steps,
tables and laminated tillers.

SIMPSON LAWRENCE LTD
218-228 Edmiston Drive,
Glasgow G51 2YT.
Tel 0141-427 5331 Fax 0141-427 5419
e-mail: info@simpson-lawrence.co.uk
Simpson Lawrence are manufacturers and
the UK's largest wholesale distributor of
quality marine equipment.

VETUS DEN OUDEN LTD
38 South Hants Industrial Park,
Totton, Southampton,
Hampshire SO40 3SA.
Tel (01703) 861033 Fax (01703) 663142
Suppliers of marine diesel equipment,
exhaust systems, steering systems, bow
propellers, propellers and shafts, hatches,
portlights, windows, electronic instruments,
batteries, ventilators, windlasses, water and
fuel tanks, chandlery items and much much
more.

WORCESTER YACHT CHANDLERS LTD
Unit 7, 75 Waterworks Road,
Barbourne,
Worcester WR1 3EZ.
Tel (01905) 22522 & 27949
Chandlery, paints, ropes, cables, chain,
clothing, footwear, shackles, books, bottled
gas, anti-foul, fastenings, oakam, fenders.
Hard storage, crane, haulage, engine
service, oils, navigation aids, buoyancy aids,
life jackets, distress flares, **small boat hire.**

GENERATORS

GENACIS
Power House, Gordon Road, Winchester, Hampshire SO23 7DD.
Tel (01962) 841828 Fax (01962) 841834
Dolphin water cooled diesel generators, 3 - 16 KVA.

GLASS FIBRE - MARINE SPECIALISTS

ROSDEN GLASS FIBRE
La Rue Durell, La Collette, St Helier, Jersey JE2 3NB.
Tel (01534) 625418 Fax (01534) 625419
Specialists in all types of glass fibre marine works, structural repairs, alterations, re-flow coating, GEL coat work, Blakes Osmosis Treatment Centre. Manufacturers of fuel tanks, bathing platforms and boat builders. General refurbishment and polishing. A division of Precision Plastics (Jersey) Ltd.

GRAPHICS

WET & WILD GRAPHICS
7 Firefly Road, Hamble Point Marina, Hamble, Southampton, Hampshire SO31 4NB.
Tel (01703) 458332 Fax (01703) 456830
Supply and application of vinyl graphics, signboards, banners and flags. Specialist materials for sails and spinnakers. Brochure available for mail order boat names. Deadlines never a problem!!!

HARBOURS

ALBERT DOCK
Albert Dock Co., 7 The Colonnades, Albert Dock, Liverpool L3 4AA.
Tel 0151-708 7334 Fax 0151-708 0929
The world-famous Albert Dock welcomes vessels for short or long-term visits. Maximum length 55m. Concessionary rates (details on application). Access by prior agreement.

BALTIC WHARF
WATER LEISURE CENTRE
Bristol Harbour, Underfall Yard, Bristol BS1 6XG.
Tel 0117-929 7608 Fax 0117-929 4454
Tuition: 0117-952 5202
Sailing school and centre, with qualified instruction in most watersports. Also moorings available throughout the Bristol harbour for all types of leisurecraft.

BEAULIEU RIVER MANAGEMENT LTD
Harbour Master's Office, Bucklers Hard Yacht Harbour, Beaulieu, Hampshire SO42 7XB.
Tel (01590) 616200 Fax (01590) 616211
110-berth yacht harbour (pontoon berths), fully serviced with back-up facilities of historic Bucklers Hard village. Agamemnon boatyard - 290 swinging moorings let on annual basis. Visiting craft welcome. Capacity 100+ pile/pontoon.

CHELSEA HARBOUR LTD
108 The Chambers, Chelsea Harbour, London SW10 0XF.
Tel 0171-351 4433 Fax 0171-352 7868
A tranquil and intimate marina of 55 berths close to the heart of the west end of London. 5-Star hotel, restaurants and bars. Overnight pontoon and amenities. 24-hour security patrols and CCTV.

CLYDE MARINA - ARDROSSAN
The Harbour, Ardrossan, Ayrshire KA22 8DB.
Tel (01294) 607077 Fax (01294) 607076
Located on the north Ayrshire coast, deep draught harbour, minimum depth 5m accommodating vessels to 100' alongside quay, and to 60' on full service pontoons. 20-ton hoist, undercover storage, diesel fuel, most facilities and services. Ancasta brokerage, also Beneteau, Nimbus, SeaRay and Marlin RIB dealers.

DUCHY OF CORNWALL
Harbour Office, St Mary's, Isles of Scilly, Cornwall TR21 0HU.
Tel/Fax (01720) 422768
Port of St Mary's, Isles of Scilly - 38 visitor moorings. New visitor centre, hot showers, toilets, launching facilities, winter storage, security lockers, fuel and fresh water. 5 minutes from town centre. Ferry terminal and airport close by. Contact Harbour Master for more information.

HAFAN PWLLHELI
Glan Don, Pwllheli, Gwynedd LL53 5YT.
Tel (01758) 701219 Fax (01758) 701443
Hafan Pwllheli has over 400 pontoon berths and offers access at virtually all states of the tide. Ashore, its modern purpose-built facilities include luxury toilets, showers, landerette, a secure boat park for winter storage, 40-ton travel hoist, mobile crane and plenty of space for car parking. Open 24-hours a day, 7 days a week.

JERSEY HARBOURS
Harbour Office, Weighbridge, St Helier, Jersey JE4 9XF.
Tel (01534) 885588 Fax (01534) 885599
A warm welcome to visiting yachtsmen! Elizabeth Marina opens in April 1998. Berths available on lease - £184.86 per metre. St Helier marina continues to cater for visitng yachts. Both marinas offer excellent facilities.

LANGSTONE HARBOUR BOARD
Ferry Road, Hayling Island, Hampshire PO11 0DG.
Tel (01705) 463419 Fax (01705) 467144
All boatyard facilities. Deep water and tidal moorings available. Water, electricity and diesel. Summer and winter storage. Public slipways. 6-ton crane. Landrover vessel and trailer recovery services.

MARINE ACTIVITIES CENTRE
North Dock Marina, Sunderland SR6 0PW.
Tel 0191-514 4721 Fax 0191-514 1847
New in 1996 with 85 fully serviced pontoon berths and 108 chain moorings accessible on all tides. Diesel fuel, 24-hour security and close circuit TV surviellance. New marina activities centre with excellent toilets and shower facilities.

THE MAYFLOWER
INTERNATIONAL MARINA
Ocean Quay, Richmond Walk, Plymouth, Devon PL1 4LS.
Tel (01752) 556633 Fax (01752) 606896
Plymouth's only Five-Gold Anchor marina. Known for its extensive facilities, courtesy and security. Owned by berth holders and run to a very high standard.

PETERHEAD BAY AUTHORITY
Bath House, Bath Street, Peterhead AB42 1DX.
Tel (01779) 474020 Fax (01779) 475712
Contact: Stephen Paterson. Peterhead Bay Marina offers fully serviced pontoon berthing for local and visiting boat owners. Local companies provide a comprehensive range of supporting services. Ideal stopover for vessels heading to/from Scandinavia or the Caledonian canal.

PORT DINORWIC MARINA
Watkin Jones (Holdings) Ltd, Port Dinorwic, Gwynedd LL56 4JN.
Tel (01248) 671500 Fax (01248) 671252
180-berths in lock basin or tidal pontoon basin. Toilets, showers and restaurant facilities. Visitors always welcome. Call channel 37 (M).

PORT OF TRURO
Harbour Office, Town Quay, Truro, Cornwall.
Tel (01872) 272130 Fax (01872) 225346
Facilities for the yachtsman include visitor pontoons located at Turnaware Bar, Ruan Creek and Boscawen Park. Visitor moorings at Woodbury. Quay facilities at Truro with free showers and toilets. Chemical toilet disposal, fresh water and garbage disposal.

RAMSGATE ROYAL HARBOUR MARINA
Harbour Office, Military Road, Ramsgate, Kent CT11 9LQ.
Tel (01843) 592277 Fax (01843) 590941
Ramsgate Royal Harbour is situated on the south east coast, making an ideal base for crossing to the Continent. 24-hour access to finger pontoons. Comprehensive security systems. Amenities: Launderette, repairs, slipways, boatpark. Competitive rates for permanent berths and discount for visitors' group bookings.

SUFFOLK YACHT HARBOUR LTD
Levington, Ipswich, Suffolk IP10 0LN.
Tel (01473) 659240 Fax (01473) 659632
420-berths - access at all states of tide (dredged to 2.5 metres at LW Springs). Boat hoist facilities up to 60 tons. Full boatyard services, chandlery, gas, diesel, petrol, engineering, sailmaking, electronics. Club house and restaurant.

WEYMOUTH OLD HARBOUR
Weymouth & Portland Borough Council,
Borough Engineers Department,
Municipal Offices,
North Quay, Weymouth, Dorset DT4 8TA.
Tel (01305) 206363/206423
Fax (01305) 206276
e-mail: cflowers@weymouth.gov.uk
http://www.weymouth.gov.uk/
marine.htm
Access at all stages of tide. Visitor berths in the centre of prime tourist resort with shops, restaurants and night life all at hand. Diesel fuelling from pontoon or tanker. Chandlery and repair facilities available.

HYDRAULIC MARINE EQUIPMENT

VOSPER THORNYCROFT
MARINE PRODUCTS LTD
Northarbour Road, Cosham,
Hampshire PO6 3TL.
Tel (01705) 383311 Fax (01705) 325133
Manufacturer and supplier of Fin stabilizers, Transverse thrusters and Vospower water jets to the luxury, commercial and naval markets worldwide.

INLAND WATERWAYS

BRITISH WATERWAYS
& THE ENVIRONMENT AGENCY
CANAL & RIVER LINE
Tel (0891) 546 555
Our canals and rivers provide: marinas, moorings, berthing, boatyard services and relaxing, picturesque waters for cruising. Find out more from **Canal and River Line** (50p minute peak rate at 45p minute other times). See Coastal and Waterways Directory, areas 1-11.

INSTRUMENTATION & POSITION FIXING

W & H CHINA
Howley Properties Ltd,
PO Box 149,
Warrington WA1 2DW.
Tel (01925) 634621 Fax (01925) 418009
Manufacturer of China chart dividers.

DIVERSE YACHT SERVICES
Unit 12, Hamble Yacht Services,
Port Hamble, Hamble,
Hampshire SO31 4NN.
Tel (01703) 453399 Fax (01703) 455288
Marine electronics and electrics. Supplied and installed. Specialists in racing yachts. Suppliers of 'Loadsense' Loadcells for marine applications.

GREENHAM MARINE
King's Saltern Road, Lymington,
Hampshire SO41 9QD.
Tel (01590) 671144 Fax (01590) 679517
Greenham Marine can offer yachtsmen one of the most comprehensive selections of marine electronic equipment currently available. Also at Poole/Weymouth 01202 676363 and Emsworth/Chichester 01243 378314.

SOFTWAVE
4 Aranmor House,
Kingston Hill, Kingston,
Surrey KT2 7LY.
Tel 0181-549 0650 Fax 0181-546 1090
www.softwave.co.uk Specialist supplier of PC based electronic navigation systems and high quality vectorized charts drawn from Admiralty and other official sources. Also tide computing, simulations, hard ware and on-board installations. *See advertisement first right hand page in this volume.*

SWALE MARINE (ELECTRICAL)
The Old Stable,
North Road, Queenborough,
Kent ME11 5EH.
Tel (01795) 580930 Fax (01795) 667280
For all your electrical and electronic needs. Authorised agents for: Furuno, Autohelm, Raytheon and most major manufacturers. Fight crime with Harbourguard monitored security: Medway and Swale coverage - Boatmark registration centre.

INSURANCE & FINANCE

BISHOP SKINNER INTERNATIONAL
INSURANCE BROKERS
Oakley Crescent, City Road,
London EC1V 1NU.
Tel 0171-566 5800 Fax 0171-608 2171
Dinghy Insurance - As insurance brokers to the RYA we offer cover for accidental damage, racing risks, 30-days European extension, discounts for dinghy instructors, third party indemnity of £2,000,000, no claim bonus (transferable) and first class security. Immediate quotation and instant cover all at competitive rates.

BOWRING MARSH & McLENNAN LTD
Yacht Division,
Havelock Chambers,
Queens Terrace,
Southampton, Hampshire SO14 3PP.
Tel (01703) 318300 Fax (01703) 318391
A member of the largest insurance broking firm in the world with associated offices in Antibes and Fort Lauderdale. Specialists in yacht insurance for craft cruising Mediterranean, Caribbean and US waters.

C CLAIMS (Marine Loss Adjusters)
PO Box 8, Romford, Essex RM4 1UY.
Tel Helpline: 0181-502 6999
Fax 0181-500 1005
C Claims are specialist marine and small craft claims adjusters with a central record of stolen vessels and equipment. They have provided a unique service to marine insurers since 1979 and welcome trade and private enquiries. They are represented throughout the world.

CRAVEN HODGSON ASSOCIATES
Suite 15, 30-38 Dock Street,
Leeds LS10 1JF.
Tel 0113-243 8443
As an independent intermediary, we are in a position to advise you in relation to all major marine insurers and consequently act as your agent.

DESMOND CHEERS & PARTNERS
44 High Street, Hampton Hill,
Middlesex TW12 1PD.
Tel 0181-943 5333 Fax 0181-943 5444
Marine insurance specialists with over 30 years' experience in arranging tailor-made policies through leading marine underwriters. For all your insurance enquiries for yachts, motorcruisers and speedboats call Tim Cheers or Daphne Bamberger.

GENERAL ACCIDENT FIRE & LIFE
ASSURANCE CORPORATION PLC
Head Office: Pitheavlis, Perth PH2 0NH.
Tel (01738) 621202 Fax (01738) 621843
Pleasurecraft insurance for small craft, yachts and motor boats. Contact your local GA office for details of our Sailplan policies.

GUARDIAN INSURANCE LTD
Head Office: Civic Drive, Ipswich,
Suffolk IP1 2AN.
Tel (01473) 212422 Fax (01473) 210035
A member of Guardian Royal Exchange Group. Marine insurers since 1720. Member of ABI and IOB. Competitive insurance for dinghies, yachts and motorcruisers. Offices throughout UK including Belfast, Glasgow, Cardiff, Leeds, Manchester, Birmingham, Southampton and Bristol.

KENDALL BECKER LTD
Kendalls, West Bracklesham,
Bracklesham Bay, Chichester,
Sussex PO20 8PH.
Tel (01243) 672142 Fax (01243) 672068
Marine insurance specialists for yachts and motor cruisers throughout the world. Vessels over 20 years old a speciality (surveys not required). Immediate quotes and cover. Call us now.

LOMBARD GENERAL INSURANCE CO LTD
Lombard House, 182 High Street,
Tonbridge, Kent TN9 1BY.
Tel (01732) 376317 Fax (01732) 369501
One of the UK's largest specialist yacht underwriters and risk carriers. For full details of the range of insurance products available for all types of pleasurecraft, please contact your local marine insurance broker or intermediary.

NORTHERN STAR INSURANCE CO LTD
London Road, Gloucester GL1 3NS.
Tel (01452) 393000
Yacht Department Direct Line:
(01452) 393109.
Founded over four decades ago and now part of the worldwide Generali Group, Northern Star underwrites most classes of insurance but specialises in insurances for homeworkers, pleasurecraft, holiday and travel, property owners and householders.

PANTAENIUS UK LTD
Registered Insurance Broker:
Marine Building Victoria Wharf,
Plymouth, Devon PL4 0RF.
Tel (01752) 223656 Fax (01752) 223637
Head Office: Cremon 32.20457 Hamburg, Germany. Tel: +49 40 370 910 Fax +49 40 3709 1109. Pantaenius is one of Europe's largest yacht insurance brokers and covers yachts sailing under more than 35 different flags in all seven seas.

SHAMROCK CHANDLERY
Shamrock Quay, William Street,
Northam, Southampton,
Hampshire S014 5QL.
Tel (01703) 632725 Fax (01703) 225611
Situated on Shamrock Quay, a busy working yard with a pub, restaurant and boutiques. Shamrock Chandlery is renowned for extensive quality stocks and service and is widely used by both the trade and boat owners.

ST MARGARETS INSURANCES LTD
153-155 High Street, Penge,
London SE20 7DL.
Tel 0181-778 6161 Fax 0181-659 1968
Marine insurance. Over 25 years dedicated to insuring yachts and pleasurecraft. Many unique policies available only through St Margarets. Immediate quotations and cover available.

WARD & McKENZIE
12 Blackhill Road West, Holton Heath Trading Park, Poole, Dorset BH16 6LS.
Tel (01202) 624690 Fax (01202) 632251
National and International Marine Surveyors, Technical and Legal Consultants, offering a comprehensive service to boat owners and those seeking to acquire pleasure yachts. All aspects of vessel search, survey, purchase and ownership undertaken, including insurance surveys, finance and disputes.

YACHTLINE
100 Fenchurch Street, London EC3M 5JJ.
Tel 0171-680 1444 Fax 0171-680 1441
Yacht insurance.

LEGAL SERVICES

SHOOSMITHS & HARRISON
Russell House, 1550 Parkway,
Solent Business Park, Fareham,
Hampshire PO15 7AG.
Tel (01489) 881010/616928
Fax (01489) 881000
Marine solicitors advising on yacht sales, purchase and charter, insurance claims, disputes, debt recovery and general advice for the yachting community. Contact: Jonathan Hadley-Piggin.

WARD & McKENZIE
12 Blackhill Road West
Holton Heath Trading Park,
Poole, Dorset BH16 6LS.
Tel (01202) 624690 Fax (01202) 632251
National and International Marine Surveyors, Technical and Legal Consultants, offering a comprehensive service to boat owners and those seeking to acquire pleasure yachts. All aspects of vessel search, survey, purchase and ownership undertaken, including insurance surveys, finance and disputes.

LIFERAFTS/INFLATABLES/ REPAIRS

A B MARINE LTD
Castle Walk, St Peter Port,
Guernsey,
Channel Islands GY1 1AU.
Tel (01481) 722378 (Fax (01481) 711080
We specialise in safety and survival equipment and are a DoT approved service station for liferafts including R.F.D., Beaufort/Dunlop, Zodiac, Plastimo and Lifeguard. We also carry a full range of new liferafts, dinghies and lifejackets, and are agents for Bukh marine engines.

ADEC MARINE LTD
4 Masons Avenue, Croydon,
Surrey CR0 1EH.
Tel 0181-686 9717 Fax 0181-680 9912
Approved liferaft service station for south east UK. Additionally we hire and sell new rafts and sell a complete range of safety equipment for yachts including pyrotechnics, fire extinguishers, lifejackets, buoys and a buoyancy bag system.

PREMIUM LIFERAFT SERVICES
Liferaft House,
Burnham Business Park,
Burnham-on-Crouch,
Essex CM0 8TE.
Tel (01621) 784858 Fax (01621) 785934
Freephone 0800 243673
e-mail: 101624.574
Hire and sales of DoT and RORC approved liferafts. Long and short-term hire from 18 depots nationwide. Servicing and other safety equipment available.

MAIL ORDER

THE CARTOON GALLERY
(Wavelength Design)
37 Lower Street, Dartmouth,
Devon TQ6 9AN.
Tel/Fax (01803) 834466
Tel (01803) 834425 Evenings
Rick, the International Cartoonist specialises in hand coloured and personalised sailing cartoon prints (eg A3 £10). Commissions are carried out in Rick's Dartmouth gallery and studio. Prints available by mail order. Telephone or fax for details.

CHICK'S MARINE LTD/VOLVO PENTA
Collings Road,
St Peter Port,
Guernsey,
Channel Islands GY1 1FL.
Tel (01481) 723716 Fax (01481) 713632
Distributor of diesel fuel biocide used to treat and protect contamination in fuel tanks where an algae (bug) is present. Most owners do not realise what the problem is, loss of power, blocked fuel filter, exhaust smoking, resulting in expensive repairs to injectors - fuel pump - or complete engine overhaul. Marine engineers, engines, spares, service - VAT free. Honda outboards, pumps and generators. Volvo Penta specialists.

FORESIGHT OPTICAL
PO Box No 184, Banbury,
Oxfordshire OX16 9RT.
Tel (01295) 264365
Suppliers of marine binoculars, waterproof, nitrogen filled, also available with integral compass, suitable for all marine uses. Telescopes, night vision equipment, high power observation and gyro stabilised binoculars. Mail order service throughout the UK and Ireland.

THE HARBOUR BOOKSHOP
12 Fairfax Place, Dartmouth,
Devon TQ6 9AE.
Tel/Fax (01803) 832448
The general bookstore with a specialised nautical section: Nautical fiction, pilots and almanacs, log books and charts, seamanship, and RYA publications. Worlwide mail order. 10% discount on nautical stock on production of this voucher/advert.

JOHN LEWCOCK
(Maritime Bookseller)
6 Chewells Lane, Haddenham, Ely,
Cambridgeshire CB6 3SS.
Tel/Fax (01353) 741152
We buy and sell secondhand and antiquarian books on yachting, naval architecture, maritime history etc. Catalogues issued regularly complemented by an excellent mail order service. Please telephone or fax your order on 01353 741152.

KELVIN HUGHES
CHARTS & MARITIME SUPPLIES
Royal Crescent Road, Southampton,
Hampshire SO14 3NP.
Tel (01703) 634911 Fax (01703) 330014
Charts, books, chandlery, safety equipment and clothing. Liferaft hire and sales. Also in London with worldwide mail order service.

SARNIA FLAGS
8 Belmont Road, St Peter Port,
Guernsey, Channel Islands GY1 1PY.
Tel (01481) 725995
Flags and pennants made to order. National flags, house, club and battle flags, and burgees made to order. Any size, shape or design. Prices on request.

TODD CHART AGENCY LTD
4 Seacliff Road, The Harbour, Bangor,
Northern Ireland BT20 5EY.
Tel (01247) 466640 Fax (01247) 471070
International Admiralty Chart Agent, chart correction service and nautical booksellers. Stockist of navigation and chartroom instruments, binoculars, clocks etc. Mail order service available. Visa, Access and American Express accepted.

WARSASH NAUTICAL BOOKSHOP
6 Dibles Road, Warsash, Southampton,
Hampshire SO31 9HZ.
Tel (01489) 572384 Fax (01489) 885756
e-mail: alan@nauticalbooks.co.uk
http://www.nauticalbooks.co.uk
Nautical bookseller and chart agent. Callers and mail order. Free new and secondhand book lists. Credit cards taken. Publishers of the Bibliography of Nautical books.

WET & WILD GRAPHICS
7 Firefly Road, Hamble Point Marina,
Hamble, Southampton,
Hampshire SO31 4NB.
Tel (01703) 458332 Fax (01703) 456830
Supply and application of vinyl graphics, signboards, banners and flags. Specialist materials for sails and spinnakers. Brochure available for mail order boat names. Deadlines never a problem!!!

CREST NICHOLSON MARINAS LTD
- BRISTOL
Parklands, Stoke Gifford,
Bristol BS12 6QU.
Tel 0117-923 6466 Fax 0117-923 6508
Marina development management and consultancy.

MARINAS

ALBERT DOCK
Albert Dock Co., 7 The Colonnades,
Albert Dock, Liverpool L3 4AA.
Tel 0151-708 7334 Fax 0151-708 0929
The world-famous Albert Dock welcomes vessels for short or long-term visits. Maximum length 55m. Concessionary rates (details on application). Access by prior agreement.

ARDFERN YACHT CENTRE
Ardfern By Lochgilphead,
Argyll PA31 8QN.
Tel (01852) 500247/636
Fax (01852) 500624
Boatyard with full repair and maintenance facilities. Timber and GRP repairs, painting and engineering. Sheltered moorings and pontoon berthing. Winter storage,

chandlery, showers, fuel, Calor, brokerage, 20-ton boat hoist. Hotel, bars and restaurant.

W BATES & SON BOATBUILDERS LTD
Bridge Wharf, Chertsey,
Surrey KT16 8LG.
Tel (01932) 562255 Fax (01932) 571161
110-berth marina in quiet picturesque area and additional riverside moorings. Full facilities including electricity to most berths, toilets and showers. 12-ton crane and hard standing for winter storage. Always a welcome to visitors from our friendly staff. Sales office open seven days a week.

BEAUCETTE MARINA
Vale, Guernsey,
Channel Islands GY3 5BQ.
Tel (01481) 45000 Fax (01481) 47071
Situated on the north east coast, Beaucette is one of Europe's most charming deep water marinas. With 140 berths, the marina offers all the services and facilities you would expect. Beaucette is a PREMIER marina.

BEAULIEU RIVER MANAGEMENT LTD
Harbour Master's Office,
Bucklers Hard Yacht Harbour,
Beaulieu, Hampshire SO42 7XB.
Tel (01590) 616200 Fax (01590) 616211
110-berth yacht harbour (pontoon berths), fully serviced with back-up facilities of historic Bucklers Hard village. Agamemnon boatyard - 290 swinging moorings let on annual basis. Visiting craft welcome. Capacity 100+ pile/pontoon.

BIRDHAM SHIPYARD LTD
Birdham Pool, Chichester,
West Sussex PO20 7BG.
Tel (01243) 512310 Fax (01243) 513163
Quiet, picturesque marina in Chichester harbour. Moorings available for boats up to 55' overall and 5'6" draught. Chandlery and all boatyard services available. Visitors welcome.

BRIGHTON MARINA
Brighton Marina Village,
Brighton, East Sussex BN2 5UF.
Tel (01273) 819919 Fax (01273) 675082
Britain's largest marina (1600 pontoon berths) with marina village under development. TYHA Five-Gold Anchors. Full boatyard and shore facilities. Brokerage

and boat sales. Club racing throughout the year. Group visits, rallies welcome.

BRUNDALL BAY MARINA
Riverside Estate, Brundall, Norwich,
Norfolk NR13 5PN.
Tel (01603) 716606 Fax (01603) 715666
200-berth marina with full facilities.

BURGH CASTLE MARINA
Butt Lane, Burgh Castle, Norfolk,
Norwich NR31 9PZ.
Tel (01493) 780331
100 serviced pontoons and quay moorings accessible at all tides. Secure car and boat parking. Adjoining boatyard services, access to holiday park showers, laundry and heated pool. Riverside pub and shop. Complex open all year.

BURNHAM YACHT HARBOUR
MARINA LTD
Burnham Yacht Harbour,
Burnham-on-Crouch, Essex CM0 8BL.
Tel (01621) 782150 Fax (01621) 785848
The only Five-Gold Anchor marina in Essex. 350 fully serviced pontoon berths and 120 deep water swing moorings. Marina access at all states of tide with minimum 2.5m depth at low water. VHF Ch80.

CALEY MARINA
Canal Road, Inverness IV3 6NF.
Tel (01463) 236539 Fax (01463) 238323
Open 08.30 - 17.30. Berths: 50 Pontoons (visitors available). Facilities: Fuel, water, pump-out facilities, provisions (nearby shops), repair, cranage, secure storage afloat and ashore. Comprehensive chandlery, showers, workshop. Situated at eastern end of Caledonian canal above Muirtown locks. Access via sea locks 4 hours either side of high water.

CARLINGFORD MARINA CLUB
- IRELAND
Carlingford, Co Louth, Ireland.
Tel/Fax +353 42 73492
Superb location in beautiful setting close to historic village of Carlingford, our friendly marina provides a top class service for all boat users. Moorings, chandlery, slipway, 16-ton cranage, power, diesel, water, laundry, showers and coffee shop. Visitors always welcome. VHF Ch16 and 37 (M). *Sailing Holidays in Ireland - Only the Best.*

CARRICKFERGUS MARINA
Rodger's Quay, Carrickfergus,
Co Antrim,
Northern Ireland BT38 8BE.
Tel (01960) 366666 Fax (01960) 350505
300 fully serviced pontoon berths with full on-shore facilities (half a mile from town centre). Steeped in a wealth of historical legend. Carrickfergus has excellent restaurants, hotels, pubs, shops and a host of recreational leisure facilities.

CASTLEPARK MARINA - IRELAND
Kinsale,
Co Cork, Ireland.
Tel +353 21 774959 Fax +353 21 774958
100-berth fully serviced marina with restaurant, laundry, showers and toilets. Waterside hostel-type accommodation available. New restaurant catering for both breakfast and evening meals. Access at all stages of the tide. *Sailing Holidays in Ireland - Only the Best.*

CHELSEA HARBOUR LTD
108 The Chambers, Chelsea Harbour,
London SW10 0XF.
Tel 0171-351 4433 Fax 0171-352 7868
A tranquil and intimate marina of 55 berths close to the heart of the west end of London. 5-Star hotel, restaurants and bars. Overnight pontoon and amenities. 24-hour security patrols and CCTV.

CHICHESTER MARINA
Birdham, Chichester,
West Sussex PO20 7EJ.
Tel (01243) 512731 Fax (01243) 513472
Situated in the north east corner of Chichester harbour, Chichester Marina enjoys one of the most attractive locations in the country. With 1100 berths, Chichester offers a unique combination of service, facilities, security and friendliness, unparalleled in UK marinas. Chichester Marina is a PREMIER Marina.

CHISWICK QUAY MARINA LTD
Marina Office,
Chiswick Quay,
London W4 3UR.
Tel 0181-994 8743
Small, secluded, peaceful marina on tidal Thames at Chiswick. Slipway, marine engineers and electricians, power, water, toilets and sluice. Some residential moorings.

CLOVELLY BAY MARINA
The Quay, Turnchapel,
Plymouth,
Devon PL9 9TF.
Tel (01752) 404231 Fax (01752) 484177
Position: Southern side of cattewater, sheltered from prevailing winds by Mountbatten Peninsula. Open: All year, 24 hours. Radio: VHF Ch37 and 80. Callsign: Clovelly Bay. Berths: 180 berths, vessels up to 150', some fore and afts, visitors welcome. Facilities: electricity, water, 24-hour security, workshop, chandlery, brokerage, showers, laundry, diesel. Calor gas, payphone, refuse, water taxi, two local pubs. **New marina opens 1st April 1998.**

CLYDE MARINA - ARDROSSAN
The Harbour, Ardrossan,
Ayrshire KA22 8DB.
Tel (01294) 607077 Fax (01294) 607076
Located on the north Ayrshire coast, deep draught harbour, minimum depth 5m accommodating vessels to 100' alongside quay, and to 60' on full service pontoons. 20-ton hoist, undercover storage, diesel fuel, most facilities and services. Ancasta brokerage, also Beneteau, Nimbus, SeaRay and Marlin RIB dealers.

COLERAINE MARINA
64 Portstewart Road, Coleraine,
Co Londonderry,
Northern Ireland BT52 1RS.
Tel (01265) 44768
Wide range of facilities.

COWES YACHT HAVEN
Vectis Yard, High Street, Cowes,
Isle of Wight PO31 7BD.
Tel (01983) 299975 Fax (01983) 200332
Cowes Yacht Haven is the Solent's premier sailing event centre offering 200 fully serviced berths right in the heart of Cowes. Our improved facilities, capability and location ensures the perfect venue and profile for every kind of boating event.

CRAOBH MARINA
By Lochgilphead, Argyll PA31 8UD.
Tel (01852) 500222 Fax (01852) 500252
250-berth marina on Loch Shuna. Water, electricity, diesel and gas. Full boatyard services. Chandlery. Brokerage. Insurance. Shops, bar. 24-hour access. VHF Ch37 and 80 (M).

CREST NICHOLSON MARINAS LTD - BANGOR
Bangor Marina, Bangor, Co Down,
Northern Ireland BT20 5ED.
Tel (01247) 453297 Fax (01247) 453450
Situated on the south shore of Belfast Lough, Bangor is Ireland's largest and most comprehensive yachting facility. The marina is within convenient walking distance of all the town's amenities and may be accessed at any time of day or state of the tide.

CREST NICHOLSON MARINAS LTD - CONWY
Conwy Marina, Conwy Morfa,
Conwy, Gwynedd LL32 8EP.
Tel (01492) 593000 Fax (01492) 572111
Conwy Marina is ideally placed on the south shore of the Conwy Estuary. The marina is set within idyllic surroundings and has comprehensive facilities. Road access is extremely convenient, with the A55 dual carriageway passing close by.

CREST NICHOLSON MARINAS LTD - PENARTH
Portway Village, Penarth,
South Glamorgan CF64 1TQ.
Tel (01222) 705021 Fax (01222) 712170
Situated within the sheltered waters of Cardiff Bay the marina provides fully serviced, secure berths and wide ranging ancilliary services. Open 24-hours, year round, we can assure visitors of a warm welcome. Please apply for details.

CROSSHAVEN BOATYARD MARINA - IRELAND
Crosshaven, Co Cork, Ireland.
Tel +353 21 831161 Fax +353 21 831603
All facilities at this 100-berth marina situated 12 miles from Cork City and close to ferryport and airport. Travel lift, full repair and maintenance services, spray painting and approved International Gelshield centre. Storage undercover and outside for 250 boats. Brokerage. RNLI and Defence contractors. Sailing Holidays in Ireland - Only the Best.

DART MARINA
Sandquay, Dartmouth,
Devon TQ6 9PH.
Tel (01803) 833351 Fax (01803) 832307
High quality 110-berth marina on the fabulous river Dart, opposite the Dart Marina hotel. A superb situation with all amenities, 24-hour security, hotel and restaurant, showers, baths and laundry, fuel berth and a warm welcome to all visitors.

DARTHAVEN MARINA LTD
Brixham Road, Kingswear, Dartmouth,
Devon TQ6 0SG.
Tel (01803) 752242 Fax (01803) 752722
Marina Office: (01803) 752545
Chandlery: (01803) 752733
Fax: (01803) 752790
All types of repair facilities available. Fully trained staff. 30-ton mobile hoist available all states of tide. Extensive chandlery open 7 days a week. Agents for Autohelm/ Raytheon, Cetrek, B&G, Simrad Stowe, Navico, Simpson Lawrence, Sowester, International Paint, Webasto, Yanmar Main Agents, Volvo Penta ASW and Vetus sales and service. Visitors welcome. 24-hour engineering call-out service mobile numbers: 0860 873553 and 0467250787 for electronics

**DEAN & REDDYHOFF LTD
- HASLAR MARINA**
Haslar Road, Gosport,
Hampshire PO12 1NU.
Tel (01705) 601201 Fax (01705) 602201
Haslar marina is just inside the entrance of
Portsmouth harbour on the Gosport side.
Included in the 600 berths is a visitors' area
which is adjacent to a converted lightship
with bar facilities and excellent toilets and
showers.

HASLAR MARINA
Superb marina berths in Portsmouth
Harbour, at £200 per metre per
annum plus VAT
Tel: 01705 601201

WEYMOUTH MARINA
Opened in 1996, this marina is
proving to be popular with visitors.
Annual berthing at £185 per metre
per annum plus VAT.
Tel: 01305 767576

**DEAN & REDDYHOFF LTD
- WEYMOUTH MARINA**
70 Commercial Road, Weymouth,
Dorset DT4 8NA.
Tel (01305) 767576 Fax (01305) 767575
This new marina in the inner harbour of
Weymouth provides facilities for visitors
which are proving very popular. The marina
is right next to Weymouth's high street, and
the area has a multitude of pubs and
restaurants.

DINGLE MARINA - IRELAND
Harbour Master, Strand Street, Dingle,
Co Kerry, Ireland.
Tel/Fax +353 66 51629
Europe's most westerly marina on the
beautiful south west coast of Ireland in the
heart of the old sheltered fishing port of
Dingle. Visitor berths, fuel and water. Shops,
52 pubs and many restaurants with
traditional music and hospitality. Harbour
easily navigable day or night. Sailing
Holidays in Ireland - Only the Best.

ELMHAVEN MARINA
Rochester Road, Halling, Rochester,
Kent ME2 1AQ.
Tel (01634) 240489
Berths and moorings with excellent secure
facilities.

FALMOUTH MARINA
North Parade, Falmouth,
Cornwall TR11 2TD.
Tel (01326) 316620 Fax (01326) 313939
The most westerly marina in England.
Falmouth is an ideal starting point for a
cruise to the Channel Islands, Brittany or

the Scilly Isles. The marina offers fully
serviced permanent and visitor berths with
a professional and friendly service you would
expect from a PREMIER marina.

FARNDON HARBOUR MOORINGS LTD
North End,
Farndon, Newark,
Nottinghamshire NG24 3SX.
Tel (01636) 705483 Fax (01636) 701457
Marina with full services. Road haulage and
brokerage.

FENIT HARBOUR MARINA - IRELAND
Fenit,
Co Kerry, Ireland.
Tel/Fax +353 66 36231
A new marina opened in July 1997 with 104
berths for all sizes of boat up to 15m x 3m
draught, with one berth available for larger
vessels up to 30m. Access at all tides.
Minimum approach depth 5m. Facilities
include smartcard access, toilets, showers,
laundry and harbour office. Visitors are
welcome to use the superb clubhouse
facilities of the Tralee Sailing Club and
participate in races Tuesdays, Thursdays
and Saturdays. *Sailing Holidays in Ireland -
Only the Best.*

FIDDLERS FERRY YACHT HAVEN
Off Station Road, Penketh,
Warrington, Cheshire WA5 2UJ.
Tel (01925) 727519
Sheltered moorings upto 6'6" draught, 50'
long. Access through lock from river Mersey
1½ hours either side of high tide. Signed
from A652. Boatyard and lift-out facilities.
Annual rate per foot £8.25.

FOX'S MARINA IPSWICH LTD
The Strand, Wherstead,
Ipswich,
Suffolk IP2 8SA.
Tel (01473) 689111 Fax (01473) 601737
The most comprehensive boatyard facility
on the east coast. Extensive chandlery.
Marina access 24-hours. Two travel hoists
to 45 tons, 10 ton crane. Full electronics,
rigging, engineering, stainless steel
services. Specialists in osmosis and spray
painting.

HAFAN PWLLHELI
Glan Don, Pwllheli,
Gwynedd LL53 5YT.
Tel (01758) 701219 Fax (01758) 701443
Hafan Pwllheli has over 400 pontoon berths
and offers access at virtually all states of
the tide. Ashore, its modern purpose-built
facilities include luxury toilets, showers,
landerette, a secure boat park for winter
storage, 40-ton travel hoist, mobile crane
and plenty of space for car parking. Open
24-hours a day, 7 days a week.

HOWTH MARINA - IRELAND
Howth, Co Dublin, Ireland.
Tel +353 1 8392777 Fax +353 1 8392430
Modern marina in beautiful, sheltered
location. Fully serviced berths with every
facility and 24-hour security. Very popular
marina for traffic in the Irish Sea. Is available
at all states of the tide with extremely easy
access. Sailing Holidays in Ireland - Only
the Best.

HULL MARINA LTD
Warehouse
13, Kingston Street,
Hull HU1 2DQ.
Tel (01482) 613451 Fax (01482) 224148
Four-Anchor marina. Situated 5 minutes
from the centre of Hull and all national and
international transport systems. First class
leisure, boatyard and brokerage facilities.
4-Star hotel and quayside restaurants.
Professional and caring staff. Competitive
rates.

JERSEY HARBOURS
Harbour Office,
Weighbridge,
St Helier, Jersey JE4 9XF.
Tel (01534) 885588 Fax (01534) 885599
A warm welcome to visiting yachtsmen!
Elizabeth Marina opens in April 1998. Berths
available on lease - £184.86 per metre. St
Helier marina continues to cater for visitng
yachts. Both marinas offer excellent
facilities.

KILMORE QUAY MARINA - IRELAND
Kilmore Quay,
Co Wexford, Ireland.
Tel/Fax +353 53 29955
Kilmore Quay in the south east of Ireland
has a new marina with 20 pontoon visitor
berths. This friendly fishing port has
pleasant hotel facilities, pubs and
restaurants offering a traditional Irish
welcome. Rosslare ferryport is only 15 miles
away. Sailing Holidays in Ireland - Only the
Best.

KILRUSH CREEK MARINA - IRELAND
Kilrush,
Co Clare, Ireland.
Tel +353 65 52072 Fax +353 65 51692
Mobile +353 87 2313870
Kilrush Creek Marina on Ireland's beautiful
west coast, is a new marina with 120 fully
serviced berths with 24-hour access. The
marina has all shore facilities including a
modern boatyard with 45-ton hoist. It
adjoins the busy market town of Kilrush
which has every facility required by the
visiting yachtsman. Sailing Holidays in
Ireland - Only the best.

KINSALE YACHT CLUB MARINA
Kinsale,
Co Cork, Ireland.
Tel +353 21 772196 Fax +353 21 774426
Mobile +353 87 449471
Magnificent deep water yacht club marina
offering Kinsale hospitality to visiting
yachtsmen. Full facilities include berths up
to 20 metres, fresh water, electricity, diesel
on pier. Club bar and wealth of pubs and
restaurants in Kinsale. Enter Kinsale harbour
- lit at night - no restrictions.

KIP MARINA
The Yacht Harbour,
Inverkip,
Renfrewshire PA16 0AS.
Tel (01475) 521485 Fax (01475) 521298
Marina berths for vessels up to 65' LOA.
Full boatyard facilities including travel hoist,
crane, on-site engineers, GRP repairs etc.
Bar, restaurant, saunas, launderette and
chandlery.

LARGS YACHT HAVEN
Irvine Road, Largs,
Ayrshire KA30 8EZ.
Tel (01475) 675333 Fax (01475) 672245
Perfectly located 600-berth marina with full services afloat and ashore. 45-ton travel hoist operational 7 days; fuel (diesel and petrol); gas and ice on sale 24-hours. Bar, coffee shop, dive shop plus usual marine services.

LITTLEHAMPTON MARINA LTD
Ferry Road,
Littlehampton,
West Sussex BN17 5DS.
Tel (01903) 713553 Fax (01903) 732264
Only 2 miles upstream of harbour entrance, we have deep water pontoon berths with electricity and lighting. Showers, toilets, changing rooms, cafe, and floating pub. Petrol, marine diesel, slipway with tractor launch, recovery service, and storage compounds. 30 miles from Isle of Wight, 18 miles from Brighton and 14 miles of navigable river which flows through the historic town of Arundel. Good diving and fishing available.

LIVERPOOL MARINA
Coburg Dock,
Sefton Street,
Liverpool L3 4BP.
Tel 0151-709 0578/(2683 after 5pm)
Fax 0151-709 8731.
300-berth yacht harbour. All serviced pontoons. Tidal access HW ± 2½ hours approximately, depending on draught. 60-ton hoist, workshops, bar and restaurant, toilets and showers. City centre one mile. Open all year. Active yacht club and yacht brokerage.

LYMINGTON YACHT HAVEN
King's Saltern Road,
Lymington,
Hampshire SO4 9XY.
Tel (01590) 677071 Fax (01590) 678186
Perfectly situated at the mouth of the Lymington river giving instant access to the Western Solent. Full marina services, boatyard, brokerage, diesel, petrol and gas.

MALAHIDE MARINA VILLAGE - IRELAND
Malahide,
Co Dublin, Ireland.
Tel +353 1 8454129 Fax +353 1 8454255
Located next to the picturesque village of Malahide our marina village is the ideal spot to enjoy and relax. There are 150 fully serviced berths, petrol and diesel available, 30-ton hoist and facilities for winter storage ashore or afloat. A fine selection of shops, and friendly pubs and restaurants serving good food are close by. Sailing Holidays in Ireland - Only the Best.

MARINE ACTIVITIES CENTRE
North Dock Marina,
Sunderland SR6 0PW.
Tel 0191-514 4721 Fax 0191-514 1847
New in 1996 with 85 fully serviced pontoon berths and 108 chain moorings accessible on all tides. Diesel fuel, 24-hour security and close circuit TV surviellance. New marina activities centre with excellent toilets and shower facilities.

THE MAYFLOWER INTERNATIONAL MARINA
Ocean Quay, Richmond Walk,
Plymouth, Devon PL1 4LS.
Tel (01752) 556633 Fax (01752) 606896
Plymouth's only Five-Gold Anchor Marina. Known for its extensive facilities, courtesy and security. Owned by berth holders and run to a very high standard.

MEDWAY BRIDGE MARINA LTD
Manor Lane, Rochester, Kent ME1 3HS.
Tel (01634) 843576 Fax (01634) 843820
A great stopover for exploring the south and east coast.

NEYLAND YACHT HAVEN LTD
Brunel Quay, Neyland,
Pembrokeshire SA73 1PY.
Tel (01646) 601601 Fax (01646) 600713
Marina operators with all facilities. 370 fully serviced pontoon berths in a sheltered, tree lined marina. On-site services include boatyard, sailmaker, sailing school, chandlery, cafe, launderette, showers and toilets. 30 visitor berths. 24-hour access and security.

NOSS-ON-DART MARINA
Noss Quay, Dartmouth, Devon TQ6 0EA.
Tel (01803) 833351 Fax (01803) 832307
Peacefully located on the east shore of the river Dart, this relaxing marina is the perfect base for cruising yachtsmen. Extensive parking, chandlery, repair and lift-out facilities, easy access from London and the Midlands. Boat taxi to Dartmouth.

PETERHEAD BAY AUTHORITY
Bath House, Bath Street,
Peterhead AB42 1DX.
Tel (01779) 474020 Fax (01779) 475712
Contact: Stephen Paterson. Peterhead Bay Marina offers fully serviced pontoon berthing for local and visiting boat owners. Local companies provide a comprehensive range of supporting services. Ideal stopover for vessels heading to/from Scandinavia or the Caledonian canal.

PORT DINORWIC MARINA
Watkin Jones (Holdings) Ltd,
Port Dinorwic, Gwynedd LL56 4JN.
Tel (01248) 671500 Fax (01248) 671252
180-berths in lock basin or tidal pontoon basin. Toilets, showers and restaurant facilities. Visitors always welcome. Call channel 37 (M).

PORT FLAIR LTD
Bradwell Marina, Waterside,
Bradwell-on-Sea, Essex CM0 7RB.
Tel (01621) 776235/776391
300 pontoon berths with water and electricity, petrol and diesel, chandlery, marine slip/hoistage to 20 tons. Repairs, winter lay-ups, licensed club, yacht brokerage.

PORT OF TRURO
Harbour Office, Town Quay,
Truro, Cornwall.
Tel (01872) 272130 Fax (01872) 225346
Facilities for the yachtsman include visitor pontoons located at Turnaware Bar, Ruan Creek and Boscawen Park. Visitor moorings at Woodbury. Quay facilities at Truro with free showers and toilets. Chemical toilet disposal, fresh water and garbage disposal.

PORT SOLENT
South Lockside,
Port Solent,
Portsmouth, Hampshire PO6 4TJ.
Tel (01705) 210765 Fax (01705) 324241
From a marine superstore and outstanding slipway services to restaurants, bars and multiscreen cinema, Port Solent offers visitors and berth holders superb facilities, unsurpassed by any other UK marina. Port Solent is a PREMIER Marina.

PREMIER MARINAS LTD
South Lockside,
Port Solent,
Portsmouth, Hampshire PO6 4TJ
Tel (01705) 214145 Fax (01705) 221876
At our marinas we're always on hand to help you. Premier Group Marinas - Beaucette - Chichester - Falmouth - Port Solent.

RAMSGATE ROYAL HARBOUR MARINA
Harbour Office, Military Road,
Ramsgate, Kent CT11 9LQ.
Tel (01843) 592277 Fax (01843) 590941
Ramsgate Royal Harbour is situated on the south east coast, making an ideal base for crossing to the Continent. 24-hour access to finger pontoons. Comprehensive security systems. Amenities: Launderette, repairs, slipways, boatpark. Competitive rates for permanent berths and discount for visitors' group bookings.

RHU MARINA LTD
Helensburgh,
Dunbartonshire G84 8LN.
Tel (01436) 820238 Fax (01436) 821039
Berths accessible at all times and moorings available situated in an area of outstanding natural beauty, by the Garsloch and 10 minutes from Loch Lomond. Hotels, shops, yacht clubs all adjacent.

RIDGE WHARF YACHT CENTRE
Ridge, Wareham,
Dorset BH20 5BG.
Tel (01929) 552650 Fax (01929) 554434
Marina with full boatyard facilities. Winter lay-up and fuels etc.

SALVE MARINE LTD - IRELAND
Crosshaven,
Co Cork, Ireland.
Tel +353 21 831145 Fax +353 21 831747
The marina is situated just 20 minutes from Cork City, Cork airport and Ringaskiddy ferry port. Located yards from Royal Cork Yacht Club and Crosshaven village centre. Facilities for yachts up to 140' x 14' draught including mains electricity 240/380 volts, telephone, fax, toilets and showers. Welding and machining in stainless steel, aluminium and bronze. Repairs and maintenance to hulls/rigging. Routine and detailed engine maintenance. Slip. *Sailing Holidays in Ireland - Only the Best.*

SHOTLEY MARINE SERVICES
Shotley Marina Ltd,
Shotley Gate,
Ipswich, Suffolk IP9 1QJ.
Tel (01473) 788982 Fax (01473) 788868
A modern state of the art marina with 350 berths offering all the services expected. Open 24-hours with full security. Access all states of tide, ideal cruising base. Well stocked chandlery and general store, repair facilities, laundry and ironing centre, showers/baths and toilets. Restaurants, bar, children's room, TV/video and function rooms with dance floor and bar. Disabled facilities.

SOUTH DOCK MARINA
South Lock Office,
Rope Street,
Plough Way, London SE16 1TX.
Tel 0171-252 2244 Fax 0171-237 3806
London's largest marina. 200+ berths. Spacious, tranquil setting. Manned 24 hours. Lift-out to 20 tonnes. Competitive mooring rates.

SOUTHDOWN MARINA
Southdown Quay, Millbrook,
Cornwall PL10 1HG.
Tel/Fax (01752) 823084
32-berth marina on edge of river Tamar in quiet location behind Rame Peninsula. Plymouth is just across the river. Quayside berths available for large vessels. Winter storage. 24-hour security. DIY facilities available.

SPARKES YACHT HARBOUR LTD
38 Wittering Road, Hayling Island,
Hampshire PO11 9SR.
Tel (01705) 463572 Fax (01705) 465741
Sparkes Marina - a small friendly, family run business offering all the facilities you require including access at all states of the tide to a depth of 2 metres at lowest low water springs. In addition to marina berths, accessible through a security gate, we also offer dry boat sailing, moorings, storage ashore plus full maintenance facilities, new boat sales and brokerage, chandlery and restaurant.

ST KATHARINE HAVEN
50 St Katharine's Way,
London E1 9LB.
Tel 0171-264 5312 Fax 0171-702 2252
In the heart of London, St Katharine's 200-berth Haven offers facilities for 100'+ vessels, access to the West End and City, its own shops, restaurants, health club and yacht club, plus water, electric, showers and sewerage disposal. Entry via a lock. Operational HW - 2hours to HW +1½hours London Bridge. October-March 0800-1800. April-August 0600-2030.

SUFFOLK YACHT HARBOUR LTD
Levington,
Ipswich, Suffolk IP10 0LN.
Tel (01473) 659240 Fax (01473) 659632
420-berths - access at all states of tide (dredged to 2.5 metres at LW Springs). Boat hoist facilities up to 60 tons. Full boatyard services, chandlery, gas, diesel, petrol, engineering, sailmaking, electronics. Club house and restaurant.

SWANSEA MARINA
Lockside,
Maritime Quarter, Swansea,
West Glamorgan SA1 1WG.
Tel (01792) 470310 Fax (01792) 463948
Access all states of the tide except LWST. City centre marina, restaurants, theatres etc. Call us on Channels 18 or 80 to check locking times. Visitors always welcome - a good destination for your annual trip.

TARQUIN YACHT HARBOUR LTD
Thorney Road,
Emsworth,
Hampshire PO10 8BP.
Tel (01243) 377727 Fax (01243) 373432
Friendly marina in Chichester harbour. Water, electricity, diesel, Calor gas, 25-tonne mobile crane, slipways, hard-standing and storage areas. Showers and toilets, car parking, chandlery, engineers and boat repairs.

TITCHMARSH MARINA
(WALTON-ON-THE-NAZE)
Coles Lane,
Walton-on-the-Naze,
Essex CO14 8SL.
Tel (01255) 672185 Fax (01255) 851901
Friendly service in the peaceful backwater. Visiting yachtsmen welcome. Sheltered marina berths. Full marina facilities: travel-lift, cranage, 16amp electricity, diesel. Winter storage. Restaurant and bar open every day. Bar meals available all day. Weekend barbecues. (See the Harbour Lights Restaurant.

TOLLESBURY MARINA
The Yacht Harbour,
Tollesbury,
Maldon, Essex CM9 8SE.
Tel (01621) 869202 Fax (01621) 868489
Dedicated to customer service, this family-run marina can offer 240 marina berths with water and electricity on all pontoons. Cruising club with bar, restaurant, swimming pool and tennis courts. Repair workshop, osmosis treatment centre. Full brokerage service listing over 200 boats. VHF Ch37 and 80.

TOWN QUAY MARINA
Town Quay,
The Waterfront,
Southampton, Hampshire.
Tel (01703) 234397
Town Quay is a growing development of bars and restaurants on an attractive waterfront environment just minutes away from the city centre.

TROON YACHT HAVEN
The Harbour,
Troon,
Ayrshire KA10 6DJ.
Tel (01292) 315553 Fax (01292) 312836
Sheltered harbour for 350 berths. Well placed for those on passage to and from the Clyde. Bar, restaurant, marine services. Attractive seafront town with good beaches and championship golf.

WEYMOUTH OLD HARBOUR
Weymouth & Portland Borough Council,
Borough Engineers Department,
Municipal Offices,
North Quay, Weymouth, Dorset DT4 8TA.
Tel (01305) 206363/206423
Fax (01305) 206276
e-mail: cflowers@weymouth.gov.uk
http://www.weymouth.gov.uk/ marine.htm
Access at all stages of tide. Visitor berths in the centre of prime tourist resort with shops, restaurants and night life all at hand. Diesel fuelling from pontoon or tanker. Chandlery and repair facilities available.

MARINE ACTIVITY CENTRES

BALTIC WHARF
WATER LEISURE CENTRE
Bristol Harbour,
Underfall Yard,
Bristol BS1 6XG.
Tel 0117-929 7608 Fax 0117-929 4454
Tuition: 0117-952 5202
Sailing school and centre, with qualified instruction in most watersports. Also moorings available throughout the Bristol harbour for all types of leisurecraft.

MARINE ACTIVITIES CENTRE
North Dock Marina,
Sunderland SR6 0PW.
Tel 0191-514 4721 Fax 0191-514 1847
New in 1996 with 85 fully serviced pontoon berths and 108 chain moorings accessible on all tides. Diesel fuel, 24-hour security and close circuit TV surviellance. New marina activities centre with excellent toilets and shower facilities.

MARINE ARTISTS/ CARTOONISTS

THE CARTOON GALLERY
(Wavelength Design)
37 Lower Street, Dartmouth,
Devon TQ6 9AN.
Tel/Fax (01803) 834466
Tel (01803) 834425 Evenings
Rick, the International Cartoonist specialises in hand coloured and personalised sailing cartoon prints (eg A3 £10). Commissions are carried out in Rick's Dartmouth gallery and studio. Prints available by mail order. Telephone or fax for details.

MARINE ENGINEERS

AILSA-TROON LTD
Harbour Road,
Troon,
Ayrshire KA10 6DN.
Tel (01292) 311311 Fax (01292) 317613
Boatyard with full repair and maintenance facilities for GRP, steel, aluminium, timber and inflatable craft. Ship repair, fabrication and new building work also undertaken in Ailsa's extensive 15 acre covered facilities.

CHICK'S MARINE LTD/VOLVO PENTA
Collings Road,
St Peter Port,
Guernsey, Channel Islands GY1 1FL.
Tel (01481) 723716 Fax (01481) 713632
Distributor of diesel fuel biocide used to treat and protect contamination in fuel tanks where an algae (bug) is present. Most owners do not realise what the problem is, loss of power, blocked fuel filter, exhaust smoking, resulting in expensive repairs to injectors - fuel pump - or complete engine overhaul. Marine engineers, engines, spares, service - VAT free. Honda outboards, pumps and generators. Volvo Penta specialists.

CHISWICK QUAY MARINA LTD
Marina Office,
Chiswick Quay,
London W4 3UR.
Tel 0181-994 8743
Small, secluded, peaceful marina on tidal Thames at Chiswick. Slipway, marine engineers and electricians, power, water, toilets and sluice. Some residential moorings.

FELTON MARINE ENGINEERING
The Boatyard,
Brighton Marina,
East Sussex BN2 5UF.
Tel (01273) 601779 Fax (01273) 673258
Main Volvo Penta marine dealer. New engines, sales and service. Genuine Volvo Penta parts and accessories. Stainless steel fabrication workshop. Eberspacher heaters, sales and service centre.

FOX'S MARINA IPSWICH LTD
The Strand,
Wherstead,
Ipswich, Suffolk IP2 8SA.
Tel (01473) 689111 Fax (01473) 601737
The most comprehensive boatyard facility on the east coast. Extensive chandlery. Marina access 24-hours. Two travel hoists to 45 tons, 10 ton crane. Full electronics, rigging, engineering, stainless steel services. Specialists in osmosis and spray painting.

GWEEK QUAY BOATYARD
Gweek Quay (Helford River),
Helston,
Cornwall TR12 6UF.
Tel (01326) 221657 Fax (01326) 221685
Head of the Helford river. Yacht repair yard, 30-ton crane, chandlery, brokerage, coffee shop, toilets and showers. Boat storage and all boat repair and service facilities. Access approximately 2 hours either side of highwater.

HIGHWAY MARINE LTD
Pillory Gate Wharf,
Strand Street,
Sandwich, Kent CT13 9EU.
Tel (01304) 613925 Fax (01304) 614814
Pontoon moorings available in town of Sandwich. Lift-out facilities and hard standing, water, electricity. OMC main dealer with full service centre. New engine sales. Brokerage and boat sales, chandlery.

OCEAN MARINE INTERNATIONAL - OMI
Mayflower International Marina,
Plymouth, Devon PL1 4LS.
Tel (01752) 500121 Fax (01752) 500221
Queen Anne's Battery Marina, Plymouth,
Devon PL1 0LP
Tel (01752) 222688
Established for over 20 years, OMI are specialists in electrical and electronic installations, as well as providing a comprehensive service, for both private and commercial vessels. Agents for Webasto and other leading manufacturers.

R K MARINE LTD
Hamble River Boatyard, Bridge Road,
Swanwick, Southampton,
Hampshire SO31 7EB.
Tel (01489) 583572 Fax (01489) 583172
Volvo Penta main dealer with all marina facilities.

S A L MARINE
Mill Lane, Lymington,
Hampshire SO41 9AZ.
Tel (01590) 679588 Fax (01590) 670032
Volva Penta, Honda and Suzuki main dealers. Sales, servicing and installation for all marine engines and outboard motors. Situated in Haven Quay with full facilities. We also offer stainless steel and aluminium fabrication and repairs.

PETER CUMBERLIDGE PHOTO LIBRARY
Sunways, Slapton, Kingsbridge,
Devon TQ7 2PR.
Tel (01548) 580461 Fax (01548) 580588
Large selection of nautical, travel and coastal colour transparencies. Specialities boats, harbours, lighthouses, marinas and inland waterways in Britain, Northern Europe, the Mediterranean and the Baltic. Commissions undertaken.

PETER DANBY SAILING PHOTOGRAPHER
Saltern Wood Quay, Yarmouth,
Isle of Wight PO41 0SE.
Tel/Fax (01983) 761353
Marine photographer

ALL SPARS (KEMP SOUTHWEST)
The Boathouse, Commercial Road,
Penryn, Falmouth, Cornwall TR10 8AE.
Tel (01326) 374177 Fax (01326) 377696
Regional centre for SELDÉN and KEMP integrated sailing systems. Full range of rigging services on-site and mobile. Large and comprehensively stocked chandlery to cover all yachting requirements. Support and back-up for retail and trade alike.

ATLANTIC SPARS (KEMP WEST)
The Loft, Mayors Avenue,
Dartmouth, Devon TQ6 9NG.
Tel (01803) 833322 Fax (01803) 835855
Regional centre for SELDÉN and KEMP integrated sailing systems. Services include standing and running rigging, repairs,

custom spars and furling systems. Aluminium design and fabrications for industry. Official suppliers to the BT Global Challenge.

CARBOSPARS LTD
Hamble Point, School Lane, Hamble,
Southampton, Hampshire SO31 4JD.
Tel (01703) 456736 Fax (01703) 455361
e-mail: carbospars@compuserve.com
Design and manufacture of carbon spars for racing and cruising and the award-winning AeroRig®.

FOX'S SPARS & RIGGING (KEMP EAST)
Fox's Marina, The Strand, Wherstead,
Ipswich, Suffolk IP2 8SA.
Tel (01473) 691235 Fax (01473) 601737
Regional centre for SELDÉN and KEMP integrated sailing systems. Fox's experience in world girdling racing and cruising yachts provides testimony to products and skills. The No 1 choice for yachtsmen everywhere. Supplier to the OYSTER range.

GUY BROOKE MASTS & RIGGING (KEMP NORTHWEST)
Conwy Marina, Conwy, Gwynedd
North Wales LL32 8GU.
Tel/Fax (01492) 592909
Mobile 0589 108860
Regional centre for SELDÉN and KEMP integrated sailing systems. Specialists in mast build and maintenance. Full rigging service for swaging, splicing and rig surveys. Personal, professional and mobile along the north Wales and north west coasts.

HARKEN - DISTRIBUTED BY SIMPSON LAWRENCE
218-228 Edmiston Drive,
Glasgow G51 2YT.
Tel 0141-427 5331/8 Fax 0141-427 5419
e-mail: info@simpson-lawrence.co.uk
Distributors of **Harken** deck hardware, ball bearing blocks in all sizes from micros to maxis, jib reefing and furling systems, from dinghies to 150 footers, winches, backstay tensioners, power sheet jammers and deck shoes. We also distribute **Head Foil** plastic luff groove systems, and **Edson** steering and pump-out systems.

IRISH SPARS & RIGGING (KEMP IRELAND)
52 Whiterock Road, Killinchy, Co Down,
Northern Ireland BT23 6PT.
Tel/Fax (01238) 541727
Regional centre for SELDÉN and KEMP integrated sailing systems. The complete and fully mobile rigging service for yachtsmen in Ireland with outlets in Dublin and Cork. A comprehensive stock of all KEMP/SELDÉN products always available.

JOSEPH P LAMB & SONS
Maritime Building (opposite Albert
Dock), Wapping, Liverpool L1 8DQ.
Tel 0151-709 4861 Fax 0151-709 2786
Situated in the centre of Liverpool, J P
Lamb have provided a service to world
shipping for over 200 years. All chandlery
supplies, clothing, rope, paint and flags are
available. Full sailmaking and repairs. Kemp
Retail Outlet for spars and rigging. Open
Mon to Fri 8am to 5.30pm - Sat 9am to
12.30pm.

KEMP MASTS LTD (Seldén Masts Ltd)
St Margaret's Lane, Titchfield, Fareham,
Hampshire PO14 4BG.
Tel (01329) 841900 Fax (01329) 847052
Now renamed Seldén, this is the UK
manufacturing and supply base for the
Seldén range of masts, booms, poles,
kickers, mainsail-furling and headsail-
furling to suit production yachts upto 45'
and custom yachts from upto 70'.

MANX MARINE
35 North Quay, Douglas,
Isle of Man IM1 4LB.
Tel/Fax (01624) 674842
The Island's leading and most established
yacht chandlery. Stockists of quality foul-
weather clothing and thermal wear. Large
stock holdings of stainless steel fixtures
and fittings and a comprehensive range of
general chandlery including rigging
facilities.

**MAST & RIGGING SERVICES LTD
(KEMP SCOTLAND)**
Kip Marina, Inverkip,
Renfrewshire PA16 0AS.
Tel (01475) 522700 Fax (01475) 522800
Regional centre for SELDÉN and KEMP
integrated sailing systems. Specialist mast
and rigging service offering - splicing,
swaging, spar maintenance and repairs
throughout Scotland. Suppliers of main
and headsail furling gears, spinnaker poles
and rod kickers.

**NORTHERN SPAR SERVICES
(KEMP NORTHWEST)**
M R Coates Marine, The Marina
Boatyard, Whitby,
North Yorkshire YO21 1EU.
Tel (01947) 604486 Fax (01947) 600580
Regional centre for SELDEN and KEMP
integrated sailing systems. 25 years'
experience of mast and rigging manu-
facturing. Surveys undertaken. UK and
export mail order service. Roll-swaging,
Talurits, wire and rope splicing. Suppliers
of furling systems.

**OFFSHORE SPARS & RIGGING
(KEMP CHANNEL ISLANDS)**
Boatworks+, Castle Emplacement,
St Peter Port, Guernsey,
Channel Islands GY1 1AU.
Tel (01481) 726071 Fax (01481) 714224
Regional centre for SELDÉN and KEMP
integrated sailing systems. Specialist in
new mast builds and maintenance for the
Channel Islands. Complete retrofit and
rigging services including FURLEX genoa
and mainsail furling, rod kickers, spinnaker
poles etc.

THE RIG SHOP LTD
Unit 1A, Cobb's Quay Marina,
Poole, Dorset BH15 4EL.
Tel/Fax (01202) 677717
Yacht riggers and mast builders with
facilities in Poole and Ocean Village Marina,
Southampton.

THE RIG SHOP LTD
Ocean Village,
Marina Service Area,
Maritime Walk,
Southampton, Hampshire SO14 3TL.
Tel/Fax (01703) 338341
Yacht riggers and mast builders with
facilities in Southampton and Cobb's Quay,
Poole.

SEA-KING BOAT BUILDERS LTD
8A High Street,
Leigh-on-Sea,
Essex SS9 2EN.
Tel (01702) 73612
Wooden boatbuilders, dinghies 12', cruisers
up to 32' clinker construction, repairs to
wooden vessels, iron work to your pattern
undertaken. Mast and spars made in wood.

SIMPSON LAWRENCE LTD
218-228 Edmiston Drive,
Glasgow G51 2YT.
Tel 0141-427 5331 Fax 0141-427 5419
e-mail: info@simpson-lawrence.co.uk
Simpson Lawrence are manufacturers and
the UK's largest wholesale distributor of
quality marine equipment.

**SOUTHERN MAST & RIGGING
(KEMP SOUTHEAST)**
Unit B The Boatyard,
Brighton Marina, Brighton,
East Sussex BN2 5UF.
Tel (01273) 818189
Fax (01273) 818188 Mobile 0802 284088
Regional centre for SELDÉN and KEMP
integrated sailing systems. Builders of
masts and spars, standing and running
rigging. Rig surveyors. Suppliers of rope,
wire, mast and deck hardware, booms,
kickers and reefing systems. Mobile service
available.

**SOUTHERN SPAR SERVICES
(KEMP SOUTH)**
Shamrock Quay, William Street,
Northam, Southampton,
Hampshire SO14 5QL.
Mobile 0850 736540
Tel (01703) 331714 Fax (01703) 230559
Regional centre for SELDÉN and KEMP
integrated sailing systems. Convectional
and furling spars for UK and abroad. Also
headsail and mainsail reefing, deck
equipment, toe rails and stanchion bases.
All forms of repairs and modifications
undertaken.

MOISTURE METERS

TRAMEX LTD
Chamco House, Shankill,
Co Dublin, Ireland.
Tel+353 1 282 3688 Fax +353 1 282 6311
Manufacturers of Moisture Meter and
osmosis detection instruments for boats.

NAVIGATION EQUIPMENT - GENERAL

DOLPHIN MARITIME SOFTWARE LTD
713 Cameron House,
White Cross,
Lancaster LA1 4XQ.
Tel/Fax (01524) 841946
e-mail: 100417.744@compuserve.com
Marine computer programs for IBM PC,
Psion and Sharp pocket computers.
Specialists in navigation, tidal prediction
and other programs for both yachting and
commercial uses.

MERIDIAN CHARTWARE LTD
Maggs House,
78 Queens Road,
Clifton, Bristol BS8 1QX.
Tel 0117-907 3327 Fax 0117-907 7548
e-mail: meridian@dial.pipex.com
http://dspace.dial.pipex.com/meridian/
Designers and suppliers of quality marine
software. Electronic charting systems for
the leisure user to the professional mariner,
using the British Admiralty Raster Chart
Service (ARCS). Dedicated Win96/NT
mariner-friendly systems. Official ARCS
chart agent. Suppliers of complete
hardware/software packages.

NAVIONICS UK
Oak Wood House, Gospel Oak Lane,
Stratford-upon-Avon,
Warwickshire CV37 0JA.
Tel (01789) 269891 Fax (01789) 262717
Navionics UK, the exclusive UK and Irish
distributor for Navionics electronic charts.
Charts suitable in chart plotters from Furuno,
Koden, Navico, Trimble, Panasonic, B&G,
Philips etc. 24-hour despatch service for
any Navionics chart worldwide.

RADIO & ELECTRONIC SERVICES LTD
Les Chenes, Rohais,
St Peter Port, Guernsey,
Channel Islands GY1 1FB.
Tel (01481) 728837 Fax (01481) 714379
Chart plotters, GPS, C-Map and Navionics
charting, radars, VHF fixed and portable
radios, autopilots. We offer full electronic
supply and service. Sales and service dealers
for Furuno, Icom, Shipmate, Cetrek,
Autohelm, Robertson and AP Navigator.

ROYAL INSTITUTE OF NAVIGATION
1 Kensington Gore,
London SW7 2AT.
Tel 0171-589 5021 Fax 0171-823 8671
Forum for all interested in navigation - Air:
Sea: Land: Space.

SWALE MARINE (ELECTRICAL)
The Old Stable,
North Road,
Queenborough, Kent ME11 5EH.
Tel (01795) 580930 Fax (01795) 667280
For all your electrical and electronic needs.
Authorised agents for: Furuno, Autohelm,
Raytheon and most major manufacturers.
Fight crime with Harbourguard monitored
security: Medway and Swale coverage -
Boatmark registration centre.

NAVIGATION LIGHT SWITCHES & MONITORS

MECTRONICS MARINE
PO Box 8, Newton Abbot,
Devon TQ12 1FF.
Tel (01626) 334453
LIGHT ACTIVATED SWITCHES, rugged solid state devices to automatically switch anchor lights at sunset and sunrise. NAVLIGHT SELECTORS, protected enclosed rotary switches internally connected to ensure approved navigation light combination on auxiliary sailing vessels. NAVLIGHT STATUS MONITORS, diagnostic displays on which the appropriate indicator flashes quickly or slowly in the event of a short or open circuit fault. Also drives an optional, audible warning device.

OUTBOARD MOTORS

S A L MARINE
Mill Lane, Lymington,
Hampshire SO41 9AZ.
Tel (01590) 679588 Fax (01590) 670032
Volva Penta, Honda and Suzuki main dealers. Sales, servicing and installation for all marine engines and outboard motors. Situated in Haven Quay with full facilities. We also offer stainless steel and aluminium fabrication and repairs.

PAINT & OSMOSIS

FOX'S MARINA IPSWICH LTD
The Strand, Wherstead,
Ipswich, Suffolk IP2 8SA.
Tel (01473) 689111 Fax (01473) 601737
The most comprehensive boatyard facility on the east coast. Extensive chandlery. Marina access 24-hours. Two travel hoists to 45 tons, 10 ton crane. Full electronics, rigging, engineering, stainless steel services. Specialists in osmosis and spray painting.

INTERNATIONAL PAINT
24-30 Canute Road, Southampton,
Hampshire SO14 3PB.
Tel (01703) 226722 Fax (01703) 335975
International Paint is the leading supplier of quality paints, epoxies, varnishes and antifoulings to the marine industry. Over half the world's pleasure craft are protected by International products.

NORTH QUAY MARINE
North Side, St Sampson's Harbour,
Guernsey, Channel Islands.
Tel (01481) 46561 Fax (01481) 43488
The complete boating centre. Full range of chandlery, rope, chain, lubricants, paint, boatwear and shoes. Fishing tackle for onshore and on-board. Inflatables and safety equipment. Electronics and small outboard engines.

> *PLEASE MENTION THE MACMILLAN NAUTICAL ALMANAC WHEN MAKING ENQUIRIES*

RICE & COLE LTD
Sea End Boathouse,
Burnham-on-Crouch, Essex CM0 8AN.
Tel/Fax (01621) 782063
Boatyard with full repair and shipwright services. Osmosis treatment, painting and spraying, GRP repairs, standing and running rigging, brokerage and chandlery. Visitors welcome to this family-run business on the river Crouch.

ROSDEN GLASS FIBRE
La Rue Durell, La Collette, St Helier,
Jersey JE2 3NB.
Tel (01534) 625418 Fax (01534) 625419
Specialists in all types of glass fibre marine works, structural repairs, alterations, reflow coating, GEL coat work, Blakes Osmosis Treatment Centre. Manufacturers of fuel tanks, bathing platforms and boat builders. General refurbishment and polishing. A division of Precision Plastics (Jersey) Ltd.

S P SYSTEMS
Love Lane, Cowes,
Isle of Wight PO31 7EU.
Tel (01983) 284000 Fax (01983) 298453
Epoxy resins for laminating, bonding, coating and filling. Usable with wood, GRP, concrete. GRP/FRP materials including glass, carbon and Kevlar fibres. Structural engineering of GRP and composite materials. Technical advice service.

TRAMEX LTD
Chamco House, Shankill,
Co Dublin, Ireland.
Tel+353 1 282 3688 Fax +353 1 282 6311
Manufacturer of Moisture Meter and osmosis detection instruments for boats.

PORT TRUST

LERWICK HARBOUR TRUST
Albert Building, Lerwick,
Shetland Isles ZE1 0LL.
Tel (01595) 692991 Fax (01595) 693452
e-mail: lkharbour@lht.zetnet.co.uk
http://www.shetland.shetland-news.co.uk/websites/lht
Lerwick - fishing, oilfield support, ferries, cargo and cruising.

PROPELLERS & STERNGEAR/ REPAIRS

BRUNTON'S PROPELLERS LTD
Units 3 & 4 Faraday Close,
Gorse Lane Industrial Estate,
Clacton-on-Sea, Essex CO15 4TR.
Tel (01255) 420005 Fax (01255) 427775
Manufacturer of the Autoprop and specialist propellers.

PROP PROTECTOR
74 Abingdon Road, Maidstone,
Kent ME16 9EE.
Tel (01622) 728738 Fax (01622) 727973
Prevention is better than cure when it comes to avoiding a fouled propeller. Prop Protectors are now accepted worldwide as the first line of defence against stray rope, netting, weed and plastic bags.

SILLETTE SONIC LTD
182 Church Hill Road, North Cheam,
Sutton, Surrey SM3 8NF.
Tel 0181-715 0100 Fax 0181-288 0742
Sillette manufactures a range of propulsion systems - stern drive, saildrives etc and sterngear. Markets Radice & Gori fixed and folding propellers. Acts as agents for Morse Controls, Yanmar and Lombardini marine engines, and Fuji Robin generators. See distribution depot Poole, Dorset - Area 2.

VETUS DEN OUDEN LTD
38 South Hants Industrial Park, Totton,
Southampton, Hampshire SO40 3SA.
Tel (01703) 861033 Fax (01703) 663142
Suppliers of marine diesel equipment, exhaust systems, steering systems, bow propellers, propellers and shafts, hatches, portlights, windows, electronic instruments, batteries, ventilators, windlasses, water and fuel tanks, chandlery items and much much more.

QUAY SERVICES

GWEEK QUAY BOATYARD
Gweek Quay (Helford River), Helston,
Cornwall TR12 6UF.
Tel (01326) 221657 Fax (01326) 221685
Head of the Helford river. Yacht repair yard, 30-ton crane, chandlery, brokerage, coffee shop, toilets and showers. Boat storage and all boat repair and service facilities. Access approximately 2 hours either side of highwater.

RADIO COURSES/SCHOOLS

R T TRAINING
286 Sea Front, Hayling Island,
Hampshire PO11 0AZ.
Tel (01705) 462122 Fax (01705) 462138
Weekend radio courses at Southampton and Port Solent for leisure and professional yachtsmen. SSB - 3-day Long Range Certificate (LRC) - optional Satellite module. Restricted to LRC upgrade course. VHF 1-day course/exam.

RADIO SCHOOL LTD
33 Island Close, Hayling Island,
Hampshire PO11 0NJ.
Tel (01705) 466450 Fax (01705) 461449
Regular weekend courses/exams for the
VHF and Long Range (SSB/Sat.) Radiotelephone Operator's Certificates in UK's
only permanent, fully equipped classroom
solely dedicated to training small-boat
sailors on a full-time, professional basis.
Established 1980.

REPAIR MATERIAL

ROSDEN GLASS FIBRE
La Rue Durell, La Collette, St Helier,
Jersey JE2 3NB.
Tel (01534) 625418 Fax (01534) 625419
Specialists in all types of glass fibre marine
works, structural repairs, alterations, re-
flow coating, GEL coat work, Blakes
Osmosis Treatment Centre. Manufacturers
of fuel tanks, bathing platforms and boat
builders. General refurbishment and
polishing. A division of Precision Plastics
(Jersey) Ltd.

S P SYSTEMS
Love Lane, Cowes,
Isle of Wight PO31 7EU.
Tel (01983) 284000 Fax (01983) 298453
Epoxy resins for laminating, bonding,
coating and filling. Usable with wood, GRP,
concrete. GRP/FRP materials including
glass, carbon and Kevlar fibres. Structural
engineering of GRP and composite
materials. Technical advice service.

SAFETY EQUIPMENT

A B MARINE LTD
Castle Walk, St Peter Port, Guernsey,
Channel Islands GY1 1AU.
Tel (01481) 722378 (Fax 01481) 711080
We specialise in safety and survival
equipment and are a DoT approved service
station for liferafts including R.F.D.,
Beaufort/Dunlop, Zodiac, Plastimo and
Lifeguard. We also carry a full range of new
liferafts, dinghies and lifejackets, and are
agents for Bukh marine engines.

ADEC MARINE LTD
4 Masons Avenue, Croydon,
Surrey CR0 1EH.
Tel 0181-686 9717 Fax 0181-680 9912
Approved liferaft service station for south
east UK. Additionally we hire and sell new
rafts and sell a complete range of safety
equipment for yachts including pyrotechnics, fire extinguishers, lifejackets,
buoys and a buoyancy bag system.

CREWSAVER LTD
Crewsaver House, Mumby Road,
Gosport, Hampshire PO12 1AQ.
Tel (01705) 528621
MARLIN - Leading manufacturer of stylish,
comfortable, hardwearing wetsuits,
lifejackets, buoyancy aids and accessories
for all seasons and all surface watersports.
YAK - Catering for all canoeing needs from
cags and decks to long johns and buoyancy
aids.

NORTH QUAY MARINE
North Side, St Sampson's Harbour,
Guernsey, Channel Islands.
Tel (01481) 46561 Fax (01481) 43488
The complete boating centre. Full range of
chandlery, rope, chain, lubricants, paint,
boatwear and shoes. Fishing tackle for onshore and on-board. Inflatables and safety
equipment. Electronics and small outboard
engines.

SEAQUEST MARINE LTD
13 Fountain Street, St Peter Port,
Guernsey, Channel Islands GY1 1BX.
Tel (01481) 721773 Fax (01481) 716738
Seaquest Marine have a fully stocked
chandlery. Agents for Sowester and
Simpson Lawrence. Sole agents for Avon,
Typhoon, Garmin Electronics and Compass
inflatables. Electronics specialising in GPS.
Inflatable specialists. Official Avon service
station. VAT free. Friendly advice.

WINTERS MARINE LTD
(Lincombe Boatyard)
Lincombe, Salcombe, Devon TQ8 8NQ.
Tel (01548) 843580
Deep water pontoon moorings. Winter
storage for 150 boats. All maintenance and
repair facilities. Slipway capacity 30 tonnes.
Inflatable craft sales and service. Lifecraft
surveys and repairs. Short and long-term
lifecraft hire.

SAILMAKERS & REPAIRS

BRUCE BANKS SAILS LTD
372 Brook Lane, Sarisbury, Southampton,
Hampshire SO31 7ZA.
Tel (01489) 582444 Fax (01489) 589789
e-mail: enquiries@banks.co.uk
http:/www.banks.co.uk
Banks Sails are manufacturers of high
quality racing and cruising sails. Banks also
offer a range of dinghy covers and accessories. Pick up points at all Hamble marinas,
Gosport and Southampton waters.

KEMP SAILS LTD
Unit 2, Sandford Lane Industrial Estate,
Wareham, Dorset BH20 4DY.
Tel (01929) 554308 Fax (01929) 554350
e-mail: kemp@eluk.co.uk
http://www.eluk.co.uk/kemp/index/html
Sailmakers and suppliers of sail handling
equipment.

NORTH SAILS UK LTD
Satchell Lane, Hamble,
Hampshire SO31 4HH.
Tel (01703) 453109 Fax (01703) 457015
e-mail:info@gb.northsails.com
At NORTH SAILS a team of highly skilled
sailors are dedicated to helping you achieve
even higher standards in your sailing -
whether it be on the race course, crossing
an ocean or enjoying a day's cruising. Benefit
from world beating research and
development programmes, new sail design
and material technology that is only available
to NORTH SAILS.

PARKER & KAY SAILMAKERS - EAST
Suffolk Yacht Harbour,
Levington,
Ipswich, Suffolk IP10 0LN.
Tel (01473) 659878 Fax (01473) 659197
A complete sailmaking service, from small
repairs to the construction of custom
designed sails for racing or cruising yachts.
Covers constructed for sail and powercraft,
plus the supply of all forms of sail handling
hardware.

PARKER & KAY SAILMAKERS - SOUTH
Port Hamble Marina,
Satchell Lane, Hamble,
Southampton, Hampshire SO31 5QD.
Tel (01703) 458213 Fax (01703) 458228
A complete sailmaking service, from small
repairs to the construction of custom
designed sails for racing or cruising yachts.
Covers constructed for sail and powercraft,
plus the supply of all forms of sail handling
hardware.

UK/McWILLIAM SAILMAKERS
Crosshaven,
Co Cork, Ireland.
Tel +353 21 831505 Fax +353 21 831700
Ireland's premier sailmaker, prompt repairs
and service.

SEA DELIVERIES

BRIAN BAGG YACHT DELIVERIES
Vine Cottage, Southampton Road,
Dibden, Southampton,
Hampshire SO45 5TA.
Tel/Fax (01703) 847514
Worldwide deliveries of sail, power and
small commercial vessels. Undertaken
with utmost care and consideration by
professional yachtmaster. 300,000 miles
and 370 deliveries completed since 1969.
Telephone or fax for a competitive quotation.

CARDINAL YACHTS
12A Grafton Court,
Grafton Road,
Torquay, Devon TQ1 1UP.
Tel/Fax (01803) 212954
Sail and power deliveries worldwide by
experienced, commercial yachtmasters.
Take the cheapest Mediterranean route with
our combined sea and road service. Owners
welcome. As an RYA recognised sea school
we offer tuition at all levels.

**DUNCAN GARRATT MARINE
TRANSPORT**
69A King Street, Plymouth,
Devon PL1 5HY.
Tel (01752) 260945
Professional yacht and powerboat deliveries
by experienced skipper and crew. Owners
welcome. Areas cover south west and west
coast of UK, Ireland, Europe and the
Canaries. Specialist extended cruising
scheme for existing owners. We can deliver
your boat to your cruising location and
return it at competitive rates.

MAX WALKER YACHT DELIVERIES
Zinderneuf Sailing,
PO Box 105,
Macclesfield, Cheshire SK10 2EY.
Tel (01625) 431712 Fax (01625) 619704
Fixed price deliveries. Sailing yachts delivered with care in north west European, UK and Eire waters by RYA/DoT yachtmaster and crew; 30 years' experience. Owners welcome. Tuition if required. References available. Your enquiries welcome 24 hours.

PETERS & MAY LTD
18 Canute Road,
Ocean Village,
Southampton, Hampshire SO14 3FJ.
Tel (01703) 480480 Fax (01703) 480400
The 'Round the World' specialists in shipping, transporting, cradling yachts and powerboats. Weekly service to USA, Far East, Mediterranean, Middle East and Caribbean.

PORT À PORT YACHT SERVICES
Studio 6, Fox's Marina, The Strand,
Ipswich, Suffolk IP2 8NJ.
Tel (01473) 692691 Fax (01473) 692693
Port à Port Services guarantee speedy and safe passage for your yacht. Our skippers are never less than instructor level and all crew hold RYA qualifications, ensuring your yacht is in the very best of hands.

RELIANCE YACHT MANAGEMENT LTD
34 Netley Street,
Farnborough,
Hampshire GU14 6AQ.
Tel (01252) 378239 Fax (01252) 521736
e-mail:100713.363@compuserve.com
With over 10 years' experience we offer a professional management and delivery service. Your yacht can be safely and expertly delivered anywhere in the world by highly experienced skippers and crews. We are also able to offer 'Total Solution Management Packages' designed to suit your needs. Offices in the Caribbean, Pacific, Asia and France.

SEALAND BOAT DELIVERIES LTD
64 Outwood Road,
Radcliffe,
Manchester, Lancashire M26 1AG.
Tel (01254) 705225 Fax (01254) 776582
http://www.btx.co.uk
Nationwide and European road transporters of all craft. No weight limit. We never close. Irish service. Worldwide shipping agents. Extrication of yachts from workshops and building yards. Salvage contractors. Established 25 years.

TREVOR VINCENT DELIVERIES
Coombe Cottage,
9 Swannaton Road,
Dartmouth, Devon TQ6 9RL.
Tel/Fax (01803) 833757
Worldwide delivery of yachts and commercial vessels undertaken at short notice by RYA/DoT Yachtmaster Ocean (with commercial endorsement). Over 28 years' experience including three masted schooners, tugs, motor yachts and hi-tec racers. For instant quotes call/fax 01803 833757.

CRINAN YACHT CHARTERS
The Pump House,
Crinan,
Argyll PA31 8SP.
Tel (01546) 830260 Fax (01546) 83025
Bareboat and skippered charters around the Hebrides. Fantastic cruising. Sheltered waters, wildlife, distilleries and isolated anchorages, yet with marine services within easy reach. 'Crinan - Where it all begins.'

ISLAND SEA SCHOOL
7 Church View,
South Milford,
Leeds LS25 5BM.
Tel/Fax (01977) 685394
e-mail: sea.school@mcmail.com
RYA practical courses from our base at Port Dinorwic on the Menai Strait: Competent Crew, Day Skipper, Coastal Skipper, Yachtmaster Preparatory, Ocean Yachtmaster Qualifying Passages. Own boat tuition. Skippered charter.

SHEARWATER CRUISES
Seaview Farm,
Kilbrittain,
Co Cork, Ireland.
Tel +353 23 49610
Come sailing in comfortable 40' ketch with experienced skipper, on Ireland's beautiful, unspoilt south west coast. Wonderful sheltered bays, fascinating off-shore islands. Tuition available. Yacht based in Kinsale.

SOUTHAMPTON INSTITUTE
East Park Terrace,
Southampton, Hampshire SO14 0YN.
Tel (01703) 319000 Fax (01703) 222259
The Young Skippers Scheme offers young people the chance to develop their seamanship and personal skills at a price which just covers running costs. Our 23' Hunter Duettes are perfect for exploring the Solent. Contact Andy Moat (01703) 319787

RAMSGATE ROYAL HARBOUR MARINA
Harbour Office, Military Road,
Ramsgate, Kent CT11 9LQ.
Tel (01843) 592277 Fax (01843) 590941
Ramsgate Royal Harbour is situated on the south east coast, making an ideal base for crossing to the Continent. 24-hour access to finger pontoons. Comprehensive security systems. Amenities: Launderette; repairs; slipways; boatpark. Competitive rates for permanent berths and discounts for visitors' group bookings.

RIVERSFORD HOTEL
Limers Lane, Bideford, Devon EX39 2RG.
Tel (01237) 474239
Peace and tranquility in gardens beside the river Torridge. A relaxing retreat with convenient slipway close by. Excellent restaurant with efficient, friendly service with a choice of imaginative food and wine from our extensive menu and wine list. Comfortable, flexible lounge bar.

ST MAWES SAILING CLUB
No 1 The Quay,
St Mawes,
Truro, Cornwall TR2 5DG.
Tel (01326) 270686 Fax (01326) 270040
Quayside sailing club in centre of village. Visitor moorings in harbour. Private slip, launching and recovery facilities. Dinghy park, post box, showers. Visitors encouraged. Chandlery and sail repairs to order. No marina but a warm welcome awaits.

TARQUIN YACHT HARBOUR LTD
Thorney Road
Emsworth,
Hampshire PO10 8BP.
Tel (01243) 377727 Fax (01243) 373432
Friendly marina in Chichester harbour. Water, electricity, diesel, Calor gas, 25-tonne mobile crane, slipways, hard-standing and storage areas. Showers and toilets, car parking, chandlery, engineers and boat repairs.

WEIR QUAY BOATYARD
Heron's Reach,
Bere Alston,
Devon PL20 7BT.
Tel (01822) 840474 Fax (01822) 840948
Deepwater swinging moorings, shore storage, full boatyard facilities and services, cranage to 12 tons, repairs, maintenance, slipway. A traditional boatyard at affordable rates 'in a superb setting' on the Tamar, with excellent security.

WINTERS MARINE LTD
(Lincombe Boatyard)
Lincombe,
Salcombe, Devon TQ8 8NQ.
Tel (01548) 843580
Deep water pontoon moorings. Winter storage for 150 boats. All maintenance and repair facilities. Slipway capacity 30 tonnes. Inflatable craft sales and service. Lifecraft surveys and repairs. Short and long-term lifecraft hire.

MARLEC ENGINEERING CO LTD
Rutland House,
Trevithick Road,
Corby, Northamptonshire NN17 5XY.
Tel (01536) 201588 Fax (01536) 400211
For wind and solar powered battery charging on board talk to Marlec. We manufacture the Rutland Marine range of windchargers, and import and distribute Solarex photovoltaic modules. Manufacturer of Leisurelights - IOW energy high efficiency 12v lamps.

THOMAS WALKER GROUP LTD
37-41 Bissell Street,
Birmingham B5 7HR.
Tel 0121-622 4475 Fax 0121-622 4478
Manufacturer of marine instruments including, Neco Autopilots, Walker Logs and Towing Logs, Walker Anemometers, Chernikeeff Logs.

SPRAYHOODS & DODGERS

MARTELLO YACHT SERVICES
Mulberry House, Mulberry Road,
Canvey Island, Essex SS8 0PR.
Tel/Fax (01268) 681970
Manufacturer and supplier of made-to-measure upholstery, covers, hoods, dodgers, sailcovers, curtains and cushions etc. Repairs undertaken. DIY materials, chandlery and fitting-out supplies.

MARTEX
Hillside, Over Road, Church Minshull,
Nantwich, Cheshire CW5 6EA.
Tel/Fax (01270) 522251
Manufacturers of sprayhoods, dodgers, sailcovers, boomtents, sun awnings etc. Retailers of acrylic 'Canvas', pvc, sailcloth, sprayhood fittings, etc. Personal callers by appointment please.

STAINLESS STEEL FITTINGS

MANX MARINE
35 North Quay, Douglas,
Isle of Man IM1 4LB.
Tel/Fax (01624) 674842
The Island's leading and most established yacht chandlery. Stockists of quality foul-weather clothing and thermal wear. Large stock holdings of stainless steel fixtures and fittings and a comprehensive range of general chandlery including rigging facilities.

SURVEYORS/ARCHITECTS

ANDREW POTTER MA AMYDSA YACHT SURVEYOR
Penrallt Cottage, Cichle Hill,
Llandegfan, Anglesey LL59 5TD.
Tel/Fax (01248) 712358
Mobile 0374 411681
Prompt and professional surveys prior to purchase and for insurance purposes throughout Wales, the north west and Midlands. Services also include valuations, osmosis inspections and consultancy.

ANTHONY STAPLEY & ASSOCIATES
Deacons Boatyard, Bridge Road,
Burlesdon, Southampton,
Hampshire SO31 8AZ.
Tel/Fax (01703) 407407 (24hrs)
Mobile 0589 038839
Condition, pre-purchase, valuation, insurance,osmosis, structural and damage surveys. Fast, detailed reports with advice. Engine inspections, oil sample analysis,rigging tests, keel bolt tests. Probably the most competitive rates in the south. National and European (French and Spanish spoken).

CAPT MEL BARRATT MNI MCMS
29 The Paddock, Tarporley,
Cheshire CW6 0BT.
Tel (01829) 732063
Tel (01758) 712873 (Wales)
Fax (01829) 733221
Mobile 0831 685569
Prompt, professional condition, pre-purchase, insurance, valuation and damage

surveys in north west England, north and mid Wales. Full member Society of Consulting Marine Engineers and Ship Surveyors. Examiner for the Code of Practice for charter vessels. Established over 25 years.

CINQUE PORTS MARINE SERVICES
'Midwater' Willow Road,
Gt Mongeham, Nr Deal, Kent CT14 0HN.
Tel/Fax (01304) 365138
Mobile 0585 844653
Marine surveyor and consultant marine engineer. Damage, pre-purchase and full condition surveys. Machinery inspections and Code of Practice - safety of small commercial motor/sailing vessels. BW/NRA Boat Safety Certificate.

F J HARRIS BSc MRINA CENG
Naval Architect,
Surveyor & Boat Builder
'Gulls Target', 24 Roa Island,
Barrow in Furness, Cumbria LA13 0QL.
Tel (01229) 826084
Surveys of yachts and small craft for condition, insurance and repair. Design of yachts and small craft in traditional and modern materials. Work for MSA codes undertaken.

N W SEWAYS
Port Dinorwic Marina, Y Felinheli,
Gwynedd, North Wales LL56 4JN.
Tel (01248) 670620 Fax (01248) 671213
Mobile 0468 794361
Condition and pre-purchase surveys and insurance valuations, damage and repair reports, underwater dive inspections. Repair and dry dock facilities available. Call in or phone your requirement for prompt, professional service at competative rates.

PETER N DAVIES SURVEYS LTD
98 The Avenue, Wivenhoe,
Colchester, Essex CO7 9PP.
Tel (01206) 823289 Fax (01206) 826969
Condition pre-purchase, insurance valuation and damage surveys, UK and abroad. All types of material and hull construction. MSA Code of Practice certification. Traditional and square rig surveys. Marina and boatyard quantification surveys. Comprehensive, informative survey reports.

WARD & McKENZIE
12 Black Hill Road,
Holton Heath Trading Park,
Poole, Dorset BH16 6LS.
Tel (01202) 624690 Fax (01202) 632251
National and International Marine Surveyors, Technical and Legal Consultants, offering a comprehensive service to boat owners and those seeking to acquire pleasure yachts. All aspects of vessel search, survey, purchase and ownership undertaken, including insurance surveys, finance and disputes.

> **PLEASE MENTION THE MACMILLAN NAUTICAL ALMANAC WHEN MAKING ENQUIRIES**

TANKS

TEK-TANKS
Unit 5B Station Approach, Four Marks,
Alton, Hampshire GU34 5HN.
Tel (01420) 564359 Fax (01420) 561605
e-mail: tek_tanks@compuserve.com
Manufacturers of made-to-measure polypropylene water, waste and HDPE diesel tanks.

TENTS/AWNINGS

MARTEX
Hillside, Over Road, Church Minshull,
Nantwich, Cheshire CW5 6EA.
Tel/Fax (01270) 522251
Manufacturers of sprayhoods, dodgers, sailcovers, boomtents, sun awnings etc. Retailers of acrylic 'Canvas', pvc, sailcloth, sprayhood fittings, etc. Personal callers by appointment please.

TRADE ASSOCIATIONS

CHART & NAUTICAL INSTRUMENT TRADE ASSOCIATION (CNITA)
The Secretaries: Dalmore House,
310 St Vincent Street, Glasgow G2 5QR.
Members of the Association are able to place their experience and service at the disposal of the shipping industry and all navigators.

TRANSPORT, YACHT DELIVERIES & HAULAGE

ANGLO EUROPEAN BOAT TRANSPORT
Baltic Wharf Shipyard, St Peters Quay,
Totnes, South Devon TQ9 5EW.
Tel/Fax (01803) 868691
Mobile 0378 873889
Local UK - European boat and yacht transport. Telephone or fax 01803 868691

BRIAN BAGG YACHT DELIVERIES
Vine Cottage, Southampton Road,
Dibden, Southampton, SO45 5TA.
Tel/Fax (01703) 847514
Worldwide deliveries of sail, power and small commercial vessels. Undertaken with utmost care and consideration by professional yachtmaster. 300,000 miles and 370 deliveries completed since 1969. Telephone or fax for a competitive quotation.

CARDINAL YACHTS
12A Grafton Court, Grafton Road,
Torquay, Devon TQ1 1UP.
Tel/Fax (01803) 212954
Sail and power deliveries worldwide by experienced, commercial yachtmasters. Take the cheapest Mediterranean route with our combined sea and road service. Owners welcome. As an RYA recognised sea school we offer tuition at all levels.

CONVOI EXCEPTIONNEL
Castleton House, High Street, Hamble,
Southampton, Hampshire SO31 4HA.
Tel (01703) 453045 Fax (01703) 454551
International marine haulage and abnormal load consultants. Specialist services up to 40 tons.

DUNCAN GARRATT MARINE TRANSPORT
69A King Street, Plymouth, Devon PL1 5HY.
Tel (01752) 260945
Professional yacht and powerboat deliveries by experienced skipper and crew. Owners welcome. Areas cover south west and west coast of UK, Ireland, Europe and the Canaries. Specialist extended cruising scheme for existing owners. We can deliver your boat to your cruising location and return it at competitive rates.

MAX WALKER YACHT DELIVERIES
Zinderneuf Sailing, PO Box 105, Macclesfield, Cheshire SK10 2EY.
Tel (01625) 431712 Fax (01625) 619704
Fixed price deliveries. Sailing yachts delivered with care in north west European, UK and Eire waters by RYA/DoT yachtmaster and crew; 30 years' experience. Owners welcome. Tuition if required. References available. Your enquiries welcome 24 hours.

NELSON MARINE TRANSPORT
Trafalgar Garage, Ashleigh Road, Arnside, Carnforth, Lancashire LA5 0HE.
Tel/Fax (01524) 761481
Nelson Marine Transport and Storage. Specialist haulage nationwide. Competitive rates handled with a friendly, caring respect for boats.

PETERS & MAY LTD
18 Canute Road, Ocean Village, Southampton, Hampshire SO14 3FJ.
Tel (01703) 480480 Fax (01703) 480400
The 'Round the World' specialists in shipping, transporting, cradling yachts and powerboats. Weekly service to USA, Far East, Mediterranean, Middle East and Caribbean.

PORT À PORT YACHT SERVICES
Studio 6, Fox's Marina, The Strand, Ipswich, Suffolk IP2 8NJ.
Tel (01473) 692691 Fax (01473) 692693
Port à Port Services guarantee speedy and safe passage for your yacht. Our skippers are never less than instructor level and all crew hold RYA qualifications, ensuring your yacht is in the very best of hands.

SEALAND BOAT DELIVERIES LTD
64 Outwood Road, Radcliffe, Manchester, Lancashire M26 1AG.
Tel (01254) 705225 Fax (01254) 776582
http://www.btx.co.uk
Nationwide and European road transporters of all craft. No weight limit. We never close. Irish service. Worldwide shipping agents. Extrication of yachts from workshops and building yards. Salvage contractors. Established 25 years.

TREVOR VINCENT DELIVERIES
Coombe Cottage, 9 Swannaton Road, Dartmouth, Devon TQ6 9RL.
Tel/Fax (01803) 833757
Worldwide delivery of yachts and commercial vessels undertaken at short notice by RYA/DoT Yachtmaster Ocean (with commercial endorsement). Over 28 years' experience including three masted schooners, tugs, motor yachts and hi-tec racers. For instant quotes call/fax 01803 833757.

TUITION SAILING SCHOOLS

CARDINAL YACHTS
12A Grafton Court, Grafton Road, Torquay, Devon TQ1 1UP.
Tel/Fax (01803) 212954
Sail and power deliveries worldwide by experienced, commercial yachtmasters. Take the cheapest Mediterranean route with our combined sea and road service. Owners welcome. As an RYA recognised sea school we offer tuition at all levels.

FIVE STAR SAILING
Stone Pier Yard, Shore Road, Warsash, Southampton, Hampshire SO31 9FR.
Tel (01489) 885599 Fax (01489) 885505
Five Star Sailing offer RYA competent crew, day skipper, coastal skipper, yachtmaster offshore and ocean. Keel boat levels 1 to 5. Racing and race training. Top school for yachtmaster - 100% pass rate for over 5 years. Top school for racing, winning the Sailing School trophy for 5 years.

HOYLAKE SAILING SCHOOL
43a Market Street, Hoylake, Wirral L47 2BG.
Tel 0151-632 4664 Fax 0151-632 4776
RYA recognised shorebased teaching establishment offering a wide range of courses including Day Skipper to Yachtmaster Ocean, VHF and First Aid. Day, evening or intensive classes. Pratical courses by arrangement. Books, charts and gifts available.

ISLAND SEA SCHOOL
7 Church View, South Milford, Leeds LS25 5BM.
Tel/Fax (01977) 685394
e-mail: sea.school@mcmail.com
RYA practical courses from our base at Port Dinorwic on the Menai Strait: Competent Crew, Day Skipper, Coastal Skipper, Yachtmaster Preparatory, Ocean Yachtmaster Qualifying Passages. Own boat tuition. Skippered charter.

NATIONAL MARINE CORRESPONDENCE SCHOOL
30 Woodside Business Park, Shore Road, Birkenhead, Merseyside L41 1EL
Tel/Fax 0151-647 6777
The UK's leading correspondence school with courses from basic navigation to ocean cruising including RYA courses Day Skipper, Coastal Skipper/Yachtmaster and Yachtmaster Ocean. RYA accredited for courses in power and sail, UK and overseas.

PECULIAR YACHTS LTD
Haslar Marina, Haslar Road, Gosport, Hampshire PO12 1NU.
Tel/Fax (01705) 589953
Mobile 0402 220983
Yacht charter both bareboat and skippered on a wide range of different boats to suit all tastes and budgets. One-way charters arranged. Also catamaran based in Spain with villa. RYA and VHF courses plus own boat tuition.

PEMBROKESHIRE CRUISING
Cleddau House, Milford Marina, Milford Haven, Pembrokeshire SA73 3AF.
Tel/Fax (01646) 690285
Sail around the dramatic and unspoilt beauty of Britain's only coastal national park. Professional RYA tuition for beginners to Yachtmaster, practical and theory. Yacht charter and skippered adventure cruises to Ireland, Cornwall and the Scillies.

SHEARWATER CRUISES
Seaview Farm, Kilbrittain, Co Cork, Ireland.
Tel +353 23 49610
Come sailing in comfortable 40' ketch with experienced skipper, on Ireland's beautiful, unspoilt south west coast. Wonderful sheltered bays, fascinating off-shore islands. Tuition available. Yacht based in Kinsale.

SOUTHAMPTON INSTITUTE
East Park Terrace, Southampton, Hampshire SO14 0YN.
Tel (01703) 319000 Fax (01703) 222259
The Young Skippers Scheme offers young people the chance to develop their seamanship and personal skills at a price which just covers running costs. Our 23' Hunter Duettes are perfect for exploring the Solent. Contact Andy Moat (01703) 319787

START POINT SAILING
Cover House, 113 Bewdley Road, Kidderminster, Worcestershire DY11 6RX.
Tel (01562) 748635 Fax (01562) 746089
Small craft training and tuition - RYA practical courses, competent crew, day skipper, yachtmaster, shorebased navigation and pilotage, diesel engine, sea survival, VHF first aid courses. Competitive yacht charter from Dartmouth and Plymouth. Beginners and families welcome.

SULU YACHT CHARTER
The Lodge House, Glenborrodale Castle, Acharacle, Argyll PH36 4JP.
Tel/Fax (01972) 500218
Two Jeanneau Melodie 35' yachts available for skippered or bareboat charters in the magnificent Western Isles of Scotland. Enjoy the holiday of a lifetime. RYA courses available. Yachts to DoT standard.

UPHOLSTERY & COVERS

BRUCE BANKS SAILS LTD
372 Brook Lane, Sarisbury, Southampton, Hampshire SO31 7ZA.
Tel (01489) 582444 Fax (01489) 589789
e-mail: enquiries@banks.co.uk
http:/www.banks.co.uk
Banks Sails are manufacturers of high quality racing and cruising sails. Banks also offer a range of dinghy covers and accessories. Pick up points at all Hamble marinas, Gosport and Southampton waters.

MARTELLO YACHT SERVICES
Mulberry House,
Mulberry Road,
Canvey Island, Essex SS8 0PR.
Tel/Fax (01268) 681970
Manufacturer and supplier of made-to-measure upholstery, covers, hoods, dodgers, sailcovers, curtains and cushions etc. Repairs undertaken. DIY materials, chandlery and fitting-out supplies.

WEATHER INFORMATION

MARINECALL - TELEPHONE INFORMATION SERVICES
Avalon House,
London EC2A 4PJ.
Tel 0171-631 6000
Marinecall provides detailed coastal weather forecasts for 17 different regions, up to 5 days ahead from the Met Office. For a full fax list of services dial 0891 24 66 80. Telephone forecasts are updated daily, morning and afternoon.

PROSSER SCIENTIFIC INSTRUMENTS LTD
Lady Lane Industrial Estate,
Hadleigh,
Ipswich, Suffolk IP7 6BQ.
Tel (01473) 823005 Fax (01473) 824095
Manufacturers of a range of marine instruments, including the WEATHERTREND digital barometer, with full 24-hour history, the unique TIDECLOCK tidal data predictor and tidal software for the PSION 3 series.

WIND POWER

ARIES VANE GEAR SPARES
48 St Thomas Street,
Penryn, Cornwall TR10 8JW.
Tel (01326) 377467 Fax (01326) 378117
Spare parts, re-build kits for all existing Aries gears.

MARLEC ENGINEERING CO LTD
Rutland House, Trevithick Road,
Corby, Northamptonshire NN17 5XY.
Tel (01536) 201588 Fax (01536) 400211
For wind and solar powered battery charging on board talk to Marlec. We manufacture the Rutland Marine range of wind windchargers, and import and distribute Solarex photovoltaic modules. Manufacturer of Leisurelights - IOW energy high efficiency 12v lamps.

WINDOWS, DOORS & HATCHES

SEAGLAZE MARINE WINDOWS LTD
Wendover Road, Rackheath, Norwich,
Norfolk NR13 6LH.
Tel (01603) 720745 Fax (01603) 721770
Manufacturer of high quality windows, doors and hatches for the marine industry. Exclusive suppliers to the RNLI. We will supply a one-off window/door or a whole set for your boat, no matter what shape, size or colour. We also offer a refurbishment service.

WOOD FITTINGS

SHERATON MARINE CABINET
White Oak Green,
Hailey,
Witney, Oxfordshire OX8 5XP.
Tel/Fax (01993) 868275
Manufacturers of quality teak and mahogany marine fittings, louvre doors, gratings and tables. Special fitting-out items to customer specification. Colour catalogue available on request.

YACHT BROKERS

ARDFERN YACHT CENTRE
Ardfern By Lochgilphead,
Argyll PA31 8QN.
Tel (01852) 500247/636 Fax (01852) 500624
Boatyard with full repair and maintenance facilities. Timber and GRP repairs, painting and engineering. Sheltered moorings and pontoon berthing. Winter storage, chandlery, showers, fuel, Calor, brokerage, 20-ton boat hoist. Hotel, bars and restaurant.

CRAOBH MARINA
By Lochgilphead,
Argyll PA31 8UD.
Tel (01852) 500222 Fax (01852) 500252
250-berth marina on Loch Shuna. Water, electricity, diesel and gas. Full boatyard services. Chandlery. Brokerage. Insurance. Shops, bar. 24-hour access. VHF Ch37 and 80 (M).

DEACONS BOATYARD LTD
Bursledon Bridge,
Southampton, Hampshire SO3 8AZ.
Tel (01703) 402253 Fax (01703) 405665
This yard provides a comprehensive range of services including moorings, laying-up of boats, boat repairs, marine engineering, rigging, sail making and repairs and brokerage etc.

YACHT CHARTERS & HOLIDAYS

CRINAN YACHT CHARTERS
The Pump House, Crinan,
Argyll PA31 8SP.
Tel (01546) 830260 Fax (01546) 83025
Bareboat and skippered charters around the Hebrides. Fantastic cruising. Sheltered waters, wildlife, distilleries and isolated anchorages, yet with marine services within easy reach. 'Crinan - Where it all begins.'

FIRSTAWAY CHARTERS
23 Orchard Lea,
Swanmore,
Southampton, Hampshire SO32 2QZ.
Tel/Fax (01489) 893889
UK charter. 30-44' fast cruising yachts.

GULLIVERS YACHT SERVICES
Antells Farm, Stour Provost,
Gillingham, Dorset SP8 5SA.
e-mail: EAJ@Gullivers.T/Me.com
Tel (01747) 838987 Fax (01747) 838853
Yacht consultancy for private and corporate clients. Complete yacht management service in UK and abroad. International

yacht charter brokers for 2000 sailing and motoryachts worldwide, including the most luxurious, fully crewed, bareboat and single berths. Member BMIF YCA.

ISLAND SEA SCHOOL
7 Church View, South Milford,
Leeds LS25 5BM.
Tel/Fax (01977) 685394
e-mail: sea.school@mcmail.com
RYA practical courses from our base at Port Dinorwic on the Menai Strait: Competent Crew, Day Skipper, Coastal Skipper, Yachtmaster Preparatory, Ocean Yachtmster Qualifying Passages. Own boat tuition. Skippered charter.

ODYSSEUS YACHTING HOLIDAYS
33 Grand Parade, Brighton,
East Sussex BN2 2QA.
Tel (01273) 695094 Fax (01273) 688855
Templecraft Yacht Charters are bonded tour operators specialising in independent yacht charter holidays in the Mediterranean and in the Caribbean, and as Odysseus Yachting Holidays in flotilla sailing holidays in Corfu and the Ionian islands.

PECULIAR YACHTS LTD
Haslar Marina, Haslar Road, Gosport,
Hampshire PO12 1NU.
Tel/Fax (01705) 589953
Yacht charter both bareboat and skippered on a wide range of different boats to suit all tastes and budgets. One-way charters arranged. Also catamaran based in Spain with villa. RYA and VHF courses plus own boat tuition.

PEMBROKESHIRE CRUISING
Cleddau House, Milford Marina,
Milford Haven,
Pembrokeshire SA73 3AF.
Tel/Fax (01646) 690285
Sail around the dramatic and unspoilt beauty of Britain's only coastal national park. Professional RYA tuition for beginners to Yachtmaster, practical and theory. Yacht charter and skippered adventure cruises to Ireland, Cornwall and the Scillies.

RELIANCE YACHT MANAGEMENT LTD
34 Netley Street, Farnborough,
Hampshire GU14 6AQ.
Tel (01252) 378239 Fax (01252) 521736
e-mail:100713.363@compuserve.com
With over 10 years' experience we offer a professional management and delivery service. Your yacht can be safely and expertly delivered anywhere in the world by highly experienced skippers and crews. We are also able to offer 'Total Solution Management Packages' designed to suit your needs. Offices in the Caribbean, Pacific, Asia and France.

SAIL IRELAND CHARTERS
Trident Hotel, Kinsale, Co Cork, Ireland.
Tel +353 21 772927 Fax +353 21 774170
Sail Ireland Charters is Ireland's premier yacht charter company. Yachts varying in size from 35' to 50' Beneteau's, Sigma's. Based in the picturesque village of Kinsale, an ideal place to commence your cruise of Europe's secret paradise of uncrowded sailing.

SAIL NORTHWEST
45 Ingrow Lane, Keighley,
West Yorkshire BD22 7BU.
Tel/Fax (01535) 602133
Sail Northwest offers yacht charter, skippered charter, and management from Maryport's marina, north Cumbria (40 minutes from M62, Lake District). We also manufacture customised fused switch panels, and refurbishment, including steps, tables and laminated tillers.

SHEARWATER CRUISES
Seaview Farm, Kilbrittain, Co Cork,
Ireland.
Tel +353 23 49610
Come sailing in comfortable 40' ketch with experienced skipper, on Ireland's beautiful, unspoilt south west coast. Wonderful sheltered bays, fascinating off-shore islands. Tuition available. Yacht based in Kinsale.

SLEAT MARINE SERVICES
Ardvasar, Isle of Skye IV45 8RU.
Tel (01471) 844216/844387
Yacht charter (bareboat and skippered) from Armadale Bay, Isle of Skye. Six yachts 34' to 40' LOA. All medium to heavy displacement blue water cruisers. Fuel, water and emergency services for passing yachts with problems.

SOUTHAMPTON INSTITUTE
East Park Terrace, Southampton,
Hampshire SO14 0YN.
Tel (01703) 319000 Fax (01703) 222259
The Young Skippers Scheme offers young people the chance to develop their seamanship and personal skills at a price which just covers running costs. Our 23' Hunter Duettes are perfect for exploring the Solent. Contact Andy Moat (01703) 319787.

ST BLANE'S YACHT CHARTER
Crofton Cottage, Ascog, Rothesay,
Isle of Bute PA20 9LN.
Tel (01700) 503108
Firth of Clyde and west coast of Scotland - Largs Marina or Rothesay Harbour. Bareboat yacht charters. Yachts available from 30' to 34' including the latest style Legend 295 and 336.

START POINT SAILING
Cover House, 113 Bewdley Road,
Kidderminster,
Worcestershire DY11 6RX.
Tel (01562) 748635 Fax (01562) 746089
Small craft training and tuition - RYA practical courses, competent crew, day skipper, yachtmaster, shorebased navigation and pilotage, diesel engine, sea survival, VHF first aid courses. Competitive yacht charter from Dartmouth and Plymouth. Beginners and families welcome.

STAYSAIL
The Old Rectory, Rectory Road,
Llangwen, Haverfordwest,
Pembrokeshire SA62 4JA.
Tel (01437) 890078 Fax (01437) 899309
Holidays for dinghy/cruiser sailors, or space and comfort for their non-sailing partners. Use our dinghies/cruisers or bring your own. Paint, draw, relax, walk and sightsee.

En-suite rooms overlooking breathtaking estuary. Scrumptious cooking.

SULU YACHT CHARTER
The Lodge House, Glenborrodale Castle,
Acharacle, Argyll PH36 4JP.
Tel/Fax (01972) 500218
Two Jeanneau Melodie 35' yachts available for skippered or bareboat charters in the magnificent Western Isles of Scotland. Enjoy the holiday of a lifetime. RYA courses available. Yachts to DoT standard.

TEMPLECRAFT YACHT CHARTERS
33 Grand Parade, Brighton,
East Sussex BN2 2QA.
Tel (01273) 695094 Fax (01273) 688855
Templecraft Yacht Charters are bonded tour operators specialising in independent yacht charter holidays in the Mediterranean and in the Caribbean, and as Odysseus Yachting Holidays in flotilla sailing holidays in Corfu and the Ionian islands.

YACHT CLUB FACILITIES

KINSALE YACHT CLUB MARINA
Kinsale, Co Cork, Ireland.
Tel +353 21 772196 Fax +353 21 774426
Mobile +353 87 449471
Magnificent deep water yacht club marina offering Kinsale hospitality to visiting yachtsmen. Full facilities include berths up to 20 metres, fresh water, electricity, diesel on pier. Club bar and wealth of pubs and restaurants in Kinsale. Enter Kinsale Harbour - lit at night - no restrictions.

PARKSTONE YACHT CLUB
Pearce Avenue, Parkstone, Poole,
Dorset BH14 8EH.
Tel (01202) 743610 Fax (01202) 716394
Deep water club haven facilities in Poole harbour. Access at all states of the tide. Berths for yachts up to 15 metres. Facilities include electricity, fresh water, toilets and showers. Visitors welcome by appointment. Club bar and restaurant.

PEMBROKESHIRE YACHT CLUB
Gellyswick Bay, Milford Haven,
Pembrokeshire SA73 3RS.
Tel (01646) 692799
Visitors welcome. Slipway, pontoon. Open every day.

ROYAL CORK YACHT CLUB
Crosshaven, Co Cork, Ireland.
Tel +353 21 831023 Fax +353 21 831586
Sheltered 120-berth marina. Visitors welcome.

ROYAL WESTERN YACHT CLUB
Queen Anne's Battery, Plymouth,
Devon PL4 0TW.
Tel (01752) 660077 Fax (01752) 224299
Home of shorthanded sailing. Visiting yachtsmen welcome. Mooring facilities available.

ST MAWES SAILING CLUB
No 1 The Quay, St Mawes, Truro,
Cornwall TR2 5DG.
Tel (01326) 270686 Fax (01326) 270040
Quayside sailing club in centre of village.

Visitor moorings in harbour. Private slip, launching and recovery facilities. Dinghy park, post box, showers. Visitors encouraged. Chandlery and sail repairs to order. No marina but a warm welcome awaits.

YACHT MANAGEMENT

GULLIVERS YACHT SERVICES
Antells Farm, Stour Provost, Gillingham,
Dorset SP8 5SA.
Tel (01747) 838987 Fax (01747) 838853
e-mail: EAJ@Gullivers.Tel/Me.com
Yacht consultancy for private and corporate clients. Complete yacht management service in UK and abroad. International yacht charter brokers for 2000 sailing and motoryachts worldwide, including the most luxurious, fully crewed, bareboat and single berths. Member BMIF YCA.

PECULIAR YACHTS LTD
Haslar Marina, Haslar Road, Gosport,
Hampshire PO12 1NU.
Tel/Fax (01705) 589953
Yacht charter both bareboat and skippered on a wide range of different boats to suit all tastes and budgets. One-way charters arranged. Also catamaran based in Spain with villa. RYA and VHF courses plus own boat tuition.

RELIANCE YACHT MANAGEMENT LTD
34 Netley Street, Farnborough,
Hampshire GU14 6AQ.
Tel (01252) 378239 Fax (01252) 521736
e-mail:100713.363@compuserve.com
With over 10 years' experience we offer a professional management and delivery service. Your yacht can be safely and expertly delivered anywhere in the world by highly experienced skippers and crews. We are also able to offer 'Total Solution Management Packages' designed to suit your needs. Offices in the Caribbean, Pacific, Asia and France.

SAIL NORTHWEST
45 Ingrow Lane, Keighley,
West Yorkshire BD22 7BU.
Tel/Fax (01535) 602133
Sail Northwest offers yacht charter, skippered charter, and management from Maryport's marina, north Cumbria (40 minutes from M62, Lake District). We also manufacture customised fused switch panels, and refurbishment, including steps, tables and laminated tillers.

YACHT REGISTRATION

WILDE MARINE SERVICES LTD
PO Box 112, Pollet House,
Lower Pollet, St Peter Port,
Guernsey, Channel Islands GY1 4EA.
Tel (01481) 725840 Fax (01481) 711156
British yacht registration, corporate yacht ownership and management, marine insurance, crew placement and management. Wilde Marine Services (previously known as International Marine Services) aims to provide a personal and individual service to its clients.

WATERSIDE ACCOMMODATION & RESTAURANTS

Sometimes after a long haul, or at the end of an arduous day carrying out necessary maintenance on your boat, or indeed as part of your holiday you may wish to enjoy the luxury of haute cuisine or simply a good meal cooked by somebody else, followed maybe, by a comfortable bed for the night. The following list guides you to hotels, restaurants and accommodation with their own private berths, or moorings close by.

ARDENTINNY HOTEL
Ardentinny, Loch Long, By Dunoon, Argyll PA23 8TR.
Tel (01369) 810209 Fax (01369) 810241
A warm Scottish welcome awaits you at the Ardentinny. Delightful dinners to a very high standard are prepared by our chef complemented by a choice of over 50 selections of French and New World wines. Excellent casual lunches served in the garden or buttery. Friendly bar, frequented by yachtsmen, with a good selection of beer. Seven moorings available.

COLUMBA HOTEL
East Pier Road, Tarbert, Loch Fyne, Argyll PA29 6UF.
Tel/Fax (01880) 820808
3-Crown Commended hotel in peaceful lochside position. Log fired bars offering rather special bar meals. Restaurant serving the best of Scottish produce imaginatively prepared. 'Taste of Scotland' recommended. Sauna, gym and solarium. Courtesy car available.

THE CREGGANS INN
Strachur, Argyll PA27 8BX.
Tel (01369) 860279 Fax (01369) 860637
The Creggans Inn has been described as 'The kind of waterside blessing every visitor to the Highlands dreams of discovering'. Owned by Sir Charles MacLean. 3-Star hotel. Award-winning restaurant specialising in local seafood and game.

DART MARINA HOTEL
Sandquay, Dartmouth, Devon TQ6 9QS.
Tel (01803) 832580 Fax (01803) 83504
All 50 bedrooms and public rooms overlook the river. Brasserie menu served on the terrace and in the River Bar. Stylish Hanley's restaurant for table d'hôte dinner. Excellent wine list. Ample parking. Marina-side location.

THE GALLEY OF LORNE INN
Ardfern, by Lochgilphead, Argyll PA31 8QN.
Egon Ronay & STB 3-Crown Commended
Tel (01852) 500284
Traditional inn on the shores of Loch Craignish, renowned for a warm welcome to yachtsmen. Well known pub with log fires and good company. Excellent restaurant specialising in local seafood. All bedrooms newly refurbished, with private facilities. Two minutes from Ardfern Yacht Centre.

GIGHA HOTEL
Isle of Gigha, Argyll PA41 7AA.
Tel (01583) 505254 Fax (01583) 505244
Beautiful island, good food, lots of booze and friendly folk. Ideal to pick up or leave your family when sailing around the Mull of Kintyre. Moorings, water, fuel, showers and laundry facilities. Self-catering cottages also available. Achamore Gardens and 9-hole golf course.

THE HARBOUR LIGHTS RESTAURANT (Walton-on-Naze) Ltd
Titchmarsh Marina, Coles Lane, Walton-on-the-Naze, Essex CO14 8SL.
Tel (01255) 672185 Fax (01255) 851901
Open 7 days a week the Harbour Lights offers a welcome to yachtsmen and land-lubbers alike. Bar meals served all day, coffee and afternoon tea. Excellent menu choice in the restaurant overlooking the marina in this peaceful backwater.

THE HAVEN ARMS PUB & RESTAURANT
Kilrush, Co Clare, Ireland.
Tel +353 65 51267 Fax +353 65 51213
'The Haven Arms' - Kilrush - *Sail* into this pub and restaurant which has become a landmark to generations of local people and visitor alike. The 'Ship' restaurant offers appetising meals complemented by good service from our friendly staff. 'MOORINGS ARE FREE'.

HULL MARINA LTD
Warehouse 13, Kingston Street, Hull HU1 2DQ.
Tel (01482) 613451 Fax (01482) 224148
Four-Anchor marina. Situated 5 minues from the centre of Hull and all national and international transport systems. First class leisure, boatyard and brokerage facilities. 4-Star hotel and quayside restaurants. Professional and caring staff. Competitive rates.

KAMES HOTEL
Kames, By Tighnabruaich, Argyll PA21 2AF.
Tel (01700) 811489 Fax (01700) 811283
On the Kyles of Bute, with 15 free moorings. Good food, real ales, fine malts. Showers availables for visitors. 10 en-suite bedrooms. Regular music nights. Fresh local seafood in season.

KING SITRIC FISH RESTAURANT
East Pier, Howth, Co Dublin, Ireland.
Tel +353 832 5235 & 6729 Fax +353 839 2442
Lovely location on the harbour front. Marina and Howth Yacht Club 3 minutes walk. Established 1971, Aidan and Joan MacManus have earned an international reputation for superb, fresh seafood, service and hospitality. Wine conoisseurs take note! Quality accommodation April 1998. Informal summer lunch - dinner all year.

MOORES HOTEL
Le Pollet, St Peter Port, Guernsey, Channel Islands GY1 1WH.
Tel (01481) 724452 Fax (01481) 714057
Minutes away from the marina. The Library Bar at Moores offers great value carverys, sumptious seafood platters and a wide selection of fresh fish. Comfortable, en-suite bedrooms for those who don't want to sleep aboard.

Shetland Islands

7

Orkney Islands

Cape Wrath

Rattray Head

8

Scotland

Loch Craignish

Crinan Canal

Eyemouth

Berwick-on-Tweed

9

6

13

Northern Ireland

Mull of Galloway

Isle of Man

5

Lambay Island

10

Liscanor Bay

Ireland

12

Bardsey Island

Wales

England **4**

11

Great Yarmouth

20

Netherlands **Germany**

Land's End

Selsey Bill

3

Nieuwpoort

Belgium

Portland Bill

2

19

Pte de Barfleur

Isles of Scilly

1

16

14

Paimpol

Portrieux

Channel Islands

Raz de Sein

15

F r a n c e

17

River Loire

Denmark

Sylt

21

Helgoland

Emden

Delfzijl

River Elbe

18

Spain

Spanish Border

AREA MAP
showing coastal divisions.

Inland waterways are classified by coastal access

Coastal and Waterways Services Directory - Area by Area

SOUTH WEST ENGLAND (AREA 1)
Scilly Isles to Portland Bill

ALL SPARS (KEMP SOUTHWEST)
The Boathouse, Commercial Road, Penryn, Falmouth, Cornwall TR10 8AE. Tel (01326) 374177 Fax (01326) 377696. Regional centre for SELDÉN and KEMP integrated sailing systems. Full range of rigging services on-site and mobile. Large and comprehensively stocked chandlery to cover all yachting requirements. Support and back-up for retail and trade alike.

ANGLO EUROPEAN BOAT TRANSPORT
Baltic Wharf Shipyard, St Peters Quay, Totnes, South Devon TQ9 5EW. Tel/Fax (01803) 868691. Mobile 0378 873889 Local UK - European boat and yacht transport. Telephone or fax 01803 868691

ARIES VANE GEAR SPARES
48 St Thomas Street, Penryn, Cornwall TR10 8JW. Tel (01326) 377467 Fax (01326) 378117. Spare parts, re-build kits for all existing Aries gears.

ATLANTIC SPARS (KEMP WEST)
The Loft, Mayors Avenue, Dartmouth, Devon TQ6 9NG. Tel (01803) 833322 Fax (01803) 835855. Regional centre for SELDÉN and KEMP integrated sailing systems. Services include standing and running rigging, repairs, custom spars and furling systems. Aluminium design and fabrications for industry. Official suppliers to the BT Global Challenge.

BRITISH WATERWAYS & THE ENVIRONMENT AGENCY
CANAL & RIVER LINE 0891 546 555. Our canals and rivers provide: marinas, moorings, berthing, boatyard services and relaxing, picturesque waters for cruising. Find out more from Canal and River Line (50p minute peak rate at 45p minute other times).

BRIXHAM YACHT SUPPLIES LTD
72 Middle Street, Brixham, Devon TQ5 8EJ. Tel (01803) 882290. We stock a complete range of sailing and leisure clothing. English and Continental pure wool traditional knitwear. Camping accessories.

CARDINAL YACHTS
12A Grafton Court, Grafton Road, Torquay, Devon TQ1 1UP. Tel/Fax (01803) 212954. Sail and power deliveries worldwide by experienced, commercial yachtmasters. Take the cheapest Mediterranean route with our combined sea and road service. Owners welcome. As an RYA recognised sea school we offer tuition at all levels.

THE CARTOON GALLERY (Wavelength Design)
37 Lower Street, Dartmouth, Devon TQ6 9AN. Tel/Fax (01803) 834466 Tel (01803) 834425 Evenings. Rick, the International Cartoonist specialises in hand coloured and personalised sailing cartoon prints (eg A3 £10). Commissions are carried out in Rick's Dartmouth gallery and studio. Prints available by mail order. Telephone or fax for details.

CHALLENGE MARINE
Freeman's Wharf, Falmouth Road, Penryn, Cornwall TR10 8AS. Tel (01326) 377222 Fax (01326) 377800. Marine engineers, chandlery, boatyard. Main Volvo Penta dealer, marina berths, brokerage and Bombard inflatables' dealer.

CLOVELLY BAY MARINA
The Quay, Turnchapel, Plymouth, Devon PL9 9TF. Tel (01752) 404231 Fax (01752) 484177. Position: Southern side of cattewater, sheltered from prevailing winds by Mountbatten Peninsula. Open: All year, 24 hours. Radio: VHF Ch37 and 80. Callsign: Clovelly Bay. Berths: 180 berths, vessels up to 150', some fore and afts, visitors welcome. Facilities: electricity, water, 24-hour security, workshop, chandlery, brokerage, showers, laundry, diesel. Calor gas, payphone, refuse, water taxi, two local pubs. NEW MARINA OPENS 1st APRIL 1998.

DART MARINA
Sandquay, Dartmouth, Devon TQ6 9PH. Tel (01803) 833351 Fax (01803) 832307. High quality 110-berth marina on the fabulous river Dart, opposite the Dart Marina hotel. A superb situation with all amenities, 24-hour security, hotel and restaurant, showers, baths and laundry, fuel berth and a warm welcome to all visitors.

DART MARINA HOTEL
Sandquay, Dartmouth, Devon TQ6 9QS. Tel (01803) 832580 Fax (01803) 83504. All 50 bedrooms and public rooms overlook the river. Brasserie menu served on the terrace and in the River Bar. Stylish Hanley's restaurant for table d'hôte dinner. Excellent wine list. Ample parking. Marina-side location.

DARTHAVEN MARINA LTD
Brixham Road, Kingswear, Dartmouth, Devon TQ6 0SG. Tel (01803) 752242 Fax (01803) 752722 Marina Office: (01803) 752545 Chandlery: (01803) 752733. Fax: (01803) 752790 All types of repair facilities available. Fully trained staff. 30-ton mobile hoist available all states of tide. Extensive chandlery open 7 days a week. Agents for Autohelm/Raytheon, Cetrek, B&G, Simrad Stowe, Navico, Simpson Lawrence, Sowester, International Paint, Webasto, Yanmar Main Agents, Volvo Penta ASW and Vetus sales and service. Visitors welcome. 24-hour engineering call-out service mobile numbers 0860 873553 and 0467 250787 for electronics.

DUCHY OF CORNWALL
Harbour Office, St Mary's, Isles of Scilly, Cornwall TR21 0HU. Tel/Fax (01720) 422768. Port of St Mary's, Isles of Scilly - 38 visitor moorings. New visitor centre, hot showers, toilets, launching facilities, winter storage, security lockers, fuel and fresh water. 5 minutes from town centre. Ferry terminal and airport close by. Contact Harbour Master for more information.

PORT FALMOUTH BOATYARD
North Parade, Falmouth, Cornwall TR11 2TB. Tel (01326) 313248
Fax (01326) 319395. Full boatyard facilities. Powered hoist, slipway
cradle.

PORT OF TRURO
Harbour Office, Town Quay, Truro, Cornwall. Tel (01872) 272130
Fax (01872) 225346. Facilities for the yachtsman include visitor
pontoons located at Turnaware Bar, Ruan Creek and Boscawen
Park. Visitor moorings at Woodbury. Quay facilities at Truro with free
showers and toilets. Chemical toilet disposal, fresh water and
garbage disposal.

RIVERSFORD HOTEL
Limers Lane, Bideford, Devon EX39 2RG. Tel (01237) 474239.
Peace and tranquility in gardens beside the river Torridge. A
relaxing retreat with convenient slipway close by. Excellent restaurant
with efficient, friendly service with a choice of imaginative food and
wine from our extensive menu and wine list. Comfortable, flexible
lounge bar.

ROYAL WESTERN YACHT CLUB
Queen Anne's Battery, Plymouth, Devon PL4 0TW. Tel (01752)
660077 Fax (01752) 224299. Home of shorthanded sailing. Visiting
yachtsmen welcome. Mooring facilities available.

THE SEA CHEST NAUTICAL BOOKS & CHARTS
Queen Anne's Battery Marina, Plymouth, Devon PL4 0LP.
Tel (01752) 222012 Fax (01752) 252679. Admiralty Chart Agent.
Worldwide mail order service.

SOUTHDOWN MARINA
Southdown Quay, Millbrook, Cornwall PL10 1HG. Tel/Fax (01752)
823084. 32-berth marina on edge of river Tamar in quiet location
behind Rame Peninsula. Plymouth is just across the river. Quayside
berths available for large vessels. Winter storage. 24-hour security.
DIY facilities available.

ST MAWES SAILING CLUB
No 1 The Quay, St Mawes, Truro, Cornwall TR2 5DG. Tel (01326)
270686 Fax (01326) 270040. Quayside sailing club in centre of
village. Visitor moorings in harbour. Private slip, launching and
recovery facilities. Dinghy park, post box, showers. Visitors
encouraged. Chandlery and sail repairs to order. No marina but a
warm welcome awaits.

START POINT SAILING
Cover House, 113 Bewdley Road, Kidderminster, Worcestershire
DY11 6RX. Tel (01562) 748635 Fax (01562) 746089. Small craft
training and tuition - RYA practical courses, competent crew, day
skipper, yachtmaster, shorebased navigation and pilotage, diesel
engine, sea survival, VHF first aid courses. Competitive yacht
charter from Dartmouth and Plymouth. Beginners and families
welcome.

TREVOR VINCENT DELIVERIES
Coombe Cottage, 9 Swannaton Road, Dartmouth, Devon
TQ6 9RL. Tel/Fax (01803) 833757. Worldwide delivery of yachts
and commercial vessels undertaken at short notice by RYA/DoT
Yachtmaster Ocean (with commercial endorsement). Over 28 years'
experience including three masted schooners, tugs, motor yachts
and hi-tec racers. For instant quotes call/fax 01803 833757.

UPPER DECK MARINE/OUTRIGGERS
Albert Quay, Fowey, Cornwall PL23 1AQ. Tel (01726) 832287
Fax (01726) 833265. Chandlery, fastenings, paints, cords, fenders,
anchors, compasses, lifejackets, Gaz. Leading names in waterproofs
and warm wear.

WEIR QUAY BOATYARD
Heron's Reach, Bere Alston, Devon PL20 7BT. Tel (01822)
840474 Fax (01822) 840948. Deepwater swinging moorings, shore
storage, full boatyard facilities and services, cranage to 12 tons,
repairs, maintenance, slipway. A traditional boatyard at affordable
rates 'in a superb setting' on the Tamar, with excellent security.

WINTERS MARINE LTD (Lincombe Boatyard)
Lincombe, Salcombe, Devon TQ8 8NQ. Tel (01548) 843580.
Deep water pontoon moorings. Winter storage for 150 boats. All
maintenance and repair facilities. Slipway capacity 30 tonnes.
Inflatable craft sales and service. Lifecraft surveys and repairs.
Short and long-term lifecraft hire.

CENTRAL SOUTHERN ENGLAND
(AREA 2)
Portland Bill to Selsey Bill

ANTHONY STAPLEY & ASSOCIATES
Deacons Boatyard, Bridge Road, Burlesdon, Southampton,
Hampshire SO31 8AZ. Mobile 0589 038839 Tel/Fax (01703)
407407 (24hrs). Condition, pre-purchase, valuation,
insurance, osmosis, structural and damage surveys. Fast, detailed
reports with advice. Engine inspections, oil sample analysis, rigging
tests, keel bolt tests. Probably the most competitive rates in the
south. National and European (French and Spanish spoken).

AQUA-MARINE MANUFACTURING (UK) LTD
216 Fair Oak Road, Bishopstoke, Eastleigh, Hampshire SO50
8NJ. Tel (01703) 694949 Fax (01703) 601381 Sales Fax (01703).
601188 e-mail: sales@aqua-marine.co.uk Manufacturer and
distributor of chandlery, including: Engel refrigeration, Dutton-
Lainson winches, Anchor fenders, Rule pumps, Aquaflow water
systems, SeaStar steering and controls, Skyblazer flares. Admiralty
small craft charts, Aquametcompasses, RWO and Holt fittings,
Danforth anchors, Aqua-Signal lights, Techimpex cookers.

BEAULIEU RIVER MANAGEMENT LTD
Harbour Master's Office, Bucklers Hard Yacht Harbour, Beaulieu,
Hampshire SO42 7XB. Tel (01590) 616200 Fax (01590) 616211.
110-berth yacht harbour (pontoon berths), fully serviced with back-
up facilities of historic Bucklers Hard village. Agamemnon boatyard
- 290 swinging moorings let on annual basis. Visiting craft welcome.
Capacity 100+ pile/pontoon.

BIRDHAM SHIPYARD LTD
Birdham Pool, Chichester, West Sussex PO20 7BG. Tel (01243) 512310 Fax (01243) 513163. Quiet, picturesque marina in Chichester harbour. Moorings available for boats up to 55' overall and 5'6" draught. Chandlery and all boatyard sevices available. Visitors welcome.

BOOK CABIN
Unit 20, Canutes Pavilion, Ocean Village, Southampton, Hampshire SO14 3JS. Tel (01703) 211199 Fax (01703) 338488. Nautical and general booksellers.

BOWRING MARSH & McLENNAN LTD
Yacht Division, Havelock Chambers, Queens Terrace, Southampton, Hampshire SO14 3PP. Tel (01703) 318300 Fax (01703) 318391. A member of the largest insurance broking firm in the world with associated offices in Antibes and Fort Lauderdale. Specialists in yacht insurance for craft cruising Mediterranean, Caribbean and US waters.

BRIAN BAGG YACHT DELIVERIES
Vine Cottage, Southampton Road, Dibden, Southampton, Hampshire SO45 5TA. Tel/Fax (01703) 847514. Worldwide deliveries of sail, power and small commercial vessels. Undertaken with utmost care and consideration by professional yachtmaster. 300,000 miles and 370 deliveries completed since 1969. Telephone or fax for a competitive quotation.

BRITISH WATERWAYS & THE ENVIRONMENT AGENCY
CANAL & RIVER LINE 0891 546 555. Our canals and rivers provide: marinas, moorings, berthing, boatyard services and relaxing, picturesque waters for cruising. Find out more from Canal and River Line (50p minute peak rate at 45p minute other times).

BRUCE BANKS SAILS LTD
372 Brook Lane, Sarisbury, Southampton, Hampshire SO31 7ZA.Tel (01489) 582444 Fax (01489) 589789 e-mail: enquiries@banks.co.uk http://www.banks.co.uk. Banks Sails are manufacturers of high quality racing and cruising sails. Banks also offer a range of dinghy covers and accessories. Pick up points at all Hamble marinas, Gosport and Southampton waters.

C T PLATON LTD
Jays Close, Viables, Basingstoke, Hampshire RG22 4BS. Tel (01256) 358258 Fax (01256) 355015. Manufacturers of Harwood water separators and filters to remove harmful water from diesel fuel. Also a range of cold starting aids for diesel engines and RO Watermakers. Contact: M Barcy.

CARBOSPARS LTD
Hamble Point, School Lane, Hamble, Southampton, Hampshire SO31 4JD. Tel (01703) 456736 Fax (01703) 455361. e-mail: carbospars@compuserve.com Design and manufacture of carbon spars for racing and cruising and the award-winning AeroRig®.

CHICHESTER MARINA
Birdham, Chichester, West Sussex PO20 7EJ. Tel (01243) 512731 Fax (01243) 513472. Situated in the north east corner of Chichester harbour, Chichester Marina enjoys one of the most attractive locations in the country. With 1100 berths, Chichester offers a unique combination of service, facilities, security and friendliness, unparalleled in UK marinas. Chichester Marina is a PREMIER Marina.

COMPASS POINT CHANDLERY
The Quay, High Street, Hamble, Hampshire SO31 4HA. Tel (01703) 452388 Fax (01703) 456942. Compass Point is adjacent to the quay at Hamble. It stocks an attractive selection of leisure clothing and foul-weather gear as well as a wide range of chandlery.

CONVOI EXCEPTIONNEL
Castleton House, High Street, Hamble, Southampton, Hampshire SO31 4HA. Tel (01703) 453045 Fax (01703) 454551. International marine haulage and abnormal load consultants. Specialist services up to 40 tons.

COWES YACHT HAVEN
Vectis Yard, High Street, Cowes, Isle of Wight PO31 7BD. Tel (01983) 299975 Fax (01983) 200332. Cowes Yacht Haven is the Solent's premier sailing event centre offering 200 fully serviced berths right in the heart of Cowes. Our improved facilities, capability and location ensures the perfect venue and profile for every kind of boating event.

CREWSAVER LTD
Crewsaver House, Mumby Road, Gosport, Hampshire PO12 1AQ. Tel (01705) 528621. MARLIN - Leading manufacturer of stylish, comfortable, hardwearing wetsuits, lifejackets, buoyancy aids and accessories for all seasons and all surface watersports. YAK - Catering for all canoeing needs from cags and decks to long johns and buoyancy aids.

CRUISAIR UK LTD
26 Old Wareham Road, Poole, Dorset BH12 4QR. Tel (01202) 716469 Fax (01202) 716478. Marine air conditioning.

D G M Boat Repairs
57 Imber Avenue, Boscombe Down, Salisbury, Wiltshire SP4 7JT. Tel (01980) 624852. GRP specialist repairs.

DEACONS BOATYARD LTD
Bursledon Bridge, Southampton, Hampshire SO3 8AZ. Tel (01703) 402253 Fax (01703) 405665. This yard provides a comprehensive range of services including moorings, laying-up of boats, boat repairs, marine engineering, rigging, sail making and repairs and brokerage etc.

DEAN & REDDYHOFF LTD - HASLAR MARINA
Haslar Road, Gosport, Hampshire PO12 1NU. Tel (01705) 601201 Fax (01705) 602201. Haslar Marina is just inside the entrance of Portsmouth harbour on the Gosport side. Included in the 600 berths is a visitors' area which is adjacent to a converted lightship with bar facilities and excellent toilets and showers.

DEAN & REDDYHOFF LTD - WEYMOUTH MARINA
70 Commercial Road, Wymouth, Dorset DT4 8NA. Tel (01305) 767576 Fax (01305) 767575. This new marina in the inner harbour of Weymouth provides facilities for visitors which are proving very popular. The marina is right next to Weymouth's high street, and the area has a multitude of pubs and restaurants.

DIVERSE YACHT SERVICES
Unit 12, Hamble Yacht Services, Port Hamble, Hamble, Hampshire SO31 4NN. Tel (01703) 453399 Fax (01703) 455288. Marine electronics and electrics. Supplied and installed. Specialists in racing yachts. Suppliers of 'Loadsense' Loadcells for marine applications.

ELKINS BOATYARD
Tidesreach, 18 Convent Meadow, The Quay, Christchurch, Dorset BH23 1BD. Tel (01202) 483141. All boatyard facilities. Moorings alongside, water and electricity, storage ashore, repairs. Boats up to 45', 10 tons maximum, haul-out.

FIRSTAWAY CHARTERS
23 Orchard Lea, Swanmore, Southampton, Hampshire SO32 2QZ. Tel/Fax (01489) 893889. UK charter. 30-44' fast cruising yachts.

FIVE STAR SAILING
Stone Pier Yard, Shore Road, Warsash, Southampton, Hampshire SO31 9FR. Tel (01489) 885599 Fax (01489) 885505. Five Star Sailing offer RYA competent crew, day skipper, coastal skipper, yachtmaster offshore and ocean. Keel boat levels 1 to 5. Racing and race training. Top school for yachtmaster - 100% pass rate for over 5 years. Top school for racing, winning the Sailing School trophy for 5 years.

GenACis
Power House, Gordon Road, Winchester, Hampshire SO23 7DD. Tel (01962) 841828 Fax (01962) 841834. Dolphin water cooled diesel generators, 3 - 16 KVA.

GREENHAM MARINE
King's Saltern Road, Lymington, Hampshire SO41 9QD. Tel (01590) 671144 Fax (01590) 679517. Greenham Marine can offer yachtsmen one of the most comprehensive selections of marine electronic equipment currently available. Also at Poole/Weymouth 01202 676363 and Emsworth/Chichester 01243 378314.

GULLIVERS YACHT SERVICES

Antells Farm, Stour Provost, Gillingham, Dorset SP8. 5SA.
e-mail: EAJ@Gullivers.Tel/Me.com Tel (01747) 838987
Fax (01747) 838853. Yacht consultancy for private and corporateclients. Complete yacht management service in UK and abroad. International yacht charter brokers for 2000 sailing and motoryachts worldwide, including the most luxurious, fully crewed, bareboat and single berths. Member BMIF YCA.

Private Yacht Management & Consultancy

EXISTING OWNERS Just enjoy your sailing
Fixed price contracts • Regular visits UK & abroad • Maintenance scheduling Yard liaison and Refit supervision • Equipment choices, Procurement, testing, sea trials
PROSPECTIVE OWNERS Make the right choices
Concept discussion and advice • New build liaison • Used market research, previews • Purchase negotiations • Equipment advice
 • Commissioning trials • Owner support

Contact EOIN ASHTON-JOHNSON MRIN Yachtmaster
GULLIVERS YACHT SERVICES Antells Farm, Gillingham, Dorset SP8 5SA
Tel 01747 838987   Fax 01747 838853   e-mail: EAJ@Gullivers.TelMe.com

---

INTERNATIONAL PAINT

24-30 Canute Road, Southampton, Hampshire SO14 3PB.
Tel (01703) 226722 Fax (01703) 335975. International Paint is the leading supplier of quality paints, epoxies, varnishes and anti-foulings to the marine industry. Over half the world's pleasure craft are protected by International products.

✖ International

International Yacht Paints is the leading supplier of quality paints, epoxies, varnishes and anti-foulings to the marine industry. Over half the world's pleasure craft are protected by International products.

INTERNATIONAL PAINT 24-30 CANUTE ROAD, SOUTHAMPTON, HANTS SO14 3PB   TEL: (01703) 226722 FAX: (01703) 335975

KELVIN HUGHES CHARTS & MARITIME SUPPLIES

Royal Crescent Road, Southampton, Hampshire SO14 3NP.
Tel (01703) 634911 Fax (01703) 330014. Charts, books, chandlery, safety equipment and clothing. Liferaft hire and sales. Also in London with worldwide mail order service.

KELVIN HUGHES

Royal Crescent Road, Southampton, Hampshire
Tel (01703) 634911 Fax (01703) 330014

Charts, books, chandlery, safety equipment and clothing. Liferaft hire and sales. Also in London, with world-wide mail order service.

KEMP MASTS LTD (Seldén Masts Ltd)

St Margaret's Lane, Titchfield, Fareham, Hampshire PO14 4BG.
Tel (01329) 841900 Fax (01329) 847052. Now renamed Seldén, this is the UK manufacturing and supply base for the Seldén range of masts, booms, poles, kickers, mainsail-furling and headsail-furling to suit production yachts upto 45' and custom yachts from upto 70'.

KEMP SAILS LTD

Unit 2, Sandford Lane Industrial Estate, Wareham, Dorset BH20 4DY. Tel (01929) 554308 Fax (01929) 554350. e-mail: kemp@eluk.co.uk   http://www.eluk.co.uk/kemp/index/html Sailmakers and suppliers of sail handling equipment.

KENDALL BECKER LTD

Kendalls, West Bracklesham, Bracklesham Bay, Chichester, Sussex PO20 8PH. Tel (01243) 672142 Fax (01243) 672068. Marine insurance specialists for yachts and motor cruisers throughout the world. Vessels over 20 years old a speciality (surveys not required). Immediate quotes and cover. Call us now.

Make use of the wide range of services presented here

LANGSTONE HARBOUR BOARD

Ferry Road, Hayling Island, Hampshire PO11 0DG. Tel (01705) 463419 Fax (01705) 467144. All boatyard facilities. Deep water and tidal moorings available. Water, electricity and diesel. Summer and winter storage. Public slipways. 6-ton crane. Landrover vessel and trailer recovery services.

MARINE EQUIPMENT FOR THE WORLD'S YACHTS

LEWMAR MARINE LTD

Southmoor Lane, Havant, Hampshire PO9 1JJ. Tel (01705) 471841 Fax (01705) 476043. Manufacturers of winches, windlasses, hatches, hardware, hydraulics and marine thrusters for boats ranging in size from 25' to 300' LOA.

LYMINGTON YACHT HAVEN

King's Saltern Road, Lymington, Hampshire SO4 9XY.
Tel (01590) 677071 Fax (01590) 678186. Perfectly situated at the mouth of the Lymington river giving instant access to the Western Solent. Full marina services, boatyard, brokerage, diesel, petrol and gas.

Tel: (01590) 677071
Fax: (01590) 678186

LYMINGTON YACHT HAVEN

Perfectly situated at the mouth of the Lymington river giving instant access to the western Solent. Full marina services, boatyard, brokerage, diesel, petrol and gas.

KING'S SALTERN ROAD, LYMINGTON, HAMPSHIRE SO4 9XY

R J MUIR

22 Seymour Close, Chandlers Ford, Eastleigh, Southampton SO5 2JE. Tel (01703) 261042. Books and Charts. DTp Certificated.

NORTH SAILS UK LTD

Satchell Lane, Hamble, Hampshire SO31 4HH. Tel (01703) 453109 Fax (01703) 457015. e-mail:info@gb.northsails.com At NORTH SAILS a team of highly skilled sailors are dedicated to helping you achieve even higher standards in your sailing - whether it be on the race course, crossing an ocean or enjoying a day's cruising. Benefit from world beating research and development programmes, new sail design and material technology that is only available to NORTH SAILS.

OCEAN WORLD LTD

46 High Street, Cowes, Isle of Wight PO31 7RR. Tel (01983) 291744 Fax (01983) 297252. Clothing and embroidery services.

S P SYSTEMS

Love Lane, Cowes, Isle of Wight PO31 7EU. Tel (01983) 284000 Fax (01983) 298453. Epoxy resins for laminating, bonding, coating and filling. Usable with wood, GRP, concrete. GRP/FRP materials including glass, carbon and Kevlar fibres. Structural engineering of GRP and composite materials. Technical advice service.

SEASTART

Unit 13 Hamble Point Marina, School Lane, Hamble, Southampton SO31 4JD. Tel 0800 885500 Fax (01703) 458000. SeaStart is the 24-hour marine breakdown membership service on both sides of the English Channel and the Channel Islands. For membership - join now on 0800 885500 using your credit card.

SHAMROCK CHANDLERY

Shamrock Quay, William Street, Northam, Southampton, Hampshire SO14 5QL. Tel (01703) 632725 Fax (01703) 225611. Situated on Shamrock Quay, a busy working yard with a pub, restaurant and boutiques. Shamrock Chandlery is renowned for extensive quality stocks and service and is widely used by both the trade and boat owners.

SHERATON MARINE CABINET

White Oak Green, Hailey, Witney, Oxfordshire OX8 5XP. Tel/Fax (01993) 868275. Manufacturers of quality teak and mahogany marine fittings, louvre doors, gratings and tables. Special fitting-out items to customer specification. Colour catalogue available on request.

SHOOSMITHS & HARRISON

Russell House, 1550 Parkway, Solent Business Park, Fareham, Hampshire PO15 7AG. Tel (01489) 881010/616928. Fax (01489) 881000 Marine solicitors advising on yacht sales, purchase and charter, insurance claims, disputes, debt recovery and general advice for the yachting community. Contact: Jonathan Hadley-Piggin.

SILLETTE SONIC LTD

Unit 5 Stepnell Reach, 541 Blandford Road, Hamworthy, Poole, Dorset BH16 5BW. Tel (01202) 621631 Fax (01202) 625877. Distribution Depot: Sillette manufactures a range of propulsion systems - stern drive, saildrives etc and sterngear. Markets Radice and Gori fixed and folding propellers. Acts as agents for Morse Controls, Yanmar and Lombardini marine engines, and Fuji Robin generators. See Area 4.

SOUTHAMPTON INSTITUTE

East Park Terrace, Southampton, Hampshire SO14 0YN. Tel (01703) 319000 Fax (01703) 222259. The Young Skippers Scheme offers young people the chance to develop their seamanship and personal skills at a price which just covers running costs. Our 23' Hunter Duettes are perfect for exploring the Solent. Contact Andy Moat (01703) 319787.

SOUTHERN SPAR SERVICES (KEMP SOUTH)

Shamrock Quay, William Street, Northam, Southampton, Hampshire SO14 5QL. Mobile 0850 736540 Tel (01703) 331714 Fax (01703) 230559. Regional centre for SELDÉN and KEMP integrated sailing systems. Convectional and furling spars for UK and abroad. Also headsail and mainsail reefing, deck equipment, toe rails and stanchion bases. All forms of repairs and modifications undertaken.

SPARKES YACHT HARBOUR LTD

38 Wittering Road, Hayling Island, Hampshire PO11 9SR. Tel (01705) 463572 Fax (01705) 465741. Sparkes Marina - a small friendly, family run business offering all the facilities you require including access at all states of the tide to a depth of 2 metres at lowest low water springs. In addition to marina berths, accessible through a security gate, we also offer dry boat sailing, moorings, storage ashore plus full maintenance facilities, new boat sales and brokerage, chandlery and restaurant.

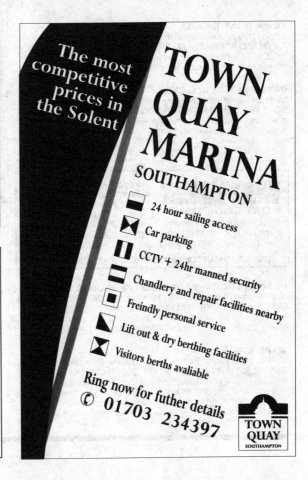

TARQUIN YACHT HARBOUR LTD
Thorney Road, Emsworth, Hampshire PO10 8BP. Tel (01243) 377727 Fax (01243) 373432. Friendly marina in Chichester harbour. Water, electricity, diesel, Calor gas, 25-tonne mobile crane, slipways, hard-standing and storage areas. Showers and toilets, car parking, chandlery, engineers and boat repairs.

TEK-TANKS
Unit 5B Station Approach, Four Marks, Alton, Hampshire GU34 5HN. Tel (01420) 564359 Fax (01420) 561605. e-mail: tek_tanks@compuserve.com Manufacturers of made-to-measure polypropylene water, waste and HDPE diesel tanks.

TOLLEY MARINE LTD
Unit 7, Blackhill Road West, Holton Heath Trading Park, Poole, Dorset BH16 6LS. Tel (01202) 632644 Fax (01202) 632622. (also at: Plymouth - Tel (01752) 222530; Brighton - Tel (01273) 424224 and London - 0171-930 3237. Agents of sales and service for Autohelm, B&G, Cetrek, Furuno, Garmin, Icom, Koden, Lo-Kata, MLR, Magnavox, Navico, Panasonic, Raytheon, Robertson, Sailor, Shipmate, Trimble.

TOWN QUAY MARINA
Town Quay, The Waterfront, Southampton, Hampshire. Tel (01703) 234397 Fax (01703) 235302. Town Quay is a growing development of bars and restaurants on an attractive waterfront environment just minutes away from the city centre.

VETUS DEN OUDEN LTD
38 South Hants Industrial Park, Totton, Southampton, Hampshire SO40 3SA. Tel (01703) 861033 Fax (01703) 663142. Suppliers of marine diesel equipment, exhaust systems, steering systems, bow propellers, propellers and shafts, hatches, portlights, windows, electronic instruments, batteries, ventilators, windlasses, water and fuel tanks, chandlery items and much much more.

VOSPER THORNYCROFT MARINE PRODUCTS LTD
Northarbour Road, Cosham, Hampshire PO6 3TL. Tel (01705) 383311 Fax (01705) 325133. Manufacturer and supplier of Fin stabilizers, Transverse thrusters and Vospower water jets to the luxury, commercial and naval markets worldwide.

WARD & McKENZIE
12 Black Hill Road, Holton Heath Trading Park, Poole, Dorset BH16 6LS. Tel (01202) 624690 Fax (01202) 632251. National and International Marine Surveyors, Technical and Legal Consultants - offering a comprehensive service to boat owners and those seeking to acquire pleasure yachts. All aspects of vessel search, survey, purchase and ownership undertaken, including insurance surveys, finance and disputes.

WARSASH NAUTICAL BOOKSHOP
6 Dibles Road, Warsash, Southampton, Hampshire SO31 9HZ. Tel (01489) 572384 Fax (01489) 885756. e-mail: alan @nauticalbooks.co.uk http://www.nautical books.co.uk Nautical bookseller and chart agent. Callers and mail order. Free new and secondhand book lists. Credit cards taken. Publishers of the Bibliography of Nautical books.

WESSEX MARINE EQUIPMENT LTD
Logistics House, 2nd Avenue Business Park, Millbrook Road East, Southampton, Hampshire SO1 0LP. Tel (01703) 510570. Books and charts.

WET & WILD GRAPHICS
7 Firefly Road, Hamble Point Marina, Hamble, Southampton, Hampshire SO31 4NB. Tel (01703) 458332 Fax (01703) 456830. Supply and application of vinyl graphics, signboards, banners and flags. Specialist materials for sails and spinnakers. Brochure available for mail order boat names. Deadlines never a problem!!!

WEYMOUTH OLD HARBOUR
Weymouth & Portland Borough Council, Borough Engineers Department, Municipal Offices, North Quay, Weymouth, Dorset DT4 8TA. Tel (01305) 206363/206423. Fax (01305) 206276 e-mail: cflowers@weymouth.gov.uk http://www.weymouth.gov.uk/marine.htm Access at all stages of tide. Visitor berths in the centre of prime tourist resort with shops, restaurants and night life all at hand. Diesel fuelling from pontoon or tanker. Chandlery and repair facilities available.

SOUTH EAST ENGLAND (AREA 3)
Selsey Bill to North Foreland

ADEC MARINE LTD
4 Masons Avenue, Croydon, Surrey CR0 1EH. Tel 0181-686 9717 Fax 0181-680 9912. Approved liferaft service station for south east UK. Additionally we hire and sell new rafts and sell a complete range of safety equipment for yachts including pyrotechnics, fire extinguishers, lifejackets, buoys and a buoyancy bag system.

BOSUN'S LOCKER
10 Military Road, Royal Harbour, Ramsgate, Kent CT11 9LG. Tel/Fax (01843) 597158. The Bosun's Locker, a friendly, family owned business, caters for a wide range of boat owners and is staffed by experienced yachtsmen. The stock is extensive, including paint, ropes, quality clothing for foul-weather and fashion, electronics, inflatables and charts.

BRIGHTON MARINA
Brighton Marina Village, Brighton, East Sussex BN2 5UF. Tel (01273) 819919 Fax (01273) 675082. Britain's largest marina (1600 pontoon berths) with marina village under development. TYHA Five-Gold Anchors. Full boatyard and shore facilities. Brokerage and boat sales. Club racing throughout the year. Group visits, rallies welcome.

BRITISH WATERWAYS & THE ENVIRONMENT AGENCY
CANAL & RIVER LINE 0891 546 555. Our canals and rivers provide: marinas, moorings, berthing, boatyard services and relaxing, picturesque waters for cruising. Find out more from Canal and River Line (50p minute peak rate at 45p minute other times).

CINQUE PORTS MARINE SERVICES
'Midwater' Willow Road, Gt Mongeham, Nr Deal, Kent CT14 0HN. Tel/Fax (01304) 365138. Mobile 0585 844653 Marine surveyor and consultant marine engineer. Damage, pre-purchase and full condition surveys. Machinery inspections and Code of Practice - safety of small commercial motor/sailing vessels. BW/NRA Boat Safety Certificate.

THAMES ESTUARY   (AREA 4)
North Foreland to Great Yarmouth

CHELSEA HARBOUR LTD
108 The Chambers, Chelsea Harbour, London SW10 0XF. Tel 0171-351 4433. Fax 0171-352 7868 A tranquil and intimate marina of 55 berths close to the heart of the west end of London. 5-Star hotel, restaurants and bars. Overnight pontoon and amenities. 24-hour security patrols and CCTV.

FOX'S MARINA IPSWICH LTD
The Strand, Wherstead, Ipswich, Suffolk IP2 8SA. Tel (01473) 689111 Fax (01473) 601737. The most comprehensive boatyard facility on the east coast. Extensive chandlery. Marina access 24-hours. Two travel hoists to 45 tons, 10 ton crane. Full electronics, rigging, engineering, stainless steel services. Specialists in osmosis and spray painting.

FOX'S SPARS & RIGGING (KEMP EAST)
Fox's Marina, The Strand, Wherstead, Ipswich, Suffolk IP2 8SA. Tel (01473) 691235 Fax (01473) 601737. Regional centre for SELDÉN and KEMP integrated sailing systems. Fox's experience in world girdling racing and cruising yachts provides testimony to products and skills. The No 1 choice for yachtsmen everywhere. Supplier to the OYSTER range.

GUARDIAN INSURANCE LTD
Head Office: Civic Drive, Ipswich, Suffolk IP1 2AN. Tel (01473) 212422 Fax (01473) 210035. A member of Guardian Royal Exchange Group. Marine insurers since 1720. Member of ABI and IOB. Competitive insurance for dinghies, yachts and motorcruisers. Offices throughout UK including Belfast, Glasgow, Cardiff, Leeds, Manchester, Birmingham, Southampton and Bristol.

HALCON MARINE LTD
The Point, Canvey Island, Essex SS8 7TL. Tel (01268) 511611 Fax (01268) 510044. Marine engineers, repairs and full boatyard services in this quiet and picturesque area. Berths, moorings, slipping facilities. Summer and winter storage. Dry dock (70t max), diesel. 1 or 2 hours ±HW. Water, electric, toilets and showers. A friendly welcome awaits you.

THE HARBOUR LIGHTS RESTAURANT (Walton-on-Naze)
Titchmarsh Marina, Coles Lane, Walton-on-the-Naze, Essex CO14 8SL. Tel (01255) 672185 Fax (01255) 851901. Open 7 days a week the Harbour Lights offers a welcome to yachtsmen and landlubbers alike. Bar meals served all day, coffee and afternoon tea. Excellent menu choice in the restaurant overlooking the marina in this peaceful backwater.

KELVIN HUGHES CHARTS & MARITIME SUPPLIES
New North Road, Hainault, Ilford, Essex IG6 2UR. Tel 0181-500 6166 Books and charts. DTp Certificated.

MARINECALL - TELEPHONE INFORMATION SERVICES
Avalon House, London EC2A 4PJ. Tel 0171-631 6000. Marinecall provides detailed coastal weather forecasts for 17 different regions, up to 5 days ahead from the Met Office. For a full fax list of services dial 0891 24 66 80. Telephone forecasts are updated daily, morning and afternoon.

MARTELLO YACHT SERVICES
Mulberry House, Mulberry Road, Canvey Island, Essex SS8 0PR. Tel/Fax (01268) 681970. Manufacturer and supplier of made-to-measure upholstery, covers, hoods, dodgers, sailcovers, curtains and cushions etc. Repairs undertaken. DIY materials, chandlery and fitting-out supplies.

PARKER & KAY SAILMAKERS - EAST
Suffolk Yacht Harbour, Levington, Ipswich, Suffolk IP10 0LN. Tel (01473) 659878 Fax (01473) 659197. A complete sailmaking service, from small repairs to the construction of custom designed sails for racing or cruising yachts. Covers constructed for sail and powercraft, plus the supply of all forms of sail handling hardware.

PETER N DAVIES SURVEYS LTD
98 The Avenue, Wivenhoe, Colchester, Essex CO7 9PP. Tel (01206) 823289 Fax (01206) 826969. Condition pre-purchase, insurance valuation and damage surveys, UK and abroad. All types of material and hull construction. MSA Code of Practice certification. Traditional and square rig surveys. Marina and boatyard quantification surveys. Comprehensive, informative survey reports.

PORT À PORT YACHT SERVICES
Studio 6, Fox's Marina, The Strand, Ipswich, Suffolk IP2 8NJ. Tel (01473) 692691 Fax (01473) 692693. Port à Port Services guarantee speedy and safe passage for your yacht. Our skippers are never less than instructor level and all crew hold RYA qualifications, ensuring your yacht is in the very best of hands.

PORT FLAIR LTD
Bradwell Marina, Waterside, Bradwell-on-Sea, Essex CM0 7RB. Tel (01621) 776235/776391. 300 pontoon berths with water and electricity, petrol and diesel, chandlery, marine slip/hoistage to 20 tons. Repairs, winter lay-ups, licensed club, yacht brokerage.

PREMIUM LIFERAFT SERVICES
Liferaft House, Burnham Business Park, Burnham-on-Crouch, Essex CM0 8TE. Tel (01621) 784858 Fax (01621) 785934. Freephone 0800 243673 e-mail: 101624.574 Hire and sales of DoT and RORC approved liferafts. Long and short-term hire from 18 depots nationwide. Servicing and other safety equipment available.

PROSSER SCIENTIFIC INSTRUMENTS LTD
Lady Lane Industrial Estate, Hadleigh, Ipswich, Suffolk IP7 6BQ. Tel (01473) 823005 Fax (01473) 824095. Manufacturers of a range of marine instruments, including the WEATHERTREND digital barometer, with full 24-hour history, the unique TIDECLOCK tidal data predictor and tidal software for the PSION 3 series.

RICE & COLE LTD
Sea End Boathouse, Burnham-on-Crouch, Essex CM0 8AN. Tel/Fax (01621) 782063. Boatyard with full repair and shipwright services. Osmosis treatment, painting and spraying, GRP repairs, standing and running rigging, brokerage and chandlery. Visitors welcome to this family-run business on the river Crouch.

S I R S NAVIGATION LTD
186a Milton Road, Swanscombe, Kent DA10 0LX. Tel (01322) 383672. Books and Charts. DTp Certificated.

SEA-KING BOAT BUILDERS LTD
8A High Street, Leigh-on-Sea, Essex SS9 2EN. Tel (01702) 73612. Wooden boatbuilders, dinghies 12', cruisers up to 32' clinker construction, repairs to wooden vessels, iron work to your pattern undertaken. Mast and spars made in wood.

SEATH INSTRUMENTS (1992) LTD
Unit 30, Colville Road Works, Colville Road, Lowestoft NR33 9QS. Tel (01502) 573811. Books and charts. DTp Certificated.

SHOTLEY MARINA LTD
Shotley Gate, Ipswich, Suffolk IP9 1QJ. Tel (01473) 788982 Fax (01473) 788868. A modern state of the art marina with 350 berths offering all the services expected. Open 24-hours with full security. Access all states of tide, ideal cruising base. Well stocked chandlery and general store, repair facilities, laundry and ironing centre, showers/baths and toilets. Restaurants, bar, children's room, TV/video and function rooms with dance floor and bar. Disabled facilities.

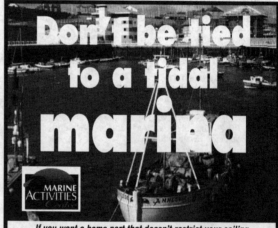

A M SMITH (MARINE) LTD
33 Epping Way, Chingford E4 7PB. Tel 0181-529 6988. Books and charts.

SOUTH DOCK MARINA
South Lock Office, Rope Street, Plough Way, London SE16 1TX. Tel 0171-252 2244 Fax 0171-237 3806. London's largest marina. 200+ berths. Spacious, tranquil setting. Manned 24 hours. Lift-out to 20 tonnes. Competitive mooring rates.

ST KATHARINE HAVEN
50 St Katharine's Way, London E1 9LB. Tel 0171-264 5312 Fax 0171-702 2252. In the heart of London, St Katharine's 200-berth Haven offers facilities for 100'+ vessels, access to the West End and City, its own shops, restaurants, health club and yacht club, plus water, electric, showers and sewerage disposal. Entry via a lock. Operational HW - 2hours to HW + 1½hours London Bridge. October-March 0800-1800. April-August 0600-2030.

ST MARGARETS INSURANCES LTD
153-155 High Street, Penge, London SE20 7DL. Tel 0181-778 6161 Fax 0181-659 1968. Marine insurance. Over 25 years dedicated to insuring yachts and pleasurecraft. Many unique policies available only through St Margarets. Immediate quotations and cover available.

SUFFOLK YACHT HARBOUR LTD
Levington, Ipswich, Suffolk IP10 0LN. Tel (01473) 659240 Fax (01473) 659632. 420-berths - access at all states of tide (dredged to 2.5 meters at LW Springs). Boat hoist facilities up to 60 tons. Full boatyard services, chandlery, gas, diesel, petrol, engineering, sailmaking, electronics. Club house and restaurant.

TITCHMARSH MARINA (WALTON-ON-THE-NAZE)
Coles Lane, Walton-on-the-Naze, Essex CO14 8SL. Tel (01255) 672185 Fax (01255) 851901. Friendly service in the peaceful backwater. Visiting yachtsmen welcome. Sheltered marina berths. Full marina facilities: travel-lift, cranage, 16amp electricity, diesel. Winter storage. Restaurant and bar open every day. Bar meals available all day. Weekend barbecues. (See the Harbour Lights Restaurant.)

TOLLESBURY MARINA
The Yacht Harbour, Tollesbury, Maldon, Essex CM9 8SE. Tel (01621) 869202 Fax (01621) 868489. Dedicated to customer service, this family-run marina can offer 240 marina berths with water and electricity on all pontoons. Cruising club with bar, restaurant, swimming pool and tennis courts. Repair workshop, osmosis treatment centre. Full brokerage service listing over 200 boats. VHF Ch37 and 80.

UPPER THAMES (AREA 4)
Navigable west of Westminster Bridge

W BATES & SON BOATBUILDERS LTD
Bridge Wharf, Chertsey, Surrey KT16 8LG. Tel (01932) 562255 Fax (01932) 571161. 110-berth marina in quiet picturesque area and additional riverside moorings. Full facilities including electricity to most berths, toilets and showers. 12-ton crane and hard standing for winter storage. Always a welcome to visitors from our friendly staff. Sales office open seven days a week.

BISHOP SKINNER INTERNATIONAL INSURANCE BROKERS
Oakley Crescent, City Road, London EC1V 1NU. Tel 0171-566 5800 Fax 0171-608 2171. Dinghy Insurance - As insurance brokers to the RYA we offer cover for accidental damage, racing risks, 30-days European extension, discounts for dinghy instructors, third party indemnity of £2,000,000, no claim bonus (transferable) and first class security. Immediate quotation and instant cover all at competitive rates.

BISHOP SKINNER INSURANCE

The RYA Insurance Scheme offers:
- Competitive rates for yachts and powerboats
- Special discounts for RYA qualifications
- First Class security with Leading Insurers
- Expert advice from Registered Insurance Brokers

Telephone: 0171-566 5800 Fax: 0171-608 2171

Bishop Skinner & Co Ltd, Oakley Crescent, City Road, London EC1V 1NU

FOR VOLVO PENTA PARTS AND SERVICE.
See Chapter 10, Areas 1-21

BRITISH WATERWAYS & THE ENVIRONMENT AGENCY
CANAL & RIVER LINE 0891 546 555. Our canals and rivers provide: marinas, moorings, berthing, boatyard services and relaxing, picturesque waters for cruising. Find out more from Canal and River Line (50p minute peak rate at 45p minute other times).

CHISWICK QUAY MARINA LTD
Marina Office, Chiswick Quay, London W4 3UR. Tel 0181-994 8743. Small, secluded, peaceful marina on tidal Thames at Chiswick. Slipway, marine engineers and electricians, power, water, toilets and sluice. Some residential moorings.

DESMOND CHEERS & PARTNERS
44 High Street, Hampton Hill, Middlesex TW12 1PD. Tel 0181-943 5333 Fax 0181-943 5444. Marine insurance specialists with over 30 years' experience in arranging tailor-made policies through leading marine underwriters. For all your insurance enquiries for yachts, motorcruisers and speedboats call Tim Cheers or Daphne Bamberger.

MARINE RADIO SERVICES LTD
3 Brook Lane Business Centre, Brook Lane North, Brentford, Middlesex TW8 0QY. Tel/Fax 0181-568 6884. Service and repair of marine radio, radar and electronic equipment.

OCEAN LEISURE LTD
11-14 Northumberland Avenue, London WC2N 5AQ. Tel 0171-930 5050 Fax 0171-930 3032. Complete range of sailing clothing, swim and beachwear stocked all year round. Chandlery includes marine electronic equipment, marine antiques, books and charts. Also canoeing, underwater photography, diving and waterskiing specialists. Learn to scuba dive.

ROYAL INSTITUTE OF NAVIGATION
1 Kensington Gore, London SW7 2AT. Tel 0171-589 5021 Fax 0171-823 8671. Forum for all interested in navigation - Air: Sea: Land: Space.

SILLETTE SONIC LTD
182 Church Hill Road, North Cheam, Sutton, Surrey SM3 8NF. Tel 0181-715 0100 Fax 0181-288 0742. Sillette manufactures a range of propulsion systems - stern drive, saildrives etc and sterngear. Markets Radice & Gori fixed and folding propellers. Acts as agents for Morse Controls, Yanmar and Lombardini marine engines, and Fuji Robin generators. See distribution depot Poole, Dorset - Area 2.

SOFTWAVE
4 Aranmor House, Kingston Hill, Kingston, Surrey KT2 7LY. Tel 0181-549 0650 Fax 0181-546 1090. www.softwave.co.uk Specialist supplier of PC based electronic navigation systems and high quality vectorized charts drawn from Admiralty and other official sources. Also tide computing, simulations, hardware and on-board installations. (See advertisement first right hand page in this volume)

YACHTLINE
100 Fenchurch Street, London EC3M 5JJ. Tel 0171-680 1444 Fax 0171-680 1441. Yacht insurance.

EAST ENGLAND (AREA 5)
Blakeney to Berwick-on-Tweed

BRITISH WATERWAYS & THE ENVIRONMENT AGENCY
CANAL & RIVER LINE 0891 546 555. Our canals and rivers provide: marinas, moorings, berthing, boatyard services and relaxing, picturesque waters for cruising. Find out more from Canal and River Line (50p minute peak rate at 45p minute other times).

BURGH CASTLE MARINA
Butt Lane, Burgh Castle, Norfolk, Norwich NR31 9PZ. Tel (01493) 780331. 100 serviced pontoons and quay moorings accessible at all tides. Secure car and boat parking. Adjoining boatyard services, access to holiday park showers, laundry and heated pool. Riverside pub and shop. Complex open all year.

B COOKE & SON LTD
Kingston Observatory, 58-59 Market Place, Hull HU1 1RH. Tel (01482) 223454. Books and Charts. DTp Certificated.

FARNDON HARBOUR MOORINGS LTD
North End, Farndon, Newark, Nottinghamshire NG24 3SX. Tel (01636) 705483 Fax (01636) 701457. Marina with full services. Road haulage and brokerage.

HULL MARINA LTD
Warehouse 13, Kingston Street, Hull HU1 2DQ. Tel (01482) 613451 Fax (01482) 224148. Four-anchor Marina. Situated 5 minutes from the centre of Hull and all national and international transport systems. First class leisure, boatyard and brokerage facilities. 4-Star hotel and quayside restaurants. Professional and caring staff. Competitive rates.

JOHN LILLEY & GILLIE LTD
Clive Street, North Shields, Tyne & Wear NE29 6LF. Tel 0191-257 2217. Books and Charts. DTp Certificated.

MARINE ACTIVITIES CENTRE
North Dock Marina, Sunderland SR6 0PW. Tel 0191-514 4721 Fax 0191-514 1847. New in 1996 with 85 fully serviced pontoon berths and 108 chain moorings accessible on all tides. Diesel fuel, 24-hour security and close circuit TV surviellance. New marina activities centre with excellent toilets and shower facilities.

NELSON MARINE TRANSPORT
Trafalgar Garage, Ashleigh Road, Arnside, Carnforth, Lancashire LA5 0HE. Tel/Fax (01524) 761481. Nelson Marine Transport and Storage. Specialist haulage nationwide. Competitive rates handled with a friendly, caring respect for boats.

NORTHERN SPAR SERVICES (KEMP NORTHWEST)
M R Coates Marine, The Marina Boatyard, Whitby, North Yorkshire YO21 1EU. Tel (01947) 604486 Fax (01947) 600580. Regional centre for SELDÉN and KEMP integrated sailing systems. 25 years' experience of mast and rigging manufacturing. Surveys undertaken. UK and export mail order service. Roll-swaging, Talurits, wire and rope splicing. Suppliers of furling systems.

SEAGLAZE MARINE WINDOWS LTD
Wendover Road, Rackheath, Norwich, Norfolk NR13 6LH. Tel (01603) 720745 Fax (01603) 721770. Manufacturer of high quality windows, doors and hatches for the marine industry. Exclusive suppliers to the RNLI. We will supply a one-off window/door or a whole set for your boat, no matter what shape, size or colour. We also offer a refurbishment service.

SOUTH EAST SCOTLAND   (AREA 6)
Eyemouth to Rattray Head

BRITISH WATERWAYS & THE ENVIRONMENT AGENCY
CANAL & RIVER LINE 0891 546 555. Our canals and rivers provide: marinas, moorings, berthing, boatyard services and relaxing, picturesque waters for cruising. Find out more from Canal and River Line (50p minute peak rate at 45p minute other times).

PETERHEAD BAY AUTHORITY
Bath House, Bath Street, Peterhead AB42 1DX. Tel (01779) 474020 Fax (01779) 475712. Contact: Stephen Paterson. Peterhead Bay Marina offers fully serviced pontoon berthing for local and visiting boat owners. Local companies provide a comprehensive range of supporting services. Ideal stopover for vessels heading to/from Scandinavia or the Caledonian canal.

THOMAS GUNN NAVIGATION SERVICES
Anchor House, 62 Regents Quay, Aberdeen AB11 5AR. Tel (01224) 595045. Books and charts. DTp Certificated.

NORTH EAST SCOTLAND   (AREA 7)
Rattray Head to Cape Wrath including Orkney and Shetland

BRITISH WATERWAYS & THE ENVIRONMENT AGENCY
CANAL & RIVER LINE 0891 546 555. Our canals and rivers provide: marinas, moorings, berthing, boatyard services and relaxing, picturesque waters for cruising. Find out more from Canal and River Line (50p minute peak rate at 45p minute other times).

CALEY MARINA
Canal Road, Inverness IV3 6NF. Tel (01463) 236539 Fax (01463) 238323. Open 08.30 - 17.30. Berths: 50 Pontoons (visitors available). Facilities: Fuel, water, pump-out facilities, provisions (nearby shops), repair, cranage, secure storage afloat and ashore. Comprehensive chandlery, showers, workshop. Situated at eastern end of Caledonian canal above Muirtown locks. Access via sea locks 4 hours either side of high water.

LERWICK HARBOUR TRUST
Albert Building, Lerwick, Shetland Isles ZE1 0LL. Tel (01595) 692991 Fax (01595) 693452. e-mail: lkharbour@lht.zetnet.co.uk http://www.shetland.shetland-news.co.uk/websites/lht Lerwick - fishing, oilfield support, ferries, cargo and cruising.

NORTH WEST/CENTRAL WEST SCOTLAND (AREA 8)
Cape Wrath to Crinan Canal

ARDENTINNY HOTEL
Ardentinny, Loch Long, By Dunoon, Argyll PA23 8TR. Tel (01369) 810209 Fax (01369) 810241. A warm Scottish welcome awaits you at the Ardentinny. Delightful dinners to a very high standard are prepared by our chef complemented by a choice of over 50 selections of French and New World wines. Excellent casual lunches served in the garden or buttery. Friendly bar, frequented by yachtsmen, with a good selection of beer. Seven moorings available.

ARDFERN YACHT CENTRE
Ardfern By Lochgilphead, Argyll PA31 8QN. Tel (01852) 500247/636 Fax (01852) 500624. Boatyard with full repair and maintenance facilities. Timber and GRP repairs, painting and engineering. Sheltered moorings and pontoon berthing. Winter storage, chandlery, showers, fuel, Calor, brokerage, 20-ton boat hoist. Hotel, bars and restaurant.

ARDFERN YACHT CENTRE
Ardfern By Lochgilphead, Argyll, Scotland PA31 8QN.
Tel: (01852) 500247/636 Fax: (01852) 500624
The ideal place to visit and keep your boat while cruising the west of Scotland.
COMPREHENSIVE FACILITIES.

ARDORAN MARINE
Lerags, Oban, Argyll PA34 4SE. Tel (01631) 566123 Fax (01631) 566611. All marine services.

BRITISH WATERWAYS & THE ENVIRONMENT AGENCY
CANAL & RIVER LINE 0891 546 555. Our canals and rivers provide: marinas, moorings, berthing, boatyard services and relaxing, picturesque waters for cruising. Find out more from Canal and River Line (50p minute peak rate at 45p minute other times).

COLUMBA HOTEL
East Pier Road, Tarbert, Loch Fyne, Argyll PA29 6UF. Tel/Fax (01880) 820808. 3-Crown Commended hotel in peaceful lochside position. Log fired bars offering rather special bar meals. Restaurant serving the best of Scottish produce imaginatively prepared. 'Taste of Scotland' recommended. Sauna, gym and solarium. Courtesy car available.

CRAOBH MARINA
By Lochgilphead, Argyll PA31 8UD. Tel (01852) 500222 Fax (01852) 500252. 250-berth marina on Loch Shuna. Water, electricity, diesel and gas. Full boatyard services. Chandlery. Brokerage. Insurance. Shops, bar. 24-hour access. VHF Ch37 and 80 (M).

CRAOBH MARINA
By Lochgilphead, Argyll PA31 8UD.
Tel: 01852 500222 Fax: 01852 500252
250 berth marina on Loch Shuna. Water. Electricity. Diesel and Gas. Full Boatyard Services. Chandlery. New amd Brokerage Boat Sales. Insurance. Shops. Bar. 1.5.0 5 second sector light making entrance. 24-hour access VHF Channels 37 (M) and 80.
CRAOBH MARINA
ARGYLL SCOTLAND

THE CREGGANS INN
Strachur, Argyll PA27 8BX. Tel (01369) 860279 Fax (01369) 860637. The Creggans Inn has been described as 'The kind of waterside blessing every visitor to the Highlands dreams of discovering'. Owned by Sir Charles MacLean. 3-Star hotel. Award-winning restaurant specialising in local seafood and game.

CRINAN BOATS LTD
Crinan, Lochgilphead, Argyll PA31 8SP. Tel (01546) 830232 Fax (01546) 830281. Boatbuilders, chandlers, engineers, slipping, repairs, charts, electricians, pontoon, moorings, showers, laundry and basic stores.

CRINAN BOATS
LIMITED
British Marine Industries Federation
Crinan, Lochgilphead, Argyll PA31 8SP
Tel: (01546) 830232 Fax: (01546) 830281
Chart Agents - Boat Builders - Marine Engineers - Outboard Sales & Repairs
Services include chandlery, slipping, repairs, electricians, engineers, Diesel, pontoon, moorings, showers, laundry and basic stores.

CRINAN YACHT CHARTERS
The Pump House, Crinan, Argyll PA31 8SP. Tel (01546) 830260 Fax (01546) 83025. Bareboat and skippered charters around the Hebrides. Fantastic cruising. Sheltered waters, wildlife, distilleries and isolated anchorages, yet with marine services within easy reach. 'Crinan - Where it all begins.'

THE GALLEY OF LORNE INN
Ardfern, by Lochgilphead, Argyll PA31 8QN. Egon Ronay & STB 3-Crown Commended Tel (01852) 500284. Traditional inn on the shores of Loch Craignish, renowned for a warm welcome to yachtsmen. Well known pub with log fires and good company. Excellent restaurant specialising in local seafood. All bedrooms newly refurbished, with private facilities. Two minutes from Ardfern Yacht Centre.

GIGHA HOTEL
Isle of Gigha, Argyll PA41 7AA. Tel (01583) 505254 Fax (01583) 505244. Beautiful island, good food, lots of booze and friendly folk. Ideal to pick up or leave your family when sailing around the Mull of Kintyre. Moorings, water, fuel, showers and laundry facilities. Self-catering cottages also available. Achamore Gardens and 9-hole golf course.

GIGHA HOTEL
Isle of Gigha
Isle of Gigha, Argyll PA41 7AA
Tel: 01583 505254 Fax: 01583 505244
Gigha Hotel is the ideal place to spend a restful holiday exploring the beautiful bays, lochs, sandy beaches, easy hillsides and birdwatching. Golf facilities and Achamore Gardens nearby. Ideal for visiting yachtsmen. Also self-catering cottages available.
ONCE YOU HAVE VISITED GIGHA YOU WILL NOT WANT TO CATCH THE FERRY HOME

KAMES HOTEL
Kames, By Tighnabruaich, Argyll PA21 2AF. Tel (01700) 811489 Fax (01700) 811 283. On the Kyles of Bute with 15 free moorings. Good food, real ales, fine malts. Showers available for visitors. 10 en-suite bedrooms. Regular music nights. Fresh local seafood in season.

SLEAT MARINE SERVICES
Ardvasar, Isle of Skye IV45 8RU. Tel (01471) 844216/844387. Yacht charter (bareboat and skippered) from Armadale Bay, Isle of Skye. Six yachts 34' to 40' LOA. All medium to heavy displacement blue water cruisers. Fuel, water and emergency services for passing yachts with problems.

Isle of Skye
6 quality yachts for charter
Emergency repair facilities
SLEAT MARINE SERVICES
Ardvasar, Isle of Skye IV45 8RU
Tel (01471) 844216/844387

SULU YACHT CHARTER
The Lodge House, Glenborrodale Castle, Acharacle, Argyll PH36 4JP. Tel/Fax (01972) 500218. Two Jeanneau Melodie 35' yachts available for skippered or bareboat charters in the magnificent Western Isles of Scotland. Enjoy the holiday of a lifetime. RYA courses available. Yachts to DoT standard.

TIGH AN EILEAN HOTEL
Shieldaig by Strathcaron, Ross-shire IV54 8XN. Tel (01520) 755251 Fax (01520) 755321. On the edge of the sea amongst some of the most dramatic landscapes in the Highlands, this friendly 12-bedroom hotel is run under the personal supervision of the proprietors. Our restaurant serves local produce cooked with flair and complemented with good wine. Excellent drying room for those wet clothes!!

THE TOBERMORAY HOTEL & RESTAURANT

53 Main Street, Tobermory, Isle of Mull, Argyll PA75 6NT. Egon Ronay & STB 3-Crown Commended Tel (01688) 302091 Fax (01688) 302254. Situated on the beautiful Tobermory Bay on the lovely Isle of Mull the Tobermoray Hotel offers a traditional Scottish welcome to all visiting yachtsmen. Come and eat at our excellent restaurant serving delicious fish and steak etc with good wines and spirits.

SOUTH WEST SCOTLAND (AREA 9)
Crinan Canal to Mull of Galloway

AILSA-TROON LTD

Harbour Road, Troon, Ayrshire KA10 6DN. Tel (01292) 311311 Fax (01292) 317613. Boatyard with full repair and maintenance facilities for GRP, steel, aluminium, timber and inflatable craft. Ship repair, fabrication and new building work also undertaken in Ailsa's extensive 15 acre covered facility.

BRITISH WATERWAYS & THE ENVIRONMENT AGENCY

CANAL & RIVER LINE 0891 546 555. Our canals and rivers provide: marinas, moorings, berthing, boatyard services and relaxing, picturesque waters for cruising. Find out more from Canal and River Line (50p minute peak rate at 45p minute other times).

BROWN SON & FERGUSON LTD

4-10 Darnley Street, Glasgow G41 2SD. Tel 0141-429 1234. Books and charts.

CLYDE MARINA - ARDROSSAN

The Harbour, Ardrossan, Ayrshire KA22 8DB. Tel (01294) 607077 Fax (01294) 607076. Located on the north Ayrshire coast, deep draught harbour, minimum depth 5m accommodating vessels to 100' alongside quay, and to 60' on full service pontoons. 20-ton hoist, undercover storage, diesel fuel, most facilities and services. Ancasta brokerage, also Beneteau, Nimbus, SeaRay and Marlin RIB dealers.

HARKEN - DISTRIBUTED BY SIMPSON LAWRENCE

218-228 Edmiston Drive, Glasgow G51 2YT. Tel 0141-427 5331/8 Fax 0141-427 5419. e-mail: info@simpson-lawrence.co.uk Distributors of *Harken* deck hardware, ball bearing blocks in all sizes from micros to maxis, jib reefing and furling systems, from dinghies to 150 footers, winches, backstay tensioners, power sheet jammers and deck shoes. We also distribute *Head Foil* plastic luff groove systems, and *Edson* steering and pump-out systems.

KIP MARINA

The Yacht Harbour, Inverkip, Renfrewshire PA16 0AS. Tel (01475) 521485 Fax (01475) 521298. Marina berths for vessels up to 65' LOA. Full boatyard facilities including travel hoist, crane, on-site

---

engineers, GRP repairs etc. Bar, restaurant, saunas, launderette and chandlery.

LARGS YACHT HAVEN

Irvine Road, Largs, Ayrshire KA30 8EZ. Tel (01475) 675333 Fax (01475) 672245. Perfectly located 600-berth marina with full services afloat and ashore. 45-ton travel hoist operational 7 days; fuel (diesel and petrol); gas and ice on sale 24-hours. Bar, coffee shop, dive shop plus usual marine services.

MAST & RIGGING SERVICES LTD (KEMP SCOTLAND)

Kip Marina, Inverkip, Renfrewshire PA16 0AS. Tel (01475) 522700 Fax (01475) 522800. Regional centre for SELDEN and KEMP integrated sailing systems. Specialist mast and rigging service offering - splicing, swaging, spar maintenance and repairs throughout Scotland. Suppliers of main and headsail furling gears, spinnaker poles and rod kickers.

THE OYSTERCATCHER RESTAURANT

Otter Ferry, Argyll PA21 2DH. Tel (01700) 821229 Fax (01700) 821300. Situated on Loch Fyne, just north of the Otter Spit, about one hour's sailing from the Crinan canal. Moorings (insured to 12t) free to patrons. French chef and superb food, seafood our speciality. 1996 Tourist Board winner 'BEST PLACE TO EAT'. Children's play area.

RHU MARINA LTD

Helensburgh, Dunbartonshire G84 8LN. Tel (01436) 820238 Fax (01436) 821039. Berths accessible at all times and moorings available situated in an area of outstanding natural beauty, by the Garsloch and 10 minutes from Loch Lomond. Hotels, shops, yacht clubs all adjacent.

SIMPSON LAWRENCE LTD

218-228 Edmiston Drive, Glasgow G51 2YT. Tel 0141-427 5331 Fax 0141-427 5419. e-mail: info@simpson-lawrence.co.uk Simpson Lawrence are manufacturers and the UK's largest wholesale distributor of quality marine equipment.

ST BLANE'S YACHT CHARTER

Crofton Cottage, Ascog, Rothesay, Isle of Bute PA20 9LN. Tel (01700) 503108. Firth of Clyde and west coast of Scotland - Largs Marina or Rothesay Harbour. Bareboat yacht charters. Yachts available from 30' to 34' including the latest style Legend 295 and 336.

TROON YACHT HAVEN

The Harbour, Troon, Ayrshire KA10 6DJ. Tel (01292) 315553 Fax (01292) 312836. Sheltered harbour for 350 berths. Well placed for those on passage to and from the Clyde. Bar, restaurant, marine services. Attractive seafront town with good beaches and championship golf.

NORTH WEST ENGLAND (AREA 10)
Isle of Man and North Wales, Mull of Galloway to Bardsey Island

A 1 PLYMOL FLAGSTAFF COMPANY
Carr Lane Industrial Estate, Hoylake, Wirral, Merseyside L47 4AY. Tel 0151-632 1354 Fax 0151-632 4912. Plymol manufacture a range of fibreglass flagstaffs from 3m to 18m. They can be supplied complete with fittings for ground or wall mounting. Plymol also supply all National flags, house flags, pvc display banners and bunting.

ALBERT DOCK
Albert Dock Co., 7 The Colonnades, Albert Dock, Liverpool L3 4AA. Tel 0151-708 7334 Fax 0151-708 0929. The world-famous Albert Dock welcomes vessels for short or long-term visits. Maximum length 55m. Concessionary rates (details on application). Access by prior agreement.

BRITISH WATERWAYS & THE ENVIRONMENT AGENCY
CANAL & RIVER LINE 0891 546 555. Our canals and rivers provide: marinas, moorings, berthing, boatyard services and relaxing, picturesque waters for cruising. Find out more from Canal and River Line (50p minute peak rate at 45p minute other times).

CAPT MEL BARRATT MNI MCMS
29 The Paddock, Tarporley, Cheshire CW6 0BT. Tel (01829) 732063 Tel (01758) 712873 (Wales) Fax (01829) 733221 Mobile 0831 685569. Prompt, professional condition, pre-purchase, insurance, valuation and damage surveys in north west England, north and mid Wales. Full member Society of Consulting Marine Engineers and Ship Surveyors. Examiner for the Code of Practice for charter vessels. Established over 25 years.

CREST NICHOLSON MARINAS LTD - CONWY
Conwy Marina, Conwy Morfa, Conwy, Gwynedd LL32 8EP. Tel (01492) 593000 Fax (01492) 572111. Conwy Marina is ideally placed on the south shore of the Conwy Estuary. The marina is set within idyllic surroundings and has comprehensive facilities. Road access is extremely convenient, with the A55 dual carriageway passing close by.

DOLPHIN MARITIME SOFTWARE LTD
713 Cameron House, White Cross, Lancaster LA1 4XQ. Tel/Fax (01524) 841946 e-mail: 100417.744@compuserve.com. Marine computer programs for IBM PC, Psion and Sharp pocket computers. Specialists in navigation, tidal prediction and other programs for both yachting and commercial uses.

DUBOIS-PHILLIPS & McCALLUM LTD
Oriel Chambers, Covent Garden, Liverpool L2 8UD. Tel 0151-236 2776. Books and charts.

FIDDLERS FERRY YACHT HAVEN
Off Station Road, Penketh, Warrington, Cheshire WA5 2UJ. Tel (01925) 727519. Sheltered moorings upto 6'6" draught, 50' long. Access through lock from river Mersey 1½ hours either side of high tide. Signed from A652. Boatyard and lift-out facilities. Annual rate per foot £8.25.

GUY BROOKE MASTS & RIGGING (KEMP NORTHWEST)
Conwy Marina, Conwy, Gwynedd, North Wales LL32 8GU. Tel/Fax (01492) 592909 Mobile 0589 108860. Regional centre for SELDÉN and KEMP integrated sailing systems. Specialists in mast build and maintenance. Full rigging service for swaging, splicing and rig surveys. Personal, professional and mobile along the north Wales and north west coasts.

HAFAN PWLLHELI
Glan Don, Pwllheli, Gwynedd LL53 5YT. Tel (01758) 701219 Fax (01758) 701443. Hafan Pwllheli has over 400 pontoon berths and offers access at virtually all states of the tide. Ashore, its modern purpose-built facilities include luxury toilets, showers, landerette, a secure boat park for winter storage, 40-ton travel hoist, mobile crane and plenty of space for car parking. Open 24-hours a day, 7 days a week.

HOYLAKE SAILING SCHOOL
43a Market Street, Hoylake, Wirral L47 2BG. Tel 0151-632 4664 Fax 0151-632 4776. RYA recognised shorebased teaching establishment offering a wide range of courses including Day Skipper to Yachtmaster Ocean, VHF and First Aid. Day, evening or intensive classes. Pratical courses by arrangement. Books, charts and gifts available.

ISLAND SEA SCHOOL
7 Church View, South Milford, Leeds LS25 5BM. Tel/Fax (01977) 685394. e-mail: sea.school@mcmail.com RYA practical courses from our base at Port Dinorwic on the Menai Strait: Competent Crew, Day Skipper, Coastal Skipper, Yachtmaster Preparatory, Ocean Yachtmster Qualifying Passages. Own boat tuition. Skippered charter.

ISLE OF ANGLESEY COUNTY COUNCIL
Highways & Technical Services Department, Council Offices, Llangefni, Anglesey LL77 7TW Tel (01248) 752331 Fax (01248) 724839. Berths and moorings available at Menai bridge, Amlwch harbour and north east Menai Straits (Beaumaris). Winter storage at competitive rates available at Beaumaris and Amlwch. Contact Maritime Officer 01248 752331 for details.

JOSEPH P LAMB & SONS
Maritime Building (opposite Albert Dock), Wapping, Liverpool L1 8DQ. Tel 0151-709 4861 Fax 0151-709 2786. Situated in the centre of Liverpool, J P Lamb have provided a service to world shipping for over 200 years. All chandlery supplies, clothing, rope, paint and flags are available. Full sailmaking and repairs. Kemp Retail Outlet for spars and rigging. Open Mon to Fri 8am to 5.30pm - Sat 9am to 12.30pm.

LIVERPOOL MARINA
Coburg Dock, Sefton Street, Liverpool L3 4BP. Tel 0151-709 0578/(2683 after 5pm). Fax 0151-709 8731. 300-berth yacht harbour. All serviced pontoons. Tidal access HW + or - 2½ hours approximately, depending on draught. 60-ton hoist, workshops, bar and restaurant, toilets and showers. City centre one mile. Open all year. Active yacht club and yacht brokerage.

MANX MARINE
35 North Quay, Douglas, Isle of Man IM1 4LB. Tel/Fax (01624) 674842. The Island's leading and most established yacht chandlery. Stockists of quality foul-weather clothing and thermal wear. Large stock holdings of stainless steel fixtures and fittings and a comprehensive range of general chandlery including rigging facilities.

MARTEX
Hillside, Over Road, Church Minshull, Nantwich, Cheshire CW5 6EA. Tel/Fax (01270) 522251. Manufacturers of sprayhoods, dodgers, sailcovers, boomtents, sun awnings etc. Retailers of acrylic 'Canvas', pvc, sailcloth, sprayhood fittings, etc. Personal callers by appointment please.

MAX WALKER YACHT DELIVERIES
Zinderneuf Sailing, PO Box 105, Macclesfield, Cheshire SK10 2EY. Tel (01625) 431712 Fax (01625) 619704. Fixed price deliveries. Sailing yachts delivered with care in north west European, UK and Eire waters by RYA/DoT yachtmaster and crew; 30 years' experience. Owners welcome. Tuition if required. References available. Your enquiries welcome 24 hours.

NATIONAL MARINE CORRESPONDENCE SCHOOL
30 Woodside Business Park, Shore Road, Birkenhead, Merseyside L41 1EL Tel/Fax 0151-647 6777. e-mail: sail@ nmcs.u.net.com www.nms.u-net.com The UK's leading correspondence school with courses from basic navigation to ocean cruising including RYA courses Day Skipper, Coastal Skipper/ Yachtmaster and Yachtmaster Ocean. RYA accredited for courses in power and sail, UK and overseas.

RESCUE EMERGENCY CARE
Hyfrydle, Capel Curig, Betws-y-Coed, Gwynedd LL24 0EU. Tel/Fax (01690) 720400. Our courses meet the requirements for organisations which require an individual to hold an H and SE First Aid Certificate, and our instructors can provide the full REC training programme for first aid at sea. If you would like to learn how to handle emergency situations, we have a programme to suit your needs. On-site or off-site courses available.

SAIL NORTHWEST
45 Ingrow Lane, Keighley, West Yorkshire BD22 7BU. Tel/Fax (01535) 602133. Sail Northwest offers yacht charter, skippered charter, and management from Maryport's marina, north Cumbria (40 minutes from M62, Lake District). We also manufacture customised fused switch panels, and refurbishment, including steps, tables and laminated tillers.

SEALAND BOAT DELIVERIES LTD
64 Outwood Road, Radcliffe, Manchester, Lancashire M26 1AG. Tel (01254) 705225 Fax (01254) 776582. http://www.btx.co.uk Nationwide and European road transporters of all craft. No weight limit. We never close. Irish service. Worldwide shipping agents. Extrication of yachts from workshops and building yards. Salvage contractors. Established 25 years.

WEST WALES, SOUTH WALES AND BRISTOL CHANNEL (AREA 11)
Bardsey Island to Lands End

ANDREW POTTER MA AMYDSA YACHT SURVEYOR
Penrallt Cottage, Cichle Hill, Llandegfan, Anglesey LL59 5TD. Tel/Fax (01248) 712358. Mobile 0374 411681 Prompt and professional surveys prior to purchase and for insurance purposes throughout Wales, the north west and Midlands. Services also include valuations, osmosis inspections and consultancy.

BALTIC WHARF WATER LEISURE CENTRE
Bristol Harbour, Underfall Yard, Bristol BS1 6XG. Tel 0117-929 7608 Fax 0117-929 4454. Tuition: 0117-952 5202 Sailing school and centre, with qualified instruction in most watersports. Also moorings available throughout the Bristol harbour for all types of leisurecraft.

BRITISH WATERWAYS & THE ENVIRONMENT AGENCY
CANAL & RIVER LINE 0891 546 555. Our canals and rivers provide: marinas, moorings, berthing, boatyard services and relaxing, picturesque waters for cruising. Find out more from Canal and River Line (50p minute peak rate at 45p minute other times).

CREST NICHOLSON MARINAS LTD - BRISTOL
Parklands, Stoke Gifford, Bristol BS12 6QU. Tel 0117-923 6466 Fax 0117-923 6508. Marina development management and consultancy.

CREST NICHOLSON MARINAS LTD - PENARTH
Portway Village, Penarth, South Glamorgan CF64 1TQ. Tel (01222) 705021 Fax (01222) 712170. Situated within the sheltered waters of Cardiff Bay the marina provides fully serviced, secure berths and wide ranging ancillary services. Open 24-hours, year round, we can assure visitors of a warm welcome. Please apply for details.

DALE SAILING CO LTD
Brunel Quay, Neyland Marina, Neyland, Pembrokeshirre SA73 1PY. Tel (01646) 601636 Fax (01646) 601061. Comprehensive chandlery. Hull and engine repair and service.

F J HARRIS BSc MRINA C Eng
Naval Architect, Surveyor & Boat Builder 'Gulls Target', 24 Roa Island, Barrow in Furness, Cumbria LA13 0QL. Tel (01229) 826084. Surveys of yachts and small craft for condition, insurance and repair. Design of yachts and small craft in traditional and modern materials. Work for MSA codes undertaken.

MERIDIAN CHARTWARE LTD
Maggs House, 78 Queens Road, Clifton, Bristol BS8 1QX. Tel 0117-907 3327 Fax 0117-907 7548. e-mail: meridian @dial.pipex.com http://dspace.dial.pipex.com/meridian/ Designers and suppliers of quality marine software. Electronic charting systems for the leisure user to the professional mariner, using the British Admiralty Raster Chart Service (ARCS). Dedicated Win96/NT mariner-friendly systems. Official ARCS chart agent. Suppliers of complete hardware/software packages.

N W SEAWAYS
Port Dinorwic Marina, Y Felinheli, Gwynedd, North Wales LL56 4JN. Tel (01248) 670620 Fax (01248) 671213. Mobile 0468 794361 Condition and pre-purchase surveys and insurance valuations, damage and repair reports, underwater dive inspections. Repair and dry dock facilities available. Call in or phone your requirement for prompt, professional service at competitive rates.

NEYLAND YACHT HAVEN LTD
Brunel Quay, Neyland, Pembrokeshire SA73 1PY. Tel (01646) 601601 Fax (01646) 600713. Marina operators with all facilities. 370 fully serviced pontoon berths in a sheltered, tree lined marina. On-site services include boatyard, sailmaker, sailing school, chandlery, cafe, launderette, showers and toilets. 30 visitor berths. 24-hour access and security.

PEMBROKESHIRE CRUISING
Cleddau House, Milford Marina, Milford Haven, Pembrokeshire SA73 3AF. Tel/Fax (01646) 690285. Sail around the dramatic and unspoilt beauty of Britain's only coastal national park. Professional RYA tuition for beginners to Yachtmaster, practical and theory. Yacht charter and skippered adventure cruises to Ireland, Cornwall and the Scillies.

PEMBROKESHIRE YACHT CLUB
Gellyswick Bay, Milford Haven, Pembrokeshire SA73 3RS. Tel (01646) 692799. Visitors welcome. Slipway, pontoon. Open every day.

PORT DINORWIC MARINA
Watkin Jones (Holdings) Ltd, Port Dinorwic, Gwynedd LL56 4JN. Tel (01248) 671500 Fax (01248) 671252. 180-berths in lock basin or tidal pontoon basin. Toilets, showers and restaurant facilities. Visitors always welcome. Call channel 37 (M).

W F PRICE & CO LTD
Northpoint House, Wapping Wharf, Bristol BS1 6UD. Tel 0117-929 2229. Books and charts. DTp Certificated.

RUDDERS BOATYARD & MOORINGS
Church Road, Burton, Milford Haven, Pembrokeshire SA73 1NU. Tel (01646) 600288. Moorings, pontoon, storage. All repairs.

ROWLANDS MARINE ELECTRONICS LTD
Unit 4 Glandon Industrial Estate, Pwllheli, Gwynedd LL53 5YT. EXPECTED TO BE SETTLED IN OUR NEW PREMISES AT PWLLHELI MARINA FOR 1998 SEASON Tel/Fax (01758) 613193. BEMA and BMIF members, dealer for Autohelm, B&G, Cetrek, ICOM, Kelvin Hughes, Marconi, Nasa, Navico, Navstar, Neco, Seafarer, Shipmate, Stowe, Racal-Decca, V-Tronix, Ampro, Walker. Equipment supplied installed and serviced.

SEVERNSIDE CONSULTANTS
Deco Court, South View Business Park, Staple Hill, Bristol BS16 5PJ. Tel 0117-956 8844. Books and charts. DTp Certificated.

STAYSAIL
The Old Rectory, Rectory Road, Llangwen, Haverfordwest, Pembrokeshire SA62 4JA. Tel (01437) 890078 Fax (01437) 899309. Holidays for dinghy/cruiser sailors, or space and comfort for their non-sailing partners. Use our dinghies/cruisers or bring your own. Paint, draw, relax, walk and sightsee. En-suite rooms overlooking breathtaking estuary. Scrumptious cooking.

SWANSEA MARINA
Lockside, Maritime Quarter, Swansea, West Glamorgan SA1 1WG. Tel (01792) 470310 Fax (01792) 463948. Access all states of the tide except LWST. City centre marina, restaurants, theatres etc. Call us on Channels 18 or 80 to check locking times. Visitors always welcome - a good destination for your annual trip.

WORCESTER YACHT CHANDLERS LTD
Unit 7, 75 Waterworks Road, Barbourne, Worcester WR1 3EZ. Tel (01905) 22522 & 27949. Chandlery, paints, ropes, cables, chain, clothing, footwear, shackles, books, bottled gas, anti-foul, fastenings, oakam, fenders. Hard storage, crane, haulage, engine service, oils, navigation aids, buoyancy aids, life jackets, distress flares, small boat hire.

SOUTHERN IRELAND   (AREA 12)
Malahide , south to Liscanor Bay

CARLINGFORD MARINA CLUB - IRELAND
Carlingford, Co Louth, Ireland. Tel/Fax +353 42 73492. Superb location in beautiful setting close to historic village of Carlingford, our friendly marina provides a top class service for all boat users. Moorings, chandlery, slipway, 16-ton cranage, power, diesel, water, laundry, showers and coffee shop. Visitors always welcome. VHF Ch16 and 37 (M). Sailing Holidays in Ireland - Only the Best.

CASTLEPARK MARINA - IRELAND
Kinsale, Co Cork, Ireland. Tel +353 21 774959 Fax +353 21 774958. 100-berth fully serviced marina with restaurant, laundry, showers and toilets. Waterside hostel-type accommodation available. New restaurant catering for both breakfast and evening meals. Access at all stages of the tide. Sailing Holidays in Ireland - Only the Best.

CROSSHAVEN BOATYARD MARINA - IRELAND
Crosshaven, Co Cork, Ireland. Tel +353 21 831161 Fax +353 21 831603. All facilities at this 100-berth marina situated 12 miles from Cork City and close to ferryport and airport. Travel lift, full repair and maintenance services, spray painting and approved International Gelshield centre. Storage undercover and outside for 250 boats. Brokerage. RNLI and Defence contractors. Sailing Holidays in Ireland - Only the Best.

DINGLE MARINA - IRELAND
Harbour Master, Strand Street, Dingle, Co Kerry, Ireland. Tel/Fax +353 66 51629. Europe's most westerly marina on the beautiful south west coast of Ireland in the heart of the old sheltered fishing port of Dingle. Visitor berths, fuel and water. Shops, 52 pubs and many restaurants with traditional music and hospitality. Harbour easily navigable day or night. Sailing Holidays in Ireland - Only the Best.

FENIT HARBOUR MARINA - IRELAND
Fenit, Co Kerry, Ireland. Tel/Fax +353 66 36231. A new marina opened in July 1997 with 104 berths for all sizes of boat up to 15m x 3m draught, with one berth available for larger vessels up to 30m. Access at all tides. Minimum approach depth 5m. Facilities include smartcard access, toilets, showers, laundry and harbour office. Visitors are welcome to use the superb clubhouse facilities of the Tralee Sailing Club and participate in races Tuesdays, Thursdays, and Saturdays. Sailing Holidays in Ireland - Only the Best.

THE HAVEN ARMS PUB & RESTAURANT
Kilrush, Co Clare, Ireland. Tel +353 65 51267 Fax +353 65 51213. 'The Haven Arms' - Kilrush - *Sail* into this pub and restaurant which has become a landmark to generations of local people and visitor alike. The 'Ship' restaurant offers appetising meals complemented by good service from our friendly staff. 'MOORINGS ARE FREE'.

HOWTH MARINA - IRELAND
Howth, Co Dublin, Ireland. Tel +353 1 8392777 Fax +353 1 8392430. Modern marina in beautiful, sheltered location. Fully serviced berths with every facility and 24-hour security. Very popular marina for traffic in the Irish Sea. Is available at all states of the tide with extremely easy access. Sailing Holidays in Ireland - Only the Best.

KILMORE QUAY MARINA - IRELAND
Kilmore Quay, Co Wexford, Ireland. Tel/Fax +353 53 29955. Kilmore Quay in the south east of Ireland has a new marina with 20 pontoon visitor berths. This friendly fishing port has pleasant hotel facilities, pubs and restaurants offering a traditional Irish welcome. Rosslare ferryport is only 15 miles away. Sailing Holidays in Ireland - Only the Best.

KILRUSH CREEK MARINA - IRELAND
Kilrush, Co Clare, Ireland. Tel +353 65 52072 Fax +353 65 51692. Mobile 087 2313870 Kilrush Creek Marina on Ireland's beautiful west coast, is a new marina with 120 fully serviced berths with 24-hour access. The marina has all shore facilities including a modern boatyard with 45-ton hoist. It adjoins the busy market town of Kilrush which has every facility required by the visiting yachtsman. Sailing Holidays in Ireland - Only the best.

KING SITRIC FISH RESTAURANT
East Pier, Howth, Co Dublin, Ireland. Tel +353 832 5235 & 6729 Fax +353 839 2442. Lovely location on the harbour front. Marina and Howth Yacht Club 3 minutes walk. Established 1971, Aidan and Joan MacManus have earned an international reputation for superb, fresh seafood, service and hospitality. Wine conoisseurs take note! Quality accommodation April 1998. Informal summer lunch - dinner all year.

KINSALE YACHT CLUB MARINA
Kinsale, Co Cork, Ireland. Tel +353 21 772196 Fax +353 21 774426. Mobile +353 87 449471. Magnificent deep water yacht club marina offering Kinsale hospitality to visiting yachtsmen. Full facilities include berths up to 20 metres, fresh water, electricity, diesel on pier. Club bar and wealth of pubs and restaurants in Kinsale. Enter Kinsale harbour - lit at night - no restrictions.

MALAHIDE MARINA VILLAGE - IRELAND
Malahide, Co Dublin, Ireland. Tel +353 1 8454129 Fax +353 1 8454255. Located next to the picturesque village of Malahide our marina village is the ideal spot to enjoy and relax. There are 150 fully serviced berths, petrol and diesel available, 30-ton hoist and facilities for winter storage ashore or afloat. A fine selection of shops, and friendly pubs and restaurants serving good food are close by. Sailing Holidays in Ireland - Only the Best.

ROYAL CORK YACHT CLUB
Crosshaven, Co Cork, Ireland. Tel +353 21 831023 Fax +353 21 831586. Sheltered 120-berth marina. Visitors welcome.

SAIL IRELAND CHARTERS
Trident Hotel, Kinsale, Co Cork, Ireland. Tel +353 21 772927 Fax +353 21 774170. Sail Ireland Charters is Ireland's premier yacht charter company. Yachts varying in size from 35' to 50' Beneteau's, Sigma's. Based in the picturesque village of Kinsale, an ideal place to commence your cruise of Europe's secret paradise of uncrowded sailing.

SALVE MARINE LTD - IRELAND
Crosshaven, Co Cork, Ireland. Tel +353 21 831145 Fax +353 21 831747. The marina is situated just 20 minutes from Cork City, Cork airport and Ringaskiddy ferry port. Located yards from Royal Cork Yacht Club and Crosshaven village centre. Facilities for yachts up to 140' x 14' draught including mains electricity 240/380 volts, telephone, fax, toilets and showers. Welding and machining in stainless steel, aluminium and bronze. Repairs and maintenance to hulls/rigging. Routine and detailed engine maintenance. Slip. Sailing Holidays in Ireland - Only the Best.

SHEARWATER CRUISES
Seaview Farm, Kilbrittain, Co Cork, Ireland. Tel +353 23 49610. Come sailing in comfortable 40' ketch with experienced skipper, on Ireland's beautiful, unspoilt south west coast. Wonderful sheltered bays, fascinating off-shore islands. Tuition available. Yacht based in Kinsale.

TRAMEX LTD
Chamco House, Shankill, Co Dublin, Ireland. Tel +353 1 282 3688 Fax +353 1 282 6311. Manufacturer of Moisture Metre and osmosis detection instruments for boats.

UK/McWILLIAM SAILMAKERS
Crosshaven, Co Cork, Ireland. Tel +353 21 831505 Fax +353 21 831700. Ireland's premier sailmaker, prompt repairs and service.

NORTHERN IRELAND   (AREA 13)
Lambay Island, north to Liscanor Bay

CARRICKFERGUS MARINA
Rodger's Quay, Carrickfergus, Co Antrim, Northern Ireland BT38 8BE. Tel (01960) 366666 Fax (01960) 350505. 300 fully serviced pontoon berths with full on-shore facilities (half a mile from town centre). Steeped in a wealth of historical legend, Carrickfergus has excellent restaurants, hotels, pubs, shops and a host of recreational leisure facilities.

COLERAINE MARINA
64 Portstewart Road, Coleraine, Co Londonderry, Northern Ireland BT52 1RS. Tel (01265) 44768. Wide range of facilities.

CREST NICHOLSON MARINAS LTD - BANGOR
Bangor Marina, Bangor, Co Down, Northern Ireland BT20 5ED. Tel (01247) 453297 Fax (01247) 453450. Situated on the south shore of Belfast Lough, Bangor is Ireland's largest and most comprehensive yachting facility. The marina is within convenient walking distance of all the town's amenities and may be accessed at any time of day or state of the tide.

DOWN MARINE CO LTD
163 Comber Road, Dundonald, Belfast, Co Down, Northern Ireland BT16 0BU. Tel/Fax (01237) 480247. Down Marine is a family owned business specialising in sailing equipment. We stock a comprehensive range of navigational instruments, paint, rope, charts, life jackets, deck hardware, seacocks, toilets, anchors, all-weather clothing and inflatables etc.

IRISH SPARS & RIGGING (KEMP IRELAND)
52 Whiterock Road, Killinchy, Co Down, Northern Ireland BT23 6PT. Tel/Fax (01238) 541727. Regional centre for SELDÉN and KEMP integrated sailing systems. The complete and fully mobile rigging service for yachtsmen in Ireland with outlets in Dublin and Cork. A comprehensive stock of all KEMP/SELDÉN products always available.

TODD CHART AGENCY LTD
4 Seacliff Road, The Harbour, Bangor, Northern Ireland BT20 5EY. Tel (01247) 466640 Fax (01247) 471070. International Admiralty Chart Agent, chart correction service and nautical booksellers. Stockist of navigation and chartroom instruments, binoculars, clocks etc. Mail order service available. Visa, Access and American Express accepted.

CHANNEL ISLANDS   (AREA 14)
Guernsey, Jersey, Alderney.

A B MARINE LTD
Castle Walk, St Peter Port, Guernsey, Channel Islands GY1 1AU. Tel (01481) 722378 (Fax 01481) 711080. We specialise in safety and survival equipment and are a DoT approved service station for liferafts including R.F.D., Beaufort/Dunlop, Zodiac, Plastimo and Lifeguard. We also carry a full range of new liferafts, dinghies and lifejackets, and are agents for Bukh marine engines.

Agents for Bukh Marine Engines. We specialise in safety and survival equipment. DOT approved service station for liferafts, including RFD, Beaufort/Dunlop, Zodiac, Plastimo and Lifeguard. Full range of liferafts, dinghies and lifejackets.
Telephone: 01481 722378
A B Marine Limited
Castle Walk, St Peter Port, Guernsey, Channel Islands.

BEAUCETTE MARINA
Vale, Guernsey, Channel Islands GY3 5BQ. Tel (01481) 45000 Fax (01481) 47071. Situated on the north east coast, Beaucette is one of Europe's most charming deep water marinas. With 140 berths, the marina offers all the services and facilities you would expect. Beaucette is a PREMIER marina.

BOATWORKS + LTD
Castle Emplacement, St Peter Port, Guernsey, Channel Islands GY1 1AU. Tel (01481) 726071 Fax (01481) 714224. Boatworks+ provides a comprehensive range of services including boatbuilding and repairs, chandlery, clothing and fuel supplies.

BOATWORKS+
Comprehensive range of services including chandlery with a good range of clothing, boatbuilders and repairs, boatyard facilities, fuel.
Castle Emplacement, St Peter Port, Guernsey GY1 1AU, Channel Islands.   Tel (01481) 726071 Fax (01481) 714224

CHICK'S MARINE LTD/VOLVO PENTA
Collings Road, St Peter Port, Guernsey, Channel Islands GY1 1FL. Tel (01481) 723716 Fax (01481) 713632. Distributor of diesel fuel biocide used to treat and protect contamination in fuel tanks where an algae (bug) is present. Most owners do not realise what the problem is, loss of power, blocked fuel filter, exhaust smoking, resulting in expensive repairs to injectors - fuel pump - or complete engine overhaul. Marine engineers, engines, spares, service - VAT free. Honda outboards, pumps and generators. Volvo Penta specialists.

JACKSON YACHT SERVICES
Le Boulevard, St Aubin, Jersey, Channel Islands JE3 8AB. Tel (01534) 43819 Fax (01534) 45952. Boatyard and chandler. Sailoft and liferaft service station.

JERSEY HARBOURS
Harbour Office, Weighbridge, St Helier, Jersey JE4 9XF. Tel (01534) 885588 Fax (01534) 885599. A warm welcome to visiting yachtsmen! Elizabeth Marina opens in April 1998. Berths available on lease - £184.86 per metre. St Helier marina continues to cater for visitng yachts. Both marinas offer excellent facilities.

MARQUAND BROS LTD - Yacht Chandlers
North Quay, St Peter Port, Guernsey, Channel Islands. Tel (01481) 720962 Fax (01481) 713974. Yacht chandlers, stockists of a comprehensive range of marine products. Guernsey distributor for International Paint. Extensive leisure and marine clothing department including Barbour, Driza-Bone, Dubarry and Quayside.

MOORES HOTEL
Le Pollet, St Peter Port, Guernsey, Channel Islands GY1 1WH. Tel (01481) 724452 Fax (01481) 714057. Minutes away from the marina. The Library Bar at Moores offers great value carverys, sumptious seafood platters and a wide selection of fresh fish. Comfortable, en-suite bedrooms for those who don't want to sleep aboard.

NORTH QUAY MARINE
North Side, St Sampson's Harbour, Guernsey, Channel Islands. Tel (01481) 46561 Fax (01481) 43488. The complete boating centre. Full range of chandlery, rope, chain, lubricants, paint, boatwear and shoes. Fishing tackle for on-shore and on-board. Inflatables and safety equipment. Electronics and small outboard engines.

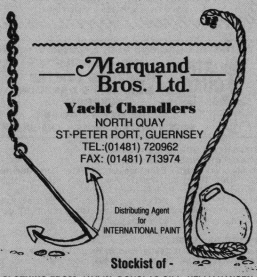

Marquand Bros. Ltd.
Yacht Chandlers
NORTH QUAY
ST-PETER PORT, GUERNSEY
TEL:(01481) 720962
FAX: (01481) 713974
Distributing Agent for INTERNATIONAL PAINT
Stockist of -
CLOTHING FROM JAVLIN, DOUGLAS GILL, HELLY HANSEN, BARBOUR, GUY COTTON
SHOES & BOOTS FROM DUBARRY, BARBOUR, QUAYSIDE, PLASTIMO & DOUGLAS GILL
CHANDLERY FROM AQUA MARINE, SIMPSON LAWRENCE, PLASTIMO, SOWESTER, E C SMITH & MARLOW ROPES.
ADMIRALTY/IMRAY/STANFORD CHARTS.
BOOKS - GALLEY EQUIPMENT
FISHING TACKLE, IRONMONGERY & D.I.Y. TOOLS
FRIENDLY FAMILY SERVICE

**OFFSHORE SPARS & RIGGING
(KEMP CHANNEL ISLANDS)**
Boatworks+, Castle Emplacement, St Peter Port, Guernsey, GY1 1AU. Tel (01481) 726071 Fax (01481) 714224. Regional centre for SELDÉN and KEMP integrated sailing systems. Specialist in new mast builds and maintenance for the Channel Islands. Complete retrofit and rigging services including FURLEX genoa and mainsail furling, rod kickers, spinnaker poles etc.

PETER DE JERSEY
La Contree de Saint, Saints Road, St Martin, Guernsey, Channel Islands GY4 6JA. Tel (01481) 36858. Boat maintenance and repairs. 24-hour service 01481 36858.

RADIO & ELECTRONIC SERVICES LTD
Les Chenes, Rohais, St Peter Port, Guernsey, Channel Islands GY1 1FB. Tel (01481) 728837 Fax (01481) 714379. Chart plotters, GPS, C-Map and Navionics charting, radars, VHF fixed and portable radios, autopilots. We offer full electronic supply and service. Sales and service dealers for Furuno, Icom, Shipmate, Cetrek, Autohelm, Robertson and AP Navigator.

ROSDEN GLASS FIBRE
La Rue Durell, La Collette, St Helier, Jersey JE2 3NB. Tel (01534) 625418 Fax (01534) 625419. Specialists in all types of glass fibre marine works, structural repairs, alterations, re-flow coating, GEL coat work, Blakes Osmosis Treatment Centre. Manufacturers of fuel tanks, bathing platforms and boat builders. General refurbishment and polishing. A division of Precision Plastics (Jersey) Ltd.

SARNIA FLAGS
8 Belmont Road, St Peter Port, Guernsey, Channel Islands GY1 1PY. Tel (01481) 725995. Flags and pennants made to order. National flags, house, club and battle flags, and burgees made to order. Any size, shape or design. Prices on request.

SEAQUEST MARINE LTD
13 Fountain Street, St Peter Port, Guernsey, Channel Islands GY1 1BX. Tel (01481) 721773 Fax (01481) 716738. Seaquest Marine have a fully stocked chandlery. Agents for Sowester and Simpson Lawrence. Sole agents for Avon, Typhoon, Garmin Electronics and Compass inflatables. Electronics specialising in GPS. Inflatable specialists. Official Avon service station. VAT free. Friendly advice.

WILDE MARINE SERVICES LTD
PO Box 112, Pollet House, Lower Pollet, St Peter Port, Guernsey, Channel Islands GY1 4EA. Tel (01481) 725840 Fax (01481) 711156. British yacht registration, corporate yacht ownership and management, marine insurance, crew placement and management. Wilde Marine Services (previously known as International MarineServices) aims to provide a personal and individual service to its clients.

THE YACHT INN
South Esplanade, St Peter Port, Guernsey, Channel Islands GY1 3AL. Tel (01481) 720969 Fax (01481) 716168. Guernsey's oldest inn, only 200 yards from visitors' marina. Two bars and restaurant serving good food at reasonable prices. 12 fully equipped bedrooms - competitive rates.

BELGIUM AND THE NETHERLANDS (AREA 20)
Nieuwpoort to Delfzijl

KELVIN HUGHES OBSERVATOR
Nieuwe Longowed 41, 3199 DC, Hoogliet, The Netherlands. Book and charts. DTp Certificated.

GERMANY (AREA 21)
Emden (new port) to the Danish Border

BOGERD NAVTEC NV
Oude Leeuwenrui 37, Antwerp 20000, Germany.
Books and charts.

MARTIN & CO
Oude Leewenrui 37, Antwerp 2000, Germany.
Books and charts. DTp Certificated.

PANTAENIUS UK LTD
Head Office: Cremon 32, 20457, Hamburg, Germany. Tel (0) 40-37 09 11 09. Pantaenius is one of Europe's largest yacht insurance brokers and covers yachts sailing under more than 35 different flags in all seven seas. (See UK office - area 1.)

IVER C WEILBACH & CO., A/S
35 Toldbodgade, Postbox 1560, DK-1253 Copenhagen K, Denmark. Books and charts.

FEEL THE COMFORT
of our waterside hotels & restaurants

From the coast of Cornwall to Mull and beyond - there is always the opportunity to take a break and stay or eat at some of the most beautiful locations in the British Isles and Ireland.

A welcome change after a long haul, to let somebody else do the work and be wined and dined in the comfort of a hotel which caters for the needs and desires of travelling yachtsmen and their families.

...ough harbour
50° 9.3' north, 05° 04' west

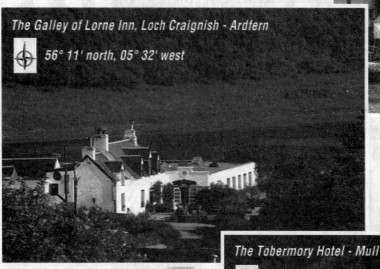
The Galley of Lorne Inn, Loch Craignish - Ardfern
56° 11' north, 05° 32' west

The Pandora Inn - Restronquet Creek - Falmouth
50° 12' north, 05° 04' west

The Tobermory Hotel - Mull
56° 37.3' north, 06° 04' west

N

Look in the Pink Pages under Waterside Accommodation & Restaurants

IN AN EMERGENCY
Look in
The Pink
and don't be in the doldrums

The PINK PAGES section at the front of the book is your own guide to marinas, harbours, services and supplies, including emergencies. With over 60 categories listed by discipline and coastal location, it is the quickest route to find what you want with simplicity and ease.

The MACMILLAN *incorporating* REED'S
NAUTICAL ALMANAC

Chapter 1
About this Almanac

Contents

Explanation

The Almanac contains important data which is subject to frequent and detailed correction (see 1.3). The 1998 Almanac is a stand-alone compendium of the essential navigational data needed by yachtsmen for the waters around the United Kingdom, Ireland and the coast of Europe from the North Sea border of Germany and Denmark to the Franco-Spanish Atlantic border. Important information is kept updated by the issue of two correcting Supplements. Much data of a permanent or semi-permanent nature has been tranferred from the Almanac to the Handbook. It is therefore essential that both books are used together and carried on board at all times.

The Macmillan & Silk Cut Yachtsman's Handbook is an enduring and valuable reference work which covers matters of a semi-permanent nature in as much detail as a single volume permits. The Handbook is not published on an annual basis, but is revised as necessary: a new third edition was published in 1995.

1.1   INTRODUCTION

1.1.1   Numbering system

There are ten chapters. For ease of reference each chapter is divided into numbered sections, prefaced by the number of the chapter. Thus the sections in Chapter 7, for example, are numbered 7.1, 7.2, etc.

Within each section the key paragraphs are numbered. Thus in section 7.2 (say) the main paragraphs are numbered 7.2.1, 7.2.2, 7.2.3, etc.

Diagrams carry the chapter number and a figure in brackets, thus: Fig. 7(1), Fig. 7(2), Fig. 7(3), etc.

Tables carry the chapter number and a figure in brackets, thus: Table 3(1), Table 3(2), etc.

1.1.2   Index

The main paragraph headings and the page numbers of each section are listed on the contents page at the start of each chapter and geographical area. A full index is located at the back of the Almanac.

1.1.3   General acknowledgments

The Editors wish to thank the many individuals and official bodies who have assisted by providing essential information and much advice in the preparation of this Almanac. They include the UK Hydrographic Office, Trinity House, Northern Lighthouse Board, Irish Lights, HM Nautical Almanac Office, HM Stationery Office, HM Customs, Meteorological Office, HM Coastguard, British Telecom, BBC and IBA, Marine Safety Agency, Royal National Lifeboat Institution, Koninklijke Nederlandse Redding Maatschappij (KNRM), Deutsche Gesellschaft zur Rettung Schiffbrüchiger (DGzRS), Port of London Authority, Associated British Ports, countless Harbour Masters and our many individual agents.

Chartlets, tidal stream diagrams and tidal curves are reproduced from Admiralty Charts and Publications with permission of the UK Hydrographic Office (Licence No HO 313/961001/01) and the Controller of HMSO.

Information from the Admiralty List of Lights, Admiralty Sailing Directions, Admiralty Tide Tables, and the Admiralty List of Radio Signals is reproduced with the permission of the UK Hydrographic Office and the Controller of HMSO.

WARNING: No National Hydrographic Office has verified the information in this product and none accept liability for the accuracy of reproduction or any modifications made thereafter. No National Hydrographic Office warrants that this product satisfies national or international regulations regarding the use of the appropriate products for navigation.

Chartlets are only intended for reference and should not be used for navigation. You should always consult navigational charts updated for the latest information.

Extracts from the following are published by permission of the Controller of HM Stationery Office: *International Code of Signals, 1969; Meteorological Office Weather Services for Shipping*.

Phases of the Moon and Astronomical data in Chapter 5 and the Astro-Supplement are derived from the current edition of the *Nautical Almanac*, and are included by permission of HM Nautical Almanac Office and of the Particle Physics and Astronomy Research Council.

1.1.4   Acknowledgments – tidal information

Acknowledgment is made to the following authorities for permission to use tidal predictions stated:

Bundesamt für Seeschiffahrt und Hydrographie, Hamburg and Rostock: Helgoland, Wilhelmshaven and Cuxhaven (BSH 8095·02/97-Z1102).

Rijkswaterstaat, Netherlands: Vlissingen (Flushing), and Hoek van Holland.

Service Hydrographique et Océanographique de la Marine, France: Dieppe, Le Havre, Cherbourg, St Malo, Brest, Pointe de Grave, authorisation (No. 89/97).

UK and foreign tidal predictions are supplied by the Hydrographic Office, Taunton, England.

The tidal stream arrows on the S and W coasts of Ireland are printed in 10.12.3 and 10.13.3 by kind permission of the Irish Cruising Club.

1.1.5   Standard terms

All bearings given in this Almanac are 'True' and arcs are measured in a clockwise direction. For example, the sector of a light shown as G (Green) 090°–180° is visible over an arc of 90° to any observer between due West and due North of that light.

Dimensions, in general, are stated in metric terms, the Imperial equivalent being included where appropriate. Distances, unless otherwise stated, are in International nautical (sea) miles, abbreviated as M. All depths and heights are shown in metres (m) unless otherwise indicated.

VHF frequencies are identified by their International Maritime VHF series channel (Ch) designator.

The 24-hour clock convention is used throughout, i.e. 0001 to 2359. Unless otherwise stated, times are in Universal Time (UT). Local times, when quoted, are indicated by LT.

The UK, Republic of Ireland and Portugal, use UT as their standard time. During the specified summer months, the UK, Republic of Ireland and Portugal use Summer Time which is UT+1 hour. In Germany, Netherlands, Belgium, France, and Spain the Standard Time is UT+1 hour; during the summer months these countries use UT+2, as Daylight Saving Time (DST).

For 1998, BST/DST will be in force for all countries from 29 Mar to 25 Oct.

1.2 IMPROVING THE ALMANAC

1.2.1 Suggestions for improvements

The Editors always welcome suggestions for improving the content or layout of the Almanac. Ideas based on experience and practical use afloat are especially welcome. It is not always feasible to implement suggestions received, but all will be very carefully considered. Even minor ideas are welcome.

If you have any comments, please write them on the Supplement application card, or alternatively send your ideas or comments by letter or fax direct to the appropriate Editor. Correspondence on nautical matters should always be sent direct to the Editors at one of the addresses below and not to the Publisher's address.

For Chapters 1 to 9 inclusive, and for those pages in Chapter 10 covering Area Maps; Coastal Lights, Fog Signals, and Waypoints; Area Waypoints; and Supplements:

The Editor, The Macmillan Nautical Almanac, Macmillan General Books, 25 Eccleston Place, London SW1W 9NF. (☎: 0171 8818001.)

For Chapter 10, Areas 1 to 21 inclusive and for the Passage Information pages: The Editor, The Macmillan Nautical Almanac, Edington House, Trent, Sherborne, Dorset DT9 4SR. (☎: 01935 850737.)

1.2.2 Notification of errors

Although very great care has been taken in compiling all the information from innumerable sources, it is recognised that in a publication of this nature some errors may occur. The Editors would be extremely grateful if their attention could be called to any such lapses, by writing to them at the appropriate address in 1.2.1 above.

1.3 KEEPING IT UP TO DATE

1.3.1 Late corrections

Late corrections are given at the back of the Almanac, before the index.

1.3.2 Sources of amendments

It is most important that charts and other navigational publications – such as this Almanac – are kept up to date. Corrections to Admiralty charts and publications are issued weekly in *Admiralty Notices to Mariners*. These are obtainable from Admiralty Chart Agents (by post if required), or they can be sighted at Customs Houses or Mercantile Marine Offices.

An alternative, but less frequent, service is given by the *Admiralty Notices to Mariners, Small Craft Edition*. This contains reprinted notices for the British Isles and the European coast from the Gironde to the Elbe. Notices concerning depths greater in general than 7 metres (23ft), or which do not affect small craft for some other reason, are not included. They are available from Admiralty Chart Agents, or through the Royal Yachting Association.

1.3.3 Our free Supplements

This Almanac contains corrections up to and including *Admiralty Notices to Mariners*, Weekly Edition No. 16/97. Subsequent corrections up to November 1997 are contained in the first of two free Supplements, published in January 1998. The second Supplement containing corrections up to April 1998, is published in May 1998.

As information contained in this Almanac is subject to constant change throughout the year, it is essential that users should **immediately** apply for the correcting Supplements in order to bring the Almanac fully up to date before using operationally.

To obtain these two free Supplements please complete and return the enclosed postcard, duly stamped, to: ESP Direct, The Old Workshops, East Avenue, Oxford OX4 1XU.

The Supplements will be sent to you free as soon as possible after publication. The Supplements also include important corrections to *The Iberian Guide* and *The Macmillan & Silk Cut Yachtsman's Handbook*.

1.3.4 Record of amendments

The amendment sheet below is intended to assist you in keeping the Almanac up to date, although it can also be used to record corrections to charts or other publications. Tick where indicated when the appropriate amendments have been made.

Weekly Notices to Mariners		Small Craft Editions	
1	27	1 Feb 1997	....
2	28		
3	29	1 May 1997	....
4	30		
5	31	1 July 1997	....
6	32		
7	33	1 Sept 1997	....
8	34		
9	35	1 Feb 1998	....
10	36		
11	37	1 May 1998	....
12	38		
13	39	1 July 1998	....
14	40		
15	41	1 Sept 1998	....
16	42		
17	43	**Late corrections**	
18	44	(see back of Almanac,	
19	45	before index)	
20	46		
21	47	**Macmillan**	
22	48	**Supplement**	
23	49	First	
24	50	(Jan 1998)	....
25	51	Second	
26	52	(May 1998)	....

1.4 ABBREVIATIONS AND GLOSSARY

1.4.1 Abbreviations and symbols

The following selected abbreviations and symbols may be encountered in this Almanac, in Supplements, in Admiralty Publications, or on Admiralty Charts. Abbreviations for harbour facilities in Chapter 10 are also printed for convenience on the loose-leaf card bookmark for HW Dover and Range.

NOTE: *   Not shown for Marinas

AB*	Alongside berth
Abm	Abeam
ABP	Associated British Ports
abt	About
AC	220-250v AC electrical supplies
AC	Admiralty Chart
ACA	Admiralty Chart Agent
✈	Airport
Aff Mar	Affaires Maritimes
ALL	Admiralty List of Lights
ALRS	Admiralty List of Radio Signals
Alt	Altitude
Al	Alternating Lt
AM	Amplitude Modulation
anch, ⚓	Anchorage
annly	Annually
ANWB	Dutch Tourist Association of Road & Waterway Users
App	Apparent
Appr.	Approaches
ARCC	Aeronautical Rescue Co-ordination Centre
ATT	Admiralty Tide Tables
Auto	Météo Répondeur Automatique
Az	Azimuth
B.	Bay
B	Black
Ⓑ	Bank (£)
Bar	Licensed bar
Bcst	Broadcast
BFO	Beat Frequency Oscillator
BH	Boat Hoist (tons)
Bk.	Bank (shoal)
bk	Broken
Bkwtr	Breakwater
Bldg	Building
Bn(s)	Beacon, beacon(s)
Bol	Bollard
brg	Bearing
BS	British Standard
BSH	German Hydrographic chart(s)
BST	British Summer Time
BT	British Telecom
Bu	Blue

BWB	British Waterways Board
By(s)	Buoy, buoys
BY	Boatyard
C.	Cape, Cabo, Cap
C	Crane (tons)
c	Coarse
ca	Cable
Cas	Castle
CD	Chart datum
CEVNI	Code Européen de Voies de la Navigation Intérieure
CG	Coastguard
ⒼⒼ, ⚓	Coastguard MRCC, MRSC
CH	Chandlery
Ch	Channel (VHF)
Ch, ✠	Church, chapel
chan.	Channel (navigational)
Chy	Chimney
cm	Centimetre(s)
Col, I	Column, pillar, obelisk
conspic	Conspicuous
const	Construction
cont	Continuous
Corr	Correction
cov	Covers
Cr.	Creek
CROSS	Centre Régional Opérationnel de Surveillance et Sauvetage
CRS, 📞, ⚔	Coast Radio Station
Cup	Cupola
⌗	Customs (see HMC)
Cy	Clay
D	Diesel fuel
Dec	Declination
decrg	Decreasing
dest	Destroyed
DF	Direction finding
DG Range	Degaussing Range
DGPS	Differential GPS
Dia	Diaphone
◆ ◇	Diamond
Dir Lt	Directional light
discont	Discontinued
dist	Distance, Distant
Dk	Dock
DLR	Dockland Light Railway
dm	Decimetre(s)
Dn(s)	Dolphin(s)
DOP	Dilution of Precision (GPS)
Dr	Doctor
dr	Dries
DR	Dead Reckoning
DSC	Digital Selective Calling
DST	Daylight Saving Time
DW	Deep Water, Deep-draught Route

DYC	Dutch Yacht Chart(s)
DZ	Danger Zone (buoy)
E	East
EC	Early closing
ECM ⌿	East Cardinal Mark
ECM	Éditions Cartographiques Maritimes
ED	Existence doubtful, European datum
El	Electrical repairs
Ⓔ	Electronics repairs
Ent.	Entrance
EP	Estimated position
Est.	Estuary
ETA	Estimated Time of Arrival
ETD	Estimated Time of Departure
exper	Experimental
explos	Explosive
ext	Extension
F&A	Fore and aft berth
📠, Fax	Facsimile
⌁	Fog signal
F	Fixed Light
f	Fine
F&A	Fore and aft berth
Fcst	Forecast
FFL	Fixed and Flashing light
Fl	Flashing light
FM	Frequency Modulation
Fog Det Lt	Fog Detector Light
Freq, Fx	Frequency
FS	Flagstaff, Flagpole
ft	Foot, feet
Ft	Fort
FV(s)	Fishing vessel(s)
FW, ⚓	Fresh water supply
G	Gravel
G, Ⓖ	Green, Green Fixed light
Gas	Calor Gas
Gaz	Camping Gaz
GC	Great-circle
GDOP (GPS)	Geometrical Dilution of Precision
GHA	Greenwich Hour Angle
GMDSS	Global Maritime Distress and Safety System
GPS	Global Positioning System
grt	Gross Registered Tonnage
Gt	Great
Gy	Grey
♿ ♿	Hearing-impaired facilities
h	Hard, Hour
H+, H–	Minutes past/before each hour
H24	Continuous
HAT	Highest Astronomical Tide
Hd.	Head, Headland

HF	High Frequency
HFP	High Focal Plane Buoy
HIE	Highlands & Islands Enterprise
HJ	Day Service only, Sunrise to Sunset
HMC, ⌗	HM Customs
HMSO	Her Majesty's Stationery Office
HN	Night Service only, Sunset to Sunrise
Hn.	Haven
Ho	House
HO	Office hours, Hydrographic Office
⚓ ⛴	Holding tank pumpout
(hor)	Horizontally disposed
Ⓗ	Hospital
Hbr	Harbour
Hrs	Hours
Hr Mr, Ⓗ	Harbour Master
ht	Height
HW	High Water
HX	No fixed hrs
Hz	Hertz
Ⓘ	Harbour information/tidal data
I	Island, islet
IALA	International Association of Lighthouse Authorities
Ident	Identification signal
IDM ⌿	Isolated Danger Mark
IHO	International Hydrographic Organisation
(illum)	Illuminated
IMO	International Maritime Organisation
incrg	Increasing
info	Information
INMARSAT	International Maritime Satellite Organisation
inop	Inoperative
INT	International
intens	Intensified
IPTS	International Port Traffic Signals
IQ	Interrupted quick flashing light
IRPCS	International Regulations for Prevention of Collision at Sea
Iso	Isophase light
ITU	International Telecommunications Union
ITZ	Inshore Traffic Zone
IUQ	Interrupted ultra quick flashing light
IVQ	Interrupted very quick flashing light
kHz	Kilohertz
km	Kilometre(s)
kn	knot(s)
Kos	Kosangas
kW	Kilowatts
L	Lake, Loch, Lough
L*, Lndg, ⌐	Landing place

▣	Launderette
Lat	Latitude
LAT	Lowest Astronomical Tide
Lanby ⟲	Large Automatic Navigational Buoy
LB, 🆑, ⚠	Lifeboat, inshore lifeboat
Ldg	Leading
L Fl	Long-flashing light
Le.	Ledge
LF	Low frequency
LHA	Local Hour Angle
LH	Left hand
LL	List of Lights
Lndg	Landing place
LOA	Length overall
Long	Longitude
LT	Local time
Lt(s)	Light(s)
Lt By	Light buoy
Lt F ⟲	Light float
Lt Ho	Lighthouse
Lt V ⟲	Light vessel
LW	Low Water
M*	Moorings available
M	Sea mile(s)
M	Mud
m	Metre(s)
mm	Millimetre(s)
Mag	Magnetic, magnitude (of Star)
ME	Marine engineering repairs
Météo	Météorologie/Weather
MF	Medium Frequency
MHWN	Mean High Water Neaps
MHWS	Mean High Water Springs
MHz	Megahertz
min(s)	Minute(s) of time
Mk	Mark
ML	Mean Level
MLWN	Mean Low Water Neaps
MLWS	Mean Low Water Springs
MMSI	Maritime Mobile Service Call Identity Code
Mo	Morse
Mon	Monument, Monday
MRCC	Maritime Rescue Co-ordination Centre
MRSC	Maritime Rescue Sub-Centre
ms	Millisecond(s); minutes, seconds
MSL	Mean Sea Level
Mt.	Mountain, Mount
N	North
NB	Notice Board
NCM ⌇	North Cardinal Mark
NGS	Naval Gunfire Support
NM	Notice(s) to Mariners
No	Number
NON	Unmodulated continuous wave emission
np	Neap tides

NP	Naval Publication
NRT	Net registered tonnage
NT	National Trust
Obscd	Obscured
Obstn	Obstruction
Oc	Occulting light
(occas)	Occasional
ODAS	Ocean Data Acquisition System
Off	Office
Or	Orange
OSGB	Ordnance Survey GB Datum (1936)
OT	Other times
✆	Partial-sighted facilities
P	Petrol
P.	Port (harbour)
P	Pebbles
(P)	Preliminary (NM)
PA	Position approximate
Pass.	Passage
Pax	Passengers
PC	Portuguese chart
PD	Position doubtful
PHM ⟰ ◢	Port-hand Mark
Pk.	Peak
⇡ ⇡	Perch, Stake (PHM & SHM)
PLA	Port of London Authority
PO, ✉	Post Office
⚓	Port Radio
pos	Position
⚠	Precautionary Area
(priv)	Private
Prog	Prognosis (weather charts)
prohib	Prohibited
proj	Projected
prom	Prominent
Pt.	Point
Pta	Punta
PV	Pilot Vessel
Pyl	Pylon
Q	Quick flashing light
QHM	Queen's Harbour Master
R, Ⓡ	Red, Red Fixed light, Rock
R.	River
R	Restaurant
R, Rk, Rky	Rock, Rocky
Ra	Coast Radar Station
Ⓡⓒ	Marine RDF Beacon
Ⓡⓒ Aero	Aeronautical RDF Beacon
Racon ◁▷	Radar Transponder Beacon
Radome	Radar dome
Ramark	Radar Beacon
RC	Non-directional radiobeacon
RCC	Rescue Co-ordination Centre
RDF	Radio direction-finding
Rds.	Roads, Roadstead

Rep	Reported
Rf.	Reef
RG	Radio Direction-Finding Station
RH	Right hand
⇌	Railway station
RNLI	Royal National Lifeboat Institution
Ro-Ro	Roll-on Roll-off (ferry terminal)
● ○	Round, circular; Ball
RT	Radiotelephony
Rtg	Rating (harbour)
Ru	Ruins
S	South
S	Sand
S, St, Ste	Saint(s)
SAR	Search and Rescue
✈	SAR helicopter base
SBM	Single buoy mooring
SC	Sailing Club, Spanish chart
Sch	School
SCM ↓	South Cardinal Mark
Sd.	Sound
SD	Sailing Directions, Semi-Diameter
SD	Sounding of doubtful depth
sec(s)	Second(s) (of time)
Sem	Semaphore
Seq	Sequence
sf	Stiff
Sh	Shells, Shoal
Sh	Shipwright, hull repairs, etc
SHA	Sidereal Hour Angle (Stars)
SHM ▲ ◮	Starboard-hand Mark
SHOM	French Hydrographic Charts
Si	Silt
Sig	Signal
SIGNI	Signalisation de Navigation Intérieure (Dutch inland buoyage)
SM	Sailmaker
◣	Slip for launching, scrubbing
SNSM	Société Nationale de Sauvetage en Mer (Lifeboats)
so	Soft
Sp	Spire
sp	Spring tides
SPM ◭ ◮ ↓	Special Mark, Single Point Mooring
SPS	Standard Positioning Service (GPS)
■ □	Square
SR	Sunrise
SS	Sunset, Signal Station
SSB	Single Sideband
St	Stones
Stbd	Starboard
Sta	Station
Str.	Strait
subm	Submerged
SWM ◉ ↓	Safe Water Mark
sy	Sticky
sync	Synchronised
(T), (temp)	Temporary (NM)
t	Ton, tonne
TD	Fog signal temp discontinued
TE	Light temp extinguished
☎, Tel	Telephone
Tfc	Traffic
Tr	Tower
▼ ▲ ▽ △	Triangle, cone
TSS	Traffic Separation Scheme
Twi	Twilight
≠	In transit with
ufn	Until further notice
uncov	Uncovers
Unintens	Unintensified
unexam	Unexamined
UQ	Ultra quick flashing light
UT	Universal Time
V	Victuals, food stores, etc
Ⓥ, Ⓠ	Visitors berth/mooring
Var	Variation
Vel	Velocity
(vert)	Vertically disposed
VHF	Very High Frequency
Vi	Violet
vis	Visibility, visible
Volmet	Weather broadcasts for aviation
VTM	Vessel Traffic Management
VTS	Vessel Traffic Service
VQ	Very quick flashing light
W	West
W, Ⓦ	White, White Fixed light
WCM ↓	West Cardinal Mark
Wd	Weed
wef	With effect from
WGS	World Geodetic System (datum)
♿	Wheelchair access
Whf	Wharf
Whis	Whistle
WIP	Work in progress
⚡ ⚡	Withy (SHM & PHM)
Wk	Wreck
WMO	World Meteorological Organisation
WPT, ⊕	Waypoint
☵, Wx	Weather (☎ or times)
Y, Ⓨ	Yellow, Amber, Orange, Yellow Fixed light
YC, ⌐	Yacht Club
⚓	Yacht harbour, Marina
⚓	Where to report, or yacht berths

1.4.2

GLOSSARY	GLOSSAIRE	WOORDENLIJST	GLOSSAR
English	**Français**	**Nederlands**	**Deutsch**

A. NAVIGATION	NAVIGATION	NAVIGATIE	NAVIGATION
Marks, Buoys, Beacons	**Bouées et Balises**	**Merken, Tonnen, Bakens**	**Tonnen, Baken**
Beacon (Bn)	Balise	Baken	Bake
Buoy	Bouée	Boei	Tonne
Can (PHM buoy)	Plate, cylindrique	Stompe ton	Stumpftonne
Chequered	A damier	Geblokt	gewürfelt
Column	Colonne	Zuil, kolom	Laternenträger
Cone, conical (SHM buoy)	Cone, conique	Spitse ton	Kegel, kegelförmig
Diamond (◊ shape)	Losange	Ruit (◊ vorm)	Raute (◊ Rautenförmig)
Dividers	Compas à pointes sèches	Steekpasser	Kartenzirkel, Stechzirkel
Framework Tower	Charpente	Traliemast	Gittermast
Isolated danger (IDM buoy)	Danger isolé	Losliggend gevaar	Einzelgefahr
Landfall (SWM buoy)	Atterrisage	Verkenningston	Ansteuerungstonne
Landmark	Amer	Oriëntatiepunt	Landmarke
Leading line, transit	Alignement	Geleidelijn	Leitlinie
Log Book	Livre de Bord	Journaal	Logbuch, Schiffstagebuch
Perch	Perche, pieu	Prik	Pricke
Pilot Station	Station de pilotage	Loodsstation	Lotsenstation
Port (side)	Bâbord	Bakboord	Backbord
Radio beacon	Radiobalise	Radiobaken	Funkfeuer
Signal station	Sémaphore	Seinstation, semafoor	Signalstelle
Special mark (SPM buoy)	Marque spéciale	Bijzondere betonning	Sonderzeichen
Square (□)	Carré	Vierkant	Viereck
Starboard (Stbd)	Tribord	Stuurboord	Steuerbord
Topmark	Voyant	Topteken	Toppzeichen
Tower (Tr)	Tour, tourelle	Toren	Turm
Watch Tr, lookout	Vigie	Uitkijk	Beobachtungsstelle

Colours	**Couleurs**	**Kleuren**	**Farben**
Black (B)	Noir	Zwart (Z)	schwarz (B)
Blue (Bu)	Bleu (Bl)	Blauw (B)	blau (Bl)
Green (G)	Vert (V)	Groen (Gn)	grün (Gn)
Grey	Gris	Grijs	grau (Gr)
Red, (R)	Rouge	Rood (r)	rot (R)
Stripe	Raie	Streep	Steifen
White (W)	Blanc (B)	Wit (W)	weiß (W)
Yellow (Y)	Jaune (J)	Geel (gl)	gelb (G)

Lights	**Feux**	**Lichten**	**Leuchtfeuer**
Alternating (Al)	Feu alternatif	Alternerend (Alt)	Wechselfeuer (Wchs)
Extinguished (Lt)	Éteint	Gedoofd	velöscht
Fixed (F)	Feu fixe	Vast licht (V)	Festfeuer (F)
Fixed and Flashing (FFl)	Fixe É	Vast en schitterend (V & S)	Mischfeuer (FFl)
Flashing	Feux à éclats	Schitterlicht (S)	Blitzfeuer (Fl)
Interrupted quick flashing (IQ)	Scintillant, interrompu	Onderbroken flikkerlicht (Int Fl)	Unterbrochenes Funkelfeuer (IQ)
Isophase (Iso)	Feu isophase (Iso)	Isofase (Iso)	Gleichtaktfeuer (Iso)
Leading Light	Feu d'alignement	Geleidelicht	Richtfeuer
Lighthouse	Phare	Vuurtoren	Leuchtturm
Lightship	Bateau-phare	Lichtschip	Feuerschiff
Obscured	Masqué	Verduisterd	verdunkelt
Occulting (Oc)	Feu à occultations (Oc)	Onderbroken (Oc)	Unterbrochenes Feuer (Oc)
Quick flashing (Q)	Feu scintillant, (Scint)	Flikkerlicht (Fl)	Funkelfeuer mitdauerndem
Temporary	Temporaire	Tijdelijk	zeitweilig
Very quick flashing (VQ)	Feu scintillant rapide	Snelflikkerlicht	Schnelles Funkelfeuer

Fog Signals	**Signaux de brume**	**Mistseinen**	**Nebelsignale**
Bell	Cloche	Bel/klok	Glocke
Explosive (fog)	Explosif	Knalmistsein	Knall
Foghorn	Corne de brume	Misthoorn	Nebelhorn
Reed (horn)	Trompette	Hoorn	Mundnebelhorn
Siren	Sirène	Sirene	Sirene
Whistle	Sifflet	Fluit	Heuler/Nebelhorn

Compass	**Compas**	**Kompas**	**Kompaß**
Compass, hand-bearing	Compas de relèvement	Handpeilkompas	Handpeilkompaß
East (E)	Est	Oost	Ost
North (N)	Nord	Noord	Nord

| South (S) | Sud | Zuid | Süd |
| West (W.) | Ouest | West | West |

Tides/Depths	**Marées/Profondeur**	**Getij/Diepten**	**Gezeiten/Tiefen**
Bay	Anse	Baai, inham	Bucht
Beach, sandy	Grève, plage	Zandstrand	Strand
Channel	Chenal, Passe	Kanaal, geul, vaarwater	Fahrwasser
Chart Datum (CD)	Zéro des cartes	Reductievlak	Kartennull
Cliff	Falaise	Klip, krijtrots	Kliff
Coastline	Contour de la côte	Kustlijn	Küstenlinien
Draught	Tirant d'eau	Diepgang	Tiefgang
Echosounder	Échosondeur	Dieptemeter	Echolot
Estuary	Estuaire	Riviermond	Flußmündung
Flood/ebb stream	Courant de flot de jusant	Vloed/eb stroom	Flutstrom/Ebbstrom
Gulf	Golfe	Golf	Golf, Haff
Height, headroom, clearance	Tirant d'air	Doorvaarthoogte	Durchfahrtshöhe
High Water (HW)	Pleine Mer	Hoogwater	Hochwasser
Island	Ile	Eiland	Insel
Knots (kn)	Nœuds	Knopen	Knoten
Low Water (LW)	Basse Mer	Laagwater	Niedrigwasser
Peninsula	Presqu'île	Schiereiland	Halbinsel
Point, headland	Pointe, pte	Punt	Huk, Landspitze
Mean Sea level	Niveau de la mer moyen	Middenstandsvlak (ML)	Wasserstand
Mean (tide)	Mi-marée	Gemiddeld	Mittelwasser
Narrows	Goulet	Zeeëngte	Enge
Neaps (np)	Morte eau	Doodtij	Nipptide
Range	Amplitude	Verval	Tidenhub
Rate (tide)	Vitesse	Snelheid	Geschwindigkeit
River	Fleuve, rivière	Rivier	Fluß
Sandhill, dunes	Dunes	Duinen	Sandhügel, Dünen
Slack water, stand	Etale	Kentering (hoog of laag)	Stauwasser
Springs (sp)	Vive eau	Springtij	Springtide
Strait(s)	Pertuis	Straat	Straße
Tidal stream al as	Atlas des Marées	Stroomatlas	Gezeitenstromatlas
Tide Tables	Annuaire des Marées	Getijtafel	Gezeitentafeln

Features	**Marques distinctives**	**Kenmerken**	**Merkmale**
Bridge	Pont	Brug	Brücke
Castle	Château	Kasteel	Schloß
Conspicuous (conspic)	Amer remarquable	Opvallend	auffällig
Railway	Chemin de fer	Spoorweg	Eisenbahn
Steeple, spire	Clocher, flèche	Toren, spits	Kirchturm
Water tower	Château d'eau	Watertoren	Wasserturm
Windmill	Moulin à vent	Windmolen	Windmühle

Dangers/Seabed	**Dangers/Fonds**	**Gevaren/Zeebodem**	**Gefahren/Meeresboden**
Aground	Dérive, Échoué	Aan de grond	Auf Grund sitzen
Bank	Chaussée, rive	Bank	Bank
Breakers	Brisants	Branding	Brandung
Clay	Argile	Klei	Lehm/Ton (Cy)
Mud (M)	Vase (V)	Modder (M)	Schlick (M)
Prohibited area	Zone interdite	Verboden gebied	Sperrgebiet
Sand (S)	Sable (S)	Zand (Z)	Sand (S)
Seaweed, kelp	Algues	Zeewier	Seetang
Shoal	Haut fond, Basse	Droogte	Untiefe
Stony, shingly	Cailloux, galets	Grind of kiezel	Steine (St)
Reef	Récif	Rif	Riff
Rock, stone	Roche, pierre	Rots, steen	Fels
Wreck	Épave	Wrak	Wrack

Ports/Harbours	**Ports**	**Havens**	**Häfen**
Alongside berth (AB)	Accostage	Aanlegplaats	Liegeplatz, Anleger
Anchorage (⚓)	Mouillage	Ankerplaats	Ankerplatz
Basin	Darse, bassin	Bassin, dok	Becken
Breakwater, mole	Digue	Havendam	Mole
Breakwater, wave-break	Brise-lames	Golfbreker	Wellenbrecher
Concrete	Béton	Beton	Beton
Dolphin	Bouée de corps mort	Dukdalf	Dalben
Downstream	Aval	Stroomafwaarts	Stromab
Dredged	Dragué	Gebaggerd	Gebaggert
Drying berth	Assèchage	Droogvallende ligplaats	Trockenplatz
Ferry	Bac	Veer	Fähre
Finger berth/pontoon	Catway	Box/Ponton	Liegeplatz/Ponton

Fishing harbour	Port de pêche	Vissershaven	Fischereihafen
Fixed bridge	Pont fixe	Vaste brug	Feste Brücke
Harbour dues	Taxes portuaires	Havengeld	Hafengebühr
Harbour Master	Maitre de Port	Havenmeester	Hafenmeister
Inner harbour	Arrière Port	Binnenhaven	Innerer Hafen
Jetty	Jetée	Pier	Anlegestelle
Landing (L)	Escalier du quai	Haventrap	Landungstreppe
Lifeboat (LB)	Canot de sauvetage	Reddingsboot	Rettungsboot
Lifting bridge	Pont basculant	Beweegbare brug	Hubbrücke
Lock	Écluse, Sas	Sluis	Schleuse
Mooring buoy	Corps-mort	Meerboei	Festmachetonne
Mooring	Coffre d'amarrage	Ligplaats	Ligeplatz
Outer harbour	Avant Port	Buitenhaven	Aussenhafen
Post, pile (mooring)	Poteau	Paal, meerpaal	Pfosten, Pfahl, Pfeiler
Roadstead	Rade	Rede	Reede
Slipway (slip)	Cale	Scheepshelling	Slip/Aufschleppe
Stone	Maçonnerie	Steen	Stein
Swing bridge	Pont tournant	Draaibrug	Drehbrücke
Upstream	Amont	Stroomopwaarts	Stromauf
Yacht harbour, marina	Port de plaisance	Jachthaven	Yachthafen, Marina

B. METEOROLOGY — MÉTÉO — METEOROLOGIE — METEOROLOGIE

Pressure — Pression — Drukgebied — Druck

Forecast	Prévision	Weervoorspelling	Wettervorhersage
Front, warm/cold	Front, chaud/froid	Front, warm/koud	Front, warm/kalt
High pressure	Haute pression, anticyclone	Hogedrukgebied	Hochdruck
Low pressure	Dépression, bas	Depressie	Tiefdruck
Ridge (high)	Crête	Rug	Rücken
Rise/fall	Monter/baisser	Rijzen/vallen	steigen/fallen
Settled	Stationnaire	Vast	beständig
To deepen	Se creuser	Dieper worden	sich vertiefen
To fill	Se combler	Opvullen	auffüllen
Trough (low)	Creux	Trog	Trog

Wind — Vent — Wind — Wind

Calm (F0)	Calme	Windstil	Ruhig
Light airs (F1)	Très légère brise	Flauw en stil	Leiser Zug
Light breeze (F2)	Légère brise	Zwakke wind	Leichte Brise
Gentle breeze (F3)	Petite brise	Matige wind	Schwache Brise
Moderate breeze (F4)	Jolie brise	Matige wind	Mäßige Brise
Fresh breeze (F5)	Bonne brise	Vrij krachtige wind	Frische Brise
Strong breeze (F6)	Vent frais	Krachtige wind	Starker Wind
Near gale (F7)	Grand frais	Harde wind	Steifer Wind
Gale (F8)	Coup de vent	Stormachtig	Stürmischer Wind
Severe gale (F9)	Fort coup de vent	Storm	Sturm
Storm (F10)	Tempête	Zware storm	Schwerer Sturm
Back	Adonner...	Krimpen	zurückdrehen
Freshening	Fraîchissant	Toenemend	zunehmend
Gust	Rafale	Windvlaag	Windstoß
Lull	Accalmie	Luwte	Vorübergehende Abflauen
Moderating	Décroissant	Afnemend	abnehmend
Squall	Grain	Bui	Bö
Veer	Vire au...	Ruimen	rechtsdrehen

Precipitation — Précipitation — Neerslag — Niederschlag

Drizzle	Bruine, crachin	Motregen	Sprühregen
Hail	Grêle	Hagel	Hagel
Rain	Pluie	Regen	Regen
Shower	Averse	Stortbui	Schauer
Sleet	Neige et pluie	Natte sneeuw	Schneeregen
Thunderstorm	Orage	Onweer	Gewitter

Cloud & Visibility — Ciel et Visibilité — Hemel en Zicht — Himmel und Sichtweite

Clearing up	Éclaircie	Opklarend	aufklarend
Cloudy	Nuageux	Bewolkt	bewölkt
Mist	Brume	Nevel	Feuchter Dunst
Fog	Brouillard	Mist	Nebel
Overcast	Couvert	Betrokken	bedeckt

Sea state — Mer — Zee — See (-gaug)

Choppy	Croisée	Kort	kabbelig
Moderate	Agitée,	Aanschietende zee	bewegt
Overfalls (tide race)	Remous (violents)	Stroomrafeling	Stromkabbelung
Rough	Forte	Ruw	grob

Smooth	Belle	Vlak	glatt
Swell	Houle	Deining	Dünung

C THE BOAT | LE BATEAU | HET JACHT | DAS BOOT

Sails/Spars/Rigging | Voiles/Mâts/Gréement | Zeilen/Masten/Tuigage Spieren/Rigg | Segel/Masten und

Backstay	Pataras	Achterstag	Achterstag
Batten (sail)	Latte	Zeillat	Segellatten
Boom	Bôme	Giek	Baum
Bosun's chair	Chaise de gabier	Bootsmanstoel	Bootsmannsstuhl
Ensign	Pavillon	Scheepsvlag	Nationalflagge
Forestay	Etai	Voorstag	Vorstag
Genoa	Génois	Genua	Genua
Halyard	Drisse	Val	Fall
Mainsail	Grand voile	Grootzeil	Grossegel
Mast	Mât	Mast	Mast
Mast, to step/unstep	Mâter/démâter	Mast plaatsen/verwijderen	Mast setzen/legen
Shackle	Manille	Sluiting	Schäkel
Sheet	Ecoute	Schoot	Schot
Spinnaker boom	Tangon de spi	Spinnakerboom	Spinnakerbaum
Splice	Epissure	Splits	Spleiß
Stainless steel	Acier inoxydable	Roestvast staal (RVS)	Rostfreier Stahl
Staysail	Trinquette	Stagfok	Fock
Topping lift	Balancine	Kraanlijn	Dirk
Turnbuckle, bottle-screw	Ridoir	Wantspanner	Wantenspanner
Whipping twine	Fil à surlier	Garen	Takelgarn

On deck | Sur le pont | Aan dek | An deck

Anchor	Ancre	Anker	Anker
Beam, breadth	Largeur	Breedte	Breite
Bilge pump	Pompe de cale	Lenspomp	Lenzpumpe
Boat hook	Gaffe	Pikhaak	Peekhaken
Bucket	Seau	Emmer, puts	Pütz
Fender	Défense	Stootkussen	Fender
Glass fibre (GRP)	Fibre de verre	Fiberglas, glasvezel	Fiberglas (GFK)
Life jacket	Gilet de sauvetage	Reddingvest	Rettungsweste
Oar	Aviron	Riem	Riemen
Pulpit/pushpit	Balcon avant/arrière	Preekstoel/Hekstoel	Bugkorb/Heckkorb
Rudder	Gouvernail, safran	Roer	Ruder
Tender	Annexe	Bijboot	Beiboot, Schlauchboot
Tiller	Barre	Helmstok	Ruderpinne
Varnish	Vernis	Lak, vernis	Lack
Winch handle	Manivelle de winch	Zwengel	Winschkurbel

Below deck | Sous le pont | Onderdeks | Unter Deck

Corkscrew	Tire-bouchon	Kurketrekker	Korkenzieher
Galley	Cuisine	Kombuis	Kombüse
Gas cooker	Réchaud à gaz	Gastoestel	Gasherd
Matches	Allumettes	Lucifers	Streichhölzer
Plug	Bouchon	Stop	Stöpsel
Saucepan	Casserole	Steelpan	Kochtopf
Tap	Robinet	Kraan	Hahn

Electrics | Électrique | Elektrisch | Elektrik

Battery (ships)	Batterie	Accu	Batterie
Bulb, lamp	Ampoule	Lamp	Glühlampe
Distilled water	Eau distillée	Gedestilleerd water	Destilliertes Wasser
Fuse	Fusible	Zekering	Sicherung
Insulating tape	Adhésif isolant	Isolatieband	Isolierband
Navigation lights	Feux de route	Navigatielichten	Positionslaternen
Solder	Soudure	Soldeer	Lötmetall
Switch	Interrupteur	Schakelaar	Schalter

Engine | Moteur | Motor | Motor

Alternator	Alternateur	Wisselstroom-dynamo	Lichtmaschine
Drive-belt	Courroie	V-snaar	Keilriemen
Fuel filter	Filtre à combustible	Brandstoffilter	Brennstofffilter
Gasket	Garniture, joint	Pakking	Dichtung, Packungsring
Grease	Graisse	Vet	Fett
Injector	Injecteur	Verstuiver	Einspritzdüse
Impeller	Turbine de pompe à eau	Impeller, Waaier	Impeller
Nut and bolt	Ecrou et boulon	Moer en bout	Mutter und Schraube
Oil, lubricating	Huile	Smeerolie	Schmieröl

Propeller	Hélice	Schroef	Schraube/Propeller
Sea-cock	Vanne	Buitenboordkraan	Seeventil
Spark plug	Bougie	Bougie	Zündkerze
Split pin	Goupille fendue	Splitpen	Splint
Starter motor	Démarreur	Startmotor	Anlasser
To bleed (air)	Purger l'air	Ontluchten	entlüften
Washer	Rondelle	Vulring	Unterlegscheibe

Tools	**Outils**	**Gereedschappen**	**Werkzeug**
Feeler gauge	Calibre d'épaisseur	Voelermaat	Fühlerlehre (Spion)
File (wood/metal)	Lime	Vijl	Feile
Hacksaw	Scie à métaux	Metaalzaag	Metallsäge, Bügelsäge
Hammer	Marteau	Hamer	Hammer
Pliers	Pince	Buigtang	Kneifzange
Screwdriver	Tournevis	Schroevedraaier	Schraubenzieher
Spanner, adjustable	Clé à molette	Sleutel, Engelse sleutel	Schlüssel, (Engländer)
Vice	Étau	Bankschroef	Schraubstock, Feilkloben

D. ASHORE	**A TERRE**	**AANLAND**	**AN LAND**
Nautical	**Nautique**	**Nautisch**	**Nautisch**
Boat hoist (BH)	Élévateur	Botenlift	Bootswinde, Bootskran
Boatyard (BY)	Chantier naval	Jachtwerf	Yachtwerft
Chandlery (CH)	Accastillage	Scheepsleverancier	Jachtausrüster
Coastguard (CG)	Sémaphore	Kustwacht	Küstenwache
Crane (C)	Grue	Hijskraan	Kran
Customs (#)	Douane	Douane	Zoll
Diesel (D)	Gas-oil, diesel	Dieselolie	Dieselöl
Dustbin	Poubelle	Vuilniscontainer	Mülltonne
Engineer (ME)	Mécanicien	Werktuigkundige/elektricien	Mechaniker
Fresh water (FW)	Eau douce, potable	Drinkwater	Trinkwasser
Fuel	Carburant	Brandstof	Kraftstoff
Methylated spirits	Alcool à brûler	Spiritus	Brennspiritus
Paraffin	Petrole	Petroleum	Petroleum
Petrol (P)	Essence	Benzine	Benzin
Power point (AC)	Prise d'électricité	Stopcontact	Steckdose
Shipwright (Sh)	Constructeur	Scheepsbouwer	Bootsbauer
Sailmaker (SM)	Voilier	Zeilmaker	Segelmacher

Non-nautical, Shopping	**Avitaillement**	**Niet nautisch, winkelen**	**Einkaufen/Shopping**
Airport (✈)	Aéroport	Vliegveld	Flughafen
Bakery	Boulangerie	Bakker	Bäcker
Butcher	Boucherie	Slager	Schlachter/Fleischer
Chemist	Pharmacie	Apotheek	Apotheke
Dentist	Dentiste	Tandarts	Zahnarzt
Doctor	Médecin	Dokter, huisarts	Arzt
Hospital (H)	Hôpital	Ziekenhuis	Krankenhaus
Ironmonger	Quincaillerie	Yzerwarenwinkel	Eisenwarenhändler
Launderette (⊙)	Laverie	Wasserette	Wäscherei
Market, food (V)	Marché	Supermarkt	Markt
Off licence	Vins et de spiriteaux	Slijter	Wein-u. Sprirituosenhändler
Post Office (✉)	Bureau de Poste	Postkantoor	Postamt
Railway station (⇌)	Gare	Spoorwegstation	Bahnhof
Stamps	Timbres	Postzegels	Briefmarken

E. FIRST AID	**PREMIERS SOINS**	**EERSTE HULP**	**ERSTE-HILFE**
Acute infection	Infection aiguë	Acute infectie	akute Infektion
Appendicitis	Appendicite	Blindedarmontsteking	Blinddarmentzündung
Burn	Brûlure	Brandwond	Brandwunde
Coma	dans le coma	Coma	Koma
Coughing blood	Cracher le sang	Bloed ophoesten	Bluthusten
Delirium	Delirium	Delirium, geest-verwarring	Delirium
Drowning	Noyade	Verdrinken	Ertrinkend
Fracture	Fracture	Breuk	Fraktur
Head injury	Traumisme cranien	Hoofdwond	Kopfverletzung
Haemorrhage	Hémorragie	Bloeding	Blutung
Laceration	Déchirure	Scheuring	Schürfwunde, Verletzung
Perforated ulcer	Ulcère perforé	Opengebarsten zweer	Magendurchbruch
Poisoning	Empoisonnement	Vergiftiging	Vergiftung
Vomiting blood	Vomir du sang	Bloed braken	Bluterbrechen
Sting (insect, jellyfish)	Piqûre	Steek (insect, kwal)	Stich, Stachel (Insekt)

Chapter 2

General Information

Contents

2

General information – introduction

Basic information on the *International Regulations for Preventing Collisions at Sea*, documentation, Customs procedures, useful addresses and conversion factors, is given in this Almanac. For further information reference should also be made to *The Macmillan & Silk Cut Yachtsman's Handbook*.

The following subjects are described in detail in Chapter 2 of *The Macmillan & Silk Cut Yachtsman's Handbook*:

limits and dangers – e.g. territorial waters; fishing limits; measured distances; hovercraft; warships on exercises; practice and exercise areas; submarines; minefields; wrecks; offshore oil and gas fields; power cables; traffic schemes; HM Customs – notice of departure; immigration; full and quick reports; Customs regulations in European countries; yacht tonnage measurement – net and gross tonnages; Lloyd's Register tonnage; dead weight tonnage; One Ton Cup etc; units and conversions; glossaries of nautical terms; yachting organisations – Royal Yachting Association; Seamanship Foundation; British Marine Industries Federation; Trinity House; useful addresses.

2.1   INTERNATIONAL REGULATIONS FOR PREVENTING COLLISIONS AT SEA

2.1.1   General

a.   The 1972 International Regulations for Preventing Collisions at Sea (IRPCS), occasionally referred to as Colregs or Rule of the Road, are given in full in *The Macmillan & Silk Cut Yachtsman's Handbook* (2.1), together with supporting diagrams and explanatory notes. The following are notes on some of the provisions of special concern to yachtsmen. It is important that these shortened notes should only be used in conjunction with the complete IRPCS and not in isolation. The numbers of the rules quoted are given for reference.

b.   The rules must be interpreted in a seaman-like way if collisions are to be avoided (Rule 2). A vessel does not have right of way over another regardless of special factors – such as other vessels under way or at anchor, shallow water or other hazards, poor visibility, traffic separation schemes, fishing boats, etc. – or the handling characteristics of the vessels concerned in the prevailing conditions. Sometimes vessels must depart from the rules to avoid a collision.

c.   A sailing vessel is so defined (Rule 3) when she is under sail only. When under power she must show the lights for a power-driven vessel, and when under sail and power a cone, point-down, forward (Rule 25).

d.   Keep a good lookout at all times, using eyes and ears as well as by radar and VHF, particularly at night or in poor visibility (Rule 5).

e.   Safe speed is dictated by visibility, traffic density, including concentrations of fishing or other vessels, depth of water, the state of wind, sea and current, proximity of navigational dangers, and the manoeuvrability of the boat with special reference to stopping distance and turning ability in the prevailing conditions (Rule 6). Excessive speed gives less time to appreciate the situation, less time to take avoiding action, and produces a worse collision if such action fails.

f.   When faced with converging vessel(s), a skipper/crew must always answer the following three questions and take action if required.

1.   Is there a risk of collision?
2.   If there is, am I the give-way vessel?
3.   If I am, what action must I take?

g.   If there is any doubt, assume that there is a risk (Rule 7). A yacht should take a series of compass bearings on a converging ship – see Fig. 2(1). Unless the bearings change appreciably, there is risk of collision. If fitted, use radar to obtain early warning of risk of collision. Take special care with large ships.

Take early and positive action to avoid collision (Rule 8). Large alterations of course and/or speed are more evident to the other skipper, particularly at night

Fig. 2(1) Rule 7. The bearing of black from white is steady. White should have taken action long before position 2 by altering course to starboard by at least 45° to pass under black's stern.

or on radar. Do not hesitate to slow down, stop (or even go astern, under power). While keeping clear of one vessel, watch out for others.

h.   In narrow channels, keep to starboard and as near to the outer limit of the channel or fairway as is safe and practical whether under power or sail (Rule 9). A yacht under 20m in length must not impede larger vessels confined to a channel. A yacht should not cross a narrow channel if such crossing would impede a vessel which can only safely navigate within the channel, and should avoid anchoring in such channels.

2.1.2   Vessels in sight of each other

a.   When two sailing vessels are in risk of collision and on opposite tacks, the one on the port tack keeps clear. If on the same tack, the windward yacht keeps clear. If a yacht with the wind on the port side sees a yacht to windward and cannot determine with certainty whether the other yacht has the wind on the port or starboard side, then keep out of the way of the other. For the purpose of this rule the windward side is deemed to be the side opposite to that on which the mainsail is carried (Rule 12). Rule 12 does not apply when either yacht is motor sailing. Fig. 2(2) illustrates the practical application of the rules in the three cases mentioned above. There are other practical situations which might give cause for doubt about the application of Rule 12. The first is when running downwind under spinnaker alone. In this case windward would be the side on which the spinnaker boom is set (normally opposite to the mainsail). The second case is when hove-to. This would have to be determined by the most likely position of the mainsail if it were set.

Fig. 2(2) **Rule 12.** Conduct between sailing vessels. In all cases the yacht on the port tack keeps clear; if both yachts are on the same tack the windward boat keeps clear. If in doubt, always keep clear.

b. Any overtaking vessel, whether power or sail, shall keep out of the way of the vessel being overtaken (Rule 13). Overtaking means approaching the other vessel from a direction more than 22½° abaft her beam (in the sector of her sternlight by night). An overtaken vessel must not hamper one overtaking: always look astern before altering course to ensure another vessel is not coming up on either quarter.

c. When two power-driven vessels approach head-on, each must alter course to starboard, to pass port to port (Rule 14). A substantial alteration may be needed, with the appropriate sound signal (see page 16 and Rule 34), to make intentions clear.

d. When two power-driven vessels are crossing and in risk of collision, the one with the other on her starboard side must keep clear and, if possible, avoid passing ahead of the other (Rule 15). The give-way vessel should normally alter to starboard; exceptionally, an alteration to port may be justified, in which case a large alteration may be needed to avoid crossing ahead of the other.

e. When one vessel has to keep clear, the other shall maintain her course and speed (Rule 17a). But if she

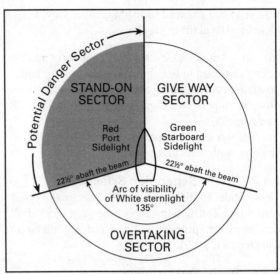

Fig. 2(3) **Rules 11 to 17.** These rules apply only to vessels in sight of one another and do not apply when vessels can only see each other on radar.

realises that the give-way vessel is failing to keep clear, she must take independent action to avoid collision (Rule 17b).

f. Using the arcs of visibility of the sidelights and sternlight to illustrate the rules, Fig. 2(3) allocates names to each arc. The arc of the sternlight is called the 'overtaking sector'; the arc of the starboard (Green) sidelight is called the 'give-way sector'; and the arc covered by the port (Red) sidelight is called the 'stand-on sector'. The stand-on sector is sometimes referred to as the 'potential danger sector' because, under Rule 17(a) (ii), as soon as it becomes apparent that the giving-way vessel is not taking action to alter course and that collision cannot be avoided by the action of the give-way vessel alone, the stand-on vessel shall take such action as will best avoid a collision. In taking such action, under Rule 17(c) a power-driven vessel should not alter course to port for a vessel on her own port side to avoid any risk of the two vessels turning towards each other. Recent court cases have held that a stand-on vessel in a crossing situation should take action in accordance with Rule 17 (a) (ii) at a distance of 2 miles or more by the good seamanship rule. This would normally involve a substantial alteration of course to starboard.

g. Under Rule 18, except where Rules 9 (Narrow Channels), 10 (Traffic Schemes) and 13 (Overtaking) otherwise require:

(a) A power-driven vessel under way keeps clear of:
   (i) a vessel not under command;
   (ii) a vessel restricted in manoeuvrability;
   (iii) a vessel engaged in fishing;
   (iv) a sailing vessel.

(b) A sailing vessel under way keeps clear of:
   (i)-(iii) in (a) above.

(c)   A vessel engaged in fishing, under way, keeps clear of: (i) and (ii) in (a) above.

(d)   (i)   Any vessel, except one not under command or one restricted in her ability to manoeuvre, shall if possible avoid impeding a vessel constrained by her draught, showing the signals prescribed in Rule 28 (see page 68).

(ii)   A vessel constrained by her draught shall navigate with particular caution.

2.1.3   Traffic Separation Schemes
Under Rule 10 all vessels, including yachts, must conform to Traffic Separation Schemes (TSS). Full details of the procedures involved are given in Chapter 10 (10.0.9).

2.1.4   Restricted visibility
In poor visibility vessels must proceed at a safe speed (Rule 19). On hearing a fog signal ahead of the beam, be prepared to reduce speed or stop. If a vessel is detected by radar, take early action to avoid collision: if the other vessel is ahead of the beam, avoid altering course to port, unless the other vessel is being overtaken: if the other vessel is abaft the beam, do not alter course towards it. Sound the appropriate fog signal; keep a good lookout; have an efficient radar reflector; keep clear of shipping lanes; and be ready to take avoiding action. In thick fog it is best to anchor in shallow water, out of the shipping channels.

2.1.5   Lights and shapes
a.   The required lights must be shown from sunset to sunrise, and by day in restricted visibility. The required shapes must be shown by day (Rule 20).
b.   The types of navigation light are defined in Rule 21, and are shown in Plate 1 on page 65, together with illustrations of the lights to be shown by power-driven vessels and sailing vessels under way. A summary of further lights and shapes to be shown by various classes of vessel is given in Plate 4 on page 68.
c.   A yacht, even with sails set, which is under engine must show the lights of a power-driven vessel, and by day, a cone, point-down, forward.
d.   In a sailing yacht up to 20m in length, the sidelights and sternlight may be combined in one tricolour lantern at the masthead. This gives excellent visibility for the lights, and maximum brightness for minimum battery drain. A tricolour light should not be switched on at the same time as the normal sidelights and sternlight, and must not be used when under power.
e.   A sailing vessel under way may, in addition to her normal sidelights and sternlight, show near the masthead two all-round lights in a vertical line, red over green. But these lights must not be shown in conjunction with the tricolour lantern described in the previous paragraph (Rule 25).
f.   A power-driven vessel under 12m in length may combine her masthead light and sternlight in one all-round white light (Rule 23).

g.   Lights required for vessels towing and being towed (Rule 24) include a special yellow towing light above the sternlight of the towing vessel. But this is not required by a yacht or other small craft not normally used for towing.
h.   In broad terms coloured lights indicate a hampered vessel. Special lights commonly encountered include fishing vessels – an all-round red over white; trawlers – all-round green over white; vessels which cannot manoeuvre – all-round red, over white, over red; and a vessel constrained by her draught – three all-round red lights; and not least the optional all-round red over green light shown by yachts so fitted. All the above lights are displayed in a vertical line. A hovercraft exhibits an all-round rapid flashing yellow light.
j.   The rules for vessels not under command, or restricted in their ability to manoeuvre (Rule 27), do not apply to vessels under 12m in length, except for showing flag 'A' International Code when engaged in diving operations. See Plates 6–7 on pages 70 and 71.
k.   A yacht less than 7m in length is not required to show an anchor light or ball when she is not anchored in or near a narrow channel, fairway or anchorage, or where other vessels normally navigate (Rule 30). A vessel under 12m in length is not required to show the lights or shapes prescribed by that rule when she is aground.

2.1.6   Distress signals
The IRPCS, Annex IV, gives details of all the signals which may be used either together or separately to indicate distress and need of assistance. These are described in more detail in Chapter 8 (8.2). For those flag and sound signals having a special meaning under IRPCS, see also Plates 6 – 7 on pages 70 and 71. For lesser emergencies use 'V' International Code – 'I require assistance'.

Distress signals must only be used when a vessel or person is in serious and immediate danger and urgent help is needed.

2.1.7   Sound signals
Sound signals required (by Rules 34 and 35) are summarised in the table below. Vessels over 12m in length must be provided with a whistle (foghorn) and a bell. A boat under 12m is not obliged to carry these sound-signalling appliances, but must have some means of making an efficient sound signal. The effectiveness of a yacht's sound signal should be judged against its audibility from the bridge of a large ship, with conflicting noises from other sources. Note that a short blast is about one second, and a prolonged blast four to six seconds in duration. A sailing vessel under way in fog sounds one prolonged blast, followed by two short blasts ('D'). The maximum interval between sound signals for vessels under way in restricted visibility is two minutes, but they should be sounded more frequently if other craft are near.

SUMMARY OF IMPORTANT SOUND SIGNALS – RULES 34 AND 35

Note: • indicates a short blast of foghorn, of about one second's duration.
     — indicates a prolonged blast of foghorn, of four to six seconds' duration.

Vessels in sight of each other (Rule 34)

•	I am altering course to starboard (power-driven vessel).
• •	I am altering course to port (power-driven vessel).
• • •	I am operating astern propulsion (power-driven vessel).
— — •	(In a narrow channel) I intend to overtake you on your starboard side.
— — • •	(In a narrow channel) I intend to overtake you on your port side.
— • — •	Agreement with the overtaking signal above.
• • • • •	I fail to understand your intentions or actions/I doubt if you are taking sufficient action to avoid collision.
—	Warning signal by vessel(s) approaching a bend in channel.

Sound signals in restricted visibility (Rule 35)

—	Power-driven vessel making way through the water.
— —	Power-driven vessel under way, but stopped and not making way through the water.
— • •	Vessel not under command, or restricted in her ability to manoeuvre, or constrained by her draught, or engaged in fishing, or towing or pushing, or a sailing vessel.
— • • •	Vessel being towed, or if more than one vessel is towed, the last vessel in the tow.
• • • •	Pilot vessel engaged on pilotage duties.

Bell rung rapidly for about 5 seconds, every minute.	Vessel at anchor.
Gong rung rapidly for about 5 seconds following above signal, every minute.	Vessel of 100m or more in length at anchor: the bell being sounded in the fore part of the vessel and the gong aft.
• — •	Vessel at anchor (optional additional signal).
Bell rung rapidly for about 5 seconds, with three separate and distinct strokes before and after.	Vessel aground.

2.2 DOCUMENTATION

2.2.1 Registration

Two forms of registration are available for British-owned yachts. Both are described more fully in section 1.5 of *The Macmillan & Silk Cut Yachtsman's Handbook*.

Full registration, under the Merchant Shipping (Registration etc.) Act 1993 and the Merchant Shipping (Registration of Ships) Regulations 1993 is a relatively complex and expensive business, since a yacht has to follow the same procedure as for a large merchant vessel. It does however have the advantage of establishing title (ownership), and is also useful for recording a marine mortgage. The register is in four parts:

Part 1	for Merchant Ships and pleasure vessels
Part 2	for fishing vessels
Part 3	for small ships
Part 4	for bareboat charter ships

The procedure for Part 1 registrations is fully described in a pamphlet issued by the Department of Transport titled *Registering British Ships in the United Kingdom* obtainable from Registry of Shipping and Seamen (RSS), PO Box 165, Cardiff CF4 5FU.

☎: 01222 747333. 📠: 01222 747877. There is a ☎ help line available on 0891 615353.

Part 3, commonly called The Small Ships Register, is for ships which only want a simple registration. This is sufficient for most purposes. A small ship is deemed to be less than 24 metres in overall length and is, or applying to be, registered on Part 3 of the Register of British Ships. It satisfies the law that a British yacht proceeding abroad must be registered, and it also meets the registration requirement for a privileged ensign. Part 3 registration does not register 'Title' and you cannot register mortgages.

The cost is only £10 for a five-year period, and measurement is a simple matter of taking the overall length of the boat – well described in the instructions which accompany the application form which is obtainable from: The Small Ships Register, PO Box 508, Cardiff CF4 5FH. ☎: 01222 761911. 📠: 01222 7747877.

2.2.2 International Certificate for Pleasure Navigation

With the introduction of The Small Ships Register, this certificate has no relevance for yachts owned by UK or Commonwealth citizens resident in the UK. It is however available for European citizens established in the UK.

2.2.3   International Certificate of Competence

The former Helmsman's Overseas Certificate of Competence (HOCC) is replaced by the International Certificate of Competence (ICC) (Pleasure Craft). If a suitable RYA Certificate (e.g. Yachtmaster offshore) is not held, the ICC will be issued by the RYA to UK residents who pass a test at an RYA recognised teaching establishment or participating Club, who already hold a HOCC, or a professional or services' seagoing qualification. The ICC period of validity is five years. Holders of existing HOCC can be renewed on expiry without the requirement of a practical test.

2.2.4   Licences

A licence is required to operate a boat on most inland waterways (e.g. the River Thames above Teddington Lock, the Norfolk Broads, Yorkshire Ouse above Naburn Lock, and canals or rivers controlled by the British Waterways Board).

2.2.5   Insurance

Any cruising boat represents a large capital investment, which should be protected against possible loss or damage by adequate insurance. It is also essential to insure against third-party risks, and cover for at least £500,000 is recommended.

The value for which a boat is insured should be the replacement cost of the boat and all equipment. Read the proposal form carefully, and fill in the details required as accurately as possible. Take care to abide by the nominated period in commission and cruising area. Note the various warranties which are implied or expressed in the policy. For example, the owner is required to keep the boat in good, seaworthy condition; insurance does not cover charter, unless specially arranged; prompt notice must be given of any claim; a reduction may be made for fair wear and tear for items such as outboards, sails and rigging; theft is only covered if forcible entry or removal can be shown; engines and other mechanical items are only covered in exceptional circumstances; personal effects are not covered, unless specially arranged; and motorboats with speeds of 17 knots or more are subject to special clauses and often to extra premiums.

2.2.6   Classification

Lloyd's Register of Shipping provides an advisory and consultancy service to owners, builders, moulders and designers, and publishes rules for the construction of yachts in various materials. Experienced surveyors approve drawings, supervise moulding, inspect fitting out, check the machinery, and certify the completed yacht. To remain 'in class' a yacht must be subjected to periodical surveys.

As an alternative to full classification, Lloyd's Register Building Certificate is provided to newly built yachts which have been constructed of any approved material in accordance with the Society's rules, and under the supervision of its surveyors, without the requirement for periodical survey.

2.2.7   Cruising formalities

Before, or while cruising abroad, certain formalities are necessary, as summarised below:

(1) Conform to HM Customs regulations, see 2.3.
(2) The yacht must be registered, see 2.2.1.
(3) Take valid passports for all the crew, and conform to health regulations (e.g. by reporting any infectious disease): exceptionally, vaccination certificates may be needed.
(4) Conform to Customs regulations in countries visited. Brief notes are given in section 2.4, but if in doubt about specific items or procedures, ask. All countries are sensitive to the importation (including carriage on board) of illegal quantities of alcohol and tobacco, and drugs of any kind.
(5) Make sure the yacht is covered by insurance for the intended cruising area, including third-party cover.
(6) It is wise for the skipper to carry a Certificate of Competence or similar document (e.g. Yachtmaster Certificate).
(7) The yacht should wear the Red Ensign (or a Special Ensign, if so authorised), and fly a courtesy ensign of the country concerned at starboard crosstree. Flag 'Q' must be carried to comply with Customs procedures.
(8) In most countries it is illegal to use a visiting cruising yacht for any commercial purpose (e.g. charter).

2.3   HM CUSTOMS

2.3.1   General information

All yachts sailing outside UK Territorial Waters must conform to Customs Notice No. 8 summarised below. This Notice, Form C1331, and further information may be obtained from any Customs and Excise Office, or from HM Customs and Excise, OAS, 5th Floor East, New King's Beam House, 22 Upper Ground, London SE1 9PJ. ☎: 0171-865 4742. Most yacht clubs and marinas hold stocks of Form C1331.

On 1st January 1993 the European Union (EU) became a single market and EU yachtsmen can now enjoy unhindered movement within the EU, provided that all taxes due, such as Customs duty, VAT, or any other Customs charges, have been paid in one of the EU countries.

Countries of the EU are: Austria, Belgium, Denmark, France, Finland, Germany, Greece, the Republic of Ireland, Italy, Luxembourg, the Netherlands, Portugal (including the Azores and Madeira), Spain (including the Balearic Islands, but not the Canary Islands), Sweden, and the United Kingdom (including the Isle of Man, but not the Channel Islands).

It is important to note that the Channel Islands and the Canary Islands do not operate a VAT system under Community rules, and for practical purposes are therefore treated as being outside the EU single market.

Yachtsmen are warned that a boat may be searched at any time. There are severe penalties for non-declaration of prohibited or restricted goods, and the carriage and non-declaration of prohibited drugs and firearms will incur the forfeiture of your boat and all its equipment. Form C1331 will be required for every voyage to or from a non-EU country. In addition yachtsmen arriving from outside the EU, including the Channel Islands need to remember to fly flag 'Q'. Failure to clear outwards and inwards in this way may result in a fine. It is clearly in the yachtsman's best interests to have a copy of Customs Notice No. 8 (Apr 1996) aboard.

2.3.2   Notice of departure

It is not necessary to report any voyage planned to another EU country, unless asked to do so by a Customs Officer. Each intended departure to a place outside the EU must be notified to HM Customs on Part 1 of Form C1331, copies of which are available at Customs offices and from most yacht clubs, etc. The form is in two parts. When completed Part I should be handed to a Customs Officer, taken to the Customs office nearest the place of departure, or put in a Customs post box, so the form arrives before departure. Retain Part 2 on board for use on your return. Form C1331 is valid for up to 48 hours after the stated time of departure. Should the voyage be abandoned, Part 2 should be delivered to the same office marked 'voyage abandoned'. Failure to give notice of departure may result in delay and inconvenience on return, and possible prosecution.

2.3.3   Stores

In general there is no restriction on taking reasonable quantities of food, fuel and other stores on which all duties and VAT have been paid elsewhere in the EU. Duty-free stores may be allowed on vessels proceeding south of Brest (France) or north of the north bank of the Eider (Germany), but you will need to apply to a Customs office in advance, and will have to meet certain conditions. Details on how to ship stores, or to re-ship previously landed surplus duty-free stores, can be obtained from any Customs office. You cannot take duty-free stores to the Republic of Ireland or the Channel Islands. If you are shipping stores under bond, or on which you are claiming repayment of Customs charges, the goods must be placed under a Customs seal on board. Such goods cannot be used in UK waters without paying duty, and you may be liable to duty if you abandon or interrupt the voyage. Further details may be obtained from any Customs office.

2.3.4   Immigration

Anyone who is not an EU national must get the Immigration Officer's permission to enter the UK. In most yachting centres the Customs Officer acts as the Immigration Officer as well. It is a skipper's responsibility to inform a Customs or Immigration Officer if there is any person on board who is not a national of the EU and who is arriving in the UK from any country other than the Isle of Man, the Channel Islands, or the Republic of Ireland.

2.3.5   Arrivals from an EU country

If arriving directly from another EU country there is no need to fly flag 'Q', complete any paperwork, or contact Customs. You must, however, contact Customs if you have goods to declare, or have non-EU nationals on board. You must declare any animals or birds; any prohibited or restricted goods such as controlled drugs, firearms, or radio transmitters not approved for use in UK; counterfeit goods; any duty-free stores; or the boat itself if duty and VAT are owed on it. Further details on which goods are classified as prohibited or restricted are given in Notice 8.

2.3.6   Arrival from countries outside the EU

If arriving directly from a country outside the EU (including the Channel Islands), yachts are subject to Customs control and on arrival you must contact a Customs Officer in person or by telephone. As soon as UK Territorial Waters are entered, i.e. the 12-mile limit, complete Part 2 of Form C1331 and fly the flag 'Q' where it can easily be seen until formalities are complete. If an officer boards your vessel, you must hand Form C1331 to him. You must declare any tobacco goods, alcoholic drinks, perfumes and toilet waters in excess of your duty-free allowance; animals or birds; prohibited or restricted goods; duty-free stores; or the boat itself if duty and VAT are owed on it. You must also declare any goods that are to be left in the UK. You must not land any persons or goods, or transfer them to another vessel until a Customs Officer says so.

2.3.7   Customs offices – telephone numbers

The telephone number of the appropriate Customs office (⌗) is given under the heading 'Telephone' for each British harbour in Chapter 10.

2.4   FOREIGN CUSTOMS – PROCEDURES

2.4.1   General

Other EU countries should follow the same regulations as described in 2.3.1 to 2.3.6 above, and any Customs formalities are likely to be minimal. However, before departure, skippers are recommended to check the procedures in force in their destination country. Currently, both the Netherlands and Belgium require a vessel to report on arrival even if coming from another EU country. If you are going directly to a country outside the EU you must inform UK Customs before departure by filling in Form C1331.

2.5.   VAT AND THE SINGLE MARKET

2.5.1   General

An EU resident can move a yacht between member states without restriction, providing VAT has been paid.

Enquiries concerning VAT on pleasure craft or on any other procedural matters on imported boats should be addressed to HM Customs and Excise, Dover Yacht Unit, Central Processing Unit, PO Box 242, Dover CT17 9GP. ☎: 01304 224421. The RYA may also be able to provide useful advice.

2.5.2   Temporary importation (TI)

A boat can only be permitted into an EU country under temporary import arrangements if:

(1)   The owner is not an EU resident (i.e. lives outside the EU for at least 185 days in any 12-month period), and

(2)   The owner does not keep the boat in the EU for more than six months in a continuous 12-month period, within the EU as a whole. The period of TI cannot be extended by moving the boat to another EU member state. It may, however, be extended by written application to the member state where the yacht is at present. For the UK, this is the Dover Yacht Unit as above.

2.6   USEFUL ADDRESSES

British Marine Industries Federation (BMIF).
Boating Industry House, Mead Lake Place,
Thorpe Lea Road, Egham, Surrey TW20 8HE.
☎: 01784 473377. 📠: 01784 439678.

British Sub-Aqua Club.
Telford's Quay, Ellesmere Port, South Wirral,
Cheshire L65 4FY.
☎: 0151-357 1951. 📠: 0151-357 1250.

British Telecom Maritime Radio Services.
43 Bartholomew Close, London EC1A 7HP.
☎: 0171-583 9416. 📠: 0171-726 8123.

British Waterways Board.
Willow Grange, Church Road, Watford,
Herts WD1 3QA.
☎: 01923 226422. 📠: 01923 226081.

Clyde Cruising Club.
Suite 408, The Pentagon Centre, 36 Washington
Street, Glasgow G3 8AZ.
☎: 0141-221 2774. 📠: 0141-221 2775.

Cowes Combined Clubs.
Secretary, 18 Bath Road, Cowes, Isle of Wight
PO31 7QN.
☎: 01983 295744. 📠: 01983 295329.

Cruising Association (CA).
CA House, 1 Northey Street, Limehouse Basin,
London E14 8BT.
☎: 0171-537 2828. 📠: 0171-537 2266.

Coastguard Headquarters.
Spring Place, 105 Commercial Road,
Southampton SO1 0ZD.
☎: 01703 329486. 📠: 01703 329351.

HM Customs and Excise.
OAS, 5th Floor East, New King's Beam House,
22 Upper Ground, London SE1 9PJ.
☎: 0171-865 4742. 📠: 0171-865 4744.

Hydrographic Office.
Admiralty Way, Taunton, Somerset TA1 2DN.
☎: 01823 337900. 📠: 01823 284077.

International Maritime Organisation (IMO).
4 Albert Embankment, London SE1 7SR.
☎: 0171-735 7611. 📠: 0171-587 3210.

**International Maritime Satellite Organisation
(Inmarsat).**
99 City Road, London EC1Y 1AX.
☎: 0171-728 1000. 📠: 0171-728 1044.

Irish Lights.
16 Lower Pembroke Street,
Dublin 2.
☎: 00-353-1-6624525. 📠: 00-353-1-6618094.

Junior Offshore Group.
43 Parklands Ave, Cowes, Isle of Wight PO31 7NH.
☎: 01983 280279. 📠: 01983 292962.

Little Ship Club.
Bell Wharf Lane, Upper Thames Street,
London EC4R 3TB.
☎: 0171-236 7729. 📠: 0171-236 9100.

Maritime Trust.
2 Greenwich Church Street, London SE10 9BG.
☎: 0181-858 2698. 📠: 0181-858 6976.

Meteorological Office.
London Road, Bracknell, Berks RG12 2SZ.
☎: 01344 420242. 📠: 01344 855921.

Northern Lighthouse Board.
84 George Street, Edinburgh EH2 3DA.
☎: 0131 226 7051. 📠: 0131 220 2093.

Radiocommunications Agency.
Ship Radio Licensing Unit,
New King's Beam House,
22 Upper Ground, London SE1 9SA.
☎: 0171 211 0215. 📠: 0171 211 0507.

Radio Licensing Centre.
Subscription Service Ltd, PO Box 885,
Bristol BS99 5LG.
☎: 0117 9258333. 📠: 0117 9219026.

Registry of Shipping and Seamen (RSS).
Anchor House, Cheviot Close, Llanishen,
Cardiff CF4 5JA.
☎: 01222 747333 Extn 289. 📠: 01222 747877.
☎: RSS Helpline 0891 615353.

Royal Cruising Club (RCC).
At the Royal Thames Yacht Club (see below).

Royal Institute of Navigation.
At the Royal Geographical Society,
1 Kensington Gore, London SW7 2AT.
☎: 0171-589 5021. 📠: 0171-823 8671.

Royal National Lifeboat Institution (RNLI).
West Quay Road, Poole, Dorset BH15 1HZ.
☎: 01202 663000. 📠: 01202 663167.

Royal Naval Sailing Association (RNSA).
17 Pembroke Road, Portsmouth, Hants PO1 2NT.
☎: 01705 823524. 📠: 01705 870654.

Royal Ocean Racing Club (RORC).
20 St James's Place, London SW1A 1NN.
☎: 0171-493 2248. 📠: 0171-493 5252.

Royal Thames Yacht Club (RTYC).
60 Knightsbridge, London SW1A 7LF.
☎: 0171-235 2121. 📠: 0171-235 5672.

Royal Yachting Association (RYA).
RYA House, Romsey Road, Eastleigh,
Hants SO5 9YA.
☎: 01703 629962. 📠: 01703 629924.

Royal Yachting Association (Scotland).
Caledonia House, South Gyle,
Edinburgh EH12 9DQ.
☎: 0131-317 7388. 📠: 0131-317 8566.

Ship Radio Licensing Unit.
Wray Castle Ltd, Ship Radio Licensing,
PO Box 5, Ambleside, LA22 0BF.
☎: 015394 34662. 📠: 015394 34663.

Small Ships Register.
Small Ships Section,
Registry of Shipping and Seamen,
PO Box 165, Cardiff CF4 5FU.
☎: 01222 747333. 📠: 01222 747877.

Solent Cruising and Racing Association.
18 Bath Road, Cowes, Isle of Wight PO31 7QN.
☎: 01983 295744. 📠: 01983 295329.

Sports Council.
16 Upper Woburn Place, London WC1H 0QP.
☎: 0171-388 1277. 📠: 0171-383 5740.

Trinity House, Corporation of.
Trinity House, Tower Hill, London EC3N 4DH.
☎: 0171-480 6601. 📠: 0171-480 7662.

UK Offshore Boating Association.
1 Carbis Close, Port Solent, Portsmouth PO6 4TW.
☎: 01705 219949. 📠: 01705 219969.

2.7 CONVERSION FACTORS

2.7.1 Conversion factors

To convert	Multiply by	To convert	Multiply by
sq in to sq mm	645·16	sq mm to sq in	0·00155
sq ft to sq m	0·0929	sq m to sq ft	10·76
in to mm	25·40	mm to in	0·0394
ft to m	0·3048	m to ft	3·2808
fathoms to m	1·8288	m to fathoms	0·5468
nautical miles to statute miles	1·1515	statute miles to nautical miles	0·8684
lb to kg	0·4536	kg to lb	2·205
tons to tonnes (1000 kg)	1·016	tonnes to tons (2240 lb)	0·9842
kilometres to nautical miles	0·539957	nautical miles to kilometres	1·852
millibars to inches	0·0295	inches to millibars	33·86
lb/sq in to kg/sq cm	0·0703	kg/sq cm to lb/sq in	14·22
lb/sq in to atmospheres	0·0680	atmospheres to lb/sq in	14·7
ft/sec to m/sec	0·3048	m/sec to ft/sec	3·281
ft/sec to miles/hr	0·682	miles/hr to ft/sec	1·467
ft/min to m/sec	0·0051	m/sec to ft/min	196·8
knots to miles/hr	1·1515	miles/hr to knots	0·868
knots to km/hr	1·8520	km/hr to knots	0·5400
cu ft to galls	6·25	galls to cu ft	0·16
cu ft to litres	28·33	litres to cu ft	0·035
pints to litres	0·568	litres to pints	1·76
galls to litres	4·546	litres to galls	0·22
Imp galls to US galls	1·2	US galls to Imp galls	0·833

2.7.2 Feet to metres, metres to feet

Explanation: The central columns of figures in **bold** type can be referred in either direction. To the left to convert metres into feet, or to the right to convert feet into metres.

For example, five lines down: 5 feet = 1·52 metres, and 5 metres = 16·40 feet.

Feet		Metres	Feet		Metres	Feet		Metres	Feet		Metres
3·28	1	0·30	45·93	14	4·27	88·58	27	8·23	131·23	40	12·19
6·56	2	0·61	49·21	15	4·57	91·86	28	8·53	134·51	41	12·50
9·84	3	0·91	52·49	16	4·88	95·14	29	8·84	137·80	42	12·80
13·12	4	1·22	55·77	17	5·18	98·43	30	9·14	141·08	43	13·11
16·40	5	1·52	59·06	18	5·49	101·71	31	9·45	144·36	44	13·41
19·69	6	1·83	62·34	19	5·79	104·99	32	9·75	147·64	45	13·72
22·97	7	2·13	65·62	20	6·10	108·27	33	10·06	150·92	46	14·02
26·25	8	2·44	68·90	21	6·40	111·55	34	10·36	154·20	47	14·33
29·53	9	2·74	72·18	22	6·71	114·83	35	10·67	157·48	48	14·63
32·81	10	3·05	75·46	23	7·01	118·11	36	10·97	160·76	49	14·94
36·09	11	3·35	78·74	24	7·32	121·39	37	11·28	164·04	50	15·24
39·37	12	3·66	82·02	25	7·62	124·67	38	11·58			
42·65	13	3·96	85·30	26	7·92	127·95	39	11·89			

2.8.1 UK PUBLIC HOLIDAYS 1997

ENGLAND & WALES: Jan 1†, Apr 10, Apr 13, May 4†, May 25, Aug 31, Dec 25, Dec 28†

NORTHERN IRELAND: Jan 1†, Mar 17, Mar 28, Apr 10, May 4†, May 25, July 13†, Aug 31, Dec 25, Dec 28†

SCOTLAND: Jan 1, Jan 2, Apr 10, May 4, May 25†, Aug 3, Dec 25, Dec 28†

† Subject to confirmation

2.8.2 PHASES OF THE MOON 1998

	New Moon		First Quarter		Full Moon		Last Quarter	
	d h m		d h m		d h m		d h m	
		Jan	05 14 18	Jan	12 17 24	Jan	20 19 40	
Jan	28 06 01	Feb	03 22 53	Feb	11 10 23	Feb	19 15 27	
Feb	26 17 26	Mar	05 08 41	Mar	13 04 34	Mar	21 07 38	
Mar	28 03 14	Apr	03 20 18	Apr	11 22 23	Apr	19 19 53	
Apr	26 11 41	May	03 10 04	May	11 14 29	May	19 04 35	
May	25 19 32	Jun	02 01 45	Jun	10 04 18	Jun	17 10 38	
Jun	24 03 50	Jul	01 18 43	Jul	09 16 01	Jul	16 15 13	
Jul	23 13 44	Jul	31 12 05	Aug	08 02 10	Aug	14 19 48	
Aug	22 02 03	Aug	30 05 06	Sep	06 11 21	Sep	13 01 58	
Sept	20 17 01	Sept	28 21 11	Oct	05 20 12	Oct	12 11 11	
Oct	20 10 09	Oct	28 11 46	Nov	04 05 18	Nov	11 00 28	
Nov	19 04 27	Nov	27 00 23	Dec	03 15 19	Dec	10 17 53	
Dec	18 22 42	Dec	26 10 46					

Note: All times UT

2.8.3 ECLIPSE NOTES 1998

1. Total Eclipse of the Sun, 26 February   Not visible from Europe
2. Annular Eclipse of the Sun, 21-22 August   Not visible from Europe

2.8.4 STANDARD TIMES
(Corrected to March 1997)
Summer time, one hour in advance of UT, is kept in all places in the European Union, including the Channel Islands, from Mar 29 01h UT to October 25 01h UT in 1998

PLACES NORMALLY KEEPING UT

Canary Islands	Great Britain	Irish Republic
Channel Islands	Iceland*	Morocco*
Faeroes, The*	Ireland, Northern**	Portugal

PLACES FAST ON UT

Algeria*	01	Germany	01	Norway	01
Balearic Islands	01	Gibraltar	01	Poland**	01
Belgium	01	Italy	01	Russia, W of 40°**	03
Corsica*	01	Latvia**	02	Sardinia	01
Denmark	01	Lithuania**	02	Spain	01
Estonia**	02	Malta**	01	Sweden	01
Finland	02	Monaco	01	Tunisia*	01
France	01	Netherlands, The	01		

The times should be *added* to UT to give Standard Time:
            subtracted from Standard Time to give UT
*   Summer time is not kept in these places
**   Summer time, may be kept

Chapter 3

Coastal Navigation

Contents

3

Coastal navigation – introduction

The following subjects are described in more detail in Chapters 3 and 15 of *The Macmillan & Silk Cut Yachtsman's Handbook:*

the terms and definitions used in coastal navigation; magnetic variation and deviation; compass checks; compass adjusting and compass swinging; charts and their symbols; lights and fog signals; methods of laying-off courses and position fixing; time, speed and distance; measured mile table; pilotage; IALA Buoyage System; passage planning; the use of calculators; practical passage making; sailing directions.

3.1 DEFINITIONS AND TERMS

3.1.1 General

The information given in this chapter covers a few of the more important aspects of basic coastal navigation in simplified form, together with useful tables.

The Macmillan and Silk Cut Yachtsman's Handbook provides a more extensive reference on coastal navigation covering terms and definitions, charts, chartwork and pilotage.

3.1.2 Position

Position on the Earth's surface can be expressed in two ways. By Latitude and Longitude, or by a bearing and distance from a known position.

The latitude of a place is its distance north or south of the Equator. It is measured in degrees (°), minutes (') and decimals of a minute from 0° to 90° north or south of the equator.

The longitude of a place is measured in degrees (°), minutes ('), and decimals of a minute from 0° to 180° east or west from the Greenwich meridian.

3.1.3 Direction

Direction is measured clockwise from north in a three-figure group, i.e. 000° to 359°. Thus east is written as 090°, and west 270°.

There are three different norths from which direction is measured. It is imperative for a navigator to distinguish clearly between each. These are:

(1) **True North** is measured from the North Geographic Pole.

(2) **Magnetic North** is measured from the Magnetic North Pole, which does not coincide with the Geographic Pole.

(3) **Compass North** is measured from the north-seeking end of the compass needle.

Wind direction is normally given in points of the compass clockwise from a cardinal or quadrantal point rather than in degrees, i.e. N, NNE, NE by N, etc. There are 32 points of the compass, with each point equal to 11¼°.

Tidal streams are always expressed in the direction towards which they are running.

3.1.4 Compass variation and deviation

The magnetic compass is the most vital navigational instrument in a cruising boat. It is affected by **variation** (the angular difference between True North and Magnetic North), which alters from place to place, and by **deviation** which is the angular difference between the direction of Magnetic North and the direction indicated by a compass needle (caused by the boat's local magnetic field).

Variation, which alters slightly from year to year, is shown on the chart – normally at the compass rose.

Deviation varies according to the boat's heading: it should be shown, for different headings, on a deviation card – produced as a result of swinging and adjusting the compass. With a properly adjusted compass, deviation should not be more than about 2° on any heading – in which case it can often be ignored except on long passages.

When converting a True course or a True bearing to Magnetic: add westerly variation or deviation and subtract easterly.

When converting a Magnetic course or bearing to True: subtract westerly variation or deviation, and add easterly.

Bearings given on charts, or quoted in Sailing Directions, are normally True bearings, from seaward.

3.1.5 Distance

Distance at sea is measured in nautical miles (M). A nautical mile is defined as the length of one minute of latitude.

The length of a nautical mile varies with latitude and measures 6,108 feet at the Pole and 6,046 at the Equator. For practical purposes the International nautical mile is taken as being 6,076 feet or 1,852 metres.

Short distances are measured in cables. A cable is one tenth of a nautical mile, and for practical purposes approximates to 200 yards, 600 feet or 100 fathoms in length and is always used for navigational purposes irrespective of the latitude.

Distances must always be measured from the latitude scale of a chart, never from the longitude scale because the length of one minute of longitude on the earth varies from being roughly equal to a minute of latitude at the Equator, to zero length at the Pole. The longitude scale is therefore of no value as a measure of distance.

3.1.6 Speed

Speed at sea is measured in knots. A knot is one nautical mile per hour. There is an important relationship between speed, time and distance. A convenient time, speed and distance table is given in Table 3(5), (see also 3.4.1 for basic formulae used to find speed when time and distance are known, or to find distance when speed and time are known).

A log measures distance run through the water and most logs today also incorporate a speed indicator. Course and speed made good over the ground can be obtained directly from electronic position-fixing receivers such as GPS, Decca or Loran-C.

3.1.7 Depth

One of the most important functions of a navigator is to ensure he keeps the boat safely afloat in sufficient water. The depth of water is therefore highly important and is measured by echo sounder (or lead line). Chart Datum (CD) is the level below which the tide never, or very rarely, falls. Soundings and drying heights shown on charts are always referred to CD. The height of tide is the height of the sea surface above Chart Datum at any given instant. It is important that you should know whether the reading of the echo sounder gives the below keel or the true depth of the water. Tidal height calculations are fully covered in Chapter 9.

3.1.8 Light sectors, arcs of visibility

The abbreviations and characteristics for lights are shown in Fig. 3.5.2 or on *Admiralty Chart 5011*.
The limits of light sectors and arcs of visibility, and the alignment of directional and leading lights, are given as seen from seaward by an observer aboard ship looking towards the light. All bearings are given in °True, starting from 000°, and going clockwise to 359°.

A typical example of a simple sectored light occurs with the Ouistreham main light, which is an Oc WR 4s 37m **W17M**, R13M having visibility sectors R115°-151°, W151°-115°. This is depicted in Fig. 3(1) below. **Bold** type indicates a light with a nominal range of >15M which is 37 metres above the level of MHWS, occulting every 4s and has red and white sectors. The red sector of the light has a nominal range of 13M; it is visible over an arc of 36°, i.e. between 115° (WNW of the light) and 151° (NW of the light). The white sector of the light is visible from 151° clockwise right round to 115°, an angular coverage of the remaining 324°; the white sector has a nominal range of 17M.

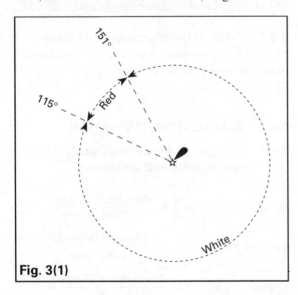

Fig. 3(1)

Coloured sector lights often mean there are special navigation problems. Sometimes they show you where the channel is so if you stray to port you see red and if you stray to starboard you see green. Or alternatively, the lights are used to cover a dangerous area. Details are always shown on charts. A slightly more complex example of a sectored light listed as Q WRG 9m 10M, vis G015°-058°(43°), W058°-065°(7°), R065°-103°(38°), G103°-143·5°(40·5°), W143·5°-145·5°(3°), R146·5°-015° (129·5°) is shown in Fig. 3(2).

Fig. 3(2)

It is a quick flashing light, with an elevation of 9 metres above MHWS, with a nominal range of 10M. It has white, red and green sectors – in fact two sectors of each colour. After plotting these sectors, it will be seen that there are two sets of WRG directional sectors, such that in each case a narrow white sector is flanked by a red sector to port and a green sector to starboard. The white sector defines the navigable channel; deviation out of the white sector is immediately obvious as the light changes colour to red or green as appropriate.

3.2   PASSAGE PLANNING

3.2.1   General

Detailed guidance on practical passage making and planning is contained in Chapter 15 of *The Macmillan and Silk Cut Yachtsman's Handbook*.

Before commencing any passage it is necessary to undertake some form of basic planning. Having decided where you want to go, the next step is to study the charts and read any relevant yachtsman's sailing directions or cruising guides.

You also need to prepare a check list of those items that need further detailed planning. Much of the required work such as laying-off courses on the chart, measuring distances, selecting waypoints and making the necessary tidal calculations can all be done at home well before you start the passage. If you possess or have access to a computer then all the tidal predictions for your entire trip can be done.

3.2.2   Passage planning check list

The following is a suggested list of navigational items which need to be considered before departure. Other more general items such as the boat, crew and feeding arrangements may also need to be taken into account.

- Note the times of HW at the reference port(s).

- Tidal streams tend to form gates to a yacht on passage so you need to know the critical points of any tidal gates which affect your passage together with the times of favourable and adverse tides.

- Insert the dates and times of HW applicable on each page of the tidal stream atlas.

- Note the critical heights and times of any tides which may affect the departure, crossing bars, or destination harbours.

- Note potential dangers en route: clearing lines, distances off dangers, Traffic Separation Schemes, busy shipping lanes, etc.

- Consider visual and radio aids to be used.

- Prepare a detailed pilotage plan for entry to any unfamiliar harbour, final destination or refuge port.

- Consider the entry criteria for alternative harbours which might be required during the planned passage.

- Ensure that charts covering the intended route and alternative harbours that might be used are up to date and on board together with a copy of the current Almanac, Yachtsman's Handbook, and correcting Supplement, or the relevant lists of lights, radio and communication aids, and pilotage information.

Having completed all the necessary planning the weather is a major factor which is likely to have considerable impact and may well cause you to alter your original plans.

3.3   NAVIGATION TABLES

3.3.1   Tables – Explanations
The tables listed below are given on pages 30-37. Here are brief explanations of their use. For greater detail see Chapter 3 in *The Macmillan & Silk Cut Yachtsman's Handbook*.

3.3.2   Table 3(1) – True bearing of Sun at sunrise and sunset
A compass can always be checked against the Sun's azimuth when rising or setting. In order to do so you only require to know the approximate latitude and the Sun's declination.

Enter with the approximate latitude and declination (extracted from the ephemeris in the *Astro Supplement*). The tabulated figure is the True bearing, measured from north if declination is north or from south if declination is south, towards the east if rising or towards the west if setting. Having extracted the True bearing, apply variation before comparing with the compass to determine deviation on course steered. The bearing of the Sun should be taken when its lower limb is a little over half a diameter above the horizon.

3.3.3   Table 3(2) – Distance off by Vertical Sextant Angle
Enter with the height of the body (in metres) and read across the page until the required sextant angle (corrected for index error) is met. Take out the distance of the object (miles) at the head of the column. Caution is needed when the base of the object (e.g. a lighthouse) is below the horizon. For precise ranges the distance that sea level is below MHWS must be added to the height of the object (above MHWS) before entering the table.

3.3.4   Table 3(3) – Distance of horizon for various heights of eye
Enter with height of eye (in metres), and extract distance of horizon (in miles). The actual distance may be affected by abnormal refraction.

3.3.5   Table 3(4) – Lights – distance off when rising or dipping
This table combines selected heights of eye with selected heights of lights, to give the range at which a light dips below or rises above the horizon.

3.3.6   Table 3(5) – Distance for a given speed and time
Enter with time (in decimals of an hour, or in minutes) and speed (in knots) to determine distance run (in M).

3.3.7   Table 3(6) – Measured mile table
Enter with time (in minutes at the head of columns and in seconds down the side of the table) to extract speed (in knots).

3.4   CALCULATOR NAVIGATION

3.4.1   Navigation by electronic calculator - speed, time and distance

$$\text{Speed (in kn)} = \frac{\text{Distance (M)} \times 60}{\text{Time (mins)}}$$

$$\text{Time (in mins)} = \frac{\text{Distance (M)} \times 60}{\text{Speed (kn)}}$$

$$\text{Distance (in M)} = \frac{\text{Speed (kn)} \times \text{Time (mins)}}{60}$$

Distances and speed

Distance of horizon (in M) = $2 \cdot 072 \times \sqrt{\text{Ht of eye (m)}}$

Distance a light is visible (M) = $2 \cdot 072 \times (\sqrt{h_o} + \sqrt{h_e})$ where heights are in metres.

Distance of mountains etc. beyond horizon, in

$$M = \sqrt{3 \cdot 71 (h_o - h_e) + (a - 1 \cdot 76 \times \sqrt{h_e})^2} - (a - 1 \cdot 76 \times \sqrt{h_e})$$

where both heights are in metres, and a is the sextant angle in minutes.

Distance to radar horizon (M)
$$= 2 \cdot 21 \times \sqrt{\text{Ht of scanner (m)}}$$

Boat speed over measured distance of lM =
$$\frac{3600}{\text{time in seconds}} \text{ (knots)}$$

Horizontal sextant angle
Radius of position circle (in M) =
$$\frac{D}{2 \times \sin A}$$
where D is distance between objects in M, and A is the angle between them in degrees.

Vertical sextant angle
$$\text{Distance off} = \frac{\text{Ht of object (above MHWS in m)}}{1852 \times \tan \text{ (sextant angle)}}$$

Note: sextant angle above is in degrees and minutes, and must be corrected for index error.

An approximate distance off, in M, adequate for most purposes is given by:

$$\text{Distance} = \frac{\text{Ht of object (in metres)} \times 1 \cdot 854}{\text{sextant angle (in minutes)}}$$

Coastal navigation
To find the DR/EP, as bearing and distance from start position; example using algebraic calculator. Key in:

1st distance run	5·2 x < > t
1st course (°T)	230 →R STO 0 x< >t STO 6
2nd distance run	1·9 x< >t
2nd course (°T)	255 →R SUM 0 x< >t SUM 6

Repeat for each subsequent Co (°T) and distance. For EP, treat Set/Drift as for Co (°T) and distance.

To display bearing and distance from start:

RCL 6 x < >t RCL 0 →P 236·6   (°T)
x< >t   6·97 (M)
Note: to find EP, treat Set/Drift as for Co (°T) and distance run.
Example: using RPN calculator. Key in:

1st course (°T)	230 ENTER
1st distance run	5·2 →R Σ+
2nd course (°T)	255 ENTER
2nd distance run	1·9 →R Σ+

Repeat for each subsequent Co (°T) and distance.

To display distance and bearing from start:

RCL 13[1] RCL 11[1]   →P   6·97   M
x ↔ y   236·6[2]   (°T)
Notes: (1) Check the actual stores used for vector summation in your calculator.
(2) If display negative (–), add 360.

To find EP, treat Set/Drift as for Co (°T) and distance run.
Distance (D, in M) of object at second bearing
$$= \frac{R \times \sin A}{\sin (B - A)}$$

Predicted distance (in M) object will be off when abeam = D x sin B, where R is distance run (M) between two relative bearings of an object, first A degrees and then B degrees.

Course to steer and speed made good
Co (°T) = Tr (°T) – sin⁻¹ – ((Drift ÷ Speed) ×
$$\qquad \sin \text{ (Set – Track))}$$
SMG   = Speed × cos (Co.T – Track) + Drift ×
$$\qquad \cos \text{ (Set – Track)}$$

Note: the drift must be less than the yacht's speed.

Conversion angle (half convergency)
Radio bearings follow great circles, and become curved lines when plotted on a Mercator chart. A correction may be needed for bearings of beacons more than about 60M away, and can be calculated from the formula:
Conversion angle = ½ d.Long × sin mid Latitude
A great circle always lies on the polar side of the rhumb line, and conversion angle is applied towards the Equator. Further information is given in Chapter 4 in *The Macmillan & Silk Cut Yachtsman's Handbook.*

Short distance sailing
(Note: these formulae should not be used for distances over 600M.)

Departure	=	Distance × sin Course
	=	d.Long × cos Mean Latitude
	=	tan Course × d.Lat
d.Lat	=	Distance × cos Course
d.Long	=	Departure ÷ cos Mean Latitude
Distance	=	Departure ÷ sin Course
	=	d.Lat × sec Course
sin Course	=	Departure ÷ Distance
cos Course	=	d.Lat ÷ Distance
tan Course	=	Departure ÷ d.Lat

Further explanation of the use of calculators, and formulae for the calculation of tracks and distances for distances over 600M are contained in Chapter 3 of *The Macmillan & Silk Cut Yachtsman's Handbook.*

3

3.5   IALA BUOYAGE

3.5.1   IALA Buoyage System (Region A)
(See also Plate 5 on page 69.)

International buoyage is harmonised into a single system which, applied to Regions A and B, differs only in the use of red and green lateral marks. In Region A (which includes all Europe) lateral marks are red on the port hand, and in Region B red on the starboard hand, related to direction of buoyage. Five types of marks are used, as illustrated in Plate 5, on page 69.

(1) *Lateral marks:* are used in conjunction with a direction of buoyage, shown by a special arrow on the chart. In and around the British Isles its general direction is from SW to NE in open waters, but from seaward when approaching a harbour, river or estuary. Where port or starboard lateral marks do not rely on can or conical buoy shapes for identification, they carry, where practicable, the appropriate topmarks. Any numbering or lettering follows the direction of buoyage, evens to port and odds to starboard.

In Region A, port-hand marks are coloured red, and port-hand buoys are can or spar shaped. Any topmark fitted is a single red can. Any light fitted is red, any rhythm. Starboard-hand marks are coloured green, and starboard-hand buoys are conical or spar shaped. Any topmark fitted is a single green cone, point up. Any light fitted is green, any rhythm. In exceptional cases starboard-hand marks may be coloured black.

At a division, the preferred channel may be shown by lateral marks with red or green bands:

Preferred channel	Indicated by	Light (if any)
To starboard	Port lateral mark with green band	Flashing red (2 + 1)
To port	Starboard lateral mark with red band	Flashing green (2 + 1)

(2) *Cardinal marks:* are used in conjunction with a compass to show where dangers exist or where the mariner may find navigable water. They are named after the quadrant in which the mark is placed, in relation to the danger or point indicated. The four quadrants (north, east, south and west) are bounded by the True bearings NW-NE, NE-SE, SE-SW and SW-NW, taken from the point of interest. The name of a cardinal mark indicates that it should be passed on the named side.

A cardinal mark may indicate the safe side on which to pass a danger, or that the deepest water is on the named side of the mark, or it may draw attention to a feature in a channel such as a bend, junction or fork, or the end of a shoal.

Cardinal marks are pillar or spar shaped, painted black and yellow, and always carry black double cone topmarks, one cone above the other. Their lights are white, and are either VQ or Q. VQ lights flash at a rate of 80 to 159 flashes per minute, usually either 100 or 120, and Q flash at a rate of between 50 to 79 flashes per minute, usually either 50 or 60. A long flash is one of not less than two seconds' duration.

North cardinal mark

Two black cones	— Points up
Colour	— Black above yellow
Light (if fitted)	— White; Q or VQ

East cardinal mark

Two black cones	— Base to base
Colour	— Black, with horizontal yellow band
Light (if fitted)	— White; Q (3) 10 sec or VQ (3) 5 sec

South cardinal mark

Two black cones	— Points down
Colour	— Yellow above black
Light (if fitted)	— White; VQ (6) plus long flash 10 sec or Q (6) plus long flash 15 sec

West cardinal mark

Two black cones	— Point to point
Colour	— Yellow, with horizontal black band
Light (if fitted)	— White; VQ (9) 10 sec or Q (9) 15 sec

(3) *Isolated danger marks:* are placed on or above an isolated danger such as a rock or a wreck which has navigable water all around it. The marks are black, with one or more broad horizontal red bands. Buoys are pillar or spar shaped. Any light is white, flashing twice. Topmark – two black spheres.

(4) *Safe water marks:* indicate that there is navigable water all round the mark, and are used for mid-channel or landfall marks. Buoys are spherical, pillar, with spherical topmark or spar, and are coloured with red and white vertical stripes. Any topmark fitted is a single red sphere. Any light fitted is white – either isophase, occulting or long-flash every 10 seconds.

(5) *Special marks:* do not primarily assist navigation, but indicate a special area or feature (e.g. spoil grounds, exercise areas, water-ski areas, cable or pipeline marks, outfalls, Ocean Data Acquisition Systems (ODAS), or traffic separation marks where conventional channel marks may cause confusion). Special marks are yellow, and any shape not conflicting with lateral or safe water marks. If can, spherical or conical are used they indicate the side on which to pass. Any topmark fitted is a yellow X. Any light fitted is yellow, and may have any rhythm not used for white lights.

New dangers (which may be natural obstructions such as a sandbank, or a wreck) are marked in accordance with the rules above, and lit accordingly. For a very grave danger one of the marks may be duplicated.

3.5.2   Light characteristics (Metric and Fathoms charts)

Reproduced by kind permission of H.M. Stationery Office and the Hydrographer of the Navy

CLASS OF LIGHT	International abbreviations	National abbreviations	Illustration — Period shown ⊢————⊣
Fixed	F		
Occulting *(total duration of light more than dark)*			
Single-occulting	Oc	Occ	
Group-occulting e.g.	Oc(2)	Gp Occ(2)	
Composite group-occulting e.g.	Oc(2+3)	Gp Occ(2+3)	
Isophase *(light and dark equal)*	Iso		
Flashing *(total duration of light less than dark)*			
Single-flashing	Fl		
Long-flashing *(flash 2s or longer)*	L Fl		
Group-flashing e.g.	Fl(3)	Gp Fl(3)	
Composite group-flashing e.g.	Fl(2+1)	Gp Fl(2+1)	
Quick *(50 to 79 – usually either 50 or 60 – flashes per minute)*			
Continuous quick	Q	Qk Fl	
Group quick e.g.	Q(3)	Qk Fl(3)	
Interrupted quick	IQ	Int Qk Fl	
Very Quick *(80 to 159 – usually either 100 or 120 – flashes per minute)*			
Continuous very quick	VQ	V Qk Fl	
Group very quick e.g.	VQ(3)	V Qk Fl(3)	
Interrupted very quick	IVQ	Int V Qk Fl	
Ultra Quick *(160 or more – usually 240 to 300 – flashes per minute)*			
Continuous ultra quick	UQ		
Interrupted ultra quick	IUQ		
Morse Code e.g.	Mo(K)		
Fixed and Flashing	F Fl		
Alternating e.g.	Al. WR	Alt. WR	

COLOUR	International abbreviations		NOMINAL RANGE in miles	International abbreviations
White	W *(may be omitted)*		Light with single range e.g.	15M
Red	R			
Green	G		Light with two different ranges e.g.	15/10M
Blue	Bu			
Violet	Vi		Light with three or more ranges e.g.	15-7M
Yellow	Y			
Orange	Y		**PERIOD** is given in seconds e.g.	90s
Amber	Y			
ELEVATION is given in metres (m) or feet (ft) above MHWS			**DISPOSITION** horizontally disposed vertically disposed	(hor) (vert)

3

TABLE 3(1)   True bearing of Sun at sunrise and sunset

DECLINATION

LAT	0°	1°	2°	3°	4°	5°	6°	7°	8°	9°	10°	11°	LAT
30°	90	88·8	87·7	86·5	85·4	84·2	83·1	81·9	80·7	79·6	78·4	77·3	30°
31°	90	88·8	87·7	86·5	85·3	84·2	83·0	81·9	80·6	79·5	78·3	77·1	31°
32°	90	88·8	87·6	86·5	85·3	84·1	82·9	81·7	80·5	79·4	78·2	77·0	32°
33°	90	88·8	87·6	86·4	85·2	84·0	82·8	81·6	80·4	79·2	78·0	76·8	33°
34°	90	88·8	87·6	86·4	85·2	84·0	82·7	81·5	80·3	79·1	77·9	76·7	34°
35°	90	88·8	87·5	86·3	85·1	83·9	82·7	81·4	80·2	79·0	77·8	76·5	35°
36°	90	88·8	87·5	86·3	85·0	83·8	82·6	81·3	80·1	78·8	77·6	76·3	36°
37°	90	88·7	87·5	86·2	85·0	83·7	82·5	81·2	80·0	78·7	77·4	76·2	37°
38°	90	88·7	87·5	86·2	84·9	83·6	82·4	81·1	79·8	78·5	77·3	76·0	38°
39°	90	88·7	87·4	86·1	84·8	83·6	82·3	81·0	79·7	78·4	77·1	75·8	39°
40°	90	88·7	87·4	86·1	84·8	83·5	82·1	80·8	79·5	78·2	76·9	75·6	40°
41°	90	88·7	87·3	86·0	84·7	83·4	82·0	80·7	79·4	78·0	76·7	75·3	41°
42°	90	88·6	87·3	86·0	84·6	83·3	81·9	80·6	79·2	77·8	76·5	75·1	42°
43°	90	88·6	87·3	85·9	84·5	83·1	81·8	80·4	79·0	77·6	76·3	74·9	43°
44°	90	88·6	87·2	85·8	84·4	83·0	81·6	80·2	78·8	77·4	76·0	74·6	44°
45°	90	88·6	87·2	85·7	84·3	82·9	81·5	80·1	78·6	77·2	75·8	74·3	45°
46°	90	88·6	87·1	85·7	84·2	82·8	81·3	79·9	78·4	77·0	75·5	74·0	46°
47°	90	88·5	87·1	85·6	84·1	82·6	81·2	79·7	78·2	76·7	75·2	73·7	47°
48°	90	88·5	87·0	85·5	84·0	82·5	81·0	79·5	78·0	76·5	75·0	73·4	48°
49°	90	88·5	86·9	85·4	83·9	82·4	80·8	79·3	77·7	76·2	74·6	73·1	49°
50°	90	88·4	86·9	85·3	83·8	82·2	80·6	79·1	77·5	75·9	74·3	72·7	50°
51°	90	88·4	86·8	85·2	83·6	82·0	80·4	78·8	77·2	75·6	74·0	72·4	51°
52°	90	88·4	86·7	85·1	83·5	81·9	80·2	78·6	76·9	75·3	73·6	71·9	52°
53°	90	88·3	86·7	85·0	83·3	81·7	80·0	78·3	76·6	74·9	73·2	71·5	53°
54°	90	88·3	86·6	84·9	83·2	81·5	79·8	78·0	76·3	74·6	72·8	71·1	54°
55°	90	88·2	86·5	84·8	83·0	81·3	79·5	77·7	76·0	74·2	72·4	70·6	55°
56°	90	88·2	86·4	84·6	82·8	81·0	79·2	77·4	75·6	73·8	71·9	70·0	56°
57°	90	88·2	86·3	84·5	82·6	80·8	78·9	77·0	75·2	73·3	71·4	69·5	57°
58°	90	88·1	86·2	84·3	82·4	80·5	78·6	76·7	74·8	72·8	70·9	68·9	58°
59°	90	88·1	86·1	84·2	82·2	80·3	78·3	76·3	74·3	72·3	70·3	68·3	59°
60°	90	88·0	86·0	84·0	82·0	80·0	77·9	75·9	73·8	71·8	69·7	67·6	60°

DECLINATION

LAT	12°	13°	14°	15°	16°	17°	18°	19°	20°	21°	22°	23°	LAT
30°	76·1	74·9	73·8	72·6	71·4	70·3	69·1	67·9	66·7	65·5	64·4	63·2	30°
31°	76·0	74·8	73·6	72·4	71·2	70·0	68·9	67·7	66·5	65·3	64·1	62·9	31°
32°	75·8	74·6	73·4	72·2	71·0	69·8	68·6	67·4	66·2	65·0	63·8	62·6	32°
33°	75·6	74·4	73·2	72·1	70·8	69·6	68·4	67·1	65·9	64·7	63·5	62·2	33°
34°	75·5	74·2	73·0	71·8	70·6	69·3	68·1	66·9	65·6	64·4	63·1	61·9	34°
35°	75·3	74·1	72·8	71·6	70·3	69·1	67·8	66·6	65·3	64·1	62·8	61·5	35°
36°	75·1	73·8	72·6	71·3	70·1	68·8	67·5	66·3	65·0	63·7	62·4	61·1	36°
37°	74·9	73·6	72·4	71·1	69·8	68·5	67·2	65·9	64·6	63·3	62·0	60·7	37°
38°	74·7	73·4	72·0	70·8	69·5	68·2	66·9	65·6	64·3	62·9	61·6	60·3	38°
39°	74·5	73·2	71·9	70·5	69·2	67·9	66·6	65·2	63·9	62·5	61·2	59·8	39°
40°	74·2	72·9	71·6	70·2	68·9	67·6	66·2	64·8	63·5	62·1	60·7	59·3	40°
41°	74·0	72·7	71·3	69·9	68·6	67·2	65·8	64·4	63·0	61·6	60·2	58·8	41°
42°	73·7	72·4	71·0	69·6	68·2	66·8	65·4	64·0	62·6	61·2	59·7	58·3	42°
43°	73·5	72·1	70·7	69·3	67·9	66·4	65·0	63·6	62·1	60·7	59·2	57·7	43°
44°	73·2	71·8	70·3	68·9	67·5	66·0	64·6	63·1	61·6	60·1	58·6	57·1	44°
45°	72·9	71·4	70·0	68·5	67·0	65·6	64·1	62·6	61·1	59·5	58·0	56·4	45°
46°	72·6	71·1	69·6	68·1	66·6	65·1	63·6	62·0	60·5	58·9	57·4	55·8	46°
47°	72·2	70·7	69·2	67·7	66·2	64·6	63·1	61·5	59·9	58·3	56·7	55·0	47°
48°	71·9	70·3	68·8	67·2	65·7	64·1	62·5	60·9	59·3	57·6	55·9	54·3	48°
49°	71·5	69·9	68·4	66·8	65·1	63·5	61·9	60·2	58·6	56·9	55·2	53·4	49°
50°	71·1	69·5	67·9	66·2	64·6	62·9	61·3	59·6	57·8	56·1	54·3	52·6	50°
51°	70·7	69·1	67·4	65·7	64·0	62·3	60·6	58·8	57·1	55·3	53·5	51·6	51°
52°	70·3	68·6	66·9	65·1	63·4	61·6	59·9	58·1	56·3	54·4	52·5	50·6	52°
53°	69·8	68·1	66·3	64·5	62·7	60·9	59·1	57·3	55·4	53·5	51·5	49·5	53°
54°	69·3	67·5	65·7	63·9	62·0	60·2	58·3	56·4	54·4	52·4	50·4	48·3	54°
55°	68·7	66·9	65·1	63·2	61·3	59·4	57·4	55·4	53·4	51·3	49·2	47·1	55°
56°	68·2	66·3	64·4	62·4	60·5	58·5	56·5	54·4	52·3	50·1	47·9	45·7	56°
57°	67·6	65·6	63·6	61·6	59·6	57·5	55·4	53·3	51·1	48·9	46·5	44·2	57°
58°	66·9	64·9	62·8	60·8	58·7	56·5	54·3	52·1	49·8	47·4	45·0	42·5	58°
59°	66·2	64·1	62·0	59·8	57·6	55·4	53·1	50·8	48·4	45·9	43·3	40·7	59°
60°	65·4	63·3	61·1	58·8	56·5	54·2	51·8	49·4	46·8	44·2	41·5	38·6	60°

TABLE 3(2) Distance off by Vertical Sextant Angle

Values are in degrees and minutes (° ').

Height of object ft	m	0·1	0·2	0·3	0·4	0·5	0·6	0·7	0·8	0·9	1·0	1·1	1·2	1·3	1·4	1·5	m	ft
33	10	3 05	1 33	1 02	0 46	0 37	0 31	0 27	0 23	0 21	0 19	0 17	0 15	0 14	0 13	0 12	10	33
39	12	3 42	1 51	1 14	0 56	0 45	0 37	0 32	0 28	0 25	0 22	0 20	0 19	0 17	0 16	0 15	12	39
46	14	4 19	2 10	1 27	1 05	0 52	0 43	0 37	0 32	0 29	0 26	0 24	0 22	0 20	0 19	0 17	14	46
53	16	4 56	2 28	1 39	1 14	0 59	0 49	0 42	0 37	0 33	0 30	0 27	0 25	0 23	0 21	0 20	16	53
59	18	5 33	2 47	1 51	1 24	1 07	0 56	0 48	0 42	0 37	0 33	0 30	0 28	0 26	0 24	0 22	18	59
66	20	6 10	3 05	2 04	1 33	1 14	1 02	0 53	0 46	0 41	0 37	0 34	0 31	0 29	0 27	0 25	20	66
72	22	6 46	3 24	2 16	1 42	1 22	1 08	0 58	0 51	0 45	0 41	0 37	0 34	0 31	0 29	0 27	22	72
79	24	7 23	3 42	2 28	1 51	1 29	1 14	1 04	0 56	0 49	0 45	0 40	0 37	0 34	0 32	0 30	24	79
85	26	7 59	4 01	2 41	2 01	1 36	1 20	1 09	1 00	0 54	0 48	0 44	0 40	0 37	0 34	0 32	26	85
92	28	8 36	4 19	2 53	2 10	1 44	1 27	1 14	1 05	0 58	0 52	0 47	0 43	0 40	0 37	0 35	28	92
98	30	9 12	4 38	3 05	2 19	1 51	1 33	1 20	1 10	1 02	0 56	0 51	0 46	0 43	0 40	0 37	30	98
105	32	9 48	4 56	3 18	2 28	1 58	1 39	1 25	1 14	1 06	0 59	0 54	0 49	0 46	0 42	0 40	32	105
112	34	10 24	5 15	3 30	2 38	2 06	1 45	1 30	1 19	1 10	1 03	0 57	0 53	0 49	0 45	0 42	34	112
118	36	11 00	5 33	3 42	2 47	2 14	1 51	1 35	1 24	1 14	1 07	1 01	0 56	0 51	0 48	0 45	36	118
125	38	11 36	5 41	3 55	2 56	2 21	1 58	1 41	1 28	1 18	1 11	1 04	0 59	0 54	0 50	0 47	38	125
131	40	12 11	6 10	4 07	3 05	2 28	2 04	1 46	1 33	1 22	1 14	1 07	1 02	0 57	0 53	0 49	40	131
138	42	12 47	6 28	4 19	3 15	2 36	2 10	1 51	1 37	1 27	1 18	1 11	1 05	1 00	0 56	0 52	42	138
144	44	13 22	6 46	4 32	3 24	2 43	2 16	1 57	1 42	1 31	1 22	1 14	1 08	1 03	0 58	0 54	44	144
151	46	13 57	7 05	4 44	3 33	2 51	2 22	2 02	1 47	1 35	1 25	1 18	1 11	1 06	1 01	0 57	46	151
157	48	14 32	7 23	4 56	3 42	2 58	2 28	2 07	1 51	1 39	1 29	1 21	1 14	1 09	1 04	0 59	48	157
164	50	15 07	7 41	5 09	3 52	3 05	2 35	2 13	1 56	1 43	1 33	1 24	1 17	1 11	1 06	1 02	50	164
171	52	15 41	7 59	5 21	4 01	3 13	2 41	2 18	2 01	1 47	1 36	1 28	1 20	1 14	1 09	1 04	52	171
177	54	16 15	8 18	5 33	4 10	3 20	2 47	2 23	2 05	1 51	1 40	1 31	1 23	1 17	1 12	1 07	54	177
184	56	16 49	8 36	5 45	4 19	3 28	2 53	2 28	2 10	1 55	1 44	1 34	1 27	1 20	1 14	1 09	56	184
190	58	17 23	8 54	5 58	4 29	3 35	2 59	2 34	2 15	2 00	1 48	1 38	1 30	1 23	1 17	1 12	58	190
197	60	17 57	9 12	6 10	4 38	3 42	3 05	2 39	2 19	2 04	1 51	1 41	1 33	1 26	1 20	1 14	60	197
203	62	18 31	9 30	6 22	4 47	3 50	3 12	2 44	2 24	2 08	1 55	1 45	1 36	1 29	1 22	1 17	62	203
210	64	19 04	9 48	6 34	4 56	3 57	3 18	2 50	2 28	2 12	1 59	1 48	1 39	1 31	1 25	1 19	64	210
217	66	19 37	10 06	6 46	5 05	4 05	3 24	2 53	2 33	2 16	2 02	1 51	1 42	1 34	1 27	1 22	66	217
223	68	20 10	10 24	6 59	5 15	4 12	3 30	3 00	2 38	2 20	2 06	1 55	1 45	1 37	1 30	1 24	68	223
230	70	20 42	10 42	7 11	5 24	4 19	3 36	3 05	2 42	2 24	2 09	1 58	1 48	1 40	1 33	1 27	70	230
236	72	21 15	11 00	7 23	5 33	4 27	3 42	3 11	2 47	2 28	2 14	2 01	1 51	1 43	1 35	1 29	72	236
246	75	22 03	11 27	7 41	5 47	4 38	3 52	3 19	2 54	2 35	2 19	2 07	1 56	1 47	1 39	1 33	75	246
256	78	22 50	11 54	7 59	6 01	4 49	4 01	3 27	3 01	2 41	2 24	2 12	2 01	1 51	1 43	1 36	78	256
266	81	23 37	12 20	8 18	6 14	5 00	4 10	3 35	3 08	2 47	2 30	2 17	2 05	1 56	1 47	1 40	81	266
276	84	24 24	12 47	8 36	6 28	5 11	4 19	3 42	3 15	2 53	2 36	2 22	2 10	2 00	1 51	1 44	84	276
289	88	25 25	13 22	9 00	6 46	5 26	4 32	3 53	3 24	3 01	2 43	2 28	2 16	2 06	1 57	1 49	88	289
302	92	26 25	13 57	9 24	7 05	5 40	4 44	4 04	3 33	3 10	2 51	2 35	2 22	2 11	2 02	1 54	92	302
315	96	27 24	14 32	9 48	7 23	5 55	4 56	4 14	3 42	3 18	2 58	2 42	2 28	2 17	2 07	1 59	96	315
328	100	28 22	15 07	10 12	7 41	6 10	5 09	4 25	3 52	3 26	3 05	2 49	2 35	2 23	2 13	2 04	100	328
341	104	29 19	15 41	10 36	7 59	6 24	5 21	4 35	4 01	3 34	3 13	2 55	2 41	2 28	2 18	2 09	104	341
358	109	30 29	16 24	11 06	8 22	6 43	5 36	4 48	4 12	3 44	3 22	3 04	2 48	2 36	2 24	2 15	109	358
374	114	31 37	17 06	11 36	8 45	7 01	5 51	5 02	4 24	3 55	3 31	3 12	2 56	2 43	2 31	2 21	114	374
394	120	32 56	17 57	12 11	9 12	7 23	6 10	5 17	4 38	4 07	3 42	3 22	3 05	2 51	2 39	2 28	120	394
427	130	35 04	19 20	13 10	9 57	8 00	6 40	5 44	5 01	4 28	4 01	3 39	3 21	3 05	2 52	2 41	130	427
459	140	37 05	20 42	14 09	10 42	8 36	7 11	6 10	5 24	4 48	4 19	3 56	3 36	3 20	3 05	2 53	140	459
492	150	39 00	22 03	15 07	11 27	9 12	7 41	6 36	5 47	5 09	4 38	4 13	3 52	3 34	3 19	3 05	150	492
574	175		25 17	17 29	13 17	10 42	8 57	7 41	6 44	6 00	5 24	4 55	4 30	4 09	3 52	3 36	175	574
656	200		28 22	19 48	15 07	12 11	10 12	8 46	7 41	6 51	6 10	5 36	5 09	4 45	4 25	4 07	200	656
738	225			22 03	16 54	13 39	11 27	9 51	8 38	7 41	6 56	6 18	5 47	5 20	4 58	4 38	225	738
820	250			24 14	18 39	15 07	12 41	10 55	9 35	8 32	7 41	7 00	6 25	5 56	5 30	5 09	250	820
902	275			26 20	20 22	16 32	13 54	11 59	10 31	9 22	8 27	7 41	7 03	6 31	6 03	5 39	275	902
984	300				22 03	17 57	15 07	13 02	11 27	10 12	9 12	8 23	7 41	7 06	6 36	6 10	300	984
1148	350					20 42	17 29	15 07	13 17	11 51	10 42	9 45	8 57	8 16	7 41	7 11	350	1148
1312	400						19 48	17 09	15 07	13 30	12 11	11 07	10 12	9 26	8 46	8 12	400	1312
ft m Height of object		0·1	0·2	0·3	0·4	0·5	0·6	0·7	0·8	0·9	1·0	1·1	1·2	1·3	1·4	1·5		m ft Height of object

Distance of object (miles)

3

TABLE 3(2)   Distance off by Vertical Sextant Angle (continued)

Height of object ft	m	1·6	1·7	1·8	1·9	2·0	2·1	2·2	2·3	2·4	2·5	2·6	2·7	2·8	2·9	3·0	m	ft
		° ′	° ′	° ′	° ′	° ′	° ′	° ′	° ′	° ′	° ′	° ′	° ′	° ′	° ′	° ′		
33	10	0 12	0 11	0 10	0 10												10	33
39	12	0 14	0 13	0 12	0 12	0 11	0 11	0 10	0 10	0 10							12	39
46	14	0 16	0 15	0 14	0 14	0 13	0 12	0 12	0 11	0 11	0 10	0 10	0 10				14	46
53	16	0 19	0 17	0 16	0 16	0 15	0 14	0 13	0 13	0 12	0 12	0 11	0 11	0 11	0 10	0 10	16	53
59	18	0 21	0 20	0 19	0 18	0 17	0 16	0 15	0 15	0 14	0 13	0 13	0 12	0 12	0 12	0 11	18	59
66	20	0 23	0 22	0 21	0 20	0 19	0 18	0 17	0 16	0 15	0 15	0 14	0 14	0 13	0 13	0 12	20	66
72	22	0 26	0 24	0 23	0 21	0 20	0 19	0 19	0 18	0 17	0 16	0 16	0 15	0 15	0 14	0 14	22	72
79	24	0 28	0 26	0 25	0 23	0 22	0 21	0 20	0 19	0 19	0 18	0 17	0 16	0 16	0 15	0 15	24	79
85	26	0 30	0 28	0 27	0 25	0 24	0 23	0 22	0 21	0 20	0 19	0 19	0 18	0 17	0 17	0 16	26	85
92	28	0 32	0 31	0 29	0 27	0 26	0 25	0 24	0 23	0 22	0 21	0 20	0 19	0 19	0 18	0 17	28	92
98	30	0 35	0 33	0 31	0 29	0 28	0 27	0 25	0 24	0 23	0 22	0 21	0 21	0 20	0 19	0 19	30	98
105	32	0 37	0 35	0 33	0 31	0 30	0 28	0 27	0 26	0 25	0 24	0 23	0 22	0 21	0 20	0 20	32	105
112	34	0 39	0 37	0 35	0 33	0 31	0 30	0 29	0 27	0 26	0 25	0 24	0 23	0 23	0 22	0 21	34	112
118	36	0 42	0 39	0 37	0 35	0 33	0 32	0 30	0 29	0 28	0 27	0 26	0 25	0 24	0 23	0 22	36	118
125	38	0 44	0 41	0 39	0 37	0 35	0 34	0 32	0 31	0 29	0 28	0 27	0 26	0 25	0 24	0 24	38	125
131	40	0 46	0 44	0 41	0 39	0 37	0 35	0 34	0 32	0 31	0 30	0 29	0 27	0 27	0 26	0 25	40	131
138	42	0 49	0 46	0 43	0 41	0 40	0 37	0 35	0 34	0 32	0 31	0 30	0 29	0 28	0 27	0 26	42	138
144	44	0 51	0 48	0 45	0 43	0 41	0 39	0 37	0 36	0 34	0 33	0 31	0 30	0 29	0 28	0 27	44	144
151	46	0 53	0 50	0 47	0 45	0 43	0 41	0 39	0 37	0 36	0 34	0 33	0 32	0 30	0 29	0 28	46	151
157	48	0 56	0 52	0 49	0 47	0 45	0 42	0 40	0 39	0 37	0 36	0 34	0 33	0 32	0 31	0 30	48	1 57
164	50	0 58	0 55	0 52	0 49	0 46	0 44	0 42	0 40	0 39	0 37	0 36	0 34	0 33	0 32	0 31	50	164
171	52	1 00	0 57	0 54	0 51	0 48	0 46	0 44	0 42	0 40	0 39	0 37	0 36	0 34	0 33	0 32	52	171
177	54	1 03	0 59	0 56	0 53	0 50	0 48	0 46	0 44	0 42	0 40	0 39	0 37	0 36	0 35	0 33	54	177
184	56	1 05	1 01	0 58	0 55	0 52	0 49	0 47	0 45	0 43	0 42	0 40	0 38	0 37	0 36	0 35	56	184
190	58	1 07	1 03	1 00	0 57	0 54	0 51	0 49	0 47	0 45	0 43	0 41	0 40	0 38	0 37	0 36	58	190
197	60	1 10	1 06	1 02	0 59	0 56	0 53	0 51	0 48	0 46	0 45	0 43	0 41	0 40	0 38	0 37	60	197
203	62	1 12	1 08	1 04	1 01	0 58	0 55	0 52	0 50	0 48	0 46	0 44	0 43	0 41	0 40	0 38	62	203
210	64	1 14	1 10	1 06	1 03	0 59	0 57	0 54	0 52	0 49	0 48	0 46	0 44	0 42	0 41	0 40	64	210
217	66	1 17	1 12	1 08	1 05	1 01	0 58	0 56	0 53	0 51	0 49	0 47	0 45	0 44	0 42	0 41	66	217
223	68	1 19	1 14	1 10	1 06	1 03	1 00	0 57	0 55	0 53	0 50	0 49	0 47	0 45	0 44	0 42	68	223
230	70	1 21	1 16	1 12	1 08	1 05	1 02	0 59	0 56	0 54	0 52	0 50	0 48	0 46	0 45	0 43	70	230
236	72	1 24	1 19	1 14	1 10	1 07	1 04	1 01	0 58	0 56	0 53	0 51	0 49	0 48	0 46	0 45	72	236
246	75	1 27	1 22	1 17	1 13	1 10	1 06	1 03	1 01	0 58	0 56	0 54	0 51	0 50	0 48	0 46	75	246
256	78	1 30	1 25	1 20	1 16	1 12	1 09	1 06	1 03	1 00	0 58	0 56	0 54	0 52	0 50	0 48	78	256
266	81	1 34	1 28	1 23	1 19	1 15	1 12	1 08	1 05	1 03	1 00	0 58	0 56	0 54	0 52	0 50	81	266
276	84	1 37	1 32	1 27	1 22	1 18	1 14	1 11	1 08	1 05	1 02	1 00	0 58	0 56	0 54	0 52	84	276
289	88	1 42	1 36	1 31	1 26	1 22	1 18	1 14	1 11	1 08	1 05	1 03	1 00	0 58	0 56	0 54	88	289
302	92	1 47	1 40	1 35	1 30	1 25	1 21	1 18	1 14	1 11	1 08	1 06	1 03	1 01	0 59	0 57	92	302
315	96	1 51	1 45	1 39	1 34	1 29	1 25	1 21	1 17	1 14	1 11	1 09	1 06	1 04	1 01	0 59	96	315
328	100	1 56	1 49	1 43	1 38	1 33	1 28	1 24	1 21	1 17	1 14	1 11	1 09	1 06	1 04	1 02	100	328
341	104	2 01	1 54	1 47	1 42	1 36	1 32	1 28	1 24	1 20	1 17	1 14	1 11	1 09	1 07	1 04	104	341
358	109	2 06	1 59	1 52	1 46	1 41	1 36	1 32	1 28	1 24	1 21	1 18	1 15	1 12	1 10	1 07	109	358
374	114	2 12	2 04	1 58	1 51	1 46	1 41	1 36	1 32	1 28	1 25	1 21	1 18	1 16	1 13	1 11	114	374
394	120	2 19	2 11	2 04	1 57	1 51	1 46	1 41	1 37	1 33	1 29	1 26	1 22	1 20	1 17	1 14	120	394
427	130	2 31	2 22	2 14	2 07	2 01	1 55	1 50	1 45	1 41	1 36	1 33	1 29	1 26	1 23	1 20	130	427
459	140	2 42	2 33	2 24	2 17	2 10	2 04	1 58	1 53	1 48	1 44	1 40	1 36	1 33	1 30	1 27	140	459
492	150	2 54	2 44	2 35	2 26	2 19	2 13	2 07	2 01	1 56	1 51	1 47	1 43	1 39	1 36	1 33	150	492
574	175	3 23	3 11	3 00	2 51	2 42	2 35	2 28	2 21	2 15	2 10	2 05	2 00	1 56	1 52	1 48	175	574
656	200	3 52	3 38	3 26	3 15	3 05	2 57	2 49	2 41	2 35	2 28	2 23	2 17	2 13	2 08	2 04	200	656
738	225	4 21	4 05	3 52	3 40	3 29	3 19	3 10	3 01	2 54	2 47	2 41	2 36	2 29	2 24	2 19	225	738
820	250	4 49	4 32	4 17	4 04	3 52	3 41	3 31	3 22	3 13	3 05	2 58	2 52	2 46	2 40	2 35	250	820
902	275	5 18	5 00	4 43	4 28	4 15	4 03	3 52	3 42	3 32	3 24	3 16	3 09	3 02	2 56	2 50	275	902
984	300	5 47	5 27	5 09	4 52	4 38	4 25	4 13	4 02	3 52	3 42	3 34	3 26	3 19	3 12	3 05	300	984
1148	350	6 44	6 21	6 00	5 41	5 24	5 09	4 55	4 42	4 30	4 19	4 09	4 00	3 52	3 44	3 36	350	1148
1312	400	7 41	7 14	6 51	6 29	6 10	5 52	5 36	5 22	5 09	4 56	4 45	4 34	4 25	4 16	4 07	400	1312
ft m Height of object		1·6	1·7	1·8	1·9	2·0	2·1	2·2	2·3	2·4	2·5	2·6	2·7	2·8	2·9	3·0	m ft Height of object	

Distance of object (miles)

TABLE 3(2) Distance off by Vertical Sextant Angle (continued)

Height of object ft	m	3·1	3·2	3·3	3·4	3·5	3·6	3·7	3·8	3·9	4·0	4·2	4·4	4·6	4·8	5·0	m	ft
		°′	°′	°′	°′	°′	°′	°′	°′	°′	°′	°′	°′	°′	°′	°′		
33	10																10	33
39	12																12	39
46	14																14	46
53	16	0 01															16	53
59	18	0 11	0 10	0 10	0 10	0 10											18	59
66	20	0 12	0 12	0 11	0 11	0 11	0 10	0 10	0 10	0 10							20	66
72	22	0 13	0 13	0 12	0 12	0 12	0 11	0 11	0 11	0 10	0 10						22	72
79	24	0 14	0 14	0 13	0 13	0 13	0 12	0 12	0 12	0 11	0 11	0 11	0 10				24	79
85	26	0 16	0 15	0 15	0 14	0 14	0 13	0 13	0 13	0 12	0 12	0 11	0 11	0 10	0 10		26	85
92	28	0 17	0 16	0 16	0 15	0 15	0 14	0 14	0 14	0 13	0 13	0 12	0 12	0 11	0 11	0 10	28	92
98	30	0 18	0 17	0 17	0 16	0 16	0 15	0 15	0 15	0 14	0 14	0 13	0 13	0 12	0 12	0 11	30	98
105	32	0 19	0 19	0 18	0 17	0 17	0 16	0 16	0 16	0 15	0 15	0 14	0 13	0 13	0 12	0 12	32	105
112	34	0 20	0 20	0 19	0 19	0 18	0 17	0 17	0 17	0 16	0 16	0 15	0 14	0 14	0 13	0 13	34	112
118	36	0 22	0 21	0 20	0 20	0 19	0 19	0 18	0 18	0 17	0 17	0 16	0 15	0 14	0 14	0 13	36	118
125	38	0 23	0 22	0 21	0 21	0 20	0 20	0 19	0 19	0 18	0 18	0 17	0 16	0 15	0 15	0 14	38	125
131	40	0 24	0 23	0 22	0 22	0 21	0 21	0 20	0 20	0 19	0 19	0 18	0 17	0 16	0 15	0 15	40	131
138	42	0 25	0 24	0 24	0 23	0 22	0 22	0 21	0 21	0 20	0 19	0 19	0 18	0 17	0 16	0 16	42	138
144	44	0 26	0 25	0 25	0 24	0 23	0 23	0 22	0 22	0 21	0 20	0 19	0 19	0 18	0 17	0 16	44	144
151	46	0 28	0 27	0 26	0 25	0 24	0 24	0 23	0 22	0 22	0 21	0 20	0 19	0 19	0 18	0 17	46	151
157	48	0 29	0 28	0 27	0 26	0 25	0 25	0 24	0 23	0 23	0 22	0 21	0 20	0 19	0 19	0 18	48	157
164	50	0 30	0 29	0 28	0 27	0 27	0 26	0 25	0 24	0 24	0 23	0 22	0 21	0 20	0 19	0 19	50	164
171	52	0 31	0 30	0 29	0 28	0 28	0 27	0 26	0 25	0 25	0 24	0 23	0 22	0 21	0 20	0 19	52	171
177	54	0 32	0 31	0 30	0 29	0 29	0 28	0 27	0 26	0 26	0 25	0 24	0 23	0 22	0 21	0 20	54	177
184	56	0 34	0 32	0 31	0 31	0 30	0 29	0 28	0 27	0 27	0 26	0 25	0 24	0 23	0 22	0 21	56	184
190	58	0 35	0 34	0 33	0 32	0 31	0 30	0 29	0 28	0 28	0 27	0 26	0 24	0 23	0 22	0 21	58	190
197	60	0 36	0 35	0 34	0 33	0 32	0 31	0 30	0 29	0 29	0 28	0 26	0 25	0 24	0 23	0 22	60	197
203	62	0 37	0 36	0 35	0 34	0 33	0 32	0 31	0 30	0 30	0 29	0 27	0 26	0 25	0 24	0 23	62	203
210	64	0 38	0 37	0 36	0 35	0 34	0 33	0 32	0 31	0 30	0 30	0 28	0 27	0 26	0 25	0 24	64	210
217	66	0 40	0 38	0 37	0 36	0 35	0 34	0 33	0 32	0 31	0 31	0 29	0 28	0 27	0 26	0 25	66	217
223	68	0 41	0 39	0 38	0 37	0 36	0 35	0 34	0 33	0 32	0 32	0 30	0 29	0 27	0 26	0 25	68	223
230	70	0 42	0 41	0 39	0 38	0 37	0 36	0 35	0 34	0 33	0 32	0 31	0 29	0 28	0 27	0 26	70	230
236	72	0 43	0 42	0 40	0 39	0 38	0 37	0 36	0 35	0 34	0 33	0 32	0 30	0 29	0 28	0 27	72	236
246	75	0 45	0 44	0 42	0 41	0 40	0 39	0 38	0 37	0 36	0 35	0 33	0 32	0 30	0 29	0 28	75	246
256	78	0 47	0 45	0 44	0 43	0 41	0 40	0 39	0 38	0 37	0 36	0 34	0 33	0 31	0 30	0 29	78	256
266	81	0 48	0 47	0 46	0 44	0 43	0 42	0 41	0 40	0 39	0 38	0 36	0 34	0 33	0 31	0 30	81	266
276	84	0 50	0 49	0 47	0 46	0 45	0 43	0 42	0 41	0 40	0 39	0 37	0 35	0 34	0 32	0 31	84	276
289	88	0 53	0 51	0 49	0 48	0 47	0 45	0 44	0 43	0 42	0 41	0 39	0 37	0 36	0 34	0 33	88	289
302	92	0 55	0 53	0 52	0 50	0 49	0 47	0 46	0 45	0 44	0 43	0 41	0 39	0 37	0 36	0 34	92	302
315	96	0 57	0 56	0 54	0 52	0 51	0 49	0 48	0 47	0 46	0 45	0 42	0 41	0 39	0 37	0 36	96	315
328	100	1 00	0 58	0 56	0 55	0 53	0 52	0 50	0 49	0 48	0 46	0 44	0 42	0 40	0 39	0 37	100	328
341	104	1 02	1 00	0 58	0 57	0 55	0 54	0 52	0 51	0 49	0 48	0 46	0 44	0 42	0 40	0 39	104	341
358	109	1 05	1 03	1 01	1 00	0 58	0 56	0 55	0 53	0 52	0 51	0 48	0 46	0 44	0 42	0 40	109	358
374	114	1 08	1 06	1 04	1 02	1 00	0 59	0 57	0 56	0 54	0 53	0 50	0 48	0 46	0 44	0 42	114	374
394	120	1 12	1 10	1 07	1 06	1 04	1 02	1 00	0 59	0 57	0 56	0 53	0 51	0 48	0 46	0 45	120	394
427	130	1 18	1 15	1 13	1 11	1 09	1 07	1 05	1 03	1 02	1 00	0 57	0 55	0 52	0 50	0 48	130	427
459	140	1 24	1 21	1 19	1 16	1 14	1 12	1 10	1 08	1 07	1 05	1 02	0 59	0 56	0 54	0 52	140	459
492	150	1 30	1 27	1 24	1 22	1 20	1 17	1 15	1 13	1 11	1 10	1 06	1 03	1 01	0 58	0 56	150	492
574	175	1 45	1 41	1 38	1 36	1 33	1 30	1 28	1 25	1 23	1 21	1 17	1 14	1 11	1 08	1 05	175	574
656	200	2 00	1 56	1 52	1 49	1 46	1 43	1 40	1 38	1 35	1 33	1 28	1 24	1 21	1 17	1 14	200	656
738	225	2 15	2 10	2 06	2 03	1 59	1 56	1 53	1 50	1 47	1 44	1 39	1 35	1 31	1 27	1 24	225	738
820	250	2 30	2 25	2 20	2 16	2 13	2 09	2 05	2 02	1 59	1 56	1 50	1 45	1 41	1 37	1 33	250	820
902	275	2 45	2 39	2 34	2 30	2 26	2 22	2 18	2 14	2 11	2 08	2 01	1 56	1 51	1 46	1 42	275	902
984	300	2 59	2 54	2 48	2 44	2 39	2 35	2 30	2 26	2 23	2 19	2 13	2 07	2 01	1 56	1 51	300	984
1148	350	3 29	3 23	3 16	3 11	3 05	3 00	2 55	2 51	2 46	2 42	2 35	2 28	2 21	2 15	2 10	350	1148
1312	400	3 59	3 52	3 44	3 38	3 32	3 26	3 20	3 15	3 10	3 05	2 57	2 49	2 41	2 35	2 28	400	1312
ft m Height of object		3·1	3·2	3·3	3·4	3·5	3·6	3·7	3·8	3·9	4·0	4·2	4·4	4·6	4·8	5·0	m ft Height of object	

Distance of object (miles)

3

TABLE 3(3)   Distance of horizon for various heights of eye

Height of eye (metres)	Height of eye (feet)	Horizon distance (M)	Height of eye (metres)	Height of eye (feet)	Horizon distance (M)	Height of eye (metres)	Height of eye (feet)	Horizon distance (M)
1	3·3	2·1	21	68·9	9·5	41	134·5	13·3
2	6·6	2·9	22	72·2	9·8	42	137·8	13·5
3	9·8	3·6	23	75·5	10·0	43	141·1	13·7
4	13·1	4·1	24	78·7	10·2	44	144·4	13·8
5	16·4	4·7	25	82·0	10·4	45	147·6	14·0
6	19·7	5·1	26	85·3	10·6	46	150·9	14·1
7	23·0	5·5	27	88·6	10·8	47	154·2	14·3
8	26·2	5·9	28	91·9	11·0	48	157·5	14·4
9	29·6	6·2	29	95·1	11·2	49	160·8	14·6
10	32·8	6·6	30	98·4	11·4	50	164·0	14·7
11	36·1	6·9	31	101·7	11·6	51	167·3	14·9
12	39·4	7·2	32	105·0	11·8	52	170·6	15·0
13	42·7	7·5	33	108·3	12·0	53	173·9	15·2
14	45·9	7·8	34	111·6	12·1	54	177·2	15·3
15	49·2	8·1	35	114·8	12·3	55	180·4	15·4
16	52·5	8·3	36	118·1	12·5	56	183·7	15·6
17	55·8	8·6	37	121·4	12·7	57	187·0	15·7
18	59·1	8·8	38	124·7	12·8	58	190·3	15·9
19	62·3	9·1	39	128·0	13·0	59	193·6	16·0
20	65·6	9·3	40	131·2	13·2	60	196·9	16·1

TABLE 3(4)   Lights – distance off when rising or dipping (M)

Height of light (metres)	Height of light (feet)	1 / 3	2 / 7	3 / 10	4 / 13	5 / 16	6 / 20	7 / 23	8 / 26	9 / 30	10 / 33
10	33	8·7	9·5	10·2	10·8	11·3	11·7	12·1	12·5	12·8	13·2
12	39	9·3	10·1	10·8	11·4	11·9	12·3	12·7	13·1	13·4	13·8
14	46	9·9	10·7	11·4	12·0	12·5	12·9	13·3	13·7	14·0	14·4
16	53	10·4	11·2	11·9	12·5	13·0	13·4	13·8	14·2	14·5	14·9
18	59	10·9	11·7	12·4	13·0	13·5	13·9	14·3	14·7	15·0	15·4
20	66	11·4	12·2	12·9	13·5	14·0	14·4	14·8	15·2	15·5	15·9
22	72	11·9	12·7	13·4	14·0	14·5	14·9	15·3	15·7	16·0	16·4
24	79	12·3	13·1	13·8	14·4	14·9	15·3	15·7	16·1	16·4	17·0
26	85	12·7	13·5	14·2	14·8	15·3	15·7	16·1	16·5	16·8	17·2
28	92	13·1	13·9	14·6	15·2	15·7	16·1	16·5	16·9	17·2	17·6
30	98	13·5	14·3	15·0	15·6	16·1	16·5	16·9	17·3	17·6	18·0
32	105	13·9	14·7	15·4	16·0	16·5	16·9	17·3	17·7	18·0	18·4
34	112	14·2	15·0	15·7	16·3	16·8	17·2	17·6	18·0	18·3	18·7
36	118	14·6	15·4	16·1	16·7	17·2	17·6	18·0	18·4	18·7	19·1
38	125	14·9	15·7	16·4	17·0	17·5	17·9	18·3	18·7	19·0	19·4
40	131	15·3	16·1	16·8	17·4	17·9	18·3	18·7	19·1	19·4	19·8
42	138	15·6	16·4	17·1	17·7	18·2	18·6	19·0	19·4	19·7	20·1
44	144	15·9	16·7	17·4	18·0	18·5	18·9	19·3	19·7	20·0	20·4
46	151	16·2	17·0	17·7	18·3	18·8	19·2	19·6	20·0	20·3	20·7
48	157	16·5	17·3	18·0	18·6	19·1	19·5	19·9	20·3	20·6	21·0
50	164	16·8	17·6	18·3	18·9	19·4	19·8	20·2	20·6	20·9	21·3
55	180	17·5	18·3	19·0	19·6	20·1	20·5	20·9	21·3	21·6	22·0
60	197	18·2	19·0	19·7	20·3	20·8	21·2	21·6	22·0	22·3	22·7
65	213	18·9	19·7	20·4	21·0	21·5	21·9	22·3	22·7	23·0	23·4
70	230	19·5	20·3	21·0	21·6	22·1	22·5	22·9	23·2	23·6	24·0
75	246	20·1	20·9	21·6	22·2	22·7	23·1	23·5	23·9	24·2	24·6
80	262	20·7	21·5	22·2	22·8	23·3	23·7	24·1	24·5	24·8	25·2
85	279	21·3	22·1	22·8	23·4	23·9	24·3	24·7	25·1	25·4	25·8
90	295	21·8	22·6	23·3	23·9	24·4	24·8	25·2	25·6	25·9	26·3
95	312	22·4	23·2	23·9	24·5	25·0	25·4	25·8	26·2	26·5	26·9
metres	feet	1	2	3	4	5	6	7	8	9	10
Height of light		3 (feet)	7	10	13	16	20	23	26	30	33

Height of eye

Table 3(5) Distance for a given speed and time

Time Decimal of hr	Mins	Speed in knots 2·5	3·0	3·5	4·0	4·5	5·0	5·5	6·0	6·5	7·0	7·5	8·0	8·5	9·0	9·5	10·0	Mins	Time Decimal of hr
·0167	1				0·1	0·1	0·1	0·1	0·1	0·1	0·1	0·1	0·1	0·1	0·2	0·2	0·2	1	·0167
·0333	2	0·1	0·1	0·1	0·1	0·1	0·2	0·2	0·2	0·2	0·2	0·2	0·3	0·3	0·3	0·3	0·3	2	·0333
·0500	3	0·1	0·1	0·2	0·2	0·2	0·2	0·3	0·3	0·3	0·3	0·4	0·4	0·4	0·4	0·5	0·5	3	·0500
·0667	4	0·1	0·2	0·2	0·3	0·3	0·3	0·4	0·4	0·4	0·5	0·5	0·5	0·6	0·6	0·6	0·7	4	·0667
·0833	5	0·2	0·2	0·3	0·3	0·4	0·4	0·5	0·5	0·5	0·6	0·6	0·7	0·7	0·7	0·8	0·8	5	·0833
·1000	6	0·2	0·3	0·3	0·4	0·4	0·5	0·5	0·6	0·6	0·7	0·7	0·8	0·8	0·9	0·9	1·0	6	·1000
·1167	7	0·3	0·4	0·4	0·5	0·5	0·6	0·6	0·7	0·8	0·8	0·9	0·9	1·0	1·1	1·1	1·2	7	·1167
·1333	8	0·3	0·4	0·5	0·5	0·6	0·7	0·7	0·8	0·9	0·9	1·0	1·1	1·1	1·2	1·3	1·3	8	·1333
·1500	9	0·4	0·4	0·5	0·6	0·7	0·7	0·8	0·9	1·0	1·0	1·1	1·2	1·3	1·3	1·4	1·5	9	·1500
·1667	10	0·4	0·5	0·6	0·7	0·8	0·8	0·9	1·0	1·1	1·2	1·3	1·3	1·4	1·5	1·6	1·7	10	·1667
·1833	11	0·5	0·5	0·6	0·7	0·8	0·9	1·0	1·1	1·2	1·3	1·4	1·5	1·6	1·6	1·7	1·8	11	·1833
·2000	12	0·5	0·6	0·7	0·8	0·9	1·0	1·1	1·2	1·3	1·4	1·5	1·6	1·7	1·8	1·9	2·0	12	·2000
·2167	13	0·5	0·6	0·8	0·9	1·0	1·1	1·2	1·3	1·4	1·5	1·6	1·7	1·8	2·0	2·0	2·2	13	·2167
·2333	14	0·6	0·7	0·8	0·9	1·0	1·2	1·3	1·4	1·5	1·6	1·7	1·9	2·0	2·1	2·2	2·3	14	·2333
·2500	15	0·6	0·7	0·9	1·0	1·1	1·2	1·4	1·5	1·6	1·8	1·9	2·0	2·1	2·2	2·4	2·5	15	·2500
·2667	16	0·7	0·8	0·9	1·1	1·2	1·3	1·5	1·6	1·7	1·9	2·0	2·1	2·3	2·4	2·5	2·7	16	·2667
·2833	17	0·7	0·8	1·0	1·1	1·3	1·4	1·6	1·7	1·8	2·0	2·1	2·3	2·4	2·5	2·7	2·8	17	·2833
·3000	18	0·7	0·9	1·0	1·2	1·3	1·5	1·6	1·8	1·9	2·1	2·2	2·4	2·5	2·7	2·8	3·0	18	·3000
·3167	19	0·8	1·0	1·1	1·3	1·4	1·6	1·7	1·9	2·1	2·1	2·4	2·5	2·7	2·9	3·0	3·2	19	·3167
·3333	20	0·8	1·0	1·2	1·3	1·5	1·7	1·8	2·0	2·2	2·3	2·5	2·7	2·8	3·0	3·2	3·3	20	·3333
·3500	21	0·9	1·0	1·2	1·4	1·6	1·7	1·9	2·1	2·3	2·4	2·6	2·8	3·0	3·1	3·3	3·5	21	·3500
·3667	22	0·9	1·1	1·3	1·5	1·7	1·8	2·1	2·2	2·4	2·6	2·8	2·9	3·1	3·3	3·5	3·7	22	·3667
·3833	23	1·0	1·1	1·3	1·5	1·7	1·9	2·1	2·3	2·5	2·7	2·9	3·1	3·3	3·4	3·6	3·8	23	·3833
·4000	24	1·0	1·2	1·4	1·6	1·8	2·0	2·2	2·4	2·6	2·8	3·0	3·2	3·4	3·6	3·8	4·0	24	·4000
·4167	25	1·0	1·3	1·5	1·7	1·9	2·1	2·3	2·5	2·7	2·9	3·1	3·3	3·5	3·8	4·0	4·2	25	·4167
·4333	26	1·1	1·3	1·5	1·7	1·9	2·2	2·4	2·6	2·8	3·0	3·2	3·5	3·7	3·9	4·1	4·3	26	·4333
·4500	27	1·1	1·3	1·6	1·8	2·0	2·2	2·5	2·7	2·9	3·1	3·4	3·6	3·8	4·0	4·3	4·5	27	·4500
·4667	28	1·2	1·4	1·6	1·9	2·1	2·3	2·6	2·8	3·0	3·3	3·5	3·7	4·0	4·2	4·4	4·7	28	·4667
·4833	29	1·2	1·5	1·7	1·9	2·2	2·4	2·7	2·9	3·1	3·4	3·6	3·9	4·1	4·3	4·6	4·8	29	·4833
·5000	30	1·2	1·5	1·7	2·0	2·2	2·5	2·7	3·0	3·2	3·5	3·7	4·0	4·2	4·5	4·7	5·0	30	·5000
·5167	31	1·3	1·6	1·8	2·1	2·3	2·6	2·8	3·1	3·4	3·6	3·9	4·1	4·4	4·7	4·9	5·2	31	·5167
·5333	32	1·3	1·6	1·9	2·1	2·4	2·7	2·9	3·2	3·5	3·7	4·0	4·3	4·5	4·8	5·1	5·3	32	·5333
·5500	33	1·4	1·6	1·9	2·2	2·5	2·7	3·0	3·3	3·6	3·8	4·1	4·4	4·7	4·9	5·2	5·5	33	·5500
·5667	34	1·4	1·7	2·0	2·3	2·6	2·8	3·1	3·4	3·7	4·0	4·3	4·5	4·8	5·1	5·4	5·7	34	·5667
·5833	35	1·5	1·7	2·0	2·3	2·6	2·9	3·2	3·5	3·8	4·1	4·4	4·7	5·0	5·2	5·5	5·8	35	·5833
·6000	36	1·5	1·8	2·1	2·4	2·7	3·0	3·3	3·6	3·9	4·2	4·5	4·8	5·1	5·4	5·7	6·0	36	·6000
·6117	37	1·6	1·8	2·1	2·4	2·8	3·1	3·4	3·7	4·0	4·3	4·6	4·9	5·2	5·5	5·8	6·1	37	·6117
·6333	38	1·6	1·9	2·2	2·5	2·8	3·2	3·5	3·8	4·1	4·4	4·7	5·1	5·4	5·7	6·0	6·3	38	·6333
·6500	39	1·6	1·9	2·3	2·6	2·9	3·2	3·6	3·9	4·2	4·5	4·9	5·2	5·5	5·8	6·2	6·5	39	·6500
·6667	40	1·7	2·0	2·3	2·7	3·0	3·3	3·7	4·0	4·3	4·7	5·0	5·3	5·7	6·0	6·3	6·7	40	·6667
·6833	41	1·7	2·0	2·4	2·7	3·1	3·4	3·8	4·1	4·4	4·8	5·1	5·5	5·8	6·1	6·5	6·8	41	·6833
·7000	42	1·7	2·1	2·4	2·8	3·1	3·5	3·8	4·2	4·5	4·9	5·2	5·6	5·9	6·3	6·6	7·0	42	·7000
·7167	43	1·8	2·2	2·5	2·9	3·2	3·6	3·9	4·3	4·7	5·0	5·4	5·7	6·1	6·5	6·8	7·2	43	·7167
·7333	44	1·8	2·2	2·6	2·9	3·3	3·7	4·0	4·4	4·8	5·1	5·5	5·9	6·2	6·6	7·0	7·3	44	·7333
·7500	45	1·9	2·2	2·6	3·0	3·4	3·7	4·1	4·5	4·9	5·2	5·6	6·0	6·4	6·7	7·1	7·5	45	·7500
·7667	46	1·9	2·3	2·7	3·1	3·5	3·8	4·2	4·6	5·0	5·4	5·8	6·1	6·5	6·9	7·3	7·7	46	·7667
·7833	47	2·0	2·3	2·7	3·1	3·5	3·9	4·3	4·7	5·1	5·5	5·9	6·3	6·7	7·0	7·4	7·8	47	·7833
·8000	48	2·0	2·4	2·8	3·2	3·6	4·0	4·4	4·8	5·2	5·6	6·0	6·4	6·8	7·2	7·6	8·0	48	·8000
·8167	49	2·0	2·5	2·9	3·3	3·7	4·1	4·5	4·9	5·3	5·7	6·1	6·5	6·9	7·4	7·8	8·2	49	·8167
·8333	50	2·1	2·5	2·9	3·3	3·7	4·2	4·6	5·0	5·4	5·8	6·2	6·7	7·1	7·5	7·9	8·3	50	·8333
·8500	51	2·1	2·5	3·0	3·4	3·8	4·2	4·7	5·1	5·5	5·9	6·4	6·8	7·2	7·6	8·1	8·5	51	·8500
·8667	52	2·2	2·6	3·0	3·5	3·9	4·3	4·8	5·2	5·6	6·1	6·5	6·9	7·4	7·8	8·2	8·7	52	·8667
·8833	53	2·2	2·6	3·1	3·5	4·0	4·4	4·9	5·3	5·7	6·2	6·6	7·1	7·5	7·9	8·4	8·8	53	·8833
·9000	54	2·2	2·7	3·1	3·6	4·0	4·5	4·9	5·4	5·8	6·3	6·7	7·2	7·6	8·1	8·5	9·0	54	·9000
·9167	55	2·3	2·8	3·2	3·7	4·1	4·6	5·0	5·5	6·0	6·4	6·9	7·3	7·8	8·3	8·7	9·2	55	·9167
·9333	56	2·3	2·8	3·3	3·7	4·2	4·7	5·1	5·6	6·1	6·5	7·0	7·5	7·9	8·4	8·9	9·3	56	·9333
·9500	57	2·4	2·8	3·3	3·8	4·3	4·7	5·2	5·7	6·2	6·6	7·1	7·6	8·1	8·5	9·0	9·5	57	·9500
·9667	58	2·4	2·9	3·4	3·9	4·4	4·8	5·3	5·8	6·3	6·8	7·3	7·7	8·2	8·7	9·2	9·7	58	·9667
·9833	59	2·5	2·9	3·4	3·9	4·4	4·9	5·4	5·9	6·4	6·9	7·4	7·9	8·4	8·8	9·3	9·8	59	·9833
1·0000	60	2·5	3·0	3·5	4·0	4·5	5·0	5·5	6·0	6·5	7·0	7·5	8·0	8·5	9·0	9·5	10·0	60	1·0000
Decimal of hr Mins		2·5	3·0	3·5	4·0	4·5	5·0	5·5	6·0	6·5	7·0	7·5	8·0	8·5	9·0	9·5	10·0	Mins	Decimal of hr
Time								Speed in knots											Time

3

Table 3(5)   Distance for a given speed and time (continued)

Time Decimal of hr	Mins	10·5	11·0	11·5	12·0	12·5	13·0	13·5	14·0	14·5	15·0	15·5	16·0	17·0	18·0	19·0	20·0	Mins	Time Decimal of hr
·0167	1	0·2	0·2	0·2	0·2	0·2	0·2	0·2	0·2	0·2	0·3	0·3	0·3	0·3	0·3	0·3	0·3	1	·0167
·0333	2	0·3	0·4	0·4	0·4	0·4	0·4	0·4	0·5	0·5	0·5	0·5	0·5	0·6	0·6	0·6	0·7	2	·0333
·0500	3	0·5	0·5	0·6	0·6	0·6	0·6	0·7	0·7	0·7	0·7	0·8	0·8	0·8	0·8	0·9	1·0	3	·0500
·0667	4	0·7	0·7	0·8	0·8	0·8	0·9	0·9	0·9	1·0	1·0	1·0	1·1	1·1	1·2	1·3	1·3	4	·0667
·0833	5	0·9	0·9	1·0	1·0	1·0	1·1	1·1	1·2	1·2	1·2	1·3	1·3	1·4	1·5	1·6	1·7	5	·0833
·1000	6	1·0	1·1	1·1	1·2	1·2	1·3	1·3	1·4	1·4	1·5	1·5	1·6	1·7	1·8	1·9	2·0	6	·1000
·1167	7	1·2	1·3	1·3	1·4	1·5	1·5	1·6	1·6	1·7	1·8	1·8	1·9	2·0	2·1	2·2	2·3	7	·1167
·1333	8	1·4	1·5	1·5	1·6	1·7	1·7	1·8	1·9	1·9	2·0	2·1	2·1	2·3	2·4	2·5	2·7	8	·1333
·1500	9	1·6	1·6	1·7	1·8	1·9	1·9	2·0	2·1	2·1	2·2	2·3	2·4	2·5	2·7	2·8	3·0	9	·1500
·1667	10	1·8	1·8	1·9	2·0	2·1	2·2	2·3	2·3	2·4	2·5	2·6	2·7	2·8	3·0	3·2	3·3	10	·1667
·1833	11	1·9	2·0	2·1	2·2	2·3	2·4	2·5	2·6	2·7	2·7	2·8	2·9	3·1	3·3	3·5	3·7	11	·1833
·2000	12	2·1	2·2	2·3	2·4	2·5	2·6	2·7	2·8	2·9	3·0	3·1	3·2	3·4	3·6	3·8	4·0	12	·2000
·2167	13	2·3	2·4	2·5	2·6	2·7	2·8	2·9	3·0	3·1	3·2	3·3	3·5	3·7	3·9	4·1	4·3	13	·2167
·2333	14	2·4	2·6	2·7	2·8	2·9	3·0	3·1	3·3	3·4	3·5	3·6	3·7	4·0	4·2	4·4	4·7	14	·2333
·2500	15	2·6	2·7	2·9	3·0	3·1	3·2	3·4	3·5	3·6	3·7	3·9	4·0	4·2	4·5	4·7	5·0	15	·2500
·2667	16	2·8	2·9	3·1	3·2	3·3	3·5	3·6	3·7	3·9	4·0	4·1	4·3	4·5	4·8	5·1	5·3	16	·2667
·2833	17	3·0	3·1	3·3	3·4	3·5	3·7	3·8	4·0	4·1	4·2	4·4	4·5	4·8	5·1	5·4	5·7	17	·2833
·3000	18	3·1	3·3	3·4	3·6	3·7	3·9	4·0	4·2	4·3	4·5	4·6	4·8	5·1	5·4	5·7	6·0	18	·3000
·3167	19	3·3	3·5	3·6	3·8	4·0	4·1	4·3	4·4	4·6	4·8	4·9	5·1	5·4	5·7	6·0	6·3	19	·3167
·3333	20	3·5	3·7	3·8	4·0	4·2	4·3	4·5	4·7	4·8	5·0	5·2	5·3	5·7	6·0	6·3	6·7	20	·3333
·3500	21	3·7	3·8	4·0	4·2	4·4	4·5	4·7	4·9	5·1	5·2	5·4	5·6	5·9	6·3	6·6	7·0	21	·3500
·3667	22	3·9	4·0	4·2	4·4	4·6	4·8	5·0	5·1	5·3	5·5	5·7	5·9	6·2	6·6	7·0	7·3	22	·3667
·3833	23	4·0	4·2	4·4	4·6	4·8	5·0	5·2	5·4	5·6	5·7	5·9	6·1	6·5	6·9	7·3	7·7	23	·3833
·4000	24	4·2	4·4	4·6	4·8	5·0	5·2	5·4	5·6	5·8	6·0	6·2	6·4	6·8	7·2	7·6	8·0	24	·4000
·4167	25	4·4	4·6	4·8	5·0	5·2	5·4	5·6	5·8	6·0	6·3	6·5	6·7	7·1	7·5	7·9	8·3	25	·4167
·4333	26	4·5	4·8	5·0	5·2	5·4	5·6	5·8	6·1	6·3	6·5	6·7	6·9	7·4	7·8	8·2	8·7	26	·4333
·4500	27	4·7	4·9	5·2	5·4	5·6	5·8	6·1	6·3	6·5	6·7	7·0	7·2	7·6	8·1	8·5	9·0	27	·4500
·4667	28	4·9	5·1	5·4	5·6	5·8	6·1	6·3	6·5	6·8	7·0	7·2	7·5	7·9	8·4	8·9	9·3	28	·4667
·4833	29	5·1	5·3	5·6	5·8	6·0	6·3	6·5	6·8	7·0	7·2	7·5	7·7	8·2	8·7	9·2	9·7	29	·4833
·5000	30	5·2	5·5	5·7	6·0	6·2	6·5	6·7	7·0	7·2	7·5	7·7	8·0	8·5	9·0	9·5	10·0	30	·5000
·5167	31	5·4	5·7	5·9	6·2	6·5	6·7	7·0	7·2	7·5	7·8	8·0	8·3	8·8	9·3	9·8	10·3	31	·5167
·5333	32	5·6	5·9	6·1	6·4	6·7	6·9	7·2	7·5	7·7	8·0	8·3	8·5	9·1	9·6	10·1	10·7	32	·5333
·5500	33	5·8	6·0	6·3	6·6	6·9	7·1	7·4	7·7	8·0	8·2	8·5	8·8	9·3	9·9	10·4	11·0	33	·5500
·5667	34	6·0	6·2	6·5	6·8	7·1	7·4	7·7	7·9	8·2	8·5	8·8	9·1	9·6	10·2	10·8	11·3	34	·5667
·5833	35	6·1	6·4	6·7	7·0	7·3	7·6	7·9	8·2	8·5	8·7	9·0	9·3	9·9	10·5	11·1	11·7	35	·5833
·6000	36	6·3	6·6	6·9	7·2	7·5	7·8	8·1	8·4	8·7	9·0	9·3	9·6	10·2	10·8	11·4	12·0	36	·6000
·6117	37	6·4	6·7	7·0	7·3	7·6	8·0	8·3	8·6	8·9	9·2	9·5	9·8	10·4	11·0	11·6	12·2	37	·6117
·6333	38	6·6	7·0	7·3	7·6	7·9	8·2	8·5	8·9	9·2	9·5	9·8	10·1	10·8	11·4	12·0	12·7	38	·6333
·6500	39	6·8	7·1	7·5	7·8	8·1	8·4	8·8	9·1	9·4	9·7	10·1	10·4	11·0	11·7	12·3	13·0	39	·6500
·6667	40	7·0	7·3	7·7	8·0	8·3	8·7	9·0	9·3	9·7	10·0	10·3	10·7	11·3	12·0	12·7	13·3	40	·6667
·6833	41	7·2	7·5	7·9	8·2	8·5	8·9	9·2	9·6	9·9	10·2	10·6	10·9	11·6	12·3	13·0	13·7	41	·6833
·7000	42	7·3	7·7	8·0	8·4	8·7	9·1	9·4	9·8	10·1	10·5	10·8	11·2	11·9	12·6	13·3	14·0	42	·7000
·7167	43	7·5	7·9	8·2	8·6	9·0	9·3	9·7	10·0	10·4	10·8	11·1	11·5	12·2	12·9	13·6	14·3	43	·7167
·7333	44	7·7	8·1	8·4	8·8	9·2	9·5	10·0	10·3	10·6	11·0	11·4	11·7	12·5	13·2	13·9	14·7	44	·7333
·7500	45	7·9	8·2	8·6	9·0	9·4	9·7	10·1	10·5	10·9	11·2	11·6	12·0	12·7	13·5	14·2	15·0	45	·7500
·7667	46	8·1	8·4	8·8	9·2	9·6	10·0	10·4	10·7	11·1	11·5	11·9	12·3	13·0	13·8	14·6	15·3	46	·7667
·7833	47	8·2	8·6	9·0	9·4	9·8	10·2	10·6	11·0	11·4	11·7	12·1	12·5	13·3	14·1	14·9	15·7	47	·7833
·8000	48	8·4	8·8	9·2	9·6	10·0	10·4	10·8	11·2	11·6	12·0	12·4	12·8	13·6	14·4	15·2	16·0	48	·8000
·8167	49	8·6	9·0	9·4	9·8	10·2	10·6	11·0	11·4	11·8	12·2	12·7	13·1	13·9	14·7	15·5	16·3	49	·8167
·8333	50	8·7	9·2	9·6	10·0	10·4	10·8	11·2	11·7	12·1	12·5	12·9	13·3	14·2	15·0	15·8	16·7	50	·8333
·8500	51	8·9	9·3	9·8	10·2	10·6	11·0	11·5	11·9	12·3	12·7	13·2	13·6	14·4	15·3	16·1	17·0	51	·8500
·8667	52	9·1	9·5	10·0	10·4	10·8	11·3	11·7	12·1	12·6	13·0	13·4	13·9	14·7	15·6	16·5	17·3	52	·8667
·8833	53	9·3	9·7	10·2	10·6	11·0	11·5	11·9	12·4	12·8	13·2	13·7	14·1	15·0	15·9	16·8	17·7	53	·8833
·9000	54	9·4	9·9	10·3	10·8	11·2	11·7	12·1	12·6	13·0	13·5	13·9	14·4	15·3	16·2	17·1	18·0	54	·9000
·9167	55	9·6	10·1	10·5	11·0	11·5	11·9	12·4	12·8	13·3	13·8	14·2	14·7	15·6	16·5	17·4	18·3	55	·9167
·9333	56	9·8	10·3	10·7	11·2	11·7	12·1	12·6	13·1	13·5	14·0	14·5	14·9	15·9	16·8	17·7	18·7	56	·9333
·9500	57	10·0	10·4	10·9	11·4	11·9	12·3	12·8	13·3	13·8	14·2	14·7	15·2	16·1	17·1	18·0	19·0	57	·9500
·9667	58	10·2	10·6	11·1	11·6	12·1	12·6	13·1	13·5	14·0	14·5	15·0	15·5	16·4	17·4	18·4	19·3	58	·9667
·9833	59	10·3	10·8	11·3	11·8	12·3	12·8	13·3	13·8	14·3	14·7	15·2	15·7	16·7	17·7	18·7	19·7	59	·9833
1·0000	60	10·5	11·0	11·5	12·0	12·5	13·0	13·5	14·0	14·5	15·0	15·5	16·0	17·0	18·0	19·0	20·0	60	1·0000
Decimal of hr Mins		10·5	11·0	11·5	12·0	12·5	13·0	13·5	14·0	14·5	15·0	15·5	16·0	17·0	18·0	19·0	20·0	Mins	Decimal of hr
Time								Speed in knots										Time

Table 3(6) Measured mile table – Knots related to time over one mile

Secs	1 min	2 min	3 min	4 min	5 min	6 min	7 min	8 min	9 min	10 min	11 min
	60·00	30·00	20·00	15·00	12·00	10·00	8·57	7·50	6·67	6·00	5·45
1	59·02	29·75	19·89	14·94	11·96	9·97	8·55	7·48	6·66	5·99	5·45
2	58·06	29·51	19·78	14·88	11·92	9·94	8·53	7·47	6·64	5·98	5·44
3	57·14	29·27	19·67	14·81	11·88	9·92	8·51	7·45	6·63	5·97	5·43
4	56·25	29·03	19·57	14·75	11·84	9·89	8·49	7·44	6·62	5·96	5·42
5	55·38	28·80	19·46	14·69	11·80	9·86	8·47	7·42	6·61	5·95	5·41
6	54·55	28·57	19·35	14·63	11·76	9·84	8·45	7·41	6·59	5·94	5·41
7	53·73	28·35	19·25	14·57	11·73	9·81	8·43	7·39	6·58	5·93	5·40
8	52·94	28·12	19·15	14·52	11·69	9·78	8·41	7·38	6·57	5·92	5·39
9	52·17	27·91	19·05	14·46	11·65	9·76	8·39	7·36	6·56	5·91	5·38
10	51·43	27·69	18·95	14·40	11·61	9·73	8·37	7·35	6·55	5·90	5·37
11	50·70	27·48	18·85	14·34	11·58	9·70	8·35	7·33	6·53	5·89	5·37
12	50·00	27·27	18·75	14·29	11·54	9·68	8·33	7·32	6·52	5·88	5·36
13	49·32	27·07	18·65	14·23	11·50	9·65	8·31	7·30	6·51	5·87	5·35
14	48·65	26·87	18·56	14·17	11·46	9·63	8·29	7·29	6·50	5·86	5·34
15	48·00	26·67	18·46	14·12	11·43	9·60	8·28	7·27	6·49	5·85	5·33
16	47·37	26·47	18·37	14·06	11·39	9·58	8·26	7·26	6·47	5·84	5·33
17	46·75	26·28	18·27	14·01	11·36	9·55	8·24	7·24	6·46	5·83	5·32
18	46·15	26·09	18·18	13·95	11·32	9·52	8·22	7·23	6·45	5·83	5·31
19	45·57	25·90	18·09	13·90	11·29	9·50	8·20	7·21	6·44	5·82	5·30
20	45·00	25·71	18·00	13·85	11·25	9·47	8·18	7·20	6·43	5·81	5·29
21	44·44	25·53	17·91	13·79	11·21	9·45	8·16	7·19	6·42	5·80	5·29
22	43·90	25·35	17·82	13·74	11·18	9·42	8·14	7·17	6·41	5·79	5·28
23	43·37	25·17	17·73	13·69	11·15	9·40	8·13	7·16	6·39	5·78	5·27
24	42·86	25·00	17·65	13·64	11·11	9·37	8·11	7·14	6·38	5·77	5·26
25	42·35	24·83	17·56	13·58	11·08	9·35	8·09	7·13	6·37	5·76	5·26
26	41·86	24·66	17·48	13·53	11·04	9·33	8·07	7·11	6·36	5·75	5·25
27	41·38	24·49	17·39	13·48	11·01	9·30	8·05	7·10	6·35	5·74	5·24
28	40·91	24·32	17·31	13·43	10·98	9·28	8·04	7·09	6·34	5·73	5·23
29	40·45	24·16	17·22	13·38	10·94	9·25	8·02	7·07	6·33	5·72	5·22
30	40·00	24·00	17·14	13·33	10·91	9·23	8·00	7·06	6·32	5·71	5·22
31	39·56	23·84	17·06	13·28	10·88	9·21	7·98	7·04	6·30	5·71	5·21
32	39·13	23·68	16·98	13·24	10·84	9·18	7·96	7·03	6·29	5·70	5·20
33	38·71	23·53	16·90	13·19	10·81	9·16	7·95	7·02	6·28	5·69	5·19
34	38·30	23·38	16·82	13·14	10·78	9·14	7·93	7·00	6·27	5·68	5·19
35	37·89	23·23	16·74	13·09	10·75	9·11	7·91	6·99	6·26	5·67	5·18
36	37·50	23·08	16·67	13·04	10·71	9·09	7·89	6·98	6·25	5·66	5·17
37	37·11	22·93	16·59	13·00	10·68	9·07	7·88	6·96	6·24	5·65	5·16
38	36·73	22·78	16·51	12·95	10·65	9·05	7·86	6·95	6·23	5·64	5·16
39	36·36	22·64	16·44	12·90	10·62	9·02	7·84	6·94	6·22	5·63	5·15
40	36·00	22·50	16·36	12·86	10·59	9·00	7·83	6·92	6·21	5·62	5·14
41	35·64	22·36	16·29	12·81	10·56	8·98	7·81	6·91	6·20	5·62	5·13
42	35·29	22·22	16·22	12·77	10·53	8·96	7·79	6·90	6·19	5·61	5·13
43	34·95	22·09	16·14	12·72	10·50	8·93	7·78	6·89	6·17	5·60	5·12
44	34·62	21·95	16·07	12·68	10·47	8·91	7·76	6·87	6·16	5·59	5·11
45	34·29	21·82	16·00	12·63	10·43	8·89	7·74	6·86	6·15	5·58	5·10
46	33·96	21·69	15·93	12·59	10·40	8·87	7·72	6·84	6·14	5·57	5·10
47	33·64	21·56	15·86	12·54	10·37	8·85	7·71	6·83	6·13	5·56	5·09
48	33·33	21·43	15·79	12·50	10·34	8·82	7·69	6·82	6·12	5·56	5·08
49	33·03	21·30	15·72	12·46	10·32	8·80	7·68	6·80	6·11	5·55	5·08
50	32·73	21·18	15·65	12·41	10·29	8·78	7·66	6·79	6·10	5·54	5·07
51	32·43	21·05	15·58	12·37	10·26	8·76	7·64	6·78	6·09	5·53	5·06
52	32·14	20·93	15·52	12·33	10·23	8·74	7·63	6·77	6·08	5·52	5·06
53	31·86	20·81	15·45	12·29	10·20	8·72	7·61	6·75	6·07	5·51	5·05
54	31·58	20·69	15·38	12·24	10·17	8·70	7·59	6·74	6·06	5·50	5·04
55	31·30	20·57	15·32	12·20	10·14	8·67	7·58	6·73	6·05	5·50	5·04
56	31·03	20·45	15·25	12·16	10·11	8·65	7·56	6·72	6·04	5·49	5·03
57	30·77	20·34	15·19	12·12	10·08	8·63	7·55	6·70	6·03	5·48	5·02
58	30·51	20·22	15·13	12·08	10·06	8·61	7·53	6·69	6·02	5·47	5·01
59	30·25	20·11	15·06	12·04	10·03	8·59	7·52	6·68	6·01	5·46	5·00
Secs	1 min	2 min	3 min	4 min	5 min	6 min	7 min	8 min	9 min	10 min	11 min

3

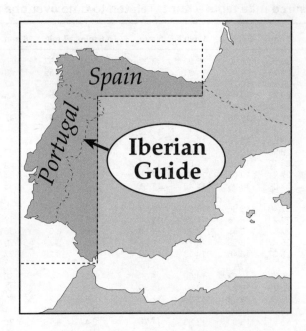

THE 1998 IBERIAN GUIDE

The second edition of this 56 page Guide extends the Almanac's coverage from the Franco-Spanish border at Hendaye (10.18.28) westward along Northern Spain and southward past the coasts of Portugal and South West Spain to Gibraltar.

It gives details and chartlets of 37 harbours, plus minor harbours and anchorages, as shown on four full page maps of the Iberian Peninsula.

Coastal lights, fog signals and Waypoints are listed, together with summaries of Navigational aids, Weather sources and Communications facilities around the Atlantic coast of Iberia.

Passage Information offers guidance on dangers and passage-making, with two Distance Tables.

Tidal predictions and curves are included for the Standard Ports of Lisboa and Gibraltar, together with their associated secondary port differences. For secondary ports in North Spain, differences are referenced to Point de Grave in Area 18 of the Almanac.

Spanish and Portuguese vocabularies of useful nautical terms are also included.

From Dec 1998 this Guide is obtainable by post direct from the Publishers by completing the card enclosed within this Almanac and forwarding it with the appropriate remittance.

Chapter 4

Radio Navigational Aids

Contents

4

Radio navigational aids – introduction

Basic information on position fixing systems such as GPS, Decca, Loran-C and the use of Waypoints, together with details of individual RDF beacons and Racons, for navigational use is given in this Almanac. Further information on procedures and possible errors, together with the other subjects listed below, is given in Chapter 4 of *The Macmillan & Silk Cut Yachtsman's Handbook:*

  aids to navigation; developments; navigational aids and position fixing systems; satellite position fixing system; Global Positioning System (GPS); differential GPS; hyperbolic position fixing systems; Decca; Loran-C; Omega; differential Omega; radar in yachts; how radar works; radar for collision avoidance; radar as a navigational aid; radar beacons (Racons); marine and aeronautical RDF beacons; DF receiving sets; directional radio beacons; beacons incorporating distance finding; aero RDF beacons operating procedures; errors in radio bearings; calibration; radio direction finding; half convergency; VHF emergency direction finding; QTG service from Coast Radio Stations.

4.1   INTRODUCTION

4.1.1   Types of systems

Four position fixing systems are available to yachtsmen. Satellite navigation is provided by the Global Positioning System (GPS), and the hyperbolic area navigation systems by Decca, Loran-C and Omega. Radio Direction Finding (RDF) is now obsolescent and will be phased out. Each aid has its merits for particular applications and geographical areas. All these aids are more fully described in *The Macmillan & Silk Cut Yachtsman's Handbook*.

The choice of navigation aids for a yacht largely depends on the usage of the boat, the owner's requirements and interests, and the particular waters sailed. GPS provides global fixes with an accuracy of approximately 100m in any weather. Loran-C and Decca provide continuous fixes within coverage areas, albeit with less accuracy and reliability. Omega provides global coverage, but the accuracy is not as good as Loran-C or Decca.

4.2   SATELLITE SYSTEMS

4.2.1   Global Positioning System (GPS)

GPS provides highly accurate, worldwide, continuous three-dimensional position fixing (latitude, longitude and altitude), together with velocity and time data in all weather conditions.

The GPS constellation, shown in Fig. 4(1), consists of 24 operational satellites configured in six orbital planes. Three of the satellites operate as active spares. The satellites circle the earth in approximately 12 hour orbits at a height of about 10,900M.

GPS provides two levels of service. These are:

    (1)   **Standard Positioning Service (SPS)**
    (2)   **Precise Positioning Service (PPS)**

It is the SPS service which is of interest to yachtsmen. SPS is available to all civil users at no cost. PPS provides higher accuracy but, at present, is reserved solely for military purposes and is only made available to selected civil users when specially authorised.

The principle on which GPS works is the accurate measurement of the range, or distance, from the receiver to a number of satellites transmitting accurately timed signals together with information on their accurate position in space. In very simplistic terms each satellite transmits a PPS and SPS code saying 'this is my position and this is the time'.

By accurately knowing the times of transmission and reception of the signal it is possible to establish the transit time. Multiply the transit time by the speed of light (161,829 miles per second) to get the range to the satellite. If similar measurements are made on three satellites, three intersecting range circles, each centred on the satellite's position at the time of transmission,

are obtained. If no other errors are present, the intersection of the three range circles represents the yacht's position.

GPS basic system errors are relatively small and are of the order of 19-20m using SPS. Current US plans for the use of SPS are based on a denial of full system accuracy by the use of cryptology. This is called Selective Availability (SA). The imposition of SA means there is no guarantee that a standard GPS yacht receiver will give a horizontal fix of better than ±100m, 140m vertically, and time to 340 nanoseconds for 95% of the time. Accuracy will be ±300m for 99·99% of the time. As fix accuracy continually varies when SA is switched on, no assumptions should be made about fix accuracy at any given time. SPS accuracy can be significantly improved by access to a differential (DGPS) service, but a user charge may be applicable.

GPS receivers vary from single-channel to multi-channel receivers. Better quality positioning is obtained by tracking more than the minimum three satellites required to produce a two-dimensional fix (latitude and longitude). A receiver with at least six dedicated channels is the most suitable for use on a yacht.

In conventional coastal navigation it is generally recommended to avoid using any visual position lines where the angle of cut is less than 30°. The accuracy of GPS fixes equally depends on the angle of cut of its position lines, but this is more difficult to appreciate because the geometry of the satellites is constantly changing. The receiver, rather than the navigator, selects those satellites which offer the best fix geometry.

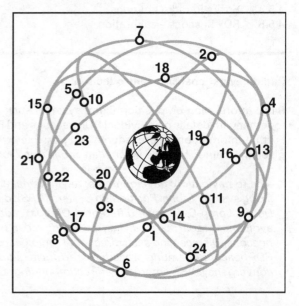

Fig. 4(1)   The GPS constellation contains 21 operational satellites and three active spares at orbital heights of 10,900M arranged in six orbital planes inclined to the equator at 55°. The satellite spacing is arranged to ensure at least four satellites are in view from anywhere on earth.

4.2.2   Dilution of precision

The efficiency of the satellite geometry is indicated by the Dilution of Precision (DOP) factor which is computed from the angular separation between various satellites. The greater the separation the better the fix geometry is, and the lower the DOP value.

Performance is most likely to be degraded when there are less than 5 satellites visible, or when DOP is greater than 5. Since high DOP is caused by poor satellite geometry, these events usually coincide.

The potential inaccuracy of a 2D GPS fix resulting from poor geometry is expressed by a factor called the Horizontal Dilution of Precision (HDOP). The accuracy of a GPS fix varies with the capability of the user's receiver and receiver-to-satellite geometry. Receivers are programmed to select satellites which give the lowest HDOP value. Should the HDOP value exceed a certain figure, usually 4 or 5, then receivers give a warning, or cease computing fixes until satellite geometry improves.

4.2.3   Datum

GPS satellites are referenced to the World Geodetic System 84 (WGS 84) datum. This means that satellite fixes cannot be directly plotted on Admiralty charts, which are referenced to a local datum. If the full potential benefit of GPS accuracy is to be achieved, then suitable corrections need to be applied.

UK Admiralty charts are based on the Ordnance Survey Great Britain 1936 (OSGB 36) datum. Admiralty charts covering the NW European Coastline are based on the European 1950 Datum (ED 50). Admiralty charts always state which datum is used in a note on 'Satellite-Derived Positions' printed under the main title. The note also indicates the amount of correction required between satellite and chart positions.

The approximate difference between WGS 84, OSGB 36 and ED 50 datums in the Dover Strait are shown in Fig. 4(2).

The amount of the error will vary at each location and can be substantial in some parts of the world such as the Pacific.

Fig. 4(2)   Chart datum differences in the Dover Strait

Good GPS receivers generally allow users a choice of many different chart datums. Navigators should always ensure that the chart datum set on the receiver is the same datum as the chart in use.

4.2.4   Differential GPS

Differential GPS (DGPS) is a method of considerably improving the basic accuracy of GPS SPS locally. DGPS is only likely to appeal to a limited number of yacht users such as those engaged in racing, or having special requirements for high accuracy.

When fully operational, a DGPS reference station compares observed GPS satellite pseudo-ranges with calculated pseudo-ranges, for all satellites in view, derived by knowing the reference station location very precisely. Observed differences in pseudo-ranges are then re-transmitted by the reference station over a suitable medium to the users' GPS receiver via a data-link. A radio receiver capable of receiving selected marine radio beacons, and equipped with a suitable demodulator for the DGPS messages is required and is interfaced to the GPS receiver. It will then automatically apply the transmitted corrections to the navigational data. Once the errors at a particular time and place have been established, differential corrections can be applied to achieve an accuracy of better than ± 10m for a limited period of time.

The Lighthouse Authorities will shortly provide a free public maritime differential GPS service for vessels navigating around the coasts of UK and Ireland. This replaces the paid service formerly provided by Scorpio Marine Electronics Ltd on behalf of Trinity House.

4.2.5   GPS integrity monitoring

Urgent information on GPS is given in BT CRS navigation warning broadcasts on VHF or MF, and by any Navtex station under message category J.

Information is also obtainable from the US Coast Guard GPS Information Centre (GPSIC) on ☎ 00 1 703 313 5907 which gives a pre-recorded daily status message. GPSIC duty personnel can be contacted on ☎ 00 1 703 313 5900.

4.3   HYPERBOLIC SYSTEMS

4.3.1   Decca

The Decca Navigator System is a very accurate short- to medium-range hyperbolic fixing system ideally suited to coastal and landfall navigation. Good coverage is available over the UK and the European coastline to a range of approximately 400M by day, and 250M by night. The six UK Decca Chains are unlikely to continue in operation beyond the year 2000. Decca Chains available in the UK and NW Europe are shown on Fig. 4(3).

The principle on which Decca works is the accurate measurement of the time difference taken by radio waves travelling between at least two transmitters. This is achieved by measuring the phase differences.

Radio wave propagation is affected by weather, season, radio noise, time of day and night, terrain over which the radio waves pass, and range from transmitters. Decca errors are mostly quite small, but are present and can have navigational significance. A good tip is to treat all Decca positions with extreme caution whenever your TV picture at home is distorted by abnormal radio propagation conditions. Such conditions are quite frequent whenever atmospheric pressure is approximately 10 Millibars (Mbs) higher than the average. Average Mean Sea Level pressure during the month of July would be approximately 1017 Mbs in the English Channel and 1012 Mbs in Scotland. Therefore, if the barometer reads 1030 Mbs abnormal radio propagation is likely to occur.

There are two main types of error:

(1) *Fixed errors:* resulting from variations in the velocity of radio waves over different types of terrain, or the presence of land between transmitter and receiver. The effect of fixed errors can be very pronounced when close to the coast. Fixed errors are constant at any given location. Racal-Decca publishes data sheets giving fixed error corrections for each Decca Chain but unfortunately these are in a form which can only be applied to large ship receivers using Decca co-ordinates, rather than latitude/longitude. It is not possible to apply fixed error corrections to yacht receivers which only give a latitude/longitude read-out.

(2) *Variable errors:* are due to the effect of skywave/groundwave interference and to the other factors mentioned above. Generally speaking, conditions are worse on winter nights than in summer and errors are bigger at the extremities of the coverage area than in the centre.

For practical navigation purposes it is unwise to assume an accuracy of better than 0·25M at ranges of 50-100M from transmitters, and up to 1·5M or more at the limits of coverage, especially when abnormal propagation conditions are present.

4.3.2   Loran-C

Loran-C is a long-range hyperbolic system suitable for coastal and offshore navigation within coverage. It provides continuous fixing and the groundwave can be received at ranges of 800-1200M. Loran-C pulses also propagate as skywaves which may be received at much greater range, but with much less accuracy.

Four new Loran-C Chains provide extensive coverage over North-West Europe, and the British Isles. See Fig. 4(4).

The basic principle on which Loran-C works is the accurate measurement of the time difference in the arrival of pulse signals transmitted from a Master and Secondary station. Loran Chains consist of three to five transmitters and operate in sequenced pairs. The time difference obtained from each pair of transmitters determines an exclusive hyperbolic curve of constant time difference and the intersection of two or more curves produces the fix. Loran-C radio wave propagation is affected by conditions similar to those already described for Decca. Several factors can affect overall system accuracy such as the type of terrain over which the radio waves pass, range from transmitters, system geometry, weather, electronic noise, angle of cut of position lines and gradient, and synchronisation errors between transmitters. Using the groundwave system, accuracy varies from about 100m at a range of 200M from transmitters, to 250m to 1M or more at 500M range.

4.4   WAYPOINTS

4.4.1   Waypoint navigation

A waypoint can be any point chosen by a navigator such as a departure point or destination, any selected position along the intended route where it is proposed to alter course, a point at a selected distance off a headland or lighthouse, a buoy, or any other position in the open sea. Always study the chart first and plot the position of any planned waypoint before loading the co-ordinates into electronic equipment. This ensures that any projected route will not take you across shallows, into danger, or even across land. It is usual to tag either a number or name to waypoint co-ordinates. A waypoint listing may be assembled in any order required to form a route or sailing plan.

Approximately 3,500 waypoints are given in Chapter 10 for navigational use. They are shown for individual harbour entrances after the harbour name and county (or equivalent abroad) which provides a good final waypoint, and also for harbour approaches under the heading of 'Navigation'. A list of selected waypoints is given in section 4 of each Area (where they are underlined in the lists of 'Coastal Lights, Fog Signals and Waypoints'). For convenience when loading waypoints into electronic equipment, or when passage planning, a tabulated listing of selected waypoints is also given for English Channel (10.1.7), the Solent area (10.2.18), East Anglian (10.4.7), the Clyde (10.9.15), and Southern North Sea (10.20.34).

The tabulated listing gives only the name and position co-ordinates of the waypoint and complements the data given in section 4 of each area.

Latitudes and longitudes are normally stated to one-hundredth of a minute, as taken from a large-scale chart. But it should be realised that a chart using a different datum or based on another survey may give a slightly different position. Charts may also contain small errors, just like the read-out from an electronic instrument.

The greatest care needs to be taken when loading waypoint co-ordinates into electronic equipment.

Fig. 4(3)   DECCA CHAINS – NORTH-WEST EUROPE

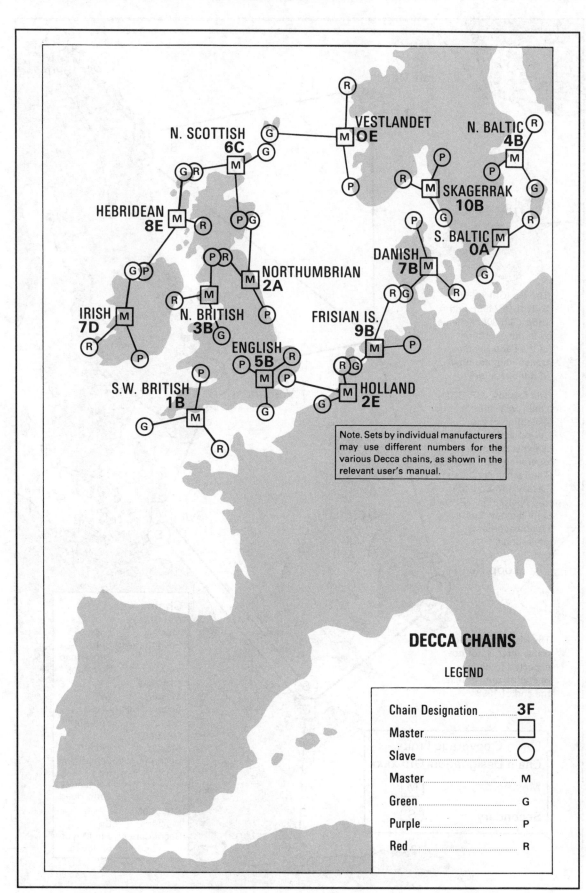

Note. Sets by individual manufacturers may use different numbers for the various Decca chains, as shown in the relevant user's manual.

DECCA CHAINS

LEGEND

Chain Designation	**3F**
Master	☐
Slave	◯
Master	M
Green	G
Purple	P
Red	R

Fig. 4(4)   LORAN-C CHAINS – NORTH-WEST EUROPE

The **Bø** (GRI 7001), **Sylt** (GRI 7499), and **Ejde** (GRI 9007) chains with the exception of the Loop Head transmitter, are now in full operation.

The **Lessay** (GRI 6731) chain, with the exception of the Loop Head transmitter is expected to be in operation from July 1997. The French stations at Lessay and Soustons will operate on GRI 8940 until the new Lessay chain becomes operational.

The Irish Loop Head transmitter is not now expected to be in operation until at least the end of 1998

Loran-C coverage limits – – –
Chain Designation **GRI xxxx**
Master   M
Secondary   S

Chains

GRI 6731
Master: Lessay
Secondaries: Sylt
                       Loop Head
                       Soustons

GRI 7499
Master: Sylt
Secondaries: Lessay
                       Værlandet

GRI 9007
Master: Ejde
Secondaries: Jan Mayen
                       Bø
                       Værlandet
                       Loop Head

GRI 7001
Master: Bø
Secondaries: Jan Mayen
                       Berlevåg

Always check that you have taken the position off the chart correctly. Any error in the entry of latitude/longitude co-ordinates into the receiver will result in navigational error if undetected. It is particularly important to understand the format required to enter data into the receiver. For example, the incorrect placing of the decimal point can result in considerable errors in the calculation of bearing and distance. Another point to watch is whether East or West longitude is assumed by the receiver. Use the ± or other designated key to change the sign from East to West if necessary.

Following the precautions listed below can assist in preventing errors being made when loading waypoints:

(1)   A published waypoint should never be used without first plotting its position on the chart.

(2)   Check that you have taken the latitude/longitude co-ordinates off the chart correctly.

(3)   Check the intended route between waypoints for navigational safety.

(4)   Measure the tracks and distances on the chart and record the results in a simplified passage plan.

(5)   Check that the waypoints have been keyed into the receiver memory correctly.

(6)   Get an independent check if possible.

After loading waypoints check the track and distances between waypoints computed by the receiver against those measured off the chart and shown in the passage plan.

One of the major advantages of modern waypoint navigation technology is its ability to present navigators with a continuous read-out of valuable navigational information in addition to position, such as course and speed made good, along and across-track error, distance and time to go to next waypoint, etc. Probably the most useful of the additional displays, especially with GPS, is the course and speed made good facility where the continuous read-out can be directly compared to the required track.

By comparison with course and speed through the water, the same data can also be used to calculate set and drift quickly. Some receivers allow the presentation of both position and course and speed made good on the same display.

Electronic systems are only aids to navigation and are subject to fixed and variable errors, or on rare occasions even total failure. It is therefore essential to maintain a record in the log of the yacht's position, course and speed from the receiver display and to plot a position on the chart at regular intervals so that you can quickly work up a DR/EP not only to cover the case of equipment failure, but also to ensure that the boat's track is keeping well clear of all dangers. Take great care when using waypoints on shore.

4.5   RDF BEACONS

4.5.1   RDF beacons – general

Radio Direction Finding (RDF) is a simple, but generally inaccurate, method whereby yachtsmen can establish an approximate position using marine or aeronautical RDF beacons and a radio receiver with a directional antenna. With the increasing use of aids such as GPS, Decca and Loran, RDF is now little used and rapidly becoming obsolescent. A number of strategically placed marine RDF beacons have been retained solely to provide a Differential GPS service (DGPS).

Marine and Aeronautical RDF beacons are non-directional and transmit on medium frequencies on a continuous basis. The navigator tunes to the listed frequency, identifies the beacon by its Morse ident (13 secs) followed by a long dash (47 secs) during which time the DF antenna is rotated until it registers the minimum or null signal. The antenna position, usually associated with a compass, then indicates the direction of the beacon.

4.5.2   Types of emission (Modes)

All marine RDF beacons transmit using A1A emission. This means transmissions are unmodulated and need a DF receiver with a built-in oscillator, called a Beat Frequency Oscillator (BFO), to be switched ON in order to receive the A1A transmissions and identify the beacon.

Aeronautical RDF beacons mostly use Non-A2A emissions which require the BFO to be switched ON for DF use, and OFF to identify the station. As individual RDF receivers vary it is necessary to consult the manufacturer's handbook for precise instructions on the use of the BFO switch.

4.5.3   RDF beacons incorporating distance finding

The RDF beacons at Castle Breakwater, St Peter Port, Guernsey and La Corbière light, Jersey, allow radio and sound signals to be synchronised for distance finding. The two signals are synchronised at an easily identifiable point in the cycle, e.g. at the start or end of a long dash.

Using a stopwatch, the difference between the two times in seconds, multiplied by 0·18, gives the distance from the horn in miles.

The system at La Corbière involves the transmission of a number of measuring signals or pips, started when the fog signal is sounded. The number of pips received before the horn is heard indicates the distance. Each pip received corresponds to a distance of 335m from the light.

4.5.4   Errors in radio bearings

The various errors to which radio bearings are subject are described in Chapter 4 of *The Macmillan & Silk*

Cut Yachtsman's Handbook. They fall into two categories – signal errors (caused by distance from the beacon, night or skywave effect particularly near sunset and sunrise, land effect or coastal refraction where the beam passes over high ground or along the coast, and synchronised transmissions of two beacons), and errors on board the boat (caused by quadrantal error due to magnetic objects re-radiating the incoming signal, compass error, the possibility of inadvertently taking a reciprocal bearing, and operating error due to inexperience or bad weather). Do not rely on radio bearings exclusively, unless three or more give an acceptable cocked hat.

4.5.5 RDF beacons – calibration

A DF set can be calibrated for quadrantal error by taking simultaneous radio and visual bearings of a beacon on different headings. Alternatively, radio bearings may be taken from a known position, and the bearing of the beacon taken from the chart. To save time it is helpful if the beacon transmits continuously. A selection of RDF beacons which provide a calibration service are shown in Table 4(1).

4.6   VHF DIRECTION FINDING

4.6.1 VHF emergency DF service

The stations listed operate a VHF DF service for emergency use only (see Fig. 4 (7)). The position of VHF DF sites is shown on maps or charts by the symbol ⓞ$_{RG}$.

UK stations are controlled by a Coastguard MRCC or MRSC as shown in brackets. On request from a yacht in distress, the station transmits her bearing *from the DF site.* Watch is kept on Ch 16. A yacht should transmit on Ch 16 (Distress only) or on Ch 67 (Ch 67 for Guernsey or 82 for Jersey, or on Ch 11 for French stations) to allow the station to determine its bearing, which is then passed back to the vessel on the same frequency.

In France, CROSS stations keep watch on Ch 16, 11, 67. Other Signal Stations or Naval Lookout Stations equipped with VHF DF keep watch on Ch 16 and other continuously scanned frequencies, which include Ch 36, 39, 48, 50, 52, 55, 56 and 60-88.

VHF DF Stations

St Mary's	(Falmouth)	49°55'·7N 06°18'·2W
Land's End	(Falmouth)	50°08'·2N 05°38'·2W
Falmouth	(Falmouth)	50°08'·7N 05°02'·7W
Rame Head	(Brixham)	50°19'·0N 04°13'·1W
Prawle	(Brixham)	50°13'·1N 03°42'·5W
Berry Head	(Brixham)	50°23'·9N 03°29'·0W
Grove Point	(Portland)	50°32'·9N 02°25'·1W
Hengistbury Head	(Portland)	50°42'·9N 01°45'·6W
Boniface	(Solent)	50°36'·2N 01°12'·0W
Selsey	(Solent)	50°43'·8N 00°48'·2W
Newhaven	(Solent)	50°46'·9N 00°03'·1E
Fairlight	(Dover)	50°52'·2N 00°38'·8E
Langdon Battery	(Dover)	51°07'·9N 01°20'·7E
North Foreland	(Dover)	51°22'·5N 01°26'·8E
Shoeburyness	(Thames)	51°31'·4N 00°46'·7E
Bawdsey	(Thames)	51°59'·6N 01°24'·6E
Trimingham	(Yarmouth)	52°54'·6N 01°20'·7E
Hunstanton	(Yarmouth)	52°56'·9N 00°29'·7E
Caister	(Yarmouth)	52°39'·6N 01°43'·0E
Easington	(Humber)	53°39'·1N 00°06'·0E
Flamborough	(Humber)	54°07'·1N 00°05'·1W
Whitby	(Humber)	54°29'·4N 00°36'·3W
Hartlepool	(Tyne Tees)	54°41'·8N 01°10'·5W
Tynmouth	(Tyne Tees)	55°01'·1N 01°24'·9W
Newton	(Tyne Tees)	55°31'·0N 01°37'·1W
Crosslaw	(Forth)	55°54'·5N 02°12'·2W
Fife Ness	(Forth)	56°16'·8N 02°35'·3W
Inverbervie	(Aberdeen)	56°51'·1N 02°15'·7W
Windyhead	(Aberdeen)	57°38'·9N 02°14'·5W
Compass Head	(Shetland)	59°52'·1N 01°16'·3W
Thrumster	(Pentland)	58°23'·6N 03°07'·3W
Dunnett Head	(Pentland)	58°40'·3N 03°22'·5W
Wideford Hill	(Pentland)	58°59'·3N 03°01'·4W
Sandwick	(Stornoway)	58°12'·7N 06°21'·3W
Barra	(Stornoway)	57°00'·8N 07°30'·4W
Rodel	(Stornoway)	57°44'·9N 06°57'·4W
Tiree	(Oban)	56°30'·6N 06°57'·7W
Kilchiaran	(Clyde)	55°45'·9N 06°27'·2W
Law Hill	(Clyde)	55°41'·8N 04°50'·5W
Snaefell	(Liverpool)	54°15'·8N 04°27'·6W
Walney Island	(Liverpool)	54°06'·6N 03°15'·9W
Great Ormes Head	(Holyhead)	53°20'·0N 03°51'·1W
Rhiw	(Holyhead)	52°50'·0N 04°37'·7W
St Ann's Head	(Milford Haven)	51°41'·0N 05°10'·5W
Hartland	(Swansea)	51°01'·2N 04°31'·3W
Trevose Head	(Falmouth)	50°32'·9N 05°01'·9W
Orlock Head	(Belfast)	54°40'·4N 05°35'·0W
West Torr	(Belfast)	55°11'·9N 06°05'·6W
Guernsey	–	49°26'·3N 02°35'·8W
Jersey	–	49°10'·9N 02°14'·3W

France

Gris Nez	(CROSS)	50°52'·2N 01°35'·0E
Jobourg	(CROSS)	49°41'·1N 01°54'·6W
Roches Douvres	(CROSS)	49°06'·5N 02°48'·8W
Fécamp	(Signal Stn)	49°46'·1N 00°22'·2E
Bréhat	(Signal Stn)	48°51'·3N 03°00'·1W
Batz	(Signal Stn)	44°48'·4N 04°00'·6W
Créac'h	(CROSS)	48°27'·6N 05°07'·7W
Pointe du Raz	(Signal Stn)	48°02'·3N 04°43'·8W
Étel	(CROSS)	47°39'·8N 03°12'·0W

Fig. 4(5) VHF EMERGENCY DF SERVICE

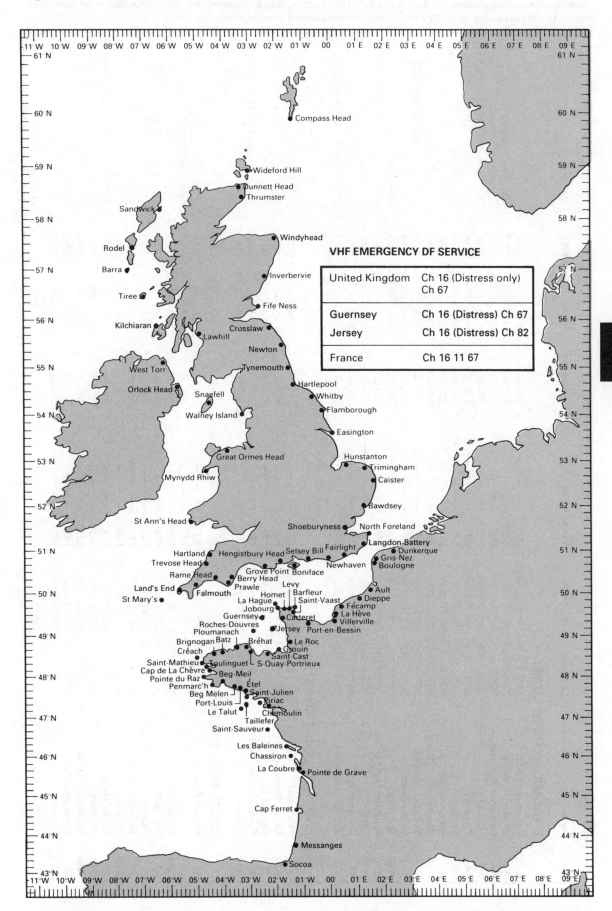

VHF EMERGENCY DF SERVICE

United Kingdom	Ch 16 (Distress only) Ch 67
Guernsey	Ch 16 (Distress) Ch 67
Jersey	Ch 16 (Distress) Ch 82
France	Ch 16 11 67

TABLE 4(1)   MARINE AND AERONAUTICAL RDF BEACONS

Note: Beacon numbers prefixed with A are Aeronautical RDF beacons. Some marine beacons also provide differential corrections for the satellite navigation system GPS (DGPS) which are transmitted on an additional signal.

No	Name	Latitude	Longitude	Morse Ident	Frequency	Mode	Range	Notes
	ENGLAND – SOUTH COAST							
1	Round Island Lt	49°58'.70N	06°19'.33W	RR	298.50	A1A	150M	
A2	St Mary's, Scilly	49°54'.82N	06°17'.43W	STM	321.00	Nøn A2A	15M	Day service: Mon-Sat
A4	Penzance Heliport	50°07'.67N	05°31'.00W	PH	333.00	Nøn A2A	15M	Day service: Mon-Sat
3	Lizard Lt	49°57'.58N	05°12'.07W	LZ	284.50	A1A	70M	DGPS service 284.00 kHz 100M
A6	Plymouth	50°25'.37N	04°06'.67W	PY	396.50	Nøn A2A	20M	
A8	Exeter	50°45'.12N	03°17'.62W	EX	337.00	Nøn A2A	15M	Day service
5	Portland Bill	50°30'.82N	02°27'.30W	PB	309.50	A1A	50M	
A10	Bournemouth/Hurn	50°46'.63N	01°50'.47W	BIA	339.00	Nøn A2A	20M	Day service
7	St Catherine's Pt	50°34'.52N	01°17'.80W	CP	293.00	A1A	50M	DGPS service 294.00 kHz 100M
A12	Bembridge	50°40'.78N	01°06'.18W	IW	426.00	Nøn A2A	15M	Day service
A14	Shoreham	50°49'.89N	00°17'.75W	SHM	332.00	Nøn A2A	10M	
9	Brighton Marina	50°48'.67N	00°05'.95W	BM	294.50	A1A	10M	
A16	Lydd	50°58'.23N	00°57'.30E	LYX	397.00	Nøn A2A	15M	
11	Dungeness Lt	50°54'.77N	00°58'.67E	DU	300.50	A1A	50M	
13	North Foreland Lt	51°22'.49N	01°26'.85E	NF	311.00	A1A	50M	DGPS service 310.50 kHz 100M
	ENGLAND – EAST COAST							
A18	Southend	51°34'.55N	00°42'.12E	SND	362.50	Nøn A2A	20M	
A20	Great Yarmouth	52°38'.10N	01°43'.73E	ND	417.00	Nøn A2A	10M	
15	Cromer Lt	52°55'.45N	01°19'.10E	CM	313.50	A1A	50M	
17	Flamborough Head Lt	54°06'.95N	00°04'.87W	FB	303.00	A1A	70M	DGPS service 302.50 kHz 100M
A22	Teeside	54°33'.57N	01°20'.03W	TD	347.50	Nøn A2A	25M	
	SCOTLAND – EAST COAST							
19	Souter Point Lt	54°58'.23N	01°21'.80W	SJ	292.00	A1A	50M	
				PT	294.50	A1A	5M	Calibration station
A24	Edinburgh	55°58'.72N	03°17'.03W	EDN	341.00	Nøn A2A	35M	
21	Inchkeith	56°02'.02N	03°08'.08W	NK	286.50	A1A	10M	
23	Fidra Lt	56°04'.40N	02°47'.02W	FD	290.00	A1A	15M	
25	Fife Ness Lt	56°16'.73N	02°35'.10W	FP	305.00	A1A	50M	
A26	Dundee	56°27'.30N	03°06'.83W	DND	394.00	Nøn A2A	25M	
27	Girdle Ness	57°08'.32N	02°02'.83W	GD	311.00	A1A	50M	DGPS service 311.50 kHz 100M
A28	Aberdeen	57°16'.13N	02°24'.18W	AOS	377.00	Nøn A2A	25M	
A30	Scotstown Head	57°33'.56N	01°48'.94W	SHD	383.00	Nøn A2A	80M	
29	Kinnards Head	57°41'.87N	02°00'.13W	KD	301.50	A1A	50M	
A32	Kinloss	57°39'.04N	03°35'.13W	KS	370.00	Nøn A2A	20M	

No.	Name	Latitude	Longitude	Ident	Freq kHz	Type	Range	Notes
A34	Wick	58°26'.83N	03°03'.70W	WIK	344.00	Nøn A2A	30M	
31	Duncansby Head	58°38'.67N	03°01'.42W	DY	290.50	A1A	50M	
A36	Kirkwall	58°58'.67N	02°54'.62W	KW	395.00	Nøn A2A	30M	
33	Sumburgh Head	59°51'.30N	01°16'.37W	SB	304.00	A1A	70M	DGPS service 304.00 kHz 150M
A38	Lerwick/Tingwall	60°11'.33N	01°14'.67W	TL	376.00	Nøn A2A	25M	
A40	Scatsa	60°27'.68N	01°12'.78W	SS	315.50	Nøn A2A	25M	Day service
A42	Unst	60°44'.33N	00°49'.17W	UT	325.00	Nøn A2A	20M	

SCOTLAND – WEST COAST

No.	Name	Latitude	Longitude	Ident	Freq kHz	Type	Range	Notes
37	Butt of Lewis	58°30'.93N	06°15'.72W	BL	289.00	A1A	70M	DGPS service 289.50 kHz 40M
A52	Stornoway	58°12'.86N	06°19'.49W	SAY	669.50	Nøn A2A	20M	
A54	St Kilda	57°49'.00N	08°35'.00W	KL	338.00	Nøn A2A	30M	
A56	Barra	57°01'.40N	07°26'.40W	BRR	316.00	Nøn A2A	20M	Occasl
A58	North Connel/Oban	56°27'.83N	05°23'.62W	CNL	404.00	Nøn A2A	15M	
39	Rhinns of Islay	55°40'.38N	06°30'.70W	RN	293.00	A1A	70M	
A60	Islay/Port Ellen	55°40'.98N	06°14'.90W	LAY	395.00	Nøn A2A	20M	
41	Cloch Point Lt	55°56'.53N	04°52'.67W	CL	300.00	A1A	8M	Calibration station. On request
A62	New Galloway	55°10'.63N	04°10'.03W	NGY	399.00	Nøn A2A	35M	

ENGLAND (WEST COAST), ISLE OF MAN, WALES

No.	Name	Latitude	Longitude	Ident	Freq kHz	Type	Range	Notes
A66	Carnane	54°08'.46N	04°29'.42W	CAR	366.50	Nøn A2A	25M	
A68	Ronaldsway/IOM	54°05'.15N	04°36'.45W	RWY	359.00	Nøn A2A	20M	
43	Walney Island	54°02'.92N	03°10'.55W	FN	306.00	A1A	50M	
A70	Barrow/Walney Island	54°07'.64N	03°15'.80W	WL	385.00	Nøn A2A	15M	
A72	Blackpool	53°46'.36N	03°01'.59W	BPL	420.00	Nøn A2A	15M	
A74	Warton	53°45'.09N	02°51'.05W	WTN	337.00	Nøn A2A	15M	Day service
45	Point Lynas Lt	53°24'.97N	04°17'.30W	PS	304.00	A1A	50M	DGPS service 305.00 kHz 100M
A76	Aberporth	52°06'.92N	04°33'.57W	AP	370.50	Nøn A2A	20M	
47	South Bishop Lt	51°51'.15N	05°24'.65W	SB	290.50	A1A	70M	Day service
A78	Swansea	51°36'.10N	04°03'.88W	SWN	320.50	Nøn A2A	15M	
A80	Cardiff/Rhoose	51°23'.57N	03°20'.23W	CDF	388.50	Nøn A2A	20M	
49	Nash Point Lt	51°24'.03N	03°33'.06W	NP	299.50	A1A	50M	DGPS service 299.00 kHz 100M
51	Lynemouth Foreland Lt	51°14'.70N	03°47'.13W	FP	294.50	A1A	5M	Calibration station. SR+1 to SS−1 hr
A82	St Mawgan	50°26'.51N	04°59'.36W	SM	356.50	Nøn A2A	20M	

4

CHANNEL ISLANDS

Ref	Name	Latitude	Longitude	Ident	Morse	kHz	Emission	Range	Remarks
A86	Alderney	49°42'·58N	02°11'·90W	ALD	.- .-.. -..	383·00	Nøn A2A	30M	DGPS service 300·50 kHz 100M
55	Castle Breakwater, St Peter Port❶	49°27'·37N	02°31'·37W	GY	--. -.--	304·50	A1A	10M	

❶ Synchronised with horn for distance finding. Horn begins simultaneously with 27 sec long dash after the four GY ident signals. Time in secs from start of long dash until horn is heard, multiplied by 0·18 gives dist in M.

Ref	Name	Latitude	Longitude	Ident	Morse	kHz	Emission	Range	Remarks
A88	Guernsey	49°26'·12N	02°38'·30W	GRB	--. .-. -...	361·00	Nøn A2A	30M	
57	La Corbière Lt❶❷	49°10'·85N	02°14'·90W	CB	-.-. -...	295·50	A1A	20M	

❶ For details of coded wind information see 7.2.15.
❷ Synchronised for distance finding. The beacon transmits on a 6 min cycle. The 6th minute signal consists of: CB 3 times, 26 sec long dash, followed by a series of pips. Horn blast (Morse 'C') begins with end of 26 sec long dash. Each pip heard before the blast corresponds to a distance of 335m from the light.

Ref	Name	Latitude	Longitude	Ident	Morse	kHz	Emission	Range	Remarks
A90	Jersey West	49°12'·37N	02°13'·30W	JW	.--- .--	329·00	Nøn A2A	25M	

IRELAND

Ref	Name	Latitude	Longitude	Ident	Morse	kHz	Emission	Range	Remarks
63	Mizen Head Lt	51°27'·05N	09°48'·80W	MZ	-- --..	300·00	A1A	100M	DGPS service 300·50 kHz 100M
65	Old Head of Kinsale Lt	51°36'·27N	08°31'·97W	OH	---	288·00	A1A	50M	Calibration station. On request
				KC	-.- -.-.	294·50	A1A	5M	
A100	Waterford	52°11'·83N	07°05'·33W	WTD	.-- - -..	368·00	Nøn A2A	25M	
67	Tuskar Rock Lt	52°12'·15N	06°12'·38W	TR	- .-.	286·00	A1A	50M	Calibration station. On request
A102	Killiney/Dublin	53°16'·17N	06°06'·33W	KLY	-.- .-.. -.--	378·00	Nøn A2A	50M	
69	Baily	53°21'·68N	06°03'·09W	BY	-... -.--	289·00	A1A	50M	
				BC	-... -.-.	286·50	A1A	5M	
A104	Rush/Dublin	53°30'·73N	06°06'·60W	RSH	.-.	326·00	Nøn A2A	30M	
71	South Rock Lt F	54°24'·47N	05°21'·92W	SU	... ..-	291·50	A1A	50M	
A106	Belfast City	54°36'·94N	05°52'·86W	HB	.... -...	420·00	Nøn A2A	15M	Calibration station. On request
73	Black Head (Antrim)	54°46'·01N	05°41'·30W	BA	-... .-	294·50	A1A	5M	
A108	Eglinton/Londonderry	55°02'·70N	07°09'·25W	EGT	. --. -	328·50	Nøn A2A	25M	
75	Tory Island Lt	55°16'·35N	08°14'·72W	TY	- -.--	313·00	A1A	100M	DGPS service 313·50 kHz 100M
77	Eagle Island Lt	54°16'·98N	10°05'·52W	GL	--. .-..	307·00	A1A	100M	
A110	Sligo	54°16'·70N	08°35'·92W	SLG	... .-.. --.	384·00	Nøn A2A	25M	
A112	Galway/Carnmore	53°18'·05N	08°56'·50W	CRN	-.-. .-. -.	321·00	Nøn A2A	25M	
A114	Ennis	52°54'·27N	08°55'·62W	ENS	. -. ...	352·00	Nøn A2A	80M	
A116	Foynes	52°33'·97N	09°11'·67W	FOY	..-. --- -.--	395·00	Nøn A2A	50M	
79	Loop Head Lt	52°33'·65N	09°55'·90W	LP	.-.. .--.	311·50	A1A	50M	DGPS service 312·00 kHz 100M

Fig. 4(6)   RDF BEACONS –
BRITISH ISLES

Fig. 4(7) RDF BEACONS –
CHANNEL ISLES AND NORTH-WEST EUROPE

FRANCE – NORTH COAST

No.	Name	Lat	Long	Ident	Morse	Freq (kHz)	Emission	Range	Notes
91	Cherbourg W Fort Lt	49°40'·50N	01°38'·87W	RB	·-· -···	302·00	A1A	20M	
A92	Granville	48°55'·10N	01°28'·87W	GV	--· ···-	321·00	A1A	25M	
93	Le Grand Jardin Lt	48°40'·27N	02°04'·90W	GJ	--· ·---	306·50	A1A	10M	
95	Cap Fréhel Lt	48°41'·10W	02°19'·07W	FÉ	··-·	286·50	A1A	20M	
97	Roches–Douvres Lt	49°06'·47N	02°48'·65W	RD	·-· -··	308·00	A1A	70M	
99	Rosédo Lt, île Bréhat	48°51'·51N	03°00'·21W	DO	-·· ---	287·50	A1A	10M	
A94	Lannion	48°43'·25N	03°18'·45W	LN	·-·· -·	345·00	A1A	50M	
101	Roscoff–Bloscon Jetty Lt	48°43'·27N	03°57'·59W	BC	-··· -·-·	304·50	A1A	10M	
A96	Landivisiau	48°32'·80W	04°08'·25W	LDV	·-·· -·· ···-	324·00	A1A	60M	
103	île Vierge Lt	48°38'·38N	04°33'·97W	VG	···- --·	314·00	A1A	70M	
105	Ouessant SW Lanby	48°31'·20N	05°49'·10W	SW	··· ·--	305·50	A1A	10M	

FRANCE – WEST COAST

No.	Name	Lat	Long	Ident	Morse	Freq (kHz)	Emission	Range	Notes
111	île d'Ouessant	48°27'·62N	05°07'·65W	CA	-·-· ·-	301·00	A1A	100M	DGPD service 291·50 kHz (planned)
113	Pointe St Mathieu Lt	48°19'·85N	04°46'·17W	SM	··· --	291·00	A1A	50M	
A100	Lanvéoc, Poulmic	48°17'·07N	04°26'·00W	BST	-··· ··· -	428·00	A1A	80M	
115	île de Sein NW Lt	48°02'·70N	04°51'·95W	SN	··· -·	289·50	A1A	70M	
117	Eckmühl Lt	47°47'·95N	04°22'·95W	ÜH	··-- ····	312·00	A1A	50M	DGPS service 312·50 kHz 40M
119	Pointe de Combrit Lt	47°51'·92N	04°06'·70W	CT	-·-· -	288·50	A1A	20M	
A102	Quimper/Pluguffan	47°58'·10N	03°59'·80W	QR	--·- ·-·	380·00	A1A		
121	Pen Men Lt, île de Groix	47°38'·97N	03°30'·36W	GX	--· -··-	298·00	A1A	50M	
A104	St Nazaire/Montoir	47°20'·02N	02°02'·57W	MT	-- -	398·00	A1A	50M	
123	Pointe de St Gildas	47°08'·10N	02°14'·67W	NZ	-· --··	308·50	A1A	40M	
125	île d'Yeu Main Lt	46°43'·10N	02°22'·90W	YE	-·-- ·	303·00	A1A	100M	
127	Les Balines Lt (île de Ré)	46°14'·70N	01°33'·60W	BN	-··· -·	299·00	A1A	40M	DGPS service 299·50 kHz 40M
129	La Rochelle	46°08'·97N	01°10'·27W	RE	·-· ·	295·50	A1A	40M	
131	Pointe de la Coubre	45°41'·87N	01°13'·93W	LK	·-·· -·-	292·00	A1A	100M	
A106	Cognac/Châteaubernard	45°40'·13N	00°18'·53W	CGC	-·-· --· -·-·	354·00	A1A	75M	
A108	Bordeaux/Mérignac	44°55'·92N	00°33'·88W	BD	-··· -··	393·00	A1A	30M	
133	Cap Ferret Lt	44°38'·77N	01°14'·81W	FT	··-· -	286·50	A1A	100M	DGPS service 287·00 kHz 40M
A110	Biarritz	43°28'·25N	01°24'·18W	BZ	-··· --··	341·00	A1A	35M	
A112	Cazaux	44°33'·08N	01°07'·13W	CAA	-·-· ·- ·-	382·00	A1A	80M	Day service

SPAIN – NORTH COAST

No.	Name	Lat	Long	Ident	Morse	Freq (kHz)	Emission	Range	Notes
A114	San Sebastian	43°23'·25N	01°47'·65W	HIG	···· ·· --·	328·00	N0N A2A	50M	
135	Cabo Machichaco Lt	43°27'·45N	02°45'·08W	MA	-- ·-	284·50	A1A	100M	
A116	Bilbao	43°19'·43N	02°58'·43W	BLO	-··· ·-·· ---	370·00	N0N A2A	70M	
137	Cabo Mayor Lt	43°29'·48N	03°47'·37W	MY	-- -·--	304·50	A1A	100M	

4

FRANCE – NORTH-EAST COAST

No.	Name	Latitude	Longitude	Ident	Morse	kHz	Emission	Range	Remarks
141	Pointe de Barfleur Lt	49°41'·87N	01°15'·87W	FG		297·00	A1A	70M	DGPS service 297·50 kHz
143	Port en Bessin Rear Lt	49°20'·98N	00°45'·48W	BS		290·00	A1A	5M	
A144	Cherbourg/Maupertus	49°38'·30N	01°22'·28W	MP		373·00	A1A	20M	
145	Pointe de Ver Lt	49°20'·47N	00°31'·05W	ER		310·00	A1A	20M	
A146	Le Havre/Octeville	49°35'·75N	00°11'·00E	LHO		346·00	A2A	15M	
149	Pointe d'Ailly Lt	49°55'·00N	00°57'·55E	AL		305·50	A1A	50M	
A148	Le Touquet/Paris Plage	50°32'·23N	01°35'·38E	LT		358·00	A2A	20M	
151	Cap d'Alprech Lt	50°41'·95N	01°33'·83E	PH		294·00	A1A	20M	
153	Calais Main Lt	50°57'·73N	01°51'·30E	CS		312·50	A1A	20M	
A150	St Inglevert	50°52'·98N	01°44'·55E	ING		387·50	A1A	50M	
A152	Calais/Dunkirk	50°59'·88N	02°03'·36E	MK		418·00	A1A	15M	Day service

BELGIUM

No.	Name	Latitude	Longitude	Ident	Morse	kHz	Emission	Range	Remarks
161	Nieuwpoort W Pier Lt	51°09'·40N	02°43'·08E	NP		285·00	A1A	5M	
163	Oostende Rear Lt	51°14'·36N	02°55'·94E	OE		312·00	A1A	40M	DGPS service 311·50 kHz 38M
165	Zeebrugge	51°21'·66N	03°11'·33E	ZB		289·00	A1A	5M	

NETHERLANDS

No.	Name	Latitude	Longitude	Ident	Morse	kHz	Emission	Range	Remarks
171	Goeree Lt	51°55'·53N	03°40'·18E	GR		296·00	A1A	48M	
173	Hoek van Holland	51°58'·90N	04°06'·83E	HH		288·00	A1A	50M	DGPS service 287·50 kHz 40M
175	IJmuiden Front Lt	52°27'·75N	04°34'·55E	YM		288·50	A1A	20M	
177	Eierland Lt	53°10'·97N	04°51'·40E	ER		301·00	A1A	20M	
179	Vlieland Lt	53°17'·80N	05°03'·57E	VL		303·50	A1A	20M	DGPS service 299·50 kHz 40M
181	Ameland Lt	53°27'·02N	05°37'·60E	AD		299·00	A1A	50M	

GERMANY

No.	Name	Latitude	Longitude	Ident	Morse	kHz	Emission	Range	Remarks
187	Borkum, Kleiner Lt	53°34'·78N	06°40'·09E	BE		302·00	A1A	20M	
189	German Bight Lt V	54°10'·80N	07°27'·60E	GB		312·00	A1A	10M	
191	Wangerooge Lt	53°47'·45N	07°51'·52E	WE		309·50	A1A	20M	
193	Düne	54°11'·20N	07°54'·38E						DGPS service 313·00 kHz 38M
195	Alte Weser Lt	53°51'·85N	08°07'·72E	AR		309·00	A1A	20M	
197	Elbe Lt F	54°00'·00N	08°06'·58E	EL		298·00	A1A	10M	
A180	Jever	53°31'·18N	08°00'·92E	JEV		390·00	Nøn A1A	50M	
A182	Glukstadt	53°51'·07N	09°27'·32E	GLX		365·00	Nøn A2A	30M	
A184	Nordholz	53°47'·18N	08°48'·47E	NDO		372·00	Nøn A2A	30M	
A186	Westerland/Sylt	54°51'·45N	08°24'·67E	SLT		387·00	Nøn A2A	25M	

4.7   RADAR

4.7.1   Radar in yachts

Radar is useful both for navigation and for collision avoidance, but to take full advantage of it and to use it in safety demands a proper understanding of its operation and of its limitations. Read the instruction book carefully, and practise using and adjusting the set so as to get optimum performance in different conditions. It is important to learn how to interpret what is seen on the display.

Radar beams do not discriminate so well in bearing as they do in range — so an accurate fix is sometimes best obtained by a radar range and a visual bearing of the same object.

The effective range of radar is approximately line of sight, but this can be decreased or increased by abnormal conditions. It is necessary to be aware that radar will not detect a low-lying coastline which is over the radar horizon.

The details of radar and its use are described in *The Macmillan & Silk Cut Yachtsman's Handbook* (4.6).

4.7.2   Radar for collision avoidance

Yacht radars invariably have a ship's head up display, with the boat at the centre, apparently stationary. If a target is moving in the same direction and at the same speed, it is stationary relative to own ship, and its echo should be sharp and well defined. If it is on a reciprocal course, it paints an echo with a long tail.

If an echo is on a steady bearing, and the range is decreasing, there is risk of collision. But to determine the proper action to take it is necessary to plot an approaching echo three or four times, in order to determine her actual course and speed, and how close she will actually approach.

4.7.3   Radar as a navigation aid

Radar cannot see behind other objects, or round corners; it may not pick up small objects, or differentiate between two targets that are close together. As already stated, radar ranges are more accurate than radar bearings. Objects with sharp features such as buildings give a better reflection than those with curved or sloping surfaces. High cliffs make a good target, but low coastlines should be approached with extreme caution as the first thing to show on radar may be hills some distance inland.

4.7.4   Radar beacons (Racons)

A Racon is a transponder beacon which, when triggered by a transmission from a vessel's radar, sends back a distinctive signal which appears on the vessel's radar display. Racons are fitted to some light-vessels, buoys and lighthouses, and are marked on charts by a magenta circle and the word Racon.

In most cases the Racon flash on the display is a line extending radially outwards from a point slightly beyond the actual position of the Racon, due to the slight delay in the response of the beacon apparatus. Thus the distance to the mark of the Racon flash is a little more than the vessel's real distance from the Racon. Some Racons give a flash composed of a Morse identification signal, often with a tail to it, the length of the tail depending on the number of Morse characters.

The maximum range of a radar beacon is usually about 10 nautical miles, but may be more. In practice, picking up a Racon at greater distances depends also on the effective range of the boat's radar. With abnormal radio propagation, a spurious Racon flash may be seen at much greater distances than the beacon's normal range, appearing at any random position along the correct bearing on the display. Only rely on a Racon flash if its appearance is consistent, and the boat is believed to be within its range. At short range a Racon sometimes causes unwelcome interference on the radar display, and this may be reduced by adjusting the rain clutter control on the set.

The characteristics of radar beacons around the coasts of Great Britain are given in Table 4(2). Details are arranged in the following columns:

(1)   Reference number.
(2)   The type of radar beacon. Unless otherwise stated, all radar beacons sweep the frequency range of marine 3cm (X-band) radar emissions. The older type of radar beacon (swept frequency Racons) take 30 to 90 seconds to sweep the band and the period of sweep is adjusted during installation to suit the individual location.

The newer type of radar beacon (agile frequency Racon) responds immediately to radar interrogations. However, in order that wanted echoes should not be obscured by the Racon signal, the agile response is switched 'on' and 'off' at a predetermined rate to suit the installation. Where indicated, radar beacons respond to both 10cm (S-band) and 3cm (X-band) emissions and are usually agile frequency Racons.
(3)   Name of the station.
(4)   Latitude and longitude.
(5)   The sector within which signals may be received, bearings being towards the beacon, clockwise from 000° to 359°. 360° indicates all-round operation.
(6)   Approximate range, in nautical miles. This also depends on the range of the yacht's radar set.
(7)   The form of the beacon's flash on the radar display. Morse signals are shown alphabetically, and are often followed by a 'tail'. Racons coded 'D' are used to mark new dangers.

Table 4(2) LIST OF RADAR BEACONS (For heading details see 4.7.4)

(1) No	(2) Type	(3) Name	(4) Lat	Long	(5) Sector	(6) Range	(7) Ident
		GREAT BRITAIN					
1	3 & 10 cm	Bishop Rock Lt	49°52'·33N	06°26'·68W	245°-215°	18M	T
3	3 & 10 cm	Seven Stones Lt V	50°03'·58N	06°04'·28W	360°	15M	O
5	3 & 10 cm	Wolf Rock Lt	49°56'·67N	05°48'·48W	360°	10M	T
7	3 & 10 cm	Eddystone Lt	50°10'·81N	04°15'·87W	360°	10M	T
9	3 & 10cm	Bridge Lt By	50°39'·59N	01°36'·80W		10M	T
11	3 cm	West Bramble Lt By	50°47'·17N	01°18'·57W	360°	3M	T
13	3 & 10 cm	Nab Tower Lt	50°40'·05N	00°57'·07W	360°	10M	T
15	3 & 10 cm	Greenwich Lt V	50°24'·50N	00°00'·00	360°	10M	T
17	3 & 10 cm	Varne Lt V	51°01'·26N	01°24'·01E	360°	10M	T
19	3 & 10 cm	Sandettié Lt V	51°09'·40N	01°47'·20E	360°	10M	T
21	3 & 10 cm	East Goodwin Lt F	51°13'·05N	01°36'·32E	360°	10M	T
23	3 & 10 cm	Inter Bank Lt By	51°16'·45N	01°52'·33E	360°	10M	M
25	3 & 10 cm	NE Goodwin Lt By	51°20'·28N	01°34'·27E	360°	10M	M
27	3 & 10 cm	Dover Strait TSS, F3 Lt V	51°23'·82N	02°00'·62E	360°	10M	T
29	3 cm	Thames Sea Reach Lt By No 1	51°29'·42N	00°52'·67E	360°	10M	T
31	3 cm	Thames Sea Reach Lt By No 7	51°30'·08N	00°37'·15E	360°	10M	T
33	3 & 10 cm	Outer Tongue Lt By	51°30'·78N	01°26'·47E	360°	10M	T
35	3 & 10 cm	Barrow Lt By No 3	51°41'·99N	01°20'·35E	360°	10M	M
37	3 & 10 cm	South Galloper Lt By	51°43'·95N	01°56'·50E	360°	10M	T
39	3 & 10 cm	Sunk Lt F	51°51'·00N	01°35'·00E	360°	10M	T
41	3 & 10 cm	Harwich Channel Lt By No 1	51°56'·11N	01°27'·30E	360°	10M	T
43	3 & 10 cm	Outer Gabbard Lt By	51°57'·80N	02°04'·30E	360°	10M	O
45	3 & 10 cm	N Shipwash Lt By	52°01'·70N	01°38'·38W	360°	10M	M
47	3 & 10 cm	Orfordness Lt	52°05'·01N	01°34'·56E		18M	T
49	3 & 10 cm	Cross Sand Lt By	52°37'·00N	01°59'·25E	360°	10M	T
51	3 & 10 cm	Winterton Old Lt Ho	52°42'·75N	01°41'·82E	360°	10M	T
53	3 & 10 cm	Smiths Knoll Lt By	52°43'·50N	02°18'·00E	360°	10M	T
55	3 & 10 cm	Newarp Lt By	52°48'·35N	01°55'·80E	360°	10M	O
57	3 & 10 cm	Cromer Lt	52°55'·45N	01°19'·10E	360°	25M	O
59	3 & 10 cm	North Haisbro Lt By	53°00'·20N	01°32'·40E	360°	10M	T
61	3 & 10 cm	North Well Lt By	53°03'·00N	00°28'·00E	360°	10M	T
63	3 & 10 cm	Dudgeon Lt By	53°16'·60N	01°17'·00E	360°	10M	O
65	3 & 10 cm	Anglia Field Platform A48/19	53°22'·03N	01°39'·21W	360°	15M	Q
67	3 & 10 cm	Inner Dowsing Lt V	53°19'·50N	00°33'·96E	360°	25M	T
69	3 & 10 cm	Dowsing Platform B1D	53°33'·65N	00°52'·75E	360°	10M	T
71	3cm	Spurn Lt F	53°33'·53N	00°14'·33E	360°	5M	M
73	3 & 10 cm	Humber Lt By	53°36'·72N	01°21'·60E	360°	7M	T
75	3 cm	Tees Fairway By	54°40'·93N	01°06'·37W	360°		B
77	3 & 10 cm	St Abb's Head Lt	55°54'·97N	02°08'·20W	360°	18M	T
77	3 cm	Inchkeith Fairway By	56°03'·50N	03°00'·00W	360°	5M	T
81	3 cm	Forth North Channel Lt By No 7	56°02'·80N	03°10'·87W	360°	5M	T
83	3 & 10 cm	Bell Rock Lt	56°26'·05N	02°23'·07W	360°	18M	M
85	3 & 10 cm	Abertay Lt By	56°27'·44N	02°40'·55W	360°	8M	T
87	3 & 10 cm	Scurdie Ness Lt	56°42'·12N	02°26'·15W	360°	15M	T
89	3 & 10 cm	Girdle Ness Lt	57°08'·35N	02°02'·82W	360°	25M	G
91	3 cm	Aberdeen Fairway By	57°09'·33N	02°01'·85W	360°	7M	T
93	3 & 10 cm	Buchan Ness Lt	57°28'·23N	01°46'·37W	360°	15M	O
95	3 & 10 cm	Rattray Head Lt	57°36'·62N	01°48'·83W	360°	15M	M
97	3 & 10 cm	Kessock Bridge Centre Mark	57°29'·99N	04°13'·71W	360°	6M	K
99	3 cm	Cromarty Firth Fairway By	57°39'·98N	03°54'·10W	360°	5M	M
101	3 & 10 cm	Tarbert Ness Lt	57°51'·92N	03°46'·52W	360°	14-16M	T
103	3 & 10 cm	Platform Chevron Alba	58°03'·20N	01°04'·88E	360°		C
105	3 & 10 cm	Platform Saltire Alpha	58°25'·05N	00°19'·85E	360°		Z
107	3 & 10 cm	Platform Piper Bravo	58°27'·68N	00°15'·07E	360°		N
109	3 & 10 cm	Duncansby Head Lt	58°38'·67N	03°01'·42W	360°	20M	T
111	3 & 10 cm	Lother Rock Lt	58°43'·82N	02°58'·59W	360°	10M	M
113	3 & 10 cm	North Ronaldsay Lt	59°23'·40N	02°22'·80W	360°	10M	T
115	3 & 10 cm	Rumble Rock Bn	60°28'·22N	01°07'·13W	360°	10M	O
117	3 & 10 cm	Gruney Island Lt	60°39'·20N	01°18'·03W	360°	14M	T
119	3 & 10 cm	Ve Skerries Lt	60°22'·40N	01°48'·67W	360°	15M	T
121	3 & 10 cm	Petrojari Foinaven 204/24	60°18'·95N	04°16'·40W			X

(1) No	(2) Type	(3) Name	(4) Lat	Long	(5) Sector	(6) Range	(7) Ident
123	3 & 10 cm	Sule Skerry Lt	59°05'·10N	04°24'·30W	360°	20M	T
125	3 & 10 cm	Eilean Glas Lt	57°51'·43N	06°38'·45W	360°	16M	T
127	3 cm	Ardivvachar	57°22'·90N	07°25'·45W	360°	16M	T
129	3 cm	Carrach Rocks Lt By	57°15'·20N	05°45'·29W	360°	5M	T
131	3 & 10cm	Hyskeir Lt	56°58'·15N	06°40'·80W	360°	14-17M	T
133	3 cm	Castlebay South By	56°56'·10N	07°27'·17W	360°	7M	T
135	3 & 10 cm	Bo Vic Chuan By	56°56'·17N	07°23'·25W	360°	5M	M
137	3 & 10 cm	Oigh Sgeir (Hyskeir) Lt	56°58'·15N	06°40'·80W	360°	14-17M	T
139	3 & 10 cm	Skerryvore Lt	56°19'·40N	07°06'·90W	360°	18M	M
141	3 cm	Dubh Sgeir Lt	56°14'·78N	05°40'·12W	360°	5M	M
143	3 cm	Sanda Lt	55°16'·50N	05°34'·90W	360°	20M	T
145	3 & 10 cm	Point of Ayre Lt	54°24'·95N	04°22'·03W	360°	13M	M
147	3 & 10 cm	Lune Deep Lt By	53°55'·80N	03°11'·00W	360°	10M	T
149	3 & 10 cm	Halfway Shoal Lt Bn	54°01'·46N	03°11'·79W	360°	10M	B
151	3 & 10 cm	Bar Lt F	53°32'·00N	03°20'·90W	360°	10M	T
153	3 & 10 cm	The Skerries Lt	53°25'·27N	04°36'·44W	360°	25M	T
155	3 & 10 cm	The Smalls Lt	51°43'·23N	05°40'·10W	360°	25M	T
157	3 & 10 cm	St Gowan Lt By	51°31'·90N	04°59'·70W	360°	10M	T
159	3 & 10 cm	West Helwick Lt By W. HWK	51°31'·37N	04°23'·58W	360°	10M	T
161	3 & 10 cm	West Scar Lt By (Swansea Bay)	51°28'·28N	03°55'·50W	360°	10M	T
163	3 & 10 cm	English & Welsh Grounds Lt By	51°26'·90N	03°00'·10W	360°	7M	O
165	3 & 10 cm	Breaksea Lt By	51°19'·85N	03°18'·98W	360°	10M	T
167		Second Severn Crossing NE	51°34'·44N	02°41'·93W			O
169		Second Severn Crossing SW	51°34'·42N	02°41'·94W			O

CHANNEL/CHANNEL ISLANDS (see also No.13)

181	3 & 10 cm	Owers Lt By	50°37'·27N	00°40'·60W		10M	O
183	3 & 10 cm	English Channel Lt By EC 1	50°05'·90N	01°48'·35W	360°	10M	T
185	3 & 10 cm	English Channel Lt By EC 2	50°12'·10N	01°12'·40W	360°	10M	T
187	3 & 10 cm	English Channel Lt By EC 3	50°18'·30N	00°36'·10W	360°	10M	T
189	3 & 10 cm	Greenwich Lt V	50°24'·50N	00°00'·00	360°	10M	M
191	3 & 10 cm	East Channel Lt By	49°58'·67N	02°28'·87W	360°	10M	T
193	3 & 10 cm	Channel Lt V	49°54'·42N	02°53'·67W	360°	15M	O
195	3 & 10 cm	Casquets Lt	49°43'·38N	02°22'·55W	360°	25M	T
197	3 cm	Platte Fougère Lt	49°30'·88N	02°29'·05W	360°		P
199	3 cm	St Helier, Demie de Pas Lt	49°09'·07N	02°06'·05W	360°	10M	T
201	3 cm	St Helier, Mont Ubé Ldg Lt	49°10'·35N	02°03'·53W	360°	14M	T

IRELAND

211	3 & 10 cm	Kish Bank Lt	53°18'·68N	05°55'·38W	360°	15M	T
213	3 & 10 cm	Codling Lanby	53°03'·02N	05°40'·70W	360°	10M	G
215	3 cm	Dublin Bay Lt By	53°19'·90N	06°04'·58W			M
217	3 & 10 cm	Arklow Lt By	52°39'·50N	05°58'·10W	360°	10M	O
219	3 & 10 cm	Tuskar Rock Lt	52°12'·15N	06°12'·38W	360°	18M	T
221	3 & 10 cm	Coningbeg Lt V	52°02'·38N	06°39'·45W	360°	13M	M
223	3 & 10 cm	Hook Head Lt	52°07'·40N	06°55'·72W	237°-177°	10M	K
225	3 & 10 cm	Fastnet Lt	51°23'·33N	09°36'·14W	360°	18M	G
227	3 & 10 cm	Cork Lt By	51°42'·90N	08°15'·50W	360°	7M	T
229	3 & 10 cm	Mizen Head Lt	51°26'·97N	09°49'·18W	360°	24M	T
231	3 & 10 cm	Inishtearaght Lt	52°04'·51N	10°39'·64W	313°-221°	18M	O
233	3 & 10 cm	Inisheer Lt	53°02'·78N	09°31'·57 W	216°-144°	13M	K
235	3 & 10 cm	Ballybunnion Lt By	52°32'·50N	09°46'·91W	360°	6M	M
237	3 & 10 cm	Rathlin O'Birne Lt	54°39'·80N	08°49'·90W	284°-203°	13M	O
239	3 & 10 cm	Tory I Lt	55°16'·35N	08°14'·92W	360°	12-23M	M
241	3 & 10 cm	Inishtrahull Lt	55°25'·85N	07°14'·60W	060°-310°[1]	24M	T

[1] Reduced or no signal 060°–310°.

243	3 & 10 cm	East Maiden Lt	54°55'·73N	05°43'·61W	360°	11-21M	M
245	3 & 10 cm	Mew Island Lt	54°41'·91N	05°30'·75W	360°	14M	O
247	3 & 10 cm	South Rock Lt V	54°24'·47N	05°21'·92W	360°	13M	T
249	3 & 10 cm	Hellyhunter Lt By	54°00'·34N	06°01'·99W		5-14M	K
251	3 & 10 cm	Greenwich Lt V	50°24'·50N	00°00'·00	360°	10M	M
253	3 & 10 cm	Rathlin East Lt	55°18'·10N	06°10'·20W	089°-003°	15-27M	G

(1) No	(2) Type	(3) Name	(4) Lat	Long	(5) Sector	(6) Range	(7) Ident

FRANCE

No	Type	Name	Lat	Long	Sector	Range	Ident
301	3 cm	BXA Lt By	45°37'·60N	01°28'·60W	360°		B
303	3 cm	St Nazaire, La Couronnée Lt By	47°07'·67N	02°20'·00W	360°	3-5M	See [1]

[1] Signals appear as a series of dots. The distance between each dot corresponds to 0·2M.

No	Type	Name	Lat	Long	Sector	Range	Ident
305	3 cm	St Nazaire Lt By SN 1	47°00'·12N	02°39'·75W	360°	3-8M	Z
307	3 cm	Chausée de Sein Lt By	48°03'·80N	05°07'·70W	360°	10M	O
309	3 cm	Pointe de Créac'h Lt	48°27'·62N	05°07'·65W	030°-248°	20M	C
311	3 & 10 cm	Ouessant SW Lanby	48°31'·20N	05°49'·10W	360°	20M	M
313	3 cm	Ouessant NE Lt By	48°45'·90N	05°11'·60W	360°	20M	B
315	3 & 10 cm	Le Havre LHA Lanby	49°31'·44N	00°09'·78W	360°	8-10M	See [1]

[1] Signals appear as a series of 8 dots or 8 groups of dots. The distance between each dot or group of dots corresponds to 0·3M.

No	Type	Name	Lat	Long	Sector	Range	Ident
317	3 cm	Antifer Approach Lt By A5	49°45'·89N	00°17'·40W	360°		K
319	3 & 10 cm	Bassurelle Lt By	50°32'·70N	00°57'·80E	360°	5-8M	B
321	3 & 10 cm	Vergoyer Lt By N	50°39'·70N	01°22'·30E	360°	5-8M	C
323	3 cm	Dunkerque Lanby	51°02'·96N	01°51'·86E	360°		See [1]

[1] Signal appears as a succession of 8 dots. The distance between each dot corresponds to 0·3M.

BELGIUM AND NETHERLANDS

No	Type	Name	Lat	Long	Sector	Range	Ident
351	3 & 10 cm	Bol Van Heist Lt MOW 3	51°23'·43N	03°11'·98E	360°	10M	H
353	3 & 10 cm	Keeten B Lt By	51°36'·40N	03°58'·12E	360°		K
355	3 & 10 cm	Zuid Vlije Lt By ZV11/SRK 4	51°38'·23N	04°14'·56E	360°		K
357	3 cm	Noord Hinder Lt By NHR-SE	51°45'·50N	02°40'·00E	360°	10M	N
359	3 cm	Noord Hinder Lt By	52°00'·15N	02°51'·20E	360°		T
361	3 cm	Noord Hinder N Lt By	52°10'·95N	03°04'·85E	360°	10M	K
363	3 cm	West Hinder Lt	51°23'·36N	02°26'·35E			W
365	3 cm	Schouwenbank Lt By	51°45'·00N	03°14'·40E	360°	10M	O
367	3 & 10 cm	Goeree Lt	51°55'·53N	03°40'·18E	360°	12-15M	T
369	3 & 10 cm	Maas Centre Lt By MC	52°01'·18N	03°53'·57E	360°	10M	M
371		Scheveningen App R&W Lt By	52°09'·00N	04°05'·50E			Z
373		Scheveningen App R Lt By	52°10'·80N	04°07'·15E			Q
375	3 & 10 cm	Rijn Field Platform P15-B	52°18'·48N	03°46'·72E	030°-270°	12-15M	B
377	3 & 10 cm	IJmuiden Lt By	52°28'·70N	04°23'·93E	360°	10M	Y
379		Horizon P9-6 Platform	52°33'·20N	03°44'·54E			Q
381	3 & 10 cm	Helm Veld A Platform	52°52'·39N	04°08'·58E	360°		T
383	3 & 10 cm	Logger Platform	53°00'·90N	04°13'·05E	060°-270°	12-15M	X
385	3 cm	Schulpengat Fairway Lt By SG	52°52'·95N	04°38'·00E			Z
387		DW Route Lt By BR/S	52°54'·95N	03°18'·15E			G
389	3 & 10 cm	NAM Field Platform K14-FA-1	53°16'·17N	03°37'·66E	360°		7
391	3 & 10 cm	Vlieland Lanby VL-Center	53°27'·00N	04°40'·00E	360°	12-15M	C
393	3 & 10 cm	Wintershall Platform L8-G	53°34'·92N	04°36'·32E	000°-340°	12-15M	G
395	3 & 10 cm	Placid Field Platform PL-K9C-PA	53°39'·20N	03°52'·45E	360°		8
397	3 & 10 cm	Markham Field Platform J6-A	53°49'·39N	02°56'·75E	000°-180°		M
399	3 & 10 cm	West Friesland Platform L2-FA-1	53°57'·65N	04°29'·85E			9
401	3 cm	DW Route Lt By FR/A	54°00'·35N	04°21'·41E	360°		M
403	3 cm	Elf Petroland Platform F15-A	54°12'·98N	04°49'·71E	360°		U
405	3 cm	DW Route Lt By EF	54°03'·30N	04°59'·80E			T
407	3 cm	DW Route Lt By EF/B	54°06'·65N	05°40'·00E			M
409	3 cm	DW Route Lt By EF/C	54°08'·30N	06°00'·00E			O
411	3 & 10 cm	NAM Field Platform F3-OLT	54°51'·30 N	04°43'·60E	360°		D

GERMANY (North Sea Coast)

No	Type	Name	Lat	Long	Sector	Range	Ident
421	3 cm	Westerems Lt By	53°36'·97N	06°19'·48E	360°	8M	T
423	3 cm	Borkumriff Lt By	53°47'·50N	06°22'·13E	360°	8M	T
425	3 cm	GW/Ems Lt F	54°10'·00N	06°20'·80E	360°	8M	T
427	3 cm	German Bight Lt V	54°10'·80N	07°27'·60E	360°	8M	T
429	3 cm	Jade/Weser Lt By	53°58'·33N	07°38'·83E	360°	8M	T
431	3 & 10 cm	Tonne 3/Jade 2 Lt By	53°52'·12N	07°47'·33E	360°	8M	T
433	3 cm	Elbe Lt F	54°00'·00N	08°06'·58E	360°	8M	T

Chapter 5

Rise and Set Tables

Contents

5

The Astro-Supplement

The information required for astro-navigation has been produced separately in a forty-eight page Astro-Supplement. This can be obtained on request by ticking the relevant box on the Supplement request card and enclosing a cheque for £4·00 made out to Macmillan Publishers Ltd.

For a general introduction to the main principles and practices of astro-navigation, Chapter 5 of the *Macmillan & Silk Cut Yachtsman's Handbook* is recommended. In particular it contains practical information on the use of a marine sextant, explaining how sextant errors are determined and how to take sights of the Sun, Moon and stars at sea.

5.1   RISING, SETTING AND TWILIGHTS

5.1.1   Rising and Setting Phenomena

The tables of Sunrise, Sunset and Twilights, Moonrise and Moonset and Phases of the Moon (see 2.8.2) enable the degree of darkness around twilight and throughout the night to be estimated.

5.1.2   Contents of Tables 5.2.1, 5.2.2 and 5.2.3

Table 5.2.1 provides Local Mean Times (LMT) for every third day of the year, of morning Nautical Twilight, Sunrise, Sunset and evening Civil Twilight for latitude 50°N and latitude variations (v). Use the left-hand sign in the tabular entry for v for Sunrise, and the right-hand sign for Sunset. The latitude correction tables in 5.2.2 for Sunrise, Sunset and Twilights, enable the LMT for latitudes in the range 30°N to 60°N to be found.

Table 5.2.3 for Moonrise and Moonset are given for each day for latitude 50°N and latitude variations (v). The latitude correction table enables the LMT for latitudes in the range 30°N to 60°N to be found.

The tabular values are for the Greenwich Meridian, which are approximately the LMT of the corresponding phenomena for the other meridians. Expressing the longitude in time, the UT is obtained from:

$$UT = LMT \, {}^{+ \, west}_{- \, east} \, longitude$$

For Moonrise and Moonset a further small correction of one minute for every seven degrees of longitude is also required, which is added to the LMT if west, subtracted if east.

At Sunrise and Sunset the upper limb of the Sun is on the horizon at sea level. The Sun's zenith distance is 96° for Civil Twilight and 102° for Nautical Twilight. At Civil Twilight the brightest stars are visible and the horizon is clearly defined. At Nautical Twilight the horizon is not visible.

At Moonrise and Moonset the Moon's upper limb is on the horizon at sea level.

5.1.3   Example (a) The Sun rising, setting and twilights

Find the UT of the beginning of morning Nautical Twilight, Sunrise, Sunset and the end of evening Civil Twilight on 22 January, 1998 for latitude 36°07'N, longitude 18°20'E.

From table 5.2.1, for 22 January, $v = +30$ for the beginning of Nautical Twilight, and $v = +51$ for Sunrise, $v = -51$ for Sunset and $v = -41$ for the end of Civil Twilight. The latitude corrections for Nautical Twilight, Sunrise, Sunset and Civil Twilight are –21m, –38m, +38m and +32m respectively. Note that for Sunset, the sign of the correction has to be reversed because v is minus.

Convert longitude from degrees and minutes to whole minutes of time, by multiplying the degrees of longitude by 4 and adding a further correction of 0m, 1m, 2m, 3m or 4m when the minutes of longitude are in the range 0' to 7', 8' to 22', 23' to 37', 38' to 52' or 53' to 59', respectively.
The longitude equivalent in time of 18°20'E is – $(18 \times 4 + 1) = -73$m.

Remarks	Naut Twi		Sunrise		Sunset		Civil Twi	
Tabular value, 22 Jan	06h	31m	07h	46m	16h	37m	17h	13m
Corr. for latitude		–21m		–38m		+38m		+32m
LMT	06h	10m	07h	8m	17h	15m	17h	45m
Corr. for longitude	–1h	13m	–1h	13m	–1h	13m	–1h	13m
UT of phenomenon	04h	57m	05h	55m	16h	02m	16h	32m

5.1.4   Example (b) The Moon rising and setting

Find the UT of Moonrise and Moonset on 11 January, 1998 for latitude 36°07'N, longitude 06°30'W.

From 5.2.3 for 11 January, $v = -51$ for Moonrise and $v = +52$ for Moonset. The latitude correction for Moonrise and Moonset is +38m and –39m, respectively. Note the reverse of the sign of the correction for Moonrise, because v is minus.

Using the method in example (a), the longitude equivalent in time of 06°30'W is +26m.

Remarks	Moonrise		Moonset	
Tabular value, 11 Jan	15h	37m	06h	25m
Corr. for latitude		+38m		–39m
LMT	16h	15m	05h	46m
Corr. for longitude		+26m		+26m
UT of phenomenon	16h	41m	06h	12m

These times can be increased by +1m to allow for the effect of longitude on the LMT of the phenomenon. (See text at end of 5.2.3 for the instructions.)

5.2.1   1998 — Sunrise, Sunset and Twilights

Date	Naut Twi	v	Sun-rise	v	Sun-set	Civil Twi	v	Date	Naut Twi	v	Sun-rise	v	Sun-set	Civil Twi	v
	h m		h m		h m	h m			h m		h m		h m	h m	
Jan 1	06 39	+ 39	07 59	+63−	16 09	16 47	−51	Jul 3	02 08	−114	03 56	−67+	20 12	20 56	+83
4	06 39	38	07 58	62	16 12	16 50	50	6	02 12	112	03 58	66	20 11	20 54	82
7	06 39	37	07 57	60	16 15	16 53	49	9	02 16	110	04 01	65	20 09	20 52	80
10	06 38	36	07 56	59	16 19	16 57	47	12	02 21	107	04 04	63	20 07	20 49	79
13	06 37	35	07 54	57	16 23	17 01	46	15	02 26	104	04 07	62	20 04	20 46	76
16	06 35	+ 34	07 52	+56−	16 28	17 05	−44	18	02 31	−100	04 11	−60+	20 01	20 42	+74
19	06 33	32	07 49	54	16 32	17 09	43	21	02 37	97	04 14	58	19 58	20 39	72
22	06 31	30	07 46	51	16 37	17 13	41	24	02 43	93	04 18	56	19 54	20 34	69
25	06 28	28	07 43	49	16 42	17 18	39	27	02 49	89	04 22	54	19 50	20 30	67
28	06 25	26	07 39	47	16 47	17 22	36	30	02 55	85	04 26	52	19 46	20 25	64
31	06 21	+ 24	07 35	+44−	16 52	17 27	−34	Aug 2	03 01	− 81	04 30	−49+	19 41	20 20	+61
Feb 3	06 18	22	07 31	42	16 57	17 32	32	5	03 07	78	04 35	47	19 37	20 14	58
6	06 14	20	07 26	39	17 02	17 37	29	8	03 13	74	04 39	44	19 31	20 09	55
9	06 09	17	07 22	36	17 08	17 42	27	11	03 19	70	04 43	42	19 26	20 03	52
12	06 05	15	07 16	34	17 13	17 47	24	14	03 25	66	04 48	39	19 21	19 57	49
15	06 00	+ 12	07 11	+31−	17 18	17 51	−22	17	03 31	− 62	04 52	−36+	19 15	19 51	+46
18	05 55	10	07 06	28	17 23	17 56	19	20	03 37	59	04 57	33	19 09	19 44	43
21	05 49	7	07 00	25	17 28	18 01	16	23	03 43	55	05 01	31	19 03	19 38	40
24	05 44	4	06 54	22	17 33	18 06	13	26	03 49	51	05 06	28	18 57	19 31	37
27	05 38	+ 2	06 48	20	17 38	18 11	11	29	03 54	48	05 10	25	18 51	19 25	34
Mar 2	05 32	− 1	06 42	+17−	17 43	18 16	− 8	Sep 1	04 00	− 44	05 14	−22+	18 45	19 18	+31
5	05 26	4	06 36	14	17 48	18 21	5	4	04 05	41	05 19	19	18 38	19 11	28
8	05 20	7	06 29	11	17 53	18 25	− 2	7	04 10	37	05 23	17	18 32	19 05	25
11	05 13	10	06 23	8	17 58	18 30	+ 1	10	04 15	34	05 28	14	18 25	18 58	22
14	05 07	13	06 17	5	18 03	18 35	4	13	04 20	31	05 32	11	18 19	18 51	19
17	05 00	− 16	06 10	+ 2−	18 08	18 40	+ 7	16	04 25	− 27	05 37	− 8+	18 12	18 44	+16
20	04 53	19	06 04	− 1+	18 13	18 45	10	19	04 30	24	05 41	5	18 05	18 38	13
23	04 46	22	05 57	4	18 17	18 50	13	22	04 35	21	05 46	− 2+	17 59	18 31	10
26	04 40	26	05 50	7	18 22	18 55	16	25	04 40	18	05 50	+ 1−	17 52	18 24	7
29	04 33	29	05 44	9	18 27	18 59	19	28	04 45	15	05 55	3	17 46	18 18	4
Apr 1	04 25	− 32	05 37	−12+	18 31	19 04	+22	Oct 1	04 50	− 12	05 59	+ 6−	17 39	18 11	+ 1
4	04 18	36	05 31	15	18 36	19 09	25	4	04 54	9	06 04	9	17 33	18 05	− 1
7	04 11	39	05 25	18	18 41	19 14	28	7	04 59	6	06 09	12	17 26	17 58	4
10	04 04	42	05 18	21	18 46	19 19	31	10	05 04	− 3	06 13	15	17 20	17 52	7
13	03 57	46	05 12	24	18 50	19 24	34	13	05 08	0	06 18	18	17 14	17 46	10
16	03 49	− 50	05 06	−27+	18 55	19 29	+37	16	05 13	+ 3	06 23	+21−	17 07	17 40	−13
19	03 42	53	05 00	30	19 00	19 34	40	19	05 17	5	06 28	24	17 01	17 34	15
22	03 35	57	04 54	32	19 04	19 40	43	22	05 22	8	06 33	26	16 56	17 29	18
25	03 28	61	04 48	35	19 09	19 45	46	25	05 27	11	06 38	29	16 50	17 23	21
28	03 21	64	04 42	38	19 14	19 50	49	28	05 31	13	06 43	32	16 44	17 18	23
May 1	03 14	− 68	04 37	−41+	19 18	19 55	+52	31	05 36	+ 16	06 48	+35−	16 39	17 13	−26
4	03 07	72	04 32	43	19 23	20 00	56	Nov 3	05 40	18	06 53	37	16 34	17 08	28
7	03 00	76	04 27	46	19 27	20 05	58	6	05 44	20	06 57	40	16 29	17 04	31
10	02 54	80	04 22	48	19 32	20 10	61	9	05 49	23	07 02	43	16 25	16 59	33
13	02 47	84	04 17	51	19 36	20 15	64	12	05 53	25	07 07	45	16 20	16 55	35
16	02 41	− 88	04 13	−53+	19 40	20 20	+67	15	05 57	+ 27	07 12	+48−	16 16	16 52	−38
19	02 35	91	04 09	55	19 45	20 25	70	18	06 02	29	07 17	50	16 13	16 49	40
22	02 29	95	04 06	57	19 48	20 29	72	21	06 06	31	07 22	52	16 09	16 46	42
25	02 24	99	04 02	59	19 52	20 34	75	24	06 10	32	07 26	54	16 06	16 43	43
28	02 19	102	03 59	61	19 56	20 38	77	27	06 13	34	07 31	56	16 04	16 41	45
31	02 15	−106	03 57	−63+	19 59	20 42	+79	30	06 17	+ 35	07 35	+58−	16 02	16 39	−47
Jun 3	02 11	109	03 55	64	20 02	20 45	81	Dec 3	06 20	37	07 39	59	16 00	16 38	48
6	02 07	111	03 53	66	20 05	20 48	82	6	06 24	38	07 43	61	15 59	16 37	49
9	02 04	114	03 52	67	20 07	20 51	84	9	06 27	39	07 46	62	15 58	16 36	50
12	02 02	116	03 51	68	20 09	20 53	85	12	06 29	39	07 49	63	15 58	16 36	51
15	02 01	−117	03 50	−68+	20 11	20 55	+85	15	06 32	+ 40	07 52	+64−	15 58	16 37	−52
18	02 00	118	03 50	69	20 12	20 57	86	18	06 34	40	07 54	64	15 59	16 38	52
21	02 00	118	03 51	69	20 13	20 58	86	21	06 36	40	07 56	64	16 00	16 39	52
24	02 01	118	03 51	69	20 13	20 58	86	24	06 37	40	07 57	64	16 02	16 40	52
27	02 03	117	03 53	68	20 13	20 58	85	27	06 38	40	07 58	64	16 04	16 42	52
30	02 05	−116	03 54	−68+	20 13	20 57	+84	30	06 39	+ 40	07 59	+63−	16 06	16 45	−51
Jul 3	02 08	−114	03 56	−67+	20 12	20 56	+83	Jan 2	06 39	+ 39	07 58	+62−	16 09	16 48	−50

5

5.2.2 — 1998 — Sunrise, Sunset and Twilights

Corrections to Sunrise and Sunset

N.Lat v	30° m	35° m	40° m	45° m	50° m	52° m	54° m	56° m	58° m	60° m
0	0	0	0	0	0	0	0	0	0	0
2	− 2	− 2	− 1	− 1	0	0	+ 1	+ 1	+ 2	+ 2
4	4	3	2	1	0	+ 1	1	2	3	4
6	6	5	4	2	0	1	2	3	4	6
8	8	6	5	3	0	1	2	4	6	7
10	−10	− 8	− 6	− 3	0	+ 1	+ 3	+ 5	+7	+ 9
12	12	10	7	4	0	2	4	6	8	11
14	14	11	8	4	0	2	4	7	10	13
16	16	13	9	5	0	2	5	8	11	15
18	18	14	10	6	0	3	6	9	12	16
20	−20	−16	−12	− 6	0	+ 3	+ 6	+10	+14	+18
22	22	18	13	7	0	3	7	11	15	20
24	24	19	14	8	0	4	7	12	16	22
26	26	21	15	8	0	4	8	13	18	24
28	28	22	16	9	0	4	9	14	19	26
30	−30	−24	−17	−10	0	+ 4	+ 9	+15	+21	+28
32	32	26	19	10	0	5	10	16	22	30
34	34	27	20	11	0	5	11	17	24	32
36	36	29	21	11	0	5	11	18	25	34
38	38	31	22	12	0	6	12	19	27	36
40	−40	−32	−23	−13	0	+ 6	+13	+20	+28	+38
42	42	34	24	13	0	6	13	21	30	40
44	44	35	26	14	0	7	14	22	31	42
46	46	37	27	15	0	7	15	23	33	44
48	48	39	28	15	0	7	15	24	35	47
50	−50	−40	−29	−16	0	+ 8	+16	+26	+36	+49
52	52	42	30	17	0	8	17	27	38	51
54	54	44	32	17	0	8	17	28	40	54
56	56	45	33	18	0	9	18	29	42	56
58	58	47	34	19	0	9	19	30	43	59
60	−60	−49	−35	−19	0	+ 9	+20	+32	+45	+62
62	62	50	36	20	0	10	20	33	47	64
64	64	52	38	21	0	10	21	34	49	67
66	66	53	39	22	0	10	22	36	51	70
68	68	55	40	22	0	11	23	37	54	74
70	−70	−57	−41	−23	0	+11	+24	+38	+56	+77

If v is negative reverse the sign of the correction

Corrections to Nautical Twilight

N.Lat v	30° m	35° m	40° m	45° m	50° m	52° m	54° m	56° m	58° m	60° m
+40	−40	−31	−22	−12	0	+ 5	+11	+17	+24	+31
30	30	23	16	9	0	4	8	12	17	22
20	20	15	10	5	0	2	5	7	10	13
+10	−10	− 7	− 5	− 2	0	+ 1	+ 2	+ 3	+ 3	+ 4
0	0	+ 1	+ 1	+ 1	0	− 1	− 1	− 2	− 3	− 4
−10	+10	+ 9	+ 7	+ 4	0	− 2	− 4	− 7	−10	−13
20	20	17	13	7	0	3	7	12	17	23
30	30	25	18	10	0	5	11	17	24	33
40	40	33	24	14	0	7	14	23	33	44
50	50	41	30	17	0	− 8	18	29	42	57
−60	+60	+49	+37	+21	0	−10	−22	−36	−52	−73
70	70	58	43	24	0	12	27	44	65	95
80	80	66	49	28	0	15	32	54	83	−136
90	90	75	56	32	0	17	39	67	−116	TAN
100	100	83	63	37	0	20	47	−88	TAN	TAN
−110	+110	+92	+70	+42	0	−24	−59	TAN	TAN	TAN
−120	+120	+101	+78	+47	0	−29	−81	TAN	TAN	TAN

Corrections to Civil Twilight

N.Lat v	30° m	35° m	40° m	45° m	50° m	52° m	54° m	56° m	58° m	60° m
−50	+50	+40	+28	+15	0	− 7	−15	−24	−33	−44
40	40	32	23	12	0	6	12	18	26	34
30	30	24	17	9	0	4	8	13	19	25
20	20	16	11	6	0	3	5	8	12	15
−10	+10	+ 8	+ 5	+ 3	0	− 1	− 2	− 4	− 5	− 7
0	0	0	0	0	0	0	+ 1	+ 1	+ 2	+ 2
+10	−10	− 8	− 6	− 4	0	+ 2	4	6	8	11
20	20	16	12	7	0	3	7	11	15	20
30	30	24	18	10	0	5	10	16	22	30
40	40	33	24	13	0	6	13	21	30	41
+50	−50	−41	−30	−17	0	+ 8	+17	+27	+39	+52
60	60	49	36	20	0	10	21	33	48	66
70	70	57	42	24	0	12	25	41	60	84
80	80	66	49	27	0	14	30	49	74	110
83	83	68	50	29	0	14	32	52	80	121
+86	−86	−71	−52	−30	0	+15	+33	+56	+86	+137

The times on the opposite page are the local mean times (LMT) of morning nautical twilight, sunrise, sunset and evening civil twilight for latitude N 50°, together with their variations v. The variations are the differences in minutes of time between the time of the phenomenon for latitudes N 50° and N 30°. The sign on the left-hand side of v (between sunrise and sunset) applies to sunrise, and the sign on the right-hand side applies to sunset. The LMT of the phenomenon for latitudes between N 30° and N 60° is found by applying the corrections in the tables above to the tabulated times as follows:

Sunrise and sunset To determine the LMT of sunrise or sunset, take out the tabulated time and v corresponding to the required date. Using v and latitude as arguments in the table of "Corrections to Sunrise and Sunset", extract the correction. This table is for positive v. If v is minus, reverse the sign of the correction. Apply the correction to the tabulated time.

Nautical twilight To determine the LMT of morning nautical twilight, follow the same method as for sunrise and sunset, but use the table of "Corrections to Nautical Twilight". This table includes both positive and negative values of v. The entry TAN stands for Twilight All Night, because the Sun does not reach an altitude of −12°.

Civil twilight To determine the LMT of evening civil twilight follow the same method as for nautical twilight, but use the table of "Corrections to Civil Twilight". This table includes both positive and negative values of v.

Convert LMT to UT by adding the longitude in time if west, or subtracting if east.

Examples on the use of these tables are given in 5.1.3 and 5.1.4.

5.2.3 — 1998 — Moonrise and Moonset

January – July (Days 1–31)

Day	JAN Rise	v	JAN Set	v	MAR Rise	v	MAR Set	v	MAY Rise	v	MAY Set	v	JUL Rise	v	JUL Set	v
	h m		h m		h m		h m		h m		h m		h m		h m	
1	09 36	+37	19 46	−34	08 15	− 9	21 31	+16	09 00	−51	24 35	+48	11 51	0	24 02	− 5
2	10 12	27	21 01	23	08 47	21	22 48	28	10 01	46	00 35	48	12 52	+10	00 02	5
3	10 43	16	22 16	−11	09 21	32	24 02	38	11 03	39	01 14	42	13 54	20	00 25	15
4	11 13	+ 5	23 31	+ 1	09 59	41	00 02	38	12 06	31	01 48	34	14 56	30	00 50	24
5	11 42	− 7	24 46	13	10 41	47	01 11	46	13 09	21	02 16	25	15 58	39	01 17	33
6	12 11	−18	00 46	+13	11 29	−51	02 13	+50	14 11	−12	02 42	+16	17 00	+46	01 48	−41
7	12 43	29	02 00	25	12 22	51	03 08	51	15 12	− 1	03 06	+ 6	18 00	51	02 25	48
8	13 18	39	03 12	35	13 19	47	03 56	49	16 14	+ 9	03 29	− 3	18 56	53	03 08	52
9	13 58	46	04 22	44	14 19	41	04 36	43	17 16	19	03 52	13	19 47	52	04 00	53
10	14 45	50	05 26	49	15 21	33	05 10	36	18 18	28	04 17	23	20 32	47	04 59	51
11	15 37	−51	06 25	+52	16 23	−24	05 40	+28	19 20	+37	04 44	−32	21 11	+39	06 05	−44
12	16 35	49	07 16	50	17 25	15	06 07	19	20 21	45	05 14	40	21 45	29	07 15	35
13	17 36	43	07 59	45	18 27	− 5	06 32	+ 9	21 20	50	05 50	47	22 16	18	08 28	24
14	18 39	36	08 36	38	19 28	+ 5	06 56	0	22 15	53	06 31	51	22 45	+ 6	09 43	−12
15	19 42	27	09 08	30	20 30	15	07 19	−10	23 06	52	07 20	53	23 13	− 6	10 58	0
16	20 45	−17	09 35	+21	21 31	+25	07 43	−19	23 51	+48	08 15	−51	23 42	−18	12 14	+12
17	21 47	− 7	10 00	11	22 32	34	08 10	28	24 30	41	09 18	46	24 14	29	13 29	24
18	22 48	+ 3	10 24	+ 2	23 33	42	08 39	37	00 30	41	10 25	38	00 14	29	14 43	35
19	23 49	13	10 47	− 8	24 32	48	09 13	44	01 05	32	11 37	27	00 49	39	15 56	44
20	24 51	23	11 12	17	00 32	48	09 52	49	01 37	21	12 51	16	01 30	47	17 03	50
21	00 51	+23	11 38	−27	01 29	+51	10 39	−52	02 07	+ 9	14 07	− 3	02 18	−52	18 04	+53
22	01 54	32	12 07	35	02 22	51	11 33	51	02 36	− 3	15 25	+ 9	03 13	53	18 56	51
23	02 56	40	12 41	43	03 10	48	12 36	46	03 06	15	16 44	22	04 13	50	19 41	46
24	03 59	47	13 21	49	03 53	42	13 46	39	03 39	27	18 03	34	05 17	43	20 18	38
25	04 59	51	14 10	52	04 32	33	15 01	29	04 16	38	19 19	44	06 23	35	20 50	29
26	05 55	+52	15 07	−51	05 07	+22	16 20	−16	04 58	−46	20 30	+50	07 29	−25	21 17	+19
27	06 46	48	16 13	47	05 39	+10	17 40	− 3	05 48	51	21 33	53	08 33	15	21 42	+10
28	07 31	42	17 25	38	06 11	− 3	19 02	+10	06 43	53	22 27	51	09 37	− 5	22 05	0
29	08 10	32	18 41	28	06 43	15	20 23	22	07 44	50	23 12	46	10 39	+ 6	22 29	−10
30	08 44	21	19 59	16	07 17	27	21 41	34	08 48	43	23 48	38	11 41	16	22 53	20
31	09 16	+ 9	21 17	− 3	07 54	−37	22 56	+43	09 52	−35	24 19	+30	12 42	+25	23 18	−29

February – August (Days 1–31)

Day	FEB Rise	v	FEB Set	v	APR Rise	v	APR Set	v	JUN Rise	v	JUN Set	v	AUG Rise	v	AUG Set	v
1	09 46	− 3	22 34	+ 9	08 36	−45	24 03	+49	10 56	−26	00 19	+30	13 44	+35	23 47	−38
2	10 16	14	23 49	21	09 23	50	00 03	49	11 59	16	00 47	20	14 45	43	24 21	45
3	10 47	26	25 03	32	10 16	51	01 03	51	13 02	− 6	01 11	10	15 45	49	00 21	45
4	11 21	35	01 03	32	11 12	49	01 54	50	14 03	+ 5	01 34	+ 1	16 43	53	01 01	50
5	11 59	43	02 13	41	12 12	43	02 37	46	15 04	15	01 57	− 9	17 37	53	01 48	53
6	12 43	−49	03 19	+47	13 14	−36	03 13	+39	16 07	+25	02 21	−19	18 25	+49	02 44	−52
7	13 32	51	04 18	51	14 16	27	03 44	31	17 09	34	02 47	28	19 07	42	03 47	47
8	14 26	50	05 11	51	15 18	18	04 12	22	18 11	42	03 16	37	19 45	33	04 57	39
9	15 25	46	05 56	47	16 19	− 8	04 37	12	19 12	49	03 49	45	20 18	22	06 12	29
10	16 27	39	06 35	41	17 21	+ 2	05 00	+ 3	20 10	53	04 29	50	20 48	+10	07 28	17
11	17 29	−30	07 08	+34	18 22	+12	05 24	− 7	21 03	+53	05 15	−53	21 17	− 2	08 45	− 4
12	18 32	21	07 38	25	19 24	22	05 48	16	21 51	50	06 09	52	21 47	14	10 02	+ 8
13	19 34	11	08 04	15	20 25	31	06 13	26	22 33	44	07 10	48	22 18	25	11 19	21
14	20 36	− 1	08 28	+ 6	21 27	39	06 41	34	23 09	35	08 16	41	22 52	36	12 34	32
15	21 38	+ 9	08 51	− 4	22 26	46	07 13	42	23 42	25	09 26	31	23 30	44	13 46	42
16	22 39	+19	09 15	−13	23 24	+51	07 50	−48	24 11	+14	10 39	−20	24 15	−50	14 54	+49
17	23 40	28	09 40	23	24 17	52	08 34	52	00 11	14	11 53	− 8	00 15	50	15 57	52
18	24 42	37	10 07	31	00 17	52	09 25	52	00 40	+ 2	13 09	+ 4	01 06	53	16 51	52
19	00 42	37	10 39	39	01 06	50	10 23	49	01 08	−10	14 25	17	02 03	51	17 37	48
20	01 43	44	11 15	46	01 50	45	11 28	43	01 39	22	15 42	29	03 05	46	18 17	41
21	02 43	+49	11 58	−50	02 28	+37	12 38	−34	02 12	−33	16 58	+39	04 10	−38	18 50	+33
22	03 40	52	12 50	52	03 03	27	13 53	23	02 51	42	18 10	47	05 15	29	19 19	23
23	04 32	50	13 50	49	03 35	16	15 11	−10	03 36	49	19 17	52	06 20	19	19 45	14
24	05 20	45	14 58	43	04 06	+ 4	16 31	+ 3	04 28	53	20 15	53	07 24	− 9	20 09	+ 4
25	06 02	37	16 13	34	04 37	− 9	17 51	16	05 26	52	21 05	49	08 26	+ 1	20 32	− 6
26	06 39	+27	17 31	−22	05 10	−21	19 12	+28	06 29	−47	21 46	+42	09 29	+12	20 56	−16
27	07 13	+15	18 52	−10	05 45	33	20 31	39	07 34	40	22 20	34	10 30	22	21 20	25
28	07 44	+ 3	20 12	+ 3	06 25	42	21 44	47	08 40	31	22 49	25	11 31	31	21 48	34
29					07 11	49	22 50	51	09 45	21	23 15	15	12 32	39	22 19	42
30					08 03	−52	23 47	+52	10 48	−10	23 39	+ 5	13 32	46	22 55	48
31													14 30	+51	23 38	−52

5

5.2.3 Continued   1998 — Moonrise and Moonset

SEPTEMBER

Day	Rise h m	v	Set h m	v
1	15 24	+53	24 29	−53
2	16 14	51	00 29	53
3	16 59	46	01 28	50
4	17 39	38	02 35	44
5	18 14	27	03 47	34
6	18 47	+16	05 04	−23
7	19 17	+ 3	06 23	−10
8	19 47	− 9	07 42	+ 3
9	20 18	21	09 02	16
10	20 52	32	10 20	28
11	21 30	−42	11 36	+39
12	22 13	49	12 47	47
13	23 03	52	13 51	52
14	23 58	52	14 48	52
15	24 58	48	15 37	50
16	00 58	−48	16 17	+44
17	02 01	41	16 52	36
18	03 05	33	17 22	27
19	04 09	23	17 48	17
20	05 13	13	18 12	+ 7
21	06 16	− 2	18 36	− 3
22	07 19	+ 8	18 59	13
23	08 20	18	19 23	22
24	09 22	28	19 49	31
25	10 23	37	20 19	39
26	11 22	+44	20 52	−46
27	12 20	50	21 32	51
28	13 15	53	22 18	53
29	14 06	53	23 12	52
30	14 51	49	24 13	47

OCTOBER

Day	Rise h m	v	Set h m	v
1	15 32	+42	00 13	−47
2	16 09	33	01 22	39
3	16 42	22	02 35	29
4	17 13	+10	03 53	17
5	17 43	− 3	05 13	− 4
6	18 15	−16	06 34	+10
7	18 48	28	07 56	23
8	19 25	39	09 16	35
9	20 08	47	10 32	45
10	20 56	52	11 42	51
11	21 51	−53	12 44	+53
12	22 51	50	13 36	51
13	23 55	44	14 19	46
14	24 57	36	14 55	39
15	00 57	36	15 26	30
16	02 01	−26	15 53	+20
17	03 05	16	16 18	11
18	04 08	− 6	16 41	+ 1
19	05 10	+ 5	17 04	− 9
20	06 12	15	17 27	19
21	07 14	+25	17 52	−29
22	08 15	34	18 20	37
23	09 16	42	18 52	45
24	10 14	49	19 29	50
25	11 10	53	20 12	53
26	12 01	+54	21 02	−54
27	12 48	52	21 59	50
28	13 29	46	23 03	44
29	14 06	38	24 12	35
30	14 39	28	00 12	35
31	15 10	+17	01 26	−23

NOVEMBER

Day	Rise h m	v	Set h m	v
1	15 39	+ 4	02 42	−11
2	16 09	− 9	04 02	+ 2
3	16 41	21	05 23	16
4	17 16	33	06 45	29
5	17 57	44	08 06	40
6	18 44	−51	09 22	+49
7	19 38	54	10 31	53
8	20 38	52	11 29	53
9	21 42	47	12 18	49
10	22 47	39	12 57	42
11	23 52	−30	13 30	+34
12	24 57	20	13 59	24
13	00 57	20	14 24	14
14	02 00	− 9	14 47	+ 4
15	03 02	+ 1	15 09	− 6
16	04 04	+11	15 32	−16
17	05 06	22	15 56	26
18	06 08	31	16 23	35
19	07 09	40	16 53	43
20	08 09	47	17 28	49
21	09 07	+52	18 09	−53
22	10 00	55	18 57	55
23	10 48	53	19 52	52
24	11 31	49	20 53	47
25	12 08	42	21 58	39
26	12 41	+33	23 08	−29
27	13 12	22	24 21	17
28	13 40	+10	00 21	17
29	14 08	− 2	01 36	− 4
30	14 37	15	02 54	+ 9

DECEMBER

Day	Rise h m	v	Set h m	v
1	15 09	−27	04 14	+22
2	15 46	38	05 34	34
3	16 29	48	06 53	45
4	17 19	53	08 07	52
5	18 18	54	09 13	55
6	19 22	−51	10 09	+52
7	20 29	44	10 54	46
8	21 37	35	11 31	38
9	22 44	24	12 02	29
10	23 49	14	12 29	18
11	24 52	− 3	12 53	+ 8
12	00 52	− 3	13 15	− 2
13	01 55	+ 7	13 38	12
14	02 57	18	14 01	22
15	03 58	28	14 26	31
16	05 00	+37	14 55	−40
17	06 01	45	15 28	47
18	07 00	51	16 07	52
19	07 56	55	16 53	55
20	08 47	55	17 46	54
21	09 32	+51	18 45	−50
22	10 11	45	19 50	42
23	10 46	36	20 58	32
24	11 17	26	22 09	21
25	11 45	15	23 22	− 9
26	12 12	+ 3	24 36	+ 3
27	12 39	− 9	00 36	3
28	13 08	21	01 52	16
29	13 41	33	03 10	28
30	14 19	43	04 27	40
31	15 04	−51	05 42	+49

Corrections to Moonrise and Moonset

N Lat v	30°	35°	40°	45°	50°	52°	54°	56°	58°	60°
	m	m	m	m	m	m	m	m	m	m
0	0	0	0	0	0	0	0	0	0	0
2	− 2	− 2	− 1	− 1	0	0	+ 1	+ 1	+ 1	+ 2
4	4	3	2	1	0	+ 1	1	2	3	4
6	6	5	3	2	0	1	2	3	4	5
8	8	6	5	3	0	1	2	4	5	7
10	−10	− 8	− 6	− 3	0	+ 1	+ 3	+ 5	+ 7	+ 9
12	12	10	7	4	0	2	4	6	8	11
14	14	11	8	4	0	2	4	7	9	12
16	16	13	9	5	0	2	5	8	11	14
18	18	14	10	6	0	3	5	9	12	16
20	−20	−16	−12	− 6	0	+ 3	+ 6	+10	+14	+18
22	22	18	13	7	0	3	7	11	15	20
24	24	19	14	8	0	3	7	12	16	22
26	26	21	15	8	0	4	8	13	18	23
28	28	22	16	9	0	4	9	14	19	25
30	−30	−24	−17	− 9	0	+ 4	+ 9	+15	+21	+27
32	32	26	18	10	0	5	10	16	22	29
34	34	27	20	11	0	5	10	17	23	31
36	36	29	21	11	0	5	11	18	25	33
38	38	31	22	12	0	6	12	19	26	35
40	−40	−32	−23	−13	0	+ 6	+12	+20	+28	+37
42	42	34	24	13	0	6	13	21	30	39
44	44	35	26	14	0	7	14	22	31	42
46	46	37	27	15	0	7	15	23	33	44
48	48	39	28	15	0	7	15	24	34	46
50	−50	−40	−29	−16	0	+ 8	+16	+25	+36	+48
52	52	42	30	17	0	8	17	26	38	51
54	54	44	32	17	0	8	17	28	39	53
56	56	45	33	18	0	9	18	29	41	56
58	58	47	34	19	0	9	19	30	43	58
60	−60	−48	−35	−19	0	+ 9	+20	+31	+45	+61
62	62	50	36	20	0	10	20	33	47	64
64	64	52	38	21	0	10	21	34	49	67
66	66	53	39	22	0	10	22	35	51	70
68	68	55	40	22	0	11	23	37	53	73
70	−70	−57	−41	−23	0	+11	+24	+38	+55	+76
72	72	58	43	24	0	11	24	40	58	80
74	74	60	44	24	0	12	25	41	60	83
76	76	62	45	25	0	12	26	43	62	87
78	78	63	46	26	0	13	27	44	65	91
80	−80	−65	−48	−27	0	+13	+28	+46	+68	+96
82	82	67	49	27	0	13	29	48	70	101
84	84	68	50	28	0	14	30	49	73	106
86	86	70	51	29	0	14	31	51	77	112
88	88	72	53	30	0	15	32	53	80	119
90	−90	−73	−54	−30	0	+15	+33	+55	+84	+127

If v is minus reverse the sign of the correction

The daily times of moonrise and moonset given above are the local mean times (LMT) of the phenomena for latitude N 50°, together with their variations v. The variations are the differences in minutes between the time of the phenomenon for latitudes N 50° and N 30°. The LMT of the phenomenon for latitudes between N 30° and N 60° is found as follows:

Take out the tabulated time and v corresponding to the required date. Using v and latitude as arguments in the table above of "Corrections to Moonrise and Moonset", extract the correction. This table is for positive v. If v is minus, reverse the sign of the correction. Apply the correction to the tabulated time.

Add a small extra correction of 1ᵐ for every 7° of longitude if west. Subtract if east.

Convert LMT to UT by adding the longitude in time if west, or subtracting if east.

Examples on the use of these tables are given in xxx

THEY'RE IN THE PINK

and just a phone call away

So look them up and widen your horizons

The PINK PAGES section at the front of the book is your own guide to marinas, harbours, services and supplies, including emergencies. With over 60 categories listed by discipline and coastal location, it is the quickest route to find what you want with simplicity and ease.

The MACMILLAN *incorporating* REED'S
NAUTICAL ALMANAC

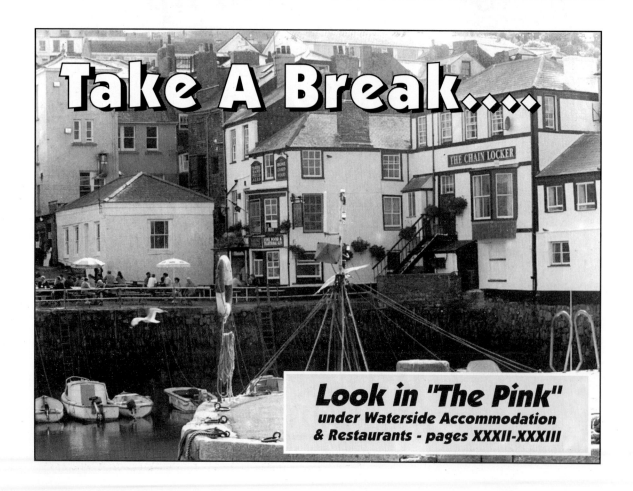

PLATE 1 – NAVIGATION LIGHTS (SEE ALSO PLATE 4)

Port sidelight (red) shows from ahead to 22½° abaft the beam

112½°

Abeam

For yachts 12-50m overall, visibility – 2 miles. For yachts under 12m – 1 mile

(May be combined with starboard sidelight in one centreline lantern in boats under 20m overall)

White masthead light shows over arc of 225° – from ahead to 22½° abaft the beam each side. Shown by vessels under power only

Ahead

225°

(Masthead light and sternlight may be combined in one all-round white light in boats under 12m overall)

For yachts 20-50m overall, visibility – 5 miles. For yachts 12-20m – 3 miles. For yachts under 12m – 2 miles

Starboard sidelight (green) shows from ahead to 22½° abaft the beam

112½°

Abeam

For yachts 12-50m overall, visibility – 2 miles. For yachts under 12m – 1 mile

(May be combined with port sidelight in one centreline lantern in boats under 20m overall)

Astern

White sternlight shows over arc of 135°, 67½° on each side of vessel

135°

For yachts under 50m overall, visibility – 2 miles

Lights for power-driven vessels underway (plan views)

Note: Also apply to sailing yachts or other sailing craft when under power

Motor boat under 7m, less than 7 knots

Motor boat under 12m (combined masthead & sternlight)

Motor yacht under 20m (combined lantern for sidelights)

Motor yacht over 20m

Larger vessel, over 50m, with two masthead lights – the aft one higher

Lights for sailing vessels underway (plan views)

Note: These lights apply to sailing craft when under sail ONLY. If motor-sailing, the appropriate lights for a power-driven vessel must be shown, as above

Masthead tricolour lantern

or

Sailing boat under 7m shows white light to prevent collision. If practicable, she should show sidelights and sternlight

Combined sidelights plus sternlight

Tricolour lantern at masthead

Separate sidelights and sternlight for sailing vessel over 20m

Sailing yacht under 20m

Bow view

If *not* using tricolour masthead lantern, a sailing yacht may show (in addition to other lights) two all-round lights near masthead, the upper red and the lower green

PLATE 2 – ADMIRALTY METRIC CHART SYMBOLS

A selection of the more common symbols from Admiralty Publication 5011

Reproduced by kind permission of H.M. Stationery Office and the Hydrographer of the Navy

RADIO AND	ARTIFICIAL FEATURES	RADIO AND RADAR
Coastline, surveyed	Sea wall	RC — Non-directional radiobeacon
Coast imperfectly known or shoreline unsurveyed	Breakwater	RD RD 269°30' — Directional radiobeacon
Steep coast, Cliffs	Groyne (always dry) Groyne (intertidal)	RW — Rotating pattern radiobeacon
Sandy shore		RG — Radio direction-finding station
Low Water Line	Patent slip	Radio/TV mast Radio/TV tower
Foreshore, Mud	Lock	Dish aerial
Foreshore, Sand	Hulk	R — Coast radio station providing QTG service
Foreshore, Boulders, Stones, Gravel and Shingle	Steps, Landing stairs	Racon Racon Racons ≠ 270° — Radar transponder beacons with bearing line
Foreshore, Rock	Overhead cable, Telephone line, Telegraph line with vertical clearance	Racon (Z) — Radar transponder beacon with identification
Foreshore, Sand and Mud	Discharge pipe, water, sewer, outfall	Radar reflector (not usually charted on IALA System buoys)
Limiting danger line	Fixed bridge with vertical clearance	Radar-conspicuous feature
Breakers along a shore	Opening bridge with vertical clearance	Aero RC — Aeronautical radiobeacon
Half-tide channel (on intertidal ground)	Ferry	
	Training wall	Racon Racon — Floating marks with Racons

PLATE 3 – ADMIRALTY METRIC CHART SYMBOLS

A selection of the more common symbols from Admiralty Publication 5011

Reproduced by kind permission of H.M. Stationery Office and the Hydrographer of the Navy

DANGERS	DANGERS	LIMITS
Rock which does not cover, height above High Water	Wreck over which the depth has been obtained by sounding, but not by wire sweep	Leading line (the firm line is the track to be followed
Rock which covers and uncovers, height above Chart Datum	Wreck over which the exact depth is unknown, but which is considered to have a safe clearance at the depth shown	Limit of sector
Rock awash at the level of Chart Datum	The remains of a wreck, or other foul area no longer dangerous to surface navigation, but to be avoided by vessels anchoring, trawling, etc.	Traffic separation scheme: one-way traffic lanes (separated by zone)
A rock or rock ledge over which the exact depth is unknown but which is considered to be dangerous to surface navigation	Obstruction, depth known	Submarine cable (telegraph and telephone)
Shoal sounding on isolated rock	Obstruction which has been swept by wire to the depth shown	Submarine cable (power)
Submerged rock not dangerous to surface navigation	Overfalls, tide rips, races	Limits of national fishing zones
Wreck which has been swept by wire to the depth shown	Eddies	Anchorage area in general. Type of anchorage may be specified, e.g. by number or name, DW (deep water), tanker, 24h (for periods up to 24 hours), small craft, etc.
Wreck showing any part of hull or superstructure at the level of Chart Datum	Kelp	
Wreck of which the mast(s) only are visible	Breakers	Anchoring prohibited
Wrecks, depth unknown. On left considered dangerous to surface navigation, and on right not considered dangerous	Fish haven, depth known	Fishing prohibited

PLATE 4 – PRINCIPAL NAVIGATION LIGHTS AND SHAPES

(*Note:* All vessels seen from starboard side)

Vessel at anchor

All-round white light; if over 50m, a second light aft and lower

Black ball forward

Not under command

Two all-round red lights, plus sidelights and sternlight when making way

Two black balls vertically

Motor sailing

Cone point down, forward

Divers down

Letter 'A' International Code

Vessel aground

Anchor light(s), plus two all-round red lights in a vertical line

Three black balls in a vertical line

Vessels being towed and towing

Vessel towed shows sidelights (forward) and sternlight

Tug shows two masthead lights, sidelights, sternlight, yellow towing light

Towing by day – Length of tow more than 200m

Towing vessel and tow display diamond shapes. By night, the towing vessel shows three masthead lights instead of two as for shorter tows

Vessel fishing

All-round red light over all-round white, plus sidelights and sternlight when underway

Fishing/Trawling

A shape consisting of two cones point to point in a vertical line one above the other

Vessel trawling

All-round green light over all-round white, plus sidelights and sternlight when underway

Pilot boat

All-round white light over all-round red, plus sidelights and sternlight when underway, or anchor light

Vessel restricted in her ability to manoeuvre

All-round red, white, red lights vertically, plus normal steaming lights when underway

Three shapes in a vertical line – ball, diamond, ball

Dredger

As left, plus two all-round red lights (or two balls) on foul side, and two all-round green (or two diamonds) on clear side

Constrained by draught

Three all-round red lights in a vertical line, plus normal steaming lights. By day – a cylinder

PLATE 5 – IALA BUOYAGE

Lateral marks

Used generally to mark the sides of well-defined navigable channels

Port Hand marks
Light:
Colour – red
Rhythm – any

Navigable channel

Direction of buoyage

Starboard Hand marks
Light:
Colour – green
Rhythm – any

Cardinal marks

Used to indicate the direction from the mark in which the best navigable water lies, or to draw attention to a bend, junction or fork in a channel, or to mark the end of a shoal.

Lights: always white

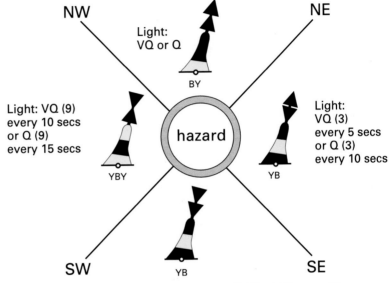

NW

Light:
VQ or Q

NE

Light: VQ (9) every 10 secs or Q (9) every 15 secs

hazard

Light:
VQ (3) every 5 secs or Q (3) every 10 secs

BY

YBY

YB

SW

YB

SE

Light: VQ (6) + L Fl every 10 secs or Q (6) + L Fl every 15 secs

Other marks

BRB   BRB

RW

RW

Y   Y   Y   Y

Isolated Danger marks
Use: To mark a small isolated danger with navigable water all round.
Light:
Colour – white
Rhythm – group flashing (2)

Safe Water marks
Use: Mid-channel or landfall
Light:
Colour – white
Rhythm – Isophase, occulting or 1 long flash every 10 seconds

Special marks
Any shape not conflicting with lateral or safe water marks.
Light:
Colour – yellow
Rhythm – different from other white lights used on buoys

Preferred Channels

At the point where the channel divides, a preferred channel is indicated by a modified Port or Starboard mark as follows:

Preferred Channel to Starboard
Light:
Colour – red
Rhythm – Fl (2+1)

RGR   RGR

Navigable channel

Direction of buoyage

GRG   GRG

Preferred channel to Port
Light:
Colour – green
Rhythm – Fl (2+1)

PLATES 6-7 – INTERNATIONAL CODE OF SIGNALS, CODE FLAGS, PHONETIC ALPHABET, MORSE SYMBOLS AND SINGLE-LETTER SIGNALS

Notes:

1. Single-letter signals may be made by any method of signalling. Those marked * when made by sound must comply with the *International Regulations for Preventing Collisions at Sea*, Rules 34 and 35.

2. Signals 'K' and 'S' have special meanings as landing signals for small boats with persons in distress.

3. In the phonetic alphabet, the syllables to be emphasised are in italics.

Code and Answering Pendant

A   Alfa   (*AL* FAH)

● ▬

I have a diver down, keep well clear at slow speed

*B   Bravo   (*BRA* VOH)

▬ ● ● ●

I am taking in, discharging, or carrying dangerous goods

*C   Charlie   (*CHAR* LEE)

▬ ● ▬ ● ▬

Yes (affirmative or 'The significance of the previous group should be read in the affirmative)

*D   Delta   (*DELL* TAH)

▬ ● ●

Keep clear of me; I am manoeuvring with difficulty

*E   Echo   (*ECK* OH)

●

I am altering my course to starboard

F   Foxtrot   (*FOKS* TROT)

● ● ▬ ●

I am disabled, communicate with me

*G   Golf   (*GOLF*)

▬ ▬ ●

I require a pilot. When made by fishing vessels operating in close proximity on the fishing grounds it means: I am hauling nets

*H   Hotel   (HOH *TELL*)

● ● ● ●

I have a pilot on board

*I   India   (*IN* DEE AH)

● ●

I am altering my course to port

J   Juliet   (JEW LEE *ETT*)

● ▬ ▬ ▬

I am on fire and have dangerous cargo on board: keep well clear of me

K   Kilo   (*KEY* LOH)

▬ ● ▬

I wish to communicate with you

L   Lima   (*LEE* MAH)

● ▬ ● ●

You should stop your vessel instantly

*M   Mike   (MIKE)

▬ ▬

My vessel is stopped and making no way through the water

N   November   (NO *VEM* BER)

▬ ●

No (negative or 'The significance of the previous group should be read in the negative'). This signal may be given only visually or by sound

O   Oscar   (*OSS* CAH)

▬ ▬ ▬

Man overboard

P   Papa   (PAH *PAH*)

● ▬ ▬ ●

In harbour: all persons should report on board as the vessel is about to proceed to sea. **At sea:** it may be used by fishing vessels to mean 'My nets have come fast upon an obstruction'

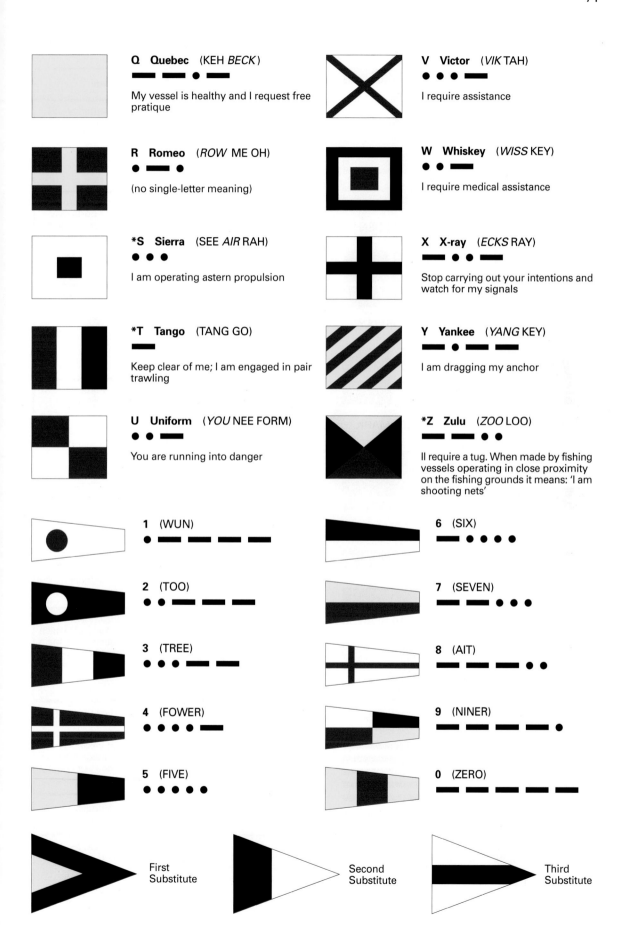

Q Quebec (KEH *BECK*)

━ ━ ● ━

My vessel is healthy and I request free pratique

R Romeo (*ROW* ME OH)

● ━ ● ●

(no single-letter meaning)

*S Sierra (SEE *AIR* RAH)

● ● ●

I am operating astern propulsion

*T Tango (TANG GO)

━

Keep clear of me; I am engaged in pair trawling

U Uniform (*YOU* NEE FORM)

● ● ━

You are running into danger

V Victor (*VIK* TAH)

● ● ● ━

I require assistance

W Whiskey (*WISS* KEY)

● ● ━

I require medical assistance

X X-ray (*ECKS* RAY)

━ ● ● ━

Stop carrying out your intentions and watch for my signals

Y Yankee (*YANG* KEY)

━ ● ━ ━

I am dragging my anchor

*Z Zulu (*ZOO* LOO)

━ ━ ● ●

Il require a tug. When made by fishing vessels operating in close proximity on the fishing grounds it means: 'I am shooting nets'

1 (WUN)

● ━ ━ ━ ━

2 (TOO)

● ● ━ ━ ━

3 (TREE)

● ● ● ━ ━

4 (FOWER)

● ● ● ● ━

5 (FIVE)

● ● ● ● ●

6 (SIX)

━ ● ● ● ●

7 (SEVEN)

━ ━ ● ● ●

8 (AIT)

━ ━ ━ ● ●

9 (NINER)

━ ━ ━ ━ ●

0 (ZERO)

━ ━ ━ ━ ━

First Substitute

Second Substitute

Third Substitute

PLATE 8 – NATIONAL ENSIGNS

UK WHITE ENSIGN

FINLAND

UK BLUE ENSIGN

SWEDEN

UK RED ENSIGN

NORWAY

IRELAND

DENMARK

GUERNSEY

GERMANY

FRANCE

NETHERLANDS

SPAIN

BELGIUM

PORTUGAL

GREECE

PANAMA

LIBERIA

PLATE 9 – INTERNATIONAL PORT TRAFFIC SIGNALS

No	Lights		Main message
1	(three flashing lights)	Flashing	Serious emergency – all vessels to stop or divert according to instructions
2	(three fixed lights)	Fixed or Slow Occulting	Vessels shall not proceed (*Note:* Some ports may use an exemption signal, as in 2a below)
3	(three lights)		Vessels may proceed. One-way traffic
4	(three lights)		Vessels may proceed. Two-way traffic
5	(three lights)		A vessel may proceed only when she has received specific orders to do so. (*Note:* Some ports may use an exemption signal, as in 5a below)
		Exemption signals and messages	
2a	(four lights)	Fixed or Slow Occulting	Vessels shall not proceed, except that vessels which navigate outside the main channel need not comply with the main message
5a	(four lights)		A vessel may proceed when she has received specific orders to do so, except that vessels which navigate outside the main channel need not comply with the main message
		Auxilliary signals and messages	
	White and/or yellow lights, displayed to the right of the main lights		Local meanings, as promulgated in local port orders

ENSIGNS

All countries have national flags and some have maritime versions (ensigns), normally based on the national flag (e.g. the United Kingdom's Red Ensign). Some countries use their national flag unaltered (e.g. France's tricolore or the Dutch flag which is also the civil and naval ensign).

On the facing page are some of the ensigns most likely to be seen in the areas covered by this Almanac. A full list can be found in *The Macmillan and Silk Cut Yachtsman's Handbook.*

The United Kingdom has three ensigns. The White worn by ships of the Royal Navy and shore establishments. Members of the Royal Yacht Squadron may also wear the White Ensign (subject to permit) in vessels of a certain size. The Blue may be worn by British Merchant Ships commanded by an RNR officer and, more commonly, by members of certain privileged yacht clubs (subject to permit). In its defaced form (i.e. with a badge) it is used by various government organisations and certain other yacht clubs (see 6.4.2.). The Red is worn by other British vessels not mentioned above, not least by merchant ships and the vast majority of yachts and motor cruisers. The defaced Red Ensign is used by a small number of privileged yacht clubs (see 6.4.2).

Most countries have a common national and maritime flag, but there are exceptions – usually for the senior yacht club which administers the sport. For instance the Royal Danish Yacht Club may use the split flag (swallow-tail) ensign of their navy with the letters YF and three golden stars in their canton. The ensign of the Royal Norwegian Yacht Club (KNS) has a swallow-tail with a tongue and a royal cypher in gold beneath the crown of the state arms. Similar privileges are accorded to the Yacht Club Italiano and the Yacht Club of Poland.

The Guernsey ensign is included as it is the only Channel Island with an approved ensign. It can be worn by any yacht based within the bailiwick of Guernsey and can be worn as an alternative to the Red Ensign as the courtesy flag by visiting yachts. The national flag of Guernsey should not be worn. UK yachts need not fly a courtesy flag in the Channel Islands.

The flags of Liberia and Panama are included since many ships are registered in these two countries by owners who are not their nationals. Known as flags of convenience, they are used to avoid the much more stringent inspections and regulations imposed by traditional maritime countries.

INT. PORT TRAFFIC SIGNALS

The international system is gradually being introduced, but its general adoption is likely to take many years.

(a) The main movement message given by a port traffic signal always comprises three lights, disposed vertically. No additional light shall be added to the column carrying the main message. (The fact that the main message always consists of three vertical lights allows the mariner to recognise it as a traffic signal, and not lights of navigational significance.) The signals may also be used to control traffic at locks and bridges.

(b) Red lights indicate 'Do not proceed'.

(c) Green lights indicate 'Proceed, subject to the conditions stipulated'. (For examples, see opposite.) Note that, to avoid confusion, red and green lights are never displayed together.

(d) Some signals may be omni-directional – i.e. exhibited to all vessels simultaneously: others must be directional, and be shown either to vessels entering or to vessels leaving harbour.

(e) The 'Serious Emergency' signal must be flashing, at least 60 flashes per minute. All other signals must be either fixed or slow occulting (the latter useful when background glare is a problem). A mixture of fixed and occulting lights must not be used.

(f) Signal No. 5 is based on the assumption that another means of communication such as VHF radio, signal lamp, loud-hailer, or auxiliary signal will be used to inform a vessel that she may specifically proceed.

(g) A single yellow light, displayed to the left of the column carrying main messages Nos. 2 or 5, at the level of the upper light, may be used to indicate that 'Vessels which can safely navigate outside the main channel need not comply with the main message'. This signal, as shown at Nos. 2a and 5a, is of obvious significance to yachtsmen.

(h) Signals which are auxiliary to the main message may be devised by local authorities. Such auxiliary signals should employ only white and/or yellow lights, and should be displayed to the right of the column carrying the main message. Ports with complex entrances and much traffic may need many auxiliary signals, which will have to be documented. See also 10.15.8 for traffic signals which may still be shown at some French ports. Smaller harbours with less traffic may only need one or two of the basic signals, such as 'Vessels shall not proceed' and 'Vessels may proceed, two-way traffic'.

THEY'RE IN THE PINK

and just a phone call away

So look them up and widen your horizons

The PINK PAGES section at the front of the book is your own guide to marinas, harbours, services and supplies, including emergencies. With over 60 categories listed by discipline and coastal location, it is the quickest route to find what you want with simplicity and ease.

The MACMILLAN *incorporating* REED'S
NAUTICAL ALMANAC

Chapter 6

Communications

Contents

6

Communications – introduction

Yachts may often need to communicate with other vessels and with shore stations. This is now commonly done by Very High Frequency (VHF) radiotelephone, so emphasis is placed on this method in this chapter. Radio broadcasts of gale warnings and weather bulletins are described in Chapter 7, while detailed information on Distress, Urgency and Safety signals is given in Chapter 8.

A full description of the various methods of signalling and the procedures that are involved, including an explanation of the *International Code of Signals*, is given in Chapter 6 of *The Macmillan & Silk Cut Yachtsman's Handbook*. This also contains more detailed notes on flag etiquette, with colour plates showing the burgees of 217 selected yacht clubs and the maritime flags of 165 nations.

6.1   INTERNATIONAL CODE

6.1.1   International Code of Signals

Most communication afloat by pleasure craft is now by radiotelephone, in plain language, and mostly using Very High Frequency (VHF) equipment, providing short range services up to 30-40 miles depending on the heights of the aerials concerned. Other forms of radiotelephony are described in section 6.4.

In more general terms marine communication is based on the *International Code of Signals* (HMSO), which provides for safety of navigation and of persons particularly where there are language problems. The code can be used by alphabetical flags and numeral pendants, by flashing light and sound signalling using the Morse code, by voice using radiotelephony or loud-hailer, by radiotelegraphy, or by hand flags.

Signals consist of: single-letter signals which are very urgent or very common; two-letter signals in the General Section; and three-letter signals starting with 'M' in the Medical Section.

6.1.2   Using the International Code

The present International Code came into force in 1969 and is presented in nine editorial languages – English, French, Italian, German, Japanese, Spanish, Norwegian, Russian and Greek. Ships, aircraft and shore stations can communicate with each other in these languages without knowing a foreign tongue if a copy of the appropriate *International Code of Signals* is held. The English language edition is published by HMSO.

An explanation of the use of the International Code is given in Chapter 6 of *The Macmillan & Silk Cut Yachtsman's Handbook*, which also contains a few selected code groups which can be useful in emergency situations.

Plates 6 and 7 on pages 70–71 of this Almanac show the International Code flags for the alphabet and for numerals, the phonetic alphabet, the phonetic figure-spelling table, the Morse symbols for letters and numerals, and the meanings of important or common single-letter signals. See 6.2.

6.2   MISCELLANEOUS SIGNALS

6.2.1   Radio time signals

The BBC broadcast time signals at the local times and on the frequencies indicated in the table below. The start of the final, longer pulse marks the minute.

BBC Radio 1   97·6–99·8 MHz
                   (97·1MHz for Channel Islands)
BBC Radio 2   88–90·2 MHz
                   (89·6 MHz for Channel Islands)
BBC Radio 3   90·2–92·4 MHz
                   (91·1 MHz for Channel Islands)
BBC Radio 4   198 kHz
                   92·4–94·6 MHz
                   (94·8 MHz for Channel Islands)

Also   603 kHz   (Tyneside)
       720 kHz   (N Ireland & London)
       756 kHz   (Redruth)
       774 kHz   (Plymouth & Enniskillen)
      1449 kHz   (Aberdeen)
      1485 kHz   (Carlisle)

Local time	Mon-Fri Radio	Sat Radio	Sun Radio
0000	2,4*	2,4*	2,4*
0600	4	3	4
0700	1,2,3,4	2,3,4	4
0800	1,2,3,4	2,4	2,4
0900	4	4	2,4
1000	4	4	
1100	4	4	
1200	4		
1300	2,4	1,4	4
1400	4	4	
1500	4		
1600	4	4	
1700	2,4		1,4
1800	4*	4*	4*
1900	4		2
2100			4
2200	4	4*	4*

* indicates Big Ben (first hour strike)

6.2.2   Pratique messages

All vessels arriving directly from outside the European Union must fly the yellow 'Q' flag where it can easily be seen, and illuminated at night, on entering the 12 mile limit. It must be kept hoisted until Customs formalities are completed.

Other pratique messages from the International Code are given in *The Macmillan & Silk Cut Yachtsman's Handbook*.

6.2.3   Distress signals and emergencies

Details of Distress signals, visual signals between shore and ships in distress, signals used by SAR aircraft, and directing signals used by aircraft are given in Chapter 8 (8.2 and 8.3).

6.2.4   Port Traffic signals

Traffic signals etc. for individual harbours are shown in Chapter 10. On the Continent Traffic signals are to some extent standardised – see 10.15.8 for France, 10.20.7 for Belgium and the Netherlands, and 10.21.7 for Germany.

International Port Traffic Signals are shown in Plate 9 and described on page 72. These are being increasingly used. Local variations are shown under individual harbours in Chapter 10.

For Port Operations and Vessel Traffic Services (VTS) on VHF RT see 6.4.19.

6.3   SHORT NOTES ON FLAG ETIQUETTE

For many years flags were the only way to pass messages at sea, and although this function has now been largely superseded by radio, flags remain a useful way of expressing identity – by national ensigns, club burgees, etc. Here is brief guidance on how they should be used.

6.3.1   Ensign

A yacht's ensign is the national maritime flag corresponding to the nationality of her owner. Thus a British yacht should wear the Red Ensign, unless she qualifies for a special ensign (see 6.3.2). It goes without saying that the national ensign should be kept clean and in good repair. At sea the ensign must be worn when meeting other vessels, when entering or leaving foreign ports, or when approaching forts, Signal and Coastguard Stations, etc. Increasingly it has become the practice to leave the ensign (and burgee) flying at all times in foreign waters – even at night in harbour, assuming that the boat' is not unattended. In British harbours it is the custom for the ensign to be hoisted at 0800 (0900 between 1 November and 14 February) or as soon after that time as people come on board; and lowered at sunset (or 2100 local time if earlier) or before that time if the crew is leaving the boat.

The ensign should normally be worn at the stern, but if this is not possible the nearest position should be used, e.g. at the peak in a gaff-rigged boat, at the mizzen masthead in a ketch or yawl, or about two-thirds up the leech of the mainsail. In harbour or at anchor the proper position is at the stern.

The ensign should not be worn when racing (after the five minute gun). It should be hoisted on finishing or when retiring.

6.3.2   Special ensigns

Members of certain clubs may apply for permission to wear a special ensign (e.g. Blue Ensign, defaced Blue Ensign, or defaced Red Ensign). For this purpose the yacht must either be a registered ship under Part I of the Merchant Shipping Act 1894 and of at least 2 tons gross tonnage, or be registered under the Merchant Shipping Act 1983 (Small Ships Register) and of at least 7 metres overall length. The owner or owners must be British subjects, and the yacht must not be used for any professional, business or commercial purpose. Full details can be obtained from the Secretaries of clubs concerned.

A special ensign must only be worn when the owner is on board or ashore in the vicinity, and only when the yacht is flying the burgee (or a Flag Officer's flag) of the club concerned. The permit must be carried on board. When the yacht is sold, or the owner ceases to be a member of the club, the permit must be returned to the Secretary of the club.

6.3.3   Burgee

A burgee shows that a yacht is in the charge of a member of the club indicated, and does not necessarily indicate ownership. It should be flown at the masthead.

Should this be impossible due to wind sensors, radio antenna, etc. the burgee may be flown at the starboard crosstrees, but this should be avoided unless absolutely necessary. A yacht should not fly more than one burgee. A burgee is not flown when a yacht is racing. If the yacht is on loan, or is chartered, it is correct to use the burgee of the skipper or charterer – not that of the absent owner. Normal practice has been to lower the burgee at night, at the same time as the ensign, but nowadays many owners leave the burgee flying if they are on board or ashore in the vicinity.

6.3.4   Flag Officer's flag

Clubs authorise their Flag Officers to fly special swallow-tailed flags, with the same design as the club burgee and in place of it. The flags of a vice-commodore and a rear-commodore carry one and two balls respectively. A Flag Officer's flag is flown day and night while he is on board, or ashore nearby. A Flag Officer should fly his flag with the Red Ensign (or special ensign, where authorised) in preference to the burgee of some other club.

6.3.5   Choice of burgee

An owner who is not a Flag Officer, and who belongs to more than one club, should normally fly the burgee (and if authorised the special ensign) of the senior club in the harbour where the yacht is lying. An exception may be if another club is staging a regatta or similar function.

6.3.6   Courtesy ensign

It is customary when abroad to fly a small maritime ensign of the country concerned at the starboard crosstrees. A courtesy ensign must not be worn in a position inferior to any flag other than the yacht's own ensign and club burgee (or Flag Officer's flag). The correct courtesy flag for a foreign yacht in British waters is the Red Ensign (not the Union Flag). British yachts do not fly a courtesy flag in the Channel Islands since these are part of the British Isles.

6.3.7   House flag

An owner may fly his personal flag when he is on board in harbour, provided it does not conflict with the design of some existing flag. A house flag is normally rectangular, and is flown at the crosstrees in a sloop or cutter, at the mizzen masthead in a ketch or yawl, or at the foremast head in a schooner.

6.3.8   Salutes

Yachts should salute all Royal Yachts, and all warships of whatever nationality. A salute is made by dipping the ensign (only). The vessel saluted responds by dipping her ensign, and then re-hoisting it, whereupon the vessel saluting re-hoists hers. It is customary for a Flag Officer to be saluted (not more than once a day) by a yacht flying the burgee of that club.

6.4   RADIO COMMUNICATIONS

6.4.1   Radiotelephones – general

Many yachts are fitted with radiotelephones, mostly Very High Frequency (VHF) sets with ranges of about 20 miles. Medium Frequency (MF) sets give much greater ranges, but must be Single Sideband (SSB). Double Sideband (DSB) transmissions are prohibited except for emergency transmissions on 2182 kHz, the international MF Distress frequency. Full details of the various licences and operating procedures are given in Chapter 6 of *The Macmillan & Silk Cut Yachtsman's Handbook*. The brief notes which follow cover only the most important points.

For a yacht which requires to maintain radio contact with shore on ocean passages it is necessary to use High Frequency (HF) radio, which is more powerful and gives a much longer range than MF, as described below.

6.4.2   Licensing requirements

A Ship Radio Licence is required for any VHF, UHF, MF, HF equipment, satellite communication or EPIRB on board. It is obtained from: Wray Castle, Ship Radio Licensing, PO Box 5, Ambleside, LA22 0BF. Tel: 015394 34662. ☎: 015394 34663. In addition to the international maritime channels, this allows the use, afloat in the UK, of Ch M and Ch M2 for communications between yachts, yacht harbours and clubs, and for race control.

A Certificate of Competence and an Authority to Operate are required by the person in charge of a set. For yachtsmen this is likely to be the Certificate of Competence, Restricted VHF Only. The Royal Yachting Association (RYA) is responsible for the conduct of this examination. Details of the syllabus and examination are in RYA booklet G26, available (with application form for the examination) from the RYA. This is to be replaced by a new Short Range radiotelephone Certificate (SRC) incorporating GMDSS procedures. For details of other certificates contact the Radiocommunications Agency (see page 20).

Neither Citizens Band or Amateur (Ham) Radio are substitutes for proper maritime radio on VHF, MF or HF, but they can be a useful means of communication for other than safety matters. CB and Amateur Radio Licences are issued by Subscription Services Ltd, Barton House, Bond Street, Bristol BS98 1TI. Tel: 0117 921 9095.

6.4.3   Radiotelephones – regulations

For details see the *Handbook for Marine Radio Communication* (Lloyds of London Press). Briefly: operators must not divulge the contents of messages heard; stations must identify themselves when transmitting; except in cases of Distress, Coast Radio Stations control communications in their areas; at sea a yacht may call other vessels or shore stations, but messages must not be sent to an address ashore except through a Coast Radio Station; in harbour a yacht may not use inter-ship channels except for safety, and may only communicate with the local Port Operations Service, British Telecom (BT) Coast Stations, or with stations on Ch M or M2; do not interfere with the

working of other stations – before transmitting, listen to see that the channel is free; it is forbidden to transmit unnecessary or superfluous signals; priority must be given to Distress calls; the transmission of bad language is forbidden; a log must be kept, recording all transmissions etc.

6.4.4   VHF radio

Very High Frequency (VHF) radio has a range slightly better than the line of sight between the aerials. It pays to fit a good aerial, as high as possible. Maximum power output is 25 watts, and a lower power (usually one watt) is used for short ranges. UK Coast Radio Stations and many harbours now have VHF, as do the principal Coastguard Stations and other rescue services.

Marine VHF frequencies are in the band 156·00–174·00 MHz. Ch 16 (156·80 MHz) is for Distress and Safety purposes, and for calling and answering. Once contact has been made, the stations concerned must switch to a working channel, except for Safety matters. Yachts at sea are encouraged to listen on Ch 16.

Basic VHF sets are 'simplex', transmitting and receiving on the same frequency, so that it is not possible to speak and listen simultaneously. 'Semi-duplex' sets transmit and receive on different frequencies, while fully 'duplex' sets can do this simultaneously so that conversation is normal.

There are three main groups of frequencies, but certain channels can be used for more than one purpose. *They are shown in order of preference.*
(1) *Public correspondence* (through Coast Radio Stations). All can be used for duplex. Ch 26, 27, 25, 24, 23, 28, 04, 01, 03, 02, 07, 05, 84, 87, 86, 83, 85, 88, 61, 64, 65, 62, 66, 63, 60, 82.
(2) *Inter-ship*. These are all simplex. Ch 06, 08, 10, 13, 09, 72, 73, 69, 67, 77, 15, 17.
(3) *Port Operations*. Simplex: Ch 12, 14, 11, 13, 09, 68, 71, 74, 10, 67, 69, 73, 17, 15. Duplex: Ch 20, 22, 18, 19, 21, 05, 07, 02, 03, 01, 04, 78, 82, 79, 81, 80, 60, 63, 66, 62, 65, 64, 61, 84.

Ch 80 (Tx 161·625 MHz Rx 157·025 MHz) is the primary working channel for yachts with yacht harbours, plus Ch M (157·85 MHz) as a stand-by. Yacht clubs may apply to use Ch M2 (161·425 MHz) for race control with Ch M as stand-by (see 6.4.2). Ch 67 (156·375 MHz) is operated in the UK by principal Coastguard Stations as the Small Craft Safety Channel, accessed via Ch 16 (see 8.2.4 and 8.4.2).

Ch 70 is reserved exclusively for digital selective calling for Distress and Safety purposes.

6.4.5   MF radio

MF radiotelephones operate in the 1605–4200 kHz wavebands. Unlike VHF and HF, MF transmissions tend to follow the curve of the earth, which makes them suitable for direction-finding equipment. For this reason, and because of their good range, the marine Distress radiotelephone frequency is in the MF band (2182 kHz). Silence periods are observed on this frequency for three minutes commencing every hour and half hour.

During these silence periods only Distress and Urgency messages may be transmitted (see 8.2.5). MF radio equipment must be Single Sideband (SSB). Double Sideband (DSB) transmissions are prohibited except for emergency-only sets operating on 2182 kHz. As for VHF, both the operator and the set must be licensed. MF sets are more complex and more expensive than VHF, and are subject to more regulations.

6.4.6 HF radio
HF radiotelephones use wavebands that are chosen, according to prevailing propagation conditions, from 4, 8, 12, 16 and 22 MHz bands (short wave). HF is more expensive than MF and absorbs more power, but it can provide worldwide coverage – although good installation and correct operation are essential for satisfactory results.

Whereas MF transmissions follow the curve of the earth, HF waves travel upwards and bounce off the ionosphere back to earth. Reception is better at night when the ionosphere is more dense. The directional properties of HF transmissions are poor, and there is no radiotelephone HF Distress frequency.

6.4.7 RT procedures
Except for Distress, Urgency or Safety messages, communications between a ship and a Coast Radio Station are controlled by the latter. Between two ship stations, the station called controls the working. A calling station must use a frequency on which the station called is keeping watch. After making contact, communication can continue on an agreed working channel. For VHF the name of the station called need normally only be given once, and that of the calling station twice. Once contact is made, each name need only be transmitted once. If a station does not reply, check the settings on the transmitter and repeat the call at three-minute intervals (if the channel is clear).

Prowords
It is important to understand the following:

ACKNOWLEDGE	'Have you received and understood?'
CONFIRM	'My version is … is that correct?'
CORRECTION	'An error has been made; the correct version is …'
I SAY AGAIN	'I repeat … (e.g. important words)'
I SPELL	'What follows is spelt phonetically'
OUT	End of work
OVER	'I have completed this part of my message, and am inviting you to reply'
RECEIVED	'Receipt acknowledged'
SAY AGAIN	'Repeat your message (or part indicated)'
STATION CALLING	Used when a station is uncertain of the identity of a station which is calling

Before making a call, decide exactly what needs to be said. It may help to write the message down. Speak clearly and distinctly. Names or important words can be repeated or spelt phonetically.

For a position, give latitude and longitude, or the yacht's bearing and distance from a charted object. For bearings use 360° True notation. For times use 24 hour notation, and specify UT, BST, etc.

6.4.8 Coast Radio Stations – general
Maritime countries operate Coast Radio Stations which control communications and link ship stations with the telephone network ashore. These Coast Radio Stations operate on nominated frequencies – for European waters see 6.5.1–6.5.6.

At scheduled times they transmit Traffic Lists, Navigation Warnings, Weather Bulletins, and (as required) Gale Warnings. They play an important part in Distress, Urgency and Safety messages (see 8.2).

6.4.9 Coast Radio Stations – United Kingdom
In the United Kingdom Coast Radio Stations are operated by BT Maritime Services, and details are shown in 6.5.1. There are eight MF stations and a larger number of VHF stations, the latter providing VHF coverage for most inshore waters.

For commercial telephone (link) calls the MF and VHF stations form one big network, and any call that comes in through any station within the UK will be answered by the first available Radio Officer, wherever he may be. A call to Land's End Radio might well be answered by an operator at Portpatrick.

For Distress and Safety, including medical advice and assistance, and for broadcasting Navigational Warnings, Weather Forecasts, Gale Warnings, etc., the stations are divided into Northern and Southern Regions. The MF stations in the Southern Region comprise Land's End, Niton, and Humber Radios. The Northern Region comprises Cullercoats, Stonehaven, Wick/Shetland, Hebrides, and Portpatrick Radios. The Southern Region controlling station is Land's End, and the Northern Region station is Stonehaven. The Commercial and Broadcasting systems are separate to reduce problems in the event of equipment or line failure.

Broadcasts are on dedicated MF frequencies and on selected VHF channels (also used for link calls). The Officer in each region making the broadcast can engage and speak over the broadcast frequencies and channels of all regional stations.

Some stations keep watch on Ch 16 or 2182 kHz, but HM Coastguard is primarily responsible for monitoring Distress, Urgency and Safety calls.

Long-range service is provided by Portishead Radio on High Frequency (HF). See 6.4.13 and 6.5.1.

6.4.10 VHF calls to UK Coast Stations
When within range (about 40 miles) you are likely to be able to call a Coast Radio Station. This allows you to make ordinary telephone calls, reverse-charge calls, YTD calls (see below), or send telegrams. There is also free access to Navigational Warnings, Weather Bulletins and Gale Warnings.

6

Except in emergency, vessels should call a UK Coast Station on one of the working frequencies shown in 6.5.1. For a Distress or Urgency call (only) use Ch 16. Avoid using the station's designated broadcast channel at about the time of a scheduled broadcast. Proceed as follows:

(1) Listen for a 'clear' channel, with no transmission at all. A busy channel will have either carrier noise, speech or the engaged signal (a series of pips).

(2) Having located a free channel, the initial call must last at least six seconds in order to activate the Coast Radio Station's ship-call latch equipment. For example: 'Land's End Radio, Land's End Radio, this is Yacht Seabird, Seabird Golf Oscar Romeo India – Channel 27, Over'.

(3) When the call is accepted by the Coast Radio Station you will hear engaged pips, indicating that you have activated and engaged the channel. Wait for the operator to speak. If you are not answered, do not change channel since you may lose your turn. If you do not hear the pips you have not activated the station's transmitter and may be out of range. Try another station or call again when you get closer.

(4) When you are answered by the Radio Officer be ready to give the following: Vessel's call sign, name, type of call and billing details (see below), and for a link call the telephone number required (and the name of the person in the case of a personal call).

It is possible to make personal calls to certain countries and collect (transferred charge) calls to the UK. Worldwide accounting for calls is arranged by quoting the 'Accounting Authority Indicator Code' (AAIC) if this has been arranged with one of the several ITU-recognised authorities such as BT. VHF link calls through BT Coast Radio Stations to the UK, or Isle of Man can be charged to the owner's home telephone by Yacht Telephone Debit (YTD). Be prepared to advise the operator accordingly. Payment can also be made by transfer charge or by BT Chargecard, which also applies to foreign calls. The operator makes the connection. Timing is automatic.

Note: St Peter Port and Jersey CRS are regarded as foreign stations by BT who add a handling charge of £4 – £7 on the bill. For Jersey, calls may be billed to a UK address. See page 85.

6.4.11 VHF calls to foreign Coast Stations

French, German and Irish stations are called on a working channel, similarly Belgian and Dutch stations, but depending on the position of the yacht. VHF calls to Scheveningen Radio should last several seconds and state the calling channel. A four-tone signal indicates temporary delay, but you will be answered when an operator is free.

6.4.12 MF calls to UK Coast Stations

Calls should be made on 2182 kHz. The Coast Station will answer on 2182 kHz, allocate a working channel, and queue you into the system.

Distress and Urgency calls should always be made on 2182 kHz, and will be answered on the same frequency. This includes urgent medical calls which should be preceded by the Urgency signal 'PAN PAN MEDICO' (see 8.4.11). For full details of radio Distress procedures see Chapter 8.

Should a Coast Radio Station be operating Distress traffic on 2182 kHz, call on 2191 kHz and listen for a reply on the station's broadcast frequency. You will then be allocated a channel. The Radio Officer will then request the following information: Vessel's call sign, name, accounting code (AAIC – see 6.4.10), and category of traffic (e.g. telegram, telephone call).

6.4.13 HF calls – Portishead Radio

The long-range service in the United Kingdom is provided by Portishead Radio, operated by BT Maritime Radio. Watch is kept on the higher bands during daylight, and on the lower bands at night. A 24-hour watch is kept on the 8 MHz band.

The bands in use are announced after the Traffic Lists, broadcast every H+00, and major changes are notified during the previous week. Channels assigned to Portishead Radio are listed in 6.5.1. R3E (SSB reduced carrier) or J3E (SSB suppressed carrier) are the modes of transmission that are mandatory in both directions, but on channel 1201 J3E should be used whenever possible and this is the preferred mode for all transmissions.

An *Optimum Transmitting Frequency Guide* is available on radiotelex from Portishead Radio Databank facility. It predicts the best band for contacting Portishead worldwide. It is only a guide, and bands should be monitored to get the best signal.

Equipment must be correctly tuned before calling, and interference not caused to calls in progress. Do not call until a channel is clear, which is announced by Portishead Radio after each period of working.

6.4.14 VHF and MF calls to a yacht

Telephone call bookings to vessels via BT Coast Stations are handled by Portishead Radio. By dialling 0800 378389 you will be connected free of charge to the ship's radiotelephone service. This number should be used to book calls on VHF, Short Range; the MF, Medium Range; or the HF, Long Range services. You will be asked for the name of the vessel, station through which vessel normally communicates, voyage details, caller's telephone number (or number to be charged if different), person to whom you wish to speak, and caller's name. Portishead Radio will route the call to the appropriate Coast Radio Station. If the vessel is subsequently contacted by other means (e.g. landline) a call via a Coast Station should be cancelled.

For receiving calls, you are called on Ch 16 or 2182 kHz when a call is ready, but it is recommended to listen to the regular Traffic Lists broadcast from the nearest Coast Radio Station. If your vessel has a selective call device, you can be alerted by a Coast Radio Station transmitting your Selcall number on Ch 16 or 2170·5 kHz. Some Selcall equipment displays the number of the station calling, but in practice when responding to a call, contact the nearest station to you.

6.4.15 Autolink RT

Autolink RT gives direct dialling from ship to shore into national and international telephone networks without going through a Coast Radio Station operator. It functions through an on-board unit which is easily connected to the radio, and which does not interfere with normal manual operation. This service on VHF, MF and HF gives quicker access, cheaper calls, call scrambling on some units where privacy is required, and simplified accounting. Last number redial and a ten-number memory store are available.

Do not use Autolink for Distress, Urgency and Safety (including medical) calls, but use the normal manual procedure on VHF Ch 16 or 2182 kHz.

6.4.16 Weather information by RT

See Chapter 7 – for example: 7.2.5 (ships at sea), 7.2.16 (broadcasts by Coast Radio Stations), 7.2.17 (broadcasts by HM Coastguard), 7.2.18 (present weather).

6.4.17 Medical help by RT

See Chapter 8 (8.4.11) for seeking medical advice or medical assistance by RT.

6.4.18 Flotilla reporting schemes

Where numbers of yachts are required to report on a regular basis to a control centre, BT offer two schemes. (1) Where vessels are given a window during which to report, and (2) where vessels report at fixed times. Details from BT Maritime Radio, 43 Bartholomew Close, London EC1A 7HP.

6.4.19 Port Operations and Vessel Traffic Services

Most harbours and marinas now have VHF RT facilities, while a few harbours also operate on MF (mostly for pilotage). The nominated channels are only for messages concerning Port Operations or, in emergency, the safety of persons, and not for public correspondence. For details of harbour RT information in Chapter 10, see 10.0.3.

An increasing number of ports are implementing Vessel Traffic Services (VTS) schemes, to improve the safety and efficiency of traffic and to protect the environment. VTS may range from the provision of information messages to the extensive management of traffic within a port or waterway, and is aimed primarily at commercial vessels which must comply with the laid down procedures.

Yachts are not normally expected to comply with VTS radio and reporting procedures, except in certain ports and waterways where larger yachts may fall within the stipulated minimum length or tonnage.

When navigating in areas covered by VTS or Port Operations Services, especially in poor visibility or at night, yachts can gain valuable information about the movement of ships by listening on the nominated working channel.

Most VTS (and some Port Operations) schemes have information broadcasts at scheduled times, typically covering traffic, weather, tidal details, and local navigational warnings. VTS radio channels are shown in Chapter 10 on Area Maps, Traffic Separation Scheme diagrams, or under RADIO TELEPHONE in port entries.

6.4.20 Distress, Urgency and Safety traffic by radiotelephone

There are agreed international procedures for passing radiotelephone messages concerning vessels in Distress – or for lesser emergencies or situations where Urgency or Safety messages are appropriate. These are fully described in 8.2. For the Global Maritime Distress and Safety System (GMDSS) see 8.3.

If you hear a Distress call, you must cease all transmissions that might interfere with it or other Distress traffic, and continue listening on the frequency concerned. Write down what you hear. You may have responsibilities for assisting the casualty or for relaying the Distress messages. This, and the general control of Distress traffic, are discussed in 8.2.5 and 8.2.8.

6.4.21 Inmarsat

Worldwide satellite communication (Satcom) is provided by the International Maritime Satellite Organisation (Inmarsat), through satellites in geostationary orbits above the equator over the Atlantic, Pacific and Indian Oceans. These satellites are the links between the Coast Earth Stations (CESs), operated by organisations such as BT, and the on-board terminals called Ship Earth Stations (SESs). Satcom is more reliable and gives better reception than HF SSB radio.

A CES connects the satellite system with the land-based communication network. A message to a ship originating on land is transmitted by the CES to one of the satellites, and thence to the ship. A call from a ship is received via the satellite by the CES, which then transmits it onwards over land-based networks.

Standard 'A' terminals, with a big antenna only suitable for larger vessels, have direct dialling telephone, Telex, data and fax facilities.

Standard 'C' are smaller, and are for sending and receiving data or text (but not voice). Both 'A' and 'C' offer speedy connection to HM Coastguard's MRCC at Falmouth for Distress, Safety, etc.

More recently, Inmarsat 'B' was launched as an improved successor to Inmarsat 'A', while Standard 'M' now makes satellite telephone, fax and data services available to a wide range of yachts, using smaller and cheaper equipment.

6.4.22 Navigational Warnings – general

The worldwide Navigational Warning Service covers 16 sea areas (Navareas) numbered I to XVI, each with a country nominated as Area Co-ordinator responsible for issuing long-range warnings. These are numbered consecutively through the year and are transmitted in English and in one or more other languages at scheduled times by WT. Other forms of transmission (RT, radiotelex and fax) may also be used. Warnings cover items such as failures or changes to navigational aids, wrecks and navigational dangers of all kinds, SAR operations, cable or pipe laying, naval exercises, etc.

6

Within each Navarea, Coastal Warnings and Local Warnings may also be issued. Coastal Warnings, up to 100 or 200 miles offshore, are broadcast in English and in the national language by Coast Radio Stations. Local Warnings are issued by harbour authorities in the national language.

6.4.23 Navigational Warnings – Europe

United Kingdom

The United Kingdom (together with Northern Europe and Scandinavia) comes within Navarea 1, with Britain as the Area Co-ordinator for long-range Navigational Warnings which are broadcast by Portishead Radio (GKA). Messages are numbered and are published in the weekly *Notices to Mariners* together with a list of warnings still in force. Navtex Warnings (see 6.4.25) are broadcast by Niton, Cullercoats, and Portpatrick Radio for the areas shown in Fig. 6(1).

Coastal Warnings are broadcast by RT at scheduled times from Coast Radio Stations for the Sea Regions lettered A-N in Fig. 6(2). Important warnings are broadcast at any time on the Distress frequencies of 2182 kHz and VHF Ch 16.

Local Warnings from harbour authorities are broadcast by nearby Coast Radio Stations. HM Coastguard broadcasts Local Warnings for inshore waters outside of harbour limits, on VHF Ch 67 after an announcement on Ch 16.

Vessels which encounter dangers to navigation should notify other craft and the nearest Coast Radio Station, prefacing the message by the Safety signal (see 8.2.3).

BT Coast Radio Stations and HM Coastguard in areas concerned make scheduled Subfacts broadcasts of submarine activity in specified exercise areas. For details see 6.5.1 on page 88.

France

Long-range warnings are broadcast in English and French for Navarea II, which includes the west coast of France, by St Lys Radio. The north coast comes within Navarea I.

Avurnavs (AVis URgents aux NAVigateurs) are regional Coastal and Local Warnings issued by regional authorities:
(1) Brestv Avurnavs for the west coast of France and the western Channel (to Mont St Michel)
(2) Cherbourg Avurnavs for the eastern Channel and the North Sea (Mont St Michel to the Belgian frontier).

Avurnavs are broadcast on MF by Coast Radio Stations; urgent ones on receipt and after next silence period, and at scheduled times (see 6.5.3). RT warnings are prefixed by *Sécurité Avurnav*, followed by the name of the station. Local warnings for coastal waters are broadcast by CROSS stations – see Table 8(2).

Belgium

Navigational Warnings are broadcast by Oostende Radio on receipt on 2761 kHz and VHF Ch 27 and at scheduled times (see 6.5.4) on 2761 kHz MF, 518 kHz (Navtex) and on Ch 27.

Netherlands

Navigational Warnings are broadcast by Scheveningen Radio on receipt and at scheduled times (see 6.5.5) on 1713 kHz (Nes) and 1890 kHz and VHF (announcement on Ch 16). Netherlands Coastguard broadcasts warnings on 518 kHz (Navtex) on receipt and at scheduled times (see 6.4.25).

Germany

Navigational Warnings are broadcast by Norddeich Radio on 2614 kHz on receipt, after the next silence period, and at scheduled times. Broadcasts commence with the Safety signal, the words *Nautische Warnnachricht*, and the serial number; they are in English and German. Decca Warnings for the German and Frisian Islands chains (*Decca Warnnachricht*) are included. Dangers to navigation should be reported to Seewarn Cuxhaven.

6.4.24 Other maritime radio services

Apart from Coast Radio Stations, Port Operations and Vessel Traffic Services, some countries operate other radio services connected with Search and Rescue (SAR) and Maritime Safety Information (MSI).

These are described in Chapter 8 (8.4 – 8.5). In most cases these stations also broadcast strong wind warnings together with scheduled weather bulletins and local Navigational Warnings.

6.4.25 Navtex

Navtex provides Navigational and Meteorological Warnings and other Safety information by automatic print-outs from a dedicated receiver, and is a component of the International Maritime Organisation (IMO) Global Maritime Distress and Safety System (GMDSS) (see 8.3).

At present, broadcasts are all in English on a single frequency of 518 kHz, with excellent coverage of coastal waters in areas such as NW Europe where the scheme originated. Interference between stations is avoided by time sharing and by limiting the range of transmitters to about 300 miles, so that three stations cover the United Kingdom. IMO is expected to make a second Navtex channel available for broadcasts in the local national language.

The use of a single frequency allows a simple receiver with a printer using cash-roll paper, although some yacht receivers have a video screen. The user programs the receiver for the vessel's area and for the types of messages required. For example, if Decca is not carried, Decca Warnings can be rejected. The receiver automatically rejects messages which are corrupt or ones that have already been printed.

Each message is prefixed by a four-character group. The first character is the code letter of the transmitting station (in the UK: S for Niton, G for Cullercoats and O for Portpatrick). The second character indicates the category of the message as in the code below. The third and fourth are message serial numbers, from 01 to 99. The serial number 00 denotes urgent traffic such as Gale Warnings and SAR alerts, and messages with this prefix are always printed.

The table below shows the Navtex stations in Navareas I and II with their identity codes and transmission times (UT). The times of Weather Bulletins are shown in bold.

Message categories

A   Navigational Warnings
B   Gale Warnings
C   Ice Reports (unlikely to apply in UK)
D   SAR information and Pirate Attack Warnings
E   Weather Forecasts
F   Pilot Service messages
G   Decca messages
H   Loran-C messages
I   Omega messages
J   Satnav messages
K   Other electronic Navaid messages
L   Subfacts and Gunfacts for the UK
V   Amplifying details of Navigation Warnings initially broadcast under A. The weekly Riglist will also be broadcast using V.
Z   No messages on hand at scheduled time

Information in a Navtex broadcast applies only to the area for which the broadcast station is responsible, as shown in Fig. 6(1). A user may accept messages from one or more stations.

Fig. 6(1)   Navtex Areas – UK and Europe

6

NAVAREA I

			Broadcast Times (UT)				
P –	**Netherlands Coast Guard,** (IJmuiden), Netherlands	0348	0748	1148	1548	1948	2348
T –	**Oostende,** Belgium	0248	**0648**	1048	1448	**1848**	2248
M –	**Oostende,** Belgium	0200	**0600**	1000	1400	**1800**	2200
G –	**Cullercoats,** UK	0048	0448	**0848**	1248	1648	**2048**
S –	**Niton,** UK	0018	0418	**0818**	1218	1618	**2018**
K –	**Niton,** UK	0140	0540	**0940**	1340	1740	**2140**
O –	**Portpatrick,** UK	0130	0530	**0930**	1330	1730	**2130**
L –	Rogaland, Norway	**0148**	0548	**0948**	**1348**	1748	**2148**
W –	**Valentia,** Ireland (On trial 1997)	0340	0740	1140	1540	1940	2340

NAVAREA II

A –	**Le Stiff,** Corsen (CROSS), France	**0000**	0400	0800	**1200**	1600	2000
G –	**Tarifa,** Spain	0100	0500	**0900**	1300	1700	**2100**
R –	**Lisboa,** Portugal	**0250**	**0650**	**1050**	**1450**	**1850**	**2250**
F –	**Horta,** Azores	**0050**	**0450**	**0850**	**1250**	**1650**	**2050**
D –	**La Coruña,** Spain	0030	0430	**0830**	1230	1630	**2030**
I –	**Las Palmas,** Islas Canarias, Spain	0100	0500	0900	1300	1700	2100

6.5   COAST RADIO STATIONS

6.5.1   UK Coast Radio Stations (VHF, MF and HF)

Notes:

a)   Except for St Peter Port Radio and Jersey Radio, services are provided by BT.

b)   MF calls to BT Coast Radio Stations are made and answered on 2182 kHz. During Distress working, call on 2191 kHz and listen for reply on the station's broadcast frequency.

c)   Channel letters and frequencies in *italics* are for Autolink RT only. Most working VHF and MF channels at BT stations are available for manual or Autolink calls.

d)   Gale Warnings are broadcast by BT stations after the first silence period after receipt, and at the next of the following times: 0303 0903 1503 2103 (UT), or if first broadcast at a scheduled time the warning is repeated after the next silence period. In the Southern Region, Weather Bulletins are broadcast at 0733 1933 (UT) or on request. In the Northern Region at 0703 1903 (UT) or on request. For further details of Gale Warnings and Weather Bulletins see Table 7(4) on page 116.

e)   Traffic Lists are sent by BT stations at all scheduled broadcast times (Navigation Warnings, Gale Warnings and Weather Bulletins).

f)   SUBFACTS and GUNFACTS are sent on the broadcast frequencies of certain stations as detailed in 8.5.1 and 8.5.2.

g)   Telephone numbers marked by an asterisk (*) are not continually manned.

Coast Station Name Position	VHF Ch other than Ch 16	Station details with MF frequencies where relevant as shown below				Navigation and Decca Warning times (UT). For Weather Bulletins and Gale Warnings see page 116. Note: Traffic Lists are sent with all scheduled broadcasts
		Distress, Urgency, Safety (kHz)	Working paired MF frequencies (kHz)			
			MF Ch	Coast Station		
				Transmit	Receive	

SOUTHERN REGION

Coast Station Name Position	VHF Ch	Station details with MF frequencies				Navigation and Decca Warning times
CELTIC RADIO 51°41'N 05°11'W	24	VHF station remotely controlled Selcall (3218): Ch 16				Broadcasts on Ch 24 at same times as Land's End below
BURNHAM RADIO 51°13'N 02°59'W	25	VHF station remotely controlled				For commercial traffic in Severn Estuary. No broadcasts
ILFRACOMBE RADIO 51°11'N 04°07'W	05	VHF station remotely controlled Selcall (3205): Ch 16				Broadcasts on Ch 05 at same times as Land's End below
LAND'S END RADIO 50°07'N 05°40'W Tel: 01736 871363	27 64[1]	2182	W X	2782 3610	2111 2120	Broadcasts on 2670 kHz and Ch 27 and Ch 64 at: 0233 0633 1033 1433 1833 2233 (Decca chains 1B 7D)
		Note (1) VHF Ch 64 directed to Scillies Selcall (3204): 2170·5 kHz Ch 16				
PENDENNIS RADIO 50°09'N 05°03'W	62	VHF station remotely controlled Selcall (3238): Ch 16				Broadcasts on Ch 62 at same times as Land's End above
START POINT RADIO 50°21'N 03°43'W	26 60	VHF station remotely controlled Selcall (3224): Ch 16				Broadcasts on Ch 26 at same times as Land's End above

CHANNEL ISLANDS

Coast Station Name Position	VHF Ch	Distress	MF Ch	Transmit	Receive	Navigation and Decca Warning times
ST PETER PORT RADIO 49°27'N 02°32'W Note: Commercial calls only. Link calls available on VHF Ch 62 only. Tel: 01481 720672	20[1] 62[2]	Ship calls on 2182 kHz Station replies on 1764 kHz	1662·5[3] 2182 1764	1662·5[3] 2182[4] 2381[5] 2108 2056		Broadcasts on 1764 kHz and Ch 20 62: *Navigation Warnings* followed by *Traffic Lists* at: 0133 0533 0933 1333 1733 2133. Ships are also called for Traffic on 2182 kHz and Ch 16
	Notes: (1) Direct calling on Ch 20 (2) Link calls on Ch 62 only (3) Trinity House and SAR only			(4) H24 (5) When 2182 is Distress working		

6.5.1   UK Coast Radio Stations (VHF, MF and HF) *continued*

CHANNEL ISLANDS continued

JERSEY RADIO 49°11'N 02°14'W Note: Link calls available on VHF Ch 25 82 only.	25 67[1] 82[2]	Ship calls on 2182 kHz Station replies on 1659 kHz (British ships) or 2182 kHz (foreign ships)	2182 1659	2182[3] 2084[4] 2045[5] 2048[5] 2534[4]	Broadcasts on 1659 kHz and Ch 25 82 after announcement on Ch 16/2182 kHz: *Navigation Warnings:* 0433 UT, 0645 0745 LT, 0833 1245 1633 1845 2033 2245 UT. *Decca Warnings:* On receipt and H+03 for next two hours (Chain 1B).
Pay by credit card, or direct bill to UK address, or to a Jersey Harbour Office account, or on arrival through contact address. *Tel: 01534 41121*		Notes:(1) Ch 67 for yacht Safety messages. Call on Ch 16 (2) Direct calling for UK ships (3) H24. When Distress working call on 2191 and listen on 1659 kHz (4) UK registered vessels (5) Foreign vessels (6) DSC (H24) on Ch 70 (GMDSS A1) MMSI 002320060			*Traffic Lists:* After *Weather Bulletins* at 0645 0745 LT 1245 1845 2245 UT. Ships are also called for traffic on 2182 kHz and Ch 16. *Gale Warnings:* On receipt, after next silence period, and at 0307 0907 1507 2107 UT

SOUTHERN REGION continued

NITON RADIO 50°35'N 01°18'W VHF service at: 50°36'N 01°12'W For NAVTEX see 6.4.25 – page 83 *Tel: 01983 730495**	04 28 64	2182 Note (1) VHF Ch 04 directed to Brighton area Selcall (3203): 2170·5 kHz Ch 16				Broadcasts on 1641 kHz and Ch 28 at: 0233 0633 1033 1433 1833 2233(2) (Decca chains 1B 5B)
HASTINGS RADIO 50°52'N 00°37'E	07	VHF station remotely controlled Selcall (3225): Ch 16				Broadcasts on Ch 07 at same times as North Foreland below
NORTH FORELAND RADIO 51°22'N 01°25'E	26	VHF station remotely controlled Selcall (3201): Ch16				Broadcasts on Ch 26 at: 0133 0533 0933 1333 1733 2133 (Decca chains 1B 5B 2E)
THAMES RADIO 51°20'N 00°20'E	02	VHF station remotely controlled Selcall (3202): Ch 16				Broadcasts on Ch 02 at same times as North Foreland above
ORFORDNESS RADIO 52°00'N 01°25'E	62	VHF station remotely controlled Selcall (3235): Ch 16				Broadcasts on Ch 62 at same times as North Foreland above
BACTON RADIO 52°51'N 01°28'E	07	VHF station remotely controlled Selcall (3214): Ch 16				Broadcasts on Ch 07 at same times as Humber below
HUMBER RADIO 53°20'N 00°17'E *Tel: 01507 473447**	26	2182 Selcall (3212): 2170·5 kHz Ch 16	Q R S 5	1925 2684 2810 3624	2105 2002 2562 3324	Broadcasts on 1869 kHz and Ch 26 at: 0133 0533 0933 1333 1733 2133 (Decca chains 5B 2A 2E 9B)
GRIMSBY RADIO 53°34'N 00°05'W	27	VHF station remotely controlled Selcall (3239): Ch 16				Broadcasts on Ch 27 at same times as Humber above

6

6.5.1   UK Coast Radio Stations (VHF, MF and HF) *continued*

Notes:
- a)   Except for St Peter Port Radio and Jersey Radio, services are provided by BT.
- b)   MF calls to BT Coast Radio Stations are made and answered on 2182 kHz. During Distress working, call on 2191 kHz and listen for reply on the station's broadcast frequency.
- c)   Channel letters and frequencies in *italics* are for Autolink RT only. Most working VHF channels at BT stations are available for manual or Autolink calls.
- d)   Gale Warnings are broadcast by BT stations after the first silence period after receipt, and at the next of the following times: 0303 0903 1503 2103 (UT), or if first broadcast at a scheduled time the warning is repeated after the next silence period. In the Southern Region, Weather Bulletins are broadcast at 0733 1933 (UT) or on request. In the Northern Region at 0703 1903 (UT) or on request. For further details of Gale Warnings and Weather Bulletins see Table 7(4) on page 116.
- e)   Traffic Lists are sent by BT stations at all scheduled broadcast times (Navigation Warnings, Gale Warnings and Weather Bulletins).
- f)   SUBFACTS and GUNFACTS are sent on the broadcast frequencies of certain stations as detailed in 8.5.1 and 8.5.2
- g)   Telephone numbers marked by an asterisk (*) are not continually manned.

Coast Station Name Position	VHF Ch other than Ch 16	Station details with MF frequencies where relevant as shown below				Navigation and Decca Warning times (UT). For Weather Bulletins and Gale Warnings see page 116. Note: Traffic Lists are sent with all scheduled broadcasts
		Distress, Urgency, Safety (kHz)	Working paired MF frequencies (kHz)			
			MF Ch	Coast Station Transmit	Receive	

NORTHERN REGION

Coast Station Name Position	VHF Ch	Distress (kHz)	MF Ch	Transmit	Receive	Navigation and Decca Warning times (UT)
WHITBY RADIO 54°29'N 00°36'W	25	VHF station remotely controlled Selcall (3231): Ch 16				Broadcasts on Ch 25 at same times as Cullercoats below
CULLERCOATS RADIO 55°04'N 01°28'W For NAVTEX see 6.4.25 – page 83 *Tel: 0191 297 0301**	26	2182 Selcall (3211): 2170·5 kHz Ch 16	N	1731	2527	Broadcasts on 2719 kHz and Ch 26 at: 0233 0633 1033 1433 1833 2233 (Decca chain 2A)
STONEHAVEN RADIO 56°57'N 02°13'W *Tel: 01569 762917*	26	2182 Selcall (3222): 2170·5 kHz Ch 16	I K M	1856 1946 3617	2555 2566 3249	Broadcasts on 2691 kHz and Ch 26 at: 0233 0633 1033 1433 1833 2233 (Decca chains 2A 6C 0E)
FORTH RADIO 55°57'N 02°27'W	62	VHF station remotely controlled Selcall (3228): Ch 16				Broadcasts on Ch 62 at same times as Stonehaven above
BUCHAN RADIO 57°36'N 02°03'W	25	VHF station remotely controlled Selcall (3237): Ch 16				Broadcasts on Ch 25 at same times as Stonehaven above
WICK RADIO 58°26'N 03°06'W Located at Norwick, Shetland 60°49'N 00°49'W. (Controlled by Wick Radio.) *Tel: 01955 602271**	28	2182 Selcall (3221): 2170·5 kHz	E F G H A C D	2705 1797 1755 2625 2751 2604 1659	2524 2060 2099 2108 2006 2013 2084	Broadcasts on 1764 kHz (Wick) and 1770 kHz (Norwick, Shetland) at: 0233 0633 1033 1433 1833 2233

Fig. 6(2)   UK Coast Radio Stations

KEY TO MF AND VHF COAST RADIO STATIONS

● = VHF Station, with Channels shown other than Ch 16. Broadcast channels are the first shown.

○ = MF Station

For UK VHF Stations call on a working channel, as described in 6.4.10. In emergency use Ch 16.

For French and German VHF Stations, call on working frequency.

For Dutch and Belgian VHF Stations, call on working frequency, as indicated in the panels for Scheveningen Radio and Oostende Radio, below.

The lettered areas (*Alfa, Bravo, Charlie,* etc.) show UK Sea Regions for Navigational Warnings – see also 6.4.23.

Scheveningen Radio (coastal stations only)

Goes	Ch 23
Rotterdam	Ch 87
Scheveningen	Ch 83
Haarlem	Ch 25
Wieringmeer	Ch 27
Platform L7	Ch 84
Terschelling	Ch 78
Nes	Ch 23
Appingedam	Ch 27

Hours of watch: H24 Call *Scheveningen Radio* in each case on working channel.

Ch 16 is for emergencies only

Oostende Radio

Vessels near	*Call on*
Zeebrugge	Ch 27 87 88
Oostende	Ch 27 85
La Panne	Ch 28

Hours of watch: H24 on Ch 16 27. Ch 88 is for Autolink only. Ch 63 and 78 are for Autolink or manual

*Map labels:*

Norwick

Alfa

November

Lewis 05
Hebrides
Wick 28

Skye 24
Bravo
Oban 07

Buchan 25
Stonehaven 26

Mike

Charlie

Islay 25

Forth 62

Portpatrick 27

NORTHERN REGION

Cullercoats 26

Lima

Whitby 25

Norddeich 28 61

Kilo

Echo
Anglesey 26 28 → 28

Grimsby 27
Humber 26
Bacton 07

Cardigan Bay 03

SOUTHERN REGION

Orfordness 62

Scheveningen (see above)

Juliett

Celtic 24

Antwerpen 7 16 24 27 81 87
Hours of watch: H24 on Ch 16 24

Oostende (see below)

Foxtrot
Ilfracombe 05
Burnham 25
Thames 02
North Foreland 26
Dunkerque 61 24

Land's End 27 64

→ 04
Niton 28 04 64
Hastings 07
India
Calais 87 01
Boulogne 23 25

Start Point 26 60
Golf
Jobourg 21
Hotel
Fécamp (16)
Dieppe 02 24

→ 64
Scillies

Pendennis 62
St Peter Port 20 62
Cherbourg 27
Carteret 64
Le Havre 26 23 28

Delta
Jersey 25 82 67
Port en Bessin 03
Rouen 25 27

Plougasnou 81

Ouessant 82 24
Brest-Le Conquet 26 28
Paimpol 84
St Malo 02 01

6

6.5.1   UK Coast Radio Stations *continued*

Coast Station Name Position	VHF Ch other than Ch 16	Station details with MF frequencies where relevant as shown below				Navigation and Decca Warning times (UT). For Weather Bulletins and Gale Warnings see page 116. Note: Traffic Lists are sent with all scheduled broadcasts
		Distress, Urgency, Safety (kHz)	Working paired MF frequencies (kHz)			
			MF Ch	Coast Station		
				Transmit	Receive	

NORTHERN REGION (continued)

Coast Station Name Position	VHF Ch	Distress (kHz)	MF Ch	Transmit	Receive	Navigation and Decca Warning times
LEWIS RADIO 58°28'N 06°14'W	05	VHF station remotely controlled Selcall (3216): Ch 16				Broadcasts on Ch 05 at same times as Hebrides below
HEBRIDES RADIO 58°14'N 07°02'W Remotely controlled		2182 Selcall (3234): Ch 16	Z	1866	2534	Broadcasts on 1866 kHz at: 0203 0603 1003 1403 1803 2203 (Decca chains 6C 8E)
SKYE RADIO 57°28'N 06°41'W	24	VHF station remotely controlled Selcall (3232): Ch 16				Broadcasts on Ch 24 at same times as Hebrides above
OBAN RADIO 56°27'N 05°44'W	07	VHF station remotely controlled Selcall (3207): Ch 16				Broadcasts on Ch 07 at same times as Portpatrick below
ISLAY RADIO 55°46'N 06°27'W	25	VHF station remotely controlled Selcall (3233): Ch 16				Broadcasts on Ch 25 at same times as Portpatrick below
PORTPATRICK RADIO 54°51'N 05°07'W For NAVTEX see 6.4.25 – page 83 *Tel: 01776 810312**	27	2182 Selcall (3207): 2170·5 kHz Ch 16	Y	1710	2135	Broadcasts on 1883 kHz and Ch 27 at: 0203 0603 1003 1403 1803 2203 (Decca chains 3B 7D 8E)
ANGLESEY RADIO 53°24'N 04°18'W	26 28	VHF station remotely controlled Selcall (3206): Ch 16				Broadcasts on Ch 26 at same times as Portpatrick above
CARDIGAN BAY RADIO 52°50'N 04°38'W	03	VHF station remotely controlled Selcall (3241): Ch 16				Broadcasts on Ch 03 at same times as Portpatrick above

SUBFACTS broadcasts announcing planned submarine activity in specified areas, and **GUNFACTS** broadcasts announcing gunnery and missile firings, are made by Coast Radio Stations as follows:

At **0733 1933 UT** (after Weather Bulletins)
by Ilfracombe Radio (Ch 05), Land's End Radio (Ch 27, 64 and 2670 kHz), Pendennis Radio (Ch 62), Start Point Radio (Ch 26), Niton Radio (Ch 28 and 1641 kHz), Celtic Radio (Ch 24), Grimsby Radio (Ch 27), Humber Radio (Ch 26 and 1869 kHz), Bacton Radio (Ch 07), Orfordness Radio (Ch 62), Thames Radio (Ch 02), North Foreland Radio (Ch 26) and Hastings Radio (Ch 07).

At **0703 1903 UT** (after Weather Bulletins)
by Wick Radio (Ch 28 and 1764, 1770 kHz), Buchan Radio (Ch 25), Stonehaven Radio (2691 kHz), Forth Radio (Ch 62), Cullercoats Radio (Ch 26 and 2719 kHz) and Whitby Radio (Ch 25).

At **0303 0703 1103 1503 1903 2303 UT** (after any Gale Warnings or Weather Bulletins)
by Hebrides Radio (1866 kHz), Lewis Radio (Ch 05), Skye Radio (Ch 24), Oban Radio (Ch 07), Islay Radio (Ch 25), Portpatrick Radio (Ch 27 and 1883 kHz), Anglesey Radio (Ch 26) and Cardigan Bay Radio (Ch 03).

6.5.1   UK Coast Radio Stations *continued*

Portishead Radio – High Frequency (HF) Long Range RT service

51°29'N 02°48'W	☎	+44 (0) 1278 772200 or 0800 378389
52°22'N 01°11'W	📠	+44 (0) 1278 792145
50°43'N 02°29'W	Telex:	46441 BTGKA G

For description of service and operation see under HF radio in 6.4.13 (page 80).

Radiotelephone HF duplex channels (carrier frequencies)				
Call sign	International channel	Portishead carrier (kHz)	Ship station carrier (kHz)	
GKT20	410	**4384**	4092	Main channel
GKT22	402	4360	4068	HF Autolink[3]
GKT26	406	4372	4080	
GKV26	426	4432	4140	
GKU46	816	**8764**	8240	Main channel
GKT42	802	8722	8198	
GKU49	819	8773	8249	HF Autolink[3]
GKV42	822	8782	8258	
GKV46	826	8794	8270	
GKW41	831	8809	8285	HF Autolink[3]
GKV54	1224	**13146**	12299	Main channel
GKT51	1201	13077	12230	
GKT52	1202	13080	12233	
GKT56	1206	13092	12245	
GKV58	1228	13158	12311	
GKV50	1230	13164	12317	
GKW52	1232	13170	12323	
GKT62	1602	**17245**	16363	Main channel
GKT66	1606	17257	16375	
GKU61	1611	17272	16390	
GKU65	1615	17284	16402	HF Autolink[3]
GKU68	1618	17293	16411	
GKV63	1623	17308	16426	
GKW62	1632	17335	16453	
GKW67	1637	17350	16468	
GKW60	1640	17359	16477	
GKT18	1801	**19755**	18780	Main channel
GKU18	1803	19761	18786	
GKT76	2206	**22711**	22015	Main channel
GKU72	2212	22729	22033	
GKU74	2214	22735	22039	
GKU70	2220	22753	22057	
GKV77	2227	22774	22078	
GKV79	2229	22780	22084	
GKX70	2240	22813	22117	
GKU25	2502	**26148**	25073	Main channel

NOTES:

(1) Assigned frequencies are 1·4 kHz above carrier frequencies shown.

(2) Portishead Radio monitors the main channel frequencies above, where vessels should make their initial call. These channels are also used for the broadcast of Traffic Lists, Distress, Urgency and Safety signals. Traffic Lists every H+00 on frequencies in use at the time. All frequencies are J3E and R3E, power 10kW. H24 frequencies are announced after the Traffic Lists. Channels marked HF Autolink are for Autolink only.

(3) Located at Niton Radio.

6.5.2   Irish Coast Radio Stations

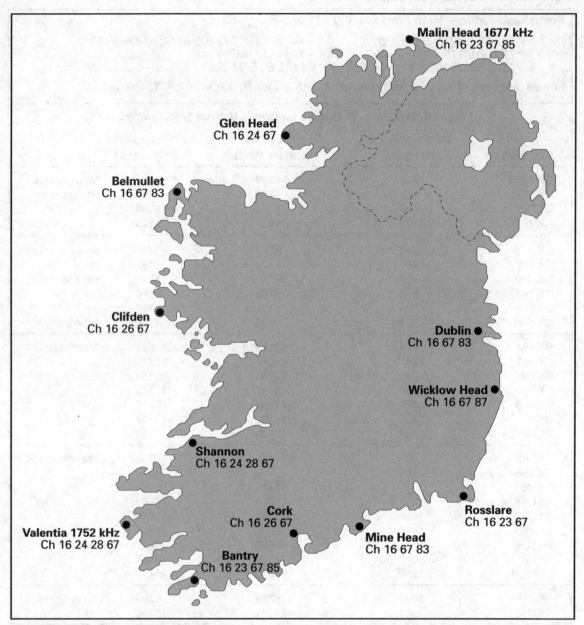

Fig. 6(3) Irish Coast Radio Stations

Irish Coast Radio Service

This service is provided by the Department of the Marine, Leeson Lane, Dublin 2. ☎ +353 1 785444. Traffic Lists, Navigational Warnings, Decca Warnings, Weather Forecasts and Gale Warnings are broadcast at the scheduled times shown in the table. Broadcasts are made on a working channel/frequency following a preliminary announcement on Ch 16 and 2182 kHz. Ch 67 is used for Safety messages only.

VHF calls to a Coast Radio Station should be made on a working channel. Only use Ch 16 in case of difficulty, or for emergency situations. Malin Head and Valentia Radios are equipped with Digital Selective Calling (DSC) on 2187·5 kHz for automatic reception of Distress calls from suitably fitted ships (H24).

Link calls are available through any of the stations on VHF or MF. Telephone calls from shore subscribers can be set up with ships at sea. Contact Malin Head or Valentia Radio by telephone or telex, giving information about the vessel's voyage or whereabouts. Ships at sea should call the nearest Coast Radio Station giving particulars of their voyage at regular intervals (track report, or TR), and listen to Traffic List broadcasts.

Malin Head. ☎ 077 70103. 📠 077 70221. Telex: 42072 MALR EI.

Valentia.   ☎ 0667 6109. 📠 0667 6289. Telex: 73968 VALR EI.

The Irish Aviation and Marine Communication Service on ☎ +353 (0) 1 785444 Ext 670 will be pleased to help with enquiries about the service.

6.5.2 Irish Coast Radio Stations

Notes:

a)   For VHF calls, direct call on working channel preferred, except in emergency.

b)   VHF Ch 67 is for Safety communications with ships, yachts, fishing vessels, etc.

c)   Decca Warnings are broadcast at scheduled times shown, and may also be broadcast on receipt and at other times after announcement on Ch 16 and/or 2182 kHz.

d)   H+... means commencing at ... minutes past the hour.

e)   For medical advice/assistance use the Urgency signal when necessary, and ask for 'Medico Service'.

f)   Normal primary working frequencies are printed in **bold** type.

g)   Irish Coast Radio Stations broadcast Gale Warnings on the respective VHF channels shown in the table on receipt and at the next of the following times 0033 0633 1233 1833 (local time). Similarly Weather Bulletins every three hours from 0103 (local time). See Table 7(4) on page 116.

h)   For further information on the Irish Coast Radio Service see page 90 opposite.

Coast Station Name Position	VHF Ch other than Ch 16	Station details with MF frequencies where relevant as shown below		Broadcast Services (Traffic Lists, Navigation Warnings, etc). For details of Gale Warnings and Weather Bulletins see Table 7(4) – page 116
		Transmits (kHz)	Receives (kHz)	
MALIN HEAD RADIO 55°22'N 07°21'W (VHF Service at Crockalough 55° 21'N 07°16'W) Tel: 353 77 70103	23 67 85	2182 **1677**[1] 1644 Notes: (1) Watches on 2045 and replies on 1677 kHz when 2182 kHz is Distress working DSC: 2187·5 kHz MMSI 002500100	2182 (H24) 2045[1] (H24) 2102 (Ch 255) 2069 (Ch 244)	Broadcasts on 1677 kHz and Ch 23. *Traffic Lists:* Every odd H+03 (not 0303 0703). *Navigation/Decca Warnings:* Every four hours from 0033. May also be broadcast on receipt and at other times after announcement on 2182 kHz/Ch 16 (Decca chains 3B 7D 8E)
GLEN HEAD RADIO 54°44'N 08°43'W	24 67	VHF station remotely controlled		Broadcasts on Ch 24 at same times as Malin Head above
BELMULLET RADIO 54°16'N 10°03'W	67 83	VHF station remotely controlled		Broadcasts on Ch 83 at same times as Malin Head above
CLIFDEN RADIO 53°30'N 09°56'W	26 67	VHF station remotely controlled		Broadcasts on Ch 26 at same times as Malin Head above
DUBLIN RADIO 53°23'N 06°04'W	67 83	VHF station		Broadcasts on Ch 83 at same times as Malin Head above
MINE HEAD RADIO 52°00'N 07°35'W	67 83	VHF station remotely controlled		Broadcasts on Ch 83 at same times as Malin Head above
ROSSLARE RADIO 52°15'N 06°20'W	23 67	VHF station remotely controlled		Broadcasts on Ch 23 at same times as Malin Head above
WICKLOW HEAD RADIO 52°58'N 06°00'W	67 87	VHF station remotely controlled		Broadcasts on Ch 87 at same time as Malin Head above
VALENTIA RADIO 51°56'N 10°21'W (VHF service at Kilkeaveragh 51°52'N 10°20'W) Tel: 353 667 6109	24 28 67	2182 1746 **1752**[1] Notes: (1) Watches on 2045 and replies on 1752 kHz when 2182 kHz is Distress working DSC: 2187·5 kHz MMSI 002500200	2182 (H24) 2045[1] (H24) 2090 (Ch 278) 2096 (Ch 280)	Broadcasts on 1752 kHz and Ch 24. *Traffic Lists:* Every odd H+33 (not 0133 0533). *Navigation/Decca Warnings:* Every four hours from 0233. May also be broadcast on receipt and at other times after announcement on 2182 kHz/Ch 16 (Decca chains 1B 7D)
SHANNON RADIO 52°31'N 09°36'W	24 28 67	VHF station remotely controlled		Broadcasts on Ch 28 at same times as Valentia above
BANTRY BAY RADIO 51°38'N 10°00'W	23 67 85	VHF station remotely controlled		Broadcasts on Ch 23 at same times as Valentia above
CORK RADIO 51°51'N 08°29'W	26 67	VHF station remotely controlled		Broadcasts on Ch 26 at same times as Valentia above

6

6.5.3   French Coast Radio Stations

Notes:
a)   At French Coast Radio Stations VHF Ch 16 operates H24 and is reserved for Distress and Safety traffic only. Normally calls must be made on working channels, which operate 0700-2200 LT.
b)   VHF channels shown in brackets are for Automatic VHF for suitably equipped ships (H24).
c)   VHF channels of Coast Radio Stations do not broadcast Traffic Lists or Navigation Warnings. They do broadcast local coastal Weather Bulletins at 0733 1533 LT, in French, on the channels indicated. For details see Table 7(5).
d)   MF Coast Radio Stations broadcast coastal and local Navigation Warnings as AVURNAVS (see 6.4.23) after announcements on 2182 kHz.

Coast Station Name Position	VHF Ch other than Ch 16	Station details with MF frequencies where relevant as shown below		Broadcast Services (Traffic Lists, Navigation Warnings, etc). For details of Gale Warnings and Weather Bulletins see Table 7(5) – page 117
		Transmits (kHz)	Receives (kHz)	
DUNKERQUE RADIO 51°02'N 02°24'E	24 61 (86)	VHF station remotely controlled See notes (a) and (b) above		*Local coastal Weather Bulletins:* Ch 61 at 0733 1533 LT, in French. See Table 7(5)
CALAIS RADIO 50°55'N 01°43'E	01 87 (60) (62)	VHF station remotely controlled See notes (a) and (b) above		*Local coastal Weather Bulletins:* Ch 87 at 0733 1533 LT, in French. See Table 7(5)
BOULOGNE-SUR-MER RADIO 50°43'N 01°37'E *Tel: 03·21·33·25·26*	23 25 (see note (a)) (64) (81) (see note (b))	**1692**[1] **1770** 2744 2747 3722 3792 3795[1] 2182 (H24) Notes: (1) For fishing vessels (2) For French vessels (3) For foreign vessels Selcall (1641): 2170.5 kHz	2045[3] 2048[1] 2051 2054 2057 2093[2] 2117[1] 3168 3314 2182 (H24)	*Traffic Lists:* 1770 kHz every odd H+03 (UT). *Navigation Warnings:* 1692 3795 kHz on receipt and every 4h from 0133 (UT) (Cherbourg AVURNAVS in French and English). 1692 3795 kHz at 0703 1833 (UT) (Cherbourg Local AVURNAVS in French). For weather see Table 7(5)
DIEPPE RADIO 49°55'N 01°03'E	02 24 (61)	VHF station remotely controlled See notes (a) and (b) above		*Local coastal Weather Bulletins:* Ch 02 at 0733 1533 LT, in French. See Table 7(5)
FÉCAMP RADIO 49°46'N 00°22'E	(65) (78)	VHF station remotely controlled See notes (a) and (b) above		No broadcast services
LE HAVRE RADIO 49°31'N 00°04'E	23 26 28 (62) (84)	VHF station remotely controlled See notes (a) and (b) above		*Local coastal Weather Bulletins:* Ch 26 at 0733 1533 LT, in French. See Table 7(5)
ROUEN RADIO 49°27'N 01°02'E	25 27 (01) (86)	VHF station remotely controlled See notes (a) and (b) above		No broadcast services
PORT-EN-BESSIN RADIO 49°20'N 00°42'W	03 (60) (66)	VHF station remotely controlled See notes (a) and (b) above		*Local coastal Weather Bulletins:* Ch 03 at 0733 1533 LT, in French. See Table 7(5)
CHERBOURG RADIO 49°38'N 01°36'W	27 (86)	VHF station remotely controlled See notes (a) and (b) above		*Local coastal weather bulletins:* Ch 27 at 0733 1533 LT, in French. See Table 7(5)
JOBOURG RADIO 49°43'N 01°56'W	21 (83)	VHF station remotely controlled See notes (a) and (b) above		No broadcast services

6.5.3   French Coast Radio Stations *continued*

Coast Station Name Position	VHF Ch other than Ch 16	Station details with MF frequencies where relevant as shown below		Broadcast Services (Traffic Lists, Navigation Warnings, etc). For details of Gale Warnings and Weather Bulletins see Table 7(5) – page 118
		Transmits (kHz)	Receives (kHz)	
CARTERET RADIO 49°23'N 01°47'W	64 (23) (88)	VHF station remotely controlled See notes (a) and (b) above		No broadcast services
ST MALO RADIO 48°38'N 02°02'W	01 02 (78) (85)	VHF station remotely controlled See notes (a) and (b) above For MF service see Brest-Le Conquet below.		*Local coastal Weather Bulletins:* Ch 02 at 0733 1533 LT, in French. See Table 7(5)
PAIMPOL RADIO 48°45'N 02°59'W	84 (87)	VHF station remotely controlled See notes (a) and (b) above		*Local coastal Weather Bulletins:* Ch 84 at 0733 1533 LT, in French. See Table 7(5)
PLOUGASNOU RADIO 48°42'N 03°48'W	81 (03)	VHF station remotely controlled See notes (a) and (b) above		*Local coastal Weather Bulletins:* Ch 81 at 0733 1533 LT, in French. See Table 7(5)
OUESSANT RADIO 48°27'N 05°05'W	24 82 (61)	VHF station remotely controlled See notes (a) and (b) above		*Local coastal Weather Bulletins:* Ch 82 at 0733 1533 LT, in French. See Table 7(5)
BREST-LE CONQUET RADIO 48°20'N 04°44'W (For MF stations at St Malo and Quimperlé see column (3)) *Tel: 02·98·89·17·89*	26 28 (see note (a)) (23) (64) (see note (b))	**1635** 1671[1] 2723 2726 3719 3722 2182 (H24) At St Malo, 48°38N 02°02'W: 2691[1] 2182 (H24) At Quimperlé, 47°52'N 03°30'W: 1876[1] 2182 (H24) Notes: (1) For fishing vessels (2) For French vessels (3) For foreign vessels Selcall (1643): 2170.5 kHz	2045[3] 2048[3] 2051 2054 2057 **2060**[2] **2096**[1] 3168 2182 (H24) 3317[1] 2182 (H24) 1992[1] 2182 (H24)	*Traffic Lists:* 1635 2691 kHz every even H+03 (UT). *Navigation Warnings:* 1671 1876 2691 kHz on receipt, after next silence period, and every 4h from 0333 UT. Brest AVURNAVS in French and English for English Channel approaches and Bay of Biscay. 1671 1876 2691 kHz at 0733 1803 (UT) (Brest local AVURNAVS in French). *Gunfire Warnings:* for Landes firing range on 1635 kHz at 0733 UT (for current day), 1803 UT (for next day). For Weather Broadcasts see Table 7(5)
PONT L'ABBÉ RADIO 47°53'N 04°13'W	86 (63) (66)	VHF station remotely controlled See notes (a) and (b) above		*Local coastal Weather Bulletins:* Ch 86 at 0733 1533 LT, in French. See Table 7(5)
LE CROUESTY RADIO (VANNES) 47°32'N 02°54'W	(02) (60)	See note (b) above		No broadcast services.
BELLE ÎLE RADIO 47°21'N 03°09'W	05 25 (65) (87)	VHF station remotely controlled See notes (a) and (b) above		*Local coastal Weather Bulletins:* Ch 25 at 0733 1533 LT, in French. See Table 7(5)
ST HERBLAIN RADIO 47°13'N 01°37'W	28 (03)	VHF station remotely controlled See notes (a) and (b) above		*Local coastal Weather Bulletins:* Ch 28 at 0733 1533 LT, in French. See Table 7(5)

6

6.5.3   French Coast Radio Stations *continued*

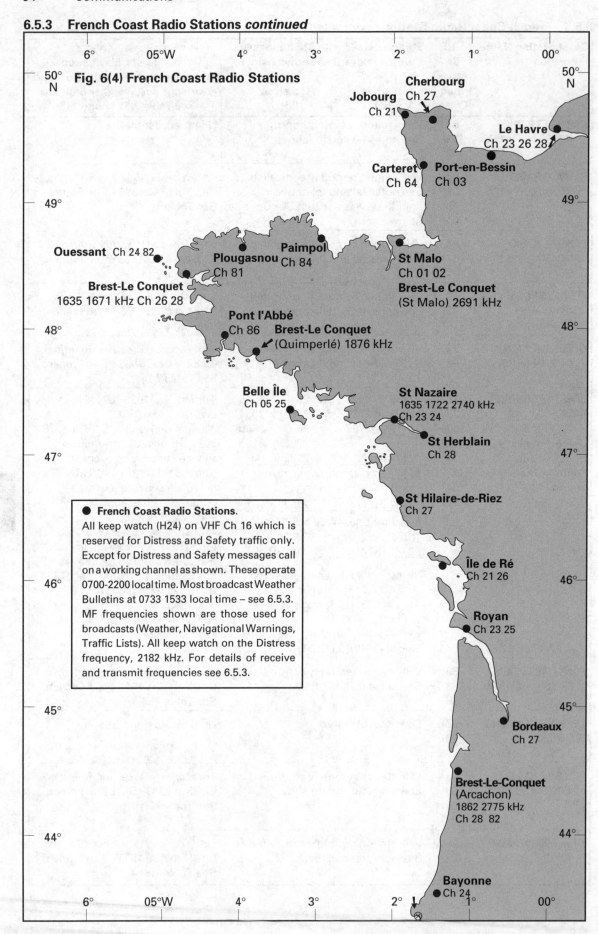

Fig. 6(4) French Coast Radio Stations

Jobourg
Ch 21

Cherbourg
Ch 27

Le Havre
Ch 23 26 28

Carteret
Ch 64

Port-en-Bessin
Ch 03

Ouessant   Ch 24 82

Plougasnou
Ch 81

Paimpol
Ch 84

St Malo
Ch 01 02

Brest-Le Conquet
(St Malo) 2691 kHz

Brest-Le Conquet
1635 1671 kHz Ch 26 28

Pont l'Abbé
Ch 86

Brest-Le Conquet
(Quimperlé) 1876 kHz

Belle Île
Ch 05 25

St Nazaire
1635 1722 2740 kHz
Ch 23 24

St Herblain
Ch 28

St Hilaire-de-Riez
Ch 27

Île de Ré
Ch 21 26

Royan
Ch 23 25

Bordeaux
Ch 27

Brest-Le-Conquet
(Arcachon)
1862 2775 kHz
Ch 28 82

Bayonne
Ch 24

● **French Coast Radio Stations.**
All keep watch (H24) on VHF Ch 16 which is
reserved for Distress and Safety traffic only.
Except for Distress and Safety messages call
on a working channel as shown. These operate
0700-2200 local time. Most broadcast Weather
Bulletins at 0733 1533 local time – see 6.5.3.
MF frequencies shown are those used for
broadcasts (Weather, Navigational Warnings,
Traffic Lists). All keep watch on the Distress
frequency, 2182 kHz. For details of receive
and transmit frequencies see 6.5.3.

6.5.3   French Coast Radio Stations *continued*

Notes:

a)   At French Coast Radio Stations VHF Ch 16 operates H24 and is reserved for Distress and Safety traffic only. Normally calls must be made on working channels, which operate 0700-2200 LT.

b)   VHF channels shown in brackets are for Automatic VHF for suitably equipped ships (H24).

c)   VHF channels of Coast Radio Stations do not broadcast Traffic Lists or Navigation Warnings. They do broadcast local coastal Weather Bulletins at 0733 1533 LT, in French, on the channels indicated. For details see Table 7(5).

e)   MF Coast Radio Stations broadcast coastal and local Navigation Warnings as AVURNAVS (see 6.4.23) after announcements on 2182 kHz.

Coast Station Name Position	VHF Ch other than Ch 16	Station details with MF frequencies where relevant as shown below		Broadcast Services (Traffic Lists, Navigation Warnings, etc). For details of Gale Warnings and Weather Bulletins see Table 7(5) – page 119
		Transmits (kHz)	Receives (kHz)	
ST NAZAIRE RADIO 47°21'N 02°06'W (Remotely controlled from Brest Le Conquet)	23 24 (see note (a)) (04) (88) (see note (b))	**1686** **1722**[1] 2586 2740[1] 3792 3795 2182 (H24)	1995[1] 2045[3] 2048[3] 2051 2054 2057 2066 2111[2] 3168 3314[1] 2182 (H24)	*Traffic Lists:* 1686 kHz every odd H+07 (UT). *Navigation Warnings:* 1635 and on receipt, and after next silence period. 1722 2740 kHz at 0733 1803 UT. Brest AVURNAVS, in French for Bay of Biscay north of 46°30'N and east of 04°00'W. For Weather Broadcasts see Table 7(5)
		Notes: (1) For fishing vessels (2) For French vessels (3) For foreign vessels Selcall (1645): 2170·5 kHz		
ÎLE D'YEU RADIO 46°43'N 02°23'W	(84)	See note (b) above		No broadcast services
ST HILAIRE-DE-RIEZ RADIO 46°43'N 01°57'W	27 (62) (85)	VHF station remotely controlled See notes (a) and (b) above		*Local coastal Weather Bulletins:* Ch 27 at 0733 1533 LT, in French. See Table 7(5)
LA ROCHELLE RADIO 46°14'N 01°33'W	(61)	See note (b) above		No broadcast services
ÎLE DE RÉ RADIO 46°12'N 01°22'W	21 26 (01) (81)	VHF station remotely controlled See notes (a) and (b) above		*Local coastal Weather Bulletins:* Ch 21 at 0733 1533 LT, in French. See Table 7(5)
ROYAN RADIO 45°34'N 00°58'W	23 25 (02) (83)	VHF station remotely controlled See notes (a) and (b) above		*Local coastal Weather Bulletins:* Ch 23 at 0733 1533 LT, in French. See Table 7(5)
BORDEAUX RADIO 44°53'N 00°30'W	27 (63)	VHF station. See notes (a) and (b) above		No broadcast services
BORDEAUX-ARCACHON RADIO 44°39'N 01°10'W (Remotely controlled from Brest-Le Conquet)	28 82 (see note (a)) (78) (86) (see note (b))	**1710** **1862**[1] 2772 2775[1] 3719 3722 2182 (H24)	1995[1] 2135[2] 2045[3] 3168 2048[3] 3317[1] 2051 2054 2057 2182 (H24)	*Navigation Warnings:* 1862 kHz on receipt, after next silence period, and every 4h from 0333 UT. Brest AVURNAVS in French and English. 1862 kHz on receipt, after next silence period, and at 0733 1803 UT. Brest local AVURNAVS in French. For Weather Broadcasts see Table 7(5)
		Notes: (1) For fishing vessels (2) For French vessels (3) For foreign vessels Selcall (1646): 2170·5 kHz		
BAYONNE RADIO 43°16'N 01°24'W	24 (03) (64)	VHF station remotely controlled See notes (a) and (b) above		*Local coastal Weather Bulletins:* Ch 24 at 0733 1533 LT, in French. See Table 7(5)

6

6.5.4   Belgian Coast Radio Stations

Coast Station Name Position	VHF Ch other than Ch 16	Station details with MF frequencies where relevant as shown below		Broadcast Services (Traffic Lists, Navigation Warnings, etc). For details of Gale Warnings and Weather Bulletins see Table 7(5) – page 119
		Transmits (kHz)	Receives (kHz)	
OOSTENDE RADIO	28[1]			*Traffic Lists:* Ch 27 every H+20. 2761 kHz every even H+20 (UT).
51°11'N 02°48'E	27[23]	1665	2090 (Ch 251)	
51°06'N 03°21'E	63[4]	1683	2108 (Ch 257)	
	78[14]	1689	2114 (Ch 259)	Following Warnings are broadcast on the channel/ frequency indicated after announcement on Ch 16/2182 kHz.
See notes below for VHF Ch to be used in different areas	85[3]			
	87[2]	1725	2069[5] (Ch 271)	
	88[25]	1728	2072 (Ch 272)	
	(Ch 16 and Ch 27 H24)	1817 1820		
For NAVTEX see 6.4.25 – page 81		1908		*Navigation Warnings:* Ch 27 and 2761 kHz on receipt, after next two silence periods and on 2761 kHz at: 0233 0633 1033 1433 1833 2233 UT, in English and Dutch.
		2087 2170.5		
		2182 (H24)	2182 (H24)	
		2253 2256		
		2373 2376		
		2484 (H24)	⎰ 2484 ⎱ (H24) ⎱ 3178 ⎰ 4095[9]	*Decca Warnings:* Ch 27 and 2761 kHz after next two silence periods after receipt, in English for chains 5B 2A 6C 8E 2E 9B.
		2761[6]		
		2817[7] 3629		
		3632[7]		
		3684[6]		

Notes:
(1) For vessels near French border
(2) For vessels near Zeebrugge
(3) For vessels near Oostende
(4) Autolink or manual calls
(5) Autolink only
(6) Working frequency Belgian ships
(7) Working frequency foreign ships
(8) Call on 2191 kHz when 2182 is Distress working
(9) 1800-0700 LT for Belgian ships
(10) DSC (GMDSS) Ch 70 and 2187·5 kHz (H24), MMSI 002050480

Tel: 32 59 706565

Ice Reports: Ch 27 and 2761 kHz every 4h from 0103 UT in English.

Fog Warnings: 2761 kHz on receipt and after next silence period, in English and Dutch, for the Schelde

---

Coast Station Name Position		Station details with MF frequencies where relevant as shown below	Broadcast Services
ANTWERPEN RADIO 51°17'N 04°20'E		VHF stations remotely controlled from Oostende Radio. VHF facilities are available (H24) at the following positions. The call in each case is Antwerpen Radio	*Traffic Lists:* Ch 24 every H+05. Following Warnings are broadcast on channel indicated after announcement on Ch 16.
Antwerpen	51°17'N 04°20'E	07 16[1] **24** 27 87[2] (Ch 16: H24)	*Navigation Warnings:*
Kortrijk	50°50'N 03°17'E	**24**[1] (H24)	Ch 24 on receipt and every H+03 H+48, in English and Dutch for the Schelde
Gent	51°02'N 03°44'E	16 **24**[1] 81 (Ch 24: H24)	
Vilvoorde	50°56'N 04°25'E	**24**[1] (H24)	
Ronquiéres	50°37'N 05°13'E	**24**[1] (H24)	
Mol	51°11'N 05°07'E	**24**[1] (H24)	
Liège	50°34'N 05°33'E	**24**[1] (H24)	

Notes:
(1) For Distress and Safety calls only, answered by Oostende Radio
(2) Ch 87 is for Autolink or manual calls
(3) DSC (GMDSS) on Ch 70, MMSI 002050485
(4) Selcall (0485): Ch 16 24

6.5.5   Netherlands Coast Radio Stations

Notes:
   a)   VHF facilities, remotely controlled, are located as below. Antennas are directed to cover either the Coastal Area (seaward) or the Inland Waters. The call in each case is Scheveningen Radio. Ch 16 is remotely controlled by Netherlands Coastguard. Except in emergency, calls must be made on working channels. Watch is kept on Ch 16 and on all working channels H24. Calls must last at least three seconds.
   b)   Netherlands Coastguard monitors Ch 16 and 2182 kHz for Distress, Urgency, Safety traffic and operates DSC on 2187·5 kHz and Ch 70 (MMSI 002442000). Do not call Scheveningen Radio on 2182 kHz for routine traffic – call on 2520 kHz and station will reply on 2824 kHz indicating working channel to be used.

Coast Station Name Position	VHF Ch other than Ch 16	Station details with MF frequencies where relevant as shown below		Broadcast Services (Traffic Lists, Navigation Warnings, etc). For details of Gale Warnings and Weather Bulletins see Table 7(5) – page 121
		Transmits (kHz)	Receives (kHz)	
SCHEVENINGEN RADIO 52°06N 04°16'E		Ch A 2824[1]	2520 (H24)	*Traffic Lists:* VHF working channels every H+05.
		B 1716	2060	1713 1890 kHz at every odd
		C 2600	1995	H+05 (UT).
VHF stations remotely controlled are located as below.		D 1674	2099	
		E –	–	*Navigation Warnings:* Coastal
Call Scheveningen Radio on working channel for routine traffic. Ch 16 is remotely controlled by Netherlands Coastguard and used only for Distress, Urgency and Safety		F 1713[2]	2138[2]	area VHF working channels –
		I 1890	2045	see col (1) opposite – and
			2048	Lelystad Ch 83 on receipt,
			2051	and after next silence period,
			2054	and (after anouncement on
			2057	Ch 16) every 4h from 0305 UT.
		Notes: (1) Ch A is calling and answering channel (H24) (2) Located at Nes 53°24'N 06°04'E (3) Ch B C D F and I are working channels, and are indicated by Ch A operator depending on ship's position and conditions		1674 1713 1890 kHz on receipt and after next silence period. 1674 1890 kHz every 4h from 0333 UT. In English and Dutch. (Decca chains 2E 9B).
Watch is kept on Ch 16 and working channels H24				
Tel: (0255) 562333		Selcall: 2170·5 kHz Ch 16.		*Ice Reports:* 1674 1890 kHz every 4h from 0333 UT. 2824 kHz at 0333 2333 UT. In English and Dutch for local waters.
Coastal Area – see Fig. 6(5):				
Goes	23	51°31'N 03°54'E		*Strong Breeze Warnings:*
Rotterdam	87	51°53'N 04°27'E		VHF working channels of Coastal
Scheveningen	83	52°04'N 04°15'E		Stations on receipt and every
Haarlem	25	52°23'N 04°40'E		H+05, in Dutch.
Tjerkgaast	–	52°55'N 05°42'E		
Wieringermeer	27	52°55'N 05°04'E		*Near Gale Warnings:*
Platform L7	84	53°34'N 04°12'E		1713 1890 kHz on recipt and after
Terschelling	78	53°21'N 05°13'E		next silence period (following
Nes	23	53°23'N 06°03'E		announcement on 2182 kHz)
Appingedam	27	53°20'N 06°51'E		in English and Dutch.
Inland VHF stations (antennas directed inland):				*Weather Messages:*
Maastricht	25	50°50'N 05°40'E		VHF working channels of Coastal
Roermond	26	51°11'N 05°59'E		Stations and Lelystad at
Arcen	28	51°30'N 06°11'E		0005 0805 1305 1905 LT, in Dutch
Goes	25	51°31'N 03°54'E		
Rotterdam	24 28	51°53'N 04°27'E		
Lopik	86	52°01'N 05°03'E		
Scheveningen	26	52°04'N 04°15'E		
Markelo	23	52°14'N 06°27'E		
Haarlem	23	52°23'N 04°40'E		
Lelystad	83	52°32'N 05°26'E		
Smilde	24	52°54'N 06°24'E		
Tjerkgaast	28	52°55'N 05°42'E		

Fig. 6(5) Netherlands VHF Service (do not call on Ch 16 except in emergency). Channels in brackets are directed to inland waters

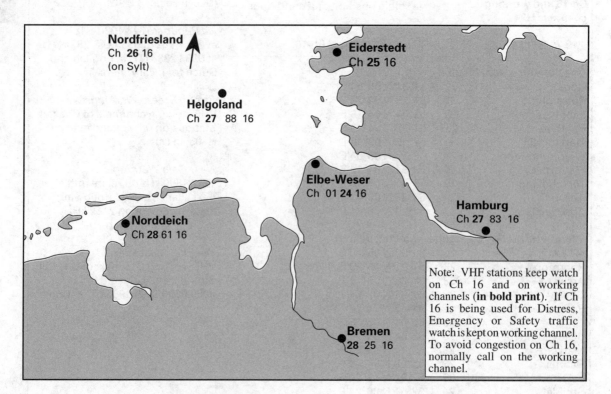

Fig. 6(6) German Coast Radio Stations

6.5.6 German Coast Radio Stations

Notes:
a) VHF stations keep watch (H24) on Ch 16 and on working channel(s) shown in **bold** print. Normally calls should be made on the indicated working channel.
b) Ch 16 is also used for selective calling.
c) All VHF stations operate Digital Selective Calling (DSC) on Ch 70 (GMDSS) (H24).

Coast Station Name Position	VHF Ch other than Ch 16	Station details with MF frequencies where relevant as shown below		Broadcast Services (Traffic Lists, Navigation Warnings, etc). For details of Gale Warnings and Weather Bulletins see Table 7(5) – page 121
		Transmits (kHz)	Receives (kHz)	
NORDDEICH RADIO 53°34'N 07°06'E 53°38'N 07°12'E 53°32'N 08°38'E 53°47'N 09°40'E *Tel: 49 4931 1830*	**28** **61**	DSC (GMDSS) 2187·5 kHz Ch 70 (H24) MMSI 002114200 Selcall: Ch 16		*Traffic Lists:* Ch 28 every H+45
BREMEN RADIO 53°05'N 08°48'E	25 **28**	VHF station remotely controlled MMSI 002114200		*Traffic Lists:* Ch 28 every H+45
HELGOLAND RADIO 54°11'N 07°53'E	**27** 88	VHF station remotely controlled MMSI 002114200		*Traffic Lists:* Ch 27 every H+45
ELBE-WESER RADIO 53°50'N 08°39'E *Tel: 49 4721 22066*	**01** **24**	Ch 24 for vessels in Nord-Ostsee Kanal VHF station remotely controlled MMSI 002114200		*Traffic Lists:* Ch 24 every H+45
HAMBURG RADIO 53°33'N 09°58'E	**27** 83	VHF station remotely controlled MMSI 002114200		*Traffic Lists:* Ch 27 every H+45
EIDERSTEDT RADIO 54°20'N 08°47'E	25	VHF station remotely controlled MMSI 002114200		*Traffic Lists:* Ch 25 every H+45
NORDFRIESLAND RADIO 54°34'N 07°07'E	26	VHF station remotely controlled MMSI 002114300		*Traffic Lists:* Ch 26 every H+45

6

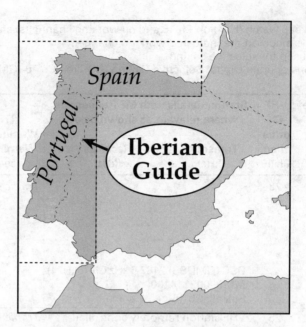

THE 1998 IBERIAN GUIDE

The second edition of this 56 page Guide extends the Almanac's coverage from the Franco-Spanish border at Hendaye (10.18.28) westward along Northern Spain and southward past the coasts of Portugal and South West Spain to Gibraltar.

It gives details and chartlets of 37 harbours, plus minor harbours and anchorages, as shown on four full page maps of the Iberian Peninsula.

Coastal lights, fog signals and Waypoints are listed, together with summaries of Navigational aids, Weather sources and Communications facilities around the Atlantic coast of Iberia.

Passage Information offers guidance on dangers and passage-making, with two Distance Tables.

Tidal predictions and curves are included for the Standard Ports of Lisboa and Gibraltar, together with their associated secondary port differences. For secondary ports in North Spain, differences are referenced to Point de Grave in Area 18 of the Almanac.

Spanish and Portuguese vocabularies of useful nautical terms are also included.

From Dec 1998 this Guide is obtainable by post direct from the Publishers by completing the card enclosed within this Almanac and forwarding it with the appropriate remittance.

Chapter 7

Weather

Contents

7

Weather – introduction

This chapter gives basic information on the content, terminology and the wide range of weather information available to yachtsmen. Particular emphasis is given to obtaining weather forecasts and reports.

Additional information on the weather and its interpretation can be found in Chapter 7 of *The Macmillan & Silk Cut Yachtsman's Handbook* where the following subjects are described in more detail:

Transfer of heat; world weather; air masses; atmospheric pressure; wind; humidity; clouds; depressions and fronts; the passage of a depression; anticyclones; fog; sea and land breezes; thunderstorms; tropical storms; glossary of meteorological terms; forecasting your own weather; bibliography.

7.1   GENERAL WEATHER INFORMATION

7.1.1   Beaufort scale

Force	Wind speed			Description	State of sea	Probable wave ht (m)
	(knots)	(km/h)	(m/sec)			
0	0–1	0–2	0–0.5	Calm	Like a mirror	0
1	1–3	2–6	0.5–1.5	Light air	Ripples like scales are formed	0
2	4–6	7–11	2–3	Light breeze	Small wavelets, still short but more pronounced, not breaking	0.1
3	7–10	13–19	4–5	Gentle breeze	Large wavelets, crests begin to break; a few white horses	0.4
4	11–16	20–30	6–8	Moderate breeze	Small waves growing longer; fairly frequent white horses	1
5	17–21	31–39	8–11	Fresh breeze	Moderate waves, taking more pronounced form; many white horses, perhaps some spray	2
6	22–27	41–50	11–14	Strong breeze	Large waves forming; white foam crests more extensive; probably some spray	3
7	28–33	52–61	14–17	Near gale	Sea heaps up; white foam from breaking waves begins to blow in streaks	4
8	34–40	63–74	17–21	Gale	Moderately high waves of greater length; edge of crests break into spindrift; foam blown in well-marked streaks	5.5
9	41–47	76–87	21–24	Severe gale	High waves with tumbling crests; dense streaks of foam; spray may affect visibility	7
10	48–55	89–102	25–28	Storm	Very high waves with long overhanging crests; dense streams of foam make surface of sea white. Heavy tumbling sea; visibility affected	9
11	56–63	104–117	29–33	Violent storm	Exceptionally high waves; sea completely covered with long white patches of foam; edges of wave crests blown into froth. Visibility affected	11
12	64 plus	118 plus	33 plus	Hurricane	Air filled with foam and spray; sea completely white with driving spray; visibility very seriously affected	14

Notes: (1) The state of sea and probable wave heights are a guide to what may be expected in the open sea, away from land. In enclosed waters, or near land with an offshore wind, wave heights will be less but possibly steeper – particularly with wind against tide.

(2) It should be remembered that the height of sea for a given wind strength depends upon the fetch and the duration for which the wind has been blowing. For further information on sea state, see Chapter 9 of *The Macmillan & Silk Cut Yachtsman's Handbook*.

7.1.2   Barometer and temperature conversion scales

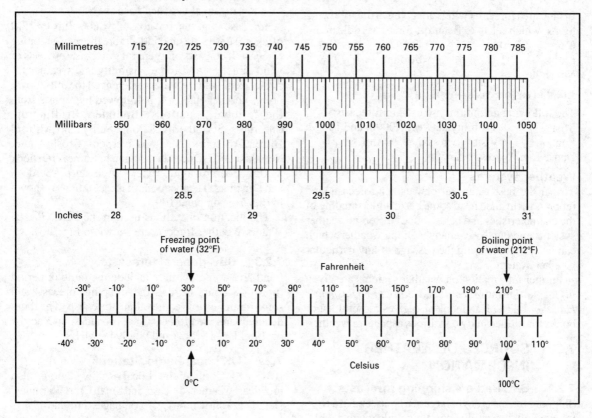

7.1.3   Meaning of terms used in weather bulletins

Speed of movement of pressure systems

Slowly:	Moving at less than 15 knots
Steadily:	Moving at 15 to 25 knots
Rather quickly:	Moving at 25 to 35 knots
Rapidly:	Moving at 35 to 45 knots
Very rapidly:	Moving at more than 45 knots

Visibility

Good:	More than 5 miles
Moderate:	2 – 5 miles
Poor:	1000 metres – 2 miles
Fog:	Less than 1000 metres

Barometric pressure changes (tendency)

Rising or falling slowly: Pressure change of 0·1 to 1·5 millibars in the preceding 3 hours.

Rising or falling: Pressure change of 1·6 to 3·5 millibars in the preceding 3 hours.

Rising or falling quickly: Pressure change of 3·6 to 6 millibars in the preceding 3 hours.

Rising or falling very rapidly: Pressure change of more than 6 millibars in the preceding 3 hours.

Now rising (or falling): Pressure has been falling (rising) or steady in the preceding 3 hours, but at the time of observation was definitely rising (falling).

Gale warnings

A **'Gale'** warning means that winds of at least force 8 (34-40 knots) or gusts reaching 43-51 knots are expected somewhere within the area, but not necessarily over the whole area. **'Severe Gale'** means winds of at least force 9 (41-47 knots) or gusts reaching 52-60 knots. **'Storm'** means winds of force 10 (48-55 knots) or gusts of 61-68 knots. **'Violent Storm'** means winds of force 11 (56-63 kn) or gusts of 69 kn or more, and **'Hurricane Force'** means winds of force 12 (64 knots or more).

Gale warnings remain in force until amended or cancelled ('gales now ceased'). If a gale persists for more than 24 hours the warning is re-issued.

Timing of gale warnings

Imminent	Within 6 hrs of time of issue
Soon	Within 6 – 12 hrs of time of issue
Later	More than 12 hrs from time of issue

Wind

Wind direction: Indicates the direction from which the wind is blowing.

Winds becoming cyclonic: Indicates that there will be considerable change in wind direction across the path of a depression within the forecast area.

Veering: The changing of the wind in a clockwise direction, i.e. SW to W.

Backing: The changing of the wind in an anti-clockwise direction, i.e. W to SW.

Land area forecasts – wind strength

In land area forecasts winds are given in the following terms, which relate to Beaufort forces as indicated:

Calm:	0	Fresh:	5
Light:	1–3	Strong:	6 – 7
Moderate:	4	Gale:	8

Land area forecasts – visibility

The following definitions are used in forecasts:

Mist:	Visibility between 2000m and 1000m
Fog:	Visibility less than 1000m
Dense fog:	Less than 50m

Weather systems

To get the best value out of weather forecasts and reports, yachtsmen need some basic understanding of the characteristics and behaviour of different weather systems and the likely changes in the weather which can be expected during the passage of any particular weather system.

Further information on weather systems are given in Chapter 7 in the *Macmillan & Silk Cut Yachtsman's Handbook*. The Handbook also gives a useful list of books for further study on various aspects of weather.

7.2   SOURCES OF WEATHER INFORMATION

7.2.1   BBC Radio 4 shipping forecasts

Shipping forecasts cover large sea areas, and in a five-minute bulletin it is difficult to include much detail – particularly variations that can and do occur near land – or to convey the right degree of confidence in the weather situation. Hence forecasts for 'Coastal Waters' (see 7.2.2), which extend up to 12M offshore, are often more helpful to yachtsmen cruising near the coast.

Shipping forecasts are broadcast by BBC Radio 4 on 198 kHz and local MF and FM frequencies at 0048, 0555, 1355 and 1750 (LT). The 0048 broadcast includes sea area Trafalgar.

The bulletins include a summary of gale warnings in force; a general synopsis of the weather for the next 24 hours and expected changes within that period; forecasts for each sea area for the next 24 hours, giving wind direction and speed, weather and visibility; and the latest reports from stations shown at the foot of page 111. For each station wind direction and Beaufort force, present weather, visibility, and (if available) sea-level pressure and tendency are given. These stations are marked by their initial letters on the chart for forecast areas on page 110.

Apart from being included in shipping forecasts, gale warnings are broadcast at the earliest juncture in the BBC Radio 4 programme after receipt, and also after the next news bulletin.

Instructions on recording and interpreting the shipping forecasts are given in 7.6.4 of *The Macmillan & Silk Cut Yachtsman's Handbook*.

The 1355 broadcast Monday–Friday includes a 24-hour forecast for the Minches (between Butt of Lewis and Cape Wrath in the north, and between Barra Head and Ardnamurchan Point in the south), after area Hebrides.

7.2.2   BBC Radio 4 coastal waters forecast

A forecast is given for coastal waters (up to 12M offshore) until 1800 at 0550, before the 0555 shipping forecast. It consists of a general synopsis, forecasts of wind direction and force, visibility and weather for stretches of inshore waters referenced to well-known points and headlands. It is followed by reports from the following stations: Boulmer, Bridlington, Sheerness, St Catherine's Point, Scilly auto, Milford Haven, Aberporth, Valley, Liverpool (Crosby) auto, Ronaldsway, Larne, Machrihanish, Larne, Greenock MRCC, Stornoway, Lerwick, Wick auto, Aberdeen and Leuchars. The locations of these stations is shown in Fig. 7(3) on page 109.

The location of stations used in the BBC Coastal Waters Weather Reports are shown in Fig. 7(3).

7.2.3   BBC general forecasts

Land area forecasts may include the outlook period (up to 48 hours beyond the shipping forecast) and some reference to weather along the coasts. The more detailed land area forecasts are broadcast on Radio 4 on 198 kHz (1515m) and 92·4-94·6 MHz.

7.2.4   UK Local Radio Stations

BBC and Commercial Local Radio stations also broadcast weather forecasts and Small Craft Warnings. Details are shown in 7.2.19 on pages 114 and 115.

7.2.5   Special forecasts for ships at sea

UK weather forecasts for yachtsmen may be obtained by listening to BBC Shipping Forecasts, BT Coast Radio Stations, Marinecall or MetFax, or by contacting the local area forecasting centre shown in 7.2.8.

When telephoning a forecast office it must be realised that during busy periods, such as occasions of bad weather, the staff may be fully occupied and there is likely to be a delay.

If a forecast is required for some future occasion or period, or if the forecast is to be kept under review and updated, the request should be addressed to: The Meteorological Office, Central Forecasting Office, London Road, Bracknell, Berks RG12 2SZ. ☎: (01344) 854893, 📠: (01344) 854412 or telex 849801 WEABKA G, giving full details of the service required. The charge for the service, including any transmissions costs, will be advised.

7.2.6   Marinecall – automatic telephone weather service

(1) Telephone forecasts

Recorded inshore forecasts are provided for 16 coastal areas around the UK coastline. In each case dial 0891 500, followed by the three-figure number for the area required (see Fig. 7(1)).

Forecasts cover the inshore waters out to 12M offshore for periods up to 48h and include: General situation, any strong wind or gale warnings in force, wind, weather, visibility, sea state, maximum air temperature and sea temperature. The two-day forecasts are immediately followed by forecasts for days three to five. Forecasts are updated at 0700 and 1900 daily. Area 432, is updated at 0700, 1300 and 1900 daily.

Two to five day planning forecasts for offshore areas beyond 12M can be obtained by ☎ as follows:

English Channel	0891 500 992
Southern North Sea	0891 500 991
Northern North Sea	0891 500 985
Irish Sea	0891 500 954
NW Scotland	0891 500 955
Biscay	0891 500 953

The local inshore forecast for Shetland is not covered by Marinecall and is available by phoning the Coastguard at Lerwick on 01595 692976. Alternatively, phone Weathercall on 0891 500 426 to obtain a general forecast for Caithness, Orkney and Shetland.

(2)   Marinecall current weather reports
For actual weather reports from 45 coastal locations ☎ 0891 226 plus the Marinecall inshore three-figure number shown in Fig. 7(1).

Each of the 16 Marinecall areas contains three weather reports (occasionally two), and are normally updated every hour.

The reports include details of wind, weather, visibility, temperature, pressure and pressure tendency. These reports are followed by the forecast for that area.

Current weather reports
451 Cape Wrath, Wick, Lossiemouth
452 Peterhead, Aberdeen, Fife Ness
453 Boulmer, Tynemouth, Teesmouth
454 Bridlington, Easington, Holbeach
455 Weybourne, Sheerness, Walton-on-the-Naze
456 Dover, Greenwich Lt V, Newhaven
457 Thorney Is, Lee-on-Solent, St Catherine's Pt
458 Brixham, Plymouth, Falmouth, St Mary's
459 Cardiff, Swansea, Milford Haven
460 Aberdaron, Aberporth, Valley
461 Rhyll, Crosby, Walney Island
462 Machrihanish, Prestwick, Greenock
463 Oban, Tiree
464 Benbecula, Altbea, Butt of Lewis
465 Ballycastle, Bangor Harbour, Malin Head

Marinecall forecast	MetFAX marine
Dial: **0891 500 plus Area No.**	*Dial:* **0836 400 plus Area No.**

Marinecall and MetFAX areas

Area	Area Title	Area Coverage
451	Scotland North	Cape Wrath to Rattray Head (and Orkney)
452	Scotland East	Rattray Hd to Berwick-on-Tweed
453	North-East	Berwick-on-Tweed to Whitby
454	East	Whitby to the Wash
455	Anglia	The Wash to North Foreland
456	Channel East	North Foreland to Selsey Bill
457	Mid-Channel	Selsey Bill to Lyme Regis
458	South-West	Lyme Regis to Hartland Point (including the Isles of Scilly)
459	Bristol Channel	Hartland Point to St David's Head
460	Wales	St David's Head to Colwyn Bay
461	North-West	Colwyn Bay to Mull of Galloway (also the Isle of Man)
462	Clyde	Mull of Galloway to Mull of Kintyre (also the North Channel)
463	Caledonia	Mull of Kintyre to Ardnamurchan
464	Minch	Ardnamurchan to Cape Wrath (including the Western Isles)
465	Northern Ireland	Lough Foyle to Carlingford Lough
432	Channel Islands	Marinecall
466	Channel Islands	MetFAX

Fig. 7(1) Marinecall and MetFAX areas

MetFAX Marine
2-to 5- day Planning Forecasts and Charts
Dial: **0336 400 Plus Area No.**

Area	*Area coverage*
468	**North West Scottish Planning Forecast** (0800) and 42/72h forecast chart (covering areas Faroes, Hebrides, Bailey, Rockall and Malin).
469	**Northern North Sea Planning Forecast** (0800) and 42/72h forecast chart (covering areas Forth, Forties, Cromarty, Viking and Fair Isle).
470	**Biscay Planning Forecast** (0800) and 48/72h forecast chart (covering areas East Sole, East Finisterre and Biscay).
471	**English Channel Planning Forecast** (0800) and 48/72h forecast chart (covering areas Plymouth, Portland, Wight and Dover).
472	**Southern North Sea Planning Forecast** (0800) and 48/72h forecast chart (covering areas Thames, Humber, German Bight, Dogger and Tyne).
473	**Irish Sea Planning forecast** (0800) and 48/72h forecast chart (covering areas Irish Sea, Lundy and Fastnet).

Fig. 7(2) MetFAX planning forecast areas

7.2.7 MetFAX Marine

Weather maps, two-day inshore forecasts, two to five day planning forecasts, satellite images and weather reports are available by facsimile. An Index for all fax products can be obtained by Fax on 0336 400 401.

Two day inshore forecasts for the areas shown on Fig 7(1) can be obtained by dialling 0336 400 plus the three figure number of the area required. It should be noted that the Channel Islands are served by two numbers, i.e. by 🖨 on 0336 400 466 and by ☎ on 0891 500 432.

Two to five day planning forecasts and 48/72h forecast chart for the Areas shown on Fig. 7(2) can be obtained by dialling 0336 400 plus the three-figure number of the area required.

Additional fax services available include:

24h shipping forecast	0336 400 441
Guide to surface charts	0336 400 446
Surface chart	0336 400 444
Surface Analysis chart	0336 400 445
Chart of UK weather reports	0336 400 447
Index to chart of weather reports	0336 400 448
3-5 day inshore forecast	0336 400 450
User guide to satellite picture	0336 400 498
Satellite picture	0336 400 499
Chart of Europe & Mediterranean plotted weather reports	0336 400 474

The charge for Marinecall, Weathercall and MetFAX Marine is 39p per minute (cheap rate) and 49p per minute at all other times, including VAT. Calls can be made through British Telecom Coast Radio Stations when the VHF per minute tariff is 95p.

7.2.8 Weather Centres

Weather Centres provide a range of services at a charge. To arrange a forecast service ring:

Southampton	(01703) 228844 or 220646
London	0171-696 0573 or 0171-405 4356
Birmingham	0121-717 0570
Norwich	(01603) 660779
Leeds	(0113) 2451990
Newcastle	(0191) 232 6453
Aberdeen Airport	(01224) 210574
Sella Ness, Scotland	(01806) 242069
Glasgow	0141-248 3451
Manchester	0161-477 1060
Cardiff	(01222) 225746
Bristol	(0117) 9279298
Belfast International Airport	(018494) 22339
Jersey	(01534) 46111 Ext 2229

Republic of Ireland

Central Forecast Office, Dublin (H24)	(01) 424655
Cork Airport Met (0900–2000)	(021) 965974
Shannon Airport Met (H24)	(061) 61333
Dublin Airport Met	(01) 379900 ext 4531

European continent

The numbers of forecast offices and recorded weather messages are shown under 'Telephone' for individual harbours in Areas 15–21 of Chapter 10.

7.2.9 Radio facsimile broadcasts

Facsimile recorders that receive pictorial images such as weather maps are now available of a type that makes them suitable for use in yachts and at port locations such as marinas.

The information available is of a general meteorological nature and not all of it is relevant to the average yachtsman, but there are many items that are of direct use, such as:

> Isobaric charts (actual and forecast)
> Sea and swell charts
> Representation of cloud satellite images
> Sea temperature charts
> Wind charts.

Internationally exchanged data is processed at various centres. In NW Europe those doing such work and transmitting facsimile broadcasts are:

Bracknell (GFA) (England)

> 2618·5*   4610   8040   14436   18261** kHz

> *   1800-0600 UT only
> **   0600-1800 UT only

Northwood (GYA) (GYZ) (GZZ) (England)

> 3652   4307   6452·5   8331·5 kHz

Selected UK Fax broadcast schedule (UT)

0230	Northwood	Schedule
0320	Northwood	Surface analysis
0341	Bracknell	Surface analysis
0400	Northwood	Surface wind and Wx prog
0431	Bracknell	24h surface analysis
0440	Northwood	Satellite pictures
0600	Northwood	Gale summary
0650	Northwood	Surface analysis
0730	Northwood	Surface wind and Wx prog
0806	Bracknell	48h & 72h surface analysis
0935	Bracknell	24h sea state prog
0941	Bracknell	Surface analysis
0950	Northwood	Surface analysis
1031	Bracknell	24h surface analysis
1040	Northwood	Satellite pictures
1045	Bracknell	48h & 72h surface analysis
1130	Northwood	Gale summary
1150	Northwood	Surface wind and Wx prog
1210	Northwood	Surface analysis
1230	Northwood	Sea and swell state prog
1330	Northwood	Satellite pictures
1500	Northwood	Surface analysis
1530	Northwood	Schedule
1541	Bracknell	Surface analysis
1631	Bracknell	24h surface analysis
1640	Northwood	Gale summary
1730	Northwood	Satellite pictures
1800	Northwood	Surface analysis
1950	Northwood	Gale summary
2018	Bracknell	24h sea state prog
2025	Northwood	Surface wind and Wx prog
2050	Northwood	Sea and swell state prog
2120	Northwood	Surface analysis
2141	Bracknell	Surface analysis
2222	Bracknell	48h & 72h surface analysis
2231	Bracknell	24h surface analysis
2320	Northwood	Surface analysis
2327	Bracknell	24h surface analysis

The quality of reception depends on the frequency used and the terrain between transmitter and receiver.

Additional frequencies to those above are also available for limited periods during any 24-hour period. Transmission frequencies and schedules are published in the *Admiralty List of Radio Signals, Vol 3* (NP 283). See also 7.6.13 of *The Macmillan & Silk Cut Yachtsman's Handbook*.

7.2.10 Navtex

Gale warnings are broadcast on receipt and are repeated at scheduled times. Weather messages are broadcast at scheduled times. Details of Navtex stations, identity codes, message categories and transmission times for Navareas I and II are given in Chapter 6 (6.4.25).

7.2.11 Volmet

Volmet is a meteorological service for aviators which continuously transmits reports of actual weather conditions and/or weather forecasts for selected airfields to aircraft in flight on HF SSB and/or VHF.

It is possible to receive HF SSB Volmet broadcasts using a suitable portable radio provided it is fitted with a Single Side Band (SSB) function.

Yachtsmen wishing to closely monitor the weather situation will find the information most useful. The continuously updated hourly reports of actual weather conditions experienced at airfields close to the UK and European coasts can be particularly valuable when drawing your own weather map.

The best broadcast is the Royal Air Force SSB Volmet which continuously broadcasts actual weather reports on HF SSB for a number of military and civil airfields, mostly in the UK, on:

5450 kHz	H24
11253 kHz	H24

The information transmitted consists of: airfield name, wind direction and speed, cloud amount and height, temperature and dew point temperature, sea level pressure (QNH), and any significant weather.

Another is the HF SSB (H3E) broadcast by Shannon which operates as follows:

3413 kHz	HN
5505 kHz	H24
8957 kHz	H24
13264 kHz	H24

The schedule commences at H+00 and at five minute intervals until all airfields have been broadcast. Weather for London/Heathrow, Prestwick and Shannon is broadcast at H+05 and H+35.

7

The names and location of selected airfields included in Volmet broadcasts are shown on Fig. 7(3).

7.2.12   Press forecasts

The delay between the time of issue and the time at which they are available next day make press forecasts of only limited value to yachtsmen. However, the better papers publish forecasts which include a synoptic chart which, in the absence of any other chart, can be helpful when interpreting the shipping forecast on first putting to sea.

7.2.13   Television forecasts

Some TV forecasts show a synoptic chart which, with the satellite pictures, can be a useful guide to the weather situation before the start of a passage.

Weather information is given on Ceefax (BBC) and Teletext (ITV). BBC Ceefax gives weather information on pages 400-428, and ITV (Teletext) gives details on pages 102-108 and 201-205. Antiope is the equivalent French system.

7.2.14   Visual storm signals

Visual storm signals used on the Continent are summarised in 10.15.8, 10.20.7 and 10.21.7.

7.2.15   Radiobeacon wind information

Wind information at La Corbière Lt (49°10'·85N 02°14'·92W) is transmitted by the radiobeacon on frequency 295·50 kHz modulated as follows: Callsign CB 3 times (16 secs), a long dash of 8 secs, a series of 1 to 8 short dashes indicating average wind direction in eight cardinal points (one dash = NE, two dashes = E, clockwise to 8 dashes = N). Up to 8 pips indicates average wind strength on the Beaufort scale (one pip = Force 1, two pips = Force 2, up to 8 pips = Force 8 or more). One or more short dashes indicates maximum gust above average Beaufort scale. A transmission consisting of 3 dashes, followed by 5 pips, followed by 2 dashes would indicate: Wind direction SE, Force 5, Gusting 7.

7.2.16   British Coast Radio Stations –
weather bulletins by R/T

Forecasts originating from the Meteorological Office are broadcast by BT Coast Radio Stations, as indicated in Table 7(4), by radiotelephone on VHF (where available) and simultaneously on MF, after an initial announcement on VHF Ch 16. BT CRS will also give a repeat of weather information at a charge of £11·50 on request (see 7.2.5). Weather messages comprise gale warnings, synopsis and 24-hour forecast for the sea area stated.

Weather broadcasts by BT Coast Radio Stations are made twice daily. There is one central Officer in each region who engages broadcast frequencies at each station from his central position, and reads the forecast for the whole of that region.

7.2.17   HM Coastguard – VHF Ch 67

Details of MRCCs and MRSCs, and their broadcasts of strong wind warnings and scheduled weather messages, are given in Chapter 8 Table 8(1). These stations may also provide information on local actual weather conditions and the current local forecast. Call on VHF Ch 16.

Dover Coastguard broadcasts gale warnings and strong wind warnings on receipt on Ch 67 following an announcement on Ch 16, and thereafter included in the next three routine CNIS broadcasts on Ch 11.

The general synopsis and shipping forecast for local sea areas will be included in routine CNIS broadcasts on VHF Ch 11, every 4 hrs commencing from 0040 UT.

7.2.18   Reports of present weather

Reports of actual local weather can be obtained from the following Meteorological Office observation stations. The locations are shown in Fig. 7(3):

From Meteorological Offices

Station Name	Telephone No
Shoeburyness	01702 292271 ext 3476
Kinloss	01309 72161 ext 674
Sella Ness (Shetlands)	01806 242069
Stornoway	01851 702256 (night 702282)
Tiree	01879 2456
Ronaldsway (IOM)	01624 823311 (night 823313)

(0700–1700 *Mon–Fri*, except Public Holidays)

From Lighthouses

Station Name	Telephone No
Whitby	01947 602107
Cromer	01263 512507
Eastbourne	01323 20634
St Catherine's	01983 730284
Lizard	01326 290431
Rhinns of Islay	01496 860223
Hyskeir	01688 2423
Butt of Lewis	01851 81201
Cape Wrath	01971 511230
Strathy Point	01641 541210

Fig. 7(3) Reports of present weather

Reports from Coastguard Stations

BBC Weather Reports (Coastal or Inshore)

Reports from Lighthouses

Reports from Meteorological Offices

HF SSB Volmet Reports

Fig. 7(4) Map of shipping forecast areas

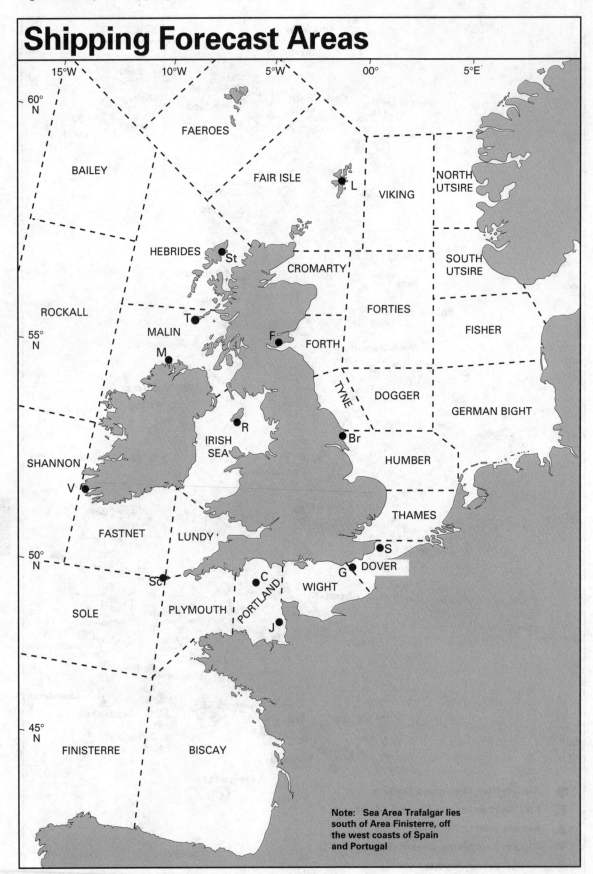

Shipping Forecast Areas

15°W 10°W 5°W 00° 5°E

60°N

FAEROES

BAILEY

FAIR ISLE

NORTH UTSIRE

L

VIKING

HEBRIDES

St

CROMARTY

SOUTH UTSIRE

ROCKALL

T

MALIN

FORTIES

55°N

M

FORTH

FISHER

F

FORTH

TYNE

DOGGER

GERMAN BIGHT

R

IRISH SEA

Br

HUMBER

SHANNON

V

THAMES

FASTNET

LUNDY

S

Scl

DOVER

G

50°N

C

PORTLAND

WIGHT

SOLE

PLYMOUTH

J

45°N

FINISTERRE

BISCAY

Note: Sea Area Trafalgar lies south of Area Finisterre, off the west coasts of Spain and Portugal

Fig. 7(5) Shipping forecast record

Shipping Forecast Record

GENERAL SYNOPSIS

at .... UT/BST

System	Present position	Movement	Forecast position	at

Gales	SEA AREA FORECAST	Wind (At first)	(Later)	Weather	Visibility
	VIKING				
	NORTH UTSIRE				
	SOUTH UTSIRE				
	FORTIES				
	CROMARTY				
	FORTH				
	TYNE				
	DOGGER				
	FISHER				
	GERMAN BIGHT				
	HUMBER				
	THAMES				
	DOVER				
	WIGHT				
	PORTLAND				
	PLYMOUTH				
	BISCAY				
	FINISTERRE				
	SOLE				
	LUNDY				
	FASTNET				
	IRISH SEA				
	SHANNON				
	ROCKALL				
	MALIN				
	HEBRIDES				
	BAILEY				
	FAIR ISLE				
	FAEROES				
	S E ICELAND				

COASTAL REPORTS at .... BST UT	Wind Direction	Force	Weather	Visibility	Pressure	Change
Tiree (T)						
Stornoway (St)						
Lerwick (L)						
Fife Ness (F)						
Bridlington (Br)						
Sandettie auto (S)						

COASTAL REPORTS	Wind Direction	Force	Weather	Visibility	Pressure	Change
Greenwich Lt V (G)						
Jersey (J)						
Channel auto (C)						
Scilly auto (Sc)						
Valentia (V)						
Ronaldsway (R)						
Malin Head (M)						

7

TABLE 7(1) BBC Radio 4 – shipping and coastal waters forecasts and gale warnings

Note: All times local

Time	Forecast	Contents	Stations and Frequencies
0048 approx	Shipping forecast – United Kingdom waters fcst areas	Gale warnings in force; synopsis; 24h fcst for United Kingdom fcst areas (including Trafalgar); reports from stations	BBC Radio 4: 198 kHz, 92·4-94·6 MHz (England and Scotland); Tyneside 603 kHz, London and Northern Ireland 720 kHz, Aberdeen 1449 kHz, Carlisle 1485 kHz, Plymouth and Enniskillen 774 kHz, Redruth 756 kHz; 92·4-96·1 MHz or 103·5-104·9 MHz (Wales and, Northern Ireland), 97·1 MHz (Channel Islands)
0550	Coastal waters UK and Northern Ireland	Fcst, valid until 1800 up to 12M offshore; synopsis; reports from selected stations	BBC Radio 4 frequencies as above
0555 and 1750	Shipping forecast – United Kingdom waters fcst areas	Gale warnings in force; synopsis; 24h fcst for United Kingdom fcst areas; reports from stations	BBC Radio 4 frequencies as above
1355	Shipping forecast – United Kingdom fcst areas	Gale warnings in force; synopsis; 24h fcst for United Kingdom fcst areas (including Mon-Fri area Minch); reports from stations	BBC Radio 4 frequencies as above

Gale warnings are broadcast at first available programme junction after receipt, and after first news bulletin after receipt – for all UK forecast areas including Trafalgar, on all Radio 4 frequencies as above. Emergency messages of unusual importance or urgency to shipping are broadcast on receipt.

TABLE 7(2) Radio Telefis Eireann – coastal waters forecasts and gale warnings

Note: All times local

Time	Contents	Stations and Frequencies
0602 1253 1823 (Sat-Sun and public holidays) 1824 (Mon-Fri) 2355	Synopsis 1h before bcst; detailed forecast and gale warnings in force for Irish coastal waters and Irish Sea; outlook for further 24h; reports from coastal stations	RTE – Radio 1: Tullamore 567 kHz, Cork 729 kHz and following main transmitters on FM network: Three Rock 88·5 MHz, Kippure 89·1 MHz, Mount Leinster 89·6 MHz, Mullaghanish 90 MHz, Maghera 88·8 MHz, Truskmore 88·2 MHz, Holywell Hill 89·2 MHz, Clermont Cam 95·2 MHz.

Gale warnings for Irish coastal waters up to 30M offshore and for Irish Sea are broadcast at the first programme junction after receipt and with news bulletins on RTE – Radio 1, frequencies as above; and on RTE – Radio 2 FM from Athlone 612 kHz, Dublin 1278 kHz and Cork 1278 kHz.

NOTE: A five-day outlook forecast is broadcast on RTE Radio 1 frequencies at 0755 LT.

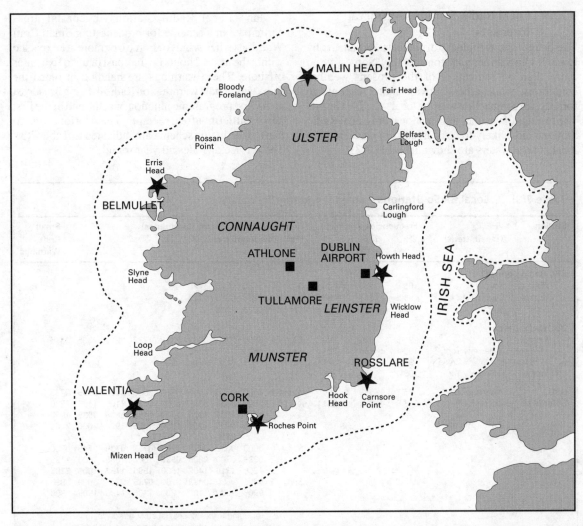

Fig. 7(6) Ireland. Coastal weather forecast areas within 30M of the coast, plus the Irish Sea. Also shown are the stations (starred) from which reports are included and the headlands used to divide up the coastline into smaller areas, depending on the expected weather situation. RTE broadcast stations are also indicated.

7

7.2.19 Local Radio Stations – coastal forecasts

The details and usefulness of forecasts broadcast by Local Radio Stations vary considerably. Some give no more than an indication of the present weather conditions, while others provide more responsible forecasts in conjunction with the local Weather Centre. The timings of weather information from Local Radio Stations most likely to be of interest to yachtsmen in local coastal waters are shown in Table 7(3).

Many Local Radio Stations in coastal areas participate in a scheme for broadcasting Small Craft Warnings when winds of Force 6 or more are expected within the next 12 hours on the coast or up to five miles offshore. These warnings are handled in much the same way as gale warnings on Radio 4, being broadcast at the first programme junction or at the end of the first news bulletin after receipt. The stations which participate in this scheme are indicated in Table 7(3). The service operates all year round.

Table 7(3)   Local Radio Stations – coastal weather forecasts

Station	VHF Transmitter(s)	Frequencies VHF (MHz)	MF (kHz)	(m)	Coastal waters forecasts (local times) (*summer months only)								Small Craft Warnings
BBC Radio Cornwall													
Redruth	Redruth	103·9	630	476	*Mon-Fri:* 0725	0825	1225						Yes
Bodmin	Caradon Hill	95·2	657	457	*Sat:* 0725	0825	1325						
Scilly	Scilly	96·0			*Sun:* 0825	0925							
BBC Radio Devon													
Exeter	Exeter	95·8	990	303	*Mon-Fri:* 0635	0733	0833	1310	1735	2212	2305	2315	Yes
Plymouth	N Hessary Tor	103·4	855	351	*Sat:* 0605	0733	0833	1310	2305				
N Devon	Huntshaw Cross	94·8	801	375	*Sun:* 0605	(0633 Bristol)	0833						
Torbay	N Hessary Tor	103·4	1458	206									
BBC Solent FM	Rowridge IOW	96·1	999	300	*Mon-Fri:* 0500	0530*	0600	0630	0635*	0700	**0735**	0745*	Yes
	Bincombe Hill	103·8	1359	221	0800	**0835**	0850*	0900	1000	1100	1135	1200	
					1235	1300	**1325**	1400	1435	1500	**1535**	1600	
					1635	1700	**1735**	1800	**1835**	1900	2000	2100	
					2305	**2305**							
					Sat: 0600	0630	0633*	0700	0730	**0735**	0745*	0800	
					0835	0900	**0905**	**0935**	1000	1035	1100	1135	
					1200	**1310**	1400	1500	**1505**	**1757**	1800	**2305**	
					Sun: 0600	0630	0633*	0700	**0735**	0745	0800	0830	
					0905	1000	1100	1200	1305	1400	**1505**	1800	
					2305								

*   =   Including forecast; coastal station reports, local Coastguards; shipping movements; tides and firings.
Bold =   live forecasts from Southampton Weather Centre

Station	VHF Transmitter(s)	Frequencies VHF (MHz)	MF (kHz)	(m)	Coastal waters forecasts (local times) (*summer months only)						Small Craft Warnings
Ocean FM											
	Fort Widley	97·5			*Mon-Fri:* 0704	0804	1704	1804			
	Crabwood Farm	96·7									
South Coast Radio											
	Farlington Marshes		1170	257	*Mon-Fri:* 0629	0729	0829	1729	1829		Yes
	Southampton		1557	193	*Sat-Sun:* 0629	0729	0829				
	Brighton		1323	227							
BBC Southern Counties Radio											
	Brighton/Hove	95·3	1485	202	*Mon-Fri:* 0623	0653	0723	0753	0823	0853	Yes
	Heathfield	104·5	1161	258	1723	1753	1823	1853	1923	1953	
	Worthing	95·3			*Sat-Sun:* 0622	0652	0722	0752	0822	0852	
	Reigate	104·0	1368	219							
	Horsham	95·1									
	Newhaven/Lewes	95·0									
BBC Radio Kent											
	Wrotham	96·7			*Mon-Fri:* 0633	0733 0833 1230 1708 1808					Yes
	Swingate	104·2	774	388	*Sat:* 0745 0845 1305						
	Folkestone	97·6	1602	187	*Sun:* 0745 0845 1305						
BBC Essex											
	Mid & N Essex	103·5	729	412	*Mon-Fri:* 0740	0840					
	SE Essex	95·3	1530	196	*Sat:* 0657	0757	0857	1205	1305		
	All Essex		765	392	*Sun:* 0657	0757	0857				
BBC Radio Suffolk											
	East Suffolk	103·9			*Mon-Fri:* 0617	0717	0817	1330	1717	1810	Yes
	Lowestoft	95·5			*Sat-Sun:* 0707	0807	1305				
	Gt. Barton	104·6									

Table 7(3) Local Radio Stations – coastal weather forecasts *Continued*

Station	VHF Transmitter(s)	VHF (MHz)	MF (kHz)	(m)	Coastal waters forecasts (local times) (*summer months only)	Small Craft Warnings
BBC Radio Norfolk	Tacolneston	95·1	855	351	*Mon-Fri:* 0630-1600 at H+00 (0850 CG report)	Yes
	Great Massingham	104·4	873	344	1700* 1800* (*summer period only)	
					Sat: 0630-1300 at H+00	
					Sun: 0630-1400 at H+00	
BBC Radio Lincolnshire	Belmont	94·9	1368	219	*Mon-Fri:* 0615 0745 1145 1650 1810	Yes
					Sat: 0720 0845 1145 1445	
					Sun: 0845 1145	
BBC Radio Humberside	High Hunsley	95·9	1485	202	*Mon-Fri:* 0635 0735 0835 1310 1633 1733 1833	Yes
					Sat-Sun: 0733 0833 1310	
BBC Radio Cleveland	Bilsdale	95·0			*Mon-Fri:* 0645 0745 0845 1345 1645 1715 1815	Yes
	Whitby	95·8			*Sat:* 0645 0745 0945 1245 1345	
					Sun: 0745 0845 0945	
BBC Radio Newcastle	Pontop Pike	95·4	1458	206	*Mon-Fri:* 0655 0755 0855 1155 1655 1755	Yes
	Chatton	96·0	in North		*Sat-Sun:* 0755 0855 0955	
Radio Forth	Craigkelly	97·3			*Mon-Sat:* 0600-1800 (every hour)	Yes
Max AM	Barns Farm		1548	194	*Sun:* 0600 0800 0900 1200 1500 1900	
Radio Tay AM	Dundee		1161	258	*Sat-Sun:* 0600 0700 0900 1200 1500 1800 2100	Yes
	Perth		1584	189	(April-October)	
Radio Clyde 2	Dechmont		1152	261	*Daily:* H24 at H+00	Yes
BBC Radio Cumbria						Yes
N Cumbria	Sandale	95·6	756	397	*Mon-Fri:* 0633 0733 0833 1710	
W Cumbria	Whitehaven	104·1	1458	206	*Sat-Sun:* 0740 0840 1115	
S Cumbria	Morecambe Bay	96·1	837	358		
Manx Radio	Snaefell	89·0			*Mon-Fri:* 0710 0810 0905 1310 1740 2303	
	Carnane	97·2			*Sat:* 0900 1310 2303	
	Jurby	103·7			*Sun:* 0803 1310 2303	
	Foxdale		1368	219		
BBC Radio Merseyside	Allerton	95·8	1485	202	*Mon-Fri:* 0743 1143 1300	
					Sat: 0800	
					Sun: 0800	
Soundwave 96·4 and Swansea Sound 1170 Sound	Kilvey Hill	96·4	1170	257	*Mon-Fri:* 0725 0825 0925	Yes
					Sat-Sun: 0825 1003	
BBC Radio Bristol	Bristol	94·9	1548	194	*Mon-Fri:* 0605 0632 0659 0733 0759 0833 0859	Yes
	Bath	104·6			1259 1633 1755	
	Avon/Somerset	95·5			*Sat:* 0758 0858	
					Sun: 0758 0858	
Brunel Radio	Tor Marton		1260	238	*Daily:* At H+30	Yes
Downtown Radio	Limavady	96·4			*Mon-Fri:* 0705 0805 0905 1005 1320 1403 503	Yes
	Knockbreckon		1026		1710 2315	
	Sheriff's Mountain	102·4			*Sat:* 0705 0805 0905 1005 1105	
	Brougher Mountain	96·6			*Sun:* 1105 2303 (0003 Mon)	
BBC Radio Guernsey		93·2	1116	269	*Mon-Fri:* 0733 1833	Yes
					Sat: 0733 0833	
					Sun: 0733	
BBC Radio Jersey		88·8	1026	292	*Mon-Fri:* 0635 0810 1835	Yes
					Sat: 0735	
					Sun: 0735	

7

TABLE 7(4)   Weather broadcasts by Coast Radio Stations in the British Isles

A.   BRITISH TELECOM (BT) COAST RADIO STATIONS (for details of other services see 6.5.1)

Weather bulletins are broadcast on request and twice daily – at 0703 1903 (UT) from Northern Region stations (see below) and at 0733 1933 (UT) from Southern Region stations (see below). Bulletins include gale warnings, synopsis and 24-hour forecast for all the sea areas listed for Northern and Southern Regions respectively.

Gale warnings are broadcast on frequencies/channels listed below after an announcement on VHF Ch 16 and 2182 kHz, at the end of the first silence period after receipt (i.e. at H+03 or H+33), and at 0303 0903 1503 2103 UT. They remain in force unless amended or cancelled, but are re-issued if the gale persists for more than 24 hours.

BT NORTHERN REGION (Routine broadcasts at **0703 1903** UT)				BT SOUTHERN REGION (Routine broadcasts at **0733 1933** UT)			
Station	Channel/Frequency		For all areas below	Station	Channel/Frequency		For all areas below
Whitby	Ch 25		Viking	**Celtic**	Ch 24		
Cullercoats	Ch 26	2719 kHz	North Utsire	**Ilfracombe**	Ch 05		Tyne
Forth	Ch 62		South Utsire	**Land's End**	Ch 27	2670 kHz	Dogger
Stonehaven	Ch 26	2691 kHz	Forties		Ch 64 (to Scilly)		German Bight
Buchan	Ch 25		Cromarty				Humber
Shetland		1770 kHz	Forth	**Pendennis**	Ch 62		Thames
Wick	Ch 28	1764 kHz	Tyne	**Start Point**	Ch 26		Dover
Lewis	Ch 05		Dogger	**Niton**	Ch 28	1641 kHz	Wight
Hebrides		1866 kHz	Fisher	**Hastings**[1]	Ch 07		Portland
Skye	Ch 24		German Bight	**Thames**[1]	Ch 02		Plymouth
Oban	Ch 07		Humber	**North Foreland**[1]	Ch 26		Biscay
Islay	Ch 25		Thames	**Orfordness**[1]	Ch 62		Finisterre
Portpatrick	Ch 27	1883 kHz	Lundy	**Bacton**	Ch 07		Sole
Anglesey	Ch 26		Irish Sea	**Humber**	Ch 26	1869 kHz	Lundy
Cardigan Bay	Ch 03		Rockall	**Grimsby**	Ch 27		Fastnet
			Malin				Irish Sea
			Hebrides				Shannon
			Bailey				
			Fair Isle				
			Faeroes				
			SE Iceland				

Note: (1) Fog warnings for River Thames broadcast when visibility falls below half a mile, at end of next silence period after receipt and repeated every two hours until amended or cancelled

B.   JERSEY RADIO (for details of other services see 6.5.1)

Weather bulletins are broadcast after announcement on Ch 16/2182 kHz and comprise near gale force 7 warnings, synopsis, 24-hour forecast and outlook for a further 24 hours and reports from meteorological stations.

Near gale force 7 warnings are broadcast on receipt, at the end of the next silence period, and at 0307 0907 1507 2107 (UT).

Station	Channel/Frequency	Area	Times of weather bulletins
Jersey	Ch 25 82 1659 kHz	Channel Islands south of 50°N and east of 3°W	On request and at 0645 0745 (LT), 0845 (LT May-Aug) and at 1245 1845 2245 (UT)

C.   IRISH COAST RADIO SERVICE (for details of other services see 6.5.2). See Fig. 6(3) for stations.

Weather bulletins are broadcast as below and comprise gale warnings, synopsis and 24-hour forecast.

Gale warnings are broadcast on VHF channels below on receipt and repeated at the next of the following times: 0033 0633 1233 1833 (LT) after announcement on Ch 16.

Valentia Radio broadcasts gale warnings on 1752 kHz at the end of the next silence period after receipt and at the next of the following times 0303 0903 1503 2103 (UT) after announcement on 2182 kHz.

Station	Channel/Frequency	Area	Times of weather bulletins
Malin Head	Ch 23		
Glen Head	Ch 24		
Belmullet	Ch 83		
Clifden	Ch 26		
Shannon	Ch 28	Irish coastal waters up	0103 0403 0703 1003 1303 1603 1903 2203 (LT)
Bantry	Ch 23	to 30 miles offshore	after announcement on Ch 16
Cork	Ch 26	and Irish Sea	
Mine Head	Ch 83		
Rosslare	Ch 23		
Wicklow Head	Ch 87		
Dublin	Ch 83		
Valentia	Ch 24	Shannon, Fastnet	As above, and on request
Valentia	1752 kHz	Shannon, Fastnet	On request and at 0833 2033 (UT)

TABLE 7(5)   Western Europe – shipping forecasts, coastal waters forecasts, and gale warnings

Notes:
(1) All times below are local or 'clock' times (LT) unless otherwise stated.
(2) Details of other broadcasts by Coast Radio Stations are given in Chapter 6 (6.5.3–6.5.6).
(3) Broadcasts in English are indicated in bold type, thus: in **English**.
(4) CROSS – Centres Régionaux Opérationnels de Surveillance et de Sauvetage. Broadcasts follow announcement on Ch 16. In the English Channel CROSS Stations broadcast weather information on request in French or in English, after a call on Ch 16. Gale warnings for coastal waters are broadcast commencing every H+03 by stations concerned.
(5) French Coast Radio Stations make a preliminary announcement on Ch 16/2182 kHz.

Station (Relay Stations)	Frequency/ Channel	Times (LT unless stated)	Weather bulletins	Areas for weather bulletins and gale warnings	Gale warnings
FRANCE – NATIONAL AND REGIONAL BROADCASTS					
France Inter	162 kHz	2005	Storm warnings, synopsis, 24h fcst and outlook, in French	French fcst areas 1-25	–
Cherbourg 100·7					
St Vaast-la-Hougue La Hague Barneville Carteret Cherbourg	85·0 MHz 99·8 MHz 99·9 MHz 100·7 MHz	0829 0829 0829 0829	Coastal fcst, storm warnings, visibility, wind strength, tidal information, small craft warnings. In French	Cherbourg peninsula coastal waters	–
Bayonne Bordeaux	1494 kHz 1206 kHz	0655	Ditto	East Atlantic and Bay of Biscay	–
Rennes Brest	711 kHz 1404 kHz	0655	Ditto	East Atlantic and English Channel	–
Paris Lille	864 kHz 1377 kHz	0655	Ditto	English Channel and North Sea	–
FRANCE – CHANNEL COAST					
Dunkerque Calais Boulogne-sur-Mer	Ch 61 Ch 87 Ch 23	0733 1533 0733 1533 0733 1533	Strong breeze/gale warnings synopsis & development, 12h fcst, outlook for further 12h, observations from Signal Stations, in French	Coastal waters from Belgian border to Dieppe	Nil
Boulogne-sur-Mer	1692 kHz 3795 kHz	0703 UT 1833 UT	Gale warnings, synopsis & development, 24h fcst and outlook, in French	French areas 1 to 14	Nil
	3795 kHz	–	–	Ditto	On receipt and every H+03 H+33 when imminent. Every odd H+03 (UT) while warning in force
CROSS[4] Gris-Nez	Ch 79 (from all four stations)	On receipt, and every H+03 H+10 and on request	–	Coastal waters from Belgian border to Cap d'Antifer	Gale warnings and information on visibility, in French and **English**
Dunkerque Gris-Nez St Frieux Ailly	Ch 79 Ch 79 Ch 79 Ch 79	0720 1920 0710 1910 0703 1903	Gale warnings, synopsis, 24h fcst, outlook for 48h. In French and **English**	Coastal waters from Belgian border to Baie de Somme	By stations concerned, commencing every H+03 station by station while warning in force

7

Station (Relay Stations)	Frequency/ Channel	Times (LT unless stated)	Weather bulletins	Areas for weather bulletins and gale warnings	Gale warnings
Dieppe Le Havre	Ch 02 Ch 26	0733 1533 0733 1533	Strong breeze/gale warnings synopsis & development, 12h fcst, outlook for further 12h, observations from Signal Stations, in French	Coastal waters from Baie de Somme to Baie de Seine	Nil
Port-en-Bessin Cherbourg	Ch 03 Ch 27	0733 1533 0733 1533		Coastal waters La Hague to Penmarc'h	
CROSS[4] Jobourg	Ch 80	On receipt and every H+20, H+50		French areas, 13 and 14	Gale warnings in French and **English**
Broadcasts from: Antifer Port-en-Bessin Jobourg	Ch 80 Ch 80 Ch 80	0803 2003 0745 1945 0733 1933	Gale warnings, synopsis, 24h fcst, reports from stations	Coastal waters, Baie de Somme to Cap de la Hague	By stations listed plus plus Gatteville and Roches Douvres as concerned, commencing every H+03, station by station while warning in force
Jobourg Granville	Ch 80 Ch 80	0715 1915 0703 1903		Coastal waters, Cape de la Hague to Penmarc'h	
St Malo	Ch 02	0733 1533	Strong breeze/gale warnings synopsis & development, 24h fcst, outlook for further 24h, observations from Ouessant, in French	Coastal waters from Le Havre to Penmarc'h	Nil
Radio France Armorique (Broadcasts from 18 sites)	101·3 MHz 103·1 MHz	0829 1229 1829	Coastal fcst, storm warnings, wind strength and direction, In French	Coast of Brittany, excluding extreme west, but including Channel Islands and Glenans	On receipt. In French
Brest-Le Conquet (at St Malo)	2691 kHz	0733 UT 1803 UT	Gale warnings, synopsis & development, 24h fcst and outlook, in French	French areas 14 to 24	Nil
CROSS[4] Corsen	1650 kHz	0745 1945	Fcsts and gale warnings	French areas 12 to 18 and 20 to 24	On receipt and every H+03
Ouessant Le Stiff	Ch 79	Every 3h from 0150 UT	Gale warnings, synopsis, 12h fcst and outlook, in French and **English**	French areas 14 to 16	On receipt and every H+10, H+40 in French and **English**
Cap Fréhel	Ch 79	0450 0733 1933	Gale warnings, synopsis, 24h fcst and outlook, in French and **English**	Coastal waters from Le Havre to Penmarc'h	In sequence, plus Bodic and Corsen, for stations concerned commencing every H+03. whilst warning in force. In French, and **English** in summer
Île de Batz	Ch 79	0445 0715 1915			
Pointe du Raz	Ch 79	0433 0703 1903			
Paimpol Plougasnou Ouessant	Ch 84 Ch 81 Ch 82	0733 1533 0733 1533 0733 1533	Strong breeze/gale warnings, synopsis & development, 24h fcst, outlook for further 24h observations from Ouessant, in French	Coastal waters from Cap de la Hague to Penmarc'h	

FRANCE – ATLANTIC COAST

Station (Relay Stations)	Frequency/ Channel	Times (LT unless stated)	Weather bulletins	Areas for weather bulletins and gale warnings	Gale warnings
Brest-Le Conquet	1671 kHz and 3722 kHz	0733 UT 1803 UT	Gale warnings, synopsis & development, 24h fcst and outlook, in French	French areas 14 to 24	Nil
	1635 kHz		–	French areas 14 to 24	Every H+03 H+33 when imminent. Every even H+03 (UT) while warning in force

Station (Relay stations)	Frequency/ Channel	Times (LT unless stated)	Weather bulletins	Areas for weather bulletins and gale warnings	Gale warnings
Brest-Le Conquet Pont l'Abbé	Ch 26 Ch 86	0733 1533 0733 1533	Strong breeze/gale warnings, synopsis & development, 24h fcst, outlook for further 24h, observations from Ouessant, in French	Coastal waters from Le Havre to Penmarc'h and from Penmarc'h to south of Vendée	Nil
Brest-Le Conquet (at Quimperlé)	1876 kHz	0733 UT 1803 UT	Gale warnings, synopsis & development, 24h fcst and outlook, in French	French areas 14 to 24	Nil
CROSS[4] Étel Broadcasts from:					On receipt and every every H+03 in winter and in **English** in summer. By stations concerned, station by station while warning in force
Penmarc'h **Étel** **Kerrouault** **L'Armandèche**	Ch 80 Ch 80 Ch 80 Ch 80	0703 1903 0715 1915 0733 1933 0745 1945	Gale warnings, synopsis, 24h fcst and outlook for further 24h, in French.	Coastal waters from Penmarc'h to L'Aiguillon	
St Nazaire	1722 kHz and 2740 kHz	0733 UT 1803 UT	Gale warnings, synopsis and development, 24h fcst and outlook, in French	French areas 14 to 24	On 1635 kHz on receipt. Every H+03 H+33 when imminent Every even H+03 (UT) while warning in force
Belle Île **St Nazaire** **St Herblain/Nantes** **St Hilaire-de-Riez**	Ch 25 Ch 23 Ch 28 Ch 27	0733 1533 0733 1533 0733 1533 0733 1533	Strong breeze/gale warnings, synopsis & development, 24h fcst, outlook for further 24h, observations from Ouessant, in French	Coastal waters from Pte du Raz (48°00'N) to south of Vendée (46°20'N)	Nil
Brest-Le Conquet (at Arcachon)	1862 kHz	0733 UT 1803 UT	Gale warnings, synopsis & development, 24h fcst and outlook, in French	French areas 14 to 24	Nil
	2775 kHz	–	–	Ditto	On receipt and every H+03 H+33 when imminent, every even H+03 (UT) while while warning in force
Île de Ré **Royan** **Arcachon** **Bayonne**	Ch 21 Ch 23 Ch 82 Ch 24	0733 1533 0733 1533 0733 1533 0733 1533	Strong breeze/gale warnings synopsis & development, 12h fcst, probabilities for next 12h, outlook, coastal reports, in French	Coastal waters from 46°20'N to Spanish border	Nil
CROSS[4] Soulac	(Note: Soulac operates 0700-2200 and night service is from Étel – see above)				
Chassiron **Soulac** **Cap Ferret** **Contis** **Biarritz**	Ch 80 Ch 80 Ch 80 Ch 80 Ch 80	0703 1903 0715 1915 0733 1933 0745 1945 0803 2003	Gale warnings, synopsis, 24h Fcst and outlook for further 24h, in French.	Coastal waters, L'Aiguillon to the Spanish border	On receipt and every H+03 in French. (**English** in summer). By stations concerned, while warning in force

7

Fig. 7(7) French shipping forecast areas

Fig. 7(7)
FRANCE
Forecast
areas

Transmissions of:
Bordeaux-Arcachon
Boulogne
Brest-Le Conquet
Radio France
St Nazaire

NORTH SEA
COMMON AREAS
AS SHOWN BELOW

French Forecast Areas
KEY
12 Dover
13 Manche Est
14 Manche Ouest
15 Ouest Bretagne
16 Nord Gascogne
17 Ouest Ecosse
18 Nord Irlande
19 Ouest Irlande
20 Mer d'Irlande
21 Sud Irlande
22 Sole
23 Cap Finisterre
24 Sud Gascogne

Fig. 7(8)
NORTH SEA
Common
shipping forecast areas

As used for forecasts from:
France
Belgium
Netherlands
Germany
Norway
United Kingdom

Notes:
(1) Numbers are as for
French forecast areas.
(2) Numbers in brackets
with prefix N are as for
German forecast areas
and for Norwegian areas
(N1) – N(4) and (N8) – (N10)

Station	Frequency/ Channel	Times (LT unless stated)	Weather bulletins	Areas for weather bulletins and gale warnings	Gale warnings
BELGIUM					
Belgische Radio en Televisie	927 kHz 91·7 MHz 94··2 MHz 95··7 MHz 98·5 MHz	0600 0900 0700 1200 0800 1700 2200	Weather report in Dutch after the news	Areas Dover, Thames, Humber, Wight, Portland	In winter only, on receipt and at 0445 0530 0630 0730 0830 1130 1545 1645 1845 2245 in Dutch
Oostende	2761 kHz and Ch 27	0820 UT 1720 UT	Strong breeze warnings and fcst, in **English** and Dutch	Areas Dover, Thames	On receipt and after next two silence periods. In **English** and Dutch
Antwerpen	Ch 24			Schelde estuary	On receipt, after next two silence periods and every odd H+05 UT. Strong wind (Force 6) warnings on receipt and every H+03, H+48 in **English** and Dutch
NETHERLANDS					
Scheveningen	1713 kHz (at Nes) and 1890 kHz	0340 UT 0940 UT 1540 UT 2140 UT	Near gale warnings, synopsis, 12h fcst, outlook for further 24h, and reports from stations, in **English** and Dutch	Dutch coastal waters up to 30M offshore (including IJsselmeer) and sea areas for southern North Sea	On receipt and after next silence period, in **English** and Dutch. Ice reports every 4h from 0333 on 1674 and 1890 kHz in **English** and Dutch
	2824 kHz	0340 UT	Ditto	Ditto	Nil
Scheveningen VHF stations					
Goes **Rotterdam** **Scheveningen** **Haarlem** **Lelystad** **Wieringermeer** **Platform L7** **Terschelling** **Nes** **Appingedam**	Ch 23 Ch 87 Ch 83 Ch 25 Ch 83 Ch 27 Ch 84 Ch 78 Ch 23 Ch 27	0005 0805 1305 1905	Strong breeze warnings, synopsis, 12h wind fcst, in Dutch. 24h wind fcst at 0005 and 1905	Dutch coastal waters up to 30M offshore (including IJsselmeer)	Strong breeze warnings on receipt and every H+05, in Dutch

7

Station	Frequency/ Channel	Times (LT unless stated)	Weather bulletins	Areas for weather bulletins and gale warnings	Gale warnings
GERMANY **Norddeutscher Rundfunk NDR 1 Welle Nord** **Helgoland Hamburg Flensburg Heide Sylt**	88·9 MHz 89·5 MHz 89·6 MHz 90·5 MHz 90·9 MHz	0830 (May - Sept)	Synopsis, 12h fcst and outlook for further 12h, and reports from stations in German. Wind fcst after the news, every H+00	Helgoland, Elbe and North Frisian coast	
Norddeutscher Rundfunk Hamburg (NDR 4)	972 kHz	On receipt 0930 2320	Wind fcst, in German Synopsis, 12h fcst and outlook for further 12h, reports from stations, in German	German Bight German areas N9–N12	Water level reports at 1000, in German
Radio Bremen Hansawelle Bremerhaven Bremen **(RB1)**	936 kHz 89·3 MHz 93·8 MHz	On receipt About 1030 2400	Wind fcst in German for next 12h Weather report, in German Synopsis, 12h fcst and outlook for further 12h, reports from stations, in German	German Bight German Bight German areas N9-N12	Water level reports 1030 2400 (Mon-Sat), 1130 2400 (Sun and Public Holidays) Nil Nil
Deutschlandfunk	1269 kHz (Gale warnings also on 88·7 MHz)	0205 0740 1205	Synopsis, 12h fcst and outlook for further 12h, reports from stations, and ice reports, in German. Water level reports at 0205 only.	German areas N9-N12	On receipt in German for German Bight
Deutschlandradio **Norddeich**	177 kHz 855 kHz 990 kHz Ch 28	0205 0740 1205 0800 1200 UT 1900	Synopsis, 12h fcst and outlook for further 12h, in German Synopsis, 12h fcst and outlook for further 12h, reports from stations, in German	German areas N9-N12 German areas N9-N12	On receipt in German for German Bight Nil
Helgoland Eiderstedt Nordfrieseland Elbe-Weser	Ch 27 Ch 25 Ch 26 Ch 24	0800 1200 UT 1900	Synopsis, 12h fcst and outlook for further 12h, reports from stations, in German	German areas N9-N12	Nil

German Traffic Centres	Traffic Centres broadcast local storm warnings, weather messages, visibility and (when appropriate) ice reports on VHF channels as follows: German Bight, Cuxhaven Elbe and Brunsbüttel Elbe broadcasts are in **English** and German, remainder in German.

German Bight Traffic	Ch 79 80	every H+00
Ems Traffic	Ch 15 18 20 21	every H+50
Jade Traffic	Ch 20 63	every H+10
Bremerhaven Weser Traffic	Ch 02 04 05 07 21 22 82	every H+20
Bremen Weser Traffic	Ch 19 78 81	every H+30
Hunte Traffic	Ch 63	every H+30
Cuxhaven Elbe Traffic	Ch 71 (outer Elbe)	every H+55
Brunsbüttel Elbe Traffic	Ch 68 (inner Elbe)	every H+05
Kiel Kanal II	Ch 02	every H+15 and H+45
(for east going vessels, in **English** on request)		

Chapter 8

Safety

Contents

8

This chapter gives information about safety equipment, emergency signals, the Global Maritime Distress and Safety System (GMDSS), and SAR operations. The following subjects are described in more detail in Chapter 8 of *The Macmillan and Silk Cut Yachtsman's Handbook: safety equipment; radar reflectors; bilge pumps; fire fighting; life jackets; safety harnesses; man overboard; life rafts; distress signals; SAR organisation; abandoning ship; helicopter rescues and first aid afloat.*

8.1   SAFETY EQUIPMENT

8.1.1   Safety equipment – general

The skipper is responsible for the safety of the boat and all on board. He must ensure that:

(1) The boat is suitable in design and in construction for her intended purpose.
(2) The boat is maintained in good condition.
(3) The crew is competent and sufficiently strong.
(4) The necessary safety and emergency equipment is carried, is in good condition, and the crew know how to use it.

Individual crew members are responsible for their personal gear. Nonslip shoes or boots are essential. So is foul-weather clothing with close fastenings at neck, wrists and ankles. At least two changes of sailing clothing should be carried, including warm sweaters and towelling strips as neck scarves. Other personal items include a sailor's knife and spike on a lanyard, a waterproof torch, and a supply of anti-seasick pills. Life jacket and safety harnesses are usually supplied on board, but if individuals bring their own, the skipper should make certain they are up to standard.

Safety guidelines for recreational boat users can be found in a useful booklet *Safety on the Sea* published jointly by the RNLI, HM Coastguard and the RYA.

8.1.2   Safety equipment – legal requirements

Yachts more than 45ft (13·7m) in length are required to carry safety equipment as in the Merchant Shipping (Life Saving Appliances) and Merchant Shipping (Fire Appliances) Rules (HMSO).

All yachts must carry navigation lights and sound signals which comply with the International Regulations for Preventing Collisions at Sea.

Racing yachts are required to carry the safety equipment specified for the class/event concerned.

8.1.3   Safety equipment – recommendations for sea-going yachts 18 – 45ft (5·5 – 13·7m) overall length

Full details of recommended safety equipment are given in *The Macmillan & Silk Cut Yachtsman's Handbook*. Below are brief reminders of the minimum equipment which should be carried for (a) coastal and (b) offshore cruising.

But prevention is better than cure, and simple precautions can eliminate accidents. Be particularly careful with bottled gas and petrol. Fit a gas detector. Turn off the gas at the bottle after use. If gas or petrol is smelt – no naked lights, and do not run electrical equipment. Test systems regularly. Insist that crew wear life jackets and harnesses when necessary, and that they do clip on. Make sure a good lookout is maintained at all times. Listen to every forecast. Double-check all navigational calculations. Take nothing for granted.

Fig. 8(1) Putting on a life jacket – first read the instructions. Hold the jacket up in front of you, put your head through the hole, and secure the waistband at the side or front as appropriate.

Safety equipment list

	(a) Coastal	(b) Offshore
Safety		
Life jackets, BS3595, or CE equivalent per person	1	1
Harnesses, BS4224, or CE equivalent per person	1	1
Navigation		
Charts, almanac, pilot	Yes	Yes
Compass with deviation card	1	1
Hand bearing compass	1	1
Chart table instruments	Yes	Yes
Watch/clock	1	2
Echo sounder	1	1
Lead line	1	1
Radio direction finding set	1	1
Radio receiver (forecasts)	1	1
Barometer	1	1
Navigation lights	Yes	Yes
Radar reflector	1	1
Foghorn	1	1
Powerful waterproof torch	1	1
Anchor with warp or chain	2	2
Towline	1	1
Man overboard		
Life buoy, with drogue and light	2	2
Buoyant heaving line	1	1
Dan buoy	–	1
Rope (or boarding) ladder	1	1

Fig. 8(2)   Life buoy with dan buoy and flag, automatic light, whistle, dye marker and drogue.

	(a) Coastal	(b) Offshore
Fire		
Fire-extinguishers	2	3
Fire blanket	1	1
Sinking		
Bilge pumps	2	2
Buckets with lanyards	2	2
Leak stopping gear	Yes	Yes
Distress signals		
Hand flares, red	2	4
Hand flares, white (warning)	4	4
Red parachute rockets	2	4
Hand smoke signals	2	–
Buoyant orange smoke signals	–	–
Emergency radio transmitter	–	1
Abandon ship		
Life raft for whole crew	1	1
	or	
Dinghy with buoyancy, or inflated inflatable	1	–
Panic bag, extra water, etc.	–	1

	Coastal	Offshore
Miscellaneous		
First-aid kit	1	1
Engine toolkit	1	1
Name/number prominently displayed	Yes	Yes
Storm canvas	Yes	Yes
Emergency steering arrangements	Yes	Yes

8.2   EMERGENCY SIGNALS

8.2.1   Distress

Distress is the most serious degree of emergency. It applies to any situation where a boat or person is threatened by grave and imminent danger and requests immediate assistance. The RT prefix associated with a Distress message is MAYDAY – see 8.2.5. A Distress call has priority over all other transmissions.

8.2.2   Urgency

Urgency is a lesser degree of emergency concerning the safety of a boat or person. Examples include, a vessel disabled but not sinking; medical problems (see also 6.4.17). The RT prefix associated with an Urgency message is PAN PAN – see 8.2.9.

8.2.3   Safety

Safety is the least serious degree of emergency, usually associated with a warning of hazardous navigational or meteorological circumstances. The RT prefix associated with a Safety message is SÉCURITÉ – see 8.2.10.

8.2.4   Emergency signals – general

Any of the distress signals listed in 8.2.5 to 8.2.10 must only be made with the authority of the skipper, and only if the boat or a person is in grave and imminent danger, and help is urgently required; or on behalf of another vessel in distress, which for some reason is unable to make a Distress signal. If subsequently the danger is overcome, the Distress call must be cancelled by whatever means are available.

For a lesser emergency, an Urgency signal (PAN PAN) as described below may be appropriate. If help is needed, but the boat is not in immediate danger, the proper signal is 'V' (Victor) International Code, meaning 'I require assistance'. This can be sent as a flag signal (a white flag with a red St Andrew's cross), or by light or sound in Morse code (··· —). Other signals of an emergency nature in the International Code are given in Chapter 6 in the Handbook.

If medical help is required, the proper signal is 'W' (Whiskey) International Code, meaning 'I require medical assistance'.

A full list of the recognised distress signals is given in Annex IV of the International Regulations for Preventing Collisions at Sea. The following are those most appropriate for yachts and small craft, together with notes on their use.

Note that an inland 999 (or 112) call to the Coastguard by cellular radiotelephone (cellphone) is **NOT** an adequate substitute for radio communication on VHF Ch 16 or 2182 kHz from a vessel in a distress/safety situation. Cellphone coverage is limited, even in coastal waters, and is not monitored in any way – unlike Ch 16, which is monitored continuously by HM Coastguard. Nor is a cellphone call heard by other vessels nearby which may be able to help. For these and other reasons (the addition of a further link in the chain of communication, the difficulty of on-scene communication, and the impossibility of calling another vessel by cellphone unless she is so fitted and her

8

number is known), the use of a cellphone for marine distress/safety communication is very strongly discouraged.

8.2.5   Radio distress signals

(1)   A signal sent by radiotelephone consisting of the spoken word MAYDAY.

This should normally be transmitted on VHF Ch 16 or 2182 kHz, but any frequency may be used if help may thereby be obtained more quickly.

Distress messages, together with Urgency and Safety messages (see below) from vessels at sea are free of charge. A distress call has priority over all other transmissions. If heard, cease all transmissions that may interfere with the distress call or messages, and listen on the frequency concerned.

Anybody in the crew should be able to pass a distress message, but this must only be done on the orders of the skipper and if the yacht or a person (or some other vessel or aircraft that cannot make a distress signal) is in serious and imminent danger and requires immediate assistance.

The full procedure is as follows:

- Check main battery switch ON
- Switch set ON, and turn power selector to HIGH
- Tune to VHF Ch 16 (or 2182 kHz for MF)
- If alarm signal generator fitted, operate for at least 30 seconds
- Press transmit button, and say slowly and distinctly:

- MAYDAY MAYDAY MAYDAY
- THIS IS (name of boat, spoken three times)
- MAYDAY (name of boat spoken once)
- MY POSITION IS (latitude and longitude, or true bearing and distance from a known point)
- Nature of distress (sinking, on fire, etc.)
- Aid required
- Number of persons on board
- Any other important, helpful information (e.g. if the yacht is drifting, whether distress rockets are being fired)
- OVER.

The yacht's position is of vital importance, and should be repeated if time allows. On completion of the distress message, release the transmit button and listen. In coastal waters an immediate acknowledgment should be expected in the following form:

> MAYDAY (name of station sending the distress message, spoken three times)
> THIS IS (name of station acknowledging, spoken three times)
> RECEIVED MAYDAY.

If an acknowledgment is not received, check the set and repeat the distress call. For 2182 kHz the call should be repeated during the three-minute silence periods which commence at H+00 and H+30.

If you hear a distress message, write down the details, and if you are able to give assistance you should acknowledge accordingly, but only after giving an opportunity for the nearest coast station or some larger vessel to do so.

If you hear a distress message from a vessel further away, and it is not acknowledged, you should pass on the message in the following form:

> MAYDAY RELAY, MAYDAY RELAY, MAYDAY RELAY
> THIS IS (name of vessel retransmitting the distress message, spoken three times)
> Followed by the intercepted message.

(2)   A signal sent by radiotelegraphy consisting of the group ··· ––– ··· in the Morse code.

The UK and France no longer keep watch on the International radiotelegraph distress frequency of 500 kHz. Larger ships are fitted with a radiotelegraph alarm signal to give notice, aurally or by triggering the auto-alarm of ships within range, of the impending transmission of a distress call and message.

8.2.6   Emergency Position Indicating Radio Beacons (EPIRBs)

Many yachts now carry EPIRBs which transmit on the emergency frequencies of 406 MHz and/or 121·5 MHz and 243·0 MHz. Transmissions on all three frequencies can be picked up by the Cospas/Sarsat (C-S) system which uses four near-polar orbital satellites to detect and localise the signals. The processed positions are passed automatically to a Mission Control Centre (MCC) for assessment of any SAR action required; the UK MCC is co-located with RCC Plymouth.

C-S location accuracy is normally better than 5 km on 406 MHz and better than 20 km on 121·5 and 243·0 MHz. Within the North American area, the maximum waiting time (i.e. the time between EPIRB activation and satellite detection) should not exceed 90 minutes and will normally be much quicker. 121·5 MHz and 243·0 MHz are not generally monitored by ships, Coast Radio Stations or the Coastguard, but are monitored by Air Traffic Control and many aircraft; survivors should switch on an EPIRB without delay.

Dedicated SAR aircraft can home on 121·5 MHz and 243·0 MHz, but not on 406 MHz. Typically a helicopter at 1,000 feet can receive homing signals from about 30M range whilst a fixed-wing aircraft at higher altitudes is capable of homing from about 60M. Overflying aircraft operating on normal commercial air routes often receive and relay information on alerts on 121·5 MHz EPIRBs at up to 200M range. Best results are likely to be obtained from 406 MHz EPIRBs which also transmit a 121·5 MHz signal for homing.

406 MHz EPIRBs transmit data with a unique code which identifies the individual beacon and therefore the individual yacht. However, it is absolutely essential for the integrity of the system that details of all yachts

on which 406 MHz EPIRBs are carried are sent for registration to: The EPIRB Register, HM Coastguard South Western, Pendennis Point, Castle Drive, Falmouth, Cornwall TR11 4WZ. Registration details should be submitted on the form provided by the EPIRB manufacturer at the point of sale. It is equally important that any changes of ownership of a 406 MHz EPIRB, or its disposal in any other way, are also notified.

The rising number of false alerts caused by inadvertent or incorrect operation of EPIRBs is putting a significant burden on SAR assets. The chances of false alerts coinciding with a real distress situation are very real and as a consequence SAR forces could be delayed in responding to a real distress – with tragic consequences.

EPIRBs must be installed and used in accordance with manufacturers' recommendations. Dependent on type, they must be installed in a proper location so they can float free and automatically activate if the yacht sinks. Many EPIRBs have lanyards intended to secure the EPIRB to a life raft or person in the water and lanyards must not be used for securing the EPIRB to the yacht. Such action will clearly prevent a float-free type from activating and would be lost with the yacht should it sink.

Once an EPIRB is activated, whether accidentally or intentionally, make every reasonable attempt to communicate with SAR authorities by other means to advise them of the situation.

8.2.7   Visual and audible distress signals

(1) Continuous sounding with any fog signalling apparatus.
In order to avoid confusion, this is best done by a succession of letters SOS in Morse (··· — — — ···).

(2) A signal made by any signalling method consisting of the group ··· — — — ··· (SOS) in the Morse code.
For a yacht the most likely methods are by sound signal as in (1) above, or by flashing light.

(3) The International Code signal 'NC'.
This can be made by flag hoist, 'N' being a blue and white chequered flag and 'C' one which is horizontally striped blue, white, red, white, blue.

(4) A signal consisting of a square flag having above or below it a ball or anything resembling a ball.
This is not too difficult to contrive from any square flag, and a round fender or anchor ball.

(5) A rocket parachute flare or a hand-held flare showing a red light.
A red flare is the most effective distress signal at night. Flares serve two purposes – first to raise the alarm, and then to pinpoint the boat's position. Within about three miles from land a hand flare will do both. At greater distances a red parachute rocket (which projects a suspended flare to a height of more than 1,000ft, or 300m, and which burns for more than 40 seconds) is needed to raise the alarm, but hand flares are useful to

indicate the boat's position. See further comments under (6) below.

(6) A smoke signal giving off orange coloured smoke.
By day orange smoke signals (hand held for short distances, or a larger buoyant type for greater ranges) are more effective than flares, although the smoke disperses quickly in a strong wind.

White flares are not distress signals, but are used to indicate the presence of a boat – to another vessel on a collision course for example. An outfit of four is suggested for boats which make night passages. Shield your eyes when using them, to protect night vision.

Pyrotechnics must be stowed where they are accessible, but protected from damp. In good storage conditions they should have a life of three years. Examine them regularly, and replace them by the expiry date. All the crew should know where the flares are stowed and how to use them. Hold hand flares firmly downwind. Rockets turn into the wind; fire them vertically in normal conditions, or aimed about 15° downwind in strong winds. Do not aim them into the wind, or they will not gain altitude. If there is low cloud, fire rockets at 45° downwind, so that the flare burns under the cloud.

(7) Slowly and repeatedly raising and lowering arms outstretched to each side.
The arms should be raised and lowered together, above and below the horizontal.

8.2.8   Control of distress traffic
A Distress (MAYDAY) call imposes general radio silence, until the vessel concerned or some other authority (e.g. the nearest MRCC, MRSC or coast station) cancels the distress. If necessary the station controlling distress traffic may impose radio silence in this form:

> SEELONCE MAYDAY, followed by its name or other identification, on the distress frequency.

> If some other station nearby believes it necessary to do likewise, it may transmit:

> SEELONCE DISTRESS, followed by its name or other identification.

When appropriate the station controlling distress traffic may relax radio silence so that normal working is resumed with caution on the distress frequency, with subsequent communications from the casualty prefixed by the Urgency signal (below).

When complete radio silence is no longer necessary on a frequency being used for distress traffic, the controlling station may relax radio silence as follows:

> MAYDAY
> HELLO ALL STATIONS (spoken three times)
> THIS IS (name or identification)
> The time
> The name of the station in distress
> PRUDONCE.

If distress working continues on other frequencies these will be identified. For example, PRUDONCE on 500 kHz (WT distress frequency) and 2182 kHz, but SEELONCE on VHF Ch 16. When all distress traffic has ceased, normal working is authorised as follows:

> MAYDAY
> HELLO ALL STATIONS (spoken three times)
> THIS IS (name or identification)
> The time
> The name of the station which was in distress
> SEELONCE FEENEE.

8.2.9   Urgency signal

The radiotelephone Urgency signal consists of the words PAN PAN, spoken three times, and indicates that the station has a very urgent message concerning the safety of a ship or person. Messages prefixed by PAN PAN take priority over all traffic except distress, and are sent on VHF Ch 16 or on 2182 kHz. The Urgency signal is appropriate when someone is lost overboard or urgent medical advice or attention is needed. It should be cancelled when the urgency is over.

After the initial call on VHF Ch 16 or 2182 kHz, the message itself should be passed on a working frequency if it is long or if it is a medical call, or in areas of heavy traffic if the message is repeated. Where necessary this should be indicated at the end of the initial call.

Here is an example of an Urgency call and message from the yacht *Seabird,* disabled off the Needles.

> PAN PAN PAN PAN PAN PAN
> HELLO ALL STATIONS
> HELLO ALL STATIONS
> HELLO ALL STATIONS
> THIS IS YACHT SEABIRD SEABIRD
> SEABIRD TWO NINE ZERO DEGREES TWO
> MILES FROM NEEDLES LIGHTHOUSE
> DISMASTED AND PROPELLER FOULED
> ANCHOR DRAGGING AND DRIFTING
> EAST NORTH EAST TOWARDS SHINGLES
> BANK REQUIRE URGENT TOW OVER.

The Urgency signal has priority over all messages except Distress, and should normally get an immediate response. If you hear an Urgency call you should respond in the same way as for a Distress call.

8.2.10   Safety signal

This consists of the word SÉCURITÉ (pronounced SAY-CURE-E-TAY) spoken three times, and indicates that the station is about to transmit an important navigational or meteorological warning. Such messages usually originate from a coast station, and are transmitted on a working frequency after an announcement on the distress frequency.

Safety messages are usually addressed to 'all stations', and often at the end of the first available silence period (see 6.4.5 – MF radio). Always listen carefully until you are sure that the message does not affect you, and do not make any transmission that will interfere.

8.3   GMDSS

8.3.1   Global Maritime Distress and Safety System (GMDSS)

The Global Maritime Distress and Safety System (GMDSS) is an improved maritime distress and safety communications system adopted by the International Maritime Organisation (IMO).

The GMDSS regulations apply to all passenger and cargo ships over 300 tons engaged in international voyages, but they affect all seagoing craft. GMDSS came into force in February 1992. GMDSS will be fully implemented worldwide by February 1999. During this period existing systems will operate together with the new.

Smaller vessels may fit GMDSS equipment on a voluntary basis, but this will become an increasing necessity towards the end of the decade as the present system for sending and receiving distress calls is run down. Although not specifically designed for yachtsmen there are features of the system which are already of interest, and as the implementation period progresses yachtsmen may see an attraction in using GMDSS.

Before the introduction of GMDSS, maritime distress and safety relied heavily on certain ships keeping a continuous radio watch on the three main international distress frequencies: i.e. Morse on 500 kHz for passenger and cargo ships over 1,600 tons, RT on 2182 kHz and VHF Ch 16 on all these ships, plus cargo ships over 300 tons. A number of Coast Radio Stations (CRS) were also obliged to maintain a watch on these frequencies. Once out of range of the Coast Radio Stations any assistance could only be provided by ships in the vicinity of the distress incident.

The objective of GMDSS is to improve distress and safety radio communications, and SAR procedures, by making use of technology such as Satcom and Satnav. The result is that shore stations, and shipping in the vicinity of a distress incident can be alerted faster and more reliably.

In addition, GMDSS provides for urgency and safety communications, and the promulgation of Marine Safety Information (MSI) such as navigational warnings, weather warnings and forecasts. Regardless of the sea area in which they operate, vessels conforming to GMDSS must be able to perform certain functions:

- transmit ship-to-shore distress alerts by two separate means
- transmit ship-to-ship distress alerts
- transmit and receive safety information such as navigation and weather warnings
- transmit signals for locating incidents
- receive shore-to-ship distress alerts
- receive ship-to-ship distress alerts
- transmit and receive communications for SAR co-ordination.

8.3.2   Distress alerting

GMDSS caters for three independent methods of distress alerting. These are:

1   Digital selective calling (DSC) using VHF Ch 70, MF 2187·5 kHz, or HF distress and alerting frequencies in the 4, 6, 8,12 and 16 MHz bands.

2   Float-free or manually operated 406 MHz EPIRBs using the Cospas/Sarsat satellite system or, in the 1·6 GHz band, the Inmarsat system. Both transmit distress messages which include the position of the vessel in distress and its identification. Some 406 MHz EPIRBs also transmit on 121·5 MHz to aid close-quarters homing.

3   Inmarsat, via ship terminals.

In addition, GMDSS includes Navtex for receiving Maritime Safety Information and Search and Rescue Transponders (SARTs). The latter are intended for operation from a lifeboat or life raft to assist homing. When interrogated by a ship's radar, the SART responds by transmitting a series of radar pulses. Some float-free 406 MHz EPIRBs include a built-in SART.

8.3.3   GMDSS communication systems

A number of terrestrial and satellite-based communications systems have been adopted for GMDSS. These are shown in 8.3.5 and 8.3.6.

8.3.4   Digital Selective Calling

DSC is a fundamental part of GMDSS and is used to transmit distress alerts from ships, and also to receive distress acknowledgments from ships or shore stations. DSC can also be used for relay purposes and for Urgency, Safety and routine calling and answering. Operationally, a distress call sent over VHF radio using DSC would roughly work as follows: yachtsman presses the distress button; the set automatically re-tunes itself to Ch 70 and transmits a coded distress message before re-tuning to Ch 16.

Any ship will reply directly by voice on Ch 16. However, a CRS would send a distress acknowledgment on Ch 70 (automatically turning off the distress transmission) before replying on Ch 16. Distress messages will be automatically repeated every four to five minutes unless already acknowledged by a CRS. Under GMDSS, every vessel will have a nine-digit identification number (referred to as an MMSI – Maritime Mobile Service Identity) that is used for identification in all DSC messages.

8.3.5   Inmarsat

GMDSS communications are also provided via four geostationary satellites covering the east and west Atlantic, Pacific and Indian Ocean regions from about 70°N to 70°S. The Inmarsat system is combined with conventional Coast Radio Stations using HF, MF and VHF to provide near-global coverage.

Additionally, 1·6 GHz satellite EPIRBs, operating through Inmarsat, can also be used for alerting as an alternative to 406 MHz EPIRBs which use Cospas/Sarsat.

8.3.6   Cospas/Sarsat

The US/Russian Cospas/Sarsat satellites complement the various Satcom systems available by not only providing an effective initial detection of an emergency signal transmitted by an EPIRB, but also its location to a high degree of accuracy. There are four Cospas/Sarsat satellites operating in low polar orbits. In addition to the low polar orbiting satellites, 406 MHz repeater systems are operating on board five geostationary satellites

8.3.7   Maritime Safety Information (MSI)

MSI includes the vital meteorological, navigational and SAR messages broadcast to all vessels at sea. For this purpose the world is divided into 16 Navareas. The UK lies in Navarea I, which covers all North-West Europe between 48°N and 71°N and to 35°W. Traditionally, these MSI broadcasts have been made from CRSs by Morse and RT on VHF and MF. Under GMDSS, broadcasts will be made 'automatically' through Inmarsat's Enhanced Group Calling (EGC) system; Inmarsat C, and, particularly for those broadcasts appertaining to the UK coast, Navtex on 518 kHz. Currently MSI is being broadcast on all these systems. A Navtex receiver meets the requirements for coastal waters up to about 300 miles from transmitters, but an Inmarsat C Enhanced Group Calling (EGC) receiver is required when operating beyond MF coverage.

8.3.8   Implementation

The speed with which the shore-based side of GMDSS is introduced varies from sea area to sea area according to the policy of its controlling government. For purposes of the GMDSS, each sea area lies within one of the following classes:

A1   an area within RT coverage of at least one VHF Coast Radio Station in which continuous alerting via Digital Selective Calling (see later in text) is available. Range: approximately 40 miles of the CRS.

A2   an area, excluding sea area A1, within RT coverage of at least one MF CRS in which continuous DSC alerting is available. Range: roughly 100-150 miles of the CRS.

A3   an area, excluding sea areas A1 and A2 within coverage of an Inmarsat satellite in which continuous alerting is available.

A4   an area outside sea areas A1, A2 and A3. In practice this means the polar regions.

The UK intends to continue to guard Channel 16 for some time ahead and has declared the UK to be an A1 area. The installation plan is for the Channel Coast and East Coast to be completed in 1997, followed by the West Coast and Northern Ireland in 1998.

The French have already declared the English Channel to be an A1 area and this came into effect in 1995. To take full advantage of GMDSS procedures it will be necessary for yachts to re-equip for operation in A1 areas.

As most UK yachtsmen will operate in an A1 area, a VHF set and a Navtex will initially suffice to meet GMDSS requirements. When suitable VHF DSC sets become available it will make sense to re-equip with DSC equipment.

8

8.4   SEARCH AND RESCUE (SAR) – UK

8.4.1   SAR – general

Around the United Kingdom, the lead authority is HM Coastguard, which initiates and co-ordinates all civil maritime SAR. To assist, Coast Radio Stations control ship/shore communications (see 6.4.8); the RNLI provide lifeboats; the Royal Navy helps with ships; and the Royal Air Force, through Military Aeronautical Rescue Co-ordination Centres (ARCC) at Kinloss and Plymouth, controls military helicopters and fixed-wing aircraft for SAR. Air Traffic Control Centres (ATCC) monitor air distress frequencies.

The ARCC at Plymouth also mans the UK Cospas/Sarsat Mission Control Centre (MCC) which receives satellite data from emergency distress beacons on 121·5 MHz, 243·0 MHz and 406 MHz (8.2.6).

8.4.2   HM Coastguard

The Coastguard initiates and co-ordinates SAR around the United Kingdom and over a large part of the eastern Atlantic. The area is divided into five Maritime Search and Rescue Regions (SRRs), supervised by Maritime Rescue Co-ordination Centres (MRCCs) at Falmouth, Dover, Great Yarmouth, Aberdeen, the Clyde and Swansea. It also includes 'Shannon' area which is the responsibility of the Republic of Ireland. Each SRR is divided into districts, each with a Maritime Rescue Sub-Centre (MRSC). Their boundaries are shown in the maps at the start of Areas 1–11 in Chapter 10. The telephone number of the nearest MRCC or MRSC (or the equivalent in other countries) is shown for each harbour.

Within each of the 21 districts thus formed there is an organisation of Auxiliary Coastguard Response Teams, grouped within sectors under the management of regular Coastguard Officers.

MRCCs and MRSCs keep watch on VHF Ch 16, and on 2182 kHz, and are connected to facsimile, telex and telephone. Some as shown in Table 8(1) keep watch on Ch 70 and/or 2187·5 kHz for Digital Selective Calling (see 8.3.4). A visual lookout is maintained when necessary. The Channel Navigation Information Service (CNIS) keeps a constant radar watch and provides a 24-hour radio safety service for all shipping in the Dover Strait. (See Table 8(1).)

There are about 560 Regular Coastguard Officers, with more than 3,500 Auxiliaries on call for emergencies. The Coastguard also has a cliff and beach rescue role.

A VHF emergency direction-finding service, controlled by the Coastguard, is operated from various stations around Britain.

The radiotelephony call sign of an MRCC or MRSC is the geographical name, followed by 'Coastguard' – for example, 'SOLENT COASTGUARD'.

The Coastguard operates a Local Warning Service related to hazards which may affect craft in inshore waters, but outside Port and Harbour Authority limits. These local warnings are broadcast on Ch 67, after an announcement on Ch 16. There is no numerical sequence, and no specific broadcast schedule; any repetition of the broadcast is at the discretion of the originating Coastguard Station. Strong wind warnings are broadcast on receipt, and forecasts for local sea areas about every four hours or on request. See also 7.2.17 and Table 8(1).

8.4.3   Yacht and Boat Safety Scheme

This free scheme provides useful information for the Coastguard to mount a successful SAR operation. Owners can obtain a Form CG66 from their local Coastguard Station, harbour master or marina. This should be completed with details of the boat and her equipment, and then posted to the local Coastguard Rescue Centre. It is desirable to enclose a recent photograph of your craft if you have one. You should inform the Coastguard if the ownership, name of the craft, or any address given on form CG66 changes. There is a tear-off section which can be given to a friend or relative so that they know the Coastguard Station to contact if they are concerned for the boat's safety.

A CG66 will remain valid for three years. If it is not renewed within that time, the old CG66 will be removed from the CG records.

It is not the function of HM Coastguard to maintain watch for boats on passage, but they will record information by phone before departure or from intermediate ports, or while on passage by visual signals or VHF Ch 67 (the Small Craft Safety Channel).

When using Ch 67 for safety messages it is requested that yachts give the name of the Coastguard Rescue Centre holding the boat's Safety Scheme card. In these circumstances the Coastguard must be told of any change to the planned movements of the boat, and it is important that they are informed of the boat's safe arrival at her ultimate destination.

8.4.4   Raising the alarm

If an accident afloat is seen from shore, dial 999 and ask for the Coastguard. You will be asked to report on the incident, and possibly to stay near the telephone for further communications. If at sea you receive a distress signal and you are in a position to give assistance, you are obliged to do so with all speed, unless, or until, you are specifically released.

When alerted the Coastguard summons the most appropriate help, they may direct vessels in the vicinity of the distress position; request the launch of an RNLI lifeboat; scramble a military or Coastguard SAR helicopter; other vessels may be alerted through Coast Radio Stations or by satellite communications.

TABLE 8(1)   HM Coastguard MRCCs and MRSCs

Notes:

(a) These stations do not accept public correspondence (link calls). They deal with Distress, Urgency and Safety traffic. The call in each case is the geographical name followed by 'Coastguard', e.g. 'Solent Coastguard', 'Belfast Coastguard', etc.

(b) They all keep watch on VHF Ch 16 and (except Oban MRSC) on 2182 kHz (H24) for Distress, Urgency and Safety calls covering UK waters. Unless stated below, stations also operate VHF Ch 10, 67, 73. Each is being equipped with VHF Ch 70 DSC in accordance with GMDSS (see 8.3), with a total of 103 stations to give coverage of all the UK coastline. Nine MRCCs/MRSCs keep watch on 2187·5 kHz DSC.

(c) Strong Wind (Force 6/7) and/or Gale Warnings are broadcast on receipt and every two hours. Weather Messages (local area forecasts) are broadcast every four hours or on request. Local Navigational Warnings are broadcast on receipt and before Weather Messages if required, and on request. All scheduled broadcasts are announced on Ch 16 and made sequentially from remote transmitter sites in each Coastguard District on Ch 67 (Dover Coastguard on Ch 11) from the times shown below for each station. They may be suspended while SAR action is in progress. See also 7.2.17.

(d) HM Coastguard VHF DF sites are shown on Area Maps.

Falmouth Coastguard (MRCC). 50°09'N 05°03'W. ☎: 01326 317575. ✒: 01326 318342.
Covers Marsland Mouth to Dodman Point.
Also operates 2226 kHz. VHF Broadcasts every 4h from 0140 LT. DSC MMSI 002320014 2187·5 kHz.

Brixham Coastguard (MRSC). 50°24'N 03°31'W. ☎: 01803 882704. ✒: 01803 882780.
Covers Dodman Point to Straight Point.
VHF Broadcasts every 4h from 0050 LT. DSC MMSI 002320013. Ch 70 planned 1997.

Portland Coastguard (MRSC). 50°36'N 02°27'W. ☎: 01305 760439. ✒: 01305 760452.
Covers Straight Point to Chewton Bunney.
VHF Broadcasts every 4h from 0220 LT. DSC MMSI 002320012. Ch 70 planned 1997.

Solent Coastguard (MRSC). 50°48'N 01°12'W. ☎: 01705 552100. ✒: 01705 551763.
Covers Chewton Bunney to Beachy Head (inc IOW).
Operates Ch 67 (H24) as calling channel for safety traffic.
VHF Broadcasts every 4h from 0040 LT. DSC MMSI 002320011. Ch 70 planned 1997.

Dover Coastguard (MRCC). 50°08'N 01°12'E. ☎: 01304 210008. ✒: 01304 202137.
Covers Beachy Head to Reculver Towers. VHF Ch 16 69 (H24) 10 11 67 73 80 (HX). 2182 kHz.
DSC MMSI 002320011. Operates Channel Navigation Information Service (CNIS) in conjunction with Gris-Nez Traffic. Ch 69 is primary working channel for routine CNIS traffic (call direct on Ch 69). CNIS broadcasts navigational and traffic information on Ch 11 every H+40 (and at H+55 in bad visibility). Weather messages every 4h from 0040 LT on Ch 11. Ch 70 planned 1997.

Thames Coastguard (MRSC). 51°51'N 01°17'E. ☎: 01255 675518. ✒: 01255 675249.
Covers Reculver to Southwold.
VHF Broadcasts every 4h from 0010 LT. DSC MMSI 002320009. Ch 70 planned 1997.

Yarmouth Coastguard (MRCC). 52°37'N 01°43'E. ☎: 01493 851338. ✒: 01493 852307.
Covers Southwold to Anderby Creek.
VHF Broadcasts every 4h from 0040 LT. DSC MMSI 002320008. Ch 70 planned 1997.

Humber Coastguard (MRSC). 54°06'N 00°11'W. ☎: 01262 672317. ✒: 01262 606915.
Covers Anderby Creek to Port Mulgrave.
VHF Broadcasts every 4h from 0340 LT. DSC MMSI 002320007 2187·5 kHz. Ch 70 planned 1997.

Tyne Tees Coastguard (MRSC). 55°01'N 01°25'W. ☎: 0191 2572691. ✒: 0191 2580373.
Covers Port Mulgrave to Goswick.
VHF Broadcasts every 4h from 0150 LT. DSC MMSI 002320006 2187·5 kHz. Ch 70 planned 1997.

Forth Coastguard (MRSC). 56°17'N 02°35'W. ☎: 01333 450666. ✒: 01333 450725.
Covers Goswick to East Haven.
VHF Broadcasts every 4h from 0205 LT. DSC MMSI 002320005. Ch 70 planned 1997.

Aberdeen Coastguard (MRCC). 57°08'N 02°05'W. ☎: 01224 592334. ✒: 01224 575920.
Covers East Haven to Ord Point.
Also operates 2226 2596 kHz and VHF Ch 06.
VHF Broadcasts every 4h from 0320 LT. DSC MMSI 00230004 2187·5 kHz. Ch 70 planned 1997.

Shetland Coastguard (MRSC). 60°09'N 01°08'W. ☎: 01595 692976. ✒: 01595 694810.
Covers Shetland Islands.
VHF Broadcasts from 0105 LT. DSC MMSI 002320001 2187·5 kHz. Ch 70 planned 1998.

Pentland Coastguard (MRSC). 58°59′N 02°57′W. ☎: 01856 873268. 📠: 01856 874202.
Covers Orkney Islands and Ord Point to Cape Wrath.
VHF Broadcasts every 4h from 0135 LT. DSC MMSI 002320002. Ch 70 planned 1998.

Stornoway Coastguard (MRSC). 58°12′N 06°22′W. ☎: 01851 702013 & 702014. 📠: 01851 704387.
Covers Cape Wrath to Applecross, Western Isles.
VHF Broadcasts every 4h from 0110 LT. DSC MMSI 002320024 2187·5 kHz. Ch 70 planned 1998.

Oban Coastguard (MRSC). 56°25′N 05°29′W. ☎: 01631 563720. 📠: 01631 564917.
Covers Applecross to Gulf of Corryvreckan. (Does not operate 2182 kHz.)
VHF Broadcasts every 4h from 0240 LT. DSC MMSI 002320023. Ch 70 planned 1998.

Clyde Coastguard (MRCC). 55°58′N 04°48′W. ☎: 01475 729988 & 729014. 📠: 01475 786955.
Covers Gulf of Corryvreckan to Mull of Galloway. Also operates 2226 kHz.
VHF Broadcasts every 4h from 0020 LT. DSC MMSI 002320022 2187·5 kHz. Ch 70 planned 1998.

Liverpool Coastguard (MRSC). 53°30′N 03°03′W. ☎: 0151 931 3341. 📠: 0151 931 3347.
Covers Mull of Galloway to Queensferry.
VHF Broadcasts every 4h from 0210 LT. DSC MMSI 002320019 2187·5 kHz. Ch 70 planned 1998.

Holyhead Coastguard (MRSC). 53°19′N 04°38′W. ☎: 01407 762051 & 763911. 📠: 01407 764373.
Covers Queensferry to Friog.
VHF Ch 16 10 67 73. 2182 kHz. VHF Broadcasts every 4h from 0235 LT. DSC MMSI 002320018.
Ch 70 planned 1998.

Milford Haven Coastguard (MRSC). 51°41′N 05°10′W. ☎: 01646 690909. 📠: 01646 692176.
Covers Friog to River Towy.
VHF Ch 16 10 67 73. 2182 kHz. VHF Broadcasts every 4h from 0335 LT. DSC MMSI 002320017 2187·5 kHz.
Ch 70 planned 1998.

Swansea Coastguard (MRCC). 51°34′N 03°58′W. ☎: 01792 366534. 📠: 01792 369005.
Covers River Towy to Marsland Mouth.
VHF Broadcasts every 4h from 0005 LT. DSC MMSI 002320016. Ch 70 planned 1998.

Belfast Coastguard (MRSC). 54°40′N 05°40′W. ☎: 01247 463933. 📠: 01247 465886.
Covers Northern Ireland.
VHF Broadcasts every 4h from 0305 LT. DSC MMSI 002320021. Ch 70 planned 1998.

CHANNEL ISLANDS
Jersey (CRS). 49°10′·85N 02°14′30W. ☎: 01534 41121. 📠: 01534 499089
Covers the Channel Islands area.
VHF DSC A1 MMSI 002320060 operational.

IRELAND
Dublin (MRCC). 53°20′N 06°15W. ☎: 01 6620922. 📠: 01 6620795.
Covers Carlingford Lough to Youghal.
DSC MMSI (To be notified).

Malin Head (MRSC). 55°22′N' 07°21W. ☎: 077 70103. 📠: 077 70221.
Covers Slyne Head to Lough Foyle.
MF DSC A2 MMSI 002500100 2187·5 kHz.
Channel 70 Planned 1998.

Valentia (MRSC). 51°56′N 10°21′W. ☎: 066 76109. 📠: 066 776289
Covers Youghal to Slyne Head.
MF DSC A2 MMSI 0025000200 2187·5 kHz.
Channel 70 Planned 1998.

8.4.5 Royal National Lifeboat Institution (RNLI)

The RNLI is a registered charity which exists to save life at sea. It provides, on call, a 24-hour lifeboat service up to 50M out from the coasts of the UK and Irish Republic. There are 215 lifeboat stations, at which are stationed 289 lifeboats ranging from 4·9 to 17·0m in length. These consist of 123 all-weather, three intermediate and 163 inshore lifeboats. There are over 100 lifeboats in the reserve fleet.

All are capable of at least 15 knots, and new lifeboats capable of 25 knots are being introduced.

When launched on service, lifeboats over 10m keep watch on 2182 kHz and Ch 16. They can also use alternative frequencies to contact other vessels, SAR aircraft, HM Coastguard or Coast Radio Stations or other SAR agencies. All lifeboats are fitted with VHF and show a quick-flashing blue light.

The RNLI's Sea Safety Initiative combines expertise from the main organisations involved with sea safety education and guidelines are available free on a variety of sea safety related topics. Details are obtainable from the RNLI, RYA, Coastguard Agency, Marine Safety Agency, BMIF or the Royal Life Saving Society.

Yachtsmen can help support the RNLI by becoming members of the RNLI and there is also a junior club for under-sixteens called 'Storm Force'. Details are available from RNLI HQ, West Quay Road, Poole, Dorset BH15 1HZ (☎ 01202 663000. ☏ 01202 663167).

Similar organisations to the RNLI exist in other countries in Western Europe.

8.4.6 Visual signals from shore to ships in distress

The following are used to a vessel in distress or stranded off the coast of the United Kingdom.

(1) Acknowledgment of distress signal.

By day: Orange smoke signal, or combined light and sound signal consisting of three signals fired at about one-minute intervals.

By night: White star rocket consisting of three single signals at about one-minute intervals.

(2) Landing signals for small boats.

'This is the best place to land' – Vertical motion of a white flag or arms (or white light or flare by night), or signalling K (—·—) by light or sound. An indication of direction may be given by placing a steady white light or flare at a lower level.

'Landing here is highly dangerous' – Horizontal motion a white flag or arms extended horizontally (or a white light or flare by night), or signalling S (···). In addition, a better landing place may be signalled by carrying a white flag (or flare or light), or by firing a white star signal in the direction indicated; or by signalling R (·—·) if a better landing is to the right in the direction of approach, or L (·—··) if it is to the left.

(3) Signals for shore life-saving apparatus.

Affirmative or specifically 'Rocket line is held', 'Tail block is made fast', 'Hawser is made fast', 'Man is in breeches buoy' or 'Haul away' – vertical motion of a white flag or the arms (or of a white light or flare).

'Negative' or specifically 'Slack away' or 'Avast hauling' – horizontal motion of a white flag or the arms (or of a white light or flare).

Rocket rescue equipment is no longer used by HM Coastguard. Some larger vessels carry a line-throwing appliance requiring on-shore liaison before use.

(4) Warning signal.

'You are running into danger' – International Code signal U (··—) or NF.

Note: Attention may be called to the above signals by a white flare, a white star rocket, or an explosive signal.

8.4.7 Signals used by SAR aircraft

A searching aircraft normally flies at about 3,000–5,000ft (900–1,500m), or below cloud, firing a green Very light every five or ten minutes and at each turning point. On seeing a green flare, a yacht in distress should take the following action:

(1) Wait for the green flare to die out.
(2) Fire one red flare.
(3) Fire another red flare after about 20 seconds. (This enables the aircraft to line up on the bearing.)
(4) Fire a third red flare when the aircraft is overhead, or appears to be going badly off course.

8.4.8 Directing signals by aircraft

(1) To direct a yacht towards a ship or aircraft in distress –the aircraft circles the yacht at least once; it then crosses low, ahead of the yacht, opening and closing the throttle or changing the propeller pitch. Finally it heads in the direction of the casualty.

(2) To indicate that assistance of the yacht is no longer required – the aircraft passes low, astern of the yacht, opening and closing the throttle or changing the propeller pitch.

8.4.9 Helicopter rescue

SAR helicopters in the UK are based at Chivenor, Culdrose, Portland, Lee-on-Solent, Wattisham, Leconfield, Boulmer, Lossiemouth, Sumburgh, Stornoway, Prestwick and Valley.

Sea King SAR helicopters can operate to a distance of 300 miles and can rescue up to 18 survivors. The Sea King has an automatic hover control system and so can effect rescues at night and in fog when there are no visual hover references available to the pilot.

In the Irish Republic a Sikorsky S61N SAR helicopter, based at Shannon, can operate to a distance of 200 miles and can rescue up to 14 survivors. A Dauphin SA 365F helicopter, based at Finner Camp, can operate to 150 miles by day and 70 miles at night.

8

SAR helicopters are generally fitted with VHF, FM and AM, UHF and HF SSB RT and can communicate with lifeboats etc. on VHF FM. Communications between ship and helicopter should normally be achieved on Marine band VHF FM (Ch 16 or 67). 2182 kHz SSB may also be available. If contact is difficult, communication can often be achieved through a Nimrod aircraft if one is on the scene, or through a lifeboat, a Coast Radio Station, or through HM Coastguard.

When the helicopter is sighted by a boat in distress, a flare, an orange smoke signal, dye marker or a well-trained Aldis lamp will assist recognition (very important if there are other vessels in the vicinity). Dodgers with the boat's name or sail number are useful aids to identification.

While hovering, the pilot has limited vision beneath him, and relies on instructions from the winch operator. Survivors from a yacht with a mast may need to be picked up from a dinghy or life raft streamed at least 100ft (30m) away. In a small yacht with no dinghy, survivors (wearing life jackets) may need to be picked up from the water, at the end of a long warp. It is very important that no survivor boards a life raft or jumps into the sea until instructed to do so by the helicopter (either by VHF Ch 16 or 67) or by the winchman (by word of mouth). Sails should be lowered and lashed and it is helpful if the drift of the boat is reduced by a sea anchor.

If a crewman descends from the helicopter, he will take charge. Obey his instructions quickly. Never secure the winch wire to the yacht, and beware that it may carry a lethal static charge if it is not dipped (earthed) in the sea before handling.

Survivors may be lifted by double lift in a strop, accompanied by the crewman in a canvas seat. Or it may be necessary, with no crewman, for a survivor to position himself in the strop. Put your head and shoulders through the strop so that the padded part is in the small of the back and the toggle is in front of the face. Pull the toggle down, as close to the chest as possible. When ready, give a thumbs-up sign with an extended arm, and place both arms close down by the side of the body (resist the temptation to hang on to the strop). On reaching the helicopter, do exactly as instructed by the crew.

In some circumstances a 'Hi-line technique' may be used. This is a rope tail, attached to the helicopter winch wire by a weak link, and weighted at its lower end. When it is lowered to the yacht do not make it fast, but coil it down carefully. The helicopter pays out the winch wire and then moves to one side of the yacht and descends, while the yacht takes in the slack (keeping it outboard and clear of all obstructions) until the winch hook and strop are on board. A member of the helicopter crew may or may not be lowered with the strop. When ready to lift, the helicopter ascends and takes in the wire. Pay out the tail, keeping enough weight on it to keep it taut until the end is reached, then cast it off well clear of the yacht. But if a further lift is to be made the tail should be retained on board (not made fast) to facilitate recovery of the strop for the next lift.

Injured persons can be lifted strapped into a special stretcher carried in the helicopter.

When alighting from a helicopter, beware of the tail rotor which can be difficult to see. Obey all instructions given by the helicopter crew.

8.4.10 Abandon ship

Although preparations must be made, do not abandon a yacht until she is doomed. She is a better target for rescue craft than a life raft, and while she is still afloat it is possible to use her resources (such as RT, for distress calls) and to select what extra equipment is put in the life raft or lashed into the dinghy (which should be taken too, if possible).

Before entering the raft, and cutting it adrift:
(1) Send a distress message (Mayday call), saying that yacht is being abandoned, and position.
(2) Dress warmly with sweaters etc. under oilskins, and life jacket on top. Take extra clothes.
(3) Fill any available containers with tops about ¾ full with fresh water, so that they will float.
(4) Collect additional food – tins and tin-opener.
(5) Collect navigational gear, torch, extra flares, bucket, length of line, First-aid kit, knife, etc.

Once in the life raft, plan for the worst. If there has not been time to collect items listed above, collect whatever flotsam is available.
(1) Keep the inside of the raft as dry as possible. Huddle together for warmth. Close the openings as necessary, but keep a good lookout for shipping and aircraft.
(2) Stream the drogue if necessary for stability, or if it is required to stay near the position.
(3) Ration fresh water to ¾ pint (½ litre) per person per day. Do not drink sea water or urine. Collect rain water.
(4) Use flares sparingly, on the skipper's orders.
(5) Issue and commence taking anti-seasick pills.

8.4.11 Medical help by RT

Medical advice can be obtained through any UK (BT) coast station by calling on a working channel and asking for a Medico call. In emergency call on Ch 16 using the Urgency signal PAN PAN, followed by the word MEDICO. Urgent requests for advice should be made on Ch 16 direct to HM Coastguard who will arrange with the coast station for a priority working channel so that your call is connected to a doctor.

Calls for medical assistance (i.e. the presence of a doctor or a casualty to be off-lifted) should be made direct to HM Coastguard on Ch 16. If such a call is received by a coast station it will be referred to HM Coastguard. A Medico message should contain:

(1) Yacht's name, call sign and nationality.
(2) Yacht's position, next port of call (with ETA) and nearest harbour if required to divert.
(3) Patient's details – name, age, sex, medical history.
(4) Present symptoms and advice required.
(5) What medication is carried on board.

When out of VHF range call on 2182 kHz. There is no charge for medical calls.

Similar arrangements apply in other countries. For France call: PAN PAN Radiomédical (name of station) in French. For Belgium call: Radiomédical Oostende, in French, Dutch, English or German. For Netherlands call: Radiomédical Scheveningen, in Dutch, English, French or German. For Germany call: Funkarzt (name of station) in German or English.

8.5   HAZARDS

8.5.1   Submarine hazard and broadcast warnings of submarine activity

There have been a number of incidents in which fishing vessels and occasionally yachts have been snagged or hit by submarines operating just below the surface.

The best advice available to yachts is:

(1) Listen to broadcasts of submarine activity (Subfacts).
(2) Where possible avoid charted submarine exercise areas.
(3) Keep clear of any surface vessel flying the International Code Flag Group 'NE2' which denotes that submarines are in the vicinity.
(4) Run your engine or generator even when under sail.
(5) Operate your echo sounder.
(6) At night show deck-level navigation lights, i.e. on pulpit and stern.

The risk is greatest in the W English Channel, Scottish and Irish waters, including the Clyde and North Channel and at night. Within these waters 104 geographic areas have been designated as submarine exercise areas (see 10.1.18, 10.8.23 and 10.9.23 for charts).

The following BT Coast Radio Stations broadcast **Subfacts – South Coast** giving details of planned submarine activity in the W English Channel at 0733 and 1933 UT after gale warnings or weather forecasts:

Celtic	(Ch 24)
Ilfracombe	(Ch 05)
Land's End	(Ch 27, 64, and 2670 kHz)
Pendennis	(Ch 62)
Start Point	(Ch 26)
Niton	(Ch 28 and 1641 kHz)
Hastings	(Ch 07)
North Foreland	(Ch 26)
Thames	(Ch 02)
Orfordness	(Ch 62),
Bacton	(Ch 07)
Humber	(Ch 26 and 1869 kHz)
Grimsby	(Ch 27)

The following BT Coast Radio Stations broadcast **Subfacts – Clyde** giving details of planned submarine activity in Scottish Waters at 0303, 0703, 1103, 1503, 1903 and 2303 UT:

Lewis	(Ch 05),
Hebrides	(1866 kHz)
Skye	(Ch 24)
Oban	(Ch 07)
Islay	(Ch 25)
Portpatrick	(Ch 27 and 1883 kHz)
Anglesey	(Ch 26)
Cardigan Bay	(Ch 03)

All BT Coast Radio Stations, East and West coasts – Northern Region broadcast Subfacts (when in force) on MF and VHF twice daily at 0703 and 1903 following the scheduled weather forecasts.

Information relating to submarine activity in the area between Cape Wrath and Latitude 54°N is also broadcast by Coastguard Stations as follows:

Stornoway	Ch 16 on request
Oban	Ch 16 on request
Clyde	Ch 67 every 4h from 0020 LT
Belfast	Ch 16 on request

8.5.2   Gunfacts

Gunfacts is a warning service to provide mariners with information on naval practice firing intentions. Such warnings pose no restriction on the passage of any vessel. The onus for safety lies with the naval unit concerned.

Gunfacts includes planned or known underwater explosions; gunnery and missile firings. Broadcasts for underwater explosions only will be made on Ch 16 at H–1, –30m, and immediately prior to detonation.

No Gunfacts broadcasts are made on days when no firings are intended. Gunfacts broadcasts will include:

(1) LT and approximate location of intended firings with a declared safe distance in M.
(2) Whether illuminants are to be fired.

Gunfacts – South Coast are promulgated by the Naval Operations room Plymouth for the English Channel areas, and for all other areas by a nominated Duty Broadcast Ship (**Gunfacts – Ship**).

Gunfacts – South Coast will cover activity in the English Channel Exercise areas, including the firing times only for the Portland and Portsmouth firing and practice exercise areas.

Gunfacts – Ship will cover activity in all other areas including Plymouth (outside the English Channel areas), Portsmouth, Scotland and Northern Ireland. Broadcasts will be made twice daily at 0800 and 1400 LT on Ch 16 before changing to Ch 06 or 67.

BT CRS Southern Region broadcast **Gunfacts** when in force at 0733 and 1933 UT following the scheduled weather forecast.

8.6   SEARCH AND RESCUE – IRELAND

8.6.1   General

The Irish Marine Emergency Service (IMES) is a division of the Department of Marine. IMES is the co-ordinating body responsible for all search and rescue operations around the coast of Ireland, and is based on MRSCs at Dublin, Malin Head and Valentia, co-located with the Coast Radio Stations (see pages 90-91) and operated by the same staff. They are co-ordinated by the MRCC at IMES Headquarters, Leeson Lane, Dublin 2 (☎: (01) 6620922). The MRSCs keep watch on marine distress frequencies.

A dedicated IMES Sikorsky S61N helicopter can provide emergency response within 15 to 45 minutes up to a radius of 200M. It is equipped with infrared search equipment.

IMES provides some 50 units around the coast and is on call 24 hours a day. Some of these units have specialised cliff climbing facilities.

The RNLI maintains four RNLI stations around the coast and some 26 lifeboats. Additionally, six individually community-run inshore rescue boats are available.

The Department of Defence provide a 24h Dauphin Helicopter at Finner Camp in Donegal and at Baldonnel, Dublin.

8.7   SEARCH AND RESCUE – FRANCE

8.7.1   General

France has five Centres Régionaux Opérationnels de Surveillance et de Sauvetage (CROSS) on the Channel and Atlantic coasts. A CROSS centre is an MRCC and a sous-CROSS centre an MRSC. They are shown in Table 8(2) and in Fig. 8(3). All keep watch on VHF Ch 16 and Ch 70 (DSC), and broadcast local navigational warnings, gale warnings and weather messages. Weather broadcasts are shown in Table 7(5).

CROSS stations have no public correspondence role. Their main functions include:

(1) Maritime Search and Rescue.
(2) Navigational surveillance.
(3) Broadcasts of navigational warnings.
(4) Broadcasts of meteorological information.
(5) Anti-pollution control.

CROSS Étel specialises in providing medical advice and responds to alerts from Cospas/Sarsat satellites.

At sea CROSS can be alerted on RT either directly, or through the Naval 'Semaphore' (signal) Stations as listed in 10.15.8 which keep watch on Ch 16 and work Ch 10, or through French Coast Radio Stations.

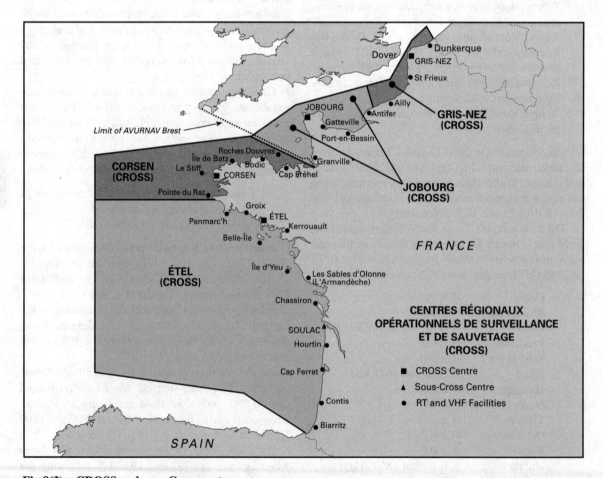

Fig 8(3) – CROSS and sous-Cross centres

TABLE 8(2)   CROSS STATIONS

Notes:
  (a)   These stations have no public correspondence role. See 8.5.1.
  (b)   For locations of stations see Fig. 8(3).
  (c)   VHF Digital Selective Calling (DSC) on Ch 70 is operational or on trial for all stations listed. The MMSI number of each controlling station is shown in the first column.
  (d)   Channels are designated for distress/safety, indicated below by (safety); for SAR Co-ordination indicated by (SAR); for calling and working indicated by (call); and for information broadcasts indicated by (info). All channels operate H24. See Table 7(5) for detailed information on CROSS Weather broadcasts

Name Position Tel: Fax: MMSI No:	Area of coverage	VHF Ch MF kHz See Note (d) above	VHF Relay stations	Navigational Warnings (in English and French unless stated). For Weather see Table 7(5)
CROSS Gris-Nez 50°52'N 01°35'E 03·21.87.21.87 03·21.87.78.55 002275100	Belgian Border to Cap d'Antifer	16 2182 (safety), 15 67 **68** 73 (SAR)	Dunkerque St Frieux Ailly	Gris-Nez Traffic (see below) bcsts general information on Ch 79 after announcement on Ch 16 every H+10 & H+25 when visibility less than 2 n miles
Gris-Nez Traffic at CROSS Gris-Nez	Dover Strait CNIS (with Dover CG)	16 (safety) 13 79 (call) 79 (info)	As above	
CROSS Jobourg 49°41'N 01°54'W 02·33.52.72.13 02·33.52.71.72 002275200	Cap d'Antifer to Mont St Michel	16 2182 (safety), 67 **68** (SAR)	Antifer Gatteville Granville Roches Douvres Port-en-Bessin	Jobourg Traffic (see below) bcsts general information on Ch 80 after announcement on Ch 16 every H+20 & H+50 or as required, and on request
Jobourg Traffic at CROSS Jobourg	Casquets TSS and ITZ (with Portland CG)	16 (safety) 13 80 (call) 80 (info)	As above	
CROSS Corsen 48°24'N 04°47'W 02·98.89.31.31 02·98.89.65.75 002275300	Mont St Michel to Pointe du Raz	16 70 (safety), 15 67 **68** 73 (SAR)	Cap Fréhel Île de Batz Bodic Le Stiff Pointe du Raz	Ouessant Traffic (see below) bcsts general information on Ch 79 after announcement on Ch 16 every H+10 & H+40 and on request
Ouessant Traffic at CROSS Corsen	Ouessant TSS and ITZ, and passages inside Ouessant	16 (safety) **13** 79 (call) 79 (info)	As above	
CROSS Étel (call: CROSSA Étel) 47°39'N 03°12'W 02·97.55.35.35 02·97.55.49.34 002275000	Pointe du Raz to 46°20'N, and to Spanish Border at night using Soulac antenna	CROSS Étel: as Corsen above. CROSSA Étel: 16 (safety), **13** 80 (call) 80 (info)	Penmarc'h Groix Kerrouault Les Sables d'Olonne Belle Ile Île d'Yeu	Urgent information on Ch 80 after announcement on Ch 16, on receipt and every 2h. Non-urgent bcsts by stations in succession after Weather Messages, commencing at 0433 and 2133 LT (in French)
sous-CROSS Soulac 45°31'N 01°07'W 05·56.09.82.00 05·56.09.79.73 002275010	46°20'N to Spanish Border 0700-2200 LT. (Night service by CROSS Etel)	CROSS Soulac: as Corsen. sous-CROSS Soulac: 16 (safety), **13** 79 (call) 79 (info)	Chassiron Hourtin Cap Ferret Contis Biarritz	Urgent warnings on Ch 79 on receipt and every 2h. Non-urgent bcsts by stations in succession after Weather Messages, commencing at 0433 and 2133 LT (in French)

8

Chapter 9

Tides

Contents

Tides – introduction

This chapter explains the use of the tidal data provided in Chapter 10 and serves as an on-board reference on tidal prediction. For fuller details of tides and the sea, reference should also be made to Chapter 9 in *The Macmillan & Silk Cut Yachtsman's Handbook* where the following subjects are described in detail:

The theory of tides; definitions of terms; calculations of times and heights of HW and LW; calculations of depths of water at specific times; calculations of times at which tide reaches certain heights; 'Twelfths' rule; tidal calculations by pocket calculator; French tidal coefficients; co-tidal and co-range charts; harmonic constituents; establishment of a port; tidal stream diamonds; tidal stream information on charts and in Sailing Directions, plus: general information on the sea – how waves are formed; freak waves; wind against tide; bars; overfalls and tide races; refraction of waves; reflected waves; ocean currents, etc.

9.1   GENERAL

9.1.1   Explanation
This chapter explains how to use the tidal information contained in Chapter 10, where the daily times and heights of High Water (HW) and Low Water (LW) for Standard Ports are given, together with time and height differences for many Secondary Ports. Tidal predictions are for average meteorological conditions. In abnormal weather the times and heights of HW and LW may vary considerably. (See 9.8.)

9.1.2   Times
The times of Standard Port predictions in Chapter 10 are given in the Zone Time indicated at the top left-hand corner of each page. Nearly all countries, and most ships, prefer to keep their clocks set to a whole number of hours ahead or behind UT.

The world is divided into 24 Time Zones. Each zone is 1 hour, or 15° of longitude wide. The zone number indicates the number of hours by which the Zone Time must be decreased or increased to obtain UT. Zones to the East of Greenwich are named minus (–), those to the West plus (+). Zone 0 is centred on the Greenwich Meridian and extends from 7½°W to 7½°E and the time kept corresponds to UT.

Tidal predictions for Standard Ports in the UK, Channel Islands and the Republic of Ireland are given in UT (Zone 0), and those for Standard Ports in France, Belgium, Netherlands and Germany are given in UT+1 (Zone –1). To convert these Zone – 0100 times to UT, subtract one hour.

Those periods in which DST (BST in UK) applies are indicated by the absence of green tinting, and one hour must be added to obtain DST (= LT).

Under each Secondary Port listed in Chapter 10 are its Time Zone, its Standard Port and the data required to calculate time differences, which when applied to the printed times of HW and LW at the Standard Port, give the times of HW and LW at the Secondary Port in the Zone Time of that Port. If DST is required, then one hour is added after the Secondary Port time difference has been applied, but not before.

9.1.3   Predicted heights
Predicted heights are given in metres and tenths of a metre above chart datum (CD) (see 9.2.1). Care must be taken when using charts which show depths in fathoms/feet. A table for converting feet to metres and metres to feet is given in 2.7.2.

9.2   DEFINITIONS

Certain definitions are given below and in Fig. 9(1). For further details see Chapter 9 of *The Macmillan & Silk Cut Yachtsman's Handbook.*

9.2.1   Chart datum
Chart datum (CD) is the reference level above which heights of tide are predicted, and below which charted depths are measured. Hence the actual depth of water is the charted depth (at that place) plus the height of tide (at that time).

Tidal predictions for most British ports use as their datum Lowest Astronomical Tide (LAT), which is the lowest sea level predicted under average meteorological conditions. All Admiralty Charts of the British Isles use LAT as chart datum, but others, particularly fathom charts, do not. Where tidal predictions and charted depths are not referenced to the same datum (e.g. LAT), errors resulting in an over-estimation of depth by as much as 0·5m can occur.

9.2.2   Charted depth
Charted depth is the distance of the sea bed below chart datum, and is shown in metres and tenths of a metre on metric charts, or in fathoms and/or feet on older charts. Make sure you know which units are used.

9.2.3   Drying height
Drying height is the height above chart datum of the top of any feature at times covered by water. The figures are underlined on the chart, in metres and tenths of a metre on metric charts, and in fathoms and feet on older charts. The depth is the height of tide (at the time) minus the drying height. If the result is negative, then that feature is above sea level.

9.2.4   Duration
Duration is the time between LW and the next HW, normally slightly more than six hours, and can be used to calculate the approximate time of LW when only the time of HW is known.

9.2.5   Height of tide
The height of the tide is the vertical distance of sea level above (or very occasionally below) chart datum, as defined in 9.2.1.

9.2.6   Interval
The interval is the period of time between a given time and the time of HW, expressed in hours and minutes before (–) or after (+) HW. Intervals are printed in increments of one hour (–1hr and +1hr) along the bottom of each tidal curve in Chapter 10. For examples, see Figs. 9(4) and 9(5).

9.2.7   Mean High Water and Low Water Springs/Neaps
Mean High Water Springs (MHWS) and Mean High Water Neaps (MHWN) are the averages of the predicted heights of the Spring or Neap tides at HW over a period of 18·6 years. Similarly, Mean Low Water Springs (MLWS) and Neaps (MLWN) are the average heights of low water for the Spring and Neap tides respectively. Charted heights of land objects such as lights, bridges, etc. are referred to the level of MHWS. On French charts these charted elevations are referred to as ML rather than MHWS.

9.2.8   Mean Level
Mean Level (ML) is the average of the heights of Mean High Water Springs (MHWS), Mean High Water Neaps (MHWN), Mean Low Water Springs (MLWS) and Mean Low Water Neaps (MLWN).

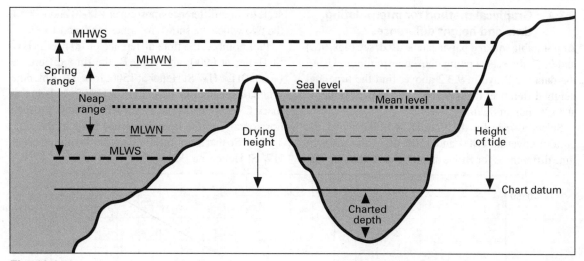

Fig. 9(1)

9.2.9   Range
The range of a tide is the difference between the heights of successive High and Low Waters.

Spring range is the difference between MHWS and MLWS, and Neap range is the difference between MHWN and MLWN.

9.2.10 Tidal Coefficients
In France the size (range) of a tide and its proximity to Springs/Neaps is quantified by Tidal Coefficients which are listed and explained in 10.16.25.

9.2.11 Rise/Fall of tide
The Rise of the tide is the amount the tide has risen since the earlier Low Water. The Fall of the tide is the amount the tide has fallen since the last High Water.

9.3   CALCULATIONS OF TIMES AND HEIGHTS OF HIGH AND LOW WATER

9.3.1   Standard Ports
The times and heights of HW and LW are tabulated for each Standard Port in Chapter 10. The conversion of Zone – 0100 time to UT and of either Zone UT or Zone – 0100 Time to Local Summer or Daylight Saving Time (DST) is dealt with in 9.1.2. See also 9.8 for the effect of wind and barometric pressure.

9.3.2   Secondary Ports – times of HW and LW
Each Secondary Port listed in Chapter 10 has a data block for the calculation of times of HW and LW as explained in 9.1.2. The following example is for Braye (Alderney):

TIDES
– 0400 Dover; ML 3·6; Duration 0545; Zone 0 (UT).

Standard Port ST HELIER (→)

Times				Height (metres)			
High Water		Low Water		MHWS	MHWN	MLWN	MLWS
0300	0900	0200	0900	11·0	8·1	4·0	1·4
1500	2100	1400	2100				
Differences BRAYE							
+0050	+0040	+0025	+0105	–4·8	–3·4	–1·5	–0·5

Thus – 0400 Dover indicates that, on average, HW Braye occurs 4 hours 00 minutes before HW Dover (the times of HW Dover, in UT, can be found on the bookmark). Duration 0545 indicates that LW Braye occurs 5 hours and 45 minutes before its HW. This is a very rough and ready method.

A more accurate and reliable method uses the Standard Port and Time Differences in the table. Thus when HW at St Helier occurs at 0900 and 2100, the Difference is + 0040, and HW at Braye occurs at 0940 and 2140. When HW at St Helier occurs at 0300 and 1500, the Difference is + 0050, and HW at Braye then occurs at 0350 and 1550. If, as is likely, HW St Helier occurs at some other time, then the Difference for Braye must be found by interpolation – by eye, by the graphical method, or by calculator. Thus, by eye, when HW St Helier occurs at 1200, the Difference is + 0045, and HW Braye occurs at 1245. The same method is used for calculating the times of LW.

The times thus obtained are in the Zone Time indicated in the Secondary Port data block. Care must be taken when the Zone Time at the Secondary Port differs from that at the Standard Port. See 9.1.2 for converting time from one zone to another and for changing to Daylight Saving Time (DST).

9.3.3   Secondary Ports – heights of HW and LW
The Secondary Port data block also contains height Differences which are applied to the heights of HW and LW at the Standard Port. Thus when the height of HW at St Helier is 11·0m (MHWS), the Difference is – 4·8m, and the height of HW at Braye is 6·2m (MHWS). When the height of HW at St Helier is 8·1m (MHWN), the Difference is – 3·4m, and the height of HW at Braye is 4·7m (MHWN). If, as is likely, the height of tide at the Standard Port does not exactly equal the Mean Spring or Neap level, then the height Difference is found. Thus if the height of HW at St Helier is 9·55m, the Difference is – 4·1m, and the height of HW at Braye is 5·45m.

9.3.4   Graphical method for interpolating time and height differences

Any suitable squared paper can be used, see Figs. 9(2) and 9(3), the scales being chosen as required. Using the data for Braye in 9.3.2 above, find the time and height differences for HW at Braye if HW St Helier is at 1126, height 8·9m.

Select a scale for the time at St Helier along the bottom covering 0900 and 1500 when the relevant time differences for Braye are known. At the side, the scale for time differences must cover + 0040 and + 0050, the two which are shown for times 0900 and 1500.

Plot point A, the time difference (+ 0040) for HW St Helier at 0900; and point B, the time difference (+ 0050) for HW St Helier at 1500. Join AB. Enter the graph on the bottom at time 1126 (HW St Helier) and mark C where that time meets AB. From C proceed horizontally to the time difference scale at the side, + 0044. So that morning HW Braye is 44 minutes after HW St Helier, i.e. 1210.

Fig. 9(2)   TIME OF HIGH WATER AT STANDARD PORT

In Fig. 9(3), the selected scales cover the height of HW at St Helier horizontally (i.e. 8·1 to 11·0m) and the relevant height differences (− 3·4 to − 4·8m) vertically. Plot point D, the height difference (− 3·4m) at Neaps when the height of HW St Helier is 8·1m; and E, the height difference (− 4·8m) at Springs when the height of HW St Helier is 11·0m. Join DE. Enter the graph at 8·9m (the height of HW St Helier that morning) and mark F where that height meets DE. From F follow the horizontal line to the scale of height differences, − 3·8m. So that morning the height of HW Braye is 5·1m.

Fig. 9(3)   HEIGHT OF HIGH WATER AT STANDARD PORT

9.4   CALCULATING INTERMEDIATE TIMES AND HEIGHTS OF TIDE

9.4.1   Standard Ports

Intermediate times and heights are best calculated from the Mean Spring and Neap Curves for Standard Ports in Chapter 10. Examples below are for Leith, on a day when the predictions are:

	UT	Ht (m)
22	0202	5·3
	0752	1·0
	1417	5·4
Tu	2025	0·5

Example: Find the height of tide at Leith at 1200.

(1)   On the Leith tidal diagram plot the heights of HW and LW each side of the required time, and join them by a sloping line, Fig. 9(4).

(2)   Enter the HW time and other times as necessary in the boxes below the curves.

(3)   From the required time, proceed vertically to the curves. The Spring Curve is a solid line, and the Neap curve (where it differs) is pecked. Interpolate between the curves by comparing the actual range – 4·4m in this example – with the Mean Ranges printed beside the curves. Never extrapolate. Here the Spring Curve applies.

(4)   Proceed horizontally to the sloping line plotted in (1), and thence vertically to the height scale, to give 4·2m.

Example: To find the time at which the afternoon height of tide falls to 3·7m.

(1)   On the Leith tidal diagram, plot the heights of HW and LW each side of the required event, and join them by a sloping line, Fig. 9(5).

(2)   Enter the HW time and others to cover the required event, in the boxes below.

(3)   From the required height, proceed vertically to the sloping line and thence horizontally to the curves. Interpolate between them as in the previous example and do not extrapolate. Here the actual range is 4·9m, and the Spring Curve applies.

(4)   Proceed vertically to the time scale, and read off the time required, 1637.

Fig. 9(4)

Fig. 9(5)

9.4.2   Secondary Ports

On coasts where there is little change of shape between tidal curves for adjacent Standard Ports, and where the duration of rise or fall at the Secondary Port is like that of the appropriate Standard Port (where the time differences for HW and LW are nearly the same), intermediate times and heights may be calculated from the tidal curves for the Standard Port in a similar manner to 9.4.1. The curves are entered with the times and heights of HW and LW at the Secondary Port, calculated as in 9.3.2 and 9.3.3.

Interpolation between the curves can be made by eye, using the range at the Standard Port as argument. Do not extrapolate, use the Spring Curve for Spring ranges or greater, and the Neap Curve for Neap ranges or less. With a large change in duration between Springs and Neaps the results may have a slight error, greater near LW.

Special curves for places between Swanage and Selsey (where the tide is very complex) are given in 10.2.12.

9.4.3   The use of factors

An alternative to the tidal curve method of tidal prediction is the use of factors which remains popular with those brought up on this method. Tidal curves show the factor of the range attained at times before and after HW. By definition a factor of 1 = HW, and 0 = LW. So the factor represents the proportion of the range (for the day in question) by which the height of tide is above the height of LW (that day) at the interval (time) concerned.

> Range × factor = Rise above LW
>
> and   Factor = Rise above LW ÷ range

In determining or using the factor it may be necessary to interpolate between the Spring and Neap curves as described in 9.4.2.

Factors are particularly useful when calculating hourly predicted heights for ports with special tidal problems (10.2.12).

9.4.4   The 'Twelfths' rule

The 'Twelfths' rule is a simple way of estimating the approximate height of the tide between HW and LW. The method assumes the duration of rise or fall is six hours and the tidal curve is symmetrical and approximates to a sine curve. The method is therefore useless in areas such as the Solent where the above conditions do not apply.

From one slack water to the next, the sea rises or falls by:

                1/12th of its range in the 1st hour
                2/12ths of its range in the 2nd hour
                3/12ths of its range in the 3rd hour
                3/12ths of its range in the 4th hour
                2/12ths of its range in the 5th hour
                1/12th of its range in the 6th hour

Fig. 9(6) Calculating vertical clearance

9.5   CALCULATIONS OF CLEARANCES UNDER BRIDGES

It is sometimes necessary to calculate whether a boat can pass underneath bridges or power cables. The vertical clearance of such objects is shown on the chart above MHWS, so the actual clearance will nearly always be greater than the figure shown. The vertical clearance is shown in metres on metric charts. It is often useful to draw a diagram, as shown in Fig. 9(6), which shows how the measurements are related to chart datum.

> Clearance = Vertical clearance of object +
>   height of MHWS minus height
>   of tide at the time + height of
>   mast above water.

9.6   TIDAL PREDICTION BY COMPUTER

By virtue of its simplicity, accuracy and speed, tidal prediction by computer or calculator is something no seaman – professional or amateur – with access to a computer can afford to ignore because it can do the job better and quicker than by conventional means.

A navigator with access to a PC or lap-top computer, can choose between two tidal prediction programs issued by the Hydrographic Office.

9.6.1   Tidecalc

Tidecalc (NP 158 v 1·1) is a simplified version of a program used by the HO for computing the daily tidal predictions published in the four volumes of Admiralty Tide Tables (ATT) NP 201 UK & Ireland (including European Channel Ports from Netherlands to Brest); NP 202 Europe (excluding UK, Ireland and Channel Ports), Mediterranean and Atlantic; NP 203 Indian Ocean and South China Sea; and NP 203 Pacific Ocean). This PC program has a worldwide application.

The software consists of a program disk, and a choice of 13 area disks (NP 158A1 to A13 which cover the world). Each area disk holds the relevant data for around 350-400 ports. Area 1 (v 4·0) covers the UK, Republic of Ireland and the Channel Islands, and Area 2 (v 4·0) covers Europe from Russia to Gibraltar excluding Iceland and Greenland, but including the Channel Islands and Mediterranean. Customised disks holding up to 400 sets of harmonic data can be supplied by the Hydrographic Office to meet individual user requirements.

Tidecalc includes a number of useful facilities to complement the usual presentation of times and heights of high and low water. The additional facilities include a choice of metres or feet; allowances for Daylight Saving Time; an indication of periods of daylight and twilight; the option to put in the yacht's draft, and the capability to display tabulated heights at specified times and time intervals. There is an option to display heights at intervals of 10, 20, 30, 40 or 50 minutes or one hour. Predictions can also be displayed graphically as a continuous plot of height against time.

Whichever method of tidal prediction is used, the basic accuracy will depend on the accuracy of the tidal observations made, the length of time over which the observations were undertaken, and whether the prediction method chosen is suitable for a particular port or area.

In some geographical areas better tide predictions may be obtained by using non-harmonic methods of prediction. Such areas include the upper reaches of many rivers like the Medway above Chatham; the Forth above Grangemouth; the Severn above Avonmouth, and the Crouch above Burnham. Other areas where non-harmonic methods result in more accurate predictions include many German ports.

Computations using Tidecalc are not intended to replace ATT but to supplement them, and it needs to be remembered that the official tide tables are the ultimate authority for tidal predictions.

9.6.2 NP 159 Harmonic Method

An alternative computer program issued by the Hydrographic Office is the Simplified Method of Harmonic Tidal Prediction (NP159A) (version 2·0).

The program automatically calculates the daily Tidal Angles and Factors which are found in Table VII in all three volumes of ATTs. The Port Harmonic Constant, and where appropriate Shallow Water Corrections and Seasonal Changes in Mean Level, are keyed in manually from data listed in Part III in all three volumes of ATTs, or from NP 160 Tidal Harmonic Constants (European Waters) Edition 2 1995.

Users are required to key the relevant data into the template boxes displayed on the screen using the ENTER key to tab through the various boxes shown. A zero is entered where no value is given in ATT. For

regularly used ports, up to twenty sets of Port Harmonic Constant data can be pre-stored for later use, but remember that the date is also stored and will need to be changed before using the data for any new prediction.

As changes in Port Harmonic Constants are made from time to time, for the best results it is recommended that only the constants listed in the latest edition of the ATTs are used. NP 160 (Constants for ATT Vol 1) will be updated approximately every five years.

9.6.3 Commercial programs

A number of commercial firms offer tidal prediction programs for use on computers or calculators. Most commercial programs are based on the Admiralty NP 159 method of tidal prediction.

9.7   TIDAL STREAMS

9.7.1   General

Tidal streams are the horizontal movement of water caused by the vertical rise and fall of the tide. They normally change direction about every six hours. They are quite different from ocean currents, such as the Gulf Stream, which run for long periods in the same direction. Tidal streams are always expressed as the direction towards which they are running.

Tidal streams are important to yachtsmen around the British Isles because they often run at about two knots, and much more strongly in a few areas, and at Spring tides. There are a few places where they can attain rates of six to eight knots.

The strength and direction of the tidal stream in the more important areas is shown in *Admiralty Tidal Stream Atlases*, as follows:

NP 209	Edition 4	Orkney and Shetland Islands, 1986
218	Edition 5	North Coast of Ireland, West Coast of Scotland, 1995
219	Edition 2	Portsmouth Harbour and Approaches, 1991
220	Edition 2	Rosyth Harbour and Approaches, 1991
221	Edition 2	Plymouth Harbour and Approaches, 1991
222	Edition 1	Firth of Clyde and Approaches, 1992
233	Edition 3	Dover Strait, 1995
249	Edition 2	Thames Estuary, 1985 (with Co-Tidal charts)
250	Edition 4	English Channel, 1992
251	Edition 3	North Sea, Southern Part, 1976
252	Edition 3	North Sea, North-Western Part, 1975
253	Edition 1	North Sea, Eastern Part, 1978
256	Edition 4	Irish Sea and Bristol Channel, 1992
257	Edition 3	Approaches to Portland, 1973

264   Edition 5 The Channel Islands and
                 Adjacent Coasts of France, 1993
265   Edition 1 France, West Coast, 1978
337   Edition 4 Solent and
                 Adjacent Waters, 1993

Extracts from the above (by permission of the Hydrographer and HMSO) are given in Chapter 10 for each area in the Almanac.

The directions of the streams are shown by arrows which are graded in weight and, where possible, in length to indicate the strength of the tidal stream. Thus ⟶ indicates a weak stream and ⟶ indicates a strong stream. The figures against the arrows give the Mean Neap and Spring rates in tenths of a knot, thus 19,34 indicates a Mean Neap rate of 1·9 knots and a mean Spring rate of 3·4 knots. The position of the comma on the Atlas indicates the approximate position at which the observations were taken.

It should be remembered that tidal atlases rarely show the details of inshore eddies, and the tide often sets towards the coast in bays. Along open coasts the turn of the tidal stream does not necessarily occur at HW and LW. It often occurs at about half tide. The tidal stream usually turns earlier inshore than offshore. On modern charts lettered diamonds give information on the tidal streams by reference to a table showing Set, Spring Rate and Neap Rate at hourly intervals before and after HW at a Standard Port. Where appropriate, normal river currents are included. Information on tidal streams and current streams is also included in *Admiralty Sailing Directions*.

9.7.2   Computation of tidal stream rates

Using Fig. 9(7) it is possible to predict the rate of a tidal stream at intermediate times, assuming that it varies with the range of tide at Dover.

Example:
It is required to predict the rate of the tidal stream off the northerly point of the Isle of Skye at 0420 UT on a day when the heights of tide at Dover are:

UT	Ht(m)
LW 0328	1·4
HW 0819	6·3
LW 1602	1·1
HW 2054	6·4

The range of the tide is therefore 6·3 – 1·4 = 4·9m. When using either the Tidal Stream Atlas NP 218, or the Tidal Stream charts for Area 8 in Chapter 10, the appropriate chart to use is that for '4 hours before HW Dover' and this gives a mean Neap and Spring rate of 09 and 17 respectively (0·9 and 1·7 kn). On Fig. 9(7), Computation of Rates, on the horizontal line marked Neaps, mark the dot above 09 on the horizontal scale;

likewise on the line marked Springs, mark the dot below the figure 17 on the horizontal scale. Join these two dots with a straight line. On the vertical scale, 'Mean Range Dover', find the range 4·9. From this point follow across horizontally until the pencil line just drawn is cut; from this intersection follow the vertical line to the scale of Tidal Stream Rates, either top or bottom, and read off the predicted rate. In this example it is 14 or 1·4 knots.

A perspex sheet, or a sheet of tracing paper can be used on top of Fig. 9(7), so as to preserve it for future use.

9.7.3   Tidal streams in rivers

Tidal streams in rivers are influenced by the local topography of the river bed as well as by the phases of the Moon. At or near Springs, in a river which is obstructed, for example, by sandbanks at the entrance, the time of HW gets later going up the river; the time of LW also gets later, but more rapidly so the duration of the flood becomes shorter, and duration of ebb becomes longer. At the entrance the flood stream starts at an interval after LW which increases with the degree of obstruction of the channel; this interval between local LW and the start of the flood increases with the distance up river. The ebb begins soon after local HW along the length of the river. Hence the duration of flood is less than that of the ebb and the difference increases with distance up river.

The flood stream is normally stronger than the ebb, and runs harder during the first half of the rise of tide.

At Neaps the flood and ebb both start soon after local LW and HW respectively, and their durations and rates are roughly equal.

9.8   METEOROLOGICAL CONDITIONS

Meteorological conditions can have a significant effect on tides and tidal streams. Broadly speaking sea level tends to rise in the direction towards which the wind is blowing and lowered in the other direction. Strong winds blowing along a coast or the sudden onset of a gale can also set up a wave or 'storm surge' which travels along the coast. Under exceptional conditions this can raise the height of the tide by two or three metres, or in the case of a 'negative' surge, can lower the height of LW by one or two metres which may be more serious for the yachtsman.

Severe conditions giving rise to a storm surge as described above are likely to be caused by a deep depression, where the low barometric pressure tends to raise the sea level still more (see 9.8.1).

Intense minor depressions can have local effects on the height of water, setting up what is known as a 'seiche' which can raise or lower the sea level a metre or more in the space of a few minutes. Certain harbours such as Wick or Fishguard are particularly susceptible to such conditions.

Tidal heights are predicted for average meteorological conditions of barometric pressure and

Fig. 9(7) Calculating Rates of Tidal Streams

wind. It therefore follows that any deviation from 'average' conditions results in a difference between the predicted and actual tide level experienced. Atmospheric pressure has the greater influence. A change of 34 millibars can cause a change of 0·3 metres in the height of sea level, although it may not be felt immediately. Higher than average atmospheric pressure is of more practical concern because the water level is always less than predictions.

In order to make an allowance for abnormal meteorological conditions it is necessary to define 'average conditions'. A good starting point is to look at the statistical tables in *Admiralty Sailing Directions*, or ask the local harbour master. Find out the average Mean Sea Level pressure for your local port and use this as a datum. For example, the pressure in the Solent area varies over the year from about 1014 to 1017mb, which gives an average of 1016mb.

Strong winds also affect tide levels and may alter the predicted times of High or Low Water by up to one hour, but are much less easy to quantify as the effect is very variable and strongly influenced by the local topography. In practical terms there is no need to consider winds of less than Force 5. Although exceptionally high or low tides may occur in one place, it is not always the case that the same effect will happen in another.

Local knowledge is the best guide and the harbour master will be able to advise on how the tide levels are affected under different pressure and wind conditions.

A good example of how localised meteorological effects on water levels can differ from the more general rules occurs in Southampton Water where strong winds between N and NE can significantly reduce tide levels. The longer and stronger the wind blows, the greater the effect. NE winds of Force 5 can be expected to reduce predicted levels by about − 0·2m, but winds of Force 8 to 10 will almost double the effect to –0·5m. Strong winds can also be associated with high-pressure systems so the total correction required to counter the combined effects of a strong wind and higher than average pressure can easily reach – 0·6m below predicted levels. Water levels at the entrances to the Newtown or Beaulieu Rivers are significantly lowered when strong N to NW winds combine with high pressure.

9.8.1 Storm Tide Warning Service

The Meteorological Office operates a Storm Tide Warning Service with the aim of providing warnings of potential coastal flooding resulting from abnormal meteorological conditions.

This service also provides warnings of abnormally low tidal levels in the Dover Strait, Thames Estuary and Southern North Sea. Warnings are issued when tidal levels measured at Dover, Sheerness or Lowestoft are expected to fall one metre or more below predicted levels.

Such warnings are broadcast on Navtex, and by the BT Coast Radio Stations on the normal VHF and MF frequencies used for navigation warnings and by the Channel Navigation Information Service.

9.9   STANDARD PORTS

The following Standard Ports, listed by Areas, are shown in Chapter 10. See also 9.1.1 and 9.3.1.

AREA

1	Falmouth*, Devonport, Dartmouth*.
2	Portland, Poole*, Southampton, Portsmouth.
3	Shoreham, Dover.
4	Sheerness, London Bridge, Burnham-on-Crouch*, Walton-on-the-Naze, Lowestoft.
5	Immingham, Tyne (North Shields).
6	Leith, Aberdeen.
7	Lerwick.
8	Ullapool, Oban.
9	Greenock.
10	Liverpool, Holyhead.
11	Milford Haven, Avonmouth.
12	Dublin, Cobh.
13	Belfast, Galway.
14	St Peter Port*, St Helier.
15	Cherbourg, St Malo.
16	Brest†.
17	Nil.
18	Pointe de Grave.
19	Le Havre, Dieppe.
20	Vlissingen, Hook of Holland.
21	Wilhelmshaven, Cuxhaven, Helgoland.

*   Daily predictions given, although not Standard Ports.

†   Brest tidal coefficients are at 10.16.25

Note: Predictions for Lisbon and Gibraltar are given in the Iberian Guide.

Chapter 10

Harbour, Coastal and Tidal Information

Contents

10

Shetland
Islands

7

Cape
Wrath

Orkney
Islands

Rattray Head

Scotland

8

6

Loch
Craignish

Crinan Canal

Eyemouth

Berwick-on-
Tweed

9

Northern
Ireland

13

Mull of
Galloway

5

Isle of
Man

10

Sylt

21

Liscanor Bay

Lambay
Island

Helgoland

Emden

Delfzijl

River
Elbe

20

12

Bardsey
Island

Wales

England

4

Great Yarmouth

Netherlands

Germany

11

Land's
End

Nieuwpoort

Belgium

Portland
Bill

Selsey Bill

3

Isles of
Scilly

1

2

19

Pte de
Barfleur

16

14

Paimpol
St Quay

Channel Islands

Raz de Sein

15

France

17

River
Loire

See IBERIAN GUIDE
for coverage to
Gibraltar

18

Denmark

Spain

Spanish Border

10.0.2 General information

Harbour, coastal and tidal information is given for each of the 21 Areas shown on the map at 10.0.1, with detailed text and chartlets of 383 harbours and notes on 405 lesser harbours and anchorages. The information provided enables a skipper to assess whether he can get into a harbour (tidal height, depth, wind direction etc), and whether he wants to enter the harbour (shelter, facilities available, early closing days etc). Abbreviations and symbols are in 1.4.1, and a four-language glossary is at 1.4.2.

Each Area is arranged as follows:

Index of the harbours covered in that area.

A diagram of the area showing the positions and characteristics of the harbours covered, principal lights, radiobeacons, coastal/port radio stations, weather information offices, LB stations and CG Centres with their boundaries.

Tidal stream chartlets for the area, based on Admiralty tidal stream atlases (by kind permission of the Hydrographer of the Navy and the Controller, HM Stationery Office), showing the rates and directions of tidal streams for each hour referenced to HW Dover and to HW at the relevant Standard Port. For how to use tidal stream charts see 9.6.2.

A list of principal coastal lights, fog signals and useful waypoints in the area. More powerful lights (range 15M or more) are in **bold** type; light-vessels and Lanbys are in *CAPITAL ITALICS*; fog signals are in *italics*. Latitude and longitude are shown for a selection of lights and marks, some of which are underlined as useful waypoints. Unless otherwise stated, lights are white. Elevations are in metres (m) above MHWS, and nominal ranges in nautical miles (M). Where appropriate, a brief description is given of the lighthouse or tower. Arcs of visibility, sector limits, and alignment of leading lights etc are true bearings as seen from seaward measured in a clockwise direction. Where a longitude is given (e.g. 04°12'·05W) W stands for West; W can also mean white. To avoid ambiguity, the words white or West may be written in full, except for longitude.

Passage information briefly calls attention in note form to some of the principal features of the coast, recommended routes, offlying dangers, tide races, better anchorages etc.

Table of distances in nautical miles by the most direct route, avoiding dangers, between selected places in that area and in adjacent areas. See also Tables of distances across the English Channel, Irish and North Seas in this Introduction.

Special notes in certain Areas (Ireland, Channel Is, France, Belgium, Netherlands and Germany) give information specific to that country or Area.

10.0.3 Harbour information

a. Below the **harbour name**, the County or Unitary Council (or equivalent abroad) is given, followed by the lat/long of the hbr entrance, or equivalent. This lat/long may be used as a final waypoint after the approach WPT ⊕ given under Navigation.
NB: A published waypoint should never be used without first plotting its position on the chart.

b. A **harbour rating** is given after the lat/long. It grades a port for ease of access, facilities available and its attractiveness as a place. Although inevitably subjective, it offers a useful shorthand as to what a yachtsman may expect to find. The rating, shown below the port name as 3 figures, eg Rtg 2.3.2, is based on the following criteria:

— Ease of access (first figure):
1. This port can be entered in *gales from any direction and at all states of tide, by day or night.*
2. Accessible in *gales* from all quarters *except one; adequate depths, marks and lights.*
3. Accessible in *strong winds* from all quarters *except one; possible tidal or pilotage constraints.*
4. Only accessible in *light winds and slight swell; brief tidal window and few marks or lights.*
5. Only accessible in *calm, settled* conditions by day with *no swell; there may be a bar and difficult pilotage.*

— Facilities available (second figure):
1. *All possible facilities* for yacht and crew.
2. *Many facilities available,* including all domestic needs, but with some limitations in chandlery and/ or major repair work.
3. *All domestic facilities,* but probably only a hauling-out slip and a boatyard capable of limited work; not necessarily attuned to yachting needs.
4. *All domestic needs;* basic marine facilities.
5. *Virtually nothing,* unless prepared to walk some distance for basic domestic needs, eg food/ water.

— Attractiveness (third figure):
1. An attractive place; visit, if necessary *going a little out of your way* to do so.
2. Normal for this part of the coast; *if convenient* visit the port concerned.
3. Visit only if alternatives are unavailable. *Expect to be disappointed* and subject to inconvenience.

This rating system, modified for harbours in this Almanac, was originated by the late Robin Brandon and used in successive editions of his *South Biscay Pilot,* published by Adlard Coles Nautical, to whom grateful ackowledgement is made.

c. **Chart numbers** for Admiralty (AC), Imray Laurie Norie & Wilson (Imray), Stanfords or foreign charts are listed, largest scale first. The *numbers* of Admiralty Small Craft editions are shown in *italics*. The Ordnance Survey (OS) Map numbers are given for UK and Eire (1:50,000 or 1¼" to 1 statute mile).

10

d.   **Chartlets** are based on British Admiralty, French, Dutch and German charts (as acknowledged in 1.1.3).

It is emphasised that these chartlets are not designed or intended for pilotage or navigation, although every effort has been made to ensure that they accurately portray the harbour concerned. The publishers and editors disclaim any responsibility for resultant accidents or damage if they are so used. The largest scale official chart, properly corrected, should always be used.

Due to limitations of scale, chartlets do not always cover the whole area referred to in the text nor do they always contain the approach waypoint ⊕. Not every depth, mark or feature can be shown. Depths and drying heights in metres are below/above Chart Datum; elevations are above MHWS. A light green tint shows drying areas, the darker tint indicates land.

e.   **Tidal predictions** are all provided by the UK Hydrographic Office, with permissions from the French, Dutch and German Hydrographic Offices.

For each Standard Port daily predictions of times and heights of HW/LW are given. Zone times are given, but no account is taken of BST or other daylight saving times (DST). In UK and Eire times are in UT.

At the foot of each page of tidal predictions is given the height difference between Chart Datum at the port in question and Ordnance Datum (Newlyn), for UK ports. For foreign ports the height difference is referenced to the relevant national Land survey datum. This enables tidal levels along a stretch of coast to be referred to a common horizontal plane. Further notes are contained in the Admiralty Tide Tables where the height differences are also tabulated.

Time and height differences for Secondary Ports are referenced to the most suitable (not always the nearest) Standard Port. An (⟵) or (⟶) points toward the Standard Port pages. The average time difference between local HW and HW Dover is given, so that the UT (±15 minutes) of local HW can be quickly found.

Times of HW Dover are in 10.3.15 and, for quick reference, on a bookmark which also lists Range together with a visual indication of the state of the tide (Springs or Neaps). Duration (quoted for most ports), if deducted from time of HW, gives the approx time of the previous LW. Mean Level (ML) is also quoted. Given ML and the height of HW, the range and therefore height of LW can also be calculated; see also Chapter 9. It should be noted, en passant, that on French charts ML, not MHWS, is used as the reference datum for elevations of lights, bridges etc.

Tidal Coefficients are listed and explained under Brest and are applicable to all French ports on the Channel and Atlantic coasts. They also provide an immediate numerical indication of the size of a tide, without resort to calculating range.

f.   **Tidal curves** are given for Standard Ports and those other ports for which full predictions are shown. Use the appropriate (np/sp) curve for tidal calculations (ie finding the height of tide at a given time, or the time for a given height). See Chapter 9 for tidal calculations.

HW −3 means 3 hrs before local HW; HW +2 means 2 hrs after. Secondary curves are given in 10.2.12 for ports between Swanage and Selsey Bill where special tidal conditions exist.

g.   **Shelter** assesses the degree of shelter and advises on access, berths (for charges see under Facilities), moorings and anchorages. Access times, if quoted, are approx figures relative to mean HW. They are purely a guide for a nominal 1·5m draft, plus safety clearance, and take no account of hull form, springs/neaps, flood/ebb, swell or nature of the bottom. Their purpose is to alert a skipper to possible tidal problems. Times of lock and bridge openings etc are local (LT), unless otherwise stated.

h.   **Navigation** gives the lat/long of a waypoint (⊕) suitable for starting the approach, with its bearing/distance from/to the hbr ent or next significant feature; some ⊕s may be off the harbour chartlet. NB: A published waypoint should never be used without first plotting its position on the chart. Approach chans, buoyage, speed limits and hazards are also described.

Wrecks around the UK which are of historic or archaeological interest are protected under the Protection of Wrecks Act 1973. About 40 sites, as detailed in Annual Notice to Mariners No 16 and depicted on the larger scale Admiralty charts, are listed in this almanac under the nearest harbour or in Passage Information. Unauthorised interference, including anchoring and diving on such sites, may lead to a substantial fine.

j.   **Lights and Marks** includes as much detail as space permits; some data may also be shown on the chartlet and/or in Coastal lights, fog signals and waypoints (10.AA.4) for that Area.

k.   **Radio Telephone** quotes VHF Channels related to each port, marina or VTS. If not obvious, the callsign of a station is shown in *italics*. Frequencies are indicated by their International Maritime Services Channel (Ch) designator. UK Marina Channels are 80 (161·625MHz) and M (157·85MHz; also known as M1 and formerly as Ch 37). M2 (161·425MHz) is allocated to some YCs for race control. MF frequencies, if shown, are in kHz.

Ch 16, the Distress, Safety and Calling Ch, is monitored by most shore stations, and is shown after the working channels. Its Distress and Safety functions can be seriously jeopardised by excessive calling, test transmissions and illegal chatter. Initial contact can usually, and very desirably, be made on the listed working Ch, rather than on Ch 16.

Where known, preferred channels are shown in bold type, thus **14**. If there is a choice of calling channel, always indicate which channel you are using; eg, *'Dover Port Control, this is NONSUCH, NONSUCH on Channel 74, over'*. This avoids confusion if the station being called is working more than one channel.

Where local times are stated, the letters LT are added. H24 means continuous watch. Times of scheduled broadcasts are shown (for example) as H +20, ie 20 minutes past the hour.

l.   **Telephone** is followed by the dialling code in brackets, which is not repeated for individual ☎ numbers. But it may be repeated or augmented under **Facilities** if different or additional codes also apply. Eg, Portsmouth and Gosport numbers are both on (01705) as listed; but Fareham's different code (01329) is quoted separately.

In the UK the ☎s of the relevant Coastguard MRCC/MRSC (see 8.4.2) are given under each port, but in an emergency dial 999 and ask for the Coastguard.

In France ☎ Nos were changed in Oct 1996 to 10 digit Nos by prefixing the new Zone codes (01 to 05), as appropriate to location. The two digit prefix for each port is shown in this almanac after the sub-heading TELEPHONE. See also 10.15.8.

The procedures for international calls from/to the UK are given in 10.12.7 (Ireland), 10.15.8 (France), 10.20.7 (Belgium & The Netherlands), and 10.21.7 (Germany). These sections also give ☎s for marine emergencies abroad. All EU countries use ☎ 112 for emergency calls to Fire, Police, Ambulance, in addition to their national emergency ☎s.

m.   **Facilities** available at the harbour, marinas and yacht clubs are listed first, followed by an abbreviated summary of those marine services provided commercially (see 1.4.1 and the Dover Range card for abbreviations). See also the Directory of Marine Services and Supplies (pink pages at the front of the Almanac) for commercial listings.
Note: Facilities at Yacht Clubs are usually available to crews who arrive by sea (as opposed to trailing a dinghy by car) and belong to a recognised YC.

The overnight cost of a visitors alongside berth for a 30ft (9·1m) LOA boat is shown in local currency at the previous year's rates. Harbour dues, if applicable, and VAT are included; in the UK the cost of mains electricity is usually extra. Note: The cost of berthing does not influence the attractiveness of a harbour, as described under 10.0.3b.

Town facilities are also listed, and whether there is a Post Office (✉), Bank (Ⓑ), Railway Station (⇌), or commercial Airport (✈) in or near the port. Where there is not, the nearest one may be shown in ( ). Abroad, the nearest port with a UK ferry link is given (see also 10.0.4 below).

FACILITIES FOR DISABLED PEOPLE

RYA Sailability is an organisation operating in the UK under the auspices of the RYA to open up sailing and its related facilities to disabled sailors. Yarmouth, Isle of Wight, and Port Solent marina at Portsmouth are amongst the first to offer special access facilities, as denoted by a wheelchair symbol. Symbols denoting facilities for those with sight or hearing disabilities will also be used. A more comprehensive listing is anticipated in future editions of this Almanac and therefore information from readers would be particularly appreciated.

10.0.4   Ferry Services

A summary is provided overleaf of most of the more popular ferry routes both within UK waters and to/from the UK, together with booking/contact ☎ numbers. Ferries on the W coast of Scotland are listed in more detail at the end of Area 8.

10.0.5/6/7   Distance Tables

In addition to the Distance Tables in each of the 21 geographic Areas, there are three Distance Tables in this Introduction. These contain port-to-port distances for passages from/to the UK across the English Channel (10.0.5), Irish Sea (10.0.6) and North Sea (10.0.7). They therefore relate to several geographic areas and may be used in conjunction with the Distance Tables in these areas.

THE 1998 IBERIAN GUIDE

This Guide extends the Almanac's coverage from the Franco-Spanish border at Hendaye (10.18.28) westward along Northern Spain and southward past the coasts of Portugal and South West Spain to Gibraltar.

It gives details and chartlets of main harbours, plus minor harbours and anchorages, as shown on four full page maps of the Iberian Peninsula.

Coastal lights, Fog signals and Waypoints are listed, together with summaries of Navigational aids, Weather sources and Communications facilities around the Atlantic coast of Iberia.

Passage Information offers guidance on dangers and passage-making, with two Distance Tables.

Tidal predictions and curves are included for the Standard Ports of Lisboa and Gibraltar, together with their associated secondary port differences. For secondary ports in North Spain, differences are referenced to Pointe de Grave in Area 18 of the Almanac.

Spanish and Portuguese vocabularies of useful nautical terms are also included.

The Guide is obtainable by post direct from the Publishers by completing the card enclosed within this Almanac and forwarding it with the appropriate remittance.

10

FERRIES AROUND UK AND TO/FROM THE CONTINENT   10.0.4

This Table is a highly condensed version of many detailed schedules. It is intended to show broadly what is available and to help when cruise plans and/or crew movements are subject to change at short notice.

NOTES: 1. **Hours** = approx duration of day crossing. 2. **Frequency** = number of one-way sailings per day in summer. Specific day(s) of the week may be shown, if non-daily. 3. ☎ **Bookings** may be via a centralised number applicable to all routes.

From	To	Hours	Frequency	Company	☎ Bookings
A.	**CROSS CHANNEL** (France, Belgium; and to Spain)				
Plymouth (Mar-Nov)	Santander	23½	M, W	Brittany	0990-360360
Plymouth	Roscoff	6	1 - 3	Brittany	Ditto
Poole	Cherbourg	4¼	1 - 2	Brittany (Truckline)	Ditto
Poole	St Malo	8	F, S, Su, M	Brittany	Ditto
Southampton	Cherbourg	5	2	Stena Line	01233-647047
Portsmouth	St Malo	8¾	1	Brittany	0990-360360
Portsmouth	Ouistreham (Caen)	6	3	Brittany	Ditto
Portsmouth (Jan-Mar)	Santander	31	Su	Brittany	Ditto
Portsmouth	Cherbourg	4¾	3	P & O European Ferries	0990-980555
Portsmouth	Le Havre	5¾	3	P & O European Ferries	Ditto
Portsmouth	Bilbao	33½	Su, Tu	P & O European Ferries	Ditto
Brighton	Fécamp	2 (Cat)	2 (May-Sep inc)	Brighton Ferries	01273-818333
Newhaven	Dieppe	4/2¼ (Cat)	2/4	Stena Line	01233-647047
Folkestone	Boulogne	55 mins	6	Hoverspeed (Cat)	0990-240241
Dover	Calais	35 mins	14	Hoverspeed (Hovercraft)	Ditto
Dover	Calais	1½/¾ (Cat)	20/7	Stena Line	01233-647047
Dover	Calais	1½	14	SeaFrance	01304-204204
Dover	Calais	1¼	25	P & O European Ferries	0990-980980
Ramsgate	Dunkerque	1¼	5	Sally	0990-595522
Ramsgate	Ostend	4/1¾ (Cat)	4/4 - 6	Sally	Ditto
B.	**NORTH SEA**				
Sheerness	Vlissingen	8	2	Eurolink	01795-581000
Harwich	Hook of Holland	6½	2	Stena Line	01233-647047
Harwich	Hamburg	18½	4 wkly	Scandinavian Seaways	0990-333000
Harwich	Esbjerg	19½	4 wkly	Scandinavian Seaways	Ditto
Harwich	Gothenburg	23½	Su, Tu	Scandinavian Seaways	Ditto
Hull	Rotterdam	12½	1	P & O N Sea Ferries	01482-377177
Hull	Zeebrugge	13¼	1	P & O N Sea Ferries	Ditto
Newcastle	IJmuiden	14	Varies; May-Sep	Scandinavian Seaways	0990-37Hò00
Newcastle	Hamburg	23½	2 wkly	Scandinavian Seaways	Ditto
Newcastle	Gothenburg	23½	F	Scandinavian Seaways	Ditto
Newcastle	Stavanger/Bergen	18½/6	M, W, S	Color	0191-296 1313
C.	**SCOTLAND**				
Aberdeen	Lerwick+Bergen	14+12½	F	P & O Scottish Ferries	01224-572615
Scrabster	Stromness	1¾	2 - 3	P & O Scottish Ferries	01856-850655
Stromness	Lerwick	8	Su, Tu	P & O Scottish Ferries	01595-5252
Ullapool	Stornoway	3½	2	Caledonian MacBrayne	01475-650000

CalMac run ferries to 23 West Scottish islands and many mainland ports; see 10.8.21 for details, inc other companies.

From	To	Hours	Frequency	Company	☎ Bookings
D.	**IRISH SEA** (and Eire-France)				
Cork	Roscoff	14	Su, Tu	Brittany	21-378401
Cork	St Malo	18	Wed	Brittany	Ditto
Cork	Cherbourg	17½	F (Jun-Aug)	Irish Ferries	01-661 0511
Cork	Le Havre	21½	Su (Jun-Aug)	Irish Ferries	Ditto
Cork	Swansea	10	1 (not Tu)	Swansea/Cork Ferries	01792-456116
Rosslare	Cherbourg	17	S, M	Irish Ferries	01-661 0511
Rosslare	Le Havre	21	Tu, W, Th	Irish Ferries	Ditto
Rosslare	Pembroke Dock	3¾	2	Irish Ferries	0345 171717
Rosslare	Fishguard	3½/1¾ (Cat)	2/5	Stena Line	01233-647047
Dun Laoghaire	Holyhead	3½/1¾ (HSS)	2/7	Stena Line	Ditto
Dublin	Holyhead	3¼	2	Irish Ferries	0345 171717
Belfast	Stranraer	1½ (Cat)	4 - 5	SeaCat	0345-523523
Belfast	Stranraer	2¼/1½ (HSS)	4/5	Stena Line	01233-647047
Belfast	Liverpool	10	1	Norse Irish Ferries	01232-779090
Larne	Cairnryan	2¼	6	P & O European Ferries	0990-980666
Douglas, IOM*	Heysham	3¾	Mo, Tu, We, Th	IOM Steam Packet Co	01624-661661
Douglas, IOM	Liverpool	4¼	Fr, Sa, Su	IOM Steam Packet Co	01624-661661

*Also less frequent sailings from Douglas to Belfast (4¾), Dublin (4¾), Fleetwood (3¼) and Ardrossan (8).

From	To	Hours	Frequency	Company	☎ Bookings
E.	**CHANNEL ISLANDS**				
Jersey	Poole	3¾	3	Condor (Cat)	01305-761551
Guernsey	Poole	2½	2	Condor (Cat)	Ditto
Jersey	St Malo	¾	4	Condor (Cat)	Ditto
Jersey	Sark	¾	1	Condor (Cat)	Ditto
Guernsey	Alderney	¾	1	Condor (Cat)	Ditto
Jersey†	St Malo	2½/1¼ (Cat)	2/5	Emeraude	02.99.40.48.40

†Also Jersey (St Helier) to Guernsey, Sark, Granville; and Jersey (Gorey) to Portbail and Carteret.

10.0.5   DISTANCES ACROSS THE ENGLISH CHANNEL

France/Cl \ England	Longships	Falmouth	Fowey	Plymouth bkwtr	Salcombe	Dartmouth	Torbay	Exmouth	Weymouth	Poole Hbr Ent	Needles Lt Ho	Nab Tower	Littlehampton	Shoreham	Brighton	Newhaven	Eastbourne	Rye	Folkestone	Dover
Le Conquet	112	112	123	125	125	137	144	155	172	188	194	212	230	240	245	249	261	278	295	301
L'Aberwrac'h	102	97	106	107	105	117	124	135	153	168	174	192	211	219	224	228	239	257	275	280
Roscoff	110	97	101	97	91	100	107	117	130	144	149	165	184	193	197	200	211	229	246	252
Trébeurden	120	105	106	102	94	102	109	120	129	142	147	164	181	190	194	197	208	226	244	249
Tréguier	132	112	110	101	94	98	102	112	116	128	132	147	162	170	174	177	188	206	224	229
Lézardrieux	142	121	118	107	94	100	105	114	115	126	130	140	157	165	169	172	184	201	219	224
St Quay-Portrieux	159	137	135	124	111	115	121	129	127	135	135	146	162	171	174	178	189	207	225	230
St Malo	172	149	146	133	118	120	124	132	125	130	130	143	157	166	170	173	184	202	220	225
St Helier	155	130	123	108	93	95	100	108	99	104	104	115	132	140	144	147	158	176	194	199
St Peter Port	139	113	104	89	73	70	75	81	71	79	83	97	112	120	124	127	135	156	174	179
Braye (Alderney)	146	116	106	89	72	69	71	75	54	60	62	73	91	100	103	106	114	136	153	159
Cherbourg	168	138	125	107	92	87	88	93	66	64	63	68	81	90	92	96	102	122	140	145
St Vaast-la-Hougue	194	164	150	132	116	111	112	116	83	76	72	71	80	87	88	90	96	115	132	138
Ouistreham	229	198	185	167	151	146	147	147	117	107	100	86	91	92	91	90	92	106	125	130
Deauville	236	205	192	174	158	153	154	154	122	111	104	88	89	88	87	85	87	101	120	125
Le Havre	231	200	187	169	153	148	148	148	118	105	97	82	82	83	82	79	80	94	115	120
Fécamp	242	212	197	179	163	157	157	157	120	105	96	75	71	68	65	62	62	72	90	95
Dieppe	268	237	222	204	188	180	180	180	142	125	117	91	80	75	70	64	63	60	70	75
Boulogne	290	258	242	224	208	198	195	191	153	135	127	97	81	71	66	59	47	33	28	25
Calais	305	272	257	239	223	213	210	209	168	150	141	111	96	86	81	74	62	43	26	22

NOTES

1. This Table applies to Areas 1 – 3, 14 – 16 and 19, each of which also contains its own internal Distance Table. Approximate distances in nautical miles are by the most direct route, while avoiding dangers and allowing for Traffic Separation Schemes.

2. For ports within the Solent, add the appropriate distances given in 10.2.6 to those shown above under either Needles light house or Nab Tower.

3. Distances across the Irish Sea, as applicable to Areas 9 – 13, are given in 10.0.6.

4. Distances across the North Sea, as applicable to Areas 3 – 7 and 19 – 21, are given in 10.0.7.

5. Some aspects of planning Cross-Channel passages are covered in Passage Information, 10.3.5 final section and 10.15.5.

10

10.0.6   DISTANCES ACROSS THE IRISH SEA

Scotland England Wales / Ireland	Port Ellen (Islay)	Campbeltown	Troon	Portpatrick	Mull of Galloway	Kirkcudbright	Maryport	Fleetwood	Pt of Ayre (IOM)	Port St Mary (IOM)	Liverpool	Holyhead	Pwllheli	Fishguard	Milford Haven	Swansea	Avonmouth	Ilfracombe	Padstow	Longships
Tory Island	75	107	132	119	134	170	185	215	156	171	238	207	260	279	307	360	406	355	372	399
Malin Head	45	76	101	88	103	139	154	184	125	140	207	176	229	248	276	329	375	324	341	368
Lough Foyle	38	61	86	73	88	124	139	169	110	125	192	161	214	233	261	314	360	309	326	353
Portrush	31	50	76	64	80	116	131	161	102	117	184	153	206	225	253	306	352	301	318	345
Carnlough	42	35	57	32	45	81	96	126	67	78	149	115	168	187	215	268	314	363	280	307
Larne	51	39	58	24	37	72	88	118	58	70	141	106	159	178	206	259	305	254	271	298
Carrickfergus	64	48	65	26	34	69	85	115	55	66	138	101	154	173	201	254	300	249	266	293
Bangor	63	48	64	22	30	65	81	111	51	62	134	97	150	169	197	250	296	245	262	289
Strangford Lough	89	72	84	36	30	63	76	97	41	37	107	69	121	141	167	219	265	214	231	258
Carlingford Lough	117	100	112	64	60	90	103	112	70	51	118	67	111	124	149	202	248	197	214	241
Dun Laoghaire	153	136	148	100	93	119	126	120	93	69	119	56	82	94	109	162	208	157	174	201
Wicklow	170	153	165	117	108	133	140	127	108	83	123	56	67	71	90	143	189	138	155	182
Arklow	182	165	177	129	120	144	149	133	117	93	131	64	71	65	79	132	179	128	144	167
Rosslare	215	202	208	161	154	179	180	164	152	125	156	90	83	55	58	109	157	110	119	137
Tuskar Rock	216	203	209	162	155	179	182	165	152	126	152	91	82	48	51	105	150	103	112	130
Dunmore East	250	237	243	196	189	213	216	199	186	160	189	127	116	79	76	130	177	124	127	136
Youghal	281	268	274	227	220	244	247	230	217	191	220	158	147	110	103	156	200	148	139	138
Crosshaven	300	287	293	246	239	263	266	249	236	210	239	177	166	131	118	170	216	163	151	144
Baltimore	346	333	339	292	285	309	312	295	282	256	285	223	212	172	160	209	254	198	178	161
Fastnet Rock	354	341	347	300	293	317	320	303	290	264	293	231	220	181	169	216	260	207	185	170

NOTES

1.   This Table applies to Areas 9 – 13, each of which also contains its own internal Distance Table. Approximate distances in nautical miles are by the most direct route, whilst avoiding dangers and Traffic Separation Schemes.

2.   Some aspects of planning passages across the Irish Sea are covered in Passage Information, 10.13.5 first section.

3.   Distances across the English Channel, as applicable to Areas 1 – 3, 14 – 16 and 19, are given in 10.0.5.

10.0.7   DISTANCES ACROSS THE NORTH SEA

Norway to France / UK	Bergen	Stavanger	Lindesnes	Skagen	Esjberg	Sylt (List)	Brunsbüttel	Helgoland	Bremerhaven	Willhelmshaven	Delfzijl	Den Helder	IJmuiden	Scheveningen	Roompotsluis	Vlissingen	Zeebrugge	Oostende	Nieuwpoort	Dunkerque
Lerwick	210	226	288	403	428	442	517	470	510	500	493	486	497	505	551	550	552	555	562	588
Kirkwall	278	275	323	438	439	452	516	467	507	497	481	460	473	481	515	514	516	519	526	545
Wick	292	283	323	437	428	440	498	449	489	479	458	433	444	451	485	484	486	489	496	514
Inverness	356	339	381	485	461	462	529	479	519	509	487	460	471	478	513	512	514	517	524	542
Fraserburgh	288	266	296	410	383	384	451	404	444	434	412	385	396	403	430	429	431	434	441	456
Aberdeen	308	279	298	411	371	378	433	382	432	412	386	353	363	369	401	400	402	405	412	426
Dundee	362	329	339	451	394	401	448	396	436	426	395	352	359	364	390	389	385	388	395	412
Port Edgar	391	355	362	472	409	413	457	405	445	435	401	355	361	366	391	390	386	389	396	413
Berwick-on-Tweed	374	325	320	431	356	361	408	355	395	385	355	310	315	320	342	341	337	340	347	364
Hartlepool	409	353	340	440	340	331	367	312	352	342	302	241	243	247	266	265	261	264	271	288
Grimsby	463	395	362	452	324	318	342	291	332	325	288	187	182	185	199	198	190	191	201	198
Kings Lynn	485	416	379	466	330	333	343	292	344	336	283	184	183	183	197	195	187	188	198	195
Lowestoft	508	431	380	453	308	300	295	262	284	271	218	118	104	98	95	99	87	87	89	106
Harwich	540	461	410	483	330	331	320	287	309	296	243	147	126	114	94	100	84	77	80	80
Brightlingsea	558	479	428	501	348	349	338	305	327	314	261	165	144	105	108	106	92	88	86	87
Burnham-on-Crouch	567	488	437	510	357	358	347	314	336	323	270	174	151	112	109	115	99	92	93	95
London Bridge	620	543	490	560	400	408	395	361	382	374	320	222	199	149	153	149	134	125	126	114
Sheerness	580	503	450	520	360	367	353	319	340	334	280	180	157	109	113	109	94	85	86	74
Ramsgate	575	498	446	516	368	346	339	305	323	315	262	161	144	121	89	85	77	65	58	42
Dover	588	511	459	529	378	359	352	328	336	328	275	174	155	132	101	92	79	65	58	44

NOTES

1. This Table applies to Areas 3 – 7 and 19 – 21, each of which also contains its own internal Distance Table. Approximate distances in nautical miles are by the most direct route, while avoiding dangers and allowing for Traffic Separation Schemes.

2. Some aspects of planning passages across the North Sea are covered in Passage Information, 10.4.5, 10.20.5 and 10.21.5.

3. Distances across the English Channel, as applicable to Areas 1 – 3, 14 – 16 and 19, are given in 10.0.5.

10.0.8 Vessel Traffic Services (VTS)

An increasing number of ports are implementing Vessel Traffic Services (VTS) Schemes, to improve the safety and efficiency of traffic management, and for environmental protection. Every harbour is different and has its own specific problems.

VTS may range from extensive traffic management to simple information broadcasts about shipping movements. Most VTS schemes are aimed at commercial vessels which must adhere to laid down procedures.

Yachts are not normally required to comply with port VTS radio and reporting procedures, but at some ports larger yachts may come within the stipulated minimum length or tonnage. When available, always use the recommended yacht tracks in preference to the main channels. When sailing in VTS areas valuable information about shipping movements can be obtained by listening continuously to the VTS frequency, especially in conditions of reduced visibility. Yachts should seldom need to transmit on a VTS or port operations channel. A possible exception to this rule might occur in fog, when it may be advisable to keep port operations informed before starting to cross a busy shipping channel.

Many of the larger ports operate VTS Traffic Information broadcasts which provide information about shipping movements, expected times of arrival or departure, and routes they will follow, in addition to weather and tidal information.

In some ports, such as Southampton, a launch is sent ahead of large ships to clear the channel. Obey any instructions given.

Fig. 10(1) *Yachts should keep well clear of the main shipping channels and whenever possible use any recommended yachts tracks. When the main channels have to be crossed, do so at right angles. Avoid crossing the bows of oncoming commercial traffic.*

10.0.9 Traffic Separation Schemes (TSS)

Yachts, like other vessels, must conform to Traffic Separation Schemes (Rule 10). Rule 10 does not however modify the IRPCS when two vessels meet or converge in a TSS with a risk of collision. TSS are essential to the safety of larger vessels and, whilst inconvenient for yachtsmen, must be accepted as another element of passage planning, or be avoided where possible. They are shown on Admiralty charts and those around the British Isles and the continental seaboard are depicted in Figs. 10(3) to 10(7).

Craft <20m LOA, and any sailing yacht, should consider using inshore traffic zones – often the most sensible action for a yacht, rather than using the main lanes. Otherwise, join or leave a lane at its extremity, but if joining or leaving at the side, do so at as shallow an angle as possible. Proceed in the correct lane, and in the general direction of traffic.

If obliged to cross a traffic lane, do so on a heading as nearly as practicable at right angles to the lane, and do not impede vessels using a traffic lane. If under sail, start motoring if speed over the ground falls below about 3 kn or if a reasonable course cannot be maintained.

Some TSS are under surveillance by radar, aircraft or patrol vessels. There are heavy penalties for breaking the rules. 'YG' in the International Code means 'You appear not to be complying with the traffic separation scheme'. See Plates 6 and 7 on pages 70 and 71.

In summary, the best advice for yachtsmen is:

● Listen out on TSS frequencies, and to TSS information broadcasts.

● Cross TSS schemes as quickly as possible on a heading at right angles to the lane, and use the engine if that makes the crossing quicker, or the speed falls below 3 kn.

● Have a good radar reflector.

● Keep a sharp lookout.

● Bear in mind that you might not easily be seen from the bridge of a big vessel, especially in a steep sea.

● Use your common sense. In poor visibility a small craft has every disadvantage imaginable.

Fig. 10(2) *When crossing a traffic lane, the **heading** of the yacht must be at right angles to the traffic flow as shown in (a) above, regardless of the course made good which is affected by tidal streams. The yacht at (b) above is not heading at right angles and is therefore on an incorrect course.*

Fig. 10(3)   Traffic Separation Schemes (TSS) and Routeing Measures

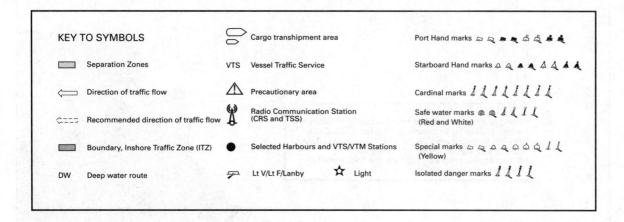

KEY TO SYMBOLS

▭ Separation Zones	⬎ Cargo transhipment area	Port Hand marks
⬅ Direction of traffic flow	VTS Vessel Traffic Service	Starboard Hand marks
⬅--- Recommended direction of traffic flow	⚠ Precautionary area	Cardinal marks
▭ Boundary, Inshore Traffic Zone (ITZ)	Radio Communication Station (CRS and TSS)	Safe water marks (Red and White)
DW Deep water route	● Selected Harbours and VTS/VTM Stations	Special marks (Yellow)
	Lt V/Lt F/Lanby ☆ Light	Isolated danger marks

Fig. 10(3)1 OFF SMALLS TSS

The TSS is located at approximately 51°46'N 05°52'W. The separation zone is 2M wide and the N- and S-bound traffic lanes are 3M wide.

Yachts are advised to listen out on Ch 16 when crossing the TSS.

Fig. 10(3)2 FASTNET ROCK TSS

The TSS is located at approximately 51°19'N 09°31'W. The separation zone and the E- and W-bound traffic lanes are all 2M wide. The ITZ extends between Fastnet Rock and the landward boundary of the TSS which is about 2M SE of the Fastnet Rk and approx 3·5M from Cape Clear.

Yachts are advised to listen out on Ch 16 when crossing the TSS or when navigating in the ITZ.

10

ATTENTION
* Always listen out on the appropriate VHF Channels when sailing in, or crossing, TSS (or VTS) areas.
* Do not transmit on TSS (or VTS) channels unless absolutely necessary or when required.
* If you have a problem, contact the TSS (or VTS) centre and give position.

PLYMOUTH VTS
Ch **14** 16

Start Point

OFF LAND'S END TSS
Falmouth CG Ch 16

Falmouth
Pendennis

TSS WEST
OF THE ISLES
OF SCILLY

TSS OFF
LAND'S END

Land's End

Seven Stones
Round I
ITZ   ITZ
St Marys
Longships
Wolf Rock
Bishop Rock
ITZ

TSS SOUTH OF
THE ISLES OF SCILLY

USHANT TSS
Ushant Tfc Ch **13** 79
Info bcsts on Ch 79 @ H+10 H+40
Weather bulletins every 3 hrs
from 0150 UT.

Corsen-Ouessant operates a
mandatory reporting system for
vessels >300grt.
This covers an area of 35M radius
based on Le Stiff Radar Tr and
includes the whole of Ushant
TSS/ITZ.
It also provides CROSS Corsen with
tfc info over the much bigger area
from Mont St Michel in the East and
Pte de Penmarc'h in the South,
thence out to 8°W.
The VTS can also provide position
and navigational assistance, if
necessary.
Monitor Ch 16 whilst in the area.

Recommended direction of traffic flow

TSS OFF
USHANT

Ouessant NE

Roscoff

Plougasnou

OUESSANT
TRAFFIC

L'Aberwrac'h

Ouessant SW

ITZ

Saint-Mathieu
Brest

Brest-Le Conquet

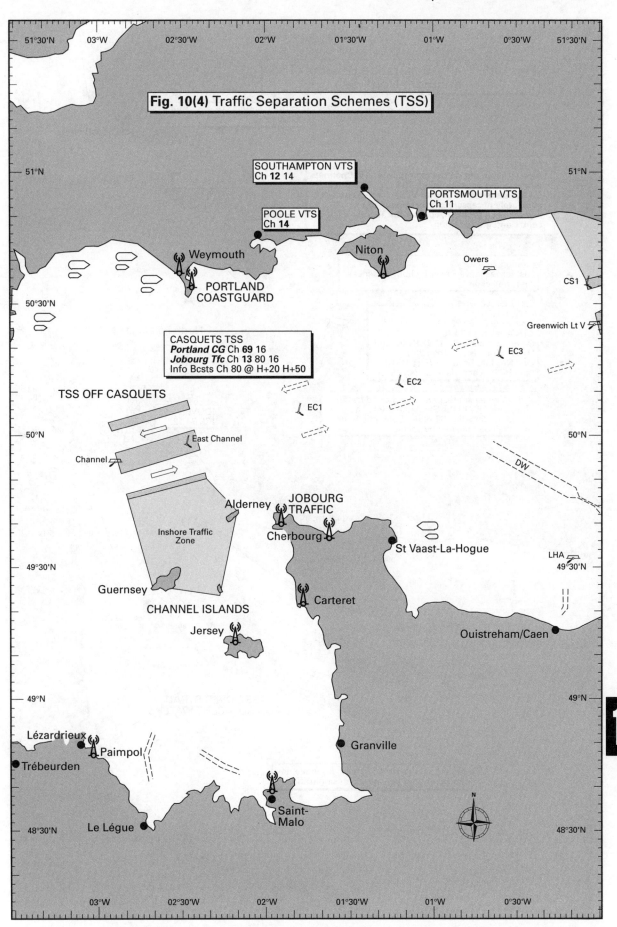

Fig. 10(4) Traffic Separation Schemes (TSS)

SOUTHAMPTON VTS
Ch **12** 14

PORTSMOUTH VTS
Ch **11**

POOLE VTS
Ch **14**

Weymouth

Niton

Owers

PORTLAND
COASTGUARD

CS1

Greenwich Lt V

CASQUETS TSS
Portland CG Ch **69** 16
Jobourg Tfc Ch **13** 80 16
Info Bcsts Ch 80 @ H+20 H+50

EC3

TSS OFF CASQUETS

EC2

EC1

East Channel

50°N

Channel

DW

Alderney

JOBOURG
TRAFFIC

Inshore Traffic
Zone

Cherbourg

St Vaast-La-Hogue

LHA
49°30'N

Guernsey

Carteret

CHANNEL ISLANDS

Jersey

Ouistreham/Caen

Lézardrieux

Paimpol

Granville

Trébeurden

N

10

Saint-
Malo

Le Légue

51°30'N   03°W   02°30'W   02°W   01°30'W   01°W   0°30'W   51°30'N
51°N   51°N
50°30'N
50°N
49°30'N
49°N   49°N
48°30'N   03°W   02°30'W   02°W   01°30'W   01°W   0°30'W   48°30'N

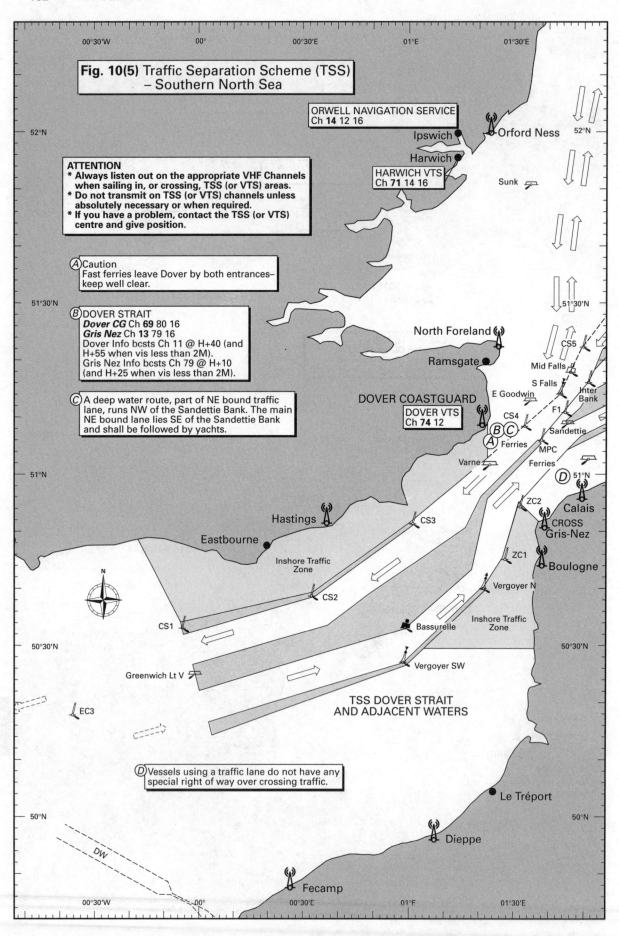

Fig. 10(5) Traffic Separation Scheme (TSS)
– Southern North Sea

ORWELL NAVIGATION SERVICE
Ch **14** 12 16

ATTENTION
* Always listen out on the appropriate VHF Channels when sailing in, or crossing, TSS (or VTS) areas.
* Do not transmit on TSS (or VTS) channels unless absolutely necessary or when required.
* If you have a problem, contact the TSS (or VTS) centre and give position.

HARWICH VTS
Ch **71** 14 16

(A) Caution
Fast ferries leave Dover by both entrances– keep well clear.

(B) DOVER STRAIT
Dover CG Ch **69** 80 16
Gris Nez Ch **13** 79 16
Dover Info bcsts Ch 11 @ H+40 (and H+55 when vis less than 2M).
Gris Nez Info bcsts Ch 79 @ H+10 (and H+25 when vis less than 2M).

(C) A deep water route, part of NE bound traffic lane, runs NW of the Sandettie Bank. The main NE bound lane lies SE of the Sandettie Bank and shall be followed by yachts.

DOVER COASTGUARD
DOVER VTS
Ch **74** 12

(D) Vessels using a traffic lane do not have any special right of way over crossing traffic.

TSS DOVER STRAIT
AND ADJACENT WATERS

52°N

51°30'N

51°N

50°30'N

50°N

Ipswich
Orford Ness
Harwich
Sunk
North Foreland
Ramsgate
CS5
Mid Falls
S Falls
Inter Bank
E Goodwin
F1
Sandettie
CS4
(B) (C)
(A) Ferries
MPC
Varne
Ferries
(D)
Hastings
ZC2
Calais
CROSS
Gris-Nez
Eastbourne
ZC1
Boulogne
Inshore Traffic Zone
CS3
Vergoyer N
CS2
Inshore Traffic Zone
CS1
Bassurelle
Greenwich Lt V
Vergoyer SW
EC3
Le Tréport
DW
Dieppe
Fecamp

N

00°30'W   00°   00°30'E   01°E   01°30'E

MAAS APPROACH
Ch 01

SCHEVENINGEN
Traffic Centre
Ch 14

TOWARDS TSS
OFF TEXEL

NORTH HINDER
NORTH TSS

NHR-N

MAAS-NORTH
TSS

MAAS WEST
INNER TSS

MW4

MN2

MN3

HOEK VAN HOLLAND
Haven Co-ordinate
Centre Ch 11 14
Traffic Centre
Ch 03 65 66 05 80 61

Noord
Hinder

MW2

Maas
Centre

52°N

Euro

MW5

Rotterdam

DW

MW3

NHR-S

MW1

SBO

CG HAAMSTEDE
Ch 74

Schouwenbank

STEENBANK
Traffic Centre
Ch 64

NHR-SE

Roompot
Locks

Oosterschelde

Westpit

OG13

TSS NORTH
HINDER SOUTH

OOSTERSCHELDE
Roompotsluis Lock Ch 18
Roompot Hbr Ch 31
Wemeldinge Ch 68

51°30'N

NE Akkaet

Goote Bank

Twin

W4

AN

Westerschelde

West Hinder Lt

F1

DW

A1bis

Sandettie N

KB

TSS AT
WEST HINDER

Antwerp

Oostende

ZEEBRUGGE
Traffic Centre
Ch 69

Nieuwpoort

BELGIUM

WANDELAAR
Traffic Centre
Ch 65

Dunkerque

51°N

51°N

D Vessels using a traffic lane do not have any
special right of way over crossing traffic.

E VESSEL TRAFFIC SERVICE (VTS)
Schelde & Estuaries (VTS-SM)
Dotted line ········ shows limits of VHF
monitoring areas.

WESTERSCHELDE VTS COMMUNICATIONS

CENTRALE
ZANDVLIET
Ch 12
(Radar Saeftinge
Ch 21)

CENTRALE
HANSWEERT
Ch 65
(Radar Ch 65)

OG13

CENTRALE
ZANDVLIET
Ch 12
(Radar Kruisschans
Ch 66)

Westerschelde

W4

E2A

46

55

76

32

60

SPR

35

65

86

CENTRALE
VLISSINGEN
Ch 14
(Radar Ch 21)

CENTRALE
ZANDVLIET
Ch 12
(Radar Waarde
Ch 19)

CENTRALE
TERNEUZEN
Ch 03
(Radar Ch 03)
Terneuzen-Gent Canal
Ch 11

CENTRALE
ZANDVLIET
Ch 12
(Radar Zandvliet
Ch 04)

Antwerp

10

Fig. 10(6) Traffic Separation Schemes (TSS) – Texel to Elbe

GERMAN BIGHT
(For South and West of Helgoland)
(Remoted from Helgoland for VTS Wilhelmshaven)

Call: *German Bight Traffic*
Helgoland Ch **80** 16 or *Borkum* **79** 16
Information Broadcasts
German Bight Traffic Ch **79 80** at H+00

RIVER ELBE
Cuxhaven-Elbe Tfc Ch 71
Brunsbuttel-Elbe Tfc Ch 68
Information Broadcasts
Cuxhaven (for Outer Elbe) on Ch 71 at H+55
Brunsbüttel Elbe (for Inner Elbe) on Ch 68 at Ch H+05

TSS JADE
APPROACH

TSS GERMAN BIGHT WESTERN APPROACH

★ Helgoland

TSS ELBE
APPROACH

Eiderstedt

GW2
GW4
GW8
GW12
GB
E1
GW/EMS
GW3/TG
GW7
GW 11
Jade
E2
E3
No 6
Grosser
Vogelsand
GW1
TG16/
Reede
TG18/
Jade
SZ-N   ELBE
No 1   No 5
★
River Elbe
*FIRING DANGER
AREA*
TG2/GW
TG12
TG19/JW2
No 1   No 5
Cuxhaven
TSS TERSCHELLING-GERMAN BIGHT
TG8
TG15
TG17/
Weser 1
Jade 1
Alte Weser
Elbe-Weser
TE14
Borkumriff
TG11
ITZ
Wangerooge
River Jade
River Weser
TG7
TG1/
EMS
Osterems
01
Bremerhaven
TE11   TE13
Westerems
Hubertgat
H3
Norddeich Radio
HUBERTGAT
★ Borkum
Wilhelmshaven
53°30'N
River Ems
GERMANY
Bremerhaven
53°30'N

CG SCHIERMONNIKOOG
Ch 05

RIVER WESER
Bremerhaven-Weser Tfc Ch 02 04 05 07 21 22 82
Bremen-Weser Tfc Ch 19 78 81
Bremen-Hunte Tfc Ch 63

No 3/Jade 2 to No 19/H Reede By: Ch 22
No 19/H Reede to No 4 Bys: Ch 22
(When Southbound) A1 to No 16A/A16 By: Ch 22
No 19/H Reede to No 37 By: Ch 02
No 37 to No 53 By: Ch 04
No 53 to No 63 By: Ch 07
No 63 to No 69 By: Ch 05 82
No 69 to No 79 By: Ch 82
No 79 to No 93 By: Ch 21

Information Broadcasts:
Bremerhaven Ch 02 04 05 07 21 22 82 at H+20
Bremen Ch 19 78 81 at H+30
Hunte Ch 63 at H+30

RIVER EMS
(Westerems and Randzel Gate No 1 to No 35 Lt
By)
Call: *Ems Tfc* Ch 18
Information Broadcasts
German Bight Traffic Ch 79 80 at H+00
Ems Traffic Ch 15 18 20 21 at H+50

RIVER JADE
(From the DB 19/Jade to Lt Bys 31/Reede/W
Siel 1 & 32)
Jade Traffic Ch 20 63 (Radar on Ch 20 63).
No 1B/Jade to No 33-34 Lt Bys: Ch 63
No 33/34 to No 58 Lt Bys: Ch 20
(Radar also on Ch 63 20)
Information Broadcasts
Jade Traffic on Ch 20 & 63 in German
every H+10

10

Fig. 10(7) Traffic Separation Schemes (TSS) and Routeing Measures

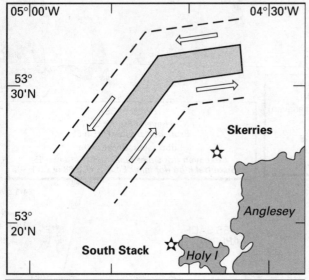

Fig. 10(7)1 OFF SKERRIES TSS

The TSS is centred upon the following positions: 53°22·8'N 04°52·0'W, 53°31'·3N 04°41'·7W and 53°32'·1N 04°31'·6W. The separation zone and the N- and S-bound traffic lanes are all 2M wide.

The passage outside the Skerries is preferable to the inside passage, except in strong offshore winds. The inside passage should not be used at night. When passing outside the Skerries allow a distance off of at least 1M to avoid the worst of the strong tidal stream.

Yachts are advised to listen out on Ch 16 when crossing the TSS.

Fig. 10(7)2 TUSKAR ROCK TSS

The TSS is centred upon the following positions: 52°14'·0N, 52°08'·5N 06°03'·8W and 52°04'·7N 06°11'·5W. The separation zone is 2M wide, and the the N- and S-bound traffic lanes each side of the separation zone are 3M wide. The designated ITZ extends between Tuskar Rock and the landward boundary of the TSS.

Yachts are advised to listen out on Ch 16 when crossing the TSS or when navigating in the ITZ.

Fig. 10(7)3 NORTH CHANNEL TSS

The TSS is centred on the following positions: 55°15'·3N 05°55'·4W, 55°22'·8'N 06°04·6W and 55°24'·0N 06°15'·0W.   The lanes, and separation zone are all 2M wide, and the ITZ about 2·5M. The NW-bound lane is only 2M from the Mull of Kintyre and its race. A strong tidal race, with overfalls, may be encountered S and SW of Mull of Kintyre. Similarly, the SE-bound lane is only 2M north of Rathlin Island where tidal streams are strong on both sides of the island.

Yachts are advised to listen out on Ch 16 when crossing the TSS.

VOLVO PENTA SERVICE

Sales and service centres in area 1

CORNWALL *Challenger Marine*, Freemans Wharf, Falmouth Road, Penryn TR10 8AS Tel (01326) 377222 *Marine Engineering Looe*, The Quay, East Looe PL13 1AQ Tel (01503) 262887 & 263009 **DEVON** *Darthaven Marine Ltd*, Brixham Road, Kingswear, Dartmouth TQ6 0SG Tel (01803) 752733 *Marine Engineering Looe*, Queen Anne's Marina, Queen Anne's Battery, Coxside, Plymouth PL4 0LP Tel (01752) 226143 *Starey Marine Services*, Lincombe Boatyard, Lincombe, Salcombe, TQ8 8NQ Tel (0154884) 3655 or 2930 *Pilkington Marine Engineering*, 9 Pottery Units, Forde Road, Brunel Trading Estate, Newton Abbot TQ12 4AD Tel (01626) 52663 *Retreat Boatyard (Topsham) Ltd*, Retreat Boatyard, Topsham, Exeter EX3 0LS Tel (01392) 874720

VOLVO PENTA

Area 1

South-West England
Isles of Scilly to Portland Bill

168

Round Island
RC 298·50 RR 150M

Seven Stones

SEPARATION ZONE

Longships ITZ

See 10-11-2

SEPARATION ZONE

ITZ

ITZ

SEPARATION ZONE

ITZ

Wolf Rock

Bishop Rock

Off Land's End TSS
Falmouth CG
VHF 16

ITZ

SEPARATION

For details of traffic
lanes see Fig. 10(4)

ZONE

St Mary's
i 10.1.9
VHF 14 16
RC Aero 321·00 STM 15M

Par*
VHF 12 16

Charlestown*
VHF 14 16

Fowey
i 10.1.15
VHF 12 09 11 16

Trevose
Head

NOTE: The coast NE from
Land's End is covered in
Area 11

St Mawgan
RC Aero 365·50 SM 20M

R. Tamar*

Lostwithiel

R. Lynher*

Penzance
i 10.1.11
VHF 12 09 16
RC Aero 333·00 PH 15M

Mevagissey
i 10.1.14
VHF 14 16

Polperro*

Whitesand
Bay

Gribbin
Hd

Rame
Hd

Godrevy I.

Pendeen

Sennen

Helford River
i 10.1.12
VHF 80 M

Porthscatho*

Gorran Haven*

Dodman Pt

Eddystone

Longships

Mousehole*

Tater-du

St. Michael's Mount

Porthleven*

Culdrose

St. Anthony Hd

Brixham CG
Falmouth CG

Looe
i 10.1.16
VHF 16

Wolf Rk

Coverack*

Black Hd

Cadgwith*

River Fal
i 10.1.13
Pendennis
VHF 62 16
VHF 12 16
Marina 80 M
VHF 62
0733 1933 UT

Mullion Cove*

Newlyn
i 10.1.10
VHF 12 09 16

Lizard
RC 284·5 LZ 70M

Land's End Radio
VHF 64 27 16
MF 2782 3610
VHF 27 64
MF 2670
0733 1933 UT

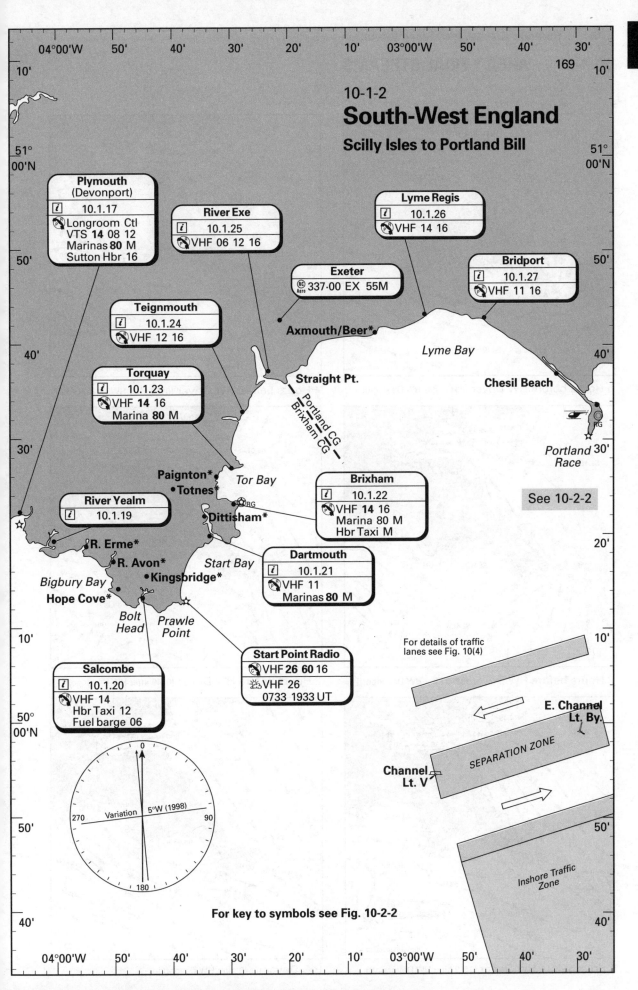

10-1-2
South-West England
Scilly Isles to Portland Bill

Plymouth
(Devonport)
[i] 10.1.17
Longroom Ctl
VTS **14** 08 12
Marinas **80** M
Sutton Hbr 16

River Exe
[i] 10.1.25
VHF 06 12 16

Lyme Regis
[i] 10.1.26
VHF 14 16

Exeter
337·00 EX 55M

Bridport
[i] 10.1.27
VHF 11 16

Teignmouth
[i] 10.1.24
VHF 12 16

Axmouth/Beer*

Lyme Bay

Straight Pt.

Chesil Beach

Torquay
[i] 10.1.23
VHF **14** 16
Marina **80** M

Portland CG
Brixham CG

Portland Race

Paignton*
•Totnes*

Tor Bay

Brixham
[i] 10.1.22
VHF **14** 16
Marina 80 M
Hbr Taxi M

River Yealm
[i] 10.1.19

Dittisham*

See 10-2-2

R. Erme*

R. Avon*
•Kingsbridge*

Start Bay

Dartmouth
[i] 10.1.21
VHF 11
Marinas **80** M

Bigbury Bay
Hope Cove*

Bolt Head

Prawle Point

For details of traffic
lanes see Fig. 10(4)

Start Point Radio
VHF **26 60** 16
VHF 26
0733 1933 UT

**E. Channel
Lt. By.**

Salcombe
[i] 10.1.20
VHF 14
Hbr Taxi 12
Fuel barge 06

**Channel
Lt. V**

SEPARATION ZONE

270
Variation 5°W (1998) 90
0
180

Inshore Traffic
Zone

For key to symbols see Fig. 10-2-2

10-1-3   AREA 1 TIDAL STREAMS

5 Hours before HW Dover (0040 after HW Devonport)

4 Hours before HW Dover (0140 after HW Devonport)

3 Hours before HW Dover (0240 after HW Devonport)

2 Hours before HW Dover (0340 after HW Devonport)

1 Hour before HW Dover (0440 after HW Devonport)

HW Dover (0540 after HW Devonport)

Eastward 10.2.3   Portland 10.2.9   Isle of Wight 10.2.24   Northward 10.11.3   Southward 10.16.3   Channel Islands 10.14.3

1 Hour after HW Dover (0545 before HW Devonport)

2 Hours after HW Dover (0445 before HW Devonport)

3 Hours after HW Dover (0345 before HW Devonport)

4 Hours after HW Dover (0245 before HW Devonport)

5 Hours after HW Dover (0145 before HW Devonport)

6 Hours after HW Dover (0045 before HW Devonport)

10.1.4 COASTAL LIGHTS, FOG SIGNALS AND WAYPOINTS

Abbreviations used below are given in 1.4.1. Principal lights are in **bold** print, places in CAPITALS, and light-vessels, light floats and Lanbys in *CAPITAL ITALICS*. Unless otherwise stated lights are white. m – elevation in metres; M – nominal range in miles. Fog signals are in *italics*. Useful waypoints are underlined – use those on land with care. All geographical positions should be assumed to be approximate. See 4.4.1. All positions are referenced to the OSGB 36 datum.

ISLES OF SCILLY TO LAND'S END

Bishop Rock 49°52'·33N 06°26'·68W Fl (2) 15s 44m **24M**; Gy ● Tr with helicopter platform; part obsc 204°-211°, obsc 211°-233°, 236°-259°; Racon (T); *Horn Mo (N) 90s.*
Gunner By 49°53'·60N 06°25'·02W; SCM.
Round Rock By 49°53'·06N 06°25'·13W; NCM.

ST MARY'S
Ldg Lts 097·3°. Front 49°55'·08N 06°18'·45W FR; W △.
Rear, 110m from front, FR; W X.
St Mary's Pool Pier Hd Fl RG 2s 5m 4M; vis R070°-099°, G099°-000°.

Bartholomew Ledges Lt By 49°54'·38N 06°19'·80W; Fl R 5s; PHM.
Spanish Ledge By 49°53'·90N 06°18'·80W; ECM; *Bell.*
Peninnis Hd 49°54'·24N 06°18'·15W Fl 20s 36m **17M**; W ● metal Tr on B frame, B cupola; vis 231°-117° but part obsc 048°-083° within 5M.
FR Lts on masts to N and NE.
Hats By 49°56'·17N 06°17'·08W; SCM.

Round I 49°58'·70N 06°19'·33W Fl 10s 55m **24M**; W ● Tr; vis 021°-288°; H24; RC; *Horn (4) 60s.*

SEVEN STONES Lt F 50°03'·58N 06°04'·28W Fl (3) 30s 12m **25M**; R hull, Lt Tr amidships; Racon (O); *Horn (3) 60s.*

Longships 50°03'·97N 05°44'·85W Iso WR 10s 35m **W18M**, **R15**/14M; Gy ● Tr with helicopter platform; vis R189°-208°, R (unintens) 208°-307°, R307°-327°, W327°- 189°; *Horn 10s.*
FR on radio mast 4·9M NE.
Wolf Rock 49°56'·70N 05°48'·50W Fl 15s 34m **23M** (H24); Racon (T); *Horn 30s.*
Runnel Stone Lt By 50°01'·15N 05°40'·30W Q (6) + L Fl 15s; SCM; *Bell, Whis.*

LAND'S END TO LIZARD POINT

Tater-du 50°03'·10N 05°34'·60W Fl (3) 15s 34m **23M**; W ● Tr; vis 241°-074°. Also FR 31m 13M vis 060°-074° over Runnel stone and in places 074°-077° within 4M; *Horn (2) 30s.*

MOUSEHOLE
N Pier Hd 50°04'·94N 05°32'·21W 2 FG (vert) 8m 4M; Gy mast; replaced by FR when hbr closed.

Low Lee Lt By 50°05'·52N 05°31'·32W Q (3) 10s; ECM.

NEWLYN
S Pier Hd 50°06'·15N 05°32'·50W Fl 5s 10m 9M; W ● Tr, R base & cupola; vis 253°-336°; *Siren 60s.*
N Pier Hd F WG 4m 2M; vis G238°-248°, W over hbr.

The Gear Bn 50°06'·59N 05°31'·56W; IDM.

PENZANCE
S Pier Hd 50°07'·03N 05°31'·63W Fl WR 5s 11m **W17M**, R12M; W ● Tr, B base; vis R (unintens) 159°-224°, R224°-268°, W268°-344·5°, R344·5°-shore.

Albert Pier Hd 50°07'·06N 05°31'·72W 2 FG (vert) 11m 2M.
Western Cressar Bn 50°07'·21N 05°31'·07W; SCM.
Ryeman Rks Bn 50°07'·22N 05°30'·27W; SCM.
Mountamopus By 50°04'·60N 05°26'·20W; SCM.

PORTHLEVEN
S Pier 50°04'·87N 05°19'·03W FG 10m 4M; G metal col, Lts shown when inner hbr is open.

Lizard 49°57'·58N 05°12'·07W Fl 3s 70m **25M**; W 8-sided Tr; vis 250°-120°, part vis 235°-250°; reflection may be seen inshore of these bearings; RC; *Siren Mo (N) 60s.*

LIZARD POINT TO START POINT

Manacles Lt By 50°02'·77N 05°01'·85W Q (3) 10s; ECM; *Bell.*
Helston Lt By 50°04'·92N 05°00'·77W Fl Y 2.5s; SPM.
August Rock By 50°06'·07N 05°04'·88W (PA); SHM (seasonal).

St Anthony Hd 50°08'·43N 05°00'·90W Oc WR 15s 22m **W22/20M**, **R20M**; W 8-sided Tr; vis W295°-004°, R004°-022° over Manacles, W (unintens) 022°-100°, W100°-172°; (H24); Fog Det Lt L Fl 5s 18m **16M** min vis 148·75°-151·25°; *Horn 30s.*

FALMOUTH
Black Rock Bn 50°08'·68N 05°01'·95W (unlit); IDM.
Black Rock Lt By 50°08'·65N 05°01'·68W Q (3) 10s; ECM.
Castle Lt By 50°08'·63N 05°01'·58W Fl G 10s; SHM.
The Governor 50°09'·12N 05°02'·32W; ECM.
E Bkwtr Hd 50°09'·31N 05°02'·90W 2 FR (vert) 2m.
N Arm East Hd Q 19m 3M.
West Narrows Lt By 50°09'·33N 05°02'·03W Fl (2) R 10s; PHM.
The Vilt Lt By 50°09'·97N 05°02'·17W Fl (4) G 15s; SHM.
Northbank Lt By 50°10'·32N 05°02'·12W Fl R 4s; PHM.
No. 1 Port By 50°09'·72N 05°04'·37W QR; PHM.

Gwineas Lt By 50°14'·47N 04°45'·30W Q (3) 10s; ECM; *Bell.*
'A' Lt By 50°08'·50N 04°46'·30W Fl Y 10s; SPM.
'B' Lt By 50°10'·90N 04°45'·50W Fl Y 5s; SPM.
'C' Lt By 50°11'·05N 04°46'·40W Fl Y 2s; SPM.

MEVAGISSEY
Victoria Pier Hd 50°16'·11N 04°46'·85W Fl (2) 10s 9m 12M; *Dia 30s.*
Cannis Rock Lt By 50°18'·35N 04°39'·88W Q (6) + L Fl 15s; SCM; *Bell.*

FOWEY
Fowey Lt Bn Tr 50°19'·62N 04°38'·75W L Fl WR 5s 28m W11M, R9M; W 8-sided Tr, R lantern; vis R284°-295°, W295°-028°, R028°-054°.
St Catherine's Pt 50°19'·66N 04°38'·59W FR 15m 2M; vis 150°-295°.
Lamp Rk 50°19'·67N 04°38'·31W Fl G 5s 7m 2M; vis 088°-205°.
Whitehouse Pt 50°19'·95N 04°38'·22W Iso WRG 3s 11m W11M, R8M, G8M; vis G017°-022°, W022°-032°, R032°-037°.

Udder Rock By 50°18'·90N 04°33'·78W; *Bell*; SCM.

POLPERRO
Tidal basin, W Pier Hd 50°19'·83N 04°30·89W F or FR 4m 4M; R when hbr closed in bad weather.
Spy House Pt 50°19'·77N 04°30'·63W Iso WR 6s 30m 7M; vis W288°-060°, R060°-288°.

LOOE
Mid Main Bn 50°20'·53N 04°26'·87W Q (3) 10s 2M; ECM.
Banjo Pier Hd 50°21'·02N 04°27'·00W Oc WR 3s 8m **W15M**, R12M; vis W013°-207°, R207°-267°, W267°-313°, R313°-332°.

Nailzee Pt 50°20'·96N 04°27'·00W *Siren (2) 30s (occas).*
Eddystone 50°10'·81N 04°15'·87W Fl (2) 10s 41m **20M**;
Gy Tr, R lantern. FR 28m 13M (same Tr) vis 112°-129° over
Hand deeps; helicopter platform, Racon (T); *Horn (3) 60s.*
Hand Deeps Lt By 50°12'·65N 04°21'·04W Q (9) 15s; WCM.

PLYMOUTH SOUND
Rame Hd, S end 50°18'·63N 04°13'·31W (unlit).
Draystone Lt By 50°18'·82N 04°11'·01W Fl (2) R 5s; PHM.
Knap Lt By 50°19'·52N 04°09'·94W Fl G 5s; SHM.
Plymouth Bkwtr W Hd 50°20'·04N 04°09'·45W Fl WR 10s
19m W12M, R9M; W ● Tr; vis W262°-208°, R208°-262°.
Iso 4s (same Tr) 12m 10M; vis 033°-037°; *Bell (1) 15s.*
Bkwtr E Hd 50°19'·98N 04°08'·18W L Fl WR 10s 9m W8M,
R6M; Vis R190°-353°, W353°-001°, R001°-018°, W018°-190°.
Queens Gnd Lt By 50°20'·26N 04°10'·02W Fl (2) R 10s; PHM.
New Gnd Lt By 50°20'·44N 04°09'·37W Fl R 2s; PHM.
Melampus Lt By 50°21'·12N 04°08'·66W Fl R 4s; PHM.
S Winter Lt By 50°21'·37N 04°08'·49W Q (6) + L Fl 15s; SCM.
S Mallard Lt By 50°21'·48N 04°08'·23W VQ (6) + L Fl 10s;
SCM.

Ldg Lts 349°. Front, Mallard Shoal 50°21'·58N 04°08'·26W
Q WRG 5m W10M, R3M, G3M; W △, Or bands; vis G233°-
043°, R043°-067°, G067°-087°, W087°-099°. Ldg sector
R099°-108°. Rear, 396m from front, West Hoe Bn Dir WRG
9m W13M, R5M, G5M. Vis FG 309°-311° F 314°-317°, FR
320°-329°; shown H24.
Asia Lt By 50°21'·53N 04°08'·81W Fl (2) R 5s; PHM.
N Drakes Is Lt By 50°21'·49N 04°09'·31W Fl R 4s; PHM.
E Vanguard Lt By 50°21'·43N 04°10'·63W QG; SHM.
Bridge Chan SE Lt Bn 50°21'·00N 04°09'·47W QG; SHM.
W Vanguard Lt By 50°21'·46N 04°09'·92W Fl G 3s; SHM.
Devils Pt Lt Bn 50°21'·55N 04°09'·97W QG 5m 3M; Fl 5s
in fog.

Duke Rk Lt By 50°20'·28N 04°08'·16W VQ (9) 10s; WCM.
Bkwtr E Hd 50°19'·98N 04°08'·18W L Fl WR 10s 9m W8M,
R6M; vis R190°-353°, W353°-001°, R001°-018°, W018°-190°.
Staddon Pt Lt Bn 50°20'·13N 04°07'·47W Oc WRG 10s 15m
W8M, R5M, G5M; W structure, R bands. vis G348°-038°,
G038°-050°, R050°-090°; H24.
Whidbey 50°19'·50N 04°07'·20W Oc (2) WRG 10s 29m
W8M, R6M, G6M; Or and W col; vis G000°-137·5°, W137·5°-
139·5°, R139·5°-159°; shown H24.
West Tinker Lt By 50°19'·22N 04°08'·57W Q (9) 15s; WCM.
East Tinker Lt By 50°19'·17N 04°08'·23W Q (3) 10s; ECM.
Bovisand Pier 50°20'·21N 04°07·65W 2 FG (vert) 4m 3M.
Wembury Pt 50°18'·97N 04°06'·55W Oc Y 10s 45m; occas.

NGS W Lt By 50°11'·10N 04°00'·78W Fl Y 5s; SPM.
NGS E Lt By 50°11'·20N 03°58'·95W Fl Y 10s; SPM.

SALCOMBE
Sandhill Pt Dir Lt 000° 50°13'·73N 03°46'·58W Dir Fl WRG
2s 27m W10M, R7M, G7M; R&W ◆ on W mast; vis R002·5°-
182·5°, G182·5°-357·5°, W357·5°-002·5°.
Wolf Rk Lt By 50°13'·47N 03°46'·52W QG; SHM.
Blackstone Rk 50°13'·57N 03°46'·43W Q (2) G 8s 4m 2M;
G & W Bn.
Starhole By 50°12'·50N 03°46'·80W; SPM; (Apr-Sep).
Gara By 50°12'·80N 03°45'·20W; SPM; (Apr-Sep).
Gammon By 50°12'·00N 03°45'·50W; SPM; (Apr-Sep).
Prawle By 50°12'·10N 03°43'·80W; SPM (Racing); (Apr-Sep).

Start Pt 50°13'·32N 03°38'·47W Fl (3) 10s 62m **25M**; W ● Tr;
vis 184°-068°. FR 55m 12M (same Tr) vis 210°-255° over
Skerries bank; *Horn 60s.*

START POINT TO STRAIGHT POINT

Skerries Bank By 50°16'·28N 03°33'·70W; PHM; *Bell.*

DARTMOUTH
Homestone By 50°19'·57N 03°33'·48W; PHM.
Castle Ledge Lt By 50°19'·95N 03°33'·05W Fl G 5s; SHM.
Checkstone Lt By 50°20'·42N 03°33'·73W Fl (2) R 5s; PHM.
Kingswear 50°20'·78N 03°34'·02W Iso WRG 3s 9m 8M; W ●
Tr; vis G318°-325°, W325°-331°, R331°-340°, (TE 1989).
Bayards Cove Fl WRG 2s 5m 6M; vis G280°-289°, W289°-
297°, R297°-shore.
RDYC 1 By 50°18'·80N 03°35'·25W; SPM; (Apr-Oct).
RDYC 2 By 50°18'·68N 03°33'·29W; SPM; (Apr-Oct).
RDYC 3 By 50°20'·07N 03°31'·42W; SPM; (Apr-Oct).
Berry Hd 50°23'·94N 03°28'·93W Fl (2) 15s 58m 14M; W Tr;
vis 100°-023°. R Lts on radio mast 5·7M NW.

BRIXHAM
Brixham Fairway Lt By 50°24'·37N 03°30'·85W Mo A 10s;
SWM.
Victoria Bkwtr Hd 50°24'·29N 03°30'·70W Oc R 15s 9m 6M.
Fairway Dir Lt 159° Dir Iso WRG 5s 4m 6M; vis G145°-157°,
W157°-161°, R161°-173°.
Prince William Marina SW end 2 Fl R 5s (vert) 4m 2M.

PAIGNTON
Outfall Lt Bn 50°25'·92N 03°33'·09W Q (3) 10s 5m 3M.
E Quay 50°25'·92N 03°33'·29W QR 7m 3M.

TORQUAY
Princess Pier Hd 50°27'·43N 03°31'·66W QR 9m 6M.
Haldon Pier Hd 50°27'·40N 03°31'·67W QG 9m 6M.
Marina S Pontoon E end 2 FR (vert) 2m.

TEIGNMOUTH
The Den 50°32'·51N 03°29'·74W FR 10m 6M; Gy ● Tr; vis
225°-135°.
Powderham Terrace 50°32'·55N 03°39'·76W FR 11m 3M.
Den Point 50°32'·38N 03°29'·98W Oc G 5·5s FG (vert); △ on
G Bn.
Outfall Lt By 50°31'·96N 03°27'·92W Fl Y 5s; SPM.

EXMOUTH
E Exe Lt By 50°35'·96N 03°21'·36W Q (3) 10s; ECM.
Straight Pt 50°36'·45N 03°21'·67W Fl R 10s 34m 7M;
vis 246°-071°.
Ldg Lts 305°. Front, 50°36'·97N 03°25'·31W Iso 2s 6m 7M.
Rear, 57m from front, Q 12m 7M.
DZS Lt By 50°36'·10N 03°19'·30W Fl Y 3s; SPM.
DZN Lt By 50°36'·80N 03°19'·20W Fl Y 3s; SPM.

SIDMOUTH/AXMOUTH
Sidmouth 50°46'·46'N 03°14'·36W Fl R 5s 2M.
Axmouth Pier Hd 50°42'·10N 03°03'·21W Fl 5s 7m 2M.

LYME REGIS
Ldg Lts 296°. Front, Victoria Pier Hd 50°43'·30N 02°56'·10W
Oc WR 8s 6m W9M. R7M; Bu col; vis R296°-116°, W116°-
296°. Rear, 240m from front, FG 8m 9M.

BRIDPORT
E Pier Hd 50°42'·52N 02°45'·74W FG 3m 2M; (occas).
W Pier Hd 50°42'·52N 02°45'·77W FR 3m 2M; (occas).
W Pier Root 50°42'·61N 02°45'·76W Iso R 2s 9m 5M.

DZ Lt By 50°36'·50N 02°42'·00W Fl Y 3s; SPM.

OFFSHORE
Channel Lt F 49°54'·42N 02°53'·67W Fl 15s 12m **25M**;
Horn 20s; Racon (O).
E Channel Lt By 49°58'·67N 02°28'·87W Fl Y 5s; Racon (T);
SPM.

NOTE: For English Channel Waypoints see 10.1.7.

10.1.5   PASSAGE INFORMATION

Refer to *West Country Cruising* (YM/Fishwick); *Shell Channel Pilot* (Imray/Cunliffe); *Isles of Scilly Pilot* (Imray/Brandon) and Admiralty *Channel Pilot*. See 10.0.5 for distances across the Channel, and 10.3.5 for notes on cross-Channel passages.

NORTH CORNWALL (charts 1149, 1156)

For the coast of North Cornwall see 10.11.5. For St Ives, Hayle, Newquay, Padstow and Bude, see 10.11.25. Certain information is repeated below for continuity and convenience.

The approaches to the Bristol Chan along N coast of Cornwall are very exposed, with little shelter in bad weather. From Land's End to St Ives the coast is rugged with high cliffs. The Brisons are 27m high rky islets 5ca SW of C Cornwall; rky ledges extend inshore and to the S and SW. Vyneck Rks lie awash about 3ca NW of C Cornwall. There are overfalls SW of Pendeen Pt (lt, fog sig). St Ives (dries) is sheltered from E and S, but exposed to N. Padstow is a refuge, but in strong NW winds the sea breaks on bar and prevents entry. In these waters yachts need to be sturdy and well equipped, since if bad weather develops no shelter may be at hand. Streams are moderate W of Lundy, but strong around the island, and much stronger towards Bristol Chan proper.

ISLES OF SCILLY (10.1.8 and charts 34, 883)

There are 50 islands, extending 21-31M WSW of Land's End, with many rky outcrops and offlying dangers. Although they are all well charted, care is needed particularly in poor vis. *St Marys Harbour and Pier* is a leaflet obtainable locally. See also 10.1.8/9 for details of this rewarding cruising ground.

Several approach transits are shown on chart *34*, and these should be followed, because the tidal streams around the islands are difficult to predict with accuracy. They run harder off points and over rks, where overfalls may occur. Yachts must expect to lie to their anchors. No one anch gives shelter from all winds and swell, so be ready to move at short notice.

Conspic landmarks are Bishop Rk lt ho, Round Island lt ho, the disused lt ho on St Agnes, the daymark at the E end of St Martin's, Penninis lt ho at the S end of St Mary's, and the TV mast and CG sig stn (at the old telegraph tower) both in the NW corner of St Mary's.

ISLES OF SCILLY TO LAND'S END (chart 1148)

Between Scilly and Land's End (chart 1148) streams are rotatory, clockwise. Relative to HW Devonport, they run ENE from HW – 1 (1kn at sp); SSE from HW + 2 (2kn at sp); WNW from HW + 6 (1kn at sp); and N from HW – 4 (1.75kn at sp).

The Seven Stones (rks) lie 7M NE of the Isles of Scilly and 15M W of Land's End; many of them dry, with ledges in between. They are marked by lt F (lt, fog sig) on E side. Wolf Rk (lt, fog sig) is 8M SW of Land's End, and is steep-to. The N/S lanes of Land's End TSS lie between Seven Stones and Wolf Rk; see Fig. 10 (4). The Longships (lt, fog sig) are a group of rks about 1M W of Land's End, with ledges 2ca further seaward. The inshore passage is about 4ca wide; drying rks on the W side are not marked.

LAND'S END TO LIZARD POINT (chart 777)

From Land's End to Gwennap Hd, 2M SE, rks extend up to 1½ca offshore, and depths are irregular to seaward causing a bad sea in strong W winds over a W-going tide. The Runnel Stone (dries 0.5m) lies 7ca S of Gwennap Hd, with rks closer inshore. These dangers are in R sectors of Longships and Tater-du Lts. No anch off Porth Curno, due to cables.

Entering Mount's B, the Bucks (dry) are 2ca ESE of Tater-du lt ho. Gull Rk (24m) is 9ca NE of Tater-du, close off the E point of Lamorna Cove. Little Heaver (dries) is 100m SW of Gull Rk, and Kemyel Rk (dries) is 1¾ca ENE. Mousehole (10.1.10) is a small drying hbr, sheltered from W and N, but exposed to E or S winds, when ent may be shut. Approach from SW side of St Clement's Is. In W winds there is good anch off the hbr.

Low Lee, a dangerous rk (1.1m), is 4ca NE of Penlee Pt, marked by ECM lt buoy. Carn Base Rk (1.8m) lies 3ca NNW of Low Lee. Newlyn (10.1.10) is only hbr in Mount's B safe to appr in strong onshore winds, but only near HW. From here to Penzance (10.1.11) beware Dog Rk and Gear Rk (1.9m).

From Penzance to St Michael's Mount the head of the Bay is shoal, drying 4ca off in places. Dangers include Cressar Rks, Long Rk, Hogus Rks, and Outer Penzeath Rk. Venton chy on with pierheads of St Michael's Mount hbr at 084° leads S of these dangers. This tiny hbr dries 2.1m, but is well sheltered, with anch about 1ca W of ent, see 10.1.11.

Two dangerous rks, Guthen Rk and Maltman Rk (0.9m), lie 2ca W and S of St Michael's Mount. 1M SE is The Greeb (7m), with rks between it and shore. The Bears (dry) lie 1¾ca E of The Greeb. The Stone (dries) is 5ca S of Cudden Pt, while offshore is Mountamopus shoal marked by SCM buoy which should be passed to seaward. Welloe Rk (dries) lies 5ca SW of Trewavas Hd.

Porthleven is a small tidal hbr, entered between Great and Little Trigg Rks and pier on S side. Dry out alongside in inner hbr, closed in bad weather when appr is dangerous. In fair weather there is good anch off Porth Mellin, about 1½ca NE of Mullion Is; Porth Mellin hbr (dries) is for temp use only.

2.5M W of Lizard Pt is The Boa, a rky shoal on which sea breaks in SW gales. The Lizard (lt, fog sig, RC) is a bold, steep headland (chart 2345). From W to E, the outer rks, all drying, are Mulvin, (2½ca SW of Lizard Pt), Taylor's Rk (2ca SSW); Clidgas Rks (5ca SW of lt ho), Men Hyr Rk (4.1m) and the Dales or Stags (5ca SSW), and Enoch Rk (3ca S). S of the rks the stream turns E at HW Devonport – 0500, and W at HW + 0155, rates up to 3kn at sp; offshore it turns an hour earlier. A dangerous race extends 2-3M S when stream is strong in either direction, worst in W'ly winds against W-going tide. Then keep at least 3M to seaward. There may be a race SE of the Point.

LIZARD POINT TO GRIBBIN HEAD (chart 1267)

E of Lizard Pt and 4ca ESE of Bass Pt, is Vrogue, a dangerous sunken rk (1.8m). Craggan Rks (1.5m) are 5ca offshore, and 1M N of Vrogue Rk. N of Black Hd rks extend at least 1ca offshore; a rk drying 1.6m lies off Chynhalls Pt. Coverack gives good anch in W winds, see 10.1.12. From Dolor Pt to E of Lowland Pt are drying rks 2½ca offshore.

The Manacles (dry), 7½ca E and SE of Manacle Pt, are marked by ECM lt buoy and are in R sector of St Anthony Hd lt. Off the Manacles the stream runs NE from HW Devonport – 0345, and SW from HW+ 0200, sp rates 1.25kn. From E of the Manacles there are no offshore dangers on courses NNW to Helford River ent (10.1.12) or N to River Fal (10.1.13).

3M NNE from St Anthony Hd, Porthscatho offers safe anch in W'lies (10.1.14). Gull Rk (38m high) lies 6ca E of Nare Hd, at W side of Veryan B. The Whelps (dry) are 5ca SW of Gull Rk. There is a passage between Gull Rk and the shore. In Veryan B beware Lath Rk (2.1m) 1M SE of Portloe.

On E side of Veryan B, Dodman Pt is a 110m flat-topped cliff, with a conspic stone cross. Depths are irregular for 1M S, with heavy overfalls in strong winds over sp tide, when it is best to pass 2M off. 3 SPM lt buoys (targets) lie 2.3 to 4.8M SSE of Dodman Pt , see 10.1.15. Gorran Haven, a sandy cove with L-shaped pier which dries at sp, is a good anch in offshore winds. 2.1M NE of Dodman Pt, and 1M ENE of Gorran Haven, is Gwineas Rk (8m high) and Yaw Rk (0.9m), marked by ECM lt buoy. Passage inside Gwineas Rk is possible, but not advised in strong onshore winds or poor vis. Portmellon and Mevagissey B, (10.1.14) are good anchs in offshore winds. For Charlestown and Par, see 10.1.15.

GRIBBIN HEAD TO START POINT (charts 1267, 1613)

Gribbin Hd has a conspic daymark, a □ tr 25m high with R & W bands. In bad weather the sea breaks on rocks round Head. Cannis Rk (4.3m) is 2½ca SE, marked by SCM lt buoy. 3M E of Fowey (10.1.15) is Udder Rk (0.6m), 5ca offshore in E part of Lantivet Bay. Larrick Rk (4.3m) is 1½ca off Nealand Pt.

Polperro hbr dries, but the inlet gives good anch in offshore winds, see 10.1.15. Beware E Polca Rk roughly in mid-chan. E of Polperro shoals lie 2½ca off Downend Pt, (memorial). The chan between Hannafore Pt and Looe (or St George's) Island nearly dries. The Ranneys (dry) are rks extending 2½ca E and SE of the Island, see 10.1.16. There are overfalls S of Looe Island in bad weather.

Eddystone rks (chart *1613*) lie 8M S of Rame Hd. Shoals extend 3ca E. Close NW of the lt ho (lt, fog sig) is the stump of old lt ho. The sea can break on Hand Deeps, sunken rks 3·5M NW of Eddystone, marked by SPM light buoy.

Rame Hd, on W side of ent to Plymouth Sound (10.1.17), is conspic cone shaped, with small chapel on top; rks extend about 1ca off and wind-over-tide overfalls may be met 1·5M to seaward. Approaching Plymouth from the W, clear Rame Hd and Penlee Point by about 8ca, then steer NNE for W end of the Breakwater. At the SE ent to Plymouth Sound, Great Mewstone (59m) is a conspic rky islet 4ca off Wembury Pt (naval gunnery range). Approaching from the E keep at least 1M offshore until clear of the drying Mewstone Ledge, 2½ca SW of Great Mewstone. The Slimers, which dry, lie 2ca E of Mewstone. E and W Ebb Rks (awash) lie 2½ca off Gara Pt (chart *30*). Wembury Bay gives access to R. Yealm (10.1.19).

Between Gara Pt and Stoke Pt, 2·5M to E, dangers extend about 4ca offshore in places. In Bigbury Bay beware Wells Rk and other dangers 5ca S of Erme Hd. From Bolt Tail to Bolt Hd keep 5ca offshore to clear Greystone Ledge, sunken rks near Ham Stone (11m), and Gregory Rks 5ca SE of Ham Stone. The Little Mew Stone and Mew Stone lie below dramatic Bolt Head. Keep approx 7½ca SE of the Mewstones before turning N for Salcombe (10.1.20).

See 10.1.18 for submarine exercise areas offshore from Start Point to the Scilly Isles.

START POINT TO STRAIGHT POINT (charts *1613, 3315*)

Start Pt (lt, fog sig) is 3M NE of Prawle Pt; it is a long headland with conspic radio masts and W lt ho near end. Rks lie 2½ca offshore, and the stream runs 4kn at sp, causing a race extending 1M to seaward. In fair weather the overfalls can be avoided by passing close to rks, but in bad weather keep at least 2M off. 3M S of Start the stream turns ENE at HW Devonport – 0150, and WSW at HW + 0420. Inshore it turns 30 minutes earlier.

Between Start Pt and Portland Bill the tidal curve becomes progressively more distorted, especially on the rising tide. The rise is relatively fast for the 1st hr after LW; then slackens

noticeably for the next 1½ hrs, before resuming the rapid rate of rise. There is often a stand at HW, not very noticeable at Start Point but lasting about 1½ hrs at Lyme Regis.

NNE of Start Point is Skerries Bank, on which sea breaks in bad weather (chart 1634). Good anch off Hallsands in offshore winds. Between Dartmouth (10.1.21) and Brixham (10.1.22) rks extend 5ca offshore.

Berry Head (lt) is a steep, flat-topped headland (55m). Here the stream turns N at HW Devonport – 0105, and S at HW + 0440, sp rates 1·5kn. In Torbay (chart *26*) the more obvious dangers are steep-to, but beware the Sunker 100m SW of Ore Stone, and Morris Rogue 5ca W of Thatcher Rk.

There are good anchs in Babbacombe B and in Anstey's cove in W winds; beware the Three Brothers (drying rks), S side of Anstey's cove. From Long Quarry Pt for 4M N to Teignmouth (10.1.24) there are no offlying dangers. Off Teignmouth the NNE-going stream begins at HW Devonport – 0135, and the SSW-going at HW+ 0510. In the ent the flood begins at HW Devonport – 0535, and the ebb at HW +0040. The stream runs hard off Ferry Pt; the ent is dangerous in onshore winds.

Between Teignmouth and Dawlish rks extend 1ca offshore. Beware Dawlish Rk (depth 2·1m) about 5ca off N end of town. Warren Sands and Pole Sands lie W of ent to the River Exe (10.1.25), and are liable to shift. Along the NE (Exmouth) side of the chan, towards Orcomb Pt and Straight Pt (lt), drying rks and shoals extend up to 2½ca from shore. There is a firing range off Straight Point.

LYME BAY (chart *3315*)

Start Pt is W end of Lyme B (chart *3315*), which stretches 50M ENE to Portland Bill. Tides are weak, rarely more than 0·75kn. Between Torbay and Portland there is no hbr accessible in onshore winds, and yachtsmen must take care not to be caught on a lee shore. There are no dangers offshore. In offshore winds there is a good anch NE of Beer Hd, the most W chalk cliff in England, see 10.1.25. 3·5M E of Lyme Regis (10.1.26) is Golden Cap (186m and conspic). High Ground and Pollock are rks 7ca offshore, 2M and 3M ESE of Golden Cap.

From 6M E of Bridport (10.1.27), Chesil Beach runs SE for about 8M to the N end of the Portland peninsula. From a distance Portland looks like an island, with its distinctive wedge-shaped profile sloping down from 144m at the N to the Bill at the S tip. It is mostly steep-to, but rks extend 2½ca from the Bill which is marked by a stone bn (18m) and conspic lt ho.

10.1.6   DISTANCE TABLE

Approximate distances in nautical miles are by the most direct route while avoiding dangers and allowing for Traffic Separation Schemes. Places in *italics* are in adjoining areas; places in **bold** are in 10.0.5, Cross-Channel Distances.

	1	2	3	4	5	6	7	8	9	10	11	12	13	14	15	16	17	18	19	20
1. *Milford Haven*	**1**																			
2. *Lundy Island*	28	**2**																		
3. *Padstow*	67	40	**3**																	
4. Longships	100	80	47	**4**																
5. St Mary's (Scilly)	120	102	69	22	**5**															
6. Penzance	115	95	62	15	37	**6**														
7. Lizard Point	123	103	72	23	40	16	**7**													
8. Falmouth	139	119	88	39	60	32	16	**8**												
9. Mevagissey	152	132	99	52	69	46	28	17	**9**											
10. Fowey	157	137	106	57	76	49	34	22	7	**10**										
11. Looe	163	143	110	63	80	57	39	29	16	11	**11**									
12. Plymouth (bkwtr)	170	150	117	70	92	64	49	39	25	22	11	**12**								
13. R. Yealm (ent)	172	152	119	72	89	66	49	39	28	23	16	4	**13**							
14. Salcombe	181	161	128	81	102	74	59	50	40	36	29	22	17	**14**						
15. Start Point	186	166	135	86	103	80	63	55	45	40	33	24	22	7	**15**					
16. Dartmouth	195	175	142	95	116	88	72	63	54	48	42	35	31	14	9	**16**				
17. Torbay	201	181	150	101	118	96	78	70	62	55	50	39	38	24	15	11	**17**			
18. Exmouth	213	193	162	113	131	107	90	82	73	67	61	51	49	33	27	24	12	**18**		
19. Lyme Regis	226	206	173	126	144	120	104	96	86	81	74	63	62	48	41	35	30	21	**19**	
20. *Portland Bill*	235	215	184	135	151	128	112	104	93	89	81	73	70	55	49	45	42	36	22	**20**

THIS PAGE IS INTENTIONALLY BLANK. IT MAY BE USEFUL FOR NOTES.

ENGLISH CHANNEL
WAYPOINTS   10-1-7

Selected waypoints and major lights for use in English Channel crossings, are listed in order from **West** to **East**. Further waypoints in coastal waters are given in section 4 of each area (i.e. 10.1.4 to 10.3.4 on the English coast, and 10.14.4 to 10.19.4 for the French coast and the Channel Islands). All positions in Areas 1, 2 and 3 are referenced to the OSGB 36 datum. Areas 14, 15, 16 and 19 are referenced to the European ED 50 datum. Offshore positions may be referenced to either datum depending on the chart used.

ENGLISH COAST

AREA 1

Bishop Rock Lt	49°52'·33N 06°26'·68W
Peninnis Hd Lt	49°54'·24N 06°18'·15W
Bartholomew Ledge Lt By	49°54'·38N 06°19'·80W
Round Is Lt	49°58'·70N 06°19'·33W
Seven Stones Lt F	50°03'·58N 06°04'·28W
Longships Lt	50°03'·97N 05°44'·85W
Wolf Rock Lt	49°56'·70N 05°48'·50W
Runnel Stone Lt By	50°01'·15N 05°40'·30W
Tater Du Lt	50°03'·10N 05°34'·60W
Low Lee Lt By	50°05'·52N 05°31'·32W
Mountamopus By	50°04'·60N 05°26'·20W
Lizard Pt Lt	49°57'·58N 05°12'·07W
August Rk By (seasonal)	50°06'·07N 05°04'·88W
Manacles Lt By	50°02'·77N 05°01'·85W
Black Rk Lt By	50°08'·65N 05°01'·68W
Castle Lt By	50°08'·63N 05°01'·58W
St Anthony Hd Lt	50°08'·43N 05°00'·90W
Helston Lt By	50°04'·92N 05°00'·77W
Gwineas Lt By	50°14'·47N 04°45'·30W
Cannis Rk Lt By	50°18'·35N 04°39'·88W
Udder Rk By	50°18'·90N 04°33'·78W
Hands Deep Lt By	50°12'·65N 04°21'·04W
Eddystone Lt	50°10'·81N 04°15'·87W
West Tinker Lt By	50°19'·22N 04°08'·57W
East Tinker Lt By	50°19'·17N 04°08'·23W
Start Point Lt	50°13'·32N 03°38'·47W
Royal Dart YC No. 1 By*	50°18'·80N 03°35'·25W
Checkstone Lt By	50°20'·42N 03°33'·73W
Royal Dart YC No. 2 By*	50°18'·68N 03°33'·29W
Castle Ledge Lt By	50°19'·95N 03°33'·05W
Royal Dart YC No. 3 By*	50°20'·07N 03°31'·42W
Brixham Fairway Lt By	50°24'·37N 03°30'·85W
Berry Head Lt	50°23'·94N 03°28'·93W
East Exe Lt By	50°35'·96N 03°21'·36W
Straight Point Lt	50°36'·45N 03°21'·67W
DZ Lt By	50°36'·50N 02°42'·00W
Portland Bill Lt	50°30'·82N 02°27'·32W

AREA 2

Portland NE Bkwtr Lt	50°35'·12N 02°24'·99W
W Shambles Lt By	50°29'·75N 02°24'·33W
E Shambles Lt By	50°30'·75N 02°20'·00W
Anvil Point Lt	50°35'·48N 01°57'·52W
Peverill Ledge By	50°36'·38N 01°56'·02W
Poole Fairway Lt By	50°38'·97N 01°54'·80W
Needles Fairway Lt By	50°38'·20N 01°38'·90W
SW Shingles Lt By	50°39'·31N 01°37'·36W
Needles Lt	50°39'·70N 01°35'·43W
N Head Lt By	50°42'·65N 01°35'·43W
NE Shingles Lt By	50°41'·93N 01°33'·32W
St Catherine's Pt Lt	50°34'·52N 01°17'·80W
W Princessa Lt By	50°40'·20N 01°03'·95W
Bembridge Ledge Lt By	50°41'·12N 01°02'·72W
New Grounds Lt By	50°41'·97N 00°58'·53W
Nab Tower Lt	50°40'·05N 00°57'·07W

AREA 3

Boulder Lt By	50°41'·53N 00°49'·00W
Outer Owers By	50°38'·75N 00°41'·30W
Owers Lt By	50°37'·27N 00°40'·60W
E Borough Hd Lt By	50°41'·50N 00°39'·00W
Littlehampton Outfall Lt By	50°46'·20N 00°30'·45W
Beacham Outfall Lt By	50°48'·45N 00°19'·40W
Shoreham Outfall Lt By	50°47'·85N 00°13'·63W
Brighton Marina W Hd Lt	50°48'·46N 00°06'·29W
Newhaven Bkwtr Lt	50°46'·52N 00°03'·60E
Beachy Hd Lt	50°44'·00N 00°14'·60E
Sovereign Hbr Lt By	50°47'·33N 00°20'·42E
Royal Sovereign Lt	50°43'·42N 00°26'·18E
St Leonard's Outfall Lt By	50°49'·27N 00°32'·00E
Hastings W Bkwtr Hd	50°51'·13N 00°35'·70E
Rye Fairway Lt By	50°54'·00N 00°48'·13E
Dungeness Outfall Lt By	50°54'·43N 00°58'·33E
Dungeness Lt	50°54'·77N 00°58'·67E
Bullock Bank Lt By	50°46'·90N 01°07'·70E
Folkestone Bkwtr Hd Lt	51°04'·53N 01°11'·79E
S Varne Lt By	50°55'·60N 01°17'·40E
Dover Pier extn Hd	51°06'·65N 01°19'·77E
Varne Mid Lt By	50°58'·90N 01°20'·00E
E Varne Lt By	50°58'·20N 01°21'·00E
Varne Lanby	51°01'·25N 01°24'·00E
W Quern Lt By	51°18'·95N 01°25'·00E
Ramsgate N Bkwtr Hd Lt	51°19'·53N 01°25'·58E
Downs Lt By	51°14'·47N 01°26'·60E
Deal Bank Lt By	51°12'·90N 01°25'·67E
North Foreland Lt	51°22'·47N 01°26'·80E
S Brake Lt By	51°15'·45N 01°26'·80E
Goodwin Fork Lt By	51°14'·30N 01°27'·23E
W Goodwin Lt By	51°15'·28N 01°27'·32E
Brake Lt By	51°16'·95N 01°28'·30E
S Goodwin Lt F	51°07'·95N 01°28'·60E
NW Goodwin Lt By	51°16'·54N 01°28'·67E

SW Goodwin Lt By	51°08'·57N 01°28'·80E
E Brake Lt By	51°19'·40N 01°29'·05E
Broadstairs Knoll Lt By	51°20'·85N 01°29'·58E
Gull Stream Lt By	51°18'·25N 01°29'·80E
Ramsgate (RA) Lt By	51°19'·57N 01°30'·23E
N Goodwin Lt By	51°17'·88N 01°30'·42E
Gull Lt By	51°19'·55N 01°31'·40E
Elbow Lt By	51°23'·20N 01°31'·70E
Goodwin Knoll Lt By	51°19'·55N 01°32'·30E
S Goodwin Lt By	51°10'·57N 01°32'·37E
NE Goodwin Lt By	51°20'·28N 01°34'·27E
SE Goodwin Lt By	51°12'·95N 01°34'·55E
E Goodwin Lt By	51°16'·00N 01°35'·60E
E Goodwin Lt F	51°13'·05N 01°36'·31E

OFFSHORE

Channel Lt F	49°54'·42N 02°53'·67W
E Channel Lt By	49°58'·67N 02°28'·87W
EC1 Lt By	50°05'·90N 01°48'·35W
EC2 Lt By	50°12'·10N 01°12'·40W
EC3 Lt By	50°18'·30N 00°36'·10W
CS1 Lt By	50°33'·67N 00°03'·83W
Greenwich Lt V	50°24'·50N 00°00'·00
CS2 Lt By	50°39'·10N 00°32'·70E
CS3 Lt By	50°52'·00N 01°02'·30E
Bullock Bank Lt By	50°46'·90N 01°07'·70E
N Colbart Lt By	50°57'·42N 01°23'·40E
CS4 Lt By	51°08'·58N 01°34'·03E
MPC Lt By	51°06'·09N 01°38'·36E
S Falls Lt By	51°13'·80N 01°44'·03E
F1 Lt By	51°11'·20N 01°45'·03E
Mid Falls Lt By	51°18'·60N 01°47'·10E
CS 5 Lt By	51°23'·00N 01°50'·00E
Inter Bank Lt By	51°16'·45N 01°52'·33E
F2 Lt By	51°20'·38N 01°56'·30E
F3 Lt By	51°23'·82N 02°00'·62E

CHANNEL ISLANDS

AREA 14

Les Hanois Lt	49°26'·16N 02°42'·06W
St Martin's Point Lt	49°25'·37N 02°31'·61W
Reffée Lt By	49°27'·80N 02°31'·18W
Petite Canupe Lt Bn	49°30'·25N 02°29'·05W
Platte Fougère Lt	49°30'·88N 02°29'·05W
Casquets Lt	49°43'·38N 02°22'·55W
Desormes Lt By	49°19'·00N 02°17'·90W
La Corbière Lt	49°10'·85N 02°14'·90W
Passage Rk Lt By	49°09'·59N 02°12'·18W
Alderney Main Lt	49°43'·81N 02°09'·77W
Diamond Rk Lt By	49°10'·18N 02°08'·56W
Canger Rk Lt By	49°07'·41N 02°00'·30W
Frouquier Aubert Lt By	49°06'·14N 01°58'·78W
Violet Lt By	49°07'·87N 01°57'·05W
NW Minquiers Lt By	48°59'·70N 02°20'·50W
N Minquiers Lt By	49°01'·70N 02°00'·50W
NE Minquiers Lt By	49°00'·90N 01°55'·20W
SE Minquiers Lt By	48°53'·50N 02°00'·00W
S Minquiers Lt By	48°53'·15N 02°10'·00W
SW Minquiers Lt By	48°54'·40N 02°19'·30W

FRENCH COAST

Selected waypoints in Area 15 and 16 are listed clockwise around the French coast from **East** to **West**, and Area 19 from **West** to **East**. All positions are referenced to the European ED 50 datum.

AREA 15

Les Équets Lt By	49°43'·68N 01°18'·28W
Basse du Rénier Lt By	49°44'·90N 01°22'·10W
Cap Lévi Lt	49°41'·80N 01°28'·40W
La Pierre Noire Lt By	49°43'·57N 01°28'·98W
Cherbourg Fort Ouest Lt	49°40'·50N 01°38'·87W
CH1 Lt By	49°43'·30N 01°42'·10W
Basse Bréfort Lt By	49°43'·70N 01°51'·05W
Cap de la Hague Lt	49°43'·37N 01°57'·19W
Flamanville Lt By	49°32'·62N 01°53'·93W
Cap de Carteret Lt	49°22'·46N 01°48'·35W
Les Trois-Grunes Lt By	49°21'·88N 01°55'·12W
Basses de Portbail (PB) By	49°18'·47N 01°44'·60W
Écrevière Lt By	49°15'·33N 01°52'·08W
Basse Jourdan Lt By	49°06'·90N 01°44'·07W
La Pierre-de-Herpin	48°43'·83N 01°48'·83W
La Catheue Lt By	48°57'·95N 01°42'·00W
Les Ardentes Lt By	48°57'·84N 01°51'·53W
Anvers Lt By	48°53'·90N 01°40'·84W
Chausey, Grand Île Lt	48°52'·25N 01°49'·27W
Le Videcoq Lt By	48°49'·70N 01°42'·02W
Pierre d'Herpin Lt By	48°43'·83N 01°48'·81W
Brunel Lt By	48°40'·88N 02°05'·26W
Buharats Ouest No. 2 Lt By	48°40'·30N 02°07'·48W
St Malo Fairway Lt By	48°41'·42N 02°07'·21W
Le Sou Lt By	48°40'·15N 02°05'·24W
Bassé NE Lt By	48°42'·51N 02°09'·34W
Banchenou Lt By	48°40'·52N 02°11'·42W
Cap Fréhel Lt	48°41'·10N 02°19'·07W
Le Rohein Lt Bn	48°38'·88N 02°37'·68W
Le Légué Lt By	48°34'·38N 02°41'·07W
Caffa Lt By	48°37'·89N 02°43'·00W
Grand Léjon Lt	48°44'·95N 02°39'·90W
La Roselière Lt By	48°37'·51N 02°46'·31W
Roc du Nord-Est By	48°39'·65N 02°44'·00W
Île Harbour	48°40'·05N 02°48'·42W

AREA 16

Roches Douvres Lt	49°06'·35N 02°48'·65W
Barnouic Lt	49°01'·70N 02°48'·33W
Roche Gautier Lt By	49°00'·49N 02°52'·92W
L'Ost Pic	48°46'·82N 02°56'·33W
Les Echaudés By	48°53'·42N 02°57'·26W
Rosédo (Bréhat) Lt	48°51'·51N 03°00'·21W
Les Héaux Lt	48°54'·57N 03°05'·10W
La Jument des Héaux Lt By	48°55'·41N 03°07'·95W
Les Sept Îles Lt	48°52'·78N 03°29'·33W
Les Triagoz Lt	48°52'·35N 03°38'·73W
Méloine By	48°45'·65N 03°50'·55W
Stolvezen By	48°42'·71N 03°53'·32W
Pot de Fer By	48°44'·29N 03°53'·93W

Bassee de Bloscon Lt By	48°43'·77N 03°57'·48W
Astan Lt By	48°44'·95N 03°57'·55W
Île de Batz Lt	48°44'·78N 04°01'·55W
Aman-ar-Ross Lt By	48°41'·94N 04°26'·96W
Lizen Van Ouest Lt By	48°40'·55N 04°33'·68W
Île Vierge Lt	48°38'·38N 04°33'·97W
Trépied By	48°37'·35N 04°37'·47W
Libenter Lt By	48°37'·57N 04°38'·35W
Rusven Est By	48°36'·37N 04°38'·53W
Petite Fourche By	48°37'·05N 04°38'·67W
Ruzven Ouest By	48°36'·15N 04°39'·34W
Le Relec By	48°36'·05N 04°40'·76W
Grande Basse Portsall Lt By	48°36'·78N 04°46'·05W
Basse Paupian By	48°35'·38N 04°46'·20W
Créac'h Lt	48°27'·62N 05°07'·72W
Ouessant NE Lt By	48°45'·90N 05°11'·60W
Ouessant SW Lanby	48°31'·20N 05°49'·10W

AREA 19

Pointe de Barfleur Lt	49°41'·83N 01°15'·87W
Îles St Marcouf Lt	49°29'·90N 01°08'·70W
Norfalk Lt By	49°28'·83N 01°03'·40W
Est du Cardonnet Lt By	49°26'·97N 01°01'·00W
Broadswood Lt By	49°25'·39N 00°52'·90W
Cussy Lt By	49°29'·50N 00°43'·25W
Ver-sur-Mer Lt	49°20'·47N 00°31'·15W
Ouistreham Lt By	49°20'·48N 00°14'·73W
Northgate Lt By	49°30'·40N 00°14'·15W
LHA Lanby	49°31'·44N 00°09'·78W
A17 Lt By	49°41'·60N 00°01'·75E
A18 Lt By	49°42'·07N 00°02'·21E
Ratier NW Lt By	49°26'·85N 00°02'·55E
Cap de la Hève Lt	49°30'·79N 00°04'·24E
Cap d'Antifer Lt	49°41'·07N 00°10'·00E
Pointe d'Ailly Lt	49°55'·13N 00°57'·56E
Bassurelle Lt By	50°32'·70N 00°57'·80E
Ecovouga Wk Lt By	50°33'·70N 00°59'·20E
Vergoyer SW Lt By	50°26'·90N 01°00'·10E
Daffodils Lt By	50°02'·52N 01°04'·10E
Colbart SW Lt By	50°48'·85N 01°16'·45E
Ridens SE Lt By	50°43'·45N 01°19'·00E

ZC1 Lt By	50°44'·94N 01°27'·30E
Ault Lt	50°06'·32N 01°27'·31E
AT-SO Lt By	50°14'·29N 01°28'·65E
Ophélie Lt By	50°43'·91N 01°30'·92E
ZC2 Lt By	50°53'·50N 01°31'·00E
Pointe de Haut Blanc Lt	50°23'·90N 01°33'·75E
Cap d'Alprech Lt	50°41'·96N 01°33'·83E
Cap Gris Nez Lt	50°52'·05N 01°35'·07E
Abbeville Lt By	50°56'·05N 01°37'·70E
CA3 Lt By	50°56'·80N 01°41'·25E
CA4 Lt By	50°58'·94N 01°45'·18E
CA6 Lt By	50°58'·30N 01°45'·70E
SW Sandettié Lt By	51°09'·72N 01°45'·73E
CA5 Lt By	50°57'·70N 01°46'·20E
Sangatte Lt	50°57'·23N 01°46'·57E
SW Ruytingen Lt By	51°04'·99N 01°46'·90E
Sandettié Lt F	51°09'·40N 01°47'·20E
CA8 Lt By	50°58'·43N 01°48'·72E
CA2 Lt By	51°00'·91N 01°48'·86E
CA10 Lt By	50°58'·68N 01°50'·00E
Ruytingen W Lt By	51°06'·90N 01°50'·60E
Sandettié WSW Lt By	51°12'·32N 01°51'·23E
Calais Lt	50°57'·73N 01°51'·28E
Calais E Hd Lt	50°58'·45N 01°50'·54E
Dunkerque Lanby	51°03'·00N 01°51'·83E
RCE Lt By	51°02'·40N 01°53'·20E
DKA Lt By	51°02'·59N 01°57'·06E
NW Ruytingen Lt By	51°09'·05N 01°57'·40E
DW5 Lt By	51°02'·20N 02°01'·00E
N Sandettié Lt By	51°18'·42N 02°04'·80E
Haut-fond de Gravelines	51°04'·10N 02°05'·10E
E Dyck Lt By	51°05'·70N 02°05'·70E
SE Ruytingen Lt By	51°09'·20N 02°09'·00E
DKB Lt By	51°03'·00N 02°09'·34E
N Ruytingen Lt By	51°13'·12N 02°10'·42E
Hinder 1 Lt By	51°20'·90N 02°11'·06E
DW23 Lt By	51°03'·60N 02°15'·25E
S Fairy Lt By	51°21'·22N 02°17'·35E
Bergues Lt By	51°17'·20N 02°18'·70E
S Bergues Lt By	51°15'·16N 02°19'·50E
DW29 Lt By	51°03'·88N 02°20'·32E
Dunkerque Lt	51°02'·98N 02°21'·94E

ISLES OF SCILLY   10-1-8

The Isles of Scilly are made up of 48 islands and numerous rocky outcrops, covering an area approx 10M by 7M and lying 21 – 31M WSW of Land's End. Only six islands are inhabited: St Mary's, St Martin's, Tresco, Bryher, St Agnes and Gugh. The islands belong to the Duchy of Cornwall. Arrangements for visiting uninhabited islands are given in a booklet *Duchy of Cornwall - Information for visiting craft* obtainable from Hr Mr, Hugh Town Hbr, St Mary's. There is a LB and a HM CG Sector Base at St Mary's.
Historic Wrecks (see 10.0.3h) are at 49°52'·6N 06°26'·5N Tearing Ledge, 2ca SE of Bishop Rk Lt; and at 49°54'·26N 06°19'·83W, Bartholomew Ledges, 5ca N of Gugh.

CHARTS
AC *883, 34* (both essential); Scilly to Lands End 1148; Imray C7; Stanfords 2, 13; OS 203
TIDES
Standard Port is Devonport. Differences for St Mary's are given in 10·1·9. Tidal heights, times, directions and rates around the islands are irregular; see AC 34 for streams.
SHELTER
The Isles of Scilly are exposed to Atlantic swell and wind. Weather can be unpredictable and fast-changing. It is not a place for inexperienced navigators or poorly equipped yachts. Normal yacht ⚓s may drag on fine sand, even with plenty of scope, but holding is mostly good. That said, the islands are attractive, interesting and rewarding.

The following are some of the many ⚓s, anti-clockwise:

HUGH TOWN HBR (St Mary's). See 10·1·9 facing.

PORTH CRESSA (St Mary's, S of Hugh Town). Beware of dangers on each side of ent and submarine cables. Good ⚓ (2m) in W/NW'lies, but exposed to swell from SE to SW.

WATERMILL COVE (NE corner of St Mary's). Excellent shelter in winds S to NW. ⚓ in approx 5m.

TEAN SOUND (St Martin's, W end). Needs careful pilotage, but attractive ⚓ in better weather. More suitable for shoal draught boats which can ⚓ or take the ground out of main tidal stream in chan. St Martin's Hotel ☎ 422092, D, FW, M (6), V, R, Bar. There are several other ⚓s which can be used in settled weather.

ST HELEN'S POOL (S of St Helen's Is). Ent via St Helen's Gap to ⚓ in 1·5m - 7m. Secure, but may be swell near HW.

OLD GRIMSBY (NE side of Tresco). Green Porth & Raven's Porth, divided by a quay, form the Old Grimsby Hbr; both dry 2·3m. Beware cable in Green Porth. ⚓s 1½ca NE of quay in 2·5m; access more difficult than New Grimsby. Well sheltered in SW'lies but open to swell if wind veers N of W. Facilities: 4 ⚓s (R cans), L (quay), hotel with slip.

NEW GRIMSBY (between Tresco and Bryher). Appr (line E) through New Grimsby Sound, or with adequate rise of tide across Tresco Flats. Good shelter except in NW'lies. Popular ⚓ between Hangman Is and the quay in 1·5 - 4·5m. Beware cables. 10 ⚓s £8 from Tresco Estate ☎ 22849, ⛟ 22807; VHF Ch 08 for R, Bar, FW, V, ⊠. Ferry to St Mary's.

THE COVE (St Agnes/Gugh). Well sheltered from W and N winds, except when the sand bar between the islands covers near HWS with a strong NW wind. Beware cables.

PORTH CONGER (St Agnes/Gugh). On the N side of the sandbar, sheltered in winds from E through S to W. May be uncomfortable when the bar is covered. Facilities: L (two quays), ferry to St Mary's; in Middle Town (¾M), St Agnes, V, ⊠, R, Bar.

NAVIGATION

For TSS to the E, S and W, see Fig. 10 (4) and 10.1.2. If ldg lines/marks cannot be identified, then it is best to lie off. Pilotage is compulsory for all vessels, except HM Ships, trawlers <47·5m LOA and yachts <20m LOA, navigating within a radius of 6M from S tip of Samson Is excluding St Mary's Hbr. Many chans between islands have dangerous shallows, often with rky ledges. Beware lobster pots.

Line A, via St Mary's Sound, is the normal ent to St Mary's Road. Appr from the E or SE to avoid Gilstone Rk (dries 4m) 3ca E of Peninnis Hd. Spanish Ledges, off Gugh, are marked by an unlit ECM By; thence past Woolpack SCM bn and PHM By Fl R 5s (Bartholomew Ledge) to ent St Mary's Rd on 040°.

Line B, which clears Woodcock Ledge (breaks in bad wx).

Line C, from SW: Broad Sound is entered between Bishops Rk lt ho and Flemming's Ledge about 7ca to the N, then twixt Round Rk NCM and Gunner SCM buoys to Old Wreck NCM buoy; beware Jeffrey Rk, close to port. Ldg marks are more than 7M off and at first not easy to see. Smith Sound, 350° between St Agnes and Annet may also be used.

Line D, from NW: North Chan is about 7ca wide, and of easy access with good ldg marks, but beware cross tide and Steeple Rk (0·1m, 2ca to port). Intercept Line C for St Mary's Road.

Line E, from the N, leads between Bryher and Tresco, into New Grimsby Hbr (see SHELTER); thence it winds across Tresco Flats (with adequate rise of tide and good vis).

Line F, from the E & NE: Crow Sound is not difficult, with sufficient rise of tide but can be rough in strong E or S winds. From NE a yacht can pass close to Menawethan and Biggal Rk, avoiding Trinity Rk and the Ridge, which break in bad weather. Hats SCM buoy marks a shoal with an old boiler, drying 0·6m, on it. Track 254° between Bar Pt and Crow Bar (dries 0·7m), passing Crow Rk IDM bn on its N side (for best water) before altering SSW for St Mary's.

LIGHTS AND MARKS

See 10·1·4 for lts, including Seven Stones lt float, Wolf Rock lt ho and Longships lt ho. A working knowledge of the following daymarks and conspic features will greatly aid pilotage (from NE to SW):

St Martin's E end: Conical bn tr (56m) with RW bands.

Round Is: conical shaped Is with W lt ho 19/55m high.

Tresco: Abbey & FS, best seen from S. Cromwell's Castle and Hangman Is from the NW.

Bryher: Watch Hill, stone bn (43m); rounded Samson Hill.

St Mary's: TV & radio masts at N end; all with R lts. Crow Rk IDM bn, 11m on rk drying 4·6m, at N.

St Agnes: Old lt ho, ○ W tr, visible from all directions.

Bishop Rk lt ho: Grey ○ tr, 44m; helo pad above lamp.

ST MARY'S   10-1-9

Isles of Scilly 49°55'·10N 06°18'·65W   Rtg 2-3-1

CHARTS
AC *883, 34*; Imray C7; Stanfords 2; OS 203

TIDES
+0607 Dover; ML 3·2; Duration 0600; Zone 0 (UT)

Standard Port DEVONPORT (→)

Times				Height (metres)			
High Water		Low Water		MHWS	MHWN	MLWN	MLWS
0000	0600	0000	0600	5·5	4·4	2·2	0·8
1200	1800	1200	1800				
Differences ST MARY'S							
−0050	−0100	−0045	−0045	+0·2	−0·1	−0·2	−0·1

SHELTER
Good in St Mary's Pool where 38 Y ⚓s lie in 5 trots close E of the LB ⌂ in at least 2m. ⚓ is prohib S of a line from the pier hd to the LB slip; to seaward of the LB ⌂; off the pier hd where the ferry turns, and in the apprs. Holding in the Pool is poor and in W/NW gales it is notorious for yachts dragging ⚓, when Porth Cressa (see 10·1·8) is safer. Hbr speed limit 3kn. NB: do not impede the ferry *Scillonian III* which arrives about 1200 and sails at 1630.

NAVIGATION
WPT via St Mary's Sound: Spanish Ledge unlit ECM buoy, 49°53'·90N 06°18'·80W, 128°/308° from/to transit line B (040°), 1·2M. See also 10·1·4 and 10·1·8. The 097° transit leads S of Bacon Ledge (0·3m); the 151° transit leads into the Pool between Bacon Ledge and the Cow & Calf (drying 0·6 and 1·8m) to the E.

LIGHTS AND MARKS
2 ldg marks, (both show FR lts for commercial ships) lead 097° into the Pool; front bn = W △ on pole on W pyramid, rear = black X on pole (hard to see). Pier hd lt is Fl RG 2s 5m 4M, R070°-099° (29°), G099°-000° (261°). Buzza Hill tr and power stn chy (48m) are conspic.

RADIO TELEPHONE
St Mary's Hbr VHF Ch 14 16 (0800-1700LT). Pilot Ch 69 16. Lands End Radio Ch 64 covers Scilly. St Mary's CG Ch 16 67 (manned in bad wx only). *Falmouth CG* provides radio cover Ch 16 of the TSS/ITZ off Land's End. Do not hesitate to call the CG Ch 16 in emergency/gales/dragging ⚓.

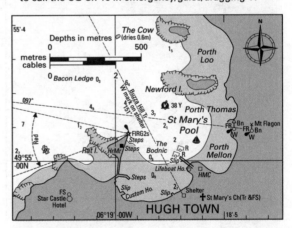

TELEPHONE (Dial code 01720)
Hr Mr 422768 (also ⛟); MRCC (01326) 317575; Marinecall 0891 500458; ⌗ 0345 231110, locally 422571; Ⓗ 422392; Dr 422628; Police 422444; Pilot 422066; Tourist Info 422536.

FACILITIES
Hbr ⚓ (Overnight dues: >9m LOA = £7.50; <9m = £6.50), L, M, Gas, Gaz, P (cans), D (bowser on quay), Slip, FW (⛽ on pier, 0930-1130, not Sat; see Hr Mr. Nil or limited quantity in summer). Hbr Office will hold mail for visiting yachts if addressed c/o Hr Mr. Services: ACA, Sh, CH, ME, El.

Hugh Town EC Wed (or Thurs depending on ferry times); limited shopping facilities, ⊠, Ⓑ, Ⓞ. Ferry sails daily (not Sun) 0915 from Penzance and 1630 from St Mary, approx 2¾hrs crossing, booking ☎ 01736-62009 (see also 10.0.4); ✈ helicopter to Penzance (⇌) and fixed wing to St Just, near Lands End, and Exeter (⇌). There are ⊠, R, V, Bar etc. at Tresco, Bryher, St Martins and St Agnes.

NEWLYN   10-1-10

Cornwall 50°06'·15N 05°32'.52W   Rtg 3-2-2

CHARTS
AC 2345, 777; Imray C7; Stanfords 13; OS 203

TIDES
+0600 Dover; ML 3·2; Duration 0555; Zone 0 (UT)

Standard Port DEVONPORT (→)

Times				Height (metres)			
High Water		Low Water		MHWS	MHWN	MLWN	MLWS
0000	0600	0000	0600	5·5	4·4	2·2	0·8
1200	1800	1200	1800				
Differences NEWLYN							
–0055	–0115	–0035	–0035	+0·1	0·0	–0·2	0·0

SHELTER
Good, except in SE winds when heavy swell enters hbr; access at all tides. FVs take priority. Yachts berth on SW side of Mary Williams Pier. No 🅥s, no ⚓ in hbr. Good ⚓ in Gwavas Lake in offshore winds.

NAVIGATION
WPT 50°06'·15N 05°31'·74W, 090°/270° from/to S pier, 0·5M. From NE, beware The Gear and Dog Rk 3½ca NE of hbr ent; from S beware Low Lee and Carn Base.

LIGHTS AND MARKS
S pier hd, Fl 5s 10m 9M; vis 253°-336°, W tr, R base and cupola; Siren 60s. N pier hd, F WG 4m 2M; vis G238°-248°, W over hbr. Old Quay hd, FR 3m 1M.

RADIO TELEPHONE
Call: *Newlyn Hbr* VHF Ch 09 **12** 16 (Mon-Fri 0800-1700, Sat 0800-1200LT).

TELEPHONE (Dial code 01736)
Hr Mr 362523; MRCC, ⌗, Marinecall, Police, Ⓗ, Dr: as for Penzance.

FACILITIES
N Pier Slip, D (cans), FW, C (6 ton); **Mary Williams Pier** £7 (every 3rd night free). **Services:** ME, Sh, SM, Gas, El, Ⓔ, CH. **Town** EC Wed; ⌕, V, R, Bar, ✉, Ⓑ (AM only), bus to Penzance for ⇌, ✈.

ADJACENT HARBOUR
MOUSEHOLE, Cornwall, 50°04'·93N 05°32'·20W. Rtg 4-5-1. AC 2345. HW +0550 on Dover; Tides as Newlyn; ML 3·2m; Duration 0600. Shelter good except in NE and SE winds; protected by St Clements Is from E'lies. Best appr from S, midway between St Clements Is and bkwtr. Ent 11m wide; hbr dries 1·8m, access HW±3. Ent is closed with timber baulks from Nov-Apl. Lts N pier 2 FG (vert) 8/6m 3M; 2 FR (vert) = hbr closed. Hr Mr ☎ (01736) 731511. £5. Facilities limited: FW, V, Slip. Buses to Penzance.

PENZANCE   10-1-11

Cornwall 50°07'·05N 05°31'·62W   Rtg 3-2-1

CHARTS
AC 2345, 777; Imray C7; Stanfords 13; OS 203

TIDES
–0635 Dover; ML 3·2; Duration 0550; Zone 0 (UT)

Standard Port DEVONPORT (→)

Times				Height (metres)			
High Water		Low Water		MHWS	MHWN	MLWN	MLWS
0000	0600	0000	0600	5·5	4·4	2·2	0·8
1200	1800	1200	1800				
Differences PENZANCE							
–0055	–0115	–0035	–0035	+0·1	0·0	–0·2	0·0
PORTHLEVEN							
–0050	–0105	–0030	–0025	0·0	–0·1	–0·2	0·0
LIZARD POINT							
–0045	–0100	–0030	–0030	–0·2	–0·2	–0·3	–0·2

SHELTER
Excellent in the wet dock (gates open HW –2 to +1), or dry out against Albert pier or ⚓ E of hbr. But Mounts Bay is an unsafe ⚓ in S or SE winds, which, if strong, also render the hbr ent dangerous. Hbr speed limit 5kn.

NAVIGATION
WPT 50°06'·70N 05°31'·10W, 135°/315° from/to S pier hd, 0·48M. Beware Gear Rk 0·4M S. Cressar (5ca NE of ent) and Long Rks are marked by SCM bns.

LIGHTS AND MARKS
There are no ldg lts/marks. Dock ent sigs, shown from FS at N side of Dock gate (may not be given for yachts).
2B ● (hor) (2FR (vert) by night) = Dock gates open.
2B ● (vert) (Ⓡ over Ⓖ by night) = Dock gates shut.

RADIO TELEPHONE
VHF Ch 09 **12** 16 (HW –2 to HW +1, and office hrs).

TELEPHONE (Dial code 01736)
Hr Mr 366113; MRCC (01326) 317575; ⌗ 0345 231110 (H24); Marinecall 0891 500458; Police 362395; Dr 363866; Ⓗ 362382.

FACILITIES
Wet Dock (50 Ⓥ) ☎ 366113, ⚓ 366114, £8 (every 3rd night free), M, D (cans), FW, AC, C (3 ton); **S Pier** D, FW; **Penzance YC** ☎ 364989, Bar, L, FW, R; **Services:** Slip (dry dock), ME, El, CH, SM, Sh, Gas, Gaz. **Town** EC Wed (winter only); ⌕, V, R, Bar, ✉, Ⓑ, ⇌, ✈.

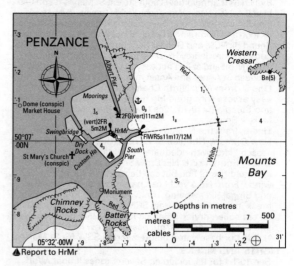

ADJACENT HARBOUR
ST MICHAEL'S MOUNT, Cornwall, 50°07'·10N 05°28'·58W. AC 2345, 777. HW +0550 on Dover; Tides as Penzance; ML 3·2m; Duration 0550. Shelter good from N to SE, but only in fair wx. Hbr dries; it has approx 3·3m at MHWS and 1·4m at MHWN. Beware Hogus Rks to NW of hbr and Outer Penzeath Rk about 3ca WSW of Hogus Rks. Also beware Maltman Rk 1ca SSW of the Mount. There are no lts. Ent between piers is 30m wide. No facilities on the island except FW; some at Marazion, 5M to N. EC Wed.

ADJACENT HARBOURS ON THE LIZARD PENINSULA

PORTHLEVEN, Cornwall, 50°04'·88N 05°19'·07W. Rtg 4-4-3. AC 2345, 777. HW +0551 on Dover; ML 3·1m; Duration 0545. See 10·1·11. Hbr dries 2m above the old LB ho but has approx 2·3m in centre of ent; access HW±3. It is open to W and SW. Beware rks round pier hd and Deazle Rks to W. Lt on S pier FG 10m 4M = inner hbr open. Inside hbr FG vis 033°-067° when required for vessels entering. Visitors go alongside the Quay on E side. Hr Mr ☎ (01326) 574270. Facilities: **Inner Hbr** AB £8, FW, L, ME, P & D (cans). **Village** EC Wed; ⊠, ⓪, R, Ⓑ, V, Bar.

MULLION COVE, Cornwall, 50°00'·86N, 05°15'·48W. AC 2345, 777. Lizard HW +0552 on Dover, −0050 and −0·2m on HW Devonport; ML 3·0m; Duration 0545. Porth Mellin hbr dries 2·4m and is open to W'lies. ⚓ in Mullion Cove is safer especially in lee of Mullion Island where there is approx 3·5m, but local knowledge advised. NT owns the island and the hbr. Due to lack of space, visiting boats may only stay in hbr briefly to load/unload. No lts. There is a slip on E side of hbr. Hr Mr ☎ (01326) 240222. Only facilities at Mullion village (1M) EC Wed; Bar, V.

Historic Wrecks (see 10.0.3h) are located at:
50°03'·40N 05°17'·10W (St Anthony), 2M SE of Porthleven.
50°02'·33N 05°16'·40W (Schiedam), 1·5M N of Mullion Is.
49°58'·50N 05°14'·45W, Rill Cove, 1·4M NW of Lizard Pt.
49°57'·45N 05°12'·92W, (Royal Anne) The Stags, Lizard Pt.

CADGWITH, Cornwall, 49°59'·18N 05°10'·62W. AC 2345, 154, 777; HW +0555 on Dover; −0030 on Devonport; −0·2m on Devonport; ML 3·0m. See Differences Lizard Pt under 10.1.11. Hbr dries; it is divided by a rky outcrop, The Todden. Beware the extension of this, rks called The Mare; also beware The Boa rks to ESE which cover at quarter tide. ⚓ off The Mare in about 2–3m, but not recommended in on-shore winds. There are no lts. Many local FVs operate from here and are hauled up on the shingle beach. Facilities: ⊠, Bar, R, V (1M at Ruan Minor).

COVERACK, Cornwall, 50°01'·40N 05°05'·60W. AC 154, 777. HW +0605 on Dover; ML 3·0m; Duration 0550. See 10·1·12. Hbr dries but has 3·3m at MHWS and 2·2m at MHWN. In good weather and off-shore winds it is better to ⚓ outside. Hbr is very small and full of FVs. From the S beware the Guthens, off Chynhalls Pt; from the N, the Dava and other rks off Lowland Pt, and Manacle Rks to the NE (ECM, Q(3) 10s bell). There are no lts. Hr Mr ☎ (01326) 280583. Facilities: EC Tues; FW (hotel) D, P (cans) from garage (2M uphill), V, ⊠.

HELFORD RIVER   10-1-12

Cornwall 50°05'·75N 05·06'·00W (Ent)   Rtg 2-3-1

CHARTS
AC 147, 154; Imray C6, Y57; Stanfords 13; OS 204

TIDES
−0613 Dover; ML 3·0; Duration 0550; Zone 0 (UT)

Reference Port FALMOUTH (⟶)

Times				Height (metres)			
High Water		Low Water		MHWS	MHWN	MLWN	MLWS
0000	0600	0000	0600	5·3	4·2	1·9	0·6
1200	1800	1200	1800				
Differences HELFORD RIVER (Ent)							
0000	−0005	−0005	0000	0·0	0·0	0·0	0·0
COVERACK							
0000	−0010	−0010	0000	0·0	0·0	0·0	0·0

SHELTER
Excellent, except in E'lies. ⚓s marked 'Visitors' on G can buoys or G pick-up buoys are administered by Moorings Officer. Ferry will collect people from yachts, if requested during normal ferry operating hrs.
⚓s at: Durgan Bay, good; off Helford, but tides strong; Navas Creek, good shelter, little room, YC wall dries 1·9m. Gillan Creek is good except in E'lies, but beware Car Croc rk in ent marked by ECM buoy in season.
Note: A local bye-law states that yachts must not ⚓ in the river and creeks W of Navas Creek due to oyster beds.

NAVIGATION
WPT 50°05'·70N 05°04'·50W, 093°/273° from/to The Voose NCM bn, 1·5M. From N beware August Rock (alias the Gedges), marked by SHM (seasonal). From SE keep well clear of Nare Pt and Dennis Hd. Speed limit 6kn in river. Keep Helford Pt open of Bosahan Pt to clear The Voose, a rky reef E of Bosahan Pt, marked by NCM (seasonal). On N side of river opposite Helford Creek avoid mud bank marked by Bar buoy SHM (seasonal). PHM & SHM buoys mark chan from Mawgan Creek to Gweek.

LIGHTS AND MARKS
Bosahan Pt on with Mawnan Shear (259°) clears August Rk (The Gedges), dangerous rks marked by unlit SHM By.

RADIO TELEPHONE
Moorings Officer VHF Ch M. Helford River SC Ch **80** M.

TELEPHONE (Dial code 01326)
Moorings Officer 221265; MRCC 317575; ☷ 0345 231110 (H24); Marinecall 0891 500458; Police 72231; Ⓗ 572151.

FACILITIES
Moorings £4.50. Please ditch rubbish only at the Helford River SC; protect the wild life of this beautiful river.
Helford River SC ☎ 231460, Slip, FW, R, Bar, ⓪;
Porth Navas YC ☎ 340419/340065 (Bar), Gas, C (3 ton), M, AC, V, R, FW; **Helford Passage** Slip, L, FW, V; **Gweek Quay** ☎ 221657, ⚓ 221685, C (30 ton), M, CH, R, EI, Sh, ME, FW, Ⓔ; **Gillan Creek** CH, FW, M;
Services: Gas, Gaz, Slip, L, Sh, CH, ⓪, D (cans).
EC Wed; ⊠ (Helford, Gweek, Mawnan-Smith, Mawgan); Ⓑ Mawnan-Smith (Jan-Sept Mon, Wed, Fri AM only. Oct-May Tues, Fri AM only); ⇌ (bus to Falmouth); ✈ (Penzance or Newquay).

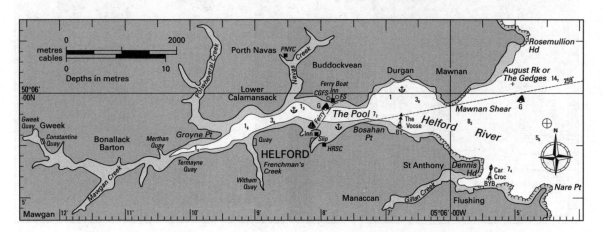

RIVER FAL   10-1-13
Cornwall 50°08'·58N 05°01'·42W (Ent)   Rtg 1-1-1

CHARTS
AC *32*, 18, *154*; Imray C6, Y58; Stanfords 13; OS 204

TIDES
−0558 Dover; ML 3·0; Duration 0550; Zone 0 (UT)
Daily Predictions and Tidal Curve are given below.
HW Truro is approx HW Falmouth +0008 and −1·8m.

NAVIGATION
WPT 50°08'·00N 05°02'·00W, 183°/003° from/to Black Rock IDM bn, 0·68M. Ent is 1M wide and deep. Hbr accessible in any weather or tide although fresh on-shore winds over an ebb tide make it a bit rough. The only hazard is Black Rk, dries 2·1m almost in the middle of the ent; pass either side, but at night the E chan is advised keeping E of the ECM By, Q (3) 10s. Outside the buoyed chans large areas are quite shallow and care is needed below half tide.

Falmouth is a deep water port, taking ships up to 90,000 tons; appropriate facilities are available. Take care not to impede shipping or ⚓ in prohib areas. Beware oyster beds, especially in Penryn and Percuil Rivers.

Mylor Creek dries or is shoal, <1m, but Mylor Pool has many moorings in up to 2·4m, and some pontoon berths. A PHM and SHM buoy mark the ent to the fairway.

Restronguet Creek has a 12m deep pool at its ent, but dries above Pandora Inn. Beware Carrick Carlys Rk 0·8m, 3ca E of ent, marked by a NCM and SCM post.

River Fal proper flows into the N end of Carrick Roads at Turnaware Pt; beware strong tides and rips. There are ⚓s off the various creeks. 8ca NW of Malpas a flood barrage, lit by 2 FR/FG (vert), is usually open; 3 Fl R lts show when it is closed. Truro dries, but can be reached on the tide.

In **St Mawes Hbr** ent keep S of the SCM buoy marking Lugo Rk, 0·6m, which is always covered. The river dries above Percuil.

LIGHTS AND MARKS
St Anthony Hd lt (H24), R sector covers the Manacles Rks.

RADIO TELEPHONE
Call: *Falmouth Hbr Radio*, VHF Ch **12** 16 (Mon-Fri 0800-1700LT); Hbr launch *Killigrew* Ch 12. Port Health Ch 12 16. Customs launch *Curlew* Ch 12 09 06 10 14 16. Falmouth Yacht Marina, Port Pendennis Marina, Royal Cornwall YC and Mylor Yacht Hbr: Ch **80**, M (H24). Visitors Yacht Haven Ch 12 16. Malpas Marine and St Mawes SC: Ch M (HO). Fuel Barge Ch 16. Falmouth CG Ch 16 67 provides radio coverage of the TSS/ITZ off Land's End; see Fig 10 (5) and 10.1.2. Pendennis Radio Ch 62 (Link calls).

TELEPHONE (Dial code Falmouth 01326; Truro 01872)
Hr Mr Falmouth 312285/314379, ☎ 211352; Hr Mr Penryn 373352; Hr Mr St Mawes 270553; MRCC 317575; ⌗ 0345 231110 (H24); Marinecall 0891 500458; Weather 42534; Police 372231; Dr 317317; Ⓗ Truro 74242.

FACILITIES
FALMOUTH
Port Pendennis Marina ☎ 311113, ☎ 313344, £11.97, AC, FW, YC (R, Bar, Ⓞ, CH); external marina is planned for 1998 (Tall Ships), 73 AB inc 40 ⓥ; max LOA 60m, draft 3.5m.

Falmouth Hbr Visitors Yacht Haven (40) ☎ 314379 (Apr-Sept inc), ☎ 211352, £11.50, P, D, FW, Access H24.

Falmouth Yacht Marina (280+20 visitors), ☎ 316620, ☎ 313939, £16.00, AC, FW, CH, V, P (cans), D, ME, El, Sh, Ⓞ, BH (30 ton), C (2 ton), Gas, Gaz, SM, Bar, R; access H24, but *least depths of 1·4m* require caution at LWS.

Services: Slip, BH (60 ton), C (48 ton), ME, Sh, El, M, SM, Gaz, CH, ACA, FW. Fuel Barge, D only, as chartlet, Ch 16.

Town V, R, Bar, ⌧, Ⓑ, ⇌, ✈ (Plymouth or Newquay).

PENRYN/FLUSHING (01326)
Challenger Marine ☎ 377222, ☎ 377800, £10, VHF Ch M, 80; 46 pontoon berths, access HW±3, visitors welcome.

Services: M, FW, P & D (cans, 500m), Slip, El, ME, C (12 ton), Sh, SM, ACA, BY, CH.

MYLOR (01326)
Mylor Yacht Hbr (250+20 visitors) ☎ 372121, ☎ 372120, BH (25 ton), CH, Gas, Gaz, AC, FW, Slip, C (4 ton), Sh, ME, El, Ⓔ, V, D, R, Bar, Ⓞ, Access HW±1.

RESTRONGUET (01326)
Restronguet Yacht Basin ☎ 373613, Slip, M, Sh; **Pandora Inn** ☎ 372678, V, R, Bar, pontoon dries 1·9m.

Services: Ⓔ, CH, Gas, Gaz.

ST MAWES (01326)
Inner Hbr FW, Slip. **Services:** M, ⚓s (contact SC), BY, ME, Sh, El, SM, Gas.

MALPAS/TRURO (01872)
Bar Creek Yacht Stn ☎ 73919, M; **Malpas Marine** ☎ 71260, M, CH, ME, El, Sh, access H24 except LWS±1.

Services: CH, Gas.

YACHT CLUBS
Port of Falmouth Sailing Association ☎ 211555; Royal Cornwall YC ☎ 311105/312126 (Sec'y), M, Slip, FW, R, Bar; Port Pendennis YC ☎ 211211; Falmouth Town SC ☎ 377061; Flushing SC ☎ 374043; Mylor YC ☎ 374391, Bar; Restronguet SC ☎ 374536; St Mawes SC ☎ 270686.

SHELTER
Excellent. There are many ⓥ berths, see below; also 12 G ⚓s clearly marked, on SW side of the fairway, owned by Falmouth Hbr Commissioners or the Royal Cornwall YC. The **Visitors Yacht Haven** operates Apr-Sept, pontoons being connected to North Quay; max draft 1·8m.

Port Pendennis marina, SW of commercial docks; access HW±3 via lock with tfc lts. External marina planned.

Falmouth Marina, 6ca beyond RCYC up the Penryn R, is accessible at most tides, but at LWS beware depths of 1·4m or less due silting. On near appr pass within 20m of outside pontoon, 2FR (vert), and leave ECM lt bn, VQ (3) 5s (hard to see), close to stbd to keep within narrow chan.

Challenger Marine pontoon, 2ca up-river, has ⓥ berths; dries at LWS. Speed limit in Penryn R is 8kn.

Up-stream on the W bank **Mylor Yacht Hbr** is sheltered from W'lies but uncomfortable in strong E'lies. Further up on the W bank is **Restronguet Creek**, a good ⚓ in pool (12·4m max depth), but most of the creek dries.

On E side **St Mawes Hbr** with 9 G ⚓s (contact SC) offers excellent shelter except from SW winds, when ⚓ above Amsterdam Pt. Off St Just is a good ⚓, but uncomfortable in strong W/SW'lies.

Up the Fal there are pontoons & ⚓s N of Tolcarne Creek; and good ⚓s in Tolcarne Creek, Channals Creek, Tolverne, Ruan Creek (ⓥ pontoon), Church Creek, Mopus Reach & Malpas (Bar Creek Yacht Stn ¼M up Tresillian R has ⚓s). 5kn speed limit in upper reaches and creeks.

ENGLAND – FALMOUTH

LAT 50°09′N   LONG   5°03′W

TIMES AND HEIGHTS OF HIGH AND LOW WATERS

YEAR **1998**

TIME ZONE (UT)
For Summer Time add ONE hour in non-shaded areas

Chart Datum: 2·91 metres below Ordnance Datum (Newlyn)

JANUARY

Day	Time	m	Time	m	Day	Time	m	Time	m
1 TH	0104	0.9	0653	5.4	**16** F	0143	1.0	0715	5.2
	1330	0.8	1920	5.2		1405	1.1	1936	4.9
2 F	0146	0.9	0737	5.4	**17** SA	0214	1.2	0747	5.1
	1413	0.9	2004	5.1		1435	1.3	2008	4.8
3 SA	0227	1.0	0822	5.3	**18** SU	0242	1.4	0821	5.0
	1455	1.0	2050	5.0		1502	1.5	2043	4.7
4 SU	0310	1.2	0910	5.2	**19** M	0309	1.5	0858	4.8
	1540	1.2	2139	4.9		1530	1.6	2122	4.5
5 M	0357	1.4	1002	5.0	**20** TU	0339	1.8	0940	4.6
	1630	1.4	2236	4.7		1603	1.8	2209	4.4
6 TU	0452	1.6	1103	4.8	**21** W	0422	2.0	1030	4.4
	1732	1.6	2345	4.6		1657	2.0	2307	4.2
7 W	0603	1.8	1216	4.6	**22** TH	0534	2.2	1134	4.3
	1849	1.7				1816	2.1		
8 TH	0057	4.5	0731	1.8	**23** F	0019	4.2	0655	2.2
	1328	4.6	2011	1.6		1248	4.3	1931	2.0
9 F	0206	4.7	0848	1.6	**24** SA	0140	4.4	0806	1.9
	1434	4.7	2119	1.5		1407	4.4	2037	1.7
10 SA	0307	4.9	0950	1.4	**25** SU	0246	4.6	0909	1.6
	1533	4.9	2216	1.3		1510	4.6	2136	1.5
11 SU	0358	5.1	1043	1.1	**26** M	0339	4.9	1006	1.4
	1622	5.0	2305	1.1		1601	4.9	2230	1.2
12 M	0443	5.3	1131	0.9	**27** TU	0423	5.2	1058	1.0
	1708	5.1	O 2350	0.9		1647	5.1	2320	0.9
13 TU	0524	5.4	1215	0.8	**28** W	0508	5.4	1148	0.8
	1750	5.1				1733 ●	5.2		
14 W	0031	0.9	0605	5.4	**29** TH	0008	0.7	0553	5.5
	1256	0.8	1829	5.1		1236	0.6	1820	5.3
15 TH	0109	0.9	0642	5.3	**30** F	0055	0.6	0640	5.6
	1332	0.9	1905	5.0		1321	0.4	1907	5.4
					31 SA	0138	0.5	0727	5.6
						1404	0.4	1953	5.3

FEBRUARY

Day	Time	m	Time	m	Day	Time	m	Time	m
1 SU	0219	0.6	0811	5.5	**16** M	0213	1.2	0757	5.0
	1444	0.6	2036	5.2		1429	1.2	2015	4.8
2 M	0259	0.6	0857	5.4	**17** TU	0235	1.3	0829	4.9
	1524	0.8	2121	5.1		1450	1.4	2048	4.7
3 TU	0340	1.1	0944	5.1	**18** W	0259	1.5	0904	4.6
	1607	1.2	2210	4.8		1516	1.6	2125	4.5
4 W	0426	1.4	1038	4.8	**19** TH	0332	1.7	0944	4.4
	1657	1.5	2311	4.5		1555	1.8	2213	4.3
5 TH	0524	1.7	1148	4.5	**20** F	0423	2.0	1041	4.2
	1804	1.8				1659	2.1	2319	4.2
6 F	0025	4.4	0649	1.9	**21** SA	0558	2.1	1154	4.1
	1303	4.4	1939	1.9		1844	2.1		
7 SA	0140	4.4	0827	1.8	**22** SU	0038	4.2	0727	2.0
	1415	4.4	2102	1.7		1321	4.2	2002	1.9
8 SU	0246	4.6	0936	1.5	**23** M	0207	4.5	0904	1.7
	1516	4.6	2201	1.5		1442	4.5	2110	1.5
9 M	0340	4.9	1030	1.3	**24** TU	0311	4.8	0942	1.3
	1607	4.8	2251	1.2		1607	4.8	2209	1.2
10 TU	0425	5.1	1116	1.0	**25** W	0400	5.1	1039	0.9
	1650	4.9	2334	1.0		1628	5.1	2303	0.8
11 W	0506	5.2	1159	0.8	**26** TH	0447	5.4	1159	0.6
	1729 O	5.0				1714	5.3	● 2353	0.5
12 TH	0014	0.8	0543	5.3	**27** F	0533	5.6	1220	0.3
	1238	0.8	1805	5.1		1801	5.4		
13 F	0051	0.8	0619	5.3	**28** SA	0040	0.2	0622	5.7
	1312	0.8	1840	5.1		1305	0.2	1849	5.5
14 SA	0122	0.9	0553	5.3					
	1342	0.9	1912	5.0					
15 SU	0149	1.0	0725	5.2					
	1407	1.1	1943	5.0					

MARCH

Day	Time	m	Time	m	Day	Time	m	Time	m
1 SU	0124	0.2	0710	5.7	**16** M	0123	0.9	0701	5.2
	1348	0.2	1935	5.5		1338	0.9	1918	5.0
2 M	0204	0.3	0756	5.6	**17** TU	0145	1.0	0733	5.0
	1427	0.3	2018	5.4		1359	1.1	1949	4.9
3 TU	0243	0.5	0839	5.4	**18** W	0207	1.2	0803	4.9
	1506	0.6	2059	5.2		1420	1.3	2017	4.8
4 W	0321	0.9	0925	5.1	**19** TH	0231	1.4	0833	4.7
	1545	1.1	2143	4.9		1446	1.5	2049	4.6
5 TH	0404	1.3	1013	4.7	**20** F	0302	1.5	0911	4.4
	1630	1.5	2236	4.5		1521	1.7	2134	4.4
6 F	0456	1.7	1121	4.3	**21** SA	0347	1.8	1007	4.2
	1729	1.9	2354	4.3		1615	2.0	2237	4.3
7 SA	0612	2.0	1244	4.2	**22** SU	0507	2.0	1119	4.1
	1903	2.1				1759	2.1	2355	4.2
8 SU	0117	4.3	0807	2.0	**23** M	0653	2.0	1242	4.2
	1358	4.2	2043	1.9		1932	1.9		
9 M	0224	4.4	0919	1.6	**24** TU	0123	4.4	0811	1.6
	1459	4.4	2143	1.5		1413	4.4	2044	1.5
10 TU	0320	4.7	1011	1.3	**25** W	0241	4.8	0918	1.3
	1549	4.7	2231	1.3		1516	4.8	2147	1.2
11 W	0404	5.0	1056	1.0	**26** TH	0336	5.1	1017	0.8
	1629	4.9	2314	1.0		1606	5.1	2243	0.7
12 TH	0442	5.1	1137	0.8	**27** F	0424	5.4	1110	0.4
	1705	5.0	2352	0.8		1653	5.4	2333	0.4
13 F	0517	5.2	1214	0.7	**28** SA	0512	5.6	1158	0.2
	1738 O	5.1				1739 ●	5.5		
14 SA	0027	0.8	0552	5.3	**29** SU	0020	0.2	0601	5.7
	1247	0.7	1813	5.1		1245	0.1	1827	5.6
15 SU	0057	0.8	0626	5.2	**30** M	0105	0.2	0650	5.7
	1315	0.8	1846	5.1		1327	0.2	1913	5.6
					31 TU	0146	0.2	0737	5.6
						1408	0.3	1956	5.5

APRIL

Day	Time	m	Time	m	Day	Time	m	Time	m
1 W	0225	0.4	0821	5.4	**16** TH	0145	1.1	0740	4.8
	1446	0.6	2036	5.2		1358	1.2	1952	4.9
2 TH	0304	0.8	0905	5.0	**17** F	0213	1.3	0811	4.7
	1525	1.1	2116	4.9		1426	1.4	2025	4.7
3 F	0345	1.3	0952	4.6	**18** SA	0246	1.5	0851	4.5
	1608	1.5	2202	4.6		1503	1.6	2110	4.6
4 SA	0436	1.6	1057	4.2	**19** SU	0331	1.6	0946	4.3
	1704	1.9	2319	4.3		1557	1.8	2210	4.4
5 SU	0545	2.0	1224	4.1	**20** M	0444	1.9	1055	4.2
	1825	2.2				1726	2.0	2325	4.4
6 M	0050	4.2	0734	2.0	**21** TU	0623	1.8	1215	4.2
	1336	4.1	2010	2.0		1902	1.9		
7 TU	0159	4.4	0852	1.7	**22** W	0048	4.5	0743	1.5
	1435	4.4	2115	1.7		1343	4.5	2017	1.5
8 W	0252	4.6	0944	1.5	**23** TH	0208	4.8	0852	1.2
	1522	4.6	2203	1.4		1448	4.8	2123	1.2
9 TH	0337	4.8	1028	1.1	**24** F	0310	5.1	0952	0.8
	1602	4.8	2245	1.1		1541	5.1	2219	0.8
10 F	0415	5.0	1107	0.9	**25** SA	0401	5.4	1046	0.5
	1637	5.0	2323	0.9		1630	5.4	2311	0.4
11 SA	0449	5.1	1144	0.8	**26** SU	0450	5.6	1136	0.2
	1710	5.1	O 2358	0.8		1716	5.5	● 2359	0.2
12 SU	0523	5.2	1217	0.8	**27** M	0538	5.6	1223	0.2
	1744	5.1				1803	5.6		
13 M	0029	0.8	0600	5.2	**28** TU	0044	0.2	0628	5.6
	1244	0.9	1819	5.1		1307	0.2	1850	5.6
14 TU	0055	0.9	0632	5.1	**29** W	0127	0.4	0717	5.5
	1309	0.9	1853	5.1		1348	0.4	1934	5.5
15 W	0120	1.0	0710	5.0	**30** TH	0208	0.5	0803	5.2
	1333	1.1	1924	5.0		1428	0.7	2014	5.2

ENGLAND – FALMOUTH

LAT 50°09′N   LONG 5°03′W

TIMES AND HEIGHTS OF HIGH AND LOW WATERS   YEAR 1998

TIME ZONE (UT)
For Summer Time add ONE hour in non-shaded areas

MAY

Day	Time	m	Day	Time	m
1 F	0248 / 0846 / 1508 / 2052	0.8 / 4.9 / 1.2 / 4.9	**16** SA	0203 / 0759 / 1418 / 2011	1.2 / 4.7 / 1.3 / 4.9
2 SA	0330 / 0932 / 1550 / 2132	1.3 / 4.6 / 1.5 / 4.6	**17** SU	0241 / 0840 / 1458 / 2056	1.3 / 4.6 / 1.5 / 4.7
3 SU	0418 / 1031 / 1642 / 2230	1.6 / 4.2 / 1.9 / 4.3	**18** M	0329 / 0933 / 1551 / 2153	1.5 / 4.4 / 1.7 / 4.6
4 M	0519 / 1155 / 1748	1.9 / 4.1 / 2.1	**19** TU	0433 / 1037 / 1705 / 2301	1.6 / 4.3 / 1.8 / 4.5
5 TU	0010 / 0639 / 1303 / 1912	4.2 / 2.0 / 4.1 / 2.1	**20** W	0554 / 1153 / 1830	1.6 / 4.3 / 1.7
6 W	0121 / 0804 / 1400 / 2028	4.3 / 1.8 / 4.3 / 1.9	**21** TH	0020 / 0713 / 1312 / 1947	4.6 / 1.5 / 4.5 / 1.5
7 TH	0216 / 0903 / 1447 / 2123	4.5 / 1.5 / 4.5 / 1.5	**22** F	0138 / 0824 / 1420 / 2055	4.8 / 1.3 / 4.8 / 1.3
8 F	0302 / 0949 / 1528 / 2208	4.7 / 1.4 / 4.7 / 1.4	**23** SA	0243 / 0926 / 1516 / 2155	5.0 / 0.9 / 5.1 / 0.9
9 SA	0341 / 1030 / 1605 / 2248	4.9 / 1.2 / 4.9 / 1.1	**24** SU	0339 / 1022 / 1607 / 2249	5.2 / 0.6 / 5.3 / 0.6
10 SU	0419 / 1107 / 1641 / 2324	5.0 / 1.0 / 5.0 / 1.0	**25** M	0429 / 1114 / 1655 / ● 2338	5.4 / 0.5 / 5.4 / 0.4
11 M	0456 / 1141 / 1716 / O 2357	5.0 / 1.0 / 5.1 / 0.9	**26** TU	0518 / 1201 / 1742	5.4 / 0.4 / 5.5
12 TU	0533 / 1213 / 1754	5.1 / 1.0 / 5.1	**27** W	0025 / 0608 / 1247 / 1828	0.4 / 5.4 / 0.4 / 5.5
13 W	0028 / 0613 / 1243 / 1830	0.9 / 5.0 / 1.0 / 5.1	**28** TH	0110 / 0659 / 1330 / 1913	0.4 / 5.3 / 0.6 / 5.4
14 TH	0059 / 0650 / 1313 / 1904	1.0 / 4.9 / 1.1 / 5.0	**29** F	0153 / 0744 / 1411 / 1954	0.6 / 5.1 / 0.8 / 5.2
15 F	0130 / 0725 / 1344 / 1935	1.1 / 4.8 / 1.2 / 5.0	**30** SA	0234 / 0828 / 1451 / 2029	0.9 / 4.9 / 1.2 / 5.0
			31 SU	0315 / 0908 / 1532 / 2105	1.2 / 4.6 / 1.5 / 4.7

JUNE

Day	Time	m	Day	Time	m
1 M	0358 / 0952 / 1617 / 2148	1.5 / 4.3 / 1.7 / 4.5	**16** TU	0326 / 0925 / 1546 / 2140	1.3 / 4.6 / 1.5 / 4.8
2 TU	0448 / 1052 / 1709 / 2250	1.7 / 4.2 / 2.0 / 4.3	**17** W	0420 / 1022 / 1644 / 2241	1.4 / 4.5 / 1.5 / 4.7
3 W	0546 / 1209 / 1812	1.9 / 4.1 / 2.1	**18** TH	0525 / 1131 / 1756 / 2354	1.5 / 4.5 / 1.6 / 4.6
4 TH	0016 / 0652 / 1310 / 1919	4.3 / 1.9 / 4.2 / 2.0	**19** F	0639 / 1243 / 1914	1.5 / 4.5 / 1.5
5 F	0124 / 0759 / 1402 / 2024	4.3 / 1.8 / 4.4 / 1.8	**20** SA	0110 / 0754 / 1351 / 2028	4.7 / 1.4 / 4.7 / 1.4
6 SA	0218 / 0855 / 1447 / 2118	4.5 / 1.5 / 4.6 / 1.5	**21** SU	0219 / 0901 / 1452 / 2132	4.8 / 1.2 / 4.9 / 1.2
7 SU	0305 / 0943 / 1531 / 2205	4.7 / 1.4 / 4.8 / 1.4	**22** M	0318 / 1001 / 1546 / 2229	5.0 / 0.9 / 5.1 / 0.9
8 M	0348 / 1026 / 1611 / 2246	4.8 / 1.2 / 4.9 / 1.2	**23** TU	0411 / 1055 / 1636 / 2321	5.1 / 0.8 / 5.3 / 0.7
9 TU	0429 / 1105 / 1651 / 2326	4.9 / 1.1 / 5.0 / 1.1	**24** W	0501 / 1144 / 1722 / ●	5.2 / 0.6 / 5.4
10 W	0511 / 1143 / 1730 / O	5.0 / 1.0 / 5.1	**25** TH	0009 / 0550 / 1231 / 1808	0.6 / 5.2 / 0.6 / 5.4
11 TH	0004 / 0551 / 1221 / 1809	1.0 / 5.0 / 1.0 / 5.1	**26** F	0055 / 0639 / 1314 / 1853	0.6 / 5.1 / 0.7 / 5.3
12 F	0042 / 0632 / 1258 / 1848	1.0 / 4.9 / 1.0 / 5.1	**27** SA	0138 / 0725 / 1355 / 1933	0.7 / 5.0 / 0.9 / 5.2
13 SA	0120 / 0713 / 1336 / 1926	1.0 / 4.9 / 1.1 / 5.1	**28** SU	0218 / 0804 / 1433 / 2005	0.9 / 4.9 / 1.1 / 5.0
14 SU	0159 / 0753 / 1415 / 2004	1.0 / 4.8 / 1.2 / 5.0	**29** M	0255 / 0837 / 1509 / 2037	1.1 / 4.7 / 1.4 / 4.7
15 M	0240 / 0835 / 1457 / 2048	1.1 / 4.7 / 1.3 / 5.0	**30** TU	0332 / 0911 / 1546 / 2114	1.4 / 4.5 / 1.5 / 4.7

JULY

Day	Time	m	Day	Time	m
1 W	0411 / 0952 / 1627 / 2200	1.6 / 4.3 / 1.8 / 4.5	**16** TH	0402 / 1005 / 1623 / 2223	1.1 / 4.7 / 1.4 / 4.8
2 TH	0456 / 1044 / 1718 / 2256	1.8 / 4.2 / 2.0 / 4.3	**17** F	0456 / 1105 / 1723 / 2331	1.4 / 4.6 / 1.5 / 4.6
3 F	0551 / 1151 / 1819	1.9 / 4.2 / 2.0	**18** SA	0604 / 1215 / 1840	1.5 / 4.5 / 1.6
4 SA	0007 / 0653 / 1302 / 1923	4.2 / 1.9 / 4.2 / 2.0	**19** SU	0046 / 0724 / 1326 / 2003	4.5 / 1.5 / 4.5 / 1.6
5 SU	0122 / 0755 / 1404 / 2025	4.3 / 1.8 / 4.4 / 1.8	**20** M	0159 / 0841 / 1431 / 2115	4.6 / 1.5 / 4.7 / 1.4
6 M	0225 / 0853 / 1456 / 2121	4.4 / 1.6 / 4.6 / 1.5	**21** TU	0302 / 0945 / 1529 / 2215	4.7 / 1.3 / 4.9 / 1.1
7 TU	0318 / 0945 / 1543 / 2211	4.6 / 1.4 / 4.8 / 1.4	**22** W	0358 / 1041 / 1619 / 2308	4.9 / 1.0 / 5.1 / 0.9
8 W	0404 / 1033 / 1626 / 2258	4.8 / 1.2 / 5.0 / 1.1	**23** TH	0446 / 1130 / 1705 / ● 2356	5.0 / 0.8 / 5.3 / 0.7
9 TH	0448 / 1119 / 1709 / O 2344	4.9 / 1.1 / 5.1 / 1.0	**24** F	0532 / 1216 / 1749	5.1 / 0.7 / 5.3
10 F	0531 / 1203 / 1751	5.0 / 1.0 / 5.2	**25** SA	0040 / 0618 / 1258 / 1830	0.7 / 5.1 / 0.7 / 5.3
11 SA	0028 / 0617 / 1247 / 1833	0.9 / 5.0 / 0.9 / 5.3	**26** SU	0121 / 0659 / 1336 / 1907	0.7 / 5.0 / 0.8 / 5.2
12 SU	0111 / 0701 / 1329 / 1915	0.9 / 5.0 / 0.9 / 5.3	**27** M	0157 / 0734 / 1410 / 1938	0.8 / 4.9 / 1.0 / 5.1
13 M	0153 / 0744 / 1409 / 1958	0.8 / 5.0 / 0.9 / 5.3	**28** TU	0230 / 0804 / 1441 / 2009	1.0 / 4.8 / 1.2 / 5.0
14 TU	0234 / 0828 / 1450 / 2041	0.8 / 5.0 / 1.0 / 5.2	**29** W	0300 / 0835 / 1510 / 2043	1.3 / 4.7 / 1.4 / 4.8
15 W	0316 / 0914 / 1534 / 2129	0.9 / 4.9 / 1.2 / 5.0	**30** TH	0328 / 0912 / 1540 / 2121	1.5 / 4.5 / 1.6 / 4.6
			31 F	0359 / 0955 / 1617 / 2206	1.7 / 4.4 / 1.9 / 4.4

AUGUST

Day	Time	m	Day	Time	m
1 SA	0444 / 1048 / 1716 / 2303	1.9 / 4.2 / 2.1 / 4.2	**16** SU	0531 / 1150 / 1809	1.6 / 4.4 / 1.8
2 SU	0554 / 1155 / 1831	2.0 / 4.2 / 2.1	**17** M	0027 / 0657 / 1306 / 1946	4.4 / 1.8 / 4.4 / 1.8
3 M	0017 / 0706 / 1314 / 1941	4.2 / 2.0 / 4.2 / 2.0	**18** TU	0145 / 0828 / 1416 / 2105	4.4 / 1.7 / 4.6 / 1.6
4 TU	0145 / 0813 / 1423 / 2045	4.3 / 1.8 / 4.5 / 1.7	**19** W	0251 / 0935 / 1516 / 2205	4.5 / 1.5 / 4.8 / 1.3
5 W	0250 / 0913 / 1517 / 2142	4.5 / 1.5 / 4.8 / 1.5	**20** TH	0347 / 1028 / 1605 / 2255	4.8 / 1.2 / 5.0 / 1.0
6 TH	0342 / 1007 / 1604 / 2235	4.7 / 1.3 / 5.0 / 1.1	**21** F	0433 / 1115 / 1647 / 2340	4.9 / 0.9 / 5.2 / 0.8
7 F	0428 / 1058 / 1647 / 2325	4.9 / 1.1 / 5.2 / 0.9	**22** SA	0513 / 1158 / 1727 / ●	5.0 / 0.8 / 5.3
8 SA	0512 / 1146 / 1730 / O	5.1 / 0.8 / 5.3	**23** SU	0021 / 0553 / 1238 / 1804	0.7 / 5.1 / 0.7 / 5.3
9 SU	0012 / 0558 / 1233 / 1816	0.7 / 5.2 / 0.7 / 5.4	**24** M	0059 / 0629 / 1313 / 1839	0.7 / 5.1 / 0.8 / 5.3
10 M	0058 / 0644 / 1317 / 1901	0.5 / 5.2 / 0.6 / 5.5	**25** TU	0132 / 0701 / 1343 / 1910	0.8 / 5.0 / 0.9 / 5.2
11 TU	0141 / 0730 / 1358 / 1946	0.5 / 5.2 / 0.6 / 5.5	**26** W	0200 / 0732 / 1409 / 1940	1.0 / 5.0 / 1.1 / 5.1
12 W	0221 / 0813 / 1438 / 2029	0.5 / 5.2 / 0.7 / 5.4	**27** TH	0223 / 0802 / 1432 / 2012	1.2 / 4.8 / 1.3 / 4.9
13 TH	0301 / 0857 / 1517 / 2114	0.7 / 5.1 / 0.9 / 5.1	**28** F	0243 / 0835 / 1453 / 2046	1.4 / 4.7 / 1.5 / 4.7
14 F	0342 / 0944 / 1601 / 2203	1.0 / 4.9 / 1.3 / 4.9	**29** SA	0304 / 0912 / 1519 / 2125	1.6 / 4.5 / 1.7 / 4.5
15 SA	0429 / 1038 / 1655 / 2306	1.4 / 4.6 / 1.5 / 4.6	**30** SU	0335 / 0958 / 1602 / 2214	1.8 / 4.3 / 2.0 / 4.2
			31 M	0431 / 1058 / 1733 / 2324	2.1 / 4.2 / 2.2 / 4.1

Chart Datum: 2·91 metres below Ordnance Datum (Newlyn)

ENGLAND – FALMOUTH

LAT 50°09′N   LONG 5°03′W

TIMES AND HEIGHTS OF HIGH AND LOW WATERS   YEAR **1998**

TIME ZONE (UT)
For Summer Time add ONE hour in non-shaded areas

SEPTEMBER

Day	DoW	Time	m	Time	m	Time	m	Time	m
1	TU	0620	2.2	1215	4.2	1905	2.1		
2	W	0055	4.1	0740	2.0	1347	4.4	2016	1.8
3	TH	0226	4.4	0846	1.7	1451	4.7	2118	1.5
4	F	0322	4.7	0945	1.4	1540	5.1	2213	1.1
5	SA	0408	5.0	1038	1.0	1625	5.3	2305	0.7
6 ○	SU	0452	5.2	1128	0.7	1709	5.5	2353	0.5
7	M	0536	5.4	1215	0.5	1754	5.6		
8	TU	0039	0.3	0623	5.4	1300	0.4	1842	5.7
9	W	0122	0.3	0709	5.5	1341	0.4	1928	5.6
10	TH	0203	0.4	0754	5.4	1421	0.6	2011	5.5
11	F	0242	0.6	0836	5.3	1500	0.9	2056	5.2
12	SA	0321	1.0	0921	5.0	1541	1.3	2143	4.8
13	SU	0405	1.5	1012	4.7	1632	1.6	2245	4.5
14	M	0503	1.8	1124	4.4	1745	2.0		
15	TU	0013	4.2	0635	2.1	1249	4.3	1935	2.0
16	W	0135	4.3	0816	1.9	1402	4.5	2054	1.7
17	TH	0242	4.5	0921	1.6	1501	4.8	2149	1.4
18	F	0334	4.7	1011	1.3	1548	5.0	2236	1.1
19	SA	0415	5.0	1055	1.0	1627	5.2	2318	0.8
20 ●	SU	0452	5.1	1135	0.8	1703	5.3	2357	0.7
21	M	0525	5.2	1213	0.8	1735	5.3		
22	TU	0032	0.7	0558	5.2	1245	0.8	1808	5.3
23	W	0102	0.8	0629	5.2	1313	0.9	1841	5.2
24	TH	0127	1.0	0702	5.1	1337	1.1	1913	5.1
25	F	0147	1.2	0733	5.0	1358	1.3	1943	4.9
26	SA	0206	1.4	0803	4.8	1418	1.5	2014	4.7
27	SU	0227	1.5	0836	4.6	1444	1.7	2050	4.5
28	M	0258	1.8	0918	4.4	1522	1.9	2140	4.3
29	TU	0344	2.1	1016	4.3	1630	2.2	2248	4.1
30	W	0521	2.3	1131	4.2	1830	2.2		

OCTOBER

Day	DoW	Time	m	Time	m	Time	m	Time	m
1	TH	0011	4.1	0708	2.2	1259	4.4	1948	1.9
2	F	0157	4.4	0820	1.8	1420	4.7	2053	1.5
3	SA	0258	4.8	0921	1.4	1515	5.1	2150	1.1
4	SU	0346	5.1	1016	1.0	1601	5.4	2242	0.7
5 ○	M	0430	5.4	1106	0.7	1646	5.6	2331	0.4
6	TU	0514	5.5	1154	0.4	1732	5.7		
7	W	0017	0.3	0600	5.6	1239	0.3	1820	5.8
8	TH	0101	0.2	0646	5.7	1322	0.3	1908	5.7
9	F	0143	0.4	0732	5.6	1403	0.5	1954	5.5
10	SA	0222	0.7	0814	5.4	1443	0.9	2038	5.2
11	SU	0302	1.1	0859	5.1	1525	1.3	2126	4.8
12	M	0346	1.5	0948	4.8	1615	1.7	2228	4.4
13	TU	0441	2.0	1059	4.5	1726	2.1	2359	4.2
14	W	0607	2.3	1228	4.3	1913	2.1		
15	TH	0118	4.2	0751	2.1	1340	4.5	2031	1.8
16	F	0221	4.4	0856	1.8	1437	4.7	2125	1.5
17	SA	0311	4.7	0945	1.5	1523	5.0	2210	1.2
18	SU	0351	4.9	1028	1.2	1601	5.1	2250	1.0
19	M	0425	5.1	1107	1.0	1636	5.3	2327	0.9
20 ●	TU	0457	5.2	1143	0.9	1708	5.3		
21	W	0001	0.9	0528	5.3	1216	0.9	1741	5.3
22	TH	0030	1.0	0601	5.3	1243	1.0	1816	5.2
23	F	0054	1.1	0634	5.2	1308	1.2	1849	5.1
24	SA	0117	1.2	0707	5.1	1331	1.3	1921	5.0
25	SU	0139	1.4	0737	5.0	1356	1.5	1952	4.8
26	M	0205	1.5	0809	4.8	1424	1.6	2027	4.6
27	TU	0237	1.7	0851	4.6	1503	1.9	2117	4.4
28	W	0322	2.0	0946	4.5	1604	2.1	2222	4.2
29	TH	0438	2.3	1056	4.3	1751	2.2	2341	4.2
30	F	0631	2.2	1216	4.5	1916	1.9		
31	SA	0115	4.4	0750	1.9	1341	4.8	2025	1.5

NOVEMBER

Day	DoW	Time	m	Time	m	Time	m	Time	m
1	SU	0227	4.8	0855	1.5	1445	5.1	2125	1.1
2	M	0320	5.1	0952	1.1	1537	5.4	2218	0.8
3	TU	0407	5.4	1044	0.7	1624	5.6	2308	0.5
4 ○	W	0452	5.6	1132	0.5	1711	5.7	2355	0.3
5	TH	0537	5.7	1219	0.4	1800	5.7		
6	F	0041	0.4	0624	5.7	1304	0.4	1849	5.6
7	SA	0124	0.5	0711	5.6	1347	0.6	1937	5.4
8	SU	0205	0.8	0756	5.4	1429	0.9	2023	5.1
9	M	0246	1.2	0839	5.2	1512	1.3	2110	4.8
10	TU	0330	1.6	0926	4.9	1600	1.7	2208	4.5
11	W	0421	2.0	1026	4.6	1701	2.0	2332	4.2
12	TH	0529	2.2	1153	4.4	1824	2.2		
13	F	0045	4.2	0709	2.3	1304	4.4	1948	2.0
14	SA	0146	4.4	0815	2.0	1402	4.6	2048	1.7
15	SU	0236	4.6	0909	1.7	1449	4.8	2135	1.5
16	M	0318	4.8	0954	1.5	1530	5.0	2216	1.3
17	TU	0355	5.0	1034	1.3	1606	5.1	2254	1.2
18	W	0428	5.2	1111	1.2	1641	5.2	2328	1.1
19 ●	TH	0502	5.3	1144	1.1	1716	5.2	2358	1.1
20	F	0536	5.3	1215	1.1	1753	5.2		
21	SA	0027	1.2	0613	5.3	1244	1.2	1829	5.1
22	SU	0055	1.2	0648	5.1	1314	1.3	1905	5.0
23	M	0123	1.4	0721	5.1	1344	1.4	1938	4.8
24	TU	0154	1.5	0754	5.0	1418	1.5	2015	4.7
25	W	0230	1.6	0834	4.8	1459	1.7	2102	4.5
26	TH	0315	1.8	0927	4.7	1554	1.8	2201	4.4
27	F	0418	2.0	1029	4.6	1712	1.9	2312	4.4
28	SA	0548	2.1	1144	4.6	1838	1.8		
29	SU	0031	4.5	0713	1.9	1301	4.7	1952	1.6
30	M	0149	4.7	0824	1.6	1412	5.0	2057	1.3

DECEMBER

Day	DoW	Time	m	Time	m	Time	m	Time	m
1	TU	0250	5.0	0926	1.3	1512	5.2	2154	1.0
2	W	0343	5.3	1022	0.9	1604	5.4	2247	0.7
3 ○	TH	0431	5.5	1113	0.7	1653	5.6	2336	0.6
4	F	0517	5.6	1201	0.5	1743	5.6		
5	SA	0022	0.5	0605	5.7	1248	0.5	1832	5.5
6	SU	0108	0.6	0653	5.6	1333	0.7	1922	5.3
7	M	0150	0.8	0738	5.5	1416	0.9	2008	5.1
8	TU	0232	1.2	0821	5.2	1458	1.2	2052	4.8
9	W	0313	1.5	0901	5.0	1542	1.5	2137	4.6
10	TH	0357	1.8	0945	4.7	1629	1.8	2232	4.3
11	F	0448	2.1	1041	4.5	1726	2.0	2348	4.2
12	SA	0549	2.2	1200	4.4	1833	2.1		
13	SU	0053	4.2	0703	2.2	1308	4.4	1945	2.0
14	M	0149	4.4	0813	2.0	1404	4.5	2045	1.8
15	TU	0237	4.6	0909	1.8	1451	4.7	2134	1.6
16	W	0320	4.8	0956	1.5	1535	4.9	2216	1.5
17	TH	0359	5.0	1037	1.4	1616	5.0	2254	1.3
18 ●	F	0438	5.2	1115	1.3	1655	5.1	2330	1.2
19	SA	0515	5.2	1151	1.2	1734	5.1		
20	SU	0005	1.2	0555	5.2	1227	1.2	1815	5.1
21	M	0040	1.2	0633	5.2	1303	1.2	1854	5.0
22	TU	0114	1.2	0710	5.2	1339	1.2	1931	4.9
23	W	0150	1.3	0746	5.1	1416	1.3	2009	4.8
24	TH	0228	1.4	0825	5.0	1456	1.4	2052	4.7
25	F	0310	1.5	0912	4.9	1543	1.5	2143	4.6
26	SA	0401	1.7	1007	4.8	1640	1.6	2244	4.5
27	SU	0506	1.8	1113	4.7	1753	1.7	2357	4.5
28	M	0627	1.8	1227	4.7	1913	1.6		
29	TU	0113	4.6	0750	1.7	1342	4.8	2027	1.5
30	W	0222	4.8	0902	1.5	1448	5.0	2132	1.3
31	TH	0321	5.1	1003	1.2	1546	5.2	2229	1.0

Chart Datum: 2·91 metres below Ordnance Datum (Newlyn)

FALMOUTH

MEAN SPRING
AND NEAP CURVES

MEAN RANGES	
Springs	4·7m
Neaps	2·3m

Springs occur 2 days
after
New and Full Moon.

**OTHER HARBOURS AND ANCHORAGES BETWEEN
ST ANTHONY HEAD AND MEVAGISSEY**

PORTSCATHO, Cornwall, 50°10'·80N 04°58'·25W. AC *154*.
HW –0600 on Dover, HW –0025 and –0·2m on Devonport;
ML 3·0m; Duration 0550. Small drying hbr, but in settled
weather and off-shore winds ⚓ outside moorings in good
holding. No lts. Hr Mr ☎ (01872) 580616. Facilities: V, FW,
R, Bar, Slip, P & D (cans), Ⓑ 1000-1230 Mon, Wed, Fri, ✉.

GORRAN HAVEN, Cornwall, 50°14'·45N 04°47'·09W. AC
148, *1267*. HW –0600 on Dover, HW –0010 and –0·1m on
Devonport. Shelter good with flat sand beach for drying
out in off-shore wind; good ⚓ 100 to 500m E of harbour.
Beware Gwineas Rk and Yaw Rk marked by ECM. Beware
pot markers on appr. Not suitable ⚓ when wind is in E.
Fin keelers without legs should not ⚓ closer than 300m
from hbr wall where depth is 1·8m at MLWS. Facilities:
✉, V, Bar, P & D (cans, 1M), R.

PORTMELLON, Cornwall, 50°15'·70N 04°46'·91W. AC 148,
1267. HW –0600 on Dover, HW –0010 and –0·1m on
Devonport; ML 3·1m; Duration 0600. Shelter good but
only suitable as a temp ⚓ in settled weather and offshore winds. There are no lts and few facilities.

MEVAGISSEY   10-1-14

Cornwall 50°16'·12N 04°46'·86W   Rtg 3-3-1

CHARTS
AC 147, 148, *1267*; Imray C6; Stanfords 13; OS 204

TIDES
–0600 Dover; ML 3·1; Duration 0600; Zone 0 (UT)

Standard Port DEVONPORT (→)

Times				Height (metres)			
High Water		Low Water		MHWS	MHWN	MLWN	MLWS
0000	0600	0000	0600	5·5	4·4	2·2	0·8
1200	1800	1200	1800				
Differences MEVAGISSEY							
–0015	–0020	–0010	–0005	–0·1	–0·1	–0·2	–0·1

SHELTER (MEVAGISSEY *continued)*
Exposed to E'lies, but available at all states of the tide.
Dangerous to appr in strong SE'lies. ❶ berth on S Quay
in about 1·6m (D available). Bilge keelers/cats may dry
out on sandy beach, SE side of W Quay. One ⚓ in Outer
hbr on request to Hr Mr. ⚓ inside the hbr is prohib due to
over-crowding and many FVs. ⚓ outside the S Pier is only
advised in settled weather with no E in the wind. Inner
hbr (dries 1·5m) is reserved for FVs, unless taking on FW.

NAVIGATION
WPT 50°16'·11N 04°46'·54W, 090°/270° from/to pier hd lt,
0·20M. Beware rky ledges off the N Quay. Hbr ent is 46m
wide. Speed limit in the hbr is 3kn. Beware FVs.

LIGHTS AND MARKS
S Quay Fl (2) 10s 9m 12M, Dia 30s (fishing).

RADIO TELEPHONE
Hr Mr VHF Ch 16 14 (Summer 0900-2100LT. Winter
0900-1700LT); call on 16 for berth.

TELEPHONE (Dial code 01726)
Hr Mr 843305, (home 842496); MRSC (01803) 882704;
⌗ 0345 231110 (H24); Marinecall 0891 500458; Police
842262; Dr 843701.

FACILITIES
Outer Hbr AB (S Quay) £5, M, FW, D; **Inner Hbr** Slip, FW,
C (1 ton). **Services:** BY, Sh (wood), CH. **Village** EC Thurs;
V, R, ▣, Gas, Bar, Ice, ✉, Ⓑ (June-Sept 1000-1430, Oct-
June 1000-1300), ⇌ (bus to St Austell), ✈ (Newquay).

GUNNERY RANGE OFF DODMAN PT AND GRIBBIN HEAD

Naval gunnery practice takes place to seaward of Dodman Pt and Gribbin Hd, under the control of Flag Officer Sea Training (FOST), HMS Drake, Plymouth PL2 2BG. Firing is by day only, approx 1-2 times per week, in a 2 hrs block, although actual firing only lasts about 15 mins. Planned firings are broadcast in Gunfacts (see 8.5.2) and Navtex. Advance details are also printed in local newspapers and are available from Hr Mrs at Fowey, Looe, Polperro and Mevagissey. Firings are not planned for two weeks over Christmas and four weeks in August.

The range is in danger areas D.006A and D.007A & B (see 10.1.18). Warships, between 2·5 and 9M SSE of Gribbin Hd, fire WSW at 3 SPM target buoys, Fl Y, which lie from 2·4 to 4·8M SSE of Dodman Pt. The RN will ensure that safety requirements can be met; if not possible, ie due to vessels in the range area, then firing will not take place. A helicopter conducts range safety surveillance. A range safety boat will advise other craft of firings and may suggest a slight course alteration to clear the area. Yachts are legally entitled to transit through the range area. For info ☎ (01752) 5557550 (H24) or call FOST OPS on VHF Ch 74, which is monitored by all warships in the areas S of Plymouth.

MINOR HARBOURS BETWEEN MEVAGISSEY AND FOWEY

CHARLESTOWN, Cornwall, 50°19'·81N 04°45'·28W. AC 31, 148, *1267*. HW –0555 on Dover, –0010 on Devonport; HW –0·1m on Devonport; ML 3·1m; Duration 0605. A china clay port; yachts should berth in the outer hbr (dries), but only in W'lies. The inner locked hbr is rarely used by commercial ships. Ent dries and should only be attempted by day and in off-shore winds with calm weather. Hbr is closed in SE winds. Waiting buoys 2ca S of hbr. N bkwtr 2FG (vert) 5m 1M; S bkwtr 2FR (vert) 5m 1M. Ent sig: ® (night) = hbr shut. VHF Ch14 16 (HW –2, only when vessel expected). Yachts should pre-arrange via Hr Mr on Ch 14 or ☎ (01726) 67526. Facilities: EC Thurs; AB, FW, P & D (cans or pre-arranged tanker), R, Bar, V at ⊠, ME, Sh.

PAR, Cornwall, 50°20'·58N 04°42'·00W. AC 31, 148, *1267*. HW –0555 on Dover; ML 3·1m; Duration 0605. See 10.1.15. A china clay port, only in emergency for yachts; dries 1·2m. 4 chys are conspic 2½ca W of ent. Beware Killyvarder Rk (dries 2·4m) 3ca SE of ent, marked by a SHM bn. Only attempt ent by day, in calm weather with off-shore winds. Ent sigs: R shape (day) or ® lt (night) = port closed or vessel leaving. VHF Ch 12 16 (by day, HW –2 to HW +1). Hr Mr ☎ (01726) 817300. Facilities: EC Thurs; Bar, FW.

FOWEY   10-1-15

Cornwall 50°19'·62N 04°38'·47W   Rtg 1-2-1

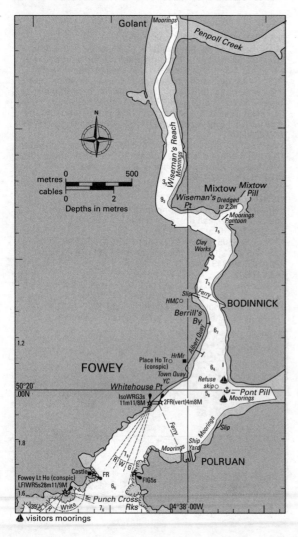

▲ visitors moorings

CHARTS
AC 31, 148, *1267*; Imray C6, Y52; Stanfords 13; OS 204
TIDES
–0540 Dover; ML 2·9; Duration 0605; Zone 0 (UT)

Standard Port DEVONPORT (→)

Times				Height (metres)			
High Water		Low Water		MHWS	MHWN	MLWN	MLWS
0000	0600	0000	0600	5·5	4·4	2·2	0·8
1200	1800	1200	1800				
Differences FOWEY							
–0010	–0015	–0010	–0005	–0·1	–0·1	–0·2	–0·2
LOSTWITHIEL							
+0005	–0010	Dries		–4·1	–4·1	Dries	
PAR							
–0005	–0015	0000	–0010	–0·4	–0·4	–0·4	–0·2

SHELTER
Good, but exposed to winds from S to SW. Gales from these directions can cause heavy swell in the lower hbr and confused seas, especially on the ebb. Entry at any tide in any conditions. Speed limit 6kn. All ⚓s are White and marked 'FHC VISITORS'. Dues £7.90 for a 30'/9m boat overnight. Pontoons are in situ May-Oct. Craft >12·5m LOA should berth/moor as directed by Hr Mr. **Pont Pill**, on the E side, offers double-berth fore and aft ⚓s and AB in 2m on a 120' floating pontoon; there is also a refuse barge and fuel barge. Opposite Albert Quay, on the E side of the chan there is a line of single swinging ⚓s and another 120' pontoon.
At **Albert Quay** the 'T' shaped landing pontoon is for short stay (2 hrs), plus FW. A second short stay (2 hrs) landing pontoon is 250m up-river, at Berrills BY.
At **Mixtow Pill** (5ca upriver) is a quieter 120' pontoon in 2·2m, but only 60' for ⚓. A ⚓ is 30m N of Wiseman's Pt.
NAVIGATION
WPT 50°19'·30N 04°38'·73W, 207°/027° from/to Whitehouse Pt lt, Iso WRG 3s, 0·72M. Appr in W sector of Fowey lt ho. W sector of Whitehouse Pt lt leads 027° through hbr ent. 3M E of ent beware Udder Rk marked by unlit SCM buoy. From SW beware Cannis Rk (4ca SE of Gribbin Hd) with SCM buoy, Q (6) + L Fl 15s. Entering hbr, keep well clear of Punch Cross Rks to stbd. Caution: Fowey is a busy commercial clay port. Unmarked chan is navigable up to Golant, but moorings restrict ⚓ space. Lerryn (1·6M) and Lostwithiel (3M) are accessible on the tide by shoal draft.

FOWEY continued

LIGHTS AND MARKS
An unlit RW tr 33m on Gribbin Hd (1·3M WSW of hbr ent) is conspic from all sea directions, as is a white house 3ca E of hbr ent. Lt ho is conspic, L Fl WR 5s 28m 11/9M, R284°-295°, W295°-028°, R028°-054°. Whitehouse Pt Iso WRG 3s 11m 11/8M, G017°-022°, W022°-032°, R032°-037°. Ent is marked by Lamp Rk SHM bn Fl G 5s 7m 2M, vis 088°-205°, and St Catherine's Pt FR 15m 2M, vis 150°-295°.

RADIO TELEPHONE
Call *Fowey Hbr Radio* Ch **12** 09 16 (HO). Hbr Patrol (0900-2000LT) Ch 12 16. *Fowey Refueller* Ch 10 16. Water taxi Ch 06. Pilots Ch 09. Tugs Ch 09 12.

TELEPHONE (Dial code 01726)
Hr Mr 832471, ⚓ 833738; MRSC (01803) 882704; Marinecall 0891 500458; ⌗ 0345 231110 (H24); Police 72313; Ⓗ 832241; Dr 832451; Fowey Refueller 833055/(0836) 519341 (mobile).

FACILITIES
Albert Quay Pontoon L, FW; **Polruan Quay** Slip, P, D, L, FW, C (3 ton); **Royal Fowey YC** ☎ 832245, FW, Showers, R, Bar; **Fowey Gallants SC** ☎ 832335, Showers, Bar; **Fowey Refueller** (0900-1800LT daily; winter Mon-Fri) VHF Ch 10, 16 or ☎ as above, D. **Services:** M, FW, Gas, Gaz, CH, ACA, Ⓔ, BY, Slip, ME, EI, Sh, C (7 ton); ⌀ and oils disposal at Berrills BY pontoon, 250m N of Albert Quay.
Town EC Wed & Sat; ✉, Ⓑ, ⇌ (bus to Par), ✈ (Newquay).

KEEPING FOWEY HARBOUR CLEAN
The Harbour Authority actively campaigns against all forms of pollution in the Harbour and estuary so as to protect and preserve the environment for both humans and wildlife. There are many species of birds, some protected, and the water supports a variety of fish and shellfish.
Yachtsmen are encouraged to use shore-side toilets and/or holding tanks and the sewage pump-out facilities at Berrill's Yard. Rubbish should be ditched in the skip on the refuse pontoon or taken ashore. Waste oils and rags must be disposed of in sealed containers.
Noise is an ever-increasing nuisance, whether caused by slapping halyards, blaring radios or noisy outboards being used in a thoughtless manner – often with the additional disturbance from wash.

MINOR HARBOUR BETWEEN FOWEY AND LOOE

POLPERRO, Cornwall, 50°19'·74N 04°30'·72W. AC 148, *1267*. HW –0554 on Dover; HW –0007 and –0·2m on Devonport; ML 3·1m; Duration 0610. Shelter good, but hbr dries about 2m. There is 3·3m at MHWS and 2·5m at MHWN. The ent is 9·8m wide (closed by gate in bad weather). AB on N quay or pick up a buoy; also temp buoys outside hbr. Beware The Ranneys to W of ent, and the rks to E. Lights: Iso WR 6s 30m 7M at Spy House Pt CG Stn, vis W288°-060°, R060°-288°. Tidal Basin, W pier hd FW 4m 4M on post; shows FR when hbr closed. Dir FW (occas) shown from measured distance bns 1M and 2·2M to ENE. Hr Mr on Fish Quay, AB £11; FW on quays. EC Sat.

LOOE   10-1-16

Cornwall 50°21'·00N 04°26'·96W   Rtg 3-3-2

CHARTS
AC 147, 148, *1267*; Imray C6; Stanfords 13; OS 201

TIDES
–0538 Dover; ML 3·0; Duration 0610; Zone 0 (UT)

Standard Port DEVONPORT (→)

Times				Height (metres)			
High Water		Low Water		MHWS	MHWN	MLWN	MLWS
0000	0600	0000	0600	5·5	4·4	2·2	0·8
1200	1800	1200	1800				
Differences LOOE							
–0010	–0010	–0005	–0005	–0·1	–0·2	–0·2	–0·2
WHITSAND BAY							
0000	0000	0000	0000	0·0	+0·1	–0·1	+0·2

SHELTER
Good, but uncomfortable in strong SE winds. ⚓ in 2m E of the pier hd; access approx HW ±1½. Ⓥ berth, above ferry, is marked in Y on W side of hbr which dries 2·4m to the ent. The W bank has rky outcrops to S of ferry.

NAVIGATION
WPT 50°19'·73N 04°24'·60W, 130°/310° from/to pier hd lt, 2·0M. Ent dangerous in strong SE'lies, when seas break heavily on the bar. From W, beware The Ranneys, rks 2ca SE of Looe Is. Do not attempt the rky passage between Looe Is and mainland except with local knowledge and at HW. From E, beware Longstone Rks extending 1½ca from shore NE of hbr ent. At sp, ebb tide runs up to 5kn.

LIGHTS AND MARKS
Looe Island (or St George's Is) is conspic (44m), 8ca S of the ent. Mid Main bn (off Hannafore Pt, halfway between pier hd and Looe Is) Q (3) 10s 2M; ECM. At night appr in W sector (267°-313°) of pier hd lt Oc WR 3s 8m 15/12M; vis W013°-207°, R207°-267°, W267°-313°, R313°-332°; siren (2) 30s, fishing. No lts inside hbr.

RADIO TELEPHONE
VHF Ch 16 (occas).

TELEPHONE (Dial code 01503)
Hr Mr 262839; CG 262138; MRSC (01803) 882704; Marinecall 0891 500458; ⌗ 0345 231110 (H24); Police 262233; Dr 263195.

FACILITIES
W Looe Quay AB £11.28, Slip, M, P & D (cans), L, FW, ME, EI, CH; **E Looe Quay** Access HW ±3, Slip, P & D (cans), L, FW, ME, EI, C (2½ ton); **Looe SC** ☎ 262559, L, R, Bar.
Services: Sh (Wood), Ⓔ, Sh, Gas.
Town EC Thurs (winter only); P, FW, V, R, Bar, ▣, ✉, Ⓑ, ⇌, ✈ (Plymouth).

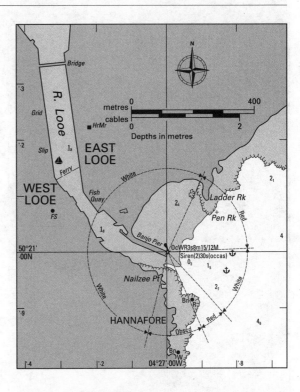

Our course down Channel had no doubt been tortuous. On June 2nd the visibility being poor, I reckoned we must be somewhere near the Manacles. But life is full of surprises. When the wind fell light we handed the mainsail in order to stitch a slender seam and while I was busy with this Noddy sighted through the haze a slender tower to the north-east – no doubt, the Eddystone. But when the sun went down and the lights came on it proved to be the Wolf Rock light. We were at least twenty miles and two points out in our reckoning. I concluded that Mischief *knew the way down Channel better than her skipper.*

Mostly Mischief: H.W.Tilman

With acknowledgements to the Executors of the estate of H.W.Tilman and to Hollis & Carter (Publishers 1966).

PLYMOUTH (DEVONPORT) 10-1-17

Devon   50°20'·00N 04°10'·00W (W Chan)   Rtg 1-1-1
50°20'·00N 04°08'·00W (E Chan)

CHARTS
AC *871*, 1902, 1901, *30*, 1967, 1900, *1267*, *1613*; Imray C14;
Stanfords 13; OS 201

TIDES
–0540 Dover; ML 3·3; Duration 0610; Zone 0 (UT)

Standard Port DEVONPORT (→)

Times				Height (metres)			
High Water		Low Water		MHWS	MHWN	MLWN	MLWS
0000	0600	0000	0600	5·5	4·4	2·2	0·8
1200	1800	1200	1800				
Differences BOVISAND PIER							
0000	–0020	0000	–0010	–0·2	–0·1	0·0	+0·1
TURNCHAPEL (Cattewater)							
0000	0000	+0010	–0015	0·0	+0·1	+0·2	+0·1
JUPITER POINT (R. Lynher)							
+0010	+0005	0000	–0005	0·0	0·0	+0·1	0·0
ST GERMANS (R. Lynher)							
0000	0000	+0020	+0020	–0·3	–0·1	0·0	+0·2
SALTASH (R. Tamar)							
0000	+0010	0000	–0005	+0·1	+0·1	+0·1	+0·1
CARGREEN (R. Tamar)							
0000	+0010	+0020	+0020	0·0	0·0	–0·1	0·0
COTEHELE QUAY (R. Tamar)							
0000	+0020	+0045	+0045	–0·9	–0·9	–0·8	–0·4

NOTE: Devonport is a Standard Port; predictions are given
below. Winds from SE to W increase the flood and retard
the ebb; vice versa in winds from the NW to E.

SHELTER

Excellent. Plymouth is a Naval Base, a busy commercial/ferry port principally using Mill Bay Docks, and an active fishing port based mainly on Sutton Harbour which is entered via a lock (see Facilities). There are marinas to E and W of the city centre, as well as in the Cattewater, off Torpoint and in Millbrook Lake. Around the Sound there are ⚓s, sheltered according to the wind, in Cawsand Bay, in Barn Pool (below Mt Edgcumbe), N of Drake's Is, below The Hoe and in Jennycliff Bay to the E. Also good shelter W of Cremyll and off the Hamoaze in the R Lynher and in the R Tamar/Tavy above Saltash (see overleaf).

NAVIGATION

WPT 50°19'·70N 04°09'·80W, 213°/033° from/to W bkwtr lt, 0·40M. The Sound can be entered via the W or E Chans which are well lit/buoyed with no real hazards. There are no shoal patches with less than 3·7m at MLWS. Yachts need not keep to the deep water chans.

The short cut to the Hamoaze via The Bridge (channel between Drake's Is and Mt Edgcumbe) is lit by 2 PHM and 2 SHM bns; the seaward pair show QR and QG, the inner pair Fl (4) R 10s and Fl (3) G 10s. The QR bn and the Fl (4) R 10s bn both have tide gauges calibrated to show height of tide above CD; charted depth is 2·1m. The E'ly of 3 conspic high-rise blocks brg 331° leads through The Bridge chan. Caution: a charted depth 1·8m is close SW of No 3 SHM bn, Fl (3) G 10s.

Speed limits: 10kn N of The Breakwater, 8kn in Cattewater (where outbound vessels have right of way), 4kn in Sutton Chan and 5kn in Sutton Hbr.

Historic Wrecks (see 10.0.3h) are at:
Cattewater, 50°21'·69N 04°07'·63W, 1ca N of Mount Batten. Penlee Pt, 2ca W and 7ca SW of: two sites at 50°18'·96N 04°11'·57W and 50°18'·57N 04°11'·98W.

LIGHTS AND MARKS

See 10.1.4 for complete detail. Bkwtr W hd, Fl WR 10s 19m 12/9M (vis W262°-208°, R208°-262°) and Iso 4s 12m 10M (vis 033°-037°). Bkwtr E hd, L Fl WR 10s 9m 8/6M (R190°-353°, W353°-001°, R001°-018°, W018°-190°). Mallard Shoal ldg lts 349°: Front Q WRG 10/3M (vis G233°-043°, R043°-067°, G067°-087°, W087°-099°, R099°-108°); rear 396m from front (on Hoe) Oc G 1·3s (vis 310°-040°).

There are Dir WRG lts, all lit H24 except **, at Whidbey (138·5°), Staddon Pt (044°), Withyhedge (070°), W Hoe bn (315°), Western King (271°), Mill Bay** (048·5°), Ravenness (225°), Mount Wise (343°), and Ocean Court** (085°).

In fog the following Dir W lts operate: Mallard (front) Fl 5s (vis 232°-110°); West Hoe bn F (vis 313°-317°); Eastern King Fl 5s (vis 259°-062°); Ravenness Fl (2) 15s (vis 160°-305°;) Mount Wise F (vis 341°-345°); Ocean Court Fl 5s (vis 270°-100°).

Notes: Principal lts in Plymouth Sound show QY if mains power fails. N of The Bkwtr, four large mooring buoys (C, D, E & F) have Fl Y lts.

RADIO TELEPHONE

Call: *Long Room Port Control* VHF Ch 08 12 **14** 16 (H24). *Mill Bay Docks* Ch 12 13 14 16 (only during ferry ops). *Sutton Lock*, for lock opening and marina, Ch **12** 16 (H24). *Cattewater Hbr* Ch 14 16 (Mon-Fri, 0900-1700LT). Mayflower, Queen Anne's Battery, Sutton Hbr & Clovelly Bay marinas and Torpoint Yacht Hbr: all Ch **80** M.

TELEPHONE (Dial code 01752)
QHM 552047; DQHM 552701; Flagstaff Port Control 552413; Longroom Control 552411/2; Cattewater Hr Mr 665934; ABP at Mill Bay 662191; MRSC (01803) 882704; ⌗ 0345 231110 (H24); Marinecall 0891 500458; Police 701188; Dr 663138; Ⓗ 668080.

FACILITIES

Marinas (W to E)
Torpoint Yacht Hbr (60+20 Ⓥ) ☎/🛠 813658, £10, access H24, dredged 2m. FW, AC, BY, C, ME, El, Sh, Diver, SM.
Southdown Marina (35 inc Ⓥ) ☎/🛠 823084, £7.50, access HW±4; AB on pontoon (2m) or on drying quay; FW, AC, D.
Mayflower Marina (300+50 Ⓥ) ☎ 556633, 🛠 606896, £18.20 inc AC, P, D, FW, ME, El, Sh, C (2 ton), BH (25 ton), CH, Slip, Gas, Gaz, Divers, SM, BY, YC, V, R, Bar, ▣.
Mill Bay Village Marina ☎ 226785, 🛠 222513, VHF Ch M. NO VISITORS. Ent lts = Oc R 4s & Oc G 4s, not on chartlet.
Queen Anne's Battery Marina (240+60 Ⓥ) ☎ 671142, 🛠 266297, £16.10, AC, P, D, ME, El, Sh, FW, BH (20 ton), C (50 ton), CH, Gas, Gaz, ▣, SM, Slip, V, Bar, YC.
Sutton Hbr Marina (310) ☎ 664186, 🛠 223521, £15, P, D, FW, AC, El, ME, Sh, CH, C (masts only), Slip. Sutton Hbr is entered via lock (Barbican flood protection scheme), which maintains 3m CD in the marina. Lock (floating fenders) operates H24, free; call *Sutton Lock* VHF Ch 12 16. When tide reaches 3m CD, gates stay open for free-flow. Tfc lts (vert): 3 Ⓡ = Stop; 3 Ⓖ = Go; 3 Fl Ⓡ = Serious hazard, wait.
Clovelly Bay Marina (180+ Ⓥ) ☎ 404231, 🛠 484177, £14.48, D, FW, AC, CH, ME, El, Gas, Gaz, V, ▣.

Clubs
Royal Western YC of England ☎ 660077, M, Bar, R; Royal Plymouth Corinthian YC ☎ 664327, VHF Ch M, M, R, Bar, Slip; Plym YC ☎ 404991; RNSA c/o QHM ☎ 555581; Mayflower SC ☎ 662526; Torpoint Mosquito SC ☎ 812508, visitors welcome, R, Bar; Saltash SC ☎ 845988.

Services All facilities available, inc ACA; consult marina/Hr Mr for details. A *Water Sports and Events Diary*, available from chandlers, marinas and some newsagents, contains much useful information.

City EC Wed; P, D, V, R, CH, ✉, Ⓑ, ⇌, ✈.

BYE LAWS/NAVAL ACTIVITY

The whole Port is under the jurisdiction of the QHM, but certain areas are locally controlled, i.e. by Cattewater Commissioners and by ABP who operate Mill Bay Docks. Beware frequent movements of naval vessels, which have right of way in the chans. Obey MOD Police orders. Info on Naval activities may be obtained from Naval Ops.

DEVONPORT

MEAN SPRING
AND NEAP CURVES

MEAN RANGES	
Springs 4.7m	———
Neaps 2.2m	– – –

Springs occur 2 days
after
New and Full Moon.

☎ 501182 (H24) or Devonport Ops Room ☎ 563777 Ext 2182/3. Submarines may secure to a buoy close N of the Breakwater; they will show a Fl Y anti-collision lt. For Subfacts in the W English Channel see 10.1.18.

TRAFFIC SIGNALS

Traffic is controlled H24 by the following combinations of 3 lts WRG (vert), Fl or Oc, shown from Drake's Island and at Flagstaff Port Control Station in the Dockyard. These signals and any hoisted by HM Ships apply to the waters off the dockyard port and 125m either side of the deep water chan out to the W Ent. The Cattewater, Mill Bay Docks and Sutton Hbr are excluded.

Signal	Meaning
Unlit	No restrictions, unless passed on VHF
Ⓡ Ⓡ All Fl Ⓡ	Serious Emergency All traffic suspended
Ⓡ Ⓖ All Oc Ⓖ	Outgoing traffic only may proceed on the recommended track. Crossing traffic to seek approval from Port Control*
Ⓖ Ⓖ All Oc Ⓡ	Incoming traffic only may proceed on the recommended track. Crossing traffic to seek approval from Port Control*
Ⓖ Ⓖ All Oc Ⓦ	Vessels may proceed in either direction, but shall give a wide berth to HM Ships using the recommended track

*Call Port Control Ch 13 or 14, but craft <20m LOA may proceed in the contrary direction, with care and not impeding the passage of vessels for which the signal is intended.

Wind Strength Warning Flags and Lights

Wind flags (R & W vert stripes) are flown at Queen Anne's Battery, Mayflower Marina and The Camber (HO only) to warn of excessive winds as follows:

1 wind flag   (1 Oc Ⓦ lt)   = Rough weather, Force 5 - 6.
2 wind flags (2 Oc Ⓦ lts, vert) = Very rough weather, > F 6.

Note: These flags are supplemented by Oc Ⓦ lt(s) shown from Drake's Island, HJ when no traffic signal is in force.

Wembury Firing Range extends 16·5M offshore in an arc of 126°–244° from 50°19′·00N 04°06′·30W. Firing usually occurs Tues - Fri, 0900 – 1600 (1630 summer); occas Mon; rarely at night, weekends or public hols. No firing at Easter, Christmas and for 3 weeks in Aug. 4 large R flags are flown at Wembury Pt when range active. 4 small Y target buoys and 3 Fl Y lt buoys are aligned 300° from a point 3½ca S of Great Mewstone to a point 8ca W of the same. Other targets may be towed 1000yds astern of tug vessel. Two SPM target buoys (NGS West, Fl Y 5s, and NGS East, Fl Y 10s) are at 50°11′·1N 04°00′·8W and 50°11′·2N 03°59′·0W; do not secure to them or loiter nearby. To enter The Sound from S during firings, keep W of Eddystone lt ho. It is not advisable to pass inside the Mewstone, due to drying ledges. For info call *Wembury Range* VHF Ch 16 (working 11), advising your position; or ☎ Freephone 0800 833608 or Range Officer ☎ (01752) 862799 (HO) or 553740 ext 77412 (OT).

Diving: Keep clear of regular diving off Bovisand Pier, The Breakwater Fort and Ravenness Point. Diving signals (Flag A) are displayed.

RIVER TAMAR (and TAVY)

The Tamar is navigable on the flood for 15M to Morwhellan. R Tavy flows into the Tamar 1¼M above the bridges, but due to power lines (8m) and a bridge (7·6m) at its mouth, is only accessible to un-masted craft up to Bere Ferrers. Cargreen village is 0·7M beyond the Tavy, on the W bank, with many local moorings and ⚓ in 2m. Weir Quay on E bank has a SC, BY, M and fuel. The river S-bends, narrowing and drying, passes Cothele Quay and then turns 90° stbd to Calstock; possible AB, M, or ⚓ above the viaduct in 2m. **Tamar River SC** ☎ 362741; **Weir Quay SC** ☎ (01822) 840474, M, CH, ME; **Calstock BY** ☎ (01822) 832502, access HW ±3, M, ME, SH, C (8 ton), BH (10 ton). Facilities: P, D, V, Bar, Ⓑ (Mon a.m.), ⇌.

RIVER LYNHER (or ST GERMANS)

This river which flows into The Hamoaze about 0·8M S of the Tamar Bridge, dries extensively but is navigable on the tide for 4M up to St Germans Quay (private); but temp AB possible by prior arrangement with Quay SC. The chan, ent at Wearde Quay, is buoyed and partly lit for the first 2M. There are ⚓s, amid local moorings, at the ent to Forder Lake (N bank); SE of Ince Pt and Castle in about 3m; and at Dandy Hole, a pool with 3m, where the river bends NW and dries almost completely. Facilities: V, Bar, ✉, (½M). **Quay SC** Moorings ☎ (01503) 30531.

ENGLAND – PLYMOUTH (DEVONPORT)

LAT 50°22′N   LONG   4°11′W

TIMES AND HEIGHTS OF HIGH AND LOW WATERS

YEAR 1998

TIME ZONE (UT)
For Summer Time add ONE hour in non-shaded areas

Chart Datum: 3·22 metres below Ordnance Datum (Newlyn)

JANUARY

Day	Time	m	Day	Time	m
1 TH	0114 / 0725 / 1340 / 1950	0.9 / 5.5 / 0.8 / 5.3	16 F	0153 / 0746 / 1415 / 2006	1.0 / 5.3 / 1.1 / 5.0
2 F	0156 / 0807 / 1423 / 2033	0.9 / 5.5 / 0.9 / 5.2	17 SA	0224 / 0816 / 1445 / 2037	1.2 / 5.2 / 1.3 / 4.9
3 SA	0237 / 0850 / 1505 / 2117	1.0 / 5.4 / 1.0 / 5.1	18 SU	0252 / 0849 / 1512 / 2110	1.4 / 5.1 / 1.5 / 4.8
4 SU	0320 / 0936 / 1550 / 2204	1.2 / 5.3 / 1.2 / 5.0	19 M	0319 / 0925 / 1540 / 2148	1.6 / 4.9 / 1.7 / 4.6
5 M	0407 / 1026 / 1640 / 2259	1.4 / 5.1 / 1.4 / 4.8	20 TU	0349 / 1005 / 1613 / 2233	1.9 / 4.7 / 1.9 / 4.5
6 TU	0502 / 1125 / 1742	1.7 / 4.9 / 1.7	21 W	0432 / 1053 / 1707 / 2329	2.1 / 4.5 / 2.1 / 4.3
7 W	0005 / 0613 / 1238 / 1859	4.7 / 1.9 / 4.7 / 1.8	22 TH	0544 / 1154 / 1826	2.3 / 4.4 / 2.2
8 TH	0121 / 0741 / 1353 / 2021	4.6 / 1.9 / 4.7 / 1.7	23 F	0041 / 0705 / 1311 / 1941	4.3 / 2.3 / 4.4 / 2.1
9 F	0233 / 0858 / 1502 / 2129	4.8 / 1.7 / 4.8 / 1.5	24 SA	0205 / 0816 / 1434 / 2047	4.5 / 2.0 / 4.5 / 1.8
10 SA	0336 / 1000 / 1603 / 2226	5.0 / 1.4 / 5.0 / 1.3	25 SU	0314 / 0919 / 1539 / 2146	4.7 / 1.7 / 4.7 / 1.5
11 SU	0429 / 1053 / 1655 / 2315	5.2 / 1.1 / 5.1 / 1.1	26 M	0409 / 1016 / 1633 / 2240	5.0 / 1.4 / 5.0 / 1.2
12 M O	0517 / 1141 / 1742	5.4 / 0.9 / 5.2	27 TU	0456 / 1108 / 1721 / 2330	5.3 / 1.0 / 5.2 / 0.9
13 TU	0000 / 0559 / 1225 / 1824	0.9 / 5.4 / 0.8 / 5.2	28 W ●	0542 / 1158 / 1808	5.5 / 0.8 / 5.3
14 W	0041 / 0639 / 1306 / 1902	0.9 / 5.5 / 0.8 / 5.2	29 TH	0018 / 0627 / 1246 / 1853	0.7 / 5.6 / 0.6 / 5.4
15 TH	0119 / 0714 / 1342 / 1936	0.9 / 5.4 / 0.9 / 5.1	30 F	0105 / 0712 / 1331 / 1938	0.6 / 5.7 / 0.4 / 5.5
			31 SA	0148 / 0757 / 1414 / 2022	0.5 / 5.7 / 0.4 / 5.4

FEBRUARY

Day	Time	m	Day	Time	m
1 SU	0229 / 0840 / 1454 / 2104	0.6 / 5.6 / 0.6 / 5.3	16 M	0223 / 0826 / 1439 / 2044	1.2 / 5.1 / 1.2 / 4.9
2 M	0309 / 0924 / 1534 / 2147	0.8 / 5.5 / 0.8 / 5.2	17 TU	0245 / 0857 / 1500 / 2115	1.3 / 5.0 / 1.4 / 4.8
3 TU	0350 / 1009 / 1617 / 2234	1.1 / 5.2 / 1.2 / 4.9	18 W	0309 / 0930 / 1526 / 2150	1.6 / 4.7 / 1.7 / 4.6
4 W	0436 / 1101 / 1707 / 2332	1.4 / 4.9 / 1.6 / 4.6	19 TH	0342 / 1009 / 1605 / 2237	1.8 / 4.5 / 1.9 / 4.4
5 TH	0534 / 1208 / 1814	1.8 / 4.6 / 1.9	20 F	0433 / 1104 / 1709 / 2340	2.1 / 4.3 / 2.2 / 4.3
6 F	0047 / 0659 / 1327 / 1949	4.5 / 2.0 / 4.5 / 2.0	21 SA	0608 / 1215 / 1854	2.2 / 4.2 / 2.2
7 SA	0205 / 0837 / 1442 / 2112	4.5 / 1.9 / 4.5 / 1.8	22 SU	0101 / 0737 / 1346 / 2012	4.3 / 2.1 / 4.3 / 2.0
8 SU	0314 / 0946 / 1546 / 2211	4.7 / 1.6 / 4.7 / 1.5	23 M	0234 / 0849 / 1510 / 2120	4.6 / 1.8 / 4.6 / 1.6
9 M	0411 / 1040 / 1639 / 2301	5.0 / 1.3 / 4.9 / 1.2	24 TU	0340 / 0952 / 1610 / 2219	4.9 / 1.3 / 4.9 / 1.2
10 TU	0458 / 1126 / 1724 / 2344	5.2 / 1.0 / 5.0 / 1.0	25 W	0432 / 1049 / 1701 / 2313	5.2 / 0.9 / 5.2 / 0.8
11 W O	0540 / 1209 / 1804	5.4 / 0.8 / 5.1	26 TH ●	0521 / 1140 / 1749	5.5 / 0.6 / 5.4
12 TH	0024 / 0617 / 1248 / 1839	0.8 / 5.4 / 0.8 / 5.2	27 F	0003 / 0608 / 1230 / 1835	0.5 / 5.7 / 0.3 / 5.5
13 F	0101 / 0652 / 1322 / 1912	0.8 / 5.4 / 0.8 / 5.2	28 SA	0050 / 0655 / 1315 / 1921	0.3 / 5.8 / 0.1 / 5.6
14 SA	0132 / 0724 / 1352 / 1943	0.9 / 5.4 / 0.9 / 5.1			
15 SU	0159 / 0755 / 1417 / 2013	1.0 / 5.3 / 1.1 / 5.1			

MARCH

Day	Time	m	Day	Time	m
1 SU	0134 / 0741 / 1358 / 2005	0.2 / 5.8 / 0.2 / 5.6	16 M	0133 / 0732 / 1348 / 1949	0.9 / 5.3 / 0.9 / 5.1
2 M	0214 / 0825 / 1437 / 2046	0.3 / 5.7 / 0.3 / 5.5	17 TU	0155 / 0803 / 1409 / 2018	1.0 / 5.1 / 1.1 / 5.0
3 TU	0253 / 0907 / 1516 / 2126	0.5 / 5.5 / 0.6 / 5.3	18 W	0217 / 0832 / 1430 / 2045	1.2 / 5.0 / 1.3 / 4.9
4 W	0331 / 0950 / 1555 / 2208	0.9 / 5.2 / 1.1 / 5.0	19 TH	0241 / 0901 / 1501 / 2116	1.4 / 4.8 / 1.5 / 4.7
5 TH	0414 / 1037 / 1640 / 2259	1.3 / 4.8 / 1.6 / 4.6	20 F	0312 / 0937 / 1531 / 2159	1.6 / 4.5 / 1.8 / 4.5
6 F	0506 / 1142 / 1739	1.8 / 4.4 / 2.0	21 SA	0357 / 1031 / 1625 / 2300	1.9 / 4.3 / 2.1 / 4.4
7 SA	0015 / 0622 / 1307 / 1913	4.4 / 2.1 / 4.3 / 2.2	22 SU	0517 / 1140 / 1809	2.1 / 4.2 / 2.2
8 SU	0141 / 0817 / 1424 / 2053	4.4 / 2.1 / 4.3 / 2.0	23 M	0016 / 0703 / 1305 / 1942	4.3 / 2.1 / 4.3 / 2.0
9 M	0252 / 0929 / 1528 / 2153	4.5 / 1.7 / 4.5 / 1.6	24 TU	0148 / 0821 / 1440 / 2054	4.5 / 1.7 / 4.5 / 1.6
10 TU	0350 / 1021 / 1620 / 2241	4.8 / 1.3 / 4.8 / 1.3	25 W	0309 / 0928 / 1545 / 2157	4.9 / 1.3 / 4.9 / 1.2
11 W	0436 / 1106 / 1702 / 2324	5.1 / 1.0 / 5.0 / 1.0	26 TH	0406 / 1027 / 1638 / 2253	5.2 / 0.8 / 5.2 / 0.7
12 TH	0516 / 1147 / 1739	5.2 / 0.8 / 5.1	27 F	0457 / 1120 / 1727 / 2343	5.5 / 0.4 / 5.5 / 0.4
13 F O	0002 / 0552 / 1224 / 1813	0.8 / 5.3 / 0.7 / 5.2	28 SA ●	0547 / 1208 / 1814	5.7 / 0.2 / 5.6
14 SA	0037 / 0626 / 1257 / 1846	0.8 / 5.4 / 0.7 / 5.2	29 SU	0030 / 0635 / 1255 / 1900	0.2 / 5.8 / 0.0 / 5.7
15 SU	0107 / 0659 / 1325 / 1918	0.8 / 5.3 / 0.8 / 5.2	30 M	0115 / 0722 / 1337 / 1944	0.1 / 5.8 / 0.1 / 5.7
			31 TU	0156 / 0807 / 1418 / 2025	0.2 / 5.7 / 0.3 / 5.6

APRIL

Day	Time	m	Day	Time	m
1 W	0235 / 0849 / 1456 / 2104	0.4 / 5.5 / 0.6 / 5.3	16 TH	0155 / 0810 / 1408 / 2021	1.1 / 4.9 / 1.2 / 5.0
2 TH	0314 / 0931 / 1535 / 2142	0.8 / 5.1 / 1.1 / 5.0	17 F	0223 / 0840 / 1436 / 2053	1.3 / 4.8 / 1.4 / 4.8
3 F	0355 / 1016 / 1618 / 2226	1.3 / 4.7 / 1.6 / 4.7	18 SA	0256 / 0918 / 1513 / 2136	1.5 / 4.6 / 1.7 / 4.7
4 SA	0446 / 1119 / 1714 / 2340	1.7 / 4.3 / 2.0 / 4.4	19 SU	0341 / 1011 / 1607 / 2234	1.7 / 4.4 / 1.9 / 4.5
5 SU	0555 / 1246 / 1835	2.1 / 4.2 / 2.3	20 M	0454 / 1117 / 1736 / 2346	2.0 / 4.3 / 2.1 / 4.5
6 M	0113 / 0744 / 1401 / 2020	4.3 / 2.1 / 4.2 / 2.1	21 TU	0633 / 1237 / 1912	1.9 / 4.3 / 2.0
7 TU	0225 / 0902 / 1503 / 2125	4.5 / 1.8 / 4.5 / 1.8	22 W	0111 / 0753 / 1408 / 2027	4.6 / 1.6 / 4.6 / 1.6
8 W	0321 / 0954 / 1552 / 2213	4.7 / 1.5 / 4.7 / 1.4	23 TH	0235 / 0902 / 1517 / 2133	4.9 / 1.2 / 4.9 / 1.2
9 TH	0407 / 1038 / 1634 / 2255	4.9 / 1.1 / 4.9 / 1.1	24 F	0339 / 1002 / 1612 / 2229	5.2 / 0.8 / 5.2 / 0.8
10 F	0447 / 1117 / 1710 / 2333	5.1 / 0.9 / 5.1 / 0.9	25 SA	0433 / 1056 / 1703 / 2321	5.5 / 0.5 / 5.5 / 0.4
11 SA O	0523 / 1154 / 1744	5.2 / 0.8 / 5.2	26 SU ●	0524 / 1146 / 1751	5.7 / 0.2 / 5.6
12 SU	0008 / 0558 / 1227 / 1818	0.8 / 5.3 / 0.8 / 5.2	27 M	0009 / 0613 / 1233 / 1837	0.2 / 5.7 / 0.1 / 5.7
13 M	0039 / 0634 / 1254 / 1852	0.8 / 5.3 / 0.9 / 5.2	28 TU	0054 / 0701 / 1317 / 1922	0.1 / 5.7 / 0.2 / 5.7
14 TU	0105 / 0708 / 1319 / 1925	0.9 / 5.2 / 0.9 / 5.2	29 W	0137 / 0748 / 1358 / 2004	0.2 / 5.6 / 0.4 / 5.6
15 W	0130 / 0741 / 1343 / 1954	1.0 / 5.1 / 1.1 / 5.1	30 TH	0218 / 0832 / 1438 / 2043	0.5 / 5.3 / 0.7 / 5.3

ENGLAND – PLYMOUTH (DEVONPORT)

LAT 50°22′N   LONG 4°11′W

TIMES AND HEIGHTS OF HIGH AND LOW WATERS

YEAR **1998**

TIME ZONE (UT)
For Summer Time add ONE hour in non-shaded areas

MAY

Day	Time	m	Time	m	Day	Time	m	Time	m
1 F	0258	0.8			**16** SA	0213	1.2		
	0913	5.0				0828	4.8		
	1518	1.2				1428	1.3		
	2119	5.0				2040	5.0		
2 SA	0340	1.3			**17** SU	0251	1.3		
	0957	4.7				0908	4.7		
	1600	1.6				1508	1.5		
	2157	4.7				2123	4.8		
3 SU	0428	1.7			**18** M	0339	1.5		
	1054	4.3				0958	4.5		
	1652	2.0				1601	1.8		
	2253	4.4				2217	4.7		
4 M	0529	2.0			**19** TU	0443	1.7		
	1216	4.2				1100	4.4		
	1758	2.2				1715	1.9		
						2323	4.6		
5 TU	0032	4.3			**20** W	0604	1.7		
	0649	2.1				1214	4.4		
	1327	4.2				1840	1.8		
	1922	2.2							
6 W	0146	4.4			**21** TH	0042	4.7		
	0814	1.9				0723	1.6		
	1426	4.4				1336	4.6		
	2038	2.0				1957	1.6		
7 TH	0243	4.6			**22** F	0203	4.9		
	0913	1.6				0834	1.3		
	1516	4.6				1447	4.9		
	2133	1.6				2105	1.3		
8 F	0331	4.8			**23** SA	0311	5.1		
	0959	1.4				0936	0.9		
	1558	4.8				1546	5.2		
	2218	1.4				2205	0.9		
9 SA	0412	5.0			**24** SU	0409	5.3		
	1040	1.2				1032	0.6		
	1637	5.0				1639	5.4		
	2258	1.1				2259	0.6		
10 SU	0452	5.1			**25** M	0502	5.5		
	1117	1.0				1124	0.5		
	1714	5.1				1729 ●	5.5		
	2334 O	1.0				2348	0.4		
11 M	0530	5.1			**26** TU	0553	5.5		
	1151	1.0				1211	0.4		
	1751 O	5.2				1816	5.6		
12 TU	0007	0.9			**27** W	0035	0.4		
	0608	5.2				0642	5.5		
	1223	1.0				1257	0.4		
	1828	5.2				1901	5.6		
13 W	0038	0.9			**28** TH	0120	0.4		
	0646	5.1				0730	5.4		
	1253	1.0				1340	0.6		
	1903	5.2				1944	5.5		
14 TH	0109	1.0			**29** F	0203	0.6		
	0722	5.0				0814	5.2		
	1323	1.1				1421	0.8		
	1935	5.1				2023	5.3		
15 F	0140	1.1			**30** SA	0244	0.9		
	0755	4.9				0856	5.0		
	1354	1.2				1501	1.2		
	2005	5.1				2057	5.1		
					31 SU	0325	1.2		
						0934	4.7		
						1542	1.5		
						2131	4.8		

JUNE

Day	Time	m	Time	m	Day	Time	m	Time	m
1 M	0408	1.6			**16** TU	0336	1.3		
	1016	4.4				0950	4.7		
	1627	1.8				1556	1.5		
	2213	4.6				2205	4.9		
2 TU	0458	1.8			**17** W	0430	1.4		
	1114	4.3				1045	4.6		
	1719	2.1				1654	1.6		
	2312	4.4				2304	4.8		
3 W	0556	2.0			**18** TH	0535	1.5		
	1230	4.2				1151	4.6		
	1822	2.2				1806	1.7		
4 TH	0038	4.4			**19** F	0015	4.7		
	0702	2.0				0649	1.5		
	1334	4.3				1304	4.6		
	1929	2.1				1924	1.6		
5 F	0149	4.4			**20** SA	0134	4.8		
	0809	1.9				0804	1.4		
	1428	4.5				1417	4.8		
	2034	1.9				2038	1.4		
6 SA	0245	4.6			**21** SU	0246	4.9		
	0905	1.6				0911	1.2		
	1516	4.7				1521	5.0		
	2128	1.6				2142	1.2		
7 SU	0334	4.8			**22** M	0348	5.1		
	0953	1.4				1011	0.9		
	1601	4.9				1617	5.2		
	2215	1.4				2239	0.9		
8 M	0419	4.9			**23** TU	0443	5.2		
	1036	1.2				1105	0.8		
	1643	5.0				1709	5.4		
	2256	1.2				2331	0.7		
9 TU	0502	5.0			**24** W	0535	5.3		
	1115	1.1				1154	0.6		
	1725	5.1				1757 ●	5.5		
	2336	1.1							
10 W	0545	5.1			**25** TH	0019	0.6		
	1153	1.0				0624	5.3		
	1805 O	5.2				1241	0.6		
						1842	5.5		
11 TH	0014	1.0			**26** F	0105	0.6		
	0625	5.1				0711	5.2		
	1231	1.0				1324	0.7		
	1843	5.2				1925	5.4		
12 F	0052	1.0			**27** SA	0148	0.7		
	0705	5.0				0755	5.1		
	1308	1.0				1405	0.9		
	1920	5.2				2003	5.3		
13 SA	0130	1.0			**28** SU	0228	0.9		
	0744	5.0				0833	5.0		
	1346	1.1				1443	1.1		
	1956	5.2				2034	5.1		
14 SU	0209	1.0			**29** M	0305	1.1		
	0822	4.9				0905	4.8		
	1425	1.2				1519	1.4		
	2033	5.1				2105	5.0		
15 M	0250	1.1			**30** TU	0342	1.4		
	0903	4.8				0937	4.6		
	1507	1.3				1556	1.6		
	2115	5.1				2140	4.8		

JULY

Day	Time	m	Time	m	Day	Time	m	Time	m
1 W	0421	1.7			**16** TH	0412	1.1		
	1016	4.4				1029	4.8		
	1637	1.9				1633	1.4		
	2224	4.6				2246	4.9		
2 TH	0506	1.9			**17** F	0506	1.4		
	1107	4.3				1127	4.7		
	1728	2.1				1733	1.6		
	2318	4.4				2351	4.7		
3 F	0601	2.0			**18** SA	0614	1.6		
	1212	4.3				1237	4.6		
	1829	2.1				1850	1.7		
4 SA	0028	4.3			**19** SU	0109	4.6		
	0703	2.0				0734	1.6		
	1326	4.3				1351	4.6		
	1933	2.1				2013	1.7		
5 SU	0147	4.4			**20** M	0225	4.7		
	0805	1.9				0851	1.5		
	1430	4.5				1459	4.8		
	2035	1.9				2125	1.4		
6 M	0253	4.5			**21** TU	0331	4.8		
	0903	1.7				0955	1.3		
	1525	4.7				1559	5.0		
	2131	1.6				2225	1.1		
7 TU	0348	4.7			**22** W	0429	5.0		
	0955	1.4				1051	1.0		
	1614	4.9				1652	5.2		
	2221	1.4				2318	0.9		
8 W	0436	4.9			**23** TH	0520	5.1		
	1043	1.2				1140	0.8		
	1659	5.1				1739 ●	5.4		
	2308	1.1							
9 TH	0522	5.0			**24** F	0006	0.7		
	1129	1.1				0607	5.2		
	1743	5.2				1226	0.7		
	2354 O	1.0				1823	5.4		
10 F	0606	5.1			**25** SA	0050	0.7		
	1213	1.0				0651	5.2		
	1825	5.3				1308	0.7		
						1903	5.4		
11 SA	0038	0.9			**26** SU	0131	0.7		
	0650	5.1				0730	5.1		
	1257	0.9				1346	0.8		
	1906	5.4				1938	5.3		
12 SU	0121	0.8			**27** M	0207	0.8		
	0732	5.1				0804	5.0		
	1339	0.9				1420	1.0		
	1946	5.4				2008	5.2		
13 M	0203	0.8			**28** TU	0240	1.0		
	0814	5.1				0833	4.9		
	1419	0.9				1451	1.2		
	2027	5.4				2038	5.1		
14 TU	0244	0.9			**29** W	0310	1.3		
	0856	5.1				0903	4.8		
	1500	1.0				1520	1.5		
	2109	5.3				2110	4.9		
15 W	0326	0.9			**30** TH	0338	1.5		
	0940	5.0				0938	4.6		
	1544	1.1				1550	1.7		
	2154	5.1				2147	4.7		
					31 F	0409	1.8		
						1019	4.5		
						1627	2.0		
						2230	4.5		

AUGUST

Day	Time	m	Time	m	Day	Time	m	Time	m
1 SA	0454	2.0			**16** SU	0541	1.7		
	1110	4.3				1210	4.5		
	1726	2.2				1819	1.9		
	2325	4.3							
2 SU	0604	2.1			**17** M	0049	4.5		
	1216	4.3				0707	1.9		
	1841	2.2				1330	4.5		
						1956	1.9		
3 M	0039	4.3			**18** TU	0210	4.5		
	0716	2.1				0838	1.8		
	1338	4.3				1443	4.7		
	1951	2.1				2115	1.7		
4 TU	0210	4.4			**19** W	0320	4.6		
	0823	1.9				0945	1.5		
	1451	4.6				1545	4.9		
	2055	1.8				2215	1.3		
5 W	0319	4.6			**20** TH	0418	4.9		
	0923	1.6				1038	1.2		
	1547	4.9				1637	5.1		
	2152	1.5				2305	1.0		
6 TH	0413	4.8			**21** F	0506	5.0		
	1017	1.3				1125	0.9		
	1636	5.1				1721	5.3		
	2245	1.1				2350	0.8		
7 F	0501	5.0			**22** SA	0548	5.1		
	1108	1.1				1208	0.8		
	1721	5.3				1802 ●	5.4		
	2335	0.9							
8 SA	0547	5.1			**23** SU	0031	0.7		
	1156	0.8				0627	5.2		
	1805	5.4				1248	0.7		
	O					1838	5.4		
9 SU	0022	0.7			**24** M	0109	0.7		
	0632	5.3				0702	5.2		
	1243	0.7				1323	0.8		
	1849	5.5				1911	5.4		
10 M	0108	0.5			**25** TU	0142	0.8		
	0716	5.3				0732	5.1		
	1327	0.6				1353	0.9		
	1932	5.6				1941	5.3		
11 TU	0151	0.5			**26** W	0210	1.0		
	0800	5.3				0802	5.1		
	1408	0.6				1419	1.1		
	2015	5.6				2010	5.2		
12 W	0231	0.5			**27** TH	0233	1.2		
	0842	5.3				0831	4.9		
	1448	0.7				1442	1.3		
	2057	5.5				2041	5.0		
13 TH	0311	0.7			**28** F	0253	1.4		
	0924	5.2				0903	4.8		
	1527	0.9				1503	1.6		
	2140	5.2				2113	4.8		
14 F	0352	1.0			**29** SA	0314	1.7		
	1009	4.9				0938	4.6		
	1611	1.3				1529	1.8		
	2227	5.0				2150	4.6		
15 SA	0439	1.4			**30** SU	0345	1.9		
	1101	4.7				1022	4.4		
	1705	1.6				1612	2.1		
	2328	4.7				2238	4.3		
					31 M	0441	2.2		
						1120	4.3		
						1743	2.3		
						2345	4.2		

Chart Datum: 3·22 metres below Ordnance Datum (Newlyn)

ENGLAND – PLYMOUTH (DEVONPORT)

LAT 50°22'N   LONG 4°11'W

TIMES AND HEIGHTS OF HIGH AND LOW WATERS   YEAR **1998**

TIME ZONE (UT)
For Summer Time add ONE hour in non-shaded areas

Chart Datum: 3·22 metres below Ordnance Datum (Newlyn)

SEPTEMBER

Day	Time	m	Time	m	Time	m	Time	m
1 TU	0630	2.3	1237	4.3	1915	2.2		
16 W	0200	4.4	0826	2.0	1428	4.6	2104	1.8
2 W	0119	4.2	0750	2.1	1413	4.5	2026	1.9
17 TH	0310	4.6	0931	1.7	1530	4.9	2159	1.4
3 TH	0254	4.5	0856	1.8	1520	4.8	2128	1.5
18 F	0404	4.8	1021	1.3	1619	5.1	2246	1.1
4 F	0352	4.8	0955	1.4	1611	5.2	2223	1.1
19 SA	0447	5.1	1105	1.0	1700	5.3	2328	0.8
5 SA	0440	5.1	1048	1.0	1658	5.4	2315	0.7
20 SU ●	0526	5.2	1145	0.8	1737	5.4		
6 SU ○	0526	5.3	1138	0.7	1743	5.6		
21 M	0007	0.7	0600	5.3	1223	0.8	1810	5.4
7 M	0003	0.5	0611	5.5	1225	0.5	1828	5.7
22 TU	0042	0.7	0632	5.3	1255	0.8	1842	5.4
8 TU	0049	0.3	0656	5.5	1310	0.4	1914	5.8
23 W	0112	0.8	0702	5.2	1323	0.9	1913	5.3
9 W	0132	0.3	0740	5.6	1351	0.4	1958	5.7
24 TH	0137	1.0	0733	5.2	1347	1.1	1944	5.3
10 TH	0213	0.4	0823	5.5	1431	0.6	2040	5.6
25 F	0157	1.2	0803	5.1	1408	1.3	2013	5.0
11 F	0252	0.6	0904	5.4	1510	0.9	2123	5.3
26 SA	0216	1.4	0832	4.9	1428	1.5	2043	4.8
12 SA	0331	1.0	0947	5.1	1551	1.3	2208	4.9
27 SU	0237	1.6	0904	4.7	1454	1.8	2117	4.6
13 SU	0415	1.5	1036	4.8	1642	1.7	2308	4.6
28 M	0308	1.9	0944	4.5	1532	2.0	2205	4.4
14 M	0513	1.9	1145	4.5	1755	2.1		
29 TU	0354	2.2	1040	4.4	1640	2.3	2310	4.2
15 TU	0035	4.3	0645	2.2	1312	4.4	1945	2.1
30 W	0531	2.4	1151	4.3	1840	2.3		

OCTOBER

Day	Time	m	Time	m	Time	m	Time	m
1 TH	0033	4.2	0718	2.3	1323	4.5	1958	2.0
16 F	0248	4.5	0906	1.9	1505	4.8	2135	1.6
2 F	0223	4.5	0830	1.9	1447	4.8	2103	1.5
17 SA	0340	4.8	0955	1.5	1553	5.1	2220	1.2
3 SA	0327	4.9	0931	1.4	1544	5.2	2200	1.1
18 SU	0422	5.0	1038	1.2	1633	5.2	2300	1.0
4 SU	0417	5.2	1026	1.0	1633	5.5	2252	0.7
19 M	0458	5.2	1117	1.0	1709	5.4	2337	0.9
5 M ○	0503	5.5	1116	0.7	1720	5.7	2341	0.4
20 TU ●	0531	5.3	1153	0.9	1742	5.4		
6 TU	0549	5.6	1204	0.4	1807	5.8		
21 W	0011	0.9	0603	5.4	1226	0.9	1815	5.4
7 W	0027	0.2	0634	5.7	1249	0.3	1853	5.9
22 TH	0040	1.0	0635	5.4	1253	1.0	1849	5.3
8 TH	0111	0.2	0718	5.8	1332	0.3	1939	5.8
23 F	0104	1.1	0707	5.3	1318	1.2	1921	5.2
9 F	0153	0.4	0802	5.7	1413	0.5	2023	5.6
24 SA	0127	1.2	0738	5.2	1341	1.3	1951	5.1
10 SA	0232	0.7	0843	5.5	1453	0.9	2106	5.3
25 SU	0149	1.4	0807	5.1	1406	1.5	2021	4.9
11 SU	0312	1.1	0926	5.2	1535	1.3	2151	4.9
26 M	0215	1.6	0838	4.9	1434	1.7	2055	4.7
12 M	0356	1.6	1013	4.9	1625	1.8	2251	4.5
27 TU	0247	1.8	0918	4.7	1513	2.0	2143	4.5
13 TU	0451	2.1	1121	4.6	1736	2.2		
28 W	0332	2.1	1011	4.6	1614	2.2	2245	4.3
14 W	0020	4.3	0617	2.4	1250	4.4	1923	2.2
29 TH	0448	2.4	1118	4.5	1801	2.3		
15 TH	0142	4.3	0801	2.2	1405	4.6	2041	1.9
30 F	0001	4.3	0641	2.3	1238	4.6	1926	2.0
31 SA	0139	4.5	0800	2.0	1406	4.9	2035	1.6

NOVEMBER

Day	Time	m	Time	m	Time	m	Time	m
1 SU	0255	4.9	0905	1.5	1513	5.2	2135	1.1
16 M	0348	4.9	1004	1.5	1600	5.1	2226	1.3
2 M	0350	5.2	1002	1.1	1607	5.5	2228	0.8
17 TU	0426	5.1	1044	1.3	1638	5.2	2304	1.2
3 TU	0439	5.5	1054	0.7	1657	5.7	2318	0.5
18 W	0501	5.3	1121	1.2	1714	5.3	2338	1.1
4 W ○	0526	5.7	1142	0.5	1746	5.8		
19 TH ●	0536	5.4	1154	1.1	1751	5.3		
5 TH	0005	0.3	0612	5.8	1229	0.4	1834	5.8
20 F	0008	1.1	0611	5.4	1225	1.1	1827	5.3
6 F	0051	0.4	0657	5.8	1314	0.4	1921	5.7
21 SA	0037	1.2	0646	5.4	1254	1.2	1902	5.2
7 SA	0134	0.5	0742	5.7	1357	0.6	2007	5.5
22 SU	0105	1.3	0720	5.3	1324	1.3	1936	5.1
8 SU	0215	0.8	0825	5.5	1439	0.9	2051	5.2
23 M	0133	1.4	0751	5.2	1354	1.4	2008	4.9
9 M	0256	1.2	0907	5.3	1522	1.3	2136	4.9
24 TU	0204	1.5	0823	5.1	1428	1.6	2044	4.8
10 TU	0340	1.7	0951	5.0	1610	1.8	2232	4.6
25 W	0240	1.7	0902	4.9	1509	1.8	2129	4.6
11 W	0431	2.1	1049	4.7	1711	2.1	2352	4.3
26 TH	0325	1.9	0952	4.8	1604	1.9	2225	4.5
12 TH	0539	2.3	1214	4.5	1834	2.3		
27 F	0428	2.1	1052	4.7	1722	2.0	2333	4.5
13 F	0108	4.3	0710	2.4	1328	4.5	1958	2.1
28 SA	0558	2.2	1204	4.7	1848	1.9		
14 SA	0212	4.5	0825	2.1	1428	4.7	2058	1.8
29 SU	0054	4.6	0723	2.0	1325	4.8	2002	1.7
15 SU	0304	4.7	0919	1.8	1518	4.9	2145	1.5
30 M	0215	4.8	0834	1.7	1439	5.1	2107	1.3

DECEMBER

Day	Time	m	Time	m	Time	m	Time	m
1 TU	0319	5.1	0936	1.3	1541	5.3	2204	1.0
16 W	0350	4.9	1006	1.6	1605	5.0	2226	1.5
2 W	0414	5.4	1032	0.9	1636	5.5	2257	0.7
17 TH	0431	5.1	1047	1.4	1648	5.1	2304	1.3
3 TH	0504	5.6	1123	0.7	1727	5.7	2346	0.6
18 F ●	0511	5.3	1125	1.3	1729	5.2	2340	1.2
4 F	0552	5.8	1211	0.5	1817	5.7		
19 SA	0550	5.3	1201	1.2	1809	5.2		
5 SA	0032	0.5	0639	5.8	1258	0.5	1905	5.6
20 SU	0015	1.2	0629	5.4	1237	1.2	1848	5.2
6 SU	0118	0.6	0725	5.7	1343	0.7	1952	5.4
21 M	0050	1.2	0706	5.3	1313	1.2	1926	5.1
7 M	0200	0.9	0808	5.6	1426	0.9	2037	5.2
22 TU	0124	1.2	0741	5.3	1349	1.2	2001	5.0
8 TU	0242	1.2	0849	5.3	1508	1.2	2119	4.9
23 W	0200	1.3	0815	5.2	1426	1.3	2038	4.9
9 W	0323	1.5	0928	5.1	1552	1.6	2202	4.7
24 TH	0238	1.4	0853	5.1	1506	1.4	2119	4.8
10 TH	0407	1.9	1010	4.8	1639	1.9	2255	4.4
25 F	0320	1.6	0938	5.0	1553	1.6	2208	4.7
11 F	0458	2.2	1104	4.6	1736	2.1		
26 SA	0411	1.8	1031	4.9	1650	1.7	2307	4.6
12 SA	0008	4.3	0559	2.3	1221	4.5	1843	2.2
27 SU	0516	1.9	1134	4.8	1803	1.8		
13 SU	0117	4.3	0713	2.3	1332	4.5	1955	2.1
28 M	0018	4.6	0637	1.9	1249	4.8	1923	1.7
14 M	0215	4.5	0823	2.1	1430	4.6	2055	1.9
29 TU	0137	4.7	0800	1.8	1407	4.9	2037	1.5
15 TU	0305	4.7	0919	1.9	1520	4.8	2144	1.7
30 W	0249	4.9	0912	1.5	1517	5.1	2142	1.3
31 TH	0351	5.2	1013	1.2	1617	5.3	2239	1.0

SUBMARINE EXERCISE AREAS (SUBFACTS)

Within the SW English Channel, those areas (see below) where dived and surfaced submarines are planned to operate during all or part of the ensuing 24 hrs will be broadcast daily on VHF at 0733 and 1933 UT by the four Coast Radio Stations shown below. Further info from Naval Ops, Plymouth; ☎ (01752) 557550. See also 6.3.15.

Submarines on the surface and at periscope depth will maintain constant listening watch on VHF Ch 16. The former will comply strictly with IRPCS; the latter will not close to within 1500 yds of a FV without permission from the FV. See 8.4.10 for general advice on submarine activity which also occurs in other sea areas.

RIVER YEALM Devon 50°18'·55N 04°04'·06W (Ent)   Rtg 3-4-1

CHARTS
AC *30*,1900,*1613*; Imray C6, C14; Stanfords 13; OS 201

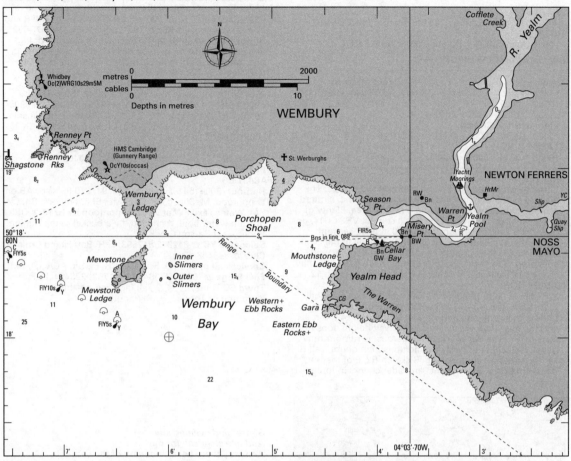

TIDES
−0522 Dover; ML 3·2; Duration 0615; Zone 0 (UT)

Standard Port DEVONPORT (◄——)

Times				Height (metres)			
High Water		Low Water		MHWS	MHWN	MLWN	MLWS
0000	0600	0000	0600	5·5	4·4	2·2	0·8
1200	1800	1200	1800				

Differences RIVER YEALM ENTRANCE

+0006	+0006	+0002	+0002	−0·1	−0·1	−0·1	−0·1

Note: Strong SW winds hold up the ebb and raise levels, as does the river if in spate.

SHELTER
Very good. Ent easy except in strong onshore winds. ‡ in Cellar Bay is open to NW winds. Ⓥ pontoon in The Pool.

NAVIGATION
WPT 50°18'·00N 04°06'·00W, 240°/060° from/to Season Pt, 1·4M. For details of **Wembury firing range** and target buoys, see 10.1.17. The SE edge of the range lies across the ent to the Yealm. The W & E Ebb rks and the Inner & Outer Slimers are dangerous, lying awash on E and W sides of Wembury Bay. Ldg bns (W △, B stripe) in line at 089° clear Mouthstone Ledge, but **not** the sand bar. The PHM buoy, Fl R 5s (Apr-Oct), marks end of sand bar and **must** be left to port on entry. When abeam, **but not before**, bn (G ▲ on W □) on S shore, turn NE toward bn (W □, R stripe) on N shore. From sand bar to Misery Pt, river carries only 1·2m at MLWS. Leave Spit PHM buoy off Warren Pt to port. It is impossible to beat in against an ebb tide. Speed limit 6kn.

LIGHTS AND MARKS
Great Mewstone (57m) is conspic 1·5M to W of river ent. Bns as above. No lights apart from PHM By Fl R 5s at ent.

TELEPHONE (Dial code 01752)
Hr Mr 872533; MRSC (01803) 882704; ⌗ 0345 231110 (H24); Marinecall 0891 500458; Police 701188; Dr 880392.

RADIO TELEPHONE None.
FACILITIES
Yealm Pool M, pontoon £8, L, FW; **Yealm YC** ☎ 872291, FW, Bar; **Newton Ferrers** L, Slip, FW, V, Gas, Gaz, R, Bar, ✉; **Services**: ME, El, Sh, SM. **Bridgend** L, Slip (HW±2½), FW; **Noss Mayo** L, Slip, FW, V, R, Bar, ✉; Nearest fuel 3M at Yealmpton. ⇌ ✈ (Plymouth).

ADJACENT ANCHORAGES IN BIGBURY BAY

RIVER ERME, Devon, 50°18'·12N 03°57'·60W. AC *1613*. HW − 0525 on Dover; +0015 and −0·6m on HW Devonport. Temp day ‡ in 3m at mouth of drying river, open to SW. Access near HW, but only in offshore winds and settled wx. Beware Wells Rk (1·2m) 1M SE of ent. Appr from SW, clear of Edwards Rk. Ent between Battisborough Is and W. Mary's Rk (dries 1·1m) keeping to the W. No facilities. Two Historic Wrecks are at 50°18'·15N 03°57'·41W and 50°18'·41N 03°57'·19W on W side of the ent; see 10.0.3h.

RIVER AVON, Devon, 50°16'·61N 03°53'·60W. AC *1613*. Tides as R Erme, above. Enter drying river HW −1, only in offshore winds and settled wx. Appr close E of conspic Burgh Is & Murray's Rks, marked by bn. Narrow chan hugs cliffy NW shore, then turns SE and N off Bantham. A recce at LW or local knowledge would assist. Streams run hard, but able to dry out in good shelter clear of moorings. V, ✉, Bar at Bantham. Aveton Gifford accessible by dinghy, 2·5M.

HOPE COVE, Devon, 50°14'·62N 03°51'·75W. AC *1613*. Tides as R Erme, above; ML 2·6m; Duration 0615. Popular day ‡ in centre of cove, but poor holding ground and only safe in offshore winds. Appr with old LB ho brg 110° and ‡ SW of pier hd. Beware rk, drying 2·5m, ½ca offshore and 3ca E of Bolt Tail. No lts. Facilities: very limited in village, EC Thurs; but good at Kingsbridge (6M bus), or Salcombe, (4M bus).

SALCOMBE   10-1-20

Devon 50°13'·55N 03°46'·60W. Rtg 3-2-1

CHARTS
AC 28, 1634, 1613; Imray C6, Y48; Stanfords 13; OS 202

TIDES
−0523 Dover; ML 3·1; Duration 0615; Zone 0 (UT)

Standard Port DEVONPORT (←—)

Times				Height (metres)			
High Water		Low Water		MHWS	MHWN	MLWN	MLWS
0100	0600	0100	0600	5·5	4·4	2·2	0·8
1300	1800	1300	1800				
Differences SALCOMBE							
0000	+0010	+0005	−0005	−0·2	−0·3	−0·1	−0·1
START POINT							
+0005	+0030	−0005	+0005	−0·2	−0·4	−0·1	−0·1

SHELTER
Perfectly protected hbr but ent exposed to S winds. The estuary is 4M long and has 8 drying creeks off it. Limited ⚓ on SE side between ferry and ⚓ prohib area. Plenty of deep water ⚓s. (Hr Mr's launch will contact VHF Ch14, on duty 0600-2100 in season; 0600-2200 in peak season). S'ly winds can cause an uncomfortable swell in the ⚓ off the town. Visitors' pontoon and ⚓s in the Bag are well sheltered. Short stay pontoon (1 hour max, 0700-1900) by Hr Mr's office has 1m. Water taxi via Hr Mr, VHF Ch 12.

NAVIGATION
WPT 50°12'·40N 03°46'·60W, 180°/000° from/to Sandhill Pt lt, 1·3M. The bar (0·7m) can be dangerous at sp ebb tides with strong on-shore winds. Access HW±4½, but at springs this window applies only if swell height does not exceed 1m. The Bar is not as dangerous as rumour may have it, except in the above conditions; if in doubt, call Hr Mr Ch 14 before approaching. Rickham Rk, E of the Bar, has 3·1m depth. Speed limit 8kn; radar checks in force.

Note: The site of a Historic Wreck (50°12'·70N 03°44'·33W) is at Moor Sand, 1M WNW of Prawle Pt; see 10.0.3h.

LIGHTS AND MARKS
Outer ldg marks: Sandhill Pt bn on with Poundstone bn 000°. Sandhill Pt Dir lt 000°, Fl WRG 2s 27m 10/7M; R and W ♦ on W mast: vis R002°-182°, G182°-357°, W357°-002°. Beware unmarked Bass Rk (dries 0·8m) close W of ldg line and Wolf Rk, marked by SHM By QG, close E of ldg line. After passing Wolf Rk, pick up Inner ldg lts, Q Fl 042°, leaving Blackstone Rk Q (2) G 8s 4m 2M to stbd.

RADIO TELEPHONE
VHF Ch 14 call Salcombe Hbr or Launch (Mon-Thurs 0900-1645, Fri 0900-1615); 14 May-14 Sept Sat/Sun 0900-1615). Call Water taxi Ch 12. Call: ICC Base (clubhouse) and Egremont (ICC floating HQ) Ch M. Fuel Barge Ch 06.

TELEPHONE (Dial code 01548)
Hr Mr 843791, ☎ 842033; MRSC (01803) 882704; ✕ 0345 231110 (H24); Marinecall 0891 500458; Police 842107; Dr 842284.

FACILITIES
Harbour (300+150 visitors) ☎ 843791, £10 for ⚓ or AB on Ⓥ pontoon. M, Slip, Ⓔ, P, D, L, ME, EI, C (15 ton), Sh, CH, SM, Water Taxi; FW at visitors' pontoon by Hr Mr's Office or from water boat; if needed, fly a bucket in the rigging. Public ⚓ at Batson Creek.
Salcombe YC ☎ 842872/842593, L, R, Bar; **Island Cruising Club** ☎ 843483, Bar, Ⓒ.
Services: Slip, M, P, D, FW, ME, CH, EI, Sh, ACA, Ⓔ, SM;
Fuel Barge ☎ (0836) 775644 or (01752) 223434, D, P.
Town EC Thurs; Ⓒ, ✉, Ⓑ, all facilities, ⇌ (bus to Plymouth or Totnes), ✈ (Plymouth).

Sunset and evening star,
And one clear call for me!
And may there be no moaning of the bar,
When I put out to sea ...

Crossing the Bar: Alfred Lord Tennyson

The opening lines of Tennyson's famous poem written whilst on board a yacht at Salcombe. The description of putting out to sea on a calm evening is actually used as a metaphor for death.

ADJACENT HARBOUR UP-RIVER

KINGSBRIDGE, Devon, 50°16'·85N 03°46'·45W. AC 28. HW = HW Salcombe +0005. Access HW±2½ for <2m draft/bilge keelers, max LOA 11m. Berth on visitors' pontoon E side or wall on W side of basin, drying 3·4m to soft mud. Best to pre-check berth availability with Hr Mr Salcombe. The 3M chan to Kingsbridge is marked beyond Salt Stone SHM perch by R/W PHM poles with R can topmarks. 6ca N of Salt Stone a secondary chan marked by PHM buoys diverges slowly E into Balcombe Creek. There is a private ferry pontoon at New Quay, 3ca before the visitors' pontoon. Facilities: Slip, SM.
Town EC Thurs; V, R, Bar, ✉, Ⓑ, Ⓒ.

ENGLAND – DARTMOUTH

LAT 50°21′N   LONG 3°34′W

TIMES AND HEIGHTS OF HIGH AND LOW WATERS

YEAR **1998**

TIME ZONE (UT)
For Summer Time add ONE hour in non-shaded areas

Chart Datum: 2·62 metres below Ordnance Datum (Newlyn)

JANUARY

Day	Time	m	Time	m	Day	Time	m	Time	m
1 TH	0114 / 0748	0.7 / 4.9	1339 / 2012	0.6 / 4.7	16 F	0152 / 0808	0.8 / 4.7	1414 / 2028	0.9 / 4.4
2 F	0155 / 0829	0.7 / 4.9	1422 / 2054	0.7 / 4.6	17 SA	0223 / 0838	1.0 / 4.6	1443 / 2058	1.1 / 4.3
3 SA	0235 / 0911	0.8 / 4.8	1503 / 2137	0.8 / 4.5	18 SU	0250 / 0910	1.2 / 4.5	1510 / 2131	1.3 / 4.2
4 SU	0318 / 0956	1.0 / 4.7	1547 / 2223	1.0 / 4.4	19 M	0317 / 0945	1.4 / 4.3	1537 / 2207	1.5 / 4.0
5 M	0404 / 1045	1.2 / 4.5	1636 / 2317	1.2 / 4.2	20 TU	0346 / 1024	1.7 / 4.1	1610 / 2251	1.7 / 3.9
6 TU	0458 / 1142	1.5 / 4.3	1737	1.5	21 W	0428 / 1111	1.9 / 3.9	1703 / 2346	1.9 / 3.7
7 W	0021 / 0608	4.1 / 1.7	1253 / 1855	4.1 / 1.6	22 TH	0539 / 1210	2.1 / 3.8	1821	2.0
8 TH	0137 / 0737	4.0 / 1.7	1410 / 2017	4.1 / 1.5	23 F	0056 / 0701	3.7 / 2.1	1326 / 1937	3.8 / 1.9
9 F	0251 / 0855	4.2 / 1.5	1521 / 2126	4.2 / 1.3	24 SA	0222 / 0812	3.9 / 1.8	1452 / 2044	3.9 / 1.6
10 SA	0356 / 0958	4.4 / 1.2	1624 / 2224	4.4 / 1.1	25 SU	0333 / 0916	4.1 / 1.5	1559 / 2144	4.1 / 1.3
11 SU	0451 / 1052	4.6 / 0.9	1718 / 2314	4.5 / 0.9	26 M	0430 / 1014	4.4 / 1.2	1655 / 2239	4.4 / 1.0
12 M	0541 / 1140	4.8 / 0.7	1806 / O 2359	4.6 / 0.7	27 TU	0519 / 1107	4.7 / 0.8	1745 / 2329	4.6 / 0.7
13 TU	0624 / 1224	4.8 / 0.6	1849	4.6	28 W	0606 / 1157	4.9 / 0.6	1833 ●	4.7
14 W	0041 / 0703	0.7 / 4.9	1306 / 1926	0.6 / 4.6	29 TH	0017 / 0652	0.5 / 5.0	1246 / 1917	0.4 / 4.8
15 TH	0119 / 0738	0.7 / 4.8	1341 / 1959	0.7 / 4.5	30 F	0105 / 0736	0.4 / 5.1	1330 / 2001	0.2 / 4.9
					31 SA	0147 / 0819	0.3 / 5.1	1413 / 2044	0.2 / 4.8

FEBRUARY

Day	Time	m	Time	m	Day	Time	m	Time	m
1 SU	0228 / 0901	0.4 / 5.0	1452 / 2125	0.4 / 4.7	16 M	0222 / 0848	1.0 / 4.5	1437 / 2105	1.0 / 4.3
2 M	0307 / 0944	0.6 / 4.9	1531 / 2206	0.6 / 4.6	17 TU	0243 / 0918	1.1 / 4.4	1458 / 2136	1.2 / 4.2
3 TU	0347 / 1028	0.9 / 4.6	1614 / 2252	1.0 / 4.3	18 W	0307 / 0950	1.4 / 4.1	1524 / 2209	1.5 / 4.0
4 W	0432 / 1119	1.2 / 4.3	1703 / 2349	1.4 / 4.0	19 TH	0339 / 1028	1.6 / 3.9	1602 / 2255	1.7 / 3.8
5 TH	0529 / 1224	1.6 / 4.0	1809	1.7	20 F	0429 / 1122	1.9 / 3.7	1705 / 2357	2.0 / 3.7
6 F	0102 / 0655	3.9 / 1.8	1343 / 1945	3.9 / 1.8	21 SA	0603 / 1231	2.0 / 3.6	1850	2.0
7 SA	0222 / 0834	3.9 / 1.7	1500 / 2109	3.9 / 1.6	22 SU	0116 / 0733	3.7 / 1.9	1403 / 2008	3.7 / 1.8
8 SU	0333 / 0944	4.1 / 1.4	1607 / 2209	4.1 / 1.3	23 M	0252 / 0846	4.0 / 1.6	1529 / 2117	4.0 / 1.4
9 M	0432 / 1039	4.4 / 1.1	1701 / 2300	4.3 / 1.0	24 TU	0400 / 0957	4.3 / 1.1	1631 / 2217	4.3 / 1.0
10 TU	0521 / 1125	4.6 / 0.8	1748 / 2343	4.4 / 0.8	25 W	0454 / 1048	4.6 / 0.7	1724 / 2312	4.6 / 0.6
11 W	0604 / 1208	4.7 / 0.6	1829 O	4.5	26 TH	0545 / 1139	4.9 / 0.4	1814 ●	4.8
12 TH	0023 / 0642	0.6 / 4.8	1248 / 1903	0.6 / 4.6	27 F	0002 / 0633	0.3 / 5.1	1230 / 1859	0.1 / 4.9
13 F	0101 / 0716	0.6 / 4.8	1322 / 1936	0.6 / 4.6	28 SA	0050 / 0719	0.1 / 5.2	1315 / 1944	-0.1 / 5.0
14 SA	0131 / 0747	0.6 / 4.8	1351 / 2006	0.7 / 4.5					
15 SU	0158 / 0817	0.8 / 4.7	1416 / 2035	0.9 / 4.5					

MARCH

Day	Time	m	Time	m	Day	Time	m	Time	m
1 SU	0133 / 0804	0.0 / 5.2	1357 / 2027	0.0 / 5.0	16 M	0132 / 0755	0.7 / 4.7	1347 / 2011	0.7 / 4.5
2 M	0213 / 0847	0.1 / 5.1	1435 / 2107	0.1 / 4.9	17 TU	0154 / 0825	0.8 / 4.5	1408 / 2040	0.9 / 4.4
3 TU	0251 / 0928	0.3 / 4.9	1514 / 2146	0.4 / 4.7	18 W	0216 / 0853	1.0 / 4.4	1429 / 2106	1.1 / 4.3
4 W	0328 / 1009	0.7 / 4.6	1552 / 2227	0.9 / 4.4	19 TH	0239 / 0922	1.2 / 4.2	1454 / 2136	1.3 / 4.1
5 TH	0411 / 1055	1.1 / 4.2	1636 / 2317	1.4 / 4.0	20 F	0310 / 0957	1.4 / 3.9	1528 / 2218	1.6 / 3.9
6 F	0502 / 1159	1.6 / 3.8	1734	1.8	21 SA	0354 / 1049	1.7 / 3.7	1622 / 2318	1.9 / 3.8
7 SA	0031 / 0617	3.8 / 1.9	1322 / 1909	3.7 / 2.0	22 SU	0513 / 1157	1.9 / 3.6	1804	2.0
8 SU	0157 / 0813	3.8 / 1.9	1442 / 2050	3.7 / 1.8	23 M	0032 / 0659	3.7 / 1.9	1320 / 1938	3.7 / 1.8
9 M	0311 / 0926	3.9 / 1.5	1548 / 2151	3.9 / 1.4	24 TU	0205 / 0817	3.9 / 1.5	1458 / 2051	3.9 / 1.4
10 TU	0411 / 1019	4.2 / 1.1	1642 / 2240	4.2 / 1.1	25 W	0328 / 0925	4.3 / 1.1	1606 / 2155	4.3 / 1.0
11 W	0458 / 1105	4.5 / 0.8	1725 / 2323	4.4 / 0.8	26 TH	0427 / 1025	4.6 / 0.6	1700 / 2252	4.6 / 0.5
12 TH	0540 / 1146	4.6 / 0.6	1803	4.5	27 F	0520 / 1119	4.9 / 0.2	1751 / 2342	4.9 / 0.2
13 F	0001 / 0617	0.6 / 4.7	1223 / 1838 O	0.5 / 4.6	28 SA	0612 / 1207	5.1 / 0.0	1839 ●	5.1
14 SA	0037 / 0651	0.6 / 4.8	1257 / 1910	0.5 / 4.6	29 SU	0030 / 0659	0.0 / 5.2	1255 / 1924	-0.2 / 5.1
15 SU	0107 / 0723	0.6 / 4.7	1325 / 1941	0.6 / 4.6	30 M	0115 / 0745	-0.1 / 5.2	1336 / 2007	-0.1 / 5.1
					31 TU	0155 / 0829	0.0 / 5.1	1417 / 2047	0.1 / 5.0

APRIL

Day	Time	m	Time	m	Day	Time	m	Time	m
1 W	0233 / 0910	0.2 / 4.9	1454 / 2125	0.4 / 4.7	16 TH	0154 / 0832	0.9 / 4.3	1407 / 2043	1.0 / 4.4
2 TH	0312 / 0951	0.6 / 4.5	1532 / 2202	0.9 / 4.4	17 F	0222 / 0901	1.1 / 4.2	1434 / 2114	1.2 / 4.2
3 F	0352 / 1035	1.1 / 4.1	1615 / 2245	1.4 / 4.1	18 SA	0254 / 0938	1.3 / 4.0	1511 / 2156	1.5 / 4.1
4 SA	0442 / 1136	1.5 / 3.7	1710 / 2357	1.8 / 3.8	19 SU	0338 / 1030	1.5 / 3.8	1604 / 2252	1.7 / 3.9
5 SU	0550 / 1301	1.9 / 3.6	1831	2.1	20 M	0450 / 1134	1.8 / 3.7	1731	1.9
6 M	0128 / 0740	3.7 / 1.9	1418 / 2016	3.6 / 1.9	21 TU	0002 / 0629	3.9 / 1.7	1252 / 1908	3.7 / 1.8
7 TU	0243 / 0859	3.9 / 1.6	1522 / 2122	3.9 / 1.6	22 W	0126 / 0749	4.0 / 1.4	1425 / 2023	4.0 / 1.4
8 W	0341 / 0952	4.1 / 1.3	1613 / 2211	4.1 / 1.2	23 TH	0253 / 0859	4.3 / 1.0	1537 / 2131	4.3 / 1.0
9 TH	0428 / 1037	4.3 / 0.9	1656 / 2254	4.3 / 0.9	24 F	0359 / 1000	4.6 / 0.6	1633 / 2227	4.6 / 0.6
10 F	0510 / 1116	4.5 / 0.7	1733 / 2332	4.5 / 0.7	25 SA	0455 / 1055	4.9 / 0.3	1726 / 2320	4.9 / 0.2
11 SA	0547 / 1153	4.6 / 0.6	1808 O	4.6	26 SU	0548 / 1145	5.1 / 0.0	1816 ●	5.0
12 SU	0007 / 0623	0.6 / 4.7	1226 / 1843	0.7 / 4.6	27 M	0008 / 0638	0.0 / 5.1	1233 / 1901	-0.1 / 5.1
13 M	0039 / 0658	0.6 / 4.7	1254 / 1916	0.7 / 4.6	28 TU	0054 / 0725	-0.1 / 5.1	1317 / 1945	0.0 / 5.1
14 TU	0105 / 0732	0.7 / 4.6	1319 / 1948	0.7 / 4.6	29 W	0136 / 0810	0.2 / 5.0	1357 / 2026	0.2 / 5.0
15 W	0130 / 0804	0.8 / 4.5	1342 / 2016	0.8 / 4.5	30 TH	0217 / 0853	0.3 / 4.7	1436 / 2104	0.5 / 4.7

ENGLAND – DARTMOUTH

LAT 50°21′N   LONG 3°34′W

TIMES AND HEIGHTS OF HIGH AND LOW WATERS

YEAR **1998**

TIME ZONE (UT)
For Summer Time add ONE hour in non-shaded areas

MAY

Day	Time	m	Day	Time	m
1 F	0256 0934 1516 2139	0.6 4.4 1.0 4.4	**16** SA	0212 0850 1427 2101	1.0 4.2 1.1 4.4
2 SA	0337 1016 1557 2216	1.1 4.1 1.4 4.1	**17** SU	0249 0929 1506 2143	1.1 4.1 1.3 4.2
3 SU	0425 1112 1648 2311	1.5 3.7 1.8 3.8	**18** M	0336 1017 1558 2236	1.3 3.9 1.6 4.1
4 M	0525 1232 1753	1.8 3.6 2.0	**19** TU	0439 1118 1711 2340	1.5 3.8 1.7 4.0
5 TU	0047 0645 1343 1918	3.7 1.9 3.6 2.0	**20** W	0559 1230 1836	1.5 3.8 1.6
6 W	0203 0810 1444 2035	3.8 1.7 3.8 1.8	**21** TH	0057 0719 1352 1953	4.1 1.4 4.0 1.4
7 TH	0301 0910 1536 2131	4.0 1.4 4.0 1.4	**22** F	0220 0831 1506 2102	4.3 1.1 4.3 1.1
8 F	0351 0957 1619 2216	4.2 1.2 4.2 1.2	**23** SA	0330 0934 1607 2203	4.5 0.7 4.6 0.7
9 SA	0433 1039 1659 2257	4.4 1.0 4.4 0.9	**24** SU	0430 1031 1701 2258	4.7 0.4 4.8 0.4
10 SU	0515 1116 1737 2333	4.5 0.8 4.5 0.8	**25** M ●	0525 1123 1753 2347	4.9 0.3 4.9 0.2
11 M O	0554 1150 1816	4.5 0.8 4.6	**26** TU	0618 1210 1841	4.9 0.2 5.0
12 TU	0006 0633 1222 1853	0.7 4.6 0.8 4.6	**27** W	0035 0706 1257 1925	0.2 4.9 0.2 5.0
13 W	0038 0710 1253 1927	0.7 4.5 0.8 4.6	**28** TH	0120 0753 1339 2007	0.2 4.8 0.4 4.9
14 TH	0109 0745 1323 1958	0.8 4.4 0.9 4.5	**29** F	0202 0836 1420 2045	0.4 4.6 0.6 4.7
15 F	0139 0817 1353 2027	0.9 4.3 1.0 4.5	**30** SA	0242 0917 1459 2118	0.7 4.4 1.0 4.5
			31 SU	0323 0954 1539 2151	1.0 4.1 1.3 4.2

JUNE

Day	Time	m	Day	Time	m
1 M	0405 1035 1624 2232	1.4 3.8 1.6 4.0	**16** TU	0333 1009 1553 2224	1.1 4.1 1.3 4.3
2 TU	0454 1132 1715 2330	1.6 3.7 1.9 3.8	**17** W	0427 1103 1650 2322	1.2 4.0 1.4 4.2
3 W	0551 1246 1817	1.8 3.6 2.0	**18** TH	0530 1207 1801	1.3 4.0 1.5
4 TH	0053 0658 1350 1925	3.8 1.8 3.7 1.9	**19** F	0031 0645 1321 1920	4.1 1.3 4.0 1.4
5 F	0206 0805 1446 2031	3.8 1.7 3.9 1.7	**20** SA	0150 0800 1435 2035	4.2 1.2 4.2 1.2
6 SA	0304 0902 1536 2125	4.0 1.4 4.1 1.4	**21** SU	0305 0908 1541 2140	4.3 1.0 4.4 1.0
7 SU	0354 0951 1622 2213	4.2 1.2 4.3 1.2	**22** M	0409 1009 1639 2238	4.5 0.7 4.6 0.7
8 M	0441 1035 1705 2255	4.3 1.0 4.4 1.0	**23** TU	0505 1104 1732 2330	4.6 0.6 4.8 0.5
9 TU	0525 1114 1749 2335	4.4 0.9 4.5 0.9	**24** W ●	0559 1153 1822	4.7 0.4 4.9
10 W O	0610 1152 1830	4.5 0.8 4.6	**25** TH	0018 0649 1241 1906	0.4 4.7 0.4 4.9
11 TH	0013 0650 1231 1907	0.8 4.5 0.8 4.6	**26** F	0105 0735 1324 1948	0.4 4.6 0.5 4.8
12 F	0052 0729 1308 1943	0.8 4.4 0.8 4.6	**27** SA	0147 0817 1404 2025	0.5 4.5 0.7 4.7
13 SA	0130 0807 1345 2018	0.8 4.4 0.9 4.6	**28** SU	0227 0854 1441 2055	0.7 4.4 0.9 4.5
14 SU	0208 0844 1424 2054	0.8 4.3 1.0 4.5	**29** M	0303 0924 1517 2126	0.9 4.2 1.2 4.4
15 M	0248 0924 1505 2136	0.9 4.2 1.1 4.5	**30** TU	0339 0957 1553 2200	1.2 4.0 1.4 4.2

JULY

Day	Time	m	Day	Time	m
1 W	0418 1035 1633 2243	1.5 3.8 1.7 4.0	**16** TH	0409 1048 1629 2304	0.9 4.2 1.2 4.3
2 TH	0502 1125 1724 2335	1.7 3.7 1.9 3.8	**17** F	0502 1144 1728	1.2 4.1 1.4
3 F	0556 1228 1824	1.8 3.7 1.9	**18** SA	0007 0609 1252 1846	4.1 1.4 4.0 1.5
4 SA	0044 0659 1342 1929	3.7 1.8 3.7 1.9	**19** SU	0124 0730 1408 2009	4.0 1.4 4.2 1.5
5 SU	0204 0801 1448 2032	3.8 1.7 3.9 1.7	**20** M	0243 0848 1518 2122	4.1 1.3 4.2 1.2
6 M	0312 0900 1545 2129	3.9 1.5 4.1 1.4	**21** TU	0351 0953 1620 2223	4.2 1.1 4.4 0.9
7 TU	0409 0953 1635 2219	4.1 1.2 4.3 1.2	**22** W	0451 1050 1715 2317	4.4 0.8 4.6 0.7
8 W	0458 1042 1722 2307	4.3 1.0 4.5 0.9	**23** TH ●	0544 1139 1803	4.5 0.6 4.8
9 TH O	0546 1128 1807 2353	4.4 0.9 4.6 0.8	**24** F	0005 0632 1225 1848	0.5 4.6 0.5 4.8
10 F	0631 1212 1850	4.5 0.8 4.7	**25** SA	0050 0715 1308 1927	0.5 4.6 0.5 4.8
11 SA	0038 0714 1257 1930	0.7 4.5 0.7 4.8	**26** SU	0130 0753 1345 2001	0.5 4.5 0.6 4.7
12 SU	0121 0755 1338 2008	0.6 4.5 0.7 4.8	**27** M	0206 0826 1419 2030	0.6 4.4 0.8 4.6
13 M	0202 0836 1418 2049	0.6 4.5 0.7 4.8	**28** TU	0238 0854 1449 2059	0.8 4.3 1.0 4.5
14 TU	0242 0917 1458 2130	0.6 4.4 0.8 4.7	**29** W	0308 0924 1518 2131	1.1 4.2 1.3 4.3
15 W	0324 1000 1541 2213	0.7 4.4 1.0 4.5	**30** TH	0335 0958 1547 2206	1.3 4.0 1.5 4.2
			31 F	0406 1038 1624 2249	1.6 3.9 1.8 3.9

AUGUST

Day	Time	m	Day	Time	m
1 SA	0450 1128 1722 2342	1.8 3.7 2.0 3.7	**16** SU	0536 1226 1814	1.5 3.9 1.7
2 SU	0559 1232 1837	1.9 3.7 2.0	**17** M	0104 0703 1346 1952	3.9 1.7 3.9 1.7
3 M	0054 0712 1354 1947	3.7 1.9 3.7 1.9	**18** TU	0227 0835 1501 2112	3.9 1.6 4.1 1.5
4 TU	0227 0819 1510 2052	3.8 1.7 4.0 1.6	**19** W	0340 0943 1606 2213	4.0 1.3 4.3 1.1
5 W	0339 0920 1608 2150	4.0 1.4 4.3 1.3	**20** TH	0440 1037 1659 2304	4.3 1.0 4.5 0.8
6 TH	0434 1015 1658 2244	4.2 1.1 4.5 0.9	**21** F	0529 1124 1745 2349	4.4 0.7 4.7 0.6
7 F	0524 1107 1745 2334	4.4 0.9 4.7 0.7	**22** SA ●	0613 1207 1827	4.5 0.6 4.8
8 SA O	0612 1155 1830	4.6 0.6 4.8	**23** SU	0031 0652 1248 1902	0.5 4.6 0.5 4.8
9 SU	0021 0656 1243 1913	0.5 4.7 0.5 4.9	**24** M	0109 0726 1323 1935	0.5 4.6 0.6 4.8
10 M	0108 0739 1327 1955	0.3 4.7 0.4 5.0	**25** TU	0141 0755 1352 2004	0.6 4.5 0.7 4.7
11 TU	0150 0822 1407 2037	0.3 4.7 0.4 5.0	**26** W	0209 0824 1418 2032	0.8 4.5 0.9 4.6
12 W	0229 0903 1446 2118	0.3 4.7 0.5 4.9	**27** TH	0231 0852 1440 2102	1.0 4.3 1.1 4.4
13 TH	0309 0944 1525 2200	0.5 4.6 0.7 4.6	**28** F	0251 0924 1501 2134	1.2 4.2 1.4 4.2
14 F	0349 1028 1608 2246	0.8 4.4 1.1 4.4	**29** SA	0312 0958 1527 2209	1.5 4.0 1.6 4.0
15 SA	0435 1119 1701 2345	1.2 4.1 1.4 4.1	**30** SU	0342 1041 1609 2256	1.7 3.8 1.9 3.7
			31 M	0437 1137 1738	2.0 3.7 2.1

Chart Datum: 2·62 metres below Ordnance Datum (Newlyn)

1

ENGLAND – DARTMOUTH

LAT 50°21′N   LONG   3°34′W

TIMES AND HEIGHTS OF HIGH AND LOW WATERS   YEAR **1998**

TIME ZONE (UT)
For Summer Time add ONE hour in non-shaded areas

Chart Datum: 2·62 metres below Ordnance Datum (Newlyn)

SEPTEMBER

	Time	m		Time	m
1 TU	0002 0626 1252 1911	3.6 2.1 3.7 2.0	**16** W	0217 0822 1446 2101	3.8 1.8 4.0 1.6
2 W	0135 0746 1430 2022	3.6 1.9 3.9 1.7	**17** TH	0329 0929 1550 2157	4.0 1.5 4.3 1.2
3 TH	0313 0853 1540 2125	3.9 1.6 4.2 1.3	**18** F	0425 1019 1641 2245	4.2 1.1 4.5 0.9
4 F	0413 0953 1632 2221	4.2 1.2 4.6 0.9	**19** SA	0510 1104 1723 2327	4.5 0.8 4.7 0.6
5 SA	0502 1047 1721 2314	4.5 0.8 4.8 0.5	**20** SU ●	0550 1144 1801	4.6 0.6 4.8
6 SU O	0550 1137 1807	4.7 0.5 5.0	**21** M	0006 0625 1222 1835	0.5 4.7 0.6 4.8
7 M	0002 0636 1224 1853	0.3 4.9 0.3 5.1	**22** TU	0042 0656 1255 1906	0.5 4.7 0.6 4.8
8 TU	0049 0720 1310 1938	0.1 4.9 0.2 5.2	**23** W	0112 0726 1323 1937	0.6 4.7 0.7 4.7
9 W	0131 0803 1350 2020	0.1 5.0 0.2 5.1	**24** TH	0136 0746 1346 2007	0.8 4.7 0.9 4.6
10 TH	0212 0845 1429 2101	0.2 4.9 0.3 5.0	**25** F	0156 0825 1407 2035	1.0 4.5 1.1 4.4
11 F	0250 0925 1508 2143	0.4 4.8 0.7 4.7	**26** SA	0215 0853 1427 2104	1.2 4.3 1.3 4.2
12 SA	0328 1006 1548 2227	0.8 4.5 1.1 4.3	**27** SU	0235 0925 1452 2137	1.4 4.1 1.6 4.0
13 SU	0412 1054 1638 2326	1.3 4.2 1.5	**28** M	0306 1004 1529 2224	1.7 3.9 1.8 3.8
14 M	0509 1202 1750	1.7 3.9 1.9	**29** TU	0351 1058 1636 2328	2.0 3.8 2.1 3.6
15 TU	0050 0637 1327 1941	3.7 2.0 3.8 1.9	**30** W	0526 1207 1836	2.2 3.7 2.1

OCTOBER

	Time	m		Time	m
1 TH	0048 0714 1339 1954	3.6 2.1 3.9 1.8	**16** F	0307 0903 1524 2133	3.9 1.7 4.2 1.4
2 F	0241 0827 1506 2100	3.9 1.7 4.2 1.3	**17** SA	0400 0953 1614 2218	4.2 1.3 4.5 1.0
3 SA	0347 0929 1604 2158	4.3 1.2 4.6 0.9	**18** SU	0444 1037 1655 2259	4.4 1.0 4.6 0.8
4 SU	0439 1024 1655 2251	4.6 0.8 4.9 0.5	**19** M	0521 1116 1732 2336	4.6 0.8 4.8 0.7
5 M O	0526 1115 1744 2340	4.9 0.5 5.1 0.2	**20** TU ●	0555 1152 1806	4.7 0.7 4.8
6 TU	0614 1203 1832	5.0 0.2 5.2	**21** W	0010 0628 1225 1840	0.7 4.8 0.7 4.8
7 W	0026 0658 1249 1917	0.0 5.1 0.1 5.3	**22** TH	0040 0659 1253 1913	0.8 4.8 0.8 4.7
8 TH	0111 0741 1331 2002	0.1 5.2 0.1 5.2	**23** F	0104 0731 1318 1944	0.9 4.7 1.0 4.6
9 F	0152 0824 1412 2045	0.2 5.1 0.3 5.0	**24** SA	0127 0803 1340 2013	1.0 4.6 1.1 4.5
10 SA	0230 0904 1451 2127	0.5 4.9 0.7 4.7	**25** SU	0148 0829 1405 2043	1.2 4.5 1.3 4.4
11 SU	0310 0946 1532 2210	0.9 4.6 1.1 4.3	**26** M	0214 0859 1432 2116	1.4 4.3 1.5 4.1
12 M	0353 1032 1622 2309	1.4 4.3 1.6 3.9	**27** TU	0245 0938 1511 2203	1.6 4.1 1.8 3.9
13 TU	0447 1138 1731	1.9 4.0 2.0	**28** W	0329 1030 1611 2303	1.9 4.0 2.0 3.7
14 W	0036 0612 1305 1919	3.7 2.2 3.8 2.0	**29** TH	0444 1135 1756	2.2 3.9 2.1
15 TH	0158 0757 1422 2038	3.7 2.0 4.0 1.7	**30** F	0017 0916 1253 1922	3.7 2.1 4.0 1.8
			31 SA	0155 0756 1423 2032	3.9 1.8 4.3 1.4

NOVEMBER

	Time	m		Time	m
1 SU	0314 0902 1532 2133	4.3 1.3 4.6 0.9	**16** M	0409 1002 1621 2224	4.3 1.3 4.5 1.1
2 M	0411 1000 1628 2226	4.6 0.9 4.9 0.6	**17** TU	0448 1043 1700 2303	4.5 1.1 4.6 1.0
3 TU	0501 1053 1720 2317	4.7 0.5 5.1 0.3	**18** W	0524 1120 1737 2337	4.7 1.0 4.7 0.9
4 W O	0550 1141 1811	5.1 0.3 5.2	**19** TH ●	0600 1153 1816	4.8 0.9 4.7
5 TH	0004 0637 1228 1858	0.1 5.2 0.2 5.2	**20** F	0007 0636 1224 1852	0.9 4.8 0.9 4.7
6 F	0051 0721 1314 1944	0.2 5.1 0.2 5.1	**21** SA	0037 0710 1254 1926	1.0 4.8 1.0 4.6
7 SA	0133 0805 1356 2029	0.3 5.1 0.4 4.9	**22** SU	0105 0743 1324 1959	1.0 4.7 1.1 4.5
8 SU	0214 0847 1437 2112	0.6 4.9 0.7 4.6	**23** M	0132 0813 1353 2030	1.2 4.6 1.2 4.3
9 M	0254 0928 1520 2156	1.0 4.6 1.1 4.3	**24** TU	0203 0845 1427 2105	1.3 4.5 1.4 4.2
10 TU	0337 1010 1607 2250	1.5 4.4 1.6 4.0	**25** W	0238 0923 1507 2149	1.5 4.3 1.6 4.0
11 W	0427 1107 1707	1.9 4.1 1.9	**26** TH	0323 1011 1601 2244	1.9 4.2 1.7 3.9
12 TH	0008 0534 1230 1830	3.7 2.1 3.9 2.1	**27** F	0425 1110 1718 2350	1.9 4.1 1.8 3.9
13 F	0123 0706 1344 1954	3.7 2.2 3.9 1.9	**28** SA	0553 1220 1844	2.0 4.1 1.7
14 SA	0229 0821 1446 2055	3.9 1.9 4.1 1.6	**29** SU	0109 0719 1341 1958	4.0 1.8 4.2 1.5
15 SU	0323 0916 1538 2143	4.1 1.6 4.3 1.3	**30** M	0233 0831 1457 2104	4.2 1.5 4.5 1.1

DECEMBER

	Time	m		Time	m
1 TU	0339 0934 1601 2202	4.5 1.1 4.7 0.8	**16** W	0411 1004 1626 2224	4.3 1.1 4.4 1.3
2 W	0435 1031 1658 2256	4.8 0.7 4.9 0.5	**17** TH	0453 1046 1711 2303	4.4 1.2 4.5 1.1
3 TH O	0527 1122 1751 2345	5.0 0.5 5.1 0.4	**18** F ●	0534 1124 1753 2339	4.7 1.1 4.6 1.0
4 F	0617 1210 1842	5.2 0.3 5.1	**19** SA	0615 1200 1834	4.7 1.0 4.6
5 SA	0032 0703 1258 1929	0.3 5.2 0.3 5.0	**20** SU	0014 0654 1237 1912	1.0 4.8 1.0 4.6
6 SU	0118 0748 1342 2014	0.4 5.1 0.5 4.8	**21** M	0050 0730 1313 1949	1.0 4.7 1.0 4.5
7 M	0159 0830 1425 2058	0.7 5.0 0.7 4.6	**22** TU	0124 0804 1348 2023	1.0 4.7 1.0 4.4
8 TU	0240 0910 1506 2139	1.0 4.7 1.0 4.3	**23** W	0159 0837 1425 2059	1.1 4.6 1.1 4.3
9 W	0321 0948 1549 2221	1.3 4.5 1.4 4.1	**24** TH	0236 0914 1504 2139	1.2 4.5 1.2 4.2
10 TH	0404 1029 1635 2313	1.7 4.2 1.7 3.8	**25** F	0318 0958 1550 2227	1.4 4.4 1.4 4.1
11 F	0454 1122 1731	2.0 4.0 1.9	**26** SA	0408 1049 1646 2325	1.6 4.3 1.5 4.0
12 SA	0024 0554 1237 1839	3.7 2.1 3.9 2.0	**27** SU	0512 1151 1758	1.7 4.2 1.6
13 SU	0133 0709 1348 1951	3.7 2.1 3.9 1.9	**28** M	0034 0633 1304 1919	4.0 1.7 4.2 1.5
14 M	0233 0819 1448 2052	3.9 1.9 4.0 1.7	**29** TU	0153 0756 1424 2034	4.1 1.6 4.3 1.3
15 TU	0324 0916 1540 2142	4.1 1.7 4.2 1.5	**30** W	0308 0909 1537 2140	4.3 1.5 4.5 1.1
			31 TH	0412 1011 1639 2238	4.6 1.0 4.7 0.8

H.W.Hts.m.

M.H.W.N.
M.H.W.S.

CHART DATUM

M.L.W.S.
M.L.W.N.

L.W.Hts.m.

L.W. -6ʰ -5ʰ -4ʰ -3ʰ -2ʰ -1ʰ H.W. +1ʰ +2ʰ +3ʰ +4ʰ +5ʰ L.W.

Factor

DARTMOUTH

MEAN SPRING
AND NEAP CURVES

MEAN RANGES
Springs 4.3m
Neaps 1.8m

Springs occur 2 days
after
New and Full Moon.

DARTMOUTH　　10-1-21

Devon 50°20'·63N 03°33'·88W　Rtg 1-1-1

CHARTS
AC *2253, 1634, 1613*; Imray C5, Y47, Y43; Stanfords 12, 13; OS 202

TIDES
−0510 Dover; ML 2·8; Duration 0630; Zone 0 (UT)

DARTMOUTH (←─)

Times				Height (metres)			
High Water		Low Water		MHWS	MHWN	MLWN	MLWS
0100	0600	0100	0600	4·9	3·8	2·0	0·6
1300	1800	1300	1800				

Differences GREENWAY QUAY (DITTISHAM)
| +0015 | +0020 | +0025 | +0010 | 0·0 | 0·0 | 0·0 | 0·0 |

TOTNES
| +0015 | +0015 | +0115 | +0035 | −1·4 | −1·5 | Dries | Dries |

NOTE: Dartmouth tidal predictions for each day of the year are given above.

SHELTER
Excellent inside hbr, but ent can be difficult in strong SE to SW winds. In mid-stream there are 8 big unlit mooring buoys for commercial vessels/FVs; do not ⚓ over their ground chains, as shown on AC 2253. Only space to ⚓ is E of fairway, from abeam Nos 3 to 5 buoys.
The 3 marinas (Darthaven, Dart and Noss-on-Dart) have Ⓥ berths. Apart from the pontoons off the Royal Dart YC, the extensive pontoons and mooring trots elsewhere in the hbr are run by the Hr Mr, who should be contacted by VHF/☎. The most likely Ⓥ berths/⚓s from S to N are:
W bank: pontoon off Dartmouth YC (May-Sep); Town jetty (W side only) near Boat Camber; N end of pontoon just S of Dart marina (26'/8m max LOA).
E of fairway: (NB six pontoons N of Darthaven marina are for locals only). Some ⚓s are in the mooring trots from abeam No 5A buoy to the cable ferry. The 2 pontoons N of Fuel barge are for visitors.

NAVIGATION
WPT 50°19'·50N 03°32'·80W, 148°/328° from/to Kingswear It, Iso WRG, 1·5M. To the E of ent, on Inner Froward Pt (153m) is a conspic daymark, obelisk (24·5m). There is no bar and the hbr is always accessible. Speed limit 6kn.

LIGHTS AND MARKS
Kingswear Main It 328°, Iso WRG 3s 9m 8M, W 325°-331°. Bayard's Cove It 293°, Fl WRG 2s 5m 6M, W 289°-297°. Entry buoys as on chartlet. Within hbr, all jetty/ pontoon Its to the W are 2FR (vert); and 2FG (vert) to the E.

RADIO TELEPHONE
Hr Mr call *Dartnav* VHF Ch 11 16 (Mon-Fri 0830-1800; Sat 0900-1200). Darthaven marina, Ch **80** M; Dart marina, Noss-on-Dart marina and Dart Sailing Centre, Ch 80. Fuel barge Ch 06. Water taxi: call Ch 16, work Ch 08 06 M.

Depths in metres

Cables
No

Dart
Marina
Fuel

Marina
Office

Cable Ferry

Small Craft Trots

Pontoons

Small Craft Trots

Fuel
No6

No5A

No5

No Visitors

Boat
Camber

No4

No3A

Darthaven
Marina

No3

HrMr
Dartmouth
YC

Pontoon

Pontoon

Station

KINGSWEAR

Royal Dart YC

TELEPHONE (Dial code 01803)
Hr Mr 832337; MRSC 882704; ⊞ 0345 231110 (H24); Police 832288; Marinecall 0891 500458; Dr 832212; Ⓗ 832255.

FACILITIES
Harbour/Marinas
Hbr Authority (450+90 **V**), ☎ 832337, 🛥 833631; £11.78 - £13.07 (W bank pontoons), M, FW, Slip, V, R;

Darthaven Marina (230+12 **V**) ☎ 752242, 🛥 752722, £16.36 inc £4.73 hbr dues, FW, ME, EI, Gas, Gaz, ▣, Sh, CH, Bar, R, BH (30 ton), AC, Ⓔ;

Dart Marina (110, inc up to 30 **V**s) ☎ 835570 Ext 241, 🛥 832307, £22.45 inc £4.73 hbr dues, D, FW, AC, ME, EI, Sh, C (9 ton), 2 Slips, Gas, Gaz, CH, Bar, R, ▣.

Noss-on-Dart Marina (150) ☎ 835570 Ext 248, 🛥 832307, £16.00 inc £4.73 hbr dues, FW, AC, ME, EI, Sh, C (18 ton), CH, Gas, Gaz, ▣;

Dart Sailing Centre ☎ 752702, AB, AC, Bar, R;

Creekside BY (Old Mill Creek) ☎ 832649, Slip, dry dock, M, ME, Sh, EI, C (1 ton), CH, AB.

Clubs
Royal Dart YC ☎ 752272, M, L, FW, Bar; **Dartmouth YC** ☎ 832305, L, FW, Bar, R. Royal Regatta, last week August.

Services
M, ME, EI, Sh, BH, CH, SM, rigging, masts, Ⓔ; **Water Taxi** ☎ 833727, (VHF Ch 16 06 08); **Fuel Barge** ☎ (0836) 775643 or 834136 out of hrs, VHF Ch 06, D; next to No 6 buoy. Galmpton Creek: CH, D, FW, L, M, C (6 ton), ME, Sh, SM, BY, Slip, AC, BH (53, 16 ton), EI, Ⓔ; Slip at Higher Ferry. **Town** EC Wed; V, P (cans), ▣ (0800-2000 daily), R, Bar, ✉, Ⓑ, ⇌ ☎ 555872 (steam train in season to Paignton, or bus to Totnes/Paignton), ✈ (Plymouth or Exeter).

UP RIVER TO DITTISHAM AND TOTNES

The River Dart is navigable on the flood to Totnes bridge, about 5·5M above Dittisham. HW Totnes = HW Dartmouth +0015. Speed limit 6kn to S end of Home Reach (1M from Totnes); then Dead Slow. No lights above The Noss. **Directions**: The Anchor Stone (2½ca below Dittisham) must be left to port. No ⚓ off Dittisham where there are ⚓s. From Dittisham brgs of 020° and 310° on successive Boat Houses lead between Lower Back and Flat Owers banks; or keep E of the latter. Thereafter 8 PHM and 3 SHM buoys, all unlit and numbered sequentially (rather than evens to port/odds to stbd), plus some perches, mark the bends up to Home Reach; the chan favours the outside of bends. Unmasted boats can go beyond the bridge to the weir. **Berthing**: Baltic Wharf BY ☎ 01803-865505, W bank just below Totnes, has drying AB (30), AC, FW, BH (16 ton), C (35 ton), ME, visitors welcomed. Steamer Quay is for ferries (leisure developments are planned). Limited, drying AB on soft mud in the W Arm near the Steam Packet Inn, ☎ 863880, AC, FW, R, Bar, ▣. Totnes: EC Thurs; usual amenities; mainline ⇌.

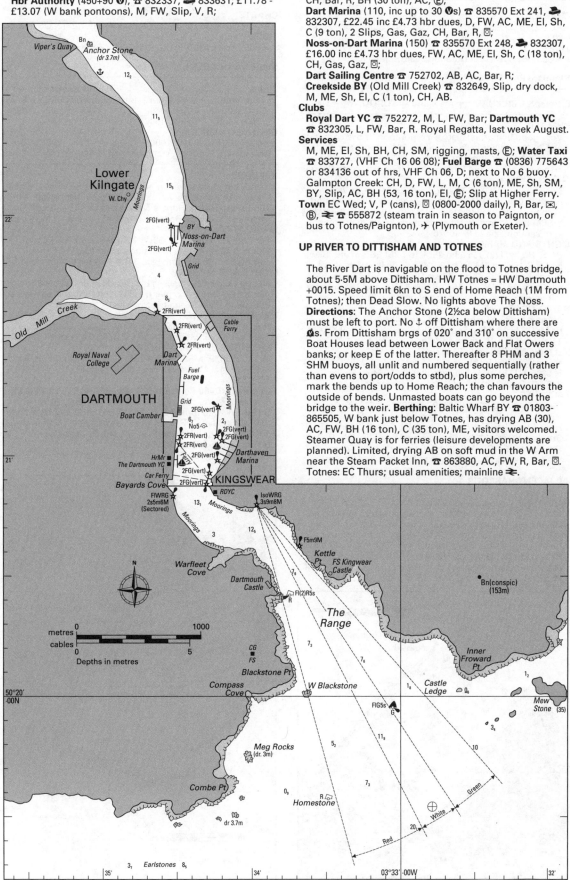

BRIXHAM   10-1-22

Devon 50°24'·28N 03°30'·79W   Rtg 2-2-2

CHARTS
AC *26, 1613, 1634, 3315*; Imray C5, Y43; Stanfords 12; OS 202

TIDES
–0505 Dover; ML 2·9; Duration 0635; Zone 0 (UT)

Standard Port DEVONPORT (⟵)

Differences BRIXHAM are the same as **TORQUAY (⟶)**

SHELTER
Very good in marina; also at YC pontoon in SW corner of hbr, but outer hbr is dangerous in NW winds. ⚓s (W) to E of main fairway. Inner hbr dries. To W of hbr are ⚓s in Fishcombe Cove and Elberry Cove (beware water skiers).

NAVIGATION
WPT 50°24'·70N 03°30'·00W, 050°/230° from/to Victoria bkwtr lt, 0·60M. No dangers; easy access. Note: Around Torbay are controlled areas, close inshore and marked by Y SPM buoys, mainly for swimmers; boats may enter with caution, speed limit 5kn.

LIGHTS AND MARKS
Berry Hd lt, Fl (2) 15s 58m 15M, is 1·2M ESE of ent. Bkwtr hd Oc R 15s 9m 6M, W tr. 3 R ● or 3 Ⓡ lts (vert) at ent = hbr closed. At SE end of hbr a Dir lt Iso WRG 5s 4m 6M, vis G145°-157°, W157°-161°, R161°-173° leads 159° into the fairway, marked by two pairs of lateral lt buoys.

RADIO TELEPHONE
Marina: Ch 80. YC and Water Taxi: *Shuttle* Ch M.
Hr Mr Ch 14 16 (May-Sept 0800-1800LT); Oct-Apr 0900-1700, Mon-Fri). Brixham CG: Ch 16 10 67 73.

TELEPHONE (Dial code 01803)
Marina 882929; Hr Mr 853321; Pilot 882214; MRSC 882704; ▦ 0345 231110 (H24); Marinecall 0891 500458; Police 882231; Dr 882731; Ⓗ 882153.

FACILITIES
Marina (480 inc Ⓥ) ☎ 882929, ⚓ 882737, £13.75, Access H24, AC, FW, D (0900-2000, Apr-Sep inc), R, Bar, ▢;
Hbr Office (New Fish Quay) Slip, M, L, FW, C (2 ton), AB, D;
Brixham YC ☎ 853332, Ⓥ pontoon, M, L, Slip, FW, R, Bar;
Services: CH, ACA, ME, (H24), P (cans), El, Ⓔ. **Town** EC Wed; R, Bar, ▢, ✉, Ⓑ, ⇌ (bus to Paignton), ✈ (Exeter).

ADJACENT HARBOUR

PAIGNTON, Devon, 50°25'·93N 03°33'·29W. AC *26, 1613*. HW –0500 on Dover, +0035 on Devonport; HW –0·6m on Devonport; ML 2·9m; Duration 0640. Hbr dries 1·3m and is only suitable for max LOA 27'/8·2m. E winds cause a heavy swell in hbr. Rks extend 180m E from E wall. Black Rk has ECM tr, Q (3) 10s 5m 3M. QR 7m 3M lt on E arm of ent. Hr Mr (summer only) ☎ (01803) 557812. **Paignton SC** ☎ 525817; Facilities: EC Wed, M, ME, Sh, Gas, CH, ACA.

TORQUAY   10-1-23

Devon 50°27'·42N 03°31'·66W   Rtg 2-2-2

CHARTS
AC *26, 1613, 3315*; Imray C5, Y43; Stanfords 12; OS 202

TIDES
–0500 Dover; ML 2·9; Duration 0640; Zone 0 (UT)

Standard Port DEVONPORT (⟵)

Times				Height (metres)			
High Water		Low Water		MHWS	MHWN	MLWN	MLWS
0100	0600	0100	0600	5·5	4·4	2·2	0·8
1300	1800	1300	1800				
Differences TORQUAY							
+0025	+0045	+0010	0000	–0·6	–0·7	–0·2	–0·1

Note: There is often a stand of about 1 hour at HW

SHELTER
Good, but some swell in hbr with strong SE winds, which may make the narrow ent difficult due to backwash. No ⚓ within hbr. NW of Hope's Nose there are ⚓s at Hope Cove, Anstey's Cove and Babbacombe Bay, sheltered in W'lies.

NAVIGATION
WPT 50°27'·00N 03°31'·50W, 165°/345° from/to Haldon pier lt, 0·40M. Access at all tides. Inner (Old) hbr dries completely. Speed limit 5kn. 3 R ● or 3 R lts = hbr closed.

LIGHTS AND MARKS
No ldg marks/lts. Princess Pier head QR 9m 6M. Haldon pier hd QG 9m 6M. S pier hd 2FG (vert) 5M. All lts may be difficult to discern against town lts.

RADIO TELEPHONE
Port VHF Ch 14 16 (May-Sept 0800-1800LT; Oct-Apr 0900-1700, Mon-Fri). Marina Ch **80** (H24), M. *Torquay Fuel* Ch M.

TELEPHONE (Dial code 01803)
Hr Mr 292429; MRSC 882704; ▦ 0345 231110 (H24); Police 0990 777444; Marinecall 0891 500458; Dr 212429; Ⓗ 614567.

FACILITIES
Marina (440+60 Ⓥ) ☎ 214624, ⚓ 291634, £17.30, FW, ME, Gas, Gaz, ▢, AC, SM, Ⓔ, El, Sh, CH, V, R, Bar, ACA.
S Pier FW, C (6 ton); P & D: Torquay Fuel ☎ 294509/mobile 0385 226839 & VHF Ch M (Apr-Sept, 0830-1900 Mon-Sat, 1000-1900 Sun); **Haldon Pier** FW, AB; **Princess Pier** L;
Royal Torbay YC ☎ 292006, R, Bar.
Town V, R, ▢, Bar, ✉, Ⓑ, ⇌, ✈ (Exeter or Plymouth).

TEIGNMOUTH   10-1-24

Devon 50°32'·36N 03°30'·00W (Abeam The Point)   Rtg 3-3-2

CHARTS
AC *26, 3315*; Imray C5, Y43; Stanfords 12; OS 192

TIDES
−0450 Dover; ML 2·7; Duration 0625; Zone 0 (UT)

Standard Port DEVONPORT (◄—)

Times				Height (metres)			
High Water		Low Water		MHWS	MHWN	MLWN	MLWS
0100	0600	0100	0600	5·5	4·4	2·2	0·8
1300	1800	1300	1800				
Differences TEIGNMOUTH (Approaches)							
+0025	+0040	0000	0000	−0·7	−0·8	−0·3	−0·2
SHALDON BRIDGE							
+0035	+0050	+0020	+0020	−0·9	−0·9	−0·2	0·0

SHELTER
Hbr completely sheltered, but difficult to enter especially with strong winds from NE to S when surf forms on the bar. Access HW±3. Appr chan is not buoyed so local advice is recommended. No AB, but two ⚓s just N of SHM lt buoy, Fl G 5s. Speed limit is 8kn.

NAVIGATION
WPT 50°32'·40N 03°29'·20W, 076°/256° from/to training wall lt, 0·43M. Bar shifts very frequently. Beware rks off the Ness; and variable extent of Salty flats. Clearance under Shaldon bridge is 4·2m at MHWS (AC 26), but it is reported locally to be at most 2·9m at MHWS and approx 5·8m at MLWS. Avoid a Historic wreck site (50°32'·92N 03°29'·17W; just off chartlet), close inshore by Church Rks to ENE of Ch Tr (see 10.0.3h).

LIGHTS AND MARKS
The Ness, high red sandstone headland, and church tower are both conspic from afar; close NE of the latter, just off N edge of chartlet, Teign Corinthian YC bldg (cream colour) is also conspic. At seaward end of outfall, 105° The Ness 1·25M, is a Y buoy, Fl Y 5s, at 50°31'·93N 03°27'·81W. Y buoy, Fl Y 2s, marks S edge of Spratt Sand. Once round The Point, Oc G 5·5s and FG (vert), two F Bu lts on quay align 022°, but are not official ldg lts.

RADIO TELEPHONE
VHF Ch 12 16 (Mon-Fri: 0800-1700; Sat 0900-1200 LT).

TELEPHONE (Dial code 01626)
Hr Mr 773165; MRSC (01803) 882704; ⌗ 0345 231110 (H24); Marinecall 0891 500458; Police 772433; Dr 774355; Ⓗ 772161.

FACILITIES
E Quay Polly Steps Slip (up to 10m); **Teign Corinthian YC** ☎ 772734, ⚓ £7.02, M, FW, Bar; **Services:** ME, CH, EI, Slip, BY, Sh, D, C (8 ton), Gas, Gaz, FW, CH, Ⓔ.
Town EC Thurs; P, D, L, FW, V, R, Ⓖ, Bar, ✉, Ⓑ, ≈, ✈ (Exeter).

AGENTS WANTED
If you are interested in becoming our agent for any of the following ports, please write to: The Editor, Edington House, Trent, Sherborne, Dorset DT9 4SR, England – and get your free copy of the Almanac annually. You do not have to live in a port to be the agent, but at least a fairly regular visitor.

Great Yarmouth	St Gilles-Croix-de-Vie
Port Ellen (Islay)	Les Sables d'Olonne
Maryport	Ile d'Oléron
Workington	River Seudre
Holyhead	Anglet/Bayonne
Lough Swilly	St Jean-de-Luz
St Peter Port, Guernsey	Hendaye
Diélette	Grandcamp-Maisy
Portbail	Port-en-Bessin
Iles Chausey	Courseulles
St Malo/Dinard	Ouistreham/Caen
Le Legue/St Brieuc	Emden
Tréguier	Dornumer-Accumersiel
Lampaul	Langeoog
L'Aberildut	Bremerhaven
Le Palais (Belle Ile)	Büsum
Morbihan/Vannes	

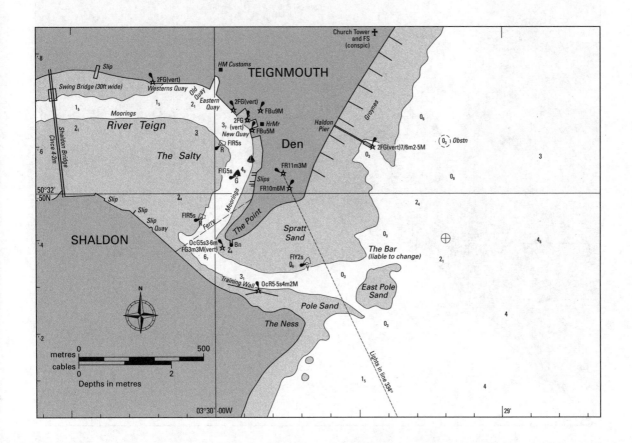

RIVER EXE   10-1-25

Devon 50°36'·91N 03°25'·33W (Abeam Exmouth)   Rtg 3-2-2

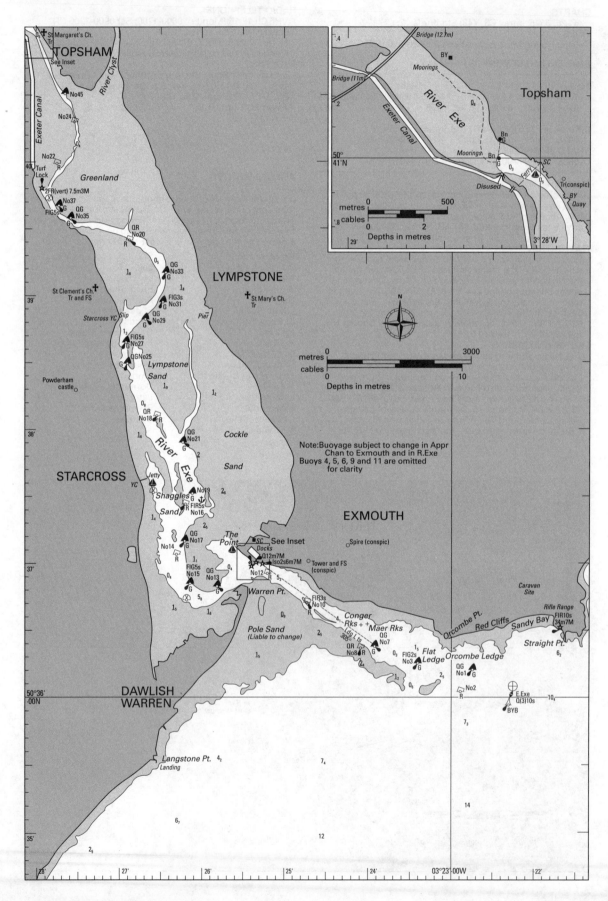

Note: Buoyage subject to change in Appr Chan to Exmouth and in R.Exe Buoys 4, 5, 6, 9 and 11 are omitted for clarity

CHARTS
AC 2290, *3315*; Imray C5, Y43; Stanfords 12; OS 192
TIDES
−0445 Dover; ML 2·1; Duration 0625; Zone 0 (UT)

Standard Port DEVONPORT (←—)

Times				Height (metres)			
High Water		Low Water		MHWS	MHWN	MLWN	MLWS
0100	0600	0100	0600	5·5	4·4	2·2	0·8
1300	1800	1300	1800				
Differences EXMOUTH (Approaches)							
+0030	+0050	+0015	+0005	−0·9	−1·0	−0·5	−0·3
EXMOUTH DOCK							
+0035	+0055	+0050	+0020	−1·5	−1·6	−0·9	−0·6
STARCROSS							
+0040	+0110	+0055	+0025	−1·4	−1·5	−0·8	−0·1
TOPSHAM							
+0045	+0105	No data		−1·5	−1·6	No data	

SHELTER
Good inside R Exe, but ent difficult in fresh winds from E and S. Caution: strong tidal streams; see below.
Exmouth Dock is a yacht basin, 2m depth (no specific ❹ berths); berth on pontoon in ent and see Dock Mr. Swing bridge opens on request; stays open HN. Water taxi will advise on ⚓s which are in The Bight (2ca SW of No 13 SHM lt buoy, near large ship's mooring By), off Starcross, Turf Lock and Topsham SC. ⚓ may be found E of Starcross clear of chan, ie 1ca SSE of No 19 buoy in 2·1m. The river at **Topsham** carries about 0·4m. Options: ⚓ in appr's, dry out at the Quay, find a mooring or berth at BY pontoon.
NAVIGATION
WPT East Exe ECM buoy Q (3)10s, 50°35'·97N 03°22'·30W, 111°/291° from/to No 7 SHM buoy, QG, 1·03M.
Caution: Royal Marine firing range at Straight Pt, just E of Exe buoy, has a danger area to SE, marked by 2 DZ SPM lt buoys. R flags are flown when the range is in use (likely times 0800-1600, Mon-Fri); call *Straight Pt Range* VHF Ch 08 16. From the E, check also with safety launch.
Best time to start appr is approx LW+2 when hazards can be seen and some shelter obtained. In the appr chan tide runs up to 3·3kn on sp ebb; with wind against tide a confused, breaking sea quickly builds. In the narrows off Warren Pt the flood stream runs at 3-4kn and the ebb can exceed 4½kn when the banks uncover.
The chan is well marked/lit, but night entry is not advised. There are drying rky ledges to the N of chan; to the south Pole Sands dry up to 2·8m. Least depths of 0·3m & 0·7m occur in the chan between Nos 5 and 7 buoys. The chan narrows to about 100m between Nos 11 and 10 buoys. After No 10 buoy it is important not to cut the corner round Warren Pt; stand on for 5ca to Exmouth Dock and No 12 PHM buoy, before altering to the WSW. Up-to-date AC 2290 is essential.
Within the estuary the bottom is sand/mud, free of rocks. Follow the curve of the chan, rather than a straight line between buoys. Some bends are marked on the outside only. The estuary is a conservation area.
Exeter Ship Canal (3·0m depth): access to Exeter is no longer available to visiting yachts. Contact Port of Exeter Hr Mr ☎ (01392) 274306 or Ch 12 for berth in the canal near Turf Lock (1M S of Topsham, abeam No 39 buoy).
LIGHTS AND MARKS
Straight Pt has conspic caravan site close W and red cliffs to W and NNE. Exmouth ⊕ tr and FS are conspic, about 2M WNW of the East Exe buoy. Ldg lts 305° at Exmouth: front Iso 2s 6m 7M; rear Q 12m 7M; do not use seaward of No 6 PHM buoy. Note: Approach buoys 4, 5, 6, 9 & 11, plus some others up-river, are not shown on chartlet due to small scale.
RADIO TELEPHONE
Exmouth Dock Mr VHF Ch 14 16; Water Taxi at Exmouth, call *Conveyance* Ch M 16. Port of Exeter Ch 12 16 (Mon-Fri: 0730-1730LT); Hbr Patrol 12 16 in summer.
TELEPHONE (Dial code Exmouth 01395)
Exmouth Dock Co 274767; Dock Mr 269314; Exeter Hr Mr 274306; MRSC (01803) 882704; ⌗ 0345 231110 (H24); Marinecall 0891 500458; Police 264651; Dr 273001; Ⓗ 279684.

FACILITIES
EXMOUTH (01395)
Yacht Basin, ☎ 269314, £17, L, FW, D, No ❻ berths or WC; **Exe SC ☎** 264607. **Town** EC Wed; P, Sh, CH, El, Ⓔ, ACA, SM, Gas, Gaz, V, R, ▣, Bar, ✉, Ⓑ, ⇌.
STARCROSS (01626)
Starcross Fishing & Cruising Club ☎ 890582; **Starcross YC ☎** 890470; **Starcross Garage ☎** 890225, P & D (cans), ME, Gas. **Village** V, Bar, ✉, Ⓑ, ⇌.
TOPSHAM (01392)
Topsham SC ☎ 877524, Slip, L, FW, Bar;
Trouts BY ☎ 873044, AB, M, D, Gas, Gaz, C, FW, Sh.
Retreat BY ☎ 874270, (access HW±2), M, D, FW, ME, C, CH, Sh.
Town P, CH, SM, ACA, R, V, ▣, Bar, ✉, Ⓑ, ⇌.
EXETER (01392)
Hr Mr, River & Canal Office, Haven Rd, Exeter EX2 8DU, ☎ 274306: canal berths, £8.50 for 2 days minimum, and laying up.
City all amenities; CH, ME, ACA, ⇌, ✈.

EXMOUTH DOCK 50°37'·00N 03°25'·37W

HARBOUR WEST OF LYME REGIS

AXMOUTH/BEER, Devon, 50°42'·10N 03°03'·20W. AC 3315. HW −0455 on Dover, +0045 and −1·1m on Devonport; ML 2·3m; Duration 0640. MHWS 4·1m, MHWN 3·1m. A small drying hbr on R Axe for boats max draught 1·2m, LOA 8·5m, able to take the ground. Appr chan to bar (dries 0·5m) is unmarked and often shifts; prior knowledge from YC is essential. Enter, in settled weather only, at HW via 7m wide ent with SHM bn; turn hard port inside. A bridge (2m clearance) crosses the river 2ca from ent. Facilities:
Axe YC ☎ (01297) 20043, Slip, pontoon, M, BH, Bar;
Services: ME, CH, D (cans), CH.
Beer Roads, 1M WSW, is ⚓ sheltered from prevailing W'ly, but open to S/SE winds. Landing on open beach.
Beer & Seaton: EC Thurs; R, V, P & D (cans), Bar, Gas, ✉.

LYME REGIS   10-1-26

Dorset 50°43'·17N 02°56'·10W   Rtg 3-3-2

CHARTS
AC *3315*; Imray C5; Stanfords 12; OS 193
TIDES
–0455 Dover; ML 2·4; Duration 0700; Zone 0 (UT)

Standard Port DEVONPORT (←)

Times				Height (metres)			
High Water		Low Water		MHWS	MHWN	MLWN	MLWS
0100	0600	0100	0600	5·5	4·4	2·2	0·8
1300	1800	1300	1800				
Differences LYME REGIS							
+0040	+0100	–0005	–0005	–1·2	–1·3	–0·5	–0·2

NOTE: Rise is relatively fast for the first hour after LW, then slackens for the next 1½ hours, after which the rapid rate is resumed. There is often a stand of about 1½ hours at HW.

SHELTER
Excellent in the hbr (dries), known as The Cobb, except in strong E or SE winds. Max LOA in hbr 9m. Keel boats can dry out alongside Victoria Pier or ⚓ as shown. Five R cylindrical ⚓s are available. Access about HW±2½.
NAVIGATION
WPT 50°43'·00N 02°55'·60W, 116°/296° from/to front ldg lt 0·35M. Rock bkwtr S of ent marked by PHM bn. Beware numerous fishing floats.
LIGHTS AND MARKS
Ldg lts 296°, see chartlet. R flag on Victoria Pier = Gale warning in force.
RADIO TELEPHONE
Call: *Lyme Regis Hbr Radio* Ch14 16. (May-Sept: 0900-1200, 1600-1800LT).
TELEPHONE (Dial code 01297)
Hr Mr 442137, ⚓ 442137; MRSC (01305) 760439; ⌗ 0345 231110 (H24); Marinecall 0891 500457; Police 442603; Dr 445777; Ⓗ 442254.
FACILITIES
Harbour (The Cobb) AB £8.90, Slip, M, P & D (cans), L, FW, ME, El, Ⓔ, Sh; **Lyme Regis SC** ☎ 442800, FW, R, Bar; **Lyme Regis Power Boat Club** ☎ 443788, R, Bar;
Services: ME, El, Ⓔ, CH, ACA (5M).
Town EC Thurs; V, R, Bar, Gas, Gaz, ✉, Ⓑ, ⇌ (bus to Axminster), ✈ (Exeter).

BRIDPORT   10-1-27

Dorset 50°42'·52N 02°45'·77W   Rtg 5-3-1

CHARTS
AC *3315*; Imray C5; Stanfords 12; OS 193
TIDES
–0500 Dover; ML 2·3; Duration 0650; Zone 0 (UT)

Standard Port DEVONPORT (←)

Times				Height (metres)			
High Water		Low Water		MHWS	MHWN	MLWN	MLWS
0100	0600	0100	0600	5·5	4·4	2·2	0·8
1300	1800	1300	1800				
Differences BRIDPORT (West Bay)							
+0025	+0040	0000	0000	–1·4	–1·4	–0·6	–0·2
CHESIL BEACH							
+0040	+0055	–0005	+0010	–1·6	–1·5	–0·5	0·0
CHESIL COVE							
+0035	+0050	–0010	+0005	–1·5	–1·6	–0·5	–0·2

NOTE: Rise is relatively fast for first hr after LW, thence a slackening for the next 1½ hrs, after which the rapid rise is resumed. There is often a stand of about 1½ hrs at HW.
SHELTER
Good in hbr, but the narrow (12m), 180m long drying ent, is dangerous in even moderate on-shore winds; access HW±2, in favourable weather. Do not attempt entry in >F4/5 S'lies. Hbr dries apart from pool and former coaster berths scoured 2·1m by sluice water. There is little space; see Hr Mr for berth or dry out at E end of Quay.
NAVIGATION
WPT 50°41'·55N 02°46'·00W, 191°/011° from/to ent, 0·75M. No offshore dangers. SPM buoy, Fl, Y 5s, marks sewer

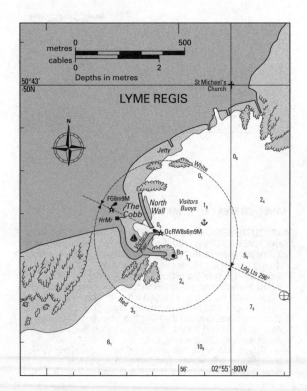

VOLVO PENTA SERVICE

Sales and service centres in area 2

BERKSHIRE *D. B. Marine*, Cookham Bridge, Cookham-on-Thames SL6 9SN Tel (01628) 526032 **BUCKINGHAMSHIRE** *M. M. S. (1981) Ltd*, Harleyford Marina, Harleyford, Marlow SL7 2DX Tel (01628) 471368 **DORSET** *Poole Marine Services*, The Marine Leisure Complex, West Quay Road, Poole BH15 1HX Tel (01202) 679577/677387 *Salterns Boatyard*, 38 Salterns Way, Lilliput, Poole BH14 8JR Tel (01202) 707391 **HAMPSHIRE** *Haven Boatyard Ltd*, King's Saltern Road, Lymington SO41 9QD Tel (01590) 677073/4/5 *R.K. Marine Ltd*, Hamble River Boatyard, Bridge Road, Swanwick, Southampton SO3 7EB Tel (01489) 583572 or 583585 *Motortech Marine Engineering Ltd*, 5 The Slipway, Port Solent, Portsmouth PO6 4TR Tel (01705) 201171 *S.A.L. Marine*, Mill Lane, Lymington SO41 9AZ Tel (01590) 679588 or 673876 *Sea Power Ltd*, Hamble Point Marina, School Lane, Hamble SO3 5JD Tel (01703) 454333 **ISLE OF WIGHT** *Power Plus Marine*, Cowes Yacht Haven, Cowes PO31 7AY Tel (01983) 200036 *Harold Hayles (Yarmouth IOW)*, The Quay, Yarmouth PO41 0RS Tel (01983) 760373 **MIDDLESEX** *M. M. S. (1981) Ltd*, Shepperton Marina, Felix Lane, Shepperton TW17 8NJ Tel (01932) 247427 **SUSSEX** *B. A. Peters plc*, Peters Shipyard Chichester Marina, Chichester PO20 7BG Tel (01243) 512831

VOLVO PENTA

2

Area 2

Central Southern England
Portland Bill to Selsey Bill

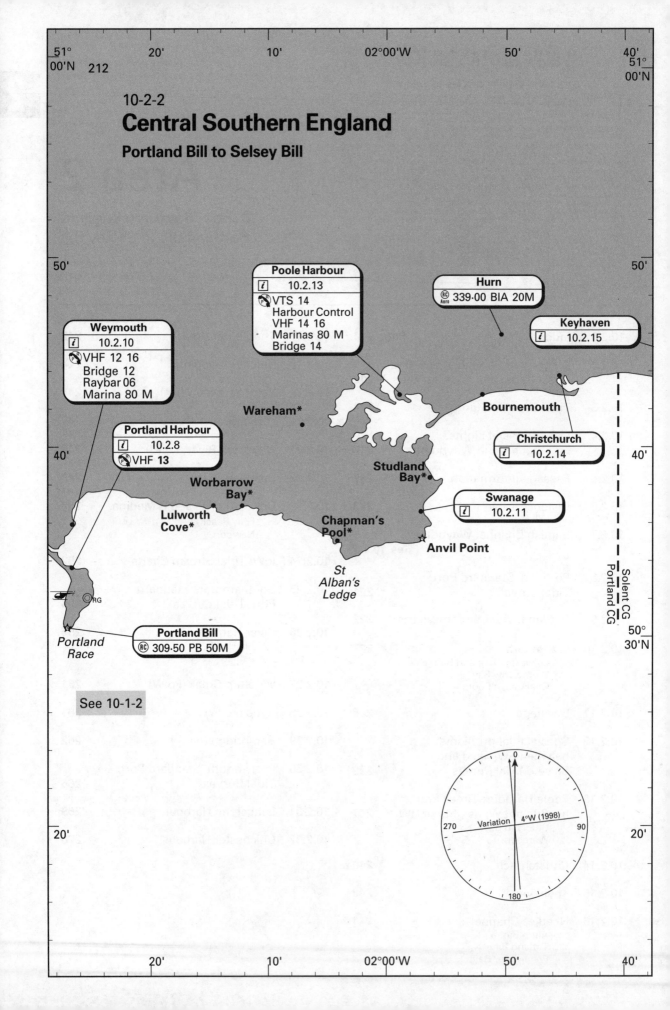

20'   10'   02°00'W   50'   40'   51°
00'N

10-2-2
Central Southern England
Portland Bill to Selsey Bill

50'   50'

Poole Harbour
| *i* | 10.2.13 |

VTS 14
Harbour Control
VHF 14 16
Marinas 80 M
Bridge 14

Hurn
RC Aero 339·00 BIA 20M

Keyhaven
| *i* | 10.2.15 |

Weymouth
| *i* | 10.2.10 |

VHF 12 16
Bridge 12
Raybar 06
Marina 80 M

Wareham*

Bournemouth

Portland Harbour
| *i* | 10.2.8 |

VHF **13**

40'   **Christchurch**
| *i* | 10.2.14 | 40'

**Worbarrow
Bay***

**Studland
Bay***

**Lulworth
Cove***

**Chapman's
Pool***

Swanage
| *i* | 10.2.11 |

Anvil Point

*St
Alban's
Ledge*

Solent CG
Portland CG

RG

Portland
Race

50°
30'N

Portland Bill
RC 309·50 PB 50M

See 10-1-2

Variation 4°W (1998)

270 ────── 90

0

180

20'   20'

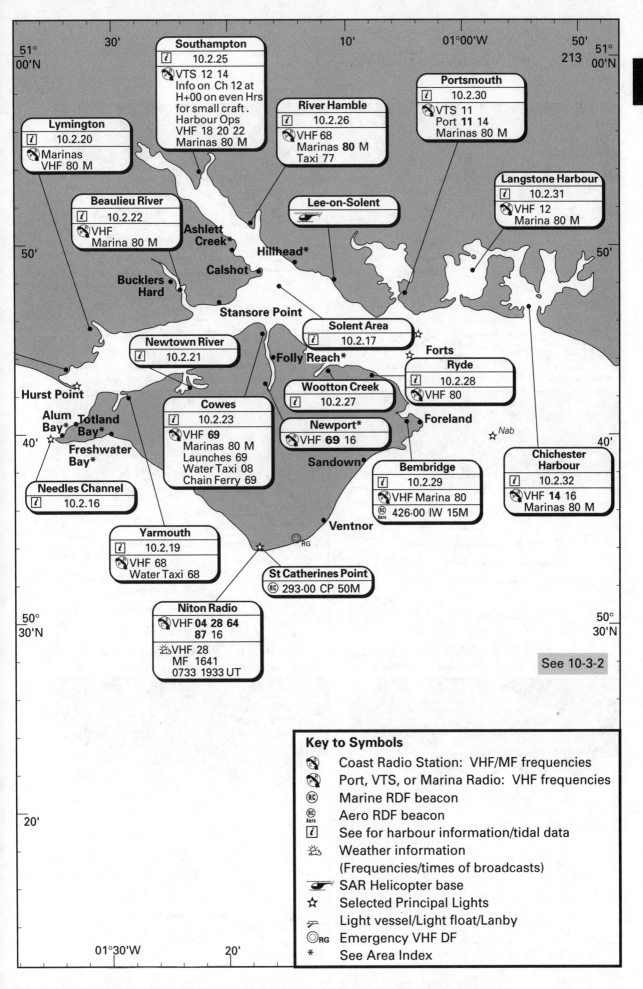

2

213

Southampton
ⓘ 10.2.25
📡 VTS 12 14
Info on Ch 12 at
H+00 on even Hrs
for small craft .
Harbour Ops
VHF 18 20 22
Marinas 80 M

Portsmouth
ⓘ 10.2.30
📡 VTS 11
Port **11** 14
Marinas 80 M

River Hamble
ⓘ 10.2.26
📡 VHF 68
Marinas **80** M
Taxi 77

Lymington
ⓘ 10.2.20
📡 Marinas
VHF 80 M

Langstone Harbour
ⓘ 10.2.31
📡 VHF 12
Marina 80 M

Beaulieu River
ⓘ 10.2.22
📡 VHF
Marina 80 M

Ashlett
Creek*

Lee-on-Solent
🚁

Hillhead*

Calshot

Bucklers
Hard

Stansore Point

Newtown River
ⓘ 10.2.21

Folly Reach*

Solent Area
ⓘ 10.2.17

☆ Forts

Ryde
ⓘ 10.2.28
📡 VHF 80

Hurst Point ☆

Alum
Bay* Totland
Bay*

Cowes
ⓘ 10.2.23
📡 VHF **69**
Marinas 80 M
Launches 69
Water Taxi 08
Chain Ferry 69

Wootton Creek
ⓘ 10.2.27

Newport*
📡 VHF **69** 16

Foreland

☆ *Nab*

**Chichester
Harbour**
ⓘ 10.2.32
📡 VHF **14** 16
Marinas 80 M

Freshwater
Bay*

Sandown*

Bembridge
ⓘ 10.2.29
📡 VHF Marina 80
📻 426·00 IW 15M

Needles Channel
ⓘ 10.2.16

Ventnor

Yarmouth
ⓘ 10.2.19
📡 VHF 68
Water Taxi 68

☆ 🔘RG

St Catherines Point
📻 293·00 CP 50M

Niton Radio
📡 VHF **04 28 64**
87 16
🌦 VHF 28
MF 1641
0733 1933 UT

See 10-3-2

Key to Symbols

📡 Coast Radio Station: VHF/MF frequencies
📡 Port, VTS, or Marina Radio: VHF frequencies
📻 Marine RDF beacon
📻 Aero RDF beacon
ⓘ See for harbour information/tidal data
🌦 Weather information
    (Frequencies/times of broadcasts)
🚁 SAR Helicopter base
☆ Selected Principal Lights
⚓ Light vessel/Light float/Lanby
🔘RG Emergency VHF DF
* See Area Index

10-2-3   AREA 2 TIDAL STREAMS

5 Hours before HW Dover (0530 before HW Portsmouth)

4 Hours before HW Dover (0430 before HW Portsmouth)

3 Hours before HW Dover (0330 before HW Portsmouth)

2 Hours before HW Dover (0230 before HW Portsmouth)

1 Hour before HW Dover (0130 before HW Portsmouth)

HW Dover (0030 before HW Portsmouth)

Westward 10.1.3   Portland 10.2.9   Isle of Wight 10.2.24   Eastward 10.3.3   Southward 10.15.3   Channel Islands 10.14.3

1 Hour after HW Dover (0030 after HW Portsmouth)

2 Hours after HW Dover (0130 after HW Portsmouth)

3 Hours after HW Dover (0230 after HW Portsmouth)

4 Hours after HW Dover (0330 after HW Portsmouth)

5 Hours after HW Dover (0430 after HW Portsmouth)

6 Hours after HW Dover (0530 after HW Portsmouth)

10.2.4 COASTAL LIGHTS, FOG SIGNALS AND WAYPOINTS

Abbreviations used below are given in 1.4.1. Principal lights are in **bold** print, places in CAPITALS, and light-vessels, light floats and Lanbys in *CAPITAL ITALICS*. Unless otherwise stated lights are white. m – elevation in metres; M – nominal range in miles. Fog signals are in *italics*. Useful waypoints are underlined – use those on land with care. All geographical positions should be assumed to be approximate. See 4.4.1. All positions are referenced to the OSGB 36 datum.

NOTE: For English Channel Waypoints see 10.1.7. For other offshore aids, near the Channel Islands and adjacent coast of France, see 10.14.4.

PORTLAND

Portland Bill 50°30'·82N 02°27'·32W Fl (4) 20s 43m **25M**; W ● Tr, R band. Changes from 1 flash to 4 flashes 221°-244°, 4 flashes 244°-117°, changes from 4 flashes to 1 flash 117°-141°; RC; FR 19m 13M (same Tr) vis 271°-291° over The Shambles. *Dia 30s.*

PORTLAND HARBOUR
Outer Bkwtr D Hd (S end) Oc R 30s 12m 5M.
Outer Bkwtr (N end) QR 14m 5M; vis 013°-268°.
NE Bkwtr (A Hd) 50°35'·12N 02°24'·99W Fl 10s 22m **20M**; W Tr.
NE Bkwtr (B Hd) 50°35'·62N 02°25'·80W Oc R 15s 11m 5M.

PORTLAND TO ISLE OF WIGHT

WEYMOUTH
S Pier Hd 50°36'·50N 02°26'·40W Q 10m 9M; tfc sigs.
Ldg Lts 239·6° both FR 5/7m 4M; R ◆ on W post.
N Pier Hd 50°36'·50N 02°26'·60W 2 FG (vert) 9m 6M. *Bell* (when vessels expected).
W Shambles Lt By 50°29'·75N 02°24'·33W Q (9) 15s; WCM; *Bell.*
E Shambles Lt By 50°30'·75N 02°20'·00W Q (3) 10s; ECM; *Bell.*
Lulworth Cove ent, E Point 50°36'·97N 02°14'·69W.
Bindon Hill 50°37'·3N 02°13'·6W and St Alban's Hd 50°34'·8N 02°03'·4W Iso R 2s (when firing taking place).
Anvil Pt 50°35'·48N 01°57'·52W Fl 10s 45m **24M**; W ● Tr; vis 237°-076°; (H24).

SWANAGE
Pier Hd 50°36'·52N 01°56'·88W 2 FR (vert) 6m 3M.
Peveril Ledge By 50°36'·38N 01°56'·02W; PHM.

POOLE
Poole Fairway Lt By 50°38'·97N 01°54'·80W L Fl 10s; SWM.
Poole Bar (No. 1) Lt By 50°39·30N 01°55'·08W QG; SHM; *Bell* (Historic wreck) 50°39'·68N 01°54'·80W Fl Y 5s; SPM.

SWASH CHANNEL
No. 2 Lt By 50°39'·19N 01°55'·16W Fl R 2s; PHM.
Swash Chan marked by PHM and SHM, unlit except for:
Training Bank Lt By 50°39'·80N 01°55'·82W QR (T).
No. 10 Lt By 50°40'·11N 01°55'·82W Fl R 4s; PHM.
No. 9 Lt By 50°40'·16N 01°55'·70W Fl G 5s; SHM.
No. 11 (Hook Sands) Lt By 50°40'·46N 01°56'·05W Fl G 3s; SHM.
No. 12 (Channel) Lt By 50°40'·41N 01°56'·18W Fl R 2s; PHM.
No. 14 Lt By 50°40'·76N 01°56'·73W Fl R 4s; PHM.
No. 13 Lt By 50°40'·84N 01°56'·62W Fl G 5s; SHM.

EAST LOOE CHANNEL
E Looe No. 16A Lt By 50°41'·02N 01°56'·03W QR; PHM.

East Hook By 50°40'·55W 01°55'·15W; PHM.
S Haven Pt, ferry landing 2 FR (vert) 5m on either side of ramp.
Ferry landing, E side 2 FG (vert) 3m, either side of ramp.
S Deep. Marked by Lt Bns and unlit Bns from ent S of Brownsea Castle to Furzey Is.

BROWNSEA ROADS
No.18 Lt By 50°41'·02N 01°57'·32W Fl R 5s; PHM.
N Haven Pt Bn 50°41'·12N 01°57'·10W Q (9) 15s 5m; WCM.
Brownsea (No. 42) Lt By 50°41'·13N 01°57'·33W Q (3) 10s; ECM.
RMYC Pier Hds 50°41'·31N 01°56'·73W 2 FG (vert) 2M.

MIDDLE SHIP CHANNEL
No. 20 Lt By 50°41'·35N 01°57'·02W Q (6) + L Fl 15s; *Bell* SCM.
Marked by PHM and SHM Lt Bys.
Aunt Betty (No. 50) Lt By 50°41'·93N 01°57'·31W Q (3) 10s; ECM.
Diver (No. 51) Lt By 50°42'·24N 01°58'·26W Q (9) 15s; WCM.

NORTH CHANNEL
The chan to Poole Hbr YC Marina and Poole Quay is marked by PHM and SHM's, mostly lit.
Bullpit Bn 50°41'·69N 01°56'·62W Q (9) 15s 7m 4M; WCM.
Salterns Marina Outer Bkwtr Hd 50°42'·20N 01°57'·01W 2 FR (vert) 2M; Tfc sigs.
Inner Bkwtr Hd 2 FG (vert) 3M.
Parkstone Yacht Haven 2 FR (vert) 4m 2M.
Parkstone YC platform 50°42'·33N 01°58'·00W Q 8m 1M; hut on dolphin.
Stakes No. 55 Lt By 50°42'·39N 01°58'·93W Q (6) + L Fl 15s; SCM.
Little Chan, E side, Oyster Bank Bn 50°42'·59N 01°59'·05W Fl (2) G 5s; SHM.

WAREHAM CHANNEL
Wareham Chan marked by PHM and SHM's initially, and then by stakes.

BOURNEMOUTH
Pier Hd 2 FR (vert) 9m 1M; W Col. *Reed (2) 120s* when vessel expected.
Boscombe Pier Hd 2 FR (vert) 7m 1M; R Col.
Hengistbury Hd, groyne, Bn 50°42'·63N 01°44'·85W (unlit).

NOTE: For waypoints of navigational buoys and racing marks in Solent area, see 10.2.18.

WESTERN APPROACHES TO THE SOLENT

Needles Fairway Lt By 50°38'·20N 01°38'·90W L Fl 10s; SWM; *Whis.*
Needles Lt 50°39'·70N 01°35'·43W Oc (2) WRG 20s 24m **W17M**, **R17M**, R14M G14M; ● Tr, R band and lantern; vis Rshore -300°, W300°-083°; R (unintens) 083°-212°, W212°-217°, G217°-224°. *Horn (2) 30s.*

NEEDLES CHANNEL
SW Shingles Lt By 50°39'·31N 01°37'·36W Fl R 2·5s; PHM.
Bridge Lt By 50°39'·59N 01°36'·80W VQ (9) 10s; Racon (T); WCM.
Shingles Elbow Lt By 50°40'·31N 01°35'·92W Fl (2) R 5s; PHM.
Mid Shingles Lt By 50°41'·18N 01°34'·58W; Fl (3) R 10s; PHM.
Totland Bay Pier Hd 2 FG (vert) 6m 2M.
Warden Lt By 50°41'·45N 01°33'·47W Fl G 2.5s; SHM; *Bell.*

NORTH CHANNEL
N Hd Lt By 50°42'·65N 01°35'·43W Fl (3) G 10s; SHM.
NE Shingles Lt By 50°41'·93N 01°33'·32W Q (3) 10s; ECM.
Hurst Pt Ldg Lts 042°. Front 50°42'·36N 01°33'·05W Iso 4s 15m 14M; R ■ Tr; vis 029°-053°. Rear 215m from front Iso WR 6s 23m W14/13M, R11M; W ● Tr; vis W (unintens) 080°-104°, W234°-244°, R244°-250°, W250°-053°.

2

THE WEST SOLENT

Sconce Lt By 50°42'·50N 01°31'·35W Q; NCM; *Bell.*
Black Rock By 50°42'·55N 01°30'·55W; SHM.
Fort Victoria Pier Hd 50°42'·42N 01°31'·08W 2 FG (vert) 4M.

YARMOUTH

YMS 2 50°42'·86N 01°29'·40W Fl Y 2·5s; SPM.
Pier Hd, centre, 50°42'·48N 01°29'·88W 2 FR (vert) 2M;
G col. High intensity FW (occas).

LYMINGTON

Jack in the Basket 50°44'·25N 01°30'·50W Fl R 2s 9m.
Ldg Lts 319·5°. Front, 50°45'·16N 01°31'·57W FR 12m 8M;
vis 309·5°-329·5°. Rear, 363m from front, FR 17m 8M.
Cross Boom No. 2 50°44'·33N 01°30'·50W Fl R 2s 4m 3M;
R □ on pile.
No. 1 50°44'·38N 01°30'·39W Fl G 2s 2m 3M; G △ on pile.
Durn's Pt obstn, S end, 50°45'·37N 01°26'·95W QR; dolphin.
Hamstead Ledge Lt By 50°43'·83N 01°26'10W Fl (2) G 5s; SHM.
W Lepe Lt By 50°45'·20N 01°24'·00W Fl R 5s; PHM.
Salt Mead Lt By 50°44'·48N 01°22'·95W Fl (3) G 10s; SHM.
Gurnard Ledge Lt By 50°45'·48N 01°20'·50W Fl G 4s; SHM.
E Lepe Lt By 50°46'·08N 01°20'·82W Fl (2) R 5s; PHM; *Bell.*
Gurnard Lt By 50°46'·18N 01°18'·75W Q; NCM.

BEAULIEU RIVER

Beaulieu Spit, E end 50°46'·83N 01°21'·67W Fl R 5s 3M;
R dolphin; vis 277°-037°.
No 2 Bn 50°46'·89N 01°21'·69W; PHM.
Ent Chan Bn Nos. 5, 9, 19, 21 Fl G 4s; Bn Nos 12, 20 Fl R 4s.

Off Stansore Pt 50°46'·89N 01°20'·34W. QR 4m 1M; R ◇, W
band, on R pile, marks cables.
NE Gurnard Lt By 50°47'·03N 01°19'·33W Fl (3) R 10s; PHM.
W Bramble Lt By 50°47'·17N 01°18'·57W VQ (9) 10s; WCM;
Bell 15s; Racon (T).
Thorn Knoll Lt By 50°47'·47N 01°18'·35W Fl G 5s; SHM.
Bourne Gap Lt By 50°47'·79N 01°18'·26W Fl R 3s; PHM.
N Thorn Lt By 50°47'·88N 01°17'·75W QG; SHM.
W Knoll By 50°47'·52N 01°17'·68W; SHM.
Outfall 50°48'·25N 01°18'·73W Iso R 10s 6m 5M; col on ■
structure; Ra refl; FR Lt on each corner; *Horn 20s.*

CALSHOT SPIT Lt F 50°48'·32N 01°17'·55W Fl 5s 12m 11M;
R hull, Lt Tr amidships; *Horn (2) 60s.*
E Knoll By 50°47'·93N 01°16'·74W; SHM.
Castle Pt Lt By 50°48'·68N 01°17'·58W IQR 10s; PHM.
Reach Lt By 50°49'·02N 01°17'·56W Fl (3) G 10s; SHM.

SOUTHAMPTON WATER

Coronation Lt By 50°49'·51N 01°17'·53W Fl Y 5s; SPM.
Hook Lt By 50°49'·49N 01°18'·21W QG 15s; SHM; *Horn.*
Fawley Chan No. 2 Lt Bn 50°49'·45N 01°18'·75W Fl R 3s; PHM.

ASHLETT CREEK

Fawley Lt By 50°49'·97N 01°19'·39W QR; PHM.

Bald Head By 50°49'·88N 01°18'·15W; SHM.
Hamble Pt Lt By 50°50'·12N 01°18'·57W Q (6) + L Fl 15s; SCM.

RIVER HAMBLE

Ldg Lts 345·5°. Front, No. 6 pile 50°50'·58N 01°18'·74W
Oc (2) R 12s 4m 2M. Rear, 820m from front, QR 12m; W
mast; vis 341·5°-349·5°.
No. 1 pile 50°50'·31N 01°18'·57W Fl G 3s 3M; SHM.
No. 2 pile 50°50'·36N 01°18'·68W Q (3) 10s 3M; ECM.
Ldg Lts 026·1°, Warsash Shore. Front, 50°50'·98N 01°18'·32W
QG; vis 010°-040°. Rear, Sailing Club, Iso G 6s; vis 022°-030°.

Esso Marine terminal, SE end 50°50'·05N 01°19'·33W 2 FR
(vert) 9m 10M.

BP Hamble Jetty 50°50'·90N 01°19'·50W 2 FG (vert) 5/3m
2M (on each side of the 4 dolphins).
Greenland Lt By 50°51'·07N 01°20'·29W IQ G 10s; SHM.
Cadland Lt By 50°50'·99N 01°20'·45W Fl R 3s; PHM.
Lains Lake Lt By 50°51'·55N 01°21'·57W Fl (2) R 4s; PHM.
Hound Lt By 50°51'·65N 01°21'·43W Fl (3) G 10s; SHM.
Netley Lt By 50°51'·99N 01°21'·72W Fl G 3s; SHM.
NW Netley Lt By 50°52'·28N 01°22'·65W Fl G 7s; SHM.
Deans Elbow Lt By 50°52'·12N 01°22'·67W Oc R 4s; PHM.
Weston Shelf Lt By 50°52'·68N 01°23'·17W Fl (3) G 15s; SHM.

HYTHE

Hythe Knock Lt By 50°52'·79N 01°23'·73W Fl R 3s; PHM.
Hythe Pier Hd 50°52'·45N 01°23'·52W 2 FR (vert) 12/5m 5M.
Marina Village Lt Bn 50°52'·23N 01°23'·48W Q (3) 10s; ECM.
Lock ent 50°52'·52N 01°23'·89W 2 FG (vert); G △ and 2 FR
(vert); R □.

SOUTHAMPTON/RIVER ITCHEN

Swinging Gd No. 1 Lt By 50°52'·97N 01°23'·35W Oc G 4s;
SHM.
E side. No. 1 dolphin 50°53'·12N 01°23'·32W QG; SHM.
No. 2 Dn 50°53'·27N 01°23'·28W Fl G 5s 2M; SHM.
No. 3 Dn 50°53'·45N 01°23'·18W Fl G 7s; SHM.
No. 4 pile 50°53'·58N 01°23'·07W QG 4m 2M; SHM.
Itchen Bridge. FW on bridge span each side marks main chan.
2 FG (vert) 2M each side on E pier. 2 FR (vert) 2M each side
on W pier.
Crosshouse Lt Bn 50°54'·01N 01°23'·11W Oc R 5s 5m 2M;
PHM.
Chapel Lt Bn 50°54'·11N 01°23'·13W Fl G 3s 5m 3M; SHM.
Shamrock Quay SW end 50°54'·46N 01°22'·84W 2 FR (vert)
4m, and NE end 2 FR (vert) 4m.
No. 5 Lt Bn 50°54'·46N 01°22'·67W Fl G 3s.
No. 6 Lt Bn 50°54'·55N 01°22'·54W Fl R 3s.
No. 7 Lt Bn 50°54'·56N 01°22'·40W Fl (2) G 5s.
No. 9 Lt Bn 50°54'·70N 01°22'·39W Fl (4) G 10s.
Kemps Marina Jetty Hd 50°54'·79N 01°22'·57W 2 FG (vert)
5m 1M.

SOUTHAMPTON/RIVER TEST

Town Quay Marina Ent 50°53'·65N 01°24'·23W 2 FG (vert).
Gymp Lt By 50°53'·14N 01°24'·21W QR; PHM.
Queen Elizabeth II terminal, S end 50°52'·97N 01°23'·64W
4 FG (vert) 16m 3M.
Lower Foul Gd Lt Bn 50°53'·23N 01°24'·46W Fl (2) R 10s; PHM.
Upper Foul Gd Lt Bn 50°53'·50N 01°24'·80W Fl (2) R 10s; PHM.
Town Quay Ldg Lts 329°, both FY 12/22m 3/2M (occas).
Gymp Elbow Lt By 50°53'·48N 01°24'·53W Oc R 4s; PHM.
Pier Hd Lt By 50°53'·64N 01°24'·57W QG; SHM.
Dibden Bay Lt By 50°53'·66N 01°24'·84W Q; NCM.
Swinging Gd No. 2 Lt By 50°53'·78N 01°25'·03W Fl (2) R 10s;
PHM.
Cracknore Lt By 50°53'·91N 01°25'·12W Oc R 8s; PHM.
Millbrook Lt By 50°54'·08N 01°26'·73W QR; PHM.
Bury Lt By 50°54'·10N 01°27'·04W Fl R 5s; PHM.
Eling Lt By 50°54'·45N 01°27'·75W Fl R 5s; PHM.

THE EAST SOLENT

NORTH CHANNEL/HILLHEAD

Calshot Lt By 50°48'·40N 01°16'·95W VQ; NCM; *Bell 30s.*
Hillhead Lt By 50°48'·04N 01°15'·92W Fl R 2·5s; PHM.
E Bramble Lt By 50°47'·20N 01°13'·56W VQ (3) 5s; ECM; *Bell.*
Hillhead Bn 50°49'·03N 01°14'·69W; Or Bn.

COWES

No. 4 Lt By 50°46'·04N 01°17'·78W QR; PHM.
No. 3 Lt By 50°46'·04N 01°17'·93W Fl G 3s; SHM.
Ldg Lts 164°. Front, 50°45'·87N 01°17'·76W Iso 2s 3m 6M.
Rear, 290m from front, Iso R 2s 5m 3M; vis 120°-240°.

E Bkwtr Hd 50°45'·84N 01°17'·43W Fl R 3s 3M.
W Cowes Marina N end 50°45'·69N 01°17'·62W 2 FG (vert) 6m.
E Cowes Marina N end 50°45'·15N 01°17'·44W 2 FR (vert).

Prince Consort Lt By 50°46'·38N 01°17'·47W VQ; NCM.
W Ryde Mid Lt By 50°46'·45N 01°15'·70W Q (9) 15s; WCM.
Norris Lt By 50°45'·92N 01°15'·40W Fl (3) R 10s; PHM.
N Ryde Mid Lt By 50°46'·58N 01°14'·30W Fl (4) R 20s; PHM.
S Ryde Mid Lt By 50°46'·10N 01°14'·08W Fl G 5s; SHM.
Peel Bank Lt By 50°45'·57N 01°13'·25W Fl (2) R 5s; PHM.
SE Ryde Mid Lt By 50°45'·90N 01°12'·00W VQ (6)+ L Fl 10s; SCM.
NE Ryde Mid Lt By 50°46'·18N 01°11'·80W Fl (2) R 10s; PHM.

WOOTTON
Lt Bn 50°44'·53N 01°12'·02W Q 1M; NCM.
No. 1 Lt Bn 50°44'·37N 01°12'·26W Fl (2) G 5s.
No. 2 Lt Bn 50°44'·22N 01°12'·38W Fl R 5s.

Mother Bank Lt By 50°45'·45N 01°11'·13W Fl R 3s; PHM.
Browndown Lt By 50°46'·54N 01°10'·87W Fl G 15s; SHM.
Stokes Bay Wk By 50°46'·67N 01°10'·58W; SHM.

RYDE
Pier, NW corner, N and E corner marked by 2 FR (vert). In fog FY from N corner, vis 045°-165°, 200°-320°.
Leisure Hbr E side 50°43'·95N 01°09'·20W 2 FR (vert) 7m 1M. FY 6m shown when depth of water in Hbr greater than 1m; 2 FY when depth exceeds 1·5m.
Hbr W side 50°43'·93N 01°09'·23W 2 FG (vert) 7m 1M.

Ft Gilkicker 50°46'·40N 01°08'·38W Oc G 10s 7M.
N Sturbridge Lt By 50°45'·31N 01°08'·15W VQ; NCM.
NE Mining Gnd Lt By 50°44'·71N 01°06'·30W Fl Y 10s; SPM.

PORTSMOUTH AND APPROACHES
Horse Sand Ft 50°44'·97N 01°04'·25W Iso G 2s 21m 8M; large ● stone structure.
Saddle Lt By 50°45'·17N 01°04'·78W VQ (3) G 10s; SHM.
Horse Sand Lt By 50°45'·48N 01°05'·17W Fl G 2·5s; SHM.
Outer Spit Lt By 50°45'·55N 01°05'·41W Q (6) + L Fl 15s; SCM.
Boyne Lt By 50°46'·12N 01°05'·17W Fl G 5s; SHM.
Spit Refuge Lt By 50°46'·02N 01°05'·37W Fl R 5s; PHM.
Spit Sand Ft, N side 50°46'·20N 01°05'·80W Fl R 5s 18m 7M; large ● stone structure.
Castle Lt By 50°46'·43N 01°05'·30W Fl (2) G 6s; SHM.
Southsea Castle N corner 50°46'·66N 01°05'·25W Iso 2s 16m 11M, W stone Tr, B band; vis 337°-071°.
Dir Lt 001·5° Dir WRG 11m W13M, R5M, G5M; same structure FG 351·5°-357·5°, Al WG 357·5°-000° (W phase incr with brg), FW 000°-003°, Al WR 003°-005·5° (R phase incr with brg), FR 005·5°-011·5°.
Ridge Lt By 50°46'·42N 01°05'·57W Fl (2) R 6s; PHM.
No. 1 Bar Lt By 50°46'·73N 01°05'·72W Fl (3) G 10s; SHM.
No. 2 Lt By 50°46'·66N 01°05'·58W Fl (3) R 10s; PHM.
No. 3 Lt By 50°47'·04N 01°06'·17W QG; SHM.
No. 4 Lt By 50°46'·98N 01°06'·27W QR; PHM.
Ft Blockhouse 50°47'·34N 01°06'·65W Dir Lt 320°; Dir WRG 6m W13M, R5M, G5M; Oc G 310°-316°, Al WG 316°-318·5° (W phase incr with brg), Oc 318·5°-321·5°, Al WR 321·5°-324° (R phase incr with brg), OcR 324°-330°. 2 FR (vert) 20m E.
Victoria Pile 50°47'·31N 01°06'·40W Oc G 15s 1M; SHM.
Dn, close E of C&N Marina, 50°47'·82N 01°06'·89W, Hbr Ent Dir Lt (Fuel Jetty) WRG 2m 1M; vis Iso G 2s 322·5°-330°, Al WG 330°-332·5°, Iso 2s 332·5°-335° (main chan), Al WR 335°-337·5°, Iso R 2s 337·5°-345° (Small Boat Chan).
Ballast Lt By 50°47'·63N 01°06'·73W Fl R 2·5s; PHM.
The Point 50°47'·54N 01°06'·48W QG 2M; SHM.
Port Solent Lock ent 50°50'·58N 01°06'·25W Fl (4) G 10s.
No Man's Land Ft 50°44'·37N 01°05'·60W Iso R 2s 21m 8M; large ● stone structure.

Horse Elbow Wk By 50°44'·40N 01°03'·35W; SHM.
Horse Elbow Lt By 50°44'·23N 01°03'·80W QG; SHM.
Warner Lt By 50°43'·84N 01°03'·93W QR; PHM; Whis.
Dean Elbow Lt By 50°43'·66N 01°01'·78W Fl (3) G 15s; SHM.
St Helens Lt By 50°40'·32N 01°02'·32W Fl (3) R 15s; PHM.
Horse Tail Lt By 50°43'·20N 01°00'·14W Fl (2) G 10s; SHM.
Nab East Lt By 50°42'·82N 01°00'·70W Fl (2) R 10s; PHM.
Dean Tail South Lt By 50°43'·10N 00°59'·49W Q (6) + L Fl 10s; SCM.
Nab End Lt By 50°42'·60N 00°59'·38W Fl R 5s; PHM.
New Grounds Lt By 50°41'·97N 00°58'·53W VQ (3) 5s; ECM.

BEMBRIDGE
St Helen's Ft (IOW) 50°42'·30N 01°05'·00W Fl (3) 10s 16m 8M; large ● stone structure.
Bembridge Tide Gauge 50°42'·45N 01°04'·95W Fl Y 2s 1M; SPM.

LANGSTONE AND APPROACHES
Winner By 50°45'·07N 01°00'·01W; SCM.
Roway Wk Bn 50°46'·08N 01°02'·20W Fl (2) 5s; IDM.
Langstone Fairway Lt By 50°46'·28N 01°01'·27W L Fl 10s; SWM.
Eastney Pt Lt Bn 50°47'·20N 01°01'·58W QR 2m 2M.
Eastney Gunnery Range Lt 50°47'·16N 01°02'·12W FR, Oc (2) Y 10s, and Y Lts (occas) when firing taking place.
S Lake 50°49'·45N 00°59'·80W Fl G 3s 3m 2M; SHM.
Binness 50°49'·60N 00°59'·85W Fl R 3s 3m 2M; PHM.

CHICHESTER ENTRANCE
Bar Lt Bn 50°45'·88N 00°56'·38W Fl WR 5s 14m W7M, R5M; vis W322°-080°, R080°-322°; Tide Gauge. Same structure, Fl (2) R 10s 7m 2M; vis 020°-080°.
Eastoke Lt Bn 50°46'·62N 00°56'·08W QR 2m 3M; R □ on pile.
W Winner Lt Bn 50°46'·85N 00°55'·88W QG; G △ on pile.

EMSWORTH CHANNEL
Verner Lt Bn 50°48'·27N 00°56'·57W Fl R 10s; PHM.
Marker Pt 50°48'·87N 00°56'·65W Fl (2) G 10s 8m; SHM.
NE Hayling Lt Bn 50°49'·60N 00°56'·77W Fl (2) R 10s 8m; PHM.
Emsworth Lt Bn 50°49'·63N 00°56'·70W Q (6) + L Fl 15s; SCM, tide gauge.

CHICHESTER CHANNEL
East Hd Lt Bn 50°47'·32N 00°54'·67W Fl (4) G 10s; G △ on pile; SHM; tide gauge.
Camber Lt Bn 50°47'·83N 00°53'·93W Q (6) + L Fl 15s; SCM.
Chalkdock Lt Bn 50°48'·46N 00°53'·27W Fl (2) G 10s; G △ on pile; SHM.
Itchenor Jetty 50°48'·43N 00°51'·90W 2 FG (vert); tide gauge.
Birdham Lt Bn 50°48'·33N 00°50'·18W Fl (4) G 10s; pile, SHM; depth gauge.
Chichester Yacht Basin Lt Bn 50°48'·42N 00°49'·87W Fl G 5s 6m; SHM; tide gauge.

St Catherine's Pt 50°34'·52N 01°17'·80W Fl 5s 41m **27M**; vis 257°-117°; RC. FR 35m **17M** (same Tr) vis 099°-116°.
Ventnor Pier 50°35'·45N 01°12'·25W 2 FR (vert) 10m 3M.
Sandown Pier Hd 50°39'·02N 01°09'·09W 2 FR (vert) 7m 2M.
W Princessa Lt By 50°40'·20N 01°03'·95W Q (9) 15s; WCM.
Bembridge Ledge Lt By 50°41'·12N 01°02'·72W Q (3) 10s; ECM.

Nab Tr. 50°40'·05N 00°57'·07W Fl 10s 27m **16M**; Horn (2) 30s; Racon (T); vis 300°-120°.

10.2.5 PASSAGE INFORMATION

Reference books include: Admiralty *Channel Pilot*; *South Coast Cruising* (YM/Fishwick); *Shell Channel Pilot* (Imray/ Cunliffe); *The Solent* (Imray/Bowskill); and *Creeks and Harbours of the Solent* (Adlard Coles). See 10.0.5 for distances across the Channel, and 10.3.5 and 10.15.5 for notes on cross-Channel passages.

THE PORTLAND RACE (chart 2255)

South of the Bill lies the Portland Race which can give severe and dangerous sea states. Even in settled weather it should be carefully avoided by small craft, although at neaps it may be barely perceptible.

The Race occurs at the confluence of two strong S-going tidal streams which run down each side of Portland for almost 10 hours out of 12 at springs. These streams meet the main E-W stream of the Channel, producing large eddies on either side of Portland and a highly confused sea state with heavy overfalls in the Race. The irregular contours of the sea-bed, which shoals abruptly from depths of over 100m some 2M south of the Bill to as little as 9m on Portland Ledge 1M further N, greatly contribute to the violence of the Race. Portland Ledge strongly deflects the flow of water upwards, so that on the flood the Race lies SE of the Bill and vice versa on the ebb. Conditions deteriorate with wind-against-tide, especially at springs; in an E'ly gale against the flood stream the Race may spread eastward to The Shambles bank. The Race normally extends about 2M S of the Bill, but further S in bad weather.

The Tidal Stream chartlets at 10.2.9 show the approx hourly positions of the Race. They are referenced to HW Portland, for the convenience of those leaving or making for Portland/ Weymouth; and to HW Dover for those on passage S of the Bill. The smaller scale chartlets at 10.2.3 show the English Chan streams referenced to HW at Dover and Portsmouth.

Small craft may avoid the Race either by passing clear to seaward of it, between 3 and 5M S of the Bill; or by using the inshore passage if conditions suit. This passage is a stretch of relatively smooth water between 1ca and 3ca off the Bill (depending on wind), which should not however be used at springs nor at night; beware lobster pots. Timing is important to catch "slackish" water around the Bill, i.e:

> **Westbound** = from HW Dover – 1 to HW + 2
> (HW Portland + 4 to HW – 6).
> **Eastbound** = from HW Dover + 5 to HW – 4
> (HW Portland – 3 to HW + 1).

From either direction, close Portland at least 2M N of the Bill to utilise the S-going stream; once round the Bill, the N-going stream will set a yacht away from the Race area.

PORTLAND TO CHRISTCHURCH BAY (chart 2615)

The Shambles bank is about 3M E of Portland Bill, and should be avoided at all times. In bad weather the sea breaks heavily on it. It is marked by buoys on its E side and at SW end. E of Weymouth are rky ledges extending 3ca offshore as far as Lulworth Cove, which provides a reasonable anch in fine, settled weather and offshore winds; as do Worbarrow Bay and Chapman's Pool (10.2.10).

A firing range extends 5M offshore between Lulworth and St Alban's Hd. Yachts must pass through this area as quickly as possible, when the range is in use, see 10.2.10. Beware Kimmeridge Ledges, which extend over 5ca seaward.

St Alban's Head (107m and conspic) is steep-to and has a dangerous race off it which may extend 3M seaward. The race lies to the E on the flood and to the W on the ebb; the latter is the more dangerous. A narrow passage, at most 5ca wide and very close inshore, avoids the worst of the overfalls. There is an eddy on W side of St Alban's Head, where the stream runs almost continuously SE. 1M S of St Alban's Head the ESE stream begins at HW Portsmouth + 0520, and the WNW stream at HW –0030, with sp rates of 4·75kn.

There is deep water quite close inshore between St Alban's Hd and Anvil Pt (lt). 1M NE of Durlston Hd, Peveril Ledge runs 2½ca seaward, causing quite a bad race which extends nearly 1M eastwards, particularly on W-going stream against a SW wind. Proceeding towards the excellent shelter of Poole Harbour (10.2.13), overfalls may be met off Ballard Pt and Old Harry on the W-going stream. Studland Bay (10.2.13 and chart *2172*) is a good anch except in NE to SE winds. Anch about 4ca WNW of Handfast Pt. Avoid foul areas on chart.

Poole Bay offers good sailing in waters sheltered from W and N winds, and with no dangers to worry the average yacht. Tidal streams are weak N of a line between Handfast Pt and Hengistbury Hd. The latter is a dark headland, S of Christchurch hbr (10.2.14), with a groyne extending 1ca S and Beerpan Rks a further 100m offshore. Beware lobster pots in this area. Christchurch Ledge extends 2·75M SE from Hengistbury Hd. The tide runs hard over the ledge at sp, and there may be overfalls. Within Christchurch Bay the streams are weak.

WESTERN APPROACHES TO SOLENT (charts *2219*, 2050)

The Needles (see 10.2.16) are distinctive rks at the W end of the Isle of Wight. The adjacent chalk cliffs of High Down are conspic from afar, but the lt ho may not be seen by day until relatively close. Goose Rk, dries, is about 50m WNW of the lt ho, 100-150m WSW of which is a drying wreck. The NW side of Needles Chan is defined by the Shingles bank, parts of which dry and on which the sea breaks violently in the least swell. The SE side of the bank is fairly steep-to, the NW side shelves more gradually. Due to shoaling near the ldg line, the SW Shingles lt buoy may be moved as necessary.

On the ebb the stream sets very strongly (3·4kn) WSW across the Shingles. In bad weather broken water and overfalls extend along The Bridge, a reef which runs 8ca W of the lt ho with extremity marked by WCM lt buoy. S to W gales against the ebb raise very dangerous seas in the Needles Chan. (In such conditions the E approach to the Solent, via Nab Tr and the Forts, should be used or shelter found at Poole or Studland). Even a SW F4 over the ebb will cause breaking seas near Bridge and SW Shingles buoys.

In strong winds the North Channel, N of the Shingles, is preferable to the Needles Channel. The two join S of Hurst Pt, where overfalls and tide rips may be met. Beware The Trap, a shoal spit 150m SE of Hurst Castle.

In E winds Alum B, close NE of the Needles, is an attractive daytime anch with its coloured cliffs, but beware Long Rk (dries) in middle of B, and Five Fingers Rk 1½ca SW of Hatherwood Pt on N side. Totland Bay is good anch in settled weather, but avoid Warden Ledge.

THE SOLENT (charts 2040, 394)

Within the Solent there are few dangers in mid-chan. The most significant is Bramble bank (dries) between Cowes and Calshot. The main shipping chan (buoyed) passes S and W of the Brambles, but yachts can use the North Chan to the NE of the Brambles at any state of tide. Tidal streams are strong at sp, but principally follow the direction of the main chan.

An Area of Concern between Cowes and Calshot provides added safety for larger ships; see 10.2.17 for details.

Several inshore spits, banks, rocks and ledges, which a yachtsman should know, include: Pennington and Lymington Spits on the N shore; Black Rk 4ca W of entrance to Yarmouth (10.2.19); Hamstead Ledge 8ca W of entrance to Newtown River (10.2.21) and Saltmead Ledge 1·5M to E; Gurnard

Ledge 1·5M W of Cowes; Lepe, Middle and Beaulieu Spit, S and W of the ent to Beaulieu R. (10.2.22); the shoals off Stone Pt, where three bns mark cable area; Shrape Mud, which extends N from the breakwater of Cowes hbr (10.2.23) and along to Old Castle Pt; the shoals and isolated rks which fringe the island shore from Old Castle Pt to Ryde (10.2.28), including either side of the ent to Wootton Creek (10.2.27); and Calshot Spit which extends almost to the lt F which marks the turn of chan into Southampton Water.

Southampton Water is a busy commercial waterway with large tankers, containerships, lesser craft and ferries. Yachts should monitor VHF Ch 12 to ascertain shipping movements. Between the Esso jetty off Fawley and the BP jetty on the E side the channel is narrow for large vessels; yachts can easily stay clear by seeking shoal water. N of this area there is adequate water for yachts close outboard of the main buoyed channel; the banks are of gently shelving soft mud, apart from foul ground between Hythe and Marchwood. Unlit marks and large mooring buoys may however be hard to see against the many shore lights. Except in strong N'lies, Southampton Water and the R Test and Itchen provide sheltered sailing. The River Hamble is convenient, but somewhat crowded.

Depending on the wind direction, there are many good anchs: For example, in W winds there is anch on E side of Hurst, as close inshore as depth permits, NE of High lt. In S winds, or in good weather, anch W of Yarmouth hbr ent, as near shore as possible; reasonably close to town, see 10.2.19.

In winds between W and N there is good anch in Stanswood Bay, about 1M NE of Stansore Pt. Just N of Calshot Spit there is shelter from SW and W. Osborne Bay, 2M E of Cowes, is sheltered from winds between S and W. In E winds Gurnard Bay, the other side of Cowes is preferable. In N winds anch in Stokes Bay. At E end of IOW there is good anch off Bembridge in winds from S, SW or W; but clear out if wind goes into E. There are also places which a shoal-draught boat can explore at the top of the tide, such as Ashlett Creek (10.2.26) between Fawley and Calshot, Eling up the R. Test, and the upper reaches of the R. Medina (10.2.23).

ISLE OF WIGHT – SOUTH COAST (chart *2045*)

From the Needles eastward to Freshwater Bay the cliffs can be approached to within 1ca, but beyond the E end of chalk cliffs there are ledges off Brook and Atherfield which require at least 5ca offing. The E-going stream sets towards these dangers. 4M SSW of the Needles the stream turns E x N at HW Portsmouth + 0530, and W at HW – 0030, sp rate 2kn.

St Catherine's lt ho (lt, RC) is conspic. It is safe to pass 2ca off, but a race occurs off the Point and can be very dangerous at or near sp with a strong opposing wind; particularly SE of the Pt on a W-going stream in a W gale, when St Catherine's should be given a berth of at least 2M. 1·25M SE of the Pt the stream turns E x N at HW Portsmouth + 0520, and W x S at HW – 0055, sp rate 3·75kn.

Rocks extend about 2½ca either side of Dunnose where a race occurs. In Sandown Bay anch off Shanklin or Sandown where the streams are weak inshore. Off the centre of the Bay they turn NE x E at HW Portsmouth + 0500, and SW x W at HW – 0100, sp rates 2 kn. The Yarborough Monument is conspic above Culver Cliff. Whitecliff Bay provides an anch in winds between W and N. From here to Foreland (Bembridge Pt) the coast is fringed by a ledge of rks (dry) extending up to 3ca offshore, and it is advisable to keep to seaward (E) of Bembridge Ledge ECM lt buoy.

EASTERN APPROACHES TO SOLENT (charts 2050, *2045*)

4·5M E of Foreland is Nab Tr (lt, fog sig), a conspic steel and concrete structure (28m), marking Nab Shoal for larger vessels and of no direct significance to yachtsmen. NW of Nab Tr, the E approach to the Solent via Spithead, presents few problems and is far safer in SW/W gales than the Needles Channel.

The main chan is well buoyed and easy to follow, but there is plenty of water for the normal yacht to the S of it when approaching No Man's Land Fort and Horse Sand Fort, between which craft must pass. Submerged barriers lie SW of the former and N of the latter. Ryde Sand dries extensively and is a trap for the unwary; so too is Hamilton Bank on the W side of the chan to Portsmouth (10.2.30).

Nab Tr is also a most useful landmark when approaching the E end of Isle of Wight, or when making for the hbrs of Langstone (10.2.31) or Chichester (10.2.32). Both these hbrs, with offlying sands, are on a dangerous lee shore in strong S'ly winds. East and West Winner flank the ent to Langstone Hbr. Similarly, E and W Pole Sands, drying 1m, lie either side of the ent chan from Chichester Bar bn. SE from Chichester Bar the whole of Bracklesham Bay is shallow, with a pronounced inshore set at certain states of the tide; yachts should keep at least 2M offshore. Further along a low-lying coast, is Selsey Bill with extensive offshore rocks and shoals. Pass these to seaward of the Owers SCM lt buoy, or via the Looe Chan (see 10.3.5) in suitable conditions. Boulder SHM lt buoy is at the W ent to this chan, about 6M SE of Chichester Bar bn. Medmery Bank, 3·7m, is 1M WNW of Boulder.

10.2.6   DISTANCE TABLE

Approximate distances in nautical miles are by the most direct route, whilst avoiding dangers and allowing for Traffic Separation Schemes. Places in *italics* are in adjoining areas; places in **bold** are also in 10.0.5, Cross-Channel Distances.

	1	2	3	4	5	6	7	8	9	10	11	12	13	14	15	16	17	18	19	20
1. *Exmouth*	1																			
2. *Lyme Regis*	21	2																		
3. Portland Bill	36	22	3																	
4. **Weymouth**	46	32	8	4																
5. Swanage	58	44	22	22	5															
6. **Poole Hbr ent**	65	51	28	26	6	6														
7. **Needles Lt Ho**	73	58	35	34	14	14	7													
8. Lymington	79	64	42	40	20	24	6	8												
9. Yarmouth (IOW)	77	63	40	39	18	22	4	2	9											
10. Beaulieu R. ent	84	69	46	45	25	29	11	7	7	10										
11. Cowes	86	71	49	46	28	27	14	10	9	2	11									
12. Southampton	93	78	55	54	34	34	20	16	16	9	9	12								
13. R. Hamble (ent)	90	75	53	51	32	34	18	12	13	6	6	5	13							
14. Portsmouth	96	81	58	57	37	35	23	19	19	12	10	18	13	14						
15. Langstone Hbr	98	84	61	59	39	39	25	21	21	14	12	21	18	5	15					
16. Chichester Bar	101	86	63	62	42	42	28	23	24	17	15	23	18	8	5	16				
17. Bembridge	97	81	59	58	38	39	24	18	19	13	10	18	15	5	6	8	17			
18. **Nab Tower**	102	86	64	63	43	44	29	23	24	18	15	24	19	10	7	6	6	18		
19. St Catherine's Pt	82	68	45	44	25	25	12	19	21	27	15	36	29	20	20	19	17	15	19	
20. *Littlehampton*	117	102	79	79	60	61	46	44	45	38	36	45	42	31	28	25	28	22	35	20

PORTLAND
MEAN SPRING
AND NEAP CURVES

MEAN RANGES
Springs 2.0m
Neaps   0.6m

Spring occurs 2 days
after
New and Full moon

PORTLAND HARBOUR   10-2-8

Dorset 50°35'·11N 02°24'·90W (E Ship Chan)   Rtg 2-4-3

CHARTS
AC 2268, 2255, *2610*; Imray C4, C5; Stanfords 12; OS 194

TIDES
–0430 Dover; ML 1·0; Zone 0 (UT)

Standard Port PORTLAND (→)

Times				Height (metres)			
High Water		Low Water		MHWS	MHWN	MLWN	MLWS
0100	0700	0100	0700	2·1	1·4	0·8	0·1
1300	1900	1300	1900				

LULWORTH COVE and MUPE BAY (Worbarrow Bay)

+0005	+0015	–0005	0000	+0·1	+0·1	+0·2	+0·1

NOTE: Portland is a Standard Port; predictions for each
day of the year are given below. Double LWs (known
locally as the Gulder) occur over a 4hr period. Predictions
are for the first LW.

SHELTER
Poor, due to lack of wind breaks. ⚓ N of the moorings off
Castletown (best in S/SW winds) or off Castle Cove. East
Fleet is only suitable for small craft with lowering masts.
Weymouth, with its old hbr and marina, is a better option
for yachtsmen. **Note:** Low flying helicopters often fly for
long periods, H24, over S part of Portland hbr.
Portland Harbour and the former Naval Base are owned
by Portland Port Ltd. The QHM remains in office until the
Hbr Revision Order is enacted, following a Public Enquiry.
Future plans include a cargo terminal and bulk storage on
Coaling Pier, Ro-Ro ferry terminal on New Quay (service
to Portugal), fishing hbr to the W of Camber jetty and a
500 berth marina in the Camber. Some of these projects
await the closure of the helicopter base in 1999. More
info, as available, in the Supplements.

NAVIGATION
WPT 50°35'·07N 02°24'·00W, 090°/270° from/to E Ship
Chan, Fort Hd, 0·50M. The S Chan is permanently closed.
Speed limit in the hbr is 12kn. Beware rky reef extending
1ca off Sandsfoot Cas, shoal areas E of Small Mouth and
hydrofoils from Weymouth. All ex-Naval buoys, lighters
and rafts have been removed. Portland Race (see 10.2.5
and 10.2.9) is extremely dangerous.

LIGHTS AND MARKS
Bill of Portland (S end) Fl (4) 20s 43m 25M; W tr, R band;
gradually changes from 1 flash to 4 flashes 221°-244°, 4
flashes 244°-117°, gradually changes from 4 flashes to 1
flash 117°-141°. FR 19m 13M, same tr, vis 271°-291° (20°)
over The Shambles, Dia 30s. Ldg lts 288° into E Fleet:
Front QG 3m 2M; rear Iso G 4s 5m 2M.

RADIO TELEPHONE
Call *Portland Harbour Control* VHF Ch 13, Mon-Fri 0800-
1600UT and when vessels >50m LOA are due. Pleasure
craft may enter the Harbour outside these times without
prior approval, provided they comply with hbr regulations.
Note: Portland CG offers radio coverage of the Casquets
TSS on Ch **69** 16.

TELEPHONE (Dial code 01305)
Portland Hbr Control 825245, 🛥 824055; QHM 820311;
MRSC 760439; ☷ 0345 231110 (H24); Marinecall 0891
500457; Police 63011; Dr 820311 (Emergency).

FACILITIES
Castle Cove SC ☎ 783708, M, L, FW; **Services:** Slip, M, L,
FW, ME, Sh, C, CH, El (mobile workshop).
Town ⊠, Ⓑ, ⇌ (bus to Weymouth), ✈ (Bournemouth).

---

*There is no set of the sea in Portland Race: no run and
sway: no regular assault. It is a chaos of pyramidical
waters leaping up suddenly without calculation, or rule
of advance. It is not a charge, but a scrimmage; a
wrestling bout; but a wrestling bout of a thousand
against one. It purposely raises a clamour to shake its
adversary's soul, wherein it most resembles a gigantic
pack of fighting dogs, for it snarls, howls, yells, and all
this most terrifically. Its purpose is to kill, and to kill with
a savage pride.*
*And all these things you find out if you get mixed up in it
on a very small boat.*

The Cruise of the Nona: Hilaire Belloc. Pimlico (Publishers).
Reprinted by permission of the Peters Fraser & Dunlop Group Ltd.

PORTLAND TIDAL STREAMS 10-2-9

6 Hours before HW Portland (0145 after HW Dover)

5 Hours before HW Portland (0245 after HW Dover)

4 Hours before HW Portland (0345 after HW Dover)

3 Hours before HW Portland (0445 after HW Dover)

2 Hours before HW Portland (0545 after HW Dover)

1 Hour before HW Portland (0540 before HW Dover)

General Area 2   10.2.3

HW Portland (0440 before HW Dover)

1 Hour after HW Portland (0340 before HW Dover)

2 Hours after HW Portland (0240 before HW Dover)

3 Hours after HW Portland (0140 before HW Dover)

4 Hours after HW Portland (0040 before HW Dover)

5 Hours after HW Portland (0020 after HW Dover)

ENGLAND – PORTLAND

LAT 50°34'N   LONG 2°26'W

TIMES AND HEIGHTS OF HIGH AND LOW WATERS

YEAR **1998**

TIME ZONE (UT)
For Summer Time add ONE hour in non-shaded areas

Chart Datum: 0·93 metres below Ordnance Datum (Newlyn)

JANUARY

Day	Reading 1 (Time m)	Reading 2	Reading 3	Reading 4
1 TH	0054 0.2	0823 2.2	1320 0.2	2045 2.0
16 F	0135 0.2	0840 2.0	1401 0.2	2105 1.8
2 F	0138 0.2	0901 2.1	1405 0.2	2123 1.9
17 SA	0209 0.3	0906 1.9	1433 0.3	2130 1.7
3 SA	0221 0.3	0940 2.0	1451 0.3	2202 1.8
18 SU	0237 0.4	0934 1.8	1459 0.4	2159 1.6
4 SU	0307 0.4	1020 1.9	1541 0.4	2246 1.7
19 M	0257 0.5	1003 1.6	1517 0.4	2231 1.4
5 M	0357 0.5	1107 1.8	1638 0.5	2338 1.6
20 TU	0321 0.5	1034 1.5	1546 0.5	2310 1.4
6 TU	0456 0.6	1204 1.7	1744 0.5	
21 W	0359 0.6	1114 1.4	1633 0.6	
7 W	0043 1.6	0608 0.7	1315 1.6	1855 0.6
22 TH	0008 1.3	0501 0.7	1218 1.4	1745 0.6
8 TH	0203 1.6	0728 0.7	1438 1.6	2007 0.6
23 F	0130 1.3	0636 0.8	1346 1.3	1914 0.6
9 F	0322 1.7	0845 0.7	1554 1.7	2112 0.5
24 SA	0254 1.4	0809 0.7	1513 1.4	2029 0.5
10 SA	0429 1.8	0948 0.6	1659 1.7	2207 0.4
25 SU	0403 1.6	0913 0.6	1624 1.6	2129 0.4
11 SU	0526 1.9	1039 0.5	1756 1.8	2256 0.4
26 M	0501 1.8	1005 0.4	1725 1.7	2222 0.3
12 M	0616 2.0	1125 0.4	1846 1.9	O 2339 0.3
27 TU	0554 2.0	1053 0.3	1821 1.9	2311 0.2
13 TU	0701 2.1	1206 0.3	1930 1.9	
28 W	0645 2.1	1140 0.2	1912 2.0	● 2358 0.1
14 W	0020 0.2	0740 2.1	1246 0.2	2008 1.9
29 TH	0733 2.2	1225 0.1	1958 2.1	
15 TH	0059 0.2	0813 2.1	1324 0.2	2039 1.9
30 F	0044 0.0	0816 2.3	1311 0.0	2039 2.1
31 SA	0128 0.0	0857 2.3	1355 0.0	2117 2.0

FEBRUARY

Day	Reading 1 (Time m)	Reading 2	Reading 3	Reading 4
1 SU	0211 0.1	0935 2.2	1439 0.1	2154 1.9
16 M	0216 0.2	0917 1.8	1430 0.2	2136 1.6
2 M	0254 0.2	1013 2.0	1524 0.2	2232 1.8
17 TU	0234 0.3	0943 1.7	1445 0.3	2201 1.5
3 TU	0338 0.3	1054 1.8	1613 0.3	2314 1.7
18 W	0254 0.4	1008 1.5	1508 0.4	2226 1.4
4 W	0427 0.5	1140 1.7	1709 0.5	
19 TH	0323 0.4	1038 1.4	1543 0.4	2304 1.3
5 TH	0006 1.6	0530 0.6	1240 1.5	1817 0.6
20 F	0408 0.6	1124 1.3	1639 0.5	
6 F	0117 1.5	0652 0.7	1404 1.4	1938 0.6
21 SA	0008 1.3	0525 0.7	1241 1.2	1810 0.6
7 SA	0250 1.5	0829 0.7	1535 1.5	2055 0.6
22 SU	0149 1.3	0718 0.7	1429 1.3	1953 0.6
8 SU	0409 1.6	0940 0.6	1646 1.6	2153 0.5
23 M	0324 1.5	0848 0.6	1559 1.5	2108 0.5
9 M	0510 1.8	1029 0.5	1744 1.7	2240 0.4
24 TU	0435 1.7	0948 0.4	1707 1.7	2205 0.3
10 TU	0601 1.9	1110 0.4	1832 1.8	2322 0.3
25 W	0534 1.9	1038 0.2	1806 1.9	2256 0.1
11 W	0645 2.0	1149 0.2	1914 1.9	O
26 TH	0628 2.1	1125 0.1	1857 2.0	● 2343 0.0
12 TH	0001 0.2	0723 2.3	1228 0.1	1950 1.9
27 F	0717 2.3	1211 -0.1	1943 2.2	
13 F	0040 0.1	0756 2.1	1305 0.1	2020 1.9
28 SA	0028 -0.1	0802 2.4	1256 -0.1	2025 2.2
14 SA	0117 0.1	0823 2.0	1340 0.1	2046 1.8
15 SU	0150 0.1	0850 1.9	1410 0.1	2111 1.8

MARCH

Day	Reading 1 (Time m)	Reading 2	Reading 3	Reading 4
1 SU	0113 -0.1	0843 2.4	1339 -0.1	2103 2.2
16 M	0127 0.1	0829 2.0	1344 0.1	2049 1.8
2 M	0155 -0.1	0921 2.3	1422 -0.1	2139 2.1
17 TU	0153 0.1	0857 1.8	1403 0.2	2114 1.7
3 TU	0235 0.2	0959 2.1	1504 0.1	2214 1.9
18 W	0211 0.2	0922 1.7	1419 0.2	2135 1.6
4 W	0317 0.2	1036 1.9	1547 0.3	2252 1.7
19 TH	0231 0.3	0946 1.5	1440 0.3	2156 1.5
5 TH	0402 0.4	1118 1.6	1637 0.5	2336 1.6
20 F	0257 0.4	1014 1.4	1510 0.4	2228 1.4
6 F	0459 0.6	1212 1.4	1741 0.6	
21 SA	0337 0.5	1056 1.3	1557 0.5	2321 1.3
7 SA	0038 1.4	0622 0.7	1339 1.3	1907 0.7
22 SU	0444 0.6	1205 1.2	1725 0.6	
8 SU	0219 1.4	0821 0.7	1521 1.4	2036 0.7
23 M	0047 1.3	0643 0.7	1350 1.3	1925 0.6
9 M	0348 1.5	0929 0.6	1632 1.5	2134 0.6
24 TU	0240 1.5	0824 0.5	1534 1.4	2047 0.5
10 TU	0449 1.7	1012 0.5	1726 1.6	2218 0.5
25 W	0405 1.7	0928 0.4	1646 1.7	2146 0.3
11 W	0539 1.8	1049 0.3	1811 1.8	2258 0.1
26 TH	0509 1.9	1019 0.2	1744 1.9	2237 0.1
12 TH	0622 1.9	1125 0.2	1851 1.9	2337 0.0
27 F	0605 2.1	1107 0.0	1836 2.1	2324 0.0
13 F	0700 2.0	1203 0.1	1927 1.9	O
28 SA	0656 2.3	1152 -0.1	1922 2.2	●
14 SA	0016 0.1	0732 2.1	1240 0.0	1956 2.0
29 SU	0010 -0.1	0741 2.4	1237 -0.2	2004 2.3
15 SU	0054 0.1	0801 2.0	1315 0.0	2023 1.9
30 M	0054 -0.1	0801 2.4	1320 -0.2	2043 2.3
31 TU	0135 -0.1	0903 2.3	1401 -0.1	2120 2.1

APRIL

Day	Reading 1 (Time m)	Reading 2	Reading 3	Reading 4
1 W	0216 0.0	0941 2.1	1442 0.1	2155 2.0
16 TH	0150 0.2	0903 1.7	1358 0.3	2114 1.7
2 TH	0256 0.2	1019 1.8	1523 0.3	2231 1.8
17 F	0213 0.3	0928 1.6	1422 0.3	2136 1.6
3 F	0340 0.4	1100 1.6	1608 0.5	2311 1.6
18 SA	0242 0.4	0959 1.5	1452 0.4	2207 1.5
4 SA	0435 0.6	1153 1.4	1707 0.7	
19 SU	0322 0.4	1042 1.4	1538 0.6	2256 1.4
5 SU	0005 1.4	0553 0.7	1322 1.3	1830 0.8
20 M	0429 0.6	1148 1.3	1705 0.7	
6 M	0141 1.4	0757 0.7	1502 1.3	2004 0.8
21 TU	0014 1.4	0616 0.6	1325 1.3	1900 0.7
7 TU	0316 1.5	0904 0.6	1607 1.5	2104 0.7
22 W	0200 1.5	0753 0.5	1504 1.5	2022 0.6
8 W	0417 1.6	0943 0.5	1657 1.6	2148 0.5
23 TH	0331 1.7	0901 0.4	1617 1.7	2123 0.4
9 TH	0506 1.7	1018 0.3	1740 1.7	2228 0.4
24 F	0439 1.9	0955 0.2	1717 1.9	2215 0.2
10 F	0549 1.9	1055 0.2	1810 1.9	2309 0.2
25 SA	0538 2.1	1044 0.0	1810 2.1	2304 0.1
11 SA	0628 2.0	1133 0.1	1856 2.0	O 2348 0.2
26 SU	0631 2.2	1131 -0.1	1858 2.3	● 2350 0.0
12 SU	0703 2.0	1211 0.1	1928 2.0	
27 M	0720 2.3	1216 -0.1	1942 2.3	
13 M	0026 0.1	0735 2.0	1300 0.1	1958 2.0
28 TU	0034 0.0	0804 2.3	1300 -0.1	2023 2.3
14 TU	0100 0.1	0807 2.0	1315 0.1	2026 1.9
29 W	0117 0.0	0846 2.2	1341 0.0	2101 2.2
15 W	0127 0.1	0836 1.9	1337 0.2	2052 1.8
30 TH	0158 0.1	0925 2.0	1421 0.2	2138 2.0

ENGLAND – PORTLAND

LAT 50°34'N   LONG 2°26'W

TIMES AND HEIGHTS OF HIGH AND LOW WATERS

YEAR **1998**

TIME ZONE (UT)
For Summer Time add ONE hour in non-shaded areas

MAY

Day	Time	m	Day	Time	m
1 F	0239	0.2	16 SA	0203	0.3
	1004	1.8		0917	1.7
	1501	0.4		1416	0.4
	2212	1.8		2126	1.7
2 SA	0322	0.4	17 SU	0238	0.4
	1045	1.6		0951	1.6
	1544	0.6		1453	0.5
	2247	1.6		2200	1.6
3 SU	0414	0.6	18 M	0323	0.4
	1133	1.4		1037	1.5
	1637	0.7		1543	0.6
	2332	1.5		2248	1.6
4 M	0521	0.7	19 TU	0427	0.5
	1248	1.3		1138	1.4
	1748	0.8		1659	0.7
				2357	1.5
5 TU	0038	1.4	20 W	0552	0.5
	0649	0.7		1301	1.4
	1423	1.3		1831	0.7
	1911	0.8			
6 W	0217	1.4	21 TH	0127	1.5
	0810	0.6		0718	0.5
	1528	1.4		1430	1.6
	2020	0.7		1951	0.6
7 TH	0327	1.5	22 F	0256	1.7
	0858	0.5		0829	0.4
	1618	1.6		1544	1.7
	2111	0.6		2056	0.5
8 F	0419	1.6	23 SA	0408	1.8
	0939	0.4		0928	0.3
	1700	1.7		1647	1.9
	2155	0.5		2152	0.3
9 SA	0505	1.7	24 SU	0511	2.0
	1019	0.3		1021	0.1
	1741	1.8		1743	2.1
	2237	0.4		2243	0.2
10 SU	0548	1.8	25 M	0608	2.1
	1059	0.2		1111	0.1
	1819	1.9		1834	2.2
	2318	0.1		● 2331	0.1
11 M	0629	1.9	26 TU	0659	2.2
	1138	0.2		1157	0.0
	1856	2.0		1921	2.3
O	2357	0.2			
12 TU	0708	1.9	27 W	0017	0.1
	1214	0.2		0746	2.2
	1932	2.0		1242	0.1
				2004	2.3
13 W	0032	0.2	28 TH	0101	0.1
	0744	1.9		0831	2.1
	1246	0.2		1324	0.1
	2004	2.0		2045	2.2
14 TH	0103	0.2	29 F	0143	0.2
	0818	1.9		0912	2.0
	1315	0.2		1404	0.3
	2034	1.9		2121	2.0
15 F	0132	0.2	30 SA	0224	0.3
	0848	1.8		0950	1.8
	1344	0.3		1443	0.4
	2100	1.8		2154	1.9
			31 SU	0306	0.4
				1027	1.6
				1524	0.5
				2224	1.7

JUNE

Day	Time	m	Day	Time	m
1 M	0351	0.5	16 TU	0324	0.4
	1106	1.5		1033	1.6
	1608	0.7		1547	0.5
	2300	1.6		2248	1.7
2 TU	0444	0.6	17 W	0420	0.4
	1155	1.4		1127	1.6
	1705	0.8		1648	0.6
	2348	1.4		2346	1.6
3 W	0551	0.7	18 TH	0528	0.5
	1302	1.3		1234	1.5
	1817	0.8		1800	0.6
4 TH	0050	1.4	19 F	0059	1.6
	0702	0.6		0643	0.5
	1421	1.4		1353	1.6
	1928	0.8		1916	0.6
5 F	0205	1.4	20 SA	0222	1.6
	0804	0.6		0757	0.4
	1522	1.5		1510	1.7
	2029	0.7		2028	0.6
6 SA	0315	1.5	21 SU	0339	1.7
	0855	0.5		0900	0.4
	1612	1.6		1619	1.8
	2119	0.6		2131	0.5
7 SU	0414	1.6	22 M	0447	1.8
	0941	0.4		1002	0.3
	1658	1.8		1720	2.0
	2205	0.5		2227	0.4
8 M	0507	1.7	23 TU	0548	1.9
	1023	0.3		1054	0.2
	1742	1.9		1814	2.1
	2247	0.4		2318	0.3
9 TU	0556	1.8	24 W	0643	2.0
	1104	0.3		1145	0.2
	1826	2.0		1904	2.2
	2327	0.3	●		
10 W	0642	1.9	25 TH	0004	0.2
	1143	0.3		0733	2.1
	1907	2.0		1228	0.2
O				1949	2.2
11 TH	0005	0.3	26 F	0049	0.2
	0725	1.9		0818	2.0
	1221	0.2		1309	0.2
	1946	2.0		2030	2.2
12 F	0042	0.3	27 SA	0130	0.2
	0808	1.9		0858	2.0
	1259	0.3		1349	0.2
	2022	2.0		2105	2.1
13 SA	0118	0.2	28 SU	0210	0.2
	0840	1.9		0933	1.8
	1336	0.3		1426	0.3
	2055	1.9		2135	1.9
14 SU	0156	0.3	29 M	0248	0.3
	0914	1.8		1003	1.7
	1415	0.3		1503	0.4
	2127	1.9		2201	1.8
15 M	0238	0.3	30 TU	0327	0.4
	0950	1.7		1032	1.5
	1458	0.4		1540	0.4
	2203	1.8		2230	1.6

JULY

Day	Time	m	Day	Time	m
1 W	0406	0.5	16 TH	0407	0.3
	1108	1.4		1111	1.7
	1619	0.7		1629	0.5
	2307	1.5		2332	1.7
2 TH	0449	0.6	17 F	0505	0.4
	1155	1.3		1206	1.6
	1711	0.7		1731	0.6
	2355	1.4			
3 F	0548	0.6	18 SA	0032	1.6
	1257	1.3		0612	0.5
	1825	0.8		1317	1.6
				1844	0.7
4 SA	0058	1.4	19 SU	0150	1.6
	0659	0.6		0729	0.5
	1410	1.4		1440	1.6
	1939	0.7		2005	0.7
5 SU	0214	1.4	20 M	0315	1.6
	0804	0.6		0845	0.5
	1519	1.5		1557	1.7
	2040	0.7		2118	0.6
6 M	0327	1.5	21 TU	0430	1.7
	0859	0.5		0949	0.4
	1618	1.6		1703	1.9
	2131	0.6		2217	0.5
7 TU	0430	1.6	22 W	0535	1.8
	0948	0.4		1042	0.4
	1710	1.8		1800	2.0
	2217	0.5		2307	0.4
8 W	0527	1.7	23 TH	0631	1.9
	1034	0.3		1129	0.3
	1759	1.9		1851	2.1
	2301	0.4	●	2352	0.3
9 TH	0620	1.8	24 F	0720	2.0
	1118	0.3		1212	0.2
	1847	2.0		1935	2.2
O	2343	0.3			
10 F	0709	1.9	25 SA	0034	0.2
	1202	0.2		0803	2.0
	1932	2.1		1252	0.2
				2014	2.2
11 SA	0025	0.2	26 SU	0113	0.2
	0753	1.9		0840	2.0
	1245	0.2		1330	0.2
	2013	2.1		2046	2.1
12 SU	0107	0.2	27 M	0151	0.2
	0834	1.9		0910	1.9
	1327	0.2		1406	0.2
	2052	2.1		2112	2.0
13 M	0149	0.2	28 TU	0227	0.2
	0911	1.9		0934	1.7
	1409	0.2		1440	0.3
	2128	2.0		2135	1.8
14 TU	0232	0.2	29 W	0259	0.3
	0947	1.8		0959	1.6
	1452	0.3		1509	0.4
	2205	1.9		2202	1.7
15 W	0317	0.2	30 TH	0325	0.4
	1026	1.8		1028	1.5
	1538	0.4		1532	0.5
	2245	1.8		2231	1.5
			31 F	0346	0.5
				1104	1.4
				1559	0.6
				2305	1.4

AUGUST

Day	Time	m	Day	Time	m
1 SA	0419	0.6	16 SU	0008	1.6
	1152	1.3		0545	0.6
	1648	0.7		1245	1.5
	2353	1.3		1819	0.7
2 SU	0516	0.6	17 M	0126	1.5
	1301	1.3		0707	0.6
	1815	0.8		1416	1.5
				1953	0.7
3 M	0110	1.3	18 TU	0303	1.5
	0645	0.7		0835	0.6
	1426	1.4		1544	1.6
	1954	0.7		2114	0.7
4 TU	0242	1.3	19 W	0423	1.6
	0814	0.6		0940	0.6
	1540	1.5		1651	1.8
	2101	0.5		2210	0.5
5 W	0359	1.5	20 TH	0525	1.7
	0918	0.5		1029	0.4
	1641	1.7		1746	1.9
	2152	0.5		2254	0.4
6 TH	0503	1.6	21 F	0617	1.8
	1010	0.4		1111	0.3
	1736	1.9		1833	2.1
	2239	0.4		2334	0.3
7 F	0600	1.8	22 SA	0702	1.9
	1058	0.3		1151	0.2
	1828	2.0		1915	2.1
	2324	0.3	●		
8 SA	0653	1.9	23 SU	0013	0.2
	1144	0.2		0741	2.0
	1916	2.2		1230	0.2
O				1951	2.2
9 SU	0008	0.1	24 M	0051	0.1
	0740	2.0		0815	2.0
	1229	0.1		1307	0.1
	2000	2.2		2021	2.1
10 M	0052	0.1	25 TU	0127	0.1
	0822	2.1		0841	1.9
	1313	0.1		1342	0.2
	2041	2.2		2045	2.0
11 TU	0136	0.1	26 W	0201	0.3
	0900	2.1		0904	1.8
	1355	0.1		1414	0.2
	2119	2.2		2109	1.9
12 W	0219	0.1	27 TH	0228	0.2
	0936	2.0		0927	1.7
	1437	0.1		1438	0.3
	2155	2.1		2134	1.7
13 TH	0302	0.1	28 F	0244	0.3
	1012	1.9		0952	1.6
	1521	0.3		1453	0.4
	2233	1.9		2159	1.6
14 F	0348	0.3	29 SA	0259	0.4
	1051	1.8		1017	1.5
	1608	0.4		1514	0.5
	2315	1.7		2224	1.4
15 SA	0441	0.4	30 SU	0326	0.5
	1140	1.6		1049	1.4
	1705	0.6		1551	0.6
				2300	1.3
			31 M	0411	0.6
				1144	1.3
				1701	0.8

Chart Datum: 0·93 metres below Ordnance Datum (Newlyn)

ENGLAND – PORTLAND

LAT 50°34'N   LONG 2°26'W

TIMES AND HEIGHTS OF HIGH AND LOW WATERS   YEAR **1998**

TIME ZONE (UT)
For Summer Time add ONE hour in non-shaded areas

SEPTEMBER

Day	Time	m	Time	m	Time	m	Time	m
1 TU	0005	1.3	0532	0.7	1320	1.3	1903	0.8
16 W	0303	1.4	0825	0.8	1531	1.6	2109	0.7
2 W	0156	1.3	0733	0.7	1501	1.5	2035	0.7
17 TH	0416	1.6	0925	0.7	1633	1.8	2155	0.6
3 TH	0335	1.4	0853	0.6	1613	1.7	2131	0.5
18 F	0510	1.7	1009	0.6	1723	1.9	2232	0.4
4 F	0444	1.6	0949	0.4	1712	1.9	2219	0.3
19 SA	0555	1.9	1015	0.3	1807	2.0	2308	0.3
5 SA	0541	1.8	1038	0.3	1805	2.1	2304	0.2
20 SU	0636	2.0	1124	0.3	1847	2.1	2345 ●	0.2
6 SU	0633	2.0	1124	0.1	1855	2.3	2349 O	0.1
21 M	0712	2.0	1202	0.2	1921	2.1		
7 M	0720	2.2	1209	0.0	1941	2.4		
22 TU	0022	0.1	0743	2.1	1240	0.2	1949	2.1
8 TU	0033	0.0	0802	2.2	1253	0.0	2022	2.4
23 W	0058	0.1	0809	2.0	1315	0.2	2015	2.0
9 W	0116	0.0	0841	2.2	1335	0.0	2101	2.3
24 TH	0130	0.2	0833	1.9	1346	0.2	2041	1.9
10 TH	0159	0.0	0917	2.1	1417	0.1	2138	2.2
25 F	0154	0.3	0857	1.8	1407	0.2	2106	1.8
11 F	0241	0.1	0952	2.0	1500	0.2	2215	2.0
26 SA	0207	0.4	0919	1.7	1421	0.4	2130	1.6
12 SA	0325	0.3	1030	1.8	1546	0.4	2257	1.7
27 SU	0222	0.4	0939	1.6	1441	0.5	2154	1.5
13 SU	0414	0.5	1115	1.7	1643	0.6	2349	1.5
28 M	0245	0.5	1007	1.5	1513	0.6	2229	1.4
14 M	0518	0.7	1217	1.5	1803	0.8		
29 TU	0322	0.6	1053	1.4	1614	0.7	2330	1.3
15 TU	0115	1.4	0647	0.8	1400	1.5	1954	0.8
30 W	0434	0.8	1212	1.4	1823	0.8		

OCTOBER

Day	Time	m	Time	m	Time	m	Time	m
1 TH	0117	1.3	0659	0.8	1414	1.5	2007	0.7
16 F	0356	1.6	0900	0.8	1603	1.7	2127	0.6
2 F	0312	1.4	0829	0.7	1541	1.7	2106	0.5
17 SA	0443	1.7	0940	0.7	1650	1.8	2200	0.5
3 SA	0422	1.7	0926	0.5	1643	1.9	2154	0.3
18 SU	0524	1.9	1016	0.5	1732	1.9	2235	0.3
4 SU	0517	1.9	1015	0.3	1738	2.1	2240	0.1
19 M	0602	2.0	1054	0.4	1810	2.0	2312	0.2
5 M	0608	2.1	1101	0.2	1828	2.3	2325 O	0.0
20 TU	0637	2.1	1132	0.3	1844	2.1	2349 ●	0.2
6 TU	0654	2.3	1146	0.1	1915	2.4		
21 W	0708	2.1	1210	0.3	1915	2.1		
7 W	0010	-0.1	0737	2.4	1231	0.0	1958	2.4
22 TH	0024	0.2	0736	2.1	1246	0.3	1945	2.0
8 TH	0053	0.0	0817	2.4	1313	0.0	2039	2.3
23 F	0056	0.2	0804	2.1	1316	0.3	2015	1.9
9 F	0136	0.0	0855	2.3	1356	0.1	2118	2.2
24 SA	0120	0.3	0830	2.0	1338	0.4	2042	1.8
10 SA	0217	0.2	0931	2.1	1438	0.3	2157	2.0
25 SU	0138	0.4	0853	1.8	1357	0.4	2107	1.7
11 SU	0259	0.4	1009	1.9	1524	0.5	2240	1.7
26 M	0157	0.5	0914	1.7	1420	0.5	2134	1.5
12 M	0346	0.6	1051	1.7	1622	0.7	2335	1.5
27 TU	0220	0.6	0941	1.6	1453	0.6	2212	1.4
13 TU	0446	0.8	1148	1.6	1743	0.8		
28 W	0256	0.7	1023	1.5	1552	0.7	2311	1.3
14 W	0110	1.4	0613	0.9	1336	1.5	1941	0.8
29 TH	0400	0.8	1133	1.5	1748	0.8		
15 TH	0252	1.5	0801	0.9	1505	1.6	2049	0.7
30 F	0046	1.3	0623	0.9	1322	1.5	1929	0.7
31 SA	0240	1.5	0757	0.8	1502	1.7	2034	0.5

NOVEMBER

Day	Time	m	Time	m	Time	m	Time	m
1 SU	0352	1.7	0859	0.6	1610	1.9	2126	0.3
16 M	0446	1.8	0941	0.6	1648	1.8	2158	0.4
2 M	0448	2.0	0950	0.4	1707	2.1	2214	0.2
17 TU	0522	1.9	1021	0.5	1727	1.9	2236	0.3
3 TU	0539	2.2	1038	0.3	1800	2.2	2301	0.1
18 W	0558	2.0	1101	0.4	1805	1.9	2315	0.3
4 W	0627	2.3	1124	0.2	1850	2.3	2346 O	0.0
19 TH	0632	2.1	1140	0.4	1843	1.9	2351 ●	0.3
5 TH	0712	2.4	1208	0.1	1936	2.4		
20 F	0706	2.1	1216	0.3	1920	2.0		
6 F	0030	0.3	0754	2.4	1253	0.1	2019	2.3
21 SA	0024	0.3	0739	2.1	1248	0.4	1954	1.9
7 SA	0113	0.1	0834	2.3	1336	0.2	2101	2.1
22 SU	0053	0.3	0810	2.0	1315	0.4	2025	1.8
8 SU	0155	0.3	0912	2.2	1419	0.4	2142	1.9
23 M	0119	0.4	0837	1.9	1342	0.4	2053	1.7
9 M	0236	0.5	0949	2.0	1506	0.5	2225	1.7
24 TU	0146	0.5	0902	1.8	1412	0.5	2124	1.6
10 TU	0320	0.7	1028	1.8	1600	0.7	2317	1.5
25 W	0216	0.6	0932	1.7	1451	0.6	2203	1.5
11 W	0413	0.8	1115	1.6	1710	0.8		
26 TH	0255	0.7	1013	1.6	1548	0.6	2258	1.4
12 TH	0039	1.4	0941	1.0	1230	1.5	1838	0.8
27 F	0358	0.8	1113	1.6	1715	0.7		
13 F	0215	1.4	0656	1.0	1415	1.5	1957	0.7
28 SA	0016	1.4	0542	0.8	1240	1.6	1844	0.6
14 SA	0320	1.5	0813	0.9	1519	1.6	2042	0.6
29 SU	0153	1.5	0715	0.8	1418	1.6	1955	0.5
15 SU	0406	1.7	0900	0.8	1606	1.7	2119	0.5
30 M	0313	1.7	0825	0.7	1534	1.8	2055	0.4

DECEMBER

Day	Time	m	Time	m	Time	m	Time	m
1 TU	0416	1.9	0923	0.5	1638	2.0	2148	0.3
16 W	0439	1.8	0949	0.6	1644	1.7	2202	0.4
2 W	0511	2.1	1015	0.4	1735	2.1	2238	0.2
17 TH	0520	1.9	1032	0.5	1731	1.8	2243	0.4
3 TH	0602	2.2	1104	0.3	1828	2.2	2326 O	0.1
18 F	0602	2.0	1112	0.4	1817	1.9	2322 ●	0.4
4 F	0650	2.3	1151	0.2	1918	2.2		
19 SA	0642	2.1	1150	0.4	1900	1.9	2359	0.3
5 SA	0011	0.1	0735	2.4	1237	0.2	2004	2.2
20 SU	0722	2.1	1225	0.4	1940	1.9		
6 SU	0056	0.2	0818	2.3	1321	0.3	2048	2.1
21 M	0035	0.3	0758	2.1	1300	0.3	2017	1.9
7 M	0138	0.3	0858	2.2	1405	0.3	2129	1.9
22 TU	0111	0.3	0831	2.0	1335	0.4	2050	1.8
8 TU	0218	0.4	0934	2.0	1449	0.5	2208	1.7
23 W	0146	0.4	0902	1.9	1412	0.4	2122	1.7
9 W	0259	0.6	1007	1.8	1536	0.6	2248	1.6
24 TH	0223	0.4	0935	1.8	1453	0.4	2159	1.6
10 TH	0343	0.7	1042	1.7	1629	0.7	2336	1.4
25 F	0304	0.5	1014	1.7	1542	0.5	2246	1.6
11 F	0438	0.9	1127	1.6	1733	0.7		
26 SA	0356	0.6	1104	1.6	1646	0.5	2346	1.5
12 SA	0042	1.4	0548	0.9	1227	1.5	1841	0.7
27 SU	0507	0.7	1210	1.6	1801	0.5		
13 SU	0208	1.4	0705	0.9	1342	1.5	1943	0.7
28 M	0101	1.5	0629	0.7	1332	1.6	1916	0.5
14 M	0310	1.5	0811	0.8	1456	1.5	2034	0.6
29 TU	0227	1.6	0748	0.7	1457	1.7	2024	0.5
15 TU	0357	1.6	0903	0.7	1553	1.6	2119	0.4
30 W	0342	1.8	0857	0.6	1611	1.8	2126	0.4
31 TH	0446	1.9	0958	0.5	1715	1.9	2221	0.3

Chart Datum: 0·93 metres below Ordnance Datum (Newlyn)

WEYMOUTH   10-2-10

Dorset 50°36'·54N 02°26'·50W   Rtg 2-2-1

CHARTS

AC *2172*, 2268, 2255, *2610*; Imray C4, C5; Stanfords 12; OS 194

TIDES

–0438 Dover; ML 1·1; Zone 0 (UT)

Standard Port PORTLAND (←—)

Predictions for Weymouth are as for Portland. Mean ranges are small: 0·6m at np and 2·0m at sp.
NOTE: Double LWs occur; predictions are for first LW. A LW stand lasts about 4 hrs at sp and 1 hr at nps.
Due to an eddy, the tidal stream in Weymouth Roads is W-going at all times except HW –0510 to HW –0310.

SHELTER

Good, but swell enters outer hbr and The Cove in strong E winds. Berthing options from seaward:
In The Cove on pontoon S side or on the N side (Custom House Quay) off RDYC. Pontoons also line part of the N side; fender boards are available elsewhere. In season rafting-up is the rule. (The quays between The Cove and the lifting bridge are reserved for FVs).
The municipal pontoons just beyond the lifting bridge (see NAVIGATION) are for residents only; no visitors.
N of these Weymouth Marina, dredged 2·5m, offers very good shelter. 85 more berths were added in March 1997, bringing current total to 185.
It is feasible to ‡ in Weymouth Bay, NE of hbr ent in about 3m, but necessarily some way offshore due to the drying sands and buoyed watersport areas inshore. See also 10.2.9 for possible ‡ in Portland Harbour.

NAVIGATION

WPT 50°36'·68N, 02°26'·10W 060°/240° from/to front ldg lt, 0·50M. The hbr ent lies deep in the NW corner of Weymouth Bay; it could in some conditions be confused with the N ent to Portland Hbr. Hbr speed limit is ‘Dead Slow’. Comply with IPTS.
The **bridge** lifts (LT) 0800, 1000, 1200, 1400, 1600, 1800 on request throughout the year. Later lifts are at 1930 Apr & Sept; 2030 May & Aug; 2000 and 2130 Jun & Jul). Five mins before lift times, craft should be visible to, and in contact on VHF Ch 12 with, the bridge. A waiting pontoon is on S side, close E of bridge. Oct to Mar, 12 hour's notice is required for the 0800 lift, and 1 hour's notice for other lifts.
Clearances when the bridge is down are approx 2·7m MHWS, 3·8m MHWN, 4·6m MLWN, 5·2m MLWS.

In winter many fishing factory ships are often at ‡ in the NE part of Weymouth Bay.
NOTE: If heading E, check Lulworth firing programme; see overleaf and Supplements for current dates.

LIGHTS AND MARKS

Conspic ch spire, 6ca NNW of hbr ent, is a useful day mark to help find the ent when approaching from SE past the Portland bkwtrs or from the E.
Portland ‘A’ Head lt ho, Fl 10s 22m 20M, is 1·7M SE of hbr ent and provides the best initial guidance at night; it is also a conspic W tr. Pierhead lts are hard to see against shore lts. Ldg lts 240°, 2 FR (H24), are 500m inside the pierhds; daymarks (same position) are R open ◊s on W poles; they are not visible until the hbr ent is opened.
IPTS must be obeyed. They are shown from a RW mast near the root of the S pier. There is one additional signal:
      2 Ⓡ over 1 Ⓖ = Ent and dep prohib (ent obstructed).
If no sigs are shown, vessels are clear to enter or leave with caution. Sigs are not too easy to see, by day/night.

RADIO TELEPHONE

Weymouth Harbour VHF Ch 12 16 (0800-2000 in summer and when vessel due); *Weymouth Town Bridge* also on 12. *Weymouth Marina* Ch 80. Ch 06 *Raybar* for diesel.

TELEPHONE (Dial code 01305)

Hr Mr 206278/206423, ☎ 760971; Bridge 206426/789357; Marina 767576; MRSC 760439; Marinecall 0891 500457; ⌗ 0345 231110 (H24); Police 251212; Ⓗ 772211.

FACILITIES

Marina ☎ 767576, ⊗ 767575; (185 inc Ⓥ; 237 berths when complete) £15.03 (£5 for <5 hrs), FW, AC;
Hbr and The Cove AB £11.50 (£4 for <4 hrs), M, Slip near WSC, FW;
Custom House Quay FW, AB, AC (not on S side), showers (free);
Royal Dorset YC ☎ 786258, M, Bar; **Weymouth SC** ☎ 785481, M, Bar;
Services: CH, Sh, ACA, Gaz, Rigging, Slip, ME, Ⓔ, EI, CH. D (Wyatt's Wharf pontoon on S bank, close W of LB; ☎ 787039, mobile 0378 570228); also D from road tanker on N side, daily 0700-1900, min quantity 25ltrs; ☎ 775465 or mobile 0860 912401 or call *Raybar* VHF Ch 06.
Town EC Wed; P & D (cans), FW, ▣, V, R, Bar, ✉, Ⓑ, ⇌, ✈ (Bournemouth).

ANCHORAGES AND RANGES EAST OF WEYMOUTH

LULWORTH COVE, Dorset, 50°36'·97N 02°14'·74W. AC *2172.* HW −0449 on Dover, see 10.2.8 Tides; ML 1·2m. Good shelter in fair weather and offshore winds, but heavy swell enters the cove in S and SW winds; if strong the ⚓ becomes untenable. Enter the cove slightly E of centre. There is a YB buoy for the range safety launch in the middle of the cove in about 4m CD. ⚓ in NE part in 2·5m. Holding is poor. 8kn speed limit. Local moorings, village and slip are on W side. Facilities: EC Wed/Sat; FW at tap in car park, Bar, ✉, R, Slip.

LULWORTH FIRING RANGES. These comprise an Inner and an Outer Sea Danger area, the former of most concern to yachts. Its limits, from Lulworth (50°36'·93N 02°14'·36W) coastwise to Kimmeridge Bay (50°36'·70N 02°08'·15W) thence clockwise to seaward, are: 50°36'·26N 02°08'·15W - 50°34'·20N 02°03'·15W - 50°33'·13N 02°06'·30W - 50°31'·60N 02°12'·20W - 50°31'·90N 02°16'·40W - 50°35'·56N 02°16'·11W - Lulworth. See AC 2610.
The Inner area extends 5·5M offshore and is used by the army as shown below. The Outer area extends to 12M; it is never active at night and rarely at weekends.
Warships may use the Inner & Outer areas, firing E'ward from Adamant Shoal (approx 02°19'W) at the 3 DZ target buoys, (up to 3M SW of St Alban's Head) which should be avoided by at least 1M. Warships fly R flags and other vessels/helicopters may patrol the area.
Army firing on the Inner range occurs most weekdays from 0930-1700 (1200 on Fri), often on Tues and Thurs nights for 3-4 hrs and for up to six weekends per year. There is NO firing in August. When firing is in progress R flags (Fl R lts at night) are flown from St Alban's Head and Bindon Hill. However, further inland, some R flags fly whether or not firing is taking place; these mark the boundary of the range Land Area. VHF Ch 08 is monitored by Range Control and the Range safety boats.
Times of firing are printed in local papers, sent to local Hr Mrs and YCs and are obtainable from the Range Officer ☎ (01929) 462721 ext. 4700/4859, 🕿 4912, during office hours and at other times from the guardroom ext 4819. Firing times are broadcast daily by: Radio Solent (221m/1359kHz, 300m/999kHz or 96·1MHz FM (see 10·2·18); Dorset FM 103.8MHz; and by 2 Counties Radio (362m/828kHz or 97.2MHz). Times can also be obtained from Portland CG (Ch 16) or Range Safety Boats (Ch 08). The annual firing weekends and No Firing periods are printed in the updating Supplements to this Almanac.
All the Land Area and the Inner Sea Danger Area (D026 Inner) are subject to the regulations laid down in *The Lulworth Ranges Byelaws 1978 operative from 10 Nov 1978 - Statutory Instruments 1978 No 1663.* A copy may be obtained from HMSO. A key passage states: *The Byelaws shall not apply to any vessel in the ordinary course of navigation, not being used for fishing, in the Sea Area and remaining in the Sea Area no longer than is reasonably necessary to pass through the Sea Area.*
Nevertheless yachts should make every reasonable effort to keep clear when firing is in progress. If on passage between Weymouth and Anvil Point, a track via 50°30'N 02°10'W will clear the S boundary of the Inner range and St Alban's Race, and is only 3·3M longer than a direct trk.

WORBARROW BAY, Dorset, 50°37'·00N 02°12'·00W. AC *2172.* Tides as Lulworth Cove/Mupe Bay, see 10.2.8. Worbarrow is a 1½M wide bay, close E of Lulworth Cove. It is easily identified from seaward by the V-shaped gap in the hills at Arish Mell, centre of bay just E of Bindon Hill. Bindon Hill also has a conspic white chalk scar due to cliff falls. Caution: Mupe Rks at W end and other rks 1ca off NW side. ⚓s in about 3m sheltered from W or E winds at appropriate end. The bay lies within Lulworth Ranges (see above); landing prohib at Arish Mell. No lights/facilities.

CHAPMAN'S POOL, Dorset, 50°35'·50N 02°03'·85W. AC *2172.* Tidal data is approx that for Swanage (10. 2.11). Chapman's Pool, like Worbarrow Bay, Brandy Bay and Kimmeridge Bay, is picturesque and convenient when the wind is off-shore. ⚓ in depths of about 3m in centre of bay to avoid tidal swirl, but beware large unlit B buoy (for Range Safety boat). From here to St Alban's Hd the stream runs SSE almost continuously due to a back eddy. There are no lights and no facilities.

SWANAGE   10-2-11

Dorset 50°36'·42N 01°56'·97W   Rtg 2-4-2

CHARTS
AC *2172, 2610,* 2175; Imray C4; Stanfords 12, 15; OS 195
TIDES
HW Sp−0235 & +0125, Np −0515 & +0120 on Dover; ML 1·5

Standard Port PORTSMOUTH (→)

Times				Height (metres)			
High Water		Low Water		MHWS	MHWN	MLWN	MLWS
0000	0600	0500	1100	4·7	3·8	1·9	0·8
1200	1800	1700	2300				
Differences SWANAGE							
−0250	+0105	−0105	−0105	−2·7	−2·2	−0·7	−0·3
POOLE HARBOUR ENTRANCE							
−0240	+0105	−0100	−0030	−2·7	−2·2	−0·7	−0·3

NOTE: Double HWs occur except at nps and predictions are for the higher HW. Near nps there is a stand, and the predictions shown are for the middle of the stand. See 10·2·12.

SHELTER
Good ⚓ in winds from SW to N, but bad in E/SE winds >F4 due to swell which may persist for 6 hrs after a blow. >F6 holding gets very difficult; Poole is nearest safe haven. Pier (open Apr-Oct) has been repaired; temp'y AB for FW, L.

NAVIGATION
WPT 50°36'·70N 01°56'·50W, 054°/234° from/to pier hd, 0·30M. Coming from S beware Peveril Ledge and its Race which can be vicious with a SW wind against the main ebb. It is best to keep 1M seaward of Durlston Head and Peveril Point. On the W side of Swanage B, keep clear of Tanville and Phippards Ledges, approx 300m offshore. To the S of the pier are the ruins of an old pier.
LIGHTS AND MARKS
The only lts are 2 FR (vert) on the pier; difficult to see due to confusing street lts. Peveril Ledge PHM buoy is unlit and hard to pick out at night due to Anvil Pt lt; keep 0·5M clear of it to the E.
RADIO TELEPHONE
None.
TELEPHONE (Dial code 01929)
MRSC (01305) 760439; ⌗ 0345 231110 (H24); Marinecall 0891 500457; Police 422004; Dr 422231; Ⓗ 422282.
FACILITIES
Pier, L, FW, AB £4 (HW only), pier access after 2100 via **Swanage SC ☎** 422987, Slip, L, FW, Bar, land access to pier after 2100; **Boat Park** (Peveril Pt), Slip, FW, L;
Services: Diving. **Town** P & D (cans, 1½M), FW, V, R, Bar, ✉, Ⓑ, ≷ (mainline connection in season), ✈ (Hurn).

SPECIAL TIDAL PROBLEMS BETWEEN SWANAGE AND SELSEY   10-2-12

Due to the complex tidal variations between Swanage and Selsey/Nab Twr, applying the usual secondary port time & height differences gives only approximate predictions. More accurate values are obtained by using the individual curves discussed below.

Individual curves, as shown on the following two pages, are given for each port to cater for the rapidly changing tidal characteristics and distorted tidal curves in this area. Because their low water (LW) points are more sharply defined than high water (HW), the times on these curves are referenced to LW, but in all other respects they are used as described in Chapter 9.

Critical curve. Since the curves at ports between Swanage and Yarmouth, IOW differ considerably in shape and duration between Springs and Neaps, the tide cannot adequately be defined by only Sp and Np curves. A third, "critical", curve is therefore shown for that Portsmouth range (as indicated in the lower right of the graph) at which the heights of the two HWs are equal for the port concerned. Interpolation should be between this critical curve and either the Sp or Np curve, as appropriate.

Note that whilst the critical curve extends throughout the tidal cycle, the spring and neap curves stop at the higher HW. Thus, for example, at 7hrs after LW Lymington, with a Portsmouth range of 3·8m (near Sp), the factor should be referenced to the next LW; whereas if the Portsmouth range had been 2·0m (near Np), it should be referenced to the previous LW.

The procedure is shown step-by-step in the following example using the **Differences SWANAGE** below and the special curves for Swanage, Poole (Ent) and Bournemouth re-printed at the foot of this page for convenience.

Example: To find the height of tide at Swanage at 0200 on a day when the tidal predictions for Portsmouth are:

19 0100 4·6
M 0613 1·1
1314 4·5
1833 0·8

Standard Port PORTSMOUTH (→)

Times				Height (metres)			
High Water		Low Water		MHWS	MHWN	MLWN	MLWS
0000	0600	0500	1100	4·7	3·8	1·9	0·8
1200	1800	1700	2300				
Differences SWANAGE							
–0250	+0105	–0105	–0105	–2·7	–2·2	–0·7	–0·3

Note: Double HWs occur, except at nps, at ports between Swanage and Christchurch. HW height differences, as given for each secondary port, always apply to the higher HW (that which reaches a factor of 1·0 on the curves). This higher HW should be used to obtain the range at the Secondary Port. HW time differences, which are not needed for this example, also refer to the higher HW.

(1) Complete the upper part of the tidal prediction form (next Col), omitting the HW time column (boxes 1, 5 & 9).
(2) On the left of the Swanage tidal curve diagram, plot the Secondary Port HW and LW heights (1·9m and 0·7m from (1) above), and join these points with a sloping line.

TIDAL PREDICTION FORM   Time or height required *0200*

		TIME		HEIGHT	
		HW	LW	HW	LW
Standard Port *Portsmouth*	1		2 *0613*	3 *4·6*	*1·1*
Differences	5		6 *–015*	7 *–2·7*	8 *–0·4*
Secondary Port *Swanage*	9		10 *0508*	11 *1·9*	12 *0·7*
Duration (or time fromHW to LW)	13		9-10 or 10-9	Range 14 Stand. Port *3·5*	3-4
				Range 15 Secdy. Port *1·2*	11-12

*Springs/Neaps/Interpolate

Start: height at given time	10 17-16	Time reqd.	16 *0200*	17+18
		Time of LW	17 *0508*	10
		Interval	18 *–0308*	Date *19th Nov*
		Factor	19 *0·84*	Time Zone *0(GMT)*
19 x 15		Rise above LW	20 *1·0*	22-21
12		Height of LW	21 *0·7*	12
20 + 21		Height reqd.	22 *1·7*	

Start: time for given height

*Delete as necessary

(3) The time required (0200) is 3hr 8min before the time of LW at the Secondary Port, so from this point draw a line vertically up towards the curves.
(4) It is necessary to interpolate for the day's range at Portsmouth (3·5m), which is about mid-way between the spring curve (3·9m) and the critical curve (2·8m). (This incidentally gives a point level with a factor of 0·84.)
(5) From this point draw a horizontal line to intersect the sloping line constructed in (2) above.
(6) From the intersection of the horizontal line and the sloping line, proceed vertically to the height scale at the top, and read off the height required, 1·7m.

The Factor method of doing the calculation, instead of the graphical method just described, is shown in the lower part of the completed tidal prediction form. The procedure follows that given in 9·4·3. Note that box 17 is amended to read 'Time of LW'.

The Table at the end of this section offers a less accurate but quicker method of finding intermediate heights of tide for certain places between Swanage and Nab Tower. It is reproduced from earlier Admiralty Tide Tables. It is useful to note that the green tinted area represents the period during which the tide stands or in which a second HW may occur. Note also that the upper of the three HW and LW height figures given is for mean spring tides, the middle for average tides and the lower for mean neap tides.

To use this table, determine whether the time required is nearer to HW or LW at Portsmouth; work out the interval (between time required and the nearest HW or LW at Portsmouth). Extract the height of the relevant predicted HW or LW. By interpolation between the heights of HW (left hand column) or LW (right hand column), read off the height of tide under the appropriate column (hours before/after HW or hours before/after LW).

TIDAL CURVES – SWANAGE TO SELSEY

Individual tidal curves for places between Swanage and Selsey are given below, and their use is explained above. In this area the times of LW are defined much more sharply than the times of HW, and the curves are therefore drawn with their times related to LW instead of HW. Apart from referencing the times to LW, the procedure for obtaining intermediate times and heights of tide with these curves is the same as for normal Secondary Ports (see 9·4·2). For places between Swanage and Yarmouth IOW a third curve is shown, for the range at Portsmouth at which the two HWs are equal at the port concerned; for interpolation between the curves see the previous page.

Note 1.* Due to the constriction of the R Medina, Newport requires special treatment since the hbr dries 1·4m. The calculation should be made using the LW time and height differences for Cowes, and the HW height differences for Newport. Any calculated heights which fall below 1·4m should be treated as 1·4m.

Note 2.* *** Wareham and Tuckton LWs do not fall below 0·7m except under very low river flow conditions.

H.W.Hts at Secondary Port

Swanage
Poole (Entrance)
Bournemouth

Range at Portsmouth
Sp ———— 3.9 m
--------- 2.8 m
Np – – – – 1.9 m

Poole (Town Quay)
(Pottery Pier)
(R.Frome,Wareham)***
(Cleavel Point)

Range at Portsmouth
Sp ———— 3.9 m
--------- 3.0 m
Np – – – – 1.9 m

Tuckton ***
Christchurch Ent

Range at Portsmouth
Sp ———— 3.9 m
--------- 2.6 m
Np – – – – 1.9 m

Lymington
Yarmouth

Range at Portsmouth
Sp ———— 3.9 m
--------- 3.1 m
Np – – – – 1.9 m

TIDAL CURVES *continued*

H.W.Hts at Secondary Ports

INTERMEDIATE HEIGHTS OF TIDE: SWANAGE TO NAB TOWER

(To be used for finding intermediate heights in metres for places named)

Place	Height of H.W. at Portsmouth	Hours before or after HIGH WATER AT PORTSMOUTH							Hours before or after LOW WATER AT PORTSMOUTH						Height of L.W. at Portsmouth
	m.	-3	-2	-1	HW	+1	+2	+3	-2	-1	LW	+1	+2	+3	m.
		m.	m.	m.	m.	m.	m.	m.	m.	m.	m.	m.	m.	m.	m.
SWANAGE	4·7	1·9	1·8	1·5	1·3	1·4	1·2	0·8	0·6	0·3	0·8	1·3	1·7	1·8	0·6
	4·3	1·6	1·6	1·5	1·5	1·2	1·4	1·1	0·9	0·8	1·0	1·3	1·5	1·6	1·2
	3·8	1·5	1·5	1·5	1·5	1·6	1·5	1·3	1·2	1·1	1·2	1·3	1·4	1·4	1·8
POOLE ENTRANCE	4·7	2·0	1·9	1·6	1·4	1·5	1·4	0·9	0·7	0·3	0·8	1·3	1·6	1·9	0·6
	4·3	1·6	1·6	1·5	1·5	1·5	1·5	1·1	1·0	0·8	0·9	1·2	1·5	1·6	1·2
	3·8	1·4	1·5	1·5	1·5	1·6	1·5	1·3	1·2	1·1	1·1	1·2	1·3	1·4	1·8
POOLE BRIDGE	4·7	2·2	2·2	1·9	1·6	1·6	1·7	1·3	1·1	0·6	0·5	1·0	1·6	1·9	0·6
	4·3	1·8	1·7	1·6	1·7	1·8	1·8	1·5	1·4	1·0	0·8	1·1	1·5	1·7	1·2
	3·8	1·5	1·5	1·6	1·7	1·8	1·8	1·5	1·5	1·3	1·2	1·3	1·5	1·5	1·8
BOURNE-MOUTH	4·7	2·1	2·0	1·7	1·5	1·5	1·5	0·9	0·7	0·3	0·6	1·2	1·7	1·9	0·6
	4·3	1·6	1·7	1·6	1·6	1·6	1·5	1·2	1·0	0·8	0·8	1·2	1·4	1·5	1·2
	3·8	1·5	1·5	1·5	1·5	1·6	1·5	1·4	1·3	1·1	1·1	1·2	1·3	1·4	1·8
CHRIST-CHURCH HARBOUR †	4·7	1·8	1·8	1·5	1·3	1·5	1·1	0·7	0·7	0·5	0·4	0·9	1·3	1·6	0·6
	4·3	1·5	1·5	1·4	1·5	1·5	1·2	0·9	0·8	0·6	0·6	1·0	1·2	1·4	1·2
	3·8	1·2	1·2	1·3	1·4	1·4	1·1	0·9	0·8	0·6	0·7	0·9	1·0	1·1	1·8
FRESHWATER BAY	4·7	2·4	2·5	2·4	2·2	2·2	1·9	1·1	0·9	0·5	0·8	1·5	2·0	2·2	0·6
	4·3	2·2	2·3	2·2	2·2	2·2	1·9	1·4	1·2	0·9	1·1	1·5	1·8	2·0	1·2
	3·8	1·9	2·0	2·2	2·2	2·2	2·0	1·6	1·6	1·3	1·3	1·6	1·7	1·8	1·8
TOTLAND BAY	4·7	2·3	2·5	2·4	2·3	2·3	2·1	1·4	1·1	0·5	0·8	1·4	1·8	2·1	0·6
	4·3	2·1	2·3	2·3	2·3	2·2	2·1	1·6	1·4	0·9	1·1	1·4	1·7	1·9	1·2
	3·8	2·0	2·1	2·3	2·3	2·2	2·1	1·8	1·7	1·4	1·4	1·6	1·8	1·8	1·8
HURST POINT	4·7	2·3	2·6	2·7	2·5	2·5	2·3	1·6	1·2	0·5	0·7	1·3	1·7	2·0	0·6
	4·3	2·0	2·3	2·5	2·5	2·4	2·3	1·7	1·5	1·1	1·0	1·4	1·7	1·9	1·2
	3·8	1·9	2·1	2·3	2·3	2·3	2·2	1·8	1·7	1·4	1·3	1·5	1·7	1·8	1·8
YARMOUTH I.O.W	4·7	2·4	2·8	3·0	2·8	2·8	2·7	1·8	1·5	0·7	0·8	1·4	1·8	1·8	0·6
	4·3	2·2	2·5	2·7	2·7	2·7	2·6	1·9	1·6	1·1	1·2	1·6	1·8	2·0	1·2
	3·8	2·0	2·3	2·5	2·5	2·5	2·3	1·9	1·7	1·5	1·5	1·6	1·7	1·8	1·8
LYMINGTON	4·7	2·2	2·6	3·0	2·8	2·9	2·8	2·1	1·7	0·7	0·5	1·1	1·6	1·9	0·6
	4·3	2·0	2·3	2·7	2·7	2·7	2·6	2·1	1·8	1·1	1·0	1·3	1·6	1·7	1·2
	3·8	1·9	2·2	2·4	2·5	2·5	2·4	2·0	1·8	1·5	1·4	1·5	1·6	1·7	1·8
SOLENT BANKS	4·7	2·4	2·9	3·4	3·3	3·2	3·0	2·2	1·8	0·7	0·6	1·2	1·8	2·0	0·6
	4·3	2·2	2·6	3·0	3·1	3·0	2·9	2·2	1·9	1·2	1·1	1·4	1·6	1·9	1·2
	3·8	2·1	2·3	2·6	2·7	2·7	2·6	2·2	2·0	1·6	1·5	1·7	1·9	2·0	1·6
COWES ROAD	4·7	2·5	3·4	4·1	4·2	4·1	3·8	3·0	2·5	1·1	0·6	1·2	1·8	2·1	0·6
	4·3	2·4	3·1	3·7	3·8	3·7	3·5	2·8	2·6	1·5	1·2	1·5	1·8	2·1	1·2
	3·8	2·5	3·0	3·3	3·4	3·4	3·2	2·7	2·5	2·0	1·7	1·9	2·0	2·2	1·8
CALSHOT CASTLE	4·7	2·6	3·6	4·3	4·4	4·3	4·1	3·2	2·6	1·2	0·7	1·3	1·9	2·2	0·6
	4·3	2·6	3·3	3·8	3·0	4·0	3·7	3·0	2·6	1·6	1·2	1·6	2·0	2·2	1·2
	3·8	2·7	3·2	3·5	3·6	3·6	3·4	2·8	2·6	2·0	1·9	2·0	2·2	2·3	1·8
LEE-ON-SOLENT	4·7	2·7	3·6	4·4	4·5	4·4	4·2	3·1	2·5	1·1	0·6	1·2	1·8	2·1	0·6
	4·3	2·7	3·4	3·9	4·1	4·0	3·7	2·9	2·5	1·4	1·2	1·6	2·0	2·2	1·2
	3·8	2·7	3·2	3·6	3·7	3·6	3·3	2·8	2·6	2·1	1·9	2·0	2·2	2·4	1·8
RYDE	4·7	2·7	3·7	4·3	4·5	4·3	4·0	2·9	2·4	1·1	0·7	1·2	1·8	2·1	0·6
	4·3	2·7	3·4	4·0	4·1	4·0	3·7	2·9	2·6	1·6	1·3	1·6	1·9	2·2	1·2
	3·8	2·7	3·2	3·6	3·7	3·6	3·4	2·9	2·7	2·1	1·9	2·0	2·2	2·4	1·8
NAB TOWER	4·7	2·9	3·8	4·4	4·5	4·3	3·6	2·4	2·0	0·9	0·6	1·0	1·5	2·1	0·6
	4·3	2·9	3·6	4·1	4·2	4·0	3·4	2·5	2·2	1·4	1·2	1·4	1·8	2·2	1·2
	3·8	2·9	3·3	3·7	3·7	3·6	3·1	2·6	2·3	1·9	1·7	1·8	2·1	2·4	1·8
SANDOWN	4·7	2·6	3·3	3·8	4·0	3·8	3·3	2·1	1·7	0·8	0·6	1·0	1·5	1·9	0·6
	4·3	2·6	3·0	3·5	3·6	3·5	3·1	2·2	1·9	1·3	1·1	1·4	1·7	2·0	1·2
	3·8	2·6	2·9	3·2	3·3	3·1	2·8	2·3	2·1	1·8	1·6	1·7	1·9	2·2	1·8
VENTNOR	4·7	2·8	3·3	3·7	3·8	3·5	2·9	2·0	1·7	1·0	0·9	1·3	1·7	2·1	0·6
	4·3	2·6	3·1	3·4	3·4	3·2	2·8	2·1	1·9	1·4	1·3	1·6	1·9	2·2	1·2
	3·8	2·5	2·8	3·1	3·1	3·0	2·8	2·3	2·2	1·8	1·7	1·9	2·1	2·3	1·8

Note–The green tinted area represents the period during which the tide stands, or during which a second high water may occur.
† Heights at Christchurch are for inside the bar; outside the bar, L.W. falls about 0·6 metres lower at Springs.

HEIGHTS OF TIDE AT POOLE (TOWN QUAY)

The four curves below are an alternative to those shown in 10.2.12. They derive from Reeds Nautical Almanac where they found favour, but their accuracy (as with many things tidal) should be treated as approximate. They enable a speedy estimate to be made of the Height of Tide at hourly intervals after the time of the preceding LW at Poole (Town Quay). The curves are drawn for LW heights of 0·3, 0·6 (MLWS), 0·9 and 1·2 metres (MLWN) above Chart Datum. The small range of tide (neaps 0·4m; springs 1·5m) is immediately apparent, as are the HW stand at neaps and the double HWs at springs.

Note: All references are to LW because at Poole (and at other ports between Swanage and Selsey; see 10.2.12) the times and heights of LW are more sharply defined than those of HW. HW times & heights are complicated by a stand of tide at HW at neaps and by double HWs at springs. The times of 1st and 2nd HWs cannot therefore be readily predicted with any accuracy.

Procedure:
1. Extract time and height of the preceding LW from the Poole tidal predictions (→).
2. Using the tidal curve graph whose LW height is closest to the predicted height of LW, enter at the time required, ie corresponding to the appropriate number of hours after last LW.
3. Extract the estimated height of tide (above CD).
3a. For a more exact estimate, repeat the process using the next nearest curve, then interpolate.

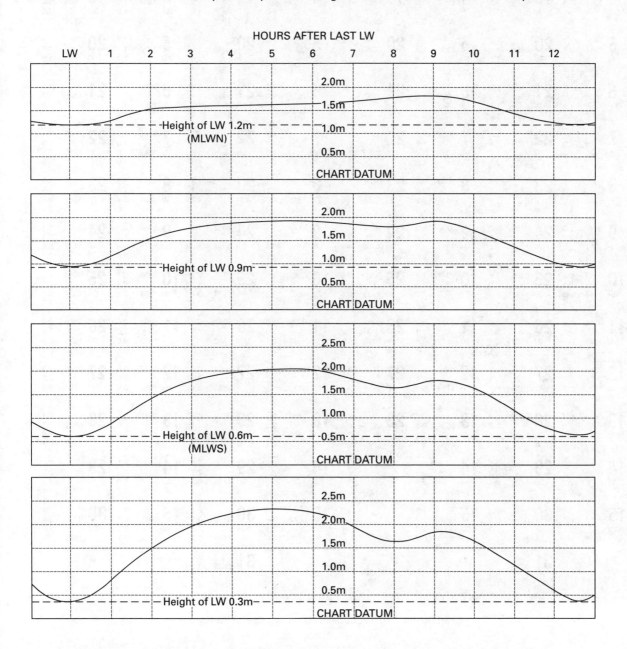

ENGLAND – POOLE HARBOUR

LAT 50°42′N   LONG 1°59′W

TIMES AND HEIGHTS OF HIGH AND LOW WATERS

YEAR **1998**

TIME ZONE (UT)
For Summer Time add ONE hour in non-shaded areas

Columns: **Time** / **m**. Each day lists the times (UT) and heights (metres) of successive waters. Symbols: ● = new moon, O = full moon.

JANUARY

Date	Day	Time — m
1	TH	0550 0.7 / 2.2 · 1816 0.5
2	F	0636 0.7 / 2.2 · 1901 0.5
3	SA	0724 2.2 / 0.7 · 1950 2.1 / 0.7
4	SU	0817 2.2 / 0.8 · 2043 2.0 / 0.7
5	M	0914 2.1 / 0.9 · 2142 2.0 / 0.8
6	TU	1021 2.0 / 1.0 · 2250 1.9 / 0.9
7	W	1135 2.0 / 1.0 · 1.9
8	TH	0002 1.0 · 1248 2.0 / 1.0 / 1.9
9	F	0113 1.0 · 1351 2.0 / 0.9 / 1.9
10	SA	0213 0.9 · 1446 2.1 / 0.8 / 2.0
11	SU	0306 0.8 · 1535 2.2 / 0.7 / 2.1
12	M O	0353 0.8 · 1619 2.2 / 0.7 / 2.1
13	TU	0434 0.7 · 1701 2.2 / 0.6
14	W	0515 2.2 / 0.7 · 1740 2.2 / 0.6
15	TH	0554 2.1 / 0.7 · 1815 2.1 / 0.6
16	F	0630 2.1 · 1850 2.1 / 0.8 / 0.7
17	SA	0704 0.8 · 1922 2.0 / 0.8
18	SU	0738 2.0 / 0.9 · 1955 2.0 / 0.9
19	M	0813 2.0 / 1.0 · 2030 1.9 / 1.0
20	TU	0854 1.9 / 1.1 · 2114 1.8 / 1.1
21	W	0948 1.9 / 1.3 · 2214 1.7 / 1.2
22	TH	1103 1.8 / 1.3 · 2332 1.6 / 1.3
23	F	1226 1.8 / 1.3 · 1.7
24	SA	0050 1.2 · 1331 1.9 / 1.1 / 1.8
25	SU	0150 1.1 · 1422 2.0 / 1.0 / 1.9
26	M	0238 0.9 · 1507 2.1 / 0.8 / 2.1
27	TU	0324 0.8 · 1551 2.1 / 0.7 / 2.1
28	W ●	0408 0.7 · 1634 2.2 / 0.5 / 2.3
29	TH	0452 0.6 · 1720 2.3 / 0.4
30	F	0539 2.3 / 0.5 · 1805 2.3 / 0.4
31	SA	0625 2.3 / 0.5 · 1850 2.3 / 0.4

FEBRUARY

Date	Day	Time — m
1	SU	0711 2.3 / 0.5 · 1936 2.2 / 0.5
2	M	0759 2.3 / 0.6 · 2024 2.1 / 0.6
3	TU	0851 2.1 / 0.7 · 2116 2.0 / 0.8
4	W	0950 2.0 / 0.9 · 2220 1.9 / 0.9
5	TH	1104 1.9 / 1.0 · 2336 1.8 / 1.0
6	F	1223 1.9 / 1.1 · 1.8
7	SA	0054 1.1 · 1335 1.9 / 1.0 / 1.9
8	SU	0202 1.0 · 1434 2.0 / 0.9 / 2.0
9	M	0256 0.9 · 1521 2.0 / 0.8 / 2.0
10	TU	0341 0.8 · 1603 2.1 / 0.7 / 2.1
11	W O	0421 0.7 · 1642 2.1 / 0.6 / 2.1
12	TH	0457 0.7 · 1719 2.1 / 0.5
13	F	0534 2.1 / 0.7 · 1753 2.1 / 0.6
14	SA	0606 2.1 · 1825 2.1 / 0.6
15	SU	0636 2.1 / 0.7 · 1853 2.0 / 0.7
16	M	0705 2.1 / 0.8 · 1920 2.0 / 0.8
17	TU	0733 2.0 / 0.9 · 1951 1.9 / 0.9
18	W	0808 2.0 / 1.0 · 2028 1.9 / 1.0
19	TH	0852 1.9 / 1.1 · 2118 1.8 / 1.1
20	F	0952 1.8 / 1.2 · 2231 1.6 / 1.3
21	SA	1121 1.7 / 1.3 · 1.6
22	SU	0006 1.3 · 1255 1.8 / 1.2 / 1.8
23	M	0124 1.1 · 1357 1.9 / 1.0 / 1.9
24	TU	0219 1.0 · 1446 2.0 / 0.8 / 2.0
25	W	0308 0.8 · 1533 2.1 / 0.6 / 2.2
26	TH ●	0353 0.6 · 1618 2.2 / 2.3
27	F	0437 0.5 · 1704 2.3 / 0.5
28	SA	0523 2.3 / 0.4 · 1749 2.3 / 0.3

MARCH

Date	Day	Time — m
1	SU	0608 2.4 / 0.3 · 1833 2.3 / 0.3
2	M	0653 2.4 / 0.4 · 1917 2.3 / 0.4
3	TU	0739 2.3 / 0.5 · 2003 2.2 / 0.5
4	W	0827 2.1 / 0.7 · 2053 2.0 / 0.7
5	TH	0923 2.0 / 0.8 · 2153 1.9 / 0.9
6	F	1033 1.9 / 1.0 · 2311 1.8 / 1.1
7	SA	1156 1.7 / 1.1 · 1.7
8	SU	0036 1.1 · 1315 1.8 / 1.0 / 1.8
9	M	0149 1.0 · 1416 1.8 / 0.9 / 1.9
10	TU	0242 0.9 · 1503 1.9 / 0.8 / 2.0
11	W	0325 0.8 · 1543 2.0 / 0.7 / 2.1
12	TH	0402 0.7 · 1619 2.0 / 0.6 / 2.1
13	F O	0436 0.6 · 1653 2.1 / 0.5 / 2.1
14	SA	0510 0.6 · 1727 2.1 / 0.5
15	SU	0542 2.1 / 0.6 · 1758 2.1 / 0.6
16	M	0609 2.1 / 0.6 · 1826 2.1 / 0.7
17	TU	0635 2.1 / 0.7 · 1851 2.0 / 0.7
18	W	0702 2.0 / 0.8 · 1920 2.0 / 0.8
19	TH	0735 0.8 / 2.0 · 1956 1.9 / 0.7
20	F	0816 2.0 / 1.0 · 2044 1.8 / 1.1
21	SA	0911 1.8 / 1.1 · 2151 1.7 / 1.2
22	SU	1034 1.7 / 1.2 · 2329 1.6 / 1.3
23	M	1217 1.7 / 1.1 · 1.8
24	TU	0058 1.1 · 1331 1.8 / 1.0 / 1.9
25	W	0159 0.9 · 1424 1.9 / 0.8 / 2.1
26	TH	0248 0.7 · 1512 2.1 / 0.5 / 2.2
27	F	0334 0.5 · 1558 2.2 / 0.4 / 2.3
28	SA ●	0420 0.4 · 1642 2.3 / 0.3 / 2.4
29	SU	0505 0.3 · 1729 2.3 / 0.3
30	M	0550 2.4 / 0.3 · 1813 2.4 / 0.3
31	TU	0635 2.4 / 0.3 · 1857 2.3 / 0.4

APRIL

Date	Day	Time — m
1	W	0719 2.3 / 0.4 · 1943 2.2 / 0.5
2	TH	0806 2.1 / 0.6 · 2031 2.1 / 0.7
3	F	0858 2.0 / 0.8 · 2130 1.9 / 0.9
4	SA	1004 1.8 / 1.0 · 2246 1.8 / 1.1
5	SU	1126 1.6 / 1.1 · 1.7
6	M	0009 1.2 · 1247 1.6 / 1.1 / 1.8
7	TU	0125 1.1 · 1349 1.8 / 1.0 / 1.9
8	W	0218 1.0 · 1435 1.9 / 0.9 / 2.0
9	TH	0300 0.8 · 1515 1.9 / 0.8 / 2.0
10	F	0335 0.7 · 1551 2.0 / 0.7 / 2.1
11	SA O	0409 0.6 · 1625 2.0 / 0.6 / 2.1
12	SU	0442 0.6 · 1658 2.0 / 0.6 / 2.1
13	M	0515 0.6 · 1732 2.0 / 0.6
14	TU	0544 2.1 / 0.6 · 1759 2.0 / 0.7
15	W	0610 2.1 / 0.7 · 1827 2.0 / 0.7
16	TH	0638 2.0 / 0.7 · 1857 2.0 / 0.8
17	F	0712 2.0 / 0.8 · 1936 1.9 / 0.9
18	SA	0754 1.9 / 0.9 · 2023 1.9 / 1.0
19	SU	0849 1.8 / 1.0 · 2129 1.8 / 1.1
20	M	1005 1.7 / 1.1 · 2259 1.8 / 1.2
21	TU	1140 1.7 / 1.1 · 1.8
22	W	0025 1.1 · 1259 1.8 / 0.9 / 1.9
23	TH	0132 0.9 · 1357 1.9 / 0.8 / 2.1
24	F	0225 0.7 · 1447 2.1 / 0.5 / 2.2
25	SA	0313 0.5 · 1534 2.2 / 0.4 / 2.3
26	SU ●	0400 0.4 · 1621 2.3 / 0.3 / 2.4
27	M	0445 0.3 · 1707 2.3 / 0.3
28	TU	0532 2.4 / 0.3 · 1753 2.3 / 0.3
29	W	0616 2.4 / 0.3 · 1838 2.3 / 0.4
30	TH	0700 2.3 / 0.4 · 1923 2.2 / 0.6

Chart Datum: 1·40 metres below Ordnance Datum (Newlyn)

2

ENGLAND – POOLE HARBOUR

LAT 50°42′N   LONG 1°59′W

TIMES AND HEIGHTS OF HIGH AND LOW WATERS

YEAR **1998**

MAY

Time	m	Time	m
1 F 0747 / 2011	2.1 0.6 2.1 0.8	**16** SA 0658 / 1923	2.0 0.7 2.0 0.8
2 SA 0837 / 2105	2.0 0.8 1.9 0.9	**17** SU 0743 / 2013	2.0 0.8 1.9 0.9
3 SU 0935 / 2212	1.8 1.0 1.8 1.1	**18** M 0839 / 2115	1.9 0.9 1.9 1.0
4 M 1049 / 2329	1.7 1.1 1.8 1.2	**19** TU 0947 / 2231	1.8 1.0 1.9 1.1
5 TU 1204	1.6 1.1 1.8	**20** W 1109 / 2350	1.8 1.0 1.9 1.0
6 W 0042 / 1308	1.1 1.6 1.0 1.9	**21** TH 1223	1.8 0.9 2.0
7 TH 0140 / 1358	1.0 1.8 0.9 1.9	**22** F 0100 / 1327	0.9 1.9 0.8 2.1
8 F 0224 / 1438	0.9 1.8 0.8 2.0	**23** SA 0159 / 1421	0.8 2.0 0.7 2.2
9 SA 0302 / 1517	0.8 1.9 0.8 2.0	**24** SU 0250 / 1512	0.6 2.1 0.5 2.3
10 SU 0338 / 1554 O	0.7 2.0 0.7 2.1	**25** M 0339 / 1600 ●	0.5 2.2 0.4 2.3
11 M 0413 / 1629 O	0.7 2.0 0.7 2.1	**26** TU 0427 / 1646	0.4 2.3 0.4 2.4
12 TU 0446 / 1703	0.6 2.0 0.7	**27** W 0514 / 1735	0.4 2.3 0.5
13 W 0518 / 1735	2.1 0.6 0.7	**28** TH 0600 / 1820	2.3 0.4 2.3 0.5
14 TH 0549 / 1806	2.1 0.7 2.0 0.7	**29** F 0644 / 1904	2.3 0.5 2.2 0.7
15 F 0622 / 1842	2.1 2.0 0.8	**30** SA 0728 / 1949	2.1 0.7 2.1 0.8
		31 SU 0814 / 2038	2.0 0.8 2.0 0.9

JUNE

Time	m	Time	m
1 M 0903 / 2133	1.9 0.9 1.9 1.1	**16** TU 0829 / 2101	2.0 0.8 2.0 0.9
2 TU 1001 / 2238	1.8 1.0 1.8 1.1	**17** W 0930 / 2206	1.9 0.9 2.0 0.9
3 W 1109 / 2347	1.6 1.1 1.8 1.2	**18** TH 1038 / 2318	1.8 0.9 2.0 1.0
4 TH 1214	1.6 1.1 1.8	**19** F 1150	1.9 0.9 2.0
5 F 0050 / 1311	1.1 1.7 1.1 1.9	**20** SA 0029 / 1259	0.9 1.9 0.8 2.1
6 SA 0141 / 1358	1.0 1.8 1.0 1.9	**21** SU 0135 / 1359	0.8 2.0 0.8 2.1
7 SU 0225 / 1440	0.9 1.9 0.9 2.0	**22** M 0231 / 1452	0.7 2.1 0.7 2.2
8 M 0305 / 1520	0.8 1.9 0.8 2.0	**23** TU 0323 / 1543 ●	0.6 2.1 0.6 2.3
9 TU 0343 / 1559	0.8 2.0 0.8 2.1	**24** W 0412 / 1631 ●	0.5 2.2 0.6 2.3
10 W 0420 / 1635 O	0.7 2.0 0.7 2.1	**25** TH 0458 / 1718	0.5 2.2 0.6
11 TH 0455 / 1713	0.7 2.1 0.7	**26** F 0544 / 1802	2.3 0.5 2.2 0.6
12 F 0533 / 1750	2.1 0.7 2.1 0.7	**27** SA 0627 / 1844	2.2 0.5 2.1 0.7
13 SA 0610 / 1831	2.1 0.7 2.1 0.7	**28** SU 0707 / 1925	2.1 0.7 2.1 0.8
14 SU 0651 / 1915	2.1 0.7 2.1 0.8	**29** M 0747 / 2007	2.0 0.8 2.0 0.9
15 M 0737 / 2004	2.0 0.7 2.0 0.8	**30** TU 0827 / 2051	1.9 0.9 2.0 1.0

JULY

Time	m	Time	m
1 W 0912 / 2142	1.8 1.0 1.9 1.1	**16** TH 0910 / 2143	2.0 0.8 2.1 0.9
2 TH 1005 / 2244	1.8 1.1 1.8 1.2	**17** F 1012 / 2251	1.9 0.9 2.0 0.9
3 F 1110 / 2351	1.7 1.2 1.8 1.2	**18** SA 1123	1.9 0.9 2.0
4 SA 1218	1.6 1.2 -1.8	**19** SU 0004 / 1236	1.0 1.9 1.0 2.0
5 SU 0055 / 1316	1.1 1.7 1.1 1.9	**20** M 0115 / 1342	0.9 1.9 0.9 2.0
6 M 0148 / 1405	1.0 1.8 1.0 1.9	**21** TU 0217 / 1440	0.8 2.0 0.8 2.1
7 TU 0234 / 1450	0.9 1.9 0.9 2.0	**22** W 0311 / 1531	0.7 2.1 0.8 2.2
8 W 0316 / 1532	0.8 2.0 0.8 2.1	**23** TH 0400 / 1618 ●	0.6 2.1 0.7 2.2
9 TH 0356 / 1613 O	0.7 2.1 0.8 2.1	**24** F 0443 / 1702	0.5 2.2 0.7
10 F 0435 / 1653	0.7 2.1 0.7 2.1	**25** SA 0526 / 1743	2.2 0.5 2.2 0.7
11 SA 0517 / 1737	0.6 2.1 0.7	**26** SU 0605 / 1822	2.1 0.5 2.1 0.7
12 SU 0559 / 1819	2.1 0.5 2.2 0.7	**27** M 0642 / 1857	2.1 0.6 2.1 0.8
13 M 0642 / 1904	2.1 0.5 2.2 0.7	**28** TU 0716 / 1932	2.0 0.7 2.1 0.8
14 TU 0727 / 1952	2.1 0.6 2.1 0.7	**29** W 0750 / 2009	2.0 0.8 2.0 0.8
15 W 0816 / 2044	2.1 0.7 2.1 0.8	**30** TH 0825 / 2048	1.9 0.9 2.0 1.0
		31 F 0906 / 2136	1.8 1.1 1.9 1.1

AUGUST

Time	m	Time	m
1 SA 0959 / 2241	1.7 1.2 1.8 1.3	**16** SU 1101 / 2342	1.9 1.0 1.9 1.0
2 SU 1113	1.6 1.3 1.8	**17** M 1220	1.8 1.1 1.9
3 M 0002 / 1233	1.3 1.7 1.3 1.8	**18** TU 0100 / 1333	1.0 1.9 1.0 1.9
4 TU 0112 / 1336	1.1 1.8 1.1 1.9	**19** W 0205 / 1432	0.9 2.0 0.9 2.0
5 W 0205 / 1425	1.0 1.9 1.0 2.0	**20** TH 0259 / 1521	0.8 2.1 0.8 2.1
6 TH 0251 / 1510	0.9 2.0 0.9 2.1	**21** F 0345 / 1604	0.7 2.1 0.7 2.1
7 F 0335 / 1553	0.7 2.1 0.8 2.1	**22** SA 0426 / 1643 ●	0.6 2.2 0.7 2.1
8 SA 0417 / 1635 O	0.6 2.2 0.7 2.2	**23** SU 0505 / 1721	0.5 2.2 0.7
9 SU 0459 / 1719	0.5 2.3 0.5	**24** M 0541 / 1756	2.1 0.5 2.1 0.7
10 M 0543 / 1803	2.2 0.4 2.3 0.5	**25** TU 0613 / 1828	2.1 0.6 2.1 0.7
11 TU 0627 / 1848	2.3 0.4 2.3 0.5	**26** W 0644 / 1858	2.1 0.7 2.1 0.8
12 W 0712 / 1935	2.2 0.5 2.3 0.5	**27** TH 0713 / 1928	2.0 0.8 2.0 0.9
13 TH 0758 / 2024	2.1 0.5 2.2 0.7	**28** F 0743 / 2001	2.0 0.9 2.0
14 F 0849 / 2119	2.0 0.7 2.1 0.8	**29** SA 0818 / 2043	1.9 1.0 1.9 1.1
15 SA 0948 / 2225	2.0 0.9 2.0 0.9	**30** SU 0904 / 2138	1.8 1.2 1.8 1.3
		31 M 1013 / 2302	1.7 1.3 1.8 1.3

Chart Datum: 1.40 metres below Ordnance Datum (Newlyn)

ENGLAND – POOLE HARBOUR

LAT 50°42'N   LONG 1°59'W

TIMES AND HEIGHTS OF HIGH AND LOW WATERS

YEAR **1998**

TIME ZONE (UT)
For Summer Time add ONE hour in non-shaded areas

SEPTEMBER

Day	Time	m	Day	Time	m
1 TU	1149	1.6 / 1.4 / 1.8	16 W	0044 / 1321	1.1 / 1.9 / 1.1 / 1.9
2 W	0036 / 1308	1.3 / 1.8 / 1.3 / 1.8	17 TH	0153 / 1420	1.0 / 2.0 / 1.0 / 2.0
3 TH	0140 / 1403	1.1 / 1.9 / 1.1 / 2.0	18 F	0243 / 1505	0.8 / 2.1 / 0.9 / 2.1
4 F	0229 / 1449	0.9 / 2.0 / 0.9 / 2.1	19 SA	0325 / 1544	0.7 / 2.1 / 0.8 / 2.1
5 SA	0314 / 1532	0.7 / 2.1 / 0.7 / 2.2	20 SU ●	0403 / 1620	0.6 / 2.2 / 0.7 / 2.1
6 SU O	0357 / 1616	0.5 / 2.3 / 0.6 / 2.3	21 M	0437 / 1654	0.6 / 2.2 / 0.7 / 2.1
7 M	0439 / 1659	0.4 / 2.3 / 0.5 / 2.3	22 TU	0512 / 1727	0.6 / 2.1 / 0.7
8 TU	0524 / 1745	0.4 / 2.4 / 0.4	23 W	0545 / 1758	2.1 / 0.6 / 2.1 / 0.7
9 W	0607 / 1829	2.3 / 0.4 / 2.4 / 0.4	24 TH	0613 / 1826	2.1 / 0.7 / 2.1 / 0.8
10 TH	0652 / 1915	2.3 / 0.4 / 2.3 / 0.5	25 F	0640 / 1853	2.1 / 0.8 / 2.1 / 0.8
11 F	0738 / 2002	2.3 / 0.5 / 2.2 / 0.6	26 SA	0708 / 1924	2.0 / 0.9 / 2.0 / 0.9
12 SA	0828 / 2056	2.1 / 0.7 / 2.1 / 0.8	27 SU	0741 / 2002	1.9 / 1.0 / 1.9 / 1.0
13 SU	0927 / 2201	2.0 / 0.9 / 1.9 / 1.0	28 M	0825 / 2054	1.8 / 1.1 / 1.8 / 1.2
14 M	1042 / 2322	1.8 / 1.1 / 1.8 / 1.1	29 TU	0929 / 2211	1.8 / 1.3 / 1.8 / 1.3
15 TU	1205	1.8 / 1.1 / 1.8	30 W	1107 / 2355	1.7 / 1.4 / 1.7 / 1.3

OCTOBER

Day	Time	m	Day	Time	m
1 TH	1238	1.8 / 1.3 / 1.8	16 F	0128 / 1358	1.0 / 2.0 / 1.0 / 1.9
2 F	0111 / 1337	1.1 / 1.9 / 1.1 / 2.0	17 SA	0218 / 1441	0.9 / 2.1 / 0.9 / 2.0
3 SA	0204 / 1426	0.9 / 2.1 / 0.9 / 2.1	18 SU	0258 / 1518	0.8 / 2.1 / 0.8 / 2.1
4 SU	0249 / 1510	0.7 / 2.2 / 0.7 / 2.2	19 M	0334 / 1553	0.7 / 2.1 / 0.7 / 2.1
5 M O	0333 / 1554	0.5 / 2.3 / 0.5 / 2.3	20 TU ●	0409 / 1626	0.7 / 2.1 / 0.7 / 2.1
6 TU	0416 / 1637	0.4 / 2.4 / 0.4 / 2.4	21 W	0442 / 1658	0.7 / 2.1 / 0.7 / 2.1
7 W	0501 / 1723	0.4 / 2.4 / 0.4	22 TH	0515 / 1730	0.7 / 2.1 / 0.7
8 TH	0546 / 1808	2.4 / 0.4 / 2.4 / 0.4	23 F	0545 / 1758	2.1 / 0.7 / 2.1 / 0.7
9 F	0631 / 1854	2.4 / 0.4 / 2.3 / 0.5	24 SA	0612 / 1825	2.1 / 0.8 / 2.1 / 0.8
10 SA	0717 / 1942	2.3 / 0.5 / 2.2 / 0.6	25 SU	0641 / 1856	2.1 / 0.9 / 2.0 / 0.9
11 SU	0808 / 2034	2.1 / 0.8 / 2.1 / 0.8	26 M	0715 / 1935	2.0 / 1.0 / 1.9 / 1.0
12 M	0906 / 2138	2.0 / 1.0 / 1.9 / 1.0	27 TU	0758 / 2024	1.9 / 1.1 / 1.9 / 1.1
13 TU	1020 / 2258	1.9 / 1.1 / 1.8 / 1.1	28 W	0859 / 2135	1.8 / 1.3 / 1.8 / 1.2
14 W	1142	1.8 / 1.2 / 1.8	29 TH	1026 / 2310	1.8 / 1.3 / 1.8 / 1.3
15 TH	0019 / 1300	1.1 / 1.9 / 1.1 / 1.8	30 F	1158	1.8 / 1.3 / 1.8
			31 SA	0031 / 1306	1.1 / 1.9 / 1.1 / 1.9

NOVEMBER

Day	Time	m	Day	Time	m
1 SU	0132 / 1358	0.9 / 2.1 / 0.9 / 2.1	16 M	0223 / 1446	0.9 / 2.1 / 0.9 / 2.0
2 M	0221 / 1445	0.7 / 2.3 / 0.7 / 2.2	17 TU	0301 / 1522	0.8 / 2.1 / 0.8 / 2.0
3 TU	0307 / 1531	0.5 / 2.4 / 0.5 / 2.3	18 W	0338 / 1558	0.8 / 2.1 / 0.8 / 2.1
4 W O	0353 / 1616	0.4 / 2.4 / 0.4 / 2.4	19 TH ●	0413 / 1631	0.8 / 2.1 / 0.7 / 2.1
5 TH	0437 / 1703	0.4 / 2.4 / 0.4	20 F	0446 / 1705	0.8 / 2.1 / 0.7
6 F	0524 / 1749	2.4 / 0.4 / 0.4	21 SA	0518 / 1735	2.1 / 0.8 / 2.1 / 0.8
7 SA	0611 / 1836	2.4 / 0.5 / 0.5	22 SU	0549 / 1805	2.1 / 0.8 / 2.1 / 0.8
8 SU	0658 / 1923	2.3 / 0.7 / 0.7	23 M	0621 / 1839	2.1 / 0.9 / 2.0 / 0.8
9 M	0748 / 2015	2.2 / 0.8 / 0.8	24 TU	0657 / 1919	2.0 / 1.0 / 2.0 / 0.9
10 TU	0845 / 2112	2.0 / 1.0 / 1.0	25 W	0743 / 2008	2.0 / 1.0 / 1.9 / 0.9
11 W	0950 / 2222	1.9 / 1.1 / 1.8 / 1.1	26 TH	0840 / 2110	1.9 / 1.1 / 1.9 / 1.1
12 TH	1108 / 2338	1.9 / 1.3 / 1.7 / 1.1	27 F	0952 / 2227	1.9 / 1.2 / 1.8 / 1.1
13 F	1222	1.9 / 1.2 / 1.8	28 SA	1114 / 2345	1.9 / 1.2 / 1.8 / 1.0
14 SA	0047 / 1323	1.1 / 1.9 / 1.1 / 1.8	29 SU	1227	2.0 / 1.1 / 1.9
15 SU	0140 / 1408	1.0 / 2.0 / 1.0 / 1.9	30 M	0054 / 1329	0.9 / 2.1 / 0.9 / 2.0

DECEMBER

Day	Time	m	Day	Time	m
1 TU	0151 / 1421	0.8 / 2.2 / 0.8 / 2.1	16 W	0227 / 1453	1.0 / 2.0 / 0.9 / 2.0
2 W	0241 / 1511	0.7 / 2.3 / 0.6 / 2.3	17 TH	0307 / 1531	0.9 / 2.1 / 0.8 / 2.0
3 TH O	0330 / 1559	0.5 / 2.4 / 0.5 / 2.3	18 F ●	0346 / 1607	0.9 / 2.1 / 0.8 / 2.1
4 F	0418 / 1646	0.5 / 2.4 / 0.5 / 2.4	19 SA	0422 / 1642	0.8 / 2.1 / 0.7 / 2.1
5 SA	0507 / 1735	0.5 / 2.4 / 0.5	20 SU	0456 / 1718	0.8 / 2.1 / 0.7
6 SU	0554 / 1822	2.3 / 0.6 / 0.5	21 M	0532 / 1752	2.1 / 0.8 / 2.1 / 0.7
7 M	0641 / 1907	2.3 / 0.7 / 0.7	22 TU	0607 / 1829	2.1 / 0.8 / 2.1 / 0.7
8 TU	0728 / 1954	2.2 / 0.8 / 0.8	23 W	0646 / 1910	2.1 / 0.9 / 2.0 / 0.8
9 W	0818 / 2043	2.1 / 0.9 / 0.9	24 TH	0731 / 1955	2.1 / 0.9 / 2.0 / 0.8
10 TH	0913 / 2138	2.0 / 1.1 / 1.8 / 1.0	25 F	0823 / 2050	2.0 / 1.0 / 2.0 / 0.9
11 F	1018 / 2243	1.9 / 1.2 / 1.8 / 1.1	26 SA	0924 / 2153	2.0 / 1.1 / 1.9 / 1.0
12 SA	1128 / 2349	1.9 / 1.3 / 1.7 / 1.2	27 SU	1036 / 2306	2.0 / 1.1 / 1.9 / 1.0
13 SU	1233	1.9 / 1.7	28 M	1151	2.0 / 1.0 / 1.9
14 M	0051 / 1328	1.1 / 1.9 / 1.1 / 1.8	29 TU	0018 / 1302	1.0 / 2.0 / 1.0 / 2.0
15 TU	0142 / 1412	1.1 / 2.0 / 1.0 / 1.9	30 W	0125 / 1402	0.9 / 2.1 / 0.8 / 2.0
			31 TH	0223 / 1456	0.8 / 2.3 / 0.7 / 2.1

Chart Datum: 1·40 metres below Ordnance Datum (Newlyn)

POOLE HARBOUR   10-2-13

Dorset 50°40'·90N 01°56'·88W (Ent)   Rtg 2-1-1

CHARTS
AC *2611, 2175*; Imray C4, Y23; Stanfords 12, 15, 7; OS 195
TIDES
Town Quay –0141, +0114 Dover; ML 1·5; Zone 0 (UT)

POOLE (TOWN QUAY) (←)

Times				Height (metres)			
High Water		Low Water		MHWS	MHWN	MLWN	MLWS
–	–	0500	1100	2·1	1·6	1·2	0·6
–	–	1700	2300				

Differences POTTERY PIER

–	–	+0005	+0005	–0·1	+0·1	+0·1	+0·2

CLEAVEL POINT

–	–	–0010	–0010	0·0	–0·1	0·0	–0·1

WAREHAM (River Frome)

–	–	+0125	+0040	+0·1	+0·1	0·0	+0·3

NOTE: Daily predictions of the times and hts of LW, but only the hts of HW, at Poole (Town Quay) are given above. See also 10·2·12. The 4 curves before these predictions simplify intermediate calculations. Double HWs occur, except at nps, and predicted hts are for the higher HW; the ht of the 2nd HW is always about 1·8m. HW occurs between LW +5 and next LW –3. At nps there is a stand; predictions are for the middle of the stand. Strong and continuous winds from E to SW may raise sea levels by 0·2m; W to NE winds can lower levels by 0·1m.
Differences POOLE HBR ENT, referenced to the Standard Port of Portsmouth, are given under 10.2.11.

SHELTER
An excellent hbr with narrow ent; access in all conditions except very strong E/SE winds. ⚓s wherever sheltered from the wind and clear of chans, moorings and shellfish beds; especially in South Deep, off W end of Brownsea Is and off Shipstal Pt. The S half of the hbr is designated as a Quiet Area (see chartlet) with speed limit of 6kn. A 6kn limit also covers from Stakes SCM By, past Poole Quay and Poole Bridge up to Cobbs Quay in Holes Bay.
A 10kn speed limit applies to the rest of the hbr, ie West from the seaward app chans (defined by an arc of radius 1400m centred on S Haven Pt, 50°40'·78N 01°56'·91W) to the junction of R Frome with R Trent at 02°04'·60W (see chartlet). Note: From 1 Oct to 31 Mar the 10kn limit does not apply in the North, Middle Ship and Wareham Chans.
NAVIGATION
WPT Poole Bar (No 1 SHM) By, QG, 50°39'·32N 01°55'·10W, 148°/328° from/to Haven Hotel, 1·95M. In strong SE-S winds the Bar is dangerous especially on the ebb. In Studland Bay and close to training bank beware lobster pots. From Poole Bar to Shell Bay a recreational **Boat Chan**, suitable for craft < 3m draught, parallels the W side of the Swash Channel, close to the E of the Training Bank.
East Looe Chan (buoyed) is liable to shift and may have less water than charted; there is only 1m 1ca ENE of East Looe PHM buoy. 5 rock groynes to the N are marked by SHM bns, the two most W'ly are lit, 2 FG (vert).
Within the hbr the two chans (Middle Ship and North) up to Poole are clearly marked by lateral buoys, mostly lit, with cardinal buoys at divisions. Outside the chans there are extensive shoal or drying areas.
Middle Ship Chan is dredged 6·0m for ferries to/from the Hamworthy terminal; it is mostly only 80m wide. Leisure craft should keep out of Middle Ship Chan, by using a **Boat Chan** which parallels S of the dredged chan between the PHM buoys and, further outboard, stakes with PHM topmarks marking the edge of the bank. Depth in this chan is 2·0m, but 1·5m closer to the stakes.
North Channel, the other option, is now dredged 4m and widened to 80m for ships. It remains suitable for yachts/leisure craft; best water is on the outside of chan bends. Yachts cruising to the W should check Lulworth gunnery range (see 10·2·10). Info is shown in the Hr Mr's office and printed in the Supplements to this Almanac.
LIGHTS AND MARKS
See chartlet and 10.2.4 for main buoys, beacons and lts.
Sandbanks Chain Ferry shows a Fl W lt (rotating) and a B ● above the leading Control cabin by D/N to indicate which way it is going. In fog it sounds 1 long and 2 short blasts every 2 mins. When stationary at night it shows a FW lt; in fog it rings a bell for 5 sec every minute.

Poole Bridge (Lights shown from bridge tr)
Ⓡ   = Do not approach bridge;
Fl Ⓖ   = Bridge lifting, proceed with caution; Ⓖ = Proceed. Bridge lifts routinely for small craft at: Mon-Fri 0930, 1030, 1230, 1430, 1630, 1830, 2130; Sat, Sun & Bank hols = as Mon-Fri, plus 0730; at 2345 daily bridge will also lift if any vessels are waiting. Each lift only permits one cycle of traffic in each direction. Pleasure craft may pass when the bridge lifts on request for a commercial vessel; monitor Ch 14. Bridge will not usually lift during weekday road traffic Rush Hours 0730-0930 and 1630-1830.
RADIO TELEPHONE
Call: *Poole Hbr Control* VHF Ch 14 16 (H24). Salterns Marina Ch M 80; Parkstone Haven Ch M; Poole YC Haven, call *Pike* Ch M; Poole Bridge, call *PB* Ch 14. Cobbs Quay, call *CQ Base* Ch 80.
TELEPHONE (Dial code 01202)
Hr Mr 440233, ⛟ 440231; Pilots 666401; Bridge 674115; MRSC (01305) 760439; ⌗ 0345 231110 (H24); Met (01703) 228844; Marinecall 0891 500457; Police 22099; Ⓗ 675100.
FACILITIES The following are some of the many facilities:
Marinas (from seaward)
Salterns Marina (300, few visitors) ☎ 709971, ⛟ 700398, £24, max draft 2·5m, AC, FW, P, D, ME, El, Ⓔ, Sh, CH, Gas, Gaz, C (5 ton), BH (45 ton), Bar, R, Ⓞ. Appr from No 31 SHM buoy, Fl G 5s.
Parkstone Haven, (Parkstone YC ☎ 743610), some Ⓥ berths, £12; dredged 2m. Access from North Chan near No 35 SHM buoy, Fl G 5s. Appr chan, dredged 2·5m, is marked by SHM buoy (Fl G 3s), 2 PHM and 3 SHM unlit buoys. Ldg daymarks 006°, both Y ◇s; ldg lts, front Iso Y 4s, rear FY. 2 FG and 2FR (vert) on bkwtr hds.
Poole Quay (AB £8.71, Sh, FW) is close to town facilities. Berthing Office on the quay is open 0800-2200, Apr-Sept. Hbr Office is at 20, New Quay Rd, Poole BH15 4AF.
Dorset Yacht Co (56 AB + 6 Ⓥ; 90M + 6Ⓐ) ☎ 674531, ⛟ 677518, P, D, AC, FW, CH, Slip, Gas/Gaz, ME, El, Sh, C (5 ton), Bar; and
Beyond Poole Bridge:
Sunseeker International Marina (50) ☎ 685335, AC, Sh, D, BH (30 ton), C (36 ton), FW, ME, El, CH, V, R, Bar;
Cobbs Quay Marina (850, some visitors) ☎ 674299, ⛟ 665217, £18, Slip, P, D, Gas, Ⓞ, SM, FW, AC, ME, El, Ⓔ, Sh, C (10 ton), CH, R, Bar;
Public Landing Places: On Poole Quay, in Holes Bay and by ferry hards at Sandbanks.
Fuel Poole Bay Fuels barge (May-Sep 0900-1800; moored near Aunt Betty buoy, No 50) P, D, Gas, Gaz, V, Off licence.
Corrals (S side of Poole Quay adjacent bridge) P & D; **Salterns marina** P & D.
Yacht Clubs: Royal Motor YC ☎ 707227, M, Bar, R; **Poole Bay YC; Parkstone YC** ☎ 743610 (Parkstone Haven); **Poole YC** ☎ 672687.
Services
A complete range of marine services is available; consult marina/Hr Mr for exact locations: M, L, FW, AB, ME, El, Sh, CH, Slip, CH, SM, D, P, C (18 ton), ACA, Ⓔ, Safety Equipment and Inflatables. **Town** EC Wed; ✉, Ⓑ, ⇌, ✈. Ferry to Cherbourg (all year) and St Malo (summer).

ADJACENT HARBOUR AND ANCHORAGE

WAREHAM, Dorset, 50°41'·00N 02°06'·48W. AC *2611*. HW –0030 (Np), +0320 (Sp) on Dover (see 10·2·12 & ·13). Shelter very good, appr narrow and winding up R Frome but well marked by buoys and posts at ent. Beware prohib ⚓s (salmon holes) marked on the chart; also many moored boats. Passage is unlit; keep to the outside of all bends. Max draft 1·2m to Wareham Quay.
Facilities: **Ridge Wharf Yacht Centre** (180+6 visitors) (½M upstream of R Frome ent) ☎ (01929) 552650, Access HW±2 approx AB, M, FW, P, D, ME, El, Gas, AC, BH (20 ton), Slip, Sh, CH; **Redclyffe YC** ☎ 551227 (½M below bridge); **Wareham Quay** AB, FW, R. **Town** EC Wed, P & D (cans), V, Gas, R, Bar, ✉, Ⓑ, ⇌, Dr ☎ 3444.

STUDLAND BAY, Dorset, 50°38'·70N 01°55'·82W. AC *2172, 2175*. Tides approx as for Swanage (10·2·11). Shelter is good except in N/ E winds. Beware Redend Rks off S shore. Best ⚓ in about 3m, 3ca NW of The Yards (three strange projections on the chalk cliffs near Handfast Pt). **Village:** EC Thurs; FW, V, R, ✉, hotel, P & D (cans), No marine facilities. A Historic Wreck (see 10.0.3h) is at 50°39'·67N 01°54'·79W, 4½ca NNE of Poole Bar buoy.

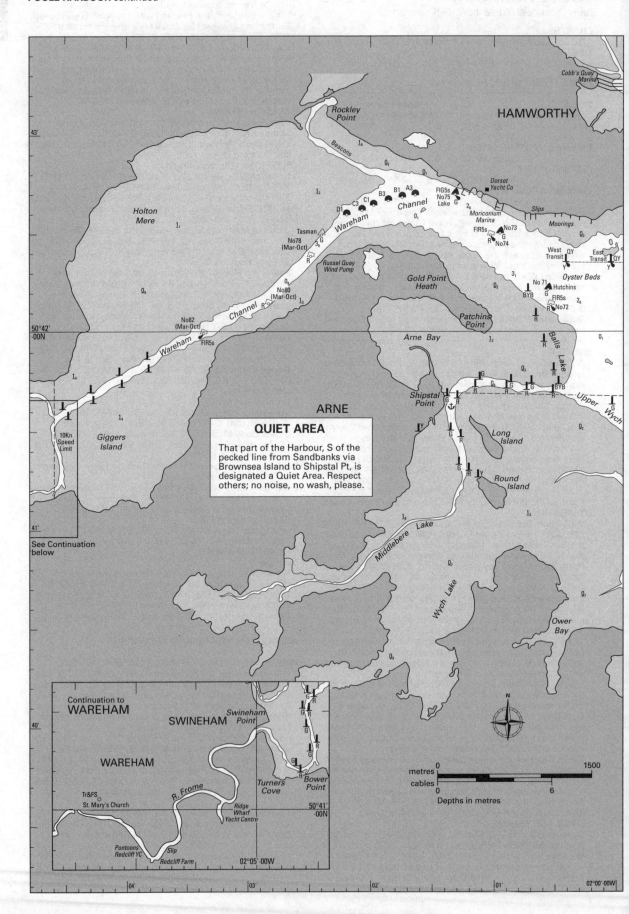

QUIET AREA

That part of the Harbour, S of the pecked line from Sandbanks via Brownsea Island to Shipstal Pt, is designated a Quiet Area. Respect others; no noise, no wash, please.

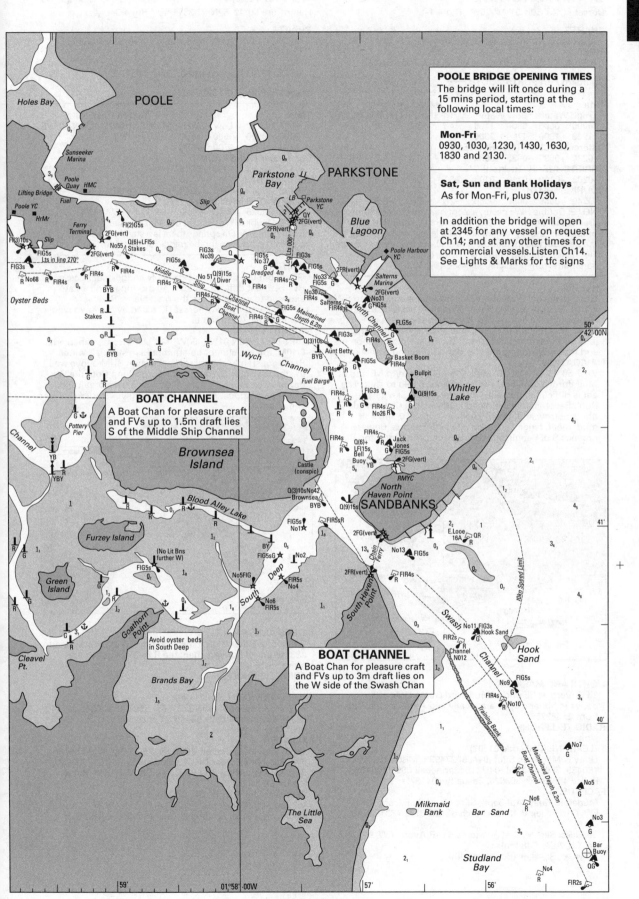

2

POOLE BRIDGE OPENING TIMES
The bridge will lift once during a 15 mins period, starting at the following local times:

Mon-Fri
0930, 1030, 1230, 1430, 1630, 1830 and 2130.

Sat, Sun and Bank Holidays
As for Mon-Fri, plus 0730.

In addition the bridge will open at 2345 for any vessel on request Ch14; and at any other times for commercial vessels. Listen Ch14. See Lights & Marks for tfc signs

POOLE

Holes Bay

PARKSTONE

Parkstone Bay

Blue Lagoon

Sunseeker Marina

Poole Quay   HMC

Lifting Bridge

Fuel

Poole YC

HrMr

Ferry Terminal

Slip

Oyster Beds

Stakes

Middle

Ship

Channel

Boat

Channel

Maintained Depth 6.2m

Parkstone YC

Poole Harbour YC

Salterns Marina

North Channel (4m)

Wych   Channel

Aunt Betty

Basket Boom

Bullpit

Fuel Barge

Whitley Lake

Jack Jones

BOAT CHANNEL
A Boat Chan for pleasure craft and FVs up to 1.5m draft lies S of the Middle Ship Channel

Pottery Pier

Brownsea Island

Castle (conspic)

Bell Buoy

North Haven Point

RMYC

SANDBANKS

Channel

Blood Alley Lake

Brownsea

Furzey Island

(No Lit Bns further W)

South   Deep

Green Island

Chain Ferry

South Haven Point

E.Looe

Swash

Hook Sand

Goathorn Point

Avoid oyster beds in South Deep

Cleavel Pt.

Brands Bay

BOAT CHANNEL
A Boat Chan for pleasure craft and FVs up to 3m draft lies on the W side of the Swash Chan

Channel

Training Bank

Hook Sand

Maintained Depth 6.2m

Boat Channel

The Little Sea

Milkmaid Bank   Bar   Sand

Studland Bay

Bar Buoy

50° 42'.00N

41'

40'

59'   01°58'.00W   57'   56'

CHRISTCHURCH   10-2-14

Dorset 50°43'·50N 01°44'·25W   Rtg 4-1-1

CHARTS
AC *2172, 2219*; Imray C4; Stanfords 7, 12; OS 195

TIDES
HW Sp −0210, Np, −0140 Dover; ML 1·2; Zone 0 (UT)

Standard Port PORTSMOUTH (→)

Times				Height (metres)			
High Water		Low Water		MHWS	MHWN	MLWN	MLWS
0000	0600	0500	1100	4·7	3·8	1·9	0·8
1200	1800	1700	2300				
Differences CHRISTCHURCH (Ent)							
−0230	+0030	−0035	−0035	−2·9	−2·4	−1·2	−0·2
CHRISTCHURCH (Tuckton)							
−0205	+0110	+0110	+0105	−3·0	−2·5	−1·0	+0·1
BOURNEMOUTH							
−0240	+0055	−0050	−0030	−2·7	−2·2	−0·8	−0·3

NOTE: Double HWs occur, except near nps; predictions are for the higher HW. Near nps there is a stand, when predictions are for mid-stand. Tidal levels are for inside the bar. Outside the bar the tide is about 0·6m lower at sp. Floods (or drought) in the two rivers cause considerable variations from predicted hts. See 10·2·12.

SHELTER
Good in lee of Hengistbury Hd, elsewhere exposed to SW winds. R Stour, navigable at HW up to Tuckton, and the R Avon up to the first bridge, give good shelter in all winds. Most ⚓s in the hbr dry. No ⚓ in chan. No berthing at ferry jetty by Mudeford sandbank. CSC has limited pontoon AB and moorings for monohulls <9m. Hbr speed limit 4kn.

NAVIGATION
WPT 50°43'·50N 01°43'·50W, 090°/270° from/to NE end of Mudeford Quay 0·5M. The bar/chan is liable to shift. The ent is difficult on the ebb which reaches 4-5kn in 'The Run'. Recommended ent/dep at HW/stand. Chan inside hbr is narrow and mostly shallow (approx 0·3m) soft mud; mean ranges are 1·2m sp and 0·7m nps. Beware groynes S of Hengistbury Hd, Beerpan and Yarranton Rks.

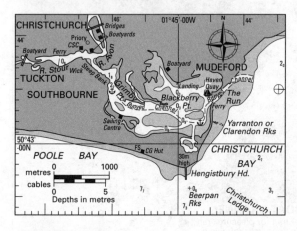

LIGHTS AND MARKS
2 FG (vert) at NE end of Mudeford Quay. Unlit chan buoys in hbr and apps are locally laid April-Oct inc; info from ☎ 483250.

RADIO TELEPHONE
None.

TELEPHONE (Dial code 01202)
Quay & Moorings Supt (01425) 274933; MRSC (01305) 760439; ⌗ 0345 231110 (H24); Marinecall 0891 500457; Police 486333; Ⓗ 303626; Casualty 704167.

FACILITIES
Mudeford Quay (Apl-Sept), Slip, AB, M, L, P (cans, ½M), FW, C (mobile), V; **Christchurch SC (CSC)** ☎ 483150, AB £8, M.
Services: Slip, M, D at Rossiter's BY (R Avon), FW, ME, EI, Sh, CH, ACA, C (8 ton).
Town ✉, Ⓑ, ⇌, ✈ (Bournemouth).

KEYHAVEN   10-2-15

Hampshire 50°42'·82N 01·33'·18W   Rtg 4-3-1

CHARTS
AC *2021, 2219, 2040*; Imray C4, C3, Y20; Stanfords 7, 11, 12; OS 196

TIDES
−0020, +0105 Dover; ML 2·0; Zone 0 (UT)

Standard Port PORTSMOUTH (→)

Times				Height (metres)			
High Water		Low Water		MHWS	MHWN	MLWN	MLWS
0000	0600	0500	1100	4·7	3·8	1·9	0·8
1200	1800	1700	2300				
Differences HURST POINT							
−0115	−0005	−0030	−0025	−2·0	−1·5	−0·5	−0·1
TOTLAND BAY							
−0130	−0045	−0040	−0040	−2·0	−1·5	−0·5	−0·1
FRESHWATER BAY							
−0210	+0025	−0040	−0020	−2·1	−1·5	−0·4	0·0

NOTE: Double HWs occur at or near sp, when predictions are for the first HW. Off springs there is a stand of about 2 hrs; predictions are then for the middle of the stand. See 10·2·12.

SHELTER
Good, but the river gets extremely congested. Access HW ±4½. Ent difficult on ebb. All moorings and ⚓s are exposed to winds across the marshland. River is administered by New Forest DC aided by the Keyhaven Consultative Committee.

NAVIGATION
WPT 50°42'·70N 01°32'·50W, 115°/295° from/to chan ent, 0·40M. Ent should not be attempted in strong E winds. Bar is constantly changing. Leave chan SHM buoys well to stbd. Beware lobster pots. Approaching from the W, beware The Shingles bank over which seas break and which partly dries. At Hurst Narrows give 'The Trap' a wide berth.

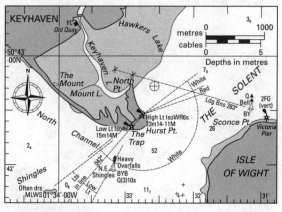

LIGHTS AND MARKS
When E of Hurst High lt, two ldg bns ('X' topmarks) lead 283° to ent of buoyed chan; the R & G ent buoys are more visible.

RADIO TELEPHONE
None.

TELEPHONE (Dial code 01590)
R. Warden 645695; MRSC (01705) 552100; ⌗ 0345 231110 (H24); Marinecall 0891 500457; Police 615101; Dr 643022; Ⓗ 677011.

FACILITIES
Quay Slip, L; **Keyhaven YC** ☎ 642165, C, M, L (on beach), FW, Bar; **New Forest District Council** ☎ (01703) 285000, Slip, M; **Milford-on-Sea** P, D, FW, CH, V, R, Bar; **Hurst Castle SC** M, L, FW;
Services: Slip, ME, EI, Sh, C (9 ton), CH.
Village EC (Milford-on-Sea) Wed; R, Bar, CH, V, ✉ and Ⓑ (Milford-on-Sea), ⇌ (bus to New Milton), ✈ (Hurn).

NEEDLES CHANNEL   10-2-16

The Needles are distinctive rks at the W end of the Isle of Wight. The adjacent chalk cliffs of High Down are conspic from afar; the lt ho may not be seen by day until relatively close. Goose Rk, dries, is about 50m WNW of the lt ho, 100-150m WSW of which is a drying wreck. The NW side of the Needles Chan is defined by the Shingles bank, parts of which dry and on which the sea breaks violently in the least swell. The SE side of the bank is fairly steep-to, the NW side shelves more gradually. On the ebb the stream sets very strongly (3·4kn) WSW across the Shingles. The Needles Chan is well lit and buoyed and in fair weather presents no significant problems. Note: The Hurst Castle ldg lts lead 042° between SW Shingles and Bridge buoys; but further NE the ldg line is outside the buoyed chan and very adjacent to the Shingles. Due to shoaling (1995) on the ldg line, the SW Shingles lt buoy has been moved 130m SSE.

In bad weather broken water and overfalls extend along The Bridge, a reef which runs 8ca W of the lt ho with extremity marked by Bridge WCM lt buoy. S to W gales against the ebb raise very dangerous seas in the Needles Chan. (In such conditions the E approach to the Solent, via Nab Tower and the Forts, should be used or shelter found at Poole or Studland). Even a SW Force 4 against the ebb will raise breaking seas near Bridge and SW Shingles buoys.

In strong winds the North Chan, N of the Shingles, is preferable to the Needles Chan. The two join S of Hurst Point where overfalls and tide rips may be met. Beware The Trap, a shoal spit extending 150m SE of Hurst Castle.

ANCHORAGES BETWEEN THE NEEDLES AND YARMOUTH

ALUM BAY, 50°40'·07N 01°34'·25W. *AC 2021.* Tides as for Totland B. Very good shelter in E and S winds, but squally in gales. Distinctive W cliffs to S and multi-coloured cliffs and chairlift to E. Appr from due W of chairlift to clear Five Fingers Rk, dries 0·6m, to the N and Long Rk, a reef drying 0·9m at its E end, to the S. ⚓ in about 4m off the new pier. A Historic Wreck (see 10.0.3h) is at 50°39'·7N 01°35'·45W.

TOTLAND BAY, 50°40'·95N 01°32'·78W. *AC 2219.* Tides, see 10.2.15 and 10.2.12; ML 1·9m. Good shelter in E'lies in wide shelving bay between Warden Ledge (rks 4ca offshore) to the N and Hatherwood Pt to the SW. Appr W of Warden SHM buoy Fl G 2·5s to ⚓ out of the tide in 2m between pier (2FG vert) and old LB house; good holding. Colwell Bay, to the N between Warden Pt and Fort Albert, is generally rky and shallow.

ANCHORAGE EAST OF THE NEEDLES, SOUTH IOW

FRESHWATER BAY, 50°40'·04N 01°30'·53W. AC *2021.* Tides see 10.2.15 and 10.2.12; ML 1·6m. Well sheltered from the N, open to the S. The bay is 3·2M E of Needles lt ho and 1·2M E of Tennyson's Cross. Redoubt Fort is conspic on W side of B, a hotel on N side and Stag, Arch and Mermaid Rks to the E. The B is shallow, with rky drying ledges ¾ca either side and a rk drying 0·1m almost in the centre. Best to ⚓ in about 2m just outside bay. Facilities: V, R, Bar, ✉.

SOLENT AREA 10-2-17

SOLENT AREA *continued*

Charts
In addition to normal ACs, the Solent and approaches are covered by AC 5600. This is a folio of 10 A2 size charts in a clear plastic wallet, price £29.50, intended for yachtsmen.

Vessel Traffic Service (VTS)
A VTS, operated by Southampton on VHF Ch 12 14, controls shipping in the Solent between the Needles and Nab Tower including Southampton Water. Portsmouth Hbr and its appr's N of a line from Gilkicker Pt to Outer Spit By are controlled on Ch 11 by QHM Portsmouth.

The VTS is primarily intended to monitor and co-ordinate the safe passage of commercial ships which must make contact at designated reporting points. The VTS includes compulsory pilotage and a radar service on request, together with berthing instructions and tug assistance.

It follows that pleasure craft, particularly at night or in poor visibility, can be forewarned of shipping movements (and likely avoiding action), simply by listening on VHF Ch 12, or Ch 11 for QHM Portsmouth. Traffic information is routinely broadcast by Southampton VTS on VHF Ch 12 every H from 0600 to 2200LT, Fri-Sun and Bank Hols from Easter to last weekend in Oct. From 1 June to 30 Sept broadcasts are daily at the same times.

Pleasure Craft and Commercial Shipping
In the interests of safety it is important that good co-operation between pleasure craft and commercial shipping be maintained. Yachtsmen should always bear in mind the restricted field of vision from large ships at close quarters, their limited ability to manoeuvre at slow speeds, and the constraints imposed by narrow and shallow channels.

An **Area of Concern** (AOC) has been designated at one of the busiest parts of the Solent to provide greater safety for large vessels. The AOC (see chartlet opposite) covers the Western Approach Channel and the Thorn Channel; it is delineated by the following lt buoys, clockwise fom Prince Consort NCM: Gurnard NCM, NE Gurnard PHM, Bourne Gap PHM, Calshot lt Float, Castle Point PHM, Black Jack PHM, Reach PHM, Calshot NCM, N Thorn SHM, Thorn Knoll SHM, W Bramble WCM and S Bramble SHM.

The AOC, which is criss-crossed by many pleasure craft, has also to be negotiated by large commercial vessels bound to/ from Southampton normally via the E Solent. Inbound ships usually pass Prince Consort NCM and turn first to the southward toward Gurnard NCM, before starting their critical stbd turn into the Thorn Chan. They turn port around Calshot to clear the AOC. Typical tracks are depicted opposite.

To minimise the risk of collision with small craft, any large vessel >150m LOA, on entering the AOC, is enclosed by a **Moving Prohibited Zone** (MPZ) which extends 1000m ahead of the vessel and 100m on either beam. *Small craft <20m LOA must remain outside this MPZ, using seamanlike anticipation of likely turns.*

The large vessel, displaying a B cylinder by day or 3 all-round ⓡ lts (vert) by night, will normally be preceded by a Hbr patrol launch showing a Fl Bu lt and working VHF Ch 12 (callsign *SP*).

VHF Ch 12, in addition to providing VTS, will identify large vessels and approx timings of MPZ as part of the hourly broadcasts (see above). All pleasure craft in the vicinity are strongly advised to monitor Ch 12 in order to create a mental picture. Be particularly alert when in, or approaching, the triangle defined by E. Lepe, Hook & W Ryde Middle buoys.

VHF Radio Telephone
The proliferation of VHF radios in yachts and, it must be said, often poor R/T procedures cause problems for legitimate users and can seriously hamper emergency situations. Yachtsmen are reminded that Ch 16 is a DISTRESS, SAFETY and CALLING Ch. If another calling Ch is available use it in preference to Ch 16; otherwise, use Ch 16 as briefly as possible to make contact before shifting to a working Ch. Note also that initial contact with Solent CG should be on Ch 67, NOT Ch 16 (see next column). For ship-to-ship messages the recognised VHF channels include 06, 08, 72 and 77. **Yachts in the Solent should listen on Ch 12 and on Ch 11 for Portsmouth.** Other Ch's are listed under each port entry.

Local Signals
Outward bound vessels normally hoist the following flag signals during daylight hours.

Signal	Meaning
International 'E' Flag over Answering Pendant }	I am bound East (Nab Tower)
Answering Pendant Over International 'W' Flag }	I am bound West (The Needles)

Southampton patrol launches have HARBOUR MASTER painted on their after cabin in B lettering on Y background. At night a Fl Bu all-round lt is shown above the W masthead lt.

Reference
Much useful information is given in the *Solent Year Book*, published by the Solent Cruising and Racing Association (SCRA); also in a free booklet *The Yachtsman's Guide to Southampton Water* and a leaflet *Enjoy the Solent*. *Solent Hazards* by Peter Bruce, published by Boldre Marine, goes closer inshore than other Pilot books.

Weather and Navigation Broadcasts
Sailing info from BBC Radio Solent: 96·1 MHz VHF and 999 kHz (300m); 103·8 MHz and 1359 kHz (221m) in West Dorset.

A   Local weather forecast.
B   Forecast, Coastal stn reports, CG reports, Shipping movements, Tidal details and Gunnery firing times.
C   Live forecast from Southampton Weather Centre.

Daily Broadcasts (LT)

0500	A (Mon-Fri)	1325	C (Mon-Fri)
0530	B (Mon-Fri)	1400	A
0600	A	1500	A (Mon-Sat)
0630	A	1505	C (Sun only)
0635	B (Mon-Fri)	1525	C (Mon-Fri)
0700	A	1600	A
0735	C	1625	C (Mon-Fri)
0745	B (Mon-Sat)	1700	A
0800	A	1735	C (Mon-Fri)
0830	A (Sun only)	1759	C (Sat only)
0835	C (Mon-Sat)	1800	A (Mon-Fri, Sun)
0850	B (Mon-Fri)	1835	C (Mon-Fri)
0900	A (Mon-Sat)	1900	A (Mon-Fri)
0905	C (Sun only)	2000	A (Mon-Fri)
1000	A	2100	A (Mon-Fri)
1100	A	2205	A (Mon-Fri)
1200	A	2305	C (Mon-Fri)
1300	A (Mon-Fri)		
1305	A (Sun only)		
1310	C (Sat only)		

Dial ☎ 0891 500 457 for Marinecall forecasts for this area, or for Marine MetFax dial 0336 400 457. Southampton Weather Centre is ☎ (01703) 228844. Solent CG broadcasts on Ch 67 local strong wind warnings on receipt; and local forecasts every 4 hrs from 0400LT, but every 2 hrs if strong wind warnings are in force.

Solent Coastguard
The Maritime Rescue Sub Centre (MRSC) at Lee-on-Solent ☎ (01705) 552100 coordinates all SAR activities in Solent District, which is bounded by a line from Highcliffe south to the EC1 buoy; E to the Greenwich Lt V; thence N to Beachy Head. It is the busiest CG District in the UK, because of the huge concentration of pleasure craft within its bounds.

It is manned H24, year round by at least 3 CG Officers who can call on the RNLI, Solent Safety rescue boats and the CG Rescue helicopter based at Lee. Sector and Auxiliary CGs are based on the IOW, Calshot, Eastney, Hayling, Littlehampton, Shoreham, Newhaven and elsewhere.

Solent CG keeps watch on VHF Ch 67 and 16. Uniquely, the initial call to *Solent Coastguard* should be made on Ch 67, the working channel; this is because Ch 16 is often very busy especially in the summer. Ch 67 is also heavily loaded and is only for essential traffic. Listen out before transmitting; be brief, to the point and use correct R/T procedures.

Save valuable R/T time by telephoning Solent CG before sailing; they will be glad to advise you. In general terms, they will always stress: Up-to-date forecasts; awareness of tidal streams; sound knowledge of "Rule of the Road" and local Notices to Mariners; adequate fuel, plus reserves, for your passage, and a sharp lookout at all times. Bon voyage!

SOLENT AREA WAYPOINTS   10.2.18

Waypoints marked with an asterisk (*) are special (yellow) racing marks, which may be removed in winter. Racing buoys marked with a bullet (•) against the longitude are only laid during Cowes week. Other waypoints are navigational buoys, unless otherwise stated. All positions are referenced to the OSGB 36 datum.

After Barn	50°51'·50N 01°20'·73W
*Air Canada	50°47'·30N 01°16'·73W
*Alpha (Cowes)	50°46'·24N 01°18'·11W•
*Alpha (Portsmouth)	50°46'·58N 01°07'·50W
*Ashlett	50°49'·95N 01°19'·67W
*Autohelm	50°46'·55N 01°21'·37W
Bald Head	50°49'·88N 01°18'·15W
Bank Lt Bn	50°53'·58N 01°23'·23W
*Bay	50°46'·02N 00°57'·81W
Bembridge Ledge	50°41'·12N 01°02'·72W
Bembridge Tide Gauge	50°42'·43N 01°04'·93W
*Berthon	50°44'·18N 01°29'·13W
*Beta (Cowes)	50°46'·25N 01°17'·53W•
*Beta (Portsmouth)	50°46'·57N 01°06'·25W
Black Jack	50°49'·10N 01°18'·00W
Black Rock	50°42'·55N 01°30'·55W
*Bob Kemp	50°45'·15N 01°09'·55W
Boulder (Looe Chan)	50°41'·53N 00°49'·00W
*Bouldnor	52°42'·70N 01°28'·90W
Bourne Gap	50°47'·79N 01°18'·26W
*Bowring	50°47'·28N 01°12'·00W
Boyne	50°46'·12N 01°05'·17W
Bramble Bn	50°47'·38N 01°17'·06W
Bridge	50°39'·59N 01°36'·80W
*Brookes & Gatehouse (ex Alpha)	50°6'·40N 01°07'·80W
Browndown	50°46'·54N 01°10'·87W
*Brunswick Gate (ex Echo)	50°46'·05N 01°05'·56W
Bury	50°54'·10N 01°27'·04W
Cadland	50°50'·99N 01°20'·45W
Calshot	50°48'·40N 01°16'·95W
Calshot Spit Lt F	50°48'·32N 01°17'·55W
*Camper & Nicholsons	50°47'·05N 01°06'·68W
Castle (NB)	50°46'·43N 01°05'·30W
Castle Point	50°48'·68N 01°17'·58W
*Cathead	50°50'·58N 01°19'·14W
*Champagne Mumm	50°45'·60N 01°23'·03W
Chi	50°45'·48N 00°56'·91W
Chichester Bar Bn	50°45'·88N 00°56'·38W
*Chilling	50°49'·18N 01°17'·37W
Chi Spit	50°45'·68N 00°56'·48W
*Clipper	50°48'·43N 01°15'·63W
*Colten ('C')	50°43'·84N 01°31'·13W
Coronation	50°49'·51N 01°17'·53W
Cowes Breakwater Lt	50°45'·84N 01°17'·43W
Cowes No. 3	50°46'·04N 01°17'·95W
Cowes No. 4	50°46'·04N 01°17'·78W
Cracknore	50°53'·91N 01°25'·12W
Crosshouse Lt Bn	50°54'·01N 01°23'·11W
*Cutter	50°49'·42N 01°16'·82W

*Daks-Simpson	50°45'·50N 01°14'·30W
*DB Marine	50°46'·13N 01°13'·00W
Dean Elbow	50°43'·66N 01°01'·78W
Deans Elbow	50°52'·12N 01°22'·67W
Deans Lake	50°51'·35N 01°21'·53W
Dean Tail South	50°43'·10N 00°59'·49W
*Deck	50°48'·60N 01°16'·57W
*Delta (Portsmouth)	50°46'·01N 01°06'·20W
Dibden Bay	50°53'·66N 01°24'·84W
*Durns	50°45'·40N 01°25'·80W•
*Dunford ('B')	50°43'·38N 01°31'·54W
Durns Pt obstn (S end)	50°45'·37N 01°26'·95W
East Bramble	50°47'·20N 01°13'·56W
East Knoll	50°47'·93N 01°16'·74W
East Lepe	50°46'·09N 01°20'·81W
*Echo (Portsmouth)	50°46'·09N 01°05'·7W
*Elephant	50°44'·60N 01°21'·80W
Eling	50°54'·45N 01°27'·75W
Fairway (Needles)	50°38'·20N 01°38'·90W
Fawley	50°49'·97N 01°19'·39W
*Gamma (Portsmouth)	50°46'·34N 01°06'·00W
Greenland	50°51'·07N 01°20'·29W
Gurnard	50°46'·18N 01°18'·76W
Gurnard Ledge	50°45'·48N 01°20'·50W
Gymp	50°53'·14N 01°24'·21W
Gymp Elbow	50°53'·49N 01°24'·53W
Hamble Point	50°50'·12N 01°18'·57W
Hamstead Ledge	50°43'·83N 01°26'·10W
*Hard	50°44'·92N 00°57'·81W
*Harwoods	50°42'·81N 01°28'·75W
Hillhead	50°48'·00N 01°15'·92W
Hook	50°49'·49N 01°18'·21W
Horse Elbow	50°44'·23N 01°03'·80W
Horse Sand	50°45'·48N 01°05'·17W
Horse Sand Fort Lt	50°44'·97N 01°04'·25W
Horse Tail	50°43'·20N 01°00'·14W
Hound	50°51'·65N 01°21'·43W
*Hurst ('A')	50°42'·87N 01°32'·46W
Hythe Knock	50°52'·79N 01°23'·73W
Jack in Basket	50°44'·25N 01°30'·50W
*Jackson ('H')	50°44'·30N 01°28'·16W
*Jardines	50°48'·10N 01°14'·55W
*Jib	50°52'·93N 01°22'·97W
*Kelvin Hughes	50°47'·30N 01°14'·50W•
Lains Lake	50°51'·55N 01°21'·56W
*Lambeth	50°41'·50N 01°41'·60W
Langstone Fairway	50°46'·28N 01°01'·27W
Lee Pt Bn	50°47'·40N 01°11'·85W
*Lucas	50°46'·24N 01°08'·67W

2

Main Passage	50°45'·98N 01°04'·02W
Marchwood	50°53'·95N 01°25'·48W
*Marina Developments	50°46'·12N 01°16'·55W
*Mark	50°49'·53N 01°18'·85W
*Meon	50°49'·15N 01°15'·62W
Mid Shingles	50°41'·18N 01°34'·58W
Milbrook	50°54'·08N 01°26'·73W
Mixon Bn	50°42'·35N 00°46'·21W
Moorhead	50°52'·52N 01°22'·81W
*Moreton	50°42'·02N 01°03'·14W
*Morse (ex Delta)	50°46'·12N 01°06'·33W
Mother Bank	50°45'·45N 01°11'·13W
Nab 1	50°41'·23N 00°56'·43W
Nab 2	50°41'·70N 00°56'·71W
Nab 3	50°42'·17N 00°57'·05W
Nab East	50°42'·82N 01°00'·70W
Nab End	50°42'·60N 00°59'·38W
Nab Tower	50°40'·05N 00°57'·07W
NE Gurnard	50°47'·03N 01°19'·33W
NE Mining Ground	50°44'·71N 01°06'·30W
NE Ryde Middle	50°46'·18N 01°11'·80W
NE Shingles	50°41'·93N 01°33'·32W
Needles Fairway	50°38'·20N 01°38'·90W
Netley	50°51'·99N 01°21'·72W
New Grounds	50°41'·97N 00°58'·53W
*Newtown	50°44'·15N 01°23'·70W•
Newtown G By	50°43'·57N 01°24'·70W
No Mans Land Fort Lt	50°44'·37N 01°05'·60W
Norris	50°45'·92N 01°15'·40W
North Head	50°42'·65N 01°35'·43W
North Ryde Middle	50°46'·58N 01°14'·28W
North Sturbridge	50°45'·31N 01°08'·15W
North Thorn	50°47'·88N 01°17'·75W
NW Netley	50°52'·28N 01°22'·65W
*Ocean Safety (ex Beken)	50°45'·75N 01°19'·67W
*ODM ('D') (Lymington)	50°44'·18N 01°30'·10W
Outer Nab	50°41'·00N 00°56'·65W
Outer Spit	50°45'·55N 01°05'·41W
Peel Bank	50°45'·57N 01°13'·25W
Peel Wreck	50°44'·85N 01°13'·30W
Pier Head	50°53'·64N 01°24'·57W
Poole Fairway	50°38'·97N 01°54'·80W
Portsmouth No. 3 Bar	50°47'·04N 01°06'·17W
Portsmouth No. 4	50°46'·98N 01°06'·27W
Prince Consort	50°46'·38N 01°17'·47W
*Pylewell ('E')	50°44'·58N 01°29'·43W
*Quinnell	50°47'·03N 01°19'·80W
*Ratsey	50°47'·63N 01°13'·56W
Reach	50°49'·02N 01°17'·56W
Ridge	50°46'·42N 01°05'·57W
*Rocwel	50°43'·02N 01°27'·04W

Roway Wk	50°46'·08N 01°02'·20W
*Royal Albert	50°46'·48N 01°05'·87W
*Royal Thames	50°47'·78N 01°19'·17W
*Royal Southern	50°48'·85N 01°15'·48W
*Ruthven	50°42'·67N 01°03'·45W
Ryde Pier Hd	50°44'·35N 01°09'·51W
*RYS flagstaff	50°45'·97N 01°17'·97W
Saddle	50°45'·17N 01°04'·78W
Salt Mead	50°44'·48N 01°22'·95W
Sconce	50°42'·50N 01°31'·35W
*Seafile	50°46'·55N 01°21'·37W
*Seascope	50°47'·38N 01°15'·82W
SE Ryde Middle	50°45'·90N 01°12'·00W
Shingles Elbow	50°40'·31N 01°35'·92W
*S.M. (Special Mark)	50°46'·12N 01°16'·76W
*Snowden (ex Trap)	50°46'·17N 01°17'·51W
South Bramble	50°46'·95N 01°17'·65W
South Ryde Middle	50°46'·10N 01°14'·08W
*Spanker	50°47'·08N 01°17'·98W
Spit Refuge	50°46'·12N 01°05'·37W
Spit Sand Fort Lt	50°46'·20N 01°05'·85W
*Sposa	50°49'·63N 01°17'·50W
St Helens	50°43'·33N 01°02'·32W
Stokes Bay Wreck	50°46'·67N 01°10'·58W
Street	50°41'·65N 00°48'·80W
*Sunsail	50°46'·40N 01°15'·00W
Swinging Ground No. 1	50°52'·97N 01°23'·35W
Swinging Ground No. 2	50°53'·79N 01°25'·03W
SW Mining Ground	50°44'·63N 01°07'·95W
SW Shingles	50°39'·31N 01°37'·36W
*Tanners ('G')	50°44'·80N 01°28'·47W
Thorn Knoll	50°47'·47N 01°18'·35W
Trinity House (Cowes)	50°46'·10N 01°17'·15W
*Vail Williams (ex Beta Portsmouth)	50°46'·80N 01°07'·25W
Warden	50°41'·45N 01°33'·47W
Warner	50°43'·84N 01°03'·93W
West Bramble	50°47'·17N 01°18'·57W
*W – E	50°45'·48N 00°58'·70W
West Knoll	50°47'·52N 01°17'·68W
West Lepe	50°45'·20N 01°24'·00W
Weston Shelf	50°52'·68N 01°23'·17W
West Princessa	50°40'·20N 01°03'·95W
West Ryde Middle	50°46'·45N 01°15'·70W
Winner	50°45'·07N 01°00'·01W
*Woolwich	50°43'·00N 01°38'·00W
Wootton Bn	50°44'·50N 01°12'·10W
*Yachting World	50°45'·08N 01°27'·25W
*Yachthaven ('D')	50°44'·18N 01°30'·10W
*YMS 2	50°42'·86N 01°29'·40W
*Yarmouth No. 4	50°46'·82N 01°28'·42W

YARMOUTH   10-2-19

Isle of Wight 50°42'·39N 01°29'·97W   Rtg 1-2-1

CHARTS

AC *2021, 2040*; Imray C3, Y20; Stanfords 11, 18; OS 196

TIDES

Sp –0050, +0150, Np +0020 Dover; ML 2·0; Zone 0 (UT)

Standard Port PORTSMOUTH (→)

Times				Height (metres)			
High Water		Low Water		MHWS	MHWN	MLWN	MLWS
0000	0600	0500	1100	4·7	3·8	1·9	0·8
1200	1800	1700	2300				
Differences YARMOUTH							
–0105	+0005	–0025	–0030	–1·6	–1·3	–0·4	0·0

NOTE: Double HWs occur at or near sp; at other times there is a stand lasting about two hrs. Predictions refer to the first HW when there are two; otherwise to the middle of the stand. See 10·2·12.

SHELTER

Good from all directions of wind and sea, but swell enters if wind strong from N/NE. Hbr dredged 2m from ent to bridge; access H24. Moor fore-and-aft on piles in 5 rows, A to E; on the Town Quay, or on pontoon if <9m LOA. Boats over 15m LOA, 4m beam or 2·4m draft should give notice of arrival. Berthing on S Quay is normally only for fuel, C, FW, or to load people/cargo. Hbr gets very full in season and may be closed to visitors. 12 Y ⚓s outside (see chartlet) and ⚓ further to the N or S.

NAVIGATION

WPT 50°42'·55N 01°29'·93W, 008°/188° from/to abeam car ferry terminal, 2ca. Dangers on appr are Black Rock and shoal water to the N of the E/W bkwtr. Beware ferries. Caution: strong ebb in the ent at sp. Speed limit 4kn in hbr apprs from abeam pierhead, in the hbr and up-river. ⚓ prohib in hbr and beyond R Yar road bridge.

This swing bridge opens for access to the moorings and BYs up-river at Saltern Quay: (May-Sept) 0800, 0900, 1000, 1200, 1400, 1600, 1730, 1830, 2000LT; and on request (Oct-May). The river is navigable by dinghy at HW almost up to Freshwater.

A **Historic Wreck** (see 10.0.3h) is at 50°42'·52N 01°29'·59W, 2ca ExN from end of pier; marked by Y SPM buoy.

LIGHTS AND MARKS

Ldg bns (2 W ◊ on B/W masts) and ldg lts (FG 5/9m 2M), on quay, 188°. When hbr is closed to visitors (eg when full in summer or at week-ends) a R flag is flown at the pier head and an illuminated board 'Harbour Full' is displayed at the ent, plus an extra Ⓡ. In fog a high intensity Ⓦ lt is shown from the pier hd and from the inner E pier, together with a Ⓨ.

RADIO TELEPHONE

Hr Mr VHF Ch 68. Water Taxi Ch 15.

TELEPHONE (Dial code 01983 = code for whole of IOW)

Hr Mr 760321, 📠 761192; MRSC (01705) 552100; ∰ 0345 231110 (H24); Marinecall 0891 500457; Police 52800; Dr 760434.

FACILITIES

Hbr £7.50 on piles, Town Quay, pontoon or ⚓; Slip, P, D, L, M, Gaz, FW, C (5 ton), Ice;
Yarmouth SC ☎ 760270, Bar, L;
Royal Solent YC ☎ 760256, Bar, R, L, M, Slip;
Services Note: Most marine services/BYs are located near Salterns Quay, 500m up-river above the bridge, or ½M by road. BY, Slip, M, ME, El, Sh, CH, Gas, Gaz, SM, C, Divers.
Town EC Wed; V, R, Bar, ✉, Ⓑ (May-Sept 1000-1445, Sept-May a.m. only), ⇌ (Lymington), ✈ (Bournemouth/Southampton).

LYMINGTON   10-2-20

Hampshire 50°45'·10N 01·31'·32W   Rtg 1-1-1

CHARTS
AC *2021, 2040, 2045*; Imray C3, Y20, Y30; Stanfords 11, 18; OS 196

TIDES
Sp –0040, +0100, Np +0020 Dover; ML 2·0; Zone 0 (UT)

Standard Port PORTSMOUTH (→)

Times				Height (metres)			
High Water		Low Water		MHWS	MHWN	MLWN	MLWS
0000	0600	0500	1100	4·7	3·8	1·9	0·8
1200	1800	1700	2300				

Differences LYMINGTON

–0110	+0005	–0020	–0020	–1·7	–1·2	–0·5	–0·1

NOTE: Double HWs occur at or near sp and on other occasions there is a stand lasting about 2hrs. Predictions refer to the first HW when there are two. At other times they refer to the middle of the stand. See 10·2·12.

RADIO TELEPHONE
Marinas VHF Ch **80** M (office hrs).

TELEPHONE (Dial code 01590)
Hr Mr 672014; MRSC (01705) 552100; ⌗ 0345 231110 (H24); Marinecall 0891 500457; Police 675411; Dr 672953; Ⓗ 677011.

FACILITIES
Marinas:
Lymington Yacht Haven (475+100 visitors), 2m depth, all tides access, ☎ 677071, 🛥 678186, £16.60, P, D, AC, FW, BY, ME, EI, Sh, C (10 ton), BH (40 ton), CH, Gas, Gaz, Ⓒ;
Lymington Marina (300+100 visitors), ☎ 673312, 🛥 676353, £14.10, Slip, P, AC, D, FW, ME, EI, Sh, CH, BH (100 ton), C, (37, 80 ton), Gas, Gaz, Ⓒ;
Town Quay AB £6.50, M, FW, Slip (see Hr Mr); **Bath Road** public pontoon, FW.
Clubs: Royal Lymington YC ☎ 672677, R, Bar; **Lymington Town SC** ☎ 674514, AB, R, Bar.
Services: M, FW, ME, EI, Sh, C (16 ton), CH, Ⓔ, SM, ACA.
Town EC Wed; every facility including ✉, Ⓑ, ⇌, ✈ (Bournemouth or Southampton).

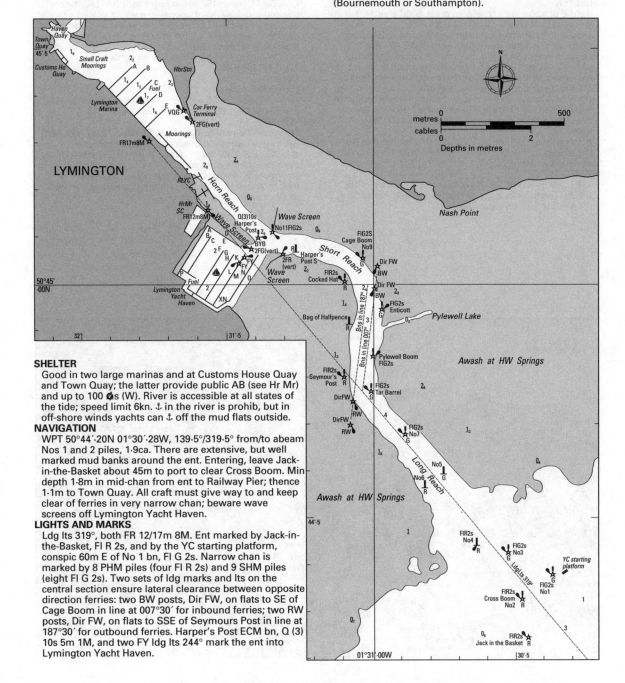

SHELTER
Good in two large marinas and at Customs House Quay and Town Quay; the latter provide public AB (see Hr Mr) and up to 100 🛥s (W). River is accessible at all states of the tide; speed limit 6kn. ⚓ in the river is prohib, but in off-shore winds yachts can ⚓ off the mud flats outside.

NAVIGATION
WPT 50°44'·20N 01°30'·28W, 139·5°/319·5° from/to abeam Nos 1 and 2 piles, 1·9ca. There are extensive, but well marked mud banks around the ent. Entering, leave Jack-in-the-Basket about 45m to port to clear Cross Boom. Min depth 1·8m in mid-chan from ent to Railway Pier; thence 1·1m to Town Quay. All craft must give way to and keep clear of ferries in very narrow chan; beware wave screens off Lymington Yacht Haven.

LIGHTS AND MARKS
Ldg Its 319°, both FR 12/17m 8M. Ent marked by Jack-in-the-Basket, Fl R 2s, and by the YC starting platform, conspic 60m E of No 1 bn, Fl G 2s. Narrow chan is marked by 8 PHM piles (four Fl R 2s) and 9 SHM piles (eight Fl G 2s). Two sets of ldg marks and Its on the central section ensure lateral clearance between opposite direction ferries: two BW posts, Dir FW, on flats to SE of Cage Boom in line at 007°30' for inbound ferries; two RW posts, Dir FW, on flats to SSE of Seymours Post in line at 187°30' for outbound ferries. Harper's Post ECM bn, Q (3) 10s 5m 1M, and two FY ldg Its 244° mark the ent into Lymington Yacht Haven.

NEWTOWN RIVER   10-2-21

Isle of Wight 50°43'·42N 01°24'·58W   Rtg 3-4-1

CHARTS
AC *2021, 2040, 1905*; Imray C3, Y20; Stanfords 11, 18; OS 196

TIDES
Sp –0108, Np +0058, Dover; ML 2·3; Zone 0 (UT)

Standard Port PORTSMOUTH (→)

Times				Height (metres)			
High Water		Low Water		MHWS	MHWN	MLWN	MLWS
0000	0600	0500	1100	4·7	3·8	1·9	0·8
1200	1800	1700	2300				

Differences SOLENT BANK (Data approximate)

–0100	0000	–0015	–0020	–1·3	–1·0	–0·3	–0·1

NOTE: Double HWs occur at or near springs; at other times there is a stand which lasts about 2hrs. Predictions refer to the first HW when there are two. At other times they refer to the middle of the stand. See 10·2·12.

SHELTER
3½M E of Yarmouth, Newtown gives good shelter, but is exposed to N winds. There are 6 ⚓s (R/W) in Clamerkin Lake and 18 (R/W) in the main arm leading to Shalfleet Quay, all are numbered; check with Hr Mr. Do not ⚓ beyond boards showing "Anchorage Limit" on account of oyster beds. Fin keel boats can stay afloat from ent to Hamstead landing or to Clamerkin Limit Boards. Public landing on E side of river N of Newtown quay by conspic black boathouse. The whole eastern peninsula ending in Fishhouse Pt is a nature reserve; yachtsmen are asked not to land there. 5kn speed limit in hbr is strictly enforced.

If no room in river, good ⚓ in 3-5m W of ent, but beware rky ledges E of Hamstead Ledge SHM buoy, Fl (2) G 5s, and piles with dolphin.

NAVIGATION
WPT 50°43'·80N 01°25'·10W, 310°/130° from/to ldg bn, 0·46M. From W, make good Hamstead Ledge SHM buoy, thence E to pick up ldg marks.

From E, keep N of Newtown gravel banks where W/SW winds over a sp ebb can raise steep breaking seas; leave R spherical bar buoy to port.

Best ent is from about HW –4, on the flood but while the mud flats are still visible. Ent lies between two shingle spits and can be rough in N winds especially near HW. There is only about 0·9m over the bar.

Inside the ent so many perches mark the mud banks that confusion may result. Near junction to Causeway Lake depth is only 0·9m and beyond this water quickly shoals. At ent to Clamerkin Lake (1·2 - 1·8m) keep to SE to avoid gravel spit off W shore, marked by two PHM perches; the rest of chan is marked by occas perches. Beware many oyster beds in Western Haven and Clamerkin Lake. There is a rifle range at top of Clamerkin Lake and in Spur Lake; R flags flown during firing. High voltage power line across Clamerkin at 50°42'·78N 01°22'·58W has clearance of only 9m and no shore markings.

LIGHTS AND MARKS
Conspic TV mast (152m) bearing about 150° (3·3M from hbr ent) provides initial approach track. In season a forest of masts inside the hbr are likely to be evident. The ldg bns, 130°, are off Fishhouse Pt in mud on NE side of ent: front bn, RW bands with Y-shaped topmark; rear bn, W with W disc in B circle. There are no lights.

RADIO TELEPHONE
None.

TELEPHONE (Dial code 01983 = code for whole of IOW)
Hr Mr 531424; MRSC (01705) 552100; ⌗ 0345 231110 (H24); Marinecall 0891 500457; Police 528000; Dr 760434.

FACILITIES
Newtown Quay M £8.00, L, FW; **Shalfleet Quay** Slip, M, L, AB; **Lower Hamstead Landing** L, FW; **R. Seabroke** ☎ 531213, Sh; **Shalfleet Village** V, Bar, P & D (cans; in emergency from garage).
Newtown EC Thurs; ⊠, Ⓑ (Yarmouth or Newport), ⇌ (bus to Yarmouth, ferry to Lymington), ✈ (Bournemouth or Southampton).

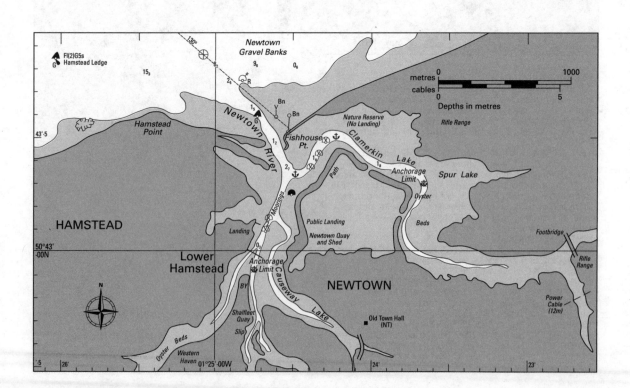

BEAULIEU RIVER   10-2-22

Hampshire 50°47'·00N 01°21'·76W (Ent)   Rtg 3-2-1

CHARTS

AC *2021, 2040, 1905*; Imray C3; Y20; Stanfords 11, 18; OS 196

TIDES

–0100 and +0140 Dover; ML 2·4; Zone 0 (UT)

Standard Port PORTSMOUTH (→)

Times				Height (metres)			
High Water		Low Water		MHWS	MHWN	MLWN	MLWS
0000	0600	0500	1100	4·7	3·8	1·9	0·8
1200	1800	1700	2300				
BUCKLER'S HARD							
–0040	–0010	+0010	–0010	–1·0	–0·8	–0·2	–0·3
STANSORE POINT							
–0050	–0010	–0005	–0010	–0·9	–0·6	–0·2	0·0

NOTE: Double HWs occur at or near springs; on other occasions there is a stand which lasts about two hrs. The predictions refer to the first HW when there are two, or to the middle of the stand. See 10.2.12.

SHELTER

Very good in all winds. ⚓ possible in reach between Lepe Ho and Beaulieu River SC, but preferable to proceed to Buckler's Hard Yacht Hbr (AB and ❶ pile moorings). Many of the landing stages/slips shown on the chartlet (and AC 2021) are privately owned and should not be used. The uppermost reaches of the river are best explored first by dinghy due to the lack of channel markers and the short duration of the HW stand.

Rabies: Craft with animals from abroad are prohibited in the river.

NAVIGATION

WPT 50°46'·50N 01°21'·25W, 144°/324° from/to abeam Beaulieu Spit dolphin (Fl R 5s), 4ca. There are patches drying 0·3m approx 100m S of Beaulieu Spit. 1ca further SSE, close W of the ldg line, are shoal depths 0·1m. Ent dangerous LW±2. The swatchway off Beaulieu River SC is closed. A speed limit of 5kn applies to the whole river.

LIGHTS AND MARKS

Ldg marks at ent 324° must be aligned exactly due to shoal water either side of ldg line. The front is No 2 bn, R with Or dayglow topmark, △ shape above ☐; the rear is Lepe Ho. Beaulieu Spit, R dolphin with W band, Fl R 5s 3M vis 277°-037°; ra refl, should be left approx 40m to port. The old CG cottages and Boat House are conspic, approx 320m E of Lepe Ho. The river is clearly marked by R and G bns and perches. SHM bns 5, 9, 19 and 21 are all Fl G 4s; PHM bns 12 and 20 are Fl R 4s. Marina pontoons A, C and E have 2FR (vert).

RADIO TELEPHONE

Buckler's Hard Yacht Harbour VHF Ch M 80.

TELEPHONE (Dial code 01590)

Hr Mr 616200/616234, 🕾 616211, Mobile (0860) 919196; MRSC (01705) 552100; ⌗ 0345 231110 (H24); Marinecall 0891 500457; Police (01703) 845511; Dr 612451 or (01703) 845955; Ⓗ 77011.

FACILITIES

Buckler's Hard Yacht Hbr £21 (110+20 visitors) ☎ 616200, 🕾 616211, Slip, M (£9 on piles), P, D, AC, FW, ME, El, Sh, C (1 ton), BH (26 ton), SM, Gas, Gaz, CH, ▣, V, R, Bar. **Village** V (Stores ☎ 616293), R, Bar, ✉ (Beaulieu), Ⓑ (Mon, Wed, Fri AM or Hythe), 🚌 (bus to Brockenhurst), ✈ (Bournemouth or Southampton).

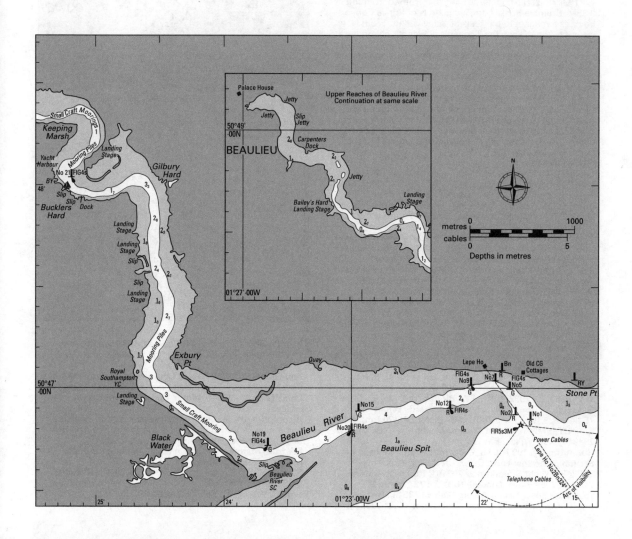

COWES/RIVER MEDINA   10-2-23

Isle of Wight 50°45'·86N 01°17'·72W   Rtg 1-1-1

CHARTS
AC *2793, 2040, 394*; Imray C3, Y20; Stanfords 11, 18; OS 196

TIDES
+0029 Dover; ML 2·7; Zone 0 (UT)

Standard Port PORTSMOUTH (→)

Times				Height (metres)			
High Water		Low Water		MHWS	MHWN	MLWN	MLWS
0000	0600	0500	1100	4·7	3·8	1·9	0·8
1200	1800	1700	2300				
Differences COWES							
−0015	+0015	0000	−0020	−0·5	−0·3	−0·1	0·0
FOLLY INN							
−0015	+0015	0000	−0020	−0·6	−0·4	−0·1	+0·2
NEWPORT							
No data		No data		−0·6	−0·4	+0·1	+0·8

NOTE: Double HWs occur at or near sp. On other occasions a stand occurs lasting up to 2hrs; times given represent the middle of the stand. See 10·2·12, especially for Newport.

SHELTER
Good at Cowes Yacht Haven and above the chain ferry, but outer hbr exposed to N and NE winds. ⚓ prohib in hbr. Visitors may pick up/secure to any mooring/piles/pontoon so labelled, ie: 4 large ⚓s N of front ldg lt (off The Parade); piles S of Cowes Yacht Haven; Thetis Pontoon (short stay/overnight only, dredged 2·5m); pontoons S of the chain ferry (W Cowes); 'E' Pontoon off E Cowes SC. See opposite for pontoons in Folly Reach; Island Harbour marina on E bank beyond Folly Inn and in Newport (dries). Good ⚓ in Osborne Bay, 2M E, sheltered from SE to W; no landing.

NAVIGATION
WPT 50°46'·20N 01°17'·90W, 344°/164° from/to front ldg lt, 0·35M. Bramble Bank, 1·1m, lying 1M N of Prince Consort buoy, is a magnet to the keels of many yachts. From N, to clear it to the W keep the 2 conspic power stn chimneys at E Cowes open of each other.

On the E side of the ent, the Shrape (mud flats) extends to Old Castle Pt. Yachts must use the main chan near W shore and are advised to motor. Caution: strong tidal streams; do not sail through or ⚓ in the mooring area. Speed limit 6kn in hbr. Beware high-speed catamarans/hydrofoils at W Cowes; car ferries at E Cowes, commercial shipping and the chain ferry which shows all round Fl W lt at fore-end, and gives way to all tfc; it runs Mon-Sat: 0435-0030, Sun 0635-0010LT. R Medina is navigable to Newport, but the upper reaches dry.

LIGHTS AND MARKS
Ldg lts 164°: Front Iso 2s 3m 6M, post by Customs Ho; rear, 290m from front, Iso R 2s 5m 3M, vis 120°-240°. Chan ent is marked by No 3 SHM buoy, Fl G 3s, and No. 4 PHM buoy, QR. E bkwtr hd Fl R 3s 3M. Jetties and some dolphins show 2FR (vert) on E side of hbr, and 2FG (vert) on W side.

RADIO TELEPHONE
Yachts should monitor *Cowes Hbr Radio* VHF Ch **69**; also used by hbr launches and for hbr authority's ⚓s. Yachts >30m LOA should advise arr/dep, and call *Chain Ferry* Ch 69 if passing. Casualties: (Ch 16/67/69) for ambulance at Fountain pontoon. Marinas Ch 80. *Water Taxi* Ch 08.

TELEPHONE (Dial code 01983 = code for whole of IOW)
Hr Mr 293952; MRSC (01705) 552100; ⊞ 0345 231110 (H24); Folly Reach Hbr Office 295722; Weather Centre (01703) 228844; Marinecall 0891 500457; Police 528000; Ⓗ 524081; Dr 295251; Cowes Yachting 280770.

FACILITIES
Marinas: Cowes Yacht Haven (CYH) (35+165 Ⓥ, £12 to £18) ☎ 299975, 🚤 200332, Access, D, Gas, Gaz (all H24), FW, AC, EI, ME, Sh, SM, Ⓔ, C (1·5 ton), BH (40 ton), R, Ice, 🛒; **Cowes Marina**, E Cowes (150+150 Ⓥ, £10.50 to £12.60) ☎ 293983, 🚤 299276, AC, FW, BH (7.5 ton), ME, EI, Sh, V, Gas, Gaz, C(7ton), SM, CH, V, R. **Shepards Wharf** (up to 75 berths, £10.50) ☎ 297821, ME, EI, Ⓔ, BH (20 ton), C (6 ton), BY, SM, Sh, CH; **UK Sailing Academy** (10 Ⓥ, £12), ☎ 294941, AC, FW, Ice, Bar, 🛒.
Hbr authority: 100 AB, £5.55-£8; FW: Thetis pontoon only.
Scrubbing berths: Town Quay, UK Sailing Academy.
YCs: Royal Yacht Squadron ☎ 292191; **Royal Corinthian YC** ☎ 292608; **Royal London YC** ☎ 299727; **Island SC** ☎ 296621; **Royal Ocean Racing Club** ☎ 295144 (manned only in Cowes Week); **Cowes Corinthian YC** ☎ 296333;

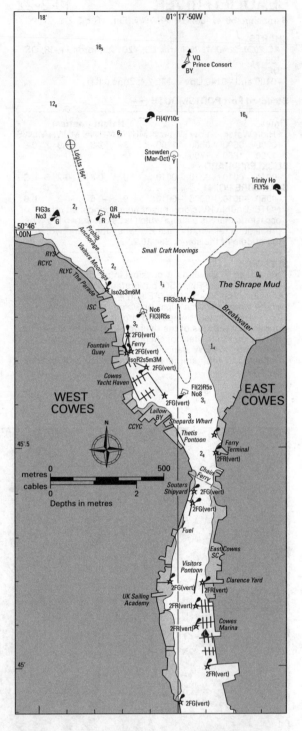

East Cowes SC ☎ 294394; **Cowes Combined Clubs** ☎ 295744. Note: Cowes Week is first full week in August.
Ferries
Red Funnel ☎ 292101, all to Southampton: Car/pax from E Cowes; Hydrofoil/Catamaran (foot pax) from W Cowes. **Chain ferry** ☎ 293041; **Water Taxi** ☎ not yet known.
Services
A comprehensive range of marine services is available. Full details in Port Handbook & Directory, free from Hr Mr, hbr launches, marinas and Cowes Yachting.
FW from marinas, Old Town Quay, Whitegates public pontoon, Thetis pontoon and Folly Inn pontoon.
Fuel: CYH, D only H24; Lallows BY (P & D); MSB pontoon off Souters BY (P & D).
Town EC Wed; P, D, Bar, 🛒, Slip, ✉, Ⓑ, Gas, Gaz.

2

RIVER MEDINA, FOLLY REACH TO NEWPORT

FOLLY REACH, 50°44'·00N 01°16'·90W. Above Medham ECM bn, VQ (3) 5s, there are depths of 1m to S Folly bn, QG. There are Ⓥ pontoons along W bank, S of residents' ones. Hr Mr ☎ 295722 and Ch 69 *Folly Launch*. **Folly Inn** ☎ 297171, AB (pontoon) £7.80, M, Slip, scrubbing berth. **Island Harbour Marina** (5ca S of Folly Inn), (150 + 100 Ⓥ berths, £11.40; 2·5m), ☎ 526020/822999, 🛥 522372, AC, BH (30 ton), C (12 ton), CH, D, El, Ⓔ, FW, Gas, Gaz, ◙, ME, BY, SM, Sh, Slip, V, Bar, R. VHF Ch 80. Excellent shelter; appr via marked, dredged chan with waiting pontoon to stbd, withies to port. Access HW ±4 to lock (HO; H24 by arrangement) with R/G tfc lts. *Ryde Queen* paddle steamer is conspic.

NEWPORT, 50°42'·18N 01°17'·35W. Tides see 10·2·12 and facing page. Above Island Hbr marina the 1·2M chan to Newport dries, but from HW Portsmouth –1½ to HW +2 it carries 2m or more. S from Folly Inn, the hbr authority is IoW Council. Speed limit 6kn up to Seaclose, S of Newport Rowing Club (NRC); thence 4kn to Newport. The chan, which is buoyed and partially lit, favours the W bank; night appr not recommended. Power lines have 33m clearance. Ldg marks/lts are 192°, W ◇ bns 7/11m, on the E bank, both lit 2FR (hor). In Newport, visitors' pontoons on the E/SE sides of the basin have 1·4m HW ±2. Bilge keelers lie alongside pontoons on soft mud; fin keelers against quay wall on firm, level bottom. Fender boards can be supplied.
Newport Yacht Hbr (40 visitors, £9), Hr Mr ☎ 525994, VHF Ch 69 (HO or as arranged), AC, FW, BY, C (10 ton).
Town EC Thurs; P & D (cans), El, Sh, Slip, Gaz, Gas, Ⓑ, Bar, Dr, Ⓗ, ✉, ◙, R, V.

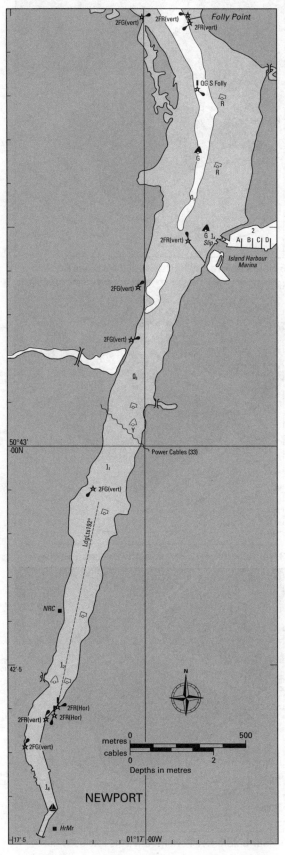

NEWPORT

10-2-24   ISLE OF WIGHT TIDAL STREAMS

5 Hours before HW Portsmouth (0445 before HW Dover)

4 Hours before HW Portsmouth (0345 before HW Dover)

3 Hours before HW Portsmouth (0245 before HW Dover)

2 Hours before HW Portsmouth (0145 before HW Dover)

1 Hour before HW Portsmouth (0045 before HW Dover)

HW Portsmouth (0015 after HW Dover)

General Area 2: 10.2.3

1 Hour after HW Portsmouth (0115 after HW Dover)

2 Hours after HW Portsmouth (0215 after HW Dover)

3 Hours after HW Portsmouth (0315 after HW Dover)

4 Hours after HW Portsmouth (0415 after HW Dover)

5 Hours after HW Portsmouth (0515 after HW Dover)

6 Hours after HW Portsmouth (0615 after HW Dover)

SOUTHAMPTON   10-2-25

Hampshire 50°52'·90N 01°23'·40W   Rtg 1-1-2

CHARTS
AC *2041, 1905, 394, 2045*; Imray C3; Stanfords 11, 18; OS 196

TIDES
HW (1st) –0001 Dover; ML 2·9; Zone 0 (UT)

Standard Port SOUTHAMPTON (→)

Times				Height (metres)			
High Water		Low Water		MHWS	MHWN	MLWN	MLWS
0400	1100	0000	0600	4·5	3·7	1·8	0·5
1600	2300	1200	1800				

Differences REDBRIDGE

–0020	+0005	0000	–0005	–0·1	–0·1	–0·1	–0·1

Southampton is a Standard Port and tidal predictions for each day of the year are given above. At sp there are two separate HWs about two hrs apart; at nps there is a long stand. Predictions are for the first HW when there are two, otherwise for the middle of the stand. See 10·2·12. NE gales combined with high barometer may lower sea level by 0·6m.

SHELTER
Good in most winds, although a heavy chop develops in SE winds ≯F4, when it may be best to shelter in marinas. **ⓥ** berths available in Hythe Marina (with lock ent), Town Quay marina (ent to R Test), and on R Itchen at Ocean Village, Itchen, Shamrock Quay and Kemp's Marinas. There are no specific yacht ⚓s but temp ⚓ is permitted (subject to Hr Mr) off club moorings at Netley, Hythe, Weston and Marchwood in about 2m. Keep clear of main or secondary chans and Hythe Pier. Public moorings for larger yachts opposite Royal Pier near Gymp Elbow PHM buoy in 4m (contact Hr Mr); nearest landing is at Town Quay Marina.

NAVIGATION
WPT Weston Shelf SHM buoy, Fl (3) G 15s, 50°52'·68N 01°23'·16W, 138°/318° from/to Port Sig Stn, 0·40M. Main chans are well marked. Yachts should keep just outside the buoyed lit fairway and are recommended to cross it at 90° abeam Fawley chy, at Cadland/Greenland buoys, abeam Hythe and abeam Town Quay. Caution: several large unlit buoys off Hythe, both sides of the main chan, and elsewhere. It is essential to keep clear of very large tankers operating from Fawley and passenger and container ships from Southampton. See also 10·2·20 for the Area of Concern between Cowes and Calshot. .

R Test   There is foul ground at Marchwood and Royal Pier; extensive container port beyond. Eling Chan dries.
R Itchen   Care is necessary, particularly at night. Above Itchen Bridge the chan bends sharply to port and favours the W side. There are unlit moorings in the centre of the river. Navigation above Northam Bridge (4·7m clearance) is not advisable.
There is a speed limit of 6kn in both rivers above the line Hythe Pier to Weston Shelf.

LIGHTS AND MARKS
Main lts are on the chartlet and in 10.2.4. Fawley chimney (198m, R lts) is conspic day/night. Note also:
(1) Hythe Marina Village, close NW of Hythe Pier: appr chan marked by Q (3) 10s, ECM bn and Fl (2) R 5s PHM bn. Lock ent, N side 2 FG (vert); S side 2 FR (vert).
(2) Southampton Water divides at Dock Head which is easily identified by conspic silos and a high lattice mast showing traffic sigs which are mandatory for commercial vessels, but may be disregarded by yachts outside the main chans. Beware large ships manoeuvering off Dock Head, and craft leaving Rivers Itchen and Test.
(3) Dock Hd, W side (Queen Elizabeth II Terminal, S end) 4 FG (vert) 3M; framework tr; marks ent to R Test. Town Quay Marina has 2 FR and 2 FG (vert) on wavebreaks.
(4) Ent to R Itchen marked by SHM Oc G 4s, beyond which piles with G lts mark E side of chan ldg to Itchen bridge (24·4m); a FW lt at bridge centre marks the main chan. Ent to Ocean Village is facing Vosper Thorneycroft sheds, conspic on E bank.
(5) Above Itchen Bridge, marked by 2 FR (vert) and 2 FG (vert), the principal marks are: Crosshouse bn Oc R 5s; Chapel bn Fl G 3s. **Caution:** 8 large unlit mooring buoys in middle of river. Shamrock Quay pontoons 2 FR (vert) at SW and NE ends; No 5 bn Fl G 3s; No 7 bn Fl (2) G 5s; Millstone Pt jetty 2 FR (vert); No 9 bn Fl (4) G 10s and Kemps Quay Marina 2 FG (vert). Northam Bridge, FR/FG, has 4·7m clearance.

RADIO TELEPHONE
Vessel Traffic Services (VTS) Centre. Call: *Southampton VTS* Ch **12** 14 16 (H24).
Traffic info for small craft broadcast on Ch 12 on the hour 0600-2200 Fri-Sun and Bank Holiday Mons from Easter to last weekend in Oct. From 1 June to 30 Sept broadcasts are every day at the same times (see 10.2.20).
Southampton Hbr Patrol Call: *Southampton Patrol* VHF Ch **12** 16, 01-28, 60-88 (H24). Marinas VHF Ch **80** M.
Fuel barges in R Itchen, call *Mr Diesel* or *Wyefuel* Ch 08.

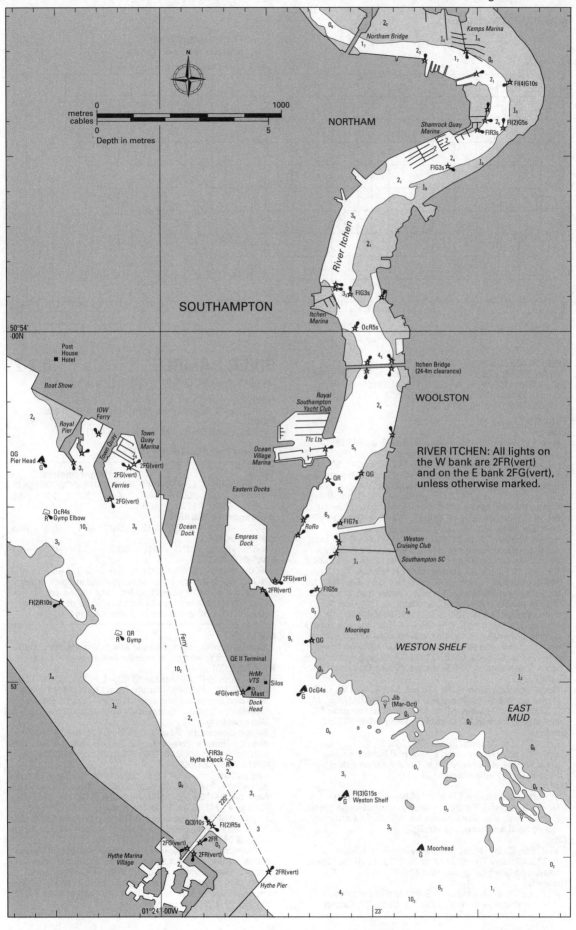

2

N

metres
cables
0 — 1000
0 — 5
Depth in metres

NORTHAM

Kemps Marina

Northam Bridge

Fl(4)G10s

Shamrock Quay
Marina

Fl(2)G5s

FlR3s

FlG3s

River Itchen

SOUTHAMPTON

FlG3s

Itchen
Marina

OcR5s

50°54'
·00N

Post
House
Hotel

Itchen Bridge
(24·4m clearance)

Boat Show

Royal
Southampton
Yacht Club

WOOLSTON

IOW
Ferry

Royal Pier

Town
Quay
Marina

QG
Pier Head
G

2FG(vert)

Ferries

2FG(vert)

Tfc Lts

Ocean
Village
Marina

QR

QG

RIVER ITCHEN: All lights on
the W bank are 2FR(vert)
and on the E bank 2FG(vert),
unless otherwise marked.

2FG(vert)

Eastern Docks

OcR4s
Gymp Elbow
R

Ocean
Dock

RoRo

FlG7s

Weston
Cruising Club

Southampton SC

Fl(2)R10s

Empress
Dock

2FG(vert)

QR
Gymp
R

Ferry

2FR(vert)

FlG5s

QG

Moorings

WESTON SHELF

QE II Terminal

HrMr
VTS

Silos

4FG(vert)

Mast

OcG4s
G

Jib
(Mar-Oct)
Y

EAST
MUD

Dock
Head

53'

FlR3s
Hythe Knock
R

Fl(3)G15s
G Weston Shelf

220°

2FG(vert)

Q(3)10s

Fl(2)R5s

2FR(vert)

2FR(vert)

Hythe Marina
Village

Moorhead
G

2FR(vert)

Hythe Pier

01°24'·00W

23'

SOUTHAMPTON continued

SOUTHAMPTON
MEAN SPRING AND NEAP CURVES
Springs occur 2 days after New and Full Moon

MEAN RANGES
Springs 4.0m
Neaps 1.9m

TELEPHONE (Dial code 01703)
Hr Mr ABP & VTS 330022, 339733 outside HO; ☎ 232991; ∰ 0345 231110 (H24); MRSC (01705) 552100; Weather Centre 228844; Marinecall 0891 500457; Police 581111; Dr 226631 (Port Health); Ⓗ 777222.

FACILITIES
Marinas

Hythe Marina (220+50 visitors; 2·5m). Pre-call VHF Ch 80. ☎ 207073, ☎ 842424, £13.44, access H24; BH (30 ton), C (12 ton), AC, P, D, El, ME, Sh, CH, FW, V, R, Bar, SM. Tfc lts (vert) at lock: 3 Ⓡ = Wait; 3 Fl R = Stop; 2 Ⓖ over Ⓦ = proceed, free-flow. Waiting pontoon outside lock, S side. Ferries from Hythe pier to Town Quay and Ocean Village.
Ocean Village Marina (450; visitors welcome). Pre-call Ch 80, ☎ 229385, ☎ 233515, £16.13, FW, V, R, Bar, CH, Slip, Gas, Gaz, Kos, ME, Sh, Ⓞ, AC, (Access H24);
Itchen Marina (50) ☎ 631500, D, BY, FW, AC, C (40 ton); No Ⓥ berths, but will not refuse a vessel in difficulty.
Shamrock Quay Marina (220+40 Ⓥ). ☎ 229461, ☎ 333384. Pre-call Ch 80. £12.89, access H24, BH (63 ton), C (12 ton), ME, El, Sh, SM, Ⓞ, R, Bar, AC, CH, FW, Gas, Gaz, Kos, V;
Kemp's Quay Marina (220; visitors welcome) ☎ 632323, £12.34, access HW±3½, AC, C (5 ton), D, FW, Gas, ME;
Town Quay Marina (136) ☎ 234397, ☎ 235302, £10.74, access H24 (2·6m), AC, FW, CH, Ⓞ, R, Bar; marina ent is a dogleg between two floating wavebreaks which appear continuous from seaward (lit by 2 FR and 2 FG). Beware adjacent fast ferries. Craft >20m LOA must get clearance from Southampton VTS to ent/dep Town Quay marina.
Yacht Clubs
Royal Southampton YC ☎ 223352, Bar, R, M, FW, L, Ⓞ; **Hythe SC** ☎ 846563; **Marchwood YC** ☎ 864641, Bar, M, C (10 ton), FW, L; **Netley SC** ☎ 454272; **Southampton SC** ☎ 446575; **Weston SC** ☎ 452527; **Eling SC** ☎ 863987.
Services
CH, ACA, Sh, Rigging, Spars, SM, ME, El, Ⓔ. Fuel barge, VHF Ch 08 *Mr Diesel*, is on E side of R Itchen, close downstream of Ocean Village. Note: nearest petrol by hose is from Hythe marina.
Hards
at Hythe, Crackmore, Eling, Mayflower Park (Test), Northam (Itchen). Public landings at Cross House hard, Cross House slip, Block House hard (Itchen), Carnation public hard & Cowporters public hard.
City
V, R, Bar, Ⓑ, ✉, ⇌, ✈, Ferries/Hydrofoil to IOW, ☎ 333042; ferry Town Quay, ☎ 840722, to Hythe. Stena Sealink to Cherbourg; see 10.0.4.
Reference
ABP publish a *Yachtsman's Guide to Southampton Water* obtainable from VTS Centre, Berth 37, Eastern Docks, Southampton SO1 1GG.

RIVER HAMBLE   10-2-26
Hampshire 50°50'·90N 01°18'·41W   Rtg 2-1-2

CHARTS
AC *2022, 1905*; Imray C3; Stanfords 11, 18; OS 196
TIDES
+0020, –0010 Dover; ML 2·9; Zone 0 (UT)

Standard Port SOUTHAMPTON (→)

Times				Height (metres)			
High Water		Low Water		MHWS	MHWN	MLWN	MLWS
0400	1100	0000	0600	4·5	3·7	1·8	0·5
1600	2300	1200	1800				
Differences WARSASH							
+0020	+0010	+0010	0000	0·0	+0·1	+0·1	+0·3
BURSLEDON							
+0020	+0020	+0010	+0010	+0·1	+0·1	+0·2	+0·2
CALSHOT CASTLE							
0000	+0025	0000	0000	0·0	0·0	+0·2	+0·3

NOTE: Double HWs occur at or near sp; at other times there is a stand of about two hrs. Predictions are for the first HW if there are two or for the middle of the stand. See 10·2·12. NE gales can decrease depths by 0·6m.

SHELTER
Excellent, with visitors berths at 4 major marinas, many YCs, SCs, BYs and on some Hbr Authority pontoons.
NAVIGATION
WPT Hamble Pt SCM buoy, Q (6) + L Fl 15s, 50°50'·12N 01°18'·58W, 166°/346° from/to front ldg lt, 0·48M. Unlit piles and buoys are a danger at night. River is extremely crowded; ⚓ prohib. Yachts may not use spinnakers above Warsash jetty.
Bridge clearances: Road 4·0m; Rly 6·0m; M27 4·3m. The site of a Historic Wreck (*Grace Dieu*) is 3ca up-river of the M27 bridge, at 50°53'·51N 01°17'·24W, (see 10.0.3h).
LIGHTS AND MARKS
Ldg lts 345°: Front Oc (2) R 12s 4m 2M, No 6 pile bn; rear, 820m from front, QR 12m, W mast on shore; vis 341°-349°. No 1 pile Fl G 3s 3M, SHM. No 2 pile Q (3) 10s 3M, ECM. No 3 pile Fl (2) G 5s, SHM. No 5 pile Fl (3) G 10s, SHM. Ldg lts 026° on E shore: front QG, pile bn; rear Iso G 6s. No 7 pile Fl G 3s, SHM. No 8 pile Fl R 3s, PHM. No 9 pile Fl (2) G 5s, SHM. No 10 pile Fl (2) R 5s, PHM.
In mid-stream between Warsash and Hamble Pt Marina there is a clearly marked visitors' pontoon, between other private pontoons. Above Warsash, jetties and pontoons on the E side are marked by 2FG (vert) lts, and those on the W side by 2FR (vert) lts. Lateral piles are Fl G 2s or Fl R 2s (see chartlet).

RIVER HAMBLE *continued*

RADIO TELEPHONE
Call: *Hamble Hbr Radio* Ch **68** 16 (April-Oct: Daily 0830-1930. Nov-Mar: Mon-Fri 0830-1700; Sat 0830-1300). Marinas Ch **80** M. Water Taxi Ch 77. See also 10.2.25 for VTS and info broadcasts.

TELEPHONE (Dial code 01703) on Hamble side. See Note. Hr Mr 576387; MRSC (01705) 552100; ☶ 0345 231110 (H24); Southampton Weather Centre 228844; Marinecall 0891 500457; Police 581111; Dr 573110.
Note: On the E side of river, Locks Heath (dial code 01489) ☎ numbers all begin 57, 58 or 88.

FACILITIES
Marinas:
Hamble Pt Marina (220+10 Ⓥ) ☎ 452464, ✆ 456440; pre-call Ch 80. Access H24; £14.81, AC, CH, D, BH (65 ton), C (7 ton), Ⓔ, EI, FW, Gas, Gaz, ME, Sh, V, YC, Bar;
Port Hamble Marina (340+ Ⓥ) ☎ 452741, ✆ 455206; pre-call Ch 80. Access H24; £13.74, AC, ▣, Bar, BH (100 ton), C (7 ton), CH, D, P, Ⓔ, FW, Gas, Gaz, ME, Sh, EI, SM, Slip;
Mercury Yacht Hbr (346+ Ⓥ) ☎ 455994, ✆ 457369; pre-call Ch 80. Access H24; £10.58, AC, Bar, BH (20 ton), EI, Slip, CH, D, Ⓔ, FW, Gas, Gaz, ME, P, Sh, SM, V, ▣;
Swanwick Marina (380+ Ⓥ) ☎ 885000 (after 1700, 885262), ✆ 885509, £12, AC, BH (60 ton), C (12 ton), CH, D, Ⓔ, FW, Gas, Gaz, ☶, ▣, ME, P, ✉, Sh, SM, V, (Access H24).

The Hbr Authority jetty in front of the conspic B/W Hr Mr's Office at Warsash has limited AB (£15 for 24hrs); also Ⓥ pontoons in mid-stream. A public jetty is on the W bank near the Bugle carpark. Ⓥ pile moorings are opposite Port Hamble marina.

Yacht Clubs:
Hamble River SC ☎ 452070; **RAFYC** ☎ 452208, Bar, R, L; **Royal Southern YC** ☎ 453271; **Warsash SC** ☎ 583575.

Services:
A very wide range of marine services is available; consult marina/Hr Mr for locations. CH, Ⓔ, BY, AB, C (12 ton), Ⓔ, FW, Gas, Gaz, M, ME, R, Sh, Slip, SM; Riggers, BH (25 ton), ACA, Divers. **Piper Marine Services** ☎ 454563, (or call *Piper Fuel* Ch M), D, P.

Hards. At Warsash, Hamble and Swanwick.
Slips at Warsash, Hamble, Bursledon & Lower Swanwick.
Scrubbing piles at Warsash by Hr Mr's slipway; on W bank upriver of public jetty near Bugle; between Port Hamble and Mercury marinas; by slip opposite Swanwick marina. ✉ (Hamble, Bursledon, Warsash and Lower Swanwick); Ⓑ (Hamble, Bursledon, Sarisbury Green, Swanwick, Warsash); ⇌ (Hamble and Bursledon); ✈ (Southampton). *Hamble River Guide* available from Hr Mr.

ADJACENT HARBOURS

ASHLETT CREEK, Hants, 50°49'·98N 01°19'·40W. AC *2022, 1905*. Tides approx as Calshot Castle (opposite). Small drying (2·1m) inlet across from R Hamble; best for shoal-draft vessels. Appr at HW via Fawley PHM buoy, QR, close to Esso Marine Terminal. Unlit chan, marked by 3 PHM buoys, 1 SHM buoy and 2 PHM bns, has four 90° bends. Ldg bns are hard to find; local knowledge desirable. Berth at drying quay. Facilities: AB, M, FW, Slip, Hard, Pub. **Esso SC.**

HILL HEAD, Hants, 50°49'·05N 01°14'·45W. AC *2022, 1905*. HW +0030 on Dover; see 10.2.30 for LEE-ON-SOLENT diffs. Short term ⚓ for small craft at mouth of R Meon. Bar dries ¼M offshore. Ent dries 1·2m at MLWS. Appr on 030° towards Hill Head SC ho (W, conspic); bns mark chan, ● topmarks to port, ▲ ones to stbd. Small hbr to W inside ent where yachts can lie in soft mud alongside bank. Facilities: **Hill Head SC** ☎ (01329) 664843. **Hill Head village** EC Thurs; ✉, CH, V, P & D (cans).

ENGLAND – SOUTHAMPTON

LAT 50°54'N   LONG 1°24'W

TIMES AND HEIGHTS OF HIGH AND LOW WATERS

YEAR **1998**

TIME ZONE (UT)
For Summer Time add ONE hour in non-shaded areas

JANUARY

Day	Time	m	Day	Time	m
1 TH	0003 / 0557 / 1218 / 1820	4.6 / 0.6 / 4.6 / 0.5	**16** F	0041 / 0634 / 1253 / 1851	4.4 / 0.8 / 4.4 / 0.7
2 F	0046 / 0640 / 1303 / 1903	4.6 / 0.7 / 4.6 / 0.6	**17** SA	0118 / 0707 / 1329 / 1922	4.3 / 0.9 / 4.3 / 0.9
3 SA	0132 / 0725 / 1350 / 1949	4.5 / 0.8 / 4.5 / 0.7	**18** SU	0155 / 0739 / 1406 / 1953	4.2 / 1.1 / 4.1 / 1.1
4 SU	0221 / 0815 / 1441 / 2039	4.4 / 1.0 / 4.3 / 0.9	**19** M	0233 / 0814 / 1445 / 2028	4.1 / 1.4 / 4.0 / 1.3
5 M	0316 / 0910 / 1538 / 2137	4.3 / 1.2 / 4.2 / 1.2	**20** TU	0315 / 0855 / 1530 / 2112	4.0 / 1.6 / 3.8 / 1.6
6 TU	0417 / 1014 / 1644 / 2244	4.2 / 1.4 / 4.0 / 1.3	**21** W	0404 / 0948 / 1624 / 2212	3.8 / 1.8 / 3.7 / 1.8
7 W	0526 / 1126 / 1757 / 2357	4.1 / 1.4 / 4.0 / 1.4	**22** TH	0505 / 1058 / 1734 / 2330	3.8 / 1.9 / 3.6 / 1.9
8 TH	0638 / 1239 / 1912	4.1 / 1.4 / 4.0	**23** F	0615 / 1216 / 1853	3.8 / 1.9 / 3.7
9 F	0108 / 0745 / 1346 / 2018	1.3 / 4.2 / 1.2 / 4.1	**24** SA	0046 / 0724 / 1324 / 2001	1.8 / 3.9 / 1.6 / 3.8
10 SA	0211 / 0844 / 1445 / 2115	1.2 / 4.3 / 1.0 / 4.2	**25** SU	0150 / 0822 / 1420 / 2055	1.6 / 4.1 / 1.0 / 4.0
11 SU	0306 / 0936 / 1536 / 2203	1.0 / 4.4 / 0.8 / 4.3	**26** M	0243 / 0911 / 1510 / 2141	1.3 / 4.3 / 1.0 / 4.3
12 M O	0354 / 1021 / 1622 / 2247	0.8 / 4.5 / 0.6 / 4.4	**27** TU	0331 / 0955 / 1557 / 2224	1.0 / 4.5 / 0.6 / 4.5
13 TU	0439 / 1102 / 1704 / 2327	0.7 / 4.5 / 0.5 / 4.4	**28** W ●	0417 / 1038 / 1643 / 2306	0.7 / 4.6 / 0.4 / 4.6
14 W	0520 / 1140 / 1743	0.6 / 4.5 / 0.5	**29** TH	0502 / 1120 / 1727 / 2349	0.5 / 4.7 / 0.2 / 4.7
15 TH	0004 / 0558 / 1217 / 1818	4.4 / 0.6 / 4.4 / 0.5	**30** F	0546 / 1204 / 1810	0.3 / 4.7 / 0.2
			31 SA	0032 / 0629 / 1248 / 1852	4.7 / 0.3 / 4.7 / 0.2

FEBRUARY

Day	Time	m	Day	Time	m
1 SU	0117 / 0713 / 1334 / 1935	4.7 / 0.4 / 4.6 / 0.4	**16** M	0122 / 0709 / 1334 / 1921	4.2 / 0.9 / 4.2 / 0.9
2 M	0203 / 0758 / 1421 / 2020	4.6 / 0.6 / 4.5 / 0.6	**17** TU	0156 / 0737 / 1409 / 1950	4.1 / 1.1 / 4.1 / 1.1
3 TU	0252 / 0846 / 1513 / 2110	4.4 / 0.9 / 4.2 / 1.0	**18** W	0232 / 0810 / 1446 / 2026	4.0 / 1.3 / 3.9 / 1.4
4 W	0347 / 0943 / 1613 / 2211	4.2 / 1.2 / 4.0 / 1.3	**19** TH	0312 / 0852 / 1531 / 2114	3.9 / 1.6 / 3.7 / 1.7
5 TH	0452 / 1052 / 1726 / 2326	4.0 / 1.4 / 3.8 / 1.5	**20** F	0403 / 0950 / 1633 / 2225	3.7 / 1.8 / 3.6 / 1.9
6 F	0609 / 1213 / 1851	3.9 / 1.5 / 3.8	**21** SA	0513 / 1113 / 1757 / 2356	3.6 / 1.9 / 3.6 / 1.9
7 SA	0047 / 0728 / 1330 / 2008	1.5 / 3.9 / 1.4 / 3.9	**22** SU	0635 / 1241 / 1921	3.7 / 1.7 / 3.7
8 SU	0158 / 0834 / 1432 / 2107	1.4 / 4.1 / 1.2 / 4.1	**23** M	0115 / 0747 / 1350 / 2026	1.7 / 3.9 / 1.4 / 4.0
9 M	0255 / 0927 / 1523 / 2155	1.1 / 4.2 / 0.9 / 4.2	**24** TU	0217 / 0845 / 1447 / 2117	1.3 / 4.2 / 1.0 / 4.2
10 TU	0342 / 1010 / 1606 / 2235	0.9 / 4.3 / 0.6 / 4.3	**25** W	0310 / 0934 / 1538 / 2203	0.9 / 4.4 / 0.6 / 4.5
11 W O	0424 / 1048 / 1646 / 2311	0.7 / 4.4 / 0.5 / 4.4	**26** TH ●	0359 / 1019 / 1625 / 2247	0.6 / 4.6 / 0.2 / 4.7
12 TH	0503 / 1122 / 1723 / 2344	0.6 / 4.4 / 0.4 / 4.4	**27** F	0446 / 1103 / 1711 / 2330	0.3 / 4.8 / 0.0 / 4.8
13 F	0539 / 1155 / 1757	0.5 / 4.4 / 0.4	**28** SA	0531 / 1146 / 1755	0.1 / 4.8 / -0.1
14 SA	0016 / 0612 / 1228 / 1827	4.4 / 0.6 / 4.4 / 0.5			
15 SU	0049 / 0641 / 1301 / 1855	4.3 / 0.7 / 4.3 / 0.7			

MARCH

Day	Time	m	Day	Time	m
1 SU	0014 / 0614 / 1231 / 1837	4.8 / 0.0 / 4.8 / -0.1	**16** M	0019 / 0615 / 1232 / 1828	4.3 / 0.5 / 4.3 / 0.6
2 M	0058 / 0657 / 1315 / 1918	4.8 / 0.1 / 4.7 / 0.1	**17** TU	0051 / 0640 / 1304 / 1852	4.2 / 0.7 / 4.2 / 0.8
3 TU	0142 / 0739 / 1401 / 2000	4.7 / 0.3 / 4.5 / 0.5	**18** W	0123 / 0705 / 1337 / 1919	4.2 / 0.9 / 4.1 / 1.0
4 W	0229 / 0823 / 1450 / 2046	4.4 / 0.7 / 4.3 / 0.9	**19** TH	0156 / 0736 / 1412 / 1952	4.1 / 1.1 / 4.0 / 1.3
5 TH	0320 / 0914 / 1547 / 2142	4.1 / 1.1 / 4.0 / 1.3	**20** F	0232 / 0814 / 1454 / 2037	3.9 / 1.3 / 3.8 / 1.6
6 F	0422 / 1020 / 1701 / 2259	3.9 / 1.4 / 3.7 / 1.6	**21** SA	0319 / 0906 / 1552 / 2142	3.8 / 1.6 / 3.7 / 1.8
7 SA	0542 / 1146 / 1833	3.7 / 1.6 / 3.6	**22** SU	0425 / 1023 / 1714 / 2314	3.6 / 1.8 / 3.6 / 1.9
8 SU	0029 / 0711 / 1312 / 1956	1.7 / 3.7 / 1.5 / 3.8	**23** M	0551 / 1200 / 1844	3.6 / 1.7 / 3.7
9 M	0146 / 0822 / 1416 / 2055	1.5 / 3.9 / 1.3 / 4.0	**24** TU	0043 / 0713 / 1320 / 1955	1.7 / 3.8 / 1.4 / 4.0
10 TU	0241 / 0913 / 1505 / 2140	1.3 / 4.1 / 1.0 / 4.2	**25** W	0152 / 0817 / 1421 / 2051	1.3 / 4.1 / 0.9 / 4.3
11 W	0325 / 0954 / 1545 / 2217	1.0 / 4.2 / 0.7 / 4.3	**26** TH	0248 / 0910 / 1514 / 2139	0.9 / 4.4 / 0.5 / 4.6
12 TH	0404 / 1029 / 1623 / 2250	0.7 / 4.3 / 0.5 / 4.3	**27** F	0339 / 0957 / 1604 / 2225	0.5 / 4.6 / 0.2 / 4.8
13 F O	0440 / 1100 / 1659 / 2320	0.5 / 4.3 / 0.4 / 4.3	**28** SA ●	0427 / 1042 / 1650 / 2309	0.2 / 4.8 / -0.1 / 4.9
14 SA	0515 / 1130 / 1732 / 2349	0.5 / 4.3 / 0.4 / 4.3	**29** SU	0513 / 1127 / 1735 / 2353	0.1 / 4.9 / -0.2 / 4.9
15 SU	0547 / 1201 / 1802	0.5 / 4.3 / 0.5	**30** M	0557 / 1211 / 1818	-0.1 / 4.9 / -0.1
			31 TU	0037 / 0638 / 1256 / 1859	4.8 / 0.0 / 4.7 / 0.1

APRIL

Day	Time	m	Day	Time	m
1 W	0122 / 0720 / 1342 / 1940	4.7 / 0.3 / 4.5 / 0.5	**16** TH	0054 / 0641 / 1312 / 1856	4.2 / 0.8 / 4.2 / 1.0
2 TH	0207 / 0802 / 1430 / 2024	4.4 / 0.6 / 4.3 / 0.9	**17** F	0128 / 0712 / 1349 / 1931	4.1 / 1.0 / 4.1 / 1.2
3 F	0256 / 0850 / 1526 / 2118	4.1 / 1.0 / 3.9 / 1.4	**18** SA	0206 / 0751 / 1432 / 2017	4.0 / 1.2 / 4.0 / 1.5
4 SA	0355 / 0951 / 1638 / 2232	3.8 / 1.4 / 3.7 / 1.7	**19** SU	0253 / 0843 / 1530 / 2120	3.8 / 1.4 / 3.8 / 1.7
5 SU	0513 / 1114 / 1810	3.6 / 1.7 / 3.6	**20** M	0357 / 0954 / 1648 / 2246	3.7 / 1.6 / 3.8 / 1.8
6 M	0004 / 0643 / 1242 / 1932	1.8 / 3.6 / 1.6 / 3.8	**21** TU	0519 / 1125 / 1812	3.7 / 1.6 / 3.9
7 TU	0122 / 0756 / 1347 / 2030	1.7 / 3.8 / 1.4 / 4.0	**22** W	0013 / 0640 / 1247 / 1924	1.6 / 3.8 / 1.3 / 4.1
8 W	0216 / 0849 / 1436 / 2114	1.4 / 4.0 / 1.1 / 4.2	**23** TH	0123 / 0748 / 1352 / 2023	1.3 / 4.1 / 1.0 / 4.4
9 TH	0259 / 0930 / 1516 / 2150	1.1 / 4.1 / 0.9 / 4.3	**24** F	0222 / 0844 / 1447 / 2114	0.9 / 4.4 / 0.6 / 4.6
10 F	0337 / 1004 / 1554 / 2222	0.8 / 4.2 / 0.7 / 4.3	**25** SA	0315 / 0934 / 1539 / 2201	0.5 / 4.6 / 0.3 / 4.8
11 SA O	0413 / 1035 / 1629 / 2251	0.6 / 4.3 / 0.5 / 4.3	**26** SU ●	0405 / 1021 / 1627 / 2247	0.2 / 4.7 / 0.1 / 4.9
12 SU	0447 / 1104 / 1703 / 2320	0.5 / 4.3 / 0.5 / 4.3	**27** M	0452 / 1107 / 1713 / 2332	0.1 / 4.8 / 0.1 / 4.9
13 M	0520 / 1134 / 1734 / 2350	0.5 / 4.3 / 0.6 / 4.3	**28** TU	0538 / 1153 / 1757	0.0 / 4.8 / 0.1
14 TU	0549 / 1205 / 1802	0.5 / 4.3 / 0.7	**29** W	0017 / 0620 / 1239 / 1839	4.8 / 0.1 / 4.7 / 0.3
15 W	0021 / 0614 / 1239 / 1827	4.3 / 0.6 / 4.3 / 0.8	**30** TH	0102 / 0702 / 1325 / 1921	4.6 / 0.3 / 4.5 / 0.6

Chart Datum: 2·74 metres below Ordnance Datum (Newlyn)

2

ENGLAND – SOUTHAMPTON

LAT 50°54′N   LONG 1°24′W

TIMES AND HEIGHTS OF HIGH AND LOW WATERS   YEAR **1998**

TIME ZONE (UT)
For Summer Time add ONE hour in non-shaded areas

MAY

Day	Time	m	Time	m	Time	m	Time	m
1 F	0147	4.4	0743	0.6	1414	4.3	2005	1.0
2 SA	0235	4.1	0829	1.0	1508	4.0	2057	1.4
3 SU	0330	3.8	0923	1.3	1614	3.8	2203	1.7
4 M	0438	3.6	1034	1.6	1732	3.7	2325	1.9
5 TU	0558	3.6	1153	1.7	1850	3.8		
6 W	0039	1.8	0713	3.7	1302	1.6	1950	4.0
7 TH	0137	1.6	0810	3.8	1354	1.4	2037	4.1
8 F	0223	1.3	0855	4.0	1439	1.1	2116	4.2
9 SA	0303	1.0	0933	4.1	1519	0.9	2149	4.3
10 SU	0341	0.8	1006	4.2	1557	0.8	2220	4.3
11 M O	0417	0.7	1038	4.2	1633	0.7	2251	4.3
12 TU	0451	0.6	1110	4.3	1707	0.7	2323	4.3
13 W	0523	0.6	1143	4.3	1738	0.8	2356	4.3
14 TH	0554	0.7	1217	4.3	1809	0.9		
15 F	0032	4.3	0624	0.8	1255	4.3	1841	1.0
16 SA	0109	4.2	0658	0.9	1335	4.2	1920	1.2
17 SU	0150	4.1	0740	1.1	1421	4.1	2008	1.4
18 M	0239	4.0	0831	1.3	1518	4.0	2109	1.6
19 TU	0341	3.9	0937	1.4	1628	4.0	2224	1.6
20 W	0454	3.8	1056	1.5	1744	4.0	2343	1.5
21 TH	0611	3.9	1213	1.3	1854	4.2		
22 F	0053	1.3	0719	4.1	1320	1.0	1955	4.4
23 SA	0155	1.0	0818	4.3	1419	0.8	2048	4.6
24 SU	0250	0.7	0912	4.5	1513	0.5	2138	4.7
25 M ●	0343	0.4	1002	4.6	1604	0.4	2226	4.8
26 TU	0432	0.3	1050	4.6	1652	0.3	2313	4.8
27 W	0519	0.2	1138	4.6	1738	0.3	2359	4.7
28 TH	0603	0.3	1224	4.6	1822	0.5		
29 F	0044	4.5	0645	0.4	1310	4.4	1905	0.7
30 SA	0129	4.4	0726	0.7	1358	4.3	1948	1.1
31 SU	0214	4.2	0808	1.0	1447	4.1	2034	1.4

JUNE

Day	Time	m	Time	m	Time	m	Time	m
1 M	0303	3.9	0854	1.3	1542	4.0	2129	1.7
2 TU	0358	3.8	0949	1.5	1644	3.9	2234	1.8
3 W	0502	3.6	1055	1.7	1752	3.8	2344	1.9
4 TH	0613	3.6	1204	1.7	1856	3.9		
5 F	0046	1.8	0718	3.7	1304	1.6	1950	4.0
6 SA	0139	1.6	0813	3.8	1356	1.4	2035	4.1
7 SU	0225	1.3	0858	4.0	1441	1.3	2115	4.2
8 M	0307	1.1	0937	4.1	1524	1.1	2150	4.3
9 TU	0346	0.9	1013	4.2	1604	1.0	2225	4.3
10 W O	0424	0.8	1048	4.3	1642	0.9	2300	4.4
11 TH	0501	0.7	1124	4.3	1718	0.9	2337	4.4
12 F	0537	0.7	1201	4.3	1755	0.9		
13 SA	0015	4.4	0612	0.7	1241	4.3	1832	1.0
14 SU	0056	4.3	0651	0.8	1324	4.3	1914	1.1
15 M	0140	4.2	0734	0.9	1411	4.3	2002	1.2
16 TU	0229	4.1	0823	1.1	1505	4.2	2057	1.3
17 W	0326	4.0	0922	1.2	1607	4.2	2203	1.4
18 TH	0432	4.0	1029	1.3	1716	4.2	2314	1.4
19 F	0542	4.0	1141	1.3	1824	4.2		
20 SA	0023	1.3	0651	4.1	1251	1.2	1928	4.4
21 SU	0129	1.1	0755	4.2	1354	1.0	2027	4.5
22 M	0228	0.9	0854	4.3	1452	0.8	2120	4.6
23 TU	0324	0.7	0947	4.4	1545	0.7	2211	4.6
24 W ●	0415	0.5	1037	4.5	1636	0.6	2258	4.6
25 TH	0503	0.4	1124	4.5	1723	0.6	2343	4.6
26 F	0547	0.4	1209	4.5	1807	0.6		
27 SA	0027	4.5	0629	0.5	1254	4.4	1848	0.8
28 SU	0109	4.4	0708	0.7	1337	4.3	1928	1.0
29 M	0151	4.2	0745	0.9	1420	4.2	2008	1.3
30 TU	0233	4.1	0823	1.2	1505	4.1	2051	1.5

JULY

Day	Time	m	Time	m	Time	m	Time	m
1 W	0318	3.9	0905	1.4	1554	4.0	2140	1.7
2 TH	0409	3.8	0956	1.7	1649	3.9	2240	1.9
3 F	0508	3.7	1059	1.8	1752	3.9	2346	1.9
4 SA	0616	3.6	1207	1.9	1855	3.9		
5 SU	0049	1.8	0723	3.7	1311	1.8	1952	4.0
6 M	0144	1.6	0820	3.9	1405	1.6	2040	4.1
7 TU	0233	1.4	0907	4.0	1453	1.4	2123	4.2
8 W	0317	1.1	0949	4.2	1537	1.2	2202	4.3
9 TH O	0400	0.9	1027	4.3	1620	1.0	2240	4.4
10 F	0441	0.7	1106	4.4	1701	0.9	2320	4.5
11 SA	0522	0.6	1145	4.4	1742	0.8		
12 SU	0000	4.5	0602	0.6	1227	4.4	1823	0.8
13 M	0043	4.5	0643	0.6	1311	4.5	1906	0.8
14 TU	0128	4.4	0726	0.7	1357	4.5	1952	0.9
15 W	0216	4.3	0812	0.9	1447	4.4	2042	1.1
16 TH	0308	4.2	0904	1.1	1544	4.3	2139	1.3
17 F	0408	4.1	1004	1.3	1647	4.2	2245	1.4
18 SA	0515	4.0	1113	1.4	1757	4.2	2357	1.4
19 SU	0628	4.0	1227	1.4	1908	4.2		
20 M	0108	1.3	0740	4.1	1337	1.3	2013	4.3
21 TU	0214	1.2	0844	4.2	1439	1.1	2110	4.4
22 W	0311	0.9	0939	4.3	1534	0.9	2201	4.5
23 TH ●	0402	0.7	1028	4.4	1623	0.8	2246	4.5
24 F	0448	0.6	1112	4.4	1709	0.7	2328	4.5
25 SA	0531	0.5	1153	4.4	1751	0.7		
26 SU	0008	4.4	0610	0.6	1233	4.4	1829	0.8
27 M	0046	4.4	0646	0.7	1310	4.4	1905	0.9
28 TU	0123	4.3	0718	0.9	1348	4.3	1938	1.1
29 W	0200	4.2	0750	1.1	1426	4.2	2011	1.3
30 TH	0238	4.0	0822	1.3	1506	4.0	2048	1.6
31 F	0320	3.9	0901	1.6	1551	3.9	2134	1.8

AUGUST

Day	Time	m	Time	m	Time	m	Time	m
1 SA	0410	3.7	0953	1.9	1646	3.8	2237	2.0
2 SU	0513	3.6	1104	2.0	1754	3.8	2352	2.0
3 M	0630	3.6	1223	2.0	1905	3.8		
4 TU	0102	1.8	0741	3.8	1330	1.8	2006	4.0
5 W	0201	1.6	0838	4.0	1425	1.6	2056	4.2
6 TH	0251	1.3	0924	4.2	1514	1.3	2139	4.3
7 F	0338	1.0	1006	4.4	1600	1.0	2221	4.5
8 SA O	0423	0.7	1046	4.5	1645	0.8	2302	4.6
9 SU	0507	0.5	1127	4.6	1728	0.6	2344	4.7
10 M	0549	0.4	1210	4.7	1811	0.5		
11 TU	0026	4.7	0631	0.4	1253	4.7	1853	0.5
12 W	0111	4.6	0714	0.5	1338	4.6	1936	0.7
13 TH	0158	4.5	0757	0.7	1426	4.5	2022	0.9
14 F	0247	4.4	0845	1.0	1519	4.3	2115	1.2
15 SA	0344	4.2	0940	1.3	1620	4.1	2218	1.4
16 SU	0452	4.0	1050	1.6	1733	4.0	2335	1.6
17 M	0612	3.9	1211	1.7	1854	4.0		
18 TU	0056	1.6	0733	4.0	1330	1.6	2007	4.1
19 W	0206	1.4	0840	4.1	1433	1.3	2105	4.3
20 TH	0302	1.1	0934	4.3	1525	1.1	2153	4.4
21 F	0349	0.9	1018	4.4	1610	0.9	2234	4.5
22 SA ●	0431	0.7	1057	4.4	1652	0.7	2311	4.5
23 SU	0511	0.6	1133	4.5	1730	0.7	2345	4.4
24 M	0547	0.6	1206	4.4	1805	0.7		
25 TU	0018	4.4	0620	0.7	1239	4.4	1837	0.8
26 W	0051	4.3	0649	0.8	1312	4.3	1905	1.0
27 TH	0125	4.2	0715	1.0	1346	4.2	1932	1.2
28 F	0159	4.1	0742	1.3	1421	4.1	2002	1.5
29 SA	0236	4.0	0815	1.6	1500	4.0	2039	1.7
30 SU	0319	3.8	0858	1.8	1548	3.8	2132	2.0
31 M	0416	3.7	1002	2.1	1653	3.7	2250	2.1

Chart Datum: 2·74 metres below Ordnance Datum (Newlyn)

ENGLAND – SOUTHAMPTON

LAT 50°54′N   LONG 1°24′W

TIMES AND HEIGHTS OF HIGH AND LOW WATERS

YEAR **1998**

TIME ZONE (UT)
For Summer Time add ONE hour in non-shaded areas

SEPTEMBER

Day	Time	m		Day	Time	m
1 TU	0536 / 1133 / 1815	3.6 / 2.2 / 3.7		**16** W	0046 / 0728 / 1323 / 1959	1.7 / 3.9 / 1.7 / 4.0
2 W	0020 / 0700 / 1256 / 1930	2.0 / 3.7 / 2.0 / 3.9		**17** TH	0156 / 0832 / 1424 / 2055	1.5 / 4.1 / 1.5 / 4.2
3 TH	0131 / 0807 / 1359 / 2028	1.7 / 4.0 / 1.7 / 4.1		**18** F	0248 / 0921 / 1510 / 2139	1.2 / 4.3 / 1.2 / 4.4
4 F	0226 / 0858 / 1451 / 2115	1.3 / 4.2 / 1.3 / 4.4		**19** SA	0330 / 1001 / 1551 / 2216	1.0 / 4.4 / 0.9 / 4.5
5 SA	0316 / 0942 / 1539 / 2159	0.9 / 4.5 / 0.9 / 4.6		**20** SU	0408 / 1036 / 1628 / 2248 ●	0.8 / 4.5 / 0.8 / 4.5
6 SU O	0403 / 1024 / 1625 / 2241	0.6 / 4.7 / 0.6 / 4.7		**21** M	0445 / 1107 / 1704 / 2318	0.6 / 4.5 / 0.7 / 4.5
7 M	0448 / 1107 / 1710 / 2324	0.4 / 4.8 / 0.4 / 4.8		**22** TU	0519 / 1136 / 1737 / 2348	0.6 / 4.5 / 0.7 / 4.4
8 TU	0532 / 1150 / 1754	0.2 / 4.9 / 0.3		**23** W	0551 / 1206 / 1807	0.7 / 4.4 / 0.8
9 W	0007 / 0614 / 1233 / 1836	4.9 / 0.2 / 4.9 / 0.3		**24** TH	0019 / 0618 / 1237 / 1833	4.4 / 0.8 / 4.4 / 0.9
10 TH	0052 / 0656 / 1318 / 1918	4.8 / 0.3 / 4.8 / 0.5		**25** F	0051 / 0642 / 1309 / 1857	4.3 / 1.0 / 4.3 / 1.1
11 F	0137 / 0738 / 1404 / 2003	4.7 / 0.6 / 4.6 / 0.8		**26** SA	0124 / 0708 / 1343 / 1925	4.2 / 1.2 / 4.2 / 1.3
12 SA	0226 / 0824 / 1455 / 2052	4.4 / 1.0 / 4.4 / 1.1		**27** SU	0159 / 0738 / 1419 / 2000	4.1 / 1.5 / 4.0 / 1.6
13 SU	0322 / 0918 / 1556 / 2154	4.2 / 1.4 / 4.1 / 1.5		**28** M	0239 / 0819 / 1503 / 2047	3.9 / 1.8 / 3.9 / 1.8
14 M	0432 / 1029 / 1713 / 2317	3.9 / 1.7 / 3.9 / 1.7		**29** TU	0334 / 0918 / 1604 / 2159	3.8 / 2.0 / 3.8 / 2.0
15 TU	0602 / 1200 / 1843	3.8 / 1.9 / 3.9		**30** W	0452 / 1047 / 1728 / 2337	3.7 / 2.2 / 3.7 / 2.0

OCTOBER

Day	Time	m		Day	Time	m
1 TH	0621 / 1221 / 1852	3.8 / 2.0 / 3.9		**16** F	0131 / 0810 / 1400 / 2031	1.6 / 4.1 / 1.6 / 4.2
2 F	0058 / 0734 / 1330 / 1956	1.7 / 4.0 / 1.7 / 4.2		**17** SA	0221 / 0857 / 1445 / 2114	1.3 / 4.3 / 1.3 / 4.3
3 SA	0159 / 0829 / 1426 / 2048	1.3 / 4.3 / 1.3 / 4.4		**18** SU	0301 / 0935 / 1523 / 2150	1.1 / 4.4 / 1.1 / 4.4
4 SU	0251 / 0916 / 1516 / 2134	0.9 / 4.6 / 0.9 / 4.7		**19** M	0338 / 1008 / 1559 / 2222	0.9 / 4.5 / 0.9 / 4.4
5 M O	0339 / 1001 / 1603 / 2219	0.5 / 4.8 / 0.5 / 4.8		**20** TU ●	0414 / 1037 / 1634 / 2251	0.8 / 4.5 / 0.7 / 4.4
6 TU	0425 / 1044 / 1649 / 2303	0.3 / 5.0 / 0.3 / 4.9		**21** W	0448 / 1106 / 1707 / 2320	0.7 / 4.5 / 0.7 / 4.4
7 W	0510 / 1128 / 1734 / 2347	0.1 / 5.0 / 0.2 / 5.0		**22** TH	0520 / 1135 / 1738 / 2351	0.7 / 4.5 / 0.8 / 4.4
8 TH	0554 / 1212 / 1818	0.1 / 5.0 / 0.3		**23** F	0549 / 1206 / 1805	0.7 / 4.4 / 0.9
9 F	0032 / 0636 / 1258 / 1900	4.9 / 0.3 / 4.9 / 0.4		**24** SA	0023 / 0620 / 1240 / 1830	4.4 / 0.9 / 4.4 / 1.0
10 SA	0118 / 0718 / 1344 / 1943	4.7 / 0.6 / 4.6 / 0.7		**25** SU	0058 / 0642 / 1314 / 1859	4.3 / 1.2 / 4.3 / 1.2
11 SU	0207 / 0804 / 1434 / 2032	4.5 / 1.0 / 4.4 / 1.1		**26** M	0133 / 0714 / 1351 / 1934	4.2 / 1.4 / 4.1 / 1.4
12 M	0304 / 0857 / 1533 / 2132	4.2 / 1.4 / 4.1 / 1.5		**27** TU	0214 / 0755 / 1434 / 2021	4.0 / 1.7 / 4.0 / 1.7
13 TU	0414 / 1008 / 1650 / 2253	3.9 / 1.8 / 3.8 / 1.8		**28** W	0308 / 0852 / 1533 / 2127	3.9 / 1.9 / 3.9 / 1.9
14 W	0544 / 1139 / 1820	3.8 / 2.0 / 3.8		**29** TH	0421 / 1013 / 1651 / 2257	3.8 / 2.0 / 3.8 / 1.9
15 TH	0022 / 0708 / 1301 / 1936	1.8 / 3.9 / 1.9 / 4.0		**30** F	0545 / 1144 / 1814	3.9 / 1.9 / 3.9
				31 SA	0021 / 0659 / 1257 / 1923	1.7 / 4.1 / 1.6 / 4.2

NOVEMBER

Day	Time	m		Day	Time	m
1 SU	0127 / 0758 / 1356 / 2020	1.3 / 4.4 / 1.3 / 4.4		**16** M	0225 / 0902 / 1449 / 2120	1.3 / 4.4 / 1.2 / 4.3
2 M	0222 / 0849 / 1449 / 2109	0.9 / 4.7 / 0.9 / 4.7		**17** TU	0304 / 0936 / 1527 / 2154	1.1 / 4.4 / 1.0 / 4.3
3 TU	0312 / 0936 / 1539 / 2156	0.6 / 4.9 / 0.6 / 4.8		**18** W	0342 / 1008 / 1604 / 2225	0.9 / 4.5 / 0.9 / 4.4
4 W O	0401 / 1022 / 1627 / 2242	0.3 / 5.0 / 0.3 / 4.9		**19** TH ●	0418 / 1038 / 1639 / 2257	0.9 / 4.5 / 0.9 / 4.4
5 TH	0447 / 1107 / 1714 / 2328	0.2 / 5.0 / 0.2 / 4.9		**20** F	0452 / 1110 / 1712 / 2329	0.8 / 4.5 / 0.8 / 4.4
6 F	0532 / 1152 / 1759	0.2 / 5.0 / 0.3		**21** SA	0524 / 1142 / 1742	0.9 / 4.5 / 0.8
7 SA	0014 / 0616 / 1238 / 1842	4.8 / 0.4 / 4.9 / 0.4		**22** SU	0003 / 0554 / 1217 / 1811	4.4 / 1.0 / 4.4 / 0.9
8 SU	0102 / 0700 / 1325 / 1926	4.7 / 0.7 / 4.6 / 0.7		**23** M	0039 / 0625 / 1253 / 1843	4.3 / 1.1 / 4.3 / 1.1
9 M	0151 / 0745 / 1414 / 2012	4.5 / 1.0 / 4.4 / 1.1		**24** TU	0117 / 0700 / 1332 / 1920	4.3 / 1.3 / 4.2 / 1.2
10 TU	0246 / 0836 / 1510 / 2107	4.2 / 1.4 / 4.1 / 1.4		**25** W	0159 / 0742 / 1417 / 2005	4.2 / 1.5 / 4.1 / 1.4
11 W	0351 / 0940 / 1616 / 2216	4.0 / 1.8 / 3.9 / 1.7		**26** TH	0251 / 0836 / 1512 / 2105	4.1 / 1.7 / 4.0 / 1.6
12 TH	0508 / 1100 / 1736 / 2336	3.9 / 2.0 / 3.8 / 1.8		**27** F	0355 / 0946 / 1620 / 2221	4.0 / 1.8 / 3.9 / 1.7
13 F	0627 / 1218 / 1853	3.9 / 1.9 / 3.8		**28** SA	0510 / 1106 / 1736 / 2341	4.0 / 1.8 / 4.0 / 1.6
14 SA	0046 / 0731 / 1320 / 1953	1.7 / 4.1 / 1.8 / 4.0		**29** SU	0622 / 1221 / 1848	4.1 / 1.6 / 4.1
15 SU	0141 / 0821 / 1408 / 2041	1.5 / 4.2 / 1.5 / 4.1		**30** M	0051 / 0726 / 1325 / 1950	1.3 / 4.4 / 1.3 / 4.3

DECEMBER

Day	Time	m		Day	Time	m
1 TU	0151 / 0821 / 1423 / 2045	1.0 / 4.6 / 1.0 / 4.5		**16** W	0229 / 0903 / 1455 / 2127	1.4 / 4.3 / 1.2 / 4.2
2 W	0246 / 0912 / 1516 / 2136	0.7 / 4.8 / 0.7 / 4.7		**17** TH	0311 / 0940 / 1535 / 2204	1.2 / 4.4 / 1.0 / 4.3
3 TH	0337 / 1001 / 1607 / 2225 O	0.5 / 4.9 / 0.5 / 4.8		**18** F ●	0351 / 1015 / 1613 / 2238	1.0 / 4.4 / 0.8 / 4.3
4 F	0426 / 1048 / 1655 / 2313	0.4 / 4.9 / 0.3 / 4.8		**19** SA	0429 / 1049 / 1649 / 2312	0.9 / 4.5 / 0.7 / 4.4
5 SA	0514 / 1135 / 1742	0.4 / 4.9 / 0.3		**20** SU	0504 / 1123 / 1724 / 2347	0.9 / 4.5 / 0.7 / 4.4
6 SU	0000 / 0559 / 1222 / 1826	4.7 / 0.5 / 4.8 / 0.4		**21** M	0539 / 1200 / 1758	0.9 / 4.5 / 0.8
7 M	0048 / 0643 / 1307 / 1909	4.6 / 0.7 / 4.6 / 0.6		**22** TU	0024 / 0613 / 1238 / 1832	4.4 / 0.9 / 4.4 / 0.8
8 TU	0136 / 0727 / 1354 / 1952	4.4 / 1.0 / 4.4 / 0.9		**23** W	0103 / 0650 / 1318 / 1910	4.4 / 1.0 / 4.3 / 1.0
9 W	0225 / 0814 / 1443 / 2038	4.3 / 1.3 / 4.2 / 1.2		**24** TH	0146 / 0732 / 1402 / 1954	4.3 / 1.2 / 4.2 / 1.1
10 TH	0319 / 0906 / 1536 / 2131	4.1 / 1.6 / 4.0 / 1.5		**25** F	0234 / 0821 / 1453 / 2046	4.2 / 1.3 / 4.1 / 1.3
11 F	0419 / 1008 / 1638 / 2235	4.0 / 1.8 / 3.8 / 1.7		**26** SA	0330 / 0920 / 1552 / 2149	4.2 / 1.5 / 4.0 / 1.4
12 SA	0527 / 1119 / 1749 / 2345	3.9 / 1.9 / 3.7 / 1.8		**27** SU	0434 / 1030 / 1700 / 2301	4.1 / 1.5 / 4.0 / 1.5
13 SU	0634 / 1226 / 1859	3.9 / 1.9 / 3.8		**28** M	0544 / 1144 / 1813	4.2 / 1.5 / 4.0
14 M	0049 / 0733 / 1323 / 1958	1.7 / 4.0 / 1.7 / 3.9		**29** TU	0015 / 0653 / 1255 / 1923	1.4 / 4.3 / 1.3 / 4.1
15 TU	0143 / 0822 / 1412 / 2046	1.6 / 4.2 / 1.5 / 4.1		**30** W	0123 / 0756 / 1359 / 2025	1.2 / 4.4 / 1.1 / 4.3
				31 TH	0224 / 0853 / 1457 / 2122	1.0 / 4.6 / 0.8 / 4.4

Chart Datum: 2·74 metres below Ordnance Datum (Newlyn)

WOOTTON CREEK   10-2-27

Isle of Wight 50°44'·06N 01°12'·68W   Rtg 1-5-1

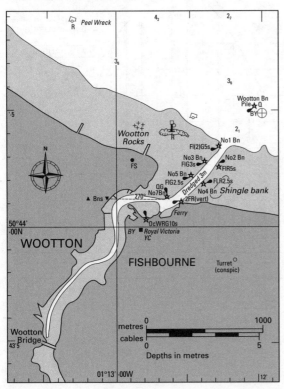

CHARTS
AC *2022, 394*; Imray C3, Y20; Stanfords 11, 18; OS 196
TIDES
+0023 Dover; ML 2·8; Zone 0 (UT). Use RYDE differences 10.2.28; see also 10.2.12.
SHELTER
Good except in stormy N or E winds. Above the ferry, the creek dries. Moor to piles or Ⓐs off RVYC. No ⚓ in the fairway. Speed limit 5kn.
NAVIGATION
WPT Wootton NCM Bn, Q, 50°44'·51N 01°12'·04W, 044°/224° from/to ferry slip, 0·64M. Beware large ferries, leaving astern and turning at Wootton Bn. It is difficult to beat in on the ebb.
LIGHTS AND MARKS
Ent to creek due S of SE Ryde Middle SCM and 1·75M W of Ryde Pier. Chan is marked by four lit SHM bns and two PHMs. Keep in W sector of Dir lt, Oc WRG 10s, G221°-224°, W224°-225½°, R225½°-230½°. By ferry terminal, turn onto ldg marks on W shore △ ▽, which form a ◇ when in transit 270°.
RADIO TELEPHONE
None.
TELEPHONE (Dial code 01983)
Royal Victoria YC 882325; MRSC (01705) 552100; Fairways Association 882763; ☎ 0345 231110 (H24); Marinecall 0891 500457; Police 528000; Dr 882424.
FACILITIES
Royal Victoria YC ☎ 882325, Slip, M, FW, R, Bar;
Village EC = Thurs, Wootton Bridge = Wed; ✉ (Wootton Bridge, Ryde), Ⓑ (Ryde), ⇌ (ferry to Portsmouth), ✈ (Southampton).

RYDE   10-2-28

Isle of Wight 50°43'·95N 01°09'·22W   Rtg 3-4-2

CHARTS
AC *394, 2045*; Imray C3, C15; Stanfords 11, 18; OS 196
TIDES
+0022 Dover; ML 2·8m; Zone 0 (UT). See 10.2.12

Standard Port PORTSMOUTH (→)

Times				Height (metres)			
High Water		Low Water		MHWS	MHWN	MLWN	MLWS
0000	0600	0500	1100	4·7	3·8	1·9	0·8
1200	1800	1700	2300				
Differences RYDE							
–0010	+0010	–0005	–0010	–0·2	–0·1	0·0	+0·1

SHELTER
Small hbr 300m E of Ryde Pier; dries approx 2·3m. Access for shoal draft approx HW–2½ to +2. Berth on E'ly of three pontoons; long and fin keel yachts should dry out against the bkwtr.

NAVIGATION
WPT 50°44'·32N 01°09'·15W, No 1 SHM buoy, 017°/197° from/to hbr ent, **6**ca. From the E, best to stay North of No Man's Land Fort and SW Mining Ground Y buoy to clear Ryde Sands. Drying channel **197**° across Ryde Sands (1·5m - 1·7m) is marked by 3 SHM and 3 PHM unlit buoys. Beware hovercraft manoeuvering between Ryde pier and marina; and ferries from/to pierhead.
LIGHTS AND MARKS
Ryde Ch spire (Holy Trinity) brg 200° gives initial appr. Ryde pier is lit by 3 sets of 2FR (vert) and a FY fog lt. Hbr ent lts are 2 FR and 2FG (vert) 7m 1M. Hbr has W floodlights inside ent.
RADIO TELEPHONE
Ryde Harbour VHF Ch 80.
TELEPHONE (Dial code 01983)
Hr Mr 613879, ⚓ 823941; MRSC (01705) 552100; ☎ 0345 231110 (H24); Marinecall 0891 500457; Police 528000; Ⓗ 524081.
FACILITIES
Marina (75+70 visitors) ☎ 613879, £7.50, FW, Slip, Ⓞ.
Services: P & D (cans) from garage, Gas, V, R, Bar,
Town EC Thurs; all domestic facilities nearby.

PORTSMOUTH

MEAN SPRING
AND NEAP CURVES

MEAN RANGES
Springs 3.9m
Neaps 1.9m

Springs occur 2 days
after
New and Full Moon.

BEMBRIDGE 10-2-29

Isle of Wight 50°41′·59N 01°06′·31W   Rtg 3-2-2

CHARTS
AC 2022, 2050, 2045; Imray C15, C3, C9; Stanfords 18; OS 196
TIDES
+0020 Dover; Zone 0 (UT). See 10.2.12

Standard Port PORTSMOUTH (→)

Times				Height (metres)			
High Water		Low Water		MHWS	MHWN	MLWN	MLWS
0000	0600	0500	1100	4·7	3·8	1·9	0·8
1200	1800	1700	2300				
Differences BEMBRIDGE HARBOUR							
−0010	+0005	+0020	0000	−1·6	−1·5	−1·4	−0·6
FORELAND (LB Slip)							
−0005	0000	+0005	+0010	−0·1	−0·1	0·0	+0·1
VENTNOR							
−0025	−0030	−0025	−0030	−0·8	−0·6	−0·2	+0·2
SANDOWN							
0000	+0005	+0010	+0025	−0·6	−0·5	−0·2	0·0

SHELTER
Good, but difficult ent in NNE gales. No access LW ±2½
for 1·5m draft; carefully check tide gauge which indicates
depth over the bar. Speed limit 6kn. Visitors' berths at
marina, Fisherman's Wharf and afloat on pontoon
between Nos 15 & 17 SHM buoys. No ‡ in chan and hbr,
but Priory Bay is sheltered ‡ in winds from S to WNW.
NAVIGATION
WPT tide gauge, Fl Y 2s, 50°42′·43N 01°04′·93W, approx 2ca E
of ent to well-buoyed, but unlit chan. The bar, between Nos 6
and 10 buoys, almost dries. Avoid the gravel banks between
St Helen's Fort, Nodes Pt and N to Seaview, by keeping to ent
times above.
LIGHTS AND MARKS
St Helens Fort Fl (3) 10s 16m 8M; no ‡ within 1ca radius of
Fort. Conspic W seamark on shore where chan turns S.
RADIO TELEPHONE
Call Bembridge Marina VHF Ch 80; Hbr Launch Ch M.

TELEPHONE (Dial code 01983)
Hr Mr 872828; MRSC (01705) 552100; ⌗ 0345 231110
(H24); Marinecall 0891 500457; Police 528000; Dr 872614.
FACILITIES
Marina (40+100 visitors) ☎ 872828, ⚓ 872922, £12, FW,
ME, EI, AC, ⊙, V, R, Bar; **St Helen's Quay** FW, CH; **Brading
Haven YC** ☎ 872289, Bar, R, FW; **Bembridge SC** ☎ 872686;
Services: M, Slip, BY, P & D (cans), ME, EI, Sh, Gas.
Town EC Thurs; V, R, Bar, ⊠, Ⓑ, ⇌ (Ryde), ✈ (So'ton).

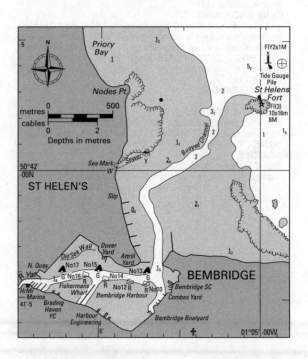

ENGLAND – PORTSMOUTH

LAT 50°48'N   LONG 1°07'W

TIMES AND HEIGHTS OF HIGH AND LOW WATERS   YEAR **1998**

TIME ZONE (UT)
For Summer Time add ONE hour in non-shaded areas

JANUARY

Day	Time	m	Time	m	Day	Time	m	Time	m
1 TH	0039	4.8	1252	4.7	**16** F	0119	4.6	1327	4.5
	0603	0.9	1829	0.7		0642	1.1	1902	1.0
2 F	0123	4.8	1336	4.7	**17** SA	0154	4.5	1402	4.4
	0648	0.9	1913	0.7		0715	1.2	1933	1.1
3 SA	0210	4.7	1424	4.6	**18** SU	0229	4.4	1438	4.3
	0735	1.0	2000	0.9		0748	1.4	2005	1.3
4 SU	0259	4.7	1514	4.4	**19** M	0306	4.3	1517	4.1
	0826	1.1	2051	1.0		0822	1.6	2039	1.5
5 M	0352	4.5	1609	4.3	**20** TU	0347	4.2	1559	4.0
	0922	1.3	2149	1.2		0902	1.8	2122	1.7
6 TU	0451	4.4	1711	4.1	**21** W	0434	4.1	1651	3.8
	1027	1.5	2255	1.4		0955	2.0	2220	1.9
7 W	0557	4.3	1824	4.1	**22** TH	0532	4.0	1759	3.7
	1141	1.6				1108	2.1	2338	2.0
8 TH	0009	1.5	1256	1.5	**23** F	0644	4.0	1919	3.8
	0709	4.3	1941	4.1		1234	2.0		
9 F	0122	1.5	1401	1.4	**24** SA	0058	1.9	1340	1.8
	0818	4.4	2051	4.2		0753	4.1	2027	4.0
10 SA	0224	1.3	1458	1.2	**25** SU	0200	1.7	1433	1.5
	0918	4.6	2150	4.4		0851	4.3	2123	4.2
11 SU	0318	1.2	1548	1.0	**26** M	0250	1.4	1519	1.2
	1009	4.7	2240	4.6		0940	4.5	2210	4.5
12 M O	0406	1.1	1633	0.9	**27** TU	0337	1.2	1604	0.9
	1055	4.7	2325	4.6		1025	4.6	2256	4.6
13 TU	0449	1.0	1715	0.8	**28** W ●	0422	1.0	1649	0.7
	1137	4.7				1110	4.7	2340	4.8
14 W	0006	4.7	1216	4.7	**29** TH	0507	0.8	1734	0.5
	0529	1.0	1753	0.8		1154	4.8		
15 TH	0044	4.6	1252	4.6	**30** F	0025	4.9	1240	4.8
	0607	1.0	1828	0.8		0552	0.7	1818	0.5
					31 SA	0110	4.9	1326	4.8
						0637	0.6	1902	0.5

FEBRUARY

Day	Time	m	Time	m	Day	Time	m	Time	m
1 SU	0156	4.9	1413	4.7	**16** M	0157	4.5	1411	4.3
	0722	0.7	1946	0.6		0716	1.1	1931	1.1
2 M	0242	4.8	1501	4.6	**17** TU	0230	4.4	1445	4.2
	0809	0.8	2033	0.8		0744	1.3	2001	1.3
3 TU	0330	4.6	1551	4.4	**18** W	0304	4.3	1521	4.1
	0859	1.0	2124	1.1		0817	1.5	2037	1.5
4 W	0423	4.4	1647	4.2	**19** TH	0343	4.1	1605	3.9
	0957	1.3	2226	1.4		0900	1.7	2126	1.8
5 TH	0524	4.2	1757	4.0	**20** F	0434	3.9	1708	3.7
	1109	1.6	2342	1.6		0959	1.9	2237	2.0
6 F	0639	4.1	1923	3.9	**21** SA	0545	3.9	1832	3.7
	1230	1.6				1127	2.0		
7 SA	0102	1.7	1344	1.5	**22** SU	0013	2.0	1303	1.9
	0759	4.1	2042	4.1		0708	3.9	1953	3.9
8 SU	0212	1.5	1445	1.3	**23** M	0133	1.8	1407	1.5
	0905	4.3	2142	4.3		0819	4.1	2057	4.2
9 M	0308	1.3	1534	1.1	**24** TU	0230	1.5	1458	1.1
	0959	4.4	2231	4.4		0915	4.3	2149	4.4
10 TU	0354	1.1	1617	0.9	**25** W	0320	1.1	1546	0.8
	1044	4.5	2313	4.5		1005	4.6	2236	4.7
11 W O	0435	1.0	1657	0.8	**26** TH ●	0406	0.8	1632	0.5
	1123	4.6	2350	4.6		1052	4.7	2322	4.8
12 TH	0512	0.9	1733	0.7	**27** F	0452	0.6	1718	0.4
	1158	4.5				1139	4.8		
13 F	0023	4.6	1232	4.5	**28** SA	0008	4.9	1226	4.9
	0547	0.9	1806	0.8		0537	0.4	1802	0.3
14 SA	0054	4.6	1304	4.5					
	0619	0.9	1837	0.8					
15 SU	0125	4.6	1337	4.4					
	0648	1.0	1905	0.9					

MARCH

Day	Time	m	Time	m	Day	Time	m	Time	m
1 SU	0054	5.0	1313	4.9	**16** M	0057	4.5	1313	4.5
	0621	0.3	1845	0.3		0622	0.8	1838	0.9
2 M	0138	5.0	1359	4.8	**17** TU	0127	4.5	1346	4.4
	0705	0.4	1928	0.4		0647	0.9	1903	1.0
3 TU	0223	4.9	1445	4.7	**18** W	0158	4.4	1419	4.3
	0749	0.6	2013	0.7		0714	1.1	1931	1.2
4 W	0308	4.6	1533	4.4	**19** TH	0229	4.3	1453	4.1
	0836	0.9	2101	1.0		0745	1.2	2006	1.4
5 TH	0356	4.4	1627	4.2	**20** F	0304	4.1	1535	4.0
	0930	1.2	2200	1.4		0825	1.5	2052	1.7
6 F	0453	4.1	1735	3.9	**21** SA	0351	3.9	1634	3.8
	1039	1.5	2317	1.7		0919	1.7	2158	1.9
7 SA	0610	3.8	1906	3.8	**22** SU	0459	3.8	1754	3.7
	1203	1.7				1040	1.9	2335	2.0
8 SU	0044	1.8	1324	1.6	**23** M	0625	3.8	1920	3.9
	0741	3.9	2029	4.0		1224	1.8		
9 M	0159	1.6	1427	1.4	**24** TU	0106	1.8	1340	1.5
	0852	4.0	2129	4.2		0746	4.0	2029	4.2
10 TU	0254	1.4	1515	1.2	**25** W	0209	1.4	1435	1.1
	0945	4.2	2215	4.4		0849	4.2	2125	4.5
11 W	0338	1.2	1556	1.0	**26** TH	0300	1.0	1524	0.7
	1028	4.3	2254	4.5		0942	4.5	2214	4.7
12 TH	0415	1.0	1633	0.8	**27** F	0347	0.7	1611	0.5
	1105	4.4	2328	4.5		1032	4.7	2301	4.9
13 F O	0451	0.8	1708	0.7	**28** SA ●	0434	0.4	1657	0.3
	1138	4.5	2358	4.6		1120	4.9	2348	5.0
14 SA	0524	0.7	1741	0.7	**29** SU	0519	0.3	1743	0.2
	1209	4.5				1208	4.9		
15 SU	0027	4.6	1241	4.5	**30** M	0033	5.0	1256	5.0
	0555	0.8	1811	0.8		0603	0.2	1826	0.2
					31 TU	0118	5.0	1342	4.9
						0647	0.3	1909	0.4

APRIL

Day	Time	m	Time	m	Day	Time	m	Time	m
1 W	0202	4.9	1429	4.7	**16** TH	0131	4.4	1356	4.3
	0730	0.5	1953	0.7		0650	1.0	1909	1.1
2 TH	0246	4.6	1516	4.5	**17** F	0203	4.3	1433	4.2
	0815	0.8	2040	1.0		0723	1.1	1946	1.3
3 F	0333	4.3	1609	4.2	**18** SA	0239	4.2	1516	4.1
	0906	1.2	2137	1.4		0804	1.3	2032	1.6
4 SA	0427	4.0	1715	3.9	**19** SU	0326	4.0	1613	3.9
	1011	1.5	2251	1.8		0857	1.6	2136	1.8
5 SU	0540	3.7	1843	3.8	**20** M	0430	3.8	1726	3.9
	1132	1.7				1012	1.7	2304	1.9
6 M	0016	1.9	1255	1.7	**21** TU	0550	3.8	1848	4.0
	0714	3.7	2004	4.0		1147	1.7		
7 TU	0134	1.7	1359	1.5	**22** W	0033	1.7	1307	1.4
	0828	3.9	2103	4.2		0711	4.0	1959	4.2
8 W	0229	1.5	1447	1.3	**23** TH	0141	1.4	1407	1.1
	0921	4.1	2148	4.3		0819	4.2	2058	4.5
9 TH	0312	1.2	1527	1.1	**24** F	0236	1.0	1459	0.7
	1003	4.2	2226	4.4		0916	4.5	2150	4.7
10 F	0348	1.0	1604	0.9	**25** SA	0325	0.7	1547	0.5
	1039	4.3	2259	4.5		1009	4.7	2239	4.9
11 SA O	0423	0.8	1639	0.8	**26** SU ●	0413	0.4	1635	0.3
	1112	4.4	2329	4.5		1100	4.8	2326	5.0
12 SU	0457	0.8	1713	0.8	**27** M	0500	0.3	1721	0.3
	1144	4.4	2358	4.5		1149	4.9		
13 M	0529	0.8	1745	0.8	**28** TU	0013	5.0	1238	4.9
	1216	4.4				0545	0.3	1806	0.3
14 TU	0029	4.5	1249	4.4	**29** W	0058	5.0	1325	4.9
	0557	0.8	1812	0.9		0629	0.3	1850	0.5
15 W	0100	4.5	1323	4.4	**30** TH	0142	4.8	1412	4.7
	0623	0.9	1839	1.0		0712	0.5	1934	0.8

Chart Datum: 2·73 metres below Ordnance Datum (Newlyn)

ENGLAND – PORTSMOUTH

LAT 50°48′N   LONG 1°07′W

TIMES AND HEIGHTS OF HIGH AND LOW WATERS   YEAR **1998**

TIME ZONE (UT)
For Summer Time add ONE hour in non-shaded areas

Chart Datum: 2·73 metres below Ordnance Datum (Newlyn)

MAY

Day	Time	m	Day	Time	m
1 F	0226 / 0757 / 1500 / 2020	4.6 / 0.8 / 4.5 / 1.1	**16** SA	0144 / 0710 / 1418 / 1934	4.4 / 1.0 / 4.3 / 1.2
2 SA	0312 / 0845 / 1551 / 2113	4.3 / 1.1 / 4.2 / 1.4	**17** SU	0224 / 0753 / 1504 / 2022	4.3 / 1.2 / 4.2 / 1.4
3 SU	0403 / 0942 / 1651 / 2218	4.0 / 1.5 / 4.0 / 1.7	**18** M	0312 / 0847 / 1558 / 2123	4.1 / 1.4 / 4.1 / 1.6
4 M	0506 / 1054 / 1805 / 2335	3.8 / 1.7 / 3.9 / 1.9	**19** TU	0412 / 0954 / 1703 / 2237	4.0 / 1.5 / 4.1 / 1.7
5 TU	0629 / 1211 / 1922	3.7 / 1.7 / 3.9	**20** W	0522 / 1114 / 1817 / 2357	4.0 / 1.5 / 4.1 / 1.6
6 W	0050 / 0746 / 1317 / 2023	1.8 / 3.7 / 1.6 / 4.1	**21** TH	0638 / 1231 / 1928	4.0 / 1.4 / 4.3
7 TH	0150 / 0843 / 1408 / 2111	1.6 / 3.9 / 1.4 / 4.2	**22** F	0108 / 0749 / 1336 / 2030	1.4 / 4.2 / 1.1 / 4.5
8 F	0235 / 0928 / 1450 / 2150	1.4 / 4.0 / 1.2 / 4.3	**23** SA	0209 / 0851 / 1432 / 2125	1.1 / 4.4 / 0.9 / 4.7
9 SA	0314 / 1006 / 1529 / 2225	1.2 / 4.2 / 1.1 / 4.4	**24** SU	0302 / 0947 / 1524 / 2217	0.8 / 4.6 / 0.7 / 4.9
10 SU	0351 / 1041 / 1607 / 2257	1.0 / 4.3 / 1.0 / 4.5	**25** M	0352 / 1040 / 1613 / ● 2306	0.6 / 4.7 / 0.5 / 4.9
11 M	0427 / 1116 / 1643 / O 2329	0.9 / 4.3 / 0.9 / 4.5	**26** TU	0441 / 1131 / 1701 / 2353	0.5 / 4.8 / 0.5 / 5.0
12 TU	0501 / 1150 / 1717	0.8 / 4.4 / 0.9	**27** W	0528 / 1221 / 1748	0.4 / 4.8 / 0.5
13 W	0002 / 0532 / 1226 / 1748	4.5 / 0.8 / 4.4 / 0.9	**28** TH	0039 / 0613 / 1309 / 1832	4.9 / 0.5 / 4.8 / 0.7
14 TH	0036 / 0602 / 1301 / 1819	4.5 / 0.9 / 4.4 / 1.0	**29** F	0124 / 0656 / 1356 / 1915	4.8 / 0.6 / 4.7 / 0.9
15 F	0109 / 0634 / 1338 / 1854	4.5 / 0.9 / 4.4 / 1.1	**30** SA	0207 / 0739 / 1442 / 1959	4.6 / 0.9 / 4.5 / 1.1
			31 SU	0250 / 0823 / 1529 / 2046	4.3 / 1.1 / 4.3 / 1.4

JUNE

Day	Time	m	Day	Time	m
1 M	0336 / 0911 / 1619 / 2140	4.1 / 1.4 / 4.1 / 1.7	**16** TU	0301 / 0838 / 1543 / 2109	4.3 / 1.1 / 4.4 / 1.3
2 TU	0427 / 1008 / 1715 / 2244	3.9 / 1.6 / 4.0 / 1.8	**17** W	0356 / 0937 / 1641 / 2213	4.2 / 1.3 / 4.3 / 1.4
3 W	0527 / 1114 / 1819 / 2354	3.7 / 1.8 / 3.9 / 1.9	**18** TH	0459 / 1044 / 1747 / 2324	4.1 / 1.3 / 4.3 / 1.5
4 TH	0638 / 1221 / 1924	3.7 / 1.8 / 4.0	**19** F	0609 / 1157 / 1857	4.1 / 1.3 / 4.3
5 F	0058 / 0746 / 1320 / 2019	1.8 / 3.8 / 1.7 / 4.1	**20** SA	0037 / 0722 / 1307 / 2003	1.4 / 4.2 / 1.2 / 4.5
6 SA	0151 / 0841 / 1408 / 2105	1.6 / 3.9 / 1.5 / 4.2	**21** SU	0144 / 0830 / 1409 / 2103	1.2 / 4.3 / 1.1 / 4.6
7 SU	0236 / 0927 / 1452 / 2146	1.4 / 4.1 / 1.3 / 4.3	**22** M	0242 / 0930 / 1504 / 2158	1.1 / 4.5 / 0.9 / 4.7
8 M	0317 / 1008 / 1533 / 2224	1.2 / 4.2 / 1.2 / 4.4	**23** TU	0336 / 1026 / 1556 / 2248	0.8 / 4.6 / 0.8 / 4.8
9 TU	0356 / 1047 / 1612 / 2301	1.1 / 4.3 / 1.1 / 4.5	**24** W	0426 / 1118 / 1645 / ● 2336	0.7 / 4.7 / 0.8 / 4.8
10 W	0434 / 1125 / 1650 / O 2337	1.0 / 4.4 / 1.0 / 4.5	**25** TH	0513 / 1207 / 1732	0.6 / 4.7 / 0.8
11 TH	0510 / 1203 / 1727	0.9 / 4.5 / 1.0	**26** F	0021 / 0557 / 1253 / 1815	4.8 / 0.6 / 4.7 / 0.8
12 F	0013 / 0546 / 1243 / 1803	4.5 / 0.9 / 4.5 / 1.0	**27** SA	0104 / 0639 / 1337 / 1856	4.7 / 0.7 / 4.6 / 1.0
13 SA	0051 / 0623 / 1323 / 1843	4.5 / 0.9 / 4.5 / 1.0	**28** SU	0145 / 0718 / 1419 / 1936	4.5 / 0.9 / 4.5 / 1.1
14 SU	0130 / 0703 / 1405 / 1926	4.5 / 0.9 / 4.5 / 1.1	**29** M	0225 / 0757 / 1500 / 2016	4.4 / 1.1 / 4.4 / 1.3
15 M	0213 / 0747 / 1452 / 2014	4.4 / 1.0 / 4.4 / 1.2	**30** TU	0305 / 0836 / 1541 / 2059	4.2 / 1.3 / 4.3 / 1.5

JULY

Day	Time	m	Day	Time	m
1 W	0347 / 0920 / 1624 / 2149	4.0 / 1.5 / 4.1 / 1.8	**16** TH	0340 / 0918 / 1618 / 2150	4.4 / 1.1 / 4.5 / 1.3
2 TH	0434 / 1012 / 1714 / 2249	3.9 / 1.7 / 4.0 / 1.9	**17** F	0437 / 1018 / 1718 / 2256	4.2 / 1.3 / 4.3 / 1.4
3 F	0530 / 1116 / 1812 / 2358	3.8 / 1.9 / 4.0 / 1.9	**18** SA	0544 / 1129 / 1827	4.1 / 1.4 / 4.3
4 SA	0638 / 1225 / 1916	3.7 / 1.9 / 4.0	**19** SU	0011 / 0700 / 1244 / 1939	1.5 / 4.1 / 1.5 / 4.3
5 SU	0103 / 0748 / 1325 / 2016	1.8 / 3.8 / 1.8 / 4.1	**20** M	0124 / 0816 / 1352 / 2046	1.4 / 4.2 / 1.4 / 4.4
6 M	0158 / 0847 / 1416 / 2107	1.6 / 4.0 / 1.6 / 4.2	**21** TU	0228 / 0921 / 1452 / 2144	1.2 / 4.4 / 1.2 / 4.6
7 TU	0245 / 0937 / 1502 / 2152	1.4 / 4.2 / 1.4 / 4.4	**22** W	0323 / 1017 / 1544 / 2235	1.0 / 4.5 / 1.1 / 4.7
8 W	0328 / 1021 / 1545 / 2233	1.2 / 4.3 / 1.2 / 4.5	**23** TH	0413 / 1107 / 1632 / ● 2321	0.8 / 4.6 / 0.9 / 4.7
9 TH	0409 / 1102 / 1627 / O 2313	1.0 / 4.3 / 1.1 / 4.5	**24** F	0458 / 1153 / 1716	0.7 / 4.7 / 0.9
10 F	0450 / 1143 / 1708 / 2353	0.9 / 4.6 / 1.0 / 4.6	**25** SA	0003 / 0540 / 1236 / 1756	4.7 / 0.7 / 4.7 / 0.9
11 SA	0531 / 1225 / 1750	0.8 / 4.6 / 0.9	**26** SU	0043 / 0618 / 1314 / 1834	4.6 / 0.7 / 4.6 / 1.0
12 SU	0034 / 0612 / 1308 / 1831	4.6 / 0.7 / 4.7 / 0.9	**27** M	0120 / 0654 / 1350 / 1909	4.5 / 0.8 / 4.6 / 1.1
13 M	0117 / 0654 / 1352 / 1915	4.6 / 0.7 / 4.7 / 0.9	**28** TU	0155 / 0727 / 1425 / 1943	4.4 / 1.0 / 4.5 / 1.2
14 TU	0202 / 0738 / 1437 / 2002	4.6 / 0.8 / 4.6 / 1.0	**29** W	0231 / 0800 / 1500 / 2018	4.3 / 1.2 / 4.4 / 1.4
15 W	0249 / 0825 / 1526 / 2052	4.5 / 0.9 / 4.6 / 1.1	**30** TH	0309 / 0834 / 1538 / 2056	4.2 / 1.4 / 4.3 / 1.6
			31 F	0349 / 0914 / 1619 / 2143	4.0 / 1.7 / 4.1 / 1.8

AUGUST

Day	Time	m	Day	Time	m
1 SA	0438 / 1006 / 1711 / 2246	3.8 / 1.9 / 4.0 / 2.0	**16** SU	0522 / 1106 / 1800 / 2349	4.1 / 1.6 / 4.1 / 1.6
2 SU	0540 / 1119 / 1816	3.7 / 2.0 / 3.9	**17** M	0645 / 1227 / 1922	4.0 / 1.7 / 4.1
3 M	0009 / 0658 / 1241 / 1929	2.0 / 3.8 / 2.0 / 4.0	**18** TU	0108 / 0809 / 1342 / 2036	1.5 / 4.1 / 1.6 / 4.2
4 TU	0121 / 0811 / 1345 / 2032	1.8 / 3.9 / 1.8 / 4.1	**19** W	0216 / 0916 / 1443 / 2134	1.4 / 4.3 / 1.4 / 4.4
5 W	0216 / 0909 / 1436 / 2123	1.6 / 4.1 / 1.6 / 4.3	**20** TH	0311 / 1009 / 1534 / 2223	1.1 / 4.5 / 1.2 / 4.5
6 TH	0303 / 0957 / 1522 / 2209	1.3 / 4.4 / 1.3 / 4.5	**21** F	0358 / 1055 / 1618 / 2306	0.9 / 4.6 / 1.0 / 4.6
7 F	0348 / 1041 / 1606 / 2251	1.0 / 4.5 / 1.1 / 4.6	**22** SA	0440 / 1136 / 1658 / ● 2344	0.8 / 4.7 / 0.9 / 4.6
8 SA	0431 / 1124 / 1650 / O 2334	0.8 / 4.7 / 0.9 / 4.7	**23** SU	0519 / 1213 / 1735	0.7 / 4.7 / 0.9
9 SU	0514 / 1207 / 1733	0.6 / 4.8 / 0.7	**24** M	0019 / 0554 / 1246 / 1809	4.6 / 0.7 / 4.6 / 0.9
10 M	0018 / 0556 / 1251 / 1816	4.7 / 0.5 / 4.8 / 0.7	**25** TU	0052 / 0626 / 1318 / 1840	4.5 / 0.8 / 4.6 / 1.0
11 TU	0103 / 0639 / 1335 / 1900	4.8 / 0.5 / 4.8 / 0.7	**26** W	0125 / 0656 / 1349 / 1910	4.5 / 0.9 / 4.5 / 1.1
12 W	0148 / 0723 / 1419 / 1945	4.7 / 0.6 / 4.8 / 0.7	**27** TH	0158 / 0724 / 1421 / 1939	4.4 / 1.1 / 4.4 / 1.3
13 TH	0234 / 0808 / 1505 / 2033	4.6 / 0.7 / 4.7 / 0.9	**28** F	0233 / 0753 / 1455 / 2011	4.3 / 1.3 / 4.3 / 1.5
14 F	0323 / 0857 / 1554 / 2127	4.4 / 1.0 / 4.5 / 1.2	**29** SA	0309 / 0827 / 1531 / 2051	4.1 / 1.6 / 4.2 / 1.7
15 SA	0417 / 0955 / 1651 / 2231	4.3 / 1.3 / 4.3 / 1.4	**30** SU	0352 / 0912 / 1617 / 2145	3.9 / 1.9 / 4.0 / 2.0
			31 M	0450 / 1019 / 1720 / 2307	3.8 / 2.1 / 3.9 / 2.1

ENGLAND – PORTSMOUTH

LAT 50°48′N   LONG   1°07′W

TIMES AND HEIGHTS OF HIGH AND LOW WATERS   YEAR **1998**

TIME ZONE (UT)
For Summer Time add ONE hour in non-shaded areas

Chart Datum: 2·73 metres below Ordnance Datum (Newlyn)

SEPTEMBER

Day	Time	m	Time	m	Time	m	Time	m
1 TU	0612	3.7	1156	2.2	1843	3.9		
16 W	0052	1.7	0801	4.1	1330	1.7	2026	4.1
2 W	0044	2.0	0736	3.9	1317	2.0	1958	4.0
17 TH	0203	1.5	0905	4.3	1431	1.5	2123	4.3
3 TH	0150	1.7	0841	4.1	1413	1.7	2056	4.3
18 F	0255	1.2	0954	4.5	1517	1.3	2208	4.5
4 F	0240	1.3	0932	4.4	1501	1.3	2144	4.5
19 SA	0338	1.0	1036	4.6	1557	1.1	2247	4.5
5 SA	0326	1.0	1017	4.6	1545	1.0	2229	4.7
20 SU ●	0417	0.8	1113	4.7	1634	0.9	2321	4.6
6 SU O	0410	0.7	1101	4.8	1630	0.8	2314	4.8
21 M	0452	0.8	1146	4.7	1709	0.9	2353	4.6
7 M	0454	0.5	1145	4.9	1714	0.6	2359	4.9
22 TU	0526	0.8	1215	4.6	1741	0.9		
8 TU	0538	0.4	1229	5.0	1758	0.5		
23 W	0023	4.6	0558	0.8	1245	4.6	1811	0.9
9 W	0044	4.9	0620	0.4	1314	5.0	1841	0.5
24 TH	0055	4.5	0626	0.9	1315	4.6	1838	1.1
10 TH	0130	4.9	0704	0.5	1358	4.9	1926	0.6
25 F	0128	4.5	0652	1.1	1346	4.5	1905	1.2
11 F	0216	4.8	0748	0.7	1443	4.7	2012	0.8
26 SA	0201	4.4	0719	1.3	1417	4.4	1935	1.4
12 SA	0304	4.6	0837	1.0	1531	4.5	2104	1.2
27 SU	0235	4.2	0751	1.5	1451	4.2	2012	1.6
13 SU	0358	4.3	0934	1.4	1626	4.2	2208	1.5
28 M	0315	4.0	0834	1.8	1533	4.0	2102	1.9
14 M	0504	4.0	1047	1.7	1737	4.0	2328	1.7
29 TU	0411	3.9	0936	2.1	1634	3.9	2217	2.1
15 TU	0632	3.9	1212	1.8	1909	4.0		
30 W	0529	3.8	1112	2.2	1756	3.8		

OCTOBER

Day	Time	m	Time	m	Time	m	Time	m
1 TH	0002	2.0	0658	3.9	1246	2.0	1921	4.0
16 F	0137	1.6	0842	4.3	1408	1.6	2101	4.2
2 F	0120	1.7	0810	4.2	1347	1.7	2026	4.3
17 SA	0229	1.4	0930	4.5	1453	1.4	2145	4.4
3 SA	0214	1.3	0904	4.5	1437	1.3	2117	4.5
18 SU	0310	1.2	1010	4.6	1530	1.1	2223	4.5
4 SU	0301	1.0	0951	4.7	1522	0.9	2205	4.7
19 M	0347	1.0	1046	4.6	1606	1.0	2255	4.5
5 M O	0346	0.7	1037	4.9	1607	0.7	2251	4.9
20 TU ●	0423	0.9	1115	4.6	1640	0.9	2326	4.5
6 TU	0430	0.5	1122	5.0	1652	0.5	2338	5.0
21 W	0457	0.9	1144	4.6	1713	0.9	2356	4.6
7 W	0515	0.4	1207	5.1	1737	0.5		
22 TH	0529	0.9	1213	4.6	1744	1.0		
8 TH	0025	5.0	0559	0.4	1252	5.0	1821	0.4
23 F	0028	4.6	0558	1.0	1244	4.6	1811	1.0
9 F	0112	5.0	0643	0.5	1337	4.9	1906	0.6
24 SA	0101	4.5	0625	1.1	1315	4.5	1837	1.2
10 SA	0158	4.8	0728	0.7	1422	4.7	1952	0.8
25 SU	0135	4.5	0653	1.3	1347	4.4	1908	1.3
11 SU	0247	4.6	0817	1.1	1510	4.5	2043	1.2
26 M	0210	4.3	0726	1.5	1421	4.2	1945	1.5
12 M	0341	4.3	0914	1.5	1604	4.2	2145	1.5
27 TU	0251	4.2	0808	1.8	1503	4.1	2033	1.8
13 TU	0447	4.1	1026	1.8	1715	3.9	2303	1.9
28 W	0344	4.0	0907	2.0	1601	3.9	2142	1.9
14 W	0613	4.0	1149	1.9	1848	3.9		
29 TH	0455	3.9	1032	2.1	1716	3.9	2315	2.0
15 TH	0026	1.8	0739	4.1	1308	1.8	2005	4.0
30 F	0618	4.0	1205	2.0	1839	4.0		
31 SA	0039	1.7	0733	4.2	1314	1.7	1951	4.2

NOVEMBER

Day	Time	m	Time	m	Time	m	Time	m
1 SU	0141	1.4	0832	4.5	1408	1.3	2048	4.5
16 M	0234	1.4	0935	4.5	1458	1.3	2152	4.3
2 M	0232	1.0	0923	4.8	1457	1.0	2140	4.7
17 TU	0313	1.2	1010	4.5	1535	1.2	2226	4.4
3 TU	0319	0.7	1011	5.0	1544	0.7	2229	4.9
18 W	0351	1.1	1042	4.6	1611	1.1	2258	4.5
4 W O	0406	0.5	1058	5.1	1630	0.5	2318	5.0
19 TH ●	0427	1.1	1113	4.6	1646	1.0	2331	4.5
5 TH	0452	0.5	1144	5.1	1717	0.5		
20 F	0501	1.1	1145	4.6	1719	1.0		
6 F	0006	5.0	0538	0.5	1231	5.1	1802	0.5
21 SA	0004	4.6	0532	1.1	1218	4.6	1748	1.1
7 SA	0054	5.0	0624	0.6	1317	4.9	1848	0.6
22 SU	0039	4.6	0602	1.2	1251	4.5	1818	1.1
8 SU	0142	4.9	0710	0.9	1402	4.7	1934	0.9
23 M	0115	4.5	0633	1.3	1324	4.4	1851	1.2
9 M	0232	4.7	0758	1.2	1450	4.5	2024	1.2
24 TU	0152	4.4	0709	1.5	1401	4.3	1930	1.4
10 TU	0325	4.4	0853	1.5	1543	4.2	2120	1.5
25 W	0235	4.3	0753	1.6	1444	4.2	2017	1.5
11 W	0426	4.1	0957	1.8	1646	4.0	2228	1.7
26 TH	0326	4.2	0848	1.8	1538	4.1	2118	1.7
12 TH	0540	4.1	1113	2.0	1806	3.8	2344	1.8
27 F	0428	4.1	0959	1.9	1644	4.0	2233	1.7
13 F	0659	4.1	1229	1.9	1926	3.9		
28 SA	0540	4.1	1120	1.9	1758	4.0	2352	1.6
14 SA	0055	1.8	0803	4.2	1332	1.8	2026	4.0
29 SU	0654	4.3	1235	1.7	1914	4.2		
15 SU	0150	1.6	0854	4.4	1419	1.5	2113	4.2
30 M	0102	1.4	0759	4.5	1338	1.4	2019	4.4

DECEMBER

Day	Time	m	Time	m	Time	m	Time	m
1 TU	0201	1.1	0855	4.7	1432	1.1	2116	4.6
16 W	0238	1.5	0932	4.4	1505	1.4	2155	4.3
2 W	0253	0.9	0947	4.9	1523	0.8	2210	4.8
17 TH	0319	1.4	1009	4.5	1544	1.2	2232	4.4
3 TH O	0343	0.7	1037	5.0	1612	0.6	2301	4.9
18 F ●	0359	1.3	1045	4.6	1621	1.1	2308	4.5
4 F	0432	0.7	1125	5.1	1701	0.6	2351	5.0
19 SA	0436	1.2	1120	4.6	1657	1.0	2344	4.5
5 SA	0521	0.7	1212	5.0	1748	0.6		
20 SU	0511	1.2	1155	4.6	1732	1.0		
6 SU	0040	4.9	0607	0.8	1259	4.9	1834	0.7
21 M	0021	4.6	0545	1.2	1231	4.6	1805	1.0
7 M	0128	4.8	0653	0.9	1344	4.7	1918	0.9
22 TU	0059	4.6	0620	1.2	1308	4.5	1841	1.0
8 TU	0217	4.7	0739	1.2	1430	4.5	2004	1.1
23 W	0138	4.6	0658	1.3	1348	4.4	1921	1.1
9 W	0306	4.5	0827	1.4	1518	4.3	2051	1.4
24 TH	0221	4.5	0742	1.4	1431	4.4	2005	1.2
10 TH	0357	4.3	0921	1.7	1609	4.0	2145	1.6
25 F	0309	4.4	0832	1.5	1521	4.3	2058	1.3
11 F	0454	4.2	1024	1.9	1707	3.9	2248	1.8
26 SA	0404	4.3	0931	1.6	1618	4.2	2200	1.5
12 SA	0557	4.1	1134	2.0	1816	3.8	2356	1.9
27 SU	0506	4.3	1042	1.7	1724	4.1	2311	1.5
13 SU	0704	4.1	1241	1.9	1929	3.8		
28 M	0616	4.3	1158	1.6	1839	4.1		
14 M	0059	1.8	0803	4.2	1337	1.8	2028	3.9
29 TU	0025	1.5	0726	4.4	1310	1.5	1952	4.3
15 TU	0152	1.7	0851	4.3	1423	1.6	2115	4.1
30 W	0134	1.3	0830	4.6	1412	1.2	2058	4.4
31 TH	0234	1.1	0927	4.8	1508	1.0	2156	4.6

PORTSMOUTH   10-2-30

Hampshire 50°47'·35N 01°06'·58W (Entrance)   Rtg 2-1-2

CHARTS
AC 2628, 2629, 2625, *2631, 394, 2050, 2045*; Imray C3, C9;
Stanfords 11, 18; OS 197

TIDES
+0029 Dover; ML 2·8; Zone 0 (UT)

Standard Port PORTSMOUTH (←—)

Times				Height (metres)			
High Water		Low Water		MHWS	MHWN	MLWN	MLWS
0500	1000	0000	0600	4·7	3·8	1·9	0·8
1700	2200	1200	1800				

Differences LEE-ON-SOLENT

−0005	+0005	−0015	−0010	−0·2	−0·1	+0·1	+0·2

Portsmouth is a Standard Port; daily predictions are
given above. See also 10·2·12. Strong winds from NE to
SE, coupled with a high barometer, may lower levels by
1m and delay times of HW and LW by 1hr; the opposite
may occur in strong W'lies with low pressure.

SHELTER
Excellent. This very large hbr affords shelter in some
area for any wind. There are two marinas on the Gosport
side, two at Fareham and one at the N end of Portchester
Lake, plus several yacht pontoons/jetties and many
moorings (see Facilities). Good shelter in The Camber,
but this is a busy little commercial dock and often full;
beware the Isle of Wight car ferry docking near the ent.
Portsmouth is a major naval base and Dockyard Port; all
vessels come under the QHM's authority. If > 20m LOA,
ask QHM's permission (VHF Ch 11) to enter, leave or move
in hbr, especially in fog. Fishing and ⚓ in chans are prohib.

NAVIGATION
WPT No 4 Bar buoy, QR, 50°46'·98N 01°06'·27W, 150°/330°
from/to hbr ent (W side), 4½ca. Beware very strong tides
in hbr ent, commercial shipping and ferries, Gosport
ferry and HM Ships.
Speed limit is 10kn within hbr and within 1000 yds of the
shore in any part of the Dockyard Port; speed = speed
through the water. Outside the hbr ent, the Dockyard Port
limits embrace the Solent from Hillhead and Old Castle
Pt (close NE of Cowes) eastward to Eastney and Shanklin
(IOW), thence almost out to Nab Tr (see AC 394 & 2050).
Historic Wrecks are at: 50°45'·8N 01°06'·2W
(site of *Mary Rose*), marked by SPM buoys; 5ca SSW of
Spit Sand Ft. *Invincible* lies at 50°44'·34N 01°02'·23W, 117°
Horse Sand Fort 1·45M, marked by SPM buoy.
Approaches: From the W, yachts can use the Swashway
Chan (to NW of Spit Sand Fort) which carries about 2m;
keep War Memorial and RH edge of block of flats on at
049°. The Inner Swashway Chan (Round Tr on 029°. NB:
rear transit, diving tank, has been demolished) carries
only 0·1m; local knowledge required.
Approaching inshore from E, the submerged barrier,
which extends from Southsea to Horse Sand Fort, should
only be crossed via the unlit Inshore Boat passage (0·9m)
1ca off the beach, marked by R & G piles; or via the Main
Passage (min depth 1·2m) 7ca further S, marked by G
pile and dolphin, QR.
A Small Boat Channel for craft < 20m LOA lies at the hbr
ent, parallel to and outboard of the W edge of the main
dredged chan. It runs from abeam No 4 Bar buoy, QR (off
Clarence Pier) to Ballast buoy, Fl R 2·5s, and extends
about 50m off Fort Blockhouse. A depth gauge is on pile
BC4. Yachts should enter by the Small Boat Chan; they
may also enter on the E side of the main chan, but clear
of it and close inshore. All yachts must leave via the
Small Boat Chan. Yachts may only cross the main chan N
of Ballast buoy or S of No 4 Bar buoy. Yachts must motor
(if so fitted) between No 4 Bar and Ballast buoys; winds
at the ent may be fickle or gusty and tides run hard. At
night the Small Boat Chan is covered by the Oc R sector
(324°-330°) of the Dir WRG lt on Fort Blockhouse (W side
of hbr ent), until close to the hbr ent. Thereafter the Iso R
2s sector (337·5°-345°) of the Dir WRG lt 2m 1M (on
dolphin E of Gosport Marina) leads 341° through the ent
and close abeam Ballast Bank PHM buoy, Fl R 2·5s.

LIGHTS AND MARKS
From E of the IOW, Nab Tower, Fl 10s 27m 16M, is conspic
about 10M SE of the hbr ent. In the inner appr's there are
3 conspic forts: Horse Sand Fort, Iso G 2s; No Man's Land

Fort, Iso R 2s, and Spit Sand Fort, Fl R 5s.
Ldg marks/lts: St Jude's ♣ spire and Southsea Castle lt ho
in transit 003° lead between Outer Spit SCM buoy, Q (6) +
L Fl 15s, and Horse Sand SHM buoy, Fl G 2·5s. At night
keep in the W sector (000°-003°) between the Al WG and
Al WR sectors of the Dir lt (H24) on Southsea Castle,
which also shows a lt Iso 2s 16m 11M, vis 337°-071° (94°).

FIRING RANGE
Tipner Rifle Range as shown on chartlet. The danger area
extends 2,500 metres from firing range. When firing is in
progress, R flag or ® lt on Tipner Range FS indicates
yachts should clear the range danger area or transit it as
quickly as possible.

RADIO TELEPHONE
Yachts should monitor Ch **11** (H24) for traffic/nav info.
For the Camber call *Portsmouth Hbr Radio* (Commercial
Port) Ch 11 14 (H24).
Haslar Marina and *Port Solent* Ch **80** M (H24). *Gosport
Marina* call Ch **80** M (HO). Fareham Marina Ch M (summer
0900-1730). Wicor Marina Ch 80 (0900-1730, Mon-Sat).
Naval activities to the S/SE of Portsmouth and IOW may
be advised by Solent CG Ch 67 or ☎ (01705) 552100; or
Naval Ops ☎ 722008. Naval vessels use Ch 13. The
positions and times of naval firings and underwater
explosions are broadcast daily at 0800 and 1400LT Ch 06;
preceded by a Securité call on Ch 16. Warnings of
underwater explosions will also be broadcast on Ch 16 at
1 hour, at 30 mins and just before the detonation.

TELEPHONE (Portsmouth/Gosport 01705; Fareham 01329)
QHM 723124; DQHM 723794/🖂 837715; Hbr Control (H24)
723694; Commercial Docks 297395; Camber Berthing
Offices ☎ 297395 Ext 310; ⌗ 0345 231110 (H24); MRSC
552100; Marinecall 0891 500457; Weather Centre (01703)
228844; Police 321111; Dr (Gosport) 80922; Fareham
Health Centre (01329) 282911; Ⓗ 822331.

FACILITIES
PORTSMOUTH (01705)

Marinas
Port Solent, Portchester, (900) ☎ 210765, 🖂 324241,
£16.11, P, D, FW, AC, ME, El, Ⓔ, Sh, BH (40 ton), CH, V, R,
Bar, Gas, Gaz, Ⓞ, Ⓖ.
Portchester Lake is marked by lit/unlit piles; unusually,
PHMs are numbered 57 to 74 (from seaward), and SHMs
95 to 75. Beware unlit naval buoys near the S end. Do not
delay crossing Tipner Range, S limit marked by piles 63/87
and N by 70/78. Portchester Castle is conspic 5ca SSW of
marina. 140m W of the lock, Piles A and B are lit Fl (4) R
10s and Fl (4) G 10s respectively. Access H24 via chan
dredged 1·5m to lock (43m x 12·5m); enter on 3 Ⓖ (vert) or
berth on waiting pontoon.
Services
FW, ME, El, Ⓔ, Sh, SM, ACA, CH; **Hbr** Moorings ☎ 832484.
City EC Wed (Southsea Sat); ⊠, Ⓑ, ⇌, ✈ (Southampton).
Ferries to Ouistreham, Cherbourg, Le Havre, St Malo,
Bilbao, Santander (winter) and IoW (see 10.0.4).

GOSPORT (01705)

Marinas
Gosport Marina (350, some visitors) ☎ 524811, 🖂 589541,
£13.47, P, D, FW, ME, El, Sh, BH (150, 40 ton), CH, V, R, AC,
Bar, Gas, Gaz, SM, Ⓞ. Note: There are RNSA pontoons at
the N end of Cold Hbr, inside the Fuel Jetty. Also 150 pile
moorings (some dry); contact Haslar Marina.
Haslar Marina, ☎ 601201, 🖂 602201, £10.47, (550+ 50 Ⓥ);
Access H24; Ⓥ at L pontoon, near conspic former lt ship;
Bar & R (☎ 219847); FW, AC, Gas, Gaz, CH, ME, Ⓔ, Ⓞ,
Slip (upstream of Haslar bridge). RNSA berths at S end.
Services: CH, P, D, ACA, El, Ⓔ, ME, Sh, BY, SM, Slip, C.
Town EC Wed; ⊠, Ⓑ, ⇌ (Portsmouth), ✈ (Southampton).
FAREHAM (01329)

Marinas
Fareham Marina ☎ 822445, M, Slip, D, FW, ME, El, Ⓔ, Sh,
V, Bar, CH; (Access HW±3); **Fareham Yacht Hbr; Wicor
Marine** (200) ☎ 237112, 🖂 825660, Slip, M, D, ME, Sh, CH,
AC, BH (10 ton), C (7 ton), FW, El, Ⓔ, Gas, Gaz. Fareham
Lake is well marked, but only partially lit up to Bedenham
Pier and unlit thereafter. Chan dries 0·9m in final 5ca to
Town Quay.
Services: M, Sh, CH, ME, Slip, El, Ⓔ, D, FW, Gas, AC, SM.
Town EC Wed; ⊠, Ⓑ, ⇌, ✈ (Southampton).
Clubs
Royal Naval & Royal Albert YC ☎ 825924, M, Bar;
Portsmouth SC ☎ 820596; **Portchester SC** ☎ 376375;
Hardway SC ☎ 581875, Slip, M, L, FW, C (mast stepping
only), AB; **Gosport CC** ☎ (01329) 47014 or (0860) 966390;
Fareham Sailing & Motor Boat Club ☎ (01329) 280738.

PORTSMOUTH continued

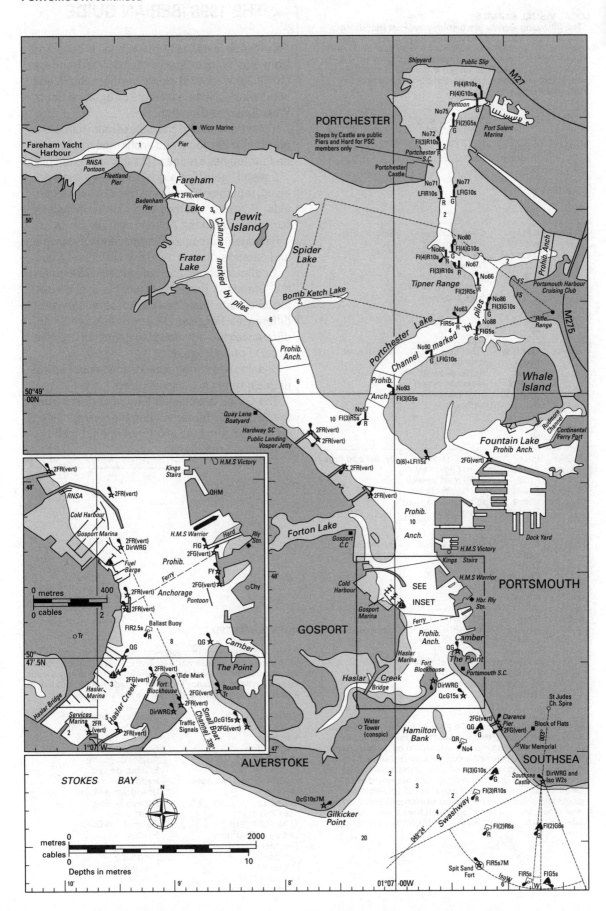

PORTCHESTER

Shipyard

Public Slip

M27

Fl(4)R10s
Fl(4)G10s
G

Pontoon
No75
Fl(2)G5s
G

Port Solent Marina

No72
Fl(3)R10s
R 2

Steps by Castle are public Piers and Hard for PSC members only

Portchester S.C.

Portchester Castle

No71
LFIR10s
R

No77
LFIG10s
G

Prohib Anch

Portsmouth Harbour Cruising Club

No80
Fl(4)G10s
G

No68
Fl(4)R10s
R

No67

No66
Fl(2)R5s
R

No86
Fl(3)G10s
G

FS

FS

Rifle Range

M275

No63
FIR5s
R

No88
FIG5s
G

Tipner Range

Channel marked by piles

No90
LFIG10s
G

Whale Island

Fl(4)R10s
R

Fl(3)R10s

Portchester Lake

Rudmore Channel

Continental Ferry Port

No93
Fl(3)G5s

Prohib. Anch.

No57
Fl(3)R5s
R

Fountain Lake
Prohib. Anch.

2FG(vert)

Quay Lane Boatyard

Hardway SC
Public Landing
Vosper Jetty

2FR(vert)
2FR(vert)

10

Q(6)+LFl15s

2FR(vert)

2FR(vert)

Prohib.
10
Anch.

Dock Yard

2FR(vert)

H.M.S Victory

Kings Stairs
H.M.S Warrior

PORTSMOUTH

Forton Lake

Gosport C.C.

SEE
INSET

Hbr. Rly Stn.

Cold Harbour

GOSPORT

Gosport Marina

Haslar Marina
Fort Blockhouse

Camber
QG
G
The Point
Portsmouth S.C.

Ferry

Prohib. Anch.

Haslar Creek
Bridge

DirWRG
QcG15s

St Judes Ch. Spire

2FG(vert)
QG
G

Clarence Pier
2FG(vert)

Block of Flats

003°

War Memorial

Hamilton Bank

Water Tower (conspic)

QR
No4
0₈

SOUTHSEA

DirWRG and Iso W2s

Southsea Castle

Fl(3)G10s
G

Fl(3)R10s
R

049°24'

Swashway

Fl(2)R6s
R

Fl(2)G6s
G

OcG10s7M

Gilkicker Point

FIR5s7M

Spit Sand Fort

Iso W

FIR5s

FIG5s

W

6'

20

ALVERSTOKE

STOKES   BAY

N

metres   0   2000
cables   0   10

Depths in metres

10'   9'   8'   01°07'·00W

2FR(vert)

RNSA

Cold Harbour

Gosport Marina

2FR(vert)
DirWRG

Fuel Barge

Prohib.

Kings Stairs

QHM

H.M.S Warrior
FIG
2FG(vert)

Hard

Rly Stn.

FY

2FG(vert)

2FR(vert)
Anchorage
Pontoon

0 metres   400
0 cables   2

Tr

FIR2.5s
R

Ballast Buoy

QG

QG

8

Camber

The Point

2FR(vert)
2FG(vert)
Fort Blockhouse

Tide Mark

Round Tr

2FG(vert)

Haslar Marina

Haslar Creek

DirWRG
2FR

Traffic Signals

OcG15s
2FG(vert)

Small Boat Channel 339°

Services Marina

2FR(vert)
2FR(vert)

1°07'W

PORTSMOUTH *continued*

LOCAL VISUAL SIGNALS

The following signals are displayed at Fort Blockhouse and sometimes in the vessel concerned and must be obeyed; except that craft <20m LOA may use the Small Boat Chan H24 despite displayed tfc sigs. Monitor Ch 11. The Channel (or main channel) is defined as the main navigable channels of the harbour and the approach channel from Outer Spit buoy.

	SIGNAL	MEANING AND APPLICATION	HOISTED/DISPLAYED BY
1. DAY	R Flag, W diagonal bar.	Clear Channel – both directions.	Blockhouse.
NIGHT	Ⓡ Ⓖ Ⓖ		
2. DAY	R Flag with W diagonal bar over B ●.	Clear Channel – only outgoing traffic allowed. No vessel shall enter the main or approach channel from seaward.	Blockhouse.
NIGHT	Ⓦ Ⓖ		
3. DAY	One B ● over R Flag with W diagonal bar.	Clear Channel – only incoming traffic allowed. No other vessel shall leave the harbour.	Blockhouse.
NIGHT	Ⓖ Ⓦ		
4. DAY	International Code Pennant above Pennant Zero.	Clear Channel – signal flown by privileged vessel. Such vessels are to be given a clear passage.	Vessel and tugs.
5. DAY	International Code Pennant above flag Alpha.	Diving – vessel conducting diving.	By vessel concerned.
6. DAY	International Code Pennant above flag Romeo above flag Yankee.	POTENTIALLY HAZARDOUS OPERATIONS. You should proceed at slow speed when passing me.	By vessel concerned.

Fog Routine is broadcast on Ch 11 and 13, when it comes into force, ie when the QHM considers that visibility is so low that normal shipping movements would be dangerous. Yachts may continue at the skipper's discretion, but with great caution and keeping well clear of the main chan. They should be aware that the presence of radar echoes from small vessels within the main channel can cause much doubt and difficulty to the Master of a large vessel. For their own safety and that of major vessels they are strongly advised not to proceed. Monitor VHF Ch 11 at all times.

LANGSTONE HARBOUR   10-2-31

Hampshire 50°47'·20N 01°01'·45W (Ent)   Rtg 3-2-2

CHARTS

AC *3418, 2045*; Imray C3, Y33; Stanfords 10, 11; OS 196, 197

TIDES

+0022 Dover; Zone 0 (UT)

Standard Port PORTSMOUTH (⟵)

Times				Height (metres)			
High Water		Low Water		MHWS	MHWN	MLWN	MLWS
0500	1000	0000	0600	4·7	3·8	1·9	0·8
1700	2200	1200	1800				
Differences LANGSTONE							
0000	0000	+0010	+0010	+0·1	+0·1	0·0	0·0
NAB TOWER							
+0015	0000	+0015	+0015	−0·2	0·0	+0·2	0·0

SHELTER

Very good in marina (2·4m) to W inside ent, access HW±3 over tidal flap 1·6m CD; waiting pontoon. Ent is 7m wide. 6 Y ⚓s at W side of hbr ent, 6 more on E side; max LOA 9m. Or ⚓ out of the fairway in Russell's Lake or Langstone Chan (water ski area); or see Hr Mr (E side of ent). Hbr speed limit 10kn.

NAVIGATION

WPT 50°46'·28N 01°01'·27W, Langstone Fairway SWM buoy, L Fl 10s, 168°/348° from/to QR lt at ent, 0·94M. Bar has about 1·8m. Ent chan lies between East and West Winner drying banks, which afford some protection. Appr is easy in most weather, best from HW −3 to +1, but avoid entry against the ebb, esp at sp and in onshore winds. In strong S/SE winds do not attempt entry.

LIGHTS AND MARKS

Ldg marks (concrete dolphins), or Fairway buoy on with conspic chy, lead 344° just clear of East Winner. The ent itself deepens and favours the W side. The narrow appr chan to Southsea Marina is marked by 7 SHM piles, only the first of which is lit, Fl G. There are 9 PHM piles; the 4th, 6th and 9th are Fl R. The lock has R/G ent sigs, as it is too narrow for 2 boats to pass; vessels going with the tide have priority.

RADIO TELEPHONE

Harbour VHF Ch 12 16 (Summer 0830-1700 daily. Winter: Mon-Fri 0830-1700; Sat-Sun 0830-1300). Marina Ch **80** M (0800-1800 daily).

TELEPHONE (Dial code 01705)

Hr Mr 463419; MRSC 552100; ⌗ 0345 231110 (H24); Marinecall 0891 500457; Police 321111; Dr 465721.

FACILITIES

Southsea Marina (300) ☎ 822719, ⚓ 822220, £10.81, AC, FW, D, Access HW±3, CH, BH (20 ton), Gaz, C (6 ton); **Hayling Pontoon** (E side of ent), AB, P, D, FW, L, Slip; **Langstone SC** ☎ 484577, Slip, M, L, FW, Bar; **Eastney Cruising Ass'n** (ECA) ☎ 734103, 6 ⚓s; **Hayling Ferry SC**; **Locks SC** ☎ 829833; **Tudor SC** (Hilsea) ☎ 662002, Slip, M, FW, Bar.
Towns: EC Havant Wed; ✉ (Eastney, Hayling), Ⓑ (Havant, Hayling, Emsworth), ⇌ (bus to Havant), ✈ (Southampton).

Contrasting views:

I dislike Langston (sic) quite as much as I like Chichester Harbour. The tide sets in very strongly, and the banks are awkward and dangerous in S or SE winds, while there are no snug nooks to get into. The small bight called Shinar Lake on the Hayling Island side is very shallow and limited in space, whilst the vast extent of mud flats are very soft, the anchor dragging in them like pins in butter.
                    Frank Cowper: Sailing Tours 1893

Many yachtsmen are under the impression that Langston is difficult to enter and that the harbour is unattractive. Far from this being the case, the entrance is straightforward. It is also comparatively sheltered from the east by Selsey Bill, and from the west by the Isle of Wight – although with an onshore wind over the tide there can be an exceedingly dangerous sea on the bar.
                    K.Adlard Coles: Creeks and Harbours of the Solent 1931

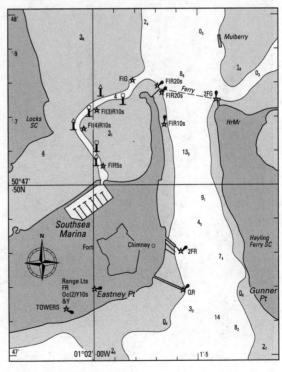

CHICHESTER HARBOUR   10-2-32
W. Sussex 50°46'·83N 00°55'·97W   Rtg 3-1-1

CHICHESTER HARBOUR *continued*

CHARTS
AC *3418, 2045*; Imray C4, C9, Y33; Stanfords 10, 11; OS 197

TIDES
+0027 Dover; ML 2·8; Zone 0 (UT); see curves on 10·2·12

Standard Port PORTSMOUTH (⟵)

Times				Height (metres)			
High Water		Low Water		MHWS	MHWN	MLWN	MLWS
0500	1000	0000	0600	4·7	3·8	1·9	0·8
1700	2200	1200	1800				
Differences HARBOUR ENTRANCE							
–0010	+0005	+0015	+0020	+0·2	+0·2	0·0	+0·1
NORTHNEY							
+0010	+0015	+0015	+0025	+0·2	0·0	–0·2	–0·3
ITCHENOR							
–0005	+0005	+0005	+0025	+0·1	0·0	–0·2	–0·2
BOSHAM							
0000	+0010	No data		+0·2	+0·1	No data	
DELL QUAY							
+0005	+0015	No data		+0·2	+0·1	No data	
SELSEY BILL							
–0005	–0005	+0035	+0035	+0·6	+0·6	0·0	0·0

SHELTER
Excellent in all five main chans, ie: Emsworth, Thorney, Chichester, Bosham, Itchenor Reach and Fishbourne. There are six yacht hbrs and marinas (see FACILITIES); also about 50 ⚓s at Emsworth and Itchenor. Recognised ⚓s in Thorney Chan off Pilsey Is; off E Head (uncomfortable in NE winds); and in Chichester Chan off Chalkdock Point. Hbr speed limit of 8kn is rigidly enforced; max fine £2500.

NAVIGATION
WPT 50°45'·50N 00°56'·50W, 193°/013° from/to Bar Bn, 0·4M. Best entry is HW –3 to +1, to avoid confused seas on the ebb, esp in onshore winds >F 5. Do not attempt entry in S'ly gales. Bar is dredged 1·5m, but after gales depths may vary ±0·75m. Leave Bar Bn (tide gauge) close to port; the chan N'ward is effectively only about 200m wide.
APPROACHES: **From the W**, the astern transit 255° of No Man's Land Fort and Ryde ✠ spire (hard to see) leads to the Bar Bn. Closer in, transit 064° of Target NCM Bn with Cakeham Tr leads 6ca S of Bar Bn; thence alter 013° as Eastoke Pt opens to E of Bar Bn. CHI SPIT unlit PHM buoy (approx 2ca SxW of Bar Bn, Apr-Nov) must be rounded to clear W Pole spit, dries 0·2m. This spit lies within the 020°-080° sector of the ☆ Fl (2) R 10s, below the main Bar blt lt. **From the E/SE** (Looe Chan) keep W for 2M, then NW; pick up an astern brg 184° of Nab Tr, toward the Bar Bn, so as to clear the shoals of Bracklesham Bay. The former Owers LANBY is now a SCM buoy, Q (6) + L Fl 15s, Whis, Racon. Note: An Historic Wreck (*Hazardous*) lies at 50°45'·10N 00°51'·47W, brg 105°/3·2M from Bar Bn; see 10.0.3h.
ENTRANCE: Pass between Eastoke bn QR and W Winner bn QG (tide gauge). Three SHM lt buoys mark the edge of The Winner shoal, dries, to stbd of the ent. At Fishery SCM buoy, Q (6) + L Fl 15s, chan divides: N to Emsworth and ENE toward Chichester. Stocker's Sand, dries 2·4m, is marked by 3 PHM lt buoys. East Head bn, Fl (4) G 10s, (tide gauge) marks start of anchorage.
EMSWORTH CHANNEL: Chan is straight, broad, deep and well marked/lit in the 2·5M reach to Emsworth SCM bn, Q (6) + L Fl 15s, where Sweare Deep forks NW to Northney. Good ⚓s especially N of Sandy Pt near ent to chan. Here an unlit ECM bn marks chan to Sparkes Yacht Hbr.
THORNEY CHANNEL: Strangers should go up at half-flood. Ent is at Camber SCM bn, Q (6) + L Fl 15s; pass between Pilsey and Thorney Lt bns, thereafter chan is marked by perches. Above Stanbury Pt chan splits, Prinsted Chan to port (full of moorings) and Nutbourne Chan to stbd; both dry at N ends. There is plenty of room to ⚓ in Thorney Chan, well protected from E and SE winds.
CHICHESTER CHANNEL: This runs up to Itchenor Reach and Bosham Chan. From NE Sandhead PHM by, Fl R 10s, transit 033° of Roman Transit bn on with Main Chan Bn and distant clump of trees leads to Chalkdock Bn, Fl (2) G 10s. Here alter 082° to Fairway buoy, Fl (3) G 10s; on this reach a measured half-mile is marked by Y perches. At Deep End SCM bn turn N into Bosham Chan, or ESE into Itchenor Reach, for Birdham Pool and Chichester Marina. ⚓ prohib in Itchenor Reach and Bosham Chan.

LIGHTS AND MARKS
Bar Bn, R/W wooden twr + R can topmark, Fl WR 5s 14m 7/5M, vis W 322°-080°, R080°-322°; and same tr, Fl (2) R 10s 7m 2M, 020°-080°; also tide gauge. 3 SHM Bys: NW Winner Fl G 10s; N Winner Fl (2) G10s; Mid Winner (3) G 10s. Fishery SCM Q (6)+L Fl 15s. All chans well marked.

RADIO TELEPHONE
Hr Mr, call *Chichester* VHF Ch **14** 16 (Patrol craft *Aella* on Ch14). (Apl-Sept: 0900-1300, 1400-1730. Oct-Mar: Mon-Fri 0900-1300, 1400-1730. Sat 0900-1300). Tarquin Yacht Hbr and Northney Marina Ch **80** M. Chichester Marina Ch M.

TELEPHONE (Dial code 01243)
Chichester Hbr Conservancy Office 512301, 🕿 513026; ⌗ 0345 231110 (H24); MRSC (01705) 552100; Weather info (01705) 8091; Marinecall 0891 500457; Police 536733; Ⓗ 787970.

FACILITIES
EMSWORTH CHANNEL
Tarquin Yacht Harbour (200+20 visitors) ☎ 375211, 🕿 378498, £11; access HW±2 over 2·4m sill which maintains 1·5m inside, Slip, Gas, ME, EI, AC, Sh, P, D, FW, BH (60 ton), C (20 ton); **Service Jetty** 50m long; access HW±4.
Slips at South St, Kings St, and Slipper Mill; contact the Warden ☎ 376422.
Services: ME, Sh, CH, EI, ACA; Emsworth EC Wed.
HAYLING ISLAND (01705)
Sparkes Yacht Hbr (150 + 30 Ⓥ) ☎ 463572, mobile 0370-365610, 🕿 465741, £12.50, access all tides via chan dredged 2m; pontoons have 1·6m. Slip, ME, EI, FW, P, D, AC, M, Gas, Gaz, ⬚, Sh, C (25 ton), CH. From close N of Sandy Pt, appr on transit 277° of two x bns; thence alter S, past 3 PHM bns to marina.
Northney Marina (260+27 visitors) ☎ 466321, 🕿 461467; pre-call Ch 80. Access all tides via chan 1m; £8.50, D, Bar, FW, AC, EI, Sh, BH (35 ton), R, CH, ME;
Services: ME, EI, Slip, BH (8 ton), P, FW, Sh, CH. EC Wed.
THORNEY CHANNEL
Thornham Marina (77+6 visitors), ☎ 375335, 🕿 371522, £7.00, appr via drying chan, P & D (cans), FW, Sh, ME, C (10 ton), BH (12 ton), Slip, R, Bar. **Services:** CH, BY.
CHICHESTER CHANNEL/ITCHENOR REACH
Hard available at all stages of the tide. There are 6 ⚓s off Itchenor jetty and a 90ft pontoon. For moorings apply Hr Mr. **Services:** Slip, P & D (cans), CH, Sh, FW, M, EI, Ⓔ, ME. Itchenor EC Thurs.
BOSHAM CHANNEL
For moorings (200+) contact the Quaymaster ☎ 573336. ⚓ prohib in chan which mostly dries, access HW±2.
Bosham Quay Hard, L, FW, AB; **Services:** SM. EC Wed.
CHICHESTER LAKE
Birdham Pool: (230+10 visitors) ☎ 512310, £12, enter chan at Birdham SHM bn, Fl (4) G 10s, with depth gauge; access HW ±3 via lock. **Services:** Slip, P, D, FW, EI, Ⓔ, AC, Sh, CH, Gas, ME, SM, C (3 ton).
Chichester Marina: (1000+50 visitors) ☎ 512731, 🕿 513472, £13.42, enter chan at CYB SHM pile, Fl G 5s, with depth gauge; 6kn speed limit. The well marked chan has approx 0·5m below CD; no access LW ±1½; a waiting pontoon is outside the lock.
Traffic sigs:
  Q Ⓡ (S of tr) = <1m water in chan.
  Q Ⓨ (top of tr) = both gates open (free flow).
Lock sigs: Ⓡ = Wait; Ⓖ = Enter.
Yachts lock out in numerical sequence, as assigned by lock-keeper on Ch 80, except during free-flow. From Easter to 30 Sep, the lock is manned Mon-Thur 0700-2100; Fri 0700 -2359; Sat, Sun, Bank Hols 0600-2359; all LT. 1 Oct to Easter: Contact ☎ 512731 or call VHF Ch M, 80.
Services: Slip, P, D, FW, ME, EI, Sh, AC, Gas, Gaz, CH, BY, BH (20 ton), V, R, Bar, ⬚, ACA, SM.
FISHBOURNE CHANNEL
Dell Quay: Possible drying berth against the Quay, apply to Hbr Office, public slip. **Services:** Sh, Slip, BH, M, L.
Clubs
Bosham SC ☎ 572341; **Chichester YC** ☎ 512918, R, Bar, ⬚; **Chichester Cruiser and Racing Club** ☎ 371731; **Dell Quay SC** ☎ 785080; **Emsworth SC** ☎ 373065; **Emsworth Slipper SC** ☎ 372523; **Hayling Island SC** (01705) 463768; **Itchenor SC** ☎ 512400; **Mengham Rithe SC** ☎ (01705) 463337; **Thorney Island SC**; **W Wittering SC**.

VOLVO PENTA SERVICE

Sales and service centres in area 3

SUSSEX *Felton Marine Engineering,* Brighton Marina, Brighton BN2 5UF Tel (01273) 601779 **LONDON** *John A. Sparks & Co. Ltd,* Ardwell Road, Streatham Hill SW2 4RT Tel 0181- 674 3434

3

Area 3

South-East England
Selsey Bill to North Foreland

VOLVO PENTA

10-3-2
South-East England
Selsey Bill to North Foreland

St Katherine Haven* **Limehouse Basin*** **Thames Barrier*** **Gallions Pt***

Chelsea Hbr* **South Dock Marina***

AREA 4
AREA 3

Key to Symbols

	Coast Radio Station: VHF/MF frequencies
	Port, VTS, or Marina Radio: VHF frequencies
RC	Marine RDF beacon
RC Aero	Aero RDF beacon
i	See for harbour information/tidal data
	Weather information (Frequencies/times of broadcasts)
	SAR Helicopter base
☆	Selected Principal Lights
	Light vessel/Light float/Lanby
◎RG	Emergency VHF DF
*	See Area Index

River Thames

i	10.4.14
Port Ctl London VHF **68** 18 20 (Sea Reach No 4 By to Crayford Ness	

Woolwich Radio
VHF **14** 22 16
(Thames above Crayford Ness)
Barrier **14** 22

Info bcsts
VHF 68 H+00 H+30
VHF 12 H+15 H+45
VHF 14 H+15 H+45

Thames Radio
VHF **02** 16
VHF 02
0733 1933 UT

Variation 3°W (1998)

Brighton Marina

i	10.3.10
VHF **80** M 68 11 16	
RC 294·50 BM 10M	

Littlehampton

i	10.3.8
VHF 71 16 Marinas 80 M	

Newhaven

i	10.3.11
VHF **12** 16 Marina 80 M	

Worthing

Bognor Regis

Shoreham

i	10.3.9
VHF **14** 16	
RC Aero 320·00 SHM 10M	

◎RG
Selsey

Eastbourne

i	10.3.12
Sovereign Hbr VHF **15** Locks/Bridge 17	

Beachy Head

Dover CG
Solent CG

See 10-2-2

Owers Lt By

5m

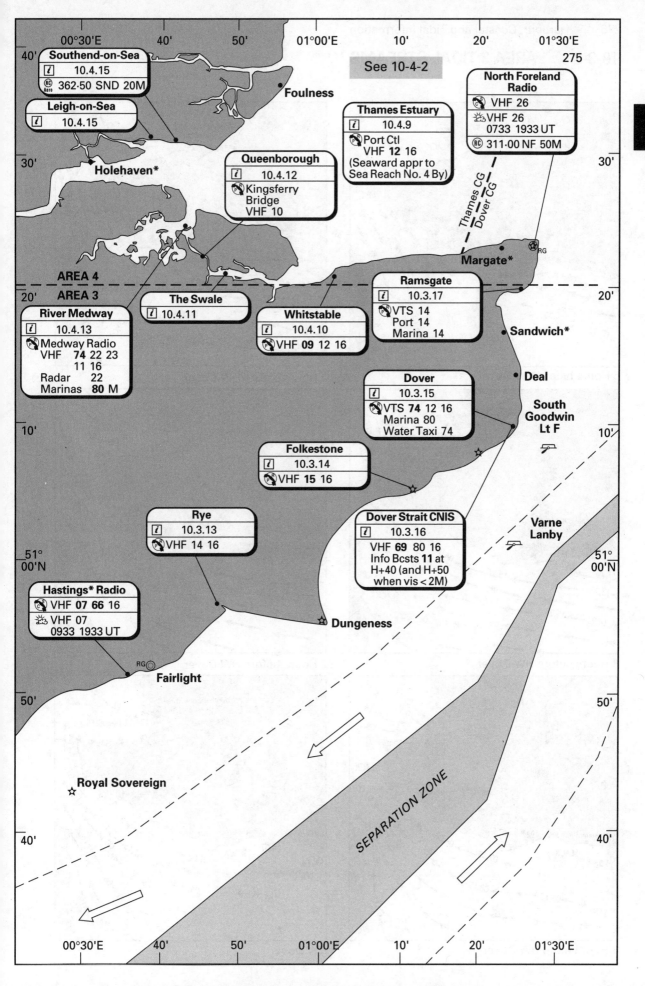

3

275

See 10-4-2

Southend-on-Sea
[i] 10.4.15
(RC) 362·50 SND 20M

Leigh-on-Sea
[i] 10.4.15

Foulness

Holehaven*

Thames Estuary
[i] 10.4.9
Port Ctl
VHF **12** 16
(Seaward appr to
Sea Reach No. 4 By)

North Foreland Radio
VHF 26
VHF 26
0733 1933 UT
(RC) 311·00 NF 50M

Queenborough
[i] 10.4.12
Kingsferry Bridge
VHF 10

Thames CG
Dover CG

Margate*

RG

AREA 4

AREA 3

River Medway
[i] 10.4.13
Medway Radio
VHF **74** 22 23
11 16
Radar 22
Marinas **80** M

The Swale
[i] 10.4.11

Whitstable
[i] 10.4.10
VHF **09** 12 16

Ramsgate
[i] 10.3.17
VTS 14
Port 14
Marina 14

Sandwich*

Deal

Dover
[i] 10.3.15
VTS **74** 12 16
Marina 80
Water Taxi 74

South
Goodwin
Lt F

Folkestone
[i] 10.3.14
VHF **15** 16

Rye
[i] 10.3.13
VHF 14 16

Dover Strait CNIS
[i] 10.3.16
VHF **69** 80 16
Info Bcsts **11** at
H+40 (and H+50
when vis < 2M)

Varne
Lanby

Hastings* Radio
VHF **07 66** 16
VHF 07
0933 1933 UT

Dungeness

RG
Fairlight

☆ **Royal Sovereign**

SEPARATION ZONE

10-3-3   AREA 3 TIDAL STREAMS

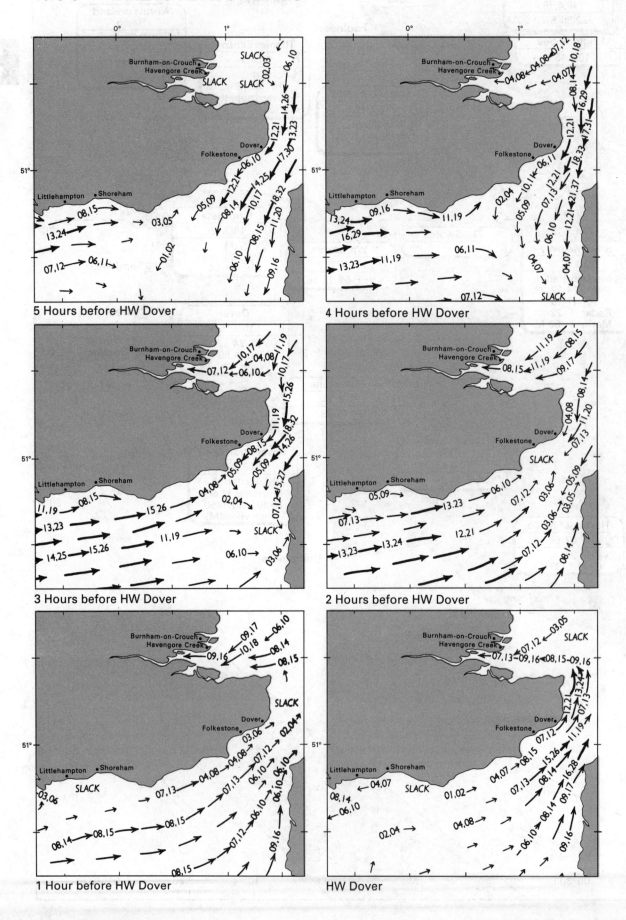

Westward 10.2.3   Southward 10.19.3   Northward 10.4.3   Thames Estuary 10.4.8   Eastward 10.20.3

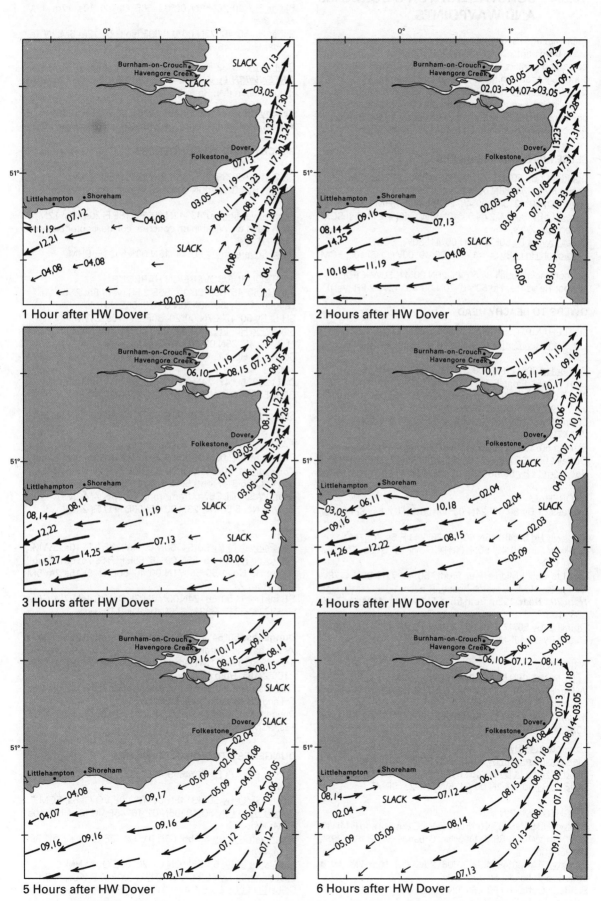

1 Hour after HW Dover

2 Hours after HW Dover

3 Hours after HW Dover

4 Hours after HW Dover

5 Hours after HW Dover

6 Hours after HW Dover

10.3.4 COASTAL LIGHTS, FOG SIGNALS AND WAYPOINTS

Abbreviations used below are given in 1.4.1. Principal lights are in **bold** print, places in CAPITALS, and light-vessels, light floats and Lanbys in *CAPITAL ITALICS*. Unless otherwise stated lights are white. m – elevation in metres; M – nominal range in miles. Fog signals are in *italics*. Useful waypoints are underlined – use those on land with care. All geographical positions should be assumed to be approximate. See 4.4.1. All positions are referenced to the OSGB 36 datum.

SELSEY BILL AND THE OWERS

Boulder Lt By 50°41'·53N 00°49'·00W Fl G 2·5s; SHM.
Street By 50°41'·65N 00°48'·80W; PHM.
Mixon Bn 50°42'·33N 00°46'·21W (unlit); PHM.
Owers Lt By 50°37'·27N 00°40'·60W Q (6) + L Fl 15s; SCM; Racon (O); *Whis.*
Outer Owers By 50°38'·75N 00°41'·30W; SCM.
E Borough Hd Lt By 50°41'·50N 00°39'·00W Q (3) 10s; ECM.

Bognor Regis Outfall By 50°45'·20N 00°41'·50W; SPM.
Bognor Regis Pier Hd 50°46'·70N 00°40'·42W 2 FR (vert).

OWERS TO BEACHY HEAD

LITTLEHAMPTON
Littlehampton Outfall Lt By 50°46'·20N 00°30'·45W Fl Y 5s; SPM.
W Pier Hd 50°47'·85N 00°32'·37W 2 FR (vert) 7m 6M.
Ldg Lts 346°. Front, E Pier Hd 50°48'·06N 00°32'·42W FG 6m 7M; B col. Rear, 64m from front, Oc WY 7·5s 9m 10M; W Tr; vis W290°-356°, Y356°-042°.
Lt Bn 50°46'·16N 00°29'·44W Fl (5) Y 20s 9m 5M.
WORTHING
Pier Hd 50°48'·38N 00°22'·02W 2 FR (vert) 6m 1M.
Outfall Lt Bn 50°48'·35N 00°20'·22W Fl R 2·5s 3m; PHM.
Beecham Lt By 50°48'·45N 00°19'·40W Fl (2) R 10s; PHM.

SHOREHAM
Express Lt By 50°47'·24N 00°17'·00W Fl Y 5s; SPM (Apr-Oct).
W Bkwtr Hd 50°49'·45N 00°14'·78W Fl R 5s 7m 7M.
E Bkwtr Hd 50°49'·50N 00°14'·70W Fl G 5s 7m 8M; *Siren 120s.*
Ldg Lts 355°. Middle Pier Front, 50°49'·72N 00°14'·78W Oc 5s 8m 10M; W watch-house, R base; tidal Lts, tfc sigs; *Horn 20s.* **Rear**, 192m from front, Fl 10s 13m **15M**; Gy Tr vis 283°-103°.
Outfall Lt By 50°47'·84N 00°13'·63W Q (6) + L Fl 15s; SCM.
Outfall By 50°49'·43N 00°14'·29W; SCM.

BRIGHTON
Lt By 50°46'·00N 00°08'·30W Fl Y 3s; SPM.
W Pier Hd 50°49'·12N 00°09'·00W Fl R 10s 13m 2M; *Bell (1) 13s* (when vessel expected).
Marine Palace Pier Hd 50°48'·88N 00°08'·12W 2 FR (vert) 10m 2M.

Lowenbrau Lt By 50°48'·40N 00°06'·40W Fl Y 4s; SPM.
Mercantile Credit Lt By 50°48'·90N 00°08'·40W Fl Y 6s; SPM.
Hand in Hand Lt By 50°46'·1N 00°08'·1W Fl Y 3s; SPM.
MHB Lt By 50°46'·2N 00°04'·5W Fl Y 2s; SPM.

BRIGHTON MARINA
E Bkwtr Hd 50°48'·53N 00°06'·27W QG 8m 7M and Fl (4) WR 20s 16m W10M, R8M; W pillar, G bands; vis R260°-295°, W295°-100°.
W Bkwtr Hd 50°48'·45N 00°06'·29W QR 10m 7M; W ● structure, R bands; *Horn (2) 30s.*
Saltdean Outfall By 50°46'·70N 00°02'·00W; SPM.

NEWHAVEN
Bkwtr Hd 50°46'·52N 00°03'·60E Oc (2) 10s 17m 12M; *Horn 30s.*
E Pier Hd 50°46'·77N 00°03'·68E Iso G 5s 12m 6M; W Tr.
W Pier Hd 50°46'·88N 00°03'·53E 2 FR (vert); SS Tfc.

CS 1 Lt By 50°33'·67N 00°03'·83W Fl Y 2·5s; SPM; *Whis.*
GREENWICH Lt V 50°24'·50N 00°00'·00 Fl 5s 12m **21M**; R hull; Racon (M); Ra refl; *Horn 30s.*

Beachy Hd 50°44'·00N 00°14'·60E Fl (2) 20s 31m **25M**; W ● Tr, R band and lantern; vis 248°-101°; (H24); *Horn 30s.*

BEACHY HEAD TO DUNGENESS

CS 2 Lt By 50°39'·10N 00°32'·70E Fl Y 5s; SPM.
CS 3 Lt By 50°52'·00N 01°02'·30E Fl Y 10s; SPM; *Bell.*

Royal Sovereign 50°43'·42N 00°26'·18E Fl 20s 28m 12M; W Tr, R band on W cabin on concrete col; helicopter platform; *Horn (2) 30s.*
Royal Sovereign By 50°44'·18N 00°25'·93E; PHM.

EASTBOURNE/SOVEREIGN HARBOUR
Pier Hd 50°45'·88N 00°17'·85E 2 FR (vert) 8m 2M.
Langney Pt By 50°46'·70N 00°20'·00E; PHM.
SH Lt By 50°47'·37N 00°20'·80E L Fl 10s; SWM.
Sovereign Hbr Lt By 50°47'·33N 00°20'·42E Fl G 5s; SHM.
Lt By 50°47'·29N 00°20'·25E Fl R 5s; PHM.
Sovereign Hbr Marina 50°47'·18N 00°19'·87E Fl (3) 15s 12m 7M.
Dir Lt 258° 50°47'·24N 00°19'·82E Dir Fl WRG 3s 4m 1M; vis G252·5°-256·5°, W256·5°-259·5°, R259·5°-262·5°.

St Leonard's Outfall Lt By 50°49'·27N 00°32'·00E Fl Y 5s; SPM.

HASTINGS
Pier Hd 50°51'·03N 00°34'·50E 2 FR (vert) 8m 5M; W hut.
W Bkwtr Hd 50°51'·13N 00°35'·70E Fl R 2·5s 5m 4M.
Ldg Lts 356·3°. Front, 50°51'·24N 00°35'·45E FR 14m 4M.
Rear, West Hill, 357m from front, FR 55m 4M; W Tr.
Groyne No. 3 50°51'·23N 00°35'·90E Fl G 5s 2m.

RYE
Rye Fairway Lt By 50°54'·00N 00°48'·13E L Fl 10s; SWM.
W Groyne Hd 50°55'·55N 00°46'·65E Fl R 5s 7m 6M; Ra refl.
E Arm Hd No. 1 50°55'·71N 00°46'·56E Q (9) 15s 7m 5M; G △; *Horn 7s.*
E Bank No. 11 50°56'·24N 00°46'·03E Oc WG 4s W7M, G6M; vis W326°-331°, G331°-326°; Tidal and Tfc sigs.

Dungeness 50°54'·77N 00°58'·67E Fl 10s 40m **27M**; B ● Tr, W bands and lantern, floodlit; Part obsc 078°-shore; RC; (H24). F RG 37m 11M (same Tr); vis R057°-073°, G073°-078°, R196°-216°; *Horn (3) 60s.*
FR Lts shown 2·4 and 5·2M WNW when firing taking place.
QR and FR on radio mast 1·2M NW.
Dungeness Outfall Lt By 50°54'·43N 00°58'·33E Q (6) + L Fl 15s; SCM.

DUNGENESS TO NORTH FORELAND

Bullock Bank Lt By 50°46'·90N 01°07'·70E VQ; NCM; *Whis.*
Ridens SE Lt By 50°43'·45N 01°19'·00E VQ (3) 5s; ECM.
Colbart SW Lt By 50°48'·85N 01°16'·45E VQ (6) + L Fl 10s; SCM; *Whis.*
South Varne Lt By 50°55'·60N 01°17'·40E Q (6) + L Fl 15s; SCM; *Whis.*
Mid Varne Lt By 50°58'·90N 01°20'·00E QG; SHM.
East Varne Lt By 50°58'·20N 01°21'·00E Fl R 2·5s; PHM.
Colbart N Lt By 50°57'·42N 01°23'·40E VQ; NCM.

3

VARNE Lanby 51°01'·25N 01°24'·00E Fl R 20s12m**19M**; Racon (T); *Horn 30s.*
CS 4 Lt By 51°08'·58N 01°34'·03E Fl (4) Y 15s; SPM; *Whis.*
CS 5 Lt By 51°23'·00N 01°50'·00E Fl (4) Y 15s; SPM.
MPC Lt By 51°06'·09N 01°38'·36E Fl Y 2·5s; SPM.
Hythe Flats Outfall Lt By 51°02'·50N 01°05'·43E Fl Y 5s; SPM.

FOLKESTONE
Bkwtr Hd   51°04'·53N 01°11'·79E Fl (2) 10s 14m **22M**; *Dia (4) 60s.* In fog Fl 2s; vis 246°-306°, intens 271·5°-280·5°.
Outer Hbr E Pier Hd 51°04'·73N 01°11'·48E QG 16m 1M.

Shakespeare Cliff W end 51°06'·05N 01°16'·12E Fl R 5s.
Shakespeare Cliff E end 51°06'·28N 01°16'·95E Fl R 5s.

DOVER
Admiralty Pier Extension Hd   51°06'·65N   01°19'·77E
Fl 7·5s 21m **20M**; W Tr; vis 096°-090°, obsc in The Downs by S Foreland inshore of 226°; *Horn 10s*; Int Port Tfc sigs.
S Bkwtr W Hd 51°06'·75N 01°19'·90E Oc R 30s 21m **18M**; W Tr.
Knuckle 51°07'·02N 01°20'·59E Fl (4) WR 10s 15m **W15M**, R13M; W Tr; vis R059°-239°, W239°-059°.
N Head 51°07'·17N 01°20'·71E Fl R 2·5s 11m 5M.
E Arm Hd 51°07'·27N 01°20'·70E Port Control Sig Stn; Fl G 5s 12m 5M; *Horn (2) 30s.*

S GOODWIN Lt F 51°07'·95N 01°28'·60E Fl (2) 20s 12m **15M**; R hull with Lt Tr amidships; *Horn (2) 60s.*
SW Goodwin Lt By 51°08'·57N 01°28'·80E Q (6) + L Fl 15s; SCM.
S Goodwin Lt By 51°10'·57N 01°32'·37E Fl (4) R 15s; PHM.
SE Goodwin Lt By 51°12'·95N 01°34'·55E Fl (3) R 10s; PHM.
E GOODWIN Lt F 51°13'·05N 01°36'·31E Fl 15s 12m **21M**; R hull with Lt Tr amidships; Racon (T); *Horn 30s.*
E Goodwin Lt By 51°16'·00N 01°35'·60E Q (3) 10s; ECM.
NE Goodwin Lt By 51°20'·28N 01°34'·27E Q (3) 10s; ECM; Racon (M).

DEAL
Pier Hd 51°13'·40N 01°24'·65E 2 FR (vert) 7m 5M.
Sandown Outfall Dn 51°14'·45N 01°24'·56E Fl R 2·5s; Ra refl.

THE DOWNS
Deal Bank Lt By 51°12'·90N 01°25'·67E; QR; PHM.
Goodwin Fork Lt By 51°14'·30N 01°27'·23E Q (6) + L Fl 15s; SCM; *Bell.*
Downs Lt By 51°14'·47N 01°26'·60E Fl (2) R 5s; PHM.

GULL STREAM
W Goodwin Lt By 51°15'·28N 01°27'·32E Fl G 5s; SHM.
S Brake Lt By 51°15'·45N 01°26'·80E Fl (3) R 10s; PHM.

NW Goodwin Lt By 51°16'·54N 01°28'·67E Q (9) 15s; WCM; *Bell.*
Brake Lt By 51°16'·95N 01°28'·30E Fl (4) R 15s; PHM; *Bell.*
N Goodwin Lt By 51°17'·88N 01°30'·42E Fl G 2·5s; SHM.
Gull Stream Lt By 51°18'·25N 01°29'·80E QR; PHM.
Gull Lt By 51°19'·55N 01°31'·40E VQ (3) 5s; ECM.
Goodwin Knoll Lt By 51°19'·55N 01°32'·30E Fl (2) G 5s; SHM.

RAMSGATE CHANNEL
B2 By 51°18'·03N 01°24'·20E; SHM.
W Quern Lt By 51°18'·95N 01°25'·50E Q (9) 15s; WCM.

RIVER STOUR/SANDWICH
Chan marked by PHM & SHM Bys and Bns.
Pegwell Bay, Sandwich app 51°18'·72N 01°23'·05E Fl R 10s 3m 4M; framework Tr; moved to meet changes in chan.

RAMSGATE
RA Lt By 51°19'·57N 01°30'·23E Q(6) + L Fl 15s; SCM.
E Brake Lt By 51°19'·40N 01°29'·05E Fl R 5s; PHM.
No. 1 Lt By 51°19'·53N 01°27'·40E QG; SHM.
No. 2 Lt By 51°19'·66N 01°27'·24E Fl (4) R 10s; PHM.
No. 3 Lt By 51°19'·32N 01°26'·42E Fl G 2·5s; SHM.
No. 4 Lt By 51°19'·26N 01°26'·67E QR; PHM.
No. 5 Lt By 51°19'·52N 01°26'·42E Q(6) + L Fl 15s; SCM.
No. 6 Lt By 51°19'·43N 01°26'·42E Fl (2) R 5s; PHM.
N Quern Lt By 51°19'·38N 01°26'·25E Q; NCM.
S Bkwtr Hd 51°19'·43N 01°25'·52E VQ R 10m 5M; W pillar, R bands.
N Bkwtr Hd 51°19'·53N 01°25'·58E Q G 10m 5M; W pillar, G bands.

W Marine terminal Dir Lt 270°, Dir Oc WRG 10s 10m 5M; B △, Or stripe; vis G259°-269°, W269°-271°, R271°-281°. Rear 493m from front Oc 5s 17m 5M; B ▽, Or stripe; vis 263°-278°.

BROADSTAIRS
Broadstairs Knoll Lt By 51°20'·85N 01°29'·58E Fl R 2·5s; PHM.
Pier SE End 51°21'·46N 01°26'·83E 2 FR (vert) 7m 4M.

N Foreland   51°22'·47N 01°26'·80E Fl (5) WR 20s 57m **W19M, R16M, R15M**; W 8-sided Tr; vis W shore-150°, R(16M)150°-181°, R(15M) 181°-200°, W200°-011°; RC.

South Falls Lt By 51°13'·80N 00°44'·03E Q (6) + L Fl 15s; SCM.
F1 Lt By 51°11'·20N 01°45'·03E; Fl (4) Y 15s; SPM.
Inter Bank Lt By 51°16'·45N 01°52'·33E Fl Y 5s; Racon (M); SPM.
Mid Falls Lt By 51°18'·60N 01°47'·10E Fl (3) R 10s; PHM; *Bell.*
F2 Lt By 51°20'·38N 01°56'·30E Fl (4) Y 15s; SPM; *Bell.*

10.3.5 PASSAGE INFORMATION

Reference books include: Admiralty *Channel Pilot*; *Shell Channel Pilot* (Imray/Cunliffe); and *South Coast Cruising* (YM/Fishwick). See 10.0.5 for cross-Channel distances.

THE EASTERN CHANNEL

This area embraces the greatest concentration of commercial shipping in the world. In such waters the greatest danger to a small yacht is being run down by a larger vessel, especially in poor visibility. In addition to the many ships plying up and down the traffic lanes, there are fast ferries, hovercraft and hydrofoils passing to and fro between English and Continental harbours; warships and submarines on exercises; fishing vessels operating both inshore and offshore; many other yachts; and static dangers such as lobster pots and fishing nets which are concentrated in certain places.

Even for coastal cruising it is essential to know about the TSS and ITZ, see Fig.10 (4); eg, note that the SW-bound TSS lane from the Dover Strait passes only 4M off Dungeness. Radar surveillance of the Dover Strait (10.3.15) is maintained at all times by the Channel Navigation Information Service (CNIS).

In this area the weather has a big effect on tidal streams, and on the range of tides. The rates of tidal streams vary with the locality, and are greatest in the narrower parts of the Channel and off major headlands. In the Dover Strait sp rates can reach 4kn, but elsewhere in open water they seldom exceed 2kn. Also N winds, which give smooth water and pleasant sailing off the shores of England, can cause rough seas on the French coast; and vice versa. With strong S'lies the English coast between Isle of Wight and Dover is very exposed, and shelter is hard to find. The Dover Strait has a funnelling effect and in strong winds can become very rough.

SELSEY BILL AND THE OWERS (chart *1652*)

Selsey Bill is a low headland, off which lie the Owers, groups of rks and shoals extending 3M to the S, and 5M to the SE. Just W and SW of the Bill, The Streets (awash) extend 1·25M seaward. 1·25M SSW of the Bill are The Grounds (or Malt Owers) and The Dries (dry). 1M E of The Dries, and about 1·25M S of the lifeboat house on E side of Selsey Bill is The Mixon a group of rks marked by bn at E end.

Immediately S of the above dangers is the Looe Chan, which runs E/W about 7½ca S of Mixon bn. It is marked by buoys at W end, where it is narrowest between Brake (or Cross) Ledge on N side and Boulder Bank to the S. In daylight, good visibility and moderate weather, the Looe Chan is an easy and useful short cut. The E-going stream begins at HW Portsmouth + 0430, and the W-going at HW Portsmouth – 0135, sp rates 2·5 kn. Beware lobster pots in this area.

In poor visibility or in bad weather (and always in darkness) keep S of the Owers SCM lt buoy, 7M SE of Selsey Bill, marking SE end of Owers. Over much of the Owers there is less than 3m, and large parts virtually dry; so a combination of tidal stream and strong wind produces heavy breaking seas and overfalls over a large area.

OWERS TO BEACHY HEAD (charts *1652, 536*)

The coast from Selsey Bill to Brighton is low, faced by a shingle beach, and with few offlying dangers, Bognor Rks (dry in places) extend 1·75M E from a point 1M W of the pier, and Bognor Spit extends E and S from the end of them. Middleton ledge are rks running 8ca offshore, about 1·5M E of Bognor pier, with depths of less than 1m. Shelley Rks lie 5ca S of Middleton ledge, with depths of less than 1m.

Winter Knoll, about 2·5M SSW of Littlehampton (10.3.9) has depths of 2·1m. Kingston Rks, depth 2m, lie about 3·25M ESE of Littlehampton. An unlit outfall bn is 3ca off Goring-on-sea (2M W of Worthing pier). Grass Banks, an extensive shoal with 2m depth at W end, lie about 1M S of Worthing pier. Elbow shoal, with depth of 3·1m, lies E of Grass Banks.

Off Shoreham (10.3.10) Church Rks, with depth of 0·3m, lie 1·5M W of the hbr ent and 2½ca offshore. Jenny Rks, with depth 0·9m, are 1·25M E of the ent, 3ca offshore.

At Brighton (10.3.11) the S Downs form the coastline, and high chalk cliffs are conspic from here to Beachy Head. There are no dangers more than 3ca offshore, until Birling Gap, where a rky ledge begins, on which is built Beachy Head lt ho (fog sig). Head Ledge (dries) extends about 4ca S. 2M S of Beachy Hd the W-going stream begins at HW Dover + 0030, and the E-going at HW Dover – 0520, sp rates 2·25kn. In bad weather there are overfalls off the Head, which should then be given a berth of 2M.

BEACHY HEAD TO DUNGENESS

Royal Sovereign lt tr (fog sig) is 7·4M E of Beachy Head. The extensive Royal Sovereign shoals lie from 3M NW of the tr to 1·5M N of it, and have a minimum depth of 3·5m. There are strong eddies over the shoals at sp, and the sea breaks on them in bad weather.

On the direct course from Royal Sovereign lt tr to clear Dungeness there are no dangers. Along the coast in Pevensey B and Rye B there are drying rky ledges or shoals extending 5ca offshore in places. These include Boulder Bank near Wish tr, S of Eastbourne (10.3.13); Oyster Reef off Cooden; Bexhill Reef off Bexhill-on-Sea; Bopeep Rks off St Leonards; and the shoals at the mouth of R Rother, at entrance to Rye (10.3.14). There are also banks 2-3M offshore, on which the sea builds in bad weather. Avoid the firing range danger area between Rye and Dungeness (lt, fog sig, RC). The nuclear power station is conspic at SE extremity of the low-lying spit. The Pt is steep-to on SE side. Good anch close NE of Dungeness.

DUNGENESS TO NORTH FORELAND (charts *1892, 1828*)

From Dungeness to Folkestone (10.3.16) the coast forms a bay. Beware Roar bank, depth 2·7m, E of New Romney: otherwise there are no offlying dangers, apart from Hythe firing range. Good anch off Sandgate in offshore winds. Off Folkestone the E-going stream starts at HW Dover – 0155, sp rate 2kn; the W-going at HW Dover + 0320, sp rate 1·5kn.

Passing Dover (10.3.17) and S Foreland keep 1M offshore. Do not pass too close to Dover, because ferries/jetfoils leave at speed, and there can be considerable backwash and lumpy seas off the breakwaters. 8M S of Dover in the TSS is the Varne, a shoal 7M long with least depth 3·3m and heavy seas in bad weather, marked by Lanby and 3 buoys. Between S and N Foreland the N-going stream begins at about HW Dover – 0150, and the S-going at about HW Dover + 0415.

The Goodwin Sands are drying, shifting shoals, extending about 10M from S to N, and 5M from W to E at their widest part. The E side is relatively steep-to; large areas dry up to 2·7m. The sands are well marked by lt Fs and buoys. Kellett Gut is an unmarked chan about 5ca wide, running SW/NE through the middle of the sands, but it is not regularly surveyed and is liable to change. The Gull Stream (buoyed) leads from The Downs, inside Goodwin Sands and outside Brake Sands to the S of Ramsgate (10.3.18). The Ramsgate chan leads inside the Brake Sands and Cross Ledge.

CROSS-CHANNEL PASSAGES

This section applies broadly to any crossing, ranging from the short (4-5hrs) Dover Strait route, through the much used, medium length Solent-Cherbourg route (13hrs; see 10.15.5), to the longer passages (20+hrs) from SW England to North Brittany. Distances are tabulated at 10.0.5. Whatever the length of passage, **thorough planning** is the key to a safe and efficient crossing. Maximum experience of crossing the Channel as crew/navigator is also invaluable, before the psychological hurdle of first skippering a boat across.

A **Planning check-list** must oblige a skipper/navigator to:

a.   Study the meteorological situation several days before departure, so that windows of opportunity, eg high pressure, may be predicted and bad weather avoided.
b.   Consider the forecast wind direction and likely shifts, so that the probability of obtaining a good slant can be improved. Prevailing winds are SW/W, except in the spring when NE/E winds are equally likely. The advantages of getting well to windward cannot be over-emphasised. If heading for St Malo from Brighton, for example, it might pay to make westing along the coast (working the tides to advantage) so as to depart from St Catherine's Point, the Needles, Anvil Point or even Portland Bill when crossing towards Barfleur, Cherbourg, Cap de la Hague or Alderney.
c.   Choose the route, departure points and landfalls so that time on passage and out of sight of identifiable marks is minimised. This can much reduce anxiety and fatigue (which may soon become apparent in a family crew). The risk of navigational errors, particularly those due to leeway and tidal streams, is also reduced. It is sound practice to take back bearings on the departure mark.
d.   Take account of tidal constraints at the point of departure and destination; and en route tidal gates, eg Hurst Narrows.
e.   Work out the hourly direction and rate of tidal streams expected during (and after) the crossing; so as to lay off the total drift angle required to make good the desired track. Only rarely do 6 hours of E-going tide cancel out 6 hours of W-going (or vice versa); streams off the French coast are usually stronger. Try to arrive up-tide of destination. Note the times and areas of races and overfalls and keep well clear.
f.   Consider actions to be taken in poor visibility/fog when the range at which marks may be seen is much reduced (and risk of collision with other vessels equally increased).

Statistically fog is unlikely in summer (except in certain notorious areas, eg off Ushant) and visibility is often greater than 6M. A landfall at night or dawn/dusk is frequently easier due to the additional range provided by lights.
g.   Observe the legal requirement to head at 90° across any TSS (10.0.9); consider motoring to expedite such crossing.
h.   Make use of additional navigational info such as soundings, for example when crossing the distinctive contours of the Hurd Deep; the rising or dipping ranges of major lights; fixing on clearly identifiable radar targets, if so equipped; and the sighting of TSS buoys and light floats. Note: The charted 2M exclusion circles around EC1, EC2 and EC3 buoys apply only to IMO-Convention vessels, ie not yachts.
j.   Keep a harbour of refuge in mind if caught out by fog, gales or gear failure. For example, if unable to make Cherbourg in a strong SSW'ly and E-going tide, it may be better to bear away and run for St Vaast in the lee of the peninsular. Or heave to and stay at sea.
k.   Finally, even if using electronic navigation, write up the ship's log and maintain a DR plot. This is both a safeguard, and a source of pride (when proven accurate); it also ensures the highest degree of navigational awareness.

Routes from ports within Area 3

Passages from Brighton, Newhaven or Eastbourne to Dieppe or adjacent French ports are relatively short and direct. The route crosses the Dover Strait TSS whose SW-bound lane lies only 7M S of Beachy Head. A departure from close W of CS2 buoy will satisfy the 90° crossing rule and minimise the time spent in the TSS. During the 19M crossing of the TSS, it is worth listening to the VHF broadcasts of navigational and traffic information made by CNIS. These include details of vessels which appear to be contravening Rule 10.

Dover to Calais or Boulogne is only about 25M (see 10.3.15) but the route crosses the congested Dover Strait TSS. Keep a very sharp lookout for ships in the traffic lanes and ferries crossing them. Do not attempt to cross in fog or poor visibility. Listen to CNIS and to the relevant hbr VHF channel.

From Ramsgate to/from Dutch/Belgian ports, see 10.20.5.

"It is better to have absolutely no idea of where one is – and to know it – than to believe confidently that one is where one is not".   Cassini (Director of the Paris Observatoire, 1770)

10.3.6   DISTANCE TABLE

Approximate distances in nautical miles are by the most direct route, whilst avoiding dangers and allowing for Traffic Separation Schemes. Places in *italics* are in adjoining areas; places in **bold** are in 10.0.5, Cross-Channel Distances; places underlined are in 10.0.7, Distances across the North Sea.

	1	2	3	4	5	6	7	8	9	10	11	12	13	14	15	16	17	18	19	20
1. *Portland Bill Lt*	1																			
2. **Nab Tower**	60	2																		
3. Boulder Lt Buoy	65	5	3																	
4. Owers Lt Buoy	69	11	8	4																
5. **Littlehampton**	78	19	13	12	5															
6. **Shoreham**	90	32	24	21	13	6														
7. **Brighton**	93	35	28	24	17	5	7													
8. **Newhaven**	97	40	34	29	24	12	7	8												
9. Beachy Head Lt	104	46	41	36	30	20	14	8	9											
10. **Eastbourne**	111	51	45	40	34	24	19	12	7	10										
11. **Rye**	129	72	67	62	56	46	41	34	25	23	11									
12. Dungeness Lt	134	76	71	66	60	50	44	38	30	26	9	12								
13. **Folkestone**	152	92	84	81	76	65	60	53	43	40	23	13	13							
14. **Dover**	157	97	89	86	81	70	65	58	48	45	28	18	5	14						
15. Ramsgate	172	112	104	101	96	85	80	73	63	60	43	33	20	15	15					
16. N Foreland Lt	175	115	107	104	99	88	83	76	66	63	46	36	23	18	3	16				
17. *Sheerness*	206	146	139	135	132	119	114	107	97	96	79	67	54	49	34	31	17			
18. *London Bridge*	248	188	184	177	177	161	156	149	139	141	124	109	96	91	76	73	45	18		
19. *Burnham-on-Crouch*	216	156	148	145	140	129	124	117	107	104	87	75	64	59	44	41	34	76	19	
20. *Harwich*	212	152	144	141	136	125	120	113	103	100	83	73	60	55	40	37	50	83	31	20

LITTLEHAMPTON   10-3-8

W. Sussex 50°47′·84N 00°32′·33W   Rtg 3-3-2

CHARTS
AC *1991, 1652*; Imray C9; Stanfords 9; OS 197

TIDES
+0015 Dover; ML 2·8; Zone 0 (UT)

Standard Port SHOREHAM (→)

Times				Height (metres)			
High Water		Low Water		MHWS	MHWN	MLWN	MLWS
0500	1000	0000	0600	6·3	4·8	1·9	0·6
1700	2200	1200	1800				
Differences LITTLEHAMPTON (ENT)							
+0010	0000	−0005	−0010	−0·4	−0·4	−0·2	−0·2
LITTLEHAMPTON (NORFOLK WHARF)							
+0015	+0005	0000	+0045	−0·7	−0·7	−0·3	+0·2
ARUNDEL							
No data	+0120	No data		−3·1	−2·8	No data	
PAGHAM							
+0015	0000	−0015	−0025	−0·7	−0·5	−0·1	−0·1
BOGNOR REGIS							
+0010	−0005	−0005	−0020	−0·6	−0·5	−0·2	−0·1

NOTE: Tidal hts in hbr are affected by flow down R Arun. Tide seldom falls lower than 0·7m above CD.

SHELTER
Good. Ent dangerous in strong SE winds which cause swell up the hbr. The bar (0·4 to 0·7m) is rough in SW'lies. Visitors berth initially at Town Quay and contact Hr Mr.

NAVIGATION
WPT 50°47′·50N 00°32′·20W, 166°/346° from/to front ldg lt, 0·60M. Bar ½M offshore. Hbr accessible from HW−3 to HW+2½ for approx 1·5m draft. The ebb runs so fast (4 – 6 kn) at sp that yachts may have difficulty entering. From HW−1 to HW+4 a strong W-going tidal stream sets across the ent; keep to E side. Speed limit 6½kn.
On E side of ent chan a training wall which covers at half-tide is marked by 7 poles and unlit bn at S end. The W pier is a long, prominent structure of wood piles; beware shoal ground within its arm. A tide gauge on end shows height of tide above CD. To obtain depth on the bar subtract 0·7m from indicated depth.

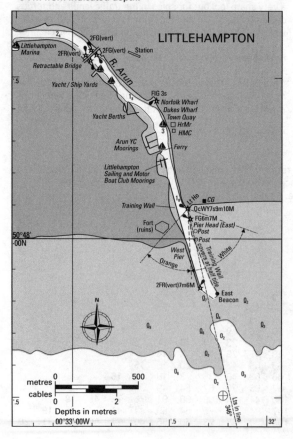

River Arun.
A retractable footbridge (3·6m clearance MHWS; 9·4m above CD) 3ca above Town Quay gives access for masted craft to Littlehampton marina. It is opened by request to Hr Mr before 1630 previous day. The River Arun is navigable on the tide by small, unmasted craft for 24M via Ford, Arundel and beyond; consult Hr Mr.

LIGHTS AND MARKS
High-rise bldg (38m) is conspic 0·4M NNE of hbr ent. A pile with small platform and ☆, Fl Y (5) 20s 5M, is 2·5M SE of hbr ent at 50°46′·1N 00°29′·5W.
Ldg lts 346°: Front FG on B column; Rear, lt ho Oc WY 7·5s at root of E bkwtr, W 290°-356°, Y 356°-042°. The Fl G 3s lt at Norfolk Wharf leads craft upstream, once inside hbr ent. When Pilot boat with P at the bow displays the Pilot flag 'H' (WR vert halves) or Ⓦ over Ⓡ lts, all boats keep clear of ent; large ship moving.
Footbridge sigs, from high mast to port:
Fl G lt = open; Fl R = closed.
Bridge's retractable centre section (22m wide) has 2 FR (vert) to port and 2 FG (vert) to stbd on each side.

RADIO TELEPHONE
Hr Mr VHF Ch 71 16 (0900-1700LT); Pilots Ch 71 16 when vessel due. Bridge Ch 71. Marinas Ch **80** M (office hrs).

TELEPHONE (Dial code 01903)
Hr Mr 721215; MRSC (01705) 552100; ⌗ 0345 231110 (H24); Marinecall 0891 500456; Police 731733; Dr 714113.

FACILITIES
Town Quay AB £10, FW, C (5 ton), ME, Sh;
Services: BY, M, Sh (Wood), ACA.
Littlehampton Sailing & Motor Club ☎ 715859, M, FW, Bar;
Arun YC (90+10 visitors), £7.50, ☎ 714533/716016, (dries; access HW±3), M, AC, FW, Bar, Slip, R, Showers;
Littlehampton Marina (120 + 30 Ⓥ), £16.33, ☎ 713553, 🕿 732264, Slip, BH (12 ton), CH, P, D, V, R, Bar, FW, AC, Sh, ME;
Ship and Anchor Marina, about 2M up-river at Ford, (182, some visitors) ☎ (01243) 551262, (access HW±4), Slip, FW, ME, Sh, CH, V, R, Bar.
Town EC Wed; P, D, V, R, Bar, ✉, Ⓑ, ⇌, ✈ (Shoreham).

3

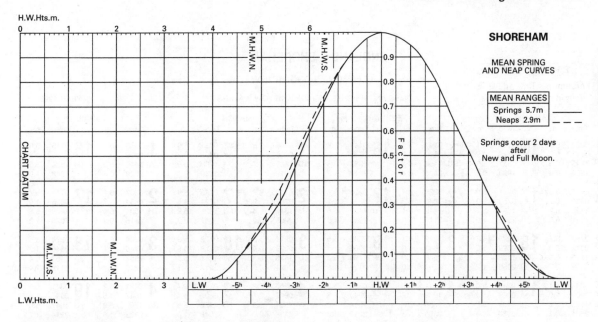

SHOREHAM

MEAN SPRING
AND NEAP CURVES

MEAN RANGES
Springs 5.7m
Neaps 2.9m

Springs occur 2 days
after
New and Full Moon.

SHOREHAM   10-3-9

W. Sussex 50°49'.50N 00°14'.76W   Rtg 3-3-2

CHARTS
AC 2044, *1652*; Imray C9; Stanfords 9; OS 197/8

TIDES
+0009 Dover; ML 3·3; Duration 0605; Zone 0 (UT)

Standard Port SHOREHAM (→)

Times				Height (metres)			
High Water		Low Water		MHWS	MHWN	MLWN	MLWS
0500	1000	0000	0600	6·3	4·8	1·9	0·6
1700	2200	1200	1800				
Differences WORTHING							
+0010	0000	−0005	−0010	−0·1	−0·2	0·0	0·0

NOTE: Shoreham is a Standard Port and tidal predictions
for the year are given below.

SHELTER
Excellent, once through the lock and into The Canal. The
shallow water (dredged 1·9m) at the ent can be very rough
in strong on-shore winds and dangerous in onshore gales.
Lady Bee and Aldrington (E end of The Canal) marinas,
least depth 2m, both welcome visitors; they are managed
by the Hbr Authority. Visiting yachtsmen are advised not
to use the drying Western Arm if possible.

NAVIGATION
WPT 50°49'.20N 00°14'.72W, 175°/355° from/to front ldg
lt, 0·52M. From E, beware Jenny Rks (0·9m) and from the
W, Church Rks (0·3m). The Eastern Arm leads to Prince
George Lock, the N'ly of two locks, which opens H24 @
H+30 for arrivals and H for departures; also, if not busy,
at other times on request VHF Ch 14. Lock ent is 6m wide,
pontoon inside on S wall; sill is 0·26m below CD, denying
access only at about LWS±1. Lock will advise exact depth

on Ch 14. Waiting space on S side of central lead-in pier.
Commercial ships use Prince Philip lock; yachts to keep
clear. Hbr speed limit = 4kn.

LIGHTS AND MARKS
Conspic, light-coloured chy (109m), 0.6M ENE of hbr ent,
is visible from 20M offshore. Radio mast is conspic 170m
N of High lt. A SCM buoy, Q(6) + L Fl 15s, marking outfall
diffusers, bears 157°/1·8M from hbr ent.
Ldg lts 355°: front Oc 5s 8m 10M; rear High lt, Fl 10s 13m 15M.
Traffic Sigs IPTS (Sigs 2 and 5, Oc) are shown from
Middle Pier. Note : Ⓨ Fl lt exempts small craft.
Oc R 3s (from LB ho, directed at E or W Arms) = No exit.
Lock Sigs (Comply strictly to avoid turbulence):
3 Ⓡ (vert)   = do not approach lock.
Ⓖ Ⓦ Ⓖ (vert) = clear to approach lock.

RADIO TELEPHONE
Call *Shoreham Hbr Radio* VHF Ch **14** 16 (H24) Hr Mr and
lock. Lock will advise Lady Bee marina of arrivals, 0830-
1800 M-Sat; 1000-1400 Sun.

TELEPHONE (Dial code 01273)
Hr Mr 592613, ☎ 592492; Locks 592366; MRSC (01705)
552100; ☷ 0345 231110 (H24); Marinecall 0891 500456;
Police 454521; Ⓗ 455622; Dr 461101 (Health Centre).

FACILITIES
Lady Bee Marina (110+10 Ⓥ) ☎ 596680, ☎ 870349, (best
to pre-arrange), £15.50 inc lock fee, £11 for subsequent
nights; Access as lock times, AB, P & D (cans), FW, AC,
CH, ME, El, Sh, SM, R, V, Slip;
Sussex YC ☎/☎ 464868, welcomes visitors, but has only
one AB in The Canal, so prior notice advised; also a drying
½ tide pontoon in the Western Arm(limited Ⓥ), R, Bar.
Services: P & D also on N side of W Arm HW±3; ACA.
Town EC Wed; ◙, ✉, Ⓑ, ⇌, ✈.

TIME ZONE (UT)
For Summer Time add ONE hour in non-shaded areas

ENGLAND – SHOREHAM

LAT 50°50′N   LONG 0°15′W

TIMES AND HEIGHTS OF HIGH AND LOW WATERS

YEAR **1998**

JANUARY

Time	m		Time	m
1 TH	0029 6.3 / 0641 0.7 / 1245 6.3 / 1906 0.6	**16** F	0119 6.1 / 0718 0.9 / 1327 5.9 / 1938 0.8	
2 F	0112 6.3 / 0725 0.7 / 1328 6.2 / 1951 0.6	**17** SA	0151 5.9 / 0753 1.0 / 1357 5.7 / 2013 1.0	
3 SA	0156 6.2 / 0812 0.8 / 1415 6.1 / 2039 0.7	**18** SU	0220 5.8 / 0829 1.2 / 1426 5.5 / 2050 1.2	
4 SU	0244 6.1 / 0905 1.0 / 1505 5.8 / 2131 0.9	**19** M	0248 5.5 / 0909 1.4 / 1459 5.4 / 2130 1.4	
5 M	0337 5.8 / 1003 1.2 / 1603 5.6 / 2229 1.1	**20** TU	0322 5.3 / 0954 1.6 / 1541 5.0 / 2215 1.7	
6 TU	0438 5.6 / 1108 1.4 / 1708 5.3 / 2337 1.3	**21** W	0409 5.0 / 1047 1.9 / 1638 4.8 / 2310 1.9	
7 W	0548 5.4 / 1221 1.4 / 1823 5.2	**22** TH	0523 4.8 / 1150 2.0 / 1806 4.7	
8 TH	0052 1.4 / 0705 5.4 / 1334 1.4 / 1946 5.3	**23** F	0018 2.0 / 0646 4.9 / 1300 1.9 / 1920 4.8	
9 F	0202 1.4 / 0819 5.6 / 1437 1.2 / 2055 5.5	**24** SA	0132 1.9 / 0750 5.1 / 1411 1.7 / 2021 5.1	
10 SA	0301 1.2 / 0920 5.8 / 1531 1.0 / 2151 5.8	**25** SU	0238 1.7 / 0845 5.4 / 1509 1.4 / 2114 5.4	
11 SU	0353 1.0 / 1012 6.0 / 1620 0.8 / 2241 6.0	**26** M	0331 1.3 / 0934 5.8 / 1557 1.0 / 2202 5.8	
12 M O	0441 0.9 / 1058 6.1 / 1706 0.7 / 2326 6.1	**27** TU	0417 1.0 / 1020 6.1 / 1641 0.7 / 2248 6.1	
13 TU	0525 0.8 / 1140 6.2 / 1749 0.6	**28** W ●	0500 0.8 / 1105 6.3 / 1725 0.5 / 2333 6.4	
14 W	0007 6.2 / 0605 0.8 / 1220 6.2 / 1827 0.6	**29** TH	0544 0.6 / 1149 6.5 / 1809 0.4	
15 TH	0045 6.2 / 0643 0.8 / 1255 6.1 / 1904 0.7	**30** F	0017 6.5 / 0628 0.5 / 1234 6.5 / 1852 0.3	
		31 SA	0101 6.6 / 0713 0.4 / 1318 6.5 / 1938 0.3	

FEBRUARY

Time	m		Time	m
1 SU	0144 6.5 / 0800 0.5 / 1403 6.4 / 2024 0.4	**16** M	0144 5.9 / 0759 1.0 / 1353 5.8 / 2018 1.0	
2 M	0229 6.4 / 0848 0.7 / 1449 6.1 / 2112 0.6	**17** TU	0209 5.7 / 0832 1.1 / 1423 5.6 / 2049 1.2	
3 TU	0317 6.1 / 0941 0.9 / 1540 5.8 / 2204 1.0	**18** W	0240 5.5 / 0906 1.4 / 1459 5.3 / 2124 1.5	
4 W	0411 5.7 / 1039 1.2 / 1639 5.4 / 2306 1.3	**19** TH	0320 5.3 / 0949 1.6 / 1544 5.0 / 2210 1.8	
5 TH	0514 5.4 / 1150 1.5 / 1749 5.1	**20** F	0411 4.9 / 1048 1.9 / 1645 4.7 / 2317 2.0	
6 F	0024 1.6 / 0628 5.1 / 1312 1.6 / 1920 5.0	**21** SA	0530 4.7 / 1206 2.0 / 1833 4.6	
7 SA	0143 1.6 / 0759 5.2 / 1420 1.5 / 2041 5.2	**22** SU	0045 2.0 / 0712 4.8 / 1329 1.8 / 1950 4.9	
8 SU	0247 1.4 / 0908 5.4 / 1517 1.2 / 2141 5.5	**23** M	0205 2.0 / 0818 5.2 / 1440 1.4 / 2050 5.4	
9 M	0341 1.2 / 1001 5.7 / 1606 1.0 / 2230 5.8	**24** TU	0307 1.4 / 0912 5.6 / 1533 1.0 / 2142 5.8	
10 TU	0427 1.0 / 1047 5.9 / 1650 0.8 / 2312 6.0	**25** W	0356 1.0 / 1002 6.0 / 1620 0.7 / 2230 6.2	
11 W O	0509 0.8 / 1127 6.1 / 1731 0.7 / 2351 6.1	**26** TH ●	0441 0.6 / 1049 6.4 / 1705 0.4 / 2316 6.5	
12 TH	0548 0.8 / 1203 6.1 / 1808 0.6	**27** F	0526 0.4 / 1135 6.6 / 1750 0.2	
13 F	0025 6.2 / 0623 0.7 / 1235 6.1 / 1842 0.6	**28** SA	0001 6.7 / 0611 0.2 / 1221 6.7 / 1834 0.1	
14 SA	0056 6.1 / 0656 0.8 / 1303 6.0 / 1914 0.7			
15 SU	0122 6.0 / 0727 0.8 / 1327 5.9 / 1946 0.8			

MARCH

Time	m		Time	m
1 SU	0046 6.8 / 0656 0.2 / 1305 6.7 / 1919 0.1	**16** M	0051 6.0 / 0702 0.7 / 1300 5.9 / 1919 0.7	
2 M	0129 6.7 / 0742 0.2 / 1349 6.5 / 2005 0.2	**17** TU	0113 5.9 / 0731 0.8 / 1326 5.9 / 1947 0.9	
3 TU	0211 6.5 / 0829 0.4 / 1433 6.3 / 2051 0.5	**18** W	0139 5.8 / 0758 0.9 / 1355 5.7 / 2014 1.1	
4 W	0256 6.2 / 0917 0.7 / 1521 5.9 / 2139 0.9	**19** TH	0210 5.7 / 0829 1.1 / 1429 5.5 / 2048 1.3	
5 TH	0346 5.7 / 1011 1.2 / 1616 5.4 / 2236 1.4	**20** F	0247 5.4 / 0909 1.4 / 1512 5.2 / 2134 1.6	
6 F	0445 5.2 / 1118 1.5 / 1722 5.0 / 2354 1.7	**21** SA	0334 5.0 / 1005 1.7 / 1607 4.9 / 2237 1.9	
7 SA	0557 4.9 / 1248 1.7 / 1852 4.8	**22** SU	0440 4.7 / 1119 1.9 / 1739 4.7	
8 SU	0123 1.8 / 0737 4.8 / 1402 1.6 / 2026 5.0	**23** M	0003 2.0 / 0633 4.7 / 1249 1.8 / 1919 4.9	
9 M	0231 1.6 / 0854 5.1 / 1459 1.3 / 2126 5.4	**24** TU	0133 1.7 / 0758 5.0 / 1409 1.4 / 2024 5.4	
10 TU	0325 1.3 / 0947 5.5 / 1548 1.1 / 2213 5.7	**25** W	0241 1.3 / 0850 5.5 / 1507 1.0 / 2119 5.9	
11 W	0410 1.0 / 1030 5.7 / 1630 0.8 / 2253 6.0	**26** TH	0333 0.8 / 0942 6.0 / 1556 0.6 / 2209 6.3	
12 TH	0449 0.8 / 1109 5.9 / 1708 0.7 / 2329 6.1	**27** F	0419 0.5 / 1031 6.4 / 1642 0.3 / 2257 6.6	
13 F O	0525 0.7 / 1142 6.0 / 1743 0.6	**28** SA ●	0505 0.2 / 1119 6.6 / 1728 0.1 / 2343 6.8	
14 SA	0001 6.1 / 0559 0.7 / 1212 6.0 / 1817 0.6	**29** SU	0551 0.1 / 1205 6.7 / 1813 0.0	
15 SU	0029 6.1 / 0631 0.7 / 1236 6.0 / 1849 0.6	**30** M	0027 6.8 / 0636 0.0 / 1251 6.7 / 1858 0.1	
		31 TU	0111 6.8 / 0722 0.1 / 1334 6.6 / 1943 0.2	

APRIL

Time	m		Time	m
1 W	0153 6.5 / 0808 0.3 / 1418 6.3 / 2029 0.5	**16** TH	0115 5.8 / 0732 0.8 / 1334 5.8 / 1948 1.0	
2 TH	0237 6.1 / 0854 0.7 / 1504 5.9 / 2116 0.9	**17** F	0146 5.7 / 0805 1.0 / 1409 5.6 / 2025 1.2	
3 F	0324 5.7 / 0945 1.1 / 1557 5.4 / 2210 1.4	**18** SA	0224 5.5 / 0846 1.2 / 1452 5.4 / 2112 1.4	
4 SA	0421 5.2 / 1047 1.5 / 1700 5.0 / 2322 1.8	**19** SU	0311 5.1 / 0941 1.5 / 1547 5.0 / 2214 1.7	
5 SU	0528 4.8 / 1219 1.8 / 1817 4.8	**20** M	0415 4.8 / 1051 1.7 / 1707 4.9 / 2333 1.8	
6 M	0059 1.9 / 0700 4.6 / 1336 1.7 / 1958 4.9	**21** TU	0555 4.7 / 1214 1.6 / 1846 5.0	
7 TU	0208 1.7 / 0830 4.9 / 1434 1.5 / 2100 5.2	**22** W	0100 1.6 / 0721 5.0 / 1337 1.4 / 1956 5.4	
8 W	0301 1.4 / 0923 5.2 / 1522 1.2 / 2146 5.6	**23** TH	0212 1.2 / 0825 5.5 / 1439 1.0 / 2054 5.9	
9 TH	0345 1.1 / 1006 5.5 / 1603 0.9 / 2226 5.8	**24** F	0307 0.8 / 0920 5.9 / 1530 0.6 / 2146 6.3	
10 F	0423 0.9 / 1043 5.7 / 1640 0.8 / 2300 5.9	**25** SA	0356 0.4 / 1011 6.3 / 1618 0.3 / 2235 6.6	
11 SA O	0459 0.7 / 1114 5.9 / 1716 0.7 / 2330 6.0	**26** SU ●	0443 0.2 / 1100 6.5 / 1705 0.2 / 2323 6.7	
12 SU	0533 0.7 / 1142 5.9 / 1750 0.7 / 2356 6.0	**27** M	0530 0.1 / 1148 6.6 / 1752 0.1	
13 M	0605 0.7 / 1208 5.9 / 1823 0.7	**28** TU	0008 6.7 / 0616 0.1 / 1235 6.6 / 1838 0.2	
14 TU	0020 6.0 / 0636 0.7 / 1236 5.9 / 1852 0.8	**29** W	0053 6.6 / 0702 0.2 / 1320 6.5 / 1923 0.3	
15 W	0046 5.9 / 0704 0.7 / 1304 5.9 / 1920 0.9	**30** TH	0136 6.4 / 0748 0.4 / 1404 6.3 / 2008 0.6	

Chart Datum: 3·27 metres below Ordnance Datum (Newlyn)

ENGLAND – SHOREHAM

LAT 50°50′N   LONG 0°15′W

TIMES AND HEIGHTS OF HIGH AND LOW WATERS

YEAR 1998

3

TIME ZONE (UT)
For Summer Time add ONE hour in non-shaded areas

MAY

Day	Time	m	Day	Time	m
1 F	0219 / 0833 / 1449 / 2054	6.0 / 0.7 / 5.9 / 1.0	**16** SA	0131 / 0750 / 1357 / 2010	5.7 / 0.9 / 5.7 / 1.1
2 SA	0305 / 0921 / 1539 / 2145	5.6 / 1.1 / 5.5 / 1.4	**17** SU	0211 / 0833 / 1442 / 2059	5.6 / 1.0 / 5.5 / 1.3
3 SU	0358 / 1017 / 1635 / 2247	5.2 / 1.4 / 5.1 / 1.7	**18** M	0300 / 0927 / 1537 / 2159	5.3 / 1.2 / 5.3 / 1.4
4 M	0458 / 1130 / 1739	4.8 / 1.7 / 4.9	**19** TU	0402 / 1031 / 1647 / 2310	5.1 / 1.4 / 5.1 / 1.5
5 TU	0016 / 0607 / 1258 / 1900	1.9 / 4.6 / 1.8 / 4.8	**20** W	0523 / 1146 / 1810	5.0 / 1.4 / 5.2
6 W	0134 / 0743 / 1359 / 2018	1.8 / 4.7 / 1.6 / 5.1	**21** TH	0029 / 0646 / 1305 / 1924	1.4 / 5.1 / 1.3 / 5.5
7 TH	0229 / 0846 / 1448 / 2108	1.5 / 5.0 / 1.4 / 5.4	**22** F	0142 / 0757 / 1411 / 2027	1.1 / 5.4 / 1.0 / 5.8
8 F	0313 / 0930 / 1531 / 2148	1.3 / 5.3 / 1.1 / 5.6	**23** SA	0241 / 0857 / 1506 / 2123	0.8 / 5.8 / 0.7 / 6.1
9 SA	0352 / 1006 / 1609 / 2222	1.0 / 5.5 / 1.0 / 5.8	**24** SU	0334 / 0951 / 1557 / 2214	0.5 / 6.1 / 0.5 / 6.4
10 SU	0429 / 1038 / 1645 / 2253	0.9 / 5.7 / 0.9 / 5.9	**25** M	0423 / 1042 / 1646 / ● 2303	0.3 / 6.3 / 0.3 / 6.5
11 M O	0504 / 1109 / 1721 / 2322	0.8 / 5.8 / 0.8 / 5.9	**26** TU	0511 / 1132 / 1734 / 2350	0.2 / 6.4 / 0.3 / 6.5
12 TU	0538 / 1141 / 1756 / 2353	0.7 / 5.9 / 0.8 / 5.9	**27** W	0559 / 1219 / 1820	0.2 / 6.5 / 0.4
13 W	0611 / 1213 / 1828	0.7 / 5.9 / 0.8	**28** TH	0036 / 0645 / 1305 / 1905	6.5 / 0.3 / 6.4 / 0.6
14 TH	0023 / 0642 / 1246 / 1858	5.9 / 0.7 / 5.9 / 0.9	**29** F	0120 / 0729 / 1349 / 1949	6.3 / 0.5 / 6.2 / 0.7
15 F	0056 / 0713 / 1320 / 1931	5.9 / 0.8 / 5.8 / 0.9	**30** SA	0202 / 0813 / 1433 / 2033	6.0 / 0.7 / 5.9 / 1.0
			31 SU	0246 / 0858 / 1518 / 2119	5.6 / 1.0 / 5.6 / 1.3

JUNE

Day	Time	m	Day	Time	m
1 M	0333 / 0946 / 1607 / 2211	5.3 / 1.3 / 5.3 / 1.6	**16** TU	0252 / 0916 / 1526 / 2145	5.6 / 1.0 / 5.6 / 1.2
2 TU	0426 / 1040 / 1701 / 2310	4.9 / 1.6 / 5.0 / 1.8	**17** W	0349 / 1014 / 1627 / 2249	5.4 / 1.1 / 5.5 / 1.3
3 W	0524 / 1144 / 1800	4.7 / 1.7 / 4.9	**18** TH	0455 / 1121 / 1736	5.2 / 1.2 / 5.4
4 TH	0025 / 0626 / 1303 / 1902	1.9 / 4.6 / 1.8 / 4.9	**19** F	0001 / 0610 / 1236 / 1849	1.3 / 5.2 / 1.2 / 5.5
5 F	0141 / 0732 / 1404 / 2003	1.7 / 4.8 / 1.6 / 5.1	**20** SA	0114 / 0727 / 1346 / 1959	1.2 / 5.3 / 1.1 / 5.7
6 SA	0233 / 0831 / 1452 / 2054	1.5 / 5.0 / 1.4 / 5.3	**21** SU	0219 / 0835 / 1446 / 2101	1.0 / 5.6 / 0.9 / 5.9
7 SU	0317 / 0917 / 1535 / 2136	1.3 / 5.3 / 1.2 / 5.6	**22** M	0315 / 0934 / 1540 / 2156	0.7 / 5.9 / 0.7 / 6.1
8 M	0356 / 0958 / 1614 / 2215	1.1 / 5.5 / 1.1 / 5.7	**23** TU	0407 / 1027 / 1631 / 2247	0.5 / 6.1 / 0.6 / 6.3
9 TU	0434 / 1037 / 1653 / 2252	0.9 / 5.7 / 1.0 / 5.9	**24** W	0456 / 1118 / 1719 / ● 2335	0.4 / 6.2 / 0.6 / 6.3
10 W O	0511 / 1116 / 1730 / 2328	0.8 / 5.8 / 0.9 / 5.9	**25** TH	0544 / 1205 / 1805	0.4 / 6.3 / 0.6
11 TH	0548 / 1153 / 1806	0.7 / 5.9 / 0.9	**26** F	0020 / 0628 / 1250 / 1848	6.3 / 0.5 / 6.3 / 0.7
12 F	0004 / 0624 / 1231 / 1841	5.9 / 0.7 / 5.9 / 0.8	**27** SA	0103 / 0711 / 1332 / 1930	6.1 / 0.6 / 6.2 / 0.8
13 SA	0042 / 0700 / 1309 / 1919	5.9 / 0.7 / 5.9 / 0.9	**28** SU	0144 / 0752 / 1413 / 2010	5.9 / 0.7 / 6.0 / 1.0
14 SU	0121 / 0740 / 1349 / 2001	5.9 / 0.8 / 5.9 / 0.9	**29** M	0223 / 0832 / 1453 / 2050	5.7 / 0.9 / 5.8 / 1.2
15 M	0203 / 0824 / 1435 / 2049	5.8 / 0.8 / 5.8 / 1.0	**30** TU	0303 / 0913 / 1534 / 2134	5.4 / 1.2 / 5.5 / 1.4

JULY

Day	Time	m	Day	Time	m
1 W	0347 / 0958 / 1620 / 2222	5.1 / 1.4 / 5.2 / 1.6	**16** TH	0332 / 0956 / 1605 / 2228	5.7 / 0.9 / 5.7 / 1.1
2 TH	0438 / 1048 / 1712 / 2317	4.9 / 1.6 / 5.0 / 1.8	**17** F	0431 / 1057 / 1706 / 2335	5.4 / 1.2 / 5.5 / 1.3
3 F	0537 / 1146 / 1810	4.7 / 1.8 / 4.9	**18** SA	0539 / 1210 / 1816	5.2 / 1.3 / 5.4
4 SA	0019 / 0638 / 1253 / 1908	1.8 / 4.7 / 1.8 / 5.0	**19** SU	0050 / 0659 / 1325 / 1934	1.3 / 5.2 / 1.4 / 5.4
5 SU	0130 / 0739 / 1402 / 2006	1.8 / 4.8 / 1.7 / 5.1	**20** M	0201 / 0818 / 1431 / 2045	1.2 / 5.3 / 1.2 / 5.6
6 M	0234 / 0835 / 1458 / 2057	1.5 / 5.1 / 1.5 / 5.4	**21** TU	0302 / 0922 / 1528 / 2145	1.0 / 5.6 / 1.0 / 5.8
7 TU	0323 / 0925 / 1544 / 2143	1.3 / 5.4 / 1.3 / 5.6	**22** W	0355 / 1017 / 1619 / 2236	0.8 / 5.9 / 0.9 / 6.0
8 W	0406 / 1010 / 1627 / 2225	1.0 / 5.6 / 1.1 / 5.8	**23** TH	0443 / 1107 / 1706 / ● 2323	0.6 / 6.1 / 0.7 / 6.1
9 TH O	0447 / 1053 / 1707 / 2307	0.9 / 5.8 / 1.0 / 6.0	**24** F	0529 / 1152 / 1750	0.6 / 6.2 / 0.7
10 F	0527 / 1134 / 1747 / 2347	0.7 / 6.0 / 0.8 / 6.1	**25** SA	0006 / 0611 / 1234 / 1831	6.2 / 0.6 / 6.2 / 0.7
11 SA	0607 / 1215 / 1827	0.6 / 6.1 / 0.8	**26** SU	0046 / 0651 / 1313 / 1908	6.1 / 0.6 / 6.2 / 0.8
12 SU	0028 / 0647 / 1257 / 1907	6.1 / 0.6 / 6.2 / 0.7	**27** M	0122 / 0727 / 1348 / 1944	6.0 / 0.7 / 6.1 / 0.9
13 M	0110 / 0729 / 1339 / 1951	6.1 / 0.6 / 6.2 / 0.7	**28** TU	0156 / 0803 / 1422 / 2019	5.8 / 0.9 / 5.9 / 1.0
14 TU	0153 / 0814 / 1423 / 2038	6.1 / 0.6 / 6.1 / 0.7	**29** W	0227 / 0839 / 1453 / 2057	5.6 / 1.1 / 5.6 / 1.2
15 W	0240 / 0902 / 1511 / 2129	5.9 / 0.7 / 6.0 / 0.9	**30** TH	0258 / 0918 / 1525 / 2139	5.3 / 1.3 / 5.4 / 1.5
			31 F	0335 / 1002 / 1604 / 2227	5.1 / 1.6 / 5.1 / 1.7

AUGUST

Day	Time	m	Day	Time	m
1 SA	0428 / 1053 / 1706 / 2324	4.8 / 1.8 / 4.9 / 1.9	**16** SU	0515 / 1146 / 1750	5.2 / 1.5 / 5.2
2 SU	0546 / 1156 / 1821	4.6 / 2.0 / 4.8	**17** M	0029 / 0638 / 1309 / 1914	1.6 / 5.0 / 1.6 / 5.1
3 M	0031 / 0658 / 1310 / 1927	1.9 / 4.7 / 2.0 / 4.9	**18** TU	0148 / 0808 / 1419 / 2037	1.5 / 5.1 / 1.5 / 5.3
4 TU	0146 / 0802 / 1422 / 2025	1.8 / 4.9 / 1.8 / 5.2	**19** W	0250 / 0915 / 1517 / 2137	1.3 / 5.5 / 1.2 / 5.6
5 W	0251 / 0857 / 1518 / 2116	1.5 / 5.3 / 1.5 / 5.5	**20** TH	0343 / 1008 / 1606 / 2226	1.0 / 5.8 / 1.0 / 5.9
6 TH	0340 / 0946 / 1603 / 2203	1.1 / 5.6 / 1.2 / 5.8	**21** F	0429 / 1054 / 1651 / 2310	0.8 / 6.1 / 0.8 / 6.1
7 F	0424 / 1032 / 1646 / 2247	0.9 / 6.0 / 0.9 / 6.1	**22** SA	0511 / 1136 / 1732 / ● 2350	0.6 / 6.2 / 0.7 / 6.1
8 SA O	0505 / 1115 / 1727 / 2330	0.6 / 6.2 / 0.7 / 6.2	**23** SU	0551 / 1214 / 1809	0.6 / 6.3 / 0.7
9 SU	0547 / 1158 / 1809	0.5 / 6.4 / 0.6	**24** M	0025 / 0626 / 1249 / 1844	6.1 / 0.6 / 6.2 / 0.8
10 M	0013 / 0629 / 1241 / 1852	6.3 / 0.4 / 6.4 / 0.5	**25** TU	0057 / 0700 / 1320 / 1916	6.0 / 0.7 / 6.1 / 0.8
11 TU	0056 / 0713 / 1324 / 1936	6.4 / 0.4 / 6.5 / 0.5	**26** W	0124 / 0733 / 1345 / 1948	5.9 / 0.8 / 5.9 / 1.0
12 W	0139 / 0758 / 1407 / 2022	6.3 / 0.4 / 6.4 / 0.6	**27** TH	0148 / 0805 / 1406 / 2022	5.7 / 1.0 / 5.7 / 1.1
13 TH	0224 / 0845 / 1452 / 2111	6.1 / 0.6 / 6.2 / 0.8	**28** F	0214 / 0839 / 1432 / 2057	5.5 / 1.2 / 5.5 / 1.3
14 F	0313 / 0935 / 1543 / 2205	5.9 / 0.9 / 5.9 / 1.1	**29** SA	0246 / 0915 / 1508 / 2138	5.3 / 1.5 / 5.3 / 1.6
15 SA	0408 / 1033 / 1641 / 2309	5.5 / 1.2 / 5.5 / 1.4	**30** SU	0328 / 1000 / 1555 / 2231	5.0 / 1.8 / 5.0 / 1.9
			31 M	0427 / 1104 / 1709 / 2342	4.7 / 2.1 / 4.7 / 2.0

Chart Datum: 3·27 metres below Ordnance Datum (Newlyn)

TIME ZONE (UT)
For Summer Time add ONE hour in non-shaded areas

ENGLAND – SHOREHAM

LAT 50°50′N   LONG 0°15′W

TIMES AND HEIGHTS OF HIGH AND LOW WATERS

YEAR 1998

SEPTEMBER

Day	Time	m	Day	Time	m
1 TU	0617 / 1225 / 1851	4.6 / 2.1 / 4.7	16 W	0133 / 0758 / 1406 / 2027	1.7 / 5.1 / 1.7 / 5.2
2 W	0103 / 0731 / 1348 / 1957	1.9 / 4.8 / 1.9 / 5.0	17 TH	0236 / 0903 / 1503 / 2125	1.4 / 5.4 / 1.4 / 5.5
3 TH	0220 / 0831 / 1452 / 2053	1.6 / 5.3 / 1.6 / 5.5	18 F	0327 / 0953 / 1550 / 2211	1.1 / 5.8 / 1.1 / 5.8
4 F	0315 / 0923 / 1540 / 2141	1.2 / 5.7 / 1.2 / 5.9	19 SA	0410 / 1036 / 1631 / 2252	0.9 / 6.1 / 0.9 / 6.0
5 SA	0400 / 1010 / 1623 / 2227	0.8 / 6.1 / 0.8 / 6.2	20 SU	0450 / 1114 / 1709 / ● 2328	0.7 / 6.2 / 0.7 / 6.1
6 SU	0442 / 1054 / 1705 / O 2312	0.5 / 6.4 / 0.6 / 6.4	21 M	0526 / 1149 / 1744	0.7 / 6.2 / 0.7
7 M	0525 / 1138 / 1748 / 2356	0.3 / 6.6 / 0.4 / 6.6	22 TU	0001 / 0600 / 1221 / 1817	6.1 / 0.7 / 6.2 / 0.8
8 TU	0609 / 1222 / 1832	0.2 / 6.7 / 0.3	23 W	0028 / 0632 / 1246 / 1848	6.0 / 0.7 / 6.1 / 0.8
9 W	0039 / 0652 / 1305 / 1917	6.6 / 0.2 / 6.7 / 0.3	24 TH	0052 / 0703 / 1307 / 1918	6.0 / 0.8 / 6.0 / 0.9
10 TH	0123 / 0737 / 1348 / 2002	6.5 / 0.3 / 6.5 / 0.5	25 F	0115 / 0733 / 1329 / 1948	5.8 / 1.0 / 5.8 / 1.1
11 F	0207 / 0824 / 1432 / 2050	6.3 / 0.6 / 6.3 / 0.7	26 SA	0141 / 0803 / 1357 / 2019	5.7 / 1.2 / 5.6 / 1.3
12 SA	0254 / 0914 / 1521 / 2142	6.0 / 0.9 / 5.9 / 1.1	27 SU	0213 / 0835 / 1431 / 2056	5.5 / 1.4 / 5.4 / 1.5
13 SU	0349 / 1011 / 1619 / 2245	5.5 / 1.3 / 5.4 / 1.5	28 M	0251 / 0918 / 1515 / 2146	5.2 / 1.8 / 5.0 / 1.8
14 M	0456 / 1124 / 1729	5.1 / 1.7 / 5.1	29 TU	0344 / 1019 / 1616 / 2256	4.9 / 2.0 / 4.7 / 2.0
15 TU	0010 / 0621 / 1254 / 1900	1.7 / 4.9 / 1.8 / 4.9	30 W	0517 / 1144 / 1813	4.6 / 2.2 / 4.6

OCTOBER

Day	Time	m	Day	Time	m
1 TH	0022 / 0700 / 1313 / 1929	2.0 / 4.8 / 2.0 / 4.9	16 F	0213 / 0839 / 1442 / 2103	1.6 / 5.4 / 1.5 / 5.4
2 F	0146 / 0804 / 1422 / 2028	1.7 / 5.3 / 1.6 / 5.4	17 SA	0304 / 0928 / 1528 / 2148	1.3 / 5.7 / 1.2 / 5.7
3 SA	0246 / 0858 / 1513 / 2119	1.2 / 5.8 / 1.1 / 5.9	18 SU	0346 / 1010 / 1607 / 2227	1.0 / 6.0 / 1.0 / 5.9
4 SU	0333 / 0946 / 1558 / 2206	0.8 / 6.2 / 0.7 / 6.3	19 M	0424 / 1046 / 1643 / 2302	0.9 / 6.1 / 0.8 / 6.0
5 M	0417 / 1031 / 1641 / O 2252	0.5 / 6.6 / 0.4 / 6.6	20 TU	0459 / 1119 / 1718 / ● 2331	0.8 / 6.2 / 0.8 / 6.0
6 TU	0501 / 1116 / 1725 / 2337	0.3 / 6.8 / 0.3 / 6.7	21 W	0533 / 1147 / 1750 / 2357	0.8 / 6.1 / 0.8 / 6.0
7 W	0546 / 1201 / 1811	0.2 / 6.8 / 0.2	22 TH	0605 / 1211 / 1822	0.8 / 6.1 / 0.8
8 TH	0022 / 0630 / 1245 / 1856	6.7 / 0.2 / 6.8 / 0.3	23 F	0022 / 0636 / 1235 / 1852	6.0 / 0.9 / 6.0 / 0.9
9 F	0107 / 0716 / 1329 / 1942	6.6 / 0.3 / 6.6 / 0.4	24 SA	0049 / 0705 / 1301 / 1921	5.9 / 1.0 / 5.9 / 1.0
10 SA	0151 / 0803 / 1413 / 2029	6.4 / 0.6 / 6.3 / 0.7	25 SU	0117 / 0734 / 1330 / 1951	5.8 / 1.2 / 5.7 / 1.2
11 SU	0239 / 0853 / 1502 / 2121	6.0 / 1.0 / 5.8 / 1.1	26 M	0149 / 0807 / 1405 / 2029	5.6 / 1.4 / 5.5 / 1.4
12 M	0333 / 0949 / 1600 / 2221	5.6 / 1.4 / 5.4 / 1.5	27 TU	0228 / 0851 / 1448 / 2118	5.4 / 1.6 / 5.2 / 1.7
13 TU	0438 / 1100 / 1707 / 2345	5.2 / 1.8 / 5.0 / 1.8	28 W	0318 / 0950 / 1547 / 2223	5.1 / 1.9 / 4.9 / 1.9
14 W	0558 / 1233 / 1836	4.9 / 1.9 / 4.8	29 TH	0433 / 1108 / 1723 / 2342	4.8 / 2.0 / 4.7 / 1.9
15 TH	0110 / 0734 / 1346 / 2006	1.8 / 5.0 / 1.8 / 5.0	30 F	0622 / 1234 / 1855	4.9 / 1.9 / 5.0
			31 SA	0106 / 0733 / 1347 / 1959	1.7 / 5.3 / 1.5 / 5.4

NOVEMBER

Day	Time	m	Day	Time	m
1 SU	0213 / 0830 / 1443 / 2054	1.3 / 5.8 / 1.1 / 5.9	16 M	0316 / 0936 / 1539 / 2156	1.3 / 5.7 / 1.1 / 5.6
2 M	0305 / 0920 / 1531 / 2143	0.9 / 6.2 / 0.7 / 6.3	17 TU	0355 / 1012 / 1616 / 2229	1.1 / 5.9 / 1.0 / 5.8
3 TU	0352 / 1008 / 1617 / 2231	0.5 / 6.6 / 0.4 / 6.5	18 W	0431 / 1043 / 1651 / 2258	1.0 / 6.0 / 0.9 / 5.9
4 W	0438 / 1054 / 1704 / O 2319	0.3 / 6.8 / 0.2 / 6.7	19 TH	0506 / 1112 / 1725 / ● 2327	0.9 / 6.0 / 0.8 / 6.0
5 TH	0524 / 1140 / 1750	0.3 / 6.8 / 0.2	20 F	0540 / 1140 / 1759 / 2358	0.9 / 6.0 / 0.9 / 6.0
6 F	0005 / 0610 / 1226 / 1837	6.7 / 0.3 / 6.8 / 0.3	21 SA	0613 / 1209 / 1831	1.0 / 6.0 / 0.9
7 SA	0052 / 0657 / 1311 / 1923	6.6 / 0.4 / 6.6 / 0.5	22 SU	0029 / 0643 / 1240 / 1901	5.9 / 1.0 / 5.9 / 1.0
8 SU	0138 / 0744 / 1357 / 2011	6.4 / 0.7 / 6.2 / 0.7	23 M	0101 / 0713 / 1313 / 1933	5.9 / 1.1 / 5.8 / 1.1
9 M	0225 / 0833 / 1445 / 2101	6.1 / 1.0 / 5.8 / 1.1	24 TU	0135 / 0749 / 1349 / 2012	5.7 / 1.3 / 5.6 / 1.2
10 TU	0317 / 0927 / 1539 / 2156	5.7 / 1.4 / 5.4 / 1.5	25 W	0215 / 0833 / 1433 / 2100	5.6 / 1.5 / 5.4 / 1.4
11 W	0416 / 1031 / 1640 / 2306	5.3 / 1.8 / 5.0 / 1.8	26 TH	0304 / 0929 / 1528 / 2159	5.3 / 1.7 / 5.1 / 1.6
12 TH	0523 / 1136 / 1751	5.0 / 1.9 / 4.8	27 F	0408 / 1038 / 1641 / 2308	5.1 / 1.8 / 5.0 / 1.7
13 F	0032 / 0646 / 1313 / 1924	1.9 / 5.0 / 1.9 / 4.8	28 SA	0532 / 1156 / 1810	5.1 / 1.7 / 5.0
14 SA	0139 / 0801 / 1411 / 2029	1.7 / 5.2 / 1.6 / 5.1	29 SU	0026 / 0653 / 1310 / 1925	1.6 / 5.4 / 1.5 / 5.3
15 SU	0232 / 0854 / 1458 / 2116	1.5 / 5.5 / 1.4 / 5.4	30 M	0138 / 0758 / 1413 / 2026	1.3 / 5.7 / 1.1 / 5.7

DECEMBER

Day	Time	m	Day	Time	m
1 TU	0237 / 0854 / 1507 / 2121	1.0 / 6.1 / 0.8 / 6.1	16 W	0323 / 0929 / 1547 / 2149	1.4 / 5.6 / 1.2 / 5.5
2 W	0329 / 0945 / 1557 / 2213	0.7 / 6.4 / 0.5 / 6.4	17 TH	0403 / 1005 / 1625 / 2226	1.2 / 5.8 / 1.0 / 5.7
3 TH	0419 / 1034 / 1646 / O 2303	0.5 / 6.6 / 0.4 / 6.5	18 F	0441 / 1040 / 1702 / ● 2302	1.1 / 5.9 / 0.9 / 5.9
4 F	0507 / 1123 / 1734 / 2351	0.4 / 6.7 / 0.3 / 6.6	19 SA	0517 / 1115 / 1738 / 2337	1.0 / 6.0 / 0.9 / 5.9
5 SA	0555 / 1210 / 1821	0.4 / 6.6 / 0.3	20 SU	0553 / 1149 / 1813	1.0 / 6.0 / 0.8
6 SU	0038 / 0641 / 1256 / 1908	6.5 / 0.5 / 6.5 / 0.5	21 M	0012 / 0626 / 1224 / 1847	6.0 / 1.0 / 6.0 / 0.9
7 M	0125 / 0728 / 1341 / 1954	6.4 / 0.7 / 6.2 / 0.7	22 TU	0048 / 0700 / 1300 / 1922	6.0 / 1.0 / 5.9 / 0.9
8 TU	0211 / 0814 / 1427 / 2040	6.1 / 1.0 / 5.9 / 1.0	23 W	0125 / 0737 / 1339 / 2000	5.9 / 1.1 / 5.8 / 1.1
9 W	0257 / 0903 / 1515 / 2128	5.8 / 1.3 / 5.5 / 1.3	24 TH	0205 / 0820 / 1422 / 2045	5.8 / 1.2 / 5.7 / 1.1
10 TH	0348 / 0956 / 1607 / 2221	5.5 / 1.6 / 5.2 / 1.6	25 F	0251 / 0910 / 1512 / 2137	5.7 / 1.3 / 5.5 / 1.2
11 F	0442 / 1056 / 1704 / 2323	5.2 / 1.8 / 4.9 / 1.8	26 SA	0346 / 1011 / 1612 / 2238	5.5 / 1.5 / 5.3 / 1.4
12 SA	0542 / 1213 / 1807	5.0 / 1.9 / 4.8	27 SU	0451 / 1121 / 1723 / 2349	5.4 / 1.5 / 5.2 / 1.5
13 SU	0040 / 0648 / 1326 / 1918	1.9 / 5.0 / 1.9 / 4.8	28 M	0608 / 1235 / 1844	5.4 / 1.5 / 5.3
14 M	0147 / 0755 / 1421 / 2024	1.8 / 5.2 / 1.7 / 5.0	29 TU	0105 / 0723 / 1346 / 1958	1.4 / 5.6 / 1.3 / 5.5
15 TU	0239 / 0848 / 1507 / 2111	1.6 / 5.4 / 1.4 / 5.3	30 W	0214 / 0829 / 1448 / 2102	1.2 / 5.8 / 1.0 / 5.8
			31 TH	0312 / 0927 / 1542 / 2158	1.0 / 6.1 / 0.7 / 6.1

Chart Datum: 3.27 metres below Ordnance Datum (Newlyn)

BRIGHTON   10-3-10
E. Sussex 50°48'·50N 00°06'·28W   Rtg 2-1-1

BRIGHTON MARINA

PL Public lavatories
YL Yachtsmen's lavatories and showers
T Public telephone
YC Yacht Club

CHARTS
AC *1991, 1652*; Imray C9; Stanfords 9; OS 198
TIDES
+0004 Dover; ML 3·5; Duration 0605; Zone 0 (UT)

Standard Port SHOREHAM (←—)

Times				Height (metres)			
High Water		Low Water		MHWS	MHWN	MLWN	MLWS
0500	1000	0000	0600	6·3	4·8	1·9	0·6
1700	2200	1200	1800				
Differences BRIGHTON							
–0010	–0005	–0005	–0005	+0·3	+0·1	0·0	–0·1

SHELTER
Good in the marina under all conditions, but in strong
S'ly winds confused seas can make the final appr very
rough. Speed limit 5kn.
NAVIGATION
WPT 50°48'·20N 00°06'·29W, 180°/000° from/to W bkwtr
lt, 0·26M. Ent chan dredged 2·5m, but after gales silting
may occur especially on E side. In heavy weather, best
appr is from SSE to avoid worst of the backlash from
bkwtrs; beware shallow water E of ent in R sector of lt Fl
(4) WR 20s. A Historic Wreck (see 8.0.3h) is at 50°48'·6N
00°06'·49W, immediately W of the marina's W bkwtr.
LIGHTS AND MARKS
The marina is at the E end of the town, where white cliffs
extend eastward. Daymark: conspic white hospital block,
brg 334° leads to ent. Y spar buoy, Fl Y 4s, is 2ca S of W
bkwtr.
Navigational lts may be hard to see against shore glare:
E bkwtr Fl (4) WR 20s (intens) 16m 10/8M; vis R260°-295°,
W295°-100°. E bkwtr hd QG 8m 7M. W bkwtr hd, tr R/W
bands, QR 10m 7M; Horn (2) 30s. RC = BM 294·5 kHz, 10M.
Inner Hbr lock controlled by normal R/G lts, 0800-2000LT.

RADIO TELEPHONE
Call: *Brighton Control* VHF Ch **M** 80 16 (H24); 68 11.
TELEPHONE (Dial code 01273)
Hr Mr 819919; BY 609235; MRSC (01705) 552100;
⌗ 0345 231110 (H24); Marinecall 0891 500456; Police
606744; Ⓗ 696955; Dr 686863.
FACILITIES
Marina (1600+200 visitors) ☎ 819919, ⬋ 675082, £15.68,
⌗, FW, P, D, AC, Gas, Gaz, Ⓞ, R, Bar, BY, BH (60 ton), C
(35 ton); **Brighton Marina YC** ☎ 818711, Bar, R.
Services El, Ⓔ, ME, Sh, SM, CH, ACA, Divers, Riggers,
Superstore.
Hbr Guides available from Hbr Office or by post.
Bus service from marina; timetable info ☎ 674881.
Electric railway runs from marina to Palace Pier, Mar-Oct.
Town V, R, Bar, ⊠, Ⓑ, ⇌, ✈ (Shoreham).

NEWHAVEN   10-3-11

E. Sussex 50°46'·80N 00°03'·63E   Rtg 2-2-2

CHARTS
AC 2154, *1652*; Imray C9; Stanfords 9; OS 198

TIDES
+0004 Dover; ML 3·6; Duration 0550; Zone 0 (UT)

Standard Port SHOREHAM (←—)

Times				Height (metres)			
High Water		Low Water		MHWS	MHWN	MLWN	MLWS
0500	1000	0000	0600	6·3	4·8	1·9	0·6
1700	2200	1200	1800				
Differences NEWHAVEN							
–0015	–0010	0000	0000	+0·4	+0·2	0·0	–0·2
EASTBOURNE							
–0010	–0005	+0015	+0020	+1·1	+0·6	+0·2	+0·1

SHELTER
Good in all weathers, but in strong on-shore winds there is often a dangerous sea at the ent. Appr from the SW, to pass 50m off bkwtr hd to avoid heavy breaking seas on E side of dredged chan. At marina, berth inside ❶ pontoon (0.0m), accessible HW±3½ due to soft silt.

NAVIGATION
WPT 50°46'·20N 00°03'·70E, 168°/348° from/to W bkwtr lt, 0·32M. Caution: Hbr silts and dredging is continuous. Ferries/cargo vessels may warp off with hawsers across the hbr. Beware fast catamarans; check on VHF Ch 12.

LIGHTS AND MARKS
Lt Ho on W bkwtr is conspic, as is an orange container crane opposite the marina.

Traffic sigs, displayed from tr on W side of river:
▼ over ●, or Ⓖ	= Only ent permitted.
● over ▼, or Ⓡ	= Only departure permitted.
● ▼ ● (vert) or	
ⓇⒼⓇ (vert)	= No ent or departure.
● or ⒼⓇ (vert)	= Entry and dep permitted with care for vessels under 15m LOA.

Swing bridge sigs:
Fl Ⓖ	= Bridge opening or closing.
Ⓡ	= Vessels may pass N to S.
Ⓖ	= Vessels may pass S to N.

RADIO TELEPHONE
Port VHF Ch 12 16 (H24). Swingbridge opening Ch 12. Marina Ch **80** M (0800-1700).

TELEPHONE (Dial code 01273)
Hr Mr 514131 (H24), ☎ 517342; Hbr Sig Stn 517922; MRSC (01705) 552100; ⌗ 0345 231110 (H24); Marinecall 0891 500456; Police 515801; Dr 515076; Ⓗ 609411 (Casualty 696955).

FACILITIES
Marina (300+50 ❶) ☎ 513881, £15, FW, fuel pontoon 200 yds N of ent, ME, El, Sh, AC, BH (18 ton), C (10 ton), CH, Gas, Gaz, Slip, V, R, Bar, ◙; **Marina YC** ☎ 513976; **Newhaven YC** ☎ 513770, AB, M, ME, El, Sh, Slip, CH; **Newhaven & Seaford SC** ☎ (01323) 890077, M, FW. **Town** EC Wed; ACA, SM, P, Ⓔ, V, R, Bar, ⊠, Ⓑ, ≷, ✈ (Shoreham). Ferry/catamaran to Dieppe; Stena Line ☎ 516699.

EASTBOURNE   10-3-12

E. Sussex 50°47'·30N 00°20'·00E   Rtg 2-1-2

CHARTS
AC *536*; Imray C8; Stanfords 9; OS 199

TIDES
–0005 Dover; ML 3·8; Duration 0540; Zone 0 (UT)

Standard Port SHOREHAM (←—)

See Differences under 10.3.11

SHELTER
Good, but apprs exposed to NE/SE winds. Access H24 via chan dredged 2·0m and twin locks into inner basin (4m).

NAVIGATION
WPT 50°47'·37N 00°20'·81E, SWM buoy 'SH', L Fl 10s (4ca off E edge of chartlet), 079°/259° from/to hbr ent, 0·45M. There are shoals to the NE in Pevensey Bay and from 2·5M SE toward Royal Sovereign lt (tide rips). From Beachy Hd, keep 0·75M offshore to clear Holywell Bank.

LIGHTS AND MARKS
Beachy Hd lt, Fl (2) 20s, is 4·7M SW; Royal Sovereign lt, Fl 20s, is 5·5M to SE. Martello tr No 66 at root of S bkwtr has high intens Xenon lt, Fl (3) 15s 12m 7M, vis H24; but hard to see by day. From E, by day R roofs are conspic WSW of ent. Dir lt, Fl WRG 5s 4m 1M, G252·5°-256·5°, W256·5°-259·5°, R259·5°-262·5°, leads 258° into chan. Ent chan buoys are a SHM buoy, Fl G 5s, then 3 SHM buoys, Fl G 3s; a PHM buoy, Fl R 5s, then a PHM buoy, Fl R 3s. Lt buoys inside bkwtrs are Fl 3s R or G. Eastbourne pier, 2 FR, is 2M S of hbr ent; an unlit PHM buoy is approx 5ca S.

RADIO TELEPHONE
Call *Sovereign Harbour* VHF Ch 15 (H24) for entry and Ch 17 for locks/bridges and berthing.

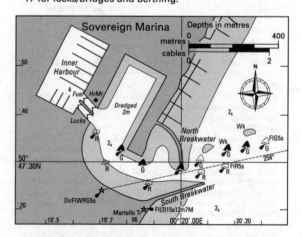

TELEPHONE (Dial code 01323)
Hr Mr 470099; MRSC (01304) 210008; ⌗ 0345 231110 (H24); Marinecall 0891 500456; Police 722522; Dr 720555; Ⓗ 417400.

FACILITIES
Sovereign Marina (332 berths), ☎ 470099, ☏ 470077, £15.08, FW, AC, D & P (H24), BH (50 tons), ME, Sh, CH, ◙, supermarket. **Town** (2½M) all facilities, ≷, ✈ (Gatwick).

RYE   10-3-13

E. Sussex 50°55'·57N 00°46'·69E   Rtg 3-4-1

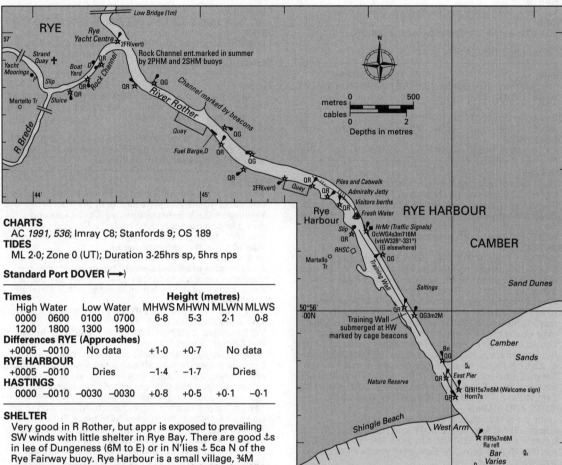

CHARTS
AC *1991, 536*; Imray C8; Stanfords 9; OS 189

TIDES
ML 2·0; Zone 0 (UT); Duration 3·25hrs sp, 5hrs nps

Standard Port DOVER (→)

Times				Height (metres)			
High Water		Low Water		MHWS	MHWN	MLWN	MLWS
0000	0600	0100	0700	6·8	5·3	2·1	0·8
1200	1800	1300	1900				
Differences RYE (Approaches)							
+0005	−0010	No data		+1·0	+0·7	No data	
RYE HARBOUR							
+0005	−0010	Dries		−1·4	−1·7	Dries	
HASTINGS							
0000	−0010	−0030	−0030	+0·8	+0·5	+0·1	−0·1

SHELTER
Very good in R Rother, but appr is exposed to prevailing SW winds with little shelter in Rye Bay. There are good ⚓s in lee of Dungeness (6M to E) or in N'lies ⚓ 5ca N of the Rye Fairway buoy. Rye Harbour is a small village, ¾M inside ent on W bank, used by commercial shipping. Hbr dries completely to soft mud. Berth initially on Admiralty Jetty and see Hr Mr for AB or M; ⚓ prohib. Speed limit 6kn. Rye Town (a Cinque Port) is 2M up river; ent via Rock Chan, visitors' AB on NE side of Strand Quay.

NAVIGATION
WPT Rye Fairway SWM By, L Fl 10s, 50°54'·00N 00°48'·13E, 150°/330° from/to W Arm tripod lt, 1·81M. Bar dries 2·75m about 2ca offshore and needs care when wind >F6 from SE to SW. Enter HW −2 to HW +3. Beware: Bar and shoals E and W of ent with ground swell or surf; narrow ent (42m) and chan (30m); flood runs 4·5kn (max HW −3 to HW −1).
Depth of water over the bar can be judged by day from how many horizontal timbers can be seen on West Arm tripod structure (approx 2ca N of the bar): 3, 2 or 1 timbers indicate water depths over the bar of about 0·5m, 2·0m or 3·5m (1·6ft, 6·5ft or 11·5ft) respectively.
Army Firing Ranges at Lydd: a Sea Danger Area extends 3M offshore and stretches E from Rye Fairway buoy to a N/S line approx 1·5M W of Dungeness lt ho. When firing takes place, about 300 days p.a. 0830–1630LT (often to 2300), R flags/R lts are displayed ashore and a Range Safety Craft may be on station. Call *Lydd Ranges* Ch 73 13 or ☎ 01303 225518/225519. Radar fixes may also be obtained by VHF. Vessels may legally transit through the Sea Danger Area, but should not enter or remain in it for other purposes. If possible vessels should transit S of Stephenson Shoal. See also 10.3.16 for Hythe ranges.

LIGHTS AND MARKS
Dir Oc WG 4s lt on Hr Mr's office has W sector (326°-331°) covering ent/river. W Arm lt Fl R 5s 7m 6M, wooden tripod, radar reflector. E Arm hd, Q (9) 15s 7m 5M; Horn 7s, G △. On E Pier a floodlit "Welcome to Rye" sign is considered too bright by some, but helpful by others. Rock Chan ent marked by a QR and QG lt buoy in season.
IPTS (Sigs 2 & 5 only) are shown to seaward (3M) from Hr Mr's office and up-river (1M) from Admiralty Jetty.

RADIO TELEPHONE
VHF Ch 14 16 (0900-1700LT, HW±2 or when vessel due). To avoid commercial ships monitor Ch 14 before arr/dep.

TELEPHONE (Dial code 01797)
Hr Mr 225225, ☎ 227429; MRCC (01304) 210008; ⌗ (01304) 224251; Marinecall 0891 500456; Police 222112; Dr 222031; Ⓗ 222109.

FACILITIES
Admiralty Jetty £9.50, Slip, M, L, FW; **Strand Quay** AB, M, P & D (50m, cans), L, FW, Shwrs; **Hbr** ME, El, BY, C (15 ton), C (3 ton), Slip (26 ton), Sh, CH, Ⓔ, ACA; **Rye Hbr SC** (Sec'ty) ☎ 344645. **Town** EC Tues; ✉, Ⓑ, ⇌, ✈ (Lydd).
Note: A Historic Wreck (*Anne*; see 10.0.3h) is about 4M WSW of Rye, close inshore at 50°53'·42N 00°41'·91E.

ADJACENT ANCHORAGE

HASTINGS, E Sussex, 50°50'·84N 00°35'·60E. AC *536*. Tides, s ee 10·3·13; ML 3·8m; Duration 0530. Strictly a settled weather ⚓ or emergency shelter; landing places on pier. The stone bkwtr is in disrepair and serves only to protect FVs. Beware dangerous wreck 3ca SE of pier head. Ldg lts 356°, both FR 14/55m 4M: front on W metal column; rear 357m from front, on 5-sided W tr on West Hill. Pier hd 2 FR (vert) 8m 5M from white hut; W bkwtr hd Fl R 2·5s 5m 4M; Fl G 5s 2m, 30m from head of No3 Groyne (E bkwtr). A Historic Wreck (*Amsterdam*; see 10.0.3h) is about 2M W of pier, close inshore at 50°50'·7N 00°31'·65E. Facilities: EC Wed; ⌗ (01304) 224251. ACA (St Leonard's). Few marine services, but all shore needs at Hastings and St Leonard's. YC ☎ (01424) 420656.

FOLKESTONE   10-3-14

Kent 51°04'·56N 01°11'·78E   Rtg 3-4-2

CHARTS
AC *1991, 1892*; Imray C8; Stanfords 9, 20; OS 179

TIDES
–0010 Dover; ML 3·9; Duration 0500; Zone 0 (UT)

Standard Port DOVER (→)

Times				Height (metres)			
High Water		Low Water		MHWS	MHWN	MLWN	MLWS
0000	0600	0100	0700	6·8	5·3	2·1	0·8
1200	1800	1300	1900				
Differences FOLKESTONE							
–0020	–0005	–0010	–0010	+0·4	+0·4	0·0	–0·1
DUNGENESS							
–0010	–0015	–0020	–0010	+1·0	+0·6	+0·4	+0·1

SHELTER
Good except in strong E-S winds when seas break at the hbr ent. Drying Inner Hbr has many FVs, so limited room for yachts; access approx HW±2. Visitors can berth on S Quay; fender board needed. Depth gauge on hd of E Pier. Ferry area is prohib to yachts; no room to ‡ off. Beware ferries and pulling off wires from the jetty.

NAVIGATION
WPT 51°04'·30N 01°12'·00E, 150°/330° from/to bkwtr hd lt, 0·26M. Beware drying Mole Hd Rks and Copt Rks to stbd of the ent; from/to the NE, keep well clear of the latter due to extended sewer outfall pipe.

Army Firing Ranges at Hythe have a Sea Danger Area extending 2M offshore, from Hythe to Dymchurch (approx 5M and 8M WSW of Folkestone hbr). Vessels may legally transit through the Sea Danger Area, but should not enter or remain in it for other purposes. When firing takes place, about 300 days p.a. 0830–1630LT (often to 2300), R flags/R lts are displayed ashore and a Range Safety Craft may be on station. Radar fixes may also be obtained by VHF. Call *Hythe Ranges* Ch 73 13 or ☎ 01303 249541 Ext 8179/8133, ☏ Ext 8138. See also 8.3.14.

LIGHTS AND MARKS
Hotel block is conspic at W end of Inner Hbr.
Ldg lts 295° at ferry terminal, FR and FG (occas). QG lt at E pierhead on brg 305° leads to inner hbr. Bu flag or 3 ⓡ (vert) at FS on S arm, ¼hr before ferry sails = hbr closed. 3 ⓖ (vert) = enter.

RADIO TELEPHONE
Call *Folkestone Port Control* VHF Ch 15, 16.

TELEPHONE (Dial code 01303)
Hr Mr 715300 (H24), ☏ 221567; MRCC (01304) 210008; ⌗ (01304) 224251; Marinecall 0891 500456; Police 850055.

FACILITIES
S Quay BR Slipway Slip (free), FW; **Folkestone Y & MB Club** ☎ 251574, D, FW, L, Slip, M, Bar.
Town EC Wed (larger shops open all day); P & D (cans, 100 yds), V, R, Bar, ⊠, Ⓑ, ⇌, ✈ (Lydd). Freight ferries and Hoverspeed (Seacat) to Boulogne.

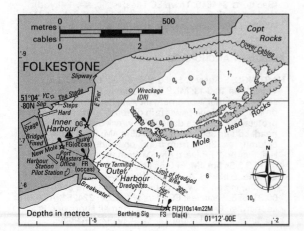

DOVER   10-3-15

Kent   51°06'·71N 01°19'·83E (W ent)   Rtg 1-1-2
        51°07'·22N 01°20'·71E (E ent)

CHARTS
AC *1698, 1828, 1892*; Imray C8; Stanfords 9, 20; OS 179

TIDES
0000 Dover; ML 3·7; Duration 0505; Zone 0 (UT)

Standard Port DOVER (→)

Times				Height (metres)			
High Water		Low Water		MHWS	MHWN	MLWN	MLWS
0000	0600	0100	0700	6·8	5·3	2·1	0·8
1200	1800	1300	1900				
Differences DEAL							
+0010	+0020	+0010	+0005	–0·6	–0·3	0·0	0·0

NOTE: Dover is a Standard Port and tidal predictions for each day of the year are given below.

SHELTER
Visiting yachts are welcomed and normally escorted by hbr launch to the complete shelter of the Marina in Wellington Dock. Berth as directed. Dock gates and swing bridge normally open HW ±1½. Waiting pontoon has 1·5m. Three pontoons (approx 2·5m) are available in tidal hbr, E of the waiting pontoon.
In the Outer Hbr the small craft moorings (33 W Øs) and ‡ are tenable in offshore winds, but exposed to winds from NE through S to SW; in gales a heavy sea builds up. Small craft may not be left unattended at ‡ in Outer Hbr.

NAVIGATION
WPT from SW, 51°06'·15N 01°19'·77E, 180°/000° from/to Admiralty Pier lt ho, 0·5M.
WPT from NE, 51°07'·27N 01°21'·51E, 090°/270° from/to S end Eastern Arm, 0·5M.
Beware lumpy seas/overfalls outside the bkwtrs and frequent ferries, hovercraft and catamarans through both ents. Strong tides across ents and high walls make ent under sail slow and difficult; use of engine very strongly recommended. Comply with tfc sigs and VHF instructions of Port Control and hbr patrol launch; advise if you have no engine. Do not go between NCM buoy, Q, (marking wreck inside W ent) and S bkwtr. Beware fast hovercraft/catamarans on rounding Prince of Wales pier.
Note: A Historic Wreck (see 8.0.3h) is adjacent to the Eastern Arm bkwtr at 51°07'·6N 01°20'·8E (see chartlet). There are four more Historic Wrecks on the Goodwin Sands in positions where a yacht would hope not to be.

LIGHTS AND MARKS
Lts as on chartlet & 10.3.4. Port Control tr (conspic) is at S end of E Arm and shows IPTS for the E ent on panels; for W ent, IPTS are on panels near Admiralty Pier sig stn.
Specific permission to ent/leave via E or W ent must first be obtained from Port Control on VHF Ch 74. Clearance for small/slow craft is not normally given until within 200m of ent. If no VHF, use following Aldis Lamp sigs:
SV (··· ···—) = I wish to enter port
SW (··· ·——) = I wish to leave port
Port Control will reply OK (——— ——·) or
                          Wait (·——— ·— ·· —·).
A Q ⓦ lt from Port Control tr or patrol launch = keep clear of ent you are approaching.
Marina sigs: In the final appr, especially near LW, stay in deep water as defined by the W sector (324°-333°) of the F WR lt, 3 unlit SHM poles and an unlit SHM buoy. IPTS are shown, plus a small Fl ⓨ lt 5 min before bridge is swung.

RADIO TELEPHONE
Call: *Dover Port Control* VHF Ch **74** 12 16. Hbr launch and Water Taxi Ch 74. *Dover Marina* Ch 80, only within tidal hbr/marina. Chan Nav Info Service (CNIS) broadcasts tfc/nav/wx/tidal info Ch 11 at H+40; also, if vis < 2M, at H+55. *Dover Coastguard* Ch **69** 16 80, gives TSS surveillance.

TELEPHONE (Dial code 01304)
Hr Mr 240400 Ext 4540; MRCC 210008; ⌗ 224251; Marinecall 0891 500456; Police 240055; Ⓗ 201624.

FACILITIES
Marina (240+150 visitors) ☎ 241663, ☏ 240465, £11.70 in marina, £12.60 in tidal hbr (both inc AC), FW, C, Slip, D; *Dover Yachtsman's Manual* from marina.
Royal Cinque Ports YC ☎ 206262, L, M, C, FW, Bar, R;
Services: D, ME, El, Sh, SM, ACA, CH, Ⓔ (H24 service).
Town EC Wed; P (cans), V, R, Bar, ⊠, Ⓑ, ⇌, ✈ (Lydd).

3

DOVER

**MEAN SPRING
AND NEAP CURVES**

MEAN RANGES	
Springs 6.0m	——
Neaps 3.2m	- - -

Springs occur 2 days
after
New and Full Moon.

H.W.Hts.m

CHART DATUM

M.H.W.N.   M.H.W.S.

Factor

M.L.W.S.   M.L.W.N.

L.W.Hts.m

L.W. -5ʰ -4ʰ -3ʰ -2ʰ -1ʰ H.W. +1ʰ +2ʰ +3ʰ +4ʰ +5ʰ +6ʰ +7ʰ L.W.

Dover Castle

FERRY TERMINAL

Restricted
area

Historic
Wreck

07'·5

RoRo

Pier A   Pier B   QR
Pier C   Siren(2)10s(occas)
Pier D   Fl(2)R5s
          Siren5s (occas)
          QcR5s

Eastern Docks
(entry restricted)

Q(6)+LFl15s
Siren(3)20s
(occas)

Fl(4)Y6s

VQ(3)5s

Eastern Arm

10₅

Port Control
Traffic Sigs
FlG5s12m5M
Horn(2)30s

DOVER

Foul

Small Craft
Moorings

1₅   3₂

3

2₅

0₉

Outer Harbour

2₅

Red

Fl.R2.5s11m5M

Knuckle
Fl(4)WR10s15m
15/13M

White

14₁

RCP
YC

HrMr

Wellington
Dock
Steps

Clock Tr

Yacht
Anchorage

Anchorage

Deep-draught Vessels only

Fl.Y4s

6₉

11₄

Southern Breakwater

Commercial Quay   Fuel
Yacht
Marina

Wellington
Dock

Marina
Office

Bridge
Gates

IPTS

Union Quay

DirFWR
Granville
Dock

Crosswall Quay

Waiting Pontoon
Dredged 1.5m Sill 1.83m CD

2₅

2₅

R
QG
324°
335°W

5.0m

Tidal
Harbour

2FR(vert)

51°07'
·00N

Pontoons
QG

OcG

Steps

Prince of Wales Pier

Hoverport
3FG(vert)

2FR
(vert)   QG
IsoR2s   QR   Fl.Y2.5s(occas)

*Inner
Harbour*

VQG14m4M
Fl.Y1.5s(occas)

Cruise
Terminal

Q
BY
(Wreck)

OcR30s21m18M

8₇

metres   0
cables   1000

0
5

Depths in metres

2FR(vert)

Admiralty Pier   Traffic Sigs   Fl7.5s21m20M
                                    Horn10s

12₂

19'   01°20'·00E   20'·5

TIME ZONE (UT)
For Summer Time add ONE hour in non-shaded areas

ENGLAND – DOVER

LAT 51°07′N   LONG 1°19′E

TIMES AND HEIGHTS OF HIGH AND LOW WATERS

YEAR **1998**

JANUARY

Day	Time	m	Time	m	Time	m	Time	m		Day	Time	m	Time	m	Time	m	Time	m
1 TH	0012	6.8	0746	0.9	1231	6.7	2005	1.0		16 F	0104	6.6	0826	1.1	1321	6.3	2034	1.3
2 F	0054	6.8	0830	0.9	1315	6.6	2047	1.0		17 SA	0139	6.5	0854	1.2	1355	6.2	2059	1.4
3 SA	0139	6.7	0914	0.9	1402	6.5	2131	1.1		18 SU	0211	6.3	0922	1.3	1428	5.9	2128	1.5
4 SU	0229	6.6	1001	1.1	1456	6.3	2217	1.3		19 M	0242	6.1	0954	1.5	1501	5.7	2204	1.7
5 M	0324	6.4	1051	1.2	1557	6.0	2310	1.5		20 TU	0317	5.8	1033	1.7	1544	5.5	2247	1.9
6 TU	0426	6.1	1149	1.5	1710	5.8			21 W	0405	5.6	1121	1.9	1651	5.2	2341	2.2
7 W	0013	1.7	0538	5.9	1254	1.6	1830	5.7		22 TH	0517	5.3	1228	2.1	1816	5.2		
8 TH	0124	1.8	0656	5.9	1404	1.6	1944	5.7		23 F	0100	2.3	0637	5.3	1349	2.1	1923	5.3
9 F	0235	1.8	0809	6.0	1516	1.5	2048	5.9		24 SA	0223	2.2	0743	5.5	1457	1.8	2018	5.6
10 SA	0349	1.6	0910	6.2	1633	1.3	2142	6.2		25 SU	0328	1.8	0836	5.8	1556	1.5	2106	6.0
11 SU	0457	1.3	1003	6.3	1733	1.2	2229	6.4		26 M	0424	1.5	0924	6.1	1650	1.2	2151	6.3
12 M	0552	1.1	1049	6.5	1821	1.0	O 2310	6.6		27 TU	0516	1.2	1009	6.4	1740	1.0	2234	6.6
13 TU	0637	1.0	1130	6.5	1901	1.0	2349	6.7		28 W	0605	0.9	1052	6.6	1828	0.9	● 2316	6.8
14 W	0718	1.0	1208	6.5	1937	1.1			29 TH	0653	0.7	1136	6.7	1915	0.7	2359	6.9
15 TH	0027	6.7	0754	1.0	1245	6.5	2008	1.2		30 F	0741	0.6	1219	6.8	2000	0.7		
										31 SA	0042	7.0	0825	0.5	1303	6.8	2041	0.7

FEBRUARY

Day	Time	m	Time	m	Time	m	Time	m		Day	Time	m	Time	m	Time	m	Time	m
1 SU	0126	7.0	0908	0.5	1348	6.7	2122	0.7		16 M	0136	6.4	0852	1.1	1347	6.1	2100	1.2
2 M	0212	6.9	0950	0.7	1437	6.5	2203	0.9		17 TU	0158	6.3	0922	1.2	1411	6.0	2133	1.4
3 TU	0303	6.6	1033	0.9	1531	6.2	2249	1.2		18 W	0227	6.1	0956	1.5	1444	5.8	2210	1.7
4 W	0359	6.3	1123	1.3	1635	5.8	2344	1.6		19 TH	0307	5.9	1036	1.7	1529	5.5	2254	2.0
5 TH	0504	5.9	1223	1.7	1750	5.5			20 F	0400	5.5	1128	2.0	1637	5.2	2356	2.2
6 F	0051	1.9	0623	5.5	1334	1.9	1915	5.5		21 SA	0533	5.2	1251	2.2	1840	5.1		
7 SA	0207	2.0	0750	5.6	1452	1.8	2032	5.6		22 SU	0135	2.3	0709	5.3	1421	2.0	1949	5.4
8 SU	0329	1.8	0903	5.8	1621	1.6	2132	5.9		23 M	0254	1.9	0813	5.7	1528	1.7	2044	5.8
9 M	0447	1.4	1004	6.1	1723	1.3	2219	6.2		24 TU	0357	1.5	0905	6.0	1626	1.3	2132	6.2
10 TU	0542	1.2	1043	6.3	1810	1.1	2258	6.5		25 W	0453	1.1	0953	6.4	1720	1.0	2216	6.6
11 W	0626	1.0	1120	6.4	1848	1.0	O 2334	6.6		26 TH	0548	0.8	1038	6.7	1813	0.7	● 2300	6.9
12 TH	0704	0.9	1153	6.5	1920	1.0			27 F	0640	0.5	1121	6.8	1907	0.4	2343	7.1
13 F	0009	6.7	0735	0.9	1226	6.4	1946	1.1		28 SA	0729	0.4	1203	6.9	1947	0.4		
14 SA	0043	6.6	0802	1.0	1257	6.4	2008	1.1										
15 SU	0113	6.5	0826	1.0	1324	6.3	2032	1.1										

MARCH

Day	Time	m	Time	m	Time	m	Time	m		Day	Time	m	Time	m	Time	m	Time	m
1 SU	0025	7.1	0813	0.3	1246	6.9	2028	0.4		16 M	0044	6.5	0758	0.9	1255	6.3	2006	1.0
2 M	0109	7.1	0854	0.3	1330	6.8	2106	0.5		17 TU	0104	6.4	0824	1.0	1314	6.3	2035	1.1
3 TU	0154	7.0	0933	0.5	1417	6.6	2146	0.7		18 W	0125	6.4	0854	1.1	1337	6.3	2106	1.3
4 W	0241	6.7	1013	0.8	1509	6.3	2228	1.1		19 TH	0154	6.3	0926	1.3	1411	6.1	2141	1.5
5 TH	0335	6.3	1059	1.3	1608	5.9	2319	1.6		20 F	0232	6.1	1002	1.6	1453	5.8	2221	1.8
6 F	0437	5.8	1157	1.7	1718	5.5			21 SA	0320	5.7	1048	1.9	1550	5.4	2316	2.1
7 SA	0025	1.9	0553	5.4	1309	2.0	1842	5.3		22 SU	0434	5.3	1156	2.2	1750	5.2		
8 SU	0144	2.1	0732	5.3	1431	2.0	2012	5.4		23 M	0047	2.2	0639	5.3	1345	2.1	1919	5.4
9 M	0311	1.9	0856	5.6	1603	1.8	2116	5.8		24 TU	0222	1.9	0751	5.6	1459	1.7	2019	5.8
10 TU	0432	1.5	0949	5.9	1705	1.4	2202	6.1		25 W	0328	1.5	0847	6.0	1600	1.3	2110	6.3
11 W	0526	1.1	1029	6.1	1750	1.2	2240	6.4		26 TH	0428	1.1	0936	6.4	1657	0.9	2157	6.6
12 TH	0608	1.0	1103	6.3	1827	1.1	2315	6.5		27 F	0526	0.7	1020	6.7	1752	0.7	2241	6.9
13 F	0643	0.9	1133	6.4	1857	1.0	O 2348	6.6		28 SA	0622	0.4	1104	6.9	1843	0.5	● 2324	7.1
14 SA	0711	0.9	1203	6.4	1920	1.0			29 SU	0712	0.3	1146	7.0	1928	0.4		
15 SU	0018	6.6	0734	0.9	1231	6.4	1941	1.0		30 M	0007	7.2	0756	0.2	1228	7.0	2009	0.3
										31 TU	0050	7.2	0836	0.3	1312	6.9	2048	0.5

APRIL

Day	Time	m	Time	m	Time	m	Time	m		Day	Time	m	Time	m	Time	m	Time	m
1 W	0135	7.0	0915	0.5	1358	6.7	2128	0.7		16 TH	0059	6.4	0830	1.1	1314	6.4	2045	1.2
2 TH	0222	6.7	0954	0.9	1449	6.4	2210	1.1		17 F	0130	6.3	0902	1.3	1348	6.3	2119	1.4
3 F	0315	6.2	1039	1.4	1546	6.0	2300	1.6		18 SA	0208	6.1	0938	1.5	1432	6.0	2200	1.7
4 SA	0415	5.8	1134	1.8	1650	5.6			19 SU	0257	5.8	1024	1.8	1530	5.6	2253	1.9
5 SU	0004	1.9	0526	5.4	1246	2.1	1805	5.3		20 M	0408	5.4	1126	2.1	1706	5.3		
6 M	0122	2.1	0702	5.2	1405	2.1	1938	5.4		21 TU	0014	2.1	0608	5.3	1307	2.1	1845	5.5
7 TU	0243	1.9	0833	5.4	1525	1.9	2048	5.7		22 W	0149	1.8	0725	5.6	1427	1.7	1951	5.8
8 W	0359	1.5	0925	5.8	1630	1.6	2135	6.0		23 TH	0258	1.4	0825	6.0	1530	1.4	2046	6.3
9 TH	0455	1.3	1004	6.0	1718	1.3	2214	6.3		24 F	0359	1.0	0915	6.4	1629	1.0	2134	6.6
10 F	0538	1.1	1036	6.2	1756	1.2	2249	6.4		25 SA	0500	0.7	1001	6.7	1726	0.7	2220	6.9
11 SA	0612	1.0	1106	6.3	1826	1.1	O 2321	6.5		26 SU	0559	0.5	1045	6.9	1819	0.5	● 2305	7.1
12 SU	0639	1.0	1135	6.4	1850	1.0	2350	6.5		27 M	0650	0.3	1128	7.0	1907	0.4	2349	7.1
13 M	0704	1.0	1203	6.4	1914	1.0			28 TU	0736	0.3	1211	7.0	1950	0.4		
14 TU	0015	6.4	0730	1.0	1227	6.4	1942	1.0		29 W	0033	7.1	0818	0.4	1256	6.9	2031	0.5
15 W	0036	6.4	0800	1.0	1248	6.4	2013	1.1		30 TH	0118	6.9	0857	0.7	1342	6.7	2112	0.8

Chart Datum: 3·67 metres below Ordnance Datum (Newlyn)

ENGLAND – DOVER

LAT 51°07′N   LONG 1°19′E

TIMES AND HEIGHTS OF HIGH AND LOW WATERS

YEAR **1998**

TIME ZONE (UT)
For Summer Time add ONE hour in non-shaded areas

MAY

Day	Time	m	Day	Time	m
1 F	0205 / 0938 / 1431 / 2155	6.6 / 1.0 / 6.4 / 1.1	**16** SA	0115 / 0846 / 1337 / 2106	6.3 / 1.3 / 6.3 / 1.3
2 SA	0257 / 1021 / 1525 / 2243	6.2 / 1.4 / 6.1 / 1.5	**17** SU	0156 / 0924 / 1423 / 2149	6.2 / 1.4 / 6.1 / 1.5
3 SU	0354 / 1113 / 1623 / 2343	5.8 / 1.8 / 5.7 / 1.9	**18** M	0247 / 1010 / 1522 / 2242	5.9 / 1.7 / 5.9 / 1.7
4 M	0458 / 1218 / 1729	5.4 / 2.1 / 5.4	**19** TU	0357 / 1110 / 1639 / 2354	5.6 / 1.8 / 5.7 / 1.8
5 TU	0052 / 0614 / 1329 / 1847	2.0 / 5.2 / 2.2 / 5.4	**20** W	0532 / 1233 / 1805	5.5 / 1.9 / 5.7
6 W	0203 / 0746 / 1438 / 2004	1.9 / 5.3 / 2.0 / 5.6	**21** TH	0116 / 0654 / 1353 / 1918	1.7 / 5.5 / 1.7 / 5.9
7 TH	0308 / 0845 / 1539 / 2057	1.7 / 5.6 / 1.8 / 5.9	**22** F	0226 / 0759 / 1458 / 2019	1.4 / 6.0 / 1.4 / 6.2
8 F	0405 / 0926 / 1631 / 2139	1.5 / 5.8 / 1.5 / 6.1	**23** SA	0329 / 0853 / 1559 / 2112	1.1 / 6.3 / 1.1 / 6.5
9 SA	0452 / 1001 / 1714 / 2215	1.3 / 6.1 / 1.3 / 6.2	**24** SU	0433 / 0942 / 1700 / 2201	0.8 / 6.5 / 0.9 / 6.8
10 SU	0530 / 1032 / 1748 / 2248	1.2 / 6.2 / 1.2 / 6.3	**25** M	0535 / 1028 / 1757 / 2248 ●	0.6 / 6.7 / 0.6 / 6.9
11 M O	0602 / 1103 / 1818 / 2318	1.1 / 6.3 / 1.1 / 6.4	**26** TU	0630 / 1113 / 1847 / 2334	0.5 / 6.8 / 0.6 / 6.9
12 TU	0634 / 1134 / 1849 / 2345	1.0 / 6.4 / 1.1 / 6.4	**27** W	0718 / 1157 / 1933	0.5 / 6.9 / 0.7
13 W	0706 / 1202 / 1922	1.0 / 6.4 / 1.1	**28** TH	0019 / 0801 / 1242 / 2016	6.9 / 0.6 / 6.8 / 0.7
14 TH	0012 / 0739 / 1229 / 1955	6.4 / 1.0 / 6.4 / 1.1	**29** F	0104 / 0842 / 1327 / 2059	6.7 / 0.8 / 6.7 / 0.9
15 F	0041 / 0812 / 1300 / 2029	6.4 / 1.1 / 6.4 / 1.2	**30** SA	0150 / 0923 / 1413 / 2141	6.5 / 1.1 / 6.5 / 1.1
			31 SU	0238 / 1003 / 1502 / 2225	6.2 / 1.4 / 6.2 / 1.4

JUNE

Day	Time	m	Day	Time	m
1 M	0330 / 1047 / 1554 / 2314	5.8 / 1.7 / 5.8 / 1.7	**16** TU	0241 / 1004 / 1513 / 2235	6.1 / 1.4 / 6.2 / 1.4
2 TU	0426 / 1139 / 1650	5.5 / 2.0 / 5.6	**17** W	0342 / 1058 / 1616 / 2336	5.9 / 1.6 / 6.0 / 1.5
3 W	0011 / 0528 / 1241 / 1754	1.9 / 5.3 / 2.1 / 5.5	**18** TH	0456 / 1205 / 1727	5.8 / 1.7 / 5.9
4 TH	0113 / 0639 / 1344 / 1904	2.0 / 5.3 / 2.1 / 5.5	**19** F	0046 / 0617 / 1318 / 1842	1.5 / 5.7 / 1.7 / 5.9
5 F	0213 / 0746 / 1444 / 2007	1.9 / 5.4 / 2.0 / 5.7	**20** SA	0155 / 0730 / 1426 / 1952	1.4 / 5.9 / 1.5 / 6.1
6 SA	0308 / 0837 / 1539 / 2055	1.7 / 5.6 / 1.8 / 5.8	**21** SU	0301 / 0831 / 1532 / 2052	1.3 / 6.1 / 1.3 / 6.3
7 SU	0359 / 0918 / 1627 / 2135	1.5 / 5.9 / 1.5 / 6.4	**22** M	0409 / 0926 / 1637 / 2147	1.1 / 6.3 / 1.1 / 6.5
8 M	0445 / 0955 / 1709 / 2210	1.3 / 6.1 / 1.4 / 6.2	**23** TU	0516 / 1016 / 1738 / 2238	0.9 / 6.5 / 0.9 / 6.6
9 TU	0527 / 1031 / 1748 / 2245	1.2 / 6.2 / 1.2 / 6.3	**24** W	0614 / 1102 / 1831 / 2325 ●	0.8 / 6.6 / 0.8 / 6.7
10 W O	0607 / 1106 / 1826 / 2319	1.1 / 6.3 / 1.1 / 6.3	**25** TH	0703 / 1146 / 1919	0.8 / 6.7 / 0.7
11 TH	0645 / 1140 / 1904 / 2354	1.1 / 6.4 / 1.1 / 6.4	**26** F	0009 / 0747 / 1229 / 2003	6.7 / 0.8 / 6.7 / 0.8
12 F	0723 / 1215 / 1942	1.0 / 6.5 / 1.0	**27** SA	0052 / 0827 / 1311 / 2044	6.6 / 1.0 / 6.7 / 0.9
13 SA	0029 / 0800 / 1251 / 2020	6.4 / 1.1 / 6.5 / 1.1	**28** SU	0133 / 0905 / 1353 / 2123	6.4 / 1.1 / 6.5 / 1.1
14 SU	0108 / 0838 / 1332 / 2100	6.4 / 1.2 / 6.4 / 1.1	**29** M	0216 / 0940 / 1436 / 2159	6.2 / 1.4 / 6.3 / 1.3
15 M	0151 / 0918 / 1418 / 2145	6.3 / 1.3 / 6.3 / 1.2	**30** TU	0301 / 1012 / 1521 / 2235	5.9 / 1.6 / 6.1 / 1.5

JULY

Day	Time	m	Day	Time	m
1 W	0349 / 1046 / 1609 / 2316	5.7 / 1.8 / 5.8 / 1.8	**16** TH	0323 / 1043 / 1553 / 2316	6.2 / 1.3 / 6.3 / 1.3
2 TH	0442 / 1131 / 1703	5.4 / 2.0 / 5.6	**17** F	0426 / 1139 / 1656	5.9 / 1.5 / 6.1
3 F	0009 / 0543 / 1234 / 1804	1.9 / 5.3 / 2.2 / 5.4	**18** SA	0017 / 0541 / 1246 / 1810	1.5 / 5.7 / 1.7 / 5.9
4 SA	0113 / 0648 / 1344 / 1909	2.0 / 5.3 / 2.2 / 5.5	**19** SU	0126 / 0703 / 1358 / 1929	1.6 / 5.7 / 1.7 / 5.8
5 SU	0216 / 0747 / 1448 / 2006	1.9 / 5.4 / 2.0 / 5.6	**20** M	0237 / 0814 / 1510 / 2040	1.5 / 5.8 / 1.6 / 6.0
6 M	0314 / 0838 / 1545 / 2054	1.7 / 5.7 / 1.7 / 5.8	**21** TU	0352 / 0916 / 1623 / 2141	1.4 / 6.1 / 1.3 / 6.2
7 TU	0407 / 0922 / 1635 / 2137	1.5 / 5.9 / 1.5 / 6.0	**22** W	0505 / 1008 / 1727 / 2233	1.2 / 6.3 / 1.1 / 6.4
8 W	0456 / 1002 / 1721 / 2218	1.3 / 6.2 / 1.3 / 6.2	**23** TH	0603 / 1054 / 1821 / 2318 ●	1.0 / 6.5 / 0.9 / 6.5
9 TH O	0543 / 1042 / 1805 / 2258	1.1 / 6.3 / 1.1 / 6.4	**24** F	0651 / 1135 / 1907 / 2358	0.9 / 6.7 / 0.9 / 6.6
10 F	0627 / 1121 / 1848 / 2337	1.0 / 6.5 / 1.0 / 6.5	**25** SA	0732 / 1214 / 1949	0.9 / 6.7 / 0.8
11 SA	0709 / 1200 / 1931	1.0 / 6.6 / 0.9	**26** SU	0036 / 0809 / 1253 / 2025	6.5 / 1.0 / 6.7 / 0.9
12 SU	0017 / 0751 / 1240 / 2014	6.5 / 1.0 / 6.7 / 0.9	**27** M	0113 / 0841 / 1331 / 2057	6.4 / 1.1 / 6.6 / 1.0
13 M	0058 / 0832 / 1322 / 2056	6.5 / 1.0 / 6.7 / 0.9	**28** TU	0149 / 0907 / 1407 / 2125	6.2 / 1.3 / 6.4 / 1.2
14 TU	0141 / 0913 / 1407 / 2139	6.5 / 1.0 / 6.6 / 0.9	**29** W	0225 / 0930 / 1443 / 2151	6.1 / 1.4 / 6.2 / 1.4
15 W	0229 / 0956 / 1457 / 2225	6.3 / 1.1 / 6.5 / 1.1	**30** TH	0302 / 0958 / 1519 / 2223	5.8 / 1.6 / 5.9 / 1.6
			31 F	0345 / 1035 / 1603 / 2305	5.6 / 1.8 / 5.7 / 1.8

AUGUST

Day	Time	m	Day	Time	m
1 SA	0442 / 1123 / 1703	5.3 / 2.1 / 5.4	**16** SU	0514 / 1218 / 1745	5.7 / 1.8 / 5.8
2 SU	0004 / 0555 / 1235 / 1816	2.1 / 5.2 / 2.3 / 5.3	**17** M	0100 / 0638 / 1334 / 1912	1.8 / 5.5 / 1.9 / 5.6
3 M	0125 / 0704 / 1401 / 1924	2.1 / 5.3 / 2.2 / 5.4	**18** TU	0219 / 0800 / 1455 / 2035	1.9 / 5.6 / 1.8 / 5.8
4 TU	0236 / 0803 / 1509 / 2022	2.0 / 5.5 / 1.9 / 5.7	**19** W	0346 / 0908 / 1617 / 2139	1.7 / 5.9 / 1.5 / 6.1
5 W	0336 / 0853 / 1606 / 2111	1.7 / 5.8 / 1.6 / 6.0	**20** TH	0459 / 1000 / 1721 / 2229	1.4 / 6.2 / 1.2 / 6.3
6 TH	0430 / 0938 / 1657 / 2155	1.4 / 6.1 / 1.3 / 6.2	**21** F	0553 / 1042 / 1811 / 2309	1.1 / 6.5 / 1.0 / 6.5
7 F	0520 / 1020 / 1745 / 2238	1.2 / 6.4 / 1.1 / 6.5	**22** SA	0636 / 1119 / 1853 / 2343 ●	1.0 / 6.7 / 0.9 / 6.5
8 SA O	0608 / 1101 / 1833 / 2320	1.0 / 6.6 / 0.9 / 6.6	**23** SU	0713 / 1156 / 1929	1.0 / 6.7 / 0.9
9 SU	0655 / 1142 / 1919	0.9 / 6.8 / 0.7	**24** M	0016 / 0744 / 1231 / 1959	6.5 / 1.1 / 6.7 / 0.9
10 M	0001 / 0739 / 1224 / 2003	6.7 / 0.8 / 6.9 / 0.6	**25** TU	0049 / 0809 / 1305 / 2024	6.4 / 1.1 / 6.6 / 1.0
11 TU	0042 / 0821 / 1306 / 2046	6.7 / 0.8 / 6.9 / 0.6	**26** W	0119 / 0829 / 1335 / 2046	6.3 / 1.2 / 6.5 / 1.2
12 W	0125 / 0901 / 1350 / 2126	6.7 / 0.8 / 6.9 / 0.7	**27** TH	0146 / 0852 / 1359 / 2111	6.2 / 1.3 / 6.3 / 1.3
13 TH	0211 / 0941 / 1437 / 2208	6.6 / 0.9 / 6.7 / 0.9	**28** F	0210 / 0921 / 1424 / 2142	6.0 / 1.5 / 6.1 / 1.5
14 F	0302 / 1024 / 1530 / 2254	6.3 / 1.1 / 6.4 / 1.2	**29** SA	0237 / 0956 / 1459 / 2220	5.8 / 1.7 / 5.8 / 1.8
15 SA	0402 / 1114 / 1632 / 2350	6.0 / 1.5 / 6.1 / 1.6	**30** SU	0318 / 1038 / 1550 / 2307	5.5 / 2.0 / 5.5 / 2.1
			31 M	0429 / 1134 / 1725	5.2 / 2.3 / 5.2

Chart Datum: 3·67 metres below Ordnance Datum (Newlyn)

ENGLAND – DOVER

LAT 51°07′N   LONG 1°19′E

TIMES AND HEIGHTS OF HIGH AND LOW WATERS

YEAR **1998**

TIME ZONE (UT)
For Summer Time add ONE hour in non-shaded areas

Chart Datum: 3·67 metres below Ordnance Datum (Newlyn)

SEPTEMBER

Day	Time	m	Time	m	Time	m	Time	m
1 TU	0021	2.3	0624	5.2	1311	2.4	1851	5.3
2 W	0201	2.2	0732	5.4	1436	2.1	1956	5.6
3 TH	0309	1.9	0827	5.8	1538	1.7	2049	5.9
4 F	0405	1.5	0914	6.2	1632	1.3	2135	6.3
5 SA	0458	1.2	0957	6.5	1724	1.0	2218	6.6
6 SU ○	0548	1.0	1039	6.8	1814	0.7	2300	6.8
7 M	0636	0.8	1121	7.0	1902	0.6	2341	6.9
8 TU	0721	0.7	1202	7.1	1947	0.5		
9 W	0022	6.9	0803	0.6	1245	7.1	2028	0.5
10 TH	0105	6.9	0842	0.7	1329	7.0	2108	0.6
11 F	0150	6.7	0922	0.8	1416	6.8	2147	0.9
12 SA	0241	6.4	1004	1.1	1509	6.5	2232	1.3
13 SU	0340	6.1	1053	1.5	1612	6.0	2326	1.7
14 M	0451	5.7	1156	1.9	1725	5.6		
15 TU	0038	2.1	0612	5.5	1316	2.1	1857	5.5
16 W	0204	2.1	0744	5.5	1445	2.0	2030	5.6
17 TH	0339	1.9	0855	5.9	1609	1.6	2131	6.0
18 F	0445	1.5	0944	6.2	1707	1.2	2215	6.2
19 SA	0534	1.2	1023	6.5	1753	1.0	2250	6.4
20 SU ●	0614	1.1	1059	6.7	1831	0.9	2321	6.5
21 M	0647	1.1	1133	6.7	1902	1.0	2351	6.5
22 TU	0713	1.1	1206	6.7	1927	1.0		
23 W	0021	6.5	0734	1.2	1236	6.6	1947	1.1
24 TH	0048	6.4	0754	1.2	1301	6.5	2010	1.2
25 F	0109	6.3	0820	1.3	1320	6.4	2038	1.3
26 SA	0128	6.2	0851	1.4	1343	6.2	2109	1.5
27 SU	0156	6.1	0925	1.7	1416	6.0	2145	1.7
28 M	0234	5.8	1004	2.0	1501	5.7	2228	2.1
29 TU	0327	5.4	1054	2.3	1614	5.3	2327	2.4
30 W	0540	5.2	1214	2.4	1821	5.2		

OCTOBER

Day	Time	m	Time	m	Time	m	Time	m
1 TH	0118	2.4	0700	5.4	1401	2.2	1930	5.5
2 F	0239	2.0	0759	5.8	1508	1.7	2026	6.0
3 SA	0338	1.6	0849	6.2	1605	1.3	2113	6.4
4 SU	0432	1.2	0933	6.6	1658	0.9	2156	6.7
5 M ○	0523	0.9	1015	7.0	1751	0.7	2238	6.9
6 TU	0612	0.7	1058	7.2	1840	0.5	2319	7.0
7 W	0658	0.6	1140	7.3	1926	0.4		
8 TH	0000	7.1	0741	0.6	1224	7.2	2007	0.5
9 F	0044	7.0	0822	0.6	1308	7.1	2047	0.7
10 SA	0130	6.8	0903	0.8	1356	6.8	2128	1.0
11 SU	0222	6.5	0946	1.2	1451	6.4	2212	1.4
12 M	0321	6.1	1035	1.6	1553	6.0	2306	1.9
13 TU	0427	5.7	1138	2.0	1704	5.6		
14 W	0018	2.2	0542	5.5	1258	2.2	1833	5.4
15 TH	0144	2.3	0713	5.5	1425	2.0	2010	5.6
16 F	0311	2.0	0828	5.8	1557	1.7	2108	5.9
17 SA	0414	1.7	0917	6.1	1639	1.3	2150	6.1
18 SU	0502	1.4	0957	6.4	1723	1.1	2223	6.3
19 M	0541	1.2	1032	6.6	1759	1.1	2253	6.5
20 TU ●	0614	1.2	1105	6.7	1828	1.1	2322	6.5
21 W	0639	1.2	1135	6.6	1851	1.1	2351	6.5
22 TH	0701	1.2	1205	6.6	1915	1.1		
23 F	0018	6.5	0726	1.2	1229	6.5	1941	1.2
24 SA	0039	6.4	0755	1.3	1249	6.4	2011	1.3
25 SU	0100	6.4	0826	1.4	1314	6.3	2043	1.5
26 M	0129	6.3	0901	1.6	1348	6.1	2119	1.7
27 TU	0208	6.0	0939	1.9	1433	5.8	2201	2.0
28 W	0300	5.7	1028	2.1	1536	5.4	2255	2.3
29 TH	0428	5.3	1138	2.2	1745	5.3		
30 F	0023	2.4	0621	5.4	1319	2.2	1900	5.6
31 SA	0201	2.1	0727	5.8	1433	1.8	1959	6.0

NOVEMBER

Day	Time	m	Time	m	Time	m	Time	m
1 SU	0305	1.7	0820	6.2	1533	1.3	2049	6.4
2 M	0401	1.3	0907	6.7	1629	1.0	2133	6.7
3 TU	0455	1.0	0951	7.0	1724	0.7	2215	6.9
4 W ○	0546	0.8	1035	7.2	1817	0.6	2258	7.1
5 TH	0635	0.6	1119	7.2	1904	0.5	2341	7.1
6 F	0720	0.6	1204	7.2	1948	0.6		
7 SA	0026	7.0	0804	0.7	1250	7.0	2030	0.8
8 SU	0114	6.8	0847	0.9	1339	6.7	2112	1.1
9 M	0205	6.6	0932	1.2	1433	6.4	2157	1.5
10 TU	0301	6.2	1022	1.6	1533	6.0	2248	1.9
11 W	0401	5.9	1120	1.9	1638	5.6	2352	2.2
12 TH	0507	5.6	1230	2.1	1753	5.4		
13 F	0106	2.3	0624	5.5	1344	2.0	1923	5.4
14 SA	0221	2.2	0743	5.7	1454	1.8	2028	5.7
15 SU	0326	1.9	0839	6.0	1554	1.6	2112	5.9
16 M	0419	1.7	0923	6.2	1641	1.4	2149	6.2
17 TU	0502	1.5	1001	6.4	1719	1.3	2221	6.3
18 W	0537	1.3	1034	6.5	1750	1.2	2252	6.4
19 TH ●	0606	1.3	1106	6.5	1818	1.2	2323	6.5
20 F	0633	1.2	1135	6.5	1848	1.2	2351	6.5
21 SA	0704	1.2	1202	6.4	1920	1.2		
22 SU	0017	6.5	0736	1.3	1228	6.4	1952	1.3
23 M	0043	6.4	0810	1.3	1257	6.3	2026	1.4
24 TU	0115	6.4	0845	1.5	1333	6.2	2102	1.6
25 W	0155	6.2	0925	1.7	1418	6.0	2143	1.8
26 TH	0246	6.0	1012	1.9	1517	5.7	2235	2.0
27 F	0355	5.7	1114	2.0	1649	5.5	2344	2.1
28 SA	0527	5.6	1236	2.0	1821	5.6		
29 SU	0114	2.0	0646	5.8	1353	1.7	1927	5.9
30 M	0226	1.8	0748	6.2	1458	1.4	2022	6.2

DECEMBER

Day	Time	m	Time	m	Time	m	Time	m
1 TU	0327	1.4	0841	6.5	1558	1.1	2111	6.5
2 W	0426	1.1	0929	6.8	1659	0.9	2157	6.8
3 TH ○	0523	0.9	1017	7.0	1756	0.7	2243	6.9
4 F	0616	0.7	1104	7.1	1847	0.7	2329	7.0
5 SA	0705	0.7	1150	7.0	1933	0.7		
6 SU	0014	6.9	0751	0.8	1237	6.9	2017	0.9
7 M	0101	6.8	0836	0.9	1325	6.6	2059	1.1
8 TU	0149	6.6	0921	1.1	1415	6.3	2142	1.4
9 W	0239	6.4	1007	1.4	1508	6.0	2226	1.7
10 TH	0332	6.1	1056	1.7	1605	5.7	2316	2.0
11 F	0429	5.8	1150	1.9	1707	5.5		
12 SA	0015	2.2	0532	5.6	1252	2.0	1816	5.3
13 SU	0121	2.3	0643	5.6	1354	2.0	1927	5.4
14 M	0225	2.2	0749	5.7	1453	1.9	2023	5.6
15 TU	0324	2.0	0842	5.9	1546	1.7	2108	5.9
16 W	0415	1.7	0924	6.1	1632	1.5	2146	6.1
17 TH	0458	1.5	1001	6.2	1713	1.3	2222	6.3
18 F ●	0535	1.4	1035	6.3	1750	1.2	2256	6.4
19 SA	0610	1.2	1109	6.4	1827	1.2	2329	6.5
20 SU	0646	1.2	1142	6.4	1903	1.2		
21 M	0001	6.5	0722	1.2	1214	6.4	1939	1.2
22 TU	0033	6.5	0800	1.2	1248	6.4	2015	1.2
23 W	0108	6.5	0838	1.3	1325	6.3	2053	1.3
24 TH	0148	6.4	0918	1.3	1408	6.2	2133	1.5
25 F	0235	6.3	1003	1.5	1500	6.0	2220	1.6
26 SA	0332	6.1	1056	1.6	1605	5.8	2317	1.8
27 SU	0440	5.9	1200	1.7	1727	5.7		
28 M	0029	1.9	0558	5.9	1314	1.7	1850	5.7
29 TU	0146	1.8	0714	6.0	1423	1.5	1957	6.0
30 W	0255	1.6	0818	6.2	1530	1.3	2054	6.2
31 TH	0401	1.3	0915	6.5	1639	1.1	2147	6.5

DOVER STRAIT   10-3-16

3

RAMSGATE   10-3-17

Kent 51°19'·48N 01°25'·60E   Rtg 1-2-1

CHARTS
AC 1827, *1828, 323*; Imray C1, C8; Stanfords 5, 9, 20; OS 179

TIDES
+0030 Dover; ML 2·7; Duration 0530; Zone 0 (UT)

Standard Port DOVER (←—)

Times				Height (metres)			
High Water		Low Water		MHWS	MHWN	MLWN	MLWS
0000	0600	0100	0700	6·8	5·3	2·1	0·8
1200	1800	1300	1900				
Differences RAMSGATE							
+0030	+0030	+0017	+0007	−1·6	−1·3	−0·7	−0·4
RICHBOROUGH							
+0015	+0015	+0030	+0030	−3·4	−2·6	−1·7	−0·7

HW Broadstairs = HW Dover +0037 approx.

SHELTER
Good in marina, min depth 3m. Access approx HW ±2 via flap gate and lifting bridge. Close ESE of the marina ent, 107 pontoon berths in 2m are accessible H24, protected by wavebreaks. Extra berths may be available in West Gully; larger vessels can berth on S Breakwater.
Anti-Rabies Byelaw: Animals, inc dogs/cats, are totally banned ashore or afloat within the Royal Harbour limits.

NAVIGATION
WPT 51°19'·40N 01°27'·80E, 090°/270° from/to S bkwtr, 1·45M. Many ferries/catamarans uses the well-marked main E-W chan (3·3M long, dredged 7·5m, 110m wide; as upper chartlet). For ent/dep yachts must use the Recommended Yacht Track parallel to, and on the S side of, the main buoyed chan.

Enter/dep under power, or advise Port Control if unable to motor. Ent/dep Royal Hbr directly; do not manoeuvre in the outer hbr. Holding area to the S of the S bkwtr must be used by yachts to keep the hbr ent clear for ferry tfc. Beware Dike Bank to the N and Quern Bank close S of the chan. Cross Ledge and Brake shoals are further S.

LIGHTS AND MARKS
Ldg lts 270°: front Dir Oc WRG 10s 10m 5M, G259°-269°, W269°-271°, R271°-281°; rear, Oc 5s 17m 5M.
N bkwtr hd = QG 10m 5M; S bkwtr hd = VQ R 10m 5M. At E Pier, **IPTS** (Sigs 2 and 3) visible from seaward and from within Royal Hbr, control appr into hbr limits (abeam Nos 1 & 2 buoys) and ent/exit to/from Royal Hbr. In addition a Fl Y lt = ferry is under way either in the chan or outer hbr; no other vessels may move without specific permission. At W Pier, depth between piers shown by:
® = >3m; ⑤ = <3m.
Ent to marina controlled by separate IPTS to stbd of ent. Siren sounded approx 10 mins before gate closes; non-opening indicated by R ● or ®.
Quern Bank, 5ca SE of the hbr ent, is marked by Quern Bank NCM lt buoy, Q, and by a WCM lt buoy, Fl (9) 15s.

RADIO TELEPHONE
A VTS operates, mainly for ferries/catamarans, but small craft must monitor Ch 14 at all times. Call *Port Control* Ch 14 (H24) to enter/cross main chan & hbr; due to frequent tfc, yachts **must** comply with all orders, which can supersede IPTS. Also on Ch 14, call *Dock Office* for marina berth.

TELEPHONE (Dial code 01843)
Hr Mr 592277, ☎ 590941; Broadstairs Hr Mr 861879; ⌗ (01304) 224251 (H24); MRCC (01304) 210008; Marinecall 0891 500 455/456; Police 581724; Dr 852853; Ⓗ 225544.

FACILITIES
Marina (400+100 visitors) ☎ 592277, ☎ 590941, £12.80, AC, FW, Slips, C (10 ton), Ⓔ, ME, El, Sh, BH, CH, ACA, Gaz, SM, ▣; **Outer Hbr** (107 berths), 2m, access H24, AC, FW. P & D from Fuel Barge, *Foy Boat* Ch 14 or ☎ 592662.
Royal Temple YC ☎ 591766, Bar.
Town EC Thurs; Gas, Gaz, V, R, Bar, ✉, Ⓑ, ⇌, ✈ (Manston).

ADJACENT HARBOUR
SANDWICH, Kent, 51°16'·80N 01°21'·30E. AC 1827 *1828*. Richborough differences above; ML 1·4m; Duration 0520. HW Sandwich Town quay is HW Richborough +1. Access HW ±1 at sp for draft 2m to reach Sandwich; arrive off ent at HW Dover. Visitors should seek local knowledge before arriving by day; night ent definitely not advised. The chan to Shell Ness is marked by bn Fl R 10s and small lateral buoys and beacons, all with rotating reflective topmarks. Visitors' berths on S bank of the River Stour at Town Quay ☎ (01304) 613283. Limited turning room before the swing bridge, 1·7m clearance when closed. Facilities: EC Wed; Slip; ⌗ ☎ 224251; **Marina** (50+some visitors) ☎ 613783 (max LOA 18m, 2·1m draft), BH (15 ton), Sh, Slip, FW, SM, CH, ME, Gas; D & P (cans from garage); **Sandwich Sailing and Motorboat Club** ☎ 611116 and **Sandwich Bay Sailing and Water Ski Clubs** offer some facilities. Both ports are administered by Sandwich Port & Haven Commissioners.

VOLVO PENTA SERVICE

Sales and service centres in area 4

KENT *John Hawkins Marine*, Ships Stores, Medway Bridge Marina, Manor Lane, Borstal, Rochester ME1 3HS Tel (01634) 840812 **ESSEX** *Volspec Ltd*, Woodrolfe Road, Tollesbury, Maldon CM9 8SE Tel (01621) 869756 *French Marine Motors Ltd*, 61/63 Waterside, Brightlingsea CO7 0AX Tel (01206) 302133 **NORFOLK** *Marinepower Engineering*, The Mill, (off Station Road), Wood Green, Salhouse, Norwich NR13 6NS Tel (01603) 720001 **NORTHAMPTONSHIRE** *CVS Pentapower*, St. Andrews Road, Northampton NN1 2LF Tel (01604) 38537/ 38409/36173 **SUFFOLK** *Northgate Marine*, 27 Acorn Units, Ellough Industrial Estate, Beccles, Suffolk NR34 7TD Tel (01502) 716657 *French Marine Motors Ltd*, Suffolk Yacht Harbour, Levington, Ipswich IP10 0LN Tel (01473) 659882 *Volspec Ltd*, Woolverstone Marina, Woolverstone, Ipswich IP9 1AS Tel (01473) 780144

VOLVO PENTA

Area 4 **4**

Thames Estuary
North Foreland to Great Yarmouth

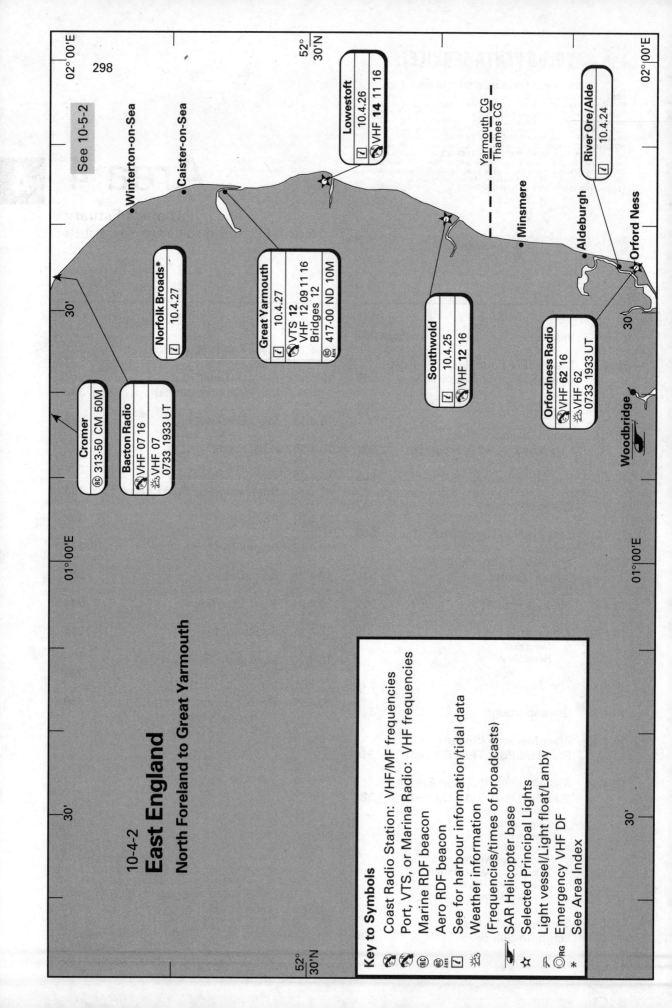

298

See 10·5·2

10·4·2
East England
North Foreland to Great Yarmouth

Cromer
RC 313·50 CM 50M

Bacton Radio
VHF 07 16
VHF 07
0733 1933 UT

Norfolk Broads*
ℹ 10.4.27

Great Yarmouth
ℹ 10.4.27
VTS 12
VHF 12 09 11 16
Bridges 12
RC 417·00 ND 10M

Southwold
ℹ 10.4.25
VHF 12 16

Orfordness Radio
VHF 62 16
VHF 62
0733 1933 UT

Lowestoft
10.4.26
VHF **14** 11 16

River Ore/Alde
ℹ 10.4.24

Yarmouth CG
Thames CG

Winterton-on-Sea
Caister-on-Sea
Minsmere
Aldeburgh
Orford Ness
Woodbridge

Key to Symbols
Coast Radio Station: VHF/MF frequencies
Port, VTS, or Marina Radio: VHF frequencies
Marine RDF beacon
Aero RDF beacon
See for harbour information/tidal data
Weather information
(Frequencies/times of broadcasts)
SAR Helicopter base
☆ Selected Principal Lights
Light vessel/Light float/Lanby
RG Emergency VHF DF
* See Area Index

THE MACMILLAN NAUTICAL ALMANAC

ORDER FORM FOR IBERIAN GUIDE 1998 AND ASTRO-SUPPLEMENT 1998

Below is an order form for the new *Macmillan Iberian Guide 1998* and the *Astro-Supplement 1998*. These are two separate publications. Please complete the form below, indicating which publication you would like to order and enclosing a cheque made payable to Macmillan Distribution Ltd for the appropriate amount.

The new **Macmillan Iberian Guide 1998** is a 56-page guide extending the Almanac's coverage from the Franco-Spanish border at Hendaye westward along Northern Spain and southward past the coasts of Portugal and South West Spain to Gibraltar. It gives all the necessary information for cruising these waters including: details and chartlets of 37 harbours, coastal lights, fog signals and waypoints, passage information, radio aids, communications and weather information, tidal predictions and curves, and distance tables. Published December 1997 at **£8.**

The **Macmillan Astro-Supplement 1997** contains an introduction to the general principles of astro-navigation, the ephemerides of the Sun and Moon, GHA Aries and the 57 navigational stars, the Pole star, tables for interpolating the ephemerides, sextant altitude correction tables, rise set tables and conversion tables, as well as algorithms for calculating the Sun emphemeris, and undertaking sight reduction by computer or program-mable calculator. Published September 1997 at **£4.**

APPLICATION FORM

I would like to order:

☐ copy(ies) of the new **Macmillan Iberian Guide 1998** at a cost of £8 per copy. (ISBN: 0 333 727681)

☐ copy(ies) of **The Macmillan Astro-Supplement 1998** at £4 per copy. (ISBN 0 333 727673)

Name

Address

Postcode

Sum enclosed   £

(Please make cheques payable to *Macmillan Distribution Ltd*)

Please send to: Direct Customer Services, Macmillan Distribution Ltd, Brunel Road, Basingstoke, RG21 6XS

4

River Deben
10.4.23
ⓘ ⚓🕐 VHF Pilot 08
Marina **80** M

River Stour
10.4.21
ⓘ ⚓🕐 VTS **71** 14 16
Hbr/Launch 11
Radar 20
Marinas **80** M

Sunk Lt F

North Foreland Radio
⚓🕐 VHF 26
📻 311·00 NF 50M
0733 1933 UT
ⓇⒼ VHF 26

Ramsgate
10.3.18
ⓘ ⚓🕐 VTS 14
Port 14

See 10-3-2

Felixstowe

Harwich

Ipswich

Walton Backwaters
10.4.20
ⓘ ⚓🕐 VHF
Marina 80

Thames CG
Dover CG

Margate* ⓇⒼ

30'

52°
00'N

River Orwell
10.4.22
ⓘ ⚓🕐 VHF **14** 12 16
Marinas 80 M

01°00'E

Brightlingsea

Clacton-on-Sea

West Mersea

River Blackwater
10.4.18
ⓘ ⚓🕐 VHF
Marinas 80 M

River Roach/Havengore
10.4.16
ⓘ ⚓🕐 Havengore
Bridge
VHF 72 16

Thames Estuary
10.4.9
ⓘ ⚓🕐 London Port Ctl
VHF **12** 16
(Seaward appr to
Sea Reach No. 4 By)

Whitstable
10.4.10
ⓘ ⚓🕐 VHF 09 12 16

Herne Bay*

Colchester

Foulness

Queenborough
10.4.12
ⓘ ⚓🕐 Kingsferry
Bridge
VHF 10

Holehaven*

01°00'E

51°
30'N

02°00'E

30'

River Colne
10.4.19
ⓘ ⚓🕐 Brightlingsea
VHF 68
Colchester
VHF 68 11 14 16

Burnham-on-Crouch
10.4.17
ⓘ ⚓🕐 VHF
Marinas 80 M

**Southend-on-Sea
and Leigh-on-Sea**
10.4.15
ⓘ 📻 362·50 SND 20M

The Swale
10.4.11
ⓘ

River Medway
10.4.13
ⓘ ⚓🕐 Medway Radio
VHF 74 22 73 11
Marinas 80 M

Variation 3°W (1998)

90

180

270

0

30'

River Thames
10.4.14
ⓘ ⚓🕐 Port Ctl London
VHF **68** 18 20
(Sea Reach No 4 By
to Crayford Ness)
Woolwich Radio
VHF **14** 22 16
(Thames above
Crayford Ness)
Barrier 14 22
Info bcsts
VHF 68 H+00 H+30
VHF 12 H+15 H+45
BHF 14 H+15 H+45

Thames Radio
VHF 02 16
⚓🕐 VHF 02
📻 0733 1933 UT

Gravesend*

52°
00'N

51°
30'N

10-4-3   AREA 4 TIDAL STREAMS

5 Hours before HW Dover (0530 before HW Walton)

4 Hours before HW Dover (0430 before HW Walton)

3 Hours before HW Dover (0330 before HW Walton)

2 Hours before HW Dover (0230 before HW Walton)

1 Hour before HW Dover (0130 before HW Walton)

HW Dover (0030 before HW Walton)

Southward 10.3.3   Thames Estuary 10.4.8   Northward 10.5.3   Eastward 10.20.3

1 Hour after HW Dover (0030 after HW Walton)

2 Hours after HW Dover (0130 after HW Walton)

3 Hours after HW Dover (0230 after HW Walton)

4 Hours after HW Dover (0330 after HW Walton)

5 Hours after HW Dover (0430 after HW Walton)

6 Hours after HW Dover (0530 after HW Walton)

10.4.4 COASTAL LIGHTS, FOG SIGNALS AND WAYPOINTS

Abbreviations used below are given in 1.4.1. Principal lights are in **bold** print, places in CAPITALS, and light-vessels, light floats and Lanbys in *CAPITAL ITALICS*. Unless otherwise stated lights are white. m – elevation in metres; M – nominal range in miles. Fog signals are in *italics*. Useful waypoints are underlined – use those on land with care. All geographical positions should be assumed to be approximate. See 4.4.1. All positions are referenced to the OSGB 36 datum.

IMPORTANT NOTE

Changes are regularly made to buoyage in the Thames Estuary. Check *Notices to Mariners* for the latest information.

THAMES ESTUARY
(Direction of buoyage generally East to West)

APPROACHES TO THAMES ESTUARY
F3 Lt F 51°23'·82N 02°00'·62E Fl 10s 12m **22M**; Racon; *Horn 10s*.
Falls Hd Lt By 51°28'·20N 01°50'·00E Q; NCM.
Drill Stone Lt By 51°25'·80N 01°43'·00E Q (3) 10s; NCM.
NE Spit Lt By 51°27'·90N 01°30'·00E VQ (3) 5s; ECM.
Elbow Lt By 51°23'·20N 01°31'·70E Q; NCM.
Foreness Pt Outfall Lt By 51°24'·60N 01°26'·10E Fl Y 5s; SPM.
Longnose By 51°24'·12N 01°26'·18E; PHM.
Longnose Spit By 51°23'·90N 01°25'·85E; NCM.

MARGATE
Promenade Pier N Hd 51°23'·64N 01°22'·90E Fl R 5s.
Stone Pier Hd FR 18m 4M. (QW marks tide gauge 385m NNW.)

GORE CHANNEL
SE Margate Lt By 51°24'·10N 01°20'·50E Q (3) 10s; ECM.
S Margate Lt By 51°23'·88N 01°16'·75E Fl G 2·5s; SHM.
Margate Hook Bn 51°24'·14N 01°14'·39E; SCM.
Hook Spit By 51°24'·05N 01°12'·65E; SHM.
E Last Lt By 51°24'·00N 01°12'·28E QR; PHM.

HERNE BAY
Pier Hd 51°22'·90N 01°07'·00E Q 8m 4M, (isolated).
Pier, near root 51°22'·36N 01°07'·30E 2 FR (vert).

WHITSTABLE
Whitstable Street Lt By 51°23'·83N 01°01'·70E Q; NCM.
Oyster Lt By 51°22'·12N 01°01'·27E Fl (2) R 10s; PHM.
NE Arm F 15m 8M; W mast; FR 10m 5M (same structure) shown when ent/dep prohib.
W Quay Dn 51°21'·82N 01°01'·55E Fl WRG 5s 2m W5M, R3M, G3M; vis W118°-156°, G156°-178°, R178°-201°.
E Quay, N End 51°21'·80N 01°01'·65E 2 FR (vert) 4m 1M.
S Quay Dir Lt 122·5° 51°21'·73N 01°01'·80E Oc WRG 5s 7m vis: G110°-121°, W121°-124°, R124°-134°.

THE SWALE
Columbine By 51°24'·23N 01°01'·45E; SHM.
Columbine Spit By 51°24'·23N 01°00'·13E; SHM.
Pollard Spit Lt By 51°22'·95N 00° 58'·67E QR; PHM.
Ham Gat By 51°23'·05N 00°58'·42E; SHM.
Sand End Lt By 51°21'·40N 00°56'·00E Fl G 5s; SHM.
Faversham Spit By 51°20'·74N 00°54'·31E; NCM.
Fowley Spit Lt By 51°21'·46N 00°51'·57E Q (3) 10s; ECM.
Queenborough Hard S1 Lt By 51°24'·96N 00°44'·28E Fl R 3s; PHM.
Queenborough Pt Lt (S) 51°25'·31N 00°44'·13E Fl R 4s.
Queenborough Pt Lt (N) 51°25'·42N 00°44'·11E QR 3m 2M.
Queenborough Spit Lt By 51°25'·78N 00°44'·03E Q (3) 10s; ECM.

QUEENS CHANNEL/FOUR FATHOMS CHANNEL
E Margate Lt By 51°27'·00N 01°26'·50E Fl R 2·5s; PHM.
Spaniard Lt By 51°26'·20N 01°04'·10E Q (3) 10s; ECM.
Spile Lt By 51°26'·40N 00°55'·80E Fl G 2·5s; SHM.

PRINCES CHANNEL
Outer Tongue Lt By 51°30'·70N 01°26'·50E L Fl 10s; SWM; Racon (T); *Whis*.
Tongue Sand S Lt By 51°29'·40N 01°22'·15E Q (6) + L Fl 15s; SCM.
Tongue Sand N Lt By 51°29'·65N 01°22'·13E Q; NCM.
E Tongue Lt By 51°28'·72N 01°18'·72E Fl (2) R 5s; PHM.
S Shingles Lt By 51°29'·20N 01°16'·12E Q (6) + L Fl 15s; SCM; *Bell*.
N Tongue Lt By 51°28'·78N 01°13'·18E Fl (3) R 10s; PHM.
SE Girdler Lt By 51°29'·47N 01°10'·00E Fl (3) G 10s; SHM.
W Girdler Lt By 51°29'·58N 01°06'·82E Q (9)15s; WCM; *Bell*.
Girdler Lt By 51°29'·15N 01°06'·50E Fl (4) R 15s; PHM.
Shivering Sand Trs 51°29'·90N 01°04'·90E. Tide gauge.
Shivering Sand Tr N Lt By 51°29'·75N 01°04'·90E Q (6) + L Fl 15s; SCM; *Bell*.
E Redsand Lt By 51°29'·38N 01°04'·15E Fl (2) R 5s; PHM.

NORTH EDINBURGH CHANNEL/KNOB CHANNEL
Edinburgh Lt By 51°31'·42N 01°21'·53E QR; PHM.
No. 1 Lt By 51°31'·55N 01°21'·92E Q (6) + L Fl 15s; SCM; *Bell*.
Patch Lt By 51°32'·24N 01°20'·91E Fl (2) R 10s; PHM.
SE Longsand Lt By 51°32'·24N 01°21'·22E QG; SHM.
No. 2 Lt By 51°32'·88N 01°20'·24E Fl (3) R 10s; PHM.
No. 3 Lt By 51°32'·98N 01°20'·46E Q (9) 15s; WCM.
No. 4 Lt By 51°33'·22N 01°19'·41E Fl R 2·5s; PHM; *Bell*.
No. 5 Lt By 51°33'·42N 01°19'·43E Fl G 2·5s; SHM.
No. 6 Lt By 51°33'·36N 01°18'·19E Fl R 2·5s; PHM.
No. 7 Lt By 51°33'·58N 01°18'·24E Fl G 2·5s; SHM.
NW Long Sand Bn 51°34'·72N 01°18'·16E; SHM.
No. 8 Lt By 51°33'·19N 01°16'·65E Fl (3) R 10s; PHM.
No. 9 Lt By 51°33'·46N 01°16'·70E Fl (3) G 10s; SHM; *Bell*.
Shingles Patch Lt By 51°32'·98N 01°15'·47E Q; NCM.
N Shingles Lt By 51°32'·66N 01°14'·35E Fl R 2·5s; PHM.
Tizard Lt By 51°32'·90N 01°13'·00E Q (6) + L Fl 15s; SCM.
Mid Shingles Lt By 51°31'·93N 01°12'·08E Fl (2) R 5s; PHM.
NE Knob Lt By 51°32'·00N 01°10'·10E QG; SHM.
NW Shingles Lt By 51°31'·23N 01°09'·83E VQ; NCM.
SE Knob Lt By 51°30'·86N 01°06'·51E Fl G 5s; SHM.
Shivering Sand Trs N Lt By 51°29'·96N 01°04'·88E Q; NCM.
Knob Lt By 51°30'·66N 01°04'·38E Iso 5s; SWM; *Bell*.

OAZE DEEP
S Oaze Lt By 51°30'·00N 01°00'·80E Fl (2) G 5s; SHM.
Red Sand Trs N Lt By 51°28'·70N 00°59'·42E Fl (3) R 10s; PHM; *Bell*.
Red Sand Trs E Lt By 51°28'·57N 00°59'·78E QG; SHM.
SW Oaze Lt By 51°29'·03N 00°57'·03E Q (6) + L Fl 15s; SCM.
W Oaze Lt By 51°29'·03N 00°55'·53E Q (9) 10s; WCM.
Cant Bn 51°27'·73N 00°55'·45E (unlit).
E Cant Lt By 51°28'·50N 00°55'·70E QR; PHM.
Mid Cant Lt Bn 51°26'·85N 00°49'·90E Q; NCM.
W Cant Lt By 51°27'·19N 00°45'·61E QR; PHM.

Medway Lt By 51°28'·80N 00°52'·92E Mo (A) 6s; SWM.

MEDWAY, SHEERNESS
Grain Edge By 51°27'·58N 00°45'·57E; SHM.
Jacobs Bank Obstn Lt By 51°26'·94N 00°45'·29E VQ; NCM.
Garrison Pt Ro Ro 51°26'·91N 00°44'·92E 2 FR (vert); Dn; *Horn (3) 30s*.
Grain Hard Lt By 51°26'·94N 00°44'·27E Fl G 5s; SHM.
Isle of Grain 51°26'·6N 00°43'·5E Q WRG 20m W13M, R7M, G8M; R & W ◊ on R Tr; vis R220°-234°, G234°-241°, W241°-013°; Ra refl.
N. Kent Lt By 51°26'·10N 00°43'·57E QG; SHM.
S. Kent Lt By 51°25'·95N 00°43'·77E Fl R 5s; PHM.
Victoria Lt By 51°25'·93N 00°42'·94E Fl (3) G 10s; SHM.
Stoke No. 13 Lt By 51°25'·73N 00°39'·91E Fl G 5s; SHM.
No. 15 Lt By 51°24'·72N 00°38'·53E Fl G 10s; SHM.

Darnett No. 23 Lt By 51°24'·57N 00°35'·72E QG; SHM.
Folly No. 25 Lt By 51°24'·07N 00°35'·33E Fl (3) G 10s; SHM.
Gillingham Reach No. 27 Lt By 51°23'·88N 00°34'·82E Fl G 10s; SHM.

RIVER THAMES

SEA REACH, NORE AND YANTLET
No. 1 Lt By 51°29'·42N 00°52'·67E Fl Y 2·5s; SPM; Racon.
No. 2 Lt By 51°29'·37N 00°49'·85E Iso 5s; SWM.
No. 3 Lt By 51°29'·30N 00°46'·63E L Fl 10s; SWM.
No. 4 Lt By 51°29'·58N 00°44'·28E Fl Y 2·5s; SPM.
No. 5 Lt By 51°29'·92N 00°41'·55E Iso 5s; SWM.
No. 6 Lt By 51°30'·00N 00°39'·95E Iso 2s; SWM.
No. 7 Lt By 51°30'·07N 00°37'·15E Fl Y 2·5s; SPM; Racon.
Nore Swatch Lt By 51°28'·26N 00°45'·65E Fl (4) R 15s; PHM.
Mid Swatch Lt By 51°28'·65N 00°44'·27E Fl G 5s; SHM.
W Nore Sand Lt By 51°29'·39N 00°40'·97E Fl (3) R 10s; PHM.
East Blyth Lt By 51°29'·68N 00°37'·90E Fl (2) R 10s; PHM.
West Lee Middle Lt By 51°30'·45N 00°38'·93E QG; SHM.
Chapman Lt By 51°30'·40N 00°37'·03E Fl (3) G 10s; SHM; Bell.
Mid Blyth Lt By 51°30'·05N 00°32'·50E Q; NCM.

LEIGH-ON-SEA/SOUTHEND-ON-SEA
South Shoebury Lt By 51°30'·40N 00°52'·50E Fl G 5s; SHM.
Shoebury Lt Bn 51°30'·28N 00°49'·38E Fl (3) G 10s 5m 5M.
Inner Shoebury Bn 51°30'·15N 00°49'·05E Fl Y 2·5s.
SE Leigh Lt By 51°29'·40N 00°47'·17E Q (6) + L Fl 15s; SCM.
West Shoebury Lt By 51°30'·20N 00°45'·83E Fl G 2·5s; SHM.
Southend Pier E End 51°30'·84N 00°43'·51E 2 FG (vert) 7m; *Horn Mo (N) 30s.*
Pier W Hd 2 FG (vert) 13m 8M.
Leigh By 51°31'·04N 00°42'·67E; SHM.

CANVEY ISLAND/HOLEHAVEN
Canvey Jetty Hd E end 51°30'·36N 00°34'·25E 2 FG (vert); *Bell (1) 10s.*
W Hd 2 FG (vert) 13m 8M.
Lts 2 FR (vert) to port, and 2 FG (vert) to stbd, are shown from wharves etc. above this Pt.
Shornmead 51°26'·97N 00°26'·63E Fl (2) WRG 10s 12m **W17M**, R13M, G13M; vis G054°-081·5°, R081·5°-086·2°, W086·2°-088·7°, G088·7°-141°, W141°-205°, R205°-213°.

GRAVESEND
Thames Navigation Service Pier 51°26'·68N 00°22'·57E FR.
Northfleet Lower 51°26'·9N 00°20'·4E Oc WR 5s 15m **W17M**, R14M; vis W164°-271°, R271°-S shore.
Northfleet Upper 51°26'·90N 00°20'·17E Oc WRG 10s 30m **W16M**, R12M, G12M; vis R126°-149°, W149°-159°, G159°-268°, W268°-279°.
Broadness 51°28'·0N 00°18'·7E Oc R 5s 12m 12M; R metal Tr.
Queen Elizabeth II Bridge NE 51°27'·95N 00°15'·72E Fl G 5s.

THAMES TIDAL BARRIER
Span E (approx centre) 51°29'·82N 00°02'·32E.

SOUTH DOCK MARINA
Greenland Pier S Hd 51°29'·64N 00°01'·80W Lt.

LIMEHOUSE BASIN MARINA/REGENT'S CANAL
Victoria Wharf W End 51°30'·52N 00°02'·14W Lt.

ST KATHARINE YACHT HAVEN
Harrison's Wharf 51°30'·33N 00°04'·23W 2 FG (vert).

CHELSEA HARBOUR MARINA
Lock SS 51°28'·45N 00°10'·73W 2 FG (vert).

THAMES ESTUARY – NORTHERN PART

KENTISH KNOCK
Kentish Knock Lt By 51°38'·50N 01°40·50E Q (3) 10s; ECM; *Whis.*
S Knock Lt By 51°34'·73N 01°36'·10E Q (6) + L Fl 15s; SCM; *Bell.*

KNOCK JOHN CHANNEL
No. 7 Lt By 51°32'·00N 01°06'·50E Fl (4) G 15s; SHM.
No. 5 Lt By 51°32'·75N 01°08'·68E Fl (3) G 10s; SHM.
No. 4 Lt By 51°32'·60N 01°08'·82E L Fl R 10s; PHM.
No. 2 Lt By 51°33'·08N 01°09'·95E Fl (3) R 10s; PHM.
No. 3 Lt By 51°33'·20N 01°09'·80E Q (6) + L Fl 15s; SCM.
No. 1 Lt By 51°33'·72N 01°10'·82E Fl G 5s; SHM.
Knock John Lt By 51°33'·46N 01°11'·08E Fl (2) R 5s; PHM.

BLACK DEEP
No. 12 Lt By 51°33'·80N 01°13'·60E Fl (4) R 15s; PHM.
No. 11 Lt By 51°34'·30N 01°13'·50E Fl (3) G 10s; SHM.
No. 10 Lt By 51°34'·70N 01°15'·70E QR; PHM.
No. 9 Lt By 51°35'·10N 01°15'·20E Q (6) + L Fl 15s; SCM.
No. 8 Lt By 51°36'·20N 01°20'·00E Q; NCM.
No. 7 Lt By 51°37'·05N 01°17'·80E QG; SHM.
No. 6 Lt By 51°38'·49N 01°24'·51E Fl R 2·5s; PHM.
No. 5 Lt By 51°39'·50N 01°23'·10E VQ (3) 5s; ECM; *Bell.*
No. 4 Lt By 51°41'·39N 01°28'·59E Fl (2) R 5s; PHM.
Long Sand Bn 51°41'·44N 01°29'·56E; SHM.
No. 3 Lt By 51°41'·95N 01°26'·07E Fl (3) G 15s; SHM.
No. 1 Lt By 51°44'·00N 01°28'·20E Fl G 5s; SHM.
Sunk Head Tr Lt By 51°46'·60N 01°30'·60E Q; NCM; *Whis.*
No. 2 Lt By 51°45'·60N 01°32'·30E Fl (4) R 15s; WCM.
Black Deep Lt By 51°46'·60N 01°34'·05E QR; PHM.
Trinity Lt By 51°49'·00N 01°36'·50E Q (6) + L Fl 15s; SCM; *Whis.*
Long Sand Hd Lt By 51°47'·87N 01°39'·53E VQ; NCM; *Bell.*

BARROW DEEP (selected Bys)
SW Barrow Lt By 51°31'·80N 01°00'·53E Q (6) + L Fl 15s; SCM; *Bell.*
Barrow No.11 Lt By 51°33'·73N 01°05'·85E Fl G 2·5s; SHM.
Barrow No. 9 Lt By 51°35'·31N 01°10'·40E VQ (3) 5s; ECM.
SW Sunk Bn 51°36'·50N 01°14'·85E; SHM.
Barrow No. 6 Lt By 51°37'·27N 01°14'·79E Fl (4) R 15s; PHM.
Barrow No. 4 Lt By 51°39'·85N 01°17'·60E VQ (9) 10s; WCM.
Barrow No. 3 Lt By 51°41'·99N 01°20'·35E Q (3) 10s; ECM; Racon (M).
Barrow No. 2 Lt By 51°41'·95N 01°23'·00E Fl (2) R 5s; PHM.
Little Sunk Bn 51°41'·89N 01°24'·85E; SHM.

WEST SWIN AND MIDDLE DEEP
Blacktail (W) Lt Bn 51°31'·43N 00°55'·30E Iso G 10s 10m 6M.
Blacktail (E) Lt Bn 51°31'·75N 00°56'·60E Iso G 5s 10m 6M.
Blacktail Spit Lt By 51°31'·45N 00°56'·85E Fl (3) G 10s; SHM.
SW Swin Lt By 51°32'·68N 01°00'·79E Fl (2) R 5s; PHM.
W Swin By 51°33'·82N 01°03'·30E; PHM.
Maplin Lt By 51°34'·00N 01°02'·40E Q (3) 10s; ECM; *Bell.*
Maplin Edge By 51°35'·30N 01°03'·75E; SHM.
Maplin Bank Lt By 51°35'·47N 01°04'·80E Fl (3) R 10s; PHM.

EAST SWIN (KING'S) CHANNEL
NE Maplin Lt By 51°37'·43N 01°04'·90E Fl G 5s; SHM; *Bell.*
W Hook Middle By 51°39'·15N 01°08'·07E; PHM.
S Whitaker Lt By 51°40'·20N 01°09'·15E Fl (2) G 10s; SHM.
N Middle By 51°41'·00N 01°12'·00E; NCM.
W Sunk Lt By 51°44'·30N 01°25'·90E Q (9) 15s; WCM.
Gunfleet Spit Lt By 51°45'·30N 01°21'·80E Q (6) + L Fl 15s; SCM; *Bell.*
Gunfleet Old Lt Ho 51°46'·08N 01°20'·52E.

WHITAKER CHANNEL AND RIVER CROUCH

Whitaker Lt By 51°41'·40N 01°10'·61E Q (3) 10s; ECM; *Bell.*
Whitaker No. 6 Lt By 51°40'·66N 01°08'·17E Q; NCM.
Swin Spitway Lt By 51°41'·92N 01°08'·45E Iso 10s; SWM; *Bell.*
Whitaker Bn 51°39'·62N 01°06'·30E; IDM.
Swallow Tail By 51°40'·44N 01°04'·81E; SHM.
Ridge Lt By 51°40'·10N 01°04'·99E Fl R 10s; PHM.
S Buxey Lt By 51°39'·82N 01°02'·60E Fl (3) G 15s; SHM.
Sunken Buxey Lt By 51°39'·50N 01°00'·60E Q; NCM.
Buxey No. 1 Lt By 51°39'·02N 01°00'·86E VQ (6) + L Fl 10s; SCM.
Buxey No. 2 Lt By 51°38'·94N 01°00'·26E Q; NCM.
Outer Crouch Lt By 51°38'·35N 00°58'·61E Q (6) + L Fl 15s; SCM.
Crouch Lt By 51°37'·60N 00°56'·49E Fl R 10s; PHM.
Inner Crouch Lt By 51°37'·19N 00°55'·22E L Fl 10s; SWM.
Horse Shoal Lt By 51°37'·08N 00°51'·62E Q; NCM.

RIVER ROACH/HAVENGORE

Branklet By 51°36'·95N 00°52'·24E; SPM.

BURNHAM-ON-CROUCH

Fairway No. 1 Lt By 51°37'·07N 00°51'·10E QG; SHM.
Fairway No. 5 Lt By 51°37'·20N 00°49'·67E QG; SHM.
Fairway No. 9 Lt By 51°37'·32N 00°48'·87E QG; SHM.
Fairway No. 11 Lt By 51°37'·43N 00°48'·40E QG; SHM.
Burnham Yacht Hbr Lt By 51°37'·48N 00°48'·31E Fl Y 5s; SPM.

RAY SAND CHANNEL

Buxey Bn 51°41'·13N 01°01'·38E (unlit); NCM.

GOLDMER GAT/WALLET

NE Gunfleet Lt By 51°49'·90N 01°27'·90E Q (3) 10s; ECM.
Wallet No. 2 Lt By 51°48'·85N 01°23'·10E Fl R 5s; PHM.
Wallet No. 4 Lt By 51°46'·50N 01°17'·33E Fl (4) R 10s; PHM.
Walton Pier Hd 51°50'·58N 01°16'·90E 2 FG (vert) 5m 2M.
Wallet Spitway Lt By 51°42'·83N 01°07'·42E L Fl 10s; SWM; *Bell.*
Knoll Lt By 51°43'·85N 01°05'·17E Q; NCM.
Eagle Lt By 51°44'·10N 01°03'·92E QG; SHM.
NW Knoll Lt By 51°44'·32N 01°02'·27E Fl (2) R 5s; PHM.
Colne Bar Lt By 51°44'·58N 01°02'·67E Fl (2) G 5s; SHM.
Bench Head By 51°44'·66N 01°01'·20E; SHM.

RIVER BLACKWATER

The Nass Lt Bn 51°45'·75N 00°54'·88E VQ (3) 5s 6m 2M; ECM.
Thirslet Lt By 51°43'·71N 00°50'·49E Fl (3) G 10s; SHM.
No. 1 By 51°43'·41N 00°48'·13E; SHM.
No. 2 Lt By 51°42'·78N 00°46'·58E Fl R 3s; PHM.
Osea I Pier Hd 51°43'·05N 00°46'·59E 2 FG (vert).
No. 3 By 51°42'·88N 00°46'·16E; SHM.
N Double No. 7 Lt By 51°43'·22N 00°44'·87E Fl G 3s; SHM.
No. 8 By 51°43'·91N 00°43'·35E; PHM.

RIVER COLNE/BRIGHTLINGSEA

Inner Bench Hd No. 2 Lt By 51°45'·93N 01°01'·86E Fl (2) R 5s; PHM.
No. 9 Lt By 51°47'·33N 01°01'·17E Fl G 3s; SHM.
No. 13 Lt By 51°47'·72N 01°00'·91E Fl G; SHM.
Brightlingsea Spit Lt By 51°48'·05N 01°00'·80E Q (6) + L Fl 15s; SCM.
Brightlingsea Lt By 51°48'·19N 01°01'·18E Fl (3) G 5s; SHM.
Ldg Lts 041°. Front, 51°48'·4N 01°01'·3E FR 7m 4M; W □, R stripe on post; vis 020°-080°. Rear, 50m from front, FR 10m 4M; W ■, R stripe on post. FR Lts are shown on 7 masts between 1·5M and 3M NW when firing occurs.
Hardway Hd 51°48'·2N 01°01'·5E 2 FR (vert) 2m.
Batemans Tr 51°48'·3N 01°00'·8E FY 12m.
Fingringhoe Wick Pier Hd 2 FR (vert) 6m (occas).
No. 23 51°50'·60N 00°59'·00E Fl G 5s 5m.
Rowhedge Wharf FY 11m.

CLACTON-ON-SEA

Berthing arm 51°47'·00N 01°09'·60E 2 FG (vert) 5m 4M; *Reed (2) 120s* (occas).

WALTON BACKWATERS

Naze Tr 51°51'·85N 01°17'·40E.
Pye End Lt By 51°55'·00N 01°18'·00E L Fl 10s; SWM.
No. 2 By 51°54'·54N 01°16'·90E; PHM; Ra refl.
No. 3 Crab Knoll By 51°54'·36N 01°16'·49E; SHM; Ra refl.
No. 4 High Hill By 51°54'·02N 01°16'·07E Fl R 10s; PHM.
No. 5 By 51°54'·25N 01°16'·33E; SHM.
No. 6 By 51°53'·76N 01°15'·80E; PHM.
No. 7 By 51°53'·78N 01°15'·65E; SHM.
No. 8 By 51°53'·39N 01°15'·53E; PHM.
Island Pt By 51°53'·27N 01°15'·44E; NCM.
No. 10 Mussel Bk By 51°53'·31N 01°15'·49E; PHM.
No. 12 By 51°53'·26N 01°15'·51E; PHM.
No. 14 Frank Bloom By 51°53'·21N 01°15'·61E; PHM.
East Coast Sails By 51°53'·14N 01°15'·66E; SHM.
Plumtrees Stone Pt By 51°53'·01N 01°15'·73E; PHM.

HARWICH APPROACHES
(Direction of buoyage North to South)

MEDUSA CHANNEL
Medusa Lt By 51°51'·20N 01°20'·46E Fl G 5s; SHM.
Stone Banks By 51°53'·16N 01°19'·33E; PHM.

CORK SAND /ROUGH SHOALS
S Cork By 51°51'·30N 01°24'·20E; SCM.
Roughs Tr SE Lt By 51°53'·61N 01°29'·05E Q (3) 10s; ECM.
Roughs Tr NW Lt By 51°53'·78N 01°28'·88E Q (9) 15s; WCM.
Rough Lt By 51°55'·16N 01°31'·11E VQ; NCM.
Cork Sand Lt Bn 51°55'·19N 01°25'·31E Q; NCM.

HARWICH CHANNEL
SUNK Lt F 51°51'·00N 01°35'·00E Fl (2) 20s 12m **24M**; R hull with Lt Tr; Racon (T); *Horn (2) 60s*.
S Threshold Lt By 51°52'·44N 01°33'·29E Q (6) + L Fl 15s.
S Shipwash Lt By 51°52'·68N 01°34'·16E Q (6) + L Fl 15s; SCM.
E Fort Massac Lt By 51°53'·33N 01°32'·90E VQ (3) 5s; ECM.
Shiphead Lt By 51°53'·76N 01°34'·01E Fl R 5s; PHM.
N Threshold Lt By 51°54'·46N 01°33'·58E Fl Y 5s; SPM.
SW Shipwash Lt By 51°54'·72N 01°34'·32E Q (9) 15s; WCM.
Haven Lt By 51°55'·73N 01°32'·67E Mo (A) 5s; SWM.
Shipway Lt By 51°56'·73N 01°30'·77E Iso 5s; SWM; *Whis.*
Cross Lt By 51°56'·20N 01°30'·59E Fl (3) Y 10s; SPM.
Harwich Chan No. 1 Lt By 51°56'·11N 01°27'·30E Fl Y 2·5s; SPM; Racon (T).
Washington Lt By 51°56'·49N 01°26'·70E QG; SHM.
Felixstowe Ledge Lt By 51°56'·30N 01°24'·53E Fl (3) G 10s; SHM.
Wadgate Ledge Lt By 51°56'·08N 01°22'·20E Fl (4) G 15s; SHM.
Platters Lt By 51°55'·61N 01°21'·07E; Q (6) + L Fl 15s; SCM.
Rolling Ground Lt By 51°55'·52N 01°19'·86E QG; SHM.
Beach End Lt By 51°55'·59N 01°19'·31E Fl (2) G 5s; SHM.
NW Beach Lt By 51°55'·87N 01°18'·98E Fl (3) G 10s; SHM; *Bell.*
Fort Lt By 51°56'·18N 01°18'·98E Fl (4) G 15s; SHM.

EDGE OF RECOMMENDED YACHT TRACK
Cork Sand Lt By 51°55'·43N 01°25'·95E Fl (3) R 10s; PHM.
Pitching Ground Lt By 51°55'·39N 01°21'·16E Fl (4) R 15s; PHM.
Inner Ridge Lt By 51°55'·31N 01°19'·68E QR; PHM.
Landguard Lt By 51°55'·35N 01°18'·98E Q; NCM.
Cliff Foot Lt By 51°55'·69N 01°18'·64E Fl R 5s; PHM.
S Shelf Lt By 51°56'·17N 01°18'·67E Fl (2) R 5s; PHM.
N Shelf Lt By 51°56'·65N 01°18'·70E QR; PHM.
Grisle Lt By 51°56'·86N 01°18'·43E Fl R 2·5s; PHM.
Guard Lt By 51°57'·03N 01°17'·88E Fl R 5s; PHM; *Bell.*

4

RIVER STOUR/HARWICH
Wharves, Jetties and Piers show 2 FR (vert).
Shotley Spit Lt By 51°57'·26N 01°17'·67E Q (6) + L Fl 15s; SCM.
Shotley Marina Lock E side Dir Lt 339·5° 51°57'·43N 01°16'·71E 3m 1M (uses Moiré pattern); Or structure.
Shotley Marina Ent E side 51°57'·23N 01°16'·84E Fl (4) G 15s; G △ on pile.
Shotley Marina 51°57'·24N 01°16'·82E VQ (3) 5s; ECM.
Shotley Ganges Pier E Hd 51°57'·18N 01°16'·34E 2 FG (vert) 4m 1M; G post.
Parkeston Lt By 51°57'·06N 01°15'·44E Fl (3) G 10s; SHM.
Erwarton Ness Lt Bn 51°57'·10N 01°13'·35E Q (6) + L Fl 15s 4M; SCM Bn.
Holbrook Lt Bn 51°57'·19N 01°10'·46E VQ (6) + L Fl 10s 4M; SCM Bn.
Mistley, Baltic Wharf 51°56'·69N 01°05'·31E 2 FR (vert).

ORWELL/IPSWICH
College Lt By 51°57'·52N 01°17'·44E Fl (2) R 10s; PHM.
Pepys Lt By 51°57'·71N 01°17'·00E Fl (4) R 15s; PHM.
Fagbury Lt By 51°57'·94N 01°16'·91E Fl G 2·5s; SHM.
Orwell Lt By 51°58'·14N 01°16'·65E Fl R 2·5s; PHM.
No. 1 Lt By 51°58'·26N 01°16'·78E Fl G 5s; SHM.
Suffolk Yacht Harbour. Ldg Lts 51°59'·77N 01°16'·22E. Front Iso Y 1M, Rear Oc Y 4s 1M.
Woolverstone Marina 52°00'·4N 01°11'·8E 2 FR (vert).
Orwell Bridge FY 39m 3M at centre; 2 FR (vert) on Pier 9 and 2 FG (vert) on Pier 10.
No. 12 Lt By (off Fox's Marina) 52°02'·08N 01°09'·45E Fl R 12s; PHM.
Ipswich Lock SS (Tfc) 52°02'·77N 01°09'·85E.

HARWICH TO ORFORDNESS

FELIXSTOWE/RIVER DEBEN/WOODBRIDGE HAVEN
Felixstowe Town Pier Hd 51°57'·37N 01°21'·02E 2 FG (vert) 7m.
Woodbridge Haven By 51°58'·15N 01°23'·90E; SWM.
Ldg Lts Fl or Fl Y moved as required (on request). Front W △ on R l. Rear; R line on l.
Felixtowe Ferry, E side 51°59'·40N 01°23'·72E 2 FG (vert). W side 2 FR (vert).

RIVER ORE/RIVER ALDE
Orford Haven By 52°01'·63N 01°27'·67E; SWM.

OFFSHORE MARKS
S Galloper Lt By 51°43'·95N 01°56'·50E Q (6) L Fl 15s; SCM; Racon (T); *Whis.*
N Galloper Lt By 51°50'·00N 01°59'·50E Q; NCM.
S Inner Gabbard Lt By 51°51'·20N 01°52'·40E Q (6) + L Fl 15s; SCM.
N Inner Gabbard Lt By 51°59'·10N 01°56'·10E Q; NCM.
Outer Gabbard Lt By 51°57'·80N 02°04'·30E Fl (3) 10s; ECM; Racon (O); *Whis.*
NHR-SE Lt By 51°45'·50N 02°40'·00E Fl G 5s; SHM; Racon (N).
NHR-S Lt By 51°51'·40N 02°28'·79E Fl Y 10s; SPM; *Bell.*

SHIPWASH/BAWDSEY BANK
E Shipwash Lt By 51°57'·05N 01°38'·00E VQ (3) 5s; ECM.
NW Shipwash Lt By 51°58'·33N 01°36'·33E Fl R 5s; PHM.
N Shipwash Lt By 52°01'·70N 01°38'·38E Q 7M; NCM; Racon (M); *Bell.*
S Bawdsey Lt By 51°57'·20N 01°30'·32E Q (6) + L Fl 15s; SCM; *Whis.*
Mid Bawdsey Lt By 51°58'·85N 01°33'·70E Fl (3) G 10s; SHM.
NE Bawdsey Lt By 52°01'·70N 01°36'·20E Fl G 10s; SHM.

CUTLER/WHITING BANKS
Cutler By 51°58'·50N 01°27'·60E; SHM.
SW Whiting By 52°01'·10N 01°30'·90E; SCM.
Whiting Hook By 52°02'·95N 01°31'·93E; PHM.
NE Whiting By 52°03'·77N 01°33'·88E; ECM.

Orford Ness 52°05'·00N 01°34'·60E Fl 5s 28m **25M**; W ● Tr, R bands. F RG 14m R14M, **G15M** (same Tr); vis R shore-210°, R038°-047°, G047°-shore; Racon (T).

ORFORDNESS TO GREAT YARMOUTH
(Direction of buoyage South to North)
Aldeburgh Ridge By 52°06'·82N 01°37'·60E; PHM.
Sizewell Power station, Pipeline Hds 52°12'·70N 01°37'·90E 2 FR (vert) 12/10m.
Sizewell Cooling Water intake and outfall 52°12'·90N 01°38'·15E each Fl R 5s.

SOUTHWOLD
Southwold Lt Ho 52°19'·60N 01°41'·00E Fl (4) WR 20s 37m **W17M**, **R15M**, R14M; W ● Tr; vis R (intens) 204°-220°, W220°-001°, R001°-032·3°.
N Pier Hd 52°18'·77N 01°40'·63E Fl G 1·5s 4m 4M.
S Pier Hd QR 4m 2M.

LOWESTOFT AND APPROACHES VIA STANFORD CHANNEL
E Barnard Lt By 52°25'·11N 01°46'·50E Q (3) 10s; ECM.
Newcome Sand Lt By 52°26'·40N 01°47'·15E QR; PHM.
S Holm Lt By 52°27'·33N 01°47'·32E VQ (6) + L Fl 10s; SCM.
Stanford Lt By 52°27'·33N 01°46'·78E Fl R 2·5s; PHM.
N Newcome Lt By 52°28'·29N 01°46'·43E Fl (4) R 15s; PHM.
SW Holm Lt By 52°28'·36N 01°47'·28E Fl (2) G 5s; SHM.
Lowestoft 52°29'·18N 01°45'·46E Fl 15s 37m **23M**; W Tr; part obscd 347°-shore.
Outer Hbr S Pier Hd Oc R 5s 12m 6M; *Horn (4) 60s;* Tfc sigs.
N Pier Hd 52°28'·29N 01°45'·50E Oc G 5s 12m 8M.
Claremont Pier 52°27'·86N 01°44'·98E 2 FR (vert) 5/4m 4M.

LOWESTOFT NORTH AND CORTON ROADS
Lowestoft Ness SE Lt By 52°28'·82N 01°46'·38E Q (6) + L Fl 15s; SCM; *Bell.*
Lowestoft Ness N Lt By 52°28'·87N 01°46'·35E VQ (3) 5s; ECM; *Bell.*
W Holm Lt By 52°29'·80N 01°47'·20E Fl (3) G 10s; SHM.
NW Holm Lt By 52°31'·90N 01°46'·80E Fl (4) G 15s; SHM.

GREAT YARMOUTH/GORLESTON APPROACHES VIA HOLM CHANNEL
E Newcome Lt By 52°28'·48N 01°49'·32E Fl (2) R 5s; PHM.
Corton Lt By 52°31'·10N 01°51'·50E Q (3) 10s; ECM; *Whis.*
E. Holm Lt By 52°31'·06N 01°49'·42E Fl (3) R 10s; PHM.
S Corton Lt By 52°32'·15N 01°50'·12E Q (6) + L Fl 15s; SCM.
NE Holm Lt By 52°32'·27N 01°48'·31E Fl R 2·5s; PHM.
Holm Lt By 52°33'·50N 01°48'·08E Fl G 2·5s; SHM.
Holm Sand Lt By 52°33'·44N 01°47'·02E Q; NCM.
W Corton Lt By 52°34'·46N 01°46'·42E Q (9) 15s; WCM.

GREAT YARMOUTH/GORLESTON
Gorleston S Pier Hd Fl R 3s 11m 11M; vis 235°-340°; *Horn (3) 60s.*
Ldg Lts 264°. Front, 52°34'·30N 01°44'·07E Oc 3s 6m 10M.
Rear, Brush Oc 6s 7m 10M, also FR 20m 6M; R ● Tr.
N Pier Hd 52°34'·36N 01°44'·49E QG 8m 6M; vis 176°-078°.
Haven Bridge 52°36'·38N 01°43'·47E marked by pairs of 2 FR (vert) and 2 FG (vert) showing up and down stream.

10.4. 5 PASSAGE INFORMATION

Reference books include: *East Coast Rivers* (YM/Coote) from the Swale to Southwold. The Admiralty *Dover Strait Pilot* also goes to Southwold. *North Sea Passage Pilot* (Imray/Navin) and *The East Coast* (Imray/Bowskill) cover the whole Area.

THE THAMES ESTUARY (chart *1183, 1975*)

To appreciate the geography of the Thames Estuary there is a well-known analogy between its major sandbanks and the fingers and thumb of the left hand, outstretched palm-down: With the thumb lying E over Margate Sand, the index finger covers Long Sand; the middle finger represents Sunk Sand and the third finger delineates West and East Barrow; the little finger points NE along Buxey and Gunfleet Sands.

The intervening channels are often intricate, but the main ones, in sequence from south to north, are:
a. between the Kent coast and thumb – Four Fathoms, Horse, Gore and South Chans; sometimes known as the overland route due to relatively shallow water.
b. between thumb and index finger – Queens and Princes Chans leading seaward to Knock Deep.
c. between index and middle fingers – Knob Chan leading to Knock Deep via the Edinburgh Chans across Long Sand and the Shingles. Knock John Chan and Black Deep, the main shipping channels.
d. between middle and third fingers – Barrow Deep.
e. between third and little fingers – W and E Swin, Middle Deep and Whitaker Chan leading seaward to King's Chan.
f. between little finger and the Essex coast – The Wallet and Goldmer Gat.

The sandbanks shift constantly in the Thames Estuary. Up-to-date charts showing the latest buoyage changes are essential, but it is unwise to put too much faith in charted depths over the banks; a reliable echosounder is vital. The main chans carry much commercial shipping and are well buoyed and lit, but this is not so in lesser chans and swatchways which are convenient for yachtsmen, particularly when crossing the estuary from N to S, or vice versa. Unlit, unmarked minor chans (eg Fisherman's Gat or S Edinburgh Chan; in the latter there is a Historic Wreck (see 10.0.3h) at 51°31'·7N 01°14'·9E) should be used with great caution, which could indeed be the hallmark of all passage-making in the Thames Estuary. Good vis is needed to pick out buoys/marks, and to avoid shipping.

CROSSING THE THAMES ESTUARY (See 10.4.9)

Study the tides carefully and understand them, so as to work the streams to best advantage and to ensure sufficient depth at the times and places where you expect to be, or might be later (see 10.4.3 and 10.4.8). In principle it is best to make most of the crossing on a rising tide, ie departing N Foreland or the vicinity of the Whitaker buoy at around LW. The stream runs 3kn at sp in places, mostly along the chans but sometimes across the intervening banks. With wind against tide a short, steep sea is raised, particularly in E or NE winds.

Making N from N Foreland to Orford Ness or beyond (or vice versa) it may be preferable to keep to seaward of the main banks, via Kentish Knock and Long Sand Head buoys, thence to N Shipwash lt buoy 14M further N.

Bound NW from N Foreland it is approximately 26M to the Rivers Crouch, Blackwater or Colne. A safe route is through either the Princes or the North Edinburgh Channels, thence S of the Tizard, Knob and West Barrow banks to the West Swin, before turning NE into Middle Deep and the East Swin. This is just one of many routes which could be followed, depending on wind direction, tidal conditions and confidence in electronic aids in the absence of marks.

A similar, well-used route in reverse, ie to the SE, lies via the Wallet Spitway, to the Whitaker lt buoy, through Barrow Swatchway to SW Sunk bn; thence via the N Edinburgh Chan, toward the E Margate lt buoy keeping E of Tongue Sand tr. Beware shoal waters off Barrow and Sunk Sands.

Port Control London can give navigational help to yachts on VHF Ch 13; Thames CG at Walton-on-the-Naze can also assist. The Thames Navigation Service has radar coverage between the Naze and Margate, eastward to near the Dutch coast.

NORTH FORELAND TO LONDON BRIDGE

N Foreland has a conspic lt ho, RC (chart *1828*), with buoys offshore. From HW Dover – 0120 to + 0045 the stream runs N from The Downs and W into Thames Estuary. From HWD + 0045 to + 0440 the N-going stream from The Downs meets the E-going stream from Thames Estuary, which in strong winds causes a bad sea. From HWD – 0450 to – 0120 the streams turn W into Thames Estuary and S towards The Downs. If bound for London, round N Foreland against the late ebb in order to carry a fair tide from Sheerness onward.

For vessels drawing less than 2m the most direct route from North Foreland to the Thames and Medway is via South Chan, Gore Chan, Horse Chan, Kentish Flats, Four Fathom Chan and Cant; but it is not well marked particularly over the Kentish Flats. An alternative, deeper route is East of Margate Sand and the Tongue, to set course through Princes Channel to Oaze Deep; larger vessels proceed via the North Edinburgh Channel. W-going streams begin at approx HW Sheerness – 0600 and E-going at HW Sheerness + 0030.

Margate or Whitstable (10.4.10) afford little shelter for yachts. The Swale (10.4.11) provides an interesting inside route S of the Isle of Sheppey with access to Sheerness and the R Medway (10.4.12). If sailing from N Foreland to the Thames, Queenborough (10.4.13) offers the first easily accessible, all-tide, deep-water shelter. The Medway Chan is the main appr to Sheerness from the Warp and the Medway Fairway buoy.

Close N is Sea Reach No 1 buoy and the start of Yanlet Chan and the Thames river which is buoyed up to Gravesend. See 10.4.13 for the Thames Barrier and 10.4.14 for yacht facilities in London and some PLA regulations on this busy river. Yachts should beware the large amount of floating debris, general turbulence and absence of bolt-holes other than listed marinas. Off Shoeburyness, Leigh Channel diverges to Southend, Leigh-on-sea (10.4.15) and Canvey Island/Benfleet.

SHOEBURYNESS TO RIVER COLNE (charts *1185, 1975*)

Maplin and Foulness Sands extend nearly 6M NE from Foulness Pt, the extremity being marked by Whitaker bn. On N side of Whitaker chan leading to R. Crouch (10.4.17) and R. Roach (10.4.16) lies Buxey Sand, inshore of which is the Ray Sand chan (dries), a convenient short cut between R. Crouch and R. Blackwater with sufficient rise of tide.

To seaward of Buxey Sand and the Spitway, Gunfleet Sand extends 10M NE, marked by buoys and drying in places. A conspic disused lt tr stands on SE side of Gunfleet Sand, about 6M SSE of the Naze tr, and here the SW-going (flood) stream begins about HW Sheerness + 0600, and the NE-going stream at about HW Sheerness – 0030, sp rates 2kn.

The Rivers Blackwater (10.4.18) and Colne (10.4.19) share a common estuary which is approached from the NE via NE Gunfleet lt buoy; thence along Goldmer Gat and the Wallet towards Knoll and Eagle lt buoys. For the Colne turn NNW via Colne Bar buoy towards Inner Bench Hd buoy keeping in mid-chan. For R. Blackwater, head WNW for NW Knoll and Bench Hd buoys. From the S or SE, make for the Whitaker ECM buoy, thence through the Spitway, via Swin Spitway and Wallet Spitway buoys to reach Knoll buoy and deeper water.

RIVER COLNE TO HARWICH (chart *1975*, 1593)

4M SW of the Naze tr at Hollands Haven a conspic radar tr (67m, unlit) is an excellent daymark. From the S, approach Walton and Harwich via the Medusa chan about 1M E of Naze tr. At N end of this chan, 1M off Dovercourt, Pye End buoy marks chan SSW to Walton Backwaters (10.4.20). Harwich and Landguard Point are close to the N. Making Harwich from the SE beware the drying Cork Sand, which lies N/S.

Sunk It Float (Fog sig, RC), 11M E of The Naze, marks the outer apprs to Harwich (10.4.21), an extensive and well sheltered hbr accessible at all times (chart *2693*). The Harwich DW channel begins 1·5M NNW of Sunk It Float and runs N between Rough and Shipwash shoals, then W past the Cork Sand PHM It buoy. It is in constant use by commercial shipping, so yachts should approach via the Recommended Track for yachts. Approaching from NE and 2M off the ent to R. Deben (10.4.23), beware Cutler shoal, with least depth of 1·2m, marked by SHM buoy on E side; Wadgate Ledge and the Platters are about 1·5M ENE of Landguard Point. S of Landguard Point the W-going (flood) stream begins at HW Harwich + 0600, and the E-going stream at HW Harwich, sp rates about 1·5kn. Note: HW Harwich is never more than 7 mins after HW Walton; LW times are about 10 mins earlier.

HARWICH TO ORFORD NESS (chart *2052*)

Shipwash shoal, buoyed and with least depth 0·5m near its S end, runs NNE from 9M E of Felixstowe to 4M SSE of Orford Ness. Inshore of this is Shipway Chan, then Bawdsey Bank, buoyed with depths of 2m, on which the sea breaks in E'ly swell. The Sledway Chan lies between Bawdsey Bank and Whiting Bank (buoyed) which is close SW of Orford Ness, and has least depth of 1m. Hollesley Chan, about 1M wide, runs inshore W and N of this bank. In the SW part of Hollesley B is the ent to Orford Haven and the R Ore/Alde (10.4.24).

There are overfalls S of Orford Ness on both the ebb and flood streams. 2M E of Orford Ness the SW-going stream begins at HW Harwich + 0605, sp rate 2·5kn; the NE-going stream begins at HW Harwich – 0010, sp rate 3kn.

Note: The direction of local buoyage becomes S to N off Orford Ness (52°05'N).

ORFORDNESS TO GREAT YARMOUTH (chart 1543)

N of Orford Ness seas break on Aldeburgh Ridge (1.3m), but the coast is clear of offlying dangers past Aldeburgh and Southwold (10.4.25), as far as Benacre Ness, 5M S of Lowestoft. Sizewell power stn is a conspic □ bldg 1·5M N of Thorpe Ness. Keep 1·5M offshore to avoid fishing floats.

Lowestoft (10.4.26) is approached from S by the buoyed/lit Stanford chan to E of Newcome Sand and SW of Holm Sand; beware possible strong set across hbr ent. From the N, approach through Yarmouth Road and then proceed S through Gorleston, Corton and Lowestoft North Roads (buoyed). From E, approach through the Holm chan. 1M E of hbr ent, the S-going stream begins at HW Dover –0600, and the N-going at HW Dover, sp rates 2·6kn.

In the approaches to Great Yarmouth (10.4.27) from seaward the banks are continually changing; use the buoyed chans. The sea often breaks on North Scroby, Middle Scroby and Caister Shoal (all of which dry), and there are heavy tide rips over parts of Corton and South Scroby Sands, Middle and South Cross Sands, and Winterton Overfalls.

1M NE of ent to Gt Yarmouth the S-going stream begins at HW Dover –0600, and the N-going at HW Dover – 0015, sp rates 2·3kn. Breydon Water (tidal) affects streams in the Haven; after heavy rain the out-going stream at Brush Quay may exceed 5kn. For Norfolk Broads, see 10.4.27. About 12M NE of Great Yarmouth lie Newarp Banks, on which the sea breaks in bad weather.

CROSSING FROM THAMES ESTUARY TO BELGIUM OR THE NETHERLANDS (charts 1610, 1872, 3371, *1406*, 1408)

Important factors in choosing a route include the need to head at 90° across the various TSSs; to avoid areas where traffic converges; to make full use of available ITZs and to keep well clear of offshore oil/gas activities (see 10.5.5). It is best to avoid the areas westward of W Hinder It, around Nord Hinder It buoy and the Maas routes W of the Hook of Holland. For Distances across N Sea, see 10.0.7 and for further notes on North Sea crossings, see 10.20.5.

Fig. 10 (5) illustrates the strategy of crossing the N Hinder South TSS and then either crossing the W Hinder TSS eastward of W Hinder It before proceeding to Belgian ports; or proceeding on a more direct route for ports between Zeebrugge and Hook of Holland.

From Rivers Crouch, Blackwater, Colne or from Harwich take departure from Long Sand Hd It buoy to S Galloper It buoy, thence to W Hinder It (see 10.20.5), crossing the TSS at right angles near Garden City It buoy; see Fig. 10 (5). Care must be taken throughout with tidal streams, which may be setting across the yacht's track. The area is relatively shallow, and in bad weather seas are steep and short.

For ports between Hook of Holland and Texel it may be best to diverge to the NE so as to cross the several Deep Water (DW) routes, and their extensions, as quickly as possible, to the N of Nord Hinder It buoy and the Maas TSS. If bound for ports NE of Texel keep well S of the TX1 It buoy and then inshore of the Off Texel-Vlieland-Terschelling-German Bight TSS, Fig. 10 (6), which is well buoyed on its S side.

10.4.6   DISTANCE TABLE

Approximate distances in nautical miles are by the most direct route, whilst avoiding dangers and allowing for Traffic Separation Schemes. Places in *italics* are in adjoining areas; places in **bold** are in 10.0.7, Distances across the North Sea.

1. *Ramsgate*	1																			
2. Whitstable	22	2																		
3. **Sheerness**	34	14	3																	
4. Gravesend	56	36	22	4																
5. **London Bridge**	76	55	45	23	5															
6. Southend-on-Sea	35	17	6	20	43	6														
7. Havengore	33	15	12	32	55	12	7													
8. **Burnham-on-Crouch**	44	36	34	53	76	33	30	8												
9. West Mersea	43	38	29	49	72	30	29	22	9											
10. **Brightlingsea**	41	36	28	47	71	28	26	22	8	10										
11. Walton-on-the-Naze	40	40	46	59	82	39	37	25	23	23	11									
12. **Harwich**	40	40	50	65	83	40	41	31	24	24	6	12								
13. Ipswich	49	49	59	74	92	49	50	40	33	33	15	9	13							
14. River Deben (ent)	45	45	55	71	89	46	46	35	38	38	10	6	15	14						
15. River Ore (ent)	47	47	60	75	93	50	51	38	43	43	14	10	19	4	15					
16. Southwold	62	67	80	95	113	70	71	58	63	63	33	30	39	23	20	16				
17. **Lowestoft**	72	77	90	105	123	80	81	68	73	73	43	40	49	33	30	10	17			
18. Great Yarmouth	79	84	97	112	130	87	88	76	81	80	51	52	61	41	38	18	7	18		
19. *Blakeney*	123	128	141	156	174	131	132	120	125	124	95	96	105	85	82	62	51	44	19	
20. *Bridlington*	207	198	224	226	244	201	215	204	205	204	181	175	184	169	165	145	135	114	79	20

EAST ANGLIAN WAYPOINTS   10-4-7

Selected waypoints and major lights for use between the Thames Estuary and the Wash are listed below. Further waypoints in adjacent waters are given in 10.3.4, 10.3.8 and 10.4.4 for the English Coast, and 10.19.4, 10.20.4 and 10.21.4 for the coasts NE France, Belgium, the Netherlands and Germany. Positions are referenced to the OSGB 36 datum.

Aldeburgh Ridge By	52°06'·82N 01°37'·60E
Barnard E Lt By	52°25'·11N 01°46'·50E
Barrow No.3 Lt By	51°41'·99N 01°20'·35E
Barrow No.6 Lt By	51°37'·27N 01°14'·79E
Barrow No.9 Lt By	51°35'·31N 01°10'·40E
Barrow No.11 Lt By	51°33'·73N 01°05'·85E
Barrow SW Lt By	51°31'·80N 01°00'·53E
Bawdsey NE Lt By	52°01'·70N 01°36'·20E
Bawdsey S Lt By	51°57'·20N 01°30'·32E
Bawdsey Mid Lt By	51°58'·85N 01°33'·70E
Bench Head Lt By	51°44'·66N 01°01'·20E
Black Deep Lt By	51°46'·60N 01°34'·05E
Black Deep No. 1 Lt By	51°44'·00N 01°28'·20E
Black Deep No. 3 Lt By	51°41'·95N 01°26'·07E
Black Deep No. 5 Lt By	51°39'·50N 01°23'·10E
Black Deep No. 7 Lt By	51°37'·05N 01°17'·80E
Black Deep No. 11 Lt By	51°34'·30N 01°13'·50E
Blacktail E Lt Bn	51°31'·75N 00°56'·60E
Blacktail W Lt Bn	51°31'·43N 00°55'·30E
Blacktail Spit Lt By	51°31'·45N 00°56'·85E
Blakeney Overfalls Lt By	53°03'·00N 01°01'·50E
Blyth E Lt By	51°29'·68N 00°37'·90E
Blyth Mid Lt By	51°30'·05N 00°32'·50E
Boston No. 1 Lt By	52°57'·87N 00°15'·22E
Boston Roads Lt By	52°57'·67N 00°16'·23E
Burnham Flats Lt By	53°07'·50N 00°35'·00E
Buxey Bn	51°41'·13N 01°01'·38E
Buxey No. 1 Lt By	51°39'·02N 01°00'·86E
Buxey No. 2 Lt By	51°38'·94N 01°00'·26E
Buxey S Lt By	51°39'·82N 01°02'·60E
Caister Mid Lt By	52°38'·96N 01°45'·77E
Cant Bn	51°27'·73N 00°55'·45E
Cant E Lt By	51°28'·50N 00°55'·70E
Cant Mid Lt Bn	51°26'·85N 00°49'·90E
Chapman Lt By	51°30'·40N 00°37'·03E
Cliff Foot Lt By	51°55'·69N 01°18'·64E
Cockle Lt By	52°44'·00N 01°43'·70E
Colne Bar Lt By	51°44'·58N 01°02'·67E
Columbine By	51°24'·23N 01°01'·45E
Columbine Spit By	51°23'·83N 01°00'·13E
Cork S By	51°51'·30N 01°24'·20E
Cork Sand Lt Bn	51°55'·19N 01°25'·31E
Cork Sand Lt By	51°55'·43N 01°25'·95E
Corton Lt By	52°31'·10N 01°51'·50E
Corton S Lt By	52°32'·15N 01°50'·12E
Corton W Lt By	52°34'·46N 01°46'·42E
Cromer Lt	52°55'·45N 01°19'·10E
Cross Sand Lt By	52°37'·00N 01°59'·25E
Cross Sand NE Lt By	52°43'·00N 01°53'·80E
Cross Sand E Lt By	52°40'·00N 01°53'·80E
Crouch Lt By	51°37'·60N 00°56'·49E
Crouch Fairway No. 1 Lt By	51°37'·08N 00°51'·11E
Crouch Inner Lt By	51°37'·19N 00°55'·22E
CS 5 Lt By	51°23'·00N 01°50'·00E
Cutler Lt By	51°58'·50N 01°27'·60E

Docking N Lt By	53°14'·80N 00°41'·60E
Docking E Lt By	53°09'·80N 00°50'·50E
Drill Stone Lt By	51°25'·80N 01°43'·00E
Eagle Lt By	51°44'·10N 01°03'·92E
East Last Lt By	51°24'·00N 01°12'·28E
Edinburgh Lt By	51°31'·42N 01°21'·53E
Elbow Lt By	51°23'·20N 01°31'·70E
F3 Lt Float	51°23'·82N 02°00'·62E
Falls Hd Lt By	51°28'·20N 01°50'·00E
Faversham Spit By	51°20'·74N 00°54'·31E
Felixstowe Ledge Lt By	51°56'·30N 01°24'·53E
Foulness Lt By	51°39'·82N 01°03'·92E
Gabbard N Inner Lt By	51°59'·10N 01°56'·10E
Gabbard S Inner Lt By	51°51'·20N 01°52'·40E
Galloper N Lt By	51°50'·00N 01°59'·50E
Galloper S Lt By	51°43'·95N 01°56'·50E
Girdler Lt By	51°29'·15N 01°06'·50E
Girdler SE Lt By	51°29'·47N 01°10'·00E
Girdler W Lt By	51°29'·58N 01°06'·82E
Grain Hard Lt By	51°26'·94N 00°44'·27E
Guard Lt By	51°57'·03N 01°17'·88E
Gunfleet NE Lt By	51°49'·90N 01°27'·90E
Gunfleet Old Lt Ho	51°46'·08N 01°20'·52E
Gunfleet Spit Lt By	51°45'·30N 01°21'·80E
Haisbro N Lt By	53°00'·20N 01°32'·40E
Haisbro Mid Lt By	52°54'·20N 01°41'·70E
Haisbro S Lt By	52°50'·80N 01°48'·40E
Hammond Knoll E Lt By	52°52'·30N 01°58'·75E
Harwich Chan No. 1	51°56'·11N 01°27'·30E
Haven Lt By	51°55'·73N 01°32'·67E
Hemsby Lt By	52°41'·84N 01°45'·00E
Holm Lt By	52°33'·50N 01°48'·08E
Holm E Lt By	52°31'·06N 01°49'·42E
Holm S Lt By	52°27'·33N 01°47'·32E
Holm SW Lt By	52°28'·36N 01°47'·28E
Holm W Lt By	52°29'·80N 01°47'·20E
Holm NW Lt By	52°31'·90N 01°46'·80E
Hook Middle W By	51°39'·15N 01°08'·07E
Hook Spit By	51°24'·05N 01°12'·65E
Horse Shoal Lt By	51°37'·07N 00°51'·62E
Kentish Knock Lt By	51°38'·50N 01°40'·50E
Knob Lt By	51°30'·66N 01°04'·38E
Knob NE Lt By	51°32'·00N 01°10'·10E
Knob SE Lt By	51°30'·86N 01°06'·51E
Knock S Lt By	51°34'·73N 01°36'·10E
Knock John Lt By	51°33'·46N 01°11'·08E
Knoll Lt By	51°43'·85N 01°05'·17E
Knoll NW Lt By	51°44'·32N 01°02'·27E
Landguard Lt By	51°55'·35N 01°18'·98E
Lee W Mid Lt By	51°30'·45N 00°38'·93E
Leigh By	51°31'·04N 00°42'·67E
Leigh SE Lt By	51°29'·40N 00°47'·17E
Little Sunk Bn	51°41'·89N 01°24'·85E
Long Sand Bn	51°41'·44N 01°29'·56E
Long Sand Hd Lt By	51°47'·87N 01°39'·53E
Long Sand SE Lt By	51°32'·24N 01°21'·22E
Long Sand NW Bn	51°34'·72N 01°18'·16E
Lowestoft Lt Ho	52°29'·18N 01°45'·46E
Lynn Knock Lt By	53°04'·40N 00°27'·31E

Maplin Lt By	51°34'·00N 01°02'·40E
Maplin NE Lt By	51°37'·43N 01°04'·90E
Maplin Bank Lt By	51°35'·47N 01°04'·80E
Margate E Lt By	51°27'·00N 01°26'·50E
Margate SE Lt By	51°24'·10N 01°20'·50E
Margate S Lt By	51°23'·88N 01°16'·75E
Margate Hook Bn	51°24'·14N 01°14'·39E
Margate Outfall Lt By	51°24'·59N 01°26'·10E
Medusa Lt By	51°51'·20N 01°20'·46E
Medway Lt By	51°28'·80N 00°52'·92E
Nass Lt Bn	51°45'·75N 00°54'·88E
Naze Tr	51°51'·85N 01°17'·40E
Newarp Lt F	52°48'·35N 01°55'·80E
Newcome N Lt By	52°28'·29N 01°46'·43E
Newcome E Lt By	52°28'·48N 01°49'·32E
Newcome Sand Lt By	52°26'·40N 01°47'·16E
NHR-S Lt By	51°51'·40N 02°28'·79E
NHR-SE Lt By	51°45'·50N 02°40'·00E
Nore Sand W Lt By	51°29'·25N 00°41'·80E
Nore Swatch Lt By	51°28'·26N 00°45'·65E
North Foreland Lt	51°22'·47N 01°26'·80E
Oaze S Lt By	51°30'·00N 01°00'·80E
Oaze SW Lt By	51°29'·03N 00°57'·03E
Oaze W Lt By	51°29'·03N 00°55'·53E
Orford Haven By	52°01'·63N 01°27'·67E
Orford Ness Lt Ho	52°05'·00N 01°34'·60E
Outer Crouch Lt By	51°38'·35N 00°58'·61E
Outer Gabbard Lt By	51°57'·80N 02°04'·30E
Outer Tongue Lt By	51°30'·70N 01°26'·50E
Oyster Lt By	51°22'·12N 01°01'·27E
Patch Lt By	51°32'·24N 01°20'·91E
Pitching Ground Lt By	51°55'·39N 01°21'·16E
Pollard Spit Lt By	51°22'·95N 00°58'·67E
Pye End Lt By	51°55'·00N 01°18'·00E
Race S Lt By	53°08'·18N 00°56'·81E
Redsand E Lt By	51°29'·38N 01°04'·15E
Red Sand Trs N Lt By	51°28'·70N 00°59'·42E
Red Sand Trs E Lt By	51°28'·57N 00°59'·78E
Ridge Lt By	51°40'·10N 01°05'·00E
Ridge Inner Lt By	51°55'·31N 01°19'·68E
Rough Lt By	51°55'·16N 01°31'·11E
Roughs Tr SE Lt By	51°53'·61N 01°29'·05E
Roughs Tr NW Lt By	51°53'·78N 01°28'·88E
Scott Patch Lt By	53°11'·10N 00°36'·50E
Scroby N Lt By	52°42'·49N 01°44'·80E
Scroby SW Lt By	52°35'·80N 01°46'·37E
Scroby NW Lt By	52°40'·35N 01°46'·44E
Scroby Elbow Lt By	52°37'·32N 01°46'·50E
Shelf N Lt By	51°56'·65N 01°18'·70E
Sheringham E Lt By	53°02'·20N 01°15'·00E
Sheringham W Lt By	53°02'·93N 01°06'·87E
Shingles N Lt By	51°32'·66N 01°14'·35E

Shingles Mid Lt By	51°31'·93N 01°12'·08E
Shingles S Lt By	51°29'·20N 01°16'·12E
Shingles NW Lt By	51°31'·23N 01°09'·83E
Shingles Patch Lt By	51°32'·98N 01°15'·47E
Shiphead Lt By	51°53'·76N 01°34'·01E
Shipwash N Lt By	52°01'·70N 01°38'·38E
Shipwash E Lt By	51°57'·05N 01°38'·00E
Shipwash S Lt By	51°52'·68N 01°34'·16E
Shipwash SW Lt By	51°54'·72N 01°34'·32E
Shipwash NW Lt By	51°58'·33N 01°36'·33E
Shivering Sand Trs N Lt By	51°29'·98N 01°04'·86E
Shivering Sand Trs S Lt By	51°29'·75N 01°04'·93E
Shoebury Lt Bn	51°30'·28N 00°49'·38E
Shoebury S Lt By	51°30'·40N 00°52'·50E
Shoebury W Lt By	51°30'·20N 00°45'·83E
Shoebury Inner Bn	51°30'·15N 00°49'·05E
Smiths Knoll Lt By	52°43'·50N 02°18'·00E
Southwold Lt Ho	52°19'·60N 01°41'·00E
Spaniard Lt By	51°26'·20N 01°04'·10E
Spile Lt By	51°26'·40N 00°55'·80E
Spit NE Lt By	51°27'·90N 01°30'·00E
Stanford Lt By	52°27'·33N 01°46'·78E
Stone Banks By	51°53'·16N 01°19'·33E
Sunk Lt F	51°51'·00N 01°35'·00E
Sunk Lt By (Wash- Cork Hole)	52°56'·27N 00°23'·50E
Sunk SW Bn	51°36'·50N 01°14'·85E
Sunk W Lt By	51°44'·30N 01°25'·90E
Sunk Head Tr Lt By	51°46'·60N 01°30'·60E
Sunken Buxey Lt By	51°39'·50N 01°00'·70E
Swallow Tail By	51°40'·44N 01°04'·81E
Swatch Mid Lt By	51°28'·65N 00°44'·27E
Swin Spitway Lt By	51°41'·92N 01°08'·45E
Swin SW Lt By	51°32'·68N 01°00'·79E
Swin W By	51°33'·82N 01°03'·30E
Tizard Lt By	51°32'·90N 01°13'·00E
Tongue N Lt By	51°28'·78N 01°13'·18E
Tongue E Lt By	51°28'·72N 01°18'·72E
Tongue Sand Tr N Lt By	51°29'·65N 01°22'·13E
Tongue Sand Tr S Lt By	51°29'·40N 01°22'·15E
Trinity Lt By	51°49'·00N 01°36'·50E
Wallet No.2 Lt By	51°48'·85N 01°23'·10E
Wallet No.4 Lt By	51°46'·50N 01°17'·33E
Wallet Spitway Lt By	51°42'·83N 01°07'·42E
Washington Lt By	51°56'·49N 01°26'·70E
Well N Lt By	53°03'·00N 00°28'·00E
Wells Fairway Lt By	52°59'·85N 00°49'·71E
Whitaker Bn	51°39'·62N 01°06'·30E
Whitaker Lt By	51°41'·40N 01°10'·61E
Whiting NE Lt By	52°03'·77N 01°33'·88E
Whiting SW Lt By	52°01'·10N 01°30'·90E
Whiting Hook By	52°02'·95N 01°31'·93E
Whitstable St Lt By	51°23'·83N 01°01'·70E
Winterton Ridge S Lt By	52°47'·20N 02°03'·60E
Woodbridge Haven By	51°58'·15N 01°23'·90E
Woolpack Lt By	53°02'·65N 00°31'·55E

4

10-4-8   THAMES ESTUARY TIDAL STREAMS

Due to very strong rates of tidal streams in some areas, eddies may occur. Where possible, some indication of these is shown, but in many areas there is insufficient information or eddies are unstable.

5 Hours before HW Sheerness (0335 before HW Dover)

4 Hours before HW Sheerness (0235 before HW Dover)

3 Hours before HW Sheerness (0135 before HW Dover)

2 Hours before HW Sheerness (0035 before HW Dover)

1 Hour before HW Sheerness (0025 after HW Dover)

HW Sheerness (0125 after HW Dover)

4

Due to very strong rates of tidal streams in some areas, eddies may occur. Where possible, some indication of these is shown, but in many areas there is insufficient information or eddies are unstable.

1 Hour after HW Sheerness (0225 after HW Dover)

2 Hours after HW Sheerness (0325 after HW Dover)

3 Hours after HW Sheerness (0425 after HW Dover)

4 Hours after HW Sheerness (0525 after HW Dover)

5 Hours after HW Sheerness (0600 before HW Dover)

6 Hours after HW Sheerness (0500 before HW Dover)

THAMES ESTUARY   10-4-9

NOTE: This chartlet is for general orientation. Due to the small scale many lights, buoys, marks and depths have been omitted. Pecked lines show some routes; timing is often critical and depths may be marginal.

WHITSTABLE 10-4-10

Kent 51°21'·83N 01°01'·56E   Rtg 3-4-2

CHARTS
AC 2571, *1607*; Imray Y14; Stanfords 5; OS 179

TIDES
+0135 Dover; ML 3·0; Duration 0605; Zone 0 (UT)

Standard Port SHEERNESS (→)

Times				Height (metres)			
High Water		Low Water		MHWS	MHWN	MLWN	MLWS
0200	0800	0200	0700	5·8	4·7	1·5	0·6
1400	2000	1400	1900				
Differences WHITSTABLE							
–0008	–0011	+0005	0000	–0·3	–0·3	0·0	–0·1
MARGATE							
–0050	–0040	–0020	–0050	–0·9	–0·9	–0·1	0·0
HERNE BAY							
–0025	–0015	0000	–0025	–0·5	–0·5	–0·1	–0·1

SHELTER
Good, except in strong winds from NNW to NE. Hbr dries up to 1·7m; access HW±1 for strangers. Yacht berths are limited to genuine refuge seekers since priority is given to commercial shipping. Fender board needed against piled quays or seek a mooring to NW of hbr, (controlled by YC).

NAVIGATION
WPT 51°22'·62N 01°01'·20E, 165°/345° from/to W Quay dolphin, 0·83M. From E keep well seaward of Whitstable Street, a hard drying sandspit, which extends 1M N from the coast; shoals a further 1M to seaward are marked by Whitstable Street NCM lt buoy. From W avoid Columbine and Pollard Spits. Appr (not before half flood) direct in the G sector or via Whitstable Oyster PHM lt buoy in W sector of dolphin lt. Beware many oyster beds and banks near approaches, which are very shallow.

LIGHTS AND MARKS
Off head of W Quay on a dolphin, ☆ Fl WRG 5s 2m 5/3M, covers the approaches, vis W118°-156°, G156°-178°, R178°-201°. At the head of the hbr a Dir lt, Oc WRG 5s, leads 122½° into hbr ent, vis G110°-121°, W121°-124°(3°), R124°-134°. Tfc sigs at NE arm: FW 15m 8M = hbr open; FR 10m 5M = hbr closed.

RADIO TELEPHONE
Call *Whitstable Harbour Radio* VHF Ch **09** 12 16 (Mon-Fri: 0800-1700LT. Other times: HW –3 to HW+1). Tidal info is available on request.

TELEPHONE (Dial code 01227)
Hr Mr 274086, ☎ 265441; MRSC (01255) 675518; ⌗ (01304) 224251 (H24); Marinecall 0891 500455; Police 770055; Dr 263844/263033.

FACILITIES
Hbr ☎ 274086, AB £10.50, FW, D, C (10 ton); **Whitstable YC** ☎ 272942, M, R, Slip, L, FW, Bar.
Services: ME, C, CH, ACA, SM, Gas, Ⓔ.
Town EC Wed; Ⓞ, P, V, R, Bar, ✉, Ⓑ, ⇌, ✈ Lydd/Manston.

MINOR HARBOURS WEST OF NORTH FORELAND

MARGATE, Kent, 51°23'·40N 01°22'·75E. AC 1827, 1828, 323; Imray Y7, C1; Stanfords 5; OS 179. HW+0045 on Dover; ML 2·6; Duration 0610; see 10.4.10. Small hbr drying 3m, inside bkwtr (Stone Pier) FR 18m 4M; exposed to NW'lies. Appr's: from E, via Longnose NCM buoy, keeping about 5ca offshore; from N, via Margate PHM buoy Fl R 2·5s; from W via Gore Chan and S Chan to SE Margate ECM buoy, Q (3) 10s. Beware ruins of old pier, known as the Iron Jetty, Fl R 5s, extending 2½ca N from root of Stone Pier. VHF none. Facilities: **Margate YC** ☎ (01843) 292602, R, Bar. **Town** EC Thurs; D & P (cans from garage), R, V, Bar, ✉, Ⓑ, ⇌, ✈ Manston.

HERNE BAY, Kent, 51°22'·37N 01°07'·32E. AC 1607. Tides see 10.4.10. Close E of pier, a 400m long bkwtr gives drying shelter for dayboats/dinghies. Lts: QW 8m 4M is 6ca offshore (former pier hd); bkwtr hd 2FR (vert); pier hd 2FG (vert). Reculvers twrs are conspic 3M to the E. Slip. **Town** EC Thurs; P, Ⓔ, R, V, Bar, ✉, Ⓑ, Ⓞ.

THE SWALE   10-4-11

Kent   Rtg 3-2-2

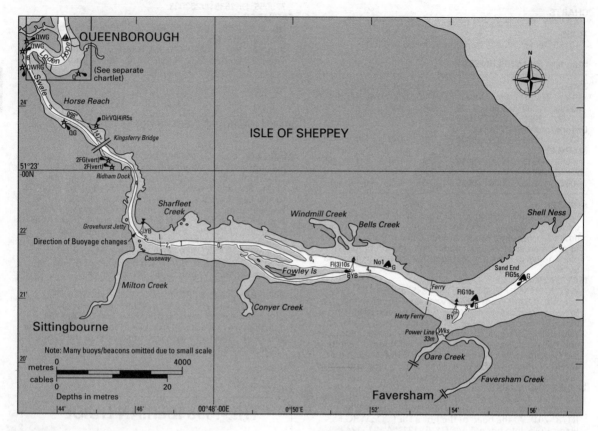

CHARTS
AC 2571, *2482*, 2572, *1834*, 3683; Imray Y18, Y14;
Stanfords 5, 8; OS 178

TIDES
Queenborough +0130 Dover; Harty Ferry +0120 Dover; ML
(Harty Ferry) 3·0; Duration 0610; Zone 0 (UT). Faversham
HW differences are –0·2m on Sheerness; no other data.

Standard Port SHEERNESS (→)

Times				Height (metres)			
High Water		Low Water		MHWS	MHWN	MLWN	MLWS
0200	0800	0200	0700	5·8	4·7	1·5	0·6
1400	2000	1400	1900				

Differences R. SWALE (Grovehurst Jetty)

–0007	0000	0000	+0016	0·0	0·0	0·0	–0·1

Grovehurst Jetty is close N of the ent to Milton Creek.

SHELTER
Excellent in the Swale, the 14M chan between the Isle of
Sheppey and the N Kent coast, from Shell Ness in the E
to Queenborough in the W. Yachts can enter the drying
creeks of Faversham, Oare, Conyer, and Milton. Beware
wrecks at ent to Faversham Creek. Many moorings line
the chan from Faversham to Conyer Creeks. See 10.4.12
for Queenborough, all-tide access.

NAVIGATION
E ent WPT: Columbine Spit SHM, 51°23´·84N 01°00´·13E,
050°/230° from/to ent to buoyed chan 1·3M. The first chan
buoys are Pollard Spit PHM QR and Ham Gat SHM unlit;
buoys are moved to suit the shifting chan. Speed limit 8kn.
The chan is well marked from Faversham to Milton
Creek. The middle section from 1·5M E of Conyer Creek
to 0·5M E of Milton Creek is narrowed by drying
mudbanks and carries least depths of 0·4m. Direction of
buoyage changes at Milton Creek. There are numerous
oyster beds in the area. Kingsferry Bridge (see below)
normally opens H and H+30 for masted craft on request,
but subject to railway trains; temp anchs off SW bank.
The **W ent** is marked by Queenborough Spit ECM buoy,
Q (3) 10s, 1M S of Garrison Pt, at 51°25´·78N 00°44´·03E.

LIGHTS AND MARKS
No fixed lts at E ent. In W Swale the following lights are
intended for large coasters using the narrow chan:
(1) Dir ent lt Q 16m 5M; vis 163°-168°.
(2) Round Loden Hope bend: two Q WG and one Q WRG
    on bns; keep in G sectors. See 10.4.13 chartlet.
(3) Horse Reach ldg lts 113°: front QG 7m 5M; rear Fl G 3s
    10m 6M. Dir lt 098°, VQ (4) R 5s 6m 5M.
(4) Kingsferry Bridge ldg lts 147°: front 2FG(vert) 9m 7M;
    rear 2 FW (vert) 11m 10M. Lts on bridge: two x 2 FG
    (vert) on SW buttresses; two x 2 FR (vert) on NE.

Kingsferry Bridge traffic sigs:

No lts	= Bridge down (3·35m MHWS).
Al Q Ⓡ/Ⓖ	= Centre span lifting.
F Ⓖ	= Bridge open (29m MHWS).
Q Ⓡ	= Centre span lowering. Keep clear.
Q Ⓨ	= Bridge out of action.

Best to request bridge opening on VHF Ch 10; normally
opens H and H+30.

RADIO TELEPHONE
Call: *Medway Radio* VHF Ch 74 16 22 (H24); Kingsferry
Bridge Ch 10 (H24).

TELEPHONE (Dial code 01795)
Hr Mr (Medway Ports Ltd) 580003; MRSC (01255) 675518;
✝ (01474) 537115 (H24); Marinecall 0891 500455; Police
536639; Dr or Ⓗ via Medway Navigation Service 663025.

FACILITIES
FAVERSHAM: **Services:** BY, AB £5, M, AC, FW, Ⓔ, ME, EI,
Sh, C (40 ton), SM, D, C (25 ton).
   Town EC Thurs; V, R, Bar, Gas, ✉, Ⓑ, ≷, ✈ Gatwick.
OARE CREEK: **Services:** AB £5, M, C (8 ton), ME, EI, Sh, CH;
   Hollow Shore Cruising Club ☎ 533254, Bar.
CONYER CREEK: **Swale Marina** ☎ 521562, ⚓ 520788, £5,
   BH (15 ton), ME, Sh, C (3 ton), Slip; **Conyer Marina** ☎
   521711 AB £5 (50 berth marina planned); **Conyer CC**.
   Services: CH, SM, Rigging, BY, ME, Sh, EI, Ⓔ, Slip, D.
MILTON CREEK (Sittingbourne): **Crown Quay** M, FW.
   Town EC Wed; V, R, Bar, ✉, Ⓑ, ≷, ✈ (Gatwick); also the
   Dolphin Yard Sailing Barge Museum.
QUEENBOROUGH: See 10.4.12.

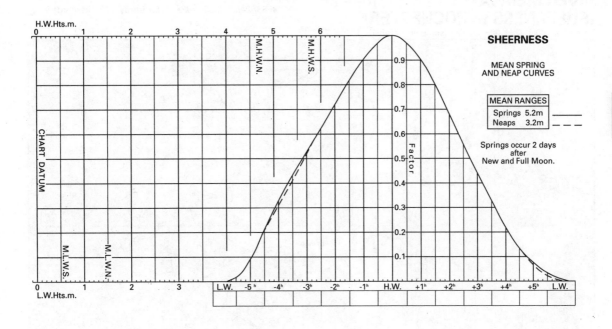

SHEERNESS

MEAN SPRING
AND NEAP CURVES

MEAN RANGES	
Springs 5.2m	——
Neaps 3.2m	– – –

Springs occur 2 days
after
New and Full Moon.

4

QUEENBOROUGH   10-4-12

Kent (Isle of Sheppey) 51°25'·01N 00°44'·29E   Rtg 1-2-2

CHARTS
AC *1834,* 3683, 2572; Imray Y14/18, C1; Stanford 8; OS 178

TIDES
Use 10.4.13 Sheerness, 2M to the N. +0130 Dover; ML 3·0;
Duration 0610; Zone 0 (UT).

SHELTER
Good, except near HW in strong N'ly winds. The first
deep-water refuge W of N Foreland, accessible at all tides
from Garrison Pt (10.4.13); or from the Swale (10.4.11) on
the tide. An all-tide pontoon/jetty (5m depth at end) on E
bank is for landing/short stay only; both sides of the jetty
are foul. 10 ⚓s on E side, N of all-tide landing; 4 Ⓥ berths
on concrete lighter on W side or at 2 Y ⚓s (4 boats on
each) close S of The Hard, a drying causeway. Speed
limit 8kn.

NAVIGATION
WPT: see 10.4.13 for appr via Garrison Pt. Enter the river
at Queenborough Spit ECM buoy, Q (3) 10s, 51°25'·78N
00°44'·03E. The chan narrows between drying banks and
moorings. See 10.4.11 if approaching from the Swale.

LIGHTS AND MARKS
Lights as chartlet. Note: Q 16m 5M lt, vis 163°-168°, on
river bend covers the appr chan. All-tide landing 2 FR
(vert). Concrete lighter Fl G 3s.

RADIO TELEPHONE
Monitor *Medway Radio* VHF Ch **74** for tfc info. Call Ch 08
Sheppey One (Q'boro Hr Mr) for berths, also water taxi at
weekends only. For QYC call *Queen Base* Ch M, 80, M2.

TELEPHONE (Dial code 01795)
Hr Mr 662051; MRSC (01255) 675518; ⊞ (01474) 537115
(H24); Marinecall 0891 500455; Police 580055; Dr 583828;
Ⓗ (01634) 830000 (Gillingham).

FACILITIES
Hbr Controller (AB/⚓ £5.00) ☎/⛴ 662051, AC, FW on all-
tide Landing. **Queenborough YC** ☎ 663955, M, R, Bar, Ⓛ,
Ⓓ, ⓦ; **The Creek** (dries) Slip, Scrubbing berth (FW, AC).
Services: BY, ME, El, Sh, CH, C (10 ton), Gas;
Town EC Wed; P & D (cans), V, R, Bar, ⊠, ⇒, ✈ (Manston).

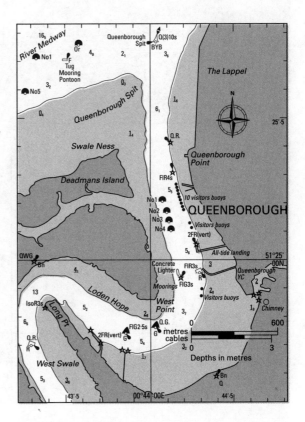

RIVER MEDWAY
(SHEERNESS to ROCHESTER)   10-4-13

Kent 51°27'·00N 00°44'·60E (Off Garrison Point)   Rtg 1-1-1

CHARTS
AC 3683, *2482*, 1835, *1834*, *1185*; Imray Y18; Stanfords 5, 8;
OS 178

TIDES
+0130 Dover; ML 3·1; Duration 0610; Zone 0 (UT)

Standard Port SHEERNESS (→)

Times				Height (metres)			
High Water		Low Water		MHWS	MHWN	MLWN	MLWS
0200	0800	0200	0700	5·8	4·7	1·5	0·6
1400	2000	1400	1900				

Differences BEE NESS
+0002	+0002	0000	+0005	+0·2	+0·1	0·0	0·0

BARTLETT CREEK
+0016	+0008	No data		+0·1	0·0		No data

DARNETT NESS
+0004	+0004	0000	+0010	+0·2	+0·1	0·0	–0·1

CHATHAM (Lock Approaches)
+0010	+0012	+0012	+0018	+0·3	+0·1	–0·1	–0·2

UPNOR
+0015	+0015	+0015	+0025	+0·2	+0·2	–0·1	–0·1

ROCHESTER (STROOD PIER)
+0018	+0018	+0018	+0028	+0·2	+0·2	–0·2	–0·3

WOULDHAM
+0030	+0025	+0035	+0120	–0·2	–0·3	–1·0	–0·3

NEW HYTHE
+0035	+0035	+0220	+0240	–1·6	–1·7	–1·2	–0·3

ALLINGTON LOCK
+0050	+0035	No data		–2·1	–2·2	–1·3	–0·4

NOTE: Sheerness tidal predictions are given below.

SHELTER
There are 3 marinas downriver of Rochester Bridge and 4 above. Sheerness is solely a commercial hbr. See 10.4.12 for Queenborough and access to/from The Swale. Lower reaches of the Medway are exposed to strong NE winds, but Stangate and Half Acre Creeks are secure in all winds and give access to lesser creeks. There are good ⚓s in Sharfleet Creek; from about HW–4 it is possible to go via the "back-door" into Half Acre Creek. Speed limit is 6kn W of Folly Pt (Hoo Island).

NAVIGATION
WPT Medway SWM buoy, Mo(A) 6s, 51°28´·80N 00°52´·92E, 069°/249° from/to Garrison Pt, 5·5M. The wreck of the 'Richard Montgomery' is visible 2M NE of river ent. The estuary offers a huge area to explore, although much of it dries out to mud. Some minor creeks are buoyed. The river is well buoyed/marked up to Rochester and tidal up to Allington Lock (21·6M). The Leisure/Sailing Guide and Medway Ports River Byelaws 1991 are obtainable from Port of Sheerness Ltd, Sheerness Docks, Kent ME12 1RX.

Bridge Clearances (MHWS):
Rochester	5·9m
Medway (M2)	29·6m
New Hythe (footbridge)	11·3m
Aylesford (Stone)	2·87m
Aylesford (Bailey)	3·26m
Maidstone Bypass (M20)	9·45m

LIGHTS AND MARKS
See 10.4.4 and chartlet for details of most lts. NB: not all buoys are shown due to small scale. Isle of Grain lt Q WRG 20m 13/7/8M R220°-234°, G234°-241°, W241°-013°. Power stn chy (242m) Oc and FR lts. Tfc Sigs: Powerful lt, Fl 7s, at Garrison Pt means large vessel under way: if shown up river = inbound; if to seaward = outbound.

RADIO TELEPHONE
Call: Medway Radio VHF Ch 74 16 (H24). Monitor Ch 74 underway and Ch 16 at ⚓. Radar assistance is available on request Ch 22. Ch 80 M for marinas: Gillingham, Hoo (H24), Medway Bridge (0900-1700LT) and Port Medway (0800-2000LT). Link calls via Thames Radio Ch 02, 83.

TELEPHONE (Dial codes 01795 Sheerness; 01634 Medway)
Hr Mr (01795) 561234, ☎ 660072; MRSC (01255) 675518; ☇ (01474) 537115 (H24); Marinecall 0891-500455; Police (01634) 811281, (01795) 661451; Dr via Medway Navigation Service (01795) 663025.

FACILITIES (all 01634 code, unless otherwise stated)
Marinas (from seaward up to Rochester Bridge)
Gillingham Marina (250+12 🆅s) ☎ 280022, ☎ 280164, £15.03 E basin (access via lock HW±4½), W basin HW±2, P, D, AC, FW, ME, El, Ⓔ, Sh, Gas, Gaz, CH, BH (20 ton), C (1 ton), Slip, V, Bar. Note: the effects of cross-tide, especially the ebb, off the lock ent are reduced by a pontoon at 90° to the stream (close W of the lock). A 2nd angled pontoon deflects the stream and is also the fuel berth; the outboard end is lit by 2FR (vert).

Medway Pier Marine ☎ 851113, D, FW, Slip, C (6 ton), BY, Ⓔ;
Hoo Marina (220) ☎ 250311, ☎ 251761, FW, Sh, ME, SM, AC, CH, El, Ⓔ, D (cans), C (20 ton), Gas, Gaz; access to W basin HW±1½; HW±3 to E basin (via sill 1m above CD); an unlit WCM buoy marks chan ent; waiting buoys in river.
Chatham Maritime. Under development, call ☎ 890331 for use of lock and possible AB in Basins 1 and 2. Basin 3 is for commercial vessels.

Marinas (between Rochester Bridge and Allington Lock)
Medway Bridge Marina (160+15 visitors) ☎ 843576, ☎ 843820, £11.75, Slip, D, P, FW, ME, El, Ⓔ, Sh, C (3 ton), BH (10 ton), Gas, Gaz, SM, AC, CH, V, R, Bar;
Port Medway Marina (50) ☎ 720033, ☎ 720315, FW, AC, BH (16 ton), C;
Cuxton Marina (150+some visitors) ☎ 721941, ☎ 290853, Slip, FW, ME, El, Ⓔ, Sh, BH (12 ton), AC, CH;
Elmhaven Marina (60) ☎ 240489, Slip, FW, ME, El, Sh, C, AC;
Allington Lock operates HW–3 to +2, ☎ (01622) 752450).
Allington Marina (120) ☎ (01622) 752057, above the lock; CH, ME, El, Sh, P, D, Slip, C (10 ton), FW, Gas, Gaz;
Notes: All moorings are administered by YCs or marinas. ACA (Sheerness). Fuel Barge at Ship Pier, Rochester, ☎ 813773. Landing (only) at Gillingham Pier, Gillingham Dock steps, Sun Pier (Chatham), Ship Pier, Town Quay (Rochester) and Strood Pier. Slips at Commodores Hard, Gillingham, and Upnor Causeway opposite The Pier pub.

Clubs
Sheppey YC (Sheerness) ☎ 663052; **Lower Halstow YC** ☎ (01227) 458554; **Medway Cruising Club** (Gillingham) ☎ 856489, Bar, M, L, FW; **Hoo Ness YC** ☎ 250052, Bar, R, M, L, FW; **Hundred of Hoo SC** ☎ 250102; **Medway Motor Cruising Club** ☎ 827194; **Medway Motor YC** ☎ 389856; **Medway YC** (Upnor) ☎ 718399; **Upnor SC** ☎ 718043; **Royal Engineers YC** ☎ 844555; **RNSA** (Chatham) ☎ 823524; **Rochester CC** ☎ 841350, Bar, R, M, FW, L, Ⓟ; **Strood YC** ☎ 718261, Bar, M, C (1·5 ton), FW, L, Slip.
Towns: EC Wed; all facilities R, V, Ⓟ, ✉, ≷, ✈ (Gatwick).

GILLINGHAM MARINA

ENGLAND – SHEERNESS

LAT 51°27′N   LONG 0°45′E

TIMES AND HEIGHTS OF HIGH AND LOW WATERS

YEAR **1998**

TIME ZONE (UT)
For Summer Time add ONE hour in non-shaded areas

Chart Datum: 2·90 metres below Ordnance Datum (Newlyn)

JANUARY

#	Time	m	#	Time	m
1 TH	0155 0811 1420 2027	5.8 0.5 5.8 0.6	**16** F	0231 0848 1456 2051	5.6 0.6 5.5 0.9
2 F	0236 0855 1503 2108	5.8 0.4 5.8 0.7	**17** SA	0305 0917 1530 2118	5.5 0.7 5.4 1.0
3 SA	0319 0940 1549 2150	5.7 0.4 5.7 0.8	**18** SU	0338 0943 1603 2145	5.4 0.8 5.3 1.1
4 SU	0404 1025 1638 2235	5.6 0.5 5.5 1.0	**19** M	0412 1014 1639 2217	5.2 0.9 5.1 1.3
5 M	0454 1114 1732 2326	5.4 0.6 5.3 1.1	**20** TU	0450 1052 1719 2258	5.0 1.0 4.9 1.4
6 TU	0552 1212 1834	5.3 0.8 5.2	**21** W	0534 1139 1809 2349	4.6 1.2 4.7 1.6
7 W	0028 0659 1320 1942	1.2 5.2 0.9 5.1	**22** TH	0631 1242 1911	4.6 1.4 4.6
8 TH	0142 0812 1434 2053	1.3 5.1 0.9 5.1	**23** F	0101 0743 1406 2023	1.7 4.6 1.4 4.7
9 F	0258 0924 1546 2201	1.2 5.2 0.9 5.3	**24** SA	0232 0859 1522 2132	1.8 4.7 1.3 4.9
10 SA	0412 1031 1649 2300	1.1 5.3 0.8 5.4	**25** SU	0345 1005 1622 2233	1.4 5.0 1.0 5.3
11 SU	0517 1129 1742 2352	0.9 5.5 0.8 5.5	**26** M	0444 1102 1715 2326	1.1 5.3 0.9 5.5
12 M O	0610 1219 1827	0.8 5.6 0.7	**27** TU	0537 1153 1803	0.8 5.5 0.7
13 TU	0036 0655 1907	5.6 0.7 0.7	**28** W	0013 0627 1239 1848	5.7 0.6 5.7 0.6
14 W	0117 0736 1343 1945	5.7 0.6 5.7 0.7	**29** TH	0058 0716 1324 1933	5.8 0.4 5.9 0.5
15 TH	0155 0814 1421 2020	5.7 0.6 5.7 0.8	**30** F	0141 0803 1407 2016	5.9 0.2 6.0 0.5
			31 SA	0223 0849 1450 2058	6.0 0.2 6.0 0.5

FEBRUARY

#	Time	m	#	Time	m
1 SU	0305 0932 1534 2138	5.9 0.2 5.9 0.6	**16** M	0312 0920 1531 2120	5.5 0.6 5.4 1.0
2 M	0349 1014 1620 2218	5.8 0.3 5.7 0.8	**17** TU	0342 0947 1603 2146	5.4 0.7 5.3 1.1
3 TU	0436 1056 1709 2301	5.2 0.5 5.4 0.9	**18** W	0414 1018 1638 2216	5.2 0.9 5.1 1.2
4 W	0528 1144 1805 2355	5.4 0.6 5.2 1.1	**19** TH	0451 1055 1720 2257	5.0 1.1 4.9 1.4
5 TH	0632 1246 1911	5.2 1.0 5.0	**20** F	0538 1144 1816 2356	4.8 1.3 4.7 1.5
6 F	0106 0746 1403 2024	1.3 5.0 1.1 4.9	**21** SA	0645 1300 1929	4.6 1.5 4.6
7 SA	0233 0906 1523 2139	1.3 5.2 1.1 5.0	**22** SU	0126 0809 1437 2050	1.6 4.6 1.4 4.8
8 SU	0359 1019 1633 2245	1.2 5.2 1.0 5.2	**23** M	0305 0930 1551 2202	1.4 4.8 1.2 5.1
9 M	0509 1119 1729 2338	0.9 5.4 0.9 5.4	**24** TU	0416 1036 1650 2301	1.1 5.1 0.9 5.4
10 TU	0602 1208 1813	0.8 5.5 0.8	**25** W	0517 1132 1744 2352	0.7 5.6 0.7 5.7
11 W O	0022 0643 1250 1851	5.6 0.6 5.6 0.8	**26** TH ●	0612 1220 1833	0.5 5.8 0.6
12 TH	0102 0720 1327 1926	5.7 0.5 5.7 0.7	**27** F	0039 0702 1306 1918	5.9 0.2 6.0 0.4
13 F O	0137 0754 1400 1959	5.7 0.5 5.7 0.7	**28** SA	0123 0750 1349 2002	6.0 0.1 6.1 0.4
14 SA	0210 0825 1431 2029	5.7 0.5 5.6 0.8			
15 SU	0241 0853 1501 2055	5.6 0.5 5.5 0.8			

MARCH

#	Time	m	#	Time	m
1 SU	0205 0834 1432 2043	6.1 0.0 6.1 0.4	**16** M	0216 0826 1432 2031	5.7 0.5 5.7 0.7
2 M	0247 0916 1514 2122	6.1 0.0 6.0 0.4	**17** TU	0245 0854 1501 2057	5.6 0.6 5.6 0.8
3 TU	0330 0955 1558 2159	6.0 0.2 5.8 0.6	**18** W	0315 0922 1532 2121	5.5 0.7 5.4 0.9
4 W	0415 1033 1644 2238	5.8 0.4 5.5 0.8	**19** TH	0345 0950 1605 2148	5.3 0.9 5.3 1.0
5 TH	0506 1116 1736 2327	5.5 0.7 5.2 1.0	**20** F	0421 1021 1645 2224	5.1 1.1 5.1 1.1
6 F	0607 1213 1839	5.2 1.1 4.9	**21** SA	0505 1104 1736 2319	4.9 1.3 4.8 1.3
7 SA	0036 0722 1333 1955	1.3 4.9 1.3 4.8	**22** SU	0606 1212 1846	4.7 1.5 4.7
8 SU	0212 0846 1500 2116	1.3 4.9 1.3 4.9	**23** M	0041 0729 1354 2011	1.4 4.6 1.5 4.7
9 M	0346 1003 1615 2225	1.1 5.1 1.2 5.1	**24** TU	0226 0857 1518 2130	1.3 4.9 1.3 5.0
10 TU	0455 1103 1712 2319	0.9 5.4 1.0 5.4	**25** W	0346 1009 1623 2234	1.0 5.3 1.0 5.4
11 W	0545 1151 1755	0.7 5.6 0.7	**26** TH	0453 1108 1720 2328	0.6 5.6 0.7 5.7
12 TH	0003 0623 1230 1831	5.5 0.6 5.6 0.8	**27** F	0551 1158 1812	0.4 5.9 0.5
13 F O	0041 0656 1304 1904	5.6 0.6 5.7 0.7	**28** SA ●	0016 0643 1245 1859	5.9 0.2 6.1 0.4
14 SA	0114 0727 1334 1935	5.7 0.5 5.7 0.7	**29** SU	0101 0730 1328 1943	6.1 0.0 6.2 0.3
15 SU	0146 0757 1403 2004	5.7 0.5 5.7 0.7	**30** M	0144 0814 1411 2025	6.2 0.0 6.2 0.3
			31 TU	0227 0854 1452 2104	6.2 0.0 6.0 0.4

APRIL

#	Time	m	#	Time	m
1 W	0311 0933 1535 2142	6.1 0.2 5.8 0.5	**16** TH	0251 0900 1506 2104	5.5 0.7 5.5 0.8
2 TH	0357 1011 1619 2220	5.8 0.5 5.6 0.7	**17** F	0324 0929 1540 2133	5.4 0.9 5.4 0.9
3 F	0447 1052 1709 2306	5.5 0.9 5.2 0.9	**18** SA	0401 1000 1620 2210	5.2 1.1 5.2 1.0
4 SA	0546 1145 1810	5.2 1.2 4.9	**19** SU	0446 1043 1710 2303	5.0 1.2 5.0 1.1
5 SU	0011 0658 1302 1924	1.2 4.9 1.5 4.7	**20** M	0545 1148 1817	4.9 1.4 4.8
6 M	0148 0820 1430 2045	1.3 4.9 1.5 4.8	**21** TU	0019 0702 1319 1938	1.2 4.8 1.5 4.8
7 TU	0318 0937 1546 2156	1.1 5.1 1.3 5.0	**22** W	0156 0826 1443 2058	1.1 5.0 1.3 5.1
8 W	0426 1037 1644 2252	0.9 5.3 1.1 5.3	**23** TH	0317 0940 1552 2204	0.8 5.3 1.0 5.4
9 TH	0515 1124 1728 2336	0.8 5.5 1.0 5.5	**24** F	0425 1041 1652 2301	0.6 5.7 0.8 5.7
10 F	0553 1202 1804	0.7 5.6 0.9	**25** SA	0526 1134 1747 2351	0.3 5.9 0.6 5.9
11 SA O	0013 0625 1235 1836	5.6 0.6 5.6 0.8	**26** SU ●	0620 1221 1836	0.2 6.1 0.4
12 SU	0047 0656 1305 1907	5.7 0.5 5.7 0.7	**27** M	0038 0707 1306 1922	6.1 0.1 6.1 0.3
13 M	0119 0727 1334 1938	5.7 0.5 5.7 0.7	**28** TU	0124 0751 1349 2006	6.2 0.1 6.1 0.3
14 TU	0149 0758 1404 2008	5.7 0.5 5.7 0.7	**29** W	0209 0832 1431 2048	6.1 0.2 6.0 0.3
15 W	0220 0829 1434 2036	5.6 0.6 5.7 0.7	**30** TH	0254 0912 1514 2128	6.0 0.4 5.8 0.5

ENGLAND – SHEERNESS

LAT 51°27'N   LONG   0°45'E

TIMES AND HEIGHTS OF HIGH AND LOW WATERS

YEAR **1998**

4

TIME ZONE (UT)
For Summer Time add ONE hour in non-shaded areas

MAY

Day	Time	m	Time	m	Time	m	Time	m
1 F	0340	5.8	0950	0.7	1558	5.5	2207	0.7
16 SA	0309	5.4	0914	0.9	1524	5.4	2128	0.8
2 SA	0430	5.5	1030	1.0	1646	5.2	2250	0.9
17 SU	0349	5.3	0950	1.0	1605	5.3	2208	0.9
3 SU	0525	5.2	1118	1.3	1742	5.0	2348	1.1
18 M	0436	5.2	1034	1.2	1655	5.1	2300	0.9
4 M	0629	4.9	1225	1.5	1849	4.8		
19 TU	0533	5.1	1134	1.3	1757	5.0		
5 TU	0111	1.2	0742	4.8	1348	1.6	2005	4.7
20 W	0009	1.0	0642	5.0	1251	1.3	1911	5.0
6 W	0234	1.1	0856	4.9	1503	1.5	2117	4.9
21 TH	0132	0.9	0758	5.1	1409	1.2	2027	5.1
7 TH	0340	1.0	0959	5.1	1603	1.3	2215	5.1
22 F	0248	0.7	0911	5.3	1518	1.0	2135	5.4
8 F	0432	0.9	1047	5.3	1650	1.1	2302	5.3
23 SA	0357	0.5	1014	5.6	1622	0.8	2235	5.6
9 SA	0513	0.8	1127	5.5	1730	1.0	2341	5.5
24 SU	0500	0.4	1121	5.8	1721	0.7	2329	5.8
10 SU	0550	0.7	1201	5.6	1806	0.8		
25 M	0555	0.3	1159	5.9	1814 ●	0.5		
11 M	0017	5.6	0623	0.6	1234	5.7	1839 O	0.8
26 TU	0019	5.9	0644	0.3	1246	6.0	1903	0.4
12 TU	0051	5.6	0657	0.6	1306	5.7	1912	0.7
27 W	0107	6.0	0729	0.3	1330	6.0	1950	0.3
13 W	0125	5.6	0732	0.6	1339	5.7	1946	0.7
28 TH	0153	6.0	0812	0.4	1413	5.9	2034	0.4
14 TH	0158	5.6	0806	0.6	1412	5.7	2020	0.7
29 F	0239	5.9	0852	0.5	1456	5.7	2116	0.5
15 F	0233	5.5	0841	0.7	1447	5.6	2053	0.7
30 SA	0325	5.7	0931	0.8	1539	5.5	2156	0.7
31 SU	0411	5.5	1009	1.1	1624	5.3	2235	0.8

JUNE

Day	Time	m	Time	m	Time	m	Time	m
1 M	0500	5.2	1050	1.3	1713	5.1	2321	1.0
16 TU	0427	5.4	1028	1.0	1644	5.3	2300	0.7
2 TU	0553	5.0	1142	1.5	1809	4.9		
17 W	0521	5.3	1120	1.1	1740	5.2	2359	0.8
3 W	0022	1.1	0653	4.8	1252	1.6	1914	4.7
18 TH	0623	5.2	1224	1.2	1846	5.1		
4 TH	0136	1.2	0800	4.8	1406	1.6	2024	4.8
19 F	0108	0.8	0731	5.2	1335	1.2	1958	5.2
5 F	0244	1.1	0905	4.9	1511	1.5	2127	4.9
20 SA	0221	0.7	0842	5.3	1446	1.1	2108	5.3
6 SA	0341	1.0	1000	5.1	1605	1.3	2220	5.1
21 SU	0331	0.6	0948	5.4	1555	1.0	2213	5.5
7 SU	0430	0.9	1045	5.3	1652	1.1	2306	5.3
22 M	0436	0.6	1047	5.6	1700	0.8	2312	5.6
8 M	0513	0.8	1126	5.5	1733	1.0	2346	5.4
23 TU	0534	0.5	1141	5.7	1758	0.6		
9 TU	0553	0.7	1204	5.6	1811	0.8		
24 W	0005	5.7	0624	0.5	1230	5.8	1849 ●	0.5
10 W	0025	5.5	0631	0.7	1241	5.7	1849 O	0.7
25 TH	0055	5.8	0710	0.5	1315	5.8	1937	0.4
11 TH	0103	5.6	0709	0.6	1319	5.7	1927	0.6
26 F	0142	5.8	0753	0.5	1359	5.8	2022	0.4
12 F	0140	5.6	0747	0.7	1356	5.7	2007	0.6
27 SA	0226	5.8	0834	0.7	1440	5.7	2103	0.5
13 SA	0218	5.6	0826	0.7	1433	5.6	2047	0.6
28 SU	0309	5.7	0912	0.8	1520	5.6	2141	0.6
14 SU	0258	5.6	0904	0.8	1513	5.5	2128	0.6
29 M	0350	5.5	0946	1.0	1600	5.4	2215	0.8
15 M	0340	5.5	0944	0.9	1555	5.4	2211	0.7
30 TU	0431	5.3	1020	1.2	1641	5.2	2249	0.9

JULY

Day	Time	m	Time	m	Time	m	Time	m
1 W	0513	5.1	1057	1.4	1726	5.1	2331	1.0
16 TH	0504	5.4	1102	1.0	1721	5.4	2342	0.6
2 TH	0600	4.9	1146	1.5	1819	4.8		
17 F	0600	5.3	1156	1.1	1821	5.2		
3 F	0027	1.2	0655	4.7	1250	1.7	1920	4.7
18 SA	0042	0.8	0704	5.2	1303	1.2	1931	5.2
4 SA	0137	1.2	0757	4.7	1406	1.6	2028	4.7
19 SU	0154	0.9	0814	5.2	1419	1.2	2046	5.2
5 SU	0247	1.2	0901	4.8	1514	1.5	2132	4.9
20 M	0308	0.9	0925	5.2	1536	1.1	2157	5.3
6 M	0346	1.1	0959	5.1	1611	1.3	2228	5.1
21 TU	0418	0.8	1030	5.4	1648	0.9	2302	5.5
7 TU	0438	0.9	1050	5.3	1701	1.1	2317	5.3
22 W	0519	0.8	1128	5.6	1749	0.7	2358	5.6
8 W	0525	0.8	1136	5.5	1746	0.9		
23 TH	0610	0.7	1218	5.7	1841 ●	0.6		
9 TH	0001	5.5	0607	0.8	1220	5.7	1829 O	0.7
24 F	0046	5.7	0655	0.7	1303	5.7	1926	0.5
10 F	0044	5.6	0649	0.7	1301	5.8	1913	0.6
25 SA	0130	5.7	0736	0.7	1343	5.8	2007	0.4
11 SA	0125	5.7	0731	0.7	1341	5.8	1957	0.5
26 SU	0210	5.8	0815	0.7	1422	5.7	2045	0.5
12 SU	0206	5.7	0813	0.6	1421	5.8	2041	0.4
27 M	0248	5.7	0850	0.8	1458	5.6	2118	0.5
13 M	0247	5.8	0855	0.7	1502	5.7	2125	0.4
28 TU	0323	5.5	0921	1.0	1533	5.5	2147	0.7
14 TU	0330	5.7	0935	0.8	1544	5.6	2208	0.4
29 W	0357	5.3	0947	1.1	1607	5.3	2214	0.8
15 W	0415	5.6	1017	0.9	1630	5.5	2253	0.5
30 TH	0432	5.2	1016	1.3	1643	5.1	2247	0.9
31 F	0510	5.0	1051	1.4	1725	4.9	2330	1.1

AUGUST

Day	Time	m	Time	m	Time	m	Time	m
1 SA	0556	4.8	1139	1.6	1818	4.7		
16 SU	0015	0.9	0636	5.1	1234	1.2	1909	5.1
2 SU	0027	1.3	0652	4.7	1245	1.7	1924	4.6
17 M	0128	1.1	0748	5.0	1357	1.3	2029	5.1
3 M	0146	1.4	0801	4.7	1414	1.7	2040	4.6
18 TU	0249	1.2	0904	5.1	1525	1.2	2147	5.2
4 TU	0303	1.3	0912	4.9	1530	1.4	2150	4.9
19 W	0404	1.1	1016	5.3	1643	1.0	2255	5.4
5 W	0405	1.1	1015	5.2	1630	1.4	2248	5.2
20 TH	0507	1.0	1115	5.5	1743	0.8	2349	5.6
6 TH	0459	1.0	1109	5.5	1722	0.9	2338	5.5
21 F	0558	0.9	1204	5.6	1830	0.6		
7 F	0547	0.8	1157	5.7	1811	0.7		
22 SA	0034	5.7	0639	0.8	1247	5.7	1909 ●	0.6
8 SA	0024	5.7	0631	0.7	1242	5.8	1858 O	0.5
23 SU	0113	5.8	0716	0.8	1324	5.8	1945	0.5
9 SU	0108	5.8	0716	0.6	1324	5.9	1945	0.3
24 M	0149	5.8	0751	0.8	1359	5.8	2018	0.5
10 M	0150	5.8	0759	0.6	1405	6.0	2030	0.2
25 TU	0222	5.7	0823	0.8	1432	5.7	2048	0.5
11 TU	0231	6.0	0841	0.6	1446	5.9	2114	0.2
26 W	0253	5.6	0851	0.9	1503	5.6	2115	0.7
12 W	0313	5.9	0921	0.7	1527	5.9	2155	0.3
27 TH	0323	5.5	0916	1.1	1534	5.5	2141	0.8
13 TH	0357	5.8	1000	0.8	1611	5.7	2236	0.4
28 F	0353	5.4	0940	1.2	1606	5.3	2210	0.9
14 F	0443	5.6	1041	0.9	1700	5.5	2320	0.7
29 SA	0427	5.2	1009	1.3	1641	5.1	2246	1.2
15 SA	0535	5.4	1129	1.1	1758	5.3		
30 SU	0507	5.0	1048	1.5	1726	4.8	2332	1.4
31 M	0558	4.8	1142	1.6	1826	4.6		

Chart Datum: 2·90 metres below Ordnance Datum (Newlyn)

ENGLAND – SHEERNESS

LAT 51°27′N   LONG 0°45′E

TIMES AND HEIGHTS OF HIGH AND LOW WATERS

YEAR **1998**

TIME ZONE (UT)
For Summer Time add ONE hour in non-shaded areas

SEPTEMBER

Day	Time	m	Day	Time	m
1 TU	0041 / 0706 / 1305 / 1947	1.6 / 4.7 / 1.7 / 4.6	**16** W	0230 / 0844 / 1516 / 2134	1.4 / 5.0 / 1.2 / 5.2
2 W	0216 / 0826 / 1446 / 2110	1.6 / 4.8 / 1.5 / 4.8	**17** TH	0349 / 0958 / 1633 / 2240	1.3 / 5.2 / 1.0 / 5.5
3 TH	0332 / 0940 / 1558 / 2218	1.4 / 5.1 / 1.2 / 5.2	**18** F	0452 / 1058 / 1728 / 2332	1.1 / 5.5 / 0.8 / 5.7
4 F	0431 / 1041 / 1657 / 2313	1.1 / 5.4 / 0.9 / 5.5	**19** SA	0539 / 1145 / 1810	1.0 / 5.6 / 0.7
5 SA	0523 / 1133 / 1751	0.9 / 5.7 / 0.6	**20** SU ●	0014 / 0617 / 1225 / 1844	5.7 / 0.9 / 5.7 / 0.7
6 SU O	0001 / 0611 / 1220 / 1840	5.8 / 0.7 / 5.9 / 0.4	**21** M	0050 / 0651 / 1301 / 1916	5.8 / 0.9 / 5.8 / 0.6
7 M	0046 / 0657 / 1303 / 1927	6.0 / 0.6 / 6.1 / 0.2	**22** TU	0122 / 0723 / 1333 / 1946	5.8 / 0.8 / 5.8 / 0.6
8 TU	0129 / 0741 / 1344 / 2012	6.1 / 0.6 / 6.1 / 0.1	**23** W	0152 / 0753 / 1404 / 2015	5.8 / 0.8 / 5.8 / 0.6
9 W	0211 / 0823 / 1425 / 2055	6.1 / 0.5 / 6.1 / 0.1	**24** TH	0220 / 0821 / 1433 / 2043	5.7 / 0.9 / 5.7 / 0.7
10 TH	0252 / 0903 / 1507 / 2135	6.1 / 0.6 / 6.1 / 0.3	**25** F	0249 / 0846 / 1503 / 2111	5.6 / 1.0 / 5.6 / 0.8
11 F	0335 / 0940 / 1551 / 2214	5.9 / 0.7 / 5.9 / 0.5	**26** SA	0319 / 0910 / 1534 / 2139	5.5 / 1.1 / 5.4 / 1.0
12 SA	0419 / 1019 / 1640 / 2256	5.7 / 0.9 / 5.6 / 0.8	**27** SU	0352 / 0937 / 1608 / 2210	5.3 / 1.2 / 5.2 / 1.2
13 SU	0510 / 1105 / 1738 / 2349	5.4 / 1.1 / 5.3 / 1.1	**28** M	0429 / 1011 / 1649 / 2250	5.1 / 1.3 / 5.0 / 1.4
14 M	0610 / 1209 / 1850	5.1 / 1.3 / 5.1	**29** TU	0516 / 1101 / 1745 / 2351	4.9 / 1.5 / 4.7 / 1.7
15 TU	0102 / 0723 / 1340 / 2012	1.4 / 4.9 / 1.4 / 5.0	**30** W	0620 / 1216 / 1901	4.7 / 1.6 / 4.6

OCTOBER

Day	Time	m	Day	Time	m
1 TH	0125 / 0742 / 1400 / 2029	1.7 / 4.7 / 1.5 / 4.8	**16** F	0322 / 0931 / 1606 / 2215	1.5 / 5.1 / 1.0 / 5.4
2 F	0254 / 0904 / 1524 / 2144	1.5 / 5.0 / 1.2 / 5.2	**17** SA	0424 / 1031 / 1659 / 2306	1.3 / 5.4 / 0.9 / 5.6
3 SA	0359 / 1010 / 1628 / 2244	1.2 / 5.4 / 0.8 / 5.6	**18** SU	0511 / 1118 / 1739 / 2347	1.1 / 5.6 / 0.8 / 5.7
4 SU	0455 / 1104 / 1725 / 2335	0.9 / 5.8 / 0.6 / 5.9	**19** M	0549 / 1158 / 1812	1.0 / 5.7 / 0.8
5 M O	0546 / 1153 / 1817	0.8 / 6.0 / 0.4	**20** TU ●	0021 / 0621 / 1233 / 1842	5.7 / 0.9 / 5.7 / 0.7
6 TU	0021 / 0633 / 1238 / 1905	6.1 / 0.6 / 6.1 / 0.2	**21** W	0052 / 0652 / 1305 / 1912	5.7 / 0.9 / 5.8 / 0.7
7 W	0105 / 0718 / 1321 / 1950	6.2 / 0.6 / 6.2 / 0.2	**22** TH	0121 / 0722 / 1335 / 1942	5.8 / 0.8 / 5.8 / 0.6
8 TH	0147 / 0801 / 1403 / 2032	6.2 / 0.5 / 6.2 / 0.2	**23** F	0150 / 0752 / 1406 / 2013	5.7 / 0.9 / 5.7 / 0.7
9 F	0229 / 0842 / 1447 / 2112	6.1 / 0.6 / 6.1 / 0.4	**24** SA	0220 / 0842 / 1437 / 2043	5.7 / 0.9 / 5.6 / 0.8
10 SA	0312 / 0922 / 1532 / 2151	5.9 / 0.7 / 5.9 / 0.6	**25** SU	0251 / 0848 / 1509 / 2113	5.6 / 1.0 / 5.4 / 1.0
11 SU	0357 / 1001 / 1622 / 2232	5.7 / 0.9 / 5.6 / 1.0	**26** M	0324 / 0917 / 1544 / 2144	5.4 / 1.1 / 5.3 / 1.2
12 M	0446 / 1047 / 1720 / 2323	5.4 / 1.1 / 5.3 / 1.3	**27** TU	0401 / 0951 / 1626 / 2222	5.3 / 1.2 / 5.1 / 1.4
13 TU	0545 / 1149 / 1829	5.1 / 1.3 / 5.0	**28** W	0447 / 1039 / 1719 / 2318	5.0 / 1.3 / 4.9 / 1.6
14 W	0034 / 0656 / 1321 / 1949	1.6 / 4.9 / 1.4 / 5.0	**29** TH	0547 / 1148 / 1829	4.8 / 1.4 / 4.8
15 TH	0203 / 0816 / 1454 / 2109	1.6 / 4.8 / 1.2 / 5.1	**30** F	0041 / 0704 / 1321 / 1952	1.7 / 4.8 / 1.4 / 4.9
			31 SA	0211 / 0826 / 1447 / 2109	1.5 / 5.0 / 1.1 / 5.2

NOVEMBER

Day	Time	m	Day	Time	m
1 SU	0321 / 0935 / 1555 / 2212	1.3 / 5.4 / 0.8 / 5.6	**16** M	0433 / 1045 / 1659 / 2312	1.3 / 5.4 / 0.9 / 5.5
2 M	0421 / 1033 / 1656 / 2307	1.0 / 5.7 / 0.5 / 5.9	**17** TU	0513 / 1126 / 1735 / 2348	1.1 / 5.5 / 0.8 / 5.6
3 TU	0516 / 1125 / 1750 / 2355	0.8 / 5.9 / 0.4 / 6.1	**18** W	0549 / 1203 / 1808	1.0 / 5.6 / 0.8
4 W O	0607 / 1212 / 1840	0.7 / 6.1 / 0.3	**19** TH ●	0020 / 0622 / 1237 / 1840	5.7 / 0.9 / 5.7 / 0.8
5 TH	0041 / 0654 / 1258 / 1925	6.1 / 0.6 / 6.2 / 0.3	**20** F	0052 / 0654 / 1310 / 1913	5.7 / 0.8 / 5.7 / 0.7
6 F	0125 / 0740 / 1344 / 2009	6.1 / 0.5 / 6.2 / 0.3	**21** SA	0124 / 0727 / 1343 / 1947	5.8 / 0.8 / 5.7 / 0.7
7 SA	0208 / 0824 / 1429 / 2050	6.1 / 0.5 / 6.1 / 0.5	**22** SU	0156 / 0800 / 1416 / 2021	5.7 / 0.8 / 5.6 / 0.8
8 SU	0252 / 0906 / 1517 / 2130	5.9 / 0.6 / 5.9 / 0.8	**23** M	0230 / 0833 / 1451 / 2054	5.5 / 0.9 / 5.5 / 1.0
9 M	0337 / 0948 / 1607 / 2211	5.6 / 0.8 / 5.6 / 1.1	**24** TU	0305 / 0907 / 1528 / 2128	5.5 / 0.9 / 5.4 / 1.1
10 TU	0425 / 1033 / 1701 / 2258	5.4 / 1.0 / 5.3 / 1.4	**25** W	0343 / 0944 / 1611 / 2206	5.3 / 1.0 / 5.2 / 1.3
11 W	0520 / 1129 / 1804	5.1 / 1.2 / 5.1	**26** TH	0428 / 1030 / 1702 / 2257	5.2 / 1.1 / 5.1 / 1.4
12 TH	0000 / 0625 / 1249 / 1914	1.6 / 4.9 / 1.3 / 4.9	**27** F	0523 / 1131 / 1805	5.0 / 1.2 / 5.0
13 F	0120 / 0739 / 1412 / 2029	1.7 / 4.8 / 1.3 / 5.0	**28** SA	0005 / 0631 / 1248 / 1918	1.5 / 4.9 / 1.2 / 5.0
14 SA	0238 / 0852 / 1522 / 2136	1.6 / 5.0 / 1.1 / 5.2	**29** SU	0126 / 0747 / 1409 / 2033	1.5 / 5.0 / 1.0 / 5.2
15 SU	0342 / 0955 / 1616 / 2230	1.4 / 5.2 / 1.0 / 5.4	**30** M	0240 / 0859 / 1521 / 2140	1.3 / 5.3 / 0.8 / 5.5

DECEMBER

Day	Time	m	Day	Time	m
1 TU	0345 / 1002 / 1626 / 2239	1.1 / 5.6 / 0.6 / 5.7	**16** W	0435 / 1052 / 1657 / 2312	1.3 / 5.3 / 0.9 / 5.4
2 W	0446 / 1059 / 1724 / 2331	0.9 / 5.8 / 0.5 / 5.9	**17** TH	0517 / 1133 / 1737 / 2350	1.1 / 5.4 / 0.8 / 5.5
3 TH	0542 / 1151 / 1816 (O)	0.7 / 5.9 / 0.4	**18** F ●	0555 / 1211 / 1814	1.0 / 5.5 / 0.8
4 F	0020 / 0634 / 1241 / 1903	6.0 / 0.6 / 6.0 / 0.4	**19** SA	0026 / 0631 / 1249 / 1850	5.7 / 0.9 / 5.6 / 0.7
5 SA	0106 / 0724 / 1329 / 1948	6.0 / 0.5 / 6.1 / 0.4	**20** SU	0103 / 0708 / 1325 / 1926	5.7 / 0.8 / 5.6 / 0.7
6 SU	0151 / 0810 / 1416 / 2031	6.0 / 0.5 / 6.0 / 0.6	**21** M	0139 / 0745 / 1401 / 2003	5.7 / 0.7 / 5.6 / 0.8
7 M	0235 / 0855 / 1503 / 2112	5.8 / 0.6 / 5.8 / 0.8	**22** TU	0215 / 0824 / 1438 / 2040	5.7 / 0.7 / 5.6 / 0.8
8 TU	0319 / 0938 / 1551 / 2151	5.6 / 0.7 / 5.6 / 1.1	**23** W	0252 / 0903 / 1517 / 2116	5.6 / 0.7 / 5.5 / 0.9
9 W	0405 / 1020 / 1639 / 2231	5.4 / 0.9 / 5.3 / 1.3	**24** TH	0331 / 0943 / 1559 / 2154	5.5 / 0.8 / 5.4 / 1.1
10 TH	0453 / 1105 / 1732 / 2319	5.2 / 1.1 / 5.1 / 1.5	**25** F	0413 / 1025 / 1647 / 2239	5.3 / 0.8 / 5.3 / 1.2
11 F	0548 / 1201 / 1830	4.9 / 1.2 / 4.9	**26** SA	0503 / 1116 / 1742 / 2334	5.2 / 0.9 / 5.1 / 1.3
12 SA	0021 / 0650 / 1311 / 1934	1.7 / 4.8 / 1.3 / 4.8	**27** SU	0602 / 1218 / 1847	5.1 / 0.9 / 5.1
13 SU	0136 / 0759 / 1421 / 2042	1.7 / 4.8 / 1.3 / 4.8	**28** M	0042 / 0711 / 1332 / 1958	1.4 / 5.1 / 0.9 / 5.1
14 M	0246 / 0906 / 1522 / 2142	1.6 / 4.9 / 1.2 / 5.0	**29** TU	0158 / 0825 / 1448 / 2109	1.3 / 5.2 / 0.9 / 5.3
15 TU	0345 / 1004 / 1613 / 2231	1.5 / 5.1 / 1.1 / 5.1	**30** W	0312 / 0935 / 1559 / 2214	1.2 / 5.3 / 0.7 / 5.4
			31 TH	0421 / 1039 / 1702 / 2312	1.0 / 5.5 / 0.6 / 5.6

Chart Datum: 2·90 metres below Ordnance Datum (Newlyn)

RIVER THAMES   10-4-14

London: from Canvey Island to Teddington lock
Ratings: 1-2 (marinas), 5 (tideway)-1 (London), 2 (tideway)-1

SEQUENCE

Information is arranged as far as possible from seaward, starting abeam Canvey Island and continuing up-river to the head of the tidal Thames at Teddington. See 10.4.15 for Southend-on-Sea and Leigh-on-Sea.

CHARTS

AC 3319, *2484*, 3337, 2151, 1186, *1185*; Imray C2, C1; Stanfords 5; OS 176, 177, 178.
Books include: *Nicholsons Guide to the Thames; River Thames Book* (Imray). The Port of London Authority (PLA), Devon House, 58-60 St Katherine's Way, London E1 9LB; ☎ (0171) 265 2656, 📠 0171 265 2699, issues free: *Yachtsman's Guide; Pleasure Users Guide; Leisure Guide.* Port of London River Byelaws & *Tide Tables* are for sale.

4

CANVEY ISLAND TO CRAYFORDNESS

CRAYFORDNESS TO TOWER BRIDGE

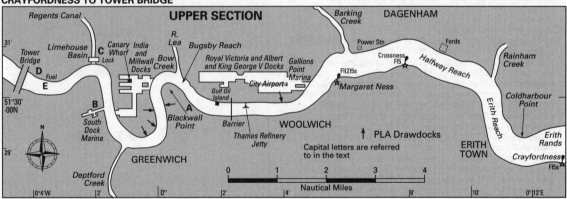

TOWER BRIDGE TO TEDDINGTON

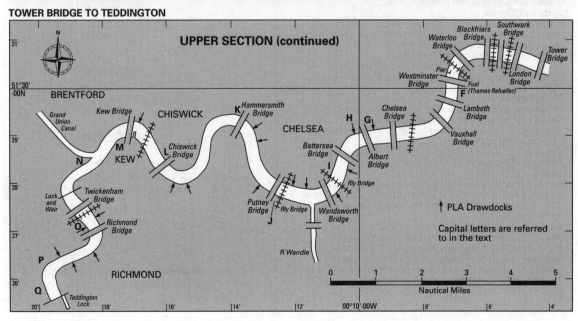

RIVER THAMES *continued*

HARBOURS IN LOWER REACHES OF RIVER THAMES

HOLEHAVEN, Essex, 51°30'·55N 00°33'·50E. AC 2484, 1186. HW +0140 on Dover; use differences for CORYTON, see 10·4·15; ML 3·0m; Duration 0610. Shelter is good, but beware swell from passing traffic. Note: There is an 8kn speed limit in the river off Coryton and Shellhaven; keep at least 60m clear of berthed tankers and refinery jetties. See Piermaster for 4 Y ⚓s on extreme W of ent with 12m at MLWS. Keep to Canvey Is side on ent. ⚓ on W edge of chan as long stone groynes extend from E side. 0·5M N of ent an overhead oil pipe crosses chan with clearance of 11m, plus 2 FY lts (horiz). PLA launch *Canvey Patrol* monitors VHF Ch 12 or 68 (not H24), depending on patrol area. Lts Coryton Refinery Jetty No 4 2 FG (vert).
Piermaster ☎ (01268) 683041; Facilities: FW at pier in office hours (also from 'The Lobster Smack' yard), P & D from Canvey Village (1M); EC Thurs; all other facilities on Canvey Is.

THAMES TIDAL BARRIER 51°29'·88N 00°02'·31E (Span G)

Description
Located at Woolwich Reach, it protects London from flooding. There are 9 piers between which gates can be rotated upwards from the river bed to form a barrier. The piers are numbered 1-9 from N to S; the spans are lettered A-K from S to N (see diagram). A, H, J & K are not navigable. C-F, with depth 5·8m, are for larger vessels; B and G, with 1·25m, are for small craft/yachts, W-bound via G and E-bound via B.
Control & Communications
The Thames Barrier Navigation Centre controls all traffic in a Zone from Margaret Ness (51°30'·5N 00°05'·6E) to Blackwall Point (51°30'·3N 00°00'·3E), using the callsign *Barrier Control* on VHF Ch **14**, 22, 16.
Inbound vessels should pass their ETA at the Barrier to *Woolwich Radio* when abeam Crayford Ness (51°28'·9N 00°12'·8E). When passing Margaret Ness they should obtain clearance to proceed through the Barrier.
Outbound vessels should use the same procedure abeam Tower Bridge (51°30'·3N 00°04'·4E) and Blackwall Point.
Non-VHF craft should, if possible, pre-notify the Barrier Control ☎ 0181-855 0315; then observe all visual signals, proceed with caution keeping clear of larger vessels and use spans B or G as appropriate. Telephone Barrier Control when passage completed. Sailing vessels should transit the Barrier under power, not sail.
Lights and Signals
At Thamesmead and Barking Power Station to the E, and Blackwall Stairs (N bank) and Blackwall Pt (S bank) to the W, noticeboards and lights indicate:
Fl ⓨ = proceed with extreme caution.
Fl ⓡ = navigation within Zone is prohibited.
Loudhailers may pass instructions and Morse K (–·–) = Barrier closed.
On the Barrier piers:
St Andrew's Cross (R lts) = barrier or span closed.
Arrows (G lts) = span indicated is open to traffic.
Spans A, H, J and K are lit with 3 ⓡ in ▽ = No passage.
Spans open for navigation
Information will be included in routine broadcasts by *Woolwich Radio* on VHF Ch 14 at H + 15 and H + 45.
Testing
The Barrier is completely closed for testing one day per month, LW –1½ to LW +1½. Dates of testing are shown in the Supplements to this Almanac. Individual spans are tested weekly.
Beware
When all spans are closed, keep 200m clear to avoid turbulence. **It is dangerous to transit a closed span, as the gate may be semi-raised.** Small craft should not navigate between Thames Refinery Jetty and Gulf Oil Island, unless intending to transit the Barrier.

GRAVESEND, Kent, 51°23'·61N 00°23'·00E. AC 1186, 2151. HW +0150 on Dover; ML 3·3m; Duration 0610. Use Tilbury diffs overleaf. Caution: Off the N bank, from Coalhouse Pt to 7ca E of Gravesend, 6 groynes (tops dry 1·0m) project approx 400m almost into the fairway; their outer ends are marked by SHM bns, Fl G 2·5s. 5 Y buoys downstream of No 6 groyne (the most E'ly) indicate that **no passage exists inshore of the Y buoys and groyne bns**. A SHM buoy *Diver*, L Fl G 10s, between Nos 3 and 2 groynes, marks the N edge of the fairway. ⚓ E of the Sea School jetty, close to S shore, but remote from town. There are ⚓s off the Club. Lock opens HW –1½ to HW on request to lock-keeper, ☎ (01474) 352392 (24hrs notice required for night tides). Boats can be left unattended in canal basin but not at ⚓s. Royal Terrace Pier hd FR. Call *Port Control London* VHF Ch 12 to seaward of Sea Reach No 4 buoy (1.4M SSE of Southend pier); and Ch 68 from No 4 buoy to Crayfordness. Broadcasts on Ch 68 every H and H+30. ⌗ 537115 (H24); **Gravesend SC** ☎ 533974, Bar, FW, M, P & D (cans); **Services**: C (at canal ent, ask at SC), CH, Ⓔ, ME, El, Sh. **Town** EC Wed, R, V.
Thurrock YC (51°28'·30N 00°19'·57E) at Grays, ☎ (01375) 373720 is 3M upriver on N bank opposite Broadness. 1 ⚓, D on site, P (2M), Bar, R (occas).

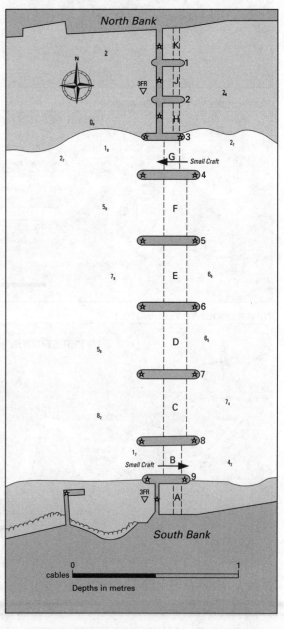

TIDES
+0252 Dover; ML 3·6; Duration 0555; Zone 0 (UT)

Standard Port LONDON BRIDGE (⟶)

Times			Height (metres)			
High Water		Low Water	MHWS	MHWN	MLWN	MLWS
0300	0900	0400	1100	7·1	5·9	1·3	0·5
1500	2100	1600	2300				

Differences TILBURY
−0055	−0040	−0050	−0115	−0·7	−0·5	+0·1	0·0

WOOLWICH (GALLIONS POINT)
−0020	−0020	−0035	−0045	−0·1	0·0	+0·2	0·0

ALBERT BRIDGE
+0025	+0020	+0105	+0110	−0·9	−0·8	−0·7	−0·4

HAMMERSMITH BRIDGE
+0040	+0035	+0205	+0155	−1·4	−1·3	−1·0	−0·5

KEW BRIDGE
+0055	+0050	+0255	+0235	−1·8	−1·8	−1·2	−0·5

RICHMOND LOCK
+0105	+0055	+0325	+0305	−2·2	−2·2	−1·3	−0·5

London Bridge is a Standard Port; daily predictions are below. The river is tidal up to Richmond Footbridge where there is a half-tide lock and a weir with overhead sluice gates. When down, ie closed, these gates maintain at least 1·72m between Richmond and Teddington bridges; the half-tide lock, on the Surrey bank, must then be used. At other times (approx HW ±2) pass through the 3 central arches. Above Putney the ht of LW may be below CD if the water flow over Teddington Weir is reduced; warnings are broadcast by Woolwich Radio qv. If the Thames Barrier (previous page) is closed, water levels will vary greatly from predictions.

TIDES – TIME DIFFERENCES ON LONDON BRIDGE
Place	MHWS	MHWN	MLWN	MLWS
Gravesend Town Pier	−0059	−0044	−0106	−0125
Broadness Lt Ho	−0052	−0040	−0101	−0119
Stoneness Lt Ho	−0048	−0037	−0059	−0114
Coldharbour Point	−0037	−0030	−0053	−0103
Royal Albert Dock Ent	−0029	−0024	−0043	−0050
Woolwich Ferry	−0028	−0024	−0042	−0047
Royal Victoria Dock Ent	−0021	−0018	−0031	−0025
India & Millwall Dock Ent	−0018	−0015	−0026	−0029
Greenwich Pier	−0014	−0012	−0020	−0023
Deptford Creek	−0012	−0011	−0018	−0021
Millwall Dock Ent	−0010	−0008	−0014	−0016
Surrey Dock Greenland Ent	−0010	−0008	−0013	−0015
London Bridge	0000	0000	0000	0000
Westminster Bridge	+0012	+0011	+0031	+0035
Battersea Bridge	+0023	+0020	+0109	+0110
Putney Bridge	+0032	+0030	+0138	+0137
Chiswick Bridge	+0049	+0044	+0235	+0224
Teddington Lock	+0106	+0056	—	—

NAVIGATION
The tidal Thames is divided by the PLA into a lower section = from sea to Crayfordness; and an upper section = Crayfordness to Teddington.
Some general points: Going up or down river, keep as far to stbd as is safe and seamanlike. Boats approaching a bridge against the tide give way to those approaching with the tide; but pleasure craft should always keep clear of commercial vessels, especially tug/barge tows. Above Cherry Garden Pier (Wapping), vessels over 40m always have priority. Speed should be such as to minimise wash, but an 8kn speed limit applies inshore off Southend, off Shellhaven and Coryton, and above Wandsworth Bridge. Some of the potential hazards are outlined below:
Lower section. In Sea Reach, keep well S of the main chan to clear tankers turning abeam Canvey Is and Shellhaven. In Lower Hope hold the NW bank until Ovens SHM buoy; long groynes extend from the N bank for the next 2M. The Tilbury landing stage is used by the Gravesend ferry and cruise liners. In Northfleet Hope beware ships/tugs turning into Tilbury Docks; container berths and a grain terminal are close up-river. Long Reach has Ro-Ro berths on both banks up/down stream of QE II bridge. Tankers berth at Purfleet (N bank).
Upper section. Avoid unhandy tug/lighter tows en route to Erith. Thames Police and PLA launches are very helpful to yachts. In emergency call *Thames Patrol* Ch 12, 68 or 14, giving position relative to landmarks, rather than by lat/long. Expect frequent passenger launches from/to Greenwich, The Tower and Westminster. Passage by night is not advised. See below for bridge warning lights.

BRIDGES
Name of Bridge	Distance from London Bridge Nautical Miles	Clearance below centre span MHWS (m)
Dartford (QEII)	17·68 below	54.1
Tower	0·49 below	8·6
London Bridge	0.00	8·9
Cannon St. Railway	0.16	7·1
Southwark	0.24	7·4
Blackfriars Railway	0.62	7·0
Blackfriars	0.63	7·1
Waterloo	1·12	8·5
Charing Cross Railway	1.32	7·0
Westminster	1·64	5·4
Lambeth	2·02	6·5
Vauxhall	2·46	5·6
Victoria Railway	3·31	6·0
Chelsea	3·40	6·6
Albert	4·04	4·9
Battersea	4·27	5·5
Battersea Railway	4·83	6·1
Wandsworth	5·46	5·8
Fulham Railway	6·31	6·9
Putney	6·45	5·5
Hammersmith	7·97	3·7
Barnes Railway	9·55	5·4
Chiswick	10·22	6·9
Kew Railway	10·98	5·6
Kew	11·33	5·3
Richmond Footbridge	13·49	5·5
Twickenham	13·64	5·9
Richmond Railway	13·67	5·3
Richmond	13·97	5·3

Tower Bridge sounds horn (10) 20s when bascules are open for shipping.
Iso W lts either side of 19 bridges (Tower to Putney) warn of an approaching large vessel/tug (which has switched on the Iso lts electronically); other craft should keep clear.
A ▽ of R discs (Ⓡ lts) below a bridge = this arch closed.

PIERS WHERE LANDING CAN BE MADE BY ARRANGEMENT
Piers with *, contact PLA Central booking Service ☎ 0171 265 2666, 📠 0171 265 2617.
Greenwich Pier*, Tower Pier*

London Bridge City Pier	0171 403 5939
Charing Cross Pier*	
Westminster Pier*	
Lambeth Pier	0171 839 2164
Festival Pier*	
Cadogan Pier	0171 349 8585
Putney Pier	0171 378 1211
Kew Pier)	0171 930 2062
Richmond Landing Stage)	
Hampton Court Pier	0181 781 9758

LIGHTS AND MARKS
Glare from the many shore lts makes navigation by night difficult or even risky. Margaret Ness Fl (2) 5s 11m 8M.

RADIO TELEPHONE
Pleasure craft are encouraged to monitor:
Port Control London   Ch 12   Sea to Sea Reach No 4 buoy;
                        Ch 68   No 4 buoy to Crayfordness.
Woolwich Radio   Ch 14   Up-river from Crayfordness.
Sea Reach No 4 buoy is 1.35M SSE of Southend pierhead at 51°29'·58N 00°44'·28E. Craft >20m LOA must have VHF radio. Smaller craft with no VHF should call ☎ 0181-855 0315 before & after transiting the Thames Barrier.
Routine traffic, weather, tidal and nav info is broadcast by *Port Control London* on Ch 12 at H +15 and H +45 and on Ch 68 at H and H +30; also by *Woolwich Radio* on Ch 14 at H +15 and H +45. The latter will warn if ht of LW upstream of Putney falls below CD. For marina VHF see next page.

TELEPHONE (Dial code 0171 Central London; 0181 Outer)
PLA: **Operational enquiries 0181 855 0315;**
General non-operational enquiries, below Crayfordness: (01474) 560311, 📠 562281;
above Crayfordness: 0171 265 2656, 📠 265 2699;
Duty Port Controller Gravesend (01474) 560311;
Duty Officer Woolwich 0181 855 0315;
Port Health Authority (Tilbury 01375) 842663 (H24);
Thames MRSC (01255) 675518; River Police HQ (Wapping) 0171 275 4421; London Weather Centre 0171 831 5968; Tower Bridge 0171 407 0922; ⌗ (01474) 537115 (H24); Richmond Lock 0181 940 0634; **Marinecall** 0891 500 455; Ⓗ 0171 987 7011.

RIVER THAMES continued

SHELTER

Very good in Marinas, see below; also at the following: Bow Creek (Bugsby's Reach), Deptford Creek (HW±2); **Upstream of fixed bridges:** at places shown under FACILITIES below and at Chas Newens (BY, Putney), Alan See (Hammersmith), Auto Marine Services (Chiswick), Howlett's BY (Twickenham) & Tough's BY (Teddington). PLA Draw Docks, arrowed on chartlets, are former barge inlets which dry to chalk/gravel; in emergency they may offer refuge but are open to wash. See also previous page for Piers where temp'y berth may be pre-arranged .

FACILITIES (Bold letters in brackets appear on chartlets)

GREENWICH (0181)

Greenwich YC (A) ☎ 8587339; VHF Ch M. FW, 1 ⛽, ME.

LIMEHOUSE REACH (0171)

See below for **S Dock Marina (B)** & **Limehouse Basin (C)**.

POOL OF LONDON (0171)

St Katharine Haven (D): see below and for Fuel barge **(E)**. *NB: ALL BRIDGES BEYOND TOWER BRIDGE ARE FIXED.*

WESTMINSTER BRIDGE (S side)

Westminster Petroleum Ltd (F) (Fuel barge). Call *Thames Refueller* VHF Ch 14, ☎ 0831 110681, Gas, CH, D, L.

CHELSEA (0171)

Cadogan Pier (G) ☎ 352 4604, M, L; **Chelsea Yacht & Boat Co (H)** ☎ 352 1427, M, Gas; **Chelsea Hbr (I)** (see over).

WANDSWORTH & HAMMERSMITH (0181)

Hurlingham YC (J) ☎ 788 5547, M, CH, ME, FW, EI, Sh; **Dove Marina (K)** ☎ 748 9474, AB, M, FW.

CHISWICK (0181)

Chiswick Quay Marina (L) (50) ☎ 994 8743, Access HW±2, M, FW, BY, M, ME, EI, Sh.

KEW (0181)

Kew Marina (M) ☎ 940 8364, M, CH, D, P, Gas, SM;

BRENTFORD (0181)

Ent to Grand Union Canal, M, AB. **Brentford Dock Marina (N)** (80+10 visitors) ☎ 568 0287 (VHF Ch M), AC, Bar, CH, EI, FW, ME, R, V, Sh, Access HW±2½;

RICHMOND (0181)

(O), **Richmond Slipway** BY, CH, D, Gas, M, FW, ME, EI, Sh.

TWICKENHAM & TEDDINGTON (0181)

(P) Eel Pie Island BY, CH, AC, ME, M, Gas, C (6 ton), Sh, EI, FW; **(Q) Swan Island Hbr**, D, M, ME, EI, Sh, FW, Gas, Slip, AB, C (30 ton), CH.

ADMIRALTY CHART AGENTS (Central London)

Brown & Perring, 36/44 Tabernacle St	☎ 0171-253 4517
Kelvin Hughes, 145 Minories	709 9076
London Yacht Centre, 13 Artillery Lane	247 0521
Ocean Leisure, 13/14 Northumberland Ave	930 5050
Stanfords, 12/14 Long Acre	836 1321
Telesonic Marine, 60/62 Brunswick Centre	837 4106
Capt. O.M.Watts, 7 Dover St	493 4633

MARINAS ON THE TIDAL THAMES (From seaward: Woolwich to Chelsea)

GALLIONS POINT MARINA, London, 51°30'·27N 00°04'·76E in original entry basin for Royal Albert Dock. AC 2151, *2484*. Tides as for Gallions Pt (10.4.14). Marina ☎ 0171-476 7054 (H24). VHF Ch 68, when vessel expected. The fuel barge LENNARD is conspic, berthed outside the lock; D, Gas on sale. Access via lock HW±5; 8m depth in basin. AB approx £9.40. Two ☆s 2FG (vert) on river pier. Usual facilities inc security H24. DLR to central London, until 0030. Woolwich ferry & foot tunnel 15 mins walk. ✈ London City airport is adjacent.

SOUTH DOCK MARINA, London, 51°29'·62N 00°01'·87W. AC 3337, *2484*. Tides as for Surrey Dock Greenland Ent (10.4.14). 1·1M above Greenwich, 2·5M below Tower Bridge. Baltic Quay building at SW end of marina is conspic with five arched rooftops. Waiting pontoon at Greenland Pier. Approx access via lock HW±2 for 2m draft; HW±4 for 1m draft. **Marina** ☎ 0171-252 2244, ⚓ 237 3806, (372 + ♥ £12). VHF Ch **M** 80. **Facilities:** AC, ME, Sh, EI, FW, CH, C (20 ton), Bar, R, V, ▣, SDYC; Dr ☎ 237 1078; Ⓗ ☎ 955 5000; Police ☎ 252 2836. ⇌, Surrey Quays Tube stn, ✈ City Airport.

SOUTH DOCK MARINA

LIMEHOUSE BASIN, London, 51°30'·54N 00°02'·17W. Entry HW±3 via swing bridge/lock, 0800-1800LT daily Apr-Oct; 0800-1630 Nov-Mar; other times by prior arrangement to Hr Mr & BWB lock, ☎ 0171-308 9930. Waiting pontoon in lock entrance is accessible outside LW±1½. Call VHF Ch 80 *Limehouse Marina*. Facilities: (90 berths £11.75) FW, AC, H24 security, ⊚, ⇌, DLR; also entry to Regents Canal and R Lea. Marina is managed by Cruising Association at: 1 Northey St, Limehouse Basin, E14 8BT, ☎ 0171-537 2828, 🖅 537 2266; temporary membership, open: 1130-1500 & 1700-2300 Mon-Fri, 1130-2300 Sat, 1200-1500 & 1900-2230 Sun; Bar, R.

4

ST KATHERINE HAVEN, London, 51°30'·33N 00°04'·25W. AC 3337, 3319. HW +0245 on Dover. Tides as London Bridge (10·4·14). Be aware of cross tide at mid-flood/ebb. Good shelter under all conditions. Tower Bridge and the Tower of London are uniquely conspic, close up-river. A waiting pontoon is close downstream of ent in 0.1 - 1.9m; or berth on inshore side of St Katherine Pier, 30m upriver of ent; limited berthing/shore access, only suitable for shoal draft. Pleasure launches berth on S side of pier.

St Katherine Haven Call *St Katherines* VHF Ch **80** M. Lock (42·7m x 9·1m with 2 small lifting bridges), access HW –2 to HW +1½, season 0600-2030, winter 0800-1800LT; other times by prior arrangement. R/G tfc lts at ent. Lock is shut Tues and Wed, Nov to Feb.

Facilities (100 + 50 Ⓥ, usually in Centre Basin or East Dock; pre-booking advised in season) ☎ 0171-481 8350 (H24)/ 488 0555, 🖅 702 2252, £13, FW, AC, CH, ME, El, Sh, Gas, Sewage pump-out, YC, Bar, R, V, ⌗, ⊚.

Fuel Barge is 400m downstream of lock ent. ☎ 0171-481 1774; VHF Ch 14 *Burgan*. D & Gas, 0900-1600 Mon-Fri; 0900-1300 Sun.

LONDON BRIDGE

MEAN SPRING
AND NEAP CURVES

MEAN RANGES
Springs 6.6m
Neaps   4.6m

Springs occur 3 days
after
New and Full Moon.

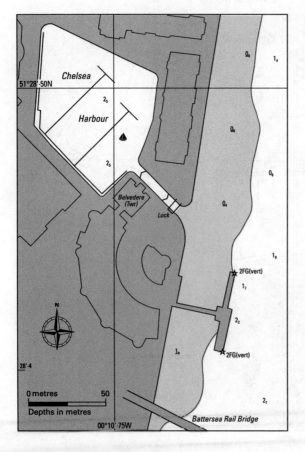

0 metres   50

Depths in metres

CHELSEA HARBOUR, London, 51°28´.45N 00°10´.72W. AC 3319. Tides: see 10·4·14. Good shelter in all conditions, 5M above Tower Bridge, reached via 14 fixed bridges. Battersea railway bridge is 120m upstream. Belvedere Tower (80m high with tide ball) is conspic, next to the lock. Basin ent is for max LOA 24m, beam 5·5m, draft 1·8m, with bascule bridge. Lock opens when 2·5m water above sill; tide gauge outside, access HW ±1½, R/G tfc lts. Limited waiting berths and shore access on Chelsea Hbr Pier (1·7m) close upriver. Call *Chelsea Hbr* VHF Ch 80. **Marina** (50+10 Ⓥ). ☎ 0171-351 4433, 📠 352 7868, Hr Mr ☎ (pager) 01893 237180, £11.75, AC, FW, Bar, R, YC, Ⓑ, V.

4

ENGLAND – LONDON BRIDGE

LAT 51°30′N   LONG 0°05′W

TIMES AND HEIGHTS OF HIGH AND LOW WATERS

YEAR **1998**

JANUARY

	Time	m		Time	m
1 TH	0315 / 1000 / 1544 / 2208	7.0 / 0.6 / 7.2 / 0.7	**16** F	0346 / 1040 / 1614 / 2237	6.7 / 0.6 / 6.8 / 1.1
2 F	0356 / 1042 / 1628 / 2246	7.0 / 0.5 / 7.2 / 0.8	**17** SA	0416 / 1108 / 1646 / 2252	6.6 / 0.8 / 6.7 / 1.1
3 SA	0438 / 1122 / 1713 / 2325	7.0 / 0.6 / 7.1 / 0.8	**18** SU	0448 / 1129 / 1721 / 2312	6.6 / 0.9 / 6.6 / 1.1
4 SU	0522 / 1201 / 1801	6.8 / 0.6 / 6.9	**19** M	0525 / 1150 / 1759 / 2344	6.5 / 0.9 / 6.5 / 1.0
5 M	0006 / 0608 / 1245 / 1854	0.9 / 6.6 / 0.8 / 6.6	**20** TU	0606 / 1224 / 1842	6.3 / 1.0 / 6.3
6 TU	0055 / 0703 / 1338 / 1955	1.1 / 6.4 / 1.0 / 6.3	**21** W	0026 / 0653 / 1310 / 1931	1.1 / 6.1 / 1.1 / 6.1
7 W	0154 / 0812 / 1443 / 2106	1.3 / 6.2 / 1.1 / 6.2	**22** TH	0117 / 0748 / 1412 / 2028	1.3 / 5.9 / 1.3 / 6.0
8 TH	0306 / 0928 / 1604 / 2214	1.4 / 6.1 / 1.2 / 6.3	**23** F	0226 / 0853 / 1523 / 2133	1.5 / 5.7 / 1.3 / 5.9
9 F	0430 / 1038 / 1722 / 2316	1.3 / 6.1 / 1.1 / 6.5	**24** SA	0344 / 1004 / 1632 / 2243	1.5 / 5.8 / 1.3 / 6.1
10 SA	0550 / 1140 / 1824	1.1 / 6.6 / 0.9	**25** SU	0454 / 1115 / 1738 / 2346	1.3 / 6.1 / 1.1 / 6.4
11 SU	0013 / 0653 / 1237 / 1917	6.7 / 0.7 / 6.8 / 0.7	**26** M	0602 / 1217 / 1841	1.1 / 6.4 / 0.9
12 M ○	0105 / 0747 / 1328 / 2006	6.9 / 0.5 / 7.0 / 0.6	**27** TU	0042 / 0709 / 1310 / 1938	6.7 / 0.9 / 6.8 / 0.7
13 TU	0152 / 0837 / 1416 / 2051	7.0 / 0.3 / 7.1 / 0.6	**28** W ●	0131 / 0812 / 1359 / 2031	6.9 / 0.6 / 7.1 / 0.6
14 W	0235 / 0923 / 1459 / 2133	7.0 / 0.3 / 7.1 / 0.7	**29** TH	0217 / 0906 / 1445 / 2119	7.1 / 0.4 / 7.3 / 0.6
15 TH	0313 / 1004 / 1538 / 2209	6.9 / 0.4 / 7.0 / 0.9	**30** F	0300 / 0955 / 1530 / 2203	7.2 / 0.3 / 7.4 / 0.5
			31 SA	0343 / 1038 / 1614 / 2243	7.2 / 0.2 / 7.4 / 0.5

FEBRUARY

	Time	m		Time	m
1 SU	0425 / 1117 / 1658 / 2320	7.2 / 0.2 / 7.3 / 0.5	**16** M	0424 / 1102 / 1651 / 2247	6.6 / 0.8 / 6.7 / 0.9
2 M	0507 / 1151 / 1743 / 2355	7.2 / 0.3 / 7.1 / 0.6	**17** TU	0458 / 1117 / 1727 / 2317	6.6 / 0.8 / 6.7 / 0.8
3 TU	0551 / 1226 / 1831	6.9 / 0.5 / 6.7	**18** W	0536 / 1226 / 1807 / 2353	6.5 / 0.5 / 6.5 / 0.8
4 W	0035 / 0639 / 1307 / 1924	0.8 / 6.6 / 0.6 / 6.3	**19** TH	0619 / 1223 / 1852	6.3 / 0.9 / 6.3
5 TH	0123 / 0739 / 1401 / 2033	1.1 / 6.2 / 1.2 / 6.0	**20** F	0035 / 0709 / 1311 / 1944	1.0 / 6.1 / 1.1 / 6.1
6 F	0225 / 0900 / 1511 / 2148	1.4 / 6.0 / 1.4 / 5.9	**21** SA	0130 / 0816 / 1424 / 2045	1.3 / 5.8 / 1.4 / 5.9
7 SA	0343 / 1018 / 1648 / 2255	1.5 / 6.0 / 1.4 / 6.1	**22** SU	0254 / 0916 / 1553 / 2157	1.5 / 5.8 / 1.4 / 5.9
8 SU	0530 / 1125 / 1802 / 2354	1.3 / 6.3 / 1.2 / 6.4	**23** M	0420 / 1035 / 1709 / 2312	1.4 / 5.9 / 1.3 / 6.2
9 M	0638 / 1223 / 1857	0.9 / 6.7 / 1.0	**24** TU	0537 / 1149 / 1818	1.2 / 6.3 / 1.0
10 TU	0047 / 0731 / 1315 / 1946	6.7 / 0.5 / 6.9 / 0.7	**25** W	0015 / 0653 / 1248 / 1920	6.5 / 0.8 / 6.8 / 0.7
11 W ○	0136 / 0819 / 1401 / 2032	6.9 / 0.3 / 7.1 / 0.6	**26** TH ●	0109 / 0758 / 1339 / 2015	7.1 / 0.5 / 7.1 / 0.5
12 TH	0218 / 0904 / 1443 / 2114	6.9 / 0.3 / 7.0 / 0.7	**27** F	0156 / 0904 / 1427 / 2106	7.2 / 0.3 / 7.4 / 0.4
13 F	0256 / 0945 / 1519 / 2152	6.8 / 0.4 / 6.9 / 0.8	**28** SA	0241 / 0941 / 1512 / 2151	7.3 / 0.0 / 7.5 / 0.3
14 SA	0327 / 1020 / 1550 / 2221	6.7 / 0.6 / 6.8 / 1.0			
15 SU	0354 / 1047 / 1619 / 2232	6.6 / 0.7 / 6.7 / 1.0			

MARCH

	Time	m		Time	m
1 SU	0324 / 1023 / 1555 / 2232	7.4 / -0.1 / 7.6 / 0.2	**16** M	0332 / 1022 / 1551 / 2213	6.6 / 0.7 / 6.7 / 0.9
2 M	0407 / 1101 / 1638 / 2308	7.5 / 0.0 / 7.5 / 0.3	**17** TU	0401 / 1034 / 1622 / 2225	6.6 / 0.8 / 6.8 / 0.8
3 TU	0449 / 1133 / 1721 / 2341	7.4 / 0.2 / 7.2 / 0.4	**18** W	0433 / 1048 / 1657 / 2253	6.6 / 0.7 / 6.8 / 0.7
4 W	0532 / 1203 / 1805	7.2 / 0.4 / 6.8	**19** TH	0510 / 1115 / 1735 / 2326	6.6 / 0.7 / 6.7 / 0.7
5 TH	0015 / 0617 / 1239 / 1852	0.6 / 6.8 / 0.8 / 6.3	**20** F	0552 / 1150 / 1819	6.5 / 0.8 / 6.4
6 F	0057 / 0713 / 1327 / 1956	1.0 / 6.3 / 1.2 / 5.9	**21** SA	0005 / 0640 / 1234 / 1909	0.8 / 6.2 / 1.1 / 6.1
7 SA	0154 / 0835 / 1432 / 2121	1.3 / 5.9 / 1.6 / 5.7	**22** SU	0054 / 0737 / 1332 / 2009	1.1 / 6.0 / 1.4 / 5.9
8 SU	0307 / 1000 / 1602 / 2232	1.6 / 5.9 / 1.7 / 5.9	**23** M	0205 / 0844 / 1513 / 2120	1.4 / 5.8 / 1.6 / 5.9
9 M	0508 / 1107 / 1736 / 2332	1.4 / 6.2 / 1.4 / 6.2	**24** TU	0351 / 1003 / 1642 / 2238	1.4 / 6.0 / 1.4 / 6.1
10 TU	0617 / 1204 / 1834	0.9 / 6.6 / 1.0	**25** W	0517 / 1122 / 1755 / 2346	1.1 / 6.3 / 1.0 / 6.5
11 W	0026 / 0709 / 1256 / 1923	6.6 / 0.5 / 6.9 / 0.7	**26** TH	0635 / 1224 / 1859	0.7 / 6.8 / 0.7
12 TH	0115 / 0756 / 1341 / 2009	6.8 / 0.3 / 7.1 / 0.6	**27** F	0042 / 0737 / 1317 / 1955	6.9 / 0.3 / 7.2 / 0.4
13 F ○	0158 / 0839 / 1421 / 2052	6.9 / 0.2 / 7.0 / 0.6	**28** SA ●	0132 / 0830 / 1405 / 2046	7.2 / 0.1 / 7.5 / 0.2
14 SA	0235 / 0919 / 1455 / 2130	6.8 / 0.3 / 6.9 / 0.7	**29** SU	0219 / 0918 / 1450 / 2132	7.4 / -0.1 / 7.6 / 0.1
15 SU	0305 / 0955 / 1524 / 2200	6.7 / 0.5 / 6.8 / 0.9	**30** M	0303 / 1001 / 1534 / 2214	7.6 / -0.2 / 7.6 / 0.0
			31 TU	0347 / 1039 / 1616 / 2252	7.6 / -0.1 / 7.5 / 0.1

APRIL

	Time	m		Time	m
1 W	0430 / 1111 / 1658 / 2325	7.5 / 0.1 / 7.2 / 0.2	**16** TH	0412 / 1025 / 1631 / 2235	6.6 / 0.8 / 6.8 / 0.7
2 TH	0514 / 1142 / 1740 / 2359	7.3 / 0.4 / 6.9 / 0.5	**17** F	0449 / 1053 / 1709 / 2308	6.6 / 0.7 / 6.7 / 0.6
3 F	0600 / 1215 / 1825	6.9 / 0.8 / 6.4	**18** SA	0532 / 1129 / 1753 / 2347	6.5 / 0.8 / 6.5 / 0.8
4 SA	0038 / 0654 / 1300 / 1921	0.8 / 6.3 / 1.2 / 5.9	**19** SU	0620 / 1212 / 1843	6.3 / 1.0 / 6.2
5 SU	0131 / 0813 / 1401 / 2050	1.2 / 5.9 / 1.6 / 5.6	**20** M	0035 / 0716 / 1308 / 1941	1.0 / 6.1 / 1.4 / 6.0
6 M	0240 / 0937 / 1521 / 2204	1.5 / 5.9 / 1.8 / 5.8	**21** TU	0143 / 0823 / 1436 / 2051	1.3 / 6.0 / 1.6 / 5.9
7 TU	0420 / 1042 / 1659 / 2304	1.4 / 6.2 / 1.6 / 5.9	**22** W	0327 / 0940 / 1615 / 2208	1.3 / 6.1 / 1.4 / 6.1
8 W	0546 / 1138 / 1804 / 2358	1.0 / 6.5 / 1.2 / 6.5	**23** TH	0455 / 1055 / 1729 / 2316	1.0 / 6.4 / 1.1 / 6.5
9 TH	0638 / 1229 / 1856	0.6 / 6.8 / 0.8	**24** F	0610 / 1158 / 1833	0.6 / 6.9 / 0.7
10 F	0047 / 0725 / 1315 / 1942	6.7 / 0.4 / 7.0 / 0.6	**25** SA	0014 / 0711 / 1252 / 1930	6.9 / 0.3 / 7.2 / 0.4
11 SA ○	0131 / 0808 / 1354 / 2025	6.8 / 0.3 / 7.0 / 0.6	**26** SU ●	0107 / 0804 / 1341 / 2022	7.2 / 0.0 / 7.5 / 0.2
12 SU	0209 / 0848 / 1428 / 2103	6.8 / 0.4 / 6.9 / 0.6	**27** M	0156 / 0852 / 1428 / 2110	7.4 / -0.1 / 7.6 / 0.0
13 M	0241 / 0924 / 1457 / 2133	6.7 / 0.5 / 6.8 / 0.8	**28** TU	0242 / 0936 / 1512 / 2155	7.6 / -0.1 / 7.5 / -0.1
14 TU	0309 / 0951 / 1525 / 2151	6.6 / 0.7 / 6.8 / 0.8	**29** W	0328 / 1016 / 1555 / 2235	7.6 / 0.0 / 7.4 / 0.0
15 W	0339 / 1006 / 1556 / 2208	6.6 / 0.8 / 6.8 / 0.8	**30** TH	0413 / 1050 / 1637 / 2311	7.5 / 0.2 / 7.2 / 0.2

Chart Datum: 3·20 metres below Ordnance Datum (Newlyn)

ENGLAND – LONDON BRIDGE

LAT 51°30′N   LONG   0°05′W

TIME ZONE (UT)
For Summer Time add ONE hour in non-shaded areas

TIMES AND HEIGHTS OF HIGH AND LOW WATERS

YEAR **1998**

Chart Datum: 3·20 metres below Ordnance Datum (Newlyn)

MAY

Day	Time	m	Day	Time	m
1 F	0459 / 1122 / 1718 / 2345	7.3 / 0.5 / 6.9 / 0.4	**16** SA	0434 / 1041 / 1650 / 2300	6.7 / 0.8 / 6.7 / 0.7
2 SA	0545 / 1156 / 1801	6.9 / 0.8 / 6.4	**17** SU	0518 / 1118 / 1733 / 2340	6.6 / 0.9 / 6.5 / 0.7
3 SU	0023 / 0638 / 1237 / 1851	0.7 / 6.4 / 1.2 / 6.0	**18** M	0607 / 1202 / 1822	6.5 / 1.0 / 6.3
4 M	0112 / 0747 / 1331 / 2010	1.0 / 6.0 / 1.6 / 5.7	**19** TU	0029 / 0702 / 1258 / 1920	0.9 / 6.3 / 1.3 / 6.1
5 TU	0214 / 0905 / 1441 / 2128	1.3 / 5.9 / 1.8 / 5.7	**20** W	0136 / 0807 / 1414 / 2029	1.1 / 6.2 / 1.4 / 6.1
6 W	0326 / 1008 / 1558 / 2229	1.3 / 6.1 / 1.7 / 6.0	**21** TH	0305 / 0920 / 1544 / 2141	1.1 / 6.3 / 1.3 / 6.2
7 TH	0450 / 1104 / 1717 / 2324	1.1 / 6.3 / 1.4 / 6.2	**22** F	0429 / 1030 / 1659 / 2248	0.9 / 6.5 / 1.1 / 6.5
8 F	0554 / 1155 / 1817	0.8 / 6.6 / 1.1	**23** SA	0542 / 1132 / 1806 / 2348	0.6 / 6.9 / 0.8 / 6.8
9 SA	0014 / 0645 / 1241 / 1906	6.5 / 0.6 / 6.8 / 0.8	**24** SU	0643 / 1227 / 1906	0.3 / 7.1 / 0.5
10 SU	0059 / 0730 / 1321 / 1950	6.6 / 0.5 / 6.9 / 0.7	**25** M	0043 / 0737 / 1319 / ●2000	7.1 / 0.1 / 7.3 / 0.2
11 M	0139 / 0811 / 1357 / O2029	6.7 / 0.5 / 6.9 / 0.7	**26** TU	0135 / 0827 / 1407 / 2050	7.3 / 0.0 / 7.4 / 0.1
12 TU	0214 / 0848 / 1429 / 2102	6.7 / 0.6 / 6.8 / 0.7	**27** W	0224 / 0913 / 1452 / 2137	7.4 / 0.0 / 7.4 / 0.0
13 W	0247 / 0918 / 1501 / 2130	6.6 / 0.7 / 6.8 / 0.7	**28** TH	0312 / 0954 / 1536 / 2219	7.5 / 0.2 / 7.3 / 0.1
14 TH	0320 / 0943 / 1535 / 2156	6.7 / 0.8 / 6.8 / 0.7	**29** F	0358 / 1032 / 1618 / 2258	7.4 / 0.4 / 7.1 / 0.2
15 F	0355 / 1009 / 1611 / 2226	6.7 / 0.8 / 6.8 / 0.7	**30** SA	0444 / 1106 / 1659 / 2334	7.2 / 0.6 / 6.8 / 0.4
			31 SU	0529 / 1139 / 1739	6.9 / 0.9 / 6.5

JUNE

Day	Time	m	Day	Time	m
1 M	0009 / 0617 / 1215 / 1823	0.7 / 6.5 / 1.2 / 6.2	**16** TU	0556 / 1157 / 1807	6.6 / 1.0 / 6.5
2 TU	0051 / 0711 / 1259 / 1919	0.9 / 6.2 / 1.4 / 5.9	**17** W	0029 / 0648 / 1249 / 1901	0.8 / 6.5 / 1.1 / 6.3
3 W	0143 / 0816 / 1357 / 2033	1.1 / 6.0 / 1.7 / 5.8	**18** TH	0127 / 0750 / 1353 / 2005	0.9 / 6.3 / 1.3 / 6.2
4 TH	0242 / 0922 / 1501 / 2141	1.2 / 5.9 / 1.7 / 5.8	**19** F	0238 / 0858 / 1509 / 2115	0.9 / 6.3 / 1.3 / 6.3
5 F	0343 / 1019 / 1605 / 2239	1.2 / 6.1 / 1.6 / 6.0	**20** SA	0357 / 1005 / 1626 / 2222	0.9 / 6.5 / 1.2 / 6.4
6 SA	0447 / 1112 / 1709 / 2333	1.0 / 6.3 / 1.4 / 6.2	**21** SU	0513 / 1108 / 1739 / 2325	0.7 / 6.7 / 0.9 / 6.7
7 SU	0549 / 1201 / 1811	0.8 / 6.5 / 1.1	**22** M	0617 / 1206 / 1843	0.5 / 6.9 / 0.6
8 M	0021 / 0642 / 1245 / 1904	6.4 / 0.7 / 6.7 / 0.9	**23** TU	0024 / 0713 / 1259 / 1940	6.9 / 0.3 / 7.1 / 0.4
9 TU	0106 / 0729 / 1326 / 1950	6.6 / 0.6 / 6.9 / 0.8	**24** W	0118 / 0804 / 1349 / ●2032	7.2 / 0.2 / 7.2 / 0.2
10 W	0147 / 0812 / 1404 / O2032	6.7 / 0.6 / 6.9 / 0.7	**25** TH	0209 / 0852 / 1435 / 2121	7.3 / 0.2 / 7.2 / 0.1
11 TH	0225 / 0850 / 1441 / 2111	6.7 / 0.6 / 6.9 / 0.7	**26** F	0258 / 0936 / 1519 / 2205	7.3 / 0.3 / 7.1 / 0.1
12 F	0303 / 0926 / 1518 / 2148	6.8 / 0.7 / 6.9 / 0.6	**27** SA	0344 / 1016 / 1600 / 2246	7.2 / 0.5 / 7.0 / 0.3
13 SA	0342 / 1000 / 1556 / 2225	6.8 / 0.7 / 6.8 / 0.6	**28** SU	0427 / 1051 / 1639 / 2321	7.1 / 0.7 / 6.8 / 0.4
14 SU	0424 / 1036 / 1636 / 2302	6.8 / 0.8 / 6.7 / 0.6	**29** M	0509 / 1122 / 1715 / 2353	7.0 / 0.9 / 6.6 / 0.6
15 M	0508 / 1114 / 1719 / 2342	6.8 / 0.8 / 6.6 / 0.7	**30** TU	0549 / 1151 / 1753	6.6 / 1.1 / 6.4

JULY

Day	Time	m	Day	Time	m
1 W	0025 / 0630 / 1224 / 1836	0.8 / 6.3 / 1.3 / 6.2	**16** TH	0022 / 0630 / 1236 / 1839	0.6 / 6.7 / 0.9 / 6.6
2 TH	0105 / 0718 / 1308 / 1928	0.9 / 6.1 / 1.4 / 6.1	**17** F	0108 / 0726 / 1329 / 1938	0.7 / 6.4 / 1.1 / 6.4
3 F	0155 / 0813 / 1405 / 2031	1.1 / 5.9 / 1.5 / 5.8	**18** SA	0206 / 0832 / 1434 / 2048	0.9 / 6.2 / 1.3 / 6.2
4 SA	0252 / 0915 / 1509 / 2138	1.2 / 5.9 / 1.6 / 5.8	**19** SU	0319 / 0941 / 1551 / 2200	1.1 / 6.2 / 1.3 / 6.2
5 SU	0353 / 1017 / 1612 / 2242	1.1 / 6.0 / 1.5 / 5.9	**20** M	0444 / 1047 / 1715 / 2308	1.0 / 6.4 / 1.1 / 6.4
6 M	0454 / 1115 / 1714 / 2341	1.0 / 6.2 / 1.3 / 6.2	**21** TU	0555 / 1147 / 1826	0.8 / 6.6 / 0.8
7 TU	0555 / 1208 / 1816	0.8 / 6.5 / 1.0	**22** W	0010 / 0653 / 1243 / 1924	6.7 / 0.6 / 6.9 / 0.5
8 W	0033 / 0650 / 1256 / 1914	6.4 / 0.7 / 6.7 / 0.8	**23** TH	0106 / 0745 / 1333 / ●2017	7.0 / 0.4 / 7.1 / 0.2
9 TH	0121 / 0741 / 1341 / O2008	6.7 / 0.6 / 6.9 / 0.7	**24** F	0157 / 0833 / 1420 / 2106	7.2 / 0.4 / 7.1 / 0.1
10 F	0205 / 0828 / 1423 / 2058	6.8 / 0.6 / 6.9 / 0.6	**25** SA	0244 / 0918 / 1503 / 2150	7.2 / 0.4 / 7.1 / 0.1
11 SA	0247 / 0913 / 1504 / 2144	6.9 / 0.6 / 7.0 / 0.5	**26** SU	0327 / 0959 / 1541 / 2230	7.1 / 0.5 / 6.9 / 0.3
12 SU	0330 / 0954 / 1544 / 2226	7.0 / 0.6 / 6.9 / 0.5	**27** M	0407 / 1036 / 1616 / 2304	7.0 / 0.7 / 6.8 / 0.5
13 M	0412 / 1034 / 1624 / 2305	7.0 / 0.7 / 6.9 / 0.5	**28** TU	0442 / 1105 / 1647 / 2332	6.8 / 0.9 / 6.7 / 0.7
14 TU	0456 / 1112 / 1706 / 2342	7.0 / 0.7 / 6.9 / 0.5	**29** W	0516 / 1125 / 1721 / 2354	6.6 / 1.0 / 6.5 / 0.8
15 W	0542 / 1152 / 1750	6.9 / 0.8 / 6.8	**30** TH	0551 / 1147 / 1759	6.5 / 1.1 / 6.4
			31 F	0021 / 0631 / 1222 / 1843	0.9 / 6.3 / 1.2 / 6.1

AUGUST

Day	Time	m	Day	Time	m
1 SA	0100 / 0717 / 1309 / 1935	1.0 / 6.1 / 1.3 / 5.9	**16** SU	0131 / 0801 / 1402 / 2021	1.0 / 6.1 / 1.3 / 6.1
2 SU	0156 / 0812 / 1414 / 2036	1.2 / 5.9 / 1.5 / 5.7	**17** M	0238 / 0917 / 1517 / 2142	1.3 / 5.9 / 1.5 / 6.0
3 M	0304 / 0917 / 1527 / 2146	1.3 / 5.9 / 1.5 / 5.7	**18** TU	0412 / 1028 / 1657 / 2255	1.4 / 6.1 / 1.3 / 6.2
4 TU	0412 / 1027 / 1634 / 2258	1.2 / 6.0 / 1.4 / 5.9	**19** W	0535 / 1130 / 1812 / 2357	1.2 / 6.4 / 0.9 / 6.6
5 W	0517 / 1132 / 1741	1.0 / 6.3 / 1.1	**20** TH	0634 / 1226 / 1909	0.8 / 6.8 / 0.5
6 TH	0001 / 0619 / 1228 / 1847	6.3 / 0.8 / 6.6 / 0.9	**21** F	0052 / 0726 / 1317 / 1959	7.0 / 0.5 / 7.0 / 0.2
7 F	0056 / 0717 / 1318 / 1950	6.6 / 0.6 / 6.9 / 0.6	**22** SA	0142 / 0814 / 1403 / ●2046	7.2 / 0.4 / 7.1 / 0.1
8 SA	0144 / 0811 / 1403 / O2045	6.9 / 0.5 / 7.0 / 0.4	**23** SU	0227 / 0859 / 1444 / 2129	7.2 / 0.4 / 7.1 / 0.1
9 SU	0229 / 0900 / 1446 / 2135	7.1 / 0.5 / 7.1 / 0.3	**24** M	0307 / 0940 / 1520 / 2208	7.1 / 0.5 / 6.9 / 0.3
10 M	0313 / 0946 / 1527 / 2219	7.2 / 0.5 / 7.1 / 0.2	**25** TU	0342 / 1017 / 1550 / 2241	6.9 / 0.7 / 6.8 / 0.5
11 TU	0356 / 1027 / 1607 / 2258	7.3 / 0.5 / 7.2 / 0.2	**26** W	0412 / 1044 / 1618 / 2305	6.8 / 0.8 / 6.7 / 0.7
12 W	0439 / 1105 / 1648 / 2333	7.2 / 0.5 / 7.1 / 0.3	**27** TH	0441 / 1057 / 1649 / 2317	6.7 / 1.0 / 6.6 / 0.9
13 TH	0522 / 1141 / 1730	7.1 / 0.6 / 7.0	**28** F	0514 / 1113 / 1725 / 2335	6.6 / 1.0 / 6.5 / 0.8
14 F	0005 / 0607 / 1219 / 1816	0.5 / 6.8 / 0.8 / 6.8	**29** SA	0551 / 1144 / 1805	6.5 / 1.0 / 6.3
15 SA	0043 / 0658 / 1304 / 1910	0.7 / 6.4 / 1.0 / 6.4	**30** SU	0008 / 0633 / 1224 / 1852	0.9 / 6.3 / 1.1 / 6.2
			31 M	0052 / 0723 / 1318 / 1948	1.2 / 6.0 / 1.4 / 5.8

ENGLAND – LONDON BRIDGE

LAT 51°30′N   LONG 0°05′W

TIMES AND HEIGHTS OF HIGH AND LOW WATERS   YEAR **1998**

TIME ZONE (UT)
For Summer Time add ONE hour in non-shaded areas

4

SEPTEMBER

Day	Time m	Time m	Time m	Time m		Day	Time m	Time m	Time m	Time m
1 TU	0202 1.5	0824 5.8	1442 1.6	2055 5.7		16 W	0336 1.7	1008 5.9	1641 1.4	2240 6.2
2 W	0332 1.5	0938 5.8	1602 1.5	2214 5.8		17 TH	0511 1.4	1110 6.3	1754 0.9	2341 6.6
3 TH	0446 1.3	1055 6.1	1714 1.2	2330 6.2		18 F	0612 1.0	1206 6.7	1848 0.4	
4 F	0554 1.0	1159 6.4	1827 0.9			19 SA	0034 7.0	0703 0.6	1256 7.0	1936 0.2
5 SA	0030 6.6	0655 0.7	1252 6.8	1932 0.5		20 SU	0122 7.2	0750 0.4	1341 7.1	● 2021 0.1
6 SU	0121 7.0	0751 0.5	1339 7.1	O 2028 0.3		21 M	0205 7.2	0835 0.4	1421 7.1	2103 0.2
7 M	0207 7.3	0843 0.4	1423 7.2	2118 0.1		22 TU	0243 7.1	0916 0.5	1455 6.9	2141 0.4
8 TU	0251 7.4	0930 0.3	1505 7.3	2202 0.1		23 W	0314 6.9	0953 0.7	1523 6.7	2213 0.6
9 W	0334 7.5	1013 0.3	1546 7.4	2241 0.1		24 TH	0340 6.8	1019 0.6	1550 6.6	2233 0.8
10 TH	0417 7.4	1051 0.3	1627 7.4	2314 0.3		25 F	0408 6.7	1027 1.0	1620 6.6	2238 0.9
11 F	0459 7.2	1126 0.5	1710 7.2	2343 0.5		26 SA	0439 6.7	1044 0.9	1654 6.6	2258 0.8
12 SA	0542 6.9	1201 0.7	1755 6.9			27 SU	0515 6.6	1113 0.9	1734 6.4	2330 0.9
13 SU	0016 0.8	0628 6.4	1242 1.0	1846 6.4		28 M	0556 6.4	1150 1.0	1819 6.2	
14 M	0100 1.2	0728 5.9	1336 1.3	1959 5.9		29 TU	0009 1.1	0643 6.1	1236 1.3	1913 5.9
15 TU	0203 1.6	0853 5.7	1450 1.5	2128 5.9		30 W	0103 1.5	0741 5.8	1347 1.6	2017 5.8

OCTOBER

Day	Time m	Time m	Time m	Time m		Day	Time m	Time m	Time m	Time m
1 TH	0241 1.7	0851 5.7	1531 1.5	2134 5.8		16 F	0437 1.7	1044 6.1	1724 1.0	2315 6.5
2 F	0415 1.5	1014 5.9	1649 1.2	2256 6.2		17 SA	0542 1.2	1139 6.5	1818 0.6	
3 SA	0526 1.2	1125 6.3	1803 0.8			18 SU	0008 6.9	0635 0.8	1229 6.9	1905 0.3
4 SU	0000 6.7	0630 0.8	1221 6.8	1908 0.5		19 M	0056 7.1	0722 0.6	1314 7.0	1950 0.2
5 M	0054 7.1	0727 0.6	1310 7.1	O 2003 0.2		20 TU	0138 7.1	0807 0.5	1354 7.0	● 2031 0.3
6 TU	0141 7.4	0820 0.4	1356 7.3	2053 0.1		21 W	0214 7.0	0848 0.6	1428 6.8	2109 0.5
7 W	0226 7.5	0909 0.2	1440 7.5	2138 0.0		22 TH	0244 6.9	0924 0.7	1457 6.7	2140 0.7
8 TH	0310 7.5	0953 0.2	1524 7.6	2217 0.1		23 F	0310 6.8	0949 0.9	1525 6.6	2157 0.9
9 F	0353 7.5	1033 0.2	1607 7.5	2252 0.3		24 SA	0338 6.8	1000 1.0	1555 6.6	2207 0.9
10 SA	0435 7.2	1110 0.3	1651 7.5	2322 0.5		25 SU	0409 6.7	1021 0.9	1630 6.6	2232 0.9
11 SU	0518 6.9	1145 0.6	1737 7.0	2354 0.8		26 M	0445 6.7	1051 0.8	1710 6.5	2305 0.9
12 M	0602 6.4	1224 0.9	1830 6.5			27 TU	0526 6.5	1128 1.0	1756 6.3	2344 1.1
13 TU	0035 1.3	0656 6.0	1316 1.2	1941 6.0		28 W	0613 6.2	1212 1.2	1848 6.1	
14 W	0134 1.7	0826 5.7	1427 1.5	2108 5.9		29 TH	0034 1.4	0708 5.9	1315 1.4	1950 6.0
15 TH	0257 1.9	0943 5.8	1610 1.4	2217 6.1		30 F	0149 1.7	1105 5.8	1458 1.5	2103 6.0
						31 SA	0338 1.6	0935 6.0	1621 1.2	2222 6.3

NOVEMBER

Day	Time m	Time m	Time m	Time m		Day	Time m	Time m	Time m	Time m
1 SU	0454 1.3	1048 6.3	1735 0.8	2328 6.7		16 M	0558 1.2	1156 6.6	1828 0.7	
2 M	0600 0.9	1147 6.7	1840 0.5			17 TU	0022 6.8	0648 0.9	1243 6.7	1913 0.6
3 TU	0024 7.1	0700 0.6	1241 7.1	1935 0.3		18 W	0105 6.9	0734 0.7	1324 6.8	1955 0.6
4 W	0115 7.4	0755 0.4	1330 7.4	O 2026 0.1		19 TH	0142 6.9	0815 0.7	1400 6.8	● 2033 0.7
5 TH	0202 7.5	0845 0.2	1417 7.5	2112 0.1		20 F	0214 6.8	0850 0.8	1432 6.7	2104 0.8
6 F	0247 7.5	0932 0.1	1504 7.6	2154 0.2		21 SA	0243 6.8	0918 0.9	1503 6.7	2126 0.9
7 SA	0331 7.4	1016 0.2	1550 7.6	2231 0.4		22 SU	0314 6.8	0940 0.9	1536 6.7	2147 0.9
8 SU	0414 7.2	1055 0.3	1636 7.4	2304 0.6		23 M	0347 6.8	1007 0.9	1612 6.7	2216 0.9
9 M	0456 6.9	1132 0.5	1723 7.0	2337 0.9		24 TU	0423 6.7	1039 0.9	1653 6.6	2251 0.9
10 TU	0540 6.5	1211 0.8	1815 6.6			25 W	0504 6.6	1117 1.0	1739 6.5	2332 1.1
11 W	0015 1.3	0629 6.1	1259 1.1	1918 6.2		26 TH	0550 6.4	1202 1.1	1830 6.3	
12 TH	0107 1.6	0747 5.7	1400 1.3	2037 6.0		27 F	0020 1.3	0642 6.1	1300 1.2	1929 6.2
13 F	0216 1.9	0908 5.7	1515 1.4	2144 6.1		28 SA	0124 1.5	0745 6.0	1421 1.5	2037 6.1
14 SA	0337 1.8	1010 6.0	1637 1.2	2242 6.3		29 SU	0252 1.5	0900 6.1	1545 1.1	2150 6.3
15 SU	0457 1.5	1105 6.3	1737 0.9	2334 6.6		30 M	0416 1.3	1013 6.3	1702 0.9	2257 6.6

DECEMBER

Day	Time m	Time m	Time m	Time m		Day	Time m	Time m	Time m	Time m
1 TU	0528 1.1	1116 6.7	1810 0.7	2356 6.9		16 W	0552 1.3	1207 6.4	1826 0.9	
2 W	0633 0.8	1214 7.0	1908 0.4			17 TH	0027 6.6	0647 1.1	1252 6.5	1912 0.8
3 TH	0049 7.2	0731 0.5	1308 7.3	O 2000 0.3		18 F	0109 6.7	0734 0.9	1333 6.7	● 1954 0.8
4 F	0139 7.3	0824 0.3	1358 7.5	2049 0.3		19 SA	0146 6.8	0815 0.8	1410 6.7	2031 0.8
5 SA	0226 7.4	0914 0.2	1447 7.5	2133 0.3		20 SU	0222 6.8	0852 0.8	1446 6.7	2104 0.9
6 SU	0312 7.3	1000 0.2	1535 7.5	2213 0.5		21 M	0256 6.8	0927 0.8	1522 6.8	2135 0.9
7 M	0355 7.1	1043 0.3	1622 7.3	2249 0.7		22 TU	0331 6.8	1002 0.8	1600 6.8	2209 0.9
8 TU	0438 6.9	1122 0.5	1708 7.1	2323 0.9		23 W	0408 6.7	1038 0.8	1641 6.8	2245 0.9
9 W	0519 6.6	1159 0.7	1755 6.7	2357 1.2		24 TH	0448 6.7	1116 0.8	1725 6.7	2325 1.0
10 TH	0601 6.3	1239 0.9	1847 6.3			25 F	0532 6.6	1158 0.9	1814 6.6	
11 F	0038 1.5	0653 6.0	1327 1.2	1948 6.0		26 SA	0010 1.1	0620 6.4	1247 1.0	1908 6.4
12 SA	0131 1.7	0809 5.7	1423 1.3	2056 5.9		27 SU	0104 1.3	0718 6.2	1348 1.1	2010 6.3
13 SU	0234 1.8	0922 5.8	1524 1.3	2157 6.0		28 M	0211 1.4	0826 6.2	1502 1.1	2120 6.2
14 M	0340 1.8	1023 5.9	1628 1.2	2251 6.1		29 TU	0332 1.4	0940 6.2	1625 1.1	2229 6.4
15 TU	0446 1.6	1117 6.1	1731 1.1	2342 6.4		30 W	0454 1.2	1050 6.4	1742 0.9	2332 6.6
						31 TH	0609 1.0	1153 6.7	1845 0.7	

Chart Datum: 3·20 metres below Ordnance Datum (Newlyn)

SOUTHEND-ON-SEA/
LEIGH-ON-SEA   10-4-15
Essex (Lat/Long as for Waypoint)   Rtg 3-5-2

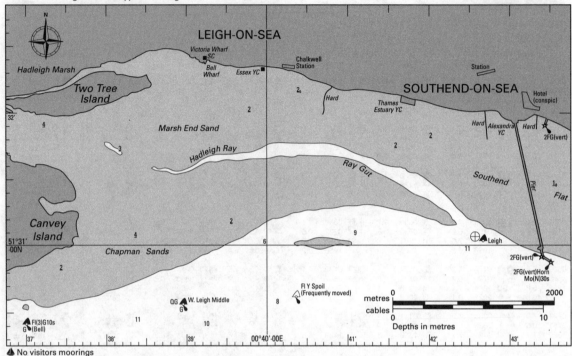

⚠ No visitors moorings

CHARTS
AC *1185, 1183*; Imray C2, Y6; Stanfords 5, 8; OS 178
TIDES
+0125 Dover; ML 3·0; Duration 0610; Zone 0 (UT)

Standard Port SHEERNESS (←—)

Times				Height (metres)			
High Water		Low Water		MHWS	MHWN	MLWN	MLWS
0200	0800	0200	0700	5·8	4·7	1·5	0·6
1400	2000	1400	1900				
Differences SOUTHEND-ON-SEA							
−0005	−0005	−0005	−0005	0·0	0·0	−0·1	−0·1
CORYTON							
+0010	+0010	0000	+0010	+0·5	+0·4	−0·1	−0·1

SHELTER
The whole area dries soon after half ebb, except Ray Gut
(0·4 - 4·8m) which leads to Leigh Creek and Hadleigh Ray,
either side of Two Tree Island, thence to Benfleet Creek; all
are buoyed, but echo-sounder is essential. At Leigh-on-Sea
some drying moorings are available; or yachts can take the
ground alongside Bell Wharf or Victoria Wharf. It is also
possible to secure at the end of Southend Pier to collect
stores, FW. NOTE: Southend-on-Sea and Leigh-on-Sea are
both part of the lower PLA Area and an 8kn speed limit is
enforced in inshore areas. Southend BC launches *Alec
White II* , *Sidney Bates II* or *Low Way* patrol area (VHF Ch
68 16), Apr-Oct.
NAVIGATION
WPT Leigh SHM buoy, 51°31´·04N 00°42´·67E, at ent to
Ray Gut; this SHM buoy can be left close to port on
entering Ray Gut, since there is now more water NE of it
than to the SW. Appr from Shoeburyness, keep outside
the W Shoebury SHM buoy, Fl G 2·5s. Beware some 3000
small boat moorings 1M either side of Southend Pier.
Speed limit in Canvey Island/Hadleigh Ray areas is 8kn.
LIGHTS AND MARKS
Pier lts as on chartlet.
RADIO TELEPHONE
Thames Navigation Service: *Port Control London* VHF Ch 68.
TELEPHONE (Dial code 01702)
Hr Mr 611889, ☎ 355110; Hr Mr Leigh-on-Sea 710561;
MRSC (01255) 675518; Essex Police Marine Section
(01268) 775533; ✇ (01473) 235704 (H24); Marinecall 0891
500455; Police 341212; Dr 49451; Ⓗ 348911.

FACILITIES
SOUTHEND-ON-SEA: **Southend Pier** ☎ 215620, AB £6.00,
M, L, FW, Bar; **Alexandra YC** ☎ 340363, Bar, FW; **Thorpe
Bay YC** ☎ 587563, Bar, L, Slip, R, FW; **Thames Estuary YC**
☎ 345967; **Halfway YC** ☎ 582025, pre-book 1 ⚓, FW;
Town EC Wed. CH, ACA, Ⓔ, V, R, Bar, ✉, Ⓑ, ⇌, ✈.
LEIGH-ON-SEA: **Essex YC** ☎ 78404, FW, Bar; **Leigh on Sea
SC** ☎ 76788, FW, Bar; **Bell Wharf**, AB (1st 24hrs free, then
£5 for subsequent 24 hrs); **Victoria Wharf** AB, SM, Slip;
Town: EC Wed, P &D (cans), ME, El, Sh, C, CH, SM.
CANVEY ISLAND: **Services**: Slip, M, D, FW, ME, El, Sh, C,
Gas, CH, Access HW±2; **Island YC** ☎ 683729.
BENFLEET: **Benfleet YC** ☎ (01268) 792278, Access HW±2½,
M, Slip, FW, D (by day), CH, ME, El, Sh, C, Bar, V, Ⓞ.

AGENTS WANTED

If you are interested in becoming our agent for any of the
following ports, please write to: The Editor, Edington House,
Trent, Sherborne, Dorset DT9 4SR, England – and get your
free copy of the Almanac annually. You do not have to live in
a port to be the agent, but at least a fairly regular visitor.

Great Yarmouth	St Gilles-Croix-de-Vie
Port Ellen (Islay)	Les Sables d'Olonne
Maryport	Ile d'Oléron
Workington	River Seudre
Holyhead	Anglet/Bayonne
Lough Swilly	St Jean-de-Luz
St Peter Port, Guernsey	Hendaye
Diélette	Grandcamp-Maisy
Portbail	Port-en-Bessin
Iles Chausey	Courseulles
St Malo/Dinard	Ouistreham/Caen
Le Legue/St Brieuc	Emden
Tréguier	Dornumer-Accumersiel
Lampaul	Langeoog
L'Aberildut	Bremerhaven
Le Palais (Belle Ile)	Büsum
Morbihan/Vannes	

RIVER ROACH/HAVENGORE

10-4-16

Essex 51°36'·95N 00°52'·24E (Branklet SPM buoy), R Roach Rtg 1-5-1. 51°33'·59N 00°50'·62E, Havengore Bridge, Rtg 5-5-3

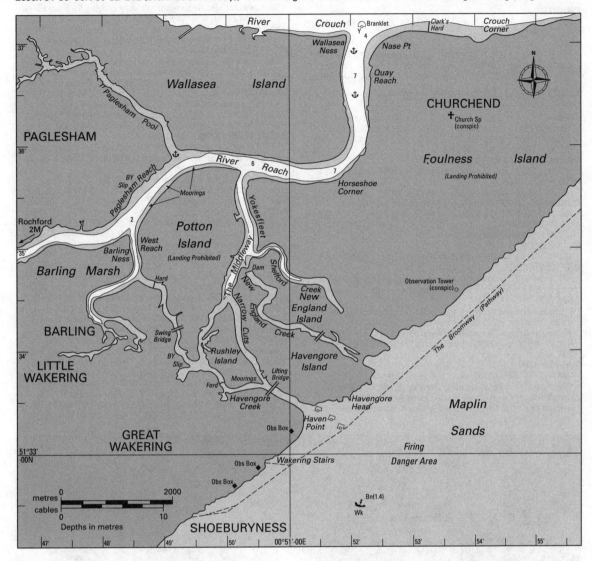

CHARTS
AC *3750, 1185*; Imray C1, Y17; Stanfords 4, 5; OS 178

TIDES
+0110 Dover; ML 2·7; Duration 0615; Zone 0 (UT)

Standard Port WALTON-ON-THE-NAZE (→)

Times				Height (metres)			
High Water		Low Water		MHWS	MHWN	MLWN	MLWS
0000	0600	0500	1100	4·2	3·4	1·1	0·4
1200	1800	1700	2300				
Differences ROCHFORD							
+0050	+0040	Dries		–0·8	–1·1	Dries	

SHELTER
Good. The Roach gives sheltered sailing and access to a network of secluded creeks, including Havengore (the "backdoor" from the Crouch to the Thames Estuary). ‡s behind sea-walls can be found for all winds at: Quay Reach (often more protected than the Crouch), Paglesham Reach (possible moorings from BY at East End), West Reach, Barling Reach and Yokes Fleet. An ↓ light is essential due to freighters H24. Speed limit 8kn. Crouch Hbr Authority controls R Roach and Crouch, out to Foulness Pt.

NAVIGATION
Normal access H24 to the Roach is from R Crouch (see 10.4.17 for WPT from seaward); the ent between Branklet SPM buoy and Nase Pt is narrowed by mudbanks. Unlit buoys up-river to Barling Ness, above which few boats go.

To exit at Havengore Creek, appr via Middleway and Narrow Cuts to reach the bridge before HW.
Entry via **Havengore Creek** is possible in good weather, with great care and adequate rise of tide (max draft 1·5m at HW sp). Shoeburyness Range is usually active Mon-Fri · 0600-1700LT; give 24hrs notice to Range Officer by ☎. Subsequent clearance on VHF by Havengore lifting bridge (☎ HW±2, HJ); no passage unless bridge raised. Least water is over the shifting bar, just inside creek ent. From the S, cross Maplin Sands at HW –1 from S Shoebury SHM buoy, Fl G 5s (51°30'·40N 00°52'·50E), leaving Pisces wreck (conspic, 1M from ent) to port.

LIGHTS AND MARKS
Unlit, but night entry to R Roach may be possible.

RADIO TELEPHONE
VHF Ch 72 16 is worked by Range Officer (*Shoe Base*) (HO); Radar Control (*Shoe Radar*) (HO); & Bridge keeper (*Shoe Bridge*) (HW±2 by day). Radar guidance may be available.

TELEPHONE (Dial code 01702= Southend)
Crouch Hbr Mr (01621) 783602; Range Officer 292271 Ext 3211; Havengore Bridge Ext 3436; Marinecall 0891 500455; ⌗ (01473) 235704 (H24); MRSC (01255) 675518; Dr 218678.

FACILITIES
Paglesham (East End) M £5, FW, D, slip, EI, ME (from BY), Sh, Bar; **Gt Wakering**: Slip, P, D, FW, ME, EI, Sh, C, CH (from BY); @ Rochford **Wakering YC** ☎ 530926, M, L, Bar. **Towns** EC Wed Gt Wakering & Rochford; V, R, Bar, ✉ (Great Wakering and Barling); most facilities, Ⓑ and ⇌ in Rochford and Shoeburyness, ✈ (Southend).

BURNHAM-ON-CROUCH   10-4-17

Essex 51°37'·47N 00°48'·33E (Yacht Hbr)   Rtg 1-1-2

CHARTS
AC *3750, 1975, 1183*; Imray Y17, Y7, Y6, C1; Stanfords 4, 5, 19, 1; OS168

TIDES
+0115 Dover; ML 2·5; Duration 0610; Zone 0 (UT). Full daily predictions for Burnham are on following pages. Ranges: Sp = 5·0m; Np = 3·2m. Use Walton Tidal Curves (10.4.20)

Standard Port WALTON-ON-THE-NAZE (→)

Times				Height (metres)			
High Water		Low Water		MHWS	MHWN	MLWN	MLWS
0000	0600	0500	1100	4·2	3·4	1·1	0·4
1200	1800	1700	2300				
Differences WHITAKER BEACON							
+0022	+0024	+0033	+0027	+0·6	+0·5	+0·2	+0·1
HOLLIWELL POINT							
+0034	+0037	+0100	+0037	+1·1	+0·9	+0·3	+0·1
BURNHAM-ON-CROUCH (but see also full predictions)							
+0050	+0035	+0115	+0050	+1·0	+0·8	−0·1	−0·2
NORTH FAMBRIDGE							
+0115	+0050	+0130	+0100	+1·1	+0·8	0·0	−0·1
HULLBRIDGE							
+0115	+0050	+0135	+0105	+1·1	+0·8	0·0	−0·1
BATTLESBRIDGE							
+0120	+0110	Dries	Dries	−1·8	−2·0	Dries	Dries

SHELTER
River is exposed to most winds. There are six marinas or yacht hbrs. ⚓ prohib in fairway but possible just E or W of the moorings. Speed limit in moorings is 8kn. Cliff Reach (off W edge of lower chartlet) is sheltered from SW'lies.

NAVIGATION
WPT 51°39'·82N 01°02'·60E, S Buxey SHM buoy, Fl (3) G 15s. Appr from East Swin, or the Wallet via Spitway, into the Whitaker Chan. From Swin Spitway SWM buoy, there is least depth of 4m between Swallowtail and Buxey Sand.

Near Sunken Buxey seas can be hazardous with strong wind over tide. Ray Sand Chan (dries 1·7m) is usable on the tide by shoal draft boats as a short cut from/to the Blackwater. Shoeburyness Artillery ranges lie E and S of Foulness Pt, clear of the fairway. Landing on Foulness and Bridgemarsh Is (up river) is prohibited. R. Crouch is navigable to Battlesbridge, 10M beyond Burnham.

LIGHTS AND MARKS
There are few landmarks to assist entering, but Whitaker Chan and the river are lit/buoyed to 0·5M W of Essex Marina. From Sunken Buxey NCM buoy, Q, the spire of St Mary's ✠ leads 233° to Outer Crouch SCM buoy, Q (6) + L Fl 15s; thence steer 240° past Foulness Pt into the river. There is a 2·2M unlit gap between Inner Crouch SWM buoy, L Fl 10s, and Horse Shoal NCM buoy, Q.

RADIO TELEPHONE
VHF Ch 80 for: Crouch Hr Mr Launch (0900-1700LT, w/e); Essex Marina; Burnham Yacht Harbour; W Wick Marina (1000-1700), also Ch M.

TELEPHONE (Dial code Maldon = 01621)
Hr Mr 783602; MRSC (01255) 675518; ⌗ (01473) 235704 (H24); Marinecall 0891 500455; Police 782121; Dr 782054.

FACILITIES
BURNHAM: Burnham Yacht Hbr ☎ 782150, ⚓ 785848, Access H24, (350) £8, D, AC, FW, ME, EI, Sh, BH (30 ton), CH, ◎, Bar, Slip; **Royal Corinthian YC** ☎ 782105, AB, FW, M, L, R, Bar; **Royal Burnham YC** ☎ 782044, FW, L, R, Bar; **Crouch YC** ☎ 782252, L, FW, R, Bar; **Services:** AB, BY, C (15 ton), D, P, FW, ME, EI, Sh, M, Slip, CH, ACA, Gas, SM, Gaz. **Town** EC Wed; V, R, Bar, ✉, Ⓑ, ➤, ✈ (Southend).
WALLASEA (01702): **Essex Marina** (400) ☎ (01702) 258531, ⚓ 258227, BY, Gas, Bar, C (13 ton), BH (40 ton), CH, D, P, EI, FW, M, ME, R, Sh, Slip, V; Ferry to Burnham Town Hard at w/ends in season, ☎ 258870; **Essex YC**; ACA.
FAMBRIDGE: N Fambridge Yacht Stn (150) ☎ 740370, Access HW±5, M, CH, Sh, ME, BY, C (5 ton), EI, FW, Slip, Gas, Gaz; **W Wick Marina** (Stow Creek) (180) ☎ 741268, Access HW±5, Gas, Gaz, CH, EI, Slip, FW, D, C (5 ton), YC, Bar; **Brandy Hole Yacht Stn** (120) ☎ (01702) 230248, L, M, ME, Sh, Slip, Gas, Gaz, Bar, BY, D, FW, Access HW±4.
ALTHORNE: Bridge Marsh Marina (125 + 6 Ⓥ) ☎ 740414, ⚓ 742216, Access HW±4, FW, Sh, ◎, ME, EI, C (8 ton), Slip.

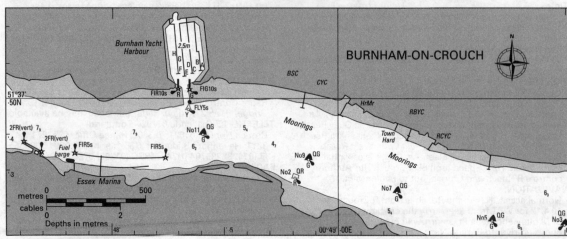

ENGLAND – BURNHAM–ON–CROUCH

LAT 51°37′N   LONG 0°48′E

TIMES AND HEIGHTS OF HIGH AND LOW WATERS   YEAR 1998

TIME ZONE (UT)
For Summer Time add ONE hour in non-shaded areas

JANUARY

Day	Time	m		Day	Time	m
1 TH	0145 / 0819 / 1412 / 2027	5.1 / 0.2 / 5.2 / 0.5		**16** F	0222 / 0858 / 1444 / 2053	5.0 / 0.3 / 5.0 / 0.7
2 F	0224 / 0859 / 1454 / 2105	5.1 / 0.2 / 5.2 / 0.5		**17** SA	0251 / 0930 / 1515 / 2121	5.0 / 0.3 / 4.8 / 0.7
3 SA	0304 / 0941 / 1538 / 2147	5.1 / 0.2 / 5.1 / 0.5		**18** SU	0322 / 1001 / 1548 / 2151	4.8 / 0.4 / 4.7 / 0.8
4 SU	0349 / 1027 / 1626 / 2232	5.0 / 0.2 / 5.0 / 0.7		**19** M	0356 / 1035 / 1624 / 2229	4.7 / 0.5 / 4.7 / 0.9
5 M	0437 / 1117 / 1720 / 2325	4.8 / 0.3 / 4.7 / 0.8		**20** TU	0436 / 1116 / 1706 / 2315	4.6 / 0.7 / 4.5 / 1.0
6 TU	0534 / 1220 / 1820	4.7 / 0.4 / 4.6		**21** W	0525 / 1209 / 1756	4.5 / 0.8 / 4.3
7 W	0033 / 0640 / 1337 / 1932	0.9 / 4.5 / 0.5 / 4.5		**22** TH	0016 / 0624 / 1315 / 1857	1.1 / 4.2 / 0.9 / 4.2
8 TH	0155 / 0756 / 1455 / 2043	0.9 / 4.5 / 0.5 / 4.5		**23** F	0130 / 0736 / 1425 / 2011	1.1 / 4.2 / 0.9 / 4.2
9 F	0316 / 0908 / 1605 / 2150	0.9 / 4.6 / 0.5 / 4.7		**24** SA	0246 / 0851 / 1532 / 2122	1.1 / 4.2 / 0.9 / 4.5
10 SA	0428 / 1014 / 1705 / 2249	0.7 / 4.8 / 0.4 / 4.8		**25** SU	0358 / 0956 / 1635 / 2223	0.9 / 4.5 / 0.8 / 4.6
11 SU	0530 / 1113 / 1756 / 2343	0.4 / 5.0 / 0.4 / 5.0		**26** M	0501 / 1053 / 1729 / 2317	0.8 / 4.7 / 0.7 / 4.8
12 M O	0623 / 1207 / 1839	0.3 / 5.1 / 0.5		**27** TU	0558 / 1145 / 1819	0.5 / 5.0 / 0.5
13 TU	0030 / 0707 / 1254 / 1917	5.0 / 0.3 / 5.1 / 0.5		**28** W ●	0005 / 0645 / 1232 / 1859	5.1 / 0.3 / 5.2 / 0.4
14 W	0112 / 0747 / 1334 / 1951	5.1 / 0.2 / 5.1 / 0.5		**29** TH	0050 / 0726 / 1317 / 1936	5.2 / 0.1 / 5.3 / 0.3
15 TH	0150 / 0824 / 1411 / 2024	5.0 / 0.2 / 5.0 / 0.7		**30** F	0132 / 0807 / 1358 / 2014	5.2 / 0.0 / 5.5 / 0.3
				31 SA	0212 / 0846 / 1440 / 2052	5.3 / 0.0 / 5.5 / 0.3

FEBRUARY

Day	Time	m		Day	Time	m
1 SU	0252 / 0927 / 1524 / 2132	5.3 / -0.1 / 5.3 / 0.3		**16** M	0257 / 0927 / 1517 / 2125	5.0 / 0.3 / 4.8 / 0.5
2 M	0334 / 1009 / 1608 / 2215	5.2 / 0.0 / 5.1 / 0.4		**17** TU	0329 / 0959 / 1551 / 2159	4.8 / 0.3 / 4.8 / 0.5
3 TU	0419 / 1055 / 1656 / 2302	5.1 / 0.2 / 4.8 / 0.5		**18** W	0405 / 1035 / 1630 / 2238	4.7 / 0.5 / 4.7 / 0.7
4 W	0510 / 1148 / 1751	4.8 / 0.4 / 4.6		**19** TH	0447 / 1120 / 1715 / 2327	4.6 / 0.7 / 4.5 / 0.9
5 TH	0000 / 0611 / 1301 / 1857	0.8 / 4.6 / 0.7 / 4.3		**20** F	0538 / 1221 / 1809	4.3 / 0.9 / 4.2
6 F	0121 / 0729 / 1425 / 2014	0.9 / 4.3 / 1.0 / 4.2		**21** SA	0035 / 0642 / 1337 / 1918	1.0 / 4.1 / 1.0 / 4.1
7 SA	0255 / 0849 / 1543 / 2128	0.9 / 4.5 / 0.8 / 4.3		**22** SU	0157 / 0803 / 1453 / 2037	1.1 / 4.1 / 1.0 / 4.2
8 SU	0416 / 1002 / 1646 / 2232	0.7 / 4.6 / 0.7 / 4.6		**23** M	0319 / 0922 / 1604 / 2149	0.9 / 4.3 / 0.9 / 4.5
9 M	0520 / 1102 / 1740 / 2327	0.5 / 4.8 / 0.7 / 4.8		**24** TU	0435 / 1027 / 1704 / 2250	0.7 / 4.7 / 0.7 / 4.7
10 TU	0613 / 1155 / 1824	0.3 / 5.0 / 0.5		**25** W	0536 / 1124 / 1756 / 2343	0.4 / 5.0 / 0.4 / 5.0
11 W O	0015 / 0654 / 1241 / 1900	5.0 / 0.2 / 5.1 / 0.5		**26** TH ●	0627 / 1214 / 1840	0.2 / 5.2 / 0.3
12 TH	0058 / 0732 / 1300 / 1932	5.0 / 0.2 / 5.1 / 0.5		**27** F	0030 / 0710 / 1300 / 1919	5.2 / 0.0 / 5.5 / 0.2
13 F	0133 / 0804 / 1353 / 2003	5.0 / 0.2 / 5.0 / 0.5		**28** SA	0114 / 0750 / 1343 / 1959	5.3 / -0.3 / 5.6 / 0.1
14 SA	0202 / 0834 / 1421 / 2029	5.0 / 0.2 / 5.0 / 0.5				
15 SU	0229 / 0900 / 1448 / 2056	5.0 / 0.3 / 4.8 / 0.5				

MARCH

Day	Time	m		Day	Time	m
1 SU	0156 / 0830 / 1424 / 2036	5.5 / -0.3 / 5.6 / 0.1		**16** M	0206 / 0831 / 1421 / 2032	5.0 / 0.3 / 5.0 / 0.4
2 M	0236 / 0909 / 1505 / 2116	5.5 / -0.3 / 5.5 / 0.1		**17** TU	0233 / 0857 / 1449 / 2101	4.8 / 0.3 / 5.0 / 0.3
3 TU	0318 / 0949 / 1549 / 2158	5.5 / -0.1 / 5.2 / 0.2		**18** W	0303 / 0927 / 1522 / 2135	5.0 / 0.3 / 5.0 / 0.4
4 W	0401 / 1032 / 1633 / 2243	5.2 / 0.1 / 5.0 / 0.4		**19** TH	0339 / 1000 / 1600 / 2211	4.8 / 0.4 / 4.8 / 0.6
5 TH	0450 / 1121 / 1724 / 2336	5.0 / 0.4 / 4.6 / 0.7		**20** F	0418 / 1039 / 1643 / 2255	4.7 / 0.7 / 4.6 / 0.7
6 F	0548 / 1227 / 1826	4.6 / 0.8 / 4.2		**21** SA	0506 / 1131 / 1736 / 2352	4.5 / 0.9 / 4.3 / 0.9
7 SA	0053 / 0705 / 1354 / 1946	0.9 / 4.3 / 1.0 / 4.1		**22** SU	0607 / 1250 / 1839	4.2 / 1.0 / 4.1
8 SU	0234 / 0832 / 1518 / 2104	0.9 / 4.3 / 1.0 / 4.2		**23** M	0116 / 0725 / 1416 / 1959	1.0 / 4.1 / 1.0 / 4.1
9 M	0358 / 0947 / 1625 / 2212	0.7 / 4.5 / 0.9 / 4.5		**24** TU	0246 / 0851 / 1532 / 2117	0.9 / 4.3 / 0.9 / 4.3
10 TU	0502 / 1046 / 1718 / 2307	0.5 / 4.7 / 0.8 / 4.7		**25** W	0407 / 1003 / 1636 / 2221	0.5 / 4.7 / 0.7 / 4.7
11 W	0554 / 1138 / 1803 / 2355	0.3 / 5.0 / 0.7 / 5.0		**26** TH	0511 / 1101 / 1730 / 2318	0.3 / 5.1 / 0.4 / 5.0
12 TH	0635 / 1221 / 1840	0.2 / 5.1 / 0.2		**27** F	0605 / 1153 / 1819	0.0 / 5.3 / 0.2
13 F O	0037 / 0709 / 1300 / 1912	5.0 / 0.2 / 5.0 / 0.4		**28** SA ●	0008 / 0650 / 1241 / 1900	5.2 / -0.1 / 5.5 / 0.1
14 SA	0111 / 0739 / 1331 / 1940	5.0 / 0.2 / 5.0 / 0.4		**29** SU	0055 / 0730 / 1325 / 1940	5.5 / -0.2 / 5.6 / 0.0
15 SU	0140 / 0806 / 1357 / 2006	5.0 / 0.2 / 4.8 / 0.4		**30** M	0137 / 0810 / 1406 / 2021	5.6 / -0.3 / 5.6 / 0.0
				31 TU	0219 / 0848 / 1447 / 2100	5.6 / -0.3 / 5.5 / 0.0

APRIL

Day	Time	m		Day	Time	m
1 W	0301 / 0928 / 1529 / 2142	5.5 / 0.0 / 5.2 / 0.1		**16** TH	0243 / 0901 / 1459 / 2115	5.0 / 0.4 / 5.0 / 0.3
2 TH	0346 / 1010 / 1613 / 2227	5.3 / 0.2 / 5.0 / 0.3		**17** F	0319 / 0934 / 1536 / 2151	4.8 / 0.5 / 4.8 / 0.4
3 F	0433 / 1057 / 1701 / 2319	5.0 / 0.5 / 4.6 / 0.5		**18** SA	0359 / 1011 / 1619 / 2234	4.7 / 0.7 / 4.6 / 0.5
4 SA	0530 / 1155 / 1800	4.6 / 0.9 / 4.2		**19** SU	0447 / 1100 / 1711 / 2329	4.5 / 0.9 / 4.3 / 0.8
5 SU	0033 / 0642 / 1320 / 1915	0.8 / 4.2 / 1.1 / 4.1		**20** M	0546 / 1209 / 1812	4.3 / 1.0 / 4.2
6 M	0208 / 0807 / 1446 / 2034	0.8 / 4.2 / 1.1 / 4.1		**21** TU	0045 / 0659 / 1339 / 1929	0.8 / 4.2 / 1.1 / 4.2
7 TU	0331 / 0921 / 1556 / 2142	0.7 / 4.5 / 1.0 / 4.3		**22** W	0216 / 0822 / 1459 / 2044	0.7 / 4.3 / 0.9 / 4.3
8 W	0435 / 1021 / 1651 / 2238	0.4 / 4.7 / 0.9 / 4.6		**23** TH	0338 / 0935 / 1606 / 2151	0.4 / 4.7 / 0.7 / 4.7
9 TH	0525 / 1110 / 1737 / 2326	0.3 / 5.0 / 0.7 / 4.8		**24** F	0443 / 1035 / 1702 / 2248	0.2 / 5.1 / 0.4 / 5.0
10 F	0608 / 1154 / 1817	0.3 / 5.0 / 0.5		**25** SA	0539 / 1128 / 1755 / 2342	0.0 / 5.3 / 0.2 / 5.2
11 SA O	0008 / 0641 / 1232 / 1849	5.0 / 0.3 / 5.0 / 0.4		**26** SU ●	0628 / 1218 / 1840	-0.1 / 5.5 / 0.1
12 SU	0044 / 0710 / 1305 / 1917	5.0 / 0.3 / 5.0 / 0.4		**27** M	0032 / 0710 / 1305 / 1923	5.5 / -0.3 / 5.5 / 0.0
13 M	0114 / 0736 / 1331 / 1943	5.0 / 0.3 / 5.0 / 0.4		**28** TU	0118 / 0750 / 1348 / 2005	5.5 / -0.3 / 5.5 / 0.0
14 TU	0142 / 0803 / 1357 / 2012	4.8 / 0.3 / 5.0 / 0.3		**29** W	0202 / 0829 / 1429 / 2047	5.6 / -0.1 / 5.3 / 0.0
15 W	0211 / 0832 / 1425 / 2042	5.0 / 0.3 / 5.0 / 0.3		**30** TH	0246 / 0909 / 1511 / 2130	5.5 / 0.1 / 5.2 / 0.1

Chart Datum: 2·35 metres below Ordnance Datum (Newlyn)

ENGLAND – BURNHAM–ON–CROUCH

LAT 51°37'N   LONG 0°48'E

TIMES AND HEIGHTS OF HIGH AND LOW WATERS

YEAR 1998

TIME ZONE (UT) — For Summer Time add ONE hour in non-shaded areas

Chart Datum: 2·35 metres below Ordnance Datum (Newlyn)

(● = new moon, O = full moon)

MAY

Date	Day	Time	m	Time	m	Time	m	Time	m
1	F	0330	5.2	0950	0.3	1554	5.0	2216	0.2
2	SA	0418	5.0	1034	0.7	1640	4.6	2306	0.4
3	SU	0511	4.6	1128	1.0	1733	4.3		
4	M	0009	0.7	0615	4.3	1239	1.2	1837	4.1
5	TU	0130	0.8	0731	4.2	1402	1.2	1952	4.1
6	W	0249	0.8	0843	4.3	1516	1.1	2101	4.3
7	TH	0354	0.7	0944	4.6	1616	1.0	2200	4.6
8	F	0446	0.4	1035	4.8	1705	0.8	2248	4.7
9	SA	0530	0.4	1120	5.0	1746	0.7	2332	4.8
10	SU	0609	0.3	1159	5.0	1822	0.5		
11	M O	0012	4.8	0640	0.3	1235	5.0	1852	0.4
12	TU	0047	4.8	0710	0.3	1305	5.0	1922	0.4
13	W	0119	4.8	0740	0.4	1334	5.0	1954	0.4
14	TH	0152	4.8	0811	0.4	1406	5.0	2026	0.3
15	F	0226	4.8	0842	0.5	1440	4.8	2101	0.3
16	SA	0303	4.8	0915	0.5	1519	4.8	2139	0.4
17	SU	0346	4.7	0954	0.7	1602	4.6	2223	0.4
18	M	0433	4.6	1042	0.9	1653	4.5	2315	0.5
19	TU	0531	4.5	1142	1.0	1752	4.3		
20	W	0024	0.7	0637	4.3	1303	1.0	1900	4.3
21	TH	0148	0.5	0754	4.5	1424	0.9	2012	4.5
22	F	0309	0.4	0904	4.7	1535	0.8	2119	4.7
23	SA	0416	0.2	1007	5.0	1636	0.5	2220	5.0
24	SU	0514	0.0	1103	5.2	1731	0.3	2317	5.1
25	M ●	0606	0.0	1155	5.3	1823	0.2		
26	TU	0011	5.3	0650	0.0	1245	5.3	1909	0.1
27	W	0101	5.3	0732	0.0	1331	5.3	1953	0.0
28	TH	0147	5.3	0813	0.1	1413	5.2	2036	0.0
29	F	0231	5.3	0851	0.3	1454	5.1	2120	0.1
30	SA	0315	5.2	0931	0.5	1535	5.0	2204	0.3
31	SU	0400	5.0	1012	0.8	1617	4.7	2249	0.3

JUNE

Date	Day	Time	m	Time	m	Time	m	Time	m
1	M	0448	4.7	1058	1.0	1703	4.5	2340	0.5
2	TU	0541	4.5	1151	1.2	1757	4.3		
3	W	0041	0.7	0641	4.2	1303	1.2	1900	4.2
4	TH	0151	0.8	0751	4.2	1419	1.2	2008	4.2
5	F	0258	0.8	0856	4.3	1527	1.1	2110	4.3
6	SA	0356	0.7	0951	4.6	1624	0.9	2206	4.6
7	SU	0446	0.5	1040	4.8	1711	0.8	2253	4.7
8	M	0530	0.4	1123	5.0	1753	0.7	2339	4.8
9	TU	0611	0.4	1204	5.0	1830	0.5		
10	W O	0019	4.8	0646	0.4	1241	5.0	1904	0.4
11	TH	0059	5.0	0719	0.4	1316	5.0	1939	0.4
12	F	0135	5.0	0754	0.4	1351	5.0	2015	0.4
13	SA	0212	5.0	0828	0.5	1427	4.8	2052	0.3
14	SU	0251	5.0	0903	0.5	1506	4.8	2131	0.3
15	M	0334	4.8	0942	0.7	1549	4.7	2214	0.3
16	TU	0421	4.8	1028	0.8	1636	4.6	2303	0.3
17	W	0515	4.7	1121	0.9	1731	4.6		
18	TH	0003	0.4	0615	4.6	1228	0.9	1832	4.5
19	F	0119	0.4	0723	4.6	1348	0.9	1942	4.6
20	SA	0239	0.4	0834	4.7	1504	0.8	2051	4.7
21	SU	0350	0.3	0940	4.8	1612	0.5	2155	4.8
22	M	0452	0.2	1040	5.0	1714	0.4	2257	5.0
23	TU	0547	0.1	1135	5.1	1812	0.3	2354	5.1
24	W ●	0635	0.2	1227	5.2	1859	0.2		
25	TH	0047	5.2	0717	0.2	1314	5.2	1945	0.1
26	F	0134	5.2	0756	0.3	1358	5.1	2026	0.1
27	SA	0217	5.2	0835	0.4	1437	5.1	2108	0.1
28	SU	0259	5.1	0910	0.5	1516	5.0	2147	0.2
29	M	0339	5.0	0947	0.8	1553	4.8	2225	0.3
30	TU	0418	4.7	1024	0.9	1631	4.7	2304	0.4

JULY

Date	Day	Time	m	Time	m	Time	m	Time	m
1	W	0500	4.6	1106	1.0	1714	4.5	2348	0.7
2	TH	0548	4.3	1159	1.1	1805	4.3		
3	F	0047	0.8	0643	4.2	1307	1.2	1907	4.2
4	SA	0151	0.8	0751	4.2	1419	1.2	2014	4.2
5	SU	0256	0.8	0858	4.3	1529	1.1	2119	4.3
6	M	0357	0.8	0956	4.6	1629	0.9	2215	4.6
7	TU	0452	0.7	1047	4.8	1722	0.8	2307	4.7
8	W	0541	0.5	1133	5.0	1809	0.7	2354	4.8
9	TH O	0624	0.5	1217	5.0	1849	0.4		
10	F	0039	5.0	0703	0.5	1258	5.1	1927	0.4
11	SA	0119	5.1	0738	0.4	1336	5.1	2005	0.3
12	SU	0158	5.1	0814	0.4	1415	5.1	2043	0.2
13	M	0238	5.1	0851	0.5	1453	5.0	2121	0.2
14	TU	0321	5.0	0929	0.5	1534	5.0	2202	0.1
15	W	0406	5.0	1012	0.5	1619	5.0	2247	0.2
16	TH	0455	4.8	1101	0.7	1709	4.8	2339	0.3
17	F	0550	4.5	1159	0.9	1807	4.6		
18	SA	0048	0.4	0654	4.6	1315	0.8	1914	4.6
19	SU	0208	0.5	0806	4.6	1437	0.9	2027	4.6
20	M	0327	0.5	0917	4.6	1556	0.7	2138	4.7
21	TU	0434	0.4	1021	4.8	1704	0.5	2244	4.8
22	W	0531	0.4	1121	5.0	1802	0.3	2344	5.0
23	TH ●	0622	0.4	1214	5.1	1851	0.2		
24	F	0037	5.1	0702	0.4	1313	5.1	1934	0.2
25	SA	0122	5.2	0739	0.4	1343	5.1	2013	0.2
26	SU	0203	5.1	0815	0.5	1419	5.1	2049	0.2
27	M	0239	5.1	0848	0.5	1453	5.0	2123	0.2
28	TU	0313	5.0	0920	0.7	1524	5.0	2153	0.3
29	W	0346	4.8	0951	0.8	1556	4.8	2226	0.4
30	TH	0419	4.7	1026	0.9	1632	4.7	2302	0.5
31	F	0458	4.6	1108	1.0	1716	4.5	2348	0.7

AUGUST

Date	Day	Time	m	Time	m	Time	m	Time	m
1	SA	0545	4.3	1204	1.1	1808	4.3		
2	SU	0051	0.9	0641	4.2	1316	1.2	1915	4.2
3	M	0200	0.9	0754	4.2	1432	1.2	2030	4.2
4	TU	0311	0.9	0907	4.3	1545	1.0	2139	4.3
5	W	0416	0.8	1011	4.6	1650	0.9	2238	4.6
6	TH	0512	0.7	1105	4.8	1745	0.7	2330	4.8
7	F	0601	0.5	1153	5.0	1832	0.4		
8	SA O	0018	5.1	0643	0.5	1238	5.1	1912	0.3
9	SU	0102	5.2	0720	0.4	1319	5.2	1950	0.1
10	M	0143	5.3	0758	0.4	1358	5.2	2028	0.0
11	TU	0222	5.3	0835	0.3	1436	5.1	2105	0.0
12	W	0303	5.3	0914	0.3	1517	5.2	2144	0.0
13	TH	0347	5.2	0955	0.4	1559	5.2	2226	0.1
14	F	0433	5.0	1041	0.5	1647	5.0	2315	0.3
15	SA	0525	4.7	1135	0.8	1743	4.7		
16	SU	0017	0.5	0626	4.5	1249	0.9	1851	4.5
17	M	0139	0.5	0741	4.5	1419	0.9	2011	4.5
18	TU	0306	0.8	0858	4.5	1545	0.8	2129	4.6
19	W	0418	0.8	1007	4.7	1655	0.5	2237	4.8
20	TH	0516	0.7	1106	5.0	1753	0.3	2334	5.0
21	F	0605	0.5	1158	5.1	1839	0.2		
22	SA ●	0024	5.1	0645	0.5	1245	5.2	1918	0.2
23	SU	0107	5.1	0720	0.5	1325	5.2	1953	0.2
24	M	0145	5.1	0754	0.5	1358	5.1	2024	0.2
25	TU	0217	5.0	0824	0.5	1427	5.0	2053	0.3
26	W	0244	5.0	0852	0.7	1454	5.0	2119	0.3
27	TH	0310	4.8	0920	0.7	1523	4.8	2147	0.4
28	F	0341	4.8	0952	0.7	1556	4.8	2220	0.5
29	SA	0416	4.7	1031	0.9	1635	4.6	2301	0.7
30	SU	0459	4.6	1119	1.0	1723	4.3	2355	0.9
31	M	0551	4.3	1225	1.2	1823	4.2		

ENGLAND – BURNHAM-ON-CROUCH

LAT 51°37′N   LONG 0°48′E

TIMES AND HEIGHTS OF HIGH AND LOW WATERS

YEAR **1998**

TIME ZONE (UT)
For Summer Time add ONE hour in non-shaded areas

4

Chart Datum: 2·35 metres below Ordnance Datum (Newlyn)

SEPTEMBER

Time	m		Time	m
1 0110 / TU 1345 / 1941	1.1 / 1.2 / 4.1	**16** W	0244 / 1531 / 2119	1.1 / 0.8 / 4.5
2 0228 / W 1505 / 2102	1.1 / 1.1 / 4.2	**17** TH	0358 / 0949 / 1639 / 2224	1.0 / 4.6 / 0.5 / 4.8
3 0340 / 0934 / TH 1619 / 2211	1.0 / 4.5 / 0.9 / 4.6	**18** F	0456 / 1047 / 1733 / 2318	0.9 / 5.0 / 0.4 / 5.1
4 0442 / 1035 / F 1718 / 2306	0.8 / 4.8 / 0.5 / 5.0	**19** SA	0543 / 1138 / 1820	0.8 / 5.1 / 0.3
5 0534 / 1126 / SA 1810 / 2355	0.7 / 5.1 / 0.3 / 5.2	**20** SU ●	0005 / 0624 / 1222 / 1855	5.2 / 0.7 / 5.2 / 0.3
6 0622 / 1213 / SU 1851 ○	0.5 / 5.2 / 0.1	**21** M	0046 / 0659 / 1301 / 1927	5.2 / 0.7 / 5.2 / 0.3
7 0041 / 0701 / M 1257 / 1931	5.3 / 0.4 / 5.3 / 0.0	**22** TU	0120 / 0730 / 1333 / 1955	5.1 / 0.5 / 5.1 / 0.3
8 0123 / 0739 / TU 1337 / 2008	5.5 / 0.3 / 5.5 / -0.1	**23** W	0149 / 0758 / 1359 / 2021	5.0 / 0.5 / 5.0 / 0.4
9 0204 / 0817 / W 1417 / 2046	5.6 / 0.2 / 5.5 / -0.1	**24** TH	0213 / 0824 / 1424 / 2046	5.0 / 0.5 / 5.0 / 0.4
10 0244 / 0857 / TH 1458 / 2123	5.5 / 0.2 / 5.5 / 0.0	**25** F	0236 / 0853 / 1453 / 2112	5.0 / 0.5 / 5.0 / 0.4
11 0327 / 0938 / F 1540 / 2205	5.3 / 0.3 / 5.3 / 0.2	**26** SA	0306 / 0925 / 1526 / 2143	5.0 / 0.7 / 4.8 / 0.5
12 0412 / 1024 / SA 1628 / 2250	5.1 / 0.4 / 5.1 / 0.4	**27** SU	0342 / 1002 / 1603 / 2219	4.8 / 0.8 / 4.7 / 0.8
13 0501 / 1116 / SU 1724 / 2347	4.8 / 0.7 / 4.7 / 0.8	**28** M	0423 / 1047 / 1648 / 2306	4.7 / 0.9 / 4.5 / 1.0
14 0602 / 1229 / M 1833	4.5 / 0.9 / 4.5	**29** TU	0513 / 1144 / 1745	4.5 / 1.1 / 4.2
15 0111 / 0718 / TU 1404 / 1959	1.0 / 4.3 / 0.9 / 4.3	**30** W	0018 / 0615 / 1305 / 1858	1.2 / 4.2 / 1.1 / 4.1

OCTOBER

Time	m		Time	m
1 0145 / TH 1429 / 2026	1.2 / 1.1 / 4.2	**16** F	0329 / 0922 / 1612 / 2200	1.2 / 4.6 / 0.7 / 4.7
2 0304 / 0856 / F 1544 / 2141	1.1 / 4.5 / 0.8 / 4.6	**17** SA	0428 / 1019 / 1706 / 2251	1.0 / 4.8 / 0.4 / 5.0
3 0409 / 1001 / SA 1648 / 2239	0.9 / 4.7 / 0.5 / 5.0	**18** SU	0516 / 1108 / 1749 / 2336	0.9 / 5.1 / 0.4 / 5.1
4 0505 / 1056 / SU 1741 / 2329	0.7 / 5.1 / 0.2 / 5.3	**19** M	0559 / 1152 / 1827	0.7 / 5.1 / 0.3
5 0554 / 1145 / M 1827 ○	0.4 / 5.3 / 0.1	**20** TU ●	0017 / 0635 / 1230 / 1857	5.1 / 0.7 / 5.1 / 0.4
6 0017 / 0638 / TU 1231 / 1907	5.5 / 0.3 / 5.5 / 0.0	**21** W	0051 / 0704 / 1304 / 1924	5.1 / 0.5 / 5.1 / 0.5
7 0101 / 0718 / W 1315 / 1946	5.6 / 0.2 / 5.6 / -0.1	**22** TH	0119 / 0732 / 1332 / 1950	5.0 / 0.5 / 5.0 / 0.5
8 0143 / 0800 / TH 1357 / 2024	5.6 / 0.2 / 5.6 / 0.0	**23** F	0143 / 0800 / 1358 / 2016	5.0 / 0.2 / 5.0 / 0.5
9 0224 / 0840 / F 1439 / 2103	5.6 / 0.2 / 5.6 / 0.1	**24** SA	0208 / 0830 / 1428 / 2045	5.0 / 0.5 / 5.0 / 0.5
10 0306 / 0923 / SA 1523 / 2144	5.3 / 0.2 / 4.8 / 0.3	**25** SU	0238 / 0903 / 1501 / 2115	5.0 / 0.7 / 4.8 / 0.7
11 0351 / 1010 / SU 1611 / 2229	5.1 / 0.4 / 5.1 / 0.7	**26** M	0314 / 0940 / 1539 / 2150	5.0 / 0.7 / 4.7 / 0.8
12 0439 / 1103 / M 1706 / 2324	4.8 / 0.7 / 4.7 / 1.0	**27** TU	0354 / 1023 / 1623 / 2233	4.7 / 0.8 / 4.6 / 1.0
13 0538 / 1213 / TU 1816	4.5 / 0.8 / 4.5	**28** W	0442 / 1116 / 1718 / 2332	4.5 / 1.0 / 4.3 / 1.2
14 0041 / 0652 / W 1344 / 1940	1.2 / 4.2 / 0.9 / 4.3	**29** TH	0542 / 1228 / 1826	4.2 / 1.0 / 4.2
15 0213 / 0812 / TH 1506 / 2056	1.3 / 4.2 / 0.8 / 4.5	**30** F	0059 / 0656 / 1353 / 1949	1.2 / 4.2 / 0.9 / 4.3
		31 SA	0224 / 0816 / 1509 / 2105	1.2 / 4.3 / 0.8 / 4.6

NOVEMBER

Time	m		Time	m
1 0333 / SU 1614 / 2207	1.0 / 0.4 / 5.0	**16** M	0443 / 1033 / 1713 / 2302	1.0 / 4.8 / 0.5 / 5.0
2 0433 / 1022 / M 1710 / 2300	0.7 / 5.0 / 0.4 / 5.2	**17** TU	0528 / 1118 / 1753 / 2343	0.8 / 5.0 / 0.5 / 5.1
3 0526 / 1114 / TU 1801 / 2350	0.4 / 5.3 / 0.1 / 5.5	**18** W	0608 / 1157 / 1826	0.7 / 5.0 / 0.5
4 0616 / 1205 / W 1846 ○	0.3 / 5.5 / 0.0	**19** TH ●	0018 / 0640 / 1233 / 1856	5.1 / 0.7 / 5.0 / 0.5
5 0038 / 0700 / TH 1253 / 1926	5.6 / 0.2 / 5.6 / 0.0	**20** F	0049 / 0710 / 1305 / 1925	5.1 / 0.5 / 5.0 / 0.5
6 0121 / 0743 / F 1338 / 2006	5.6 / 0.1 / 5.6 / 0.1	**21** SA	0117 / 0740 / 1336 / 1954	5.0 / 0.5 / 5.0 / 0.7
7 0204 / 0826 / SA 1422 / 2046	5.5 / 0.1 / 5.6 / 0.2	**22** SU	0146 / 0813 / 1409 / 2024	5.0 / 0.5 / 5.0 / 0.7
8 0246 / 0910 / SU 1507 / 2126	5.3 / 0.2 / 5.3 / 0.4	**23** M	0217 / 0847 / 1443 / 2056	5.0 / 0.5 / 5.0 / 0.7
9 0330 / 0959 / M 1555 / 2210	5.1 / 0.3 / 5.1 / 0.8	**24** TU	0253 / 0924 / 1522 / 2131	4.8 / 0.7 / 4.8 / 0.8
10 0416 / 1051 / TU 1649 / 2301	4.8 / 0.5 / 4.8 / 1.1	**25** W	0332 / 1006 / 1606 / 2213	4.7 / 0.7 / 4.7 / 1.0
11 0511 / 1153 / W 1751	4.5 / 0.7 / 4.5	**26** TH	0418 / 1056 / 1657 / 2305	4.6 / 0.8 / 4.5 / 1.1
12 0004 / 0617 / TH 1311 / 1904	1.3 / 4.3 / 0.8 / 4.3	**27** F	0514 / 1156 / 1800	4.3 / 0.8 / 4.5
13 0128 / 0733 / F 1427 / 2018	1.5 / 4.2 / 0.8 / 4.3	**28** SA	0015 / 0621 / 1314 / 1913	1.2 / 4.3 / 0.9 / 4.5
14 0247 / 0842 / SA 1532 / 2123	1.3 / 4.5 / 0.7 / 4.6	**29** SU	0138 / 0737 / 1431 / 2027	1.1 / 4.5 / 0.7 / 4.6
15 0351 / 0942 / SU 1627 / 2216	1.1 / 4.6 / 0.7 / 4.8	**30** M	0253 / 0847 / 1540 / 2133	1.0 / 4.6 / 0.4 / 4.8

DECEMBER

Time	m		Time	m
1 0359 / TU 1641 / 2231	0.8 / 0.3 / 5.1	**16** W	0453 / 1040 / 1714 / 2305	0.9 / 4.7 / 0.7 / 4.8
2 0459 / 1046 / W 1737 / 2324	0.5 / 5.2 / 0.2 / 5.3	**17** TH	0538 / 1124 / 1755 / 2346	0.8 / 4.8 / 0.7 / 5.0
3 0555 / 1141 / TH 1826 ○	0.3 / 5.3 / 0.1	**18** F ●	0618 / 1205 / 1832	0.7 / 5.0 / 0.7
4 0015 / 0645 / F 1233 / 1909	5.3 / 0.2 / 5.5 / 0.1	**19** SA	0022 / 0650 / 1244 / 1904	5.0 / 0.5 / 5.0 / 0.7
5 0103 / 0731 / SA 1322 / 1950	5.3 / 0.1 / 5.5 / 0.2	**20** SU	0056 / 0724 / 1319 / 1937	5.0 / 0.5 / 5.0 / 0.7
6 0147 / 0816 / SU 1408 / 2030	5.3 / 0.1 / 5.5 / 0.3	**21** M	0130 / 0800 / 1354 / 2010	5.0 / 0.4 / 5.0 / 0.7
7 0229 / 0901 / M 1453 / 2109	5.2 / 0.1 / 5.3 / 0.5	**22** TU	0203 / 0835 / 1430 / 2042	5.0 / 0.4 / 5.0 / 0.7
8 0311 / 0947 / TU 1539 / 2151	5.1 / 0.2 / 5.1 / 0.8	**23** W	0238 / 0912 / 1508 / 2118	5.0 / 0.4 / 5.0 / 0.7
9 0354 / 1035 / W 1626 / 2234	4.8 / 0.4 / 4.8 / 1.0	**24** TH	0317 / 0953 / 1552 / 2158	4.8 / 0.4 / 4.8 / 0.8
10 0440 / 1126 / TH 1718 / 2324	4.6 / 0.5 / 4.6 / 1.2	**25** F	0400 / 1038 / 1639 / 2245	4.7 / 0.5 / 4.7 / 0.9
11 0533 / 1225 / F 1816	4.3 / 0.8 / 4.3	**26** SA	0449 / 1129 / 1734 / 2340	4.6 / 0.5 / 4.6 / 1.0
12 0028 / 0637 / SA 1331 / 1925	1.3 / 4.2 / 0.8 / 4.2	**27** SU	0548 / 1236 / 1836	4.5 / 0.5 / 4.5
13 0145 / 0749 / SU 1436 / 2032	1.3 / 4.2 / 0.9 / 4.3	**28** M	0053 / 0657 / 1353 / 1950	1.0 / 4.5 / 0.5 / 4.5
14 0259 / 0854 / M 1537 / 2130	1.2 / 4.5 / 0.8 / 4.5	**29** TU	0213 / 0811 / 1507 / 2100	1.0 / 4.6 / 0.5 / 4.7
15 0402 / 0950 / TU 1628 / 2221	1.1 / 4.6 / 0.8 / 4.7	**30** W	0329 / 0921 / 1617 / 2204	0.8 / 4.7 / 0.4 / 4.8
		31 TH	0438 / 1024 / 1716 / 2302	0.5 / 5.0 / 0.3 / 5.0

RIVER BLACKWATER   10-4-18
Essex 51°45'·30N 00°55'·00E (5ca S of Nass bn)
Rtgs: Maldon 3-4-2; Heybridge Basin 3-5-2

CHARTS
AC *3741, 1975, 1183*; Imray, Y17; OS 168
TIDES
Maldon +0130 Dover; ML 2·8; Duration 0620; Zone 0 (UT)

Standard Port WALTON-ON-THE-NAZE (→)

Times				Height (metres)			
High Water		Low Water		MHWS	MHWN	MLWN	MLWS
0000	0600	0500	1100	4·2	3·4	1·1	0·4
1200	1800	1700	2300				
Differences SUNK HEAD							
0000	+0002	−0002	+0002	−0·3	−0·3	−0·1	−0·1
CLACTON-ON-SEA							
+0012	+0010	+0025	+0008	+0·3	+0·1	0·0	0·0
WEST MERSEA							
+0035	+0015	+0055	+0010	+0·9	+0·4	+0·1	+0·1
BRADWELL							
+0035	+0023	+0047	+0004	+1·1	+0·8	+0·2	+0·1
OSEA ISLAND							
+0057	+0045	+0050	+0007	+1·1	+0·9	+0·1	0·0
MALDON							
+0107	+0055	No data		−1·3	−1·1	No data	

SHELTER
Good, as appropriate to wind. Marinas at Tollesbury, Bradwell and Maylandsea. ‡ restricted by oyster beds and many moorings. At W Mersea there is a pontoon for landing (limited waiting); also pile moorings in Ray Chan or ‡ in Mersea Quarters, access approx HW±1½. Berths at Heybridge Basin, access via lock approx HW −1 to HW; a SHM buoy opposite the lock marks the deep water ent. Access to Chelmer & Blackwater Canal (not navigable).

NAVIGATION
WPT Knoll NCM, Q, 51°43'·85N 01°05'·17E, 107°/287° from/to Nass bn, ECM VQ (3) 5s, 6·7M. Speed liimit 8kn W of Osea Is.
WEST MERSEA: Beware oyster beds between Cobmarsh Is and Packing Marsh Is and in Salcott Chan.
BRADWELL: No dangers, but only suitable for small craft and area gets very crowded; see below under Lts & Marks.
TOLLESBURY FLEET: Proceeding via S Chan up Woodrolfe Creek, a tide gauge shows depth over marina ent sill (approx 3m at MHWS and 2m at MHWN). Speed limits: Woodrolfe Creek 4kn upper reaches; Tollesbury Fleet S Chan 8kn.

LIGHTS AND MARKS
Bradwell Creek ent has bn QR with tide gauge showing depth in ft in Creek; this bn must be left to <u>STBD</u> on entry. 4 PHM buoys, 3 SHM withies and 2 B/W △ ldg bns mark the chan which doglegs past a SHM buoy to marina ent. Power stn is conspic 7ca NNE.
MALDON: From S of Osea Is, 'The Doctor', No 3 SHM buoy on with Blackwater SC lt, Iso G 5s, lead 300° approx up the chan; or No 3 and No 8 buoys in line at 305°. Beyond No 8 buoy, the chan which shifts and carries 0·2m, is buoyed up to Maldon. Access near HW; pontoons dry to soft mud.

RADIO TELEPHONE
Bradwell and Tollesbury Marinas VHF Ch **80** M (HO).
Blackwater Marina VHF Ch M, 0900-2300.

TELEPHONE (Dial code 01621 Maldon; 01206 Colchester/ West Mersea)
Hr Mr 856726; R. Bailiff (Maldon Quay) 856487, Office 875837, Mobile 0860 456802; Canal lockmaster 853506; MRSC (01255) 675518; ⌗ (01473) 235704 (H24); Marinecall 0891 500455; Police (Colchester) 762212, (W Mersea) 382930; Dr 854118, or W Mersea 382015.

FACILITIES
WEST MERSEA (01206)
Town EC Wed; P, D, FW, ME, EI, CH, V, R, Bar, ⊠, Ⓑ, ≋ (bus to Colchester, Ⓗ ☎ 01206-853535), ✈ (Southend/ Stansted).
TOLLESBURY (01621)
Tollesbury Marina (240+20 visitors) ☎ 868471, ⚓ 868489, Slip, D, AC, BH (10 ton), Gas, Gaz, FW, ME, EI, Sh, C (5 ton), CH, V, R, Bar, ▣, Access HW±1½;
Tollesbury Cruising Club ☎ 869561, Bar, R, M, C (20 ton), D, CH, FW, L, Slip, AC, ME, EI, Sh;
Services: Slip access HW±2 , FW, ME, EI, Sh, CH.
Village EC Wed; P, V, R, Bar, ⊠, Ⓑ (Tues, Thurs 1000-1430), ≋ (bus to Witham), ✈ (Southend or Cambridge).
BRADWELL (01621)
Bradwell Marina (280, some Ⓥ) ☎ 776235, ⚓ 776393, £9.75, Slip, AC, Gas, Gaz, D, P, FW, ME, EI, Sh, BH (16 ton), CH, R, Bar, Access HW±4½, approx 2m; **Bradwell Quay YC** ☎ 776539, M, FW, Bar, L, Slip. **Town** ⊠, ≋ (bus/ taxi to Southminster), ✈ (Southend).
MAYLANDSEA
Blackwater Marina (230) ☎ 740264, ⚓ 742122, £7, Slip, D, Sh, CH, R, Bar; Access HW±2. 150 moorings in chan. Taxi to Southminster ≋.
MALDON (01621)
Maldon Quay Hr Mr/River bailiff ☎ 856487, Mobile ☎ 0860 456802, VHF Ch 16 *Highspirits* (work boat); M, P, D, FW, AB, Slip; **Maldon Little Ship Club** ☎ 854139, Bar; **Services:** Slip, D, Sh, CH, M, ACA, SM, ME, EI, Ⓔ.
Town EC Wed; ⊠, Ⓑ, ≋ (bus to Chelmsford, Ⓗ ☎ (01245) 440761), ✈ (Southend, Cambridge or Stansted).
HEYBRIDGE BASIN (01621)
Lockmaster ☎ 853506**Blackwater SC** ☎ 853923, L, FW; **Services:** Slip, D, L, M, FW, ME, EI, SH, C. Bus to Heybridge/Maldon.

RIVER COLNE   10-4-19

Essex 51°47′·95N 01°00′·70E (Brightlingsea)   Rtg 3-2-2

CHARTS
AC *3741, 1975, 1183*; Imray, Y17; Stanfords 4, 5; OS 168

TIDES
+0050 Dover; ML 2·5; Duration 0615; Zone 0 (UT)

Standard Port WALTON-ON-THE-NAZE (→)

Times				Height (metres)			
High Water		Low Water		MHWS	MHWN	MLWN	MLWS
0000	0600	0500	1100	4·2	3·4	1·1	0·4
1200	1800	1700	2300				
Differences BRIGHTLINGSEA							
+0025	+0021	+0046	+0004	+0·8	+0·4	+0·1	0·0
COLCHESTER							
+0035	+0025	Dries out		0·0	−0·3	Dries out	

LIGHTS AND MARKS
Well buoyed/lit up to Wivenhoe. Ldg lts/marks 041° for Brightlingsea: both FR 7/10m 4M; dayglo W □, orange stripe on posts; adjusted to suit the chan. Then Spit SCM buoy, Q (6) + L Fl 15s, and chan buoys Fl (3) G 5s and Fl R 5s, plus NCM bn Q where chan is divided by Cindery Is. Bateman's Tr (conspic) by Westmarsh Pt has a FY sodium lt 12m. Pyefleet Chan and other creeks are unlit.
The flood barrier is marked by 2FR/FG (vert) on both sides and there are bns, QR/QG, up/downstream on the river banks. To facilitate the passage of large vessels, Dir lts above and below the barrier are as follows: for up-stream tfc 305°, Oc WRG 5s 5/3M, vis G300°-304.7°, W304·7°-305·3°, R305·3°-310°; and for down-stream tfc 125°, Oc WRG 5s 5/3M, vis G120°-124.8, W°124.8°-125.2°, R125.2°-130°. Daymarks are W ▽ with Or vert stripe.

RADIO TELEPHONE
Brightlingsea Port Radio VHF Ch 68. Colchester Ch **68** 11 14 16 (Office hrs and HW−2 to HW+1).

TELEPHONE (Dial code 01206 Brightlingsea & Colchester) Hr Mr (Brightlingsea) 302200; Hr Mr (Colchester) 827316; MRSC (01255) 675518; ☰ (01473) 235704 (H24); Marinecall 0891 500455; Police (01255) 221312; Dr 303875.

SHELTER
Suitable shelter can be found for most winds, but outer hbr is exposed to W'lies. Some pile moorings for visitors in the creek S of Cindery Is; none to the N. ⚓s to the NW of Mersea Stone Pt and in Pyefleet Chan, E of Pewit Is. R Colne is navigable for 4·5m draft to Wivenhoe, where the river dries; and to The Hythe, Colchester (3m draft).

NAVIGATION
WPT Colne Bar By, SHM Fl (2) G 5s, 51°44′·58N 01°02′·66E, 160°/340° from/to Mersea Stone, 3·6M. See also 10·4·18. Extensive mud and sand banks flank the ent chan. Much traffic in the Colne; large coasters use the Brightlingsea chans. The ent to Brightlingsea Creek is very narrow at LW and carries about 1m.
A flood barrier 2ca below Wivenhoe church is normally open (30m wide) allowing unrestricted passage; keep to stbd, max speed 5kn. Tfc lts on N pier are 3FR (vert), vis up/downstream. When lit, they indicate either the barrier gates are shut or a large vessel is passing through; other traffic must keep clear. (See LIGHTS AND MARKS).
Speed limits in the approaches and up-river:
No 13 buoy to Fingringhoe (No 24 buoy) = 8kn; but Nos 12 to 16 buoys = 5kn;
No 24 buoy to Colchester = 4kn;
Brightlingsea Harbour = 4kn.

FACILITIES
BRIGHTLINGSEA
Town Hard ☎ 303535, L, FW, Pile moorings £5; **Colne YC** ☎ 302594, L, FW, R, Bar; **Brightlingsea SC** Slip, Bar;
Services: M, L, FW, ME, El, Ⓔ, Sh, CH, ACA, P & D (cans), Gas, SM, BY, C, Slip.
Town P & D (cans), FW, ME, El, Sh, C (mobile), CH, V, R, Bar, ✉, Ⓑ, ⇌ (bus to Wivenhoe or Colchester), ✈ (Southend or Stansted).
WIVENHOE: **Wivenhoe SC**.
Village P, V, Bar, ✉, Ⓑ (AM only), ⇌.

WALTON ON THE NAZE

MEAN SPRING
AND NEAP CURVES

MEAN RANGES
Springs 3.8m
Neaps 2.3m

Springs occur 2 days
after
New and Full Moon.

WALTON BACKWATERS   10-4-20

Essex 51°54'.54N 01°16'.90E (No 2 PHM buoy)   Rtg 3-1-2

CHARTS
AC *2695, 2052*; Imray, Y16; Stanfords 5, 6; OS 169

TIDES
+0030 Dover; ML 2·2; Duration 0615; Zone 0 (UT). Walton
is a Standard Port. Predictions are for Walton Pier, ie to
seaward. Differences for Bramble Creek (N of Hamford
Water) are +10, −7, −5, +10 mins; heights are all +0·3m.

SHELTER
Good in all weather, but ent not advised if a big sea is
running from the NE. Berth HW±5 in Titchmarsh Marina,
ent dredged 1·3m; or on adjacent pontoons in the Twizzle.
Good ⚓s in Hamford Water (keep clear of Oakley Creek)
and in N end of Walton Chan, 2ca S of Stone Pt on E side.
Walton Yacht Basin more suited for long stay; appr dries.

NAVIGATION
WPT Pye End SWM buoy, L Fl 10s, 51°55'.00N 01°18'.00E,
054°/234° from/to buoyed chan ent, 1·0M. NB this stretch
carries only 0·9m. From S, appr via Medusa Chan; from N
and E via the Harwich recomended yacht track. At narrow
ent to Walton Chan leave No. 9 NCM buoy to stbd, and 3
PHM buoys close to port; after a fourth PHM off Stone Pt
stay mid-chan. Beware lobster pots off the Naze and Pye
Sands and oyster beds in the Backwaters.

LIGHTS AND MARKS
Naze Tr (49m) is conspic 3M S of Pye End buoy. 2M NNE
at Felixstowe, cranes and Y flood lts are conspic D/N.
Chan buoys inward from Pye End are unlit, except No 4.

RADIO TELEPHONE
Titchmarsh marina Ch 80, 0800-2000 in season.

TELEPHONE (Dial code 01255)
Hr Mr 851887; MRSC 675518; ⌗ (01473) 235704 (H24);
Marinecall 0891 500455; Police 241312; Ⓗ 502446.

FACILITIES
Titchmarsh Marina (450+visitors), ☎ 672185, 🛥 851901,
£9, Access HW±5 over sill 1·3m, D, FW, AC, Gas, Gaz, ME,
CH, El, BH (10 ton), TraveLift (35 ton), Slip, R, Bar;
Walton Yacht Basin/Walton & Frinton YC (60) ☎ 675526,
AB (long stay), FW, AC, R, Bar;
Services: Slip, M, D, C (½ ton), El. **Town** EC Wed; P, SM,
V, R, Bar, ✉, Ⓑ, ➤, ✈ (Southend/Cambridge).

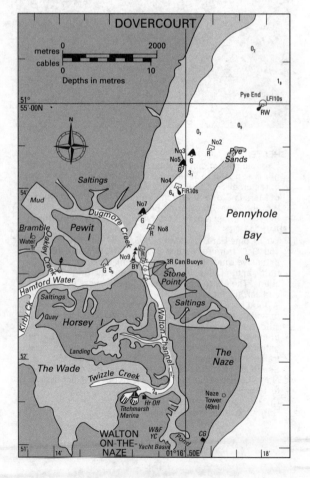

DOVERCOURT

metres
cables
Depths in metres

Pye End LFl10s
RW

No2
No3 R
No5 G
Pye
Sands
No4
6₄ Fl R10s

Saltings
Mud
Dugmore Creek
Pewit I
No7
G
No8
R

Bramble Io Water
Oakley Creek
Tr
No9
G 5s
BY
3R Can Buoys
Stone
Point
Saltings

Hamford Water
Saltings
Quay
Horsey I
Landing

The Wade
Twizzle Creek
Hr Off
Titchmarsh
Marina

Pennyhole
Bay

Walton Channel
Saltings
The Naze

Naze
Tower
(49m)

WALTON
ON THE
NAZE
W&F
YC
Pond
CG
Yacht Basin

ENGLAND – WALTON–ON–THE–NAZE

LAT 51°51′N   LONG 1°16′E

TIMES AND HEIGHTS OF HIGH AND LOW WATERS

YEAR 1998

TIME ZONE (UT)
For Summer Time add ONE hour in non-shaded areas

JANUARY

Day	Time	m	Day	Time	m
1 TH	0057 / 0713 / 1325 / 1922	4.1 / 0.4 / 4.2 / 0.7	16 F	0136 / 0756 / 1359 / 1950	4.0 / 0.5 / 4.0 / 0.8
2 F	0138 / 0757 / 1409 / 2003	4.1 / 0.4 / 4.2 / 0.7	17 SA	0206 / 0830 / 1431 / 2020	4.0 / 0.5 / 3.9 / 0.8
3 SA	0220 / 0842 / 1455 / 2048	4.1 / 0.4 / 4.1 / 0.7	18 SU	0238 / 0903 / 1505 / 2053	3.9 / 0.4 / 3.8 / 0.9
4 SU	0306 / 0931 / 1545 / 2136	4.0 / 0.4 / 4.0 / 0.8	19 M	0314 / 0940 / 1543 / 2133	3.8 / 0.7 / 3.8 / 1.0
5 M	0357 / 1025 / 1641 / 2233	3.9 / 0.5 / 3.8 / 0.9	20 TU	0356 / 1024 / 1627 / 2223	3.7 / 0.8 / 3.6 / 1.1
6 TU	0456 / 1128 / 1744 / 2340	3.8 / 0.6 / 3.7 / 1.0	21 W	0447 / 1118 / 1719 / 2324	3.6 / 0.9 / 3.5 / 1.2
7 W	0605 / 1240 / 1854	3.6 / 0.7 / 3.6	22 TH	0548 / 1220 / 1821	3.4 / 1.0 / 3.4
8 TH	0057 / 0717 / 1353 / 2003	1.0 / 3.6 / 0.7 / 3.6	23 F	0034 / 0658 / 1325 / 1932	1.2 / 3.4 / 1.0 / 3.4
9 F	0213 / 0827 / 1458 / 2107	1.0 / 3.7 / 0.7 / 3.8	24 SA	0145 / 0810 / 1428 / 2040	1.2 / 3.4 / 1.0 / 3.6
10 SA	0320 / 0930 / 1554 / 2204	0.8 / 3.9 / 0.6 / 3.9	25 SU	0252 / 0913 / 1526 / 2139	1.0 / 3.6 / 0.9 / 3.7
11 SU	0418 / 1027 / 1642 / 2255	0.6 / 4.0 / 0.6 / 4.0	26 M	0351 / 1008 / 1617 / 2230	0.9 / 3.8 / 0.8 / 3.9
12 M	0509 / 1118 / 1726 / O 2341	0.5 / 4.0 / 0.7 / 4.0	27 TU	0444 / 1057 / 1704 / 2316	0.7 / 4.0 / 0.7 / 4.1
13 TU	0556 / 1204 / 1806	0.5 / 4.1 / 0.7	28 W	0532 / 1143 / 1747 ●	0.5 / 4.2 / 0.6
14 W	0023 / 0639 / 1246 / 1843	4.1 / 0.4 / 4.1 / 0.7	29 TH	0000 / 0616 / 1228 / 1827	4.2 / 0.3 / 4.3 / 0.5
15 TH	0102 / 0719 / 1324 / 1918	4.0 / 0.4 / 4.0 / 0.8	30 F	0043 / 0700 / 1311 / 1908	4.2 / 0.2 / 4.4 / 0.4
			31 SA	0125 / 0743 / 1355 / 1949	4.3 / 0.2 / 4.4 / 0.5

FEBRUARY

Day	Time	m	Day	Time	m
1 SU	0207 / 0827 / 1440 / 2032	4.3 / 0.1 / 4.3 / 0.5	16 M	0212 / 0827 / 1433 / 2025	4.0 / 0.5 / 3.9 / 0.7
2 M	0251 / 0912 / 1526 / 2118	4.2 / 0.2 / 4.1 / 0.6	17 TU	0245 / 0901 / 1508 / 2101	3.9 / 0.5 / 3.9 / 0.7
3 TU	0338 / 1001 / 1617 / 2209	4.1 / 0.4 / 3.9 / 0.7	18 W	0323 / 0940 / 1549 / 2143	3.8 / 0.7 / 3.8 / 0.8
4 W	0431 / 1058 / 1714 / 2309	3.9 / 0.6 / 3.7 / 0.9	19 TH	0407 / 1028 / 1636 / 2235	3.7 / 0.8 / 3.6 / 1.0
5 TH	0535 / 1207 / 1821	3.7 / 0.8 / 3.5	20 F	0500 / 1129 / 1733 / 2342	3.5 / 1.0 / 3.4 / 1.1
6 F	0025 / 0651 / 1325 / 1935	1.0 / 3.5 / 0.9 / 3.4	21 SA	0607 / 1240 / 1841	3.3 / 1.1 / 3.3
7 SA	0153 / 0809 / 1438 / 2046	1.0 / 3.6 / 0.9 / 3.5	22 SU	0059 / 0724 / 1352 / 1957	1.2 / 3.3 / 1.1 / 3.4
8 SU	0308 / 0918 / 1537 / 2147	0.8 / 3.7 / 0.8 / 3.7	23 M	0216 / 0840 / 1457 / 2106	1.0 / 3.5 / 1.0 / 3.6
9 M	0408 / 1016 / 1627 / 2240	0.7 / 3.9 / 0.8 / 3.9	24 TU	0326 / 0943 / 1553 / 2205	0.8 / 3.8 / 0.8 / 3.8
10 TU	0458 / 1107 / 1710 / 2326	0.5 / 4.0 / 0.7 / 4.0	25 W	0423 / 1037 / 1642 / 2255	0.6 / 4.0 / 0.6 / 4.0
11 W	0542 / 1151 / 1748 / O	0.4 / 4.1 / 0.7	26 TH	0513 / 1125 / 1727 / ● 2341	0.4 / 4.2 / 0.5 / 4.2
12 TH	0008 / 0622 / 1231 / 1823	4.0 / 0.4 / 4.1 / 0.7	27 F	0559 / 1132 / 1809	0.2 / 4.4 / 0.4
13 F	0044 / 0657 / 1305 / 1856	4.0 / 0.4 / 4.0 / 0.7	28 SA	0025 / 0642 / 1255 / 1851	4.3 / 0.0 / 4.5 / 0.3
14 SA	0115 / 0729 / 1335 / 1924	4.0 / 0.4 / 4.0 / 0.7			
15 SU	0143 / 0758 / 1403 / 1953	4.0 / 0.5 / 3.9 / 0.7			

MARCH

Day	Time	m	Day	Time	m
1 SU	0108 / 0725 / 1338 / 1932	4.4 / 0.0 / 4.5 / 0.3	16 M	0119 / 0726 / 1335 / 1927	4.0 / 0.5 / 4.0 / 0.6
2 M	0151 / 0807 / 1421 / 2015	4.4 / 0.0 / 4.4 / 0.3	17 TU	0147 / 0755 / 1404 / 1959	4.0 / 0.5 / 4.0 / 0.5
3 TU	0234 / 0850 / 1506 / 2100	4.4 / 0.1 / 4.2 / 0.4	18 W	0219 / 0827 / 1438 / 2035	4.0 / 0.5 / 4.0 / 0.6
4 W	0319 / 0936 / 1553 / 2148	4.2 / 0.3 / 4.0 / 0.5	19 TH	0256 / 0902 / 1518 / 2114	3.9 / 0.6 / 3.9 / 0.7
5 TH	0410 / 1029 / 1646 / 2245	4.0 / 0.6 / 3.7 / 0.8	20 F	0337 / 0944 / 1603 / 2201	3.8 / 0.8 / 3.7 / 0.8
6 F	0511 / 1135 / 1751 / 2359	3.7 / 0.9 / 3.4 / 1.0	21 SA	0427 / 1040 / 1658 / 2302	3.6 / 1.0 / 3.5 / 1.0
7 SA	0629 / 1256 / 1908	3.5 / 1.1 / 3.3	22 SU	0531 / 1156 / 1804	3.4 / 1.1 / 3.3
8 SU	0134 / 0752 / 1415 / 2023	1.0 / 3.5 / 1.1 / 3.4	23 M	0021 / 0648 / 1317 / 1920	1.1 / 3.3 / 1.1 / 3.3
9 M	0252 / 0904 / 1517 / 2128	0.8 / 3.6 / 1.0 / 3.6	24 TU	0145 / 0810 / 1428 / 2035	1.0 / 3.5 / 1.0 / 3.5
10 TU	0352 / 1001 / 1607 / 2221	0.7 / 3.8 / 0.9 / 3.8	25 W	0300 / 0919 / 1527 / 2137	0.7 / 3.8 / 0.8 / 3.8
11 W	0440 / 1050 / 1649 / 2307	0.5 / 4.0 / 0.8 / 4.0	26 TH	0400 / 1015 / 1618 / 2231	0.5 / 4.1 / 0.6 / 4.0
12 TH	0521 / 1132 / 1727 / 2347	0.4 / 4.1 / 0.7 / 4.0	27 F	0451 / 1105 / 1704 / 2319	0.2 / 4.3 / 0.4 / 4.2
13 F	0558 / 1210 / 1801 / O	0.4 / 4.0 / 0.7	28 SA	0537 / 1151 / 1748 / ●	0.1 / 4.4 / 0.3
14 SA	0022 / 0630 / 1242 / 1831	4.0 / 0.4 / 4.0 / 0.6	29 SU	0005 / 0620 / 1236 / 1831	4.4 / 0.0 / 4.5 / 0.2
15 SU	0052 / 0659 / 1309 / 1859	4.0 / 0.4 / 3.9 / 0.6	30 M	0049 / 0703 / 1319 / 1915	4.5 / 0.0 / 4.5 / 0.2
			31 TU	0133 / 0745 / 1402 / 1958	4.5 / 0.0 / 4.4 / 0.2

APRIL

Day	Time	m	Day	Time	m
1 W	0217 / 0828 / 1446 / 2043	4.4 / 0.2 / 4.2 / 0.3	16 TH	0158 / 0759 / 1414 / 2014	4.0 / 0.6 / 4.0 / 0.5
2 TH	0303 / 0913 / 1532 / 2131	4.3 / 0.4 / 4.0 / 0.5	17 F	0235 / 0834 / 1453 / 2053	3.9 / 0.7 / 3.9 / 0.6
3 F	0353 / 1003 / 1622 / 2227	4.0 / 0.7 / 3.7 / 0.7	18 SA	0317 / 0914 / 1538 / 2139	3.8 / 0.8 / 3.7 / 0.7
4 SA	0452 / 1105 / 1723 / 2340	3.7 / 1.0 / 3.4 / 0.9	19 SU	0407 / 1006 / 1632 / 2238	3.6 / 1.0 / 3.5 / 0.9
5 SU	0607 / 1224 / 1838	3.4 / 1.2 / 3.3	20 M	0508 / 1118 / 1736 / 2352	3.5 / 1.1 / 3.4 / 0.9
6 M	0109 / 0728 / 1345 / 1954	0.9 / 3.4 / 1.2 / 3.3	21 TU	0623 / 1242 / 1851	3.4 / 1.2 / 3.4
7 TU	0227 / 0839 / 1450 / 2059	0.8 / 3.6 / 1.1 / 3.5	22 W	0117 / 0743 / 1357 / 2004	0.8 / 3.5 / 1.0 / 3.5
8 W	0326 / 0937 / 1541 / 2153	0.7 / 3.8 / 1.0 / 3.7	23 TH	0233 / 0852 / 1459 / 2108	0.6 / 3.8 / 0.8 / 3.8
9 TH	0413 / 1024 / 1624 / 2239	0.5 / 4.0 / 0.8 / 3.9	24 F	0334 / 0950 / 1552 / 2203	0.4 / 4.1 / 0.6 / 4.0
10 F	0453 / 1106 / 1702 / 2319	0.5 / 4.0 / 0.7 / 4.0	25 SA	0426 / 1041 / 1642 / 2254	0.2 / 4.3 / 0.4 / 4.2
11 SA	0528 / 1143 / 1736 / O 2354	0.5 / 4.0 / 0.6 / 4.0	26 SU	0514 / 1129 / 1727 / ● 2343	0.1 / 4.4 / 0.3 / 4.4
12 SU	0559 / 1215 / 1806	0.5 / 4.0 / 0.6	27 M	0559 / 1215 / 1813	0.0 / 4.4 / 0.2
13 M	0025 / 0627 / 1242 / 1834	4.0 / 0.5 / 4.0 / 0.6	28 TU	0029 / 0642 / 1300 / 1858	4.4 / 0.0 / 4.4 / 0.2
14 TU	0054 / 0656 / 1309 / 1905	3.9 / 0.5 / 4.0 / 0.5	29 W	0115 / 0724 / 1343 / 1944	4.5 / 0.1 / 4.3 / 0.2
15 W	0124 / 0727 / 1339 / 1938	4.0 / 0.5 / 4.0 / 0.5	30 TH	0201 / 0807 / 1427 / 2030	4.4 / 0.3 / 4.2 / 0.3

Chart Datum: 2·16 metres below Ordnance Datum (Newlyn)

ENGLAND – WALTON–ON–THE–NAZE

LAT 51°51′N   LONG   1°16′E

TIMES AND HEIGHTS OF HIGH AND LOW WATERS

YEAR **1998**

TIME ZONE (UT)
For Summer Time add ONE hour in non-shaded areas

MAY

Day	Time	m	Time	m	Day	Time	m	Time	m
1 F	0247	4.2			**16** SA	0219	3.9		
	0851	0.5				0814	0.7		
	1512	4.0				1435	3.8		
	2119	0.4				2040	0.6		
2 SA	0337	4.0			**17** SU	0303	3.8		
	0939	0.8				0856	0.8		
	1600	3.7				1520	3.7		
	2213	0.6				2127	0.6		
3 SU	0432	3.7			**18** M	0353	3.7		
	1036	1.1				0947	1.0		
	1655	3.5				1613	3.6		
	2318	0.8				2223	0.7		
4 M	0539	3.5			**19** TU	0453	3.6		
	1146	1.3				1051	1.1		
	1802	3.3				1715	3.5		
						2332	0.8		
5 TU	0034	0.9			**20** W	0602	3.5		
	0653	3.4				1208	1.1		
	1304	1.3				1824	3.5		
	1914	3.3							
6 W	0148	0.9			**21** TH	0051	0.7		
	0803	3.5				0715	3.6		
	1413	1.2				1324	1.0		
	2020	3.5				1933	3.6		
7 TH	0248	0.8			**22** F	0206	0.6		
	0901	3.7				0823	3.8		
	1508	1.1				1430	0.9		
	2116	3.7				2037	3.8		
8 F	0337	0.6			**23** SA	0308	0.4		
	0950	3.9				0923	4.0		
	1554	0.9				1527	0.7		
	2203	3.8				2136	4.0		
9 SA	0418	0.6			**24** SU	0403	0.2		
	1033	4.0				1017	4.2		
	1633	0.8				1619	0.5		
	2245	3.9				2230	4.1		
10 SU	0454	0.5			**25** M ●	0452	0.2		
	1111	4.0				1107	4.3		
	1708	0.7				1709	0.4		
	2323	3.9				2322	4.3		
11 M O	0527	0.5			**26** TU	0538	0.2		
	1145	4.0				1155	4.3		
	1740	0.6				1758	0.3		
	2357	3.9							
12 TU	0559	0.5			**27** W	0011	4.3		
	1215	4.0				0622	0.2		
	1812	0.6				1242	4.3		
						1845	0.2		
13 W	0030	3.9			**28** TH	0059	4.3		
	0631	0.6				0706	0.3		
	1246	4.0				1326	4.2		
	1846	0.6				1932	0.2		
14 TH	0104	3.9			**29** F	0145	4.3		
	0704	0.6				0748	0.5		
	1319	4.0				1409	4.1		
	1921	0.5				2019	0.3		
15 F	0140	3.9			**30** SA	0231	4.2		
	0738	0.7				0831	0.7		
	1355	3.9				1452	4.0		
	1959	0.5				2106	0.4		
					31 SU	0318	4.0		
						0915	0.9		
						1536	3.8		
						2155	0.5		

JUNE

Day	Time	m	Day	Time	m
1 M	0408 3.8		**16** TU	0340 3.9	
	1004 1.1			0932 0.9	
	1624 3.6			1556 3.7	
	2249 0.7			2210 0.5	
2 TU	0503 3.6		**17** W	0436 3.8	
	1101 1.3			1029 1.0	
	1720 3.5			1653 3.7	
	2348 0.8			2312 0.6	
3 W	0606 3.4		**18** TH	0539 3.7	
	1208 1.3			1136 1.0	
	1824 3.4			1757 3.6	
4 TH	0053 0.9		**19** F	0023 0.6	
	0713 3.4			0646 3.7	
	1320 1.3			1251 1.0	
	1929 3.4			1904 3.7	
5 F	0156 0.9		**20** SA	0138 0.6	
	0815 3.5			0754 3.8	
	1423 1.2			1402 0.9	
	2029 3.5			2010 3.8	
6 SA	0250 0.8		**21** SU	0244 0.5	
	0908 3.7			0857 3.9	
	1516 1.0			1505 0.7	
	2122 3.7			2112 3.9	
7 SU	0337 0.7		**22** M	0342 0.4	
	0955 3.9			0955 4.0	
	1600 0.9			1603 0.6	
	2208 3.8			2211 4.0	
8 M	0418 0.6		**23** TU	0434 0.3	
	1036 4.0			1048 4.1	
	1639 0.8			1657 0.5	
	2251 3.9			2306 4.1	
9 TU	0456 0.6		**24** W ●	0521 0.4	
	1115 4.0			1138 4.2	
	1716 0.7			1747 0.4	
	2330 3.9			2357 4.2	
10 W O	0533 0.6		**25** TH	0606 0.4	
	1151 4.0			1225 4.2	
	1753 0.6			1836 0.3	
11 TH	0009 4.0		**26** F	0045 4.2	
	0609 0.6			0648 0.5	
	1227 4.0			1310 4.1	
	1830 0.6			1921 0.3	
12 F	0047 4.0		**27** SA	0131 4.2	
	0646 0.6			0730 0.6	
	1303 4.0			1352 4.1	
	1909 0.5			2006 0.3	
13 SA	0125 4.0		**28** SU	0214 4.1	
	0723 0.7			0809 0.7	
	1341 3.9			1432 4.0	
	1949 0.5			2048 0.4	
14 SU	0206 4.0		**29** M	0256 4.0	
	0801 0.7			0853 0.8	
	1422 3.9			1510 3.9	
	2031 0.5			2129 0.5	
15 M	0251 3.9		**30** TU	0337 3.8	
	0843 0.8			0928 1.0	
	1506 3.8			1550 3.8	
	2117 0.5			2211 0.6	

JULY

Day	Time	m	Day	Time	m
1 W	0421 3.7		**16** TH	0416 3.9	
	1013 1.1			1007 0.8	
	1635 3.6			1630 3.9	
	2258 0.8			2248 0.5	
2 TH	0510 3.5		**17** F	0513 3.8	
	1108 1.2			1108 1.0	
	1728 3.5			1730 3.7	
	2353 0.9			2354 0.6	
3 F	0608 3.4		**18** SA	0618 3.7	
	1212 1.3			1220 1.0	
	1830 3.4			1837 3.7	
4 SA	0053 0.9		**19** SU	0109 0.7	
	0713 3.4			0727 3.7	
	1320 1.3			1337 1.0	
	1935 3.4			1947 3.7	
5 SU	0154 0.9		**20** M	0223 0.7	
	0817 3.5			0835 3.7	
	1425 1.2			1450 0.8	
	2037 3.5			2055 3.8	
6 M	0251 0.9		**21** TU	0325 0.6	
	0913 3.7			0937 3.9	
	1521 1.0			1553 0.7	
	2131 3.7			2159 3.9	
7 TU	0342 0.8		**22** W	0419 0.6	
	1002 3.9			1034 4.0	
	1610 0.9			1648 0.5	
	2221 3.8			2256 4.0	
8 W	0428 0.7		**23** TH	0507 0.6	
	1046 4.0			1125 4.1	
	1654 0.8			1739 0.4	
	2306 3.9		●	2347 4.1	
9 TH	0510 0.7		**24** F	0550 0.6	
	1128 4.0			1212 4.1	
	1736 0.6			1825 0.4	
O	2349 4.0				
10 F	0551 0.7		**25** SA	0033 4.2	
	1208 4.1			0630 0.6	
	1817 0.6			1255 4.1	
				1907 0.4	
11 SA	0030 4.1		**26** SU	0116 4.1	
	0629 0.6			0709 0.7	
	1248 4.1			1333 4.1	
	1858 0.5			1946 0.4	
12 SU	0111 4.1		**27** M	0154 4.1	
	0708 0.6			0745 0.7	
	1328 4.1			1408 4.0	
	1939 0.4			2022 0.4	
13 M	0153 4.1		**28** TU	0229 4.0	
	0748 0.7			0819 0.8	
	1408 4.0			1440 4.0	
	2020 0.4			2055 0.5	
14 TU	0237 4.1		**29** W	0303 3.9	
	0829 0.7			0853 0.9	
	1451 4.0			1514 3.9	
	2104 0.3			2130 0.6	
15 W	0324 4.0		**30** TH	0338 3.8	
	0915 0.7			0930 1.0	
	1538 4.0			1552 3.8	
	2152 0.4			2209 0.7	
			31 F	0419 3.7	
				1015 1.1	
				1637 3.6	
				2258 0.8	

AUGUST

Day	Time	m	Day	Time	m
1 SA	0507 3.5		**16** SU	0551 3.6	
	1113 1.2			1155 1.0	
	1732 3.5			1815 3.6	
	2357 1.0				
2 SU	0606 3.4		**17** M	0042 0.9	
	1221 1.3			0703 3.6	
	1838 3.4			1320 1.0	
				1932 3.6	
3 M	0102 1.0		**18** TU	0204 0.9	
	0715 3.4			0817 3.6	
	1332 1.3			1440 0.9	
	1950 3.4			2047 3.7	
4 TU	0208 1.0		**19** W	0310 0.9	
	0826 3.5			0923 3.8	
	1440 1.1			1545 0.7	
	2056 3.5			2152 3.9	
5 W	0308 0.9		**20** TH	0405 0.8	
	0927 3.7			1020 4.0	
	1540 1.0			1639 0.5	
	2153 3.7			2247 4.0	
6 TH	0401 0.8		**21** F	0451 0.7	
	1019 3.9			1110 4.1	
	1632 0.8			1726 0.4	
	2243 3.9			2335 4.1	
7 F	0447 0.7		**22** SA ●	0532 0.7	
	1105 4.0			1155 4.2	
	1718 0.6			1807 0.4	
	2329 4.1				
8 SA O	0530 0.7		**23** SU	0018 4.1	
	1148 4.1			0610 0.7	
	1801 0.5			1236 4.2	
				1845 0.4	
9 SU	0012 4.2		**24** M	0057 4.1	
	0610 0.6			0646 0.7	
	1230 4.2			1311 4.1	
	1842 0.3			1919 0.4	
10 M	0055 4.3		**25** TU	0130 4.0	
	0650 0.6			0719 0.7	
	1310 4.2			1341 4.0	
	1923 0.2			1950 0.5	
11 TU	0136 4.3		**26** W	0159 4.0	
	0731 0.5			0749 0.8	
	1351 4.3			1409 4.0	
	2003 0.2			2018 0.5	
12 W	0219 4.3		**27** TH	0226 3.9	
	0813 0.5			0819 0.8	
	1433 4.2			1439 3.9	
	2045 0.2			2048 0.6	
13 TH	0304 4.2		**28** F	0258 3.9	
	0857 0.6			0854 0.8	
	1517 4.2			1514 3.9	
	2130 0.3			2124 0.7	
14 F	0353 4.0		**29** SA	0335 3.8	
	0946 0.7			0935 1.0	
	1607 4.0			1555 3.7	
	2222 0.5			2207 0.8	
15 SA	0447 3.8		**30** SU	0420 3.7	
	1044 0.9			1027 1.1	
	1705 3.8			1644 3.5	
	2325 0.7			2305 1.0	
			31 M	0514 3.5	
				1133 1.3	
				1747 3.4	

Chart Datum: 2·16 metres below Ordnance Datum (Newlyn)

ENGLAND – WALTON–ON–THE–NAZE

LAT 51°51′N   LONG 1°16′E

TIMES AND HEIGHTS OF HIGH AND LOW WATERS

YEAR **1998**

4

TIME ZONE (UT)
For Summer Time add ONE hour in non-shaded areas

SEPTEMBER

Day	Time	m	Time	m	Time	m	Time	m
1 TU	0015	1.2	0621	3.4	1248	1.3	1903	3.3
2 W	0128	1.2	0739	3.4	1403	1.2	2021	3.4
3 TH	0235	1.1	0851	3.6	1511	1.0	2127	3.7
4 F	0333	0.9	0950	3.9	1607	0.7	2220	4.0
5 SA	0422	0.8	1039	4.1	1655	0.5	2307	4.2
6 SU	0507	0.7	1124	4.2	1739	0.3	O 2351	4.3
7 M	0549	0.6	1207	4.3	1821	0.2		
8 TU	0034	4.4	0630	0.5	1249	4.4	1901	0.1
9 W	0117	4.5	0711	0.4	1331	4.4	1942	0.1
10 TH	0159	4.4	0754	0.4	1413	4.4	2023	0.2
11 F	0243	4.3	0839	0.5	1457	4.1	2107	0.4
12 SA	0330	4.1	0928	0.6	1547	4.1	2156	0.6
13 SU	0422	3.9	1024	1.0	1645	3.8	2257	0.9
14 M	0525	3.6	1137	1.0	1758	3.6		
15 TU	0016	1.1	0641	3.5	1306	1.0	1920	3.5
16 W	0143	1.2	0758	3.5	1427	0.9	2037	3.6
17 TH	0252	1.1	0906	3.7	1530	0.7	2140	3.9
18 F	0346	1.0	1002	4.0	1621	0.6	2231	4.1
19 SA	0430	0.9	1050	4.1	1705	0.5	2316	4.2
20 SU	0510	0.8	1133	4.2	1743	0.5	● 2356	4.2
21 M	0547	0.8	1211	4.2	1817	0.5		
22 TU	0031	4.1	0620	0.7	1244	4.1	1847	0.5
23 W	0101	4.0	0650	0.7	1312	4.0	1915	0.6
24 TH	0126	4.0	0719	0.7	1338	4.0	1942	0.6
25 F	0151	4.0	0750	0.7	1408	4.0	2011	0.6
26 SA	0222	4.0	0825	0.8	1442	3.9	2044	0.7
27 SU	0259	3.9	0904	0.9	1521	3.8	2123	0.9
28 M	0342	3.8	0952	1.0	1608	3.6	2213	1.1
29 TU	0434	3.6	1054	1.2	1707	3.4	2326	1.3
30 W	0539	3.4	1210	1.2	1822	3.3		

OCTOBER

Day	Time	m	Time	m	Time	m	Time	m
1 TH	0048	1.3	0657	3.4	1329	1.2	1946	3.4
2 F	0202	1.2	0815	3.6	1439	0.9	2058	3.7
3 SA	0302	1.0	0917	3.8	1538	0.7	2154	4.0
4 SU	0354	0.8	1010	4.1	1628	0.4	2242	4.3
5 M	0440	0.6	1057	4.3	1713	0.3	O 2328	4.4
6 TU	0525	0.5	1142	4.4	1756	0.2		
7 W	0011	4.5	0608	0.4	1226	4.5	1838	0.1
8 TH	0055	4.5	0652	0.4	1309	4.5	1919	0.2
9 F	0138	4.5	0736	0.4	1354	4.5	2001	0.3
10 SA	0222	4.3	0823	0.4	1439	4.3	2045	0.5
11 SU	0308	4.1	0913	0.6	1529	4.1	2133	0.8
12 M	0359	3.9	1010	0.8	1627	3.8	2232	1.1
13 TU	0500	3.6	1122	0.9	1740	3.6	2348	1.3
14 W	0616	3.4	1247	1.0	1902	3.5		
15 TH	0114	1.4	0733	3.5	1404	0.9	2015	3.6
16 F	0225	1.3	0840	3.7	1505	0.8	2116	3.8
17 SA	0320	1.1	0935	3.9	1555	0.6	2206	4.0
18 SU	0405	1.0	1022	4.1	1636	0.6	2249	4.1
19 M	0445	0.8	1104	4.1	1713	0.5	2328	4.1
20 TU	0521	0.8	1141	4.1	1745	0.6	●	
21 W	0001	4.1	0553	0.7	1214	4.1	1814	0.6
22 TH	0030	4.0	0623	0.7	1243	4.0	1842	0.7
23 F	0055	4.0	0653	0.7	1311	4.0	1910	0.7
24 SA	0121	4.0	0725	0.7	1342	4.0	1941	0.7
25 SU	0153	4.0	0801	0.8	1417	3.9	2014	0.8
26 M	0230	4.0	0841	0.8	1452	3.8	2051	0.9
27 TU	0312	3.9	0927	0.9	1542	3.7	2138	1.1
28 W	0402	3.6	0952	0.9	1639	3.5	2241	1.3
29 TH	0504	3.4	1136	1.1	1750	3.4		
30 F	0005	1.3	0620	3.4	1255	1.0	1911	3.5
31 SA	0124	1.3	0737	3.5	1406	0.9	2024	3.7

NOVEMBER

Day	Time	m	Time	m	Time	m	Time	m
1 SU	0229	1.1	0842	3.8	1507	0.6	2123	4.0
2 M	0324	0.8	0938	4.0	1559	0.4	2214	4.2
3 TU	0414	0.6	1028	4.3	1647	0.3	2302	4.4
4 W	0501	0.5	1116	4.4	1733	0.2	O 2348	4.5
5 TH	0548	0.4	1203	4.5	1816	0.2		
6 F	0032	4.5	0634	0.3	1250	4.5	1859	0.3
7 SA	0117	4.4	0721	0.3	1336	4.5	1942	0.4
8 SU	0201	4.3	0809	0.4	1423	4.3	2026	0.6
9 M	0247	4.1	0901	0.5	1513	4.1	2113	0.9
10 TU	0335	3.9	0957	0.7	1609	3.9	2207	1.2
11 W	0432	3.6	1103	0.8	1714	3.6	2313	1.4
12 TH	0541	3.5	1216	0.9	1828	3.5		
13 F	0032	1.5	0655	3.4	1327	0.9	1939	3.5
14 SA	0146	1.4	0802	3.6	1428	0.8	2041	3.7
15 SU	0245	1.2	0859	3.8	1519	0.8	2132	3.9
16 M	0334	1.1	0948	3.9	1602	0.7	2216	4.0
17 TU	0416	0.9	1031	4.0	1639	0.7	2255	4.1
18 W	0453	0.8	1109	4.0	1712	0.7	2329	4.1
19 TH	0527	0.8	1144	4.0	1744	0.7	● 2359	4.1
20 F	0559	0.7	1216	4.0	1815	0.7		
21 SA	0028	4.0	0631	0.7	1248	4.0	1846	0.8
22 SU	0058	4.0	0706	0.7	1322	4.0	1919	0.8
23 M	0131	4.0	0744	0.7	1358	4.0	1953	0.8
24 TU	0208	3.9	0824	0.8	1438	3.9	2031	0.8
25 W	0249	3.8	0909	0.8	1524	3.8	2116	1.1
26 TH	0337	3.7	1002	0.9	1618	3.6	2212	1.2
27 F	0435	3.5	1106	0.9	1723	3.6	2323	1.3
28 SA	0545	3.5	1219	0.9	1836	3.6		
29 SU	0041	1.2	0659	3.6	1331	0.8	1947	3.7
30 M	0152	1.1	0807	3.7	1435	0.6	2050	3.9

DECEMBER

Day	Time	m	Time	m	Time	m	Time	m
1 TU	0253	0.9	0906	4.0	1532	0.5	2146	4.1
2 W	0349	0.7	1001	4.2	1624	0.4	2237	4.3
3 TH	0441	0.5	1053	4.3	1712	0.3	O 2326	4.3
4 F	0532	0.4	1144	4.4	1758	0.2		
5 SA	0013	4.3	0621	0.3	1233	4.4	1842	0.4
6 SU	0059	4.2	0710	0.3	1321	4.4	1925	0.5
7 M	0143	4.2	0759	0.3	1408	4.3	2008	0.7
8 TU	0227	4.1	0848	0.4	1456	4.1	2052	0.9
9 W	0312	3.9	0940	0.6	1545	3.9	2139	1.1
10 TH	0400	3.7	1034	0.7	1639	3.7	2232	1.3
11 F	0455	3.5	1133	0.9	1740	3.5	2336	1.4
12 SA	0602	3.4	1235	0.9	1848	3.4		
13 SU	0048	1.4	0711	3.4	1336	1.0	1952	3.5
14 M	0157	1.3	0813	3.6	1432	0.9	2048	3.6
15 TU	0255	1.2	0907	3.7	1520	0.9	2137	3.8
16 W	0343	1.0	0955	3.8	1603	0.8	2219	3.9
17 TH	0425	0.9	1037	3.9	1641	0.8	2258	4.0
18 F	0503	0.8	1116	4.0	1718	0.8	● 2333	4.0
19 SA	0538	0.7	1154	4.0	1753	0.8		
20 SU	0006	4.0	0614	0.7	1230	4.0	1828	0.8
21 M	0041	4.0	0652	0.6	1306	4.0	1903	0.8
22 TU	0116	4.0	0731	0.6	1344	4.0	1938	0.8
23 W	0153	4.0	0811	0.6	1424	4.0	2017	0.8
24 TH	0233	3.9	0855	0.6	1509	3.9	2100	0.9
25 F	0318	3.8	0943	0.7	1559	3.8	2150	1.0
26 SA	0409	3.7	1038	0.7	1656	3.7	2249	1.1
27 SU	0511	3.6	1143	0.7	1801	3.6	2359	1.1
28 M	0621	3.6	1255	0.7	1912	3.6		
29 TU	0114	1.1	0732	3.7	1405	0.7	2019	3.8
30 W	0225	0.9	0839	3.8	1509	0.6	2120	3.9
31 TH	0329	0.7	0940	4.0	1605	0.5	2216	4.0

Chart Datum: 2·16 metres below Ordnance Datum (Newlyn)

RIVERS STOUR, ORWELL AND DEBEN

Rtg 1-1-1

10-4-21, 22 & 23

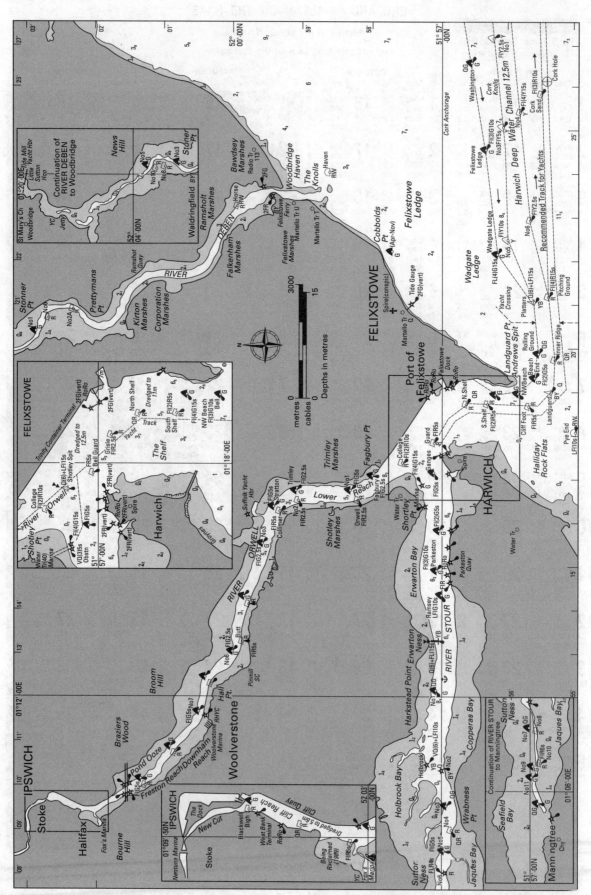

RIVER STOUR   10-4-21

Essex/Suffolk 51°57'·03N 01°17'·88E (Guard PHM buoy)

CHARTS
AC *2693*, 1594, 1491, 1593, *2052*; Imray Y16; Stanfords 5, 6; OS 169
TIDES
Harwich+0050 Dover; ML 2·1; Duration 0630; Zone 0 (UT)

Standard Port WALTON-ON-THE-NAZE (←—)

Times				Height (metres)			
High Water		Low Water		MHWS	MHWN	MLWN	MLWS
0000	0600	0500	1100	4·2	3·4	1·1	0·4
1200	1800	1700	2300				
Differences HARWICH							
+0007	+0002	–0010	–0012	–0·2	0·0	0·0	0·0
WRABNESS							
+0017	+0015	–0010	–0012	–0·1	0·0	0·0	0·0
MISTLEY							
+0032	+0027	–0010	–0012	0·0	0·0	–0·1	–0·1

Note: Although Harwich is a Standard Port, it has only two Secondary Ports referenced to it. Harwich HW and LW times differ by only 5 and 10 minutes from Walton-on-the-Naze.

SHELTER
Good at Shotley Pt Marina, access at all tides via a chan dredged 2m, outer limits lit, to lock. AB also at Harwich Pound (dries; access only near HW), Mistley, Manningtree (both dry). No yachts at Parkeston Quay. ⌕s off Erwarton Ness, Wrabness Pt, Holbrook Creek and Stutton Ness.
NAVIGATION
WPT Cork Sand PHM lt buoy, Fl (3) R 10s, 51°55'·43N 01°25'·95E, 087°/267° from/to position 7ca S of Landguard Pt, 4M. Keep clear of commercial shipping. Stay out of the DW chan by using recommended yacht track, parallel to S of it from the WPT and thence to W of it past Harwich. **Caution**: Bkwtr, ESE of Blackman's Hd, covers at HW; it is marked by small inconspic unlit PHM bn, only 5ca W of main chan. The Guard shoal (0·8m), about 2ca S of Guard PHM buoy, lies close to the recommended yacht track. Outside the hbr, yachts should cross the DW chan at 90° between Rolling Ground and Platters buoys. See 10.4.5. The R Stour is well marked; speed limit 8kn. Beware 'The Horse' 4ca NE and a drying bank 1½ca NW of Wrabness Pt. From Mistley Quay local knowledge is needed for the narrow, tortuous chan to Manningtree.
Special Local Sound Signals
Commercial vessels may use these additional sigs:

Four short and rapid blasts followed by one short blast } = I am turning short around to stbd.

Four short and rapid blasts followed by two short blasts } = I am turning short around to port.

One prolonged blast = I am leaving a dock, quay or ⌕.

LIGHTS AND MARKS
The R Stour to Mistley Quay is lit. At Cattawade, 8M up river, a conspic chy leads 270° through the best water up to Harkstead Pt.
Shotley Pt Marina: a Dir lt at lock indicates the dredged chan (2·0m) by Inogen (or Moiré) visual marker lts which are square, ambered displays; a vert B line indicates on the appr centre line 339°. If off the centre line, arrows indicate the direction to steer to regain it.
RADIO TELEPHONE
Harwich Hbr Radio Ch **71** 11 14 16 (H24). Yachts should monitor Ch 71 for tfc info, but not transmit. Weather, tidal info and possibly help in poor vis may be available on request. The Hbr Patrol launch listens on Ch 11. Hbr Radar Ch 20. Shotley Pt Marina Ch **80** M (lock master).
TELEPHONE (Dial code 01255)
Harwich Hr Mr 243030; Hbr Ops 243000; Marinecall 0891 500455; MRSC 675518; ⌗ 508966/502267 (H24) and (01473) 235704 (H24); Police 241312; Dr 506451; Ⓗ 502446.
FACILITIES
HARWICH: **Town Pier** L, FW, AB (tidal). **Town** EC Wed; P, D, ME, SM, Gas, El, Sh, V, R, Bar, ✉, Ⓑ, ⇌, ✈ (Cambridge).
SHOTLEY: (01473) **Shotley Pt Marina** (350, visitors welcome) ☎ 788982, ☎ 788868, £13.75, access H24 via lock; FW, AC, D, P, Ⓓ, ME, El, Ⓔ, Sh, BH (30 ton) C, V, BY, CH, SM, Bar, R; **Shotley SC** ☎ 787500, Slip, FW, Bar. WRABNESS: M, FW, V. MISTLEY and MANNINGTREE: AB, M, FW, V, P & D (cans), Gas, Bar. **Stour SC** ☎ (01206) 393924 M, Bar.

RIVER ORWELL   10-4-22

Suffolk 51°57'·03N 01°17'·88E (Guard PHM buoy)   Rtg 1-1-1

CHARTS
AC *2693*, 1491, *2052*; Imray Y16; Stanfords 5, 6; OS 169. A *Yachting Guide to Harwich Harbour and its Rivers* has much useful info, inc Harwich tidal predictions; it can be obtained free from Harwich Haven Authority, Angel Gate, Harwich CO12 3EJ; ☎ (01255) 243000, ☎ 241325.
TIDES
Pin Mill +0100 Dover; Ipswich +0115 Dover; ML 2·4; Duration 0555; Zone 0 (UT)

Standard Port WALTON-ON-THE-NAZE (←—)

Times				Height (metres)			
High Water		Low Water		MHWS	MHWN	MLWN	MLWS
0000	0600	0500	1100	4·2	3·4	1·1	0·4
1200	1800	1700	2300				
Differences IPSWICH							
+0022	+0027	0000	–0012	0·0	0·0	–0·1	–0·1
PIN MILL							
+0012	+0015	–0008	–0012	–0·1	0·0	0·0	0·0

SHELTER
Good. Ent and river well marked, but many unlit moorings line both banks. ⌕s above Shotley Pt on W side, or off Pinmill. No yacht facilities at Felixstowe. Visitors' berths (by pre-arrangement) at Suffolk Yacht Hbr, Woolverstone Marina and Fox's Marina (Ipswich). Ipswich Dock opens from HW –2 to HW+¾; for entry, it is essential first to call *Ipswich Port Radio* Ch 14 before arrival, then call *Neptune Marina* also Ch 14 for alongside berth in 5m.
NAVIGATION
Appr/ent from sea as in 10.4.21. WPT Shotley Spit SCM buoy, Q (6)+L Fl 15s, 51°57'·22N 01°17'·70E, at river ent. Keep clear of the many merchant ships, ferries from/to Harwich, Felixstowe & Ipswich, especially container ships turning between Trinity container terminal and Shotley Spit and Guard buoys. 6kn is max speed in R Orwell.
LIGHTS AND MARKS
Suffolk Yacht Hbr appr marked by four bns and ldg lts: front Iso Y; rear Oc Y 4s. Woolverstone Marina: 2 FR (vert). A14 bridge lts: Centre FY (clearance 38m)

No 9 Pier 2 FR (vert)) shown up and
No 10 Pier 2 FG (vert)) down stream.

Ⓡ and Ⓖ tfc lts control ent to Ipswich Dock (H24).
New Cut, W of Ipswich Dock: 3 FR (vert) = Cut closed, ie a water velocity control structure is raised from the river bed to just below water level; vessels must not proceed.
RADIO TELEPHONE
Call: *Ipswich Port Radio* VHF Ch **14** 16 12 (H24). Once above Shotley Pt, monitor Ch 14 continuously for tfc info. Suffolk Yacht Hbr, Woolverstone Marina, Fox's Marina: Ch 80 M. Neptune Marina: Ch M 14 (0800-1730LT).
TELEPHONE (Dial code 01473)
Orwell Navigation Service 231010 (also Ipswich Hr Mr and Port Radio); MRSC (01255) 675518; ⌗ 235704 (H24); Marinecall 0891 500455; Police 233000; Ⓗ 712233.
FACILITIES
LEVINGTON
Suffolk Yacht Hbr (500+ Ⓥ welcome) ☎ 659240, ☎ 659632, £10.93, Slip, Ⓑ,P, D, FW, ME, El, Ⓔ, Sh, C (15 ton), BH (10/60 ton), CH, V, Gas, Gaz, AC, SM, Ⓓ, Access H24;
  Haven Ports YC ☎ 659658, R, Bar. **Town** ✉, Ⓑ (Felixstowe), ⇌ (bus to Ipswich), ✈ (Cambridge/Norwich).
PIN MILL
Hr Mr ☎ 780276, M £4.50, L, CH, C (6 ton), SH, ME, El, FW, D (cans), Bar, R; **Pin Mill SC** ☎ 780271; Facilities at Ipswich.
WOOLVERSTONE
Woolverstone Marina (300 + Ⓥ welcome) ☎ 780206, ☎ 780273, £12.97, Slip, D, FW, BY, ME, El, Sh, AC, Gas, Gaz, Ⓓ, C (20 ton), SM, CH, V; **Royal Harwich YC** ☎ 780319, R, Bar. **Town** EC Chelmondiston Wed; ✉, V.
IPSWICH
Fox's Marina (100+some visitors) ☎ 689111, ☎ 601737, £10.50, FW, AC, P & D (cans), BY, Gas, Gaz, BH (26 and 44 ton), C (7 ton), ME, El, Ⓔ, Sh, CH, ACA, Rigging, Bar; **Neptune Marina** (100+100 Ⓥ), ☎ 215204, ☎ 780366, £12, near town centre, wet Dock (5·8m), access via lock HW –2 to HW+¾, waiting pontoon, max LOA 80'/24m, FW, AC, D, P (cans), SH, ME (14 ton), BY, El, Ⓔ, Gas, Gaz, R, Bar; **Orwell YC** ☎ 602288, Slip, L, FW, Bar. **City** No EC; ✉, Ⓑ, ⇌, ✈ (Cambridge/Norwich).

RIVER DEBEN   10-4-23

Suffolk 51°59'·35N 01°23'·69E (Felixstowe Ferry)   Rtg 5-2-1

CHARTS
AC *2693, 2052*; Imray C28, Y15; Stanfords 3, 5, 6; OS 169
TIDES
Woodbridge Haven +0025 Dover; Woodbridge +0105 Dover; ML 1·9; Duration 0635; Zone 0 (UT)

Standard Port WALTON-ON-THE-NAZE (←—)

Times				Height (metres)			
High Water		Low Water		MHWS	MHWN	MLWN	MLWS
0100	0700	0100	0700	4·2	3·4	1·1	0·4
1300	1900	1300	1900				
Differences FELIXSTOWE PIER							
−0005	−0007	−0018	−0020	−0·5	−0·4	0·0	0·0
BAWDSEY							
−0010	−0012	−0028	−0032	−0·8	−0·7	−0·2	−0·2
WOODBRIDGE HAVEN (Ent)							
0000	−0005	−0020	−0025	−0·5	−0·5	−0·1	+0·1
WOODBRIDGE (Town)							
+0045	+0025	+0025	−0020	−0·2	−0·3	−0·2	0·0

SHELTER
Good in Tide Mill Yacht Harbour (TMYH) at Woodbridge. Ent by No 24 PHM buoy; depth over sill, dries 1·5m, is 1·6m @ MHWN and 2·5m MHWS, with very accurate tide gauge and 8 waiting buoys. ⚓s up-river above Horse Sand, at: Ramsholt, Waldringfield, Methersgate, Kyson Point and Woodbridge (9M from ent), keeping clear of moorings.
NAVIGATION
WPT Woodbridge Haven unlit SWM buoy, 51°58'·36N 01°24'·20E, 306°/126° from/to Martello tower T, 0·65M. If a pilot is required call VHF Ch 08 or dip the burgee when passing Martello tower T. The shifting shingle bar, with SHM buoy, may be crossed at HW−4 to HW depending on draft. It is recommended to enter after half-flood, and to leave on the flood. The ent is only 1ca wide and in strong on-shore winds gets dangerously choppy; the chan is well buoyed and marked. Keep E of Horse Sand, just up river of the SC. No commercial tfc. Speed limit is 8kn above Green Reach. Note: For current sketch map of approaches, send SAE (plus 2 first-class stamps for the RNLI LB) to Tidemill Yacht Hbr, Woodbridge, Suffolk IP12 1BP.
LIGHTS AND MARKS
Ldg marks (unlit), between Martello trs T and U, are: Front W △ on R ■ background, rear R ■; moved according to the chan. No lights. Bawdsey Radio tower (113m) is conspic.
RADIO TELEPHONE
Pilot Ch 08, call *Late Times* (pilot launch). Tide Mill Yacht Hbr VHF Ch **80** M (some VHF dead spots down-river).
TELEPHONE (Dial code 01394)
Pilot 270853; MRSC (01255) 675518; Marinecall 0891 500 455; ⌗ (01473) 235704 (H24); Police 383377.
FACILITIES
FELIXSTOWE FERRY (01394) **Quay** Slip, M, L, FW, ME, El, Sh, CH, V, R, Bar; **Felixstowe Ferry SC** ☎ 283785; **Felixstowe Ferry BY** ☎ 282173, M (200), Gas, Slip.
RAMSHOLT **Services:** M, FW, Bar.
WALDRINGFIELD (01473) **Waldringfield SC** ☎ 736633, Bar; **Services:** BY, C, Slip, D, FW, CH, Gas, Gaz, V.
WOODBRIDGE (01394) **Tide Mill Yacht Hbr** (150+50 ⓥ) ☎ 385745, 🖂 380735, £11.50, D, L, FW, ME, El, Sh, C (10 ton), AC, V; Tide Mill is conspic daymark. **Services:** CH, Slip, C, M, ACA; **Deben YC. Town** P, D, L, FW, CH, V, R, Bar, ✉, Ⓑ, ⇌, ✈ (Cambridge or Norwich).

RIVER ORE/ALDE   10-4-24

Suffolk 52°02'·10N 01°27'·60E (Ent)   Rtg 4-2-1

CHARTS
AC *2695, 2693*, 1543, *2052*; Imray Y15, C28; Stanfords 3, 6; OS 169
TIDES
Ent. +0015 Dover Slaughden Quay +0155 Dover; ML1·6; Duration 0620; Zone 0 (UT)

Standard Port WALTON-ON-THE-NAZE (←—)

Times				Height (metres)			
High Water		Low Water		MHWS	MHWN	MLWN	MLWS
0100	0700	0100	0700	4·2	3·4	1·1	0·4
1300	1900	1300	1900				
Differences ORFORD HAVEN BAR							
−0015	−0017	−0038	−0042	−1·0	−0·8	−0·2	−0·1
ORFORD QUAY							
+0040	+0040	+0055	+0055	−1·6	−1·3	+0·2	0·0
SLAUGHDEN QUAY							
+0100	+0100	+0115	+0115	−1·3	−1·0	+0·2	0·0
SNAPE							
+0200	+0200	No data		−1·3	−1·0	−0·3	+0·4

SHELTER
Good shelter within the river, but the entrance should not be attempted in strong E/ESE onshore winds and rough seas. Good ⚓s as shown and at Iken; also ⚓s between Martello Tr and Slaughden Quay. Landing on Havergate Is, a bird sanctuary, is prohib.
NAVIGATION
WPT Orford Haven unlit SWM By, 52°01'·63N 01°27'·67E; buoy may be moved annually, as the bar shifts. The chartlet below (at larger scale than that opposite) depicts a layout of the ent, to which current info can be referred. It is strongly advised that the latest plan of ent (£1) is obtained from: The Alde & Ore Ass'n, Woodlands, Sandy Lane, Snape, Suffolk IP17 1SD; or Aldeburgh YC.

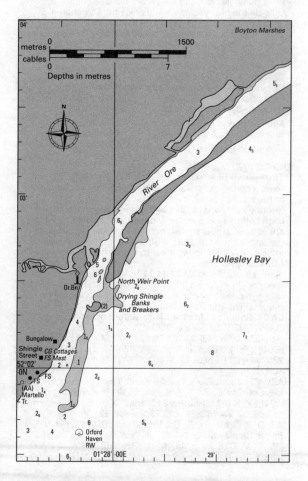

RIVER ORE/ALDE *continued*

The bar (approx 0·5m) shifts after onshore gales and is dangerous in rough or confused seas. These result from tidal streams offshore running against those within the shingle banks. Sp ebb reaches 6kn. Without local info do not enter before half flood or at night. For a first visit, appr at about LW+2½ in settled conditions and at nps. Beware shoals off the Or ♦ bn on W shore just inside ent (keep well to E side), and S to SW of Dove Pt (the most SW point of Havergate Island). R Ore, which changes its name to R Alde between Orford and Slaughden Quay, is navigable up to Snape. The upper reaches are shallow and winding, and although marked by withies these may be damaged.

LIGHTS AND MARKS

Orfordness lt ho, W tr/R bands, Fl 5s, is 5·5M NE of Haven buoy. Shingle Street, about 2ca S of ent, is identified by Martello tr 'AA', CG Stn, terrace houses and DF aerial. The Haven SWM buoy and Or ♦ bn are rarely moved; buoy does not indicate the chan. Up-river, Orford Ch & Cas are conspic; also Martello Tr 'CC', 3ca S of Slaughden Quay.

RADIO TELEPHONE

None.

TELEPHONE (Dial codes 01394 Orford/Shottisham; 01728 Aldeburgh)

Hr Mr Orford 450481; Orford River Warden 450267; Hr Mr Aldeburgh 453057; Marinecall 0891 500455; MRSC (01255) 675518; ✠ (01394) 674777; Police (01473) 613500; Orford Dr 450315 (HO); Aldeburgh Dr 452027 (HO); for Dr outside HO and at weekends, call Ipswich (01473) 717717.

FACILITIES

ORFORD **Orford Quay** Slip, AB (1 hour free, then £10/hour), M £5 night, L, FW, D (cans), C (mobile 5 ton), CH, Sh (small craft), Orford SC (OSC), R, Bar.
Village (¼M). EC Wed; P & D (cans), Gas, Gaz, ⊠, V, R, Bar, ⇌ (occas. bus to Woodbridge).
ALDEBURGH **Slaughden Quay** L, FW, Slip, BH (20 ton), CH; **Aldeburgh YC** (AYC) ☎ 452562. **Slaughden SC** (SSC).
Services: M £4, Sh, Slip, D, ME, BY, Gas, Gaz, P. **Town** (¾M), EC Wed; P, V, R, Bar, ⊠, Ⓑ, ⇌ (bus to Wickham Market), ✈ (Norwich).

SOUTHWOLD   10-4-25

Suffolk 52°18'·75N 01°40'·65E Rtg 3-3/4-1

CHARTS

AC *2695*, 1543; Imray C28; Stanfords 3; OS 156

TIDES

–0105 Dover; ML 1·5; Duration 0620; Zone 0 (UT)

Standard Port LOWESTOFT (→)

Times				Height (metres)			
High Water		Low Water		MHWS	MHWN	MLWN	MLWS
0300	0900	0200	0800	2·4	2·1	1·0	0·5
1500	2100	1400	2000				
Differences SOUTHWOLD							
+0105	+0105	+0055	+0055	0·0	0·0	–0·1	0·0
MINSMERE							
+0110	+0110	+0110	+0110	0·0	–0·1	–0·2	–0·2
ALDEBURGH (seaward)							
+0120	+0120	+0120	+0110	+0·3	+0·4	–0·1	–0·1
ORFORD NESS							
+0135	+0135	+0135	+0125	+0·4	+0·6	–0·1	0·0

Note: HW time differences (above) for Southwold apply up the hbr. At the ent mean HW is HW Lowestoft +0035.

SHELTER

Good, but the ent is dangerous in strong winds from N through E to S. Visitors berth on a staging 6ca from the ent, on N bank near to the Harbour Inn. If rafted, shore lines are essential due to current.

NAVIGATION

WPT 52°18'·06N 01°41'·80E, 135°/315° from/to N Pier lt, 1M. Enter on the flood since the ebb runs up to 6kn. Some shoals are unpredictable; a sand and shingle bar, extent/depth variable, lies off the hbr ent and a shoal builds inside N Pier. Obtain details of appr chans from Hr Mr before entering (Ch 12 or ☎ 724712). Enter between piers in midstream. When chan widens, at The Knuckle (2 FG vert), turn stbd towards LB House; keep within 10m of quay wall until it ends, when resume midstream. Unlit low footbridge ¾M upstream of ent.

LIGHTS AND MARKS

Ldg lines as chartlet. In addition: Walberswick ✠ on with N Pier lt = 268°. Hbr ent opens on 300°. 3 FR (vert) at N pier = port closed. Lt ho, W ○ tr, is in Southwold town, 0·86M NNE of hbr ent, Fl (4) WR 20s 37m 18/17/14M; vis R (intens) 204°-220°, W220°-001°, R001°-032°.

RADIO TELEPHONE

Southwold Port Radio Ch 12 16 09 (as required).

TELEPHONE (Dial code 01502)

Hr Mr 724712; MRCC (01493) 851338; ✠ (01473) 235704 (H24); Marinecall 0891 500455; Weather (01603) 660779; Police 722666; Dr 722326; Ⓗ 723333; Pilot 724712.

FACILITIES

Hbr AB £9.35, FW, D, BY, CH, ME, Sh, Slip, BH (20 ton), SM. **Southwold SC; Town** (¾M), EC Wed (Southwold & Walberswick); Gas, Gaz, Kos, P (cans, 1M), R, V, ⊠, Ⓑ, ⇌ (bus to Brampton/Darsham), ✈ (Norwich).

LOWESTOFT

MEAN SPRING
AND NEAP CURVES

MEAN RANGES
Spring 1.9m ——
Neaps 1.1m - - -

Springs occur 2 days
after
New and Full Moon

LOWESTOFT 10-4-26

Suffolk 52°28'·28N 01°45'·50E Rtg 1-1-1

CHARTS
AC 1536, 1543; Imray C28; Stanfords 3; OS 156/134

TIDES
−0133 Dover; ML 1·6; Duration 0620; Zone 0 (UT)
Lowestoft is a Standard port and tidal predictions for each day of the year are given below

SHELTER
Good; hbr accessible H24. Wind over tide, esp ebb, can make the ent lively. Fairway is dredged 4·7m. Speed limit 4kn.Yacht Basin in SW corner of Outer Hbr is run by RN & S YC; new ent is on N side (former E ent is closed off) pontoons in 2·5m. No berthing on N side of S Pier. Bridge to Inner Hbr (and Lake Lothing) lifts at the following local times (20 mins notice required):
Mon-Fri 0700, 0930, 1100, 1600, 1900, 2100
Sat/Sun, Bank Hols 0745, 0930, 1100, 1400, 1730, 1900, 2100
and also, by prior arrangement, when ships transit. Small craft may pass under the bridge (clearance 2·2m) at any time but VHF Ch 14 contact advisable.

NAVIGATION
Sands continually shift. Beware shoals and drying areas; do not cross banks in bad weather nor at mid flood/ebb.
From S, WPT is E Barnard ECM buoy, Q (3) 10s, 52°25'·11N 01°46'·50E; thence via Stanford Chan E of Newcome Sand QR, Stanford Fl R 2.5s and N Newcome Fl (4) R 15s, all PHM buoys. S Holm SCM, VQ (6)+L Fl 10s, and SW Holm SHM, Fl (2) G 5s, buoys mark the seaward side of this chan.
From E, WPT is Corton ECM buoy, Q (3) 10s Whis, 52°31'·10N 01°51'·50E; then via Holm Chan (buoyed) into Corton Road. Or approach direct to S Holm SCM buoy for Stanford Chan.
From N, appr via Yarmouth, Gorleston and Corton Roads.

LIGHTS AND MARKS
N Newcome PHM lt buoy bears 086°/5·5ca from hbr ent. Lowestoft lt ho, Fl 15s 37m 23M, is 1M N of hbr ent.
Tfc Sigs: Comply with IPTS (only Nos 2 & 5 are shown) on S pierhead; also get clearance on VHF Ch 14 when entering or leaving, due to restricted vis in appr and ent.
Bridge Sigs (on N side of bridge):
Ⓨ = bridge operating, keep 150m clear.
Ⓖ = vessels may enter/leave Inner Hbr.

RADIO TELEPHONE
Lowestoft Hbr Control (ABP) VHF Ch **14** 16 11 (H24). Pilot Ch 14. RN & SYC Ch M, 14 (occas).

TELEPHONE (Dial code 01502)
Hr Mr & Bridge Control 572286; Mutford Bridge and Lock 531778 (+Ansafone, checked daily at 0830, 1300 & 1730); Oulton Broad Yacht Stn 574946; MRCC (01493) 851338; Pilot 560277; ⌗ (01473) 235704 (H24); Weather (01603) 660779; Marinecall 0891 500455; Police 562121; Ⓗ 600611.

FACILITIES
Royal Norfolk & Suffolk YC ☎ 566726, 🛥 517981, £12.50 inc YC facilities, AB, D, L, FW, C (2 ton), Slip, R, Bar;
Lowestoft Cruising Club ☎ 574376 (occas), AB £5 (no club facilities), M, L, FW, Slip;
Services: ME, El, Sh, CH, SM, Gas, Gaz, Ⓔ, ACA.
Town EC Thurs; V, R, Bar, ✉, Ⓑ, 🚆, ✈ (Norwich).

Entry to the Broads: Passage to Oulton Broad, from Lake Lothing via two bridges and Mutford Lock (openings are coordinated; fee £5), is available 7 days/wk in working hrs HJ as pre-arranged with Mutford Br/Lock ☎ (01502) 531778/523003 or VHF Ch 09 14 (occas), who will also advise visitors drawing >1·7m. Mutford Control operates in response to bookings and daily 0800-1100 and 1300-1600LT. Oulton Broad Yacht Station ☎ (01502) 574946. From Oulton Broad, access into the R. Waveney is via Oulton Dyke. New Cut is a short cut from the R. Waveney to the R Yare for air draft <7·3m. See 10.4.27 for Broads.

ENGLAND – LOWESTOFT

LAT 52°28′N   LONG 1°45′E

TIMES AND HEIGHTS OF HIGH AND LOW WATERS

YEAR **1998**

TIME ZONE (UT)
For Summer Time add ONE hour in non-shaded areas

4

JANUARY

Day	Time	m	Day	Time	m
1 TH	0457 / 1114 / 1703 / 2315	0.5 / 2.5 / 0.8 / 2.6	**16** F	0547 / 1158 / 1728 / 2342	0.5 / 2.2 / 0.9 / 2.5
2 F	0541 / 1157 / 1744 / 2356	0.5 / 2.4 / 0.8 / 2.6	**17** SA	0620 / 1231 / 1756	0.6 / 2.2 / 1.0
3 SA	0626 / 1241 / 1827	0.5 / 2.4 / 0.9	**18** SU	0017 / 0655 / 1309 / 1827	2.5 / 0.6 / 2.1 / 1.0
4 SU	0040 / 0714 / 1332 / 1912	2.6 / 0.5 / 2.3 / 1.0	**19** M	0055 / 0738 / 1355 / 1903	2.4 / 0.8 / 2.1 / 1.1
5 M	0129 / 0808 / 1434 / 2004	2.5 / 0.6 / 2.2 / 1.0	**20** TU	0139 / 0831 / 1452 / 1951	2.3 / 0.9 / 2.1 / 1.2
6 TU	0222 / 0915 / 1558 / 2105	2.4 / 0.7 / 2.2 / 1.1	**21** W	0230 / 0929 / 1556 / 2121	2.2 / 0.9 / 2.0 / 1.3
7 W	0327 / 1033 / 1708 / 2234	2.3 / 0.7 / 2.2 / 1.1	**22** TH	0332 / 1027 / 1657 / 2242	2.2 / 1.0 / 2.1 / 1.3
8 TH	0501 / 1148 / 1807	2.3 / 0.7 / 2.2	**23** F	0449 / 1122 / 1755 / 2345	2.1 / 1.0 / 2.2 / 1.2
9 F	0014 / 0614 / 1253 / 1859	1.0 / 2.3 / 0.7 / 2.3	**24** SA	0558 / 1216 / 1846	2.2 / 0.9 / 2.2
10 SA	0121 / 0717 / 1348 / 1947	0.8 / 2.3 / 0.7 / 2.3	**25** SU	0044 / 0658 / 1307 / 1932	1.1 / 2.2 / 0.9 / 2.3
11 SU	0215 / 0814 / 1437 / 2032	0.7 / 2.4 / 0.7 / 2.4	**26** M	0139 / 0753 / 1357 / 2016	0.9 / 2.3 / 0.8 / 2.4
12 M O	0305 / 0908 / 1522 / 2115	0.5 / 2.4 / 0.7 / 2.5	**27** TU	0230 / 0845 / 1444 / 2058	0.7 / 2.3 / 0.8 / 2.5
13 TU	0350 / 0958 / 1602 / 2156	0.4 / 2.4 / 0.8 / 2.5	**28** W ●	0319 / 0934 / 1528 / 2139	0.6 / 2.4 / 0.7 / 2.6
14 W	0433 / 1043 / 1636 / 2234	0.4 / 2.3 / 0.8 / 2.5	**29** TH	0405 / 1019 / 1611 / 2220	0.4 / 2.5 / 0.7 / 2.7
15 TH	0512 / 1123 / 1703 / 2309	0.4 / 2.3 / 0.9 / 2.6	**30** F	0449 / 1102 / 1652 / 2301	0.3 / 2.5 / 0.6 / 2.7
			31 SA	0531 / 1143 / 1731 / 2342	0.3 / 2.5 / 0.6 / 2.7

FEBRUARY

Day	Time	m	Day	Time	m
1 SU	0614 / 1225 / 1812	0.3 / 2.4 / 0.7	**16** M	0618 / 1227 / 1757	0.6 / 2.2 / 0.8
2 M	0026 / 0657 / 1310 / 1854	2.7 / 0.4 / 2.3 / 0.8	**17** TU	0029 / 0648 / 1306 / 1829	2.4 / 0.7 / 2.1 / 0.9
3 TU	0112 / 0746 / 1402 / 1942	2.6 / 0.5 / 2.2 / 0.9	**18** W	0110 / 0725 / 1350 / 1909	2.3 / 0.8 / 2.1 / 1.0
4 W	0205 / 0842 / 1517 / 2039	2.4 / 0.7 / 2.1 / 1.0	**19** TH	0156 / 0820 / 1443 / 2001	2.2 / 0.9 / 2.0 / 1.1
5 TH	0313 / 0952 / 1635 / 2155	2.3 / 0.8 / 2.1 / 1.0	**20** F	0249 / 0943 / 1556 / 2148	2.1 / 1.0 / 2.0 / 1.2
6 F	0449 / 1121 / 1739 / 2358	2.2 / 0.9 / 2.1 / 1.0	**21** SA	0355 / 1048 / 1709 / 2313	2.1 / 1.0 / 2.0 / 1.1
7 SA	0605 / 1240 / 1835	2.2 / 0.9 / 2.1	**22** SU	0521 / 1147 / 1809	2.1 / 1.0 / 2.1
8 SU	0110 / 0711 / 1338 / 1926	0.8 / 2.2 / 0.9 / 2.3	**23** M	0018 / 0634 / 1244 / 1900	1.0 / 2.1 / 0.9 / 2.2
9 M	0205 / 0809 / 1427 / 2013	0.6 / 2.3 / 0.8 / 2.3	**24** TU	0119 / 0736 / 1338 / 1947	0.8 / 2.2 / 0.9 / 2.3
10 TU	0253 / 0901 / 1510 / 2057	0.5 / 2.3 / 0.8 / 2.4	**25** W	0214 / 0830 / 1429 / 2032	0.6 / 2.3 / 0.8 / 2.5
11 W O	0337 / 0947 / 1548 / 2138	0.4 / 2.3 / 0.8 / 2.5	**26** TH ●	0305 / 0917 / 1515 / 2116	0.4 / 2.4 / 0.7 / 2.6
12 TH	0417 / 1027 / 1620 / 2214	0.4 / 2.3 / 0.8 / 2.5	**27** F	0351 / 1001 / 1558 / 2200	0.3 / 2.5 / 0.6 / 2.7
13 F	0452 / 1100 / 1643 / 2247	0.4 / 2.3 / 0.8 / 2.5	**28** SA	0434 / 1042 / 1639 / 2244	0.1 / 2.5 / 0.5 / 2.7
14 SA	0522 / 1126 / 1704 / 2319	0.5 / 2.2 / 0.8 / 2.5			
15 SU	0549 / 1154 / 1729 / 2353	0.5 / 2.2 / 0.8 / 2.5			

MARCH

Day	Time	m	Day	Time	m
1 SU	0516 / 1122 / 1718 / 2327	0.1 / 2.5 / 0.5 / 2.7	**16** M	0516 / 1121 / 1705 / 2330	0.5 / 2.5 / 0.7 / 2.4
2 M	0557 / 1203 / 1757	0.2 / 2.4 / 0.5	**17** TU	0542 / 1154 / 1734	0.6 / 2.3 / 0.7
3 TU	0011 / 0638 / 1245 / 1838	2.7 / 0.3 / 2.3 / 0.6	**18** W	0006 / 0609 / 1229 / 1806	2.4 / 0.7 / 2.2 / 0.8
4 W	0059 / 0723 / 1332 / 1924	2.5 / 0.5 / 2.2 / 0.7	**19** TH	0046 / 0642 / 1307 / 1844	2.3 / 0.8 / 2.1 / 0.8
5 TH	0153 / 0815 / 1434 / 2021	2.4 / 0.7 / 2.1 / 0.8	**20** F	0131 / 0724 / 1352 / 1932	2.2 / 0.9 / 2.1 / 1.0
6 F	0310 / 0918 / 1600 / 2135	2.2 / 0.9 / 2.0 / 0.9	**21** SA	0222 / 0824 / 1445 / 2039	2.1 / 1.1 / 2.0 / 1.0
7 SA	0441 / 1048 / 1710 / 2343	2.1 / 1.0 / 2.0 / 0.9	**22** SU	0323 / 1006 / 1548 / 2239	2.1 / 1.1 / 2.0 / 1.0
8 SU	0557 / 1227 / 1810	2.2 / 1.0 / 2.1	**23** M	0450 / 1118 / 1717 / 2353	2.1 / 1.1 / 2.1 / 0.9
9 M	0055 / 0702 / 1324 / 1903	0.7 / 2.2 / 1.0 / 2.2	**24** TU	0617 / 1221 / 1821	2.1 / 1.0 / 2.2
10 TU	0148 / 0759 / 1411 / 1952	0.6 / 2.3 / 0.9 / 2.3	**25** W	0057 / 0720 / 1319 / 1914	0.7 / 2.2 / 0.9 / 2.3
11 W	0235 / 0847 / 1453 / 2036	0.5 / 2.3 / 0.9 / 2.3	**26** TH	0153 / 0811 / 1411 / 2004	0.5 / 2.3 / 0.8 / 2.4
12 TH	0317 / 0928 / 1530 / 2116	0.4 / 2.3 / 0.8 / 2.4	**27** F	0244 / 0856 / 1458 / 2052	0.3 / 2.4 / 0.6 / 2.5
13 F O	0354 / 1001 / 1559 / 2151	0.4 / 2.3 / 0.8 / 2.4	**28** SA ●	0331 / 0938 / 1542 / 2139	0.2 / 2.5 / 0.5 / 2.7
14 SA	0426 / 1027 / 1620 / 2224	0.5 / 2.3 / 0.8 / 2.4	**29** SU	0415 / 1019 / 1624 / 2226	0.1 / 2.5 / 0.4 / 2.7
15 SU	0451 / 1052 / 1640 / 2256	0.5 / 2.3 / 0.7 / 2.4	**30** M	0457 / 1059 / 1704 / 2311	0.1 / 2.5 / 0.3 / 2.7
			31 TU	0537 / 1139 / 1744 / 2358	0.1 / 2.4 / 0.4 / 2.6

APRIL

Day	Time	m	Day	Time	m
1 W	0618 / 1221 / 1826	0.3 / 2.3 / 0.4	**16** TH	0541 / 1159 / 1750	0.7 / 2.3 / 0.7
2 TH	0047 / 0701 / 1310 / 1913	2.5 / 0.5 / 2.2 / 0.6	**17** F	0025 / 0616 / 1237 / 1829	2.3 / 0.8 / 2.2 / 0.7
3 F	0146 / 0750 / 1403 / 2010	2.3 / 0.8 / 2.1 / 0.7	**18** SA	0109 / 0659 / 1320 / 1918	2.2 / 0.9 / 2.1 / 0.8
4 SA	0307 / 0849 / 1524 / 2124	2.2 / 1.0 / 2.0 / 0.8	**19** SU	0200 / 0753 / 1410 / 2021	2.1 / 1.1 / 2.1 / 0.9
5 SU	0431 / 1004 / 1638 / 2314	2.1 / 1.2 / 2.0 / 0.8	**20** M	0302 / 0905 / 1507 / 2158	2.1 / 1.2 / 2.1 / 0.9
6 M	0543 / 1201 / 1740	2.2 / 1.2 / 2.1	**21** TU	0433 / 1039 / 1614 / 2325	2.1 / 1.2 / 2.1 / 0.8
7 TU	0029 / 0645 / 1300 / 1836	0.7 / 2.2 / 1.1 / 2.2	**22** W	0558 / 1153 / 1737	2.2 / 1.1 / 2.2
8 W	0123 / 0739 / 1347 / 1926	0.6 / 2.3 / 1.0 / 2.2	**23** TH	0031 / 0658 / 1255 / 1841	0.6 / 2.3 / 0.9 / 2.3
9 TH	0209 / 0824 / 1428 / 2011	0.5 / 2.3 / 0.9 / 2.3	**24** F	0129 / 0747 / 1349 / 1937	0.4 / 2.3 / 0.8 / 2.4
10 F	0250 / 0859 / 1504 / 2050	0.5 / 2.3 / 0.8 / 2.3	**25** SA	0220 / 0831 / 1437 / 2029	0.3 / 2.4 / 0.6 / 2.5
11 SA O	0325 / 0927 / 1532 / 2125	0.5 / 2.3 / 0.8 / 2.4	**26** SU ●	0308 / 0913 / 1523 / 2119	0.2 / 2.5 / 0.4 / 2.6
12 SU	0353 / 0952 / 1553 / 2200	0.6 / 2.3 / 0.7 / 2.4	**27** M	0353 / 0955 / 1608 / 2208	0.1 / 2.5 / 0.3 / 2.6
13 M	0417 / 1022 / 1617 / 2234	0.6 / 2.3 / 0.7 / 2.4	**28** TU	0436 / 1036 / 1651 / 2256	0.1 / 2.5 / 0.3 / 2.6
14 TU	0443 / 1054 / 1645 / 2310	0.6 / 2.3 / 0.6 / 2.4	**29** W	0517 / 1118 / 1733 / 2345	0.2 / 2.5 / 0.3 / 2.5
15 W	0511 / 1126 / 1716 / 2346	0.6 / 2.3 / 0.6 / 2.3	**30** TH	0558 / 1200 / 1817	0.4 / 2.4 / 0.4

Chart Datum: 1·50 metres below Ordnance Datum (Newlyn)

ENGLAND – LOWESTOFT

LAT 52°28'N   LONG 1°45'E

TIMES AND HEIGHTS OF HIGH AND LOW WATERS

YEAR 1998

TIME ZONE (UT)
For Summer Time add ONE hour in non-shaded areas

MAY

Day	Time m	Time m	Time m	Time m
1 F	0037 2.4	0639 0.6	1245 2.3	1905 0.5
16 SA	0008 2.3	0558 0.8	1214 2.3	1821 0.7
2 SA	0139 2.3	0725 0.9	1337 2.2	2002 0.6
17 SU	0052 2.2	0641 0.9	1257 2.3	1911 0.7
3 SU	0257 2.2	0820 1.1	1448 2.1	2110 0.7
18 M	0143 2.2	0732 1.0	1346 2.2	2010 0.8
4 M	0412 2.1	0923 1.2	1600 2.1	2230 0.8
19 TU	0245 2.1	0833 1.1	1440 2.2	2126 0.7
5 TU	0518 2.1	1047 1.3	1704 2.1	2351 0.7
20 W	0417 2.1	0944 1.2	1541 2.1	2254 0.7
6 W	0617 2.2	1223 1.2	1802 2.2	
21 TH	0533 2.2	1114 1.1	1659 2.2	
7 TH	0049 0.7	0709 2.2	1315 1.1	1853 2.2
22 F	0002 0.6	0631 2.3	1226 1.0	1813 2.3
8 F	0136 0.7	0751 2.3	1357 1.0	1938 2.3
23 SA	0102 0.4	0721 2.3	1324 0.8	1913 2.4
9 SA	0215 0.7	0821 2.3	1432 0.9	2018 2.3
24 SU	0156 0.3	0806 2.4	1417 0.6	2009 2.5
10 SU	0247 0.7	0850 2.3	1459 0.8	2057 2.3
25 M	0245 0.3	0933 2.5	1506 0.5	2102 2.5 ●
11 M	0314 0.7	0922 2.4	1524 0.8	2135 2.3 O
26 TU	0332 0.2	0933 2.5	1553 0.4	2154 2.5
12 TU	0342 0.6	0956 2.4	1554 0.7	2213 2.3
27 W	0416 0.3	1016 2.5	1639 0.3	2244 2.5
13 W	0412 0.7	1031 2.4	1627 0.6	2251 2.3
28 TH	0458 0.4	1058 2.5	1724 0.3	2335 2.4
14 TH	0445 0.7	1103 2.4	1702 0.6	2328 2.3
29 F	0538 0.6	1141 2.5	1809 0.3	
15 F	0520 0.7	1136 2.4	1740 0.6	
30 SA	0027 2.3	0617 0.7	1225 2.4	1856 0.4
31 SU	0127 2.2	0658 0.9	1312 2.3	1948 0.5

JUNE

Day	Time m	Time m	Time m	Time m
1 M	0234 2.2	0746 1.1	1409 2.3	2045 0.6
16 TU	0127 2.2	0713 1.0	1326 2.4	1958 0.6
2 TU	0340 2.1	0842 1.2	1514 2.2	2143 0.7
17 W	0227 2.2	0807 1.1	1418 2.3	2103 0.6
3 W	0441 2.1	0942 1.3	1617 2.2	2244 0.8
18 TH	0351 2.2	0908 1.1	1516 2.3	2220 0.6
4 TH	0537 2.1	1047 1.3	1716 2.2	2346 0.8
19 F	0503 2.2	1026 1.1	1631 2.3	2332 0.6
5 F	0627 2.2	1200 1.2	1811 2.2	
20 SA	0603 2.2	1154 1.0	1751 2.3	
6 SA	0038 0.8	0706 2.2	1302 1.1	1859 2.2
21 SU	0036 0.5	0655 2.3	1302 0.9	1856 2.4
7 SU	0120 0.8	0740 2.3	1343 1.0	1944 2.3
22 M	0134 0.5	0743 2.4	1400 0.7	1955 2.4
8 M	0156 0.8	0817 2.4	1419 0.9	2028 2.3
23 TU	0226 0.4	0829 2.4	1452 0.5	2051 2.4
9 TU	0233 0.7	0855 2.4	1456 0.8	2111 2.3
24 W	0315 0.5	0914 2.5	1542 0.4	2144 2.4 ●
10 W	0309 0.7	0933 2.5	1534 0.7	2154 2.3 O
25 TH	0400 0.5	0958 2.5	1629 0.3	2236 2.4
11 TH	0347 0.7	1010 2.5	1613 0.7	2235 2.4
26 F	0442 0.6	1040 2.6	1714 0.3	2325 2.4
12 F	0424 0.7	1045 2.5	1652 0.6	2315 2.4
27 SA	0520 0.7	1122 2.6	1757 0.3	
13 SA	0503 0.7	1119 2.5	1733 0.6	2355 2.3
28 SU	0014 2.3	0554 0.8	1202 2.5	1840 0.4
14 SU	0543 0.8	1156 2.5	1816 0.6	
29 M	0104 2.2	0629 0.9	1243 2.5	1924 0.5
15 M	0038 2.3	0626 0.9	1239 2.4	1903 0.6
30 TU	0157 2.1	0709 1.1	1327 2.4	2011 0.6

JULY

Day	Time m	Time m	Time m	Time m
1 W	0253 2.1	0759 1.2	1420 2.3	2101 0.7
16 TH	0201 2.3	0743 0.9	1358 2.5	2039 0.6
2 TH	0347 2.1	0857 1.2	1521 2.2	2153 0.8
17 F	0315 2.2	0840 1.0	1455 2.4	2148 0.6
3 F	0440 2.1	0959 1.3	1624 2.2	2245 0.8
18 SA	0433 2.2	0950 1.1	1614 2.3	2303 0.7
4 SA	0531 2.1	1100 1.3	1724 2.2	2337 0.9
19 SU	0536 2.2	1125 1.0	1738 2.3	
5 SU	0619 2.2	1200 1.2	1820 2.2	
20 M	0015 0.7	0632 2.3	1246 0.9	1846 2.3
6 M	0027 0.9	0704 2.3	1255 1.1	1912 2.2
21 TU	0118 0.7	0722 2.4	1348 0.7	1947 2.4
7 TU	0115 0.9	0747 2.4	1346 1.0	2002 2.3
22 W	0213 0.7	0810 2.4	1442 0.5	2045 2.4
8 W	0200 0.8	0829 2.4	1433 0.9	2050 2.3
23 TH	0302 0.7	0856 2.5	1532 0.4	2138 2.4 ●
9 TH	0244 0.8	0911 2.5	1518 0.8	2136 2.4 O
24 F	0347 0.7	0940 2.6	1617 0.3	2227 2.4
10 F	0326 0.8	0950 2.5	1601 0.6	2221 2.4
25 SA	0426 0.7	1022 2.6	1659 0.3	2311 2.4
11 SA	0407 0.7	1026 2.6	1643 0.6	2302 2.4
26 SU	0501 0.8	1100 2.6	1739 0.3	2352 2.3
12 SU	0447 0.7	1103 2.6	1725 0.5	2342 2.4
27 M	0530 0.9	1136 2.6	1815 0.4	
13 M	0528 0.7	1141 2.6	1807 0.4	
28 TU	0029 2.2	0558 0.9	1212 2.5	1851 0.5
14 TU	0023 2.4	0609 0.8	1222 2.6	1851 0.5
29 W	0105 2.2	0631 1.0	1249 2.5	1930 0.7
15 W	0108 2.3	0654 0.9	1308 2.5	1941 0.5
30 TH	0147 2.1	0711 1.1	1331 2.4	2017 0.8
31 F	0241 2.1	0805 1.2	1421 2.3	2111 0.9

AUGUST

Day	Time m	Time m	Time m	Time m
1 SA	0342 2.1	0916 1.2	1525 2.2	2206 0.9
16 SU	0400 2.2	0928 1.0	1608 2.3	2235 0.9
2 SU	0442 2.1	1023 1.3	1638 2.1	2300 1.0
17 M	0510 2.2	1107 1.0	1731 2.3	
3 M	0539 2.2	1125 1.2	1744 2.2	2353 1.0
18 TU	0000 0.9	0609 2.3	1237 0.9	1841 2.3
4 TU	0631 2.3	1224 1.1	1845 2.2	
19 W	0109 0.9	0702 2.3	1339 0.7	1942 2.3
5 W	0045 0.9	0718 2.4	1320 1.0	1940 2.3
20 TH	0203 0.8	0751 2.4	1431 0.5	2038 2.4
6 TH	0136 0.9	0803 2.4	1413 0.8	2031 2.3
21 F	0250 0.8	0837 2.5	1517 0.4	2127 2.4
7 F	0223 0.8	0845 2.5	1502 0.7	2120 2.4
22 SA	0332 0.8	0920 2.6	1600 0.4	2211 2.4 ●
8 SA	0309 0.8	0926 2.6	1548 0.6	2204 2.5
23 SU	0408 0.8	1000 2.6	1639 0.4	2249 2.4
9 SU	0351 0.7	1005 2.7	1631 0.4	2245 2.5
24 M	0439 0.8	1036 2.6	1713 0.4	2320 2.3
10 M	0432 0.7	1044 2.7	1712 0.3	2324 2.5
25 TU	0503 0.8	1108 2.6	1743 0.5	2345 2.3
11 TU	0512 0.7	1124 2.7	1753 0.3	
26 W	0527 0.9	1142 2.5	1812 0.6	
12 W	0003 2.5	0553 0.7	1206 2.7	1834 0.4
27 TH	0013 2.3	0555 0.9	1217 2.5	1844 0.7
13 TH	0044 2.4	0635 0.7	1250 2.6	1920 0.5
28 F	0049 2.2	0627 1.0	1256 2.4	1922 0.8
14 F	0131 2.3	0722 0.8	1340 2.5	2013 0.7
29 SA	0132 2.2	0704 1.1	1340 2.3	2018 1.0
15 SA	0231 2.2	0817 0.9	1439 2.4	2117 0.8
30 SU	0228 2.1	0800 1.2	1433 2.2	2126 1.1
31 M	0348 2.1	0949 1.2	1547 2.1	2227 1.1

Chart Datum: 1·50 metres below Ordnance Datum (Newlyn)

ENGLAND – LOWESTOFT

LAT 52°28′N   LONG 1°45′E

TIMES AND HEIGHTS OF HIGH AND LOW WATERS

YEAR **1998**

4

TIME ZONE (UT)
For Summer Time add ONE hour in non-shaded areas

SEPTEMBER

Day	Time	m	Day	Time	m
1 TU	0458 / 1057 / 1712 / 2325	2.2 / 1.2 / 2.1 / 1.1	**16** W	0545 / 1224 / 1834	2.3 / 0.8 / 2.3
2 W	0557 / 1159 / 1822	2.2 / 1.1 / 2.2	**17** TH	0055 / 0640 / 1323 / 1933	1.1 / 2.4 / 0.7 / 2.4
3 TH	0021 / 0647 / 1258 / 1922	1.0 / 2.3 / 1.0 / 2.3	**18** F	0147 / 0730 / 1412 / 2024	1.0 / 2.4 / 0.5 / 2.4
4 F	0114 / 0733 / 1353 / 2014	1.0 / 2.4 / 0.8 / 2.4	**19** SA	0232 / 0815 / 1456 / 2109	0.9 / 2.5 / 0.5 / 2.4
5 SA	0205 / 0816 / 1443 / 2100	0.9 / 2.5 / 0.6 / 2.5	**20** SU ●	0311 / 0857 / 1537 / 2147	0.9 / 2.5 / 0.5 / 2.4
6 SU O	0251 / 0858 / 1529 / 2143	0.8 / 2.6 / 0.4 / 2.5	**21** M	0346 / 0935 / 1612 / 2217	0.9 / 2.6 / 0.5 / 2.4
7 M	0335 / 0940 / 1612 / 2222	0.7 / 2.7 / 0.3 / 2.6	**22** TU	0412 / 1008 / 1642 / 2241	0.9 / 2.6 / 0.6 / 2.4
8 TU	0416 / 1023 / 1654 / 2300	0.6 / 2.8 / 0.2 / 2.6	**23** W	0433 / 1041 / 1707 / 2306	0.8 / 2.6 / 0.6 / 2.4
9 W	0456 / 1105 / 1734 / 2339	0.6 / 2.8 / 0.3 / 2.6	**24** TH	0458 / 1115 / 1731 / 2336	0.8 / 2.5 / 0.7 / 2.4
10 TH	0536 / 1149 / 1814	0.6 / 2.8 / 0.3	**25** F	0526 / 1150 / 1756	0.8 / 2.5 / 0.8
11 F	0018 / 0618 / 1234 / 1857	2.5 / 0.6 / 2.7 / 0.5	**26** SA	0010 / 0556 / 1228 / 1823	2.4 / 0.9 / 2.4 / 0.9
12 SA	0102 / 0704 / 1325 / 1947	2.4 / 0.7 / 2.5 / 0.7	**27** SU	0047 / 0631 / 1311 / 1859	2.3 / 1.0 / 2.3 / 1.0
13 SU	0156 / 0801 / 1432 / 2049	2.2 / 0.9 / 2.3 / 0.9	**28** M	0130 / 0717 / 1400 / 1955	2.2 / 1.1 / 2.2 / 1.2
14 M	0324 / 0915 / 1606 / 2209	2.2 / 1.0 / 2.2 / 1.1	**29** TU	0222 / 0846 / 1502 / 2146	2.2 / 1.2 / 2.1 / 1.2
15 TU	0443 / 1100 / 1726 / 2349	2.2 / 1.0 / 2.2 / 1.1	**30** W	0332 / 1028 / 1642 / 2255	2.2 / 1.2 / 2.1 / 1.2

OCTOBER

Day	Time	m	Day	Time	m
1 TH	0511 / 1134 / 1803 / 2355	2.2 / 1.0 / 2.3 / 1.2	**16** F	0032 / 0614 / 1259 / 1915	1.2 / 2.4 / 0.7 / 2.4
2 F	0608 / 1234 / 1904	2.3 / 0.9 / 2.3	**17** SA	0123 / 0705 / 1347 / 2003	1.1 / 2.4 / 0.6 / 2.4
3 SA	0051 / 0657 / 1329 / 1953	1.0 / 2.4 / 0.7 / 2.4	**18** SU	0207 / 0750 / 1430 / 2043	1.0 / 2.5 / 0.6 / 2.4
4 SU	0143 / 0743 / 1419 / 2036	0.9 / 2.6 / 0.5 / 2.4	**19** M	0245 / 0831 / 1508 / 2115	1.0 / 2.5 / 0.6 / 2.4
5 M O	0231 / 0829 / 1506 / 2117	0.8 / 2.7 / 0.3 / 2.6	**20** TU ●	0318 / 0907 / 1540 / 2141	0.9 / 2.5 / 0.6 / 2.4
6 TU	0315 / 0915 / 1550 / 2156	0.7 / 2.8 / 0.2 / 2.6	**21** W	0342 / 0935 / 1605 / 2206	0.9 / 2.5 / 0.7 / 2.4
7 W	0358 / 1001 / 1632 / 2235	0.6 / 2.8 / 0.2 / 2.6	**22** TH	0404 / 1016 / 1628 / 2235	0.8 / 2.5 / 0.7 / 2.5
8 TH	0440 / 1047 / 1713 / 2315	0.5 / 2.8 / 0.3 / 2.6	**23** F	0431 / 1051 / 1654 / 2307	0.8 / 2.5 / 0.7 / 2.5
9 F	0521 / 1132 / 1753 / 2355	0.5 / 2.8 / 0.4 / 2.5	**24** SA	0502 / 1127 / 1721 / 2340	0.8 / 2.4 / 0.8 / 2.5
10 SA	0604 / 1220 / 1835	0.6 / 2.6 / 0.6	**25** SU	0535 / 1205 / 1752	0.8 / 2.4 / 0.9
11 SU	0038 / 0651 / 1315 / 1922	2.4 / 0.7 / 2.5 / 0.8	**26** M	0015 / 0612 / 1247 / 1830	2.4 / 0.9 / 2.3 / 1.0
12 M	0128 / 0750 / 1429 / 2020	2.3 / 0.8 / 2.3 / 1.1	**27** TU	0057 / 0658 / 1335 / 1919	2.3 / 1.0 / 2.2 / 1.2
13 TU	0247 / 0906 / 1559 / 2136	2.2 / 0.9 / 2.2 / 1.2	**28** W	0146 / 0802 / 1432 / 2025	2.3 / 1.1 / 2.2 / 1.3
14 W	0412 / 1045 / 1714 / 2324	2.2 / 0.9 / 2.3 / 1.3	**29** TH	0241 / 0952 / 1610 / 2203	2.2 / 1.1 / 2.1 / 1.3
15 TH	0517 / 1201 / 1819	2.3 / 0.8 / 2.3	**30** F	0343 / 1105 / 1738 / 2321	2.3 / 1.0 / 2.2 / 1.4
			31 SA	0509 / 1207 / 1838	2.3 / 0.8 / 2.3

NOVEMBER

Day	Time	m	Day	Time	m
1 SU	0023 / 0616 / 1302 / 1926	1.1 / 2.4 / 0.6 / 2.4	**16** M	0137 / 0721 / 1359 / 2009	1.1 / 2.4 / 0.7 / 2.4
2 M	0118 / 0710 / 1353 / 2009	1.0 / 2.6 / 0.5 / 2.5	**17** TU	0215 / 0802 / 1434 / 2038	1.0 / 2.4 / 0.7 / 2.4
3 TU	0208 / 0802 / 1441 / 2050	0.8 / 2.7 / 0.3 / 2.6	**18** W	0246 / 0839 / 1502 / 2106	1.0 / 2.4 / 0.8 / 2.4
4 W O	0255 / 0852 / 1527 / 2131	0.7 / 2.7 / 0.3 / 2.6	**19** TH ●	0309 / 0917 / 1526 / 2138	0.9 / 2.4 / 0.8 / 2.5
5 TH	0340 / 0941 / 1610 / 2212	0.5 / 2.8 / 0.3 / 2.6	**20** F	0337 / 0954 / 1554 / 2211	0.8 / 2.4 / 0.8 / 2.5
6 F	0425 / 1030 / 1652 / 2253	0.5 / 2.8 / 0.4 / 2.6	**21** SA	0410 / 1032 / 1625 / 2244	0.8 / 2.4 / 0.8 / 2.5
7 SA	0509 / 1118 / 1733 / 2335	0.5 / 2.7 / 0.5 / 2.6	**22** SU	0445 / 1110 / 1657 / 2316	0.8 / 2.4 / 0.8 / 2.5
8 SU	0554 / 1209 / 1814	0.6 / 2.6 / 0.7	**23** M	0521 / 1147 / 1732 / 2352	0.8 / 2.4 / 0.9 / 2.5
9 M	0018 / 0643 / 1307 / 1857	2.5 / 0.6 / 2.4 / 0.9	**24** TU	0601 / 1228 / 1811	0.8 / 2.3 / 1.0
10 TU	0106 / 0741 / 1421 / 1950	2.4 / 0.7 / 2.3 / 1.1	**25** W	0033 / 0646 / 1315 / 1857	2.4 / 0.9 / 2.2 / 1.1
11 W	0211 / 0852 / 1542 / 2053	2.3 / 0.8 / 2.2 / 1.3	**26** TH	0120 / 0743 / 1409 / 1953	2.4 / 0.9 / 2.2 / 1.2
12 TH	0333 / 1012 / 1651 / 2217	2.3 / 0.8 / 2.2 / 1.4	**27** F	0212 / 0857 / 1520 / 2059	2.3 / 0.9 / 2.2 / 1.3
13 F	0441 / 1127 / 1753 / 2355	2.3 / 0.8 / 2.3 / 1.3	**28** SA	0308 / 1027 / 1702 / 2222	2.3 / 0.9 / 2.2 / 1.3
14 SA	0541 / 1227 / 1847	2.4 / 0.8 / 2.3	**29** SU	0412 / 1134 / 1805 / 2348	2.3 / 0.7 / 2.3 / 1.2
15 SU	0051 / 0634 / 1316 / 1932	1.2 / 2.4 / 0.7 / 2.4	**30** M	0535 / 1233 / 1856	2.4 / 0.6 / 2.4

DECEMBER

Day	Time	m	Day	Time	m
1 TU	0050 / 0642 / 1327 / 1941	1.0 / 2.5 / 0.5 / 2.4	**16** W	0134 / 0730 / 1347 / 2002	1.1 / 2.3 / 0.9 / 2.4
2 W	0145 / 0739 / 1417 / 2025	0.8 / 2.6 / 0.4 / 2.5	**17** TH	0207 / 0812 / 1418 / 2038	1.0 / 2.3 / 0.9 / 2.4
3 TH O	0237 / 0833 / 1505 / 2108	0.7 / 2.6 / 0.4 / 2.6	**18** F ●	0240 / 0854 / 1452 / 2115	0.9 / 2.4 / 0.8 / 2.5
4 F	0326 / 0926 / 1551 / 2151	0.5 / 2.6 / 0.4 / 2.6	**19** SA	0317 / 0937 / 1527 / 2151	0.8 / 2.4 / 0.8 / 2.5
5 SA	0413 / 1017 / 1634 / 2234	0.5 / 2.6 / 0.5 / 2.6	**20** SU	0355 / 1018 / 1603 / 2225	0.8 / 2.4 / 0.8 / 2.5
6 SU	0500 / 1108 / 1715 / 2317	0.4 / 2.6 / 0.6 / 2.6	**21** M	0433 / 1057 / 1639 / 2258	0.7 / 2.4 / 0.8 / 2.5
7 M	0547 / 1200 / 1754 / 2359	0.4 / 2.5 / 0.8 / 2.6	**22** TU	0512 / 1135 / 1716 / 2333	0.7 / 2.4 / 0.9 / 2.5
8 TU	0634 / 1256 / 1833	0.5 / 2.3 / 1.0	**23** W	0552 / 1214 / 1756	0.7 / 2.3 / 0.9
9 W	0043 / 0726 / 1402 / 1917	2.5 / 0.6 / 2.2 / 1.1	**24** TH	0014 / 0635 / 1257 / 1839	2.5 / 0.7 / 2.3 / 1.0
10 TH	0134 / 0824 / 1512 / 2009	2.4 / 0.7 / 2.2 / 1.3	**25** F	0059 / 0725 / 1346 / 1928	2.5 / 0.7 / 2.2 / 1.1
11 F	0246 / 0926 / 1616 / 2110	2.3 / 0.8 / 2.1 / 1.4	**26** SA	0148 / 0822 / 1443 / 2024	2.4 / 0.8 / 2.2 / 1.2
12 SA	0351 / 1031 / 1715 / 2217	2.3 / 0.9 / 2.2 / 1.4	**27** SU	0242 / 0936 / 1614 / 2127	2.4 / 0.8 / 2.1 / 1.2
13 SU	0456 / 1136 / 1808 / 2342	2.3 / 0.9 / 2.2 / 1.3	**28** M	0341 / 1057 / 1728 / 2302	2.3 / 0.7 / 2.2 / 1.1
14 M	0555 / 1231 / 1853	2.3 / 0.9 / 2.2	**29** TU	0500 / 1204 / 1826	2.3 / 0.7 / 2.3
15 TU	0053 / 0645 / 1314 / 1929	1.2 / 2.3 / 0.9 / 2.3	**30** W	0024 / 0620 / 1304 / 1915	1.0 / 2.4 / 0.6 / 2.4
			31 TH	0128 / 0723 / 1358 / 2002	0.8 / 2.4 / 0.6 / 2.4

Chart Datum: 1·50 metres below Ordnance Datum (Newlyn)

GREAT YARMOUTH   10-4-27

Norfolk 52°34'·33N 01°44'·50E   Rtg 3-5-2

CHARTS

AC 1536, 1543; Imray C28; Stanfords 3; OS 134

TIDES

–0210 Dover; ML 1·5; Duration 0620; Zone 0 (UT)

Standard Port LOWESTOFT (←)

Times				Height (metres)			
High Water		Low Water		MHWS	MHWN	MLWN	MLWS
0300	0900	0200	0800	2·4	2·1	1·0	0·5
1500	2100	1400	2000				

Differences GORLESTON (To be used for Great Yarmouth)
–0035	–0035	–0030	–0030	0·0	–0·1	0·0	0·0

CAISTER-ON-SEA
–0130	–0130	–0100	–0100	0·0	–0·1	0·0	0·0

WINTERTON-ON-SEA
–0225	–0215	–0135	–0135	+0·8	+0·5	+0·2	+0·1

Rise of tide occurs mainly during 3½ hours after LW. From HW Lowestoft –3 until HW the level is usually within 0·3m of predicted HW. Flood tide runs until about HW +1½ and Ebb until about LW +2½. See also under NAVIGATION.

SHELTER

Excellent on Town Hall Quay, close S of Haven Bridge; ⚓ prohib in hbr which is a busy commercial port.

NAVIGATION

WPT 52°34'·40N 01°45'·67E, 084°/264° from/to front ldg lt, 1·0M. Access is H24, subject to clearance, but small craft must not attempt ent in strong SE winds which cause dangerous seas, especially on the ebb. Except at local slack water, which occurs at HW+1½ and LW+1¾, tidal streams at the ent are strong. On the flood, the stream eddies NW past S pier, thence up-river; beware being set onto N pier; a QY tidal lt on S pier warns of this D/N. Temp shoaling may occur in the ent during strong E'lies, with depths 1m less than those charted. Beware strong tidal streams that sweep through the Haven Bridge.

LIGHTS AND MARKS

Main lt Fl R 3s 11m 11M, vis 235°-340°, Horn (3) 60s. (Note: Tfc Sigs and the tidal QY are co-located with the Main lt on a R brick bldg, W lower half floodlit, at S pier). Ldg lts 264°: front Oc 3s 6m 10M; rear Oc 6s 7m 10M, (below the FR 20m 6M on Brush lt ho). N pier lt, QG 8m 6M, vis 176°-078° (262°). Ent and bend marked by five x 2 FG and seven x 2FR (all vert).

TRAFFIC SIGNALS

VTS instructions (Ch 12) must always be obeyed. Tfc sigs on S pier: 3 Ⓡ (vert), vis 235°-295° = No entry. VTS office: 3 Ⓡ (vert) = no vessel to go down-river S of the LB shed. Haven and Breydon bridges: 3 Ⓡ (vert) = passage prohib.

RADIO TELEPHONE

Call: *Yarmouth* Ch **12** (both H24) 09. Both bridges Ch 12.

TELEPHONE (Dial code 01493)

Hr Mr 855151; VTS (H24) 855153; MRCC 851338; ⌗ (01473) 235704 (H24); Police 336200; Breydon Bridge 651275; Broads Navigation Authority (01603) 610734.

FACILITIES

Town Hall Quay (50m stretch) AB £10, may be limited to only 2 nights in season.
Burgh Castle Marina (on Breydon Water) (90+10 visitors) ☎ 780263, Slip, D, FW, ME, El, Sh, C (6 ton), Ⓞ, Gas, Gaz, CH, V, R, Bar, Access HW ±4; **Services:** BY, P & D, ME, El, FW, Slip, Diving, AB, L, M, Sh, SM, ACA.
Town EC Thurs; P, D, CH, V, R, Bar, ✉, Ⓑ, ⇌, ✈ (Norwich).

Entry to the Broads: Pass up R Yare at slack LW, under Haven Bridge (2·3m MHWS) thence to Breydon Water via Breydon Bridge (4·0m) or to R Bure. Both bridges lift in co-ordination to pass small craft in groups.They are manned 0800-1700 Mon-Thurs, 0800-1600 Fri, but do not open 0800-0900 or 1700-1800. Call the Bridge Officer on VHF Ch 12. R Bure has two fixed bridges (2·3m MHWS).

NORFOLK BROADS: The Broads comprise about 120 miles of navigable rivers and lakes in Norfolk and Suffolk. The main rivers (Bure, Yare and Waveney) are tidal, flowing into the sea at Great Yarmouth. The N Broads have a 2·3m headroom limit. Unlimited headroom restricts cruising to R Yare (Great Yarmouth to Norwich, but note that 3M E of Norwich, Postwick viaduct on S bypass has 10.67m clearance) and River Waveney (Lowestoft to Beccles). The Broads may be entered from sea at Great Yarmouth (as above) or at Lowestoft (10.4.26).

Tidal data on the rivers and Broads is based on the time of LW at Yarmouth Yacht Stn (mouth of R Bure), which is LW Gorleston +0100 (see TIDES). Add the differences below to time of LW Yarmouth Yacht Stn to get local LW times:

R Bure		R Waveney	
Acle Bridge	+0230	Burney Arms	+0100
Horning	+0300	St Olaves	+0115
Potter Heigham	+0400	Oulton Broad	+0300
R Yare		Beccles	+0320
Reedham	+0115		
Cantley	+0200		
Norwich	+0430		

LW at Breydon (mouth of R Yare) is LW Yarmouth Yacht Stn +0100. Tide starts to flood on Breydon Water whilst still ebbing from R Bure. Max draft is 1·8m; 2m with care. Tidal range varies from 0·6m to 1·8m.

Licences are compulsory; get temp one from The Broads Authority, 18 Colegate, Norwich NR3 1BQ, ☎ 01603-610734; from Mutford Lock or from River Inspectors. *Hamilton's Guide to the Broads* is recommended.

VOLVO PENTA SERVICE

Sales and service centres in area 5

YORKSHIRE *Auto Unit Repairs (A division of Anderson Towers Ltd)*, The Engine Centre, Henshaw Lane, Yeadon, Leeds LS19 7XY Tel (01132) 501222 *Anglo Dansk Engineering Co Ltd*, Robinson Lane, Fish Docks, Grimsby DN31 3SF Tel (01472) 351457/8/9 **NOTTINGHAM** *Newark Marina Ltd*, 26 Farndon Road, Newark NG24 4SD Tel (01636) 704022 **TYNE & WEAR** *Fox and Hounds Marine (A division of Royston Marine Ltd)*, 40 Bell Street, Fish Quay, Tyne & Wear NE30 1HF Tel (0191) 259 6797 *Royston Engineering Group Ltd*, Unit 3, Walker Riverside, Wincomblee Road, Newcastle upon Tyne NE36 3PF (0191) 295 8000

VOLVO PENTA

Area 5

East England
Blakeney to Berwick-on-Tweed

5

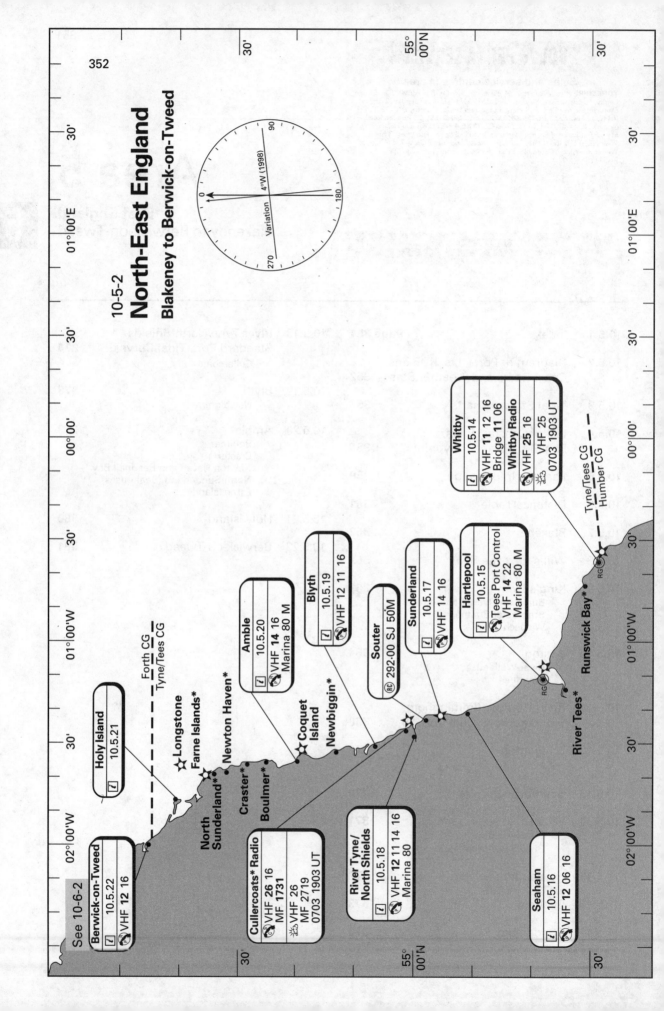

352

10·5·2
North-East England
Blakeney to Berwick-on-Tweed

Variation
4°W (1998)

See 10·6·2

Berwick-on-Tweed
ℹ 10.5.22
📞 VHF 12 16

Holy Island
ℹ 10.5.21

Longstone
Farne Islands*
Newton Haven*

Forth CG
Tyne/Tees CG

North Sunderland*
Craster*
Boulmer*

Coquet Island
Newbiggin*

Amble
10.5.20
ℹ
📞 VHF 14 16
Marina 80 M

Blyth
ℹ 10.5.19
📞 VHF 12 11 16

Cullercoats* Radio
📞 VHF 26 16
MF 1731
📞 VHF 26
MF 2719
0703 1903 UT

River Tyne/ North Shields
ℹ 10.5.18
📞 VHF 12 11 14 16
Marina 80

Souter
◉ 292·00 SJ 50M

Sunderland
ℹ 10.5.17
📞 VHF 14 16

Seaham
10.5.16
ℹ
📞 VHF 12 06 16

Hartlepool
ℹ 10.5.15
📞 Tees Port Control
VHF 14 22
Marina 80 M

River Tees*
Runswick Bay*

RG

RG

Tyne/Tees CG
Humber CG

Whitby
ℹ 10.5.14
📞 VHF 11 12 16
Bridge 11 06
Whitby Radio
📞 VHF 25 16
📞 VHF 25
0703 1903 UT

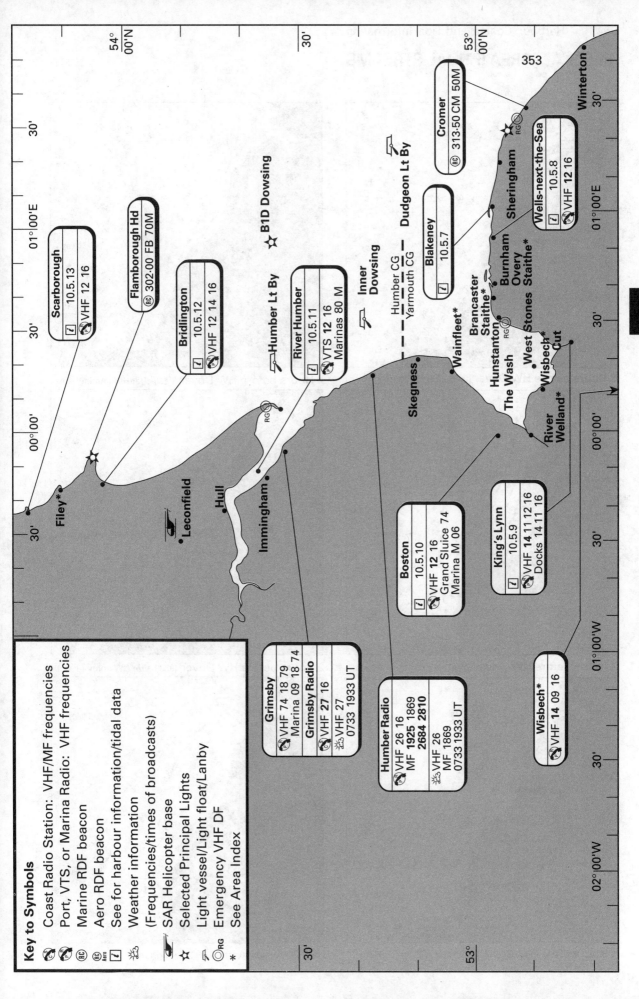

Key to Symbols

Coast Radio Station: VHF/MF frequencies
Port, VTS, or Marina Radio: VHF frequencies
Marine RDF beacon
Aero RDF beacon
See for harbour information/tidal data
Weather information
(Frequencies/times of broadcasts)
SAR Helicopter base
Selected Principal Lights
Light vessel/Light float/Lanby
Emergency VHF DF
* See Area Index

Scarborough
10.5.13
VHF 12 16

Flamborough Hd
302·00 FB 70M

Bridlington
10.5.12
VHF 12 14 16

Filey*

Leconfield

Hull

Immingham

Grimsby
VHF 74 18 79
Marina 09 18 74
Grimsby Radio
VHF 27 16
VHF 27
0733 1933 UT

Humber Radio
VHF 26 16
MF **1925** 1869
2684 2810
VHF 26
MF 1869
0733 1933 UT

Humber Lt By

River Humber
10.5.11
VTS **12** 16
Marinas 80 M

B1D Dowsing

Inner
Dowsing

Skegness

Wainfleet*

Humber CG
Yarmouth CG

Dudgeon Lt By

Blakeney
10.5.7

Cromer
313·50 CM 50M

Sheringham

Burnham
Overy
Staithe*
Brancaster
Staithe*

Wells-next-the-Sea
10.5.8
VHF 12 16

Winterton

353

Hunstanton
The Wash
West Stones*
Wisbech
Cut
River
Welland*

Boston
10.5.10
VHF **12** 16
Grand Sluice 74
Marina M 06

King's Lynn
10.5.9
VHF **14** 11 12 16
Docks 14 11 16

Wisbech*
VHF **14** 09 16

5

10-5-3   AREA 5 TIDAL STREAMS

5 Hours before HW Dover (0030 after HW Immingham)

4 Hours before HW Dover (0130 after HW Immingham)

3 Hours before HW Dover (0230 after HW Immingham)

2 Hours before HW Dover (0330 after HW Immingham)

1 Hour before HW Dover (0430 after HW Immingham)

HW Dover (0530 after HW Immingham)

Northward 10.6.3   Southward 10.4.3

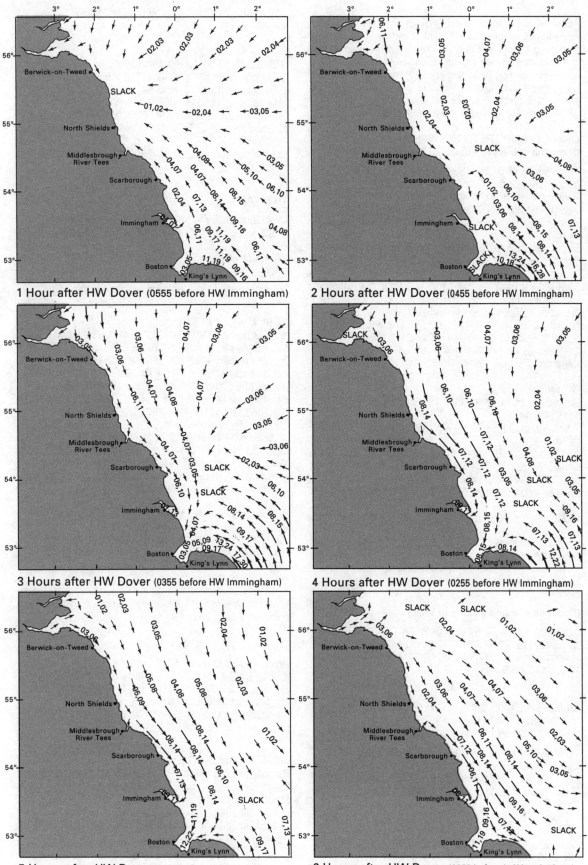

1 Hour after HW Dover (0555 before HW Immingham)

2 Hours after HW Dover (0455 before HW Immingham)

3 Hours after HW Dover (0355 before HW Immingham)

4 Hours after HW Dover (0255 before HW Immingham)

5 Hours after HW Dover (0155 before HW Immingham)

6 Hours after HW Dover (0055 before HW Immingham)

10.5.4 COASTAL LIGHTS, FOG SIGNALS AND WAYPOINTS

Abbreviations used below are given in 1.4.1. Principal lights are in **bold** print, places in CAPITALS, and light-vessels, light floats and Lanbys in *CAPITAL ITALICS*. Unless otherwise stated lights are white. m – elevation in metres; M – nominal range in miles. Fog signals are in *italics*. Useful waypoints are underlined – use those on land with care. All geographical positions should be assumed to be approximate. See 4.4.1. All positions are referenced to the OSGB 36 datum.

GREAT YARMOUTH TO THE WASH
(Direction of buoyage South to North)

YARMOUTH AND CAISTER ROADS/COCKLE GATWAY
South Denes Outfall 52°35'·10N 01°44'·50E QR 5m 2M; R △.
Wellington Pier Hd 52°35'·92N 01°44'·42E 2 FR (vert) 8m 3M.
Jetty Hd 52°36'·10N 01°44'·48E 2 FR (vert) 7m 2M.
Britannia Pier Hd 52°36'·47N 01°44'·57E 2 FR (vert) 11m 4M; W col.
SW Scroby Lt By 52°35'·80N 01°46'·37E Fl G 2·5s; SHM.
Scroby Elbow Lt By 52°37'·32N 01°46'·50E Fl (2) G 5s; SHM; *Bell*.
Mid Caister Lt By 52°38'·96N 01°45'·77E Fl (2) R 5s; PHM; *Bell*.
NW Scroby Lt By 52°40'·35N 01°46'·44E Fl (3) G 10s; SHM.
N Caister Lt By 52°40'·40N 01°45'·66E Fl (3) R 10s; PHM.
Hemsby Lt By 52°41'·84N 01°45'·00E Fl R 2·5s; PHM.
N Scroby Lt By 52°42'·49N 01°44'·80E VQ; NCM; *Whis*.
Cockle Lt By 52°44'·00N 01°43'·70E VQ (3) 5s; ECM; *Bell*.
Winterton Old Lt Ho 52°42'·75N 01°41'·80E Racon (T).

OFFSHORE ROUTE
Cross Sand Lt By 52°37'·00N 01°59'·25E L Fl 10s 6m 5M; SWM; Racon (T).
E Cross Sand Lt By 52°40'·00N 01°53'·80E Fl (4) R 15s; PHM.
NE Cross Sand Lt By 52°43'·00N 01° 53'·80E VQ (3) 5s; ECM.
Smith's Knoll Lt By 52°43'·50N 02°18'·00E Q (6) + L Fl 15s 7M; SCM; Racon (T); *Whis*.
S Winterton Ridge Lt By 52°47'·20N 02°03'·60E Q (6) + L Fl 15s; SCM.
E Hammond Knoll Lt By 52°52'·30N 01°58'·75E Q (3) 10s; ECM.
Hammond Knoll Lt By 52°49'·72N 01°57'·70E Q (9) 15s; WCM.
NEWARP Lt F 52°48'·35N 01°55'·80E Fl 10s 12m **21M** (H24); Racon (O); *Horn 20s* (continuous).
S Haisbro Lt By 52°50'·80N 01°48'·40E Q (6) + L Fl 15s; SCM; *Bell*.

(Direction of buoyage East to West)

Mid Haisbro Lt By 52°54'·20N 01°41'·70E Fl (2) G 5s; SHM.
N Haisbro Lt By 53°00'·20N 01°32'·40E Q; NCM; Racon (T); *Bell*.
Happisburgh Lt Ho 52°49'·20N 01°32'·30E Fl (3) 30s 41m 14M; W Tr, 3 R bands.

CROMER
Cromer 52°55'·45N 01°19'·10E Fl 5s 84m **23M**; W 8-sided Tr; RC; vis 102°-307°; Racon (O).
Lifeboat Ho 52°56'·00N 01°18'·20E 2 FR (vert) 8m 5M.

Tayjack Wk Lt By 52°57'·60N 01°15'·47E Fl R 2·5s; PHM.
E Sheringham Lt By 53°02'·20N 01°15'·00E Q (3) 10s; ECM.
W Sheringham Lt By 53°02'·93N 01°06'·87E Q (9) 15s; WCM.
Blakeney Overfalls Lt By 53°03'·00N 01°01'·50E Fl (2) R 5s; PHM; *Bell*.

BLAKENEY
Fairway By 52°59'·17N 00°57'·38E; SPM.
Hjordis Wk By 52°58'·98N 00°58'·16E; PHM.
Bar Lt By 52°59'·11N 00°58'·23E QY; SPM.

WELLS-NEXT-THE-SEA/BRANCASTER STAITHE
Wells Fairway Lt By 52°59'·85N 00°49'·71E Q; SWM.
Bridgirdle By 53°01'·72N 00°44'·10E; PHM.
Brancaster Club Ho 52°58'·45N 00°38'·25E Fl 5s 8m 3M; vis 080°-270°.

APPROACHES TO THE WASH
S Race Lt By 53°08'·18N 00°56'·81E Q (6) + L Fl 15s; SCM; *Bell*.
E Docking Lt By 53°09'·80N 00°50'·50E Fl R 2·5s; PHM.
N Race Lt By 53°14'·97N 00°44'·00E Fl G 5s; SHM; *Bell*.
N Docking Lt By 53°14'·80N 00°41'·60E Q; NCM.
Scott Patch Lt By 53°11'·10N 00°36'·50E VQ (3) 5s; ECM.
S Inner Dowsing Lt By 53°12'·10N 00°33'·80E Q (6) + L Fl 15s; SCM; *Bell*.
Burnham Flats Lt By 53°07'·50N 00°35'·00E Q (9) 15s; WCM; *Bell*.

THE WASH

Lynn Knock Lt By 53°04'·40N 00°27'·31E QG; SHM.
North Well Lt By 53°03'·00N 00°28'·00E L Fl 10s; SWM; *Whis*; Racon (T).
Woolpack Lt By 53°02'·65N 00°31'·55E Fl R 10s; PHM.

ROARING MIDDLE Lt F 52°58'·61N 00°21'·15E Q 5m 8M; NCM. Replaced May-June annually by B&Y pillar By Q.

CORK HOLE/KING'S LYNN
Sunk Lt By 52°56'·27N 00°23'·50E Q (9) 15s; WCM.
No. 1 Lt By 52°56'·00N 00°20'·00E VQ; NCM; *Bell*.
No. 3 Lt By 52°54'·63N 00°19'·25E Fl (2) G 6s; SHM.
No. 3A Lt By 52°53'·67 N 00°18'·38E Fl G 5s; SHM.
No. 5 Lt By 52°52'·39N 00°18'·26E Q (3) 10s; ECM.
West Stones Lt Bn 52°49'·66N 00°21'·22E Q 3m 2M; NCM.
No. 13A Lt By 52°49'·48N 00°21'·30E Fl G 3s; SHM.
No. 15 Lt By 52°48'·63N 00°21'·22E Fl G 4s; SHM.
'E' Lt Bn 52°48'·18N 00°21'·52E Fl Y 3s 3m 2M.
No. 17 Lt By 52°47'·67N 00°21'·94E Fl G 3s; SHM.
West Bank Lt Bn 52°47'·44N 00°22'·13E Fl Y 2s 3m 4M.
King's Lynn W Bk Ferry 52°45'·35N 00°23'·46E Fl Y 2s 5m 2M (when tide is falling) and 2 FG (vert).

WISBECH CHANNEL/RIVER NENE
(Note: Bns are moved as required).
Bar Flat Lt By 52°55'·10N 00°16'·47E Q (3) 10s; ECM.
Big Tom 52°49'·57N 00°13'·17E Fl (2) R 10s; R Bn.
West End 52°49'·38N 00°13'·02E Fl (3) G 10s 3M; B mast.
Marsh 52°49'·03N 00°13'·00E QR.
Scottish Sluice West Bk 52°48'·5N 00°12'·75E FG 9m; Mast; Masts on W side of River Nene to Wisbech carry FG Lts and those on E side QR or FR Lts.

FREEMAN CHANNEL
Boston Roads Lt By 52°57'·67N 00°16'·23E L Fl 10s; SWM.
Boston No. 1 Lt By 52°57'·87N 00°15'·22E Fl G 3s; SHM.
No. 3 Lt By 52°58'·10N 00°14'·15E Fl G 6s; SHM.
No. 5 Lt By 52°58'·52N 00°12'·78E Fl G 3s; SHM.
Freeman Inner Lt By 52°58'·45N 00°11'·43E Q (9) 15s; WCM.
Delta Lt By 52°58'·34N 00°11'·26E Fl R 6s; PHM.

BOSTON LOWER ROAD
Boston No. 7 Lt By 52°58'·57N 00°10'·00E Fl G 3s; SHM.
Boston No. 9 Lt By 52°57'·58N 00°08'·45E Fl G 3s; SHM.
Boston No. 11 Lt By 52°56'·51N 00°07'·64E Fl (2) G 6s; SHM.
Boston No. 13 Lt By 52°56'·22N 00°07'·13E Fl G 3s; SHM.
Boston No. 15 Lt By 52°56'·29N 00°05'·70E Fl (2) G 6s; SHM.

Welland Lt Bn 52°56'·06N 00°05'·37E QR 5m; R □ on Bn.
Tabs Hd 52°55'·99N 00°05'·01E Q WG 4m 1M; R □ on W mast; vis W shore-251°, G251°-shore; Ra refl.

BOSTON, NEW CUT AND RIVER WITHAM
Ent N side, <u>Dollypeg Lt Bn</u> 52°56'·10N 00°05'·15E QG 4m
1M; B △ on Bn; Ra refl.
Tabs Hd Q WG 4m 1M; vis shore-251°, G251°-shore.
New Cut 52°55'·97N 00°04'·79E Fl G 3s; △ on pile.
New Cut Ldg Lts 240°. Front, No. 1 52°55'·82N 00°04'·49E
F 5m 5M. Rear, 90m from front, F 8m 5M.
Boston Ldg Lts 324°. Front, No. 10 52°58'·02N 00°00'·49W
F. Rear, No. 10A 150m from front, F.

WELLAND CUT/RIVER WELLAND
SE side Iso R 2s; NW side Iso G 2s. Lts QR (to port) and
QG (to stbd) mark the chan upstream.
Fosdyke Bridge 52°52'·26N 00°02'·45W FY.

(Direction of buoyage North to South)

BOSTON DEEP/WAINFLEET ROADS
Wainfleet Range UQ R, with FR on Trs SW & NE.
<u>Scullridge By</u> 52°59'·68N 00°14'·00E; SHM.
<u>Friskney By</u> 53°00'·48N 00°16'·68E; SHM.
<u>Long Sand By</u> 53°01'·10N 00°18'·30E; SHM.
<u>Pompey By</u> 53°02'·20N 00°19'·37E; SHM.
<u>Swatchway By</u> 53°03'·76N 00°19'·80E; SHM.
<u>Inner Knock By</u> 53°04'·85N 00°20'·50E; PHM.
<u>Wainfleet Roads By</u> 53°06'·22N 00°21'·55E; PHM.
<u>Skegness S By</u> 53°06'·70N 00°23'·35E; SHM.

WASH TO THE RIVER HUMBER

(Direction of buoyage South to North)
<u>Dudgeon Lt By</u> 53°16'·60N 01°17'·00E Q (9) 15s 7M; WCM;
Racon (O); *Whis*.
<u>E Dudgeon Lt By</u> 53°19'·70N 00°58'·80E Q (3) 10s; ECM; *Bell*.
<u>Mid Outer Dowsing Lt By</u> 53°24'·80N 01°07'·90E Fl (3) G 10s;
SHM; *Bell*.
<u>N Outer Dowsing Lt By</u> 53°33'·50N 00°59'·70E Q; NCM.
B.1D Platform Dowsing 53°33'·71N 00°52'·72E Fl (2) 10s
28m **22M**; Morse (U) R 15s 28m 3M; *Horn (2) 60s*; Racon (T).

RIVER HUMBER APPROACHES
<u>W Ridge Lt By</u> 53°19'·05N 00°44'·60E Q (9) 15s; WCM.
Inner Dowsing Lt F 53°19'·50N 00°33'·96E Fl 10s 12m **15M**;
Racon (T); *Horn 60s*.
<u>Protector Lt By</u> 53°24'·83N 00°25'·25E Fl R 2·5s; PHM.
<u>DZ No. 4 Lt By</u> 53°27'·12N 00°19'·17E Fl Y 5s; SPM.
<u>DZ No. 3 Lt By</u> 53°29'·17N 00°19'·19E Fl Y 2·5s; SPM.
<u>Rosse Spit Lt By</u> 53°30'·40N 00°17'·04E Fl (2) R 5s; PHM.
<u>Haile Sand No. 2 Lt By</u> 53°32'·14N 00°12'·80E Fl (3) R 10s;
PHM.
<u>Humber Lt By</u> 53°36'·72N 00°21'·60E L Fl 10s; SWM; *Whis*;
Racon (T).
<u>N Binks Lt By</u> 53°36'·22N 00°18'·70E Fl Y 2·5s; SPM.
<u>Outer Haile Lt By</u> 53°34'·80N 00°18'·70E Fl (4) Y 15s; SPM.
<u>S Binks Lt By</u> 53°34'·72N 00°16'·65E Fl Y 5s; SPM.
SPURN Lt F 53°33'·54N 00°14'·33E Q (3) 10s 10m 8M; ECM;
Horn 20s; Racon (M).
SE CHEQUER Lt F 53°33'·37N 00°12'·65E VQ (6) + L Fl 10s
6m 6M; SCM; Ra refl; *Horn 30s*.
<u>No. 3 Chequer Lt By</u> 53°33'·05N 00°10'·70E Q (6) + L Fl 15s;
SCM.
Tetney Monobuoy 53°32'·34N 00°06'·85E 2 VQ Y (vert); Y
SBM; *Horn Mo (A) 60s*; QY on 290m floating hose.

RIVER HUMBER/GRIMSBY/HULL
Spurn Pt Lt Bn 53°34'·36N 00°06'·59E Fl G 3s 11m 5M; G △.
BULL Lt F 53°33'·78N 00°05'·65E VQ 8m 6M; NCM;
Horn (2) 20s.
<u>North Fort Lt By</u> 53°33'·78N 00°04'·29E Q; NCM.
<u>South Fort Lt By</u> 53°33'·63N 00°04'·06E Q (6) + L Fl 15s; SCM.
Haile Sand Fort 53°32'·05N 00°02'·14E Fl R 5s 21m 3M.
<u>Haile Chan No. 4 Lt By</u> 53°33'·63N 00°02'·94E Fl R 4s; PHM.

<u>Middle No. 7 Lt F</u> VQ (6) + L Fl 10s; SCM; *Horn 20s*.
<u>Grimsby Royal Dock ent E side</u> 53°35'·06N 00°03'·93W Fl (2)
R 6s 10m 8M; Dn.
Killingholme Lts in line 292°. Front, 53°38'·78N 00°12'·87W
Iso R 2s 10m 14M. Rear, 189m from front, Oc R 4s 21m 14M.
Immingham Oil Terminal SE end 53°37'·68N 00°09'·32W
2 QR (vert) 8m 5M; *Horn Mo (N) 30s*.
<u>Clay Huts No.13 Lt F</u> 53°38'·52N 00°11'·28W Iso 2s 5m 9M;
SWM.
<u>Sand End No.16 Lt F</u> 53°42'·52N 00°14'·47W Fl R 4s 5m 3M;
PHM.
<u>Hebbles No. 21 Lt By</u> 53°44'·03N 00°15'·88W Fl G 1·5s; SHM.
<u>Lower W Middle No. 24 Lt By</u> 53°44'·26N 00°18'·24W
Fl R 4s; PHM.
<u>Hull Marina, Humber Dk Basin, E ent</u> 53°44'·22N 00°20'·05W
2 FG (vert).

RIVER HUMBER TO WHITBY
<u>Canada & Giorgios Wk Lt By</u> 53°42'·33N 00°07'·22E
VQ (3) 5s; ECM.
<u>Hornsea Sewer Outfall Lt By</u> 53°55'·02N 00°08'·27E
Fl Y 20s; SPM.
<u>Atwick Sewer Outfall Lt By</u> 53°57'·10N 00°10'·25W
Fl Y 10s; SPM.

BRIDLINGTON
<u>SW Smithic Lt By</u> 54°02'·40N 00°09'·10W Q (9) 15s; WCM.
<u>N Pier Hd</u> 54°04'·77N 00°11'·10W Fl 2s 12m 9M; *Horn 60s*;
(Tidal Lts) Fl R or Fl G.
<u>N Smithic Lt By</u> 54°06'·20N 00°03'·80W VQ; NCM; *Bell*.

Flamborough Hd 54°06'·97N 00°04'·87W Fl (4) 15s 65m
24M; W ● Tr; RC; Horn *(2) 90s*.

FILEY/SCARBOROUGH/WHITBY
Filey on cliff above CG Stn FR 31m 1M; vis 272°-308°.
<u>Filey Brigg Lt By</u> 54°12'·73N 00°14'·48W Q (3) 10s; ECM;
Bell.
<u>Scarborough E Pier Hd</u> 54°16'·87N 00°23'·27W QG 8m 3M.
Scarborough Lt Ho Pier Iso 5s 17m 9M; W ● Tr; vis 219°-039°
and FY 8m; vis 233°-030°; (tide sigs); *Dia 60s*.
<u>Scalby Ness Diffusers Lt By</u> 54°18'·60N 00°23'·25W Fl R 5s;
PHM.
<u>Whitby Lt By</u> 54°30'·32N 00°36'·48W Q; NCM; *Bell*.
High Lt Ling Hill 54°28'·60N 00°34'·00W Iso RW 10s 73m
18M, R16M; W 8-sided Tr and dwellings; vis R128°-143°,
W143°-319°.
Whitby E Pier Hd 54°29'·63N 00°36'·63W FR 14m 3M; R Tr.
Whitby W Pier Hd 54°29'·63N 00°36'·70W FG (occas) 14m
3M; G Tr; *Horn 30s*.

WHITBY TO RIVER TYNE
RUNSWICK/REDCAR
Runswick Bay Pier 54°31'·99N 00°44'·90W 2 FY (occas).
Boulby Outfall Lt By 54°34'·51N 00°48'·15W Fl (4) Y 10s;
SPM.
<u>Outfall Lt By</u> 54°36'·63N 01°00'·30W Fl Y 10s; SPM.
<u>Salt Scar Lt By</u> 54°38'·10N 01°00'·00W VQ; NCM; *Horn (1)
15s; Bell*.
Luff Way Ldg Lts 197°. Front, on Esplanade, FR 8m 7M; vis
182°-212°. Rear, 115m from front, FR 12m 7M; vis 182°-212°.
High Stone. Lade Way Ldg Lts 247°. Front, 54°37'·15N
01°03'·81W Oc R 2·5s 9m 7M. Rear, 43m from front, Oc R
2·5s 11m 7M; vis 232°-262°.

TEES APPROACHES/HARTLEPOOL
<u>Tees Fairway Lt By</u> 54°40'·95N 01°06'·23W Iso 4s 9m 8M;
SWM; Racon (B); *Horn 5s*.
<u>Tees N (Fairway) Lt By</u> 54°40'·33N 01°07'·03W Fl G 5s; SHM.

Tees S (Fairway) Lt By 54°40'·22N 01°06'·87W Fl R 5s; PHM.

Bkwtr Hd **S Gare** 54°38'·83N 01°08'·13W Fl WR 12s 16m **W20M, R17M**; W ● Tr; vis W020°-274°, R274°-357°; *Sig Stn; Horn 30s.*

Ldg Lts 210·1° Front, 54°37'·22N 01°10'·08W. Both FR 18/20m 13/**16M**.

Longscar Lt By 54°40'·85N 01°09'·80W Q (3) 10s; ECM; *Bell.*

The Heugh 54°41'·80N 01°10'·47W Fl (2) 10s 19m **19M** (H24); W Tr.

Hartlepool Old Pier Hd 54°41'·59N 01°10'·99W QG 13m 7M; B Tr.

W Hbr N Pier Hd 54°41'·31N 01°11'·47W Oc G 5s 12m 2M.

Harlepool Yacht Haven Lock Dir Lt 308° 54°41'·43N 01°11'·80W Dir Fl WRG 2s 6m 3M; vis G305·5°-307°, W307°-309°, R309°-310·5°.

N Sands, Pipe Jetty Hd 54°42'·80N 01°12'·40W 2 FR (vert) 1M; *Bell 15s.*

SEAHAM/SUNDERLAND

Seaham N Pier Hd 54°50'·25N 01°19'·15W Fl G 10s 12m 5M; W col, B bands; *Dia 30s.*

Sunderland Roker Pier Hd 54°55'·27N 01°21'·05W Fl 5s 25m **23M**; W ● Tr, 3 R bands and cupola: vis 211°-357°; *Siren 20s.*

Old N Pier Hd 54°55'·12N 01°21'·52W QG 12m 8M; Y Tr; *Horn 10s.*

Whitburn Steel By 54°56'·30N 01°20'·80W; PHM.

Whitburn Firing Range 54°57'·2N 01°21'·3W and 54°57'·7N 01°21'·2W both FR when firing is taking place.

DZ Lt Bys 54°57'·04N 01°18'·81W and 54°58'·58N 01°19'·80W, both Fl Y 2·5s; SPM.

TYNE ENTRANCE/NORTH SHIELDS

Ent N Pier Hd 55°00'·87N 01°24'·08W Fl (3) 10s 26m **26M**; Gy ● Tr, W lantern; *Horn 10s.*

S Pier Hd 55°00'·67N 01°23'·97W Oc WRG 10s 15m W13M, R9M, G8M; Gy ● Tr, R&W lantern; vis W075°-161°, G161°-179° over Bellhues rk, W179°-255°, R255°-075°; *Bell (1) 10s* (TD 1995).

Fish Quay Ldg Lts 258°. **Front,** 55°00'·54N 01°25'·98W F 25m **20M**; W ■ Tr. **Rear,** 220m from front, F 39m **20M**; W ■ Tr.

Herd Groyne Hd 55°00'·48N 01°25'·34W Oc WR 10s 13m W13M, R11M, R1M; R pile structure, R&W lantern; vis R (unintens) 080°-224°, W224°-255°, R255°-277°; *Bell (1) 5s.*

Saint Peter's Marina ent 54°57'·93N 01°34'·25E (unmarked).

RIVER TYNE TO BERWICK-ON-TWEED

CULLERCOATS/BLYTH/NEWBIGGIN

Cullercoats Ldg Lts 256°. Front, 55°02'·05N 01°25'·77W FR 27m 3M. Rear, 38m from front, FR 35m 3M.

Blyth Ldg Lts 324°. Front, 55°07'·42N 01°29'·72W F Bu 11m 10M. Rear, 180m from front, F Bu 17m 10M. Both Or ◊ on Tr.

Blyth Fairway Lt By 55°06'·58N 01°28'·50W Fl G 3s; SHM; *Bell.*

Blyth E Pier Hd 55°06'·98N 01°29'·11W Fl (4) 10s 19m **21M**; W Tr. FR 13m 13M, (same Tr); vis 152°-249°; *Horn (3) 30s.*

Blyth W Pier Hd 55°06'·98N 01°29'·27W 2 FR (vert) 7m 8M; W Tr.

Newbiggin Bkwtr Hd 55°11'·00N 01°30'·22W Fl G 10s 4M.

Newbiggen Outfall Lt By 55°12'·50N 01°30'·70W Fl R 10s; PHM.

COQUET ISLAND/WARKWORTH AND AMBLE

Coquet 55°20'·03N 01°32'·28W Fl (3) WR 30s 25m **W23M, R19M**; W ■ Tr, turreted parapet, lower half Gy; vis R330°-140°, W140°-163°, R163°-180°, W180°-330°; sector boundaries are indeterminate and may appear as Alt WR; *Horn 30s.*

Outfall Lt By 55°20'·32N 01°33'·63W Fl R 10s; PHM; *Bell.*

Amble S Pier Hd 55°20'·38N 01°34'·14W Fl R 5s 9m 5M; W ● Tr, R bands, W base.

N Pier Hd 55°20'·38N 01°34'·15W Fl G 6s 12m 6M; W pylon.

BOULMER/CRASTER/NEWTON HAVEN/BEADNELL BAY

Boulmer Haven Bn 55°24'·75N 01°34'·40W; SHM.

Craster Hbr 55°28'·37N 01°35'·45W (unmarked).

Newton Rk By 55°32'·17N 01°35'·75W; PHM.

N SUNDERLAND (SEAHOUSES)/BAMBURGH/FARNE ISLANDS

The Falls By 55°34'·62N 01°37'·02W; PHM.

N Sunderland NW Pier Hd 55°35'·03N 01°38'·84W FG 11m 3M; W Tr; vis 159°-294°; Tfc Sigs; *Siren 90s* (occas).

N. Sunderland Bkwtr Hd 55°35'·05N 01°38'·79W Fl R 2·5s 6m.

Shoreston Outcars By 55°35'·88N 01°39'·22W; PHM.

Black Rocks Pt **Bamburgh** 55°37'·00N 01°43'·35W Oc (2) WRG 15s 12m **W17M**, R13M, G13M; W bldg; vis G122°-165°, W165°-175°, R175°-191°, W191°-238°, R238°-275°, W275°-289°, G289°-300°.

Inner Farne 55°36'·93N 01°39'·25W Fl (2) WR 15s 27m W10M, R7M; W ● Tr; vis R119°-280°, W280°-119°.

Longstone W side 55°38'·63N 01°36'·55W Fl 20s 23m **24M**; R Tr, W band; *Horn (2) 60s.*

Swedman By 55°37'·65N 01°41'·52W; SHM.

HOLY ISLAND

Goldstone By 55°40'·12N 01°43'·45W; SHM.

Ridge By 55°39'·70N 01°45'·87W; ECM.

Triton Shoal By 55°39'·58N 01°46'·72W; SHM.

Old Law E Bn (Guile Pt) 55°39'·49N 01°47'·50W Oc WRG 6s 9m 4M; Vis G182°-262°, W262°-264°, R264°-shore.

Heugh 55°40'·09N 01°47'·89W Oc WRG 6s 24m 5M; R △ on Tr; vis G135°-308°, W308°-311°, R311°-shore°.

Plough Seat By 55°40'·37N 01°44'·87W; PHM.

BERWICK-ON-TWEED

Bkwtr Hd 55°45'·88N 01°58'·95W Fl 5s 15m 10M; W ● Tr, R cupola and base; vis E of Seal Carr ledges-shore; FG (same Tr) 8m 1M; vis 010°-154°.

10.5.5   PASSAGE INFORMATION

For directions and pilotage refer to: *The East Coast* (Imray/Bowskill) as far as The Wash; *Tidal Havens of the Wash and Humber* (Imray/Irving) carefully documents the hbrs of this little-frequented cruising ground. N from R. Humber see the Royal Northumberland YC's *Sailing Directions, Humber to Rattray Head*. The Admiralty Pilot *North Sea (West)* covers the whole coast. *North Sea Passage Pilot* (Imray/Navin) goes as far N as Cromer and across to Den Helder.

NORTH NORFOLK COAST (charts 106, 108)

The coast of N Norfolk is unfriendly in bad weather, with no hbr accessible when there is any N in the wind. The hbrs all dry, and seas soon build up in the entrances or over the bars, some of which are dangerous even in a moderate breeze and an ebb tide. But in settled weather and moderate offshore winds it is a peaceful area to explore, particularly for boats which can take the ground. At Blakeney and Wells (see 10.5.7 and 10.5.8) chans shift almost every year, so local knowledge is essential and may best be acquired in advance from the Hr Mr; or in the event by following a friendly FV of suitable draft.

Haisborough Sand (buoyed) lies parallel to and 8M off the Norfolk coast at Happisburgh lt ho, with depths of less than 1m in many places, and drying 0·3m near the mid-point. The shoal is steep-to, on its NE side in particular, and there are tidal eddies. Even a moderate sea or swell breaks on the shallower parts. There are dangerous wks near the S end. Haisborough Tail and Hammond Knoll (with wk depth 1m) lie to the E of S end of Haisborough Sand. Newarp lt F is 5M SE. Similar banks lie parallel to and up to 60M off the coast.

The streams follow the generally NW/SE direction of the coast and offshore chans. But in the outer chans the stream is somewhat rotatory: when changing from SE-going to NW-going it sets SW, and when changing from NW-going to SE-going it sets NE, across the shoals. Close S of Haisborough Sand the SE-going stream begins at HW Immingham –0030; the NW-going at HW Immingham +0515, sp rates up to 2·5kn. It is possible to carry a fair tide from Gt Yarmouth to the Wash.

If proceeding direct from Cromer to the Humber, pass S of Sheringham Shoal (buoyed) where the ESE-going stream begins at HW Immingham – 0225, and the WNW-going at + 0430. Proceed to NE of Blakeney Overfalls and Docking Shoal, and to SW of Race Bank, so as to fetch Inner Dowsing lt tr (lt, fog sig). Thence pass E of Protector Overfalls, and steer for Rosse Spit buoy at SE ent to R Humber (10.5.11).

THE WASH (charts 108,1200)

The Wash is formed by the estuaries of the rivers Great Ouse, Nene, Welland and Witham; it is an area of shifting sands, most of which dry. Important features are the strong tidal streams, the low-lying shore, and the often poor vis. Keep a careful watch on the echo sounder, because buoys may (or may not) have been moved to accommodate changes in the chan. Near North Well, the in-going stream begins at HW Immingham – 0430, and the out-going at HW Immingham + 0130, sp rates about 2kn. The in-going stream is usually stronger than the out-going, but its duration is less. Prolonged NE winds cause an in-going current, which can increase the rate and duration of the in-going stream and raise the water level at the head of the estuary. Do not attempt entry to the rivers too early on the flood, which runs hard in the rivers.

North Well SWM lt buoy and Roaring Middle lt F are the keys to entering the Wash from N or E. But from the E it is also possible to appr via a shallow route N of Stiffkey Overfalls and

Bridgirdle PHM buoy; thence via Sledway and WoolpackPHM lt buoy to North Well and into Lynn Deeps. Near north end of Lynn Deeps there are overfalls over Lynn Knock at sp tides. For King's Lynn (10.5.9) and R Nene (Wisbech) follow the buoyed/lit Cork Hole and Wisbech Chans. Boston (10.5.10) and R Welland are reached via Freeman Chan, westward from Roaring Middle; or via Boston Deep, all lit.

The NW shore of The Wash is fronted by mudflats extending 2–3M offshore and drying more than 4m; a bombing range is marked by Y bns and buoys. Wainfleet Swatchway should only be used in good vis; the buoyed chan shifts constantly, and several shoals (charted depths unreliable) off Gibraltar Pt obstruct access to Boston Deep. For Wainfleet, see 10.5.10.

THE WASH TO THE RIVER HUMBER (charts 108, 107)

Inner Dowsing is a narrow N/S sandbank with a least depth of 1·2m, 8M offshore between Skegness and Mablethorpe. There are overfalls off the W side of the bank at the N end. Inner Dowsing lt float (fog sig) is 1M NE of the bank.

In the outer approaches to The Wash and R. Humber there are many offlying banks, but few of them are of direct danger to yachts. The sea however breaks on some of them in bad weather, when they should be avoided. Fishing vessels may be encountered, and there are many oil/gas installations offshore (see below).

RIVER HUMBER (charts 109, 1188, 3497)

R. Humber is formed by R. Ouse and R. Trent, which meet 13M above Kingston-upon-Hull. It is commercially important and gives access to these rivers and inland waterways; it also drains most of Yorkshire and the Midlands. Where the Humber estuary reaches the sea between Northcoates Pt and Spurn Hd it is 4M wide. A VTS scheme is in operation to regulate commercial shipping in the Humber, Ouse and Trent and provide full radar surveillance. Yachts are advised to listen out on the Humber VTS frequency.

Approaching from the S, a yacht should make good Rosse Spit and then Haile Sand No 2, both PHM lt buoys, before altering westward to intercept the buoyed appr chan, which leads SW from the Humber fairway lt buoy to Spurn lt float.

If bound to/from the N, avoid The Binks, a shoal (dries 0·4m in places) extending 3M E from Spurn Hd, with a rough sea when wind is against tide. Depths offshore are irregular and subject to frequent change; it would be best to round the Outer Binks ECM buoy, unless in calm conditions and with local knowledge.

Haile Sand and Bull Sand Forts are both conspic to the SW of Spurn Head; beyond them it is advisable to follow one of the buoyed chans, since shoals are liable to change. Hawke Chan (later Sunk) is the main dredged chan to the N. Haile Chan favours the S side and Grimsby. Bull Chan takes a middle course before merging with Haile Chan. There are good yachting facilities at Grimsby and Hull (10.5.11).

Streams are strong, even fierce at sp; local info suggests that they are stronger than shown in 10.5.3, which is based upon NP 251 (Admiralty Tidal Stream Atlas). 5ca S of Spurn Hd the flood sets NW from about HW Immingham – 0520, sp rate 3·5kn; the ebb sets SE from about HW Immingham, sp rate 4kn. The worst seas are experienced in NW gales against a strong flood tide. 10M E of Spurn Hd the tidal streams are not affected by the river; relative to HW Immingham, the S-going stream begins at – 0455, and the N-going at + 0130. Nearer the entrance the direction of the S-going stream becomes more W'ly, and that of the N-going stream more E'ly.

R HUMBER TO HARTLEPOOL (charts 107, 121, 129, 134)

Air gunnery and bombing practice is carried out 3M off Cowden, 17M S of Bridlington. The range is marked by 6 SPM buoys; 3 seaward ones Fl Y 10s, the 3 inner ones Fl Y 2s or 5s. Bridlington Bay (chart 1882) is clear of dangers apart from Smithic Shoals (marked by N and S cardinal lt buoys), about 3M off Bridlington (10.5.12); the seas break on these shoals in strong N or E winds even at HW.

Flamborough Head (lt, fog sig, RC) is a steep, W cliff with conspic lt ho on summit. The lt may be obsc by cliffs when close inshore. An old lt ho, also conspic, is 2½ca WNW. Tides run hard around the Head which, in strong winds against a sp tide, is best avoided by 2M. From here the coast runs NW, with no offshore dangers until Filey Brigg where rky ledges extend 5ca ESE, marked by an ECM lt buoy. There is anch in Filey B (10.5.12) in N or offshore winds. NW of Filey Brigg beware Old Horse Rks and foul ground 5ca offshore; maintain this offing past Scarborough (10.5.13) to Whitby High lt. Off Whitby (10.5.14) beware Whitby Rk and The Scar (dry in places) to E of hbr, and Upgang Rks (dry in places) 1M to WNW; swell breaks heavily on all these rocks.

From Whitby to Hartlepool (10.5.15) there are no dangers more than 1M offshore. Runswick B (10.5.14 and AC 1612), 5M NW of Whitby, provides anch in winds from S and W but is dangerous in onshore winds. 2½M further NW the little hbr of Staithes is more suitable for yachts which can take the ground, and only in good weather and offshore winds.

Redcliff, dark red and 205m high is a conspic feature of this coast which, along to Hunt Cliff, is prone to landslides and is fringed with rky ledges which dry for about 3ca off. There is a conspic radio mast 4ca SSE of Redcliff. Off Redcar and Coatham beware Salt Scar and West Scar, drying rky ledges lying 1 – 8ca offshore. Other ledges lie close SE and S of Salt Scar which has NCM lt buoy. Between R. Tees (10.5.14) and Hartlepool beware Long Scar, detached rky ledge (dries 2m) with extremity marked by ECM lt buoy. Tees and Hartlepool Bays are exposed to strong E/SE winds. The R. Tees and Middlesbrough are highly industrialised and of little interest to yachts.

HARTLEPOOL TO COQUET ISLAND (charts 134, 152, 156)

From The Heugh an offing of 1M clears all dangers until past Seaham (10.5.16) and approaching Sunderland (10.5.17), where White Stones, rky shoals with depth 2·6m, lie 1·75M SSE of Roker Pier lt ho, and Hendon Rk, depth 0·9m, lies 1·25M SE of the lt ho. 1M N of Sunderland is Whitburn Steel, a rky ledge with less than 2m over it; a dangerous wreck (buoyed) lies 1ca SE of it. A firing range at Souter Pt is marked by R flags (R lts) when active. Along this stretch of coast industrial smoke haze may reduce vis and obscure lights.

The coast N of Tynemouth (10.5.18) is foul, and on passage to Blyth (10.5.19) it should be given an offing of 1M. 3·5M N of Tynemouth is St Mary's Island (with disused lt ho), joined to mainland by causeway. The small, drying hbr of Seaton Sluice, 1M NW of St Mary's Island, is accessible only in offshore winds via a narrow ent.

Proceeding N from Blyth, keep well seaward of The Sow and Pigs rks, and set course to clear Newbiggin Pt and Beacon Pt by about 1M. There are conspic measured mile bns here. Near Beacon Pt are conspic chys of aluminium smelter and power stn. 2M NNW of Beacon Pt is Snab Pt where rks extend 3ca seaward. Further offshore Cresswell Skeres, rky patches with depth 3m, lie about 1·5M NNE of Snab Pt.

COQUET ISLAND TO FARNE ISLANDS (chart 156)

Coquet Is (lt, fog sig) lies about 5ca offshore at SE end of Alnmouth B, and nearly 1M NNE of Hauxley Pt, off which dangerous rks extend 6ca offshore, drying 1·9m. On passage, normally pass 1M E of Coquet Is in the W sector of the lt. Coquet chan may be used in good vis by day; but it is only 2ca wide, not buoyed, has least depth of 0·3m near the centre; and the stream runs strongly: S-going from HW Tyne – 0515 and N-going from HW Tyne + 0045. In S or W winds, there are good anchs in Coquet Road, W and NW of the Island.

Amble (Warkworth) hbr ent (10.5.20) is about 1M W of Coquet Is, and 1·5M SE of Warkworth Castle (conspic). 4ca NE and ENE of ent is Pan Bush, rky shoal with least depth of 0·3m on which dangerous seas can build in any swell. The bar has varying depths, down to less than 1m. The entrance is dangerous in strong winds from N/E when broken water may extend to Coquet Is. Once inside, the hbr is safe.

Between Coquet Is and the Farne Is, 19M to N, keep at least 1M offshore to avoid various dangers. To seaward, Craster Skeres lie 5M E of Castle Pt, and Dicky Shad and Newton Skere lie 1·75M and 4·5M E of Beadnell Pt; these are three rky banks on which the sea breaks heavily in bad weather. For Newton Haven and N Sunderland (Seahouses), see 10.5.20.

FARNE ISLANDS (charts 111, 160)

The coast between N Sunderland Pt (Snook) and Holy Island, 8M NW, has fine hill (Cheviots) scenery fronted by dunes and sandy beaches. The Farne Is and offlying shoals extend 4·5M offshore, and are a mini-cruising ground well worth visiting in good weather. The islands are a bird sanctuary, owned and operated by the National Trust, with large colonies of sea birds and grey seals. AC 111 is essential.

Inner Sound separates the islands from the mainland; in good conditions it is a better N/S route than keeping outside the whole group; but the stream runs at 3kn at sp, and with strong wind against tide there is rough water. If course is set outside Farne Is, pass 1M E of Longstone (lt, fog sig) to clear Crumstone Rk 1M to S, and Knivestone (dries 3·6m) and Whirl Rks (depth 0·6m) respectively 5 and 6ca NE of Longstone lt ho. The sea breaks on these rks.

The islands, rks and shoals are divided by Staple Sound, running NW/SE, into an inner and outer group. The former comprises Inner Farne, W and E Wideopens and Knock's Reef. Inner Farne (lt) is the innermost Is; close NE there is anch called The Kettle, sheltered except from NW, but anch out of stream close to The Bridges connecting Knock's Reef and W Wideopen. 1M NW of Inner Farne Is and separated by Farne Sound, which runs NE/SW, lies the Megstone, a rk 5m high. Beware Swedman reef (dries 0·5m), marked by SHM buoy 4ca WSW of Megstone.

The outer group of Islands comprises Staple and Brownsman Islands, N and S Wamses, the Harcars and Longstone. There is occas anch between Staple and Brownsman Is. Piper Gut and Crafords Gut may be negotiated in calm weather and near HW, stemming the S-going stream.

HOLY ISLAND TO BERWICK (charts 1612, 111, 160)

Near the Farne Is and Holy Is the SE-going stream begins at HW Tyne – 0430, and the NW-going at HW Tyne + 0130. Sp rates are about 2·5kn in Inner Sound, 4kn in Staple Sound and about 3·5kn 1M NE of Longstone, decreasing to seaward. There is an eddy S of Longstone on NW-going stream.

Holy Is (or Lindisfarne; 10.5.21) lies 6M WNW of Longstone, and is linked to mainland by a causeway covered at HW. There is a good anch on S side (chart 1612) with conspic daymarks and dir lts. The castle and a W obelisk at Emanuel Head are also conspic. The stream runs strongly in and out of hbr, W-going from HW Tyne + 0510, and E-going from HW Tyne – 0045. E of Holy Is, Goldstone chan runs N/S between Goldstone Rk (dries) SHM buoy on E side and Plough Seat Reef and Plough Rk (both dry) on W side, with PHM buoy.

Berwick Bay has some offlying shoals. Berwick-upon-Tweed (10.5.22) is easily visible against the low shoreline, which rises again to high cliffs further north. The hbr entrance is restricted by a shallow bar, dangerous in onshore winds.

OIL AND GAS INSTALLATIONS

Any yacht going offshore in the N Sea is likely to encounter oil or gas installations. These are shown on Admiralty charts, where scale permits; the position of mobile rigs is updated in weekly NMs. Safety zones of radius 500m are established round all permanent platforms, mobile exploration rigs, and tanker loading moorings, as described in the Annual Summary of Admiralty Notices to Mariners No 20. Some of these platforms are close together or inter-linked. Unauthorised vessels, including yachts, must not enter these zones except in emergency or due to stress of weather.

Platforms show a main lt, Fl Mo (U) 15s 15M. In addition secondary lts, Fl Mo (U) R 15s 2M, synchronised with the main lt, may mark projections at each corner of the platform if not marked by a W lt. The fog signal is Horn Mo (U) 30s. See the Admiralty List of Lights and Fog Signals, Vol A.

NORTH SEA PASSAGES

See 10.0.7 for Distances across the North Sea. There are also further passage Notes in 10.4.5 for the Southern North Sea TSS; in 10.6.5 for crossing to Norway and the Baltic; in 10.20.5 for crossings from Belgium and the Netherlands; and in 10.21.5 for crossings from the Frisian Is and German Bight.

HARTLEPOOL TO SOUTHERN NETHERLANDS
(charts 2182A, 1191, *1190*, 1503, 1408, 1610, 3371, 110)

From abeam Whitby the passage can, theoretically, be made on one direct course, but this would conflict with oil/gas activities and platforms including Rough and Amethyst fields off Humber, Hewett off Cromer and very extensive fields further offshore. Commercial, oil-rig support and fishing vessels may be met S of Flamborough Hd and particularly off NE Norfolk where it is advisable to follow an inshore track.

After passing Flamborough Hd, Dowsing B1D, Dudgeon lt buoy and Newarp lt F, either:
Proceed SxE'ly to take departure from the Outer Gabbard; thence cross N Hinder South TSS (Fig. 10(5)) at right angles before heading for Roompotsluis via Middelbank and subsequent buoyed chan.
Or set course ESE from the vicinity of Cross Sand lt buoy and Smith's Knoll, so as to cross the N/S deep-water traffic routes to the E (see 10.20.5). Thence alter SE toward Hoek van Holland, keeping N of Maas Approaches TSS, Figs 10 (5) & (6) and diagram above 10.20.22.

HARTLEPOOL TO THE GERMAN BIGHT
(charts 2182A, 1191, 266, 1405)

Taking departure eastward from abeam Whitby High lt, skirt the SW Patch off Dogger Bank, keeping clear S of Gordon Gas Field and then N of German Bight W Approach TSS (Fig. 10(6)). Thence head for the Elbe or Helgoland; the latter may also serve as a convenient haven in order to adjust the passage for Elbe tides and streams (10.21.5), without greatly increasing passage distance. Tidal streams are less than 1kn away from the coast and run E/W along much of the route.

10.5.6   DISTANCE TABLE

Approximate distances in nautical miles are by the most direct route, whilst avoiding dangers and allowing for Traffic Separation Schemes. Places in *italics* are in adjoining areas; places in **bold** are in 10.0.7, Distances across the North Sea.

	1	2	3	4	5	6	7	8	9	10	11	12	13	14	15	16	17	18	19	20
1. *Great Yarmouth*	**1**																			
2. Blakeney	44	**2**																		
3. **King's Lynn**	85	42	**3**																	
4. Boston	83	39	34	**4**																
5. Humber Lt Buoy	82	45	55	54	**5**															
6. **Grimsby**	99	54	61	58	17	**6**														
7. Hull	113	68	75	72	31	14	**7**													
8. Bridlington	114	79	87	83	35	44	58	**8**												
9. Scarborough	130	96	105	98	50	59	81	20	**9**											
10. Whitby	143	101	121	114	66	75	97	35	16	**10**										
11. River Tees (ent)	166	122	138	135	87	96	118	56	37	21	**11**									
12. **Hartlepool**	169	126	140	137	89	98	122	58	39	24	4	**12**								
13. Seaham	175	137	151	145	100	106	133	66	47	33	15	11	**13**							
14. Sunderland	180	142	156	149	105	110	138	70	51	36	20	16	5	**14**						
15. Tynemouth	183	149	163	154	112	115	145	75	56	41	27	23	12	7	**15**					
16. Blyth	190	156	171	162	120	123	153	83	64	49	35	31	20	15	8	**16**				
17. Amble	203	170	185	176	126	143	157	102	81	65	46	42	32	27	21	14	**17**			
18. Holy Island	225	191	196	198	148	166	180	126	104	88	68	65	54	50	44	37	22	**18**		
19. **Berwick-on-Tweed**	232	200	205	205	157	166	189	126	107	91	82	78	67	61	55	47	31	9	**19**	
20. *Eyemouth*	240	208	213	213	165	174	197	134	115	99	90	86	75	69	63	55	39	17	8	**20**

BLAKENEY   10-5-7

Norfolk 52°59'·10N 00°58'·35E   Rtg 4-3-1

CHARTS
AC 108, 1190; Imray C28; Stanfords 19; OS 133
TIDES
−0445 Dover; ML Cromer 2·8; Duration 0530; Zone 0 (UT)

Standard Port IMMINGHAM (⟶)

Times				Height (metres)			
High Water		Low Water		MHWS	MHWN	MLWN	MLWS
0100	0700	0100	0700	7·3	5·8	2·6	0·9
1300	1900	1300	1900				
Differences BLAKENEY							
+0115	+0055	No data		−3·9	−3·8		No data
BLAKENEY BAR							
+0035	+0025	+0030	+0040	−1·6	−1·3		No data
CROMER							
+0050	+0030	+0050	+0130	−2·1	−1·7	−0·5	−0·1

SHELTER
Very good, but hbr inaccessible with fresh on-shore winds
when conditions in the ent deteriorate very quickly,
especially on the ebb. Entry, sp HW ±2½, nps HW ±1.
Moorings in The Pit or at Stiffkey Sluices. Speed limit 8kn.
NAVIGATION
WPT 53°00'·00N 00°58'·20E, approx 045°/225° 1M from/to
Fairway RW buoy (52°59'·17N 00°56'·38E, April-Oct) at ent
to chan. Large dangerous wk, approx 1·5M E of ent, is
marked by unlit R PHM buoy. The bar is shallow and shifts
often. The chan is marked by 15 unlit G SHM buoys.
Beware mussel lays, drying, off Blakeney Spit.
LIGHTS AND MARKS
Y ldg bns on dunes at Blakeney Pt are erected only when
the chan ent moves adjacent to the Pt. Conspic marks are:
Blakeney and Langham churches; a chy on the house on
Blakeney Pt neck; TV mast (R lts) approx 2M S of ent.
RADIO TELEPHONE
None.
TELEPHONE (Dial code 01263)
Hr Mr 740362; MRCC (01493) 851338; ≢ (01473) 235704
(H24); Marinecall 0891 500455; Dr 740314; Pilot 740362.
FACILITIES
Quay AB (Free), Slip, M, D, FW, El, C (15 ton); CH;
Services: Pilot (☎ 740362), AB, BY, M, P & D (cans), FW,
ME, El, Sh, SM, Gas, Gaz, AC. **Village** EC Wed; V, R, Bar,
⊠, Ⓑ, ⇌ (Sherringham), ✈ (Norwich).

WELLS-NEXT-THE-SEA   10-5-8

Norfolk 52°59'·30N 00°49'·75E (ent shifts)   Rtg 4-3-1

CHARTS
AC 108, 1190; Imray C28, Y9; OS 132
TIDES
−0445 Dover; ML 1·2 Duration 0540; Zone 0 (UT)

Standard Port IMMINGHAM (⟶)

Times				Height (metres)			
High Water		Low Water		MHWS	MHWN	MLWN	MLWS
0100	0700	0100	0700	7·3	5·8	2·6	0·9
1300	1900	1300	1900				
Differences WELLS-NEXT-THE-SEA							
+0035	+0045	+0340	+0310	−3·8	−3·8	Not below CD	
WELLS BAR							
+0020	+0020	+0020	+0020	−1·3	−1·0	No data	

Note: LW time differences at Wells are for the end of a LW
stand which lasts about 4 hrs at sp and about 5 hrs at nps.

SHELTER
Good, except in strong N winds when swell renders entry
impossible for small craft. Max draft 3m at sp. Access from
HW −1½ to HW +1, but recommended on the flood.
NAVIGATION
WPT Fairway SWM buoy, 52°59'·85N 00°49'·71E, 020°/
200° from/to chan ent, 0·7M. A SPM buoy, Fl (5) Y 20s, is
at 53°04'·07N 00°50'·23E, off chartlet. The bar and ent vary
in depth and position; buoys are altered to suit. Best to
seek Hr Mr's advice or follow FV of appropriate draft.
Keep to port side of chan from No 12 PHM lt buoy to quay.

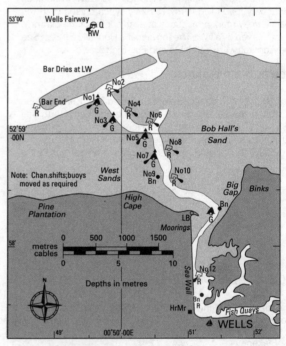

LIGHTS AND MARKS
Fairway buoy SWM, Q. Chan is marked by 10 SHM buoys,
of which 4 are Fl 3s, and two Fl G 3s; and by 9 PHM buoys
of which 7 are Fl R 3s; the rest unlit. Temp buoys may be
laid when chan changes. A white LB ho with R roof is
conspic at hbr ent, with a pine plantation visible close W.
RADIO TELEPHONE
Wells Hbr Radio Ch 12 16, HW−2 and when vessel due.
TELEPHONE (Dial code 01328 Fakenham)
Hr Mr 711744, ☎ 710623; MRCC (01493) 851338;
≢ (01473) 235704 (H24); Marinecall 0891 500 455; Police
710212; Ⓗ 710218.
FACILITIES
Main Quay M (see Hr Mr), AB (£11), FW, ME, El, Sh, C (5
ton mobile), CH, V, R, Bar; **E Quay** Slip, M; **Wells SC** ☎
711320, Slip, Bar; **Services:** Ⓔ, ACA. **Town** EC Thurs; P &
D (bowser on quay; up to 500 galls), Gas, V, R, Bar, ⊠, Ⓑ,
⇌ (bus to Norwich/King's Lynn), ✈ (Norwich).

KING'S LYNN 10-5-9

Norfolk 52°49'·72N 00°21'·30E (West Stones bn)   Rtg 3-5-2

CHARTS
AC 1200, 108, *1190*; Imray Y9; OS 132

TIDES
−0443 Dover; ML 3·6; Duration 0340 Sp, 0515 Np;
Zone 0 (UT)

Standard Port IMMINGHAM (→)

Times				Height (metres)			
High Water		Low Water		MHWS	MHWN	MLWN	MLWS
0100	0700	0100	0700	7·3	5·8	2·6	0·9
1300	1900	1300	1900				
Differences KING'S LYNN							
+0030	+0030	+0305	+0140	−0·5	−0·8	−0·8	+0·1
BURNHAM OVERY STAITHE							
+0045	+0055	No data		−5·0	−4·9		No data
HUNSTANTON							
+0010	+0020	+0105	+0025	+0·1	−0·2	−0·1	0·0
WEST STONES							
+0025	+0025	+0115	+0040	−0·3	−0·4	−0·3	+0·2
WISBECH CUT							
+0020	+0025	+0200	+0030	−0·3	−0·7	−0·4	No data

SHELTER
Port is well sheltered 1½M up river; entry is recommended HW±3. A commercial port with virtually no facilities for yachts which are not encouraged. Some mid-river moorings are free, via Hr Mr, but passage up to Denver (12M) is preferred. Alexandra dock is open from about HW −1½ to HW and yachts can be left there only with the Dockmaster's permission. Drying moorings at S Quay, S side of Boal Quay or at Friars Fleet; keep clear of FV moorings.

NAVIGATION
WPT 52°58'·61N 00°21'·15E, Roaring Middle lt float SWM, L Fl 10s 7m 8M, 013°/193° from/to No 1 NCM lt buoy, Q, 2·58M; thence 1·3M SSW to No 3 ECM buoy, Q (3) 10s, at 52°54'·65N 00°19'·25E, marking the ent to Teetotal Chan, now the main buoyed/lit appr route.
NB: Roaring Middle lt float (WPT) is replaced temporarily every May/Jun by a NCM pillar buoy, Q, for maintenance. Extensive shifting sand banks extend several miles into the Wash. Chans are subject to frequent changes. S of W Stones bn deeper water is on E side of chan. Advice may be obtained from Pilot launches which are often near to 52°56'·92N 00°21'·50E (boarding point); or call VHF Ch 14.

LIGHTS AND MARKS
Conspic white lt ho (disused, 18m) on Hunstanton cliffs. West Stones bn NCM, Q 3m 2M. Lynn Cut ldg lts 155°: front Fl R 5s 11m 3M; rear FW 16m 4M, both on masts. Entry sigs for Alexandra Dock:
Bu flag or Ⓡ = Vessels can enter;
R flag or Ⓖ = Vessels leaving dock.

RADIO TELEPHONE
Call *KLCB* VHF Ch **14** 16 11 12 (Mon-Fri: 0800-1730 LT. Other times: HW −4 to HW+1).
King's Lynn Docks (ABP) Ch **14** 16 11 (HW−2½ to HW+1).

TELEPHONE (Dial code 01553)
Hr Mr 773411; Dock 691555; MRCC (01493) 851338; Dr via Hr Mr; ⌗ (01473) 235704 (H24); Marinecall 0891 500455.

FACILITIES
Docks ☎ 691555, AB £42 for 48 hrs, FW, C (32 ton);
Services: CH, Sh, ME, El, Ⓔ, D.
Town EC Wed; P, D, V, R, Bar, ✉, Ⓑ, ⇌, ✈ (Humberside or Norwich).
Note: 24M up the Great Ouse river, Ely Marina ☎ (01353) 664622, Slip, M, P, D, FW, ME, El, Sh, C (10 ton), CH. Lock half-way at Denver Sluice ☎ (01366) 382340/VHF Ch 73, and low bridges beyond.

ADJACENT HARBOURS

BURNHAM OVERY STAITHE, Norfolk, 52°59'·00N 00°46'·50E. Rtg 4-5-1. AC 108, *1190*. HW −0420 on Dover. See 10·5·9. Small drying hbr; ent chan has 0·3m MLWS. ⚓ off the Staithe only suitable in good weather. No lts. Scolt Hd is conspic to W and Gun Hill to E; Scolt Hd Island is conspic 3M long sandbank which affords some shelter. Chan varies constantly and buoys are moved to suit. Local knowledge advisable. Facilities: (01328) **Burnham Overy Staithe SC** ☎ 738348, M, L; **Services:** CH, M, ME, Sh, Slip, FW; **Burnham Market** EC Wed; Bar, P and D (cans), R, V.

BRANCASTER STAITHE, Norfolk, 52°59'·00N 00°38'·50E. Rtg 4-4-1. AC 108, *1190*. HW −0425 on Dover; See 10.5.9. Small drying hbr; dangerous to enter except by day in settled weather. Speed limit 6kn. Appr from due N. Conspic golf club house with lt, Fl 5s 8m 3M, is 0·5M S of chan ent and Fairway buoy. Beware wk shown on chart. Sandbanks vary constantly and buoys changed to suit. Scolt Hd conspic to E. Local knowledge or Pilot advised. ⚓s available occas in The Hole. Hr Mr ☎ (01485) 210638. Facilities: **Brancaster Staithe SC** ☎ 210249, R, Bar; **Services:** BY, CH, El, FW, P & D (cans), ME, R, Sh, Bar, V.

WISBECH, Cambridgeshire, 52°40'·00N 00°09'·65E. Rtg 3-5-3. AC 1200, *1190*. HW −0450 on Dover; ML 3·5m; Duration 0520. See 10·5·9. Excellent shelter. Vessels of 4·8m draft can reach Wisbech at sp (3·4m at nps), but depths vary. Ent to R Nene and inland waterways. Landing at W Nene tr; moorings at Sutton Port (W bank 0·5M downstream from Sutton Bridge) or at Wisbech town quay. Ent well marked with lit buoys and bns from RAF No 6 ECM buoy to Nene trs. Best ent HW −3. Big Tom bn, Fl (2) R 10s 10m 3M, to Sutton br is 3½M, thence to Wisbech 6M, with FG lts to stbd. Call on VHF Ch 16 09 **14** or ☎ (01945) 582125, HW −3 to HW. Take care when ships entering or leaving the berthing area. Hr Mr ☎ (01406) 351530 at Sutton Bridge, not H24. **Town** P & D (cans), Bar, R, V, Gas.

BOSTON   10-5-10
Lincs 52°56'·00N 00°05'·00E (Tabs Head bn)   Rtg 3-4-2

CHARTS
AC 1200, 108; Imray Y9; OS 131
TIDES
−0415 Dover; ML 3·3; Duration Flood 0500, Ebb 0700;
Zone 0 (UT)

Standard Port IMMINGHAM (→)

Times				Height (metres)			
High Water		Low Water		MHWS	MHWN	MLWN	MLWS
0100	0700	0100	0700	7·3	5·8	2·6	0·9
1300	1900	1300	1900				
Differences BOSTON							
0000	+0010	+0140	+0050	−0·5	−1·0	−0·9	−0·5
TABS HEAD (WELLAND RIVER)							
0000	+0005	+0125	+0020	+0·2	−0·2	−0·2	−0·2
SKEGNESS							
+0010	+0015	+0030	+0020	−0·4	−0·5	−0·1	0·0
INNER DOWSING LIGHT TOWER							
0000	0000	+0010	+0010	−0·9	−0·7	−0·1	+0·3

SHELTER
Very good. Except in emergency berthing in the Dock is
prohib. Yachts secure just above Dock ent and see Hr Mr.
The port is administered by Port of Boston Ltd. Moorings
may be possible (on S side) below first fixed bridge.
Yachts which can lower masts should pass the Grand
Sluice lock into fresh water (24 hrs notice required); the
lock is 22·7m x 4·6m and opens approx HW±2. It leads
into the R Witham Navigation which goes 31M to Lincoln.
Marina is to stbd immediately beyond the sluice. British
Waterways have 50 moorings, with FW and AC, beyond
Grand Sluice.
NAVIGATION
WPT Boston Rds SWM lt buoy, L Fl 10s, 52°57'·53N
00°16'·23E, 100°/280° from/to Freeman Chan ent, 0·70M.
Thence Bar Chan is well marked, but liable to change.
SW of Clay Hole a new chan has formed approx 0·5M to
NW of former chan; it is marked by SHM lt buoys Nos
11N, 13N, and 15. Note: former chan is still buoyed ufn.
Tabs Head marks the ent to the river; it should be passed
not earlier than HW−3 to enable the Grand Sluice to be
reached before the start of the ebb. On reaching Boston
Dock, masts should be lowered to negotiate swing bridge
(cannot always be opened) and three fixed bridges. Chan
through town is narrow and un-navigable at LW.

LIGHTS AND MARKS
St Boltoph's ch tr, (the Boston Stump) is conspic from
afar. New Cut and R Witham are marked by bns with
topmarks. FW lts mark ldg lines: six pairs going upstream
and six pairs going downstream.
RADIO TELEPHONE
All boats between Golf buoy and Grand Sluice must
listen Ch 12. Call: *Boston Dock* VHF Ch 12 11 16 (Mon-Fri
0700-1700 LT & HW −2½ to HW +1½). *Grand Sluice* Ch 74.
TELEPHONE (Dial code 01205)
Hr Mr 362328; MRCC (01493) 851338; Port Sig Stn 362328;
Ⓗ (01473) 235704 (H24); Lock Keeper 364864; Marinecall
0891 500455; Police 366222; Ⓗ 364801.
FACILITIES
Boston Marina (50 + some visitors) ☎ 364420, £4, FW, AC,
D (cans), ACA, CH, C in dock, see Hr Mr (emergency only)
Access HW±2; **BWB** moorings: 1st night free, then £4.
Services: El, ME, Sh, Gas.
Town EC Thurs; V, R, Bar, ⊠, Ⓑ, ≈, ✈ (Humberside).

ADJACENT HARBOURS

RIVER WELLAND, Lincolnshire, 52°56'·00N 00°05'·00E
(Tabs Head bn). AC 1200, 1190. At Welland Cut HW −0440
on Dover; ML 0·3m; Duration 0520. See 10.5.10. At Tabs
Head bn HW ±3, ent Welland Cut which is defined by
training walls and lt bns. Beware sp flood of up to 5kn.
Berth 6M up, at Fosdyke on small quay 300m NE of
bridge on stbd side. Recommended for short stay only.
Very limited facilities.

WAINFLEET, Lincolnshire, 53°04'·77N 00°20'·00E (chan
ent). AC 108. Skegness HW +0500 on Dover. See 10.5.10
(Skegness). ML 4·0m; Duration 0600. Shelter good, but
emergency only. Drying chan starts close WSW of Inner
Knock PHM buoy. Swatchway buoyed but not lit; chan
through saltings marked by posts with radar reflectors
and lateral topmarks. Enter HW ±1½. No lts. Facilities: M,
AB (larger boats at fishing jetties, smaller at YC), FW at
Field Study Centre on stbd side of ent. All shore facilities
at Skegness (3½ miles), EC Thurs.

ENGLAND – IMMINGHAM

LAT 53°38′N LONG 0°11′W

TIMES AND HEIGHTS OF HIGH AND LOW WATERS

YEAR **1998**

TIME ZONE (UT)
For Summer Time add ONE hour in non-shaded areas

5

JANUARY

Day	Time	m	Day	Time	m
1 TH	0130 / 0729 / 1344 / 1938	1.1 / 7.2 / 1.3 / 7.4	**16** F	0213 / 0809 / 1413 / 2010	1.2 / 6.8 / 1.6 / 7.1
2 F	0214 / 0813 / 1427 / 2020	1.0 / 7.1 / 1.3 / 7.4	**17** SA	0246 / 0841 / 1443 / 2043	1.3 / 6.6 / 1.7 / 6.9
3 SA	0259 / 0859 / 1511 / 2105	1.1 / 7.0 / 1.5 / 7.3	**18** SU	0318 / 0913 / 1513 / 2116	1.5 / 6.4 / 1.9 / 6.6
4 SU	0346 / 0949 / 1558 / 2156	1.2 / 6.7 / 1.7 / 7.0	**19** M	0353 / 0949 / 1547 / 2153	1.8 / 6.2 / 2.1 / 6.4
5 M	0437 / 1045 / 1651 / 2253	1.4 / 6.5 / 2.0 / 6.7	**20** TU	0432 / 1032 / 1627 / 2237	2.1 / 6.0 / 2.4 / 6.1
6 TU	0535 / 1152 / 1754	1.7 / 6.3 / 2.3	**21** W	0521 / 1125 / 1722 / 2336	2.3 / 5.8 / 2.7 / 5.8
7 W	0002 / 0642 / 1306 / 1910	6.5 / 1.9 / 6.1 / 2.4	**22** TH	0623 / 1238 / 1835	2.5 / 5.7 / 2.9
8 TH	0121 / 0757 / 1415 / 2029	6.4 / 2.0 / 6.2 / 2.3	**23** F	0059 / 0730 / 1354 / 1951	5.7 / 2.5 / 5.7 / 2.8
9 F	0235 / 0906 / 1518 / 2138	6.4 / 1.9 / 6.4 / 2.0	**24** SA	0220 / 0837 / 1458 / 2101	5.8 / 2.4 / 6.0 / 2.5
10 SA	0339 / 1005 / 1613 / 2236	6.6 / 1.7 / 6.6 / 1.6	**25** SU	0323 / 0936 / 1551 / 2203	6.1 / 2.1 / 6.4 / 2.1
11 SU	0437 / 1057 / 1701 / 2327	6.8 / 1.6 / 6.9 / 1.3	**26** M	0417 / 1029 / 1638 / 2257	6.4 / 1.8 / 6.8 / 1.7
12 M ○	0528 / 1144 / 1745	6.9 / 1.5 / 7.1	**27** TU	0505 / 1118 / 1721 / 2347	6.8 / 1.5 / 7.1 / 1.3
13 TU	0015 / 0614 / 1228 / 1824	1.1 / 7.0 / 1.4 / 7.2	**28** W ●	0550 / 1204 / 1803	7.0 / 1.3 / 7.4
14 W	0059 / 0656 / 1306 / 1902	1.0 / 7.0 / 1.4 / 7.2	**29** TH	0034 / 0634 / 1249 / 1843	0.9 / 7.2 / 1.1 / 7.6
15 TH	0138 / 0734 / 1341 / 1937	1.1 / 6.9 / 1.5 / 7.2	**30** F	0121 / 0717 / 1333 / 1924	0.7 / 7.3 / 1.0 / 7.7
			31 SA	0205 / 0801 / 1416 / 2007	0.6 / 7.3 / 1.0 / 7.7

FEBRUARY

Day	Time	m	Day	Time	m
1 SU	0248 / 0844 / 1458 / 2051	0.6 / 7.2 / 1.1 / 7.6	**16** M	0251 / 0840 / 1447 / 2046	1.3 / 6.6 / 1.6 / 6.8
2 M	0331 / 0930 / 1542 / 2138	0.8 / 7.0 / 1.4 / 7.3	**17** TU	0319 / 0911 / 1514 / 2117	1.6 / 6.5 / 1.8 / 6.6
3 TU	0416 / 1019 / 1628 / 2231	1.0 / 6.6 / 1.7 / 6.9	**18** W	0348 / 0945 / 1546 / 2153	1.8 / 6.2 / 2.1 / 6.3
4 W	0506 / 1117 / 1722 / 2335	1.6 / 6.3 / 2.1 / 6.5	**19** TH	0423 / 1026 / 1630 / 2239	2.1 / 6.0 / 2.4 / 5.9
5 TH	0606 / 1229 / 1833	2.0 / 6.0 / 2.4	**20** F	0517 / 1122 / 1734 / 2343	2.5 / 5.7 / 2.7 / 5.6
6 F	0055 / 0725 / 1344 / 2006	6.1 / 2.3 / 5.9 / 2.5	**21** SA	0636 / 1250 / 1900	2.7 / 5.6 / 2.8
7 SA	0217 / 0845 / 1453 / 2124	6.0 / 2.3 / 6.1 / 2.2	**22** SU	0132 / 0755 / 1420 / 2023	5.6 / 2.6 / 5.8 / 2.6
8 SU	0328 / 0949 / 1553 / 2224	6.2 / 2.1 / 6.3 / 1.8	**23** M	0257 / 0905 / 1523 / 2135	5.9 / 2.3 / 6.2 / 2.1
9 M	0429 / 1042 / 1644 / 2315	6.4 / 1.9 / 6.6 / 1.4	**24** TU	0358 / 1004 / 1614 / 2236	6.3 / 1.9 / 6.7 / 1.6
10 TU	0519 / 1129 / 1728 / 2329	6.7 / 1.6 / 6.9 / 1.1	**25** W	0449 / 1057 / 1659 / 2329	6.7 / 1.5 / 7.1 / 1.1
11 W ○	0000 / 0601 / 1211 / 1807	1.2 / 6.8 / 1.5 / 7.1	**26** TH ●	0535 / 1146 / 1743	7.1 / 1.2 / 7.5
12 TH	0042 / 0639 / 1249 / 1843	1.0 / 6.9 / 1.4 / 7.2	**27** F	0018 / 0619 / 1233 / 1825	0.7 / 7.4 / 0.9 / 7.8
13 F	0119 / 0713 / 1322 / 1917	1.0 / 6.9 / 1.4 / 7.2	**28** SA	0105 / 0701 / 1318 / 1907	0.4 / 7.5 / 0.7 / 7.9
14 SA	0152 / 0743 / 1352 / 1948	1.1 / 6.8 / 1.4 / 7.1			
15 SU	0222 / 0811 / 1420 / 2017	1.2 / 6.8 / 1.5 / 7.0			

MARCH

Day	Time	m	Day	Time	m
1 SU	0148 / 0743 / 1401 / 1950	0.3 / 7.5 / 0.7 / 7.9	**16** M	0156 / 0741 / 1358 / 1952	1.1 / 6.9 / 1.3 / 7.0
2 M	0231 / 0824 / 1443 / 2034	0.4 / 7.4 / 0.8 / 7.7	**17** TU	0223 / 0809 / 1423 / 2020	1.3 / 6.8 / 1.4 / 6.8
3 TU	0312 / 0907 / 1524 / 2120	0.6 / 7.1 / 1.1 / 7.4	**18** W	0248 / 0838 / 1448 / 2049	1.5 / 6.6 / 1.6 / 6.6
4 W	0353 / 0952 / 1607 / 2211	1.1 / 6.7 / 1.5 / 6.9	**19** TH	0312 / 0909 / 1518 / 2123	1.7 / 6.4 / 1.8 / 6.4
5 TH	0438 / 1045 / 1657 / 2313	1.6 / 6.3 / 1.9 / 6.3	**20** F	0344 / 0947 / 1559 / 2207	2.0 / 6.1 / 2.1 / 6.0
6 F	0532 / 1154 / 1802	2.2 / 5.9 / 2.4	**21** SA	0432 / 1037 / 1657 / 2307	2.4 / 5.8 / 2.4 / 5.7
7 SA	0036 / 0650 / 1315 / 1946	5.9 / 2.6 / 5.7 / 2.5	**22** SU	0544 / 1147 / 1820	2.7 / 5.6 / 2.6
8 SU	0202 / 0825 / 1429 / 2109	5.8 / 2.6 / 5.8 / 2.2	**23** M	0043 / 0716 / 1335 / 1950	5.5 / 2.7 / 5.7 / 2.4
9 M	0317 / 0932 / 1532 / 2207	6.0 / 2.4 / 6.1 / 1.8	**24** TU	0234 / 0835 / 1451 / 2109	5.8 / 2.4 / 6.1 / 2.0
10 TU	0418 / 1024 / 1624 / 2256	6.3 / 2.0 / 6.5 / 1.5	**25** W	0339 / 0940 / 1547 / 2213	6.3 / 1.9 / 6.6 / 1.4
11 W	0505 / 1109 / 1708 / 2339	6.5 / 1.7 / 6.8 / 1.2	**26** TH	0431 / 1035 / 1635 / 2307	6.8 / 1.5 / 7.1 / 0.9
12 TH	0543 / 1150 / 1746	6.7 / 1.5 / 7.0	**27** F	0517 / 1126 / 1720 / 2357	7.2 / 1.0 / 7.5 / 0.5
13 F ○	0018 / 0617 / 1227 / 1821	1.1 / 6.8 / 1.3 / 7.1	**28** SA ●	0600 / 1213 / 1805	7.4 / 0.7 / 7.8
14 SA	0054 / 0647 / 1300 / 1853	1.0 / 6.9 / 1.3 / 7.1	**29** SU	0043 / 0641 / 1259 / 1848	0.2 / 7.6 / 0.5 / 7.9
15 SU	0126 / 0714 / 1330 / 1923	1.0 / 6.9 / 1.3 / 7.0	**30** M	0128 / 0721 / 1343 / 1933	0.2 / 7.6 / 0.5 / 7.9
			31 TU	0210 / 0802 / 1426 / 2018	0.3 / 7.4 / 0.6 / 7.7

APRIL

Day	Time	m	Day	Time	m
1 W	0250 / 0843 / 1508 / 2104	0.6 / 7.2 / 0.9 / 7.3	**16** TH	0222 / 0812 / 1429 / 2028	1.5 / 6.7 / 1.5 / 6.6
2 TH	0330 / 0927 / 1550 / 2155	1.1 / 6.8 / 1.3 / 6.7	**17** F	0249 / 0844 / 1501 / 2105	1.7 / 6.6 / 1.7 / 6.4
3 F	0412 / 1016 / 1638 / 2257	1.7 / 6.3 / 1.8 / 6.2	**18** SA	0323 / 0922 / 1543 / 2151	1.9 / 6.3 / 1.9 / 6.1
4 SA	0503 / 1122 / 1741	2.3 / 5.9 / 2.3	**19** SU	0410 / 1011 / 1640 / 2252	2.3 / 6.0 / 2.1 / 5.8
5 SU	0020 / 0613 / 1245 / 1922	5.7 / 2.8 / 5.7 / 2.4	**20** M	0517 / 1117 / 1758	2.6 / 5.8 / 2.3
6 M	0144 / 0755 / 1401 / 2045	5.7 / 2.8 / 5.7 / 2.2	**21** TU	0019 / 0643 / 1248 / 1924	5.7 / 2.6 / 5.8 / 2.1
7 TU	0256 / 0906 / 1505 / 2142	5.9 / 2.5 / 6.0 / 1.8	**22** W	0207 / 0805 / 1415 / 2042	5.9 / 2.4 / 6.1 / 1.7
8 W	0355 / 0958 / 1558 / 2229	6.2 / 2.2 / 6.4 / 1.5	**23** TH	0314 / 0913 / 1516 / 2147	6.4 / 1.9 / 6.6 / 1.2
9 TH	0440 / 1043 / 1642 / 2310	6.5 / 1.8 / 6.6 / 1.3	**24** F	0407 / 1011 / 1609 / 2242	6.8 / 1.5 / 7.1 / 0.8
10 F	0517 / 1123 / 1720 / 2348	6.7 / 1.5 / 6.8 / 1.1	**25** SA	0454 / 1103 / 1658 / 2333	7.2 / 1.0 / 7.4 / 0.5
11 SA ○	0549 / 1200 / 1754	6.8 / 1.4 / 6.9	**26** SU ●	0538 / 1153 / 1745	7.4 / 0.7 / 7.7
12 SU	0023 / 0617 / 1234 / 1826	1.1 / 6.9 / 1.3 / 6.9	**27** M	0020 / 0619 / 1241 / 1831	0.3 / 7.6 / 0.5 / 7.8
13 M	0057 / 0645 / 1306 / 1857	1.1 / 6.9 / 1.3 / 6.9	**28** TU	0106 / 0700 / 1326 / 1917	0.3 / 7.6 / 0.4 / 7.7
14 TU	0128 / 0713 / 1335 / 1927	1.2 / 6.9 / 1.3 / 6.9	**29** W	0148 / 0741 / 1410 / 2003	0.5 / 7.4 / 0.6 / 7.5
15 W	0156 / 0742 / 1401 / 1957	1.3 / 6.8 / 1.4 / 6.8	**30** TH	0229 / 0822 / 1453 / 2050	0.8 / 7.2 / 0.8 / 7.1

Chart Datum: 3·90 metres below Ordnance Datum (Newlyn)

ENGLAND – IMMINGHAM

LAT 53°38′N   LONG 0°11′W

TIMES AND HEIGHTS OF HIGH AND LOW WATERS

YEAR **1998**

TIME ZONE (UT)
For Summer Time add ONE hour in non-shaded areas

Chart Datum: 3·90 metres below Ordnance Datum (Newlyn)

MAY

#	Time	m	#	Time	m
1 F	0309 0905 1536 2141	1.3 6.8 1.2 6.6	16 SA	0234 0828 1454 2057	1.6 6.7 1.5 6.4
2 SA	0351 0953 1624 2241	1.8 6.4 1.7 6.1	17 SU	0313 0908 1539 2145	1.8 6.5 1.7 6.2
3 SU	0438 1052 1721 2357	2.3 6.0 2.1 5.7	18 M	0401 0958 1635 2245	2.1 6.3 1.8 6.0
4 M	0538 1208 1840	2.7 5.7 2.3	19 TU	0502 1100 1743	2.3 6.1 1.9
5 TU	0114 0659 1325 2005	5.6 2.9 5.7 2.2	20 W	0003 0616 1217 1900	5.9 2.4 6.1 1.8
6 W	0222 0825 1431 2105	5.8 2.7 5.9 2.0	21 TH	0134 0735 1339 2015	6.0 2.3 6.3 1.6
7 TH	0320 0922 1525 2152	6.0 2.4 6.2 1.7	22 F	0243 0845 1447 2120	6.4 1.9 6.6 1.2
8 F	0406 1009 1611 2233	6.3 2.0 6.4 1.5	23 SA	0340 0946 1545 2218	6.7 1.5 7.0 0.9
9 SA	0444 1050 1649 2312	6.5 1.7 6.6 1.3	24 SU	0430 1042 1638 2310	7.0 1.1 7.2 0.7
10 SU	0516 1129 1724 2350	6.7 1.5 6.7 1.2	25 M ●	0516 1134 1728 2359	7.3 0.8 7.4 0.6
11 M O	0546 1205 1758	6.8 1.4 6.8	26 TU	0600 1223 1817	7.4 0.6 7.5
12 TU	0026 0616 1241 1832	1.2 6.9 1.3 6.8	27 W	0045 0642 1311 1905	0.6 7.4 0.6 7.4
13 W	0100 0649 1313 1906	1.3 6.9 1.3 6.8	28 TH	0129 0723 1356 1952	0.7 7.3 0.6 7.2
14 TH	0131 0721 1344 1940	1.3 6.9 1.4 6.7	29 F	0211 0805 1440 2039	1.0 7.1 0.9 6.9
15 F	0201 0753 1417 2016	1.5 6.8 1.4 6.6	30 SA	0251 0847 1523 2127	1.4 6.9 1.2 6.5
			31 SU	0330 0931 1607 2219	1.8 6.5 1.6 6.2

JUNE

#	Time	m	#	Time	m
1 M	0413 1022 1656 2320	2.2 6.2 1.9 5.8	16 TU	0353 0949 1629 2236	1.8 6.7 1.5 6.3
2 TU	0502 1124 1753	2.6 5.9 2.2	17 W	0448 1046 1728 2343	2.0 6.5 1.6 6.2
3 W	0028 0602 1235 1857	5.7 2.8 5.8 2.3	18 TH	0552 1153 1836	2.2 6.4 1.7
4 TH	0133 0711 1342 2005	5.7 2.8 5.8 2.2	19 F	0100 0704 1309 1948	6.2 2.2 6.4 1.6
5 F	0232 0823 1441 2101	5.8 2.6 6.0 2.0	20 SA	0211 0817 1421 2056	6.3 2.0 6.5 1.5
6 SA	0322 0922 1531 2150	6.1 2.3 6.2 1.8	21 SU	0313 0924 1525 2156	6.5 1.7 6.7 1.3
7 SU	0404 1011 1614 2234	6.3 2.0 6.4 1.6	22 M	0408 1023 1623 2251	6.8 1.4 7.0 1.1
8 M	0440 1055 1654 2316	6.6 1.8 6.5 1.5	23 TU	0457 1118 1717 2341	7.0 1.1 7.1 1.0
9 TU	0515 1136 1733 2356	6.8 1.6 6.6 1.4	24 W ●	0543 1209 1808	7.2 0.8 7.2
10 W O	0551 1216 1811	6.9 1.4 6.7	25 TH	0028 0626 1258 1856	1.0 7.3 0.7 7.2
11 TH	0034 0627 1254 1850	1.3 7.0 1.3 6.8	26 F	0113 0708 1344 1941	1.0 7.2 0.8 7.1
12 F	0111 0704 1332 1929	1.4 7.0 1.3 6.8	27 SA	0154 0748 1426 2025	1.2 7.1 0.9 6.9
13 SA	0147 0740 1410 2009	1.4 7.0 1.3 6.7	28 SU	0232 0828 1506 2107	1.4 7.0 1.1 6.6
14 SU	0225 0818 1451 2052	1.5 6.9 1.3 6.6	29 M	0309 0908 1545 2148	1.7 6.7 1.4 6.3
15 M	0306 0901 1537 2140	1.6 6.8 1.4 6.5	30 TU	0345 0950 1625 2233	2.0 6.4 1.7 6.0

JULY

#	Time	m	#	Time	m
1 W	0426 1038 1710 2323	2.3 6.1 2.0 5.8	16 TH	0431 1030 1709 2318	1.7 6.8 1.4 6.4
2 TH	0514 1135 1802	2.5 5.9 2.2	17 F	0527 1131 1810	2.0 6.6 1.7
3 F	0023 0611 1240 1900	5.7 2.7 5.7 2.3	18 SA	0028 0634 1245 1921	6.2 2.2 6.4 1.8
4 SA	0127 0716 1346 2003	5.7 2.7 5.8 2.3	19 SU	0141 0741 1401 2035	6.2 2.2 6.3 1.8
5 SU	0227 0824 1446 2103	5.9 2.6 5.9 2.1	20 M	0248 0906 1511 2140	6.3 2.0 6.5 1.7
6 M	0319 0927 1539 2157	6.1 2.3 6.1 1.9	21 TU	0348 1010 1614 2236	6.5 1.6 6.7 1.5
7 TU	0405 1021 1626 2245	6.4 2.0 6.4 1.7	22 W	0440 1107 1711 2327	6.8 1.3 6.9 1.3
8 W	0448 1109 1711 2330	6.7 1.7 6.6 1.5	23 TH ●	0527 1158 1800	7.0 1.0 7.0
9 TH O	0529 1155 1754	6.9 1.5 6.8	24 F	0014 0610 1246 1845	1.2 7.1 0.9 7.0
10 F	0013 0608 1239 1835	1.4 7.1 1.4 6.9	25 SA	0057 0651 1329 1926	1.2 7.2 0.8 7.0
11 SA	0054 0648 1322 1917	1.3 7.2 1.1 7.0	26 SU	0137 0730 1409 2004	1.3 7.2 0.9 6.9
12 SU	0134 0727 1403 2000	1.3 7.3 1.0 7.0	27 M	0212 0807 1444 2039	1.4 7.1 1.1 6.7
13 M	0215 0808 1446 2043	1.3 7.3 1.0 6.9	28 TU	0245 0842 1518 2112	1.6 6.9 1.3 6.5
14 TU	0257 0850 1530 2129	1.3 7.2 1.0 6.8	29 W	0316 0917 1551 2146	1.6 6.6 1.6 6.3
15 W	0342 0937 1616 2220	1.5 7.0 1.2 6.6	30 TH	0350 0954 1628 2225	2.0 6.4 1.9 6.0
			31 F	0428 1038 1712 2315	2.3 6.1 2.2 5.8

AUGUST

#	Time	m	#	Time	m
1 SA	0516 1135 1808	2.6 5.8 2.4	16 SU	0607 1225 1855	2.2 6.2 2.2
2 SU	0022 0619 1251 1912	5.7 2.8 5.6 2.5	17 M	0113 0731 1347 2018	6.0 2.4 6.1 2.3
3 M	0135 0732 1405 2020	5.7 2.8 5.7 2.4	18 TU	0225 0855 1502 2127	6.1 2.2 6.2 2.1
4 TU	0240 0844 1509 2123	5.9 2.5 6.0 2.2	19 W	0330 1001 1609 2224	6.3 1.8 6.5 1.8
5 W	0335 0950 1604 2218	6.3 2.2 6.3 1.9	20 TH	0424 1055 1704 2313	6.6 1.4 6.7 1.6
6 TH	0423 1046 1652 2307	6.6 1.8 6.6 1.6	21 F	0510 1144 1749 2357	6.9 1.1 6.9 1.4
7 F	0507 1136 1737 2353	7.0 1.4 6.9 1.4	22 SA ●	0552 1228 1828	7.1 0.9 7.0
8 SA O	0549 1223 1821	7.2 1.1 7.1	23 SU	0038 0630 1309 1904	1.3 7.2 0.9 7.0
9 SU	0036 0629 1308 1903	1.2 7.4 0.8 7.2	24 M	0115 0707 1345 1937	1.3 7.2 0.9 6.9
10 M	0119 0710 1351 1945	1.0 7.6 0.7 7.3	25 TU	0148 0741 1417 2006	1.3 7.1 1.1 6.8
11 TU	0201 0752 1432 2027	1.0 7.6 0.7 7.2	26 W	0218 0813 1447 2034	1.4 7.0 1.3 6.7
12 W	0243 0835 1514 2110	1.0 7.5 0.8 7.1	27 TH	0246 0844 1516 2104	1.6 6.8 1.5 6.5
13 TH	0325 0920 1557 2157	1.2 7.3 1.0 6.8	28 F	0314 0915 1545 2137	1.8 6.5 1.8 6.3
14 F	0411 1011 1645 2251	1.5 7.0 1.4 6.5	29 SA	0344 0949 1618 2217	2.1 6.2 2.2 6.0
15 SA	0502 1110 1741 2358	1.9 6.6 1.9 6.1	30 SU	0424 1033 1707 2313	2.4 5.9 2.5 5.7
			31 M	0524 1144 1820	2.7 5.6 2.8

5

TIME ZONE (UT)
For Summer Time add ONE hour in non-shaded areas

ENGLAND – IMMINGHAM

LAT 53°38′N   LONG 0°11′W

TIMES AND HEIGHTS OF HIGH AND LOW WATERS

YEAR **1998**

SEPTEMBER

	Time	m		Time	m
1 TU	0044 0644 1328 1940	5.6 2.8 5.6 2.7	**16** W	0203 0844 1451 2111	6.0 2.2 6.1 2.4
2 W	0205 0806 1443 2052	5.8 2.7 5.8 2.5	**17** TH	0309 0946 1558 2206	6.2 1.8 6.4 2.1
3 TH	0307 0922 1543 2152	6.2 2.2 6.3 2.1	**18** F	0404 1037 1648 2253	6.6 1.4 6.7 1.7
4 F	0358 1023 1634 2244	6.6 1.7 6.7 1.7	**19** SA	0449 1122 1728 2335	6.9 1.1 6.9 1.5
5 SA	0443 1115 1719 2331	7.1 1.2 7.1 1.3	**20** SU	0529 1204 1804 ●	7.1 1.0 7.0
6 SU O	0526 1202 1802	7.4 0.9 7.3	**21** M	0014 0606 1242 1836	1.3 7.2 1.0 7.0
7 M	0016 0607 1248 1843	1.0 7.7 0.6 7.5	**22** TU	0050 0640 1316 1905	1.3 7.2 1.0 7.0
8 TU	0100 0649 1330 1924	0.9 7.8 0.4 7.5	**23** W	0121 0713 1346 1932	1.3 7.2 1.2 7.0
9 W	0142 0731 1412 2004	0.8 7.9 0.5 7.4	**24** TH	0150 0743 1414 1959	1.4 7.0 1.3 6.9
10 TH	0224 0815 1453 2046	0.8 7.8 0.7 7.2	**25** F	0217 0812 1440 2027	1.5 6.9 1.5 6.7
11 F	0306 0901 1534 2131	1.0 7.5 1.0 6.9	**26** SA	0242 0841 1503 2057	1.7 6.6 1.8 6.5
12 SA	0350 0951 1618 2222	1.4 7.0 1.5 6.5	**27** SU	0310 0913 1531 2133	1.9 6.3 2.1 6.2
13 SU	0440 1051 1711 2327	1.8 6.5 2.1 6.1	**28** M	0347 0954 1613 2219	2.2 6.0 2.5 5.9
14 M	0543 1209 1826	2.3 6.1 2.6	**29** TU	0441 1053 1721 2332	2.6 5.7 2.8 5.6
15 TU	0047 0717 1334 2000	5.9 2.5 5.9 2.6	**30** W	0601 1246 1855	2.8 5.5 2.9

OCTOBER

	Time	m		Time	m
1 TH	0125 0730 1417 2017	5.7 2.6 5.8 2.7	**16** F	0242 0922 1532 2140	6.2 1.9 6.3 2.3
2 F	0235 0851 1520 2123	6.1 2.2 6.3 2.2	**17** SA	0337 1011 1621 2226	6.5 1.6 6.6 1.9
3 SA	0329 0955 1611 2217	6.6 1.7 6.7 1.7	**18** SU	0422 1054 1700 2307	6.8 1.3 6.8 1.6
4 SU	0416 1048 1657 2306	7.1 1.1 7.1 1.3	**19** M	0502 1133 1734 2345	7.0 1.2 6.9 1.4
5 M O	0500 1136 1736 2352	7.5 0.7 7.6 1.0	**20** TU	0539 1209 1805 ●	7.1 1.1 7.0
6 TU	0543 1222 1820	7.8 0.5 7.6	**21** W	0020 0612 1243 1833	1.3 7.1 1.2 7.0
7 W	0037 0626 1306 1859	0.7 8.0 0.4 7.6	**22** TH	0053 0644 1314 1901	1.3 7.1 1.3 7.0
8 TH	0121 0710 1348 1940	0.6 8.0 0.4 7.6	**23** F	0122 0716 1342 1929	1.4 7.0 1.4 7.0
9 F	0205 0755 1429 2021	0.7 7.8 0.7 7.3	**24** SA	0150 0746 1408 1958	1.5 6.9 1.6 6.9
10 SA	0247 0816 1510 2105	1.0 7.5 1.1 7.0	**25** SU	0216 0816 1433 2028	1.6 6.7 1.8 6.7
11 SU	0331 0933 1552 2154	1.3 7.0 1.7 6.5	**26** M	0246 0850 1503 2102	1.8 6.4 2.1 6.4
12 M	0420 1034 1642 2257	1.8 6.4 2.3 6.1	**27** TU	0324 0932 1545 2147	2.1 6.1 2.4 6.1
13 TU	0523 1152 1752	2.3 6.0 2.8	**28** W	0416 1029 1644 2249	2.4 5.8 2.7 5.9
14 W	0018 0657 1316 1932	5.9 2.5 5.8 2.9	**29** TH	0528 1157 1808	2.6 5.7 2.9
15 TH	0136 0822 1429 2046	5.9 2.3 6.0 2.6	**30** F	0023 0654 1342 1937	5.8 2.5 5.8 2.7
			31 SA	0153 0815 1449 2048	6.1 2.1 6.3 2.3

NOVEMBER

	Time	m		Time	m
1 SU	0254 0922 1543 2146	6.6 1.6 6.7 1.8	**16** M	0352 1019 1626 2235	6.6 1.6 6.6 1.9
2 M	0345 1017 1630 2238	7.1 1.1 7.1 1.3	**17** TU	0433 1058 1702 2314	6.8 1.5 7.0 1.6
3 TU	0433 1108 1714 2327	7.5 0.8 7.4 1.0	**18** W	0510 1134 1733 2350	6.9 1.4 7.0 1.5
4 W O	0519 1155 1755	7.8 0.6 7.6	**19** TH	0545 1209 1804 ●	7.0 1.4 7.0
5 TH	0015 0605 1241 1836	0.7 7.9 0.5 7.7	**20** F	0024 0619 1243 1834	1.4 7.0 1.4 7.1
6 F	0101 0651 1325 1917	0.6 7.9 0.6 7.6	**21** SA	0057 0653 1314 1906	1.4 6.9 1.5 7.0
7 SA	0146 0738 1407 1959	0.7 7.7 0.9 7.4	**22** SU	0127 0726 1343 1936	1.5 6.8 1.6 7.0
8 SU	0231 0827 1448 2042	0.9 7.4 1.3 7.1	**23** M	0158 0800 1412 2008	1.6 6.7 1.7 6.9
9 M	0316 0918 1529 2129	1.3 6.9 1.8 6.7	**24** TU	0231 0837 1447 2044	1.7 6.5 1.9 6.6
10 TU	0404 1017 1615 2227	1.7 6.4 2.3 6.3	**25** W	0311 0920 1529 2129	1.9 6.3 2.2 6.4
11 W	0502 1129 1713 2341	2.1 6.0 2.8	**26** TH	0401 1014 1622 2225	2.1 6.1 2.5 6.2
12 TH	0619 1244 1835	2.4 5.8 3.0	**27** F	0505 1123 1731 2335	2.2 5.9 2.7 6.1
13 F	0058 0743 1354 2003	5.9 2.3 5.9 2.9	**28** SA	0619 1254 1853	2.2 6.0 2.6
14 SA	0206 0846 1454 2104	6.1 2.1 6.1 2.5	**29** SU	0059 0737 1410 2009	6.2 2.0 6.2 2.4
15 SU	0303 0936 1545 2153	6.4 1.9 6.4 2.2	**30** M	0214 0847 1510 2114	6.4 1.7 6.6 1.9

DECEMBER

	Time	m		Time	m
1 TU	0314 0947 1602 2212	6.9 1.3 6.9 1.5	**16** W	0401 1018 1627 2240	6.4 1.8 6.6 1.9
2 W	0409 1041 1649 2305	7.3 1.0 7.2 1.1	**17** TH	0442 1059 1703 2320	6.6 1.7 6.8 1.7
3 TH O	0500 1131 1733 2355	7.5 0.8 7.4 0.9	**18** F ●	0520 1138 1738 2359	6.7 1.6 7.0 1.6
4 F	0550 1219 1816	7.6 0.8 7.6	**19** SA	0557 1215 1813	6.8 1.5 7.1
5 SA	0044 0638 1304 1858	0.7 7.6 0.8 7.5	**20** SU	0036 0635 1250 1847	1.5 6.9 1.5 7.1
6 SU	0131 0726 1347 1941	0.7 7.5 1.1 7.4	**21** M	0112 0712 1324 1921	1.5 6.9 1.6 7.1
7 M	0217 0814 1429 2024	0.9 7.2 1.4 7.2	**22** TU	0147 0749 1358 1955	1.4 6.8 1.6 7.0
8 TU	0302 0903 1508 2108	1.2 6.9 1.8 6.9	**23** W	0224 0828 1436 2033	1.5 6.7 1.7 6.9
9 W	0347 0956 1549 2157	1.5 6.5 2.2 6.5	**24** TH	0304 0910 1517 2116	1.5 6.6 1.9 6.8
10 TH	0435 1054 1636 2256	1.9 6.1 2.6 6.2	**25** F	0350 0959 1605 2205	1.7 6.4 2.1 6.6
11 F	0529 1159 1732	2.2 5.8 2.8	**26** SA	0444 1056 1702 2305	1.8 6.2 2.3 6.5
12 SA	0006 0633 1305 1840	6.0 2.4 5.8 3.0	**27** SU	0547 1205 1812	1.9 6.1 2.4
13 SU	0117 0744 1406 1959	5.9 2.4 5.9 2.8	**28** M	0015 0658 1326 1930	6.4 1.9 6.1 2.4
14 M	0220 0844 1501 2105	6.0 2.2 6.1 2.6	**29** TU	0135 0813 1435 2045	6.4 1.8 6.4 2.1
15 TU	0314 0934 1547 2156	6.2 2.0 6.3 2.2	**30** W	0248 0920 1535 2150	6.6 1.6 6.6 1.8
			31 TH	0351 1019 1628 2248	6.9 1.4 7.0 1.4

Chart Datum: 3·90 metres below Ordnance Datum (Newlyn)

RIVER HUMBER

10-5-11

S bank: NE and N Lincolnshire
Grimsby marina (53°35'·10N 00°03'·87W Rtg 2-2-2).

N bank: E Riding of Yorks and City of Kingston-upon-Hull
Hull marina (53°44'·22N 00°20'·60W Rtg 3-1-1)

CHARTS
AC 109, 3497, 1188, *1190*; Imray C29; OS 107; ABP (local)

TIDES
–0510 Immingham, –0452 Hull, Dover; ML 4·1; Duration 0555; Zone 0 (UT)

Standard Port IMMINGHAM (←)

Times				Height (metres)			
High Water		Low Water		MHWS	MHWN	MLWN	MLWS
0100	0700	0100	0700	7·3	5·8	2·6	0·9
1300	1900	1300	1900				
Differences BULL SAND FORT							
–0020	–0030	–0035	–0015	–0·4	–0·3	+0·1	+0·2
GRIMSBY							
–0003	–0011	–0015	–0002	–0·3	–0·2	0·0	+0·1
HULL (ALBERT DOCK)							
+0019	+0019	+0033	+0027	+0·3	+0·1	–0·1	–0·2
HUMBER BRIDGE							
+0024	+0022	+0047	+0036	–0·1	–0·4	–0·7	–0·7
BURTON STATHER (R. Trent)*							
+0105	+0045	+0335	+0305	–2·1	–2·3	–2·3	Dries
KEADBY (R. Trent)*							
+0135	+0120	+0425	+0410	–2·5	–2·8	Dries	Dries
BLACKTOFT (R. Ouse)†							
+0100	+0055	+0325	+0255	–1·6	–1·8	–2·2	–1·1
GOOLE (R. Ouse)†							
+0130	+0115	+0355	+0350	–1·6	–2·1	–1·9	–0·6

NOTE: Daily predictions for Immingham are given above.

* Normal river level at Burton Stather is about 0·1m below CD, and at Keadby 0·1m to 0·2m below CD.

† Heights of LW can increase by up to 0·3m at Blacktoft and 0·6m at Goole when river in spate. HW heights are little affected.

SHELTER
R Humber is the estuary of R Ouse and R Trent. Yachts can ⚓ inside Spurn Hd, except in strong SW/NW winds. ABP is the Authority for the Humber and owns the ports of Hull, Grimsby, Immingham and Goole. Immingham should be used by yachts only in emergency. If unable to reach Hull on the tide, in S to W winds there is a good ⚓ off the SW bank 8ca above Killingholme Oil jetty, well out of main chan. In N'lies ⚓ off Hawkin's Pt, N of S9 buoy. The **marinas** at Grimsby, Hull, S Ferriby and the docks at Goole are all entered by lock, access HW±3. S Ferriby should not be attempted without up-to-date ABP charts which cover the ever-changing buoyed chan above Hull. Entry to Winteringham (HW±½) and Brough Havens (HW±1) should not be attempted without first contacting Humber Yawl Club for latest details of approach channel and mooring availability. Both havens dry to soft mud. Winteringham was badly silted 1996; to be dredged 1997.

NAVIGATION
WPT 53°33'·50N 00°08'·00E, 095°/275° from/to Bull Sand Fort, 2·3M. The Humber is a busy commercial waterway best entered at LW. Sp tides are fierce; 4·4kn ebb off Spurn Head and Immingham.

RIVER HUMBER *continued*

IMMINGHAM

MEAN SPRING
AND NEAP CURVES

MEAN RANGES	
Springs 6·4m	——
Neaps 3·2m	– – –

Springs occur 2 days
after
New and Full Moon.

5

From the S, make for Rosse Spit PHM buoy, then keep N of the Haile Sand buoys via Haile Chan.

From the N, make good Spurn Lt Float to keep clear of the Binks; then enter the estuary to the S of the Chequers buoys and Spurn Head for Hawke or Bull Chans. Hawke and Sunk Channels are marked by S1-S9 SHM buoys, all Fl G 1·5s (S8 is a SHM bn, Fl G 1·5s with tide gauge); and by P2-P9 PHM buoys, all Fl R 1·5s. Hawke Chan carries 10·4m and Sunk Chan is dredged continuously to 8·8m. Off R Hull there is a tidal eddy and streams can be rotatory, ie the flood makes W up Hull Roads for ¾hr whilst the ebb is already running down-river over Skitter Sand on the opposite bank (reaches 2½kn at springs). Humber bridge has 30m clearance.

LIGHTS AND MARKS
The Humber is well buoyed/lit for its whole length. At Grimsby a conspic tr (94m) marks ent to Royal Dock. IPTS control entry to Grimsby (shown W of ent to Royal Dock), Immingham, Killingholme, Hull and Goole.

RADIO TELEPHONE
Monitor Ch **12** 16 *VTS Humber* (at Queen Elizabeth Dock, Hull ☎ (01482) 701787) for traffic, nav, wx & safety info; also tides on request. VTS covers the R Humber, Ouse and Trent and broadcasts weather (inc vis reports), nav & tidal info every odd H+03 on Ch 12. Other VHF stns: *Grimsby Docks Radio* Ch 74 (H24) 18 79. Marina Ch 09 18. *Immingham Docks Radio* Ch 19 68 (H24).
R Hull Port Ops Service call *Drypool Radio* Ch 22 11 (Ch 22: Mon-Fri HW–2 to HW+1; Sat 0900-1100 LT). Hull Marina, Ch M **80** (H24); Albert Dock Ch 09.
S Ferriby lock/marina Ch 74. Humber YC, Ch M (if racing). Monitor Ch 08 R. Trent and Ch 14 R. Ouse.
Goole Docks Radio Ch 14 (H24) 09 19. Boothferry Bridge Ch 09 (H24). Selby Railway and Toll Bridges Ch 09.
TELEPHONE (Dial codes: Grimsby 01472; Hull 01482)
HUMBER Hr Mr (Hull) 327171 controls whole estuary/river. GRIMSBY Port Mgr 359181; # (01482) 782107 (H24); MRSC (01262) 672317; Marinecall 0891 500454; Police 359171.

HULL Marina 593451 & lock 593455; MRSC (01262) 672317; # 782107; Marinecall 0891 500454; Police 26111; Dr contact Humber VTS 701787.
FACILITIES
GRIMSBY (01472; NE Lincs)
 Grimsby Marina (150+25 visitors) ☎ 360404, D, P (cans), FW, ME, AC, Gas, Gaz, El, Sh, BH (30 ton), R, CH, Bar, (access HW±3 via Royal Dock and Union Dock, but fixed bridge clearance is only 4·45m; marina is just off the SW corner of chartlet).
The **Fish Docks** are entered by lock 300m E of conspic tr. Access is HW±3, with R/G tfc lts, but yachts should enter HW±2, "on the level", after being cleared in by *Fish Dock Island* Ch 74. Inside No 2 Fish Dock is:
Meridian Quay Marina,100 berths + 20 visitors on pontoon along the W quay, £10 inc AC. Contact Humber Cruising Association ☎ (01472) 268424; usual facilities. Rtg 2-2-2
Grimsby and Cleethorpes YC ☎ 356678, Bar, R, M, FW, ◎.
Town EC Thurs; all facilities, ACA.
HULL (01482; City of Kingston-upon-Hull)
Hull Marina, ent at 53°44'·22N 00°20'·07W, (310 + 20 Ⓥ), ☎ 593451, ⚓ 224148; £12.70, access HW±3 via lock, (wait at pontoons in tidal basin, accessible HW±4½; or at Victoria Pier, 150m to the E). Marina office open 0900-1700 daily; VHF Ch 80 (H24); P, D, FW, AC, CH, Gas, #, ME, El, Sh, BH (50 ton), C (2 ton), ◎, SM, ACA.
SOUTH FERRIBY, N Lincs. Rtg 3-3-2.
Marina (100+20 visitors) ☎ (01652) 635620; access HW±3, £8 inc lock fee, D, P (cans), FW, ME, El, Sh, C (30 ton), CH, Gas, Gaz. **Village** V, Bar.
WINTERINGHAM HAVEN, N Lincs (belongs to Humber Yawl Club) ☎ (01724) 734452, ✉.
BROUGH HAVEN, E Riding of Yorkshire, **Humber Yawl Club** ☎ (01482) 667224, Slip, FW, Bar, limited AB; contact club.
NABURN (R Ouse, 4M S of York and 80M above Spurn Pt).
Naburn Marina (450+50 visitors) ☎ (01904) 621021; £6.00; VHF Ch **80** M; CH, P, D, FW, AC, Sh, ME, BH (16 ton), R.

BRIDLINGTON   10-5-12

E Riding of Yorkshire 54°04′·77N 00°11′·12W   Rtg 3-4-1

CHARTS
AC 1882, 121, 129, 1191, *1190*; Imray C29; OS 101

TIDES
+0553 Dover; ML 3·6; Duration 0610; Zone 0 (UT)

Standard Port RIVER TYNE (NORTH SHIELDS) (⟶)

Times				Height (metres)			
High Water		Low Water		MHWS	MHWN	MLWN	MLWS
0200	0800	0100	0800	5·0	3·9	1·8	0·7
1400	2000	1300	2000				
Differences BRIDLINGTON							
+0119	+0109	+0109	+0104	+1·1	+0·8	+0·5	+0·4
FILEY BAY							
+0101	+0101	+0101	+0048	+0·8	+1·0	+0·6	+0·3

SHELTER
Good, except in E, SE and S winds. Hbr dries completely to soft mud; access HW±3 (for draft of 2·7m). Visitors normally berth on S pier or near Hr Mr's Office.

NAVIGATION
WPT SW Smithic WCM, Q (9) 15s, 54°02′·41N 00°09′·10W, 153°/333° from/to ent, 2·6M. Close-in appr is with N pier hd lt on brg 002° to keep W of drying patch (The Canch). Beware bar, 1m at MLWN, could dry out at MLWS.

LIGHTS AND MARKS
Hbr is 4M WSW of Flamborough Hd lt, Fl (4) 15s 65m 24M. Y racing marks are laid in the Bay, Apr-Oct. Tidal sigs, by day from S pier: R flag = >2·7m in hbr; No flag = < 2·7m. At night from N pier: Fl Ⓡ = >2·7m in hbr; Fl Ⓖ = < 2·7m.

RADIO TELEPHONE
VHF Ch **12** 16 14 (occas).

TELEPHONE (Dial code 01262)
Hr Mr 670148/9, ☎ 602041, mobile 0402 201613; MRSC 672317; Marinecall 0891 500454; ⌗ (01482) 782107 (H24); Police 672222; Ⓗ 673451.

FACILITIES
S Pier FW, C (5 ton), C, Slip; See Hr Mr for M, AB £10.06; **Royal Yorks YC** ☎ 672041, L, FW, R, Bar. **Town** EC Thurs; P & D (cans), CH, ME, El, V, R, Bar, ⊠, Ⓑ, ⇌, ✈ (Humberside).

ADJACENT ANCHORAGE

FILEY, N Yorkshire, 54°12′·80N 00°16′·10W, AC 1882, 129. HW +0532 on Dover; ML 3·5m; Duration 0605. See 10.5.12. Good ⚓ in winds from S to NNE in 4 – 5m on hard sand. Lt on cliff above CG Stn, G metal column, FR 31m 1M vis 272°-308°. The natural bkwtr, Filey Brigg marked by ECM buoy, Q(3)10s, Bell. Beware Horse Rk, N of Filey Brigg, foul ground extending ½M from shore. Facilities EC Wed; V, R, Bar, L, Ⓗ ☎ (01723) 68111, ⊠, Ⓑ, ⇌.

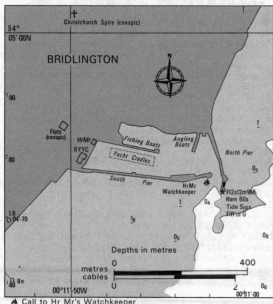

⚓ Call to Hr Mr's Watchkeeper

SCARBOROUGH   10-5-13

N. Yorkshire 54°16′·87N 00°23′·28W   Rtg 3-2-1

CHARTS
AC 1612, 129, 1191; Imray C29; OS 101

TIDES
+0527 Dover; ML 3·5; Duration 0615; Zone 0 (UT)

Standard Port RIVER TYNE (NORTH SHIELDS) (⟶)

Times				Height (metres)			
High Water		Low Water		MHWS	MHWN	MLWN	MLWS
0200	0800	0100	0800	5·0	3·9	1·8	0·7
1400	2000	1300	2000				
Differences SCARBOROUGH							
+0059	+0059	+0044	+0044	+0·7	+0·7	+0·5	+0·2

⚓ Contact Watchman on duty at Lt Ho

SHELTER
Good in E Hbr, access HW±3 via narrow (10m) ent by E pier, but not in strong E/SE'lies. Ⓥ drying berths on Old Pier just N of the drawbridge. 15 drying pontoon berths, inc 4 Ⓥ (max LOA 10.3m, draft 1.8m), were installed 1997 in the SW corner of E Hbr, just below lt ho. The Old Hbr is strictly for FVs.

NAVIGATION
WPT 54°16′·50N 00°22′·00W, 122°/302° from/to E pier lt, 0.83M. Beware rks SW of E pier running out for approx 20m. Appr from the E to avoid Ramsdale Scar, rky patch 0·9m. Keep careful watch for salmon nets E & SE of ent.

LIGHTS AND MARKS
Lt ho (conspic), Iso 5s 17m 9M, on Old Pier. No ldg lts/marks. Tidal sigs on Old Pier:
Ⓨ = 1·8 - 3·7m depth;
Iso 5s or B ● = >3·7m.
At W pier: 2FR (vert) 5m 4M = >1·8m.
These depths are for Old Hbr; E hbr ent has approx 1·5m less.

RADIO TELEPHONE
Call *Scarborough lt ho* VHF Ch **12** 16 (H24). Watchkeeper will offer guidance to approaching visitors and help them to moor.

TELEPHONE (Dial code 01723)
Hr Mr (HO) 373530 and ☎, 360684 (OT); CG 372323; MRSC (01262) 672317; ⌗ (01482) 782107 (H24); Marinecall 0891 500454; Police 500300; Ⓗ 368111.

FACILITIES
East Harbour AB £6.00, M (Long waiting list – 4 drying Ⓥ berths available), FW, AC, C (3 ton), Slip, D; **Scarborough YC** ☎ 373821, AB, Slip, M*, L, FW, ME, El, Ⓞ;
Services: ME, El, Sh, CH, P & D (cans), Ⓔ.
Town EC Wed; P, D, V, R, Bar, ⊠, Ⓑ, ⇌, ✈ (Humberside).

WHITBY   10-5-14

N. Yorkshire 54°29'·64N 00°36'·68W   Rtg 3-2-1

CHARTS
AC 1612, 134, 129; Imray C29; OS 94
TIDES
+0500 Dover; ML 3·3; Duration 0605; Zone 0 (UT)

Standard Port RIVER TYNE (NORTH SHIELDS) (→)

Times				Height (metres)			
High Water		Low Water		MHWS	MHWN	MLWN	MLWS
0200	0800	0100	0800	5·0	3·9	1·8	0·7
1400	2000	1300	2000				
Differences WHITBY							
+0034	+0049	+0034	+0019	+0·6	+0·4	+0·1	+0·1

SHELTER
Good, except in lower hbr in strong NW to NE winds. Hbr is available from HW±4 for drafts of approx 2m. Marina (dredged approx 2m) is 2ca beyond swing bridge; visitor berths at seaward end of long pontoon. Bridge opens on request at ½ hr intervals HW±2; extra openings at week-ends as arranged with WYC. FG lts = open; FR lts = shut.
NAVIGATION
WPT 54°30'·20N 00°36'·86W, 349°/169° from/to ent, 0·57M. Hbr can be approached safely from any direction except SE. In strong winds from NW through N to SE the sea breaks a long way out and ent is difficult. From the SE beware Whitby Rk; leave Whitby NCM buoy, Q, to port. Beware strong set to E from HW –2 to HW, when nearing piers. Vessels >37m LOA must embark pilot; via Hr Mr.
LIGHTS AND MARKS
Whitby High lt ho, Iso RW 10s 73m 18/16M, (R128°-143°, W143°-319°), is 2M ESE of hbr ent. Ldg lines:
(1)   Chapel spire in line 176° with E lt ho.
(2)   FR lt or 2 bns, seen between E and W pier extension, lts (FR and FG), lead 169° into hbr. Continue on this line until bns (W △ and W ○ with B stripe) on E pier (two FY lts) are abeam.
(3)   On course 209° keep these same bns in line astern.

RADIO TELEPHONE
VHF Ch 11 16 12 (H24). Whitby Bridge Ch 11 16 06 (listens on Ch 16 HW–2 to HW+2).
TELEPHONE (Dial code 01947)
Hr Mr 602354; MRSC (01262) 672317; ⌗ (01482) 782107 (H24); Marinecall 0891 500454/453; Police 603443; Dr 820888.
FACILITIES
Whitby Marina (200+10 visitors) ☎ 600165, £14.16, AC, D, FW, P (cans), Slip, ME, El, Sh, C, CH; Fish Quay M, D, L, FW, C (1 ton), CH, AB, R, Bar; Whitby YC ☎ 603623, M, L, Bar; Services: ME, El, Sh, CH, BH, ACA, SM, Gas, Gaz.
Town EC Wed; usual amenities, ✉, ⑧, ⇌, ✈ (Teesside).

ADJACENT ANCHORAGE

RUNSWICK BAY, N. Yorkshire, 54°32'·10N 00°44'·10W. AC 1612. HW +0505 on Dover: Differences on R Tyne are approx as Whitby; ML 3·1m; Duration 0605. Good shelter in all winds from NW by W to SSE. Enter bay at 225° keeping clear of many rks at base of cliffs. Two W posts (2FY by night when required by lifeboat) 18m apart are ldg marks 270° to LB ho and can be used to lead into ⚓. Good holding in 6m to 9m in middle of bay. Facilities: Runswick Bay Rescue Boat Station ☎ (01947) 840965. Village Bar, R, V.

The Skipper must not only know his vessel and how to handle her, but he must be able to navigate her and must know the sea. He must be watchful and careful. He needs 'nerve', coolness and endurance, this endurance being a mental rather than a physical quality. Above all he must not be liable to panic in a sudden emergency.

I have known men who, faced with an awkward situation and knowing exactly what should be done, lose their heads and do something quite different – perhaps run for a difficult harbour on a lee shore, thereby taking a risk twenty times greater than that which they are trying to avoid. They, fortunately, are exceptions.

Of the average man R.L.Stevenson has truly said:
'It is a commonplace that we cannot answer for ourselves until we have been tried. But it is not so common a reflection, and surely more consoling, that we usually find ourselves a great deal braver and better than we thought. I believe this is every one's experience.'

Yacht Cruising: Claud Worth 1910.

ADJACENT PORT (3M SSE OF HARTLEPOOL)

RIVER TEES/MIDDLESBROUGH, Middlesbrough/Stockton, 54°38'·93N 01°08'·38W. Rtg 4-5-3. AC 2566, 2567, 152; Imray C29; OS 93. HW +0450 Dover; Differences see 10.5.15. ML 3·1; Duration 0605. R. Tees & Middlesbrough form a major industrial area, with virtually no berths or facilities for yachts/pleasure craft. Hartlepool marina, 3M to the NNW is a far better choice with all facilities. Entry to R. Tees is not recommended for small craft in heavy weather, especially with strong winds from NE to SE. Tees Fairway SWM buoy, Iso 4s, Horn 5s, Racon, is at 54°40'·94N 01°06'·39W, 030°/2·4M from S Gare bkwtr. At Old CG stn a Q lt, or 3 ⑱ (vert), = no entry without Hr Mr's consent. Ldg lts 210°, FR on framework trs. The channel is well marked to beyond Middlesbrough. Call: Tees Hbr Radio VHF Ch 14 22 16 12 (H24). Monitor Ch 14; also info Ch 14 22. Tees Barrage Radio Ch M (37). Hr Mr ☎ (01642) 468127 (HO)/ 452541 (H24); Police 248184. S Gare Marine Club ☎ 491039 (occas), M, FW, Slip; Castlegate Marine Club ☎ 583299 Slip, M, FW, ME, El, Sh, CH, V; Tees Motor Boat Club M; Services: El, ME, Ⓔ, ACA. City EC Wed; ✉, ⑧, ⇌, ✈.

HARTLEPOOL   10-5-15

Hartlepool 54°41'·30N 01°11'·49W (West Hbr ent) Rtg 3-1-2

CHARTS
AC 2566, 2567, 152; Imray C29; OS 93

TIDES
+0437 Dover; ML 3·0; Duration 0600; Zone 0 (UT)

Standard Port RIVER TYNE (NORTH SHIELDS) (→)

Times				Height (metres)			
High Water		Low Water		MHWS	MHWN	MLWN	MLWS
0200	0800	0100	0800	5·0	3·9	1·8	0·7
1400	2000	1300	2000				
Differences HARTLEPOOL							
+0015	+0015	+0008	+0008	+0·4	+0·3	0·0	+0·1
MIDDLESBROUGH							
+0019	+0021	+0014	+0011	+0·6	+0·6	+0·3	+0·1

SHELTER
Excellent in marina (5m), access HW±4½ via chan dredged 0·8m and lock (ent 9m wide; pontoon on S side). Speed limit 4kn in W Hbr and marina. Strong E/SE winds raise broken water and swell in the bay, making ent channel hazardous, but possible. In such conditions, call VHF Ch M to shelter in the lock, awaiting tide. Or call *Tees Port Control* Ch 14 for short-stay in Victoria Hbr (commercial dock, not normally for yachts), access H24.

NAVIGATION
WPT Longscar ECM buoy, Q (3) 10s, Bell, 54°40'·85N 01°09'·79W, 115°/295° from/to W Hbr ent 1·06M; (or, for Victoria Hbr, 128°/308° from/to Nos 1/2 buoys, 0·65M). From S, beware Longscar Rks, only 0·4M WSW of WPT. Note: Tees Fairway SWM buoy, Iso 4s 8M, (54°40'·95N 01°06'·23W) is 2M E of Longscar ECM buoy and may assist the initial landfall.

LIGHTS AND MARKS
The Heugh lt ho Fl (2) 10s 19m 19M, H24. Dir lt Fl WRG 2s 6m 3M leads 308° to W Hbr/marina lock; vis G305·5°-307°, W307°-309°, R309°-310·5°. W Hbr outer piers, Oc R/G 5s 12m 2M; bright street lts on S pier. Inner piers, FR/FG 7m 2M.
Lock sigs: Ⓖ = Proceed; Ⓡ = Wait; 2Ⓡ = Lock closed.
Dir lt Iso WRG 3s 42m, W324·4°-325·4°, leads 325° via lit buoyed chan to Victoria Hbr. 2 FG (vert) on Kafiga pontoons.

RADIO TELEPHONE
Marina Ch **M** 80. *Tees Port Control* info Ch 14 22 (H24). *Hartlepool Dock Radio* Ch 12, only for ship docking.

TELEPHONE (Dial code 01429)
Marina 865744; Hr Mr 266127; MRSC (0191) 257 2691; Tees & Hartlepool Port Authority 276771; Marinecall 0891 500453; ⌗ (0191) 257 9441; Police 221151; Dr 272679.

FACILITIES
Hartlepool Marina (262 + visitors) ☎ 865744, ⌨ 865947, £11.83, FW, AC, D, P (cans), BY, EI, Sh, ▣, BH (40 tons), C (15 ton), Gas, Gaz; **Hartlepool YC** ☎ 274931, Bar; **Tees SC** ☎ 267151, Bar, Slip; **Services:** CH, ME, EL, Sh, C (mobiles).
Town EC Wed; P (cans), V, R, Bar, ✉, Ⓑ, ⇌, ✈ (Teesside).

SEAHAM   10-5-16

Durham 54°50'·23N 01°19'·17W Rtg 3-3-2

CHARTS
AC 1627, 152; Imray C29; OS 88

TIDES
+0435 Dover; ML 3·0; Duration 0600; Zone 0 (UT)

Standard Port RIVER TYNE (NORTH SHIELDS) (→)

Times				Height (metres)			
High Water		Low Water		MHWS	MHWN	MLWN	MLWS
0200	0800	0100	0800	5·0	3·9	1·8	0·7
1400	2000	1300	2000				
Differences SEAHAM							
+0004	+0004	−0001	−0001	+0·2	+0·2	+0·2	0·0

SHELTER
Small boats normally berth in N Dock where shelter is excellent, but it dries. Larger boats may lock into S Dock; gates open from HW −2 to HW+1. Speed limit 5kn. Or ⚓ 2½ca offshore with clock tr in transit 240° with St John's church tr.

NAVIGATION
WPT 54°50'·35N 01°18'·50W (off chartlet), 076°/256° from/to N bkwtr lt ho, 0·40M. Shoals and rks to S of S bkwtr (Liddle Scars). Ent should not be attempted in strong on-shore winds.

LIGHTS AND MARKS
No ldg lts, but hbr is easily identified by lt ho (W with B bands) on N pier, Fl G 10s 12m 5M (often shows FG in bad weather), Dia 30s (sounded HW−2½ to +1½). FS at NE corner of S dock on with N lt ho leads in 256° clear of Tangle Rks. 3FR lts on wave screen are in form of a △. Traffic sigs at S Dock:
Ⓡ = Vessels enter
Ⓖ = Vessels leave

RADIO TELEPHONE
VHF Ch **12** 16 06 (HW−2½ to HW+1½ between 0800-1800 LT Mon-Fri).

TELEPHONE (Dial code 0191)
Hr Mr 581 3246; Hbr Ops Office 581 3877; MRSC 257 2691; ⌗ (0191) 257 9441; Marinecall 0891 500453; Police 581 2255; Dr 581 2332.

FACILITIES
S Dock (Seaham Hbr Dock Co) ☎ 5813877, 🗲 5130700, AB £4 but normally no charge for the odd night, L, FW, C (40 ton), AB; **N Dock** M.
Town (½M) EC Wed; P, D, FW, ME, EI, CH (5M), V, R, Bar, ✉, Ⓑ, ⇌, ✈ (Teesside or Newcastle).

SUNDERLAND   10-5-17

Tyne and Wear 54°55'·22N 01°21'·05W Rtg 1-3-2

CHARTS
AC 1627, 152; Imray C29; OS 88

TIDES
+0430 Dover; ML 2·9; Duration 0600; Zone 0 (UT)

Standard Port RIVER TYNE (NORTH SHIELDS) (→)

Times				Height (metres)			
High Water		Low Water		MHWS	MHWN	MLWN	MLWS
0200	0800	0100	0800	5·0	3·9	1·8	0·7
1400	2000	1300	2000				
Differences SUNDERLAND							
+0002	−0002	−0002	−0002	+0·2	+0·3	+0·2	+0·1

SHELTER
Very good, but strong E'lies cause heavy swell in ent and outer hbr. There are 88 pontoon berths and 110 fore-and-aft ⚓s in Sunderland Marina (3·8m), protected by floating bkwtr; access H24. App to marina ent is marked by SHM dolphin, Fl G 5s, and E jetty, Fl (2) G 10s.

NAVIGATION
WPT 54°55'·20N 01°20'·00W, 098°/278° from/to Roker Pier lt, 0·61M. Beware wreck at Whitburn Steel about 1M N of ent, and Hendon Rk (0·9m), 1·2M SE of hbr ent.

LIGHTS AND MARKS
3 FL Ⓡ at Pilot Stn (Old N Pier) = danger in hbr; no ent/dep.

RADIO TELEPHONE
Sunderland Marina Ch M. Port VHF Ch 14 16 (H24); tide and visibility reports on request.

TELEPHONE (Dial code 0191)
Marina 514 4721; Hr Mr 514 0411 (HO), 567 2626 (OT); MRSC 257 2691; ⌗ (0191) 257 9441; Marinecall 0891 500453; Police 5102020; Ⓗ 565 6256.

FACILITIES
Sunderland Marina (88 pontoon berths, max LOA 12m; and 110 moorings) ☎ 514 4721, 🗲 514 1847, AB £12.74, M £5.88, D, Slip, FW;
Sunderland YC ☎ 567 5133, FW, AB, Bar, Slip (dinghy);
Wear Boating Association ☎ 567 5313, AB.
Town EC Wed; P (cans), Gas, Gaz, CH, EI, ME, SM, V, R, Bar, ✉, 🖲, Ⓑ, ⇌, ✈ (Newcastle).

R. TYNE/NORTH SHIELDS 10-5-18

Tyne and Wear 55°00'·78N 01°24'·00W   Rtg 2-2-2

CHARTS
AC 1934, 152; Imray C29; OS 88

TIDES
+0430 Dover; ML 3·0; Duration 0604; Zone 0 (UT)

Standard Port RIVER TYNE (NORTH SHIELDS) (→)

Times				Height (metres)			
High Water		Low Water		MHWS	MHWN	MLWN	MLWS
0200	0800	0100	0800	5·0	3·9	1·8	0·7
1400	2000	1300	2000				

Differences NEWCASTLE-UPON-TYNE

+0003	+0003	+0008	+0008	+0·3	+0·2	+0·1	+0·1

SHELTER
Good in all weathers. Access H24, but in strong E and NE winds appr may be difficult for smaller craft due to much backwash off the piers; confused seas can build at the ent in severe weather. The river is less industrialised and busy than of old. St Peter's Marina with usual facilities is 7·8M upriver, and 1M E of city centre. Hebburn and Friars Goose marinas have a few club berths. In emergency or as a refuge yachts may berth on Fish Quay (at W edge of chartlet) or 1M further up river in Albert Edward Dock on NW bank; contact Hr Mr. A one-off £10 conservancy fee may be levied by the Port Authority on all visiting craft.

NAVIGATION
WPT 55°01'·00N 01°22'·22W, 078°/258° from/to front ldg lt, 2·2M. From S, no dangers. From N, beware Bellhues Rk (approx 1M N of hbr and ¾M off shore); give N pier a wide berth. Dredged chan in Lower Hbr is buoyed.

The six bridges at Newcastle have least clearance 25m, or 4m when swing bridge closed.

LIGHTS AND MARKS
Ldg lts 258°, FW 25/39m 20M, two W trs; but disregard once inside pier heads. Castle conspic on cliff, N of ent. Ent to St Peter's marina is on N bank, 500m beyond Fl (G) 10s on G pile structure with platform.

RADIO TELEPHONE
Call: *Tyne Hbr Radio* VHF Ch **12** 16 11 14 (H24). St Peter's Marina Ch **80** M.

TELEPHONE (Dial code 0191)
Hr Mr 257 2080, ➤ 258 3238; MRSC 257 2691; ⊞ 257 9441; Marinecall 0891 500453; Met 2326453; Police 232 3451; Dr via Tyne Hbr Radio 257 2080; Ⓗ (Tynemouth) 259 6660; Ⓗ (Newcastle) 232 5131.

FACILITIES
St Peter's Marina (140 + 20 Ⓥ) ☎ 265 4472, ➤ 276 2618; £10.52. Access approx HW±3½ over sill 0·8m below CD; 2·5m retained within; traffic lts at ent; AC, FW, Ⓞ. Close E of ent a waiting pontoon in 2m also has D & P.
Hebburn Marina (50) ☎ 483 2876, FW, Slip; **Friars Goose Marina** (50) ☎ 469 2545, FW, ME, EI, CH, Slip;
Tynemouth SC ☎ 2529157; **South Shields SC** ☎ 4565821;
Services: Slip, M, L, FW, ME, EI, Sh, C, CH, AB, ACA, Ⓔ.
City EC Wed; All amenities, ⇌ (Newcastle/S Shields), ✈ (Newcastle). North Sea ferries as in 10.0.4.

ADJACENT HARBOUR

CULLERCOATS, Tyne and Wear, 55°02'·07N 01°25'·71W. AC 1191. +0430 Dover. Tides as 10.5.18. Small drying hbr 1·6M N of R Tyne ent. Appr on ldg line 256°, two bns (FR lts), between drying rks. An occas fair weather ⚓ or dry against S pier. Facilities at Tynemouth.

ENGLAND – NORTH SHIELDS

LAT 55°01′N   LONG   1°26′W

TIMES AND HEIGHTS OF HIGH AND LOW WATERS   YEAR **1998**

TIME ZONE (UT)
For Summer Time add ONE hour in non-shaded areas

5

JANUARY

Day	Time	m	Time	m		Day	Time	m	Time	m
1 TH	0456 / 1109 / 1705 / 2338	5.1 / 0.9 / 5.2 / 0.7				**16** F	0535 / 1136 / 1741	4.8 / 1.3 / 5.0		
2 F	0541 / 1151 / 1749	5.0 / 1.0 / 5.2				**17** SA	0009 / 0611 / 1208 / 1816	1.0 / 4.7 / 1.4 / 4.8		
3 SA	0024 / 0629 / 1237 / 1836	0.7 / 4.9 / 1.2 / 5.1				**18** SU	0043 / 0649 / 1242 / 1855	1.2 / 4.5 / 1.6 / 4.6		
4 SU	0113 / 0721 / 1326 / 1929	0.8 / 4.7 / 1.4 / 4.9				**19** M	0120 / 0729 / 1319 / 1939	1.3 / 4.3 / 1.8 / 4.4		
5 M	0207 / 0819 / 1423 / 2029	1.0 / 4.6 / 1.5 / 4.7				**20** TU	0203 / 0816 / 1406 / 2029	1.6 / 4.1 / 2.0 / 4.2		
6 TU	0308 / 0924 / 1530 / 2138	1.2 / 4.4 / 1.7 / 4.6				**21** W	0255 / 0910 / 1506 / 2128	1.8 / 4.0 / 2.1 / 4.1		
7 W	0418 / 1034 / 1646 / 2253	1.4 / 4.4 / 1.7 / 4.5				**22** TH	0358 / 1014 / 1624 / 2238	1.9 / 3.9 / 2.2 / 4.0		
8 TH	0533 / 1144 / 1803	1.4 / 4.4 / 1.6				**23** F	0511 / 1123 / 1746 / 2350	1.9 / 4.0 / 2.1 / 4.1		
9 F	0006 / 0642 / 1248 / 1909	4.6 / 1.4 / 4.6 / 1.4				**24** SA	0620 / 1227 / 1853	1.8 / 4.2 / 1.9		
10 SA	0111 / 0741 / 1343 / 2007	4.7 / 1.3 / 4.6 / 1.2				**25** SU	0054 / 0716 / 1321 / 1945	4.3 / 1.6 / 4.4 / 1.6		
11 SU	0207 / 0831 / 1431 / 2057	4.8 / 1.2 / 4.9 / 1.0				**26** M	0147 / 0805 / 1406 / 2032	4.5 / 1.4 / 4.7 / 1.2		
12 M O	0256 / 0914 / 1513 / 2141	4.9 / 1.1 / 5.1 / 0.9				**27** TU	0233 / 0849 / 1448 / 2116	4.8 / 1.1 / 5.0 / 0.9		
13 TU	0339 / 0954 / 1552 / 2222	5.0 / 1.1 / 5.1 / 0.8				**28** W ●	0316 / 0932 / 1527 / 2159	5.0 / 0.9 / 5.2 / 0.6		
14 W	0419 / 1030 / 1629 / 2300	5.0 / 1.1 / 5.1 / 0.8				**29** TH	0359 / 1014 / 1608 / 2243	5.2 / 0.8 / 5.3 / 0.4		
15 TH	0458 / 1104 / 1705 / 2335	4.9 / 1.2 / 5.1 / 0.9				**30** F	0442 / 1056 / 1650 / 2327	5.2 / 0.7 / 5.4 / 0.3		
						31 SA	0526 / 1138 / 1733	5.2 / 0.7 / 5.4		

FEBRUARY

Day	Times	Heights		Day	Times	Heights
1 SU	0011 / 0612 / 1221 / 1819	0.4 / 5.1 / 0.9 / 5.3		**16** M	0011 / 0613 / 1211 / 1822	1.0 / 4.6 / 1.3 / 4.7
2 M	0056 / 0700 / 1306 / 1910	0.6 / 4.9 / 1.1 / 5.1		**17** TU	0043 / 0648 / 1243 / 1900	1.2 / 4.5 / 1.5 / 4.6
3 TU	0145 / 0753 / 1357 / 2006	0.9 / 4.6 / 1.3 / 4.8		**18** W	0119 / 0727 / 1322 / 1943	1.4 / 4.3 / 1.7 / 4.3
4 W	0240 / 0853 / 1500 / 2113	1.2 / 4.4 / 1.6 / 4.6		**19** TH	0202 / 0814 / 1411 / 2036	1.6 / 4.1 / 1.9 / 4.1
5 TH	0348 / 1003 / 1618 / 2231	1.5 / 4.2 / 1.7 / 4.4		**20** F	0257 / 0912 / 1518 / 2143	1.9 / 3.9 / 2.1 / 4.0
6 F	0508 / 1119 / 1745 / 2353	1.7 / 4.2 / 1.7 / 4.3		**21** SA	0411 / 1024 / 1647 / 2302	2.0 / 3.9 / 2.1 / 3.9
7 SA	0627 / 1231 / 1901	1.7 / 4.4 / 1.5		**22** SU	0535 / 1141 / 1814	1.9 / 4.0 / 1.9
8 SU	0105 / 0731 / 1333 / 2000	4.4 / 1.6 / 4.6 / 1.3		**23** M	0020 / 0646 / 1247 / 1918	4.1 / 1.7 / 4.3 / 1.5
9 M	0203 / 0821 / 1422 / 2049	4.6 / 1.4 / 4.8 / 1.1		**24** TU	0122 / 0742 / 1340 / 2010	4.4 / 1.4 / 4.6 / 1.1
10 TU	0249 / 0903 / 1503 / 2130	4.7 / 1.3 / 4.9 / 0.9		**25** W	0212 / 0829 / 1425 / 2057	4.7 / 1.1 / 4.9 / 0.9
11 W O	0328 / 0939 / 1539 / 2206	4.8 / 1.2 / 5.0 / 0.8		**26** TH ●	0258 / 0914 / 1507 / 2142	5.0 / 0.8 / 5.2 / 0.4
12 TH	0404 / 1012 / 1612 / 2239	4.9 / 1.1 / 5.1 / 0.8		**27** F	0341 / 0957 / 1549 / 2226	5.2 / 0.6 / 5.5 / 0.2
13 F	0437 / 1043 / 1644 / 2310	4.9 / 1.1 / 5.1 / 0.8		**28** SA	0424 / 1039 / 1631 / 2309	5.3 / 0.5 / 5.6 / 0.1
14 SA	0509 / 1112 / 1716 / 2340	4.8 / 1.1 / 5.0 / 0.9				
15 SU	0541 / 1141 / 1748	4.7 / 1.2 / 4.9				

MARCH

Day	Times	Heights		Day	Times	Heights
1 SU	0507 / 1120 / 1715 / 2352	5.3 / 0.5 / 5.6 / 0.2		**16** M	0511 / 1115 / 1721 / 2340	4.8 / 1.0 / 4.9 / 0.9
2 M	0551 / 1202 / 1802	5.2 / 0.6 / 5.4		**17** TU	0541 / 1144 / 1754	4.7 / 1.1 / 4.7
3 TU	0036 / 0637 / 1247 / 1851	0.4 / 5.0 / 0.8 / 5.2		**18** W	0010 / 0613 / 1216 / 1829	1.1 / 4.6 / 1.2 / 4.6
4 W	0122 / 0727 / 1336 / 1947	0.8 / 4.7 / 1.1 / 4.8		**19** TH	0044 / 0649 / 1252 / 1910	1.3 / 4.4 / 1.4 / 4.4
5 TH	0214 / 0824 / 1436 / 2053	1.2 / 4.4 / 1.4 / 4.5		**20** F	0122 / 0732 / 1337 / 2000	1.5 / 4.2 / 1.6 / 4.1
6 F	0319 / 0933 / 1555 / 2213	1.6 / 4.2 / 1.7 / 4.2		**21** SA	0213 / 0827 / 1439 / 2106	1.8 / 4.0 / 1.8 / 4.0
7 SA	0444 / 1053 / 1729 / 2339	1.9 / 4.1 / 1.7 / 4.1		**22** SU	0324 / 0937 / 1604 / 2227	2.0 / 3.9 / 1.9 / 3.9
8 SU	0612 / 1212 / 1849	1.9 / 4.2 / 1.5		**23** M	0455 / 1058 / 1736 / 2349	2.0 / 4.0 / 1.7 / 4.1
9 M	0054 / 0718 / 1317 / 1948	4.3 / 1.7 / 4.4 / 1.3		**24** TU	0616 / 1212 / 1849	1.7 / 4.2 / 1.4
10 TU	0151 / 0807 / 1406 / 2033	4.4 / 1.5 / 4.6 / 1.1		**25** W	0056 / 0716 / 1311 / 1945	4.4 / 1.4 / 4.6 / 0.9
11 W	0234 / 0846 / 1446 / 2110	4.6 / 1.3 / 4.8 / 0.9		**26** TH	0149 / 0806 / 1359 / 2034	4.7 / 1.0 / 4.9 / 0.5
12 TH	0310 / 0921 / 1519 / 2143	4.7 / 1.2 / 4.9 / 0.8		**27** F	0236 / 0852 / 1444 / 2120	5.1 / 0.7 / 5.3 / 0.2
13 F O	0342 / 0950 / 1551 / 2213	4.8 / 1.1 / 5.0 / 0.7		**28** SA ●	0319 / 0936 / 1527 / 2205	5.3 / 0.5 / 5.5 / 0.0
14 SA	0412 / 1019 / 1620 / 2242	4.8 / 1.0 / 5.0 / 0.7		**29** SU	0402 / 1019 / 1611 / 2248	5.4 / 0.3 / 5.6 / 0.0
15 SU	0442 / 1047 / 1650 / 2311	4.8 / 1.0 / 5.0 / 0.8		**30** M	0445 / 1101 / 1656 / 2331	5.3 / 0.3 / 5.5 / 0.2
				31 TU	0528 / 1145 / 1744	5.2 / 0.4 / 5.4

APRIL

Day	Times	Heights		Day	Times	Heights
1 W	0014 / 0613 / 1230 / 1835	0.5 / 5.0 / 0.7 / 5.1		**16** TH	0545 / 1156 / 1807	4.6 / 1.1 / 4.5
2 TH	0059 / 0702 / 1320 / 1931	0.9 / 4.7 / 1.0 / 4.7		**17** F	0016 / 0621 / 1234 / 1849	1.2 / 4.5 / 1.2 / 4.4
3 F	0149 / 0757 / 1419 / 2036	1.3 / 4.4 / 1.3 / 4.3		**18** SA	0056 / 0704 / 1319 / 1940	1.4 / 4.3 / 1.4 / 4.2
4 SA	0252 / 0903 / 1534 / 2153	1.7 / 4.1 / 1.5 / 4.1		**19** SU	0145 / 0757 / 1419 / 2044	1.6 / 4.2 / 1.6 / 4.0
5 SU	0415 / 1022 / 1705 / 2317	2.0 / 4.0 / 1.6 / 4.0		**20** M	0254 / 0905 / 1537 / 2201	1.8 / 4.0 / 1.6 / 4.0
6 M	0545 / 1143 / 1825	2.0 / 4.1 / 1.5		**21** TU	0421 / 1022 / 1703 / 2321	1.9 / 4.0 / 1.5 / 4.1
7 TU	0031 / 0653 / 1250 / 1922	4.1 / 1.8 / 4.2 / 1.3		**22** W	0543 / 1137 / 1817	1.7 / 4.3 / 1.2
8 W	0126 / 0742 / 1340 / 2006	4.3 / 1.6 / 4.4 / 1.1		**23** TH	0028 / 0646 / 1240 / 1916	4.4 / 1.4 / 4.6 / 0.8
9 TH	0208 / 0820 / 1420 / 2041	4.5 / 1.4 / 4.6 / 1.0		**24** F	0124 / 0740 / 1332 / 2008	4.7 / 1.0 / 4.9 / 0.5
10 F	0243 / 0853 / 1453 / 2113	4.6 / 1.2 / 4.7 / 0.9		**25** SA	0212 / 0828 / 1420 / 2056	5.0 / 0.7 / 5.2 / 0.2
11 SA O	0315 / 0924 / 1525 / 2143	4.7 / 1.1 / 4.8 / 0.8		**26** SU ●	0256 / 0914 / 1506 / 2142	5.2 / 0.5 / 5.4 / 0.1
12 SU	0344 / 0954 / 1555 / 2213	4.8 / 0.9 / 4.9 / 0.7		**27** M	0339 / 0959 / 1552 / 2226	5.3 / 0.3 / 5.5 / 0.1
13 M	0414 / 1023 / 1626 / 2243	4.8 / 0.9 / 4.9 / 0.8		**28** TU	0422 / 1044 / 1640 / 2310	5.3 / 0.3 / 5.4 / 0.3
14 TU	0443 / 1053 / 1658 / 2312	4.8 / 0.9 / 4.8 / 0.9		**29** W	0506 / 1129 / 1729 / 2353	5.2 / 0.4 / 5.2 / 0.6
15 W	0513 / 1123 / 1731 / 2343	4.7 / 1.0 / 4.7 / 1.0		**30** TH	0552 / 1215 / 1821	5.0 / 0.6 / 4.9

Chart Datum: 2·60 metres below Ordnance Datum (Newlyn)

ENGLAND – NORTH SHIELDS

LAT 55°01′N   LONG 1°26′W

TIMES AND HEIGHTS OF HIGH AND LOW WATERS

YEAR 1998

TIME ZONE (UT)
For Summer Time add ONE hour in non-shaded areas

MAY

Date	Time	m	Time	m	Time	m	Time	m
1 F	0037	1.0	0639	4.7	1305	0.9	1915	4.6
2 SA	0125	1.4	0732	4.5	1401	1.1	2016	4.3
3 SU	0222	1.7	0832	4.2	1508	1.4	2124	4.0
4 M	0335	2.0	0943	4.0	1625	1.5	2239	3.9
5 TU	0459	2.0	1100	4.0	1741	1.5	2350	4.0
6 W	0611	1.9	1208	4.1	1841	1.4		
7 TH	0048	4.2	0704	1.7	1302	4.3	1927	1.2
8 F	0133	4.3	0745	1.5	1345	4.4	2004	1.1
9 SA	0210	4.5	0822	1.3	1422	4.6	2039	1.0
10 SU	0244	4.6	0855	1.1	1457	4.7	2112	0.9
11 M O	0315	4.8	0928	1.0	1530	4.7	2144	0.8
12 TU	0346	4.8	1001	0.9	1603	4.8	2216	0.8
13 W	0418	4.8	1033	0.9	1637	4.7	2249	0.9
14 TH	0450	4.8	1107	0.9	1713	4.7	2322	1.0
15 F	0524	4.7	1143	0.9	1752	4.6	2358	1.1
16 SA	0602	4.6	1223	1.0	1836	4.4		
17 SU	0040	1.3	0646	4.5	1311	1.1	1927	4.3
18 M	0131	1.5	0738	4.3	1408	1.3	2028	4.2
19 TU	0234	1.7	0841	4.2	1517	1.3	2139	4.1
20 W	0351	1.7	0952	4.2	1633	1.2	2252	4.2
21 TH	0508	1.6	1105	4.4	1745	1.0	2359	4.4
22 F	0615	1.4	1210	4.6	1848	0.8		
23 SA	0057	4.7	0712	1.1	1307	4.9	1943	0.6
24 SU	0148	4.9	0805	0.8	1359	5.1	2034	0.4
25 M ●	0235	5.1	0854	0.6	1449	5.2	2121	0.4
26 TU	0319	5.2	0942	0.4	1537	5.3	2207	0.4
27 W	0403	5.2	1029	0.4	1626	5.2	2251	0.6
28 TH	0447	5.1	1116	0.4	1716	5.0	2334	0.8
29 F	0532	5.0	1202	0.6	1806	4.8		
30 SA	0016	1.1	0617	4.8	1249	0.8	1856	4.5
31 SU	0101	1.4	0706	4.6	1338	1.0	1949	4.3

JUNE

Date	Time	m	Time	m	Time	m	Time	m
1 M	0149	1.7	0759	4.3	1432	1.3	2047	4.1
2 TU	0246	1.9	0859	4.1	1534	1.5	2150	3.9
3 W	0356	2.0	1005	4.0	1641	1.5	2256	3.9
4 TH	0510	2.0	1113	4.0	1744	1.5	2357	4.0
5 F	0614	1.9	1213	4.1	1838	1.4		
6 SA	0049	4.2	0704	1.7	1305	4.2	1924	1.3
7 SU	0133	4.4	0747	1.5	1349	4.4	2004	1.2
8 M	0211	4.5	0826	1.3	1428	4.5	2042	1.1
9 TU	0247	4.7	0903	1.1	1505	4.6	2118	1.0
10 W O	0321	4.8	0939	1.0	1542	4.7	2154	0.9
11 TH	0355	4.8	1016	0.9	1619	4.7	2230	0.9
12 F	0430	4.9	1053	0.8	1658	4.7	2307	1.0
13 SA	0506	4.9	1133	0.8	1739	4.7	2346	1.0
14 SU	0547	4.8	1215	0.8	1824	4.6		
15 M	0029	1.2	0631	4.7	1303	0.9	1914	4.5
16 TU	0118	1.3	0722	4.6	1356	1.0	2011	4.4
17 W	0215	1.5	0820	4.5	1456	1.1	2115	4.3
18 TH	0321	1.6	0925	4.4	1604	1.1	2223	4.3
19 F	0433	1.5	1117	4.5	1715	1.1	2331	4.4
20 SA	0544	1.4	1144	4.6	1822	1.0		
21 SU	0032	4.6	0649	1.2	1248	4.7	1922	0.9
22 M	0128	4.8	0747	1.0	1345	4.9	2016	0.8
23 TU	0217	4.9	0840	0.8	1438	5.0	2105	0.7
24 W ●	0303	5.1	0930	0.6	1528	5.1	2151	0.6
25 TH	0347	5.1	1018	0.5	1616	5.0	2234	0.8
26 F	0430	5.1	1103	0.5	1702	4.9	2315	0.9
27 SA	0513	5.0	1146	0.6	1747	4.8	2354	1.1
28 SU	0555	4.9	1227	0.8	1832	4.6		
29 M	0032	1.3	0637	4.7	1309	1.0	1916	4.4
30 TU	0112	1.5	0723	4.5	1352	1.2	2004	4.2

JULY

Date	Time	m	Time	m	Time	m	Time	m
1 W	0157	1.7	0812	4.3	1440	1.4	2056	4.0
2 TH	0251	1.9	0908	4.1	1537	1.6	2154	4.0
3 F	0358	2.0	1010	4.0	1640	1.7	2256	4.0
4 SA	0511	2.0	1117	4.0	1744	1.7	2357	4.1
5 SU	0618	1.9	1219	4.1	1842	1.6		
6 M	0051	4.2	0712	1.7	1314	4.3	1931	1.4
7 TU	0138	4.4	0758	1.4	1400	4.4	2014	1.3
8 W	0219	4.6	0840	1.2	1442	4.6	2055	1.1
9 TH O	0257	4.8	0920	1.0	1522	4.7	2134	1.0
10 F	0334	4.9	1000	0.8	1602	4.8	2213	0.9
11 SA	0411	5.0	1040	0.6	1642	4.9	2253	0.9
12 SU	0450	5.1	1122	0.6	1725	4.9	2334	0.9
13 M	0531	5.1	1205	0.6	1809	4.9		
14 TU	0016	1.0	0615	5.0	1250	0.6	1857	4.7
15 W	0102	1.1	0703	4.9	1339	0.8	1949	4.6
16 TH	0153	1.3	0758	4.8	1433	1.0	2048	4.4
17 F	0253	1.4	0900	4.6	1537	1.1	2154	4.3
18 SA	0403	1.5	1010	4.5	1648	1.3	2304	4.3
19 SU	0520	1.5	1125	4.5	1802	1.3		
20 M	0012	4.4	0633	1.4	1236	4.6	1908	1.2
21 TU	0113	4.6	0737	1.2	1339	4.7	2004	1.1
22 W	0206	4.8	0832	0.9	1433	4.8	2053	1.0
23 TH ●	0252	5.0	0922	0.7	1520	4.9	2137	1.0
24 F	0334	5.1	1006	0.6	1604	5.0	2217	1.0
25 SA	0414	5.1	1047	0.6	1644	4.9	2254	1.0
26 SU	0452	5.1	1125	0.6	1724	4.8	2328	1.1
27 M	0529	5.0	1200	0.8	1802	4.7		
28 TU	0001	1.2	0606	4.8	1235	0.9	1839	4.5
29 W	0035	1.4	0645	4.7	1311	1.1	1919	4.4
30 TH	0112	1.6	0723	4.5	1351	1.4	2003	4.2
31 F	0156	1.8	0816	4.3	1439	1.6	2054	4.1

AUGUST

Date	Time	m	Time	m	Time	m	Time	m
1 SA	0252	2.0	0913	4.1	1537	1.8	2154	4.0
2 SU	0404	2.1	1019	4.0	1647	1.9	2301	4.0
3 M	0525	2.0	1132	4.0	1758	1.8		
4 TU	0007	4.1	0635	1.8	1239	4.1	1858	1.7
5 W	0104	4.3	0731	1.6	1334	4.4	1949	1.4
6 TH	0151	4.6	0817	1.3	1420	4.6	2033	1.2
7 F	0232	4.8	0900	1.0	1502	4.8	2114	1.0
8 SA O	0311	5.0	0942	0.7	1543	5.0	2155	0.8
9 SU	0350	5.2	1023	0.5	1624	5.1	2236	0.7
10 M	0430	5.3	1105	0.3	1706	5.2	2317	0.7
11 TU	0511	5.4	1148	0.3	1749	5.1	2359	0.8
12 W	0555	5.3	1231	0.4	1835	5.0		
13 TH	0042	0.9	0643	5.2	1318	0.7	1925	4.7
14 F	0130	1.2	0736	4.9	1409	1.0	2021	4.5
15 SA	0227	1.4	0838	4.7	1510	1.3	2126	4.3
16 SU	0339	1.6	0952	4.4	1625	1.6	2240	4.3
17 M	0504	1.6	1114	4.4	1748	1.6	2355	4.4
18 TU	0625	1.5	1231	4.4	1859	1.5		
19 W	0101	4.5	0732	1.2	1336	4.6	1956	1.4
20 TH	0156	4.8	0825	1.0	1427	4.8	2042	1.3
21 F	0240	4.9	0910	0.8	1510	4.9	2122	1.1
22 SA ●	0319	5.1	0949	0.7	1547	4.9	2157	1.1
23 SU	0355	5.1	1025	0.6	1622	5.0	2230	1.0
24 M	0428	5.1	1058	0.7	1656	4.9	2301	1.1
25 TU	0502	5.1	1129	0.8	1729	4.8	2331	1.2
26 W	0535	5.0	1159	0.9	1802	4.7		
27 TH	0001	1.3	0610	4.8	1232	1.1	1837	4.5
28 F	0034	1.5	0648	4.6	1307	1.3	1916	4.4
29 SA	0112	1.7	0732	4.4	1348	1.6	2002	4.2
30 SU	0201	1.9	0825	4.1	1441	1.9	2058	4.0
31 M	0306	2.1	0930	4.0	1551	2.0	2206	4.0

Chart Datum: 2·60 metres below Ordnance Datum (Newlyn)

ENGLAND – NORTH SHIELDS

LAT 55°01′N   LONG 1°26′W

TIMES AND HEIGHTS OF HIGH AND LOW WATERS   YEAR **1998**

TIME ZONE (UT)
For Summer Time add ONE hour in non-shaded areas

SEPTEMBER

Day	Time	m	Day	Time	m
1 TU	0431 / 1047 / 1714 / 2321	2.1 / 3.9 / 2.0 / 4.0	**16** W	0617 / 1224 / 1848	1.5 / 4.4 / 1.8
2 W	0558 / 1204 / 1827	1.9 / 4.1 / 1.8	**17** TH	0047 / 0722 / 1327 / 1943	4.5 / 1.3 / 4.5 / 1.6
3 TH	0028 / 0702 / 1307 / 1923	4.3 / 1.6 / 4.3 / 1.6	**18** F	0141 / 0811 / 1414 / 2025	4.7 / 1.1 / 4.7 / 1.4
4 F	0122 / 0752 / 1356 / 2010	4.6 / 1.2 / 4.7 / 1.3	**19** SA	0224 / 0852 / 1452 / 2101	4.9 / 0.9 / 4.9 / 1.2
5 SA	0206 / 0837 / 1439 / 2053	4.9 / 0.9 / 5.0 / 1.0	**20** SU	0300 / 0926 / 1525 / ● 2133	5.0 / 0.8 / 4.9 / 1.1
6 SU	0246 / 0920 / 1521 / O 2134	5.2 / 0.5 / 5.2 / 0.8	**21** M	0332 / 0957 / 1556 / 2204	5.1 / 0.7 / 5.0 / 1.1
7 M	0326 / 1002 / 1601 / 2215	5.4 / 0.3 / 5.3 / 0.6	**22** TU	0403 / 1027 / 1627 / 2233	5.1 / 0.7 / 5.0 / 1.0
8 TU	0407 / 1044 / 1643 / 2256	5.6 / 0.2 / 5.4 / 0.6	**23** W	0434 / 1057 / 1657 / 2303	5.1 / 0.8 / 4.9 / 1.1
9 W	0449 / 1127 / 1726 / 2338	5.6 / 0.2 / 5.3 / 0.6	**24** TH	0506 / 1126 / 1728 / 2332	5.0 / 0.9 / 4.8 / 1.2
10 TH	0534 / 1209 / 1811	5.5 / 0.4 / 5.1	**25** F	0540 / 1156 / 1801	4.8 / 1.1 / 4.7
11 F	0022 / 0623 / 1254 / 1859	0.8 / 5.3 / 0.7 / 4.9	**26** SA	0004 / 0616 / 1229 / 1836	1.4 / 4.7 / 1.3 / 4.5
12 SA	0110 / 0717 / 1344 / 1954	1.1 / 5.0 / 1.1 / 4.6	**27** SU	0040 / 0657 / 1307 / 1918	1.5 / 4.4 / 1.6 / 4.3
13 SU	0207 / 0821 / 1446 / 2100	1.4 / 4.6 / 1.5 / 4.3	**28** M	0124 / 0747 / 1354 / 2011	1.8 / 4.2 / 1.9 / 4.1
14 M	0321 / 0938 / 1605 / 2217	1.6 / 4.3 / 1.8 / 4.2	**29** TU	0224 / 0850 / 1502 / 2117	2.0 / 4.0 / 2.1 / 4.0
15 TU	0452 / 1104 / 1735 / 2338	1.7 / 4.3 / 1.9 / 4.3	**30** W	0346 / 1008 / 1630 / 2236	2.0 / 3.9 / 2.1 / 4.0

OCTOBER

Day	Time	m	Day	Time	m
1 TH	0517 / 1130 / 1753 / 2350	1.9 / 4.1 / 2.0 / 4.3	**16** F	0023 / 0700 / 1305 / 1920	4.4 / 1.3 / 4.5 / 1.7
2 F	0629 / 1236 / 1854	1.6 / 4.4 / 1.6	**17** SA	0118 / 0747 / 1350 / 2002	4.6 / 1.2 / 4.7 / 1.5
3 SA	0048 / 0723 / 1329 / 1943	4.6 / 1.2 / 4.7 / 1.3	**18** SU	0200 / 0825 / 1427 / 2036	4.8 / 1.0 / 4.8 / 1.3
4 SU	0137 / 0810 / 1414 / 2027	4.9 / 0.8 / 5.1 / 1.0	**19** M	0236 / 0903 / 1459 / 2108	4.9 / 0.9 / 4.9 / 1.2
5 M	0220 / 0854 / 1456 / O 2110	5.3 / 0.4 / 5.3 / 0.7	**20** TU	0308 / 0927 / 1529 / ● 2138	5.0 / 0.9 / 5.0 / 1.1
6 TU	0301 / 0938 / 1537 / 2152	5.5 / 0.2 / 5.5 / 0.5	**21** W	0339 / 0957 / 1559 / 2208	5.1 / 0.9 / 5.0 / 1.1
7 W	0344 / 1021 / 1619 / 2235	5.7 / 0.1 / 5.5 / 0.5	**22** TH	0410 / 1027 / 1628 / 2238	5.0 / 0.9 / 5.0 / 1.1
8 TH	0428 / 1104 / 1701 / 2318	5.7 / 0.2 / 5.4 / 0.5	**23** F	0442 / 1057 / 1658 / 2309	5.0 / 1.0 / 4.9 / 1.2
9 F	0515 / 1147 / 1746	5.5 / 0.5 / 5.2	**24** SA	0515 / 1147 / 1730 / 2341	4.8 / 1.2 / 4.8 / 1.3
10 SA	0004 / 0605 / 1232 / 1834	0.7 / 5.3 / 0.9 / 4.9	**25** SU	0551 / 1159 / 1805	4.7 / 1.4 / 4.6
11 SU	0054 / 0702 / 1322 / 1929	1.0 / 4.9 / 1.3 / 4.6	**26** M	0017 / 0631 / 1236 / 1845	1.4 / 4.5 / 1.6 / 4.5
12 M	0152 / 0806 / 1423 / 2034	1.3 / 4.5 / 1.7 / 4.4	**27** TU	0101 / 0720 / 1321 / 1935	1.6 / 4.3 / 1.8 / 4.3
13 TU	0306 / 0923 / 1542 / 2151	1.5 / 4.3 / 2.0 / 4.2	**28** W	0157 / 0820 / 1425 / 2038	1.8 / 4.1 / 2.1 / 4.1
14 W	0434 / 1047 / 1713 / 2313	1.6 / 4.2 / 2.1 / 4.3	**29** TH	0311 / 0934 / 1548 / 2154	1.9 / 4.0 / 2.1 / 4.1
15 TH	0557 / 1205 / 1827	1.5 / 4.3 / 1.9	**30** F	0435 / 1054 / 1713 / 2309	1.8 / 4.1 / 2.0 / 4.3
			31 SA	0551 / 1203 / 1820	1.5 / 4.4 / 1.7

NOVEMBER

Day	Time	m	Day	Time	m
1 SU	0013 / 0650 / 1259 / 1913	4.6 / 1.1 / 4.8 / 1.3	**16** M	0130 / 0751 / 1356 / 2008	4.6 / 1.3 / 4.7 / 1.5
2 M	0106 / 0741 / 1347 / 2001	5.0 / 0.8 / 5.1 / 1.0	**17** TU	0208 / 0825 / 1430 / 2042	4.8 / 1.2 / 4.8 / 1.3
3 TU	0153 / 0828 / 1431 / 2046	5.3 / 0.5 / 5.3 / 0.8	**18** W	0243 / 0858 / 1502 / 2115	4.9 / 1.1 / 4.9 / 1.2
4 W	0238 / 0914 / 1513 / O 2131	5.5 / 0.3 / 5.4 / 0.6	**19** TH	0316 / 0930 / 1533 / ● 2147	4.9 / 1.0 / 5.0 / 1.1
5 TH	0324 / 0959 / 1556 / 2216	5.6 / 0.3 / 5.5 / 0.5	**20** F	0349 / 1001 / 1603 / 2219	4.9 / 1.0 / 5.0 / 1.1
6 F	0411 / 1043 / 1639 / 2302	5.6 / 0.4 / 5.4 / 0.5	**21** SA	0422 / 1033 / 1634 / 2251	4.9 / 1.1 / 4.9 / 1.1
7 SA	0500 / 1127 / 1725 / 2350	5.5 / 0.7 / 5.2 / 0.7	**22** SU	0457 / 1104 / 1707 / 2325	4.8 / 1.1 / 4.9 / 1.2
8 SU	0552 / 1212 / 1813	5.2 / 1.0 / 5.0	**23** M	0533 / 1138 / 1742	4.7 / 1.4 / 4.8
9 M	0041 / 0648 / 1301 / 1906	0.9 / 4.9 / 1.4 / 4.7	**24** TU	0003 / 0614 / 1216 / 1822	1.3 / 4.6 / 1.5 / 4.6
10 TU	0138 / 0750 / 1358 / 2006	1.2 / 4.5 / 1.8 / 4.5	**25** W	0046 / 0701 / 1301 / 1910	1.4 / 4.4 / 1.7 / 4.5
11 W	0244 / 0859 / 1509 / 2118	1.4 / 4.3 / 2.1 / 4.4	**26** TH	0139 / 0757 / 1358 / 2008	1.5 / 4.3 / 1.9 / 4.4
12 TH	0400 / 1014 / 1632 / 2235	1.6 / 4.1 / 2.2 / 4.3	**27** F	0243 / 0904 / 1510 / 2116	1.6 / 4.2 / 2.0 / 4.3
13 F	0519 / 1128 / 1749 / 2346	1.6 / 4.2 / 2.1 / 4.3	**28** SA	0357 / 1017 / 1630 / 2228	1.6 / 4.2 / 1.9 / 4.4
14 SA	0623 / 1229 / 1847	1.5 / 4.3 / 1.9	**29** SU	0511 / 1127 / 1741 / 2337	1.4 / 4.4 / 1.7 / 4.6
15 SU	0044 / 0712 / 1317 / 1930	4.5 / 1.4 / 4.5 / 1.7	**30** M	0616 / 1228 / 1842	1.2 / 4.7 / 1.4

DECEMBER

Day	Time	m	Day	Time	m
1 TU	0036 / 0713 / 1321 / 1936	4.9 / 0.9 / 4.9 / 1.1	**16** W	0139 / 0753 / 1401 / 2016	4.5 / 1.4 / 4.6 / 1.5
2 W	0130 / 0805 / 1408 / 2026	5.2 / 0.7 / 5.2 / 0.9	**17** TH	0219 / 0831 / 1437 / 2053	4.7 / 1.3 / 4.8 / 1.4
3 TH	0221 / 0854 / 1453 / O 2115	5.3 / 0.6 / 5.3 / 0.7	**18** F	0256 / 0906 / 1510 / ● 2128	4.8 / 1.2 / 4.9 / 1.2
4 F	0310 / 0941 / 1537 / 2203	5.5 / 0.6 / 5.4 / 0.6	**19** SA	0331 / 0940 / 1542 / 2203	4.8 / 1.2 / 5.0 / 1.1
5 SA	0359 / 1026 / 1622 / 2251	5.5 / 0.7 / 5.4 / 0.5	**20** SU	0406 / 1014 / 1615 / 2237	4.8 / 1.2 / 5.0 / 1.0
6 SU	0449 / 1111 / 1707 / 2339	5.3 / 0.9 / 5.3 / 0.6	**21** M	0442 / 1048 / 1649 / 2314	4.8 / 1.2 / 5.0 / 1.0
7 M	0540 / 1155 / 1754	5.1 / 1.1 / 5.1	**22** TU	0519 / 1124 / 1725 / 2353	4.8 / 1.2 / 4.9 / 1.0
8 TU	0028 / 0632 / 1240 / 1843	0.8 / 4.8 / 1.4 / 4.9	**23** W	0559 / 1203 / 1805	4.7 / 1.3 / 4.8
9 W	0118 / 0726 / 1328 / 1936	1.1 / 4.6 / 1.7 / 4.6	**24** TH	0035 / 0644 / 1246 / 1850	1.1 / 4.6 / 1.5 / 4.7
10 TH	0212 / 0824 / 1424 / 2036	1.3 / 4.3 / 2.0 / 4.4	**25** F	0123 / 0735 / 1336 / 1942	1.2 / 4.5 / 1.6 / 4.6
11 F	0313 / 0928 / 1532 / 2143	1.6 / 4.1 / 2.1 / 4.2	**26** SA	0218 / 0834 / 1436 / 2043	1.3 / 4.4 / 1.8 / 4.6
12 SA	0420 / 1035 / 1648 / 2253	1.7 / 4.2 / 2.2 / 4.2	**27** SU	0322 / 0941 / 1547 / 2152	1.4 / 4.3 / 1.8 / 4.5
13 SU	0528 / 1139 / 1757 / 2358	1.7 / 4.1 / 2.1 / 4.3	**28** M	0433 / 1051 / 1702 / 2304	1.4 / 4.4 / 1.7 / 4.6
14 M	0626 / 1235 / 1852	1.7 / 4.3 / 1.9	**29** TU	0545 / 1158 / 1813	1.3 / 4.5 / 1.6
15 TU	0052 / 0712 / 1322 / 1936	4.4 / 1.5 / 4.5 / 1.7	**30** W	0012 / 0650 / 1258 / 1916	4.7 / 1.2 / 4.7 / 1.3
			31 TH	0115 / 0748 / 1351 / 2013	4.9 / 1.0 / 5.0 / 1.0

Chart Datum: 2·60 metres below Ordnance Datum (Newlyn)

RIVER TYNE (NORTH SHIELDS)

MEAN SPRING
AND NEAP CURVES

MEAN RANGES	
Springs	4·3m
Neaps	2·1m

Springs occur 2 days
after
New and Full Moon.

BLYTH   10-5-19

Northumberland 55°06'·98N 01° 29'·17W   Rtg 2-4-2

CHARTS
AC 1626, 152, 156; Imray C29; OS 81, 88

TIDES
+0430 Dover; ML 2·8; Duration 0558; Zone 0 (UT)

Standard Port RIVER TYNE (NORTH SHIELDS) (⟵)

Times				Height (metres)			
High Water		Low Water		MHWS	MHWN	MLWN	MLWS
0200	0800	0100	0800	5·0	3·9	1·8	0·7
1400	2000	1300	2000				
Differences BLYTH							
+0005	−0007	−0001	+0009	0·0	0·0	−0·1	+0·1

SHELTER
Very good; access H24. Yachts go to SE part of South Hbr; visitors may find berth on RNYC pontoons on E side of Middle Jetty (4·4m least depth) or pick up RNYC mooring.

NAVIGATION
WPT Fairway SHM buoy, Fl G 3s, Bell, 55°06'·58N 01°28'·50W, 140°/320° from/to E pier lt, 0·53M. From N, beware The Pigs, The Sow and Seaton Sea Rks. No dangers from S. At LW in strong SE winds, seas break across ent.

LIGHTS AND MARKS
7 wind turbines (X on chartlet) are conspic on the E pier, plus 1 just off N edge of chartlet. Outer ldg lts 324°, F Bu 11/17m 10M, Or ◊ on framework trs. Inner ldg lts 338°, F Bu 5/11m 10M, front W 6-sided tr; rear W △ on mast.

RADIO TELEPHONE
Call: Blyth Hbr Control VHF Ch 12 11 16 (H24).

TELEPHONE (Dial code 01670)
Hr Mr 352678; MRSC (0191) 257 2691; ⌗ (0191) 257 9441; Marinecall 0891 500453; Police (01661) 872555; Dr 363334.

FACILITIES
R Northumberland YC ☎ 353636, (50) AB £10, M, FW, C (1½ ton), Bar; **South Hbr** ☎ 352678, FW, C (30 ton), Slip. **Town** EC Wed; P & D (cans), V, R, Bar, ✉, Ⓑ, bus to Newcastle ⇌ ✈.

ADJACENT ANCHORAGE

NEWBIGGIN, Northumberland, 55°10'·75N 01°30'·00W. AC 156. Tides approx as for Blyth, 3·5M to the S. Temp, fair weather ⚓ in about 4m in centre of Bay, sheltered from SW to N winds. Caution: offlying rky ledges to N and S. Two pairs of framework trs (marking a measured mile) bracket the bay. Conspic church on N side of bay; bkwtr lt Fl G 10s 4M. Facilities: **SC** (dinghies). **Town** V, R, Bar.

AMBLE   10-5-20
Northumberland 55°20'·37N 01°34'·15W   Rtg 3-2-1

CHARTS
AC 1627, 156; Imray C29; OS 81

TIDES
+0412 Dover; ML 3·1; Duration 0606; Zone 0 (UT)

Standard Port RIVER TYNE (NORTH SHIELDS) (←)

Times				Height (metres)			
High Water		Low Water		MHWS	MHWN	MLWN	MLWS
0200	0800	0100	0800	5·0	3·9	1·8	0·7
1400	2000	1300	2000				
Differences AMBLE							
–0023	–0015	–0023	–0014	0·0	+0·2	+0·2	+0·1
COQUET ISLAND							
–0010	–0010	–0020	–0020	+0·1	+0·1	0·0	+0·1

SHELTER
The hbr (also known as Warkworth Hbr) is safe in all weathers, but ent is dangerous in strong N to E winds or in swell which causes heavy breakers on Pan Bush shoal and on the bar at the hbr ent; least depth 0·1m at hbr ent. Once inside the N bkwtr, beware drying banks to stbd, ie on S side of ruined N jetty; chan favours the S quays. Visitors should go to Amble marina on S bank of R Coquet, approx 5ca from ent, access HW±4 via sill (0·75m above CD); the sill is marked by PHM and ECM buoys, both unlit. 4kn speed limit in hbr.

NAVIGATION
WPT 55°21'·00N 01°33'·00W, 045°/225° from/to hbr ent, 0·9M. Ent recommended from NE, passing N and W of Pan Bush. A wreck, 3·0m, lies 1·5ca ENE of N pier hd. The S-going stream sets strongly across ent. In NE'ly gales, when broken water can extend to Coquet Island, keep E of island and go to Blyth where app/ent may be safer. Coquet Chan (min depth 0·3m) is not buoyed and should only be used with local knowledge, by day, in fair weather and with adequate rise of tide.

LIGHTS AND MARKS
Coquet Island lt ho, (conspic) W □ tr, turreted parapet, lower half grey; Fl (3) WR 30s 25m 23/19M R330°-140°, W140°-163°, R163°-180°, W180°-330°. Sector boundaries are indeterminate and may appear as Al WR. Horn 30s.

RADIO TELEPHONE
Call *Amble Marina* Ch 80 (H24). *Warkworth Hbr* VHF, listens Ch 16, works Ch 14 (Mon-Fri 0900-1700 LT). Coquet YC Ch M (occas).

TELEPHONE (Dial code 01665)
Hr Mr 710306; MRSC (0191) 257 9441; local CG 710575; ⌗ (0191) 257 9441 (H24); Marinecall 0891 500453; Ⓗ (01670) 521212.

FACILITIES
Amble Marina (210+40 visitors) ☎ 712168, £12.74, AC, BY, C, Gas, FW, D, P, R, Gaz, Slip, BH (20 ton), ME, El, Sh, Ⓔ, SM, Bar; V, CH, ▣; **Hbr** D, AB; **Coquet YC** ☎ 711179 Slip, Bar, M, FW, L; **Services**: ME, Slip, CH, El, Sh, SM, Ⓔ. **Town** EC Wed; V, R, Bar, ✉, ≠ (Alnmouth), ✈ (Newcastle).

HARBOURS AND ANCHORAGES BETWEEN AMBLE AND HOLY ISLAND

BOULMER, Northumberland, 55°25'·00N 01°33'·80W. AC 156. Tides approx as for Amble, 4·5M to the S. A small haven almost enclosed by N and S Rheins, rky ledges either side of the narrow (30m) ent, Mar mouth; only advised in settled offshore weather. 2 unlit bns lead approx 262° through the ent, leaving close to stbd a bn on N Rheins. ‡ just inside in about 1·5m or dry out on sand at the N end. Few facilities: Pub, ✉ in village. Alnwick is 4M inland.

CRASTER, Northumberland, 55°28'·40N 01°35'·20W. AC 156. Tidal differences: interpolate between Amble (10.5.20) and N Sunderland (10.5.21). Strictly a fair weather ‡ in offshore winds, 1M S of the conspic Dunstanburgh Castle (ru). The ent, 40m wide, is N of Muckle Carr and S of Little Carr which partly covers and has a bn on its S end. ‡ in about 3·5m just inshore of these 2 rocky outcrops; or berth at the E pier on rk/sand inside the tiny drying hbr. Facilities: V, R, Bar.

NEWTON HAVEN and BEADNELL BAY, Northumberland, 55°30'·90N 01° 36'·60W. AC 156. HW +0342 on Dover; Tidal differences: interpolate between Amble (10.5.20) and N Sunderland (10.5.21). ML 2·6m; Duration 0625. A safe ‡ in winds from NNW to SE via S but susceptible to swell. Ent to S of Newton PHM buoy and Newton Pt. Beware Fills Rks. ‡ between Fills Rks and Low Newton by the Sea in 4/5m. A very attractive ‡ with no lts, marks or facilities except a pub. Further ‡ S of Beadnell Pt (1M N of Newton Pt) in 4-6m; small, private hbr; Beadnell SC. Village 0·5M.

5

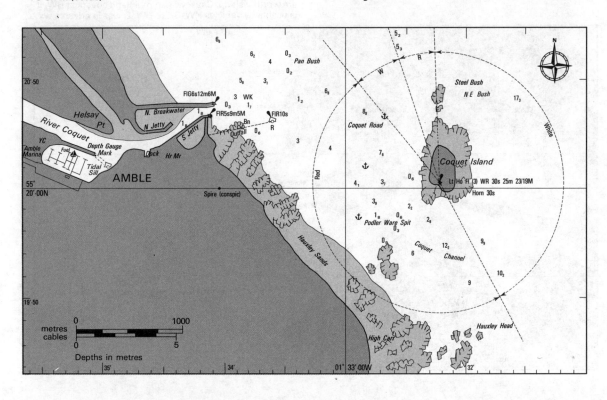

Continued

NORTH SUNDERLAND (Seahouses), Northumberland, 55°35'·04N 01°38'·81W. AC 1612. HW +0340 on Dover; ML No data; Duration 0618. See 10.5.21. Good shelter except in on-shore winds when swell makes outer hbr berths (0·7m) very uncomfortable and dangerous. Access HW±3. Inner hbr has excellent berths but usually full of FVs. Beware The Tumblers (rks) to the W of ent and rks protruding NE from bkwtr hd Fl R 2·5s 6m; NW pier hd FG 11m 3M; vis 159°-294°, on W tr; traffic sigs; Siren 90s when vessels expected. When it is dangerous to enter a Ⓡ is shown over the FG lt (or R flag over a Bu flag) on NW pier hd. Facilities: EC Wed; Gas; all facilities.

FARNE ISLANDS, Northumberland, 55°37'·00N 01°39'·00W. AC 111, 156, 160. HW +0345 on Dover; ML 2·6m; Duration 0630. See 10.5.21. The islands are a NT nature reserve in a beautiful area; they should only be attempted in good weather. Landing is only allowed on Farne Island, Staple Is and Longstone. In the inner group, ⌕ in The Kettle on the NE side of Inner Farne; near the Bridges (which connect Knocks Reef to West Wideopen); or to the S of West Wideopen. In the outer group, ⌕ in Pinnacle Haven (between Staple Is and Brownsman). Beware turbulence over Knivestone and Whirl Rks and eddy S of Longstone during NW tidal streams. Lts and marks: Black Rocks Pt, Oc (2) WRG 15s 12m 17/13M; G122°-165°, W165°-175°, R175°-191°, W191°-238°, R238°-275°, W275°-289°, G289°-300°. Bamburgh Castle is conspic 6ca to the SE. Farne Is lt ho at SW Pt, Fl (2) WR 15s 27m 8/6M; W ○ tr; R119°-280°, W280°-119°. Longstone Fl 20s 23m 24M, R tr with W band (conspic), RC, horn (2) 60s. Caution: reefs extend about 7ca seaward. No facilities.

HOLY ISLAND   10-5-21

Northumberland 55°40'·00N 01°48'·00W   Rtg 3-5-1

CHARTS
AC 1612, 111; Imray C24; OS 75
TIDES
+0344 Dover; ML No data; Duration 0630; Zone 0 (UT)

Standard Port RIVER TYNE (NORTH SHIELDS) (←)

Times				Height (metres)			
High Water		Low Water		MHWS	MHWN	MLWN	MLWS
0200	0800	0100	0800	5·0	3·9	1·8	0·7
1400	2000	1300	2000				
Differences HOLY ISLAND							
−0043	−0039	−0105	−0110	−0·2	−0·2	−0·2	0·0
NORTH SUNDERLAND (Seahouses)							
−0048	−0044	−0058	−0102	−0·7	−0·6	−0·4	−0·2

SHELTER
Good S of The Heugh in 3-6m, but ⌕ is uncomfortable in fresh W/SW winds esp at sp flood. Better shelter in The Ouse on sand/mud if able to dry out; but not in S/SE winds.
NAVIGATION
WPT 55°39'·76N 01°44'·78W, 080°/260° from/to Old Law E bn 1·55M. From N identify Emanuel Hd, conspic W △ bn, then appr via Goldstone Chan leaving Plough Seat PHM buoy to stbd. From S, clear Farne Is thence to WPT. Outer ldg bns lead 260° close past Ridge End ECM and Triton Shoal SHM buoys. Possible overfalls in chan across bar (2·1m) with sp ebb up to 4kn. Inner ldg marks lead 310° to ⌕. Inshore route, round Castle Pt via Hole Mouth and The Yares, may be more sheltered, but is not for strangers.
LIGHTS AND MARKS
Outer ldg marks/lts are Old Law bns (conspic), 2 reddish obelisks 21/25m on 260°; E bn has dir lt, Oc WRG 6s 9m 4M, G182°-2620°, W262°-264°, R264°-shore. Inner ldg marks/lts are The Heugh tr, R △, on with St Mary's ch belfry 310°. The Heugh has dir lt, Oc WRG 6s 24m 5M, G135°-308°, W308°-311°, R311°-shore. Dir lts Oc WRG are aligned on 263° and 309·5° respectively.
RADIO TELEPHONE
None.
TELEPHONE (Dial code 01289)
Hr Mr 389217; MRSC 0191-257 2691.
FACILITIES
Limited. FW on village green, R, Bar, limited V, P & D from Beal (5M); bus (occas) to Berwick. Note Lindisfarne is ancient name; Benedictine Abbey (ruins) and Castle (NT) are worth visiting. Causeway to mainland covers at HW. It is usable by vehicles HW+3½ to HW−2; less in adverse wx.

BERWICK-ON-TWEED   10-5-22

Northumberland 55°45'·87N 01°58'·95W   Rtg 3-3-2

CHARTS
AC 1612, 111, 160; OS 75

TIDES
+0348 Dover; ML 2·5; Duration 0620; Zone 0 (UT)

Standard Port RIVER TYNE (NORTH SHIELDS) (←)

Times				Height (metres)			
High Water		Low Water		MHWS	MHWN	MLWN	MLWS
0200	0800	0100	0800	5·0	3·9	1·8	0·7
1400	2000	1300	2000				
Differences BERWICK							
–0053	–0053	–0109	–0109	–0·3	–0·1	–0·5	–0·1

SHELTER
Good shelter or ⚓ except in strong E/SE winds. Yachts lie in Tweed Dock (the dock gates have been removed; 0·6m in ent, approx 1·2m inside at MLWS) or temporarily at W end of Fish Jetty (1·2m).

NAVIGATION
WPT 55°45'·65N 01°58'·00W, 114°/294° from/to bkwtr lt ho, 0·58M. On-shore winds and ebb tides cause very confused state over the bar (0·6m). Access HW ±4 at sp. From HW–2 to HW+1 strong flood tide sets S across the ent; keep well up to bkwtr. The sands at the mouth of the Tweed shift so often that local knowledge is essential. The Berwick bridge (first and lowest) has about 3m clearance.

LIGHTS AND MARKS
Town hall clock tr and lt ho in line at 294°. When past Crabwater Rk, keep bns at Spittal in line at 207°. Bns are B and Orange with △ top marks (both FR). Caution: The 207° ldg line did not clear (1997) the sands off Spittal Point which have encroached W'wards; best water is further W.

RADIO TELEPHONE
Hr Mr VHF Ch 12 16 (HO).

TELEPHONE (Dial code 01289)
Hr Mr 307404; MRSC 01333 450666; ⌗ 307547 or (01482) 782107 (H24); Marinecall 0891 500453/452; Police 307111; Dr 307484.

FACILITIES
Tweed Dock ☎ 307404, AB £4.00, M, P, D, FW, ME, El, Sh, C (Mobile 3 ton), Slip, SM.
Town EC Thurs; P, V, R, Bar, ⊠, ⑧, ⇌ and ✈ (Newcastle or Edinburgh).

AGENTS WANTED
If you are interested in becoming our agent for any of the following ports, please write to: The Editor, Edington House, Trent, Sherborne, Dorset DT9 4SR, England – and get your free copy of the Almanac annually. You do not have to live in a port to be the agent, but at least a fairly regular visitor.

Great Yarmouth	St Gilles-Croix-de-Vie
Port Ellen (Islay)	Les Sables d'Olonne
Maryport	Ile d'Oléron
Workington	River Seudre
Holyhead	Anglet/Bayonne
Lough Swilly	St Jean-de-Luz
St Peter Port, Guernsey	Hendaye
Diélette	Grandcamp-Maisy
Portbail	Port-en-Bessin
Iles Chausey	Courseulles
St Malo/Dinard	Ouistreham/Caen
Le Legue/St Brieuc	Emden
Tréguier	Dornumer-Accumersiel
Lampaul	Langeoog
L'Aberildut	Bremerhaven
Le Palais (Belle Ile)	Büsum
Morbihan/Vannes	

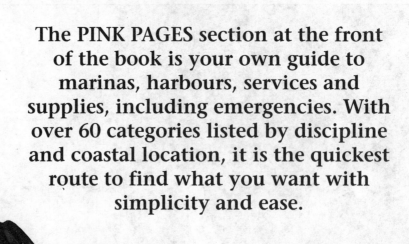

VOLVO PENTA SERVICE

Sales and service centres in area 6

LOTHIAN *Ferry Marine Ltd*, Port Edgar Marina, South Queensferry, Nr. Edinburgh EH30 9SQ Tel 0131-331 1233

VOLVO PENTA

Area 6

South-East Scotland
Eyemouth to Rattray Head

6

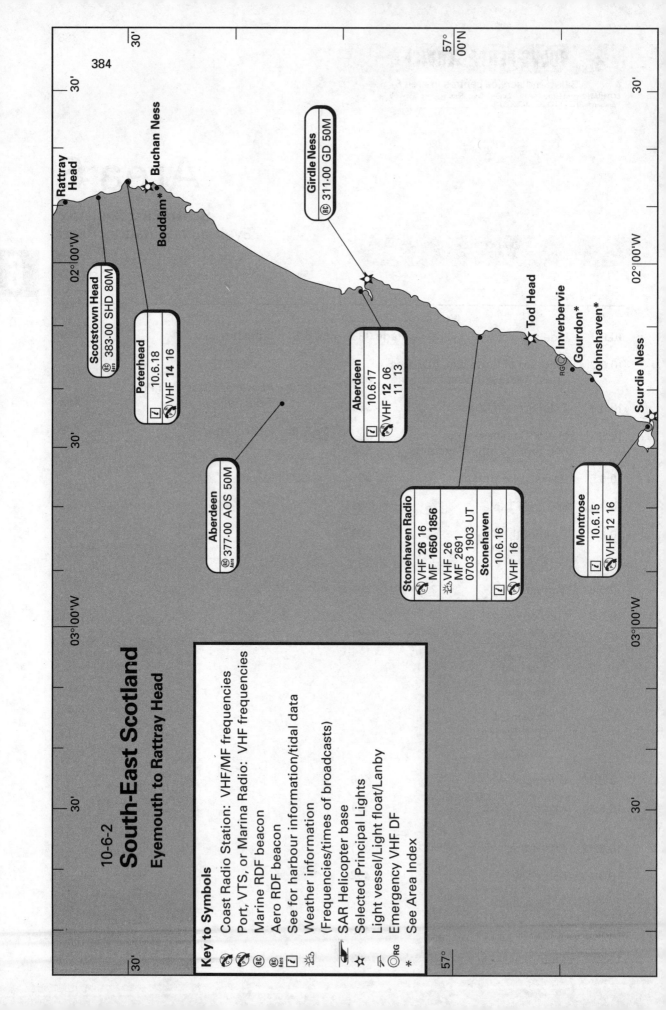

384

10-6-2 South-East Scotland
Eyemouth to Rattray Head

Key to Symbols

- Coast Radio Station: VHF/MF frequencies
- Port, VTS, or Marina Radio: VHF frequencies
- Marine RDF beacon
- Aero RDF beacon
- *i* See for harbour information/tidal data
- Weather information (Frequencies/times of broadcasts)
- SAR Helicopter base
- ☆ Selected Principal Lights
- Light vessel/Light float/Lanby
- ○RG Emergency VHF DF
- * See Area Index

Rattray Head

Buchan Ness

Boddam*

Scotstown Head
383·00 SHD 80M

Peterhead
i 10.6.18
VHF 14 16

Girdle Ness
311·00 GD 50M

Aberdeen
377·00 AOS 50M

Aberdeen
10.6.17
VHF 12 06 11 13

Tod Head

Inverbervie
RG

Gourdon*

Johnshaven*

Scurdie Ness

Stonehaven Radio
VHF 26 16
MF 1650 1856
VHF 26
MF 2691
0703 1903 UT

Stonehaven
10.6.16
VHF 16

Montrose
10.6.15
VHF 12 16

02°00'W

03°00'W

30'

30'

57°00'N

57°00'N

02°00'W

03°00'W

30'

30'

30'

30'

30'

6

See 10-5-2

Eyemouth
10.6.7
ℹ ⚓ VHF 12 16

Dunbar
10.6.8
ℹ

St Abbs Head*
RG

Burnmouth*

Barns Ness

Bass Rock

Fidra
290·00 FD 15M

North
Berwick*

Forth Radio
⚓ VHF 62 16
📡 VHF 62
📻 0703 1903 UT

Fisherrow*

Firth of Forth
10.6.9
ℹ ⚓ VTS 71 20 12
QHM 74
Marina 80 M

Leith
Cramond*
Granton
Port Edgar
Rosyth
Aberdour*

Inchcolm*

Inchkeith
286·50 NK 10M

Kirkcaldy*

Burntisland
10.6.10
ℹ ⚓ Methil Docks
VHF 14 16

Methil
10.6.11
ℹ ⚓ VHF 14 16

Elie* Elie Ness

St Monans*
Pittenweem*
Crail*
RG

Anstruther
10.6.12
ℹ

Isle of May*

St Andrews*

Fife Ness
305·00 FP 50M

Bell Rock

Tayport

Arbroath
10.6.14
ℹ

River Tay
10.6.13
ℹ ⚓ VHF 12 16
Perth Hbr 09 16

Perth*

Aberdeen CG
Forth CG

Variation 5°W (1998)

30'

02°00'W

56°
00'N

30'

02°00'W

30'

03°00'W

03°00'W

30'

56°

30'

30'

10-6-3   AREA 6 TIDAL STREAMS

5 Hours before HW Dover (0340 after HW Leith)

4 Hours before HW Dover (0440 after HW Leith)

3 Hours before HW Dover (0540 after HW Leith)

2 Hours before HW Dover (0545 before HW Leith)

1 Hour before HW Dover (0445 before HW Leith)

HW Dover (0345 before HW Leith)

Northward 10.7.3   Southward 10.5.3

1 Hour after HW Dover (0245 before HW Leith)

2 Hours after HW Dover (0145 before HW Leith)

3 Hours after HW Dover (0045 before HW Leith)

4 Hours after HW Dover (0015 after HW Leith)

5 Hours after HW Dover (0115 after HW Leith)

6 Hours after HW Dover (0215 after HW Leith)

10.6.4 COASTAL LIGHTS, FOG SIGNALS AND WAYPOINTS

Abbreviations used below are given in 1.4.1. Principal lights are in **bold** print, places in CAPITALS, and light-vessels, light floats and Lanbys in *CAPITAL ITALICS*. Unless otherwise stated lights are white. m – elevation in metres; M – nominal range in miles. Fog signals are in *italics*. Useful waypoints are underlined – use those on land with care. All geographical positions should be assumed to be approximate. See 4.4.1. All positions are referenced to the OSGB 36 datum.

BERWICK-UPON-TWEED TO BASS ROCK

BURNMOUTH
Ldg Lts 274°. Front, 55°50'·55N 02°04'·12W FR 29m 4M. Rear, 45m from front, FR 35m 4M. Both on W posts.

EYEMOUTH
Ldg Lts 174°. Front, W Bkwtr Hd, 55°52'·47N 02°05'·18W FG 9m 6M. Rear, elbow 55m from front, FG 10m 6M.
E Bkwtr Hd 55°52'·51N 02°05'·18W Iso R 2s 8m 8M; *Siren 30s*.

ST ABB'S
Hd of inside Jetty 55°53'·95N 02°07'·60W FR 4m 1M.
St Abb's Hd 55°54'·97N 02°08'·20W Fl 10s 68m **26M**; W Tr; Racon (T).
Torness Power Station Pier Hd 55°58'·40N 02°24'·32W Fl R 5s 10m 5M.
Barns Ness Lt Bn Tr 55°59'·21N 02°26'·68W Iso 4s 36m 10M; W ● Tr.

DUNBAR
Bayswell Hill Ldg Lts 198°. Front, 56°00'·26N 02°31'·08W Oc G 6s 15m 3M; W ▲ on Or col; intens 188°-208°. Rear, Oc G 6s 22m 3M; ▼ on Or col; synch with front, intens 188°-208°.
Victoria Hbr, Middle Quay, 56°00'·32N 02°30'·80W QR 6m 3M; vis through cliffs at hbr ent.

Bellhaven Bay Outfall By 56°00'·98N 02°33'·00W; SPM.
S Carr Bn (12) 56°03'·44N 02°37'·60W.
Bass Rock, S side, 56°04'·60N 02°38'·37W Fl (3) 20s 46m 10M; W Tr; vis 241°-107°.

FIRTH OF FORTH AND SOUTH SHORE
(Direction of buoyage East to West)

NORTH BERWICK
Outfall Lt By 56°04'·30N 02°40'·70W Fl Y 5s; SPM.
N Pier Hd 56°03'·73N 02°42'·92W F WR 7m 3M; vis R seaward, W over hbr. Not lit if ent closed by weather.

Fidra, near summit 56°04'·40N 02°47'·00W Fl (4) 30s 34m **24M**; W Tr; RC; obsc by Bass Rk, Craig Leith and Lamb Is.
Wreck Lt By 56°04'·40N 02°52'·30W Fl (2) R 10s; PHM.

PORT SETON/COCKENZIE/FISHERROW/SOUTH CHANNEL
Port Seton, E Pier Hd, 55°58'·40N 02°57'·10W Iso WR 4s 10m W9M, R6M; R shore-105°, W105°-225°, R225°-shore; *Bell* (occas).
Cockenzie Power Station, Jetty Hd 55°58'·25N 02°58'·32W QR 6m 1M.
Fisherrow E Pier Hd 55°58'·80N 03°04'·03W Oc W 6s 5m 6M; framework Tr.
South Chan Appr Lt By 56°01'·42N 03°02'·15W L Fl 10s; SWM.
Narrow Deep Lt By 56°01'·47N 03°04'·50W Fl(2) R 10s; PHM.
Herwit Lt By 56°01'·05N 03°06'·43W Fl (3) G 10s; SHM; *Bell*.
North Craig By 56°00'·75N 03°03'·80W, SHM.
Craigh Waugh Lt By 56°00'·27N 03°04'·38W Q; NCM.

Diffuser Hds By (Outer) 55°59'·81N 03°07'·75W; NCM.
Diffuser Hds By (Inner) 55°59'·38N 03°07'·94W; SCM.
Leith Approach Lt By 55°59'·95N 03°11'·42W Fl R 3s; PHM.

LEITH
East Bkwtr Hd 55°59'·48N 03°10'·85W Iso R 4s 7m 9M; *Horn (3) 30s*.
W Bkwtr Hd L Fl G 6s.

GRANTON
E Pier Hd 55°59'·28N 03°13'·17W Fl R 2s 5m 6M; W ■ Bldg.

CRAMOND
Church Tr 55°58'·67N 03°17'·92W.

NORTH CHANNEL/MIDDLE BANK
Inchkeith Fairway Lt By 56°03'·50N 03°00'·00W Iso 2s; SWM; Racon (T).
No. 1 Lt By 56°03'·23N 03°03'·63W Fl G 9s; SHM.
No. 2 Lt By 56°02'·90N 03°03'·63W Fl R 9s; PHM.
No. 3 Lt By 56°03'·23N 03°06'·00W Fl G 6s; SHM.
No. 4 Lt By 56°02'·90N 03°06'·00W Fl R 6s; PHM.
No. 5 Lt By 56°03'·18N 03°07'·80W Fl G 3s; SHM.
No. 6 Lt By 56°03'·05N 03°08'·35W Fl R 3s; PHM.
No. 8 Lt By 56°02'·95N 03°09'·54W Fl R 9s; PHM.
Inchkeith, summit 56°02'·01N 03°08'·09W Fl 15s 67m **22M**; stone Tr; RC.
E Stell Pt *Horn 15s*.
Pallas Rock Lt By 56°01'·50N 03°09'·22W VQ (9) 10s; WCM.
East Gunnet Lt By 56°01'·42N 03°10'·30W Q (3) 10s; ECM.
West Gunnet Lt By 56°01'·35N 03°10'·97W Q (9) 15s; WCM.
No. 7 Lt By 56°02'·80N 03°10'·87W QG; *Bell*; Racon (T).
No. 9 Lt By 56°02'·37N 03°13'·38W Fl G 6s; SHM.
No. 10 Lt By 56°02'·05N 03°13'·30W Fl R 6s; PHM.
No. 11 Lt By 56°02'·08N 03°15'·15W Fl G 3s; SHM.
No. 12 Lt By 56°01'·77N 03°15'·05W Fl R 3s; PHM.
No. 13 Lt By 56°01'·77N 03°16'·94W Fl G 9s; SHM.
No. 14 Lt By 56°01'·52N 03°16'·82W Fl R 9s; PHM.
Oxcars Lt Bn Tr 56°01'·36N 03°16'·74W Fl (2) WR 7s 16m W13M, R12M; W Tr, R band; vis W072°-087°, R087°-196°, W196°-313°, R313°-072°; Ra refl.
Inchcolm E Pt 56°01'·73N 03°17'·75W Fl (3) 15s 20m 10M; Gy Tr; part obsc 075°-145°; *Horn (3) 45s*.
No. 15 Lt By 56°01'·43N 03°18'·70W Fl G 6s; SHM.

MORTIMER'S DEEP.
Hawkcraig Pt Ldg Lts 292°. Front, 56°03'·03N 03°16'·97W Iso 5s 12m 14M; W Tr; vis 282°-302°. Rear, 96m from front, Iso 5s 16m 14M; W Tr; vis 282°-302°.
No. 1 Lt By 56°02'·68N 03°15'·19W QG; SHM.
No. 2 Lt By 56°02'·70N 03°15'·76W QR; PHM.
No. 3 Lt By 56°02'·51N 03°17'·44W Fl (2) G 5s; SHM.
No. 4 Lt By 56°02'·38N 03°17'·35W Fl (2) R 5s; PHM.
No. 5 Lt By 56°02'·37N 03°17'·86W Fl G 4s; SHM.
No. 6 Lt By 56°02'·28N 03°17'·78W Fl R 4s; PHM.
No. 7 Lt By 56°01'·94N 03°18'·92W Fl (2) G 5s; SHM.
No. 8 Lt By 56°02'·10N 03°18'·17W Fl R 2s; PHM.
No. 9 Lt By 56°01'·69N 03°19'·08W QG; SHM.
No. 10 Lt By 56°01'·83N 03°18'·48W Fl (2) R 5s; PHM.
No. 14 Lt By 56°01'·56N 03°18'·96W Q (9) 15s; WCM.
Inchcolm S Lts in line 066°. Front, 84m from rear, Q 7m 7M; W Tr; vis 062·5°-082·5°. Common Rear, 56°01'·80N 03°18'·13W Iso 5s 11m 7M; W Tr; vis 062°-082°.
N Lts in line 076·7°. Front, 80m from rear, Q 7m 7M; W Tr; vis 062·5°-082·5°.

APPROACHES TO FORTH BRIDGES
No. 16 Lt By 56°00'·75N 03°19'·81W Fl R 3s; PHM.
No. 17 Lt By 56°01'·17N 03°20'·12W Fl G 3s; SHM.
No. 19 Lt By 56°00'·72N 03°22'·40W Fl G 9s; SHM.
Hound Pt Terminal NE Dn 56°00'·48N 03°21'·14W 2 FR 7m 5M.

Centre Pier 2 Aero FR 47m 5M.
Hound Pt SW Dn 56°00'·28N 03°21'·83W FR 7m 5M.
Inch Garvie, NW end 56°00'·01N 03°23'·29W L Fl 5s 9m 11M; B ● Bn, W lantern.
N Queensferry. Oc 5s and QR or QG tfc signals.
Forth Rail Bridge. Centres of spans have W Lts and ends of cantilevers R Lts, defining N and S chans.
Forth Road Bridge. N suspension Tr Iso G 4s 7m 6M on E and W sides; 2 Aero FR 155m 11M and 2 FR 109m 7M on same Tr. Main span, N part QG 50m 6M on E and W sides. Main span, centre Iso 4s 52m 8M on E and W sides. Main span, S part QR 50m 6M on E and W sides. S suspension Tr Iso R 4s 7m 6M on E and W sides; 2 Aero FR 155m and 2 Fr 109m 7M on same Tr.

PORT EDGAR
Dir Lt 244°. W Bkwtr Hd 55°59'·85N 03°24'·69W Dir Fl R 4s 4m 8M; W blockhouse; 4 QY mark floating bkwtr.
3 x 2 FR (vert) mark N ends of Marina pontoons inside hbr.

Beamer Rk Lt Bn Tr 56°02'·28N 03°24'·66W Fl 3s 6m 9M; W Tr, R top.

FIRTH OF FORTH – NORTH SHORE (INWARD)

BURNTISLAND
W Pier outer Hd 56°03'·2N 03°22'·2W Fl (2) R 6s 7m; W Tr.
E Pier outer Hd 56°03'·23N 03°14'·08W Fl (2) G 6s 7m 5M.

ABERDOUR/BRAEFOOT BAY/INCHCOLM
Hawkcraig Pt (see MORTIMER'S DEEP above)
Aberdour Bay Outfall Bn 56°02'·97N 03°17'·62W; Y Bn.
Braefoot Bay Terminal, W Jetty. Ldg Lts 247·25°. **Front,** 56°02'·15N 03°18'·63W Fl 3s 6m **15M**; W ▲ on E dolphin; vis 237·2°-257·2°; four dolphins marked by 2 FG (vert). **Rear,** 88m from front, Fl 3s 12m **15M**; W ▼ on appr gangway; vis 237·2°-257·2°; synch with front.
Inchcolm Abbey Tr 56°01'·81N 03°18'·02W.

INVERKEITHING BAY
St David's Dir Lt Bn 56°01'·37N 03°22'·20W Dir 098° Fl G 5s 3m 7M; Or □, on pile.
Channel Lt By 56°01'·43N 03°22'·94W QG; SHM.
Channel Lt By 56°01'·44N 03°23'·30W QR; PHM.

HM NAVAL BASE, ROSYTH
Main Chan Dir Lt 323·5°. Bn A 56°01'·19N 03°25'·53W Dir Oc WRG 7m 4M; R ■ on W post with R bands, on B&W diagonal ■ on W Bn; vis G318°-321°, W321°-326°, R326°-328° (H24).
Dir Lt 115°, Bn C 56°00'·61N 03°24'·17W Dir Oc WRG 6s 7m 4M; W ▼ on W Bn; vis R110°-113°, W113°-116·5°, G116·5°-120°.
Dir Lt 295°, Bn E 56°01'·30N 03°26'·83W Dir Oc 6s 11m 4M; vis 293·5°-296·5°.
No. 1 Lt By 56°00'·54N 03°24'·48W Fl (2) G 10s; SHM.
Whale Bank No. 2 Lt By 56°00'·70N 03°25'·10W Q (3) 10s; ECM.
No. 3 Lt By 56°00'·87N 03°24'·98W Fl G 5s; SHM.
No. 4 Lt By 56°00'·82N 03°25'·18W Fl R 3s; PHM.
No. 5 Lt By 56°01'·08N 03°25'·80W QG; SHM.
No. 6 Lt By 56°01'·01N 03°25'·94W QR; PHM.
S Arm Jetty Hd 56°01'·08N 03°26'·48W L Fl (2) WR 12s 5m W9M; R6M; vis W010°-280°, R280°-010°; Siren 20s (occas).

RIVER FORTH

ROSYTH TO GRANGEMOUTH
Dhu Craig Lt By 56°00'·76N 03°27'·15W Fl G 5s; SHM.
Blackness Lt By 56°01'·07N 03°30'·22W QR; PHM.
Charlestown. Lts in line. Front 56°02'·20N 03°30'·60W FG 4m 10M; Y ▲ on Y pile; vis 017°-037°; marks line of HP gas main. Rear FG 6m 10M; Y ▼ on Y pile; vis 017°-037°.

Crombie Jetty, downstream dolphin 56°01'·94N 03°31'·76W 2 FG (vert) 8m 4M; Horn (2) 60s.
Crombie Jetty, upstream dolphin 56°02'·00N 03°32'·03W 2 FG (vert) 8m 4M.
Tancred Bank Lt By 56°01'·59N 03°31'·83W Fl (2) R 10s; PHM.
Dods Bank Lt By 56°02'·03N 03°33'·99W Fl R 3s; PHM.
Bo'ness Lt By 56°02'·23N 03°35'·31W Fl R 10s; PHM.
Bo'ness. Carriden outfall 56°01'·32N 03°33'·62W Fl Y 5s 3M; Y ■ on Y Bn.
Torry 56°02'·47N 03°35'·20W Fl G 10s 5m 7M; G ● structure.
Bo'ness Platform 56°01'·84N 03°36'·13W QR 3m 2M; R pile Bn.

GRANGEMOUTH
Grangemouth App No. 1 pile 56°02'·13N 03°38'·01W Fl (3) R 20s 4m 6M.
Hen & Chickens Lt By 56°02'·37N 03°38'·00W Fl (3) G 20s; SHM.
No. 2 pile 56°02'·35N 03°39'·13W Fl G 5s 4m 6M; G ■ on pile.
No. 3 pile 56°02'·26N 03°39'·13W Fl R 5s 4m 6M.
No. 4 pile 56°02'·39N 03°39'·83W Fl G 2s 4m 5M.
No. 5 pile 56°02'·25N 03°39'·82W Fl R 2s 4m 5M.
Grangemouth W Lt By 56°02'·38N 03°40'·50W QG; SHM.
Dock entrance, E Jetty; Horn 30s; docking signals.

Longannet Power Station, intake L Fl G 10s 5m 6M.
Inch Brake By 56°03'·62N 03°43'·19W; SHM.

KINCARDINE
Swing bridge 56°03'·9N 03°43'·5W FW at centre of each span; FR Lts mark each side of openings.

FIRTH OF FORTH – NORTH SHORE (OUTWARD)

KIRKCALDY
East Pier Hd 56°06'·78N 03°08'·81W Fl WG 10s 12m 8M; vis G156°-336°, W336°-156°.
S Pier Hd 56°06'·81N 03°08'·88W 2 FR (vert) 7m 5M.

W Rockheads By 56°07'·00N 03°06'·90W; SHM.
E Rockheads By 56°07'·15N 03°06'·33W; SHM.
Kirkcaldy Wreck Lt By 56°07'·26N 03°05'·20W Fl (3) G 18s; SHM.

METHIL
Outer Pier Hd 56°10'·77N 03°00'·39W Oc G 6s 8m 5M; W Tr; vis 280°-100°.

ELIE
Thill Rk By 56°10'·88N 02°49'·60W; PHM.
Elie Ness 56°11'·05N 02°48'·65W Fl 6s 15m **18M**; W Tr.

ST MONANCE
Bkwtr Hd 56°12'·20N 02°45'·80W Oc WRG 6s 5m W7M, R4M, G4M; vis G282°-355°, W355°-026°, R026°-038°.
E Pier Hd 2 FG (vert) 6m 4M; Or tripod; Bell (occas).
W Pier near Hd, 2 FR (vert) 6m 4M.

PITTENWEEM
Ldg Lts 037° Middle Pier Hd. Front, FR 4m 5M. Rear, FR 8m 5M. Both Gy Cols, Or stripes.
E Bkwtr Hd 56°12'·36N 02°43'·36W Fl (2) RG 5s 9m R9M, G6M; vis R265°-345°, G345°-055°.
Beacon Rk Lt Bn QR 3m 2M.
W Pier Elbow, Horn 90s (occas).

ANSTRUTHER EASTER
Ldg Lts 019°. Front 56°13'·29N 02°41'·68W FG 7m 4M.
Rear, 38m from front, FG 11m 4M, (both W masts).
W Pier Hd 2 FR (vert) 5m 4M; Gy mast; Horn (3) 60s (occas).
E Pier Hd 56°13'·15N 02°41'·72W Fl G 3s 6m 4M.

MAY ISLAND
Isle of May, Summit 56°11'·13N 02°33'·30W Fl (2) 15s 73m **22M**; ■ Tr on stone dwelling.

CRAIL
Ldg Lts 295°. Front, 56°15'·48N 02°37'·70W FR 24m 6M (not lit when hbr closed). Rear, 30m from front, FR 30m 6M.

Fife Ness Lt 56°16'·73N 02°35'·10W Iso WR 10s 12m **W21M, R20M**; W bldg; vis W143°-197°, R197°-217°, W217°-023°; RC.

FIFE NESS TO MONTROSE

N Carr Lt By 56°18'·07N 02°32'·85W Q (3) 10s; ECM.
Bell Rk Lt Tr 56°26'·05N 02°23'·07W Fl 5s 28m **18M**; W ● Tr; Racon (M).

RIVER TAY/TAYPORT/DUNDEE/PERTH
Tay Fairway Lt By 56°28'·92N 02°37'·42W L Fl 10s; SWM; Bell.
Middle Green Lt By (N) 56°28'·45N 02°39'·25W Fl (3) G 18s; SHM.
Middle Red Lt By (S) 56°28'·33N 02°38'·80W Fl (2) R 12s; PHM.
Abertay N Lt By 56°27'·44N 02°40'·55W Q (3) 10s; ECM; Racon (T).
Abertay S (Elbow) Lt By 56°27'·17N 02°40'·00W Fl R 6s; PHM.

High Lt Ho Dir Lt 269°, 56°27'·17N 02°53'·85W Dir Iso WRG 3s 24m **W22M, R17M, G16M**; W Tr; vis G267°-268°, W268°-270°, R270°-271°.
Inner Lt Buoy 56°27'·10N 02°44'·23W Fl (2) R 12s; PHM.
N Lady Lt By 56°27'·43N 02°46'·56W Fl (3) G 18s; SHM.
S Lady Lt By 56°27'·20N 02°46'·76W Fl (3) R 18s; PHM.
Pool Lt By 56°27'·15N 02°48'·50W Fl R 6s; PHM.
Tentsmuir Pt 56°26'·6N 02°49'·5W Fl Y 5s; Y Bn; vis 198°-208°; marks gas pipeline.
Monifieth 56°28'·9N 02°47'·8W Fl Y 5s; Y Bn; vis 018°-028°; marks gas pipeline.
Horse Shoe Lt By 56°27'·28N 02°50'·11W VQ (6) + L Fl 15s; SCM.
Larick Scalp Lt By 56°27'·19N 02°51'·50W Fl (2) R 12s; PHM; Bell.
Broughty Castle 56°27'·76N 02°52'·10W 2 FG (vert) 10m 4M; Gy col; FR is shown at foot of old Lt Ho at Buddon Ness, 4M to E, and at other places on firing range when practice is taking place.
Craig Lt By 56°27'·48N 02°52'·94W QR; PHM.
Newcombe Shoal Lt By 56°27'·73N 02°53'·50W Fl R 6s; PHM.
Dundee Tidal Basin E Ent 56°27'·92N 02°55'·92W 2 FG (vert).
Middle Bank Lt By 56°27'·40N 02°56'·39W Q (3) 10s; ECM.
West Deep Lt By 56°27'·15N 02°56'·15W Fl R 3s; PHM.
Tay Road Bridge N navigation span, centre 56°27'·03N 02°56'·44W 2 x VQ 27m.
Tay Road Bridge S navigation span, centre 56°27'·01N 02°56'·38W 2 x VQ 28m.
Tay Railway Bridge navigation 56°26'·28N 02°59'·20W 2 x 2 F (vert) 23m.
Jock's Hole 56°21'·75N 03°12'·10W QR 8m 2M.
Cairnie Pier 56°21'·50N 03°17'·80W.
Pipeline S by Elcho Castle 56°22'·50N 03°20'·80W Iso R 4s 4m 4M.

ARBROATH
Outfall Lt By 56°32'·64N 02°34'·97W Fl Y 3s; SPM.
Ldg Lts 299·2°. Front, 56°33'·30N 02°35'·07W FR 7m 5M; W col. Rear, 50m from front, FR 13m 5M; W col.

W Bkwtr E end, VQ (2) 6s 6m 4M; W post.
E Pier S Elbow 56°33'·26N 02°34'·89W Fl G 3s 8m 5M; W Tr; shows FR when hbr closed; Siren (3) 60s (occas).

MONTROSE
Scurdie Ness 56°42'·12N 02°26'·15W Fl (3) 20s 38m **23M**; W Tr; Racon (T).
Ldg Lts 271·5°. Front, FR 11m 5M; W twin pillars, R bands. Rear, 272m from front, FR 18m 5M; W Tr, R cupola.
Scurdie Rks Lt By 56°42'·15N 02°25'·42W QR; PHM.
Annat Lt By 56°42'·24N 02°25'·85W Fl G 3s; SHM.
Annat Shoal Lt By 56°42'·38N 02°25'·50W QG; SHM.

MONTROSE TO RATTRAY HEAD
JOHNSHAVEN
Ldg Lts 316°. Front, 56°47'·65N 02°20'·05W FR 5m; R structure. Rear, 85m from front, FG 20m; G structure; shows R when unsafe to enter hbr.

GOURDON HARBOUR
Ldg Lts 358°. Front, 56°49'·70N 02°17'·10W FR 5m 5M; W Tr; shows G when unsafe to enter; Siren (2) 60s (occas). Rear, 120m from front, FR 30m 5M; W Tr.
W Pier Hd 56°49'·62N 02°17'·15W Fl WRG 3s 5m W9M, R7M, G7M; vis G180°-344°, W344°-354°, R354°-180°.
E Bkwtr Hd Q 3m 7M.

Todhead 56°53'·00N 02°12'·85W Fl (4) 30s 41m **18M**; W Tr.

STONEHAVEN
Outer Pier Hd 56°57'·59N 02°11'·89W Iso WRG 4s 7m W11M, R7M, G8M; vis G214°-246°, W246°-268°, R268°-280°.

Girdle Ness 57°08'·35N 02°02'·82W Fl (2) 20s 56m **22M**; W ● Tr; obsc by Greg Ness when brg more than about 020°; RC; Racon (G).

ABERDEEN
Fairway Lt By 57°09'·33N 02°01'·85W Mo (A); SWM; Racon (T).
Ldg Lts 235·7°. Front, 57°08'·39N 02°04'·41W FR or G 14m 5M; W Tr; R when ent safe, FG when dangerous to navigation; vis 195°-279°. Rear, 205m from front, FR 19m 5M; W Tr; vis 195°-279°.
S Bkwtr Hd 57°08'·70N 02°03'·23W Fl (3) R 8s 23m 7M.
N Pier Hd 57°08'·75N 02°03'·58W Oc WR 6s 11m 9M; W Tr; vis W145°-055°, R055°-145°. In fog FY 10m (same Tr) vis 136°-336°; Bell (3) 12s.

Buchan Ness 57°28'·23N 01°46'·37W Fl 5s 40m **28M**; W Tr, R bands; Racon (O); Horn (3) 60s.
Cruden Scaurs Lt By 57°23'·25N 01°50'·00W Fl R 10s; PHM; Bell.

PETERHEAD
Kirktown Ldg Lts 314°. Front, 57°30'·23N 01°47'·10W FR 13m 8M; R mast, W ▲ on Or mast. Rear, 91m from front, FR 17m 8M; W ▼ on Or mast.
S Bkwtr Hd 57°29'·81N 01°46'·43W Fl (2) R 12s 24m 7M; W ● Tr with B base.
N Bkwtr Hd 57°29'·85N 01°46'·22W Iso RG 6s 19m 11M; W tripod; vis R165°-230°, G230°-165°; Horn 30s.
Marina Bkwtr Hd 57°29'·82N 01°47'·33W Fl R 3s 6m 2M.

Rattray Hd. Ron Rk 57°36'·62N 01°48'·90W Fl (3) 30s 28m **24M**; W Tr; Racon (M); Horn (2) 45s.

10.6.5   PASSAGE INFORMATION

For these waters refer to the Admiralty *North Sea (West) Pilot*; R Northumberland YC's *Sailing Directions Humber to Rattray Head*, and the *Forth Yacht Clubs Association Pilot Handbook*, which covers the Firth of Forth in detail.

BERWICK-UPON-TWEED TO BASS ROCK (charts 160,175)

From Berwick-upon-Tweed to the Firth of Forth there is no good hbr which can be approached with safety in strong onshore winds. So, if on passage with strong winds from N or E, plan accordingly and keep well to seaward. In late spring and early summer fog (haar) is likely in onshore winds.

The coast N from Berwick is rky with cliffs rising in height to Burnmouth, then diminishing gradually to Eyemouth (10.6.7). Keep 5ca offshore to clear outlying rks. Burnmouth, although small, has more alongside space than Eyemouth, which is a crowded fishing hbr. 2M NW is St Abb's Hbr (10.6.7), with temp anch in offshore winds in Coldingham B close to the S.

St Abb's Hd (lt) is a bold, steep headland, 92m high, with no offlying dangers. The stream runs strongly round the Hd, causing turbulence with wind against tide; this can be largely avoided by keeping close inshore. The ESE-going stream begins at HW Leith – 0345, and the WNW-going at HW Leith + 0240. There is a good anch in Pettico Wick, on NW side of Hd, in S winds, but dangerous if the wind shifts onshore. There are no off-lying dangers between St Abb's Hd and Fast Castle Hd, 3M WNW. Between Fast Castle Hd and Barns Ness, about 8M NW, is the attractive little hbr of Cove; but it dries and should only be approached in ideal conditions.

Torness Power Station (conspic; lt on bkwtr) is 1·75M SE of Barns Ness (lt) which lies 2·5M ESE of Dunbar (10.6.8) and is fringed with rks; tidal streams as for St Abb's Hd. Conspic chys are 7½ca WSW inland of Barns Ness. Between here and Dunbar keep at least 2½ca offshore to clear rky patches. Sicar Rk (7·9m depth) lies about 1·25M ENE of Dunbar, and sea breaks on it in onshore gales.

The direct course from Dunbar to Bass Rk (lt) is clear of all dangers; inshore of this line beware Wildfire Rks (dry) on NW side of Bellhaven B. In offshore winds there is anch in Scoughall Road. Great Car is ledge of rks, nearly covering at HW, 1M ESE of Gin Hd, with Car bn (stone tr surmounted by cross) at its N end. Drying ledges of rks extend 1M SE of Great Car, up to 3ca offshore. Keep at least 5ca off Car bn in strong onshore winds. Tantallon Castle (ruins) is on cliff edge 1M W of Great Car. Bass Rk (lt) lies 1·25M NNE of Gin Hd, and is a sheer, conspic rk (115m) with no offlying dangers; landing difficult due to swell.

FIRTH OF FORTH, SOUTH SHORE (chart 734, 735)

Westward of Bass Rk, Craigleith (51m), Lamb Is (24m) and Fidra (31m) lie 5ca or more offshore, while the coast is generally foul. Craigleith is steep-to, and temporary anchorage can be found on SE and SW sides; if passing inshore of it keep well to N side of chan. N Berwick hbr (dries) lies S of Craigleith, but is unsafe in onshore winds. Between Craigleith and Lamb Is, beware drying rks up to 3ca from land. Lamb Is is 1·5M WNW of N Berwick (10.6.8) and has a rky ledge extending 2½ca SW. Fidra Is (lt, RC) is a bird reserve, nearly connected to the shore by rky ledges, and should be passed to the N; passage and anch on S side are tricky. Anchor on E or W sides, depending on wind, in good weather.

In the B between Fidra and Edinburgh some shelter can be found in SE winds in Aberlady B and Gosford B. The best anch is SW of Craigielaw Pt. Port Seton is a drying fishing hbr 7½ca E of the conspic chys of Cockenzie Power Station; the E side of the hbr can be entered HW ±3, but not advisable in strong onshore wind or sea. Cockenzie (dries) is close to power station; beware Corsik Rk 400m to E. Access HW ± 2·5, but no attractions except boatyard. For Fisherrow, see 10.6.8.

There are no dangers on the direct course from Fidra to Inchkeith (lt, RC), which stands between the buoyed deep water chans. Rks extend 7½ca SE from Inchkeith, and 5ca off the W side where there is a small hbr below the lt ho; landing is forbidden without permission. N Craig and Craig Waugh (least depth 0·6m) are buoyed shoals 2·5M SE from Inchkeith lt ho. For Cramond and Inchcolm, see 10.6.8.

In N Chan, close to Inchkeith the W-going (flood) stream begins about HW Leith – 0530, and the E-going at HW Leith + 0030, sp rates about 1kn. The streams gather strength towards the Forth bridges, where they reach 2·25kn and there may be turbulence.

Leith is wholly commercial; Granton has yacht moorings in the E hbr; Port Edgar (10.6.9) is a major yacht hbr close W of Forth road bridge. Hound Point oil terminal is an artificial 'island-jetty' almost in mid-stream, connected to the shore by underwater pipeline (no ⌕). Yachts may pass the terminal on either side at least 30m off and well clear of tankers berthing.

RIVER FORTH TO KINCARDINE (charts 736, 737, 738)

The main shipping chan under the N span of the rail bridge is busy with commercial traffic for Grangemouth and warships to/from Rosyth dockyard. In the latter case a Protected Chan may be activated; see 10.6.9 for details. W of Beamer Rk the Firth widens as far as Bo'ness (small drying hbr) on the S shore where the chan narrows between drying mudbanks. Charlestown (N bank) dries, but is a secure hbr. Grangemouth is industrially conspic. Caution: gas carriers, tankers, cargo vessels; no yacht facilities. Few yachts go beyond Kincardine swing bridge, clearance 9m, which is no longer opened.

FIRTH OF FORTH, NORTH SHORE (charts 734, 190)

From Burntisland (10.6.10) the N shore of Firth of Forth leads E to Kinghorn Ness. 1M SSW of Kinghorn Ness Blae Rk (SHM lt buoy) has least depth of 4·1m, and seas break on it in E gales. Rost Bank lies halfway between Kinghorn Ness and Inchkeith, with tide rips at sp tides or in strong winds.

From Kinghorn Ness to Kirkcaldy, drying rks lie up to 3ca offshore. Kirkcaldy hbr (10.6.11) is effectively closed, but yachts can enter inner dock near HW by arrangement; ent is dangerous in strong E'lies, when seas break a long way out.

Between Kirkcaldy and Methil (10.6.11) the only dangers more than 2ca offshore are The Rockheads, extending 4ca SE of Dysart, and marked by 2 SHM buoys. Largo B is anch, well sheltered from N and E, but avoid gaspipes near E side. Close SW of Elie, beware W Vows (dries) and E Vows (dries, bn). There is anch close W of Elie Ness (10.6.8). Ox Rk (dries 2m) lies 5ca ENE of Elie Ness, and 2½ca offshore; otherwise there are no dangers more than 2ca offshore past St Monans, Pittenweem (10.6.8) and Anstruther (10.6.12), but in bad weather the sea breaks on Shield Rk 4ca off Pittenweem. From Anstruther to Crail (10.6.8) and on to Fife Ness keep 3ca offshore to clear Caiplie Rk and other dangers.

May Island (lt) (10.6.8) lies about 5M S of Fife Ness; its shores are bold except at NW end where rks extend 1ca off. Anch near N end at E or W Tarbert, on lee side according to winds; in good weather it is possible to land. Lt ho boats use Kirkhaven, close SE of lt ho

FIFE NESS TO MONTROSE (chart 190)

Fife Ness is fringed by rky ledges, and a reef extends 1M NE to N Carr Rk (dries 1·4m, marked by bn). In strong onshore winds keep to seaward of N Carr ECM lt buoy. From here keep 5ca offshore to clear dangers entering St Andrews B, where there is anch; the little hbr (10.6.13) dries, and should not be approached in onshore winds.

Northward from Firth of Forth to Rattray Hd the coast is mostly rky and steep-to, and there are no out-lying dangers within 2M of the coast except those off R. Tay and Bell Rk. But in an onshore blow there are few safe havens; both yachts and crews need to be prepared for offshore cruising rather than coast-crawling.

R. Tay (10.6.13 and chart 1481) is approached from the NE via Fairway buoy; it is dangerous to cut corners from the S. The Bar, NE of Abertay lt buoy, is dangerous in heavy weather, particularly in strong onshore wind or swell. Abertay Sands extend nearly 4M E of Tentsmuir Pt on S side of chan (buoyed); Elbow is a shoal extension eastward. Gaa Sands running 1·75M E from Buddon Ness, are marked by Abertay lt buoy (Racon) on N side of chan. Passage across Abertay and Gaa Sands is very dangerous. The estuary is shallow, with many shifting sandbanks; Tayport is a good passage stop and best yacht hbr (dries) in the Tay. S of Buddon Ness the W-going (flood) stream begins about HW Aberdeen − 0400, and the E-going at about HW Aberdeen + 0230, sp rates 2kn.

Bell Rk (lt, Racon) lies about 11·5M E of Buddon Ness. 2M E of Bell Rk the S-going stream begins HW Aberdeen − 0220, and the N-going at HW Aberdeen + 0405, sp rates 1kn. W of Bell Rk the streams begin earlier.

N from Buddon Ness the coast is sandy. 1·25M SW of Arbroath (10.6.14) beware Elliot Horses, rky patches with depth 1·9m, which extend about 5ca offshore. Between Whiting Ness and Scurdie Ness, 9·5M NNE, the coast is clear of out-lying dangers, but is mostly fringed with drying rks up to 1ca off. In offshore winds there is temp anch in SW of Lunan B, off Ethie Haven.

Scurdie Ness (lt, Racon) is conspic on S side of ent to Montrose (10.6.15). Scurdie Rks (dry) extend 2ca E of the Ness. On N side of chan Annat Bank dries up to about 5ca E of the shore, opposite Scurdie Ness (chart 1438). The in-going stream begins at HW Aberdeen − 0500, and the outgoing at HW Aberdeen + 0115; both streams are very strong, up to 7kn at sp, and there is turbulence off the ent on the ebb. The ent is dangerous in strong onshore winds, with breaking seas extending to Scurdie Ness on the ebb. In marginal conditions the last quarter of the flood is best time to enter.

MONTROSE TO ABERDEEN (chart 210)

N from Montrose the coast is sandy for 5M to Milton Ness, where there is anch on S side in N winds. Johnshaven (10.6.16), 2M NE, is a small hbr (dries) with tight entrance, which should not be approached with onshore wind or swell. 5ca NE, off Brotherton Cas, drying rks extend 4ca offshore. Gourdon (10.6.16) has a small hbr (mostly dries) approached on ldg line between rky ledges; inner hbr has storm gates. Outside the hbr rks extend both sides of entrance, and the sea breaks heavily in strong E winds. Keep a sharp lookout for lobster pot dan buoys between Montrose and Stonehaven.

North to Inverbervie the coast is fringed with rky ledges up to 2ca offshore. Just N of Todhead Pt (lt) is Catterline, a small B which forms a natural anch in W winds, but open to E. Downie Pt, SE of Stonehaven (10.6.16) should be rounded 1ca off. The Bay is encumbered by rky ledges up to 2ca from shore and exposed to the E; anch 6ca E of Bay Hotel or berth afloat in outer hbr.

From Garron Pt to Girdle Ness the coast is mostly steep-to. Fishing nets may be met off headlands during fishing season. Craigmaroinn and Seal Craig (dry) are parts of reef 3ca offshore SE of Portlethen, a fishing village with landing sheltered by rks. Cove B has a very small fishing hbr, off which there is anch in good weather; Mutton Rk (dries 2·1m) lie 1½ca offshore. From Cove to Girdle Ness keep 5ca offshore, avoiding Hasman Rks (dries 3·4m) 1ca off Altens .

Greg Ness and Girdle Ness (lt, RC, Racon), at SE corner of Aberdeen B (10.6.17), are fringed by rks. Girdlestone is a rky patch, depth less than 2m, 2ca ENE of lt ho. A drying patch lies 2ca SE of lt ho. Off Girdle Ness the S-going stream begins at HW Aberdeen − 0430, and the N-going at HW Aberdeen + 0130, sp rates 2·5kn. A race forms on S-going stream.

ABERDEEN TO RATTRAY HEAD (chart 213)

From Aberdeen there are few offshore dangers to Buchan Ness. R. Ythan, 1·75M SSW of Hackley Hd, is navigable by small craft, but chan shifts constantly. 3M North is the very small hbr of Collieston (mostly dries), only accessible in fine weather. 4·75M NNE of Hackley Head lie The Skares, rks (marked by PHM lt buoy) extending 3½ca from S point of Cruden B, where there is anch in offshore winds. On N side of Cruden B is Port Erroll (dries 2·5m).

Buchan Ness (lt, fog sig, Racon) is a rky peninsula. 2ca N is Meikle Mackie islet, close W of which is the small hbr of Boddam (dries) (10.6.18). 3ca NE of Meikle Mackie is The Skerry, a rk 6m high on S side of Sandford B; rks on which the sea breaks extend 2ca NNE. The chan between The Skerry and the coast is foul with rks and not advised. Peterhead (10.6.18) is easy to enter in almost all conditions and is an excellent passage port with marina at SW corner of the Bay.

Rattray Hd (with lt, fog sig on The Ron, rk 2ca E of Hd) has rky foreshore, drying for 2ca off. Rattray Briggs is a detached reef, depth 0·2m, 2ca E of lt ho. Rattray Hard is a rky patch, depth 10·7m, 1·5M ENE of lt ho, which raises a dangerous sea during onshore gales. Off Rattray Hd the S-going stream begins at HW Aberdeen − 0420, and the N-going at HW Aberdeen + 0110, sp rates 3kn. In normal conditions keep about 1M E of Rattray Hd, but pass 5M off in bad weather, preferably at slack water. Conspic radio masts with R lts lie 2·5M WNW and 2·2M W of lt ho.

For notes on offshore oil/gas installations, see 10.5.5.

NORTH SEA PASSAGE
For distances across the N Sea, see 10.0.7.

FORTH TO NORWAY AND BALTIC (charts 2182B, 2182C)

Heading ENE'ly from the Firth of Forth the main hazards result from offshore industrial activities and their associated traffic. In summer particularly, oil/gas exploration, movement of drilling rigs, pipe laying etc create situations which could endanger other vessels. Rig movements and many of the more intense activities are published in Notices to Mariners, but even so it is wise to avoid the gas and oil fields where possible and never to approach within 500m of installations (see 10.5.5). There are TSS to be avoided off the S and SW coast of Norway. Strong currents and steep seas may be experienced in the approaches to the Skagerrak.

10.6.6   DISTANCE TABLE

Approximate distances in nautical miles are by the most direct route, whilst avoiding dangers and allowing for Traffic Separation Schemes. Places in *italics* are in adjoining areas; places in **bold** are in 10.0.7, Distances across the North Sea.

1.	*Great Yarmouth*	1																		
2.	*Berwick-on-Tweed*	232	2																	
3.	Eyemouth	240	10	3																
4.	Dunbar	257	26	17	4															
5.	North Berwick	266	35	25	9	5														
6.	Granton	285	54	44	27	19	6													
7.	**Port Edgar**	290	58	50	34	26	7	7												
8.	Burntisland	283	53	43	26	18	5	8	8											
9.	Methil	276	45	36	20	13	14	20	12	9										
10.	Anstruther	269	38	29	14	10	23	29	22	11	10									
11.	Fife Ness	269	38	29	17	14	28	34	27	16	5	11								
12.	Bell Rock	276	43	36	27	25	40	47	39	28	17	12	12							
13.	**Dundee**	289	58	49	37	34	48	54	47	36	25	20	20	13						
14.	Arbroath	284	51	44	34	31	45	51	44	33	22	17	10	15	14					
15.	Montrose	291	59	51	43	41	55	61	54	43	32	27	17	27	12	15				
16.	Stonehaven	300	72	66	60	58	72	78	71	60	49	44	32	45	30	20	16			
17.	**Aberdeen**	308	82	78	73	70	84	90	83	72	61	56	44	57	42	32	13	17		
18.	Peterhead	318	105	98	93	95	106	108	105	94	83	78	68	80	64	54	35	25	18	
19.	*Fraserburgh*	334	121	114	109	108	122	128	121	110	99	94	83	96	79	68	51	39	16	19
20.	*Wick*	391	178	171	166	165	179	185	178	167	156	151	140	153	136	125	108	96	72	57	20

EYEMOUTH   10-6-7

Borders 55°52′·51N 02°05′·19W   Rtg 3-3-1

CHARTS
AC 1612, 160; OS 67

TIDES
+0330 Dover; ML No data; Duration 0610; Zone 0 (UT)

Standard Port LEITH (⟶)

Times				Height (metres)			
High Water		Low Water		MHWS	MHWN	MLWN	MLWS
0300	0900	0300	0900	5·6	4·5	2·1	0·8
1500	2100	1500	2100				
Differences EYEMOUTH							
−0015	−0025	−0014	−0004	−0·9	−0·8	No data	

EYEMOUTH

⚓ Report to Hr Mr

SHELTER
Good in all weathers but entry should not be attempted in strong N/E'lies. Busy FV hbr, but yachts are welcome; expect to berth at E quay knuckle, near lifting bridge in about 2m; or ⚓ in bay, only in off-shore winds. Work on a new FV basin on E side of ent (thus more room for yachts in old hbr eventually) began 11/96; due to complete 9/98. Dredging ent to 3m is due in first half of '98.

NAVIGATION
WPT 55°53′·00N 02°05′·28W, 354°/174° from/to E bkwtr lt, 0·50M. Appr can be made N or S of Hurkar Rks but there are no ldg marks to the S; keep in mid-chan. To the N, beware Blind Buss. Ent and basin dredged to 0·9m.

LIGHTS AND MARKS
St. Abbs Hd lt ho Fl 10s 68m 26M is 3M NW. Ldg lts 174° (orange column) both FG 9/10m 6M on W pier. Ⓡ or R flag = unsafe to enter.

RADIO TELEPHONE
VHF Ch 16 12 (No regular watch).

TELEPHONE (Dial code 018907)
Hr Mr 50223; MRSC (01333) 450666; ⌗ (0141) 887 9369 (H24); Marinecall 0891 500452; Police 50217; Dr 50599.

FACILITIES
Jetty AB £4.00, FW, D (by delivery), P (cans), Slip;
Services: BY, ME, Sh, El, C (12 ton mobile), Ⓔ.
Town EC Wed; LB, P, D, CH, V, R, Bar, ✉, ▣, Gas, Gaz, Ⓑ, ≉ (bus to Berwick-on-Tweed), ✈ (Edinburgh).

ADJACENT HARBOURS

BURNMOUTH, Borders, 55°50′·60N 02°04′·00W. AC 160. HW +0315 on Dover, −0025 on Leith; Duration 0615. Use Eyemouth tides 10.6.7. From S beware Quarry Shoal Rks; and E & W Carrs from N. 2 W posts (FR 29/35m 4M) 45m apart, lead 253° to close N of the hbr; as hbr mouth opens, enter on about 185° with outer hbr ent in line with 2FG (vert). Min depth at ent at LWS is 0·6m. Shelter is good especially in inner hbr (dries). With on-shore winds, swell makes outer hbr uncomfortable. Hr Mr (018907) 81283. Facilities: AB £4, FW, limited V, Bar at top of valley.

ST ABBS, Borders, 55°54′·100N 02°07′·65W. AC 175. HW +0330 on Dover, −0017 on Leith; HW −0·6m on Leith; Duration 0605. Ldg line (about 228°) S face of Maw Carr on village hall (conspic R roof) leads SW until the hbr ent opens to port and the 2nd ldg line (about 167°) can be seen 2FR 4/8m 1M, or Y LB ho visible thru' ent. On E side of ent chan, beware Hog's Nose and on W side the Maw Carr. Shelter good. In strong on-shore winds outer hbr suffers from waves breaking over E pier. Inner hbr is best but often full of FVs and dries. Access HW±3. Hr Mr will direct visitors. Hr Mr (018907) 71323. Facilities: AB £6, FW on quay, R, V, more facilities & bar at Coldingham (5M).

DUNBAR   10-6-8

East Lothian 56°00′·39N 02°31′·00W   Rtg 3-4-1

CHARTS
AC 734, 175; Imray 27; OS 67

TIDES
+0330 Dover; ML 3·0; Duration 0600; Zone 0 (UT)

Standard Port LEITH (→)

Times				Height (metres)			
High Water		Low Water		MHWS	MHWN	MLWN	MLWS
0300	0900	0300	0900	5·6	4·5	2·1	0·8
1500	2100	1500	2100				
Differences DUNBAR							
−0005	−0010	+0010	+0017	−0·4	−0·3	−0·1	−0·1
FIDRA							
+0006	+0006	−0006	−0006	−0·2	−0·2	0·0	0·0

SHELTER
Outer (Victoria) Hbr is subject to surge in strong NW to NE winds. N side dries; berth on S quay and contact Hr Mr. Inner (Old or Cromwell) Hbr dries, but is safe except in strong onshore winds near HWS when swell enters: entry is through a bridge, lifted on request to Hr Mr.

NAVIGATION
WPT 56°00′·70N 02°30′·80W, 018°/198° from/to front ldg lt 198°, 0·50M. Beware Outer Buss Rk (0·6m), 4ca to E. Ent is unsafe in heavy on-shore swell. Min depth at ent 0·9m. Keep to port on entry to avoid rockfall off castle.

LIGHTS AND MARKS
Church and Castle ruin both conspic. From NE, ldg lts, Oc G 6s 15/22m 3M, synch, intens 188°-208°, 2 W △ on Or cols, lead 198° through the outer rks to the Roads; thence narrow ent opens with QR brg 132°. From NW, appr on brg 132° between bns on Wallaces Head and Half Ebb Rk.

RADIO TELEPHONE
None.

TELEPHONE (Dial code 01368)
Hr Mr 863206; MRSC (01333) 450666; ⌗ (0141) 887 9369 (H24); Police 862718; Marinecall 0891 500452; Dr 862327; Ⓗ (031) 2292477.

FACILITIES
Quay AB £5, Slip, FW, D (delivery), P (cans); **N Wall** M, AB; **Inner Hbr** Slip, AB; **Services** ME, Gas, Gaz.
Town EC Wed; LB, P, Ⓣ, V, R, Bar, ⊠, Ⓑ, ⇌, ✈ Edinburgh.

FIRTH OF FORTH   10-6-9

E and W Lothian/City of Edinburgh/Fife

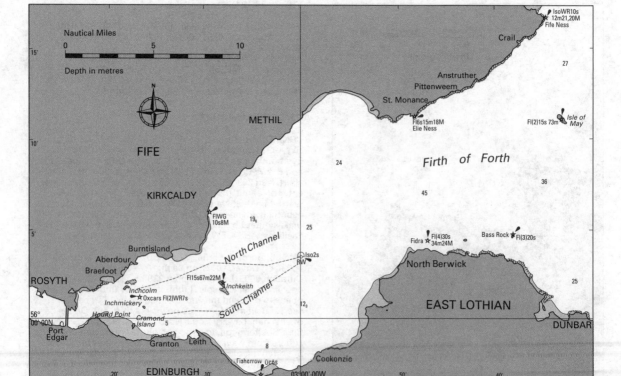

FIRTH OF FORTH *Continued*

CHARTS
AC 734, 735, 736; Imray C27; OS 66, 59

TIDES
+0350 (Granton) Dover; ML 3·3; Duration 0620; Zone 0 (UT)

Standard Port LEITH (→)

Times				Height (metres)			
High Water		Low Water		MHWS	MHWN	MLWN	MLWS
0300	0900	0300	0900	5·6	4·5	2·1	0·8
1500	2100	1500	2100				

Differences COCKENZIE

| −0007 | −0015 | −0013 | −0005 | −0·2 | 0·0 | No data | |

GRANTON: Same as LEITH
Kincardine: Time difference Leith +0030.
Alloa: Time difference Leith +0048.
Leith is a Standard Port and tidal predictions for each day of the year are given below.

SHELTER
Granton mostly dries and is open to swell in N'lies, but pontoons installed with 20 visitors' berths. Some berths also on E side of Middle pier in about 1·2m; Pilot boats berth at seaward end. W side is mainly for FVs.
Port Edgar marina offers good shelter, but prone to silting; do not enter E of wavebreak; 3kn speed limit. Leith is wholly commercial. Rosyth Naval Base to be used only in emergency.

NAVIGATION
WPT Granton 56°00'·00N 03°13'·22W, 000°/180° from/to ent, 0·72M.
WPT Port Edgar 56°N 03°24'·2W, 064°/244° from/to Dir Lt, Fl R 4s, on W bkwtr, 3ca. Beware Hound Pt terminal; Forth railway and road bridges; HM Ships entering and leaving Rosyth Naval Base. On N shore, no vessel may enter Mortimer's Deep (Braefoot gas terminal) without prior approval from Forth Navigation Service. 12kn speed limit W of Forth Rly Bridge.
Note: Forth Ports Authority controls the Forth Estuary, all commercial impounded docks and Granton Hbr.
A Protected Chan 150m wide extends from Nos 13 and 14 lt buoys (NNW of Oxcars) under the bridges (N of Inch Garvie and Beamer Rk), to the ent of Rosyth Dockyard. When the Protected Chan is in operation an Oc 5s lt and a QR lt are shown from N Queensferry Naval sig stn, and all other vessels must clear the chan for naval traffic.

LIGHTS AND MARKS
Granton: R flag with W diagonal cross (or Ⓖ lt) on signal mast at middle pier hd = Entry prohib.
Port Edgar: On W pier Dir lt Fl R 4s 4m 8M 244°; 4 QY lts mark floating bkwtr; 3 x 2 FR (vert) mark N ends of marina pontoons.

RADIO TELEPHONE
Call *Forth Navigation* (at Leith) Ch **71** (calling and short messages, H24) 16; 20 12 will be requested if necessary. Traffic, nav and weather info available on request.
Port Edgar Marina Ch M **80** (Apl-Sept 0900-1930; Oct-Mar 0900-1630 LT). Granton marina, call *Boswell* Ch M.
N Queensferry Naval Sig Stn at Battery Pt, call: *Queensferry* VHF Ch **74** 71 16 (H24).
Rosyth Naval Base, call *QHM* Ch 74 73 (Mon-Fri: 0730-1700).
Grangemouth Docks Ch 14 (H24). Leith Hbr Radio Ch 12.

TELEPHONE (Dial code 0131)
Hr Mr Leith 554 3661; MRSC (01333) 450666; ⌘ (0141) 887 9369 (H24); Weather (0141) 248 3451; Marinecall 0891 500452; Police (S. Queensferry) 331 1798; Ⓗ Edinburgh Royal Infirmary 229-2477; Flag Officer Scotland/Northern Ireland (01436) 674321 ext 3206, for Naval activities off N and E Scotland; Forth Yacht Clubs Ass'n 552 3452.

FACILITIES
GRANTON
Hr Mr ☎ 552 3385, AB £11.50, Access HW±3½, FW, Slip; **Royal Forth YC** ☎ 552 3006, ⚓ 552 8560, Slip, M, L, FW, C (5 ton), D, El, Bar; **Forth Corinthian YC** ☎ 552 5939, Slip, M, L, Bar; **Services:** Gas, Gaz, Sh, CH, ME.
Town D, P, V, R, Bar, ✉, Ⓑ, ⇌, ✈ (Buses to Edinburgh).
SOUTH QUEENSFERRY
Port Edgar Marina (300+8 visitors) ☎ 331 3330, ⚓ 331 4878, £12.33, Access H24, M, Slip, AC, CH, D, C (5 ton) on N end of main pier, El, Ⓔ, ME, Sh, SM, Gas, Gaz, FW, R; Port Edgar YC, Bar.
Town EC Wed; P, V, R, Bar, ✉, Ⓑ, ⇌ (Dalmeny), ✈ Edinburgh.
EDINBURGH: ACA.   *Continued overleaf*

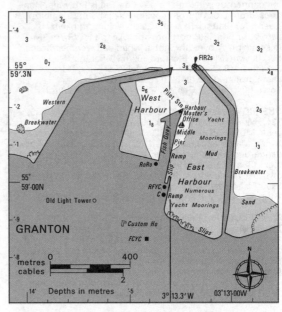

HARBOURS AND ANCHORAGES ON THE NORTH SHORE OF THE FIRTH OF FORTH

INCHCOLM, Fife, 56°01'·85N, 03°17'·80W. AC 736. Tides see 10.6.10. Best ⚓ in 4m, N of abbey (conspic); appr from NW or ESE, to land at pier close E (small fee). Meadulse Rks (dry) on N side. Ends of island foul. At SE end, lt Fl (3) 15s, obsc 075°-145°, horn (3) 45s. No facilities. ☎ 0131-244 3101. Keep clear of large ships under way in Mortimer's Deep.

ABERDOUR, Fife, 56°03'·00N 03°17'·40W. AC 735, 736. HW +0345 on Dover; +0005 on Leith; HW 0·5m on Leith; ML 3·3m; Duration 0630. See 10.6.10. Good shelter except in SE when a swell occurs. The ⚓ between The Little Craigs and the disused pier is good but exposed to winds from E to SW. Temp berths £2 are available in hbr (dries) alongside the quay wall. Beware Little Craigs (dries 2·2m) and outfall 2ca N marked by bn. There are no lts/ marks. Hr Mr ☎ (01383) 860452. Facilities: FW (tap on pier), P, R, V, Bar in village, EC Wed; **Aberdour BC** ☎ (01592) 202827.

BURNTISLAND: See 10.6.10
KIRKCALDY: See 10.6.11
METHIL: See 10.6.11

ELIE, Fife, 56°11'·20N 02°49'·20W. AC 734. HW +0325 on Dover, −0015 on Leith; HW −0·1m on Leith; ML 3·0m; Duration 0620; Elie B provides good shelter from N winds for small craft but local knowledge is needed. Hbr dries; 3 short term waiting buoys available. Beware ledge off end of pier which dries. From E beware Ox Rk (dries 1m) 5M ENE of Elie Ness; from W beware rks off Chapel Ness, W Vows, E Vows (surmounted by cage bn) and Thill Rk, marked by PHM buoy. Lt: Elie Ness Fl 6s 15m 18M, W tr. Hr Mr ☎ (01333) 330502; AB (3) drying £5, M, AC, FW, CH, SC, Slip. Police 310333. Dr ☎ 330302; **Services**: P & D (tanker), Gas, Gaz. El. In Elie & Earlsferry: R, V, Bar, ⊠, Ⓑ.

ST MONANS, Fife, 56°12'·25N 02°45'·85W. AC 734. HW +0335 on Dover, −0020 on Leith; HW −0·1m on Leith; ML 3·0m; Duration 0620. Shelter good except in strong SE to SW winds when scend occurs in the hbr (dries). Berth alongside E pier until contact with Hr Mr. From NE keep at least 2½ca from coast. Bkwtr hd Oc WRG 6s 5m 7/4M; E pier hd 2 FG (vert) 6m 4M. W pier hd 2 FR (vert) 6m 4M. Facilities: Hr Mr ☎ (01333) 730428; AB £5.10, FW, AC, El; **Services**: Gas, P & D (tanker), AC. **Village** R, Bar, V, ⊠, Ⓑ.

HARBOURS AND ANCHORAGES ON THE SOUTH SHORE OF THE FIRTH OF FORTH

NORTH BERWICK, East Lothian, 56°03'·74N 02°42'·95W. AC 734. Fidra HW +0344 on Dover; ML 3·0m; Duration 0625. See 10.6.8 Fidra. Shelter good with winds from S to W but dangerous with on-shore winds. Ent is 8m wide. Hbr dries. From E or W, from position 0·25M S of Craigleith, steer S for Plattock Rks, thence SSW 40m off bkwtr before turning 180° port into hbr. Bkwtr lt F WR 7m 3M, R to seaward, W over hbr; not lit when bad weather closes hbr. Beware Maiden Rks (bn) 100m NW of this lt. Facilities: AB £5.70, P & D (cans), FW on pier, CH; **East Lothian YC** ☎ (01620) 2698, M, 🛢s, Bar. **Town** EC Thurs; V, Gas, Ⓑ, ⊠, ⇌ and bus Edinburgh.

FISHERROW, East Lothian, 55°56'·79N 03°04'·00W. AC 735, 734. HW +0345 on Dover, −0005 on Leith; HW −0·1m on Leith; ML 3·0m; Duration 0620. Shelter good except in NW winds. Mainly a pleasure craft hbr, dries 5ca offshore. Appr dangerous in on-shore winds. Access HW±2. High-rise block (38m) is conspic 9ca W of hbr. E pier lt, Oc 6s 5m 6M on metal framework tr. Berth on E pier. Hr Mr ☎ (0131) 665 5900; **Fisherrow YC** FW. **Town** EC Wed; V, P & D from garage, R, Bar, Ⓑ, ⊠, SM.

CRAMOND, City of Edinburgh, 55°59'·80N 03°17'·40W. AC 736. Tides as Leith (see 10.6.9). Cramond Island, approx 1M offshore, is connected to the S shore of the Firth by a drying causeway. A chan, marked by 7 SHM posts, leads W of Cramond Island to Cramond hbr at the mouth of R Almond, conspic white houses. Access HW±2; AB free or ⚓ off the Is. Seek local advice from: **Cramond Boat Club** ☎ (0131) 336 1356, FW, M, Bar. **Village** V, R, Pub, Bus.

PITTENWEEM, Fife, 56°12'·60N 02°43'·70W. AC 734. HW +0325 Dover; −0015 and −0·1m on Leith; ML 3m. Duration 0620. Busy fishing hbr, dredged 1-2m, access all tides, but not in onshore winds. Yachts not encouraged; contact Hr Mr for berth at W end of inner hbr, but only for emergency use. Outer hbr dries to rock; is only suitable for temp stop in calm weather. Appr 037° on ldg marks/lts, Gy cols/Y stripe, both FR 3/8m 5M. Rks to port marked by bn, QR 3m 2M, and 3 unlit bns. E bkwtr lt Fl (2) RG 5s 9m 9/6M, R265°-345°, G345°-055°. No VHF. Hr Mr ☎ (01333) 312591. Facilities: FW, CH, D & P (tanker), Gas, V, Bar.

ANSTRUTHER: See 10.6.12

CRAIL, Fife, 56°15'·35N 02°37'·20W. AC 175. HW +0320 on Dover, −0020 on Leith; HW −0·2m on Leith; ML 3·0m; Duration 0615. Good shelter but only for boats able to take the ground alongside. Appr between S pier and bn on rks to S following ldg line 295°, two W concrete pillars with FR lts, 24/30m 6M. Turn 150° to stbd for ent. Call Forth CG on VHF Ch 16 before entering. Hr Mr ☎ (01333) 450820. Facilities: AB £5.10, El, FW, AC, Slip, P. **Village** EC Wed; Bar, R, V, ⊠, Ⓑ.

ISLE OF MAY, Fife, 56°11'·40N 02°33'·60W. AC 734. HW +0325 on Dover, −0025 on Leith. In settled weather only, and depending on the wind, ⚓ at E or W Tarbert in 4m; landing at Altarstanes. Near the SE tip there is a tiny hbr at Kirkhaven, with narrow, rky ent; yachts can moor fore-and-aft to rings in rks, in about 1-1·5m. SDs are needed. Beware Norman Rk to N of Island, and Maiden Hair Rk to S. At the summit, a ☐ tr on stone ho, Fl (2) 15s 73m 22M. The island is a bird sanctuary, owned by Scottish Natural Heritage ☎ (01334) 654038. Avoid the breeding season, mid-Mar to end Jul. Landing only at Altarstanes or Kirkhaven, 1000-1700; not on Tues, April to July inc.

SCOTLAND – LEITH

LAT 55°59′N   LONG   3°11′W

TIMES AND HEIGHTS OF HIGH AND LOW WATERS   YEAR **1998**

TIME ZONE (UT)
For Summer Time add ONE hour in non-shaded areas

6

JANUARY

Day	Time	m	Day	Time	m
1 TH	0409 / 1000 / 1622 / 2230	5.6 / 0.9 / 5.6 / 0.7	**16** F	0447 / 1013 / 1702 / 2244	5.3 / 1.3 / 5.3 / 1.0
2 F	0453 / 1043 / 1705 / 2315	5.6 / 1.0 / 5.6 / 0.8	**17** SA	0524 / 1038 / 1739 / 2312	5.1 / 1.4 / 5.2 / 1.2
3 SA	0539 / 1128 / 1752	5.5 / 1.2 / 5.5	**18** SU	0603 / 1109 / 1817 / 2346	5.0 / 1.6 / 5.0 / 1.4
4 SU	0000 / 0630 / 1215 / 1843	0.9 / 5.3 / 1.4 / 5.3	**19** M	0644 / 1145 / 1900	4.8 / 1.8 / 4.8
5 M	0049 / 0726 / 1308 / 1943	1.2 / 5.1 / 1.7 / 5.1	**20** TU	0028 / 0729 / 1231 / 1947	1.6 / 4.6 / 2.1 / 4.6
6 TU	0146 / 0828 / 1415 / 2051	1.4 / 5.0 / 1.8 / 5.0	**21** W	0121 / 0819 / 1335 / 2042	1.9 / 4.5 / 2.3 / 4.5
7 W	0301 / 0936 / 1533 / 2203	1.6 / 4.9 / 1.9 / 5.0	**22** TH	0228 / 0915 / 1506 / 2144	2.1 / 4.4 / 2.4 / 4.4
8 TH	0424 / 1045 / 1649 / 2313	1.6 / 4.9 / 1.8 / 5.0	**23** F	0351 / 1017 / 1635 / 2252	2.1 / 4.4 / 2.3 / 4.5
9 F	0536 / 1151 / 1756	1.6 / 5.1 / 1.6	**24** SA	0506 / 1123 / 1740	2.0 / 4.6 / 2.0
10 SA	0018 / 0633 / 1250 / 1855	5.1 / 1.5 / 5.2 / 1.3	**25** SU	0000 / 0602 / 1226 / 1832	4.6 / 1.8 / 4.8 / 1.7
11 SU	0115 / 0722 / 1341 / 1947	5.3 / 1.3 / 5.4 / 1.1	**26** M	0059 / 0650 / 1319 / 1919	4.9 / 1.5 / 5.1 / 1.3
12 M O	0205 / 0806 / 1426 / 2033	5.4 / 1.2 / 5.5 / 0.9	**27** TU	0147 / 0736 / 1403 / 2005	5.2 / 1.2 / 5.4 / 1.0
13 TU	0249 / 0846 / 1508 / 2115	5.5 / 1.1 / 5.5 / 0.8	**28** W ●	0229 / 0820 / 1444 / 2051	5.5 / 1.0 / 5.6 / 0.7
14 W	0331 / 0921 / 1548 / 2152	5.5 / 1.1 / 5.5 / 0.8	**29** TH	0311 / 0904 / 1524 / 2136	5.7 / 0.8 / 5.8 / 0.4
15 TH	0410 / 0950 / 1626 / 2221	5.4 / 1.2 / 5.4 / 0.9	**30** F	0352 / 0948 / 1604 / 2220	5.8 / 0.7 / 5.9 / 0.3
			31 SA	0435 / 1032 / 1648 / 2303	5.8 / 0.7 / 5.9 / 0.4

FEBRUARY

Day	Time	m	Day	Time	m
1 SU	0521 / 1114 / 1735 / 2345	5.7 / 0.8 / 5.7 / 0.6	**16** M	0529 / 1043 / 1744 / 2315	5.1 / 1.3 / 5.1 / 1.2
2 M	0610 / 1155 / 1825	5.5 / 1.1 / 5.5	**17** TU	0607 / 1108 / 1821 / 2347	4.9 / 1.5 / 4.9 / 1.4
3 TU	0026 / 0702 / 1239 / 1921	1.0 / 5.2 / 1.4 / 5.3	**18** W	0647 / 1139 / 1902	4.7 / 1.8 / 4.7
4 W	0113 / 0801 / 1337 / 2027	1.3 / 5.0 / 1.7 / 5.0	**19** TH	0024 / 0732 / 1222 / 1951	1.7 / 4.6 / 2.0 / 4.5
5 TH	0218 / 0908 / 1501 / 2141	1.7 / 4.8 / 1.9 / 4.8	**20** F	0119 / 0825 / 1334 / 2052	2.0 / 4.4 / 2.3 / 4.3
6 F	0356 / 1020 / 1634 / 2257	1.9 / 4.7 / 1.9 / 4.8	**21** SA	0243 / 0927 / 1536 / 2204	2.2 / 4.3 / 2.3 / 4.3
7 SA	0522 / 1134 / 1751	1.9 / 4.8 / 1.7	**22** SU	0426 / 1039 / 1710 / 2322	2.2 / 4.4 / 2.1 / 4.5
8 SU	0010 / 0623 / 1240 / 1852	4.9 / 1.8 / 5.0 / 1.4	**23** M	0537 / 1151 / 1812	1.9 / 4.7 / 1.7
9 M	0110 / 0711 / 1333 / 1941	5.1 / 1.6 / 5.2 / 1.2	**24** TU	0030 / 0630 / 1251 / 1902	4.8 / 1.6 / 5.0 / 1.3
10 TU	0159 / 0752 / 1418 / 2022	5.2 / 1.4 / 5.4 / 1.0	**25** W	0123 / 0718 / 1339 / 1950	5.2 / 1.2 / 5.4 / 0.8
11 W O	0239 / 0827 / 1457 / 2058	5.4 / 1.2 / 5.4 / 0.8	**26** TH ●	0208 / 0803 / 1421 / 2036	5.5 / 0.8 / 5.7 / 0.4
12 TH	0315 / 0859 / 1532 / 2129	5.4 / 1.1 / 5.5 / 0.8	**27** F	0250 / 0848 / 1502 / 2120	5.8 / 0.5 / 5.9 / 0.1
13 F	0349 / 0927 / 1605 / 2155	5.3 / 1.1 / 5.4 / 0.8	**28** SA	0331 / 0932 / 1544 / 2204	5.9 / 0.4 / 6.0 / 0.0
14 SA	0421 / 0952 / 1637 / 2220	5.3 / 1.1 / 5.4 / 0.8			
15 SU	0454 / 1017 / 1709 / 2247	5.2 / 1.2 / 5.3 / 1.0			

MARCH

Day	Time	m	Day	Time	m
1 SU	0415 / 1015 / 1629 / 2246	5.9 / 0.4 / 6.0 / 0.2	**16** M	0426 / 0957 / 1643 / 2222	5.2 / 1.0 / 5.3 / 0.9
2 M	0500 / 1056 / 1716 / 2326	5.8 / 0.6 / 5.9 / 0.5	**17** TU	0500 / 1020 / 1716 / 2247	5.1 / 1.1 / 5.1 / 1.1
3 TU	0548 / 1135 / 1807	5.5 / 0.8 / 5.6	**18** W	0535 / 1039 / 1751 / 2310	5.0 / 1.3 / 5.0 / 1.3
4 W	0003 / 0638 / 1216 / 1902	0.9 / 5.2 / 1.2 / 5.3	**19** TH	0612 / 1104 / 1830 / 2338	4.8 / 1.5 / 4.8 / 1.6
5 TH	0043 / 0735 / 1309 / 2007	1.4 / 4.9 / 1.6 / 4.9	**20** F	0653 / 1141 / 1917	4.6 / 1.7 / 4.5
6 F	0142 / 0841 / 1437 / 2120	1.9 / 4.7 / 1.9 / 4.7	**21** SA	0021 / 0743 / 1240 / 2015	1.9 / 4.5 / 2.0 / 4.4
7 SA	0332 / 0954 / 1625 / 2239	2.2 / 4.6 / 1.9 / 4.6	**22** SU	0145 / 0845 / 1432 / 2126	2.2 / 4.3 / 2.2 / 4.3
8 SU	0508 / 1113 / 1745 / 2357	2.1 / 4.6 / 1.7 / 4.7	**23** M	0349 / 0959 / 1637 / 2246	2.2 / 4.4 / 2.0 / 4.5
9 M	0610 / 1224 / 1843	1.9 / 4.8 / 1.4	**24** TU	0510 / 1116 / 1746 / 2359	1.9 / 4.6 / 1.6 / 4.8
10 TU	0058 / 0655 / 1319 / 1926	4.9 / 1.7 / 5.0 / 1.2	**25** W	0607 / 1220 / 1840	1.5 / 5.0 / 1.1
11 W	0145 / 0732 / 1402 / 2003	5.1 / 1.4 / 5.2 / 0.6	**26** TH	0056 / 0655 / 1311 / 1929	5.2 / 1.1 / 5.3 / 0.6
12 TH	0222 / 0804 / 1439 / 2034	5.2 / 1.2 / 5.3 / 0.8	**27** F	0143 / 0741 / 1356 / 2015	5.6 / 0.7 / 5.7 / 0.3
13 F O	0254 / 0834 / 1511 / 2101	5.3 / 1.0 / 5.4 / 0.7	**28** SA ●	0226 / 0827 / 1439 / 2100	5.8 / 0.4 / 6.0 / 0.0
14 SA	0324 / 0903 / 1541 / 2128	5.3 / 0.9 / 5.4 / 0.7	**29** SU	0309 / 0912 / 1523 / 2144	5.9 / 0.2 / 6.1 / 0.0
15 SU	0354 / 0931 / 1612 / 2155	5.3 / 0.9 / 5.4 / 0.7	**30** M	0353 / 0956 / 1610 / 2226	5.9 / 0.2 / 6.1 / 0.1
			31 TU	0438 / 1039 / 1658 / 2306	5.8 / 0.4 / 5.9 / 0.5

APRIL

Day	Time	m	Day	Time	m
1 W	0526 / 1120 / 1750 / 2343	5.5 / 0.7 / 5.6 / 1.0	**16** TH	0507 / 1021 / 1729 / 2243	5.0 / 1.1 / 5.0 / 1.3
2 TH	0616 / 1200 / 1846	5.2 / 1.1 / 5.2	**17** F	0543 / 1046 / 1808 / 2309	4.9 / 1.3 / 4.8 / 1.5
3 F	0018 / 0711 / 1251 / 1948	1.5 / 4.9 / 1.5 / 4.8	**18** SA	0624 / 1124 / 1855 / 2353	4.7 / 1.5 / 4.6 / 1.8
4 SA	0114 / 0815 / 1417 / 2057	2.0 / 4.6 / 1.8 / 4.6	**19** SU	0713 / 1223 / 1952	4.5 / 1.8 / 4.5
5 SU	0302 / 0927 / 1606 / 2212	2.3 / 4.5 / 1.8 / 4.5	**20** M	0118 / 0813 / 1404 / 2100	2.1 / 4.4 / 1.9 / 4.4
6 M	0440 / 1044 / 1723 / 2330	2.2 / 4.5 / 1.7 / 4.6	**21** TU	0316 / 0926 / 1600 / 2216	2.1 / 4.4 / 1.7 / 4.6
7 TU	0542 / 1156 / 1817	2.0 / 4.7 / 1.5	**22** W	0438 / 1042 / 1714 / 2328	1.8 / 4.6 / 1.4 / 4.9
8 W	0033 / 0626 / 1252 / 1858	4.8 / 1.7 / 4.9 / 1.3	**23** TH	0537 / 1148 / 1812	1.5 / 5.0 / 1.0
9 TH	0119 / 0702 / 1336 / 1932	5.0 / 1.5 / 5.0 / 1.1	**24** F	0027 / 0628 / 1242 / 1903	5.2 / 1.1 / 5.3 / 0.6
10 F	0156 / 0734 / 1412 / 2001	5.1 / 1.2 / 5.2 / 0.9	**25** SA	0117 / 0717 / 1330 / 1951	5.5 / 0.7 / 5.7 / 0.3
11 SA O	0227 / 0805 / 1445 / 2029	5.2 / 1.0 / 5.3 / 0.8	**26** SU ●	0202 / 0805 / 1416 / 2038	5.8 / 0.4 / 5.9 / 0.1
12 SU	0256 / 0837 / 1515 / 2058	5.2 / 0.9 / 5.3 / 0.7	**27** M	0246 / 0852 / 1503 / 2123	5.9 / 0.2 / 6.0 / 0.1
13 M	0327 / 0908 / 1547 / 2128	5.3 / 0.8 / 5.3 / 0.7	**28** TU	0331 / 0939 / 1552 / 2207	5.9 / 0.2 / 6.0 / 0.3
14 TU	0359 / 0937 / 1620 / 2157	5.2 / 0.9 / 5.2 / 0.9	**29** W	0418 / 1024 / 1642 / 2248	5.7 / 0.3 / 5.8 / 0.7
15 W	0433 / 1002 / 1653 / 2222	5.2 / 1.0 / 5.1 / 1.1	**30** TH	0506 / 1107 / 1735 / 2324	5.5 / 0.6 / 5.5 / 1.1

Chart Datum: 2·90 metres below Ordnance Datum (Newlyn)

SCOTLAND – LEITH

LAT 55°59′N   LONG   3°11′W

TIMES AND HEIGHTS OF HIGH AND LOW WATERS

YEAR **1998**

TIME ZONE (UT)
For Summer Time add ONE hour in non-shaded areas

MAY

Day	Time	m	Time	m	Time	m	Time	m
1 F	0556	5.2	1149	1.0	1829	5.1	2358	1.6
2 SA	0650	4.9	1237	1.4	1927	4.8		
3 SU	0046	2.0	0750	4.6	1348	1.7	2028	4.6
4 M	0212	2.2	0855	4.5	1524	1.8	2134	4.4
5 TU	0348	2.3	1004	4.4	1640	1.7	2245	4.5
6 W	0455	2.1	1114	4.5	1735	1.5	2350	4.6
7 TH	0544	1.8	1213	4.7	1817	1.4		
8 F	0041	4.8	0624	1.6	1301	4.9	1851	1.2
9 SA	0121	4.9	0700	1.3	1340	5.0	1923	1.0
10 SU	0155	5.1	0735	1.1	1415	5.1	1956	0.9
11 M ○	0227	5.2	0810	1.0	1449	5.2	2029	0.8
12 TU	0301	5.2	0845	0.9	1523	5.2	2103	0.8
13 W	0335	5.2	0918	0.9	1558	5.2	2135	0.9
14 TH	0410	5.2	0950	0.9	1633	5.1	2205	1.1
15 F	0444	5.1	1018	1.0	1710	5.0	2234	1.2
16 SA	0521	5.0	1048	1.2	1751	4.9	2306	1.5
17 SU	0603	4.9	1130	1.3	1838	4.8	2356	1.7
18 M	0652	4.7	1231	1.5	1934	4.7		
19 TU	0114	1.9	0750	4.6	1352	1.6	2038	4.6
20 W	0243	1.9	0859	4.6	1522	1.5	2148	4.7
21 TH	0401	1.7	1011	4.7	1639	1.3	2258	4.9
22 F	0505	1.5	1118	5.0	1742	1.4	2359	5.2
23 SA	0600	1.1	1216	5.3	1837	0.7		
24 SU	0052	5.4	0652	0.8	1309	5.5	1928	0.5
25 M	0140	5.6	0744	0.5	1358	5.7	●2017	0.4
26 TU	0227	5.7	0835	0.4	1448	5.8	2104	0.4
27 W	0313	5.7	0925	0.3	1537	5.8	2148	0.6
28 TH	0400	5.6	1012	0.4	1628	5.6	2230	0.8
29 F	0448	5.5	1056	0.6	1718	5.4	2306	1.2
30 SA	0537	5.2	1136	0.9	1809	5.1	2336	1.5
31 SU	0628	5.0	1215	1.2	1900	4.9		

JUNE

Day	Time	m	Time	m	Time	m	Time	m
1 M	0013	1.8	0721	4.7	1302	1.5	1953	4.6
2 TU	0112	2.1	0818	4.6	1409	1.7	2049	4.5
3 W	0233	2.2	0918	4.5	1528	1.8	2148	4.4
4 TH	0351	2.2	1020	4.4	1633	1.7	2250	4.5
5 F	0453	2.0	1121	4.5	1725	1.6	2348	4.6
6 SA	0542	1.8	1216	4.7	1808	1.4		
7 SU	0037	4.8	0625	1.5	1303	4.8	1846	1.3
8 M	0119	4.9	0705	1.3	1344	5.0	1924	1.1
9 TU	0158	5.1	0744	1.1	1422	5.1	2001	1.0
10 W	0236	5.2	0823	1.0	1500	5.2	○2039	1.0
11 TH	0313	5.3	0901	0.9	1537	5.2	2116	0.9
12 F	0349	5.3	0940	0.8	1614	5.2	2154	1.0
13 SA	0426	5.2	1019	0.8	1653	5.2	2233	1.1
14 SU	0504	5.2	1100	0.9	1736	5.1	2315	1.3
15 M	0547	5.1	1144	1.0	1823	4.7		
16 TU	0003	1.4	0635	5.0	1235	1.1	1916	4.9
17 W	0102	1.6	0730	4.9	1335	1.3	2016	4.9
18 TH	0210	1.7	0834	4.8	1447	1.3	2122	4.8
19 F	0324	1.7	0944	4.8	1604	1.3	2230	4.9
20 SA	0434	1.5	1052	5.0	1714	1.2	2334	5.1
21 SU	0536	1.3	1155	5.2	1816	1.0		
22 M	0031	5.3	0634	1.0	1253	5.4	1910	0.9
23 TU	0123	5.4	0730	0.8	1346	5.5	2000	0.8
24 W	0212	5.6	0823	0.6	1436	5.6	●2047	0.7
25 TH	0259	5.6	0913	0.5	1525	5.6	○2131	0.8
26 F	0346	5.6	0959	0.5	1613	5.5	2210	0.9
27 SA	0432	5.5	1046	0.6	1659	5.4	2244	1.2
28 SU	0517	5.3	1115	0.8	1744	5.2	2309	1.4
29 M	0602	5.1	1144	1.1	1828	4.9	2339	1.6
30 TU	0648	4.9	1217	1.3	1914	4.7		

JULY

Day	Time	m	Time	m	Time	m	Time	m
1 W	0022	1.9	0736	4.7	1304	1.6	2002	4.6
2 TH	0120	2.1	0828	4.5	1404	1.8	2054	4.4
3 F	0235	2.2	0923	4.4	1517	1.9	2149	4.4
4 SA	0355	2.2	1022	4.4	1629	1.8	2248	4.5
5 SU	0500	2.0	1125	4.5	1726	1.7	2348	4.6
6 M	0553	1.8	1223	4.7	1813	1.5		
7 TU	0042	4.8	0638	1.5	1313	4.8	1856	1.4
8 W	0129	5.0	0721	1.3	1357	5.0	1937	1.2
9 TH	0212	5.2	0815	1.0	1437	5.2	○2019	1.0
10 F	0251	5.3	0846	0.8	1525	5.3	2100	0.9
11 SA	0329	5.4	0929	0.7	1555	5.4	2143	0.8
12 SU	0407	5.5	1010	0.6	1636	5.4	2225	0.9
13 M	0447	5.5	1055	0.6	1719	5.4	2308	1.0
14 TU	0530	5.4	1138	0.7	1805	5.3	2353	1.1
15 W	0618	5.3	1223	0.9	1856	5.2		
16 TH	0041	1.4	0710	5.2	1313	1.1	1953	5.0
17 F	0138	1.6	0811	5.0	1414	1.3	2056	4.9
18 SA	0250	1.7	0921	4.9	1533	1.5	2204	4.9
19 SU	0409	1.7	1033	4.9	1655	1.5	2313	5.0
20 M	0522	1.5	1142	5.0	1802	1.4		
21 TU	0017	5.1	0626	1.2	1246	5.2	1858	1.2
22 W	0113	5.3	0723	1.0	1340	5.3	1946	1.1
23 TH	0203	5.4	0814	0.7	1429	5.5	●2031	1.0
24 F	0248	5.5	0900	0.6	1513	5.5	2111	0.9
25 SA	0332	5.5	0942	0.6	1555	5.5	2147	1.0
26 SU	0413	5.5	1018	0.6	1636	5.4	2216	1.1
27 M	0453	5.4	1046	0.8	1714	5.2	2240	1.2
28 TU	0531	5.2	1110	1.0	1753	5.0	2306	1.4
29 W	0610	5.0	1139	1.2	1834	4.9	2339	1.6
30 TH	0652	4.8	1216	1.4	1917	4.7		
31 F	0021	1.9	0737	4.6	1304	1.7	2004	4.5

AUGUST

Day	Time	m	Time	m	Time	m	Time	m
1 SA	0120	2.1	0829	4.5	1406	2.0	2057	4.4
2 SU	0244	2.3	0927	4.4	1527	2.1	2155	4.4
3 M	0416	2.2	1032	4.4	1646	2.0	2259	4.5
4 TU	0523	2.0	1141	4.5	1744	1.8		
5 W	0004	4.7	0615	1.7	1242	4.8	1832	1.6
6 TH	0100	5.0	0702	1.4	1331	5.0	1917	1.3
7 F	0147	5.2	0746	1.0	1414	5.3	2000	1.0
8 SA	0228	5.5	0831	0.7	1455	5.5	○2043	0.8
9 SU	0307	5.6	0914	0.4	1534	5.7	2127	0.6
10 M	0346	5.8	0958	0.3	1615	5.7	2210	0.6
11 TU	0427	5.8	1041	0.3	1659	5.7	2253	0.7
12 W	0511	5.7	1123	0.4	1745	5.5	2334	0.9
13 TH	0558	5.6	1204	0.7	1834	5.3		
14 F	0018	1.2	0650	5.4	1247	1.1	1929	5.1
15 SA	0110	1.5	0752	5.1	1343	1.5	2032	4.9
16 SU	0224	1.7	0903	4.9	1509	1.8	2142	4.8
17 M	0356	1.8	1019	4.8	1644	1.8	2256	4.8
18 TU	0519	1.6	1135	4.9	1755	1.7		
19 W	0006	5.0	0625	1.3	1242	5.1	1848	1.5
20 TH	0106	5.2	0719	1.0	1335	5.3	1933	1.3
21 F	0154	5.4	0804	0.8	1420	5.4	2012	1.2
22 SA	0236	5.5	0844	0.7	1458	5.4	●2048	1.0
23 SU	0315	5.5	0918	0.6	1534	5.4	2119	1.0
24 M	0351	5.5	0948	0.6	1609	5.4	2147	1.0
25 TU	0424	5.4	1013	0.7	1642	5.3	2211	1.1
26 W	0458	5.3	1037	0.8	1718	5.2	2235	1.3
27 TH	0533	5.2	1104	1.1	1755	5.0	2301	1.5
28 F	0611	5.0	1135	1.4	1835	4.8	2332	1.7
29 SA	0653	4.7	1212	1.7	1919	4.6		
30 SU	0013	2.0	0741	4.5	1303	2.0	2009	4.5
31 M	0123	2.3	0838	4.4	1423	2.3	2108	4.4

Chart Datum: 2·90 metres below Ordnance Datum (Newlyn)

SCOTLAND – LEITH

LAT 55°59′N   LONG 3°11′W

TIMES AND HEIGHTS OF HIGH AND LOW WATERS   YEAR **1998**

TIME ZONE (UT)
For Summer Time add ONE hour in non-shaded areas

6

SEPTEMBER

Day	Time	m	Day	Time	m
1 TU	0321 / 0945 / 1605 / 2215	2.4 / 4.3 / 2.3 / 4.4	16 W	0517 / 1125 / 1744 / 2353	1.7 / 4.8 / 2.0 / 5.0
2 W	0455 / 1100 / 1717 / 2326	2.1 / 4.4 / 2.0 / 4.6	17 TH	0619 / 1232 / 1834	1.4 / 5.0 / 1.7
3 TH	0554 / 1209 / 1810	1.7 / 4.7 / 1.7	18 F	0052 / 0706 / 1323 / 1913	5.2 / 1.1 / 5.2 / 1.5
4 F	0029 / 0642 / 1304 / 1856	5.0 / 1.3 / 5.1 / 1.3	19 SA	0139 / 0745 / 1403 / 1948	5.4 / 1.0 / 5.3 / 1.3
5 SA	0119 / 0728 / 1349 / 1940	5.3 / 0.9 / 5.5 / 1.0	20 SU ●	0218 / 0819 / 1438 / 2020	5.5 / 0.8 / 5.4 / 1.1
6 SU O	0201 / 0812 / 1430 / 2023	5.6 / 0.5 / 5.7 / 0.7	21 M	0253 / 0848 / 1509 / 2050	5.5 / 0.7 / 5.4 / 1.0
7 M	0241 / 0855 / 1511 / 2107	5.9 / 0.2 / 5.9 / 0.5	22 TU	0324 / 0915 / 1540 / 2118	5.5 / 0.7 / 5.4 / 1.0
8 TU	0322 / 0939 / 1553 / 2151	6.0 / 0.1 / 5.9 / 0.4	23 W	0355 / 0940 / 1611 / 2144	5.5 / 0.8 / 5.4 / 1.1
9 W	0404 / 1021 / 1636 / 2233	6.1 / 0.1 / 5.9 / 0.5	24 TH	0428 / 1006 / 1645 / 2208	5.4 / 0.9 / 5.3 / 1.2
10 TH	0450 / 1102 / 1722 / 2315	6.0 / 0.4 / 5.7 / 0.8	25 F	0502 / 1031 / 1721 / 2229	5.2 / 1.1 / 5.1 / 1.4
11 F	0539 / 1142 / 1812 / 2357	5.7 / 0.8 / 5.4 / 1.1	26 SA	0538 / 1056 / 1758 / 2254	5.0 / 1.4 / 4.9 / 1.6
12 SA	0633 / 1222 / 1907	5.4 / 1.3 / 5.1	27 SU	0618 / 1124 / 1839 / 2329	4.8 / 1.7 / 4.8 / 1.9
13 SU	0049 / 0735 / 1317 / 2010	1.5 / 5.1 / 1.8 / 4.9	28 M	0704 / 1204 / 1928	4.6 / 2.0 / 4.6
14 M	0207 / 0848 / 1452 / 2122	1.8 / 4.8 / 2.1 / 4.7	29 TU	0024 / 0759 / 1322 / 2026	2.1 / 4.4 / 2.3 / 4.5
15 TU	0352 / 1006 / 1635 / 2239	1.9 / 4.7 / 2.1 / 4.8	30 W	0219 / 0906 / 1522 / 2135	2.3 / 4.4 / 2.4 / 4.5

OCTOBER

Day	Time	m	Day	Time	m
1 TH	0419 / 1022 / 1647 / 2249	2.1 / 4.5 / 2.1 / 4.7	16 F	0558 / 1209 / 1808	1.5 / 4.9 / 1.9
2 F	0527 / 1135 / 1744 / 2355	1.7 / 4.8 / 1.8 / 5.0	17 SA	0027 / 0642 / 1259 / 1845	5.1 / 1.3 / 5.1 / 1.6
3 SA	0618 / 1234 / 1832	1.3 / 5.2 / 1.3	18 SU	0114 / 0717 / 1338 / 1918	5.2 / 1.1 / 5.3 / 1.4
4 SU	0048 / 0704 / 1322 / 1916	5.4 / 0.8 / 5.6 / 1.0	19 M	0153 / 0746 / 1422 / 1949	5.4 / 1.0 / 5.4 / 1.2
5 M O	0133 / 0748 / 1404 / 2000	5.7 / 0.4 / 5.8 / 0.6	20 TU ●	0227 / 0814 / 1442 / 2021	5.4 / 0.9 / 5.4 / 1.1
6 TU	0215 / 0833 / 1446 / 2045	6.0 / 0.2 / 6.0 / 0.4	21 W	0258 / 0841 / 1511 / 2051	5.5 / 0.8 / 5.4 / 1.0
7 W	0257 / 0917 / 1529 / 2130	6.2 / 0.1 / 6.1 / 0.4	22 TH	0329 / 0910 / 1543 / 2120	5.4 / 0.9 / 5.4 / 1.1
8 TH	0343 / 1000 / 1613 / 2215	6.2 / 0.2 / 6.0 / 0.5	23 F	0402 / 0938 / 1617 / 2146	5.4 / 1.0 / 5.3 / 1.2
9 F	0431 / 1042 / 1700 / 2258	6.0 / 0.5 / 5.8 / 0.7	24 SA	0437 / 1042 / 1651 / 2208	5.2 / 1.1 / 5.2 / 1.3
10 SA	0522 / 1122 / 1750 / 2343	5.8 / 0.9 / 5.5 / 1.1	25 SU	0513 / 1027 / 1727 / 2233	5.1 / 1.4 / 5.0 / 1.5
11 SU	0617 / 1201 / 1845	5.5 / 1.5 / 5.1	26 M	0552 / 1052 / 1807 / 2308	4.9 / 1.7 / 4.9 / 1.7
12 M	0035 / 0720 / 1254 / 1949	1.5 / 5.2 / 2.0 / 4.9	27 TU	0637 / 1129 / 1854	4.7 / 2.0 / 4.7
13 TU	0155 / 0831 / 1430 / 2101	1.8 / 4.8 / 2.3 / 4.7	28 W	0001 / 0731 / 1240 / 1950	1.9 / 4.6 / 2.3 / 4.6
14 W	0340 / 0946 / 1612 / 2216	1.9 / 4.7 / 2.3 / 4.7	29 TH	0138 / 0835 / 1440 / 2059	2.1 / 4.5 / 2.4 / 4.6
15 TH	0500 / 1103 / 1719 / 2328	1.7 / 4.7 / 2.1 / 4.9	30 F	0332 / 0948 / 1610 / 2213	2.0 / 4.6 / 2.1 / 4.7
			31 SA	0450 / 1100 / 1712 / 2320	1.6 / 4.9 / 1.8 / 5.0

NOVEMBER

Day	Time	m	Day	Time	m
1 SU	0547 / 1202 / 1803	1.2 / 5.2 / 1.4	16 M	0041 / 0639 / 1306 / 1845	5.1 / 1.4 / 5.1 / 1.6
2 M	0016 / 0636 / 1253 / 1850	5.4 / 0.8 / 5.6 / 1.0	17 TU	0123 / 0710 / 1341 / 1920	5.2 / 1.2 / 5.2 / 1.4
3 TU	0105 / 0723 / 1338 / 1937	5.7 / 0.5 / 5.8 / 0.7	18 W	0159 / 0740 / 1414 / 1954	5.3 / 1.1 / 5.3 / 1.2
4 W O	0150 / 0809 / 1422 / 2024	6.0 / 0.3 / 6.0 / 0.5	19 TH ●	0233 / 0811 / 1446 / 2027	5.3 / 1.0 / 5.1 / 1.1
5 TH	0236 / 0855 / 1506 / 2112	6.1 / 0.2 / 6.0 / 0.4	20 F	0306 / 0843 / 1519 / 2100	5.4 / 1.0 / 5.4 / 1.1
6 F	0324 / 0940 / 1552 / 2159	6.1 / 0.4 / 5.9 / 0.5	21 SA	0341 / 0915 / 1553 / 2131	5.3 / 1.1 / 5.3 / 1.1
7 SA	0414 / 1024 / 1640 / 2246	6.0 / 0.7 / 5.8 / 0.7	22 SU	0416 / 0945 / 1628 / 2200	5.3 / 1.2 / 5.3 / 1.2
8 SU	0507 / 1105 / 1730 / 2332	5.7 / 1.1 / 5.5 / 1.0	23 M	0453 / 1013 / 1703 / 2230	5.1 / 1.4 / 5.1 / 1.4
9 M	0602 / 1143 / 1826	5.4 / 1.6 / 5.2	24 TU	0532 / 1042 / 1742 / 2307	5.0 / 1.6 / 5.0 / 1.5
10 TU	0023 / 0702 / 1229 / 1927	1.4 / 5.1 / 2.0 / 4.9	25 W	0616 / 1121 / 1828 / 2359	4.9 / 1.8 / 4.9 / 1.7
11 W	0131 / 0806 / 1346 / 2034	1.7 / 4.8 / 2.3 / 4.7	26 TH	0708 / 1226 / 1922	4.8 / 2.1 / 4.8
12 TH	0302 / 0913 / 1523 / 2142	1.9 / 4.7 / 2.4 / 4.7	27 F	0113 / 0808 / 1400 / 2026	1.8 / 4.7 / 2.2 / 4.7
13 F	0422 / 1022 / 1635 / 2250	1.8 / 4.7 / 2.3 / 4.8	28 SA	0242 / 0916 / 1525 / 2137	1.8 / 4.7 / 2.1 / 4.8
14 SA	0520 / 1129 / 1727 / 2351	1.7 / 4.8 / 2.1 / 4.9	29 SU	0405 / 1026 / 1634 / 2246	1.6 / 4.7 / 1.8 / 5.0
15 SU	0604 / 1223 / 1809	1.5 / 5.0 / 1.8	30 M	0511 / 1130 / 1732 / 2347	1.3 / 5.2 / 1.5 / 5.3

DECEMBER

Day	Time	m	Day	Time	m
1 TU	0608 / 1225 / 1825	1.0 / 5.5 / 1.2	16 W	0050 / 0634 / 1308 / 1853	4.9 / 1.5 / 5.0 / 1.6
2 W	0041 / 0700 / 1315 / 1916	5.6 / 0.8 / 5.7 / 0.9	17 TH	0132 / 0710 / 1346 / 1931	5.1 / 1.4 / 5.2 / 1.4
3 TH	0131 / 0749 / 1402 / 2008	5.8 / 0.6 / 5.9 / 0.6	18 F ●	0210 / 0745 / 1423 / 2007	5.2 / 1.3 / 5.3 / 1.2
4 F	0221 / 0837 / 1448 / 2059	6.0 / 0.6 / 5.9 / 0.5	19 SA	0246 / 0821 / 1458 / 2044	5.3 / 1.2 / 5.4 / 1.1
5 SA	0310 / 0924 / 1535 / 2148	6.0 / 0.7 / 5.9 / 0.5	20 SU	0322 / 0857 / 1534 / 2121	5.3 / 1.2 / 5.4 / 1.1
6 SU	0401 / 1008 / 1623 / 2235	5.9 / 0.9 / 5.7 / 0.7	21 M	0358 / 0933 / 1609 / 2158	5.3 / 1.2 / 5.4 / 1.1
7 M	0452 / 1049 / 1713 / 2320	5.7 / 1.2 / 5.5 / 0.9	22 TU	0435 / 1008 / 1644 / 2235	5.3 / 1.3 / 5.3 / 1.1
8 TU	0545 / 1124 / 1805	5.4 / 1.6 / 5.3	23 W	0514 / 1045 / 1723 / 2315	5.2 / 1.4 / 5.2 / 1.2
9 W	0003 / 0638 / 1157 / 1900	1.2 / 5.1 / 1.9 / 5.0	24 TH	0558 / 1125 / 1807 / 2359	5.1 / 1.6 / 5.1 / 1.3
10 TH	0049 / 0733 / 1246 / 1959	1.6 / 4.8 / 2.2 / 4.8	25 F	0647 / 1215 / 1857	5.0 / 1.8 / 5.0
11 F	0149 / 0831 / 1400 / 2059	1.8 / 4.7 / 2.4 / 4.7	26 SA	0052 / 0741 / 1320 / 1955	1.5 / 4.9 / 1.9 / 4.9
12 SA	0307 / 0930 / 1525 / 2201	1.9 / 4.6 / 2.4 / 4.6	27 SU	0157 / 0844 / 1437 / 2102	1.6 / 4.9 / 2.0 / 4.9
13 SU	0418 / 1032 / 1634 / 2303	1.9 / 4.6 / 2.3 / 4.7	28 M	0315 / 0952 / 1554 / 2214	1.6 / 4.9 / 1.9 / 5.0
14 M	0512 / 1133 / 1728	1.8 / 4.7 / 2.0	29 TU	0435 / 1100 / 1703 / 2322	1.5 / 5.0 / 1.7 / 5.2
15 TU	0001 / 0556 / 1225 / 1812	4.8 / 1.7 / 4.9 / 1.8	30 W	0544 / 1202 / 1806	1.3 / 5.2 / 1.4
			31 TH	0023 / 0642 / 1257 / 1903	5.4 / 1.1 / 5.5 / 1.1

Chart Datum: 2·90 metres below Ordnance Datum (Newlyn)

H.W.Hts.m.

LEITH
MEAN SPRING
AND NEAP CURVES

MEAN RANGES	
Springs	4·8m ———
Neaps	2·4m - - - -

Springs occur 2 days
after
New and Full Moon.

CHART DATUM

M.H.W.N.   M.H.W.S.

Factor

M.L.W.S.   M.L.W.N.

L.W.Hts.m.

L.W −5ʰ −4ʰ −3ʰ −2ʰ −1ʰ H.W +1ʰ +2ʰ +3ʰ +4ʰ +5ʰ L.W

BURNTISLAND

Fife 56°03′·23N 03°14′·12W   Rtg 3-5-3

10-6-10

CHARTS
AC 733, 739, 735; Imray C27; OS 66

TIDES
+0340 Dover; ML 3·3; Duration 0625; Zone 0 (UT)

Standard Port LEITH (←—)

Times				Height (metres)			
High Water		Low Water		MHWS	MHWN	MLWN	MLWS
0300	0900	0300	0900	5·6	4·5	2·1	0·8
1500	2100	1500	2100				
Differences BURNTISLAND							
+0002	−0002	+0002	−0003	0·0	0·0	+0·1	+0·1

SHELTER
Outer hbr gives only fair shelter, not suitable for yachts in strong winds. Island Jetty is unsafe. Good shelter in the industrial docks; E Dock access HW−3 to HW, but only in emergency.

NAVIGATION
WPT 56°03′·00N 03°14′·00W, 163°/343° from/to ent, 0·23M. To the E, beware Black Rks (off chartlet) and to the W, Familars Rks. Keep clear of ships using DG ranges SW of port. Commercial barge operations can cause delays.

LIGHTS AND MARKS
Conspic marks: Radio mast 1·1M N of hbr ent; shed to NW; lt tr on W pier head; radar tr at root of E pier. Lts as chartlet. Tfc sigs are for E dock only.

RADIO TELEPHONE
Forth Navigation Ch **71** 16 12 20 (H24), for ent to E Dock.

TELEPHONE (Dial code 01592)
Hr Mr (01333) 426725; MRSC (01333) 450666; ⊞ (0141) 887 9369 (H24); Marinecall 0891 500452; Police 204444; Dr 872761.

FACILITIES
Dock ☎ 872236, AB (limited) £20, FW, C (10 ton); **Outer Hbr** Slip, FW, AB (limited); **Burntisland YC** M or AB for small fee, if room in Boat Shelter; FW; **Services**: D, ME ☎ 872939, El, Ⓔ, Sh, BY, C (80 & 30 ton), CH, Gas, Gaz. **Town** EC Wed; P, D, ME, El, C, V, R, Bar, ⊠, Ⓑ, ⇌, Ⓗ Kirkcaldy, ✈ Edinburgh.

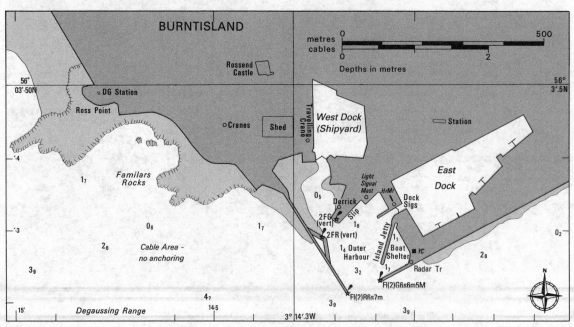

BURNTISLAND

Rossend
Castle

metres   0   500
cables
                        2
Depths in metres

56°
03′·50N   56°
                                                           3′·5N
  DG Station
Ross Point   Travelling Crane   West Dock
                                                        (Shipyard)   Station
·4   Cranes   Shed
                                                                          East
          Familars   Dock
          Rocks
·3   Light Signal Mast   HrMr   Dock Sigs
                                0·5   Derrick   0·2
                        0·8   2FG (vert)   Slip 1·8
                                             1·7
                        2·6   2FR (vert)
          Cable Area –   1·4 Outer   Boat   ■ YC
          no anchoring   Harbour Shelter
3·9   3·2 1·7 Radar Tr   2·6
                                                  Fl(2)G6s6m5M
                              4·2   Fl(2)R6s7m
                    Degaussing Range 14·5   3·9   3·9
15′   3° 14′·3W

METHIL　　10-6-11

Fife 56°10'·76N 03°00'·45W　Rtg 3-5-3

CHARTS
AC 739, 734; Imray C27; OS 59

TIDES
+0330 Dover; ML 3·0; Duration 0615; Zone 0 (UT)

Standard Port LEITH (←)

Times				Height (metres)			
High Water		Low Water		MHWS	MHWN	MLWN	MLWS
0300	0900	0300	0900	5·6	4·5	2·1	0·8
1500	2100	1500	2100				
Differences METHIL							
+0007	+0007	−0007	−0007	0·0	0·0	+0·1	+0·1
KIRKCALDY							
+0009	+0009	−0009	−0009	−0·3	−0·3	−0·2	−0·2

SHELTER
Commercial port, but good emergency shelter in No 2 dock.

NAVIGATION
WPT 56°10'·50N 03°00'·00W, 140°/320° from/to pier hd lt, 0·34M. Beware silting. A sand bar forms rapidly to seaward of the lt ho and dredged depth is not always maintained.

LIGHTS AND MARKS
By day and night (vert lts):

®/Ⓖ　=　Dangerous to enter; Bring up in roads.

®/Ⓦ　=　Clear to enter No 2 dock.

®　=　Remain in roads until another signal is made.

RADIO TELEPHONE
Methil Docks Radio VHF Ch 14 16 (HW−3 to +1). Forth Navigation Ch 71 (H24).

TELEPHONE (Dial code 01592)
Hr Mr (Port Manager) (01333) 426725; MRSC (01333) 450666; ⌗ (0141) 887 9369 (H24); Marinecall 0891 500452; Police 712881; Dr (01333) 426913.

FACILITIES
Hbr No 2 Dock £20, FW, C (7 ton).
Town EC Thurs; P, D, Gas, Gaz, V, R, Bar, ✉, Ⓑ, ⇌ (bus to Markinch or Kirkcaldy), Ⓗ Kirkcaldy, ✈ Edinburgh.

ADJACENT HARBOUR, 6M to SW.

KIRKCALDY, Fife, 56°06'·81N 03°08'·86W. AC 739. HW +0345 on Dover, −0005 on Leith; HW −0·1m on Leith; ML 3·2m; Duration 0620. See 10.6.11. Shelter good except in strong E winds; an emergency refuge. Officially the hbr is closed (no commercial tfc) and unmanned; depths may be less than charted due to silting. Small craft should contact Forth Ports Authority ☎ (01333) 426725, or call Forth Navigation Ch 71 (H24) or *Methil Docks Radio* Ch 16 14 for advice.

ANSTRUTHER　　10-6-12

Fife 56°13'·16N 02°41'·72W　Rtg 3-2-2

CHARTS
AC 734, 175; Imray C27; OS 59

TIDES
+0315 Dover; ML 3·1; Duration 0620; Zone 0 (UT)

Standard Port LEITH (←)

Times				Height (metres)			
High Water		Low Water		MHWS	MHWN	MLWN	MLWS
0300	0900	0300	0900	5·6	4·5	2·1	0·8
1500	2100	1500	2100				
Differences ANSTRUTHER EASTER							
−0010	−0035	−0020	−0020	−0·1	−0·1	−0·1	−0·1

SHELTER
Good, but dangerous to enter in strong E & S winds. Hbr dries; access approx HW±2. Caution: ledge at base of W pier. No ⚓ to W of hbr; do not go N of W pier lt due to rks.

NAVIGATION
WPT 56°12'·60N 02°42'·10W, 199°/019° from/to ent, 0·60M. Beware lobster pots and FVs.

LIGHTS AND MARKS
Conspic tr on W pier. Ldg lts 019°, both FG 7/11m 4M. Pier lts as chartlet. Horn (3) 60s in conspic tr.

RADIO TELEPHONE
None. Call Forth CG or Forth Navigation Service Ch 71.

TELEPHONE (Dial code 01333)
Hr Mr 310836; MRSC (01333) 450666; ⌗ (01382) 200822 (HO) or (0141) 887 9369 (H24); Marinecall 0891 500452; Police 310333; Dr 310352.

FACILITIES
Hbr AB £6.50, £12.00 >12m LOA, Slip, FW, LB, AC, Shwrs;
Services: D (tanker), CH, ACA, ME, Gas, Gaz, El, Ⓔ, Ⓢ.
Town EC Wed; P, V, R, Bar, ✉, Ⓑ, ⇌ (bus Cupar or Leuchars), Ⓗ St Andrews, ✈ Edinburgh/Dundee.

RIVER TAY   10-6-13

Fife/Angus   Tayport (56°27'·11N 02°52'·78W)   Rtg 3-3-2

CHARTS
AC 1481, 190; OS 54, 59

TIDES
+0401 (Dundee) Dover; ML 3·1; Duration 0610; Zone 0 (UT)

Standard Port ABERDEEN (→)

Times				Height (metres)			
High Water		Low Water		MHWS	MHWN	MLWN	MLWS
0000	0600	0100	0700	4·3	3·4	1·6	0·6
1200	1800	1300	1900				
Differences BAR							
+0100	+0100	+0050	+0110	+0·9	+0·8	+0·3	+0·1
DUNDEE							
+0140	+0120	+0055	+0145	+1·1	+0·9	+0·3	+0·1
NEWBURGH							
+0215	+0200	+0250	+0335	−0·2	−0·4	−1·1	−0·5
PERTH							
+0220	+0225	+0510	+0530	−0·9	−1·4	−1·2	−0·3

NOTE: At Perth LW time differences give the start of the rise, following a LW stand of about 4 hours.

SHELTER
Good in the Tay Estuary, but ent is dangerous in strong E/SE winds or on-shore swell. **Tayport** is best place for yachts on passage, access HW±4. Hbr partly dries except W side of NE pier; S side is full of yacht moorings. At **Dundee** commercial dock (Camperdown), gates open HW−2 to HW (Fl R lt = no entry/exit). Possible moorings off Royal Tay YC. ⚓s as on chartlet: the ⚓ off the city is exposed and landing difficult. Off S bank good shelter at Woodhaven and ⚓s from Wormit BC. There are ⚓s up river at Balmerino, Newburgh and Inchyra.

NAVIGATION
WPT Tay Fairway SWM buoy, L Fl 10s, Bell, 56°28'·92N 02°37'·42W, 046°/226° from/to the Middle Bar buoys, 9½ca. Chan is well buoyed, least depth 5·2m. Beware strong tidal streams. Do not attempt to cross Abertay or Gaa Sands as charted depths are unreliable.

LIGHTS AND MARKS
Tayport High It Dir 269° Iso WRG 3s, W sector 268°-270°. The HFP "Abertay" ECM buoy, Q (3) 10s (Racon), at E end of Gaa Sands is a clear visual mark. Keep N of Larick, a conspic disused lt bn.

RADIO TELEPHONE
Dundee Hbr Radio VHF Ch **12** 16 (H24); local nav warnings, weather, vis and tides on request. Royal Tay YC, Ch M.

TELEPHONE (Dial code 01382)
Hr Mr (Dundee) 224121/☎ 200834; Hr Mr (Perth) (01738) 624056; MRSC (01333) 450666; ⊞ 200822; Marinecall 0891 500452; Tayport Boatowners' Ass'n 553679; Police (Tayport) 552222, (Dundee) 223200; Dr 221953; Ⓗ 223125.

FACILITIES
N BANK: **Camperdown Dock**, AB £15, FW, ME, El, C (8 ton); **Victoria Dock** FW, ME, C (8 ton), AB; **Royal Tay YC** (Broughty Ferry) ☎ 477516, ⚓s free, L, R, Bar; **Services:** CH, M, L, ME, El, Sh, C (2 ton), ACA. **Dundee City** EC Wed; P, D, CH, V, R, Bar, ✉, Ⓑ, ⇌, ✈.
S BANK: **Tayport Hbr** ☎ 553679 AB £7.05, Slip, L, FW, AC; **Wormit Boating Club** ☎ 541400 ⚓s free, Slip, L, FW, V.

ADJACENT HARBOURS

PERTH, Perth & Kinross, 56°22'·90N 03°25'·65W. AC 1481; OS 53, 58. Tides, see 10.6.13. FYCA Pilot Handbook is needed. Leave Tay rly bridge at about HW Dundee −2 to carry a fair tide the 16·5M to Perth. The buoyed/lit chan favours the S bank for 9M to Newburgh. Here care is needed due to mudbanks in mid-stream; keep S of Mugdrum Is. Up-river, power cables have clearance of 33m and Friarton bridge 26m. Keep S of Willow Is, past the gasworks to hbr on the W bank. Hbr has approx 1·5m; keep clear of coasters. See Hr Mr, ☎ (01738) 624056, for berth. VHF Ch 09 16. FW, D & P (cans), usual city amenities, ⇌, ✈.

ST ANDREWS, Fife, 56°20'·33N 02°46'·70W. AC 190. HW −0015 Leith. Small drying hbr 7M S of Tay Estuary and 8M NW of Fife Ness. In strong onshore winds breaking seas render appr/ent impossible. Appr at HW±2 on 270°; N bkwtr bn in transit with conspic cathedral tr; no lights. Keep about 10m S of the bkwtr for best water. Berth on W side of inner hbr (drying 2·5m). 8m wide ent has lock gates, usually open, and retractable footbridge. Facilities: FW, SC. EC Thurs; All amenities of university town, inc golf course.

ARBROATH   10-6-14

Angus 56°33'·24N 02°34'·88W   Rtg 3-4-2

CHARTS
AC 1438, 190; OS 54

TIDES
+0317 Dover; ML 2·9; Duration 0620; Zone 0 (UT)

Standard Port ABERDEEN (→)

Times				Height (metres)			
High Water		Low Water		MHWS	MHWN	MLWN	MLWS
0000	0600	0100	0700	4·3	3·4	1·6	0·6
1200	1800	1300	1900				
Differences ARBROATH							
+0056	+0037	+0034	+0055	+0·7	+0·7	+0·2	+0·1

SHELTER
Good, especially in Wet Dock, but ent can be dangerous in moderate SE swell. Dock gates normally remain open, but will be closed on request. Or small craft can dry out in the SW corner of inner hbr; inside ent, turn stbd and stbd again.

NAVIGATION
WPT 56°33'·00N 02°34'·10W, 119°/299° from/to ent, 0·5M. Entry should not be attempted LW±2½. Beware Knuckle rks to stbd and Cheek Bush rks to port on entering.

LIGHTS AND MARKS
Ldg lts 299°, both FR 7/13m 5M; or twin trs of St Thomas' ✠ visible between N pier lt ho and W bkwtr bn.
Entry sigs: Fl Ⓖ   = Entry safe
               Ⓡ   = Entry dangerous

⚠ Report to Senior Harbour Assistant

RADIO TELEPHONE
None.

TELEPHONE (Dial code 01241)
Hr Mr 872166; MRSC (01224) 592334; ⌗ (0141) 887 9369 (H24); Marinecall 0891 500452; Police 722222; Dr 876836.

FACILITIES
Pier Slip, D, L, FW, AB; Services: BY, Slip, L, ME, El, Sh, C (8 ton) Ⓔ, M, Gas, CH.
Town EC Wed; P, D, V, R, Bar, ✉, Ⓑ, ⇌, ✈ (Dundee).

MONTROSE   10-6-15

Angus 56°42'·21N 02°26'·49W   Rtg 3-4-2

CHARTS
AC 1438, 190; OS 54

TIDES
+0320 Dover; ML 2·9; Duration 0645; Zone 0 (UT)

Standard Port ABERDEEN (→)

Times				Height (metres)			
High Water		Low Water		MHWS	MHWN	MLWN	MLWS
0000	0600	0100	0700	4·3	3·4	1·6	0·6
1200	1800	1300	1900				
Differences MONTROSE							
+0055	+0055	+0030	+0040	+0·5	+0·4	+0·2	0·0

SHELTER
Good; yachts are welcome in this busy commercial port. Contact Hr Mr for AB, usually available, but beware wash from other traffic. Double mooring lines advised due to strong tidal streams (up to 6kn).

NAVIGATION
WPT 56°42'·20N 02°25'·00W, 091°/271° from/to front ldg lt, 1·25M. Beware Annat Bank to N and Scurdie Rks to S of ent chan. In quiet weather best access is LW to LW+1, but in strong onshore winds only safe access would be from HW –2 to HW. Ent is dangerous with strong onshore winds against ebb tide as heavy overfalls develop.

LIGHTS AND MARKS
Scurdie Ness lt ho Fl (3) 20s 38m 23M (conspic). Two sets of ldg lts: Outer 271·5°, both FR 11/18m 5M. Inner 265°, both FG 21/33m 5M, Orange △ front and ▽ rear.

RADIO TELEPHONE
VHF Ch 12 16 (H24).

TELEPHONE (Dial code 01674)
Hr Mr 672302; MRCC (01224) 592334; Marinecall 0891 500 452; ⌗ (01224) 212666; Police 672222; Dr 672554/673400.

FACILITIES
N Quay ☎ 672302, AB £6.00, D (by tanker via Hr Mr), FW, ME, El, C (1½ to 40 ton), CH, Gas.
Town EC Wed; V, R, P, Bar, ✉, Ⓑ, ⇌, ✈ (Aberdeen).

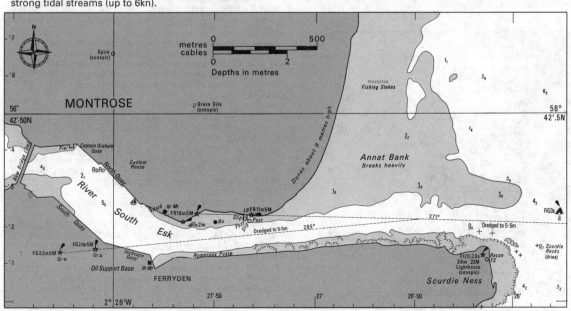

HARBOURS SOUTH OF STONEHAVEN

JOHNSHAVEN, Aberdeenshire, 56°47'·61N 02°19'·96W. AC
210. HW +0245 on Dover; +0025 and +0·4m on Aberdeen;
ML 2·7m; Duration 0626. Very small, attractive drying hbr
6·5M N of Montrose. Ent impossible in strong onshore
winds; strictly a fair weather visit with great caution. Even
in calm weather swell is a problem inside the hbr. Appr
from 5ca SE at HW±2½. Conspic W shed at N end of hbr.
Ldg marks/lts on 316°: front, R structure with FR 5m; rear
is G structure, 20m up the hill and 85m from front, with
FG (FR when entry unsafe). Transit leads between rky
ledges to very narrow (20m) ent. Turn 90° port into Inner
Basin (dries 2·5m) and berth on outer wall or secure to
mooring chains, rigged NE/SW. Hr Mr ☎ (01561) 362262
(home). Facilities: Slip, AB, AC, C (5 ton), FW, V, R, ME,
Bar, ✉. Bus to Montrose/Aberdeen.

GOURDON, Aberdeenshire, 56°49'·50N 02°17'·10W. AC
210. HW +0240 on Dover; +0020 on Aberdeen; HW +0·4m
on Aberdeen; ML 2·7m; Duration 0620. Shelter good in
inner W hbr (drys about 2m; protected by storm gates);
access from about mid-flood. E (or Gutty) hbr is rky, with
difficult access. Beware rky ledges marked by bn and
extending 200m S from W pier end. A dangerous rk dries
on the ldg line about 1½ca S of pier heads. Ldg marks/lts
358°, both FR 5/30m 5M, 2 W trs; front lt shows G when
not safe to enter. W pier hd Fl WRG 3s 5m 9/7M, vis
G180°-344°, W344°-354° (10°), R354°-180°. E bkwtr hd Q
3m 7M. Hr Mr ☎ (01569) 762741 (part-time, same as
10.6.16). Facilities: Slip, FW from standpipe, D, ME, AC,
M, V, R, Bar. Fish market held Mon-Fri 1130 and 1530.

BERTHING FEES. Aberdeenshire and Moray Councils offer
a "single entry" Rover fee (£8 inc VAT) valid for 1 week
from date of first entry at any or all of the following hbrs:
Johnshaven, Gourdon, Stonehaven; and in Area 7
(Moray Firth): Rosehearty, Banff, Portsoy, Cullen,
Portknockie, Findochty, Hopeman and Burghead. Berths
are of course subject to availability.

AGENTS WANTED

If you are interested in becoming our agent for any of the
following ports, please write to: The Editor, Edington House,
Trent, Sherborne, Dorset DT9 4SR, England – and get your
free copy of the Almanac annually. You do not have to live in
a port to be the agent, but at least a fairly regular visitor.

Great Yarmouth	St Gilles-Croix-de-Vie
Port Ellen (Islay)	Les Sables d'Olonne
Maryport	Ile d'Oléron
Workington	River Seudre
Holyhead	Anglet/Bayonne
Lough Swilly	St Jean-de-Luz
St Peter Port, Guernsey	Hendaye
Diélette	Grandcamp-Maisy
Portbail	Port-en-Bessin
Iles Chausey	Courseulles
St Malo/Dinard	Ouistreham/Caen
Le Legue/St Brieuc	Emden
Tréguier	Dornumer-Accumersiel
Lampaul	Langeoog
L'Aberildut	Bremerhaven
Le Palais (Belle Ile)	Büsum
Morbihan/Vannes	

STONEHAVEN   10-6-16

Aberdeenshire 56°57'·58N 02°11'·91WZ   Rtg 3·4·2

CHARTS
AC 1438, 210; OS 45
TIDES
+0235 Dover; ML 2·6; Duration 0620; Zone 0 (UT)

Standard Port ABERDEEN (→)

Times				Height (metres)			
High Water		Low Water		MHWS	MHWN	MLWN	MLWS
0000	0600	0100	0700	4·3	3·4	1·6	0·6
1200	1800	1300	1900				
Differences STONEHAVEN							
+0013	+0008	+0013	+0009	+0·2	+0·2	+0·1	0·0

SHELTER
Good, especially from offshore winds. Berth in outer hbr
(1·0m) on bkwtr or N wall; sandbank forms in middle to
W side. Or ⚓ outside in fair weather. Hbr speed limit 3kn.
Inner hbr dries 3·4m and in bad weather is closed. Do not
go S of ldg line, to clear rks close E of inner hbr wall.
NAVIGATION
WPT 56°57'·70N 02°11'·00W, 078°/258° from/to bkwtr lt,
0·50M. Give Downie Pt a wide berth. Do not enter in
strong on-shore winds. Radar assistance on Ch 16 in fog.
LIGHTS AND MARKS
N pier Iso WRG 4s 7m 11/7M; appr in W sector, 246°-268°.
Inner hbr ldg lts 273°, only apply to inner hbr: front FW 6m
5M; rear FR 8m 6M. FG on SE pier is shown when inner
hbr is closed by a boom in bad weather.
RADIO TELEPHONE
Hr Mr VHF Ch 11. Maritime Rescue International Ch 16.
TELEPHONE (Dial code 01569)
Hr Mr (part-time) 762741; MRCC (01224) 592334; ⌗ (0141)
887 9369 (H24); Marinecall 0891 500452; Police 762963;
Dr 762945; Maritime Rescue International ☎ 764065.
FACILITIES
Hbr AB £9.00 for 7 days, M, FW, AC, Slip, C (1·5 ton), LB, D
by tanker, Fri early am; **Aberdeen & Stonehaven YC** Slip,
Bar. **Town** EC Wed; V, R, Bar, ✉, Ⓑ, ⇌, ✈ (Aberdeen).

ABERDEEN

MEAN SPRING
AND NEAP CURVES

MEAN RANGES	
Springs	3·7m
Neaps	1·8m

Springs occur 2 days
after
New and Full Moon.

ABERDEEN   10-6-17

Aberdeenshire 57°08'·72N 02°03'·48W   Rtg 2-5-2

CHARTS
AC 1446, 210; OS 38

TIDES
+0231 Dover; ML 2·5; Duration 0620; Zone 0 (UT)
Note: Aberdeen is a Standard Port and tidal predictions
for each day of the year are given below.

SHELTER
Good in hbr; open at all tides, but do not enter in strong
NE/ESE winds. For berthing instructions call Hr Mr VHF
Ch 12 or berth at Pocra Quay first. Yachts usually lie in
Upper Dock or on N side of Albert Basin alongside
floating linkspan, but are not encouraged in this busy
commercial port. ⚓ in Aberdeen Bay gives some shelter
from S and W winds.

NAVIGATION
WPT Fairway SWM buoy, Mo (A) 5s, Racon, 57°09'·32N

02°01'·83W, 056°/236° from/to hbr ent 1·05M. Give Girdle
Ness a berth of at least ¼M (more in bad weather) and do
not pass close round pier hds. Strong tidal streams and,
with river in spate, possible overfalls. Chan dredged to
6m on ldg line.

LIGHTS AND MARKS
Ldg lts 236° (FR = port open; FG = port closed).
Traffic sigs at root of N pier:

Ⓖ   =   Entry prohib
Ⓡ   =   Dep prohib
Ⓡ & Ⓖ   =   Port closed

RADIO TELEPHONE
VHF Ch 06 11 **12** 13 16 (H24).

TELEPHONE (Dial code 01224)
Hr Mr 592571, ☎ 571507; MRCC 592334, ☎ 575920; ⌗
212666; Weather 722334; Marinecall 0891 500 452/0839
406189; Police 639111.

FACILITIES
Services: AB £15 for a period of up to 5 days , El, Ⓔ, CH,
ME, ACA.
City EC Wed/Sat; all amenities, ⇌, ✈.

⚓ After berthing at Pocra Quay report to HrMr

SCOTLAND – ABERDEEN

LAT 57°09′N   LONG 2°05′W

TIMES AND HEIGHTS OF HIGH AND LOW WATERS

YEAR 1998

TIME ZONE (UT)
For Summer Time add ONE hour in non-shaded areas

JANUARY

Day	Time	m	Time	m	Time	m	Time	m	Day	Time	m	Time	m	Time	m	Time	m
1 TH	0251	4.3	0843	0.9	1459	4.4	2113	0.7	16 F	0330	4.1	0914	1.2	1535	4.2	2145	1.0
2 F	0337	4.3	0926	1.0	1543	4.4	2159	0.7	17 SA	0407	4.0	0947	1.3	1611	4.1	2220	1.1
3 SA	0425	4.2	1012	1.1	1630	4.3	2249	0.8	18 SU	0444	3.8	1022	1.5	1649	4.0	2258	1.3
4 SU	0517	4.0	1103	1.3	1723	4.2	2344	1.0	19 M	0526	3.7	1101	1.6	1732	3.8	2341	1.4
5 M	0615	3.9	1202	1.4	1823	4.0			20 TU	0613	3.6	1148	1.8	1823	3.6		
6 TU	0046	1.1	0720	3.8	1310	1.6	1931	3.9	21 W	0033	1.6	0707	3.5	1249	2.0	1923	3.5
7 W	0156	1.3	0830	3.7	1425	1.6	2046	3.9	22 TH	0137	1.8	0810	3.4	1405	2.0	2033	3.5
8 TH	0311	1.3	0941	3.8	1542	1.5	2201	3.9	23 F	0248	1.8	0918	3.5	1525	1.9	2146	3.5
9 F	0421	1.3	1044	3.9	1648	1.4	2306	4.0	24 SA	0357	1.7	1022	3.6	1631	1.7	2250	3.7
10 SA	0518	1.2	1138	4.1	1744	1.2			25 SU	0453	1.5	1115	3.8	1722	1.5	2342	3.8
11 SU	0001	4.1	0606	1.2	1225	4.2	1832	1.0	26 M	0540	1.3	1200	4.0	1807	1.2		
12 M ○	0050	4.2	0649	1.1	1307	4.3	1916	0.8	27 TU	0028	4.1	0623	1.1	1242	4.2	1849	0.9
13 TU	0133	4.2	0729	1.1	1346	4.4	1957	0.8	28 W ●	0112	4.2	0705	0.9	1322	4.4	1933	0.6
14 W	0214	4.2	0805	1.1	1424	4.4	2035	0.8	29 TH	0154	4.2	0747	0.8	1403	4.5	2016	0.4
15 TH	0253	4.2	0840	1.1	1500	4.3	2111	0.8	30 F	0237	4.4	0829	0.7	1444	4.6	2100	0.4
									31 SA	0321	4.4	0912	0.8	1527	4.6	2144	0.4

FEBRUARY

Day	Time	m	Time	m	Time	m	Time	m	Day	Time	m	Time	m	Time	m	Time	m
1 SU	0406	4.3	0955	0.9	1613	4.5	2231	0.6	16 M	0407	3.9	0949	1.2	1616	4.0	2220	1.1
2 M	0455	4.1	1042	1.0	1703	4.4	2321	0.8	17 TU	0443	3.8	1022	1.4	1654	3.9	2256	1.3
3 TU	0548	3.9	1135	1.2	1800	4.1			18 W	0524	3.6	1101	1.5	1739	3.7	2340	1.5
4 W	0018	1.1	0648	3.8	1240	1.5	1907	3.9	19 TH	0611	3.5	1151	1.7	1833	3.5		
5 TH	0126	1.4	0758	3.6	1357	1.6	2026	3.8	20 F	0036	1.7	0710	3.4	1301	1.9	1940	3.4
6 F	0246	1.6	0915	3.6	1524	1.6	2148	3.7	21 SA	0149	1.8	0821	3.4	1428	1.9	2100	3.4
7 SA	0406	1.6	1027	3.7	1639	1.4	2300	3.8	22 SU	0312	1.8	0937	3.4	1552	1.7	2217	3.4
8 SU	0508	1.5	1126	3.9	1737	1.2	2356	3.9	23 M	0423	1.6	1042	3.7	1655	1.4	2318	3.8
9 M	0557	1.3	1214	4.1	1824	1.0			24 TU	0517	1.3	1134	3.9	1745	1.1		
10 TU	0042	4.0	0637	1.2	1255	4.2	1904	0.9	25 W	0008	4.0	0603	1.1	1220	4.2	1830	0.7
11 W ○	0122	4.1	0714	1.1	1331	4.3	1940	0.8	26 TH ●	0053	4.4	0647	0.8	1302	4.4	1914	0.4
12 TH	0157	4.2	0748	1.0	1406	4.3	2014	0.7	27 F	0135	4.4	0730	0.6	1343	4.6	1958	0.2
13 F	0231	4.1	0820	1.0	1438	4.3	2046	0.8	28 SA	0218	4.5	0811	0.5	1425	4.7	2041	0.2
14 SA	0303	4.1	0850	1.1	1510	4.2	2117	0.8									
15 SU	0335	4.0	0919	1.1	1542	4.1	2147	1.0									

MARCH

Day	Time	m	Time	m	Time	m	Time	m	Day	Time	m	Time	m	Time	m	Time	m
1 SU	0300	4.5	0853	0.5	1509	4.7	2125	0.3	16 M	0304	4.0	0853	1.0	1515	4.1	2116	0.9
2 M	0344	4.4	0936	0.6	1555	4.6	2209	0.5	17 TU	0335	4.0	0921	1.0	1549	4.0	2146	1.0
3 TU	0430	4.2	1021	0.8	1645	4.4	2256	0.8	18 W	0408	3.8	0953	1.1	1625	3.9	2219	1.2
4 W	0521	4.0	1113	1.0	1741	4.1	2350	1.2	19 TH	0445	3.7	1029	1.3	1707	3.7	2259	1.4
5 TH	0619	3.7	1215	1.3	1849	3.8			20 F	0529	3.6	1114	1.5	1758	3.5	2350	1.6
6 F	0056	1.5	0728	3.5	1334	1.5	2009	3.6	21 SA	0623	3.4	1218	1.6	1903	3.4		
7 SA	0221	1.7	0849	3.5	1508	1.5	2136	3.5	22 SU	0103	1.8	0733	3.3	1344	1.7	2024	3.3
8 SU	0350	1.7	1007	3.6	1628	1.4	2250	3.6	23 M	0232	1.7	0853	3.4	1514	1.6	2146	3.5
9 M	0455	1.6	1109	3.7	1724	1.2	2344	3.8	24 TU	0352	1.6	1007	3.6	1626	1.2	2252	3.7
10 TU	0542	1.4	1157	3.9	1808	1.0			25 W	0452	1.3	1105	3.8	1720	0.9	2344	4.0
11 W	0027	3.9	0620	1.2	1237	4.1	1844	0.8	26 TH	0541	1.0	1153	4.1	1808	0.5		
12 TH	0103	4.0	0654	1.1	1312	4.2	1917	0.8	27 F	0030	4.3	0626	0.7	1238	4.4	1852	0.3
13 F ○	0135	4.1	0726	1.0	1344	4.2	1949	0.7	28 SA ●	0113	4.4	0709	0.5	1321	4.6	1936	0.1
14 SA	0205	4.1	0756	0.9	1414	4.2	2019	0.7	29 SU	0155	4.5	0751	0.4	1405	4.7	2019	0.1
15 SU	0235	4.1	0825	0.9	1444	4.2	2047	0.8	30 M	0238	4.5	0834	0.3	1450	4.7	2103	0.2
									31 TU	0321	4.4	0917	0.4	1538	4.5	2147	0.5

APRIL

Day	Time	m	Time	m	Time	m	Time	m	Day	Time	m	Time	m	Time	m	Time	m
1 W	0406	4.2	1004	0.6	1629	4.3	2233	0.8	16 TH	0339	3.9	0931	1.0	1603	3.8	2151	1.1
2 TH	0455	3.9	1055	0.9	1726	4.0	2325	1.2	17 F	0416	3.8	1008	1.1	1645	3.7	2231	1.3
3 F	0552	3.7	1156	1.2	1833	3.7			18 SA	0459	3.6	1054	1.2	1736	3.5	2322	1.5
4 SA	0029	1.6	0659	3.5	1312	1.4	1950	3.5	19 SU	0552	3.5	1156	1.4	1840	3.4		
5 SU	0151	1.8	0818	3.4	1444	1.4	2114	3.4	20 M	0034	1.6	0658	3.4	1317	1.4	1957	3.4
6 M	0324	1.8	0937	3.5	1605	1.3	2227	3.5	21 TU	0200	1.7	0816	3.4	1441	1.3	2117	3.5
7 TU	0431	1.6	1042	3.6	1700	1.2	2321	3.6	22 W	0320	1.5	0931	3.6	1554	1.1	2224	3.7
8 W	0518	1.4	1131	3.7	1742	1.0			23 TH	0424	1.2	1033	3.8	1653	0.7	2318	4.0
9 TH	0002	3.8	0555	1.3	1211	3.9	1816	0.9	24 F	0516	1.0	1126	4.1	1743	0.5		
10 F	0037	3.9	0629	1.1	1246	4.0	1849	0.8	25 SA	0005	4.2	0602	0.7	1214	4.3	1829	0.2
11 SA ○	0108	4.0	0701	0.9	1318	4.1	1919	0.7	26 SU ●	0050	4.4	0647	0.5	1300	4.5	1914	0.1
12 SU	0137	4.0	0731	0.9	1349	4.1	1949	0.7	27 M	0133	4.4	0731	0.3	1346	4.6	1958	0.2
13 M	0206	4.0	0800	0.8	1420	4.1	2018	0.7	28 TU	0216	4.4	0816	0.3	1434	4.5	2042	0.3
14 TU	0236	4.0	0829	0.8	1452	4.0	2047	0.8	29 W	0259	4.3	0902	0.4	1523	4.4	2126	0.6
15 W	0306	4.0	0859	0.9	1526	3.9	2118	0.9	30 TH	0345	4.2	0949	0.5	1615	4.1	2212	0.9

Chart Datum: 2·25 metres below Ordnance Datum (Newlyn)

SCOTLAND – ABERDEEN

LAT 57°09′N   LONG 2°05′W

TIMES AND HEIGHTS OF HIGH AND LOW WATERS

YEAR **1998**

TIME ZONE (UT)
For Summer Time add ONE hour in non-shaded areas

6

MAY

Day	Time	m	Time	m	Time	m	Time	m
1 F	0433	3.9	1040	0.8	1711	3.8	2302	1.3
16 SA	0355	3.8	0957	0.9	1631	3.7	2215	1.2
2 SA	0527	3.7	1138	1.0	1814	3.6		
17 SU	0439	3.7	1045	1.0	1722	3.6	2307	1.4
3 SU	0000	1.5	0629	3.5	1246	1.2	1923	3.4
18 M	0531	3.6	1145	1.1	1824	3.5		
4 M	0113	1.7	0740	3.4	1405	1.3	2038	3.3
19 TU	0013	1.5	0634	3.5	1256	1.2	1934	3.5
5 TU	0238	1.8	0855	3.4	1524	1.3	2149	3.4
20 W	0131	1.5	0745	3.5	1412	1.1	2047	3.5
6 W	0351	1.7	1003	3.5	1622	1.2	2245	3.5
21 TH	0246	1.4	0857	3.6	1523	0.9	2154	3.7
7 TH	0443	1.5	1055	3.6	1706	1.1	2328	3.6
22 F	0353	1.2	1003	3.8	1625	0.7	2252	3.9
8 F	0524	1.3	1138	3.7	1743	1.0		
23 SA	0450	1.0	1101	4.0	1719	0.6	2342	4.1
9 SA	0004	3.8	0559	1.2	1216	3.8	1816	0.9
24 SU	0541	0.8	1153	4.2	1808	0.4		
10 SU	0037	3.9	0633	1.0	1250	3.9	1849	0.8
25 M	0028	4.2	0629	0.5	1243	4.4	● 1855	0.4
11 M	0108	4.0	0705	0.9	1324	4.0	O 1920	0.8
26 TU	0113	4.3	0716	0.4	1332	4.4	1940	0.4
12 TU	0139	4.0	0736	0.8	1357	4.0	1951	0.8
27 W	0157	4.3	0800	0.4	1421	4.4	2024	0.5
13 W	0210	4.0	0808	0.8	1431	3.9	2023	0.8
28 TH	0241	4.3	0849	0.4	1510	4.2	2108	0.7
14 TH	0243	4.0	0841	0.8	1507	3.9	2056	0.9
29 F	0326	4.2	0936	0.5	1601	4.0	2151	1.0
15 F	0317	3.9	0917	0.8	1547	3.8	2133	1.0
30 SA	0412	4.0	1024	0.7	1653	3.8	2237	1.2
31 SU	0502	3.8	1115	0.9	1748	3.6	2328	1.5

JUNE

Day	Time	m	Time	m	Time	m	Time	m
1 M	0556	3.6	1211	1.1	1846	3.4		
16 TU	0515	3.8	1132	0.9	1806	3.7	2354	1.3
2 TU	0027	1.7	0656	3.5	1314	1.3	1948	3.3
17 W	0613	3.8	1235	1.0	1910	3.6		
3 W	0137	1.8	0801	3.4	1424	1.4	2053	3.3
18 TH	0101	1.4	0718	3.7	1343	1.0	2017	3.6
4 TH	0253	1.8	0908	3.4	1529	1.4	2154	3.4
19 F	0213	1.4	0828	3.7	1453	1.0	2125	3.7
5 F	0357	1.7	1009	3.4	1622	1.3	2244	3.5
20 SA	0323	1.3	0938	3.8	1600	0.9	2228	3.8
6 SA	0446	1.5	1059	3.6	1705	1.2	2327	3.7
21 SU	0428	1.1	1042	4.0	1700	0.8	2322	4.0
7 SU	0528	1.3	1143	3.7	1744	1.1		
22 M	0525	0.9	1140	4.1	1753	0.7		
8 M	0005	3.8	0605	1.2	1223	3.8	1819	1.0
23 TU	0012	4.1	0616	0.7	1233	4.2	1840	0.7
9 TU	0040	3.9	0640	1.0	1300	3.9	1854	0.9
24 W	0058	4.2	0705	0.6	1323	4.3	● 1925	0.7
10 W	0114	4.0	0715	0.9	1337	3.9	O 1928	0.9
25 TH	0142	4.3	0752	0.5	1411	4.2	2009	0.8
11 TH	0148	4.0	0751	0.8	1414	4.0	2004	0.9
26 F	0225	4.3	0837	0.5	1457	4.2	2050	0.9
12 F	0223	4.1	0828	0.7	1453	4.0	2041	0.9
27 SA	0308	4.2	0921	0.6	1543	4.0	2130	1.0
13 SA	0300	4.1	0907	0.7	1534	3.9	2121	1.0
28 SU	0350	4.1	1003	0.7	1628	3.9	2210	1.2
14 SU	0340	4.0	0950	0.8	1619	3.8	2205	1.1
29 M	0434	4.0	1046	0.9	1714	3.7	2252	1.4
15 M	0424	3.9	1038	0.8	1709	3.7	2255	1.2
30 TU	0519	3.8	1131	1.1	1802	3.5	2339	1.6

JULY

Day	Time	m	Time	m	Time	m	Time	m
1 W	0609	3.6	1220	1.3	1854	3.4		
16 TH	0551	4.0	1211	0.9	1843	3.7		
2 TH	0035	1.7	0704	3.5	1318	1.4	1950	3.3
17 F	0033	1.3	0653	3.9	1316	1.1	1949	3.7
3 F	0142	1.8	0806	3.4	1423	1.5	2052	3.4
18 SA	0144	1.4	0804	3.8	1427	1.2	2059	3.7
4 SA	0256	1.8	0912	3.4	1528	1.5	2152	3.4
19 SU	0300	1.4	0920	3.8	1541	1.2	2208	3.8
5 SU	0402	1.7	1015	3.5	1624	1.4	2246	3.6
20 M	0413	1.3	1032	3.9	1647	1.2	2308	3.9
6 M	0454	1.5	1109	3.6	1711	1.3	2332	3.7
21 TU	0516	1.1	1134	4.0	1743	1.1		
7 TU	0537	1.3	1156	3.7	1752	1.2		
22 W	0000	4.1	0610	0.9	1228	4.1	1830	1.0
8 W	0013	3.9	0617	1.1	1238	3.8	1830	1.1
23 TH	0046	4.2	0657	0.7	1316	4.2	● 1913	0.9
9 TH	0051	4.0	0655	0.9	1318	4.0	O 1909	0.9
24 F	0129	4.3	0741	0.6	1359	4.2	1953	0.9
10 F	0128	4.1	0734	0.7	1358	4.1	1948	0.9
25 SA	0209	4.3	0822	0.6	1440	4.2	2030	0.9
11 SA	0205	4.2	0815	0.6	1438	4.1	2028	0.8
26 SU	0248	4.3	0900	0.6	1520	4.1	2106	1.0
12 SU	0244	4.3	0856	0.5	1520	4.1	2109	0.8
27 M	0325	4.2	0937	0.7	1558	3.9	2140	1.1
13 M	0325	4.3	0939	0.5	1604	4.1	2152	0.9
28 TU	0402	4.1	1012	0.9	1636	3.8	2215	1.3
14 TU	0409	4.2	1025	0.6	1652	4.0	2238	1.0
29 W	0440	3.9	1049	1.1	1716	3.7	2253	1.5
15 W	0457	4.1	1115	0.7	1744	3.9	2331	1.2
30 TH	0523	3.8	1130	1.3	1800	3.6	2338	1.6
31 F	0611	3.6	1218	1.5	1851	3.4		

AUGUST

Day	Time	m	Time	m	Time	m	Time	m
1 SA	0035	1.8	0708	3.5	1317	1.6	1950	3.4
16 SU	0120	1.5	0747	3.8	1404	1.4	2036	3.6
2 SU	0147	1.9	0815	3.4	1427	1.7	2056	3.4
17 M	0244	1.5	0910	3.7	1528	1.5	2151	3.7
3 M	0308	1.9	0928	3.4	1539	1.7	2202	3.5
18 TU	0407	1.4	1028	3.8	1639	1.4	2256	3.9
4 TU	0418	1.7	1035	3.5	1638	1.5	2259	3.7
19 W	0511	1.2	1131	3.9	1734	1.3	2349	4.0
5 W	0510	1.4	1130	3.7	1726	1.4	2345	3.9
20 TH	0603	1.0	1222	4.0	1819	1.2		
6 TH	0554	1.2	1216	3.9	1809	1.2		
21 F	0034	4.2	0646	0.8	1305	4.1	1858	1.1
7 F	0027	4.1	0635	0.9	1258	4.1	1849	1.0
22 SA	0113	4.3	0725	0.7	1343	4.2	● 1934	1.0
8 SA	0107	4.3	0716	0.6	1339	4.2	O 1930	0.8
23 SU	0149	4.4	0801	0.6	1418	4.2	2007	1.0
9 SU	0145	4.4	0757	0.4	1420	4.3	2011	0.7
24 M	0224	4.3	0834	0.7	1452	4.1	2039	1.0
10 M	0225	4.5	0839	0.3	1501	4.4	2052	0.7
25 TU	0257	4.3	0906	0.7	1524	4.1	2110	1.1
11 TU	0306	4.5	0922	0.3	1544	4.3	2134	0.8
26 W	0330	4.2	0936	0.9	1557	4.0	2140	1.2
12 W	0350	4.5	1006	0.5	1630	4.2	2218	0.9
27 TH	0405	4.0	1008	1.0	1632	3.8	2213	1.4
13 TH	0437	4.4	1053	0.7	1720	4.0	2308	1.1
28 F	0443	3.9	1044	1.2	1712	3.7	2251	1.5
14 F	0530	4.2	1146	0.9	1816	3.8		
29 SA	0527	3.7	1125	1.5	1758	3.6	2340	1.7
15 SA	0007	1.3	0632	4.0	1249	1.2	1921	3.7
30 SU	0620	3.5	1219	1.7	1854	3.4		
31 M	0046	1.9	0726	3.4	1329	1.8	2002	3.4

Chart Datum: 2·25 metres below Ordnance Datum (Newlyn)

SCOTLAND – ABERDEEN

LAT 57°09′N   LONG 2°05′W

TIMES AND HEIGHTS OF HIGH AND LOW WATERS

YEAR **1998**

TIME ZONE (UT)
For Summer Time add ONE hour in non-shaded areas

SEPTEMBER

Day	Time	m	Time	m	Time	m	Time	m
1 TU	0212	1.9	0843	3.4	1452	1.9	2116	3.5
16 W	0359	1.4	1022	3.7	1628	1.6	2242	3.8
2 W	0339	1.8	1001	3.5	1606	1.7	2223	3.6
17 TH	0502	1.2	1122	3.9	1721	1.5	2334	4.0
3 TH	0441	1.5	1103	3.7	1701	1.5	2316	3.9
18 F	0549	1.0	1209	4.0	1802	1.3		
4 F	0529	1.1	1152	3.9	1746	1.2		
19 SA	0016	4.2	0628	0.9	1247	4.1	1838	1.2
5 SA	0001	4.1	0612	0.8	1235	4.2	1828	1.0
20 SU	0053	4.3	0702	0.8	1320	4.2	● 1910	1.0
6 SU	0042	4.4	0654	0.5	1316	4.4	O 1909	0.7
21 M	0126	4.3	0734	0.7	1351	4.2	1942	1.0
7 M	0122	4.6	0736	0.3	1357	4.5	1950	0.6
22 TU	0158	4.3	0804	0.7	1421	4.2	2012	1.0
8 TU	0203	4.7	0818	0.2	1438	4.5	2031	0.6
23 W	0229	4.3	0834	0.8	1451	4.1	2040	1.0
9 W	0245	4.7	0900	0.2	1521	4.5	2112	0.6
24 TH	0301	4.2	0902	0.9	1521	4.1	2109	1.1
10 TH	0330	4.7	0943	0.4	1605	4.3	2157	0.8
25 F	0334	4.1	0932	1.1	1554	4.0	2141	1.3
11 F	0418	4.5	1029	0.7	1654	4.1	2247	1.0
26 SA	0411	3.9	1005	1.2	1631	3.8	2216	1.4
12 SA	0512	4.2	1121	1.1	1750	3.9	2347	1.3
27 SU	0453	3.8	1043	1.5	1714	3.7	2301	1.6
13 SU	0617	3.9	1225	1.4	1857	3.7		
28 M	0543	3.6	1131	1.7	1807	3.5		
14 M	0102	1.5	0735	3.7	1344	1.7	2014	3.6
29 TU	0002	1.8	0646	3.4	1241	1.9	1913	3.4
15 TU	0233	1.5	0903	3.7	1515	1.7	2134	3.7
30 W	0126	1.8	0805	3.4	1407	1.9	2031	3.5

OCTOBER

Day	Time	m	Time	m	Time	m	Time	m
1 TH	0256	1.7	0926	3.5	1530	1.8	2145	3.6
16 F	0440	1.3	1102	3.8	1658	1.6	2311	3.9
2 F	0408	1.4	1033	3.7	1632	1.5	2243	3.9
17 SA	0525	1.1	1145	3.9	1739	1.4	2353	4.1
3 SA	0500	1.1	1124	4.0	1720	1.2	2331	4.2
18 SU	0602	1.0	1221	4.1	1813	1.2		
4 SU	0546	0.7	1209	4.3	1803	0.9		
19 M	0028	4.2	0648	0.9	1253	4.2	1845	1.1
5 M	0015	4.4	0629	0.4	1251	4.5	O 1845	0.7
20 TU	0101	4.2	0704	0.8	1322	4.2	● 1916	1.0
6 TU	0057	4.7	0711	0.2	1332	4.6	1927	0.5
21 W	0132	4.3	0734	0.8	1352	4.2	1946	1.0
7 W	0140	4.8	0754	0.2	1414	4.6	2009	0.5
22 TH	0204	4.2	0803	0.9	1421	4.2	2015	1.0
8 TH	0224	4.8	0837	0.3	1457	4.6	2052	0.5
23 F	0236	4.2	0832	1.0	1451	4.1	2045	1.1
9 F	0311	4.7	0920	0.5	1541	4.4	2138	0.7
24 SA	0310	4.1	0902	1.1	1524	4.1	2117	1.2
10 SA	0401	4.5	1007	0.8	1630	4.2	2230	0.9
25 SU	0346	3.9	0935	1.3	1559	3.9	2153	1.3
11 SU	0458	4.2	1059	1.2	1725	3.9	2331	1.2
26 M	0428	3.8	1012	1.5	1640	3.8	2236	1.4
12 M	0604	3.9	1201	1.6	1832	3.7		
27 TU	0517	3.6	1059	1.6	1730	3.6	2334	1.6
13 TU	0045	1.4	0721	3.6	1320	1.8	1949	3.6
28 W	0618	3.5	1204	1.8	1834	3.5		
14 W	0214	1.5	0846	3.6	1452	1.9	2109	3.7
29 TH	0050	1.7	0732	3.4	1328	1.9	1949	3.5
15 TH	0340	1.4	1003	3.7	1607	1.8	2218	3.8
30 F	0215	1.6	0851	3.5	1451	1.8	2104	3.7
31 SA	0329	1.3	0959	3.8	1558	1.6	2207	3.9

NOVEMBER

Day	Time	m	Time	m	Time	m	Time	m
1 SU	0428	1.0	1054	4.0	1651	1.3	2301	4.2
16 M	0529	1.2	1150	4.0	1746	1.4		
2 M	0518	0.7	1142	4.3	1738	1.0	2348	4.5
17 TU	0000	4.0	0603	1.1	1224	4.1	1819	1.2
3 TU	0604	0.5	1226	4.5	1822	0.7		
18 W	0036	4.1	0635	1.0	1255	4.2	1852	1.1
4 W	0034	4.7	0648	0.3	1309	4.6	O 1906	0.6
19 TH	0109	4.2	0706	1.0	1325	4.2	● 1924	1.1
5 TH	0120	4.8	0732	0.3	1351	4.6	1950	0.5
20 F	0143	4.2	0737	1.0	1356	4.2	1955	1.0
6 F	0207	4.8	0816	0.4	1434	4.6	2036	0.5
21 SA	0216	4.1	0808	1.1	1427	4.2	2027	1.0
7 SA	0256	4.6	0901	0.7	1520	4.4	2125	0.7
22 SU	0251	4.1	0840	1.1	1500	4.1	2101	1.1
8 SU	0348	4.4	0947	1.0	1608	4.2	2217	0.9
23 M	0328	4.0	0914	1.3	1536	4.0	2138	1.2
9 M	0445	4.1	1038	1.3	1702	4.0	2315	1.1
24 TU	0410	3.9	0952	1.4	1616	3.9	2222	1.3
10 TU	0548	3.8	1136	1.6	1804	3.8		
25 W	0457	3.7	1039	1.6	1704	3.8	2316	1.4
11 W	0021	1.3	0658	3.6	1246	1.9	1915	3.7
26 TH	0554	3.6	1138	1.7	1802	3.7		
12 TH	0139	1.5	0813	3.5	1409	2.0	2031	3.6
27 F	0022	1.4	0701	3.6	1252	1.8	1910	3.7
13 F	0301	1.5	0927	3.6	1528	1.9	2141	3.7
28 SA	0137	1.4	0814	3.6	1409	1.8	2023	3.8
14 SA	0405	1.4	1027	3.7	1625	1.7	2238	3.8
29 SU	0249	1.3	0923	3.8	1520	1.6	2131	3.9
15 SU	0451	1.3	1113	3.8	1709	1.6	2322	3.9
30 M	0354	1.1	1024	4.0	1620	1.3	2231	4.2

DECEMBER

Day	Time	m	Time	m	Time	m	Time	m
1 TU	0450	0.9	1116	4.2	1713	1.1	2325	4.4
16 W	0532	1.3	1153	4.0	1755	1.4		
2 W	0541	0.7	1203	4.4	1803	0.8		
17 TH	0011	3.9	0608	1.2	1229	4.1	1830	1.3
3 TH	0016	4.5	0628	0.6	1249	4.5	O 1852	0.7
18 F	0049	4.0	0642	1.2	1303	4.2	● 1904	1.1
4 F	0106	4.6	0714	0.6	1333	4.6	1938	0.6
19 SA	0125	4.1	0716	1.1	1335	4.2	1938	1.0
5 SA	0155	4.6	0800	0.7	1417	4.6	2025	0.5
20 SU	0200	4.1	0749	1.1	1408	4.2	2013	1.0
6 SU	0245	4.5	0844	0.9	1502	4.5	2114	0.6
21 M	0236	4.1	0824	1.1	1442	4.1	2049	1.0
7 M	0336	4.3	0930	1.1	1549	4.3	2203	0.8
22 TU	0314	4.1	0900	1.2	1519	4.2	2128	1.0
8 TU	0429	4.1	1016	1.3	1639	4.1	2254	1.0
23 W	0355	4.0	0939	1.3	1559	4.1	2211	1.0
9 W	0524	3.9	1106	1.6	1733	3.9	2349	1.2
24 TH	0440	3.9	1023	1.4	1644	4.0	2259	1.1
10 TH	0623	3.7	1202	1.8	1833	3.8		
25 F	0532	3.8	1115	1.5	1737	4.0	2356	1.2
11 F	0051	1.4	0726	3.5	1310	2.0	1939	3.6
26 SA	0631	3.7	1217	1.6	1837	3.9		
12 SA	0200	1.6	0833	3.5	1427	2.0	2048	3.6
27 SU	0101	1.3	0737	3.7	1329	1.7	1946	3.9
13 SU	0310	1.6	0937	3.6	1538	1.9	2152	3.6
28 M	0212	1.3	0847	3.8	1442	1.6	2058	3.9
14 M	0407	1.5	1031	3.7	1632	1.8	2246	3.7
29 TU	0323	1.2	0954	3.9	1552	1.5	2207	4.0
15 TU	0453	1.4	1115	3.8	1716	1.6	2331	3.8
30 W	0428	1.1	1054	4.1	1655	1.3	2310	4.2
31 TH	0525	1.0	1146	4.2	1750	1.0		

Chart Datum: 2·25 metres below Ordnance Datum (Newlyn)

PETERHEAD   10-6-18

Aberdeenshire 57°29'·83N 01°46'·31W   Rtg 1-4-2

CHARTS
AC 1438, 213; OS 30
TIDES
+0140 Dover; ML 2·3; Duration 0620; Zone 0 (UT)

Standard Port ABERDEEN (←—)

Times				Height (metres)			
High Water		Low Water		MHWS	MHWN	MLWN	MLWS
0000	0600	0100	0700	4·3	3·4	1·6	0·6
1200	1800	1300	1900				
Differences PETERHEAD							
–0035	–0045	–0035	–0040	–0·5	–0·3	–0·1	–0·1

SHELTER
Good in marina (2·8m). A useful passage hbr, also a major fishing and oil/gas industry port. Access any weather/tide.
NAVIGATION
WPT 57°29'·46N 01°45'·64W, 134°/314° from/to ent, 0·5M. No dangers. 5kn speed limit in Bay; 4kn in marina. Chan between marina bkwtr and SHM lt buoy is <30m wide.
LIGHTS AND MARKS
Power stn chy (183m) is conspic 1·25M S of ent, with Fl W lts H24. Ldg marks 314°, front △, rear ▽ on Y cols; lts as chartlet. Marina bkwtr ☆ Fl R 3s 6m 2M is atop 2·5m high ⚓ symbol.

RADIO TELEPHONE
All vessels, inc yachts, must call *Peterhead Harbour Radio* VHF Ch **14** 9 16 for clearance to enter/depart the Bay.
TELEPHONE (Dial code 01779)
Hr Control (H24) 474281; Hr Mr (Bay Authority) 474020; MRCC (01224) 592334; ⌗ (01224) 212666; Marinecall 0891 500452; Police 472571; Dr 474841; Ⓗ 472316.
FACILITIES
Marina ☎ via 474020 (HO)/⤷ 475712, 92 berths, max LOA 17m; access all tides, 2·3m at ent, D, Gas, AC, FW, V and Ⓦ at caravan site; **Peterhead SC** ☎ (011358) 751340 (Sec); **Services:** D available in S Hbr, Slip, ME, El, Ⓔ, Sh, C, Gas. **Town** EC Wed; P, D, V, R, ✉, bus to Aberdeen for ⇌ & ✈.

ADJACENT HARBOUR

BODDAM, Aberdeenshire, 57°28'·38N 01°46'·30W. AC 213. HW +0145 on Dover; Tides as 10.6.18. Good shelter in the lee of Meikle Mackie, the island just N of Buchan Ness, Fl 5s 40m 28M Horn (3) 60s. Hbr dries/unlit. Beware rks around Meikle Mackie and to the SW of it. Appr from 1½ca NW of The Skerry. Yachts lie alongside N wall. All facilities at Peterhead, 4 miles N.

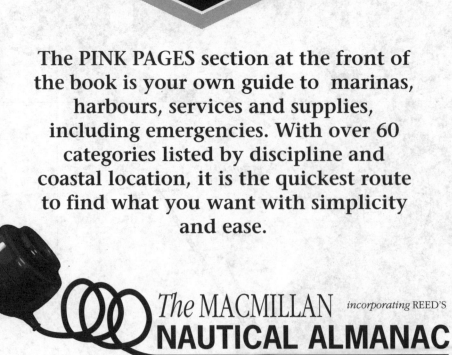

VOLVO PENTA SERVICE

Sales and service centres in area 7
HIGHLANDS AND ISLANDS *Caley Marina*, Canal Road, Muirtown, Inverness
1V3 6NF Tel (01463) 236539

**VOLVO
PENTA**

Area 7

North-East Scotland
Rattray Head to Cape Wrath
including Orkney and Shetland Islands

7

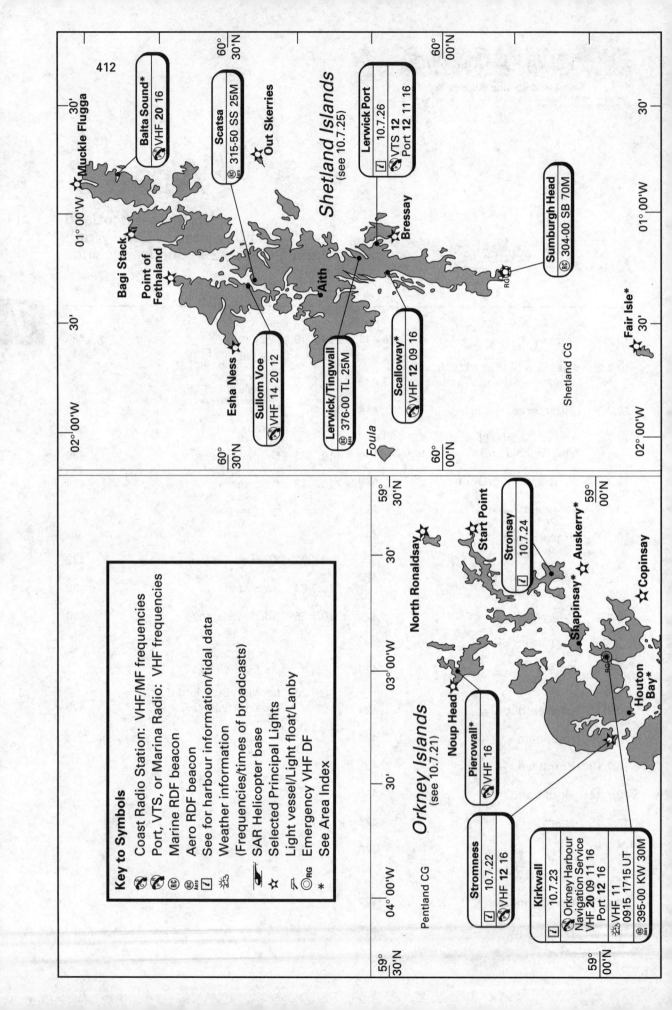

Key to Symbols

📻 Coast Radio Station: VHF/MF frequencies
📻 Port, VTS, or Marina Radio: VHF frequencies
(RC) Marine RDF beacon
(RC)Aero Aero RDF beacon
🛥 See for harbour information/tidal data
ℹ️ Weather information
(Frequencies/times of broadcasts)
🚁 SAR Helicopter base
☆ Selected Principal Lights
⌂ Light vessel/Light float/Lanby
◉RG Emergency VHF DF
* See Area Index

Shetland Islands
(see 10.7.25)

Muckle Flugga ☆
Bagi Stack
Point of Fethaland
Esha Ness ☆

Balta Sound*
🛥 VHF 20 16

Scatsa
(RC)Aero 315·50 SS 25M

Out Skerries ☆

Lerwick Port
10.7.26
ℹ️ 🛥 VTS 12
Port 12 11 16

Aith
Bressay

Sullom Voe
🛥 VHF 14 20 12

Lerwick/Tingwall
(RC)Aero 376·00 TL 25M

Scalloway*
🛥 VHF 12 09 16

Foula

Sumburgh Head
(RC)Aero 304·00 SB 70M

RG

Fair Isle* ☆

Shetland CG

02°00'W   30'   01° 00'W   30'   01° 00'W

60°30'N   60°00'N   60°30'N   60°00'N

Orkney Islands
(see 10.7.21)

North Ronaldsay ☆
Start Point ☆
Stronsay
10.7.24 ℹ️

Noup Head ☆
Pierowall*
🛥 VHF 16

Shapinsay*
Auskerry* ☆
Copinsay ☆

Houton Bay*
RG

Stromness
10.7.22
ℹ️ 🛥 VHF 12 16

Kirkwall
10.7.23
ℹ️
📻 Orkney Harbour
Navigation Service
VHF 20 09 11 16
Port 12 16
🚁 VHF 11
0915 1715 UT
(RC)Aero 395·00 KW 30M

Pentland CG

04° 00'W   30'   03° 00'W   30'   02° 00'W

59°30'N   59°30'N   59°00'N   59°00'N

10-7-2

North-East Scotland, Orkney and Shetland

Rattray Head to Cape Wrath

7

Variation
6°W (1998)

Loch Eriboll*

Kyle of
Tongue*

See 10-8-2

Muckle
Skerry

Long Hope

Cantick
Head

Stroma/
Swilkie Pt

Dunnet
Head RG

Duncansby Head
RC 290·50 DY 50M

Noss Head

Wick Radio
VHF 28 16
MF 1797 1755
2625 3528 3775
VHF 28
MF 1764
0703 1903 UT

Pentland CG
Aberdeen CG

Scrabster
10.7.20
VHF 12 16

Wick
10.7.19
VHF 14 16
RC 344·00 WIK 30M

Clythness*
Lybster*

Helmsdale
VHF 12 16

Portmahomack
10.7.17

Dornoch
Firth*
Golspie*

Tarbat
Ness

Kinloss
370·0 KS 20M

Hopeman
10.7.12

Lossiemouth
10.7.11
VHF 12 16

Inverness
10.7.16
VHF 06 12 16
Marinas 80 M
Lock 74 16

Fortrose*

Invergordon
VHF 11 13 16

Cromarty Firth*

Nairn
10.7.15
VHF M (HJ)

Findhorn
10.7.14
VHF M (HJ)

Covesea
Skerries

Burghead
10.7.13
VHF 12 14 16

Buckie
10.7.10
VHF 12 16

Findochty
Portknockie
Cullen
Portsoy*

Whitehills
10.7.9
VHF 09 08 16

Macduff and Banff
10.7.8
VHF 12 16

Kinnairds Head
RC 301·50 KD 50M

Fraserburgh
10.7.7
VHF 12 16

Buchan Radio
VHF 25 16
VHF 25
0703 1903 UT

See 10-6-2

Rosehearty*

Rattray
Head

RG

04°00'W   30'   03°00'W   30'   02°00'W   30'   01°00'W

58°
00'N

58°
00'N

57°
30'N

10-7-3   AREA 7 TIDAL STREAMS

5 Hours before HW Dover (0500 after HW Aberdeen)

4 Hours before HW Dover (0600 after HW Aberdeen)

3 Hours before HW Dover (0520 before HW Aberdeen)

2 Hours before HW Dover (0420 before HW Aberdeen)

1 Hour before HW Dover (0320 before HW Aberdeen)

HW Dover (0220 before HW Aberdeen)

Southward 10.6.3   Westward 10.8.3

1 Hour after HW Dover (0120 before HW Aberdeen)

2 Hours after HW Dover (0020 before HW Aberdeen)

3 Hours after HW Dover (0040 after HW Aberdeen)

4 Hours after HW Dover (0140 after HW Aberdeen)

5 Hours after HW Dover (0240 after HW Aberdeen)

6 Hours after HW Dover (0340 after HW Aberdeen)

10.7.4 COASTAL LIGHTS, FOG SIGNALS AND WAYPOINTS

Abbreviations used below are given in 1.4.1. Principal lights are in **bold** print, places in CAPITALS, and light-vessels, light floats and Lanbys in *CAPITAL ITALICS*. Unless otherwise stated lights are white. m – elevation in metres; M – nominal range in miles. Fog signals are in *italics*. Useful waypoints are underlined – use those on land with care. All geographical positions should be assumed to be approximate. See 4.4.1. All positions are referenced to the OSGB 36 datum.

RATTRAY HEAD TO INVERNESS

FRASERBURGH
Cairnbulg Briggs 57°41'·12N 01°56'·35W Fl (2) 10s 9m 6M.
Ldg Lt 291°. 57°41'·58N 02°00'·03W QR 12m 5M. Rear, 75m from front, Oc R 6s 17m 5M.
Balaclava Bkwtr Hd 57°41'·53N 01°59'·63W Fl (2) G 8s 26m 6M; dome on W Tr; vis 178°-326°; *Siren 20s* (fishing).

Kinnaird Hd 57°41'·87N 02°00'·15W Fl 5s 25m **22M**; vis 092°-297°; W Tr; RC.
Bombing range Lt By 57°43'·80N 02°00'·75W Fl Y 5s; SPM.
Target float 57°41'·70N 02°09'·40W Fl Y 10s (unreliable).
Target float 57°42'·60N 02°09'·70W Fl Y 3s (unreliable).

MACDUFF/BANFF/WHITEHILLS
Macduff Lt Ho Pier Hd 57°40'·26N 02°29'·90W Fl (2) WRG 6s 12m W9M, R7M; W Tr; vis G shore-115°, W115°-174°, R174°-210°; *Horn (2) 20s*.
Macduff W Pier Hd 57°40'·23N 02°29'·88W QG 4m 5M.
Whitehills Pier Hd 57°40'·82N 02°34'·75W Fl WR 3s 7m W9M, R6M; W Tr; vis R132°-212°, W212°-245°.

PORTSOY
Pier Ldg Lts 160°. Front 57°41'·18N 02°41'·30W F 12m 5M; Tr. Rear FR 17m 5M; mast.

BUCKIE
West Muck 57°41'·07N 02°57'·93W QR 5m 7M; tripod.
NW Pier Hd 57°40'·85N 02°57'·62W 2 FR (vert) 7m 11M; R col. (3 FR when Hbr closed.)
Ldg Lts 125°. **Front**, 57°40'·85N 02°57'·56W Oc R 10s 15m **15M**; W Tr; *Siren (2) 60s*. **Rear**, 365m from front, Iso WG 2s 20m **W16M**, G12M; vis G090°-110°, W110°-225°.
W Pier, NW corner 2 FG (vert) 4m 9M; G col.

LOSSIEMOUTH
S Pier Hd 57°43'·44N 03°16'·59W Fl R 6s 11m 5M; *Siren 60s*.
Covesea Skerries 57°43'·50N 03°20'·30W Fl WR 20s 49m **W24M, R20M**; W Tr; vis W076°-267°, R267°-282°.

HOPEMAN
W Pier Hd 57°42'·71N 03°26'·20W Oc G 4s 8m 4M shown 1/8-30/4.
Ldg Lts 081°. Front, 57°42'·73N 03°26'·09W FR 3m. Rear, 10m from front, FR 3m. Shown 1/8-30/4.

BURGHEAD/FINDHORN
Burghead N Bkwtr Hd 57°42'·10N 03°29'·94W Oc 8s 7m 5M.
Burghead Spur 57°42'·11N 03°29'·94W Hd QR 3m 5M; vis from SW only.
Findhorn By 57°40'·40N 03°37'·65W; SWM.

NAIRN
W Pier Hd 57°35'·62N 03°51'·56W QG 5m 1M; Gy post.
E Pier Hd Oc WRG 4s 6m 5M; 8-sided Tr; vis Gshore-100°, W100°-207°, R207°-shore.
Whiteness Hd, McDermott Base Dir Lt 142·5° 57°35'·88N 04°00'·15W Dir Iso WRG 4s 6m 10M; vis G138°-141°, W141°-144°, R144°-147°.

INVERNESS FIRTH
Riff Bank E Lt By 57°38'·40N 03°58'·07W Fl Y 10s; SPM.
Navity Bank Lt By 57°38'·18N 04°01'·10W Fl (3) G 15s; SHM.
Riff Bank N Lt By 57°37'·18N 04°02'·30W Fl (2) R 12s; PHM.
Riff Bank W Lt By 57°35'·80N 04°03'·95W Fl Y 5s; SPM.

South Channel
Riff Bank S Lt By 57°36'·75N 04°00'·87W Q (6) + LFl 15s; SCM.
Craigmee Lt By 57°35'·32N 04°04'·90W Fl R 6s; PHM.
Chanonry 57°34'·46N 04°05'·48W Oc 6s 12m **15M**; W Tr; vis 148°-073°.
Avoch 57°34'·04N 04°09'·82W 2 FR (vert) 7/5m 5M; (occas).
Munlochy Lt By 57°32'·93N 04°07'·55W L Fl 10s; SWM.
Petty Bk Lt By 57°31'·83N 04°08'·51W Fl R 5s; PHM.
Meikle Mee Lt By 57°30'·27N 04°11'·94W Fl G 3s; SHM.
Longman Pt 57°30'·02N 04°13'·22W Fl WR 2s 7m W5M, R4M; R ▲ Bn; vis W078°-258°, R258°-078°.
Craigton Pt 57°30'·07N 04°14'·01W Fl WRG 4s 6m W11M, R7M, G7M; vis W312°-048°, R048°-064°, W064°-085°, G085°-shore.
Kessock Bridge N Trs Oc G 6s 28m 5M and QG 3m 3M; S Trs Oc R 6s 28m 5M and QR 3m 3M. Centre mark ▽ 57°29'·99N 04°13'·71W; Racon (K).

INVERNESS
R. Ness Outer Bn 57°29'·84N 04°13'·85W QR 3m 4M.
Inner Bn 57°29'·73N 04°14'·02W QR 3m 4M.
Embankment Hd Fl G 2s 8m 4M; G framework Tr.
E side Fl R 3s 7m 6M.

CALEDONIAN CANAL
Clachnaharry, S training wall Hd 57°29'·44N 04°15'·78W Iso G 4s 5m 2M; W △ on W mast; tfc signals.
N Training Wall Hd QR 5m 2M.

INVERNESS TO DUNCANSBY HEAD
CROMARTY FIRTH/INVERGORDON
Fairway Lt By 57°39'·98N 03°54'·10W L Fl 10s; SWM; Racon.
Cromarty Bank Lt By 57°40'·68N 03°56'·69W Fl (2) G 10s; SHM.
Buss Bank Lt By 57°41'·00N 03°59'·45W Fl R 3s; PHM.
The Ness 57°40'·99N 04°02'·10W Oc WR 10s 18m **W15M**, R11M; W Tr; vis R079°-088°, W088°-275°, obsc by N Sutor when brg less than 253°.
Nigg Ferry Jetty, SE corner 2 FG (vert) 6m 2M.
SW corner 2 FG (vert) 6m 2M.
Nigg Oil Terminal Pier Hd 57°41'·57N 04°02'·51W Oc G 5s 31m 5M; Gy Tr, floodlit.
E and W ends marked by 2 FG (vert) 9 4M.
Nigg Sands E Lt By 57°41'·62N 04°04'·25W Fl (2) G 10s; SHM.
Nigg Sands W Lt By 57°41'·29N 04°07'·15W Fl G 3s; SHM.
British Alcan Pier Hd 57°41'·30N 04°08'·27W QG 17m 5M.
Invergordon Dockyard Pier Hd 57°41'·17N 04°09'·64W Fl (3) G 10s 15m 4M.
Supply Base, SE corner Iso G 4s 9m 6M; Gy mast.
Quay, W end Oc G 8s 9m 6M; Gy mast.
Queen's Dock, W Arm Iso G 2s 9m 6M.
Three Kings Lt By 57°43'·75N 03°54'·17W Q (3) 10s; ECM.
Tarbat Ledge/Culloden Rk By 57°52'·45N 03°45'·45W; PHM.
Lt By 57°53'·00N 03°47'·00W Fl Y 5s; SPM.

DORNOCH FIRTH/TAIN
Tarbat Ness 57°51'·92N 03°46'·52W Fl (4) 30s 53m **24M**; W Tr, R bands; Racon (T).
Firing range 57°49'·45N 03°57'·50W Fl R 5s, when firing occurs.
Target float 57°51'·59N 03°52'·46W Fl Y 5s.

HELMSDALE/LYBSTER
Ben-a-chielt 58°19'·80N 03°22'·20W Aero 5 FR (vert) 448-265m; radio mast.

Lybster, S Pier Hd 58°17'·80N 03°17'·25W Oc R 6s 10m 3M;
W Tr; (occas).
Clythness 58°18'·70N 03°12'·50W Fl (2) 30s 45m **16M**; W Tr,
R band.

WICK

S Pier Hd 58°26'·36N 03°04'·64W Fl WRG 3s 12m W12M,
R9M, G9M; W 8-sided Tr; vis G253°-270°, W270°-286°,
R286°-329°; *Bell (2) 10s (occas).*
Dir Lt 288·5° 58°26'·56N 03°05'·26W Dir F WRG 9m W10M,
R7M, G7M; col on N end of bridge; vis G283·5°-287·2°,
W287·2°-291·7°, R289·7°-293·5°.
Noss Hd 58°28'·75N 03°02'·90W Fl WR 20s 53m **W25M, R
21M**; W Tr; vis R shore-191°, W191°-shore.

DUNCANSBY HEAD TO CAPE WRATH

Duncansby Hd 58°38'·62N 03°01'·44W Fl 12s 67m **22M**;
W Tr; RC; Racon (T).
Pentland Skerries 58°41'·43N 02°55'·39W Fl (3) 30s 52m
23M; W Tr; *Horn 45s.*
Lother Rock 58°43'·80N 02°58'·58W Q 11m 6M; Racon.
S Ronaldsay, Burwick Bkwtr Hd 2 FR (vert) 8m 5M.
Swona, near SW end 58°44'·28N 03°04'·13W Fl 8s 17m 9M;
W col; vis 261°-210°.
Swona N Hd 58°45'·13N 03°03'·00W Fl (3) 10s 16m 10M.
Stroma, Swilkie Pt 58°41'·78N 03°06'·92W Fl (2) 20s 32m
26M; W Tr; *Horn (2) 60s.*
Inner sound, John O'Groats, Pier Hd 58°38'·73N 03°04'·12W
Fl R 3s 4m 2M; W post; Ra refl.
Dunnet Hd 58°40'·31N 03°22'·48W Fl (4) 30s 105m **23M**; W
Tr; RG.

THURSO/SCRABSTER

Holburn (Little) Hd 58°36'·90N 03°32'·28W Fl WR 10s 23m
W15M, R11M; W Tr; vis W198°-358°, R358°-shore.
Thurso Bkwtr Hd 58°35'·97N 03°30'·63W QG 5m 4M; G post;
shown 1/9-30/4.
Thurso Ldg Lts 195°. Front, 58°35'·98N 03°30'·65W FG 5m
4M; Gy post. Rear, FG 6m 4M; Gy mast.
Scrabster Outer Pier Hd 58°36'·63N 03°32'·48W QG 6m 4M.

Strathy Pt 58°36'·10N 04°01'·00W Fl 20s 45m **26M**; W Tr
on W dwelling.
Sule Skerry 59°05'·10N 04°24'·30W Fl (2) 15s 34m **21M**;
W Tr; Racon (T).
North Rona 59°07'·30N 05°48'·80W Fl (3) 20s 114m **24M**;
W Tr.
Sula Sgeir 59°05'·65N 06°09'·50W Fl 15s 74m 11M;
■ structure.
Loch Eriboll, White Hd 58°31'·10N 04°38'·80W Fl WR 3s 18m
W13M, R12M; W Tr and bldg; vis W030°-172°, R172°-191°,
W191°-212°.
Cape Wrath 58°37'·55N 04°59'·87W Fl (4) 30s 122m **24M**;
W Tr; *Horn (3) 45s.*

ORKNEY ISLANDS

Tor Ness 58°46'·71N 03°17'·70W Fl 3s 21m 10M; W Tr.
S Walls, SE end, **Cantick Hd** 58°47'·25N 03°07'·76W Fl 20s
35m **18M**; W Tr.

SCAPA FLOW AND APPROACHES
Ruff Reef, off Cantick Hd 58°47'·48N 03°07'·68W Fl (2) 10s
10m 6M; B Bn.
Long Hope, S Ness Pier Hd, 58°48'·08N 03°12'·22W Fl WRG
3s 6m W7M, R5M, G5M; vis G082°-242°, W242°-252°, R252°-
082°.
Hoxa Hd 58°49'·35N 03°01'·93W Fl WR 3s 15m W9M, R6M;
W Tr; vis W026°-163°, R163°-201°, W201°-215°.

Stanger Hd 58°48'·98N 03°04'·60W Fl R 5s 25m 8M.
Roan Hd 58°50'·75N 03°03'·81W Fl (2) R 6s 12m 7M.
Nevi Skerry 58°50'·70N 03°02'·60W Fl (2) 6s 7m 6M; IDM.
Calf of Flotta 58°51'·30N 03°03'·90W QR 8m 4M.
Flotta Terminal, N end of E Jetty. 2 FR (vert) 10m 3M.
West Jetty 2 FR (vert) 10m 3M; *Bell (1)10s.*
Mooring dolphins, E and W, both QR 8m 3M.
SPM Tr No. 1 58°52'·20N 03°07'·37W Fl Y 5s 12m 3M;
Horn Mo(A) 60s.
SPM Tr No. 2 58°52'·27N 03°05'·82W Fl (4) Y 15s 12m 3M;
Horn Mo(N) 60s.
Gibraltar Pier 58°50'·29N 03°07'·77W 2 FG (vert) 7m 3M.
Golden Wharf, N end 58°50'·16N 03°11'·36W 2 FR (vert)
7m 3M.
Lyness Wharf, S end 58°50'·04N 03°11'·31W 2 FR (vert)
7m 3M.
St Margaret's Hope, Needle Pt Reef 58°50'·12N 02°57'·38W
Fl G 3s 6m 3M; ◆ on post.
Pier Hd 2 FG (vert) 6m 2M.
Ldg Lts 196°, both FR 7/11m.
Rose Ness 58°52'·36N 02°49'·80W Fl 6s 24m 8M; W Tr.
Scapa Pier W end 58°57'·44N 02°58'·32W Fl G 3s 6m 8M;
W mast.
Barrel of Butter 58 53'·45N 03°07'·47W Fl (2) 10s 6m 7M; Gy
platform on ● Tr.
Cava Lt Tr 58°53'·26N 03°10'·58W Fl WR 3s 11m W10M,
R8M; W ● Tr; vis W351°-143°, R143°-196°, W196°-251°,
R251°- 271°, W271°-298°.
Houton Bay Ldg Lts 316°. Front, 58°55'·00N 03°11'·46W
Fl G 3s 8m. Rear, 200m from front, FG 16m both R ▲ on
W pole, B bands, vis 312°-320°.
Ro-Ro terminal, S end Iso R 4s 7m 5M.

CLESTRAN SOUND
Peter Skerry Lt By 58°55'·28N 03°13'·42W Fl G 6s; SHM.
Riddock Shoal Lt By 58°55'·90N 03°15'·07W Fl (2) R 12s; PHM.

HOY SOUND
Ebbing Eddy Rks Lt By 58°56'·62N 03°16'·90W Q; NCM.
Graemsay Is Ldg Lts 104°. **Front**, 58°56'·46N 03°18'·50W
Iso 3s 17m **15M**; W Tr; vis 070°-255°. **Rear**, 1·2M from front,
Oc WR 8s 35m **W20M, R16M**; W Tr; vis R097°-112°, W112°-
163°, R163°-178°, W178°-332°; obsc on Ldg line within 0·5M.
Skerry of Ness 58°56'·98N 03°17'·73W Fl WG 4s 7m W7M,
G4M; vis W shore-090°, G090°-shore.

STROMNESS
Stromness Can Lt By 58°57'·27N 03°17'·52W QR; PHM.
Stromness Conical Lt By 58°57'·43N 03°17'·55W Fl G 3s.
Ldg Lts 317°. Front, 58°57'·64N 03°18'·06W FR 29m 11M;
post on W Tr. Rear, 55m from front FR 39m 11M; both vis 307°-
327°.
N Pier Hd 58°57'·78N 03°17'·62W Fl R 3s 8m 5M.

AUSKERRY.
Copinsay 58°53'·82N 02°40'·25W Fl (5) 30s 79m **21M**; W Tr;
Horn (4) 60s. Fog Det Lt UQ, vis 192°.
Auskerry 59°01'·58N 02°34'·25W Fl 20s 34m **18M**; W Tr.

Helliar Holm, S end 59°01'·17N 02°53'·95W Fl WRG 10s 18m
W14M, R10M; W Tr; vis G256°-276°, W276°-292°, R292°-
098°, W098°-116°, G116°-154°.
Balfour Pier, Shapinsay 59°01'·89N 02°54'·40W Q WRG 5m
W3M, R2M, G2M; vis G270°-010°, W010°-020°, R020°-090°.

KIRKWALL
Scargun Shoal By 59°00'·83N 02°58'·57W; SHM.
Pier N end 58°59'·32N 02°57'·62W Iso WRG 5s 8m **W15M**,
R13M, G13M; W Tr; vis G153°-183°, W183°-192°, R192°-210°.

WIDE FIRTH

Linga Skerry Lt By 59°02'·42N 02°57'·45W Q (3) 10s; ECM.

Boray Skerries Lt By 59°03'·68N 02°57'·55W Q (6) + L Fl 15s; SCM.

Skertours Lt By 59°04'·15N 02°56'·61W Q; NCM.

Galt Skerry Lt By 59°05'·25N 02°54'·10W Q; NCM.

Brough of Birsay 59°08'·25N 03°20'·30W Fl (3) 25s 52m **18M**; W castellated Tr and Bldg.

Papa Stronsay NE end, The Ness 59°09'·38N 02°34'·80W Iso 4s 8m 9M; W Tr.

STRONSAY, PAPA SOUND

Quiabow Lt By 59°09'·85N 02°36'·20W Fl (2) G 12s; SHM.

No. 1 Lt By (off Jacks Reef) 59°09'·20N 02°36'·40W Fl G 5s; SHM.

No. 2 Lt By 59°08'·95N 02°36'·50W Fl R 5s; PHM.

No. 3 Lt By 59°08'·73N 02°36'·08W Fl (2) G 5s; SHM.

No. 4 Lt By 59°08'·80N 02°36'·37W Fl (2) R 5s; PHM.

Whitehall Pier 50°08'·61N 02°35'·79W 2 FG (vert) 8m 4M.

SANDAY ISLAND/NORTH RONALDSAY

Start Pt 59°16'·70N 02°22'·50W Fl (2) 20s 24m **19M**; W Tr, B stripes.

Kettletoft Pier Hd 59°13'·90N 02°35'·72W Fl WRG 3s 7m W7M, R5M, G5M; W Tr; vis W351°-011°, R011°-180°, G180°-351°.

N Ronaldsay NE end, 59°23'·40N 02°22'·80W Fl 10s 43m **19M**; R Tr, W bands; Racon; *Horn 60s*.

Nouster Pier Hd 59°21'·32N 02°26'·35W QR 5m.

EDAY/EGILSAY

Calf Sound 59°14'·30N 02°45'·70W Iso WRG 5s 8m W8M, R7M, G6M; W Tr; vis R shore-216°, W216°-223°, G223°-302°, W302°-307°.

Backaland Pier 59°09'·45N 02°44'·75W Fl R 3s 5m 4M; vis 192°-250°.

Egilsay Graand Lt By 59°06'·90N 02°54'·30W Q(6) + L Fl 15s; SCM.

Egilsay Pier, S end 59°09'·32N 02°56'·65W Fl G 3s 4m 4M.

WESTRAY/PIEROWALL.

Noup Hd 59°19'·90N 03°04'·10W Fl 30s 79m **22M**; W Tr; vis 335°-242°, 248°-282°; obsc on E bearings within 0·8M, part obsc 240°-275°.

Pierowall E Pier Hd 59°19'·39N 02°58'·41W Fl WRG 3s 7m W11M, R7M, G7M; vis G254°-276°, W276°-291°, R291°-308°, G308°-215°.

Papa Westray, Moclett Bay Pier Hd 59°19'·65N 02°53'·40W Fl WRG 5s 7m W5M, R3M, G3M; vis G306°-341°, W341°-040°, R040°-074°.

SHETLAND ISLES

FAIR ISLE

Skadan, S end 59°30'·85N 01°39'·08W Fl (4) 30s 32m **24M**; W Tr; vis 260°-146°, obsc inshore 260°-282°; *Horn (2) 60s*.

Skroo, N end 59°33'·16N 01°36'·49W Fl (2) 30s 80m **22M**; W Tr; vis 086·7°-358°; *Horn (3) 45s*.

MAINLAND, SOUTH

Sumburgh Hd 59°51'·30N 01°16'·37W Fl (3) 30s 91m **23M**; W Tr; RC.

Pool of Virkie, Marina E Bkwtr Hd 59°53'·05N 01°17'·00W 2 FG (vert) 6m 5M.

Mousa, Perie Bard 59°59'·85N 01°09'·40W Fl 3s 20m 10M; W Tr.

Aithsvoe 60°02'·30N 01°12'·83W Fl R 3s 3m 2M.

BRESSAY/LERWICK

Kirkabister Ness 60°07'·25N 01°07'·18W Fl (2) 20s 32m **23M**; W Tr.

Cro of Ham 60°08'·20N 01°07'·40W Fl 3s 3M.

Twageos Pt 60°08'·95N 01°07'·83W L Fl 6s 8m 6M; W Bn.

Maryfield, Ferry Terminal 60°09'·47N 01°07'·32W Oc WRG 6s 5m 5M; vis W008°-013°, R013°-111°, G111°-008°.

Bkwtr N Hd 60°09'·27N 01°08'·29W 2 FR (vert) 5m 4M.

N Ness 60°09'·60N 01°08'·66W Iso WG 4s 4m 5M; vis G158°-216°, W216°-158°.

Loofa Baa 60°09'·75N 01°08'·67W Q (6) + L Fl 15s 4m 5M; SCM.

Soldian Rk Lt By 60°12'·54N 01°04'·61W VQ(6) + L Fl 15s; SCM.

N ent Dir Lt 215° 60°10'·49N 01°09'·40W Dir Oc WRG 6s 27m 8M; Y ▲, Or stripe; vis R211°-214°, W214°-216°, G216°-221°.

Gremista Marina S Bkwtr Hd 60°10'·23N 01°09'·49W Iso R 4s 3m 2M.

Greenhead 60°10'·87N 01°08'·98W Q (4) R 10s 4m 3M.

Rova Hd 60°11'·45N 01°08'·45W Fl (3) WRG 18s 10m W8M, R7M, G6M; W Tr; vis R shore-180°, W180°-194°, G194°-213°, R213°-241°, W241°-261·5°, G261·5°-009°, W009°-shore.

The Brethren Rk Lt By 60°12'·38N 01°08'·12W Q (9) 15s; WCM.

The Unicorn Rk Lt By 60°13'·54N 01°08'·35W VQ (3) 5s; ECM.

Dales Voe 60°11'·82N 01°11'·10W Fl (2) WRG 8s 5m W4M, R3M, G3M; vis G220°-227°, W227°-233°, R233°-240°.

Dales Voe Quay 60°11'·60N 01°10'·48W 2 FR (vert) 9m 3M.

Laxfirth Pier Hd 60°12'·77N 01°12'·01W 2 FG (vert) 4m 2M.

Hoo Stack 60°14'·99N 01°05'·25W Fl (4) WRG 12s 40m W7M, R5M, G5M; W pylon; vis R169°-180°, W180°-184°, G184°-193°, W193°-169°. Dir Lt 182°. Dir Fl (4) WRG 12s 33m W9M, R6M, G6M; same structure; vis R177°-180°, W180°-184°, G184°-187°; synch with upper Lt.

Mull (Moul) of Eswick 60°15'·80N 01°05'·80W Fl WRG 3s 50m W9M, R6M, G6M; W Tr; vis R028°-200°, W200°-207°, G207°-018°, W018°-028°.

WHALSAY/SKERRIES

Symbister Ness 60°20'·46N 01°02'·15W Fl (2) WG 12s 11m W8M, G6M; W Tr; vis W shore-203°, G203°-shore.

Symbister Bay S Bkwtr Hd 60°20'·60N 01°01'·50W QG 4m 2M.

N Bkwtr Hd 60°20'·67N 01°01'·60W Oc G 7s 3m 3M.

E Bkwtr Hd Oc R 7s 3m 3M.

Marina N pontoon 60°20'·50N 01°01'·40W 2 FG (vert) 2m 3M.

Skate of Marrister 60°21'·42N 01°01'·25W Fl G 6s 4m 4M; G mast with platform.

Suther Ness 60°22'·15N 01°00'·05W Fl WRG 3s 8m W10M, R8M, G7M; vis W shore-038°, R038°-173°, W173°-206°, G206°-shore.

Mainland, Laxo Voe ferry terminal   60°21'·1N 01°10'·0W 2 FG (vert) 4m 2M.

Bound Skerry 60°25'·50N 00°43'·50W Fl 20s 44m **20M**; W Tr.

South Mouth. Ldg Lts 014°. Front, 60°25'·37N 00°44'·89W FY 3m 2M. Rear, FY 12m 2M.

Bruray Bn D Fl (3) G 6s 3m 3M.

Bruray Bn B VQ G 3m 3M.

Housay Bn A VQ R 3m 3M.

Bruray ferry berth 60°25'·4N 00°45'·10W 2 FG (vert) 6m 4M.

Muckle Skerry 60°26'·40N 00°51'·70W Fl (2) WRG 10s 13m W7M, R5M, G5M; W Tr; vis W046°-192°, R192°-272°, G272°-348°, W348°-353°, R353°-046°.

YELL SOUND

S ent, Lunna Holm 60°27'·38N 01°02'·39W Fl (3) WRG 15s 19m W10M, R7M, G7M; W ● Tr; vis R shore-090°, W090°-094°, G094°-209°, W209°-275°, R275°-shore.

Firths Voe, N shore 60°27'·24N 01°10'·50W Oc WRG 8s 9m **W15M**, R10M, G10M; W Tr; vis W189°-194°, G194°-257°, W257°-261°, R261°-339°, W339°-066°.

Linga Is. Dir Lt 60°26'·83N 01°09'·00W Dir Q (4) WRG 8s 10m W9M, R9M, G9M; concrete col; vis R145°-148°, W148°-152°, G152°-155°. Q (4) WRG 8s 10m W7M, R4M, G4M; same structure; vis R052°-146°, G154°-196°, W196°-312°; synch with Dir Lt.

The Rumble Bn 60°28'·20N 01°07'·12W R Bn; Racon (O).
Yell, Ulsta Ferry Terminal Bkwtr Hd 60°29'·78N 01°09'·40W
Oc RG 4s 7m R5M, G5M; vis G shore-354°, R044°-shore.
Same structure; Oc WRG 4s 5m W8M, R5M, G5M; vis
G shore-008°, W008°-036°, R036°-shore.
Toft ferry terminal 60°28'·06N 01°12'·26W 2 FR (vert) 5m 2M.
Ness of Sound, W side 60°31'·38N 01°11'·15W Iso WRG 5s
18m W9M, R6M, G6M; vis G shore-345°, W345°-350°,
R350°-160°, W160°-165°, G165°-shore.
Brother Is. Dir Lt 329° 60°30'·99N 01°13'·99W Dir Fl (4) WRG
8s 16m W10M, R7M, G7M; vis G323·5°-328°, W328°-330°,
R330°-333·5°.
Mio Ness 60°29'·70N 01°13'·55W Q (2) WR 10s 12m W7M,
R4M; W ● Tr; W282°-238°, R238°-282°.
Tinga Skerry 60°30'·52N 01°14'·73W Q (2) G 10s 9m 5M; W ● Tr.

YELL SOUND, NORTH ENTRANCE
Bagi Stack 60°43'·55N 01°07'·40W Fl (4) 20s 45m 10M; W Tr.
Gruney Is 60°39'·20N 01°18'·03W Fl WR 5s 53m W8M,
R6M; W Tr; vis R064°-180°, W180°-012°; Racon (T).
Point of Fethaland 60°38'·09N 01°18'·58W Fl (3) WR 15s
65m **W24M**, **R20M**; W Tr; vis R080°-103°, W103°-160°,
R160°-206°, W206°-340°.
Muckle Holm 60°34'·85N 01°15'·90W Fl (4) 10s 32m 10M; W Tr.
Little Holm 60°33'·46N 01°15'·75W Iso 4s 12m 6M; W Tr.
Outer Skerry 60°33'·08N 01°18'·20W Fl 6s 12m 8M; W col,
B bands.
Quey Firth 60°31'·48N 01°19'·46W Oc WRG 6s 22m W12M,
R8M, G8M; W Tr; vis W shore (through S and W-290°, G290°-
327°, W327°-334°, R334°-shore.
Lamba, S side 60°30'·76N 01°17'·70W Fl WRG 3s 30m
W8M, R5M, G5M; W Tr; vis G shore-288°, W288°-293°,
R293°-327°, W327°-044°, R044°-140°, W140°-shore. Dir Lt
290·5° Dir Fl WRG 3s 24m W10M, R7M, G7M; vis 285·5°-
288°, W288°-293°, R293°-295·5°.

SULLOM VOE
Gluss Is Ldg Lts 194·7° (H24). **Front**, 60°29'·81N 01°19'·31W
F 39m **19M**; ■ on Gy Tr. **Rear**, 0·75M from front, F 69m **19M**;
■ on Gy Tr. Both Lts 9M by day.
Little Roe 60°30'·05N 01°16'·35W Fl (3) WR 10s 16m W5M,
R4M; Y and W structure; vis R036°-095·5°, W095·5°-036°.
Skaw Taing 60°29'·13N 01°16'·72W Fl (2) WRG 5s 21m
W8M, R5M, G5M; Or and W structure; vis W049°-078°,
G078°-147°, W147°-154°, R154°-169°, W169°-288°.
Ness of Bardister 60°28'·22N 01°19'·50W Oc WRG 8s 20m
W9M, R6M, G6M; Or and W structure; vis W180·5°-240°,
R240°-310·5°, W310·5°-314·5°, G314·5°-030·5°.
Vats Houllands 60°27'·97N 01°17'·48W Oc WRGY 3s 73m
6M; Gy Tr; vis W343·5°-029·5°, Y029·5°-049°, G049°-074·5°,
R074·5°-098·5°, G098·5°-123·5°, Y123·5°-148°, W148°-163·5°.
Fugla Ness. Lts in line 212·3°. Rear, 60°27'·3N 01°19'·7W Iso
4s 45m 14M. Common front 60°27'·48N 01°19'·43W Iso 4s
27m 14M; synch with rear Lts. Lts in line 203°. Rear,
60°27'·3N 01°19'·6W Iso 4s 45m 14M.
Sella Ness. Upper Lt 60°26'·92N 01°16'·52W Q WRG 14m
7M; Gy Tr; vis G084·5°-098·7°, W098·7°-099·7°, W126°-
128·5°, R128·5°-174·5°; by day F WRG 2M (occas). Lower Lt.
Q WRG 10m 7M; vis: G084·5°-106·5°, W106·5°-115°, R115°-
174·5°; by day F WRG 2M (occas).
Tug Jetty finger, Pier Hd 60°26'·79N 01°16'·25W Iso G 4s 4m 3M.
Garth Pier N arm Hd 60°26'·72N 01°16'·22W Fl (2) G 5s 4m 3M.
Scatsa Ness Upper Lt 60°26'·52N 01°18'·13W Oc WRG 5s
14m 7M; Gy Tr; vis G161·5°-187·2°, W187·2°-188·2°, W207·2°-
208·2°, R208·2°-251·5°; by day F WRG 2M (occas). Lower Lt

Oc WRG 5s 10m 7M; vis G161·5°-197·2°, W197·2°-202·2°,
R202·2°-251·5°; by day F WRG 2M (occas).
Ungam Is 60°27'·27N 01°18'·50W VQ (2) 5s 2m 2M; W col;
Ra refl.

EAST YELL /UNST/BALTA SOUND
Whitehill 60°34'·85N 01°00'·01W Fl WR 3s 24m W9M, R6M;
vis W shore-163°, R163°-211°, W211°-349°, R349°-shore.
Uyea Sound 60°41'·19N 00°55'·37W Fl (2) 8s 8m 7M; R & W Tr.
Balta Sound 60°44'·47N 00°47'·56W Fl WR 10s 17m 10M,
R7M; vis W249°-010°, R010°-060°, W060°-154°; Q Lt (occas)
marks Unst Aero RC 0·7M W.
Balta Marina Bkwtr Hd 60°45'·60N 00°50'·20W Fl R 6s 2m 2M.
Holme of Skaw 60°49'·92N 00°46'·19W Fl 5s 8m 8M.
Muckle Flugga 60°51'·33N 00°53'·00W Fl (2) 20s 66m **22M**;
W Tr.
Yell. Cullivoe Bkwtr Hd 60°41'·91N 00°59'·66W Oc R 7s 5m
2M; Gy col.

MAINLAND, WEST
Esha Ness 60°29'·35N 01°37'·55W Fl 12s 61m **25M**; W ■Tr.
Hillswick, S end of Ness 60°27'·20N 01°29'·70W Fl (4) WR 15s
34m W9M, R6M; W house: vis W217°-093°, R093°-114°.
Muckle Roe, Swarbacks Minn, 60°21'·05N 01°26'·90W Fl WR
3s 30m W9M, R6M; vis W314°-041°, R041°-075°, W075°-
137°.
W Burra Firth Outer Lt 60°17'·84N 01°33'·47W Oc WRG
8s 27m W9M, R7M, G7M; vis G136°-142°, W142°-150°,
R150°-156°.
W Burra Firth Inner Lt 60°17'·84N 01°32'·03W F WRG 9m
W15M, R9M, G9M; vis G095°-098°, W098°-102°, W098°-
102°, R102°-105°.
Aith Bkwtr. RNLI berth 60°17'·20N 01°22'·30W QG 5m 3M.
W Burra Firth Transport Pier Hd 60°17'·75N 01°32'·30W Iso
G 4s 4m 4M.
Ve Skerries 60°22'·40N 01°48'·67W Fl (2) 20s 17m 11M; W
Tr; Racon (T).
Rams Hd 60°12'·00N 01°33'·40W Fl WG 8s 16m W9m, G6M,
R6M; W house; vis G265°-355°, W355°-012°, R012°-090°,
W090°-136°, obsc by Vaila I when brg more than 030°.
Vaila Pier 60°13'·47N 01°34'·00W 2 FR (vert) 4m.
Skeld Voe, Skeld Pier Hd 60°11'·20N 01°26'·10W 2 FR (vert)
4m 3M.
North Havra 60°09'·88N 01°20'·17W Fl WRG 12s 24m
W7M, R5M, G5M; W Tr; vis G001°-053·5°, W053·5°-060·5°,
G274°-334°, W334°-337·5°, R337·5°-001°.

SCALLOWAY
Pt of the Pund 60°08'·02N 01°18'·20W Fl WRG 5s 20m
W7M, R5M, G5M; W Tr; vis R350°-090°, G090°-111°, R111°-
135°, W135°-140°, G140°-177°, W267°-350°.
Whaleback Skerry Lt By 60°07'·98N 01°18'·79W Q; NCM.
Moores slipway Jetty Hd 60°08'·21N 01°16'·72W 2 FR (vert)
4m 1M.
Centre Pier 60°08'·06N 01°16'·47W Oc WRG 10s 10m W11M,
G8M, R8M; vis G052°-063·5°, W063·5°-065·5°, R065·5°-
077°.

Fugla Ness 60°06'·40N 01°20'·75W Fl (2) WRG 10s 20m
W10M, R7M, G7M; W Tr; vis G014°-032°, W032°-082°,
R082°-134°, W134°-shore.

FOULA
60°06'·78N 02°03'·72W Fl (3) 15s 36m **18M**; W Tr. Obscured
123°-221°.

7

10.7.5   PASSAGE INFORMATION

Refer to the *N Coast of Scotland Pilot*; the CCC's SDs (3 vols) for *N and NE coasts of Scotland*; *Orkney*; and *Shetland*.

MORAY FIRTH: SOUTH COAST (charts 115, 222, 223)

Crossing the Moray Firth from Rattray Hd (lt, fog sig) to Duncansby Hd (lt,RC, Racon) heavy seas may be met in strong W winds. Most hbrs in the Firth are exposed to NE-E winds. For oil installations, see 10.5.5; the Beatrice Field is 20M S of Wick. Tidal streams attain 3kn at sp close off Rattray Hd, but 5M NE of the Head the NE-going stream begins at HW Aberdeen + 0140, and the SE-going stream at HW Aberdeen − 0440, sp rates 2kn. Streams are weak elsewhere in the Moray Firth, except in the inner part. In late spring/early summer fog (haar) is likely in onshore winds.

In strong winds the sea breaks over Steratan Rk and Colonel Rk, respectively 3M E and 1M ENE of Fraserburgh (10.7.7). Rosehearty firing range is N & W of Kinnairds Hd (lt); tgt buoys often partially submerged. Banff B is shallow; N of Macduff (10.7.8) beware Collie Rks. Banff hbr dries, and should not be approached in fresh NE-E winds, when seas break well offshore; Macduff would then be a feasible alternative.

From Meavie Pt to Scar Nose dangers extend up to 3ca from shore in places. Beware Caple Rk (depth 0·2m) 7½ca W of Logie Hd. Spey B is clear of dangers more than 7½ca from shore; anch here, but only in offshore winds. Beware E Muck (dries) 5ca SW of Craigenroan, an above-water rky patch 5ca SW of Craig Hd, and Middle Muck and W Muck in approach to Buckie (10.7.10); Findochty & Portknockie are 2 and 3.5M ENE. Halliman Skerries (dry; bn) lie 1·5M WNW of Lossiemouth (10.7.11). Covesea Skerries (dry) lie 5ca NW of their lt ho.

Inverness Firth is approached between Nairn (10.7.15) and S Sutor. In heavy weather there is a confused sea with overfalls on Guillam Bank, 9M S of Tarbat Ness. The sea also breaks on Riff Bank (S of S Sutor) which dries in places. Chans run both N and S of Riff Bank. Off Fort George, on E side of ent to Inverness Firth (chart 1078), the SW-going stream begins HW Aberdeen + 0605, sp rate 2·5kn; the NE-going stream begins at HW Aberdeen − 0105, sp rate 3·5kn. There are eddies and turbulence between Fort George and Chanonry Pt when stream is running hard. Much of Inverness Firth is shallow, but a direct course from Chanonry Pt to Kessock Bridge, via Munlochy SWM and Meikle Mee SHM lt buoys, carries a least depth of 2·1m. Meikle Mee bank dries 0·2m. For Fortrose and Avoch, see 10.7.16.

MORAY FIRTH: NORTH WEST COAST (chart 115)

Cromarty Firth (charts 1889, 1890) is entered between N Sutor and S Sutor, both fringed by rks, some of which dry. Off the entrance the in-going stream begins at HW Aberdeen + 0605, and the out-going at HW Aberdeen − 0105, sp rates 1·5 kn. Good sheltered anchs within the firth, see 10.7.19.

The coast NE to Tarbat Ness (lt) is fringed with rks. Beware Three Kings (dries) about 3M NE of N Sutor. Culloden Rk, a shoal with depth of 1·8m, extends 2½ca NE of Tarbat Ness, where salmon nets between Tarbat Ness and Portmahomack (10.7.17). Dornoch Firth (10.7.19) is shallow, with shifting banks, and in strong E winds the sea breaks heavily on the bar E of Dornoch Pt.

At Lothbeg Pt, 5M SW of Helmsdale (10.7.18), a rky ledge extends 5ca offshore. Near Berriedale, 7M NE of Helmsdale, The Pinnacle, a detached rk 61m high, stands close offshore. The Beatrice oil field lies on Smith Bank, 28M NE of Tarbat Ness, and 11M off Caithness coast. Between Dunbeath and Lybster (10.7.18) there are no dangers more than 2ca offshore. Clyth Ness (lt) is fringed by detached and drying rks. From here to Wick (10.7.19) the only dangers are close inshore. There is anch in Sinclair's B in good weather, but Freswick B further N is better to await the tide in Pentland Firth (beware wreck in centre of bay). Stacks of Duncansby and Baxter Rk (depth 2·7m) lie 1M and 4ca S of Duncansby Hd.

PENTLAND FIRTH (charts 2162, 2581)

This potentially dangerous chan should only be attempted with moderate winds (less than F4), good vis, no swell and a fair np tide; when it presents few problems. A safe passage depends on a clear understanding of tidal streams and correct timing. The Admiralty Tidal Stream Atlas for Orkney and Shetland (NP 209) gives large scale vectors and is essential. Even in ideal conditions the races off Duncansby Hd, Swilkie Pt (N end of Stroma), and Rks of Mey (Merry Men of Mey) must be avoided as they are always dangerous to small craft. Also avoid the Pentland Skerries, Muckle Skerry, Old Head, Lother Rock (S Ronaldsay), and Dunnet Hd on E-going flood. For passages across the Firth see CCC SDs for Orkney.

At E end the Firth is entered between Duncansby Hd and Old Hd (S Ronaldsay), between which lie Muckle Skerry and the Pentland Skerries. Near the centre of Firth are the Islands of Swona (N side) and Stroma (S side). Outer Sound (main chan, 2·5M wide) runs between Swona and Stroma; Inner Sound (1·5M wide) between Stroma and the mainland. Rks of Mey extend about 2ca N of St John's Pt. The W end of the Firth is between Dunnet Hd and Tor Ness (Hoy).

Tidal streams reach 8-9kn at sp in the Outer Sound, and 9-12kn between Pentland Skerries and Duncansby Hd. The resultant dangerous seas, very strong eddies and violent races should be avoided by yachts at all costs. Broadly the E-going stream begins at HW Aberdeen + 0500, and the W-going at HW Aberdeen − 0105. **Duncansby Race** extends ENE towards Muckle Skerry on the SE-going stream, but by HW Aberdeen − 0440 it extends NW from Duncansby Hd. Note: HW at Muckle Skerry is the same time as HW Dover. A persistent race off **Swilkie Pt** at N end of Stroma, is very dangerous with a strong W'ly wind over a W-going stream. The most dangerous and extensive race in the Firth is **Merry Men of Mey**, which forms off St John's Pt on W-going stream at HW Aberdeen − 0150 and for a while extends right across to Tor Ness with heavy breaking seas even in fine weather.

Passage Westward: This is the more difficult direction due to prevailing W winds. Freswick B, 3·5M S of Duncansby Hd, is a good waiting anch; here an eddy runs N for 9 hrs. Round Duncansby Hd close in at HW Aberdeen −0220, as the ebb starts to run W. Take a mid-course through the Inner Sound to appr the Rks of Mey from close inshore. Gills Bay is a temp anch if early; do not pass Rks of Mey until ebb has run for at least 2 hrs. Pass 100m N of the Rks (awash).

Passage Eastward: With a fair wind and tide, no race forms and the passage is easier. Leave Scrabster at local LW+1 so as to be close off Dunnet Hd at HW Aberdeen +0240 as the E-going flood starts to make. If late, give the Hd a wide berth. Having rounded the Rks of Mey, steer S initially to avoid being set onto the rky S tip of Stroma, marked by unlit SCM bn. Then keep mid-chan through the Inner Sound and maintain this offing to give Duncansby Hd a wide berth.

PENTLAND FIRTH TO CAPE WRATH (chart 1954)

Dunnet B, S of Dunnet Hd (lt) gives temp anch in E or S winds, but dangerous seas enter in NW'lies. On W side of Thurso B is Scrabster (10.7.20) sheltered from S and W. Between Holborn Hd and Strathy Pt the E-going stream begins at HW Ullapool − 0150, and the W-going at HW Ullapool + 0420, sp rates 1·8kn. Close to Brims Ness off Ushat Hd the sp rate is 3kn, and there is often turbulence.

SW of Ushat Hd the Dounreay power stn is conspic, near shore. Dangers extend 2½ca seaward off this coast.

Along E side of Strathy Pt (lt) an eddy gives almost continuous N-going stream, but there is usually turbulence off the Pt where this eddy meets the main E or W stream. Several small B's along this coast give temp anch in offshore winds, but must not be used or approached with wind in a N quarter.

Kyle of Tongue (10.7.19) is entered from E through Caol Raineach, S of Eilean nan Ron, or from N between Eilean Iosal and Cnoc Glass. There is no chan into the kyle W of Rabbit Is, to which a drying spit extends 0·5M NNE from the mainland shore. Further S there is a bar across entrance to inner part of kyle. There are anchs on SE side of Eilean nan Ron, SE side of Rabbit Is, off Skullomie, or S of Eilean Creagach off Talmine. Approach to the latter runs close W of Rabbit Islands, but beware rks to N and NW of them.

Loch Eriboll, (chart 2076 and 10.7.19), provides secure anchs, but in strong winds violent squalls blow down from mountains. Eilean Cluimhrig lies on W side of entrance; the E shore is fringed with rks up to 2ca offshore. At White Hd (lt) the loch narrows to 6ca. There are chans W and E of Eilean Choraidh. Best anchs in Camas an Duin (S of Ard Neackie) or in Rispond B close to entrance (but not in E winds, and beware Rispond Rk which dries).

The coast to C. Wrath (10.8.5) is indented, with dangers extending 3ca off the shore and offlying rks and Is. Once a yacht has left Loch Eriboll she is committed to a long and exposed passage until reaching Loch Inchard. The Kyle of Durness is dangerous if the wind or sea is onshore. Give Cape Wrath a wide berth when wind-against-tide which raises a severe sea. A firing exercise area extends 8M E of C. Wrath, and 4M offshore. When in use, R flags or pairs of R lts (vert) are shown from E and W limits, and yachts should keep clear.

ORKNEY ISLANDS (10.7.21 and charts 2249, 2250)

The Islands are mostly indented and rky, but with sandy beaches especially on NE sides. Pilotage is easy in good vis, but in other conditions great care is needed since tides run strongly. For details refer to Clyde Cruising Club's *Orkney Sailing Directions* and the Admiralty Tidal Atlas NP 209.

When cruising in Orkney it is essential to understand and use the tidal streams to the best advantage, avoiding the various tide races and overfalls, particularly near sp. A good engine is needed since, for example, there are many places where it is dangerous to get becalmed. Swell from the Atlantic or North Sea can contribute to dangerous sea conditions, or penetrate to some of the anchorages. During summer months winds are not normally unduly strong, and can be expected to be Force 7 or more on about two days a month. But in winter the wind reaches this strength for 10-15 days per month, and gales can be very severe in late winter and early spring. Cruising conditions are best near midsummer, when of course the hours of daylight are much extended.

Stronsay Firth and Westray Firth run SE/NW through the group. The many good anchs, include: Deer Sound (W of Deer Ness); B of Firth, B of Isbister, and off Balfour in Elwick B (all leading from Wide Firth); Rysa Sound, B of Houton, Hunda Sound (in Scapa Flow); Rousay Sound; and Pierowall Road (Westray). Plans for some of these are on chart 2622. For Houton Bay, Shapinsay, Auskerry and Pierowall, see 10.7.22. There is a major oil terminal and prohibited area at Flotta, on the S side of Scapa Flow.

Tide races or dangerous seas occur at the entrances to most of the firths or sounds when the stream is against strong winds. This applies particularly to Hoy Sound, Eynhallow Sound, Papa Sound (Westray), Lashy Sound, and North Ronaldsay Firth. Also off Mull Head, over Dowie Sand, between Muckle Green Holm and War Ness (where violent turbulence may extend right across the firth), between Faraclett Head and Wart Holm, and off Sacquoy Hd. Off War Ness the SE-going stream begins at HW Aberdeen + 0435, and the NW-going at HW Aberdeen – 0200, sp rates 7kn.

SHETLAND ISLANDS (10.7.25 and charts 3281, 3282, 3283)

These Islands mostly have bold cliffs and are relatively high, separated by narrow sounds through which the tide runs strongly, so that in poor vis great care is needed. Avoid sp tides, swell and wind against tide conditions. Although there are many secluded and attractive anchs, remember that the weather can change very quickly, with sudden shifts of wind. Also beware salmon fisheries and mussel rafts (unlit) in many Voes, Sounds and hbrs. Lerwick (10.7.26) is the busy main port and capital; for Scalloway and Balta Sound see 10.7.25. Refer to the Clyde Cruising Club's *Shetland Sailing Directions*.

Coming from the S, beware a most violent and dangerous race (roost) off Sumburgh Hd (at S end of Mainland) on both streams. Other dangerous areas include between Ve Skerries and Papa Stour; the mouth of Yell Sound with strong wind against N-going stream; and off Holm of Skaw (N end of Unst). Tidal streams run mainly NW/SE and are not strong except off headlands and in the major sounds; the Admiralty Tidal Atlas NP 209 gives detail. The sp range is about 2m.

The 50M passage from Orkney can conveniently be broken by a stop at Fair Isle (North Haven). Note that races form off both ends of the Is, especially S (Roost of Keels); see 10.7.25. Recommended Traffic Routes: NW-bound ships pass to the NE (no closer than 10M to Sumburgh Hd) or SW of Fair Isle; SE-bound ships pass no closer than 5M off N Ronaldsay (Orkney). Lerwick to Bergen, Norway is about 210M.

10.7.6   DISTANCE TABLE

Approximate distances in nautical miles are by the most direct route, whilst avoiding dangers and allowing for Traffic Separation Schemes. Places in *italics* are in adjoining areas; places in **bold** are in 10.0.7, Distances across the North Sea.

		1	2	3	4	5	6	7	8	9	10	11	12	13	14	15	16	17	18	19	20
1.	*Peterhead*	**1**																			
2.	**Fraserburgh**	16	**2**																		
3.	Banff/Macduff	33	18	**3**																	
4.	Buckie	46	31	15	**4**																
5.	Lossiemouth	56	41	25	11	**5**															
6.	Findhorn	69	54	38	24	13	**6**														
7.	Nairn	79	64	48	34	23	10	**7**													
8.	**Inverness**	90	75	59	45	34	23	13	**8**												
9.	Tarbat Ness	72	57	41	27	18	14	17	27	**9**											
10.	Helmsdale	74	59	44	33	26	28	32	43	16	**10**										
11.	**Wick**	72	57	50	46	44	51	58	69	42	29	**11**									
12.	Duncansby Head	82	67	62	58	57	64	71	81	54	41	13	**12**								
13.	Scrabster	100	85	80	76	75	82	89	99	72	59	31	18	**13**							
14.	**Kirkwall**	115	100	95	91	90	97	104	114	87	74	46	34	50	**14**						
15.	Stromness	104	89	84	80	79	86	92	103	76	63	35	22	25	32	**15**					
16.	Fair Isle	122	111	116	118	120	130	137	148	121	108	79	68	85	55	77	**16**				
17.	**Lerwick**	160	150	156	160	162	172	170	190	162	148	120	109	124	95	110	42	**17**			
18.	Loch Eriboll (ent)	137	122	117	113	112	119	126	136	109	96	68	55	37	80	50	110	150	**18**		
19.	Cape Wrath	145	130	125	121	120	127	134	144	117	104	76	63	47	79	58	120	155	13	**19**	
20.	*Ullapool*	198	183	178	174	173	180	179	197	170	157	129	116	100	132	111	173	208	66	53	**20**

FRASERBURGH   10-7-7

Aberdeenshire 57°41'·52N 01°59'·70W   Rtg 1-2-3

CHARTS
AC 1462, 222,115; OS 30
TIDES
+0120 Dover; ML 2·3; Duration 0615; Zone 0 (UT)

Standard Port ABERDEEN (←)

Times				Height (metres)			
High Water		Low Water		MHWS	MHWN	MLWN	MLWS
0000	0600	0100	0700	4·3	3·4	1·6	0·6
1200	1800	1300	1900				
Differences FRASERBURGH							
–0105	–0115	–0120	–0110	–0·6	–0·5	–0·2	0·0

SHELTER
A safe refuge, but ent is dangerous in NE/SE gales. A very busy FV hbr where yachts are not encouraged but may find a berth in S Hbr (3.4m). The hbr is dredged 6·5m.
NAVIGATION
WPT 57°41'·32N 01°58'·71W, 111°/291° from/to ent, 0·57M. FVs come and go H24. Good lookout on entering/leaving. Yachts can enter under radar control in poor visibility.
LIGHTS AND MARKS
Kinnairds Hd lt ho, Fl 5s 25m 22M, is 0·45M NNW of ent. Cairnbulg Briggs bn, Fl (2) 10s 9m 6M, is 1·8M ESE of ent. Ldg lts 291°: front QR 12m 5M; rear Oc R 6s 17m 5M.
RADIO TELEPHONE
Call on approach VHF Ch 12 16 (H24) for directions/berth.
TELEPHONE (Dial code 01346)
Port Office 515858; Watch Tr 515926; MRCC (01224) 592334; ⌗ (0141) 887 9369 (H24); Marinecall 0891 500 451; Police 513151; Dr 518088.
FACILITIES
Port ☎ 515858, AB £10 (in S Hbr), Slip, P (cans), D, FW, CH, ME, El, Sh, C (30 ton & 70 ton mobile), SM, V, R, Bar; **Town** EC Wed; ✉, Ⓑ, ⇌, ✈ (bus to Aberdeen).

ADJACENT HARBOURS

ROSEHEARTY, Aberdeen, 57°42'·10N 02°06'·78W. Rtg 4-5-2. AC 222, 213. HW Aberdeen –1. E pier and inner hbr dry, but end of W pier is accessible at all tides. Ent exposed in N/E winds; in E/SE winds hbr can be uncomfortable. Ldg marks B/W on approx 220°; rks E of ldg line. When 30m from pier, steer midway between ldg line and W pier. Port Rae, close to E, has unmarked rks; local knowledge. Hr Mr ☎ (01346) 571292 (home), AB £8. **Town** V, R, Bar, ✉. Firing range: for info ☎ (01436) 571634; see also 10.7.5.
Pennan Cove, 5M to the W, has council ⚓s (10 tons max) at approx 57°40'·95N 02°15'·60W. There are similar ⚓s at **Gardenstown** (Gamrie Bay), approx 57°40'·90N 02°19'·50W.

MACDUFF/BANFF   10-7-8

Aberdeenshire Macduff 57°40'·27N 02°29'·94W Rtg 2-3-2
               Banff   57°40'·24N 02°31'·18W Rtg 4-4-2

CHARTS
AC 1462, 222, 115; OS 29
TIDES
+ 0055 Dover; ML 2·0; Duration 0615; Zone 0 (UT)

Standard Port ABERDEEN (←)

Times				Height (metres)			
High Water		Low Water		MHWS	MHWN	MLWN	MLWS
0200	0900	0400	0900	4·3	3·4	1·6	0·6
1400	2100	1600	2100				
Differences BANFF							
–0100	–0150	–0150	–0050	–0·4	–0·2	–0·1	+0·2

SHELTER
Macduff: Reasonably good, but ent not advised in strong NW/N winds. Slight/moderate surge in outer hbr with N/NE gales. Hbr ent is 17m wide with 3 basins; approx 2·6m in outer hbr and 2m inner hbr. A busy cargo/fishing port with limited space for yachts.
Banff: Popular hbr (dries); access HW±4. When Macduff ent is very rough in strong NW/N winds, Banff can be a safe refuge; berth in outside basin and contact Hr Mr. In strong N/ENE winds Banff is unusable.
NAVIGATION
WPT 57°40'·50N 02°30'·50W, 307°/127° from/to Macduff ent, 0·4M. Same WPT 056°/236° from/to Banff ent, 0·44M. Beware Feachie Craig, Collie Rks and rky coast N and S of hbr ent.
LIGHTS AND MARKS
Macduff: Ldg lts/marks 127° both FR 44/55m 3M, orange △s. Pier hd lt, Fl (2) WRG 6s 12m 9/7M, W tr; W115°-174°. Banff: W bn (unlit) at head of N pier.

RADIO TELEPHONE
Macduff VHF Ch 12 16 (H24); Banff Ch 14 (part time).
TELEPHONE (Dial code 01261)
Hr Mr (Macduff) 832236, ⚓ 833612, Watch tr 833962; Hr Mr (Banff) 815544; MRCC (01224) 592334; ⌗ (0141) 887 9369 (H24); Marinecall 0891 500 451; Police 812555; Dr (Banff) 812027.
FACILITIES
MACDUFF: **Hbr** Slip, P (cans), D, FW, ME, El, Sh, CH. **Town** EC Wed; V, R, Bar, ✉, ⇌ (bus to Keith). BANFF: **Hbr** £8, FW, AC, Slip, new toilet block; **Banff SC**: showers. **Town**, P, D, V, R, Bar, ⇌, Ⓑ, ✈ (Aberdeen).

ADJACENT HARBOUR (3·5M W of WHITEHILLS)

PORTSOY, Aberdeenshire, 57°41'·36N 02°41'·50W. Rtg 4-5-1. AC 222. HW +0047 on Dover; –0132 and Ht –0·3m on Aberdeen. Small drying hbr; ent exposed to NW/NE'lies. New Hbr to port of ent partially dries; inner hbr dries to clean sand. ⚓ to W of hbr at 57°41'·2N 02°41'·6W. Ldg lts 160°, front FW 12m 5M on twr; rear FR 17m 5M. Hr Mr ☎ (01261) 815544. Facilities: few. AB, Slip, FW, V, R, Bar, ✉. **Sandend Bay**, 1·7M W (57°41'N 02°44'·5W). There are Y ⚓s.

WHITEHILLS 10-7-9

Aberdeenshire 57°40'·82N 02°34'·78W   Rtg 2-4-2

CHARTS
AC 222, 115; OS 29

TIDES
+0050 Dover; ML 2·4; Duration 0610; Zone 0 (UT)

Standard Port ABERDEEN (←)

Times				Height (metres)			
High Water		Low Water		MHWS	MHWN	MLWN	MLWS
0200	0900	0400	0900	4·3	3·4	1·6	0·6
1400	2100	1600	2100				
Differences WHITEHILLS							
−0122	−0137	−0117	−0127	−0·4	−0·3	+0·1	+0·1

SHELTER
Safe. In strong NW/N winds beware surge in the narrow ent and outer hbr (2·4m), when ent is best not attempted. See Hr Mr for vacant pontoon berth (1·2m), or berth on N or E walls of inner hbr (1·8m) as space permits.

NAVIGATION
WPT 57°42'·00N 02°34'·80W, 000°/180° from/to bkwtr lt, 1·2M. Reefs on S side of chan marked by 2 rusty/white SHM bns. Beware fishing floats.

LIGHTS AND MARKS
Fl WR 25s (timing is unreliable) on pier hd, vis R132°–212°, W212°–245°; appr in R sector.

RADIO TELEPHONE
Whitehills Hbr Radio VHF Ch 09 08 16.

TELEPHONE (Dial code 01261)
Hr Mr 861291; MRCC (01224) 592334; ⌗ (0141) 887 9369 (H24); Marinecall 0891 500451; Police (01542) 32222; Dr 812027.

FACILITIES
Harbour AB £5, P, D, FW, ME, EI, CH.
Town V, R, Bar, ⊠, Ⓑ (AM only), ⇌ (bus to Keith), ✈ (Aberdeen).

ADJACENT HARBOURS

CULLEN, Moray, 57°41'·65N 02°49'·20W. Rtg 5-4-2. AC 222. HW +0045 on Dover, HW −0135 & −0·3m on Aberdeen; Duration 0555; ML 2·4m. Shelter good, but ent hazardous in strong W/N winds. Appr on 180° toward conspic viaduct and W bn on N pier. Caple Rk, 0·2m, is 5ca NE of hbr. Access HW ±2 approx to small drying unlit hbr, best for shoal draft. Moor S of Inner jetty if < 1m draft. Beware moorings across inner basin ent. Y ⚓s (10 ton max) about 400m WNW of hbr in 1·5m, 57°41'·7N 02°49'·5W. Hr Mr ☎ (01261) 842477 (home, part-time), £8. **Town** V, R, Bar, ⊠.

PORTKNOCKIE, Moray, 57°42'·30N 02°51'·70W. Rtg 2-5-1. AC 222. HW +0045 on Dover; −0135 and ht −0·3m Aberdeen; ML 2·3m; Duration 0555; access H24. Good shelter in one of the safest hbrs on S side of Moray Firth, but scend is often experienced; care needed in strong NW/N winds. FW ldg lts, on white-topped poles, lead approx 143°, to ent. Orange street lts surround the hbr. Berth N quay of outer hbr on firm sand; most of inner hbr dries. Hr Mr ☎ (01542) 840833; Facilities: Slip, AB £8, FW, Sh; Dr ☎ 840272. **Town** EC Wed; Ⓑ, P & D, ⊠, V, Bar.

BUCKIE 10-7-10

Moray 57°40'·84N 02°57'·63W   Rtg 3-1-2

CHARTS
AC 1462, 222, 115; OS 28

TIDES
+0040 Dover; ML 2·4; Duration 0550; Zone 0 (UT)

Standard Port ABERDEEN (←)

Times				Height (metres)			
High Water		Low Water		MHWS	MHWN	MLWN	MLWS
0200	0900	0400	0900	4·3	3·4	1·6	0·6
1400	2100	1600	2100				
Differences BUCKIE							
−0130	−0145	−0125	−0140	−0·2	−0·2	0·0	+0·1

SHELTER
Good in all weathers, but in strong NNW to NE winds there is a dangerous swell over the bar at hbr ent; access H24. Berth in No 4 basin as directed by Hr Mr.

NAVIGATION
WPT 57°41'·32N 02°58'·80W, 306°/126° from/to ent, 0·80M. Beware W Muck (QR 5m tripod, 7M), Middle Muck and E Muck Rks, 3ca off shore.

LIGHTS AND MARKS
The Oc R 10s 15m 15M, W tr on N bkwtr, in line 125° with Iso WG 2s 20m 16/12M, W tr, R top, lead clear of W Muck. NB: this line does not lead into hbr ent; but 2FG (vert) on W pier in transit with same Iso WG 2s do lead 119° to ent (24m wide). White tr of ice plant on pier No. 2 is conspic. Entry sigs on N pier:
3 Ⓡ lts = hbr closed. Traffic is controlled by VHF.

RADIO TELEPHONE
VHF Ch 12 16 (H24).

TELEPHONE (Dial code 01542)
Hr Mr 831700; MRCC (01224) 592334; ⌗ (0141) 887 9369 (H24); Marinecall 0891 500 451; Police 832222; Dr 831555.

FACILITIES
No 4 Basin AB £10, FW; **Services:** D & P (delivery), BY, ME, EI, Sh, CH, ACA, SM, BH, Slip, C (15 ton), Gas.
Town EC Wed; V, Bar, Ⓑ, ⊠, ⇌ (bus to Elgin), ✈ (Aberdeen or Inverness).

ADJACENT HARBOUR (2M ENE of BUCKIE)

FINDOCHTY, Moray, 57°41'·96N 02°54'·20W. AC 222. HW +0045 on Dover, HW −0140 & ht −0·2m on Aberdeen; ML 2·3m; Duration 0550. Ent is about 2ca W of conspic church belfry. 1ca N of ent, leave Beacon Rock (3m high) to stbd. Y ⚓ is in 5m, 150m N of hbr ent, close E of Beacon Rock. Ldg lts, FW, lead approx 166° into Outer Basin which dries 0·2m and has many rky outcrops; access HW ±2 for 1·5m draft. Ent faces N and is 20m wide; unlit white bn at hd of W pier. Good shelter in inner basin for 100 yachts on 3 pontoons (the 2 W'ly pontoons dry); AB £10. Hr Mr ☎ (01542) 831466 (home, part-time). **Town** V, R, Bar, ⊠, Ⓑ.

LOSSIEMOUTH   10-7-11
Moray 57°43'·43N 03°16'·54W   Rtg 3-4-2

CHARTS
AC 1462, 223; OS 28

TIDES
+0040 Dover; ML 2·3; Duration 0605; Zone 0 (UT)

Standard Port ABERDEEN (←—)

Times				Height (metres)			
High Water		Low Water		MHWS	MHWN	MLWN	MLWS
0200	0900	0400	0900	4·3	3·4	1·6	0·6
1400	2100	1600	2100				
Differences LOSSIEMOUTH							
−0125	−0200	−0130	−0130	−0·2	−0·2	0·0	0·0

SHELTER
Very good in winds from SSE to NW. In N to SE winds
>F6 appr to ent can be dangerous, with swell in outer
hbr. Turn hard port for marina in S Basin, dredged 2m;
access HW±4. But chan and Basin are prone to silting; a
vessel drawing 2m would have little clearance at LWS ±1.
West (or New) Basin is for commercial and FVs. 2 Y ⚓s
have been laid in 4m at 57°43'·41N 03°16'·18W, 350m E of
the hbr ent.

NAVIGATION
WPT 57°43'·40N 03°16'·00W, 097°/277° from/to ent, 0·30M.
Rks to N and S of hbr ent; appr from E. Near ent, beware
current from R Lossie setting in N'ly direction, causing
confused water in N to SE winds at sp.

LIGHTS AND MARKS
Covesea Skerries, W lt ho, Fl WR 20s 49m 24M, is 2M W
of the hbr ent; a SPM buoy, Fl Y 5s, is 5ca NE of hbr. Ldg
lts 292°, both FR 5/8m (for FVs); S pier hd Fl R 6s 11m 5M.
Traffic sigs: B ● at S pier ((R) over Fl R 6s) = hbr shut.

RADIO TELEPHONE
VHF Ch 12 16 HO. Call before ent/dep due to restricted
visibility in entrance.

TELEPHONE (Dial code 01343)
Hr Mr ☎/📠 813066/HN 814696; MRCC (01224) 592334; ⌗
(0141) 887 9369 (H24); Marinecall 0891 500451; Police
812022; Dr 812277.

FACILITIES
Marina (43), ☎ 813066, £16.00 inc AC, FW, ▣; **Hbr** ME, El,
Sh, C, SM (see Hr Mr); **Lossiemouth CC** ☎ 544454;
Lossiemouth SC ☎ 812928 (dinghies, at West Beach);
Hbr Service Stn ☎ 813001, Mon-Fri 0800-2030, Sat 0000-
1800, Sun 0930-1730, P & D cans, Gas. **Town** EC Thurs;
CH, V, R, Bar, ✉, (B), ⇌ (bus to Elgin), ✈ (Inverness).

HOPEMAN   10-7-12
Moray 57°42'·72N 03°26'·22W   Rtg 3-4-2

CHARTS
AC 1462, 223; OS 28

TIDES
+0050 Dover; ML 2·4; Duration 0610; Zone 0 (UT)

Standard Port ABERDEEN (←—)

Times				Height (metres)			
High Water		Low Water		MHWS	MHWN	MLWN	MLWS
0200	0900	0400	0900	4·3	3·4	1·6	0·6
1400	2100	1600	2100				
Differences HOPEMAN							
−0120	−0150	−0135	−0120	−0·2	−0·2	0·0	0·0

SHELTER
Once in SW basin, shelter good from all winds; but hbr
dries, access HW ± 2 (for 1·5m draft). Ent is difficult in
winds from NE to SE. A popular yachting hbr with AB
and good facilities; run by Moray Council.

NAVIGATION
WPT 57°42'·68N, 03°26'·50W, 263°/083° from/to ent, 0·17M.
Dangerous rks lie off hbr ent. Do not attempt entry in
heavy weather. Beware salmon stake nets E and W of hbr
(Mar to Aug) and lobster pot floats.

LIGHTS AND MARKS
Ldg lts 081°, FR 3/4m; S pier hd FG 4s 8m 4M. All lit only
1 Aug – 30 Apr.

RADIO TELEPHONE
None.

TELEPHONE (Dial code 01343)
Hr Mr 830650 (home, part-time); MRCC (01224) 592334;
⌗ (0141) 887 9369 (H24); Marinecall 0891 500 451; Police
830222; Dr 543141.

FACILITIES
Hbr AB £10, D, FW, Slip.
Services: CH, ME, Gas, Sh, El, P (cans).
Town EC Wed; V, R, Bar, ✉, (B), ⇌ (bus to Elgin), ✈
(Inverness).

BERTHING FEES. Aberdeenshire and Moray Councils offer
a "single entry" Rover fee (£8 inc VAT) valid for 1 week
from date of first entry to any or all of the following hbrs:
Rosehearty, Banff, Portsoy, Cullen, Portknockie,
Findochty, Hopeman and Burghead; and in Area 6:
Johnshaven, Gourdon and Stonehaven. Berths are of
course subject to availability.

BURGHEAD   10-7-13

Moray 57°42'·08N 03°29'·93W   Rtg 3-4-2

CHARTS
AC 1462, 223; OS 28

TIDES
+0035 Dover; ML 2·4; Duration 0610; Zone 0 (UT)

Standard Port ABERDEEN (←)

Times				Height (metres)			
High Water		Low Water		MHWS	MHWN	MLWN	MLWS
0200	0900	0400	0900	4·3	3·4	1·6	0·6
1400	2100	1600	2100				
Differences BURGHEAD							
−0120	−0150	−0135	−0120	−0·2	−0·2	0·0	0·0

SHELTER
One of the few Moray Firth hbrs open in strong E winds. 1·2m depth in ent chan and hbr. Go alongside where available and contact Hr Mr. Can be very full with FVs.

NAVIGATION
WPT 57°42'·30N 03°30'·30W, 317°/137° from/to N pier lt QR, 0·28M. Chan is variable due to sand movement. Appr from SW. Access HW ±4.

LIGHTS AND MARKS
No ldg lts but night ent is safe after identifying the N pier lts: QR 3m 5M and Oc 8s 7m 5M. S pier hd QG 3m 5M.

RADIO TELEPHONE
Hr Mr VHF Ch 12 14 16 (HO and when vessel due).

TELEPHONE (Dial code 01343)
Hr Mr 835337; MRCC (01224) 592334; ☏ (0141) 887 9369 (H24); Marinecall 0891 500 451; Dr 812277.

FACILITIES
Hbr £10, D, FW, AB, C (50 ton mobile), L, Slip, BY, Sh.
Town EC Thurs; Bar, ✉, V, P (cans), Ⓑ, ⇌ (bus to Elgin), ✈ (Inverness).

FINDHORN   10-7-14

Moray 57°39'·66N 03°37'·38W   Rtg 3-3-1

CHARTS
AC 223; OS 27

TIDES
+0110 Dover; ML 2·5; Duration 0615; Zone 0 (UT)

Standard Port ABERDEEN (←)

Times				Height (metres)			
High Water		Low Water		MHWS	MHWN	MLWN	MLWS
0200	0900	0400	0900	4·3	3·4	1·6	0·6
1400	2100	1600	2100				
Differences FINDHORN							
−0120	−0150	−0135	−0130	0·0	−0·1	0·0	+0·1

SHELTER
⚓ in pool off boatyard or off N pier or dry out alongside, inside piers and ask at YC; or pick up Y ⚓ off N pier. Do not attempt entry in strong NW/NE winds or with big swell running; expect breakers/surf either side of ent. THE OLD BAR. The original mouth of Findhorn River 4M SW of Findhorn gives excellent shelter in all weathers. Chan changes; local knowledge needed.

NAVIGATION
WPT 57°40'·31N 03°38'·55W, SWM spar buoy, 313°/133° from/to Ee Point, 0·85M. Access HW±2. 100m SE of the spar buoy there are 2 Y waiting ⚓s in 4m. From WPT, proceed SSE to the buoys marking the gap in the sand bar; thence ESE via SHM buoy to 3 poles with PHM topmarks to be left a boat's length to port. Once past The Ee, turn port inside G buoys. The S part of Findhorn Bay dries extensively.

LIGHTS AND MARKS
Unlit. There is a windsock on FS by The Ee. Boatyard building is conspic.

RADIO TELEPHONE
VHF Ch M *Chadwick Base* (when racing in progress).

TELEPHONE (Dial code 01309)
MRCC (01224) 592334; ☏ (0141) 887 9369 (H24); Findhorn Pilot (G. Mackenzie) 690546; Marinecall 0891 500 451; Police 672224; Dr 672221.

FACILITIES
Royal Findhorn YC ☎ 690247, M, FW, Bar;
Services: BY, L, M, AC, FW, Slip, C (16 ton), P & D (cans), El, ME, CH, ACA, Gas, Sh.
Town V, R, Bar, ✉, Ⓑ, ⇌ (Forres), ✈ (Inverness).

7

NAIRN   10-7-15

Highland 57°35'·63N 03°51'·56W   Rtg 3-4-2

CHARTS
AC 1462, 223; OS 27

TIDES
+0110 Dover; ML 2·2; Duration 0615; Zone 0 (UT)

Standard Port ABERDEEN (←)

Times				Height (metres)			
High Water		Low Water		MHWS	MHWN	MLWN	MLWS
0200	0900	0400	0900	4·3	3·4	1·6	0·6
1400	2100	1600	2100				
Differences NAIRN							
−0120	−0150	−0135	−0130	0·0	−0·1	0·0	+0·1

SHELTER
Good, but entry difficult in fresh NNE'ly. Pontoons in hbr with ⓥ berths. Best entry HW ± 1½. Two Y ⚓s are close to the WPT, approx 400m NNW of the pierheads; the W'ly buoy in 2·5m, the E'ly in 1·5m. No commercial shipping.

NAVIGATION
WPT 57°35'·90N 03°51'·80W, 335°/155° from/to ent, 0·3M. The approach dries to 100m off the pierheads. Inside, the best water is to the E side of the river chan.

LIGHTS AND MARKS
Lt ho on E pier hd, Oc WRG 4s 6m 5M, vis G shore-100°, W100°-207°, R207°-shore. Keep in W sector. McDermott Base, 4·5M to the W, has a large conspic cream-coloured building; also useful if making for Inverness Firth.

RADIO TELEPHONE
None. Ch M (weekends only).

TELEPHONE (Dial code 01667)
Hr Mr 454704; MRCC (01224) 592334; ⌗ (0141) 887 9369 (H24); Clinic 455092; Marinecall 0891 500 451; Police 452222; Dr 453421.

FACILITIES
Nairn Basin AB £10, FW (standpipes), Slip, AC (110 volts), P, D; **Nairn SC** ☎ 453897, Bar.
Town EC Wed; V, R, Bar, ✉, Ⓑ, ⇌, ✈ (Inverness).

▲ Nairn, apply to SC

INVERNESS   10-7-16

Highland 57°29'·75N 04°14'·08W   Rtg 3-2-2

CHARTS
AC 1078, 1077, 223; OS 26/27

TIDES
+0100 Dover; ML 2·7; Duration 0620; Zone 0 (UT)

Standard Port ABERDEEN (←)

Times				Height (metres)			
High Water		Low Water		MHWS	MHWN	MLWN	MLWS
0300	1000	0000	0700	4·3	3·4	1·6	0·6
1500	2200	1200	1900				
Differences INVERNESS							
−0050	−0150	−0200	−0150	+0·5	+0·3	+0·2	+0·1
FORTROSE							
−0125	−0125	−0125	−0125	0·0	0·0	No data	
CROMARTY							
−0120	−0155	−0155	−0120	0·0	0·0	+0·1	+0·2
INVERGORDON							
−0105	−0200	−0200	−0110	+0·1	+0·1	+0·1	+0·1
DINGWALL							
−0045	−0145	No data		+0·1	+0·2	No data	

SHELTER
Good in all weathers. Berth at Longman Yacht Haven (3m at LW) or alongside quays in R Ness; or at 2 marinas in Caledonian Canal, ent to which can be difficult in strong tides (see 10.8.18). The sea lock is normally available HW±4 in canal hours.

NAVIGATION
WPT Meikle Mee SHM By Fl G 3s, 57°30'·28N 04°11'·93W, 070°/250° from/to Longman Pt bn, 0·74M. Ent to R Ness is very narrow but deep.Tidal streams strong S of Craigton Pt (E-going stream at sp exceeds 5kn). Beware marine farms S of Avoch (off chartlet).

LIGHTS AND MARKS
Longman Pt bn Fl WR 2s 7m 5/4M, vis W078°-258°, R258°-078°. Craigton Pt lt, Fl WRG 4s 6m 11/7M vis W312°-048°, R048°-064°, W064°-085°, G085°-shore. Caledonian Canal ent marked by QR and Iso G 4s on ends of training walls.

RADIO TELEPHONE
Call: *Inverness Hbr Office* VHF Ch 06 12 16 (Mon-Fri: 0900 -1700 LT). Inverness Boat Centre Ch 80 M (0900-1800 LT). Ch 74 is used by all stns on the Canal. Call: *Clachnaharry Sea Lock*; or for office: *Caledonian Canal*.

TELEPHONE (Dial code 01463)
Hr Mr 715715; Clachnaharry Sea Lock 713896; Canal Office 233140; MRCC (01224) 592334; ⌗ 222787; Marinecall 0891 500 451; Police 239191; Dr 234151.

FACILITIES
Longman Yacht Haven L-shaped pontoon, (15+5 visitors) ☎ 715715, FW, access H24 (3m at LW);
Citadel and Shore Street Quays (R Ness) ☎ 715715, AB, P, D, FW, ME, El; (used mainly by commercial shipping).
Muirtown Marina, (20 + 20 ⓥ) ☎ 239475, ⚓ 710942, £10, AC, D, FW, Gas, Gaz, C (40 ton), access HW±4;
Caley Marina (25 + 25 visitors) ☎ 236539, £10, AC, D, FW, CH, ACA, ME, El, Sh;
Services: Slip, M, ME, El, C (100 ton), CH, FW, P, SM, Gas.
Town EC Wed; V, R, Bar, ✉, Ⓑ, ⇌, ✈.

MINOR HARBOURS IN INVERNESS FIRTH

FORTROSE, Highland, 57°34'·73N 04°07'·95W. AC 1078. Tides 10.7.16. HW +0055 on Dover; ML 2·5m; Duration 0620. Small drying unlit hbr, well protected by Chanonry Ness to E; access HW±2, limited space. Follow ldg line 296°, Broomhill Ho (conspic on hill to NW) in line with school spire until abeam SPM buoy; then turn W to avoid Craig an Roan rks (1·8m) ESE of ent. Chanonry Pt lt, Oc 6s 12m 15M, obscd 073°-shore. Hr Mr ☎ (01381) 620861; Dr ☎ 620909. Facilities: EC Thurs; AB £3, L, M, P, D, Slip, Gas, R, V, ✉, Ⓑ; **Chanonry SC** (near pier) ☎ 621010.

AVOCH, Highland, 57°34'·05N 04°09'·85W. AC 1078. Tides as Fortrose (1·25M to the ENE). Hbr dries, mostly on the N side, but is bigger than Fortrose; access HW±2. Small craft may stay afloat at nps against the S pier, which has 2FR (vert) at E-facing ent. Facilities: AB, FW. **Village**: ✉, V, R, Bar, P & D (cans), ME.

INVERNESS *continued*

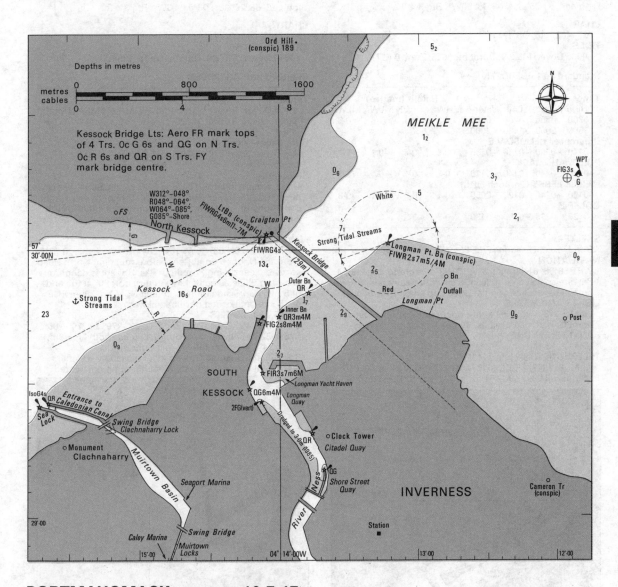

PORTMAHOMACK   10-7-17

Highland 57°50'.30N 03°49'.70W Rtg 4-5-2

CHARTS
AC 223, 115; OS 21

TIDES
+0035 Dover; ML 2·5; Duration 0600; Zone 0 (UT); See
10.7.18 for Differences

SHELTER
Good, but uncomfortable in SW/NW winds. Access to hbr
at HW only. Hbr dries but good ⚓ close SW of pier.

NAVIGATION
WPT SPM buoy, FlY 5s, 57°53'·03N 03°47'·02W, 346°/166°
from/to Tarbat Ness lt, 1·13M. Beware Curach Rks which
lie from 2ca SW of pier to the shore. Rks extend N and W
of the pier. Beware lobster pot floats and salmon nets N
of hbr. Tain Range activity shown by R flags or R lts.

LIGHTS AND MARKS
Tarbert Ness lt ho Fl (4) 30s 53m 24M, W twr R bands, is
2·6M to NE of hbr. Pier hd 2 FR (vert) 7m 5M.

RADIO TELEPHONE
None.

TELEPHONE (Dial code 01862)
Hr Mr 871441; MRCC (01224) 592334; ⌗ (0141) 887 9369
(H24); Marinecall 0891 500 451; Dr 892759.

FACILITIES
Hbr, AB £16.25, M, L, FW. **Town** EC Wed; R, V, Bar, ✉, ⇌
(bus to Tain), ✈ (Inverness).

HELMSDALE   10-7-18

Highland 58°06'·85N 03°38'·80W Rtg 3-4-2

CHARTS
AC 1462, 115; OS 17
TIDES
+0035 Dover; ML 2·2; Duration 0615; Zone 0 (UT)

Standard Port ABERDEEN (←)

Times				Height (metres)			
High Water		Low Water		MHWS	MHWN	MLWN	MLWS
0300	0800	0200	0800	4·3	3·4	1·6	0·6
1500	2000	1400	2000				
Differences HELMSDALE							
–0140	–0200	–0150	–0135	–0·5	–0·4	–0·1	–0·1
PORTMAHOMACK							
–0120	–0210	–0140	–0110	–0·2	–0·1	+0·1	+0·1
MEIKLE FERRY (Dornoch Firth)							
–0100	–0140	–0120	–0055	+0·1	0·0	–0·1	0·0
GOLSPIE							
–0130	–0215	–0155	–0130	–0·3	–0·3	–0·1	0·0

SHELTER
Good, except in strong E/SE'lies. AB on NW pier, approx 1m.
NAVIGATION
WPT 58°06'·61N 03°38'·3W, 133°/313° from/to ent, 0·35M.
Beware spate coming down river after heavy rain. Shoal
both sides of chan and bar builds up when river in spate.
LIGHTS AND MARKS
Ldg lts 313°. Front FG (= hbr open) or FR (= hbr closed);
rear FG; both on W masts. By day Or disc on each mast.
RADIO TELEPHONE
VHF Ch 12 16.
TELEPHONE (Dial code 01431)
Hr Mr 821347; MRCC (01224) 592334; ⌗ (01955) 603650;
Marinecall 0891 500 451; Dr 821221, or 821225 (Home).

FACILITIES
Hbr AB £16.25, M (See Hr Mr), FW, Slip.
Town EC Wed; P, D, Gas, V, R, Bar, ⌧, Ⓑ (Brora), ⇌ (Wick).

ADJACENT HARBOUR
LYBSTER, Highland, 58°17'·75N 03°17'·30W. AC 115. HW
+0020 on Dover; HW –0150 sp, –0215 np; HW ht –0·6m on
Aberdeen; ML 2·1m; Duration 0620. Excellent shelter in
basin (SW corner of inner hbr); AB on W side of pier in
about 1·2m. Most of hbr dries to sand/mud and is much
used by FVs; no bollards on N wall. Appr on about 350°.
Beware rks close on E side of ent; narrow (10m) ent is
difficult In strong E to S winds. Min depth 2·5m in ent. S
pier hd, Oc R 6s 10m 3M, occas in fishing season. AB
£16.25, FW on W quay. **Town** EC Thurs; Bar, D, P, R, V.

WICK   10-7-19

Highland 58°26'·38N 03°04'·63W Rtg 3-4-2

CHARTS
AC 1462, 115; OS 12
TIDES
+0010 Dover; ML 2·0; Duration 0625; Zone 0 (UT)

Standard Port ABERDEEN

Times				Height (metres)			
High Water		Low Water		MHWS	MHWN	MLWN	MLWS
0300	0800	0200	0800	4·3	3·4	1·6	0·6
1500	2000	1400	2000				
Differences WICK							
–0155	–0220	–0210	–0220	–0·9	–0·7	–0·2	–0·1

SHELTER
Good, except in strong NNE to SSE winds. Berth where
directed in the Inner Hbr, 2·4m. A good hbr to await right
conditions for W-bound passage through Pentland Firth
(see 10.7.5). NB: The River Hbr is leased and must *not* be
entered without prior approval.
NAVIGATION
WPT 58°26'·20N 03°·30W, 104°/284° from/to S pier, 0·72M.
From the N, open up hbr ent before rounding North Head
so as to clear drying Proudfoot Rks. Hbr ent is dangerous
in strong E'lies as boats have to turn port 90° at the end
of S pier. On S side of bay, an unlit NCM bn, 300m ENE
of LB slip, marks end of ruined bkwtr.
LIGHTS AND MARKS
S pier lt, Fl WRG 3s 12m 12/9M, G253°-270°, W270°-286°,
R286°-329°, Bell (2) 10s (fishing). Ldg lts , both FR 5/8m,
lead 234° into outer hbr. Traffic signals:
B ● (Ⓖ) at CG stn on S Head = hbr closed by weather.
B ● (Ⓡ) at S pier head = caution; hbr temp obstructed.

RADIO TELEPHONE
VHF Ch 14 16 (when vessel expected).
TELEPHONE (Dial code 01955)
Hr Mr 602030; MRSC (01856) 873268; ⌗ 603650; Police
603551; Ⓗ 602434, 602261.
FACILITIES
Inner Hbr AB (£5; see Hr Mr), Slip, L, ME, V; **Outer Hbr** L,
ME; **Fish Jetty** D, L, FW, CH;
Services: ME, EI, Sh, CH, Slip, Gas, C (15 to 100 ton).
Town EC Wed; P, V, R, Bar, ⌧, Ⓑ, ⇌, ✈.

OTHER HARBOURS ON THE NORTH WEST SIDE OF THE MORAY FIRTH

CROMARTY FIRTH, Highland, 57°41'·20N 04°02'·00W. AC 1889, 1890. HW +0100 on Dover; ML 2·5m; Duration 0625. See 10.7.16. Excellent hbr extending 7·5M W, past Invergordon, then 9M SW. Good shelter always available, depending on wind direction. Beware rks and reefs round N and S Sutor at the ent; many unlit oil rig mooring buoys and fish cages within the firth. Cromarty Village Hbr (partly dries) is formed by 2 piers, but crowded with small craft and probably foul ground; ⌕ 2ca W of S pier hd in approx 6m. Hr Mr ☎ (01381) 600502. Cromarty lt ho, on the Ness, Oc WR 10s 18m 15/11M, R079°–088°, W088°–275°, obsc by N Sutor when brg < 253°. *Cromarty Firth Port Control* VHF Ch 11 16 13 (H24) ☎ (01349) ☎ 852308; ⌗ 852221. **Invergordon Boat Club** Hon Sec ☎ 877612. Facilities: AB, Bar, C (3 ton), D, FW, ✉, P, R, V, Gas, L; EC Wed. Ferry: Local to Nigg; also Invergordon-Kirkwall.

DORNOCH FIRTH, Highland. 57°51'·30N 03°59'·30W. AC 223, 115. HW +0115 on Dover; ML 2·5m; Duration 0605; see 10.7.17. Excellent shelter but difficult ent. There are many shifting sandbanks, especially near the ent, from N edge of Whiteness Sands to S edge of Gizzen Briggs. ⌕s in 7m ¾M ESE of Dornoch Pt (sheltered from NE swell by Gizzen Briggs); in 7m 2ca SSE of Ard na Cailc; in 3·3m 1M below Bonar Bridge. Firth extends 15M inland, but AC coverage ceases ¼M E of Ferry Pt. The A9 road bridge, 3·3M W of Dornoch Pt, with 11m clearance, has 3 spans lit on both sides; span centres show Iso 4s, N bank pier Iso G 4s, S bank pier Iso R 4s and 2 midstream piers QY. Tarbat Ness lt ho Fl (4) 30s 53m 24M. Fl R 5s lt shown when Tain firing range active. Very limited facilities at Ferrytown and Bonar Bridge. CG ☎ (01862) 810016. **Dornoch:** EC Thur; V, P, ✉, Dr, Ⓑ, R, Bar.

GOLSPIE, Highland, 57°58'·73N 03°56'·70W. AC 223. HW +0045 on Dover; ML 2·3m; Duration 0610. See 10.7.18. Golspie pier projects 60m SE across foreshore with arm projecting SW at the hd, giving shelter during NE winds. Beware The Bridge, a bank (0·3m to 1·8m) running parallel to the shore ¼M to seaward of pier hd. Seas break heavily over The Bridge in NE winds. There are no lts. To enter, keep Duke of Sutherland's Memorial in line 316° with boathouse SW of pier, until church spire in village is in line 006° with hd of pier, then keep on those marks. Hbr gets very congested; good ⌕ off pier. **Town** EC Wed; Bar, D, Dr, Ⓗ, L, M, P, Gas, ✉, R, ⇌, V, Ⓑ.

ANCHORAGES BETWEEN SCRABSTER AND CAPE WRATH

KYLE OF TONGUE, Highland, 58°32'·00N 04°22'·60W (ent). +0050 on Ullapool; HW ht −0·4m on Ullapool. The Kyle runs about 7M inland. Entry (see 10.7.5) should not be attempted in strong N winds. ⌕ at Talmine (W of Rabbit Is) protected from all but NE winds; at Skullomie Hr, protected from E winds; off Mol na Coinnle, a small bay on SE side of Eilean nan Ron, protected from W and N winds; off S of Rabbit Is, protected from W to N winds. No ldg lts/marks. Facilities: Limited supplies at Talmine (½M from slip) or at Coldbachie (1½M from Skullomie).

LOCH ERIBOLL, Highland, 58°32'·60N 04°37'·40W. AC 2076. HW −0345 on Dover; ML 2·7m; Duration 0610. See 10.8.7. Enter between Whiten Hd and Klourig Is in W sector of White Hd lt, Fl WR 3s, vis W030°-172°, R172°-191°, W191°-212°. In SW winds fierce squalls funnel down the loch. Yachts can enter Rispond Hbr, access approx HW ± 3, and dry out alongside; no lts/marks and very limited facilities. Good ⌕s: at Rispond Bay on W side of loch, ent good in all but E winds, in approx 5m; off Portnancon in 5·5m; at the head of the loch; at Camus an Duin and in bays to N and S of peninsula at Heilam on E side of loch.

SCRABSTER   10-7-20
Highland 58°36'·63N 03°32'·52W   Rtg 1-4-1

CHARTS
AC 1462, 2162, 1954; OS 12

TIDES
-0240 Dover; ML 3·2; Duration 0615; Zone 0 (UT)

Standard Port ABERDEEN (←)

Times				Height (metres)			
High Water		Low Water		MHWS	MHWN	MLWN	MLWS
0300	1000	0100	0800	4·3	3·4	1·6	0·6
1500	2200	1300	2000				
Differences SCRABSTER							
−0455	−0510	−0500	−0445	+0·7	+0·3	+0·5	+0·2
STROMA							
−0320	−0320	−0320	−0320	−1·2	−1·1	−0·3	−0·1
DUNCANSBY HEAD							
−0320	−0320	−0320	−0320	−1·2	−1·0		No data

SHELTER
Very good except for swell in NW'lies. Yachts usually lie in the Inner (0·9 - 1·2m) or Centre Basins (0·9 - 2·7m). ⌕ is not advised. A good hbr to await the right conditions for E-bound passage through Pentland Firth (see 10.7.5).

NAVIGATION
WPT 58°36'·60N 03°32'·00W, 098°/278° from/to E pier lt, 0·25M. Can be entered at all tides in all weathers. Beware FVs, merchant ships and the Orkney ferries.

LIGHTS AND MARKS
No ldg marks/lts. Entry is simple once the conspic ice plant tr and/or the pier lt, QG 6m 4M, have been located. Do not confuse hbr lts with the shore lts of Thurso.

RADIO TELEPHONE
Call Hr Mr VHF Ch 12 16 (H24) for berthing directions, before entering hbr.

TELEPHONE (Dial code 01847)
Hr Mr 892779, ⛴ 892353; MRSC (01856) 873268; ⌗ (01955) 603650; Marinecall 0891 500 451; Police 893222; Dr 893154.

FACILITIES
Hbr AB £5.28 (£6.46 for 4th and subsequent days), FW, D, P (cans), ME, El, C (15, 30 & 100 ton mobiles), Slip, CH; **Pentland Firth YC** M, R, Bar. **Thurso** EC Thurs; V, R, Bar, ✉, Ⓑ, ⇌, ✈ (Wick). Ferry to Stromness.

ORKNEY ISLANDS   10-7-21

The Orkney Islands number about 70, of which some 24 are inhabited. They extend from Duncansby Hd 5 to 50M NNE, and are mostly low-lying, but Hoy in the SW of the group reaches 475m (1560ft). Coasts are generally rky and much indented, but there are many sandy beaches. A passage with least width of about 3M runs NW/SE through the group. The islands are separated from Scotland by the Pentland Firth, a very dangerous stretch of water (see 10.7.5). The principal island is Mainland (or Pomona) on which stands Kirkwall, the capital.

Severe gales blow in winter and early spring (see 10.7.5). The climate is mild but windy, and very few trees grow. There are LBs at Longhope, Stromness and Kirkwall. There is a CG MRSC at Kirkwall, ☎ (01856) 873268, with Auxiliary (Watch & Rescue) Stns at Longhope (S Walls), Brough Ness (S Ronaldsay), Stromness and Deerness (both Mainland), Westray, Papa Westray, N Ronaldsay, Sanday, and all inhabited isles except Egilsay and Wyre.

CHARTS
AC 2249, 2250 and 2162 at medium scale. For larger scale charts, see under individual hbrs. OS sheets 5 and 6.

TIDES
Aberdeen (10.6.17) is the Standard Port. Tidal streams are strong, particularly in Pentland Firth and in the firths and sounds among the islands (see 10.7.5).

SHELTER
There are piers (fender board advised) at all main islands. Yachts can pay 4 or 14 day hbr dues (£10.20 or £19.00 in 1997) to berth on all Council-operated piers, except St Margaret's Hope. Some of the many ⚓s are listed below:

Mainland
SCAPA BAY: good except in S winds. No yacht berths alongside pier due to heavy hbr traffic. Only ents to Scapa Flow are via Hoy Snd, Hoxa Snd or W of Flotta.
ST MARYS (known as Holm, pronounced Ham): N side of Kirk Sound; ⚓ in B of Ayre or berth E side of pier HW±4. P & D (cans), ✉, Bar, R, Bus to Kirkwall & Burwick Ferry.
KIRK SOUND (E ent): ⚓ N of Lamb Holm; beware fish cages.
DEER SOUND: ⚓ in Pool of Mirkady or off pier on NW side of sound; very good shelter, no facilities.

Burray
E WEDDEL SOUND: ⚓ to E of pier in E'lies, sheltered by No 4 Churchill Barrier; pier is exposed in strong W'lies. P & D (cans), BY, Slip, V, ✉, Bar, R, Bus to Kirkwall.
HUNDA SOUND: good ⚓ in all winds.

S Ronaldsay
ST MARGARET'S HOPE: Rtg 3-4-2. ⚓ in centre of bay; or AB £6.25 at pier, beware salmon farm. Hr Mr ☎ 831454; Dr 831206. FW, P & D (cans), V, R, Bar, ✉, Bus Kirkwall.
WIDEWALL BAY: ⚓ sheltered from all but SW winds.

Flotta
Berth on Sutherland Pier, SW of oil terminal. Hr Mr ☎ 701411. P & D (cans), V, ✉.

Hoy
LONG HOPE: ⚓ E of S Ness pier, used by steamers, or berth on pier (safest at slack water) ☎ 701273; Dr 701209. Facilities: FW, P & D (cans), ✉, V, Bar.
LYNESS: berth on pier; keep clear of disused piles. Also ⚓ in Ore Bay. Hr Mr ☎ 791228. FW, P & D (cans), Bar, ✉. Beware fish cages
PEGAL B: good ⚓ except in strong W winds.

Rousay
WYRE SOUND: ⚓ E of Rousay pier, or berth on it. ✉, V, R.

Eday
FERSNESS Bay: good holding, sheltered from S winds.
BACKALAND Bay: berth on pier clear of ferry or ⚓ to NW. Beware cross tides. FW, P & D, V, ✉.
CALF SND: ⚓ in Carrick B; good shelter from SW-NW'lies.

Papa Westray
B OF MOCLETT: Good ⚓ but open to S.
SOUTH WICK: ⚓ off the old pier or ESE of pier off Holm of Papa.

Sanday
LOTH B: berth on pier, clear of ferry. Beware strong tides.
KETTLETOFT B: ⚓ in bay or berth on pier; very exposed to SE'lies. Hr Mr ☎ 600227. P & D (cans), ✉, ⓑ, V, hotel.
NORTH BAY: on NW side of island, exposed to NW.
OTTERSWICK: good ⚓ except in N or E winds.

N Ronaldsay
SOUTH B: ⚓ in middle of bay or berth on pier; open to S and W, and subject to swell. V, ✉.
LINKLET B: ⚓ off jetty at N of bay, open to E.

NAVIGATION
From the mainland, appr from Scrabster to Stromness and Scapa Flow via Hoy Mouth and Hoy Sound. From the Moray Firth (Wick) keep well E of the Pentland Skerries if going N to Kirkwall. Or, if bound for Scapa Flow via Hoxa Sound, keep close to Duncansby Head, passing W of the Pentland Skerries and between Swona and S Ronaldsay. Keep well clear of Lother Rk (dries 1.8m; lt, Q, Racon) off SW tip of S Ronaldsay. Time this entry for slack water in the Pentland Firth (about HW Aberdeen −1¾ and +4). Be aware of tankers off Flotta oil terminal and in the S part of Scapa Flow.
Elsewhere in Orkney navigation is easy in clear weather, apart from the strong tidal streams in all the firths and sounds. Beware races and overfalls off Brough of Birsay (Mainland), Noup Head (Westray) and Dennis Head (N Ronaldsay); see also 10.7.5. Keep a good lookout for the many lobster pots (creels).

LIGHTS AND MARKS
The main hbrs and sounds are well lit; for details see 10.7.4. Powerful lts are shown offshore from Cantick Hd, Graemsay Island, Copinsay, Auskerry, Kirkwall, Brough of Birsay, Sanday Island, N Ronaldsay and Noup Hd.

RADIO TELEPHONE
Orkney Hbrs Navigation Service (call: *Orkney Hbr Radio*, Ch 09 11 20 16 (H24)) covers Scapa Flow and appr's, Wide Firth, Shapinsay Sound and Kirkwall Bay. It also broadcasts Orkney, Scapa and Pentland Firth forecasts for 12 hrs and outlook for further 12 hrs on Ch 11 at 0915 and 1715. For other local stations see individual hbrs.
TELEPHONE Area Code for islands SW of Stronsay and Westray Firths is 01856; islands to the NE are 01857.

MEDICAL SERVICES
Doctors are available at Kirkwall, Stromness, Rousay, Hoy, Shapinsay, Eday, S and N Ronaldsay, Stronsay, Sanday and Westray (Pierowall); Papa Westray is looked after by Westray. The only hospital (and dentist) are at Kirkwall. Serious cases are flown to Aberdeen (1 hour).

ORKNEY *continued*

Fish cages/farms may be found anywhere in sheltered waters within anchoring depths. Some are well buoyed, others are marked only by poles. Those known are listed.

SALMON CAGES

Beware salmon cages (may be marked by Y buoys/lts) at:

Rysa Sound	Pegal Bay (Hoy)
Lyrawa Bay	Hunda Sound
Ore Bay (Hoy)	Kirk Sound
Widewall Bay (S Ronaldsay)	Carness Bay
St Margaret's Hope	Bay of Ham
Backaland Bay (Eday)	Bay of London (Eday)

OYSTERS AND LONGLINES

Beware oysters and longlines at:

Widewall Bay	Bay of Firth
Swandister Bay	Damsay Sound
Water Sound	Millburn Bay (Gairsay)
Hunda Sound	Pierowall
Deer Sound	Bay of Skaill (Westray)
Inganess Bay	Longhope

STROMNESS   10-7-22

Orkney Islands, Mainland 58°57'·81N 03°17'·62W   Rtg 2-2-1

CHARTS

AC 2568, 2249; OS 6

TIDES

-0145 Dover; ML 2·0; Duration 0620; Zone 0 (UT)

Standard Port ABERDEEN (←)

Times				Height (metres)			
High Water		Low Water		MHWS	MHWN	MLWN	MLWS
0300	1100	0200	0900	4·3	3·4	1·6	0·6
1500	2300	1400	2100				
Differences STROMNESS							
−0430	−0355	−0415	−0420	−0·7	−0·8	−0·1	−0·1
ST MARY'S (Scapa Flow)							
−0345	−0345	−0345	−0345	−0·1	−0·1	−0·2	−0·2
BURRAY NESS (Burray)							
−0200	−0200	−0155	−0155	−1·0	−0·9	−0·3	0·0
WIDEWALL BAY (S Ronaldsay)							
−0400	−0400	−0355	−0355	−0·7	−0·7	−0·3	−0·2
BUR WICK (S Ronaldsay)							
−0255	−0320	−0400	−0410	−0·8	−0·6	0·0	0·0
MUCKLE SKERRY (Pentland Firth)							
−0230	−0230	−0225	−0225	−1·7	−1·4	−0·6	−0·2

SHELTER

Very good. Northern Lights Board have sole use of pier near to ldg lts. ↓ in hbr or berth at ferry piers further N.

OTHER HARBOURS IN THE ORKNEY ISLANDS

HOUTON BAY, Mainland, 58°54'·88N 03°11'·23W. AC 2568, 35. HW −0140 on Dover, −0400 on Aberdeen; HW ht +0·3m on Kirkwall; ML 1·8m; Duration 0615. ↓ in the bay in approx 5·5m at centre, sheltered from all winds. The ent is to the E of the island Holm of Houton; ent chan dredged 3·5m for 15m each side of ldg line. Keep clear of merchant vessels/ferries plying to Flotta.
Ldg lts 316°: front Fl G 3s 8m, rear FG 16m; both R △ on W pole, B bands. Ro Ro terminal in NE corner marked by Iso R 4s. Bus to Kirkwall; Slip close E of piers. Yachtsmen may contact **M. Grainger** ☎ 811356 for help.

SHAPINSAY, Orkney Islands, 59°02'·00N 02°54'·00W. AC 2584, 2249. HW −0015 on Dover, −0330 on Aberdeen; HW ht −1·0m on Aberdeen. Good shelter in Elwick Bay off Balfour on SW end of island in 2·5-3m. Enter bay passing W of Helliar Holm which has lt Fl WRG 10s on S end. Keep mid-chan. Balfour Pier lt Q WRG 5m 3/2M; vis G270°-010°, W010°-020°, R020°-090°. Tides in The String reach 5kn at sp. Facilities: ✉, P & D (cans), shop, Bar.

AUSKERRY, Orkney Islands, 59°02'·05N 02°34'·55W. AC 2250. HW −0010 on Dover, −0315 on Aberdeen, HW ht −1m on Aberdeen. Small island at ent to Stronsay Firth with small hbr on W side. Safe ent and good shelter except in SW winds. Ent has 3·5m; 1·2m alongside pier. Yachts can lie secured between ringbolts at ent and the pier. Auskerry Sound and Stronsay Firth are dangerous with wind over tide. Auskerry lt at S end, Fl 20s 34m 18M, W tr. No facilities.

PIEROWALL, Westray, 59°19'·35N 02°58'·41W. AC 2622, 2250. HW −0135 on Dover; ML 2·2m; Duration 0620. See 10·7.24. The bay is a good ↓ in 2-7m and well protected. Deep water AB at Gill Pt piers may be available; see Hr Mr. From S, beware Skelwick Skerry rks, and from the N the rks extending approx 1ca off Vest Ness. The N ent via Papa Sound needs local knowledge; tide race on the ebb. A dangerous tide race runs off Mull Hd at the N of Papa Westray. Lights: E pier hd Fl WRG 3s 7m 11/7M, G254°-276°, W276°-291°, R291°-308°, G308°-215°. W pier hd 2 FR (vert) 4/6m 3M. VHF Ch 16. Hr Mr ☎ (01857) 677273. Facilities: FW (at Gill Pier), P & D (cans), Bar, ✉, Ⓑ, R, V.
RAPNESS: Berth on pier, clear of Ro-Ro. Open to SSW.

NAVIGATION

WPT 58°57'·00N 03°16'·90W, 137°/317° from/to front ldg lt, 0·88M. Entry from the W should not be attempted with strong wind against tide due to heavy overfalls; if entering against the ebb, stand on to avoid being swept onto Skerry of Ness. Tides in Hoy Sound are very strong (>7kn sp). No tidal stream in hbr.

LIGHTS AND MARKS

For Hoy Sound, ldg lts 104° on Graemsay Is: front Iso 3s 17m 15M, W tr; rear Oc WR 8s 35m 20/16M, ldg sector is R097°-112°. Skerry of Ness, Fl WG 4s 7m 7/4M; W shore-090°, G090°-shore.
Hbr ldg lts 317°, both FR 29/39m 11M (H24), W trs, vis 307°-327°.

RADIO TELEPHONE

VHF Ch 12 16 (0900-1700 LT). (See also Kirkwall).

TELEPHONE (Dial code 01856)

Hr Mr 850744; Fuel 851286; MRSC 873268; ⌗ 872108; Marinecall 0891 500 451; Police 850222; Dr 850205.

FACILITIES

Services: Sh, El, Ⓔ, ME, C (mobile, 30 ton), Slip.
Town EC Thurs; FW, D, V, R, Bar, Gas, ✉, ◎, Ⓑ, ⇌ (ferry to Scrabster, bus to Thurso), ✈ (Kirkwall).
Yachtsmen may contact for help/advice: **Mr J. Stout** ☎ 850100, **Mr S. Mowat** ☎ 850624 or **Capt A. Johnston** ☎ 850366.

KIRKWALL   10-7-23
Orkney Islands, Mainland 58°59'·33N 02°57'·60W   Rtg 2-3-1

CHARTS
AC 1553, 2584, 2249, 2250; OS 6
TIDES
−0045 Dover; ML 1·7; Duration 0620; Zone 0 (UT)

Standard Port ABERDEEN (←)

Times				Height (metres)			
High Water		Low Water		MHWS	MHWN	MLWN	MLWS
0300	1100	0200	0900	4·3	3·4	1·6	0·6
1500	2300	1400	2100				
Differences KIRKWALL							
−0237	−0302	−0252	−0301	−1·3	−1·0	−0·3	−0·1
DEER SOUND							
−0245	−0245	−0245	−0245	−1·1	−0·9	−0·3	0·0
TINGWALL							
−0355	−0345	−0355	−0340	−1·2	−1·0	−0·3	−0·1

SHELTER
Good except in N winds or W gales when there is a surge
at the ent. At SW end of main pier, enter inner hbr (very
full in Jun/Jul); or safe ⚓ between pier and Crow Ness Pt.
NAVIGATION
WPT 59°01'·40N 02°57'·00W, 008°/188° from/to pier hd lt,
2·2M. Appr in W sector of pier hd lt. Bay is shoal to SW.

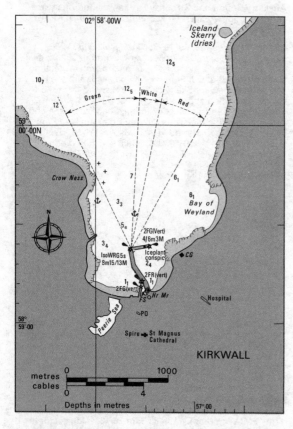

LIGHTS AND MARKS
Appr with St Magnus Cathedral (very conspic) brg 190°.
RADIO TELEPHONE
Kirkwall Hbr Radio VHF Ch 12 16 (0800-1700 LT). Orkney
Hbrs Navigation Service, call: *Orkney Hbr Radio* Ch 09 11
20 16 (H24). Local weather on Ch 11 at 0915 and 1715 LT.
TELEPHONE (Dial code 01856)
Hr Mr 872292; Port Office 873636; Fuel 873105; MRSC
873268; ⌗ 872108; Weather 873802; Marinecall 0891 500
451; Police 872241; Dr 885400 (Ⓗ).
FACILITIES
Pier P, D, FW, CH, C (mobile, 25 ton); **N and E Quays** M;
Orkney SC ☎ 872331, M, L, C, AB, Slip.
Town EC Wed; P, D, ME, El, Sh, CH, V, Gas, R, Bar, ✉, Ⓑ,
▣, ⇌ (Ferry to Scrabster, bus to Thurso), ✈.

STRONSAY   10-7-24
Orkney Islands, Stronsay 59°08'·60N 02°35'·90W   Rtg 3-4-2

CHARTS
AC 2622, 2250; OS 6
TIDES
−0140 Dover; ML 1·7; Duration 0620; Zone 0 (UT)

Standard Port ABERDEEN (←)

Times				Height (metres)			
High Water		Low Water		MHWS	MHWN	MLWN	MLWS
0300	1100	0200	0900	4·3	3·4	1·6	0·6
1500	2300	1400	2100				
Differences LOTH (Sanday)							
−0257	−0257	−0308	−0308	−1·0	−0·9	−0·2	+0·2
KETTLETOFT PIER (Sanday)							
−0230	−0230	−0225	−0225	−1·1	−0·9	−0·3	0·0
RAPNESS (Westray)							
−0410	−0410	−0410	−0410	−0·5	−0·6	0·0	0·0
PIEROWALL (Westray)							
−0355	−0355	−0350	−0350	−0·6	−0·6	−0·2	−0·1

SHELTER
Good from all winds. Good ⚓ between seaward end of
piers, or berth on outer end of W pier and contact Hr Mr.
The extended E pier head is berth for Ro-Ro ferry. There
are many other sheltered ⚓s around the bay.
NAVIGATION
WPT 59°09'·85N 02°36'·20W, Quiabow SHM By, Fl (2) G
12s, 009°/189° from/to No 1 lt buoy, 6·5ca. 800m NE of
Huip Ness is Quiabow, a submerged rk. Jack's Reef
extends 400m E from Huip Ness, and is marked by No 1
SHM buoy Fl G 5. A bank extends 350m SW from Papa
Stronsay. Crampie Shoal is in mid-chan, marked by No 3
buoy. The buoyed chan to Whitehall pier is dredged
3·5m. Spit to E of Whitehall pier extends 400m N. The E
ent is narrow and shallow and should not be attempted.
LIGHTS AND MARKS
As chartlet. Pier hd lts, 2FG (vert).
RADIO TELEPHONE
See Kirkwall.
TELEPHONE (Dial code 01857)
Hr Mr 616257; MRSC (01856) 873268; ⌗ (01856) 872108;
Marinecall 0891 500451; Police (01856) 872241; Dr 616321.
FACILITIES
W Pier M, L, AB; **Main (E) Pier** M, L, FW, AB clear of ferry.
Village (Whitehall) EC Thurs; P, D, V, Bar, ✉, Ⓑ, ⇌ (ferry
to Scrabster, bus to Thurso), ✈.

SHETLAND ISLANDS   10-7-25

The Shetland Islands consist of approx 100 islands, holms and rks of which fewer than 20 are inhabited. They lie 90 to 150M NNE of the Scottish mainland. By far the biggest island is Mainland with Lerwick (10.7.26), the capital, on the E side and Scalloway (overleaf), the only other town and old capital, on the W side. At the very S is Sumburgh airport and there are airstrips at Baltasound, Scalsta and Tingwall. Two islands of the Shetland group not shown on the chartlet are Fair Isle (see overleaf), 20M SSW of Sumburgh Hd and owned by the NT for Scotland, and Foula (see below) 12M WSW of Mainland.

There are LBs at Lerwick and Aith. The CG MRSC is at Lerwick ☎ (01595) 692976, with a Sector Base at Sella Ness (Sullom Voe) and an Auxiliary Station (Watch & Rescue) at Fair Isle.

CHARTS
AC: Med scale 3281, 3282, 3283; larger scale 3290, 3291, 3292, 3293, 3294, 3295, 3297, 3298; OS sheets 1-4.

TIDES
Lerwick is the Standard Port. Tidal streams run mostly N/ S or NW/SE and in open waters to the E and W are mostly weak. But rates >6kn can cause dangerous disturbances at the N and S extremities of the islands and in the two main sounds (Yell Snd and Bluemull/Colgrave Snds). Keep 3M off Sumburgh Head to clear a dangerous race (roost) or pass close inshore.

SHELTER
Weather conditions are bad in winter; yachts should only visit Apr – Sept. Around mid-summer it is day light H24. Some 12 small, non-commercial "marinas" are asterisked below; they are mostly full of local boats but supposedly each reserves 1 berth for visitors. Often only 1 boat lies between 2 fingers so that she can be held off by warps all round. Of the many ⚓s, the following are safe to enter in most weathers:

AGENTS WANTED

If you are interested in becoming our agent for any of the following ports, please write to: The Editor, Edington House, Trent, Sherborne, Dorset DT9 4SR, England – and get your free copy of the Almanac annually. You do not have to live in a port to be the agent, but at least a fairly regular visitor.

Great Yarmouth	St Gilles-Croix-de-Vie
Port Ellen (Islay)	Les Sables d'Olonne
Maryport	Ile d'Oléron
Workington	River Seudre
Holyhead	Anglet/Bayonne
Lough Swilly	St Jean-de-Luz
St Peter Port, Guernsey	Hendaye
Diélette	Grandcamp-Maisy
Portbail	Port-en-Bessin
Iles Chausey	Courseulles
St Malo/Dinard	Ouistreham/Caen
Le Legue/St Brieuc	Emden
Tréguier	Dornumer-Accumersiel
Lampaul	Langeoog
L'Aberildut	Bremerhaven
Le Palais (Belle Ile)	Büsum
Morbihan/Vannes	

Mainland (anti-clockwise from Sumburgh Head)
GRUTNESS VOE*: 1·5M N of Sumburgh Hd, a convenient passage ⚓, open to NE. Beware 2 rks awash in mid-ent.
CAT FIRTH: excellent shelter, ⚓ in approx 6m. Facilities: ✉ (Skellister), FW, V (both at Lax Firth).
GRUNNA VOE: off S side of Dury Voe, good shelter and holding, ⚓ in 5-10m; beware prohib ⚓ areas. Facilities: V, FW, ✉ (Lax Firth).
WHALSAY*: FV hbr at Symbister. FW, D, V, ✉.
OUT SKERRIES*: Quay and ⚓ at Bruray. FW, D, V, ✉.
S OF YELL SOUND*: Tides –0025 on Lerwick. W of Lunna Ness, well-protected ⚓s with good holding include: Boatsroom Voe, W Lunna Voe (small hotel, FW), Colla Firth* (excellent pier) and Dales Voe. Facilities: none.
SULLOM VOE: tides –0130 on Lerwick. 6·5M long deep water voe, partly taken over by the oil industry. ⚓ S of the narrows. Facilities at Brae: FW, V, ✉, D, ME, El, Sh, Bar.
HAMNA VOE: Tides –0200 on Lerwick; very good shelter. Ldg line 153° old house on S shore with prominent rk on pt of W shore 3ca within ent. Almost land-locked; ⚓ in 6m approx, but bottom foul with old moorings. Facilities: ✉ (0·5M), Vs, D (1·5M), L (at pier).
URA FIRTH: NE of St Magnus Bay, ⚓ off Hills Wick on W side or in Hamar Voe on E side, which has excellent shelter in all weathers and good holding, but no facilities. Facilities: Hills Wick FW, ✉, D, ME, El, Sh, V, R, Bar.
OLNA FIRTH: NE of Swarbacks Minn, beware rk 1ca off S shore which dries. ⚓ in firth, 4-8m or in Gon Firth or go alongside pier at Voe. Facilities: (Voe) FW, V, D, ✉, Bar.
SWARBACKS MINN*: a large complex of voes and isles SE of St Magnus Bay. Best ⚓ Uyea Sound or Aith Voe*, both well sheltered and good holding. Facilities: former none; Aith FW, ✉, V, Bar, LB.
VAILA SOUND: on SW of Mainland, ent via Easter Sound (do not attempt Wester Sound); very good shelter, ⚓ N of Salt Ness in 4-5m in mud. See WALLS* overleaf: FW, V, ✉.
GRUTING VOE*: tides –0150 on Lerwick, ⚓ in main voe or in Seli, Scutta or Browland* voes. Facilities: V and ✉ at Bridge of Walls (hd of Browland Voe).

Yell
MID YELL VOE: tides –0040 on Lerwick, enter through S Sd or Hascosay Sd, good ⚓ in wide part of voe 2·5– 10m. Facilities: ✉, FW at pier on S side, D, V, ME, Sh, El.
BASTA VOE: good ⚓ above shingle bank in 5-15m; good holding in places. Facilities: FW, V, Hotel, ✉.
BLUE MULL SND*: ⚓ at Cullivoe, pier and slip. D, FW, V.
Foula: Ham Voe on E side has tiny hbr/pier, unsafe in E'ly; berth clear of mailboat. Avoid Hoevdi Grund, 2M ESE.

NAVIGATION
A careful lookout must be kept for salmon farming cages, mostly marked by Y buoys and combinations of Y lts. The Clyde Cruising Club's *Shetland Sailing Directions and Anchorages* are essential for visitors. For general passage information see 10.7.5. Weather forecasting and the avoidance of wind-over-tide conditions assume yet more significance than elsewhere in the UK. Local magnetic anomalies may be experienced.
Note: There are two Historic Wrecks (*Kennemerland* and *Wrangels Palais*) on Out Skerries at 60°25'·2N 00°45'·0W and 60°25'·5N 00°43'·27W (see 10.0.3h).

LIGHTS AND MARKS
See 10.7.4. Powerful lights show offshore from Fair Isle, Sumburgh Head, Kirkabister Ness, Bound Skerry, Muckle Flugga, Pt of Fethaland, Esha Ness and Foula.

RADIO TELEPHONE
Shetland Coast Radio Station closed in 1997. For Port Radio services see 10.7.26.

TELEPHONE (Dial code 01595)
MRSC 692976; Sullom Voe Port Control 242551; Weather 692239; Forecaster 242069; Sumburgh Airport 460654.

FACILITIES
See SHELTER. All stores can be obtained in Lerwick and to a lesser extent in Scalloway. Elsewhere in Shetland there is little available and yachts should be stored for extended offshore cruising.

Continued

OTHER HARBOURS IN THE SHETLAND ISLANDS

FAIR ISLE, Shetland Islands, 59°32'·40N 01°36'·10W (North Haven). AC 2622. HW −0030 on Dover; ML 1·4m; Duration 0620. See 10.7.26 Good shelter in N Haven, but in NE winds uncomfortable. Lie alongside pier or ⚓ in approx 2m. Beware cross-tides in the apprs and rks all round the island, particularly in S Haven and South Hbr which are not recommended. Ldg marks 199° into N Haven: front, Stack of N Haven (only visible as a dark "tooth" sticking up from the jumble of blocks which form the bkwtr) in transit with conspic top of Sheep Craig (rear). Dir lt, 209° into North Haven, Oc WRG 8s 10m 6M, vis G204°-208°, W208°- 211°, R211°-221°. Other lts: In the S, Skadan Fl (4) 30s 32m **24**M, vis 260°-146°, but obscd close inshore from 260°–282°, Horn (2) 60s. In the N, Skroo Fl (2) 30s 80m **22**M, vis 086·7°–358°, Horn (3) 45s. Facilities: V, ✉ at N Shriva, and a bi-weekly mail boat ("Good Shepherd") to Shetland.

SCALLOWAY, Mainland, 60°07'·80N 01°16'·60W. AC 3294. HW −0200 on Dover; ML 0·9m; Duration 0620. See 10.7.26. A well sheltered ⚓ in all weathers, but care is needed passing through the islands in strong SW winds. The N Channel is easier and safer than the S Channel. ⚓s off Scalloway 6 -10m or in Hamna Voe (W Burra). Lts: Fugla Ness Fl (2) WRG 10s 20m 10/7M, W tr; W sector, 032°-082° covers the S Chan. Dir Oc 064·5°, WRG 10s 10m 11/8M, grey post on hbr quay (60°08'·05N 01°16'·47W), vis G052°-063·5°, W063·5°-065·5°, R065·5°-077°. Hbr lts: Moores Slipway jetty hd 2 FR (vert) 4/3m 1M. Blacksness W pier hd 2 FG (vert) 6/4m 3M; E pier hd Oc R 7s 5m 3M. *Scalloway Hbr Radio* VHF Ch **12** 09 16 (Mon-Fri: 0600-1800; Sat: 0600-1230 LT). Hr Mr/Port Control ☎ (01595) 880574 (H24). Facilities: **Scalloway Boat Club** ☎ 880409 welcomes visitors; AB on pontoon. **Town** EC Thurs; AB, M, Slip, P, D, FW, SM, BY, CH, C, El, ME, Sh, ✉, R, V, Bar.

VAILA SOUND (WALLS), Mainland, 60°13'·68N 01°33'·75W. AC 3295. Tides approx as Scalloway (above); see 10.7.26. Appr to E of Vaila island (do not attempt Wester Sound) in the W sector (355°-012°) of Rams Head lt, Fl WRG 8s 16m 9/6M. Gruting Voe lies to the NE. Enter Easter Sound and go N for 1·5M, passing E of Linga islet, to Walls at the head of Vaila Voe. Navigate by echo sounder. Beware fish farms. Temp'y AB on Bayhaa pier (covers). Close E of this, AB £1 on pontoon of Peter Georgeson **marina**; Sec ☎ (01595) 809273, FW. **Walls Regatta Club** welcomes visitors; showers, Bar, Slip. **Village**: P & D (cans), V, ✉.

BALTA SOUND, Unst, 60°44'·35N 00°48'·00W. AC 3293. HW −0105 on Dover; ML 1·3; Duration 0640. See 10.7.26. Balta Sound is a large almost landlocked inlet with good shelter from all winds. Beware bad holding on kelp. Safest entry is via S Chan between Huney Is and Balta Is; inner chan marked by an unlit SPM buoy and two lit PHM buoys. N Chan is deep but narrow; keep to Unst shore. ⚓ off Sandisons Wharf (2FG vert) in approx 6m or enter marina close W (one visitor's berth, very shallow); jetty has Fl R 6s 2m 2M. S end of Balta Is, Fl WR 10s 17m 10/7M, W249°-010°, R010°-060°, W060°-154°. VHF Ch 16; 20 (HO or as required). Facilities: BY, FW, D, El, ME, Sh; Hotel by pier. **Baltasound village**, Bar, R, V, ✉.

LERWICK   10-7-26

Shetland Is, Mainland 60°09'·29N 01°08'·30W   Rtg 1-3-2

CHARTS
AC 3290, 3291, 3283; OS 4
TIDES
–0001 Dover; ML 1·4; Duration 0620; Zone 0 (UT)

Standard Port LERWICK (→)

Times				Height (metres)			
High Water		Low Water		MHWS	MHWN	MLWN	MLWS
0000	0600	0100	0800	2·2	1·7	1·0	0·6
1200	1800	1300	2000				
Differences FAIR ISLE							
–0006	–0015	–0031	–0037	0·0	0·0	0·0	0·0
SUMBURGH (Grutness Voe)							
+0006	+0008	+0004	–0002	–0·4	–0·3	–0·3	–0·2
DURY VOE							
–0015	–0015	–0010	–0010	–0·1	–0·1	–0·1	–0·3
BURRA VOE (YELL SOUND)							
–0025	–0025	–0025	–0025	+0·2	+0·2	0·0	0·0
BALTA SOUND							
–0055	–0055	–0045	–0045	+0·1	+0·2	–0·1	–0·1
BLUE MULL SOUND							
–0135	–0135	–0155	–0155	+0·4	+0·2	–0·1	–0·1
SULLOM VOE							
–0135	–0125	–0135	–0120	0·0	0·0	–0·2	–0·2
HILLSWICK (URA FIRTH)							
–0220	–0220	–0200	–0200	0·0	–0·4	–0·4	–0·1
SCALLOWAY							
–0150	–0150	–0150	–0150	–0·6	–0·3	–0·3	0·0
FOULA (23M West of Scalloway)							
–0140	–0130	–0140	–0120	–0·2	–0·1	–0·1	–0·1

Lerwick is a Standard Port and tidal predictions for each day of the year are given below.

SHELTER
Good. Hr Mr allocates berths in Small Dock or Albert Dock. FVs occupy most alongside space. ⚓ prohib for about 2ca off the waterfront. Gremista marina in N hbr, is mainly for local boats, and is about 1M from the town.
NAVIGATION
WPT 60°06'·00N 01°08'·50W, 190°/010° from/to Maryfield lt, 3·5M, in W sector. From S, Bressay Sound is clear of dangers. From N, WPT 60°11'·60N 01°07'·88W, 035°/215° from/to N ent Dir lt, 1·34M; lt Oc WRG 6s, W sector 214°-216°. Beware Soldian Rk (dries), Nive Baa (0·6m), Green Holm (10m) and The Brethren (two rks 2m and 1·5m).
LIGHTS AND MARKS
Kirkabister Ness, Fl (2) 20s 32m 23M; Cro of Ham, Fl 3s 3M; Maryfield, Oc WRG 6s, W 008°-013°; all on Bressay. Twageos Pt, L Fl 6s 8m 6M. Loofa Baa SCM lt bn, as on chartlet. 2 SHM lt buoys mark Middle Ground in N Hbr.

RADIO TELEPHONE
Lerwick Harbour VHF Ch **12** 11 16 (H24) for VTS, radar and information.
Other stns: *Sullom Voe Hbr Radio* broadcasts traffic info and local forecasts on request Ch **14** 12 20 16 (H24).
TELEPHONE (Dial code 01595)
Hr Mr 692991; MRSC 692976; ⌗ 696166; Weather 692239; Police 692110; Dr 693201.
FACILITIES
Hbr Slip, M, P, D, L, FW, ME, Sh, Gas; **Lerwick Hbr Trust** ☎ 692991, AB £17 for 5 days (£1.70/metre), M, FW, D, P; **Lerwick Boating Club** ☎ 692407, L, C, Bar, Ⓘ;
Services: ME, EI, Ⓔ, Sh, Slip, BY, CH, SM, Gas, ACA.
Town EC Wed (all day); V, R, Bar, ✉, Ⓑ, ⇌, (ferry to Aberdeen), ✈.

LERWICK

MEAN SPRING
AND NEAP CURVES

MEAN RANGES	
Springs	1·6m
Neaps	0·7m

Springs occur 1 day
after
New and Full Moon.

SCOTLAND – LERWICK

LAT 60°09′N   LONG 1°08′W

TIMES AND HEIGHTS OF HIGH AND LOW WATERS

YEAR **1998**

TIME ZONE (UT)
For Summer Time add ONE hour in non-shaded areas

JANUARY

Day	Time	m	Time	m	Time	m	Time	m
1 TH	0020	2.3	0613	0.8	1228	2.5	1846	0.6
16 F	0059	2.2	0643	1.0	1307	2.4	1916	0.8
2 F	0104	2.3	0656	0.8	1312	2.4	1931	0.6
17 SA	0136	2.2	0719	1.0	1343	2.3	1953	0.8
3 SA	0151	2.2	0742	0.9	1359	2.4	2021	0.7
18 SU	0214	2.1	0756	1.1	1422	2.2	2032	0.9
4 SU	0241	2.2	0832	1.0	1449	2.3	2115	0.8
19 M	0256	2.0	0837	1.2	1504	2.1	2115	1.0
5 M	0336	2.1	0929	1.1	1546	2.2	2218	0.9
20 TU	0342	2.0	0923	1.2	1553	2.0	2205	1.1
6 TU	0440	2.0	1038	1.1	1653	2.1	2337	1.0
21 W	0435	1.9	1021	1.3	1654	1.9	2308	1.2
7 W	0556	2.0	1207	1.1	1818	2.1		
22 TH	0536	1.9	1156	1.3	1805	1.9		
8 TH	0056	1.0	0713	2.1	1325	1.1	1938	2.1
23 F	0034	1.2	0641	1.9	1322	1.3	1914	2.0
9 F	0158	1.0	0816	2.2	1425	1.0	2042	2.2
24 SA	0141	1.2	0742	2.0	1418	1.2	2015	2.1
10 SA	0250	1.0	0909	2.3	1516	0.9	2135	2.3
25 SU	0233	1.1	0836	2.1	1504	1.0	2108	2.2
11 SU	0336	0.9	0956	2.4	1603	0.8	2222	2.3
26 M	0317	1.0	0923	2.3	1546	0.9	2156	2.3
12 M ○	0419	0.9	1039	2.4	1646	0.7	2306	2.3
27 TU	0358	0.9	1007	2.4	1627	0.7	2240	2.4
13 TU	0458	0.9	1119	2.5	1727	0.7	2346	2.3
28 W ●	0438	0.8	1049	2.5	1707	0.6	2323	2.4
14 W	0535	0.9	1156	2.5	1805	0.7		
29 TH	0518	0.8	1131	2.6	1749	0.5		
15 TH	0023	2.3	0609	0.9	1232	2.4	1840	0.7
30 F	0005	2.5	0558	0.7	1214	2.6	1831	0.5
31 SA	0049	2.4	0641	0.8	1258	2.6	1915	0.5

FEBRUARY

Day	Time	m	Time	m	Time	m	Time	m
1 SU	0134	2.4	0726	0.8	1344	2.5	2002	0.6
16 M	0139	2.2	0727	1.0	1348	2.2	1956	0.6
2 M	0221	2.3	0813	0.9	1433	2.4	2052	0.8
17 TU	0215	2.1	0804	1.0	1423	2.1	2034	1.0
3 TU	0311	2.2	0907	1.0	1526	2.3	2150	0.9
18 W	0252	2.0	0844	1.1	1502	2.0	2117	1.1
4 W	0407	2.1	1011	1.1	1628	2.2	2306	1.1
19 TH	0334	2.0	0931	1.2	1551	1.9	2207	1.2
5 TH	0517	2.0	1147	1.2	1754	2.1		
20 F	0428	1.9	1032	1.3	1704	1.9	2316	1.2
6 F	0039	1.1	0646	2.0	1315	1.1	1928	2.0
21 SA	0542	1.9	1230	1.3	1834	1.9		
7 SA	0147	1.1	0801	2.1	1417	1.0	2035	2.1
22 SU	0104	1.2	0700	1.9	1350	1.1	1948	1.9
8 SU	0240	1.1	0857	2.2	1509	0.9	2128	2.2
23 M	0208	1.1	0806	2.0	1441	1.0	2047	2.1
9 M	0326	1.0	0944	2.3	1553	0.8	2213	2.2
24 TU	0255	1.0	0859	2.2	1525	0.8	2137	2.2
10 TU	0407	1.0	1026	2.4	1633	0.7	2253	2.3
25 W	0337	0.9	0947	2.4	1606	0.6	2222	2.3
11 W ○	0443	0.9	1104	2.4	1710	0.7	2329	2.3
26 TH ●	0417	0.7	1031	2.5	1647	0.5	2305	2.4
12 TH	0517	0.9	1138	2.4	1743	0.7		
27 F	0458	0.6	1045	2.6	1728	0.4	2348	2.5
13 F	0001	2.3	0547	0.9	1210	2.4	1814	0.7
28 SA	0540	0.6	1158	2.6	1811	0.4		
14 SA	0033	2.3	0619	0.9	1241	2.4	1846	0.7
15 SU	0105	2.2	0652	0.9	1314	2.3	1920	0.8

MARCH

Day	Time	m	Time	m	Time	m	Time	m
1 SU	0031	2.5	0622	0.6	1243	2.6	1854	0.4
16 M	0034	2.2	0626	0.7	1245	2.2	1849	0.7
2 M	0115	2.4	0707	0.6	1328	2.5	1940	0.6
17 TU	0105	2.1	0700	0.8	1318	2.1	1923	0.7
3 TU	0159	2.3	0754	0.7	1416	2.4	2028	0.7
18 W	0138	2.1	0736	0.8	1352	2.0	2000	0.8
4 W	0246	2.2	0846	0.8	1508	2.2	2122	0.9
19 TH	0212	2.0	0814	0.9	1430	1.9	2041	1.0
5 TH	0338	2.0	0949	1.0	1608	2.0	2238	1.1
20 F	0251	2.0	0900	1.0	1517	1.8	2129	1.1
6 F	0442	1.9	1132	1.1	1735	1.9		
21 SA	0339	1.8	0957	1.1	1620	1.8	2231	1.1
7 SA	0022	1.2	0617	1.9	1301	1.0	1919	1.9
22 SU	0442	1.8	1116	1.1	1755	1.7		
8 SU	0132	1.1	0744	1.9	1403	0.9	2026	1.9
23 M	0004	1.1	0612	1.8	1314	0.9	1921	1.8
9 M	0225	1.1	0842	2.0	1453	0.8	2115	2.0
24 TU	0136	1.0	0733	1.9	1412	0.8	2024	1.9
10 TU	0310	1.0	0928	2.1	1536	0.7	2157	2.1
25 W	0228	0.9	0833	2.0	1458	0.6	2115	2.1
11 W	0349	0.9	1009	2.2	1613	0.7	2234	2.1
26 TH	0311	0.7	0924	2.2	1541	0.4	2201	2.2
12 TH	0423	0.8	1045	2.2	1646	0.6	2307	2.1
27 F	0353	0.6	1011	2.4	1623	0.3	2245	2.3
13 F ○	0454	0.8	1116	2.3	1715	0.6	2335	2.2
28 SA ●	0436	0.5	1056	2.5	1705	0.2	2328	2.3
14 SA	0523	0.7	1144	2.3	1744	0.6		
29 SU	0519	0.4	1141	2.5	1748	0.2		
15 SU	0003	2.2	0553	0.7	1214	2.2	1815	0.6
30 M	0010	2.3	0603	0.4	1227	2.5	1832	0.3
31 TU	0054	2.3	0648	0.4	1313	2.4	1917	0.5

APRIL

Day	Time	m	Time	m	Time	m	Time	m
1 W	0138	2.2	0736	0.5	1401	2.2	2004	0.6
16 TH	0108	1.9	0712	0.6	1330	1.9	1931	0.7
2 TH	0224	2.1	0828	0.6	1452	2.0	2056	0.8
17 F	0144	1.9	0752	0.7	1411	1.8	2013	0.8
3 F	0314	1.9	0931	0.8	1552	1.8	2208	1.0
18 SA	0224	1.8	0839	0.7	1500	1.7	2102	0.9
4 SA	0413	1.8	1113	0.8	1715	1.7	2357	1.1
19 SU	0311	1.7	0935	0.8	1601	1.6	2202	0.9
5 SU	0540	1.7	1238	0.8	1859	1.7		
20 M	0411	1.7	1047	0.8	1724	1.6	2319	0.9
6 M	0108	1.0	0715	1.7	1339	0.8	2005	1.7
21 TU	0530	1.7	1224	0.7	1851	1.6		
7 TU	0202	1.0	0816	1.8	1429	0.7	2052	1.8
22 W	0052	0.9	0657	1.7	1336	0.5	1957	1.8
8 W	0247	0.9	0904	1.9	1510	0.6	2132	1.8
23 TH	0154	0.7	0805	1.9	1427	0.4	2050	1.9
9 TH	0325	0.8	0944	1.9	1545	0.6	2208	1.9
24 F	0243	0.6	0900	2.0	1513	0.3	2138	2.0
10 F	0357	0.7	1019	2.0	1615	0.5	2238	2.0
25 SA	0329	0.4	0950	2.2	1558	0.2	2223	2.1
11 SA ○	0427	0.6	1049	2.0	1643	0.5	2305	2.0
26 SU ●	0414	0.3	1038	2.3	1642	0.1	2307	2.2
12 SU	0457	0.6	1118	2.0	1714	0.5	2333	2.0
27 M	0459	0.2	1124	2.3	1726	0.2	2350	2.2
13 M	0529	0.5	1147	2.0	1747	0.5		
28 TU	0545	0.2	1211	2.2	1810	0.3		
14 TU	0003	2.0	0602	0.5	1220	2.0	1820	0.5
29 W	0034	2.2	0631	0.2	1258	2.1	1855	0.4
15 W	0035	2.0	0636	0.6	1254	2.0	1854	0.6
30 TH	0118	2.1	0720	0.3	1347	2.0	1941	0.6

Chart Datum: 1·22 metres below Ordnance Datum (Local)

SCOTLAND – LERWICK

LAT 60°09'N   LONG 1°08'W

TIMES AND HEIGHTS OF HIGH AND LOW WATERS

YEAR **1998**

TIME ZONE (UT)
For Summer Time add ONE hour in non-shaded areas

MAY

Date	Time	m	Time	m	Time	m	Time	m
1 F	0203	2.0	0812	0.4	1438	1.8	2031	0.7
16 SA	0123	1.8	0737	0.5	1358	1.7	1952	0.7
2 SA	0252	1.8	0913	0.6	1535	1.7	2134	0.9
17 SU	0206	1.8	0824	0.5	1448	1.6	2042	0.7
3 SU	0347	1.7	1040	0.6	1644	1.5	2317	0.9
18 M	0254	1.7	0920	0.5	1547	1.6	2140	0.8
4 M	0456	1.6	1203	0.7	1811	1.5		
19 TU	0351	1.7	1025	0.5	1658	1.5	2249	0.8
5 TU	0032	0.9	0622	1.6	1305	0.6	1925	1.5
20 W	0501	1.6	1143	0.5	1817	1.6		
6 W	0130	0.8	0734	1.6	1355	0.6	2016	1.6
21 TH	0010	0.7	0622	1.7	1258	0.4	1926	1.7
7 TH	0216	0.8	0826	1.7	1435	0.5	2057	1.7
22 F	0121	0.6	0735	1.8	1357	0.3	2023	1.8
8 F	0254	0.7	0909	1.7	1509	0.5	2132	1.7
23 SA	0217	0.5	0837	1.9	1447	0.2	2114	1.9
9 SA	0327	0.6	0945	1.8	1540	0.5	2203	1.8
24 SU	0308	0.4	0931	2.0	1535	0.2	2202	2.0
10 SU	0359	0.5	1017	1.9	1612	0.4	2233	1.9
25 M ●	0356	0.3	1021	2.1	1621	0.2	2247	2.1
11 M O	0432	0.5	1050	1.9	1646	0.4	2304	1.9
26 TU	0443	0.2	1110	2.1	1706	0.2	2331	2.1
12 TU	0507	0.4	1123	1.9	1721	0.4	2336	1.9
27 W	0531	0.2	1157	2.1	1751	0.3		
13 W	0542	0.4	1158	1.9	1755	0.5		
28 TH	0015	2.1	0617	0.2	1244	2.0	1835	0.4
14 TH	0009	1.9	0617	0.4	1235	1.8	1830	0.5
29 F	0059	2.0	0705	0.3	1332	1.9	1919	0.6
15 F	0045	1.9	0655	0.4	1314	1.8	1909	0.6
30 SA	0143	1.9	0755	0.3	1420	1.7	2005	0.7
31 SU	0229	1.8	0849	0.4	1511	1.6	2055	0.8

JUNE

Date	Time	m	Time	m	Time	m	Time	m
1 M	0319	1.7	0951	0.5	1606	1.5	2202	0.9
16 TU	0240	1.8	0904	0.4	1530	1.7	2119	0.7
2 TU	0415	1.6	1106	0.6	1706	1.5	2335	0.9
17 W	0334	1.8	1003	0.5	1631	1.6	2223	0.7
3 W	0518	1.5	1214	0.6	1812	1.4		
18 TH	0437	1.7	1111	0.5	1742	1.6	2336	0.7
4 TH	0043	0.9	0625	1.5	1308	0.6	1913	1.5
19 F	0551	1.5	1224	0.5	1854	1.7		
5 F	0135	0.8	0728	1.5	1351	0.6	2003	1.6
20 SA	0052	0.7	0709	1.5	1331	0.5	1957	1.8
6 SA	0217	0.7	0820	1.6	1429	0.6	2045	1.7
21 SU	0158	0.6	0817	1.9	1427	0.4	2053	1.9
7 SU	0255	0.6	0904	1.7	1505	0.5	2124	1.7
22 M	0253	0.5	0915	1.9	1518	0.4	2143	2.0
8 M	0332	0.6	0945	1.7	1543	0.5	2201	1.8
23 TU	0344	0.4	1008	2.0	1605	0.4	2230	2.1
9 TU	0410	0.5	1024	1.8	1621	0.5	2237	1.9
24 W ●	0432	0.3	1057	2.0	1650	0.4	2315	2.1
10 W O	0448	0.4	1102	1.8	1658	0.5	2312	1.9
25 TH	0519	0.2	1144	2.0	1734	0.5	2358	2.1
11 TH	0525	0.4	1140	1.9	1735	0.5	2348	2.0
26 F	0605	0.2	1229	2.0	1816	0.5		
12 F	0603	0.4	1219	1.9	1813	0.5		
27 SA	0040	2.1	0648	0.3	1313	1.9	1856	0.6
13 SA	0026	2.0	0642	0.4	1301	1.8	1852	0.5
28 SU	0122	2.0	0732	0.4	1356	1.8	1937	0.7
14 SU	0107	1.9	0724	0.4	1346	1.8	1936	0.6
29 M	0203	1.9	0816	0.4	1440	1.7	2019	0.8
15 M	0151	1.9	0812	0.4	1435	1.7	2024	0.7
30 TU	0247	1.8	0901	0.5	1525	1.6	2105	0.8

JULY

Date	Time	m	Time	m	Time	m	Time	m
1 W	0335	1.7	0951	0.6	1615	1.6	2202	0.9
16 TH	0315	2.0	0940	0.5	1604	1.8	2158	0.8
2 TH	0428	1.6	1049	0.7	1709	1.5	2318	0.9
17 F	0414	1.9	1043	0.6	1708	1.7	2309	0.8
3 F	0527	1.6	1155	0.8	1807	1.6		
18 SA	0525	1.8	1158	0.7	1823	1.7		
4 SA	0038	0.9	0630	1.6	1257	0.8	1904	1.6
19 SU	0034	0.8	0650	1.8	1314	0.7	1936	1.8
5 SU	0137	0.9	0731	1.6	1349	0.7	1959	1.7
20 M	0148	0.7	0805	1.9	1416	0.7	2037	1.9
6 M	0224	0.8	0826	1.7	1435	0.7	2048	1.8
21 TU	0246	0.6	0907	1.9	1507	0.7	2130	2.0
7 TU	0308	0.7	0915	1.8	1518	0.7	2131	1.9
22 W	0337	0.5	0959	2.0	1554	0.6	2217	2.1
8 W	0349	0.6	1000	1.8	1600	0.6	2212	2.0
23 TH ●	0424	0.4	1047	2.0	1637	0.6	2301	2.2
9 TH O	0429	0.5	1042	1.9	1639	0.6	2250	2.0
24 F	0507	0.4	1130	2.0	1717	0.6	2342	2.2
10 F	0509	0.4	1124	1.9	1717	0.5	2329	2.1
25 SA	0548	0.4	1211	2.0	1755	0.6		
11 SA	0548	0.3	1203	2.0	1756	0.5		
26 SU	0020	2.2	0626	0.4	1250	2.0	1831	0.6
12 SU	0009	2.1	0627	0.3	1246	2.0	1836	0.5
27 M	0056	2.1	0703	0.4	1326	1.9	1907	0.6
13 M	0051	2.1	0710	0.3	1330	1.9	1919	0.6
28 TU	0133	2.1	0740	0.5	1404	1.9	1944	0.8
14 TU	0136	2.1	0756	0.3	1417	1.9	2006	0.6
29 W	0212	2.0	0819	0.6	1444	1.8	2025	0.8
15 W	0223	2.0	0845	0.4	1508	1.8	2058	0.7
30 TH	0254	1.9	0900	0.7	1528	1.7	2111	0.9
31 F	0341	1.8	0947	0.8	1618	1.7	2205	1.0

AUGUST

Date	Time	m	Time	m	Time	m	Time	m
1 SA	0436	1.7	1043	0.9	1714	1.7	2324	1.1
16 SU	0506	1.9	1141	0.9	1756	1.8		
2 SU	0541	1.6	1158	1.0	1816	1.7		
17 M	0027	0.9	0642	1.8	1307	0.9	1922	1.9
3 M	0055	1.0	0650	1.7	1313	0.9	1918	1.7
18 TU	0143	0.8	0803	1.9	1409	0.9	2027	2.0
4 TU	0157	0.9	0754	1.7	1410	0.9	2015	1.8
19 W	0241	0.7	0902	1.9	1459	0.8	2120	2.1
5 W	0245	0.8	0850	1.8	1457	0.8	2104	1.9
20 TH	0328	0.6	0951	2.0	1542	0.8	2205	2.2
6 TH	0328	0.7	0938	1.9	1539	0.7	2148	2.1
21 F	0411	0.5	1034	2.0	1622	0.7	2246	2.2
7 F	0409	0.5	1022	1.9	1619	0.6	2229	2.2
22 SA ●	0450	0.5	1114	2.1	1658	0.7	2323	2.2
8 SA O	0449	0.4	1104	2.1	1658	0.6	2309	2.3
23 SU	0525	0.4	1149	2.1	1731	0.7	2356	2.2
9 SU	0528	0.3	1145	2.2	1737	0.5	2351	2.3
24 M	0559	0.4	1221	2.1	1804	0.7		
10 M	0609	0.3	1227	2.2	1818	0.5		
25 TU	0027	2.2	0631	0.5	1252	2.0	1837	0.7
11 TU	0033	2.3	0651	0.3	1310	2.1	1901	0.5
26 W	0101	2.1	0705	0.6	1326	2.0	1913	0.7
12 W	0118	2.3	0735	0.4	1355	2.1	1947	0.6
27 TH	0136	2.0	0741	0.6	1402	1.9	1951	0.8
13 TH	0205	2.2	0823	0.5	1443	2.0	2037	0.7
28 F	0213	2.0	0819	0.8	1441	1.9	2031	0.9
14 F	0256	2.1	0916	0.6	1536	1.9	2135	0.8
29 SA	0253	1.9	0900	0.9	1523	1.8	2117	1.0
15 SA	0354	2.0	1018	0.8	1637	1.8	2249	0.9
30 SU	0341	1.8	0949	1.0	1615	1.7	2217	1.1
31 M	0450	1.7	1054	1.1	1723	1.7		

7

Chart Datum: 1·22 metres below Ordnance Datum (Local)

SCOTLAND – LERWICK

LAT 60°09′N   LONG 1°08′W

TIMES AND HEIGHTS OF HIGH AND LOW WATERS

YEAR **1998**

TIME ZONE (UT)
For Summer Time add ONE hour in non-shaded areas

Chart Datum: 1·22 metres below Ordnance Datum (Local)

SEPTEMBER

Day	Time	m	Time	m	Time	m	Time	m
1 TU	0008	1.1	0612	1.7	1238	1.1	1838	1.7
2 W	0129	1.0	0727	1.7	1346	1.0	1943	1.8
3 TH	0221	0.9	0827	1.9	1434	0.9	2037	2.0
4 F	0305	0.7	0917	2.0	1516	0.8	2124	2.1
5 SA	0345	0.5	1001	2.1	1556	0.6	2207	2.3
6 SU ○	0425	0.4	1043	2.2	1635	0.5	2249	2.4
7 M	0505	0.3	1124	2.3	1716	0.5	2332	2.5
8 TU	0546	0.2	1205	2.3	1758	0.4		
9 W	0015	2.5	0628	0.3	1248	2.3	1841	0.5
10 TH	0101	2.4	0713	0.4	1332	2.2	1927	0.6
11 F	0148	2.3	0800	0.5	1419	2.1	2017	0.7
12 SA	0239	2.1	0851	0.7	1510	2.0	2116	0.8
13 SU	0337	2.0	0954	0.9	1610	1.9	2237	0.9
14 M	0454	1.8	1131	1.0	1734	1.8		
15 TU	0022	0.9	0642	1.8	1257	1.0	1910	1.9
16 W	0133	0.8	0759	1.8	1357	1.0	2015	1.9
17 TH	0228	0.7	0853	1.9	1445	0.9	2105	2.0
18 F	0313	0.6	0937	2.0	1526	0.8	2149	2.1
19 SA	0352	0.6	1017	2.0	1602	0.8	2227	2.2
20 SU ●	0426	0.5	1051	2.1	1635	0.7	2301	2.2
21 M	0458	0.5	1122	2.1	1706	0.6	2330	2.2
22 TU	0528	0.5	1149	2.1	1738	0.6	2358	2.2
23 W	0559	0.5	1218	2.1	1811	0.7		
24 TH	0029	2.1	0632	0.6	1250	2.1	1845	0.7
25 F	0103	2.1	0706	0.7	1323	2.0	1921	0.8
26 SA	0137	2.0	0742	0.8	1357	1.9	1958	0.9
27 SU	0214	1.9	0821	0.9	1433	1.9	2042	1.0
28 M	0259	1.8	0907	1.0	1518	1.8	2136	1.0
29 TU	0401	1.7	1005	1.1	1620	1.7	2258	1.1
30 W	0535	1.7	1143	1.1	1750	1.7		

OCTOBER

Day	Time	m	Time	m	Time	m	Time	m
1 TH	0055	1.0	0659	1.7	1316	1.1	1908	1.8
2 F	0152	0.8	0802	1.9	1407	0.9	2008	2.0
3 SA	0237	0.6	0852	2.0	1450	0.8	2058	2.1
4 SU	0318	0.4	0937	2.1	1531	0.6	2144	2.3
5 M ○	0359	0.3	1020	2.2	1612	0.5	2229	2.4
6 TU	0440	0.3	1101	2.3	1654	0.4	2313	2.5
7 W	0523	0.2	1144	2.3	1738	0.4	2358	2.5
8 TH	0606	0.3	1226	2.3	1823	0.4		
9 F	0044	2.4	0651	0.4	1311	2.3	1910	0.6
10 SA	0133	2.3	0737	0.6	1357	2.2	2001	0.6
11 SU	0224	2.1	0828	0.8	1447	2.0	2101	0.8
12 M	0324	1.9	0931	1.0	1546	1.9	2228	1.0
13 TU	0443	1.8	1114	1.1	1708	1.8		
14 W	0005	0.9	0630	1.7	1237	1.1	1847	1.8
15 TH	0113	0.8	0742	1.8	1336	1.0	1953	1.9
16 F	0205	0.7	0833	1.9	1423	0.9	2043	2.0
17 SA	0249	0.7	0915	1.9	1504	0.8	2126	2.0
18 SU	0326	0.6	0952	2.0	1539	0.8	2203	2.1
19 M	0359	0.6	1011	2.1	1611	0.7	2234	2.1
20 TU ●	0428	0.6	1051	2.1	1642	0.6	2302	2.1
21 W	0458	0.6	1118	2.1	1714	0.6	2331	2.1
22 TH	0530	0.6	1147	2.1	1747	0.6		
23 F	0003	2.1	0603	0.6	1218	2.1	1821	0.7
24 SA	0036	2.1	0637	0.7	1251	2.1	1856	0.8
25 SU	0112	2.0	0713	0.8	1324	2.0	1934	0.8
26 M	0150	1.9	0751	0.9	1402	1.9	2018	0.9
27 TU	0238	1.8	0836	1.0	1446	1.8	2111	1.0
28 W	0335	1.7	0933	1.1	1543	1.8	2220	1.0
29 TH	0457	1.7	1047	1.1	1700	1.8		
30 F	0003	0.9	0624	1.7	1230	1.1	1828	1.8
31 SA	0115	0.8	0731	1.8	1333	0.9	1936	2.0

NOVEMBER

Day	Time	m	Time	m	Time	m	Time	m
1 SU	0206	0.6	0825	2.0	1421	0.8	2032	2.1
2 M	0250	0.5	0912	2.1	1506	0.6	2122	2.3
3 TU	0334	0.4	0956	2.3	1550	0.5	2210	2.4
4 W ○	0417	0.3	1040	2.3	1635	0.4	2256	2.5
5 TH	0501	0.3	1123	2.4	1721	0.4	2343	2.5
6 F	0546	0.4	1207	2.4	1807	0.4		
7 SA	0030	2.4	0631	0.5	1252	2.3	1856	0.5
8 SU	0120	2.2	0717	0.7	1338	2.2	1948	0.6
9 M	0211	2.1	0807	0.9	1427	2.1	2048	0.7
10 TU	0309	1.9	0907	1.0	1522	2.0	2207	0.8
11 W	0419	1.8	1039	1.1	1632	1.9	2334	0.9
12 TH	0550	1.7	1203	1.1	1802	1.8		
13 F	0040	0.8	0707	1.7	1305	1.1	1917	1.9
14 SA	0134	0.8	0801	1.8	1355	1.0	2011	1.9
15 SU	0219	0.8	0843	1.9	1438	0.9	2055	2.0
16 M	0256	0.7	0920	2.0	1514	0.8	2132	2.0
17 TU	0329	0.7	0951	2.0	1547	0.8	2205	2.1
18 W	0400	0.7	1020	2.1	1620	0.7	2236	2.1
19 TH ●	0432	0.7	1049	2.2	1654	0.7	2308	2.1
20 F	0506	0.7	1121	2.2	1729	0.7	2342	2.1
21 SA	0540	0.7	1153	2.2	1804	0.7		
22 SU	0017	2.1	0614	0.8	1227	2.2	1839	0.7
23 M	0054	2.0	0649	0.9	1302	2.1	1917	0.8
24 TU	0135	2.0	0728	0.9	1342	2.1	2001	0.8
25 W	0222	1.9	0814	1.0	1427	2.0	2052	0.9
26 TH	0316	1.8	0908	1.1	1520	1.9	2154	0.9
27 F	0424	1.8	1013	1.1	1626	1.9	2309	1.0
28 SA	0543	1.8	1133	1.1	1745	1.9		
29 SU	0030	0.7	0655	1.9	1253	1.0	1903	2.0
30 M	0133	0.7	0755	2.0	1353	0.9	2007	2.2

DECEMBER

Day	Time	m	Time	m	Time	m	Time	m
1 TU	0225	0.6	0847	2.2	1444	0.7	2102	2.3
2 W	0312	0.6	0935	2.3	1533	0.6	2154	2.4
3 TH ○	0358	0.6	1021	2.4	1620	0.5	2243	2.4
4 F	0444	0.5	1106	2.4	1708	0.5	2331	2.4
5 SA	0529	0.6	1151	2.5	1756	0.5		
6 SU	0019	2.4	0614	0.7	1235	2.4	1844	0.5
7 M	0107	2.3	0659	0.8	1320	2.3	1934	0.6
8 TU	0156	2.1	0746	0.9	1406	2.2	2028	0.7
9 W	0247	2.0	0836	1.1	1456	2.1	2130	0.8
10 TH	0342	1.9	0940	1.2	1552	2.0	2245	0.9
11 F	0445	1.8	1110	1.2	1657	1.9	2356	1.0
12 SA	0557	1.8	1223	1.2	1811	1.9		
13 SU	0054	1.0	0705	1.8	1321	1.1	1920	1.9
14 M	0142	1.0	0757	1.9	1408	1.1	2013	1.9
15 TU	0223	0.9	0838	2.0	1448	1.0	2057	2.0
16 W	0259	0.9	0915	2.1	1525	0.9	2135	2.1
17 TH	0335	0.9	0950	2.2	1601	0.9	2212	2.1
18 F ●	0411	0.9	1025	2.2	1638	0.8	2249	2.2
19 SA	0447	0.8	1059	2.3	1714	0.8	2325	2.2
20 SU	0523	0.8	1133	2.3	1751	0.8		
21 M	0002	2.2	0557	0.9	1209	2.3	1826	0.7
22 TU	0041	2.2	0633	0.9	1246	2.3	1905	0.7
23 W	0122	2.1	0712	0.9	1327	2.3	1947	0.8
24 TH	0207	2.0	0756	1.0	1411	2.2	2035	0.8
25 F	0257	2.0	0846	1.1	1501	2.2	2129	0.9
26 SA	0354	2.0	0944	1.1	1559	2.1	2232	0.9
27 SU	0500	1.9	1053	1.1	1709	2.1	2347	0.9
28 M	0615	2.0	1214	1.1	1830	2.1		
29 TU	0103	0.9	0725	2.1	1330	1.0	1945	2.2
30 W	0205	0.8	0825	2.2	1430	0.9	2047	2.3
31 TH	0257	0.8	0918	2.3	1523	0.8	2142	2.4

VOLVO PENTA SERVICE

Sales and service centres in area 8
ARGYLL *Crinan Boats Ltd*, Crinan, PA31 8SP Tel (01546) 830232

Area 8

North-West Scotland
Cape Wrath to Crinan Canal

**VOLVO
PENTA**

8

Key to Symbols

🕿 🕿	Coast Radio Station: VHF/MF frequencies
🕿	Port, VTS, or Marina Radio: VHF frequencies
Ⓡ🄱	Marine RDF beacon
Ⓡ🄱 Aero	Aero RDF beacon
_i_	See for harbour information/tidal data
☁	Weather information
	(Frequencies/times of broadcasts)
⛟	SAR Helicopter base
☆	Selected Principal Lights
⛟	Light vessel/Light float/Lanby
◯RG	Emergency VHF DF
*	See Area Index

10-8-2 North-West Scotland
Cape Wrath to Crinan Canal

440

Shetland CG

Stornoway CG

Cape Wrath

Loch Eriboll

● Loch Inchard*

● Loch Laxford*

Badcall Bay

● Loch Inver*

Loch Nedd

Kinlochbervie
10.8.8
_i_
🕿 VHF 6 16

Ullapool
10.8.9
_i_
🕿 VHF 14 12 16

Stornoway CG
Oban CG

☆ Stoerhead

Summer Isles*◇

● Loch Ewe*

Loch ● Gairloch*

Loch ● Torridon*

Loch a'Bhraige*

Lewis Radio
🕿 VHF 05 16
☁ VHF 05
0703 1903 UT

Stornoway
10.8.7
_i_
🕿 VHF 12 16
Ⓡ🄱 Aero 669·50 SAY 20M

Rubn'Re
(Rubha ☆
Reidh)

Sound of ☆
Raasay

Rona

Raasay

☆ Tiumpan Head

Butt of Lewis
Ⓡ🄱 289·00 BL 70M

Loch Shell

Shiant
Isles*

Eilean Glas ☆

Uig

Portree
10.8.10
_i_
🕿 VHF 12 16

Hebrides Radio
🕿 MF 1866
☁ MF 1866
0703 1903 UT

● Carloway

Lewis

● Little Bernera

Loch Seaforth

Harris

East Loch
Tarbert

Leverburgh

◯RG
Rodel

Stornoway CG
Oban CG

Skye Radio
🕿 VHF 24 16
☁ VHF 24
0703 1903 UT

Loch ●
Dunvegan*

West Loch Tarbert

Loch Maddy*
🕿 VHF 12 16

North Uist

Scolpaig

Ballivanich

Neist Point

St Kilda*
🕿 VHF 16; 08
Ⓡ🄱 Aero 338·00 KL 30M

Shilley

58°
00'N

58°
00'N

05°00'W

05°00'W

06°00'W

07°00'W

07°00'W

08°00'W

08°00'W

30'

30'

30'

30'

30'

30'

30'

8

Plockton
10.8.11

Kyle of Loch Alsh*

Caledonian Canal
10.8.18
VHF 74
Locks 74

**Fort William/
Corpach**
10.8.17
VHF 74 16

Corpach

Oban/North Connel
404·00 CNL 15M

Oban
10.8.19
VHF 12 16
Oban Radio
VHF 07 16
VHF 07
0703 1903 UT

**Loch
Leven***

Loch Etive*
Bonawe

Mallaig
10.8.13
VHF 09 16

Loch Hourn*

Kyle
Rhea

Loch Nevis*

Sound of
Sleat*

Loch Sunart*
10.8.14

Corran Narrows*

Loch Crean*
Lismore

Dunstaffnage Bay*

Lynn of Lorn*
Loch Feochan*
Puilladobhrain*
Cuan Sound*

Loch Melfort
10.8.20
Marina 80 M

Crinan Canal
10.9.8
VHF 74 16

Crowlin
Is*

Armadale Bay*

Arisaig*

Loch Moidett*

Loch Aline
10.8.16

Craignure*

Seil*
Carsaig B*

Ardinamar*

Gulf of
Corryvrecken

Loch
Harport*

Kyle Akin
10.8.12

Skye

Soay*

Figg*

Muck*

Salen*

Loch
Spelve*

Loch Lathaich*

Jura

Loch
Skiport*
07°00'W

Loch Boispale*

Canna*

Rhum*

Oigh Sgeir*

Ardnamurchan Point

Rubha nan Gall

Mull

Ulva
Sound

Loch
na Keal*

Gometra*

Staffa*

Sound of Iona*
Iona
Tinkers Hole*

**Craobh Marina
(Loch Shuna)**
10.8.21
VHF M 80

Colonsay

Oban CG
Clyde CG

South
Uist

Loch Carnan
30'

Tobermory
10.8.15
VHF 12 16

Treshnish I*

Arinagour*

Gott Bay*
Tiree

Tiree

Skerryvore

Dubh Artach

Oronsay

Stornoway CG
Oban CG
08°00'W

Barra Island

Barra

Castle Bay*

Barra Head

Barra Head

Loch Craignish
10.8.22
Ardfern YC
VHF 80

Variation

9°W (1998)

90

180

270

0

57°
00'N

57°
00'N

56°
00'N

10-8-3   AREA 8 TIDAL STREAMS

5 Hours before HW Dover (0050 before HW Ullapool)

4 Hours before HW Dover (0010 after HW Ullapool)

3 Hours before HW Dover (0110 after HW Ullapool)

2 Hours before HW Dover (0210 after HW Ullapool)

1 Hour before HW Dover (0310 after HW Ullapool)

HW Dover (0410 after HW Ullapool)

Eastward 10.7.3   Southward 10.9.3

1 Hour after HW Dover (0510 after HW Ullapool)

2 Hours after HW Dover (0615 before HW Ullapool)

3 Hours after HW Dover (0515 before HW Ullapool)

4 Hours after HW Dover (0415 before HW Ullapool)

5 Hours after HW Dover (0315 before HW Ullapool)

6 Hours after HW Dover (0215 before HW Ullapool)

10.8.4 COASTAL LIGHTS, FOG SIGNALS AND WAYPOINTS

Abbreviations used below are given in 1.4.1. Principal lights are in **bold** print, places in CAPITALS, and light-vessels, light floats and Lanbys in *CAPITAL ITALICS*. Unless otherwise stated lights are white. m – elevation in metres; M – nominal range in miles. Fog signals are in *italics*. Useful waypoints are underlined – use those on land with care. All geographical positions should be assumed to be approximate. See 4.4.1. All positions are referenced to the OSGB 36 datum.

Rockall 57°35'·8N 13°41'·3W Fl 15s 19m 13M (unreliable). Extinguished (T) 1997.

CAPE WRATH TO LOCH TORRIDON

Cape Wrath 58°37'·55N 04°59'·87W Fl (4) 30s 122m **17M**; W Tr; *Horn (3) 45s.*

LOCH INCHARD/LOCH LAXFORD
Rubha na Lecaig 58°27'·43N 05°04'·51W Fl (2) 10s 30m 8M. Kinlochbervie Ldg Lts 327°. Front, 58°27'·52N 05°03'·01W Oc G 8s 16m 9M W□, Or △ on Gy Tr. Rear, 330m from front, Oc G 8s 26m 9M; W □, Or ▽ on Gy Tr.
Stoer Hd 58°14'·43N 05°24'·08W Fl 15s 59m **24M**; W Tr.

LOCH INVER
Soyea I 58°08'·58N 05°19'·59W Fl (2) 10s 34m 6M; Y post.
Glas Leac 58°08'·69N 05°16'·28W Fl WRG 3s 7m 5M; Gy col; vis W071°-078°, R078°-090°, G090°-103°, W103°-111°, R111°-243°, W243°-247°, G247°-071°.

Hbr Bkwtr Hd 58°08'·91N 05°15'·02W QG 3m 1M; B col, W bands.
Culag Hbr Pier Hd 58°08'·93N 05°14'·61W 2 FG (vert) 6m.

SUMMER ISLES
Old Dornie, new Pier Hd 58°02'·59N 05°25'·31W Fl G 3s 5m.

Rubha Cadail 57°55'·53N 05°13'·30W Fl WRG 6s 11m W9M, R6M, G6M; W Tr; vis G311°-320°, W320°-325°, R325°-103°, W103°-111°, G111°-118°, W118°-127°, R127°-157°, W157°-199°.

ULLAPOOL
Ullapool Pt Lt By 57°53'·43N 05°10'·35W QR; PHM.
Ullapool Pt 57°53'·62N 05°09'·67W Iso R 4s 8m 6M.
Cailleach Hd 57°55'·83N 05°24'·15W Fl (2) 12s 60m 9M; W Tr; vis 015°-236°.

LOCH EWE/LOCH GAIRLOCH
Fairway Lt By 57°52'·00N 05°40'·02W L Fl 10s; SWM.
NATO Jetty, NW corner Fl G 4s 5m 3M.
Rubha Reidh 57°51'·55N 05°48'·61W Fl (4) 15s 37m **24M**.
Glas Eilean 57°42'·82N 05°42'·36W Fl WRG 6s 9m W6M, R4M; vis W080°-102°, R102°-296°, W296°-333°, G333°-080°.

OUTER HEBRIDES – EAST SIDE

LEWIS
Butt of Lewis 58°30'·93N 06°15'·72W Fl 5s 52m **25M**; R Tr; vis 056°-320°; RC.
Tiumpan Hd 58°15'·6N 06°08'·3W Fl (2) 15s 55m **25M**; W Tr.

STORNOWAY
Arnish Pt 58°11'·50N 06°22'·17W Fl WR 10s 17m **W19M**, **R15M**; W ● Tr; vis W088°-198°, R198°-302°, W302°-013°.

Sandwick Bay, NW side Oc WRG 6s 10m 9M; vis G334°-341°, W341°-347°, R347°-354°.
Eitshal 58°10'·7N 06°35'·0W 4 FR (vert) on radio mast.

LOCH ERISORT/LOCH SHELL/EAST LOCH TARBERT
Tabhaidh Bheag 58°07'·22N 06°23'·15W Fl 3s 13m 3M.
Eilean Chalabrigh 58°06'·81N 06°26'·62W QG 5m 3M.
Gob na Milaid Pt 58°01'·0N 06°21'·8W Fl 15s 14m 10M.
Rubh' Uisenis 57°56'·2N 06°28'·2W Fl 5s 24m 11M; W Tr.
Sgeir Inoe Lt By 57°50'·95N 06°33'·90W Fl G 6s; SHM.
Shiants Lt By 57°54'·60N 06°25'·60W QG; SHM.
Scalpay, **Eilean Glas** 57°51'·43N 06°38'·45W Fl (3) 20s 43m **23M**; W Tr, R bands; Racon (T).
Scalpay N Hbr Lt By 57°52'·58N 06°42'·16W Fl G 2s; SHM.
Dun Cor Mòr Fl R 5s 10m 5M.
Sgeir Graidach Lt By 57°50'·38N 06°41'·31W Q (6) + L Fl 15s; SCM.
Sgeir Ghlas 57°52'·38N 06°45'·18W Iso WRG 4s 9m W9M, R6M, G6M; W ● Tr; vis G282°-319°, W319°-329°, R329°-153°, W153°-164°, G164°-171°.

SOUND OF HARRIS/LEVERBURGH
Stumbles Rk Lt By 57°45'·15N 07°01'·75W Fl (2) R 10s; PHM.
Dubh Sgeir 57°45'·54N 07°02'·56W Q (2) 5s 9m 6M; R Tr, B bands.
Leverburgh Ldg Lts 014·7°. Front, 57°46'·25N 07°01'·98W Q 10m 4M. Rear, Oc 3s 12m 4M.
Jane's Tr 57°45'·79N 07°02'·05W Q (2) G 5s 6m 4M; obsc 273°-318°.
Leverburgh Pier Hd 57°46'·04N 07°01'·56W Oc WRG 8s 5m 2M; Gy col; vis G305°-059°, W059°-066°, R066°-125°.

BERNERAY
W side, **Barra Hd** 57°47'·13N 07°39'·18W Fl 15s 208m **18M**; W Tr; obsc by islands to NE.
Berneray Bkwtr Hd 57°42'·9N 07°10'·0W Iso R 4s 6m 4M.
Drowning Rock Q (2) G 8s 2m 2M; G pillar.
Reef Chan No. 1 QG 2m 4M.
Reef Chan No. 2 Iso G 4s 2m 4M.

NORTH UIST
Eilean Fuam 57°41'·9N 07°10'·6W Q 6m 2M; W col.
Newton Jetty Root 57°41'·5N 07°11'·5W 2 FG (vert) 9m 4M.
Griminish Hbr Ldg Lts 183°. Front, 57°39'·41N 07°26'·62W QG 6m 4M. Rear, 110m from front, QG 7m 4M.
Pier Hd 57°39'·3N 07°26'·3W 2 FG (vert) 6m 4M; Gy col (shown Mar-Oct).

LOCH MADDY
Weaver's Pt 57°36'·51N 07°05'·95W Fl 3s 21m 7M; W hut.
Glas Eilean Mòr 57°35'·97N 07°06'·64W Fl G 4s 8m 5M.
Rubna Nam Pleàc 57°35'·78N 07°06'·70W Fl R 4s 7m 5M.
Ruigh Liath E Islet 57°35'·74N 07°08'·36W QG 6m 5M.

Vallaquie I 57°35'·52N 07°09'·34W Fl (3) WRG 8s 11m W7M, R5M, G5M; W pillar; vis G shore-205°, W205°-210°, R210°-240°, G240°-254°, W254°-257°, R257°-shore (P).

Lochmaddy Ldg Lts 298°. Front, Ro-Ro Pier 57°35'·79N 07°09'·29W 2 FG (vert) 8m 4M. Rear, 110m from front, Oc G 8s 10m 4M; vis 284°-304°.

GRIMSAY
Kallin Hbr Bkwtr, NE corner 57°28'·90N 07°12'·25W 2 FR (vert) 6m 5M; Gy col.

SOUTH UIST, LOCH CARNAN
Landfall Lt By 57°22'·30N 07°11'·45W L Fl 10s; SWM.
No. 2 Lt By 57°22'·41N 07°14'·87W Fl R 2s; PHM.
No. 3 Lt By 57°22'·33N 07°15'·54W Fl R 5s; PHM.
No. 4 Lt By 57°22'·27N 07°15'·82W QR; PHM.
Ldg Lts 222°. Front 57°22'·02N 07°16'·28W Fl R 2s 7m 5M; W ◊ on post. Rear, 58m from front, Iso R 10s 11m 5M; W ◊ on post.
Ushenish (S Uist) 57°17'·91N 07°11'·50W Fl WR 20s 54m **W19M, R15M**; W Tr; vis W193°-356°, R356°-013°.

LOCH BOISDALE

Calvay E End 57°08'·55N 07°15'·32W Fl (2) WRG 10s 16m W7M, R4M, G4M; W Tr; vis W111°-190°, G190°-202°, W202°-286°, R286°-111°.

N side 57°08'·99N 07°16'·98W Fl G 6s 3m 3M.

Eilean Dubh 57°09'·09N 07°18'·13W Fl (2) R 5s 2m 3M.

Gasay I Fl WR 5s 10m W7M, R4M; W Tr; vis W120°-284°, R284°-120°, .

Channel Lt By 57°09'·04N 07°17'·38W QG; SHM.

Sgeir Rk Lt By 57°09'·11N 07°17'·70W Fl G 3s; SHM.

Ro-Ro Jetty Hd 57°09'·15N 07°18'·17W Iso RG 4s 8m 2M; vis G shore-283°, R283°-shore; 2 FG (vert) 8m 3M on dn 84m W.

Sgeir Dhearg Lt By 57°00'·75N 05°49'·43W QG; SHM.

LUDAIG

Ludaig Dir Lt 297° 57°06'·2N 07°19'·7W Dir Oc WRG 6s 8m W7M, R4M, G4M; vis G287°-296°, W296°-298°, R298°-307°.

Stag Rk 57°05'·88N 07°18'·31W Fl (2) 8s 7m 4M.

The Witches Lt By 57°05'·75N 07°20'·77W Fl R 5s; PHM.

Ludaig Pier 2 FG (vert) 5m 3M.

ERISKAY

Bank Rk 57°05'·60N 07°17'·51W Q (2) 4s 5m 4M.

Haun Dir Lt 236° Dir Oc WRG 3s 9m W7M, R4M, G4M; vis G226°-234·5°, W234·5°-237·5°, R237·5°-246°.

Pier 2 FG (vert) 5m 5M.

Acairseid Mhor Ldg Lts 285°. Front, 57°03'·92N 07°17'·18W Oc R 6s 9m 4M. Rear, 24m from front, Oc R 6s 10m 4M.

BARRA/CASTLEBAY, VATERSAY SOUND

Drover Rks Lt By 57°04'·18N 07°23'·58W Fl (2) 10s; IDM.

Curachan Lt By 56°58'·58N 07°20'·45W Q (3) 10s; ECM.

Ardveenish 57°00'·23N 07°24'·37W Oc WRG 6m 9/6M; vis G300°-304°, W304°-306°, R306°-310°.

Bo Vich Chuan Lt By 56°56'·17N 07°23'·27W Q (6) + L Fl 15s; SCM; Racon (M).

Channel Rk Lt Bn 56°56'·25N 07°28'·88W Fl WR 6s 4m W6M, R4M; vis W121·5°-277°, R277°-121·5°.

Sgeir Dubh 56°56'·42N 07°28'·86W Q (3) WG 6s 6m W6M, G4M; vis W280°-117°, G117°-280°. In line 283° with Sgeir Leadh (Liath) below.

Sgeir Leadh (Liath) 56°56'·65N 07°30'·72W Fl 3s 7m 8M.

Castlebay 56°57'·23N 07°29'·22W Fl R 5s 2m 3M.

Rubha Glas. Ldg Lts 295°. Front, 56°56'·78N 07°30'·59W FG 9m 11M; Or △ on W Tr. Rear, 457m from front, FG 15m 11M; Or ▽ on W Tr.

OUTER HEBRIDES – WEST SIDE

Flannan I, Eilean Mór 58°17'·32N 07°35'·23W Fl (2) 30s 101m **20M**; W Tr; obsc in places by Is to W of Eilean Mór.

EAST LOCH ROAG

Aird Laimishader Carloway 58°17'·06N 06°49'·50W L Fl 12s 61m 8M; W hut; obsc on some brgs.

Ardvanich Pt 58°13'·48N 06°47'·68W Fl G 3s 4m 2M.

Tidal Rk 58°13'·45N 06°47'·57W Fl R 3s 2m 2M (synch with Ardvanich Pt above).

Gt Bernera Kirkibost Jetty 2 FG (vert) 7m 2M.

Grèinam 58°13'·30N 06°46'·16W Fl WR 6s 8m W8M, R7M; W Bn; vis R143°-169°, W169°-143°.

Rubha Arspaig Jetty Hd 2 FR (vert) 10m 4M.

NORTH UIST/SOUTH UIST

Vallay I 57°39'·70N 07°26'·10W Fl WRG 3s 8m; vis W206°-085°, G085°-140°, W140°-145°, R145°-206°.

Falconet Tr 57°21'·5N 07°23'·6W FR 25m 8M (3M by day); shown 1h before firing, changes to Iso R 2s 15 min before firing until completion.

ST KILDA

Ldg Lts 270°. Front, 57°48'·36N 08°34'·27W Oc 5s 26m 3M. Rear, 100m from front, Oc 5s 38m 3M; synch.

SKYE

Eilean Troddday 57°43'·65N 06°17'·87W Fl (2) WRG 10s 49m W12M, R9M, G9M; W Bn; vis W062°-088°, R088°-130°, W130°-322°, G322°-062°.

RONA/LOCH A'BHRAIGE

NE Point 57°34'·71N 05°57'·48W Fl 12s 69m **19M**; W Tr; vis 050°-358°.

Sgeir Shuas 57°35'·04N 05°58'·54W Fl R 2s 6m 3M; vis 070°-199°.

Jetty, NE end 57°34'·68N 05°57'·86W 2 FR (vert).

Rock 57°34'·62N 05°57'·94W Fl R 5s 4m 3M.

Ldg Lts 136·5°. Front, No. 9 Bn 57°34'·43N 05°58'·02W Q WRG 3m W4M, R3M; W and Or Bn; vis W135°-138°, R138°-318°, G318°-135°. Rear, No. 10 Iso 6s 28m 5M; W Bn.

No. 1 Bn Fl G 3s 91m 3M, Or Bn.

Rubha Chùiltairbh Fl 3s 6m 5M; W Bn.

No. 11 Bn QY 6m 4M; Or Bn.

No. 3 Bn Fl (2) 10s 9m 4M; W Bn and Or stripes.

No. 12 Bn QR 5m 3M; Or Bn.

Garbh Eilean SE Pt No. 8 Bn Fl 3s 8m 5M; W Bn.

INNER SOUND

Ru Na Lachan 57°29'·04N 05°52'·07W Oc WR 8s 21m 10M; Tr; vis W337°-022°, R022°-117°, W117°-162°.

SOUND OF RAASAY, PORTREE

Portree Pier Hd 57°24'·66N 06°11'·34W 2 FR (vert) 6m 4M; (occas).

CROWLIN ISLANDS

Eilean Beag 57°21'·23N 05°51'·33W Fl 6s 32m 6M; W Bn.

RAASAY/LOCH SLIGACHAN

Suisnish 2 FG (vert) 8m 2M.

Eyre Pt 57°20'·03N 06°01'·22W Fl WR 3s 5m W9M, R6M; W Tr; vis W215°-266°, R266°-288°, W288°-063°.

Sconser Ferry Terminal 57°18'·9N 06°06'·6W QR 8m 3M.

McMillan's Rk Lt By 57°21'·13N 06°06'·24W Fl (2) G 12s; SHM.

LOCH CARRON

No. 1 Lt By 57°21'·43N 05°38'·82W Fl G 3s; SHM.

Old Lt Ho 57°20'·97N 05°38'·81W (unlit).

KYLE AKIN AND KYLE OF LOCH ALSH

Kyle Akin Lt Ho 57°16'·68N 05°44'·48W (unlit).

Carragh Rk Lt By 57°17'·20N 05°45'·30W Fl (2) G 12s; SHM; Racon (T).

Bow Rk Lt By 57°16'·78N 05°45'·85W Fl (2) R 12s; PHM.

Fork Rks Lt By 57°16'·86N 05°44'·87W Fl G 6s; SHM.

Black Eye Rk Lt By 57°16'·73N 05°45'·24W Fl R 6s; PHM.

Kyle Akin Bridge Centre 57°16'·58N 05°44'·51W Oc 6s.

Eileanan Dubha E 57°16'·58N 05°42'·25W Fl (2) 10s 9m 8M; vis obscured 104°-146°.

Eileanan Dubha W 57°16'·62N 05°42'·61W Fl G 6s 5m 4M.

String Rk Lt By 57°16'·51N 05°42'·82W Fl R 6s; PHM.

Allt-an-Avaig Jetty 2 FR (vert) 10m; vis 075°-270°.

S shore, ferry slipway QR 6m (vis in Kyle of Loch Alsh).

Mooring dolphin 57°16'·38N 05°43'·36W Q 5m 3M.

Ferry Pier, W and E sides, 2 FG (vert) 6/5m 5/4M.

Butec Jetty W end, N corner 57°16'·77N 05°42'·36W Oc G 6s 5m 3M each end, synch.

Sgeir-na-Caillich 57°15'·63N 05°38'·83W Fl (2) R 6s 3m 4M.

SOUND OF SLEAT

Kyle Rhea 57°14'·24N 05°39'·85W Fl WRG 3s 7m W11M, R9M, G8M; W Bn; vis R shore-219°, W219-228°, G228°-338°, W338°-346°, R346°-shore.

Sandaig I, NW point Fl 6s 12m 8M; W 8-sided Tr.

Ornsay, N end 57°09'·10N 05°46'·5W Fl R 6s 8m 4M; W Tr.

Ornsay, SE end 57°08'·60N 05°46'·80W Oc 8s 18m **15M**; W Tr; vis 157°-030°.

Eilean Iarmain, off Pier Hd 2 FR (vert) 3m 2M.

Armadale Bay Pier Centre Oc R 6s 6m 6M.

8

Pt of Sleat 57°01'·11N 06° 01'·00W Fl 3s 20m 9M; W Tr.
Elgol 57°08'·80N 06°06'·43W Fl G 3s 4m 4M.

MALLAIG, ENTRANCE TO LOCH NEVIS

Sgeir Dhearg Lt By 57°00'·75N 05°49'·43W QG; SHM.
Northern Pier E end 57°00'·48N 05°49'·43W Iso WRG 4s 6m
W9M, R6M, G6M; Gy Tr; vis G181°-185°, W185°-197°,
R197°-201°. Fl G 3s 14m 6M; same structure.
Sgeir Dhearg 57°00'·64N 05°49'·53W Fl (2) WG 8s 6m 5M;
Gy Bn; vis G190°-055°, W055°-190°.

NW SKYE, UIG/LOCH DUNVEGAN/LOCH HARPORT

Uig, Edward Pier Hd 57°35'·14N 06°22'·22W Iso WRG 4s 9m
W7M, R4M, G4M; vis W180°-008°, G008°-052°, W052°-075°,
R075°-180°.
Waternish Pt 57°36'·5N 06°38'·0W Fl 20s 21m 8M; W Tr.
Loch Dunvegan, Uiginish Pt 57°26'·8N 06°36'·5W Fl WG
3s 14m W7M, G5M; W hut; vis G040°-128°, W128°-306°,
obsc by Fiadhairt Pt when brg more than 148°.
Neist Pt 57°25'·4N 06°47'·2W Fl 5s 43m **16M**; W Tr.
Loch Harport, Ardtreck Pt 57°20'·4N 06°25'·8W Iso 4s 17m
9M; small W Tr.

SMALL ISLES AND WEST OF MULL

CANNA, RHUM
E end, Sanday Is 57°02'·84N 06°27'·92W Fl 6s 32m 9M; W
Tr; vis 152°-061°.

ÒIGH SGEIR/EIGG/ARISAIG
Humla Lt By 57°00'·43N 06°37'·40W Fl G 6s; SHM.
S end, **Hyskeir** 56°58'·13N 06°40'·80W Fl (3) 30s 41m **24M**;
W Tr. N end Horn 30s.
SE point of Eigg (Eilean Chathastail) 56°52'·25N 06°07'·20W
Fl 6s 24m 8M; W Tr; vis 181°-shore.
Bo Faskadale Lt By 56°48'·18N 06°06'·35W Fl (3) G 18s; SHM.
Ardnamurchan 56°43'·64N 06°13'·46W Fl (2) 20s 55m **24M**;
Gy Tr; vis 002°-217°; Horn (2) 20s.
Cairns of Coll, Suil Ghorm 56°42'·27N 06°26'·70W Fl 12s 23m
10M; W Tr.

COLL/ARINAGOUR
Loch Eatharna, Bogha Mor Lt By 56°36'·67N 06°30'·90W
Fl G 6s; SHM.
Arinagour Pier 2 FR (vert) 12m.

TIREE
Roan Bogha Lt By 56°32'·25N 06°40'·10W Q (6) + L Fl 15s; SCM.
Placaid Bogha Lt By 56°33'·24N 06°43'·93W Fl G 4s; SHM.
Scarinish, S side of ent 56°30'·02N 06°48'·20W Fl 3s 11m
16M; W ▓ Tr; vis 210°-030°.
Gott Bay Ldg Lts 286·5°. Front 56°30'·63N 06°47'·75W FR
8m. Rear 30m from front FR 11m.
Skerryvore 56°19'·40N 07°06'·75W Fl 10s 46m **23M**; Gy Tr;
Racon (M); Horn 60s.

LOCH NA LÀTHAICH (LOCH LATHAICH)
Eileanan na Liathanaich, SE end 56°20'·58N 06°16'·30W
Fl WR 6s 12m W8M, R6M; vis R088°-108°, W108°-088°.
Dubh Artach 56°07'·95N 06°37'·95W Fl (2) 30s 44m **20M**;
Gy Tr, R band; Horn 45s.

SOUND OF MULL

LOCH SUNART/TOBERMORY/LOCH ALINE
Ardmore Pt 56°39'·39N 06°07'·62W Fl (2) 10s 17m 8M.
New Rks Lt By 56°39'·07N 06°03'·22W Fl G 6s; SHM.
Rubha nan Gall 56°38'·33N 06°03'·91W Fl 3s 17m **15M**,
W Tr.
Bogha Bhuilg By 56°36'·15N 05°59'·07W; SHM.
Hispania Wk Lt By 56°34'·70N 05°59'·30W Fl (2) R 10s; PHM.
Bo Rks By 56°31'·54N 05°55'·47W; SHM.
Eileanan Glasa, Green I (Dearg Sgeir) 56°32'·27N 05°54'·72W
Fl 6s 7m 0M; W ● Tr.
Fuinary Spit Lt By 56°32'·66N 05°53'·09W Fl G 6s; SHM.

Avon Rk By 56°30'·80N 05°46'·72W; PHM.
Lochaline Lt By 56°32'·99N 05°46'·41W QR; PHM.
Lochaline Ldg Lts 356°. Front, 56°32'·40N 05°46'·40W F 2M.
Rear, 88m from front, F 4M; H24.
Ardtornish Pt 56°31'·10N 05°45'·15W Fl (2) WRG 10s 7m
W8M, R5M, G5M; W Tr; vis G shore-302°, W302°-310°,
R310°-342°, W342°-057°, R057°-095°, W095°-108°, G108°-
shore.
Yule Rk By 56°30'·03N 05°43'·88W; PHM.
Glas Eileanan Gy Rks 56°29'·78N 05°42'·76W Fl 3s 11m 6M;
W ● Tr on W base.
Craignure Ldg Lts 240·9°. Front, 56°28'·30N 05°42'·21W FR 10m.
Rear, 150m from front, FR 12m; vis 225·8°-255·8° (on req).

MULL TO CALEDONIAN CANAL AND OBAN

Lismore, SW end 56°27'·35N 05°36'·38W Fl 10s 31m **19M**;
W Tr; vis 237°-208°.

Lady's Rk 56°26'·91N 05°36'·98W Fl 6s 12m 5M; R ● on W Bn.
Duart Pt 56°26'·85N 05°38'·69W Fl (3) WR 18s 14m W5M,
R3M; vis W162°-261°, R261°-275°, W275°-353°, R353°-shore.

LOCH LINNHE
Ent W side, Corran Pt 56°43'·27N 05°14'·47W Iso WRG 4s
12m W10M, R7M; W Tr; vis R shore-195°, W195°-215°,
G215°-305°, W305°-030°, R030°-shore.
Corran Narrows NE 56°43'·62N 05°13'·83W Fl 5s 4m 4M;
W Tr; vis S shore-214°.
Jetty 56°43'·42N 05°14'·56W Fl R 5s 7m 3M; Gy mast.

FORT WILLIAM/CALEDONIAN CANAL
Corpach, Caledonian Canal Lock ent Iso WRG 4s 6m 5M;
W Tr; vis G287°-310°, W310°-335°, R335°-030°.

LYNN OF LORN
Sgeir Bhuidhe Appin 56°33'·65N 05°24'·57W Fl (2) WR 7s 7m
9M; W Bn; vis R184°-220°, W220°-184°.
Dearg Sgeir, off Aird's Point Lt Bn 56°32'·22N 05°25'·15W Fl
WRG 2s 2m 3/1M; PHM; vis R196°-246°, W246°-258°,
G258°-041°, W041°058°, R058°-093°, W093°-139°.
Eriska NE Pt, QG 2m 2M; G col; vis 128°-329°.

DUNSTAFFNAGE BAY
Pier Hd, NE end 56°27'·22N 05°26'·10W 2 FG (vert) 4m 2M.

OBAN
N spit of Kerrera 56°25'·50N 05°29'·50W Fl R 3s 9m 5M;
W col, R bands.
Dunollie 56°25'·39N 05°28'·98W Fl (2) WRG 6s 7m W5M,
G4M, R4M; vis G351°-009°, W009°-047°, R047°-120°, W120°-
138°, G138°-143°.
Rubbh'a' Chruidh 56°25'·33N 05°29'·22W QR 3m 2M.

OBAN TO LOCH CRAIGNISH

Kerrera Sound, Dubh Sgeir 56°22'·82N 05°32'·20W Fl (2) 12s
7m 5M; W ● Tr.

Fladda 56°14'·90N 05°40'·75W Fl (2) WRG 9s 13m W11M,
R9M, G9M; W Tr; vis R169°-186°, W186°-337°, G337°-344°.
W344°-356°, R356°-026°.
Dubh Sgeir (Luing) 56°14'·78N 05°40'·12W Fl WRG 6s 9m
W6M, R4M. G4M; W Tr; vis W000°-010°, R010°-025°, W025°-
199°, G199°-000°; Racon (M).
The Garvellachs, Eileach an Naoimh, SW end 56°13'·05N
05°48'·97W Fl 6s 21m 9M; W Bn; vis 240°-215°.

LOCH MELFORT/CRAOBH HAVEN
Fearnach Bay Pier 56°16'·15N 05°30'·11W 2 FR (vert) 6/5m
3M; (Private shown 1/4 to 31/10).
Craobh Haven Bkwtr Hd 56°12'·79N 05°33'·44W Iso WRG 5s
10m 5/3M; vis G114°-162°, W162°-183°, R183°-200°.

For Colonsay, and Sounds of Jura and Islay see 10.9.4.

10.8.5 PASSAGE INFORMATION

It is essential to carry large scale charts, and pilotage information as in *W Coast of Scotland Pilot*; Clyde Cruising Club's *Sailing Directions, Pt 2 Kintyre to Ardnamurchan* and *Pt 3 Ardnamurchan to Cape Wrath*; and the *Yachtsman's Pilot to W Coast of Scotland* (3 Vols) by Martin Lawrence/Imray. See 10.9.5 for some of the more relevant terms in Gaelic.

The West coast of Scotland provides splendid, if sometimes boisterous, sailing and matchless scenery. In summer the long daylight hours and warmth of the Gulf Stream compensate for the lower air temperatures and higher wind speeds experienced when depressions run typically north of Scotland. Inshore winds are often unpredictable, due to geographical effects of lochs, mountains and islands offshore; calms and squalls can alternate rapidly. Good anchors, especially on kelp/weed, are essential. HIE and public ⚓s are listed, but it should not be assumed that these will always be available. Particularly in N of area, facilities are very dispersed. VHF communications with shore stations may be limited by high ground. Beware ever more fish farms in many inlets. Local magnetic anomalies occur in Kilbrannan Sound, Passage of Tiree, Sound of Mull, Canna, and East Loch Roag. Submarines exercise throughout these waters; see 10.8.23.

CAPE WRATH TO ULLAPOOL (charts 1785, 1794)

C. Wrath (lt, fog sig) is a steep headland (110m). To N of it the E-going stream begins at HW Ullapool – 0350, and W- going at HW Ullapool + 0235, sp rates 3kn. Eddies close inshore cause almost continuous W-going stream E of Cape, and N-going stream SW of it. Where they meet is turbulence, with dangerous seas in bad weather. Duslic Rk, 7ca NE of lt ho, dries 3·4m. 6M SW of C. Wrath is Islet of Am Balg (45m), foul for 2ca around.

There are anchs in Loch Inchard (chart 2503), the best shelter being in Loch Bervie (10.8.8) on N shore; also good anchs among Is along S shore of Loch Laxford, entered between Ardmore Pt and Rubha Ruadh (see 10.8.8). Handa Is to WSW is a bird sanctuary. Handa Sound is navigable with care, but beware Bogha Morair in mid-chan and associated overfalls. Tide turns 2hrs earlier in the Sound than offshore.

Strong winds against tide raise a bad sea off Pt of Stoer. The best shelter is 8M S at Loch Inver (10.8.8 and chart 2504), with good anch off hotel near head of loch. S lies Enard Bay.

ULLAPOOL TO LOCH TORRIDON (charts 1794, 2210)

The Summer Isles (chart 2501), 12M NW of the major fishing port of Ullapool (10.8.9), offer some sheltered anchs and tight approaches. The best include the Bay on E side of Tanera Mor; off NE of Tanera Beg (W of Eilean Fada Mor); and in Caolas Eilean Ristol, between the Is and mainland.

Loch Ewe (10.8.9 and chart 3146) provides good shelter and easy access. Best anchs are in Poolewe Bay (beware Boor Rks off W shore) and in SW corner of Loch Thuirnaig (entering, keep close to S shore to avoid rks extending from N side). Off Rubha Reidh (lt) seas can be dangerous. The NE-going stream begins at HW Ullapool – 0335; the SW-going at HW Ullapool + 0305. Sp rates 3kn, but slacker to SW of point.

Longa Is lies N of ent to Loch Gairloch (10.8.9 and chart 2528). The chan N of it is navigable but narrow at E end. Outer loch is free of dangers, but exposed to swell. Best anch is on S side of loch in Caolas Bad a' Chrotha, W of Eilean Horrisdale.

Loch Torridon (chart 2210) has few dangers. Streams are weak except where they run 2-3 kn in narrows between Loch Shieldaig and Upper Loch Torridon. Entering Loch Torridon from S or W beware Murchadh Breac (dries 1·5m) 3ca NNW of Rubha na Fearna. Best anchs are SW of Eilean Mor (to W of Ardheslaig); in Loch a 'Chracaich, 7ca further SE; E of Shieldaig Is; and near head of Upper Loch Torridon.

OUTER HEBRIDES (charts 1785, 1794, 1795)

The E sides of these Is have many good, sheltered anchs, but W coasts give little shelter. The Clyde Cruising Club's *Outer Hebrides Sailing Directions* are advised. The Minches and Sea of the Hebrides can be very rough, particularly in the Little Minch between Skye and Harris, and around Shiant Is where tide runs locally 4kn at sp, and heavy overfalls can be met. The NE-going stream begins at HW Ullapool – 0335; the SW-going stream at HW Ullapool + 0250, sp rates 2·5kn.

From N to S, the better hrbs in Outer Hebrides include:
Lewis. Stornoway (10.8.7); Loch Grimshader (beware Sgeir a'Chaolais, dries in entrance); Loch Erisort; Loch Odhairn; Loch Shell (10.8.7). Proceeding S from here, or to E Loch Tarbert beware Sgeir Inoe (dries 2·3m) 3M ESE of Eilean Glas lt ho at SE end of Scalpay.
Harris. E Loch Tarbert; Loch Scadaby; Loch Stockinish; Loch Finsby; W Loch Tarbert; Loch Rodel (HIE ⚓). A well buoyed/lit ferry chan connects Leverburgh (South Harris) to Berneray.
N Uist. Loch Maddy (HIE ⚓); Loch Eport, Kallin Hbr (HIE ⚓).
S Uist. Loch Carnan (HIE ⚓); Loch Skiport; Loch Eynort; Loch Boisdale (HIE ⚓).
Barra. Castlebay (HIE ⚓), see 10.8.7, and Berneray, on N side, E of Shelter Rk.

Activity at the Army Artillery Range, Benbecula ☎ (01870) 602384 Ext 4441, is broadcast at 1000LT (1 Apr - 30 Oct) on VHF Ch 12 (Ch 73 emergency only) and on MF 2660 kHz.

SKYE TO ARDNAMURCHAN PT (charts 1795, 2210, 2209, 2208, 2207)

Skye and the islands around it provide many good and attractive anchs, of which the most secure are: Acairseid Mhor on the W side of Rona; Portree (10.8.10); Isleornsay; Portnalong, near the ent to Loch Harport, and Carbost at the head; Loch Dunvegan; and Uig Bay in Loch Snizort. HIE ⚓s at Stein (Loch Dunvegan), Portree, Acairseid Mhor (Rona), Churchton Bay (Raasay) and Armadale Bay (S tip).

Tides are strong off Rubha Hunish at N end of Skye, and heavy overfalls occur with tide against fresh or strong winds. Anch behind Fladday Is near the N end of Raasay can be squally and uncomfortable; and Loch Scavaig (S. Skye, beneath the Cuillins) more so, though the latter is so spectacular as to warrant a visit in fair weather. Soay Is has a small, safe hbr on its N side, but the bar at ent almost dries at LW sp.

Between N. Skye and the mainland there is the choice of Sound of Raasay or Inner Sound. **The direction of buoyage in both Sounds is Northward.** In the former, coming S from Portree, beware Sgeir Chnapach (3m) and Ebbing Rk (dries 2·9m), both NNW of Oskaig Pt. At the Narrows (chart 2534) the SE- going stream begins at HW Ullapool – 0605, and the NW-going at HW Ullapool + 0040; sp rate 1·4kn in mid-chan, but more near shoals each side. Beware McMillan's Rk (0·4m depth) in mid-chan, marked by SHM lt buoy.

The chan between Scalpay and Skye narrows to 2½ca with drying reefs each side and least depth 0·1m. Here the E-going stream begins at HW Ullapool + 0550, and W-going at HW Ullapool – 0010, sp rate 1kn.

Inner Sound, which is a Submarine exercise area, is wider and easier than Sound of Raasay; the two are connected by Caol Rona and Caol Mor, respectively N and S of Raasay. Dangers extend about 1M N of Rona, and Cow Is lies off the mainland 8M to S; otherwise approach from N is clear to Crowlin Is, which should be passed to W. There is a good anch between Eilean Mor and Eilean Meadhonach, see 10.8.10.

A torpedo range in the Inner Sound does not normally restrict passage, but vessels may be requested to keep to the E side of the Sound if the range is active. Range activity is broadcast at 0800 and 1600LT on VHF Ch 08, 16 and is indicated by R Flags and International Code NE4 flown at the range building at Applecross, by all range vessels and at the naval pier at Kyle of Lochalsh (10.8.12), ☎ (01599) 534262.

Approaching Kyle Akin (chart 2540) from W, beware dangerous rks to N, off Bleat Is (at S side of entrance to Loch Carron); on S side of chan, Bogha Beag (dries 0·6m) and Black Eye Rk (depth 3·8m), respectively 6ca and 4ca W of bridge. For Plockton (Loch Carron), see 10.8.11. Pass at least 100m N or S of Eileanan Dubha in Kyle Akin. On S side of chan String Rk (dries) is marked by PHM lt buoy. For Loch Alsh, see 10.8.12.

Kyle Rhea connects Loch Alsh with NE end of Sound of Sleat. The tidal streams are very strong: N-going stream begins HW Ullapool + 0600, sp rate 6-7kn; S-going stream begins at HW Ullapool, sp rate 8kn. Eddies form both sides of the Kyle and there are dangerous overfalls off S end in fresh S'ly winds on S-going stream. Temp anch in Sandaig Bay, 3M to SW.

The Sound of Sleat widens to 4M off Point of Sleat and is exposed to SW winds unless Eigg and Muck give a lee. Mallaig (10.8.13) is a busy fishing and ferry hbr, convenient for supplies. Further S the lochs require intricate pilotage. 6M NE of Ardnamurchan Pt (lt, fog sig) are Bo Faskadale rks, drying 0·5m and marked by SHM lt buoy, and Elizabeth Rk with depth of 0·7m. Ardnamurchan Pt is an exposed headland onto which the ebb sets. With onshore winds, very heavy seas extend 2M offshore and it should be given a wide berth. Here the N-going stream begins at HW Oban – 0525, and the S-going at HW Oban + 0100, sp rates 1·5kn.

THE SMALL ISLES (charts 2207, 2208)

These consist of Canna, Rhum, Eigg (10.8.13) and Muck. Dangers extend SSW from Canna: at 1M Jemina Rk (depth 1·5m) and Belle Rk (depth 3·6m); at 2M Humla Rk (5m high), marked by buoy and with offlying shoals close W of it; at 5M Oigh Sgeir (lt, fog sig), the largest of a group of small islands; and at 7M Mill Rks (with depths of 1·8m).

The tide runs hard here, and in bad weather the sea breaks heavily up to 15M SW of Canna. Between Skerryvore and Neist Pt the stream runs generally N and S, starting N-going at HW Ullapool + 0550, and S-going at HW Ullapool – 0010. It rarely exceeds 1kn, except near Skerryvore, around headlands of The Small Isles, and over rks and shoals.

1M off the N side of Muck are Godag Rks, some above water but with submerged dangers extending 2ca further N. Most other dangers around the Small Isles are closer inshore, but there are banks on which the sea breaks heavily in bad weather. A local magnetic anomaly exists about 2M E of Muck. The hbrs at Eigg (SE end), Rhum (Loch Scresort) and Canna (between Canna and Sanday) are all exposed to E'lies; Canna has best shelter and is useful for the Outer Hebrides.

ARDNAMURCHAN TO CRINAN (charts 2171, 2169)

S of Ardnamurchan the route lies either W of Mull via Passage of Tiree (where headlands need to be treated with respect in bad weather); or via the more sheltered Sound of Mull and Firth of Lorne. The former permits a visit to Coll and Tiree, where best anchs are at Arinagour (HIE ⚓s) and Gott Bay respectively. Beware Cairns of Coll, off the N tip.

The W coast of Mull is rewarding in settled weather, but careful pilotage is needed. Beware tide rip off Caliach Pt (NW corner) and Torran Rks off SW end of Mull (large scale chart 2617 required). Apart from the attractions of Iona and of Staffa (Fingal's Cave), the remote Treshnish Is are worth visiting. The best anchs in this area are at Ulva, Gometra, Bull Hole and Tinker's Hole in Iona Sound. The usual passage through Iona Sound avoids overfalls W of Iona, but heed shoal patches. Loch Lathaich on the N side of Ross of Mull is 5M to the E; a good base with anch and boatyard at Bunessan.

The Sound of Mull gives access to Tobermory (10.8.15, HIE ⚓), Dunstaffnage Bay, Oban (10.8.19), and up Loch Linnhe through Corran Narrows (where tide runs strongly) to Fort William (10.8.17) and to Corpach for the Caledonian Canal (10.8.18). But, apart from these places, there are dozens of lovely anchs in the sheltered lochs inside Mull, as for example in Loch Sunart (10.8.14) with HIE ⚓s at Kilchoan; also at Craignure and Salen Bays on Sound of Mull. For Loch Aline see 10.8.16.

On the mainland shore Puilladobhrain is a sheltered anch. Cuan Sound (see 10.8.19 for details) is a useful short cut to Loch Melfort, (10.8.20) and Craobh Marina (10.8.21). Good shelter, draft permitting, in Ardinamar B, SW of Torsa.

Sound of Luing (chart 2326) between Fladda (lt), Lunga and Scarba on the W side, and Luing and Dubh Sgeir (lt) on the E side, is the normal chan to or from Sound of Jura, despite dangers at the N end and strong tidal streams. The N and W-going flood begins at HW Oban + 0430; the S and E-going ebb at HW Oban –0155. Sp rates are 2·5kn at S end of Sound, increasing to 6kn or more in Islands off N entrance, where there are eddies, races and overfalls.

At N end of Sound of Jura (chart 2326) is Loch Craignish (10.8.22). From the N, beware very strong streams, eddies and whirlpools in Dorus Mor, off Craignish Pt. The W and N-going stream begins at HW Oban + 0330, and the E and S-going at HW Oban – 0215, sp rates 8kn.

For Gulf of Corryvreckan, Colonsay, Islay, Loch Crinan and passage south through the Sound of Jura, see 10.9.5.

10.8.6   DISTANCE TABLE

Approximate distances in nautical miles are by the most direct route, keeping East of Skye and Mull where appropriate, and avoiding dangers. Places in *italics* are in adjoining areas.

	1	2	3	4	5	6	7	8	9	10	11	12	13	14	15	16	17	18	19	20
1. *Cape Wrath*	1																			
2. Ullapool	54	2																		
3. Stornoway	53	45	3																	
4. East Loch Tarbert	75	56	33	4																
5. Portree	83	57	53	42	5															
6. Loch Harport	110	82	65	45	66	6														
7. Kyle of Lochalsh	91	63	62	63	21	53	7													
8. Mallaig	112	82	83	84	42	33	21	8												
9. Eigg	123	98	97	75	54	34	35	14	9											
10. Castlebay (Barra)	133	105	92	69	97	43	76	59	46	10										
11. Tobermory	144	114	115	87	74	52	53	32	20	53	11									
12. Loch Aline	157	127	128	100	87	65	66	45	33	66	13	12								
13. Fort William	198	161	162	134	121	99	98	75	63	96	43	34	13							
14. Oban	169	138	139	111	100	76	77	56	44	77	24	13	29	14						
15. Loch Lathaich	160	130	124	98	91	62	67	49	35	56	31	53	77	48	15					
16. Loch Melfort	184	154	155	117	114	92	93	69	61	92	40	27	45	18	45	16				
17. Craobh Haven	184	155	155	117	114	93	92	70	60	93	40	27	50	21	43	5	17			
18. Loch Craignish	188	158	159	131	118	95	96	70	64	98	44	31	55	26	46	17	14	18		
19. *Crinan*	187	157	158	129	112	95	95	74	63	97	42	30	54	25	45	14	9	6	19	
20. *Mull of Kintyre*	232	203	189	175	159	133	143	121	105	120	89	87	98	72	78	62	57	54	51	20

STORNOWAY   10-8-7

Lewis (Western Isles) 58°11'·60N 06°21'·75W   Rtg 2-3-2

CHARTS
AC 2529, 1794, 1785; OS 8
TIDES
–0428 Dover; ML 2·8; Duration 0610; Zone 0 (UT)

Standard Port ULLAPOOL (⟶)

Times				Height (metres)			
High Water		Low Water		MHWS	MHWN	MLWN	MLWS
0100	0700	0300	0900	5·2	3·9	2·1	0·7
1300	1900	1500	2100				
Differences STORNOWAY							
–0010	–0010	–0010	–0010	–0·4	–0·2	–0·1	0·0
LOCH ERIBOLL (Portnancon) (See 10.7.20)							
+0055	+0105	+0055	+0100	0·0	+0·1	+0·1	+0·2
KYLE OF DURNESS (See 10.7.20)							
+0030	+0030	+0050	+0050	–0·6	–0·4	–0·3	–0·1
LOCH SHELL (Harris)							
–0023	–0010	–0010	–0027	–0·4	–0·3	–0·2	0·0
EAST LOCH TARBERT (Harris)							
–0035	–0020	–0020	–0030	–0·2	–0·2	0·0	+0·1
LEVERBURGH (Sound of Harris)							
–0051	–0030	–0025	–0035	–0·6	–0·4	–0·2	–0·1
LOCH MADDY (N.Uist)							
–0054	–0024	–0026	–0040	–0·4	–0·3	–0·2	–0·1
LOCH CARNAN (S.Uist)							
–0100	–0020	–0030	–0050	–0·7	–0·7	–0·2	–0·1
LOCH SKIPORT (S.Uist)							
–0110	–0035	–0034	–0034	–0·6	–0·4	–0·4	–0·2
LOCH BOISDALE (S.Uist)							
–0105	–0040	–0030	–0050	–1·1	–0·9	–0·4	–0·2
BARRA (North Bay)							
–0113	–0041	–0044	–0058	–1·0	–0·7	–0·3	–0·1
CASTLEBAY (Barra)							
–0125	–0050	–0055	–0110	–0·9	–0·8	–0·4	–0·1
BARRA HEAD (Berneray)							
–0125	–0050	–0055	–0105	–1·2	–0·9	–0·3	+0·1
WEST LOCH TARBERT (W.Harris)							
–0025	–0025	–0056	–0056	–1·5	–1·1	–0·6	0·0
LITTLE BERNERA (W.Lewis)							
–0031	–0021	–0027	–0037	–0·9	–0·8	–0·5	–0·2
CARLOWAY (W.Lewis)							
–0050	+0010	–0045	–0025	–1·0	–0·7	–0·5	–0·1
BALIVANICH (W.Benbecula)							
–0113	–0027	–0041	–0055	–1·1	–0·8	–0·6	–0·2
SCOLPAIG (W North Uist)							
–0043	–0043	–0050	–0050	–1·4	–1·1	–0·6	0·0
SHILLAY (Monach Islands)							
–0113	–0053	–0057	–0117	–1·0	–0·9	–0·8	–0·3

Standard Port ULLAPOOL (⟶)

Times				Height (metres)			
High Water		Low Water		MHWS	MHWN	MLWN	MLWS
0000	0600	0300	0900	5·2	3·9	2·1	0·7
1200	1800	1500	2100				
VILLAGE BAY (St Kilda)							
–0050	–0050	–0055	–0055	–1·8	–1·4	–0·9	–0·3
FLANNAN ISLES							
–0036	–0026	–0026	–0036	–1·3	–0·9	–0·7	–0·2
ROCKALL							
–0105	–0105	–0115	–0115	–2·2	–1·7	–1·0	–0·2

SHELTER
Good. A small marina, max LOA 12m, at the N end of the Inner Hbr, beyond the LB berth, has depths 1·4 - 3·3m. Or AB for larger boats on Cromwell St Quay, close S; or lie alongside FVs in the inner hbr. Ullapool ferries use No 1 pier. S'ly swells can make anchoring uncomfortable. ⌀s as on chartlet at: Poll nam Portan facing commercial quays, clear of LB moorings; Glumaig Hbr is best ⌀, but oil works may preclude this; in bay NW of Coul Is. Visitors land at steps N of FG ldg lts and report to Hr Mr.
NAVIGATION
WPT 58°10'·00N 06°20'·80W, 163°/343° from/to Oc WRG lt, 2·3M. Reef Rk, W side of ent marked by PHM buoy, QR. An unlit G bn marks the rky patch off Holm Pt, on which is a conspic memorial. A local magnetic anomaly exists over a small area in mid-hbr, 1·75ca N of Seid Rks bn.
LIGHTS AND MARKS
Arnish sheds are conspic 3ca SW of Arnish Pt lt, Fl WR 10s 17m 19/15M, W tr; W sector 302°-013° covers ent. Then in turn follow W sectors of: Sandwick B lt, (close E of water tr, 3 power stn chys and fuel tanks; all conspic) Oc WRG 6s 10m 9M, W341°-347°; then Stoney Field Fl WRG 3s 8m 11M, vis W102°-109° across hbr; and finally No 1 Pier, Q WRG 5m 11M, W335°-352°. Ldg lts FG 325° to Ro-Ro jetty.
RADIO TELEPHONE
VHF Ch 12 16 (H24).
TELEPHONE (Dial code 01851)
Hr Mr 702688; MRSC 702013; ⌗ 703626; Marinecall 0891 500464; Police 702222; Dr 703145.
FACILITIES
Marina 27 berths, inc 8 🅥, £8 via Hr Mr Ch 12; FW, AC.
Nos 1 & 2 Piers FW, C (10 ton), CH, AB, Slip, P.
Services: ACA, ME, El, Sh.
Town EC Wed; P (cans), D, El, V, R, Bar, Gas, ✉, Ⓑ, ≋ (ferry to Ullapool, bus to Garve), ✈.

8

HARBOURS AND ANCHORAGES ON THE EAST SIDE OF THE OUTER HEBRIDES (Western Isles)

LOCH SHELL, Harris, 58°00'·00N 06°25'·00W. AC 1794. HW –0437 on Dover; ML 2·7m. See 10.8.7. Pass S of Eilean Iuvard; beware rks to W of Is. ⚓ in Tob Eishken, 2½M up loch on N shore (beware rk awash on E side of ent), or at head of loch (exposed to E winds; dries some distance). Facilities: ✉/Stores at Lemreway.

SHIANT ISLANDS, Lewis, 58°53'·70N 06°21'·30W. AC 1794, 1795. Tides as Loch Shell 10.8.7. Beware strong tidal streams and overfalls in Sound of Shiant. Strictly a fair weather ⚓; in W winds ⚓ E of Mol Mor, isthmus between Garbh Eileen (160m) and Eileen an Tighe. In E winds ⚓ W of Mol Mor. No lights or facilities.

EAST LOCH TARBERT, Harris, 57°50'·00N 06°41'·00W. AC 2905. HW –0446 on Dover; ML 3·0m; Duration 0605. See 10.8.7. Appr via Sound of Scalpay; beware Elliot Rk (2m) 2½ca SSW of Rubha Crago. Eilean Glas lt ho at E end of Scalpay, Fl (3) 20s 43m 23M; W tr, R bands. In Sound of Scalpay, stream sets W from HW +3, and E from HW –3. ⚓ off Tarbert WSW of steamer pier in about 2·5m. Facilities: EC Thurs; Bar, D, Dr, FW, P, ✉, R, V, ferry to Uig. Alternatively Scalpay N Hbr gives good shelter. Beware rk 5ca off Aird an Aiseig, E side of ent. SHM By marks wk off Coddem; 5ca E of the By is a rk, depth 1·1m. Fish pier at SE end of hbr has 2FG (vert) lts; ⚓ 7ca N, in about 3m. Facilities: FW at pier, ✉, V, ferry to Harris.

LOCH MADDY, North Uist, 57°36'·00N 07°06'·00W. AC 2825 HW –0500 on Dover. See 10.8.7. With strong wind against tide there can be bad seas off ent. Appr clear, but from S beware submerged rk ½ca N of Leacnam Madadh. Lts: Weaver's Pt Fl 3s 21m 7M; Glas Eilean Mor Fl (2) G 4s 8m 5M; Rubna Nam Pleac Fl R 4s 7m 5M. Inside loch: Ruigh Liath QG 6m 5M; Vallaquie Is Fl (3) WRG 8s. Ferry pier ldg lts 298°: front 2FG(vert) 4M; rear Oc G 8s 10m 4M, vis 284°-304°. 2 HIE ⚓s in Bagh Aird nam Madadh; 5 HIE ⚓s SW of pier ☎ (01870) 602425; 2 HIE ⚓s E of Oronsay. ⚓s off Steamer Pier; in Charles Hbr; Oronsay, berth on private pier, but ⚓ not recommended due to moorings; Sponish Hbr; Loch Portain; Vallaquie. VHF Ch 12 16. Port Manager ☎ (01876) 5003337 (day), 5003226 (night). Facilities: Lochmaddy, EC Wed; Shop, Ⓑ, Gas, ✉, P, D, FW; Loch Portain ✉, Shop.

LOCH SKIPORT, South Uist, 57°20'·00N 07°13'·60W. AC 2825, 2904. HW –0602 on Dover; see 10.8.7. Easy ent 3M NNE of Hecla (604m). No lights, but 2¼M SSE is Usinish lt ho Fl WR 20s 54m 19/15M. ⚓s at: Wizard Pool in 7m; beware Float Rk, dries 2·3m; Caolas Mor in 7m on N side; Bagh Charmaig in 5m. Linne Arm has narrow ent, many fish farms and poor holding. No facilities.

LOCH BOISDALE, South Uist, 57°08'·80N 07°16'·00W. AC 2770. HW –0455 on Dover; ML 2·4m; Duration 0600. See 10.8.7. Good shelter except in SE gales when swell runs right up the 2M loch. From N, appr between Rubha na Cruibe and Calvay Is; ldg line 245°: Hollisgeir (0·3m) on with pier (ru). From S beware Clan Ewan Rk, dries 1·2m, and McKenzie Rk (2·4m), marked by PHM lt buoy Fl (3) R 15s. Chan to Boisdale Hbr lies N of Gasay Is; beware rks off E end. ⚓ off pier in approx 4m, or SW of Gasay Is in approx 9m. 4 HIE ⚓s NE of pier ☎ (01870) 602425. There are fish cages W of Rubha Bhuailt. Lts: E end of Calvay Is Fl (2) WRG 10s 16m 7/4M. Gasay Is Fl WR 5s 10m 7/4M. N side of loch, opp Gasay Is, Fl G 6s. Ro-Ro terminal Iso RG 4s 8m 2M; and close SE, Fl (2) R 5s. See 10.8.4. Facilities: EC Tues; Bar, FW (on pier), P, ✉, R, V, ferry to mainland.

CASTLEBAY, Barra, 56°56'·80N 07°29'·60W. AC 2769. HW –0525 on Dover; ML 2·3m; Duration 0600. See 10.8.7. Very good shelter & holding. Best ⚓ in approx 8m NW of Kiessimul Castle (on an island); NE of castle are rks. 8 HIE ⚓s lie to W of pier ☎ (01870) 602425. Or ⚓ in Vatersay Bay in approx 9m. W end of Vatersay Sound is closed by a causeway. Beware rks NNW of Sgeir Dubh a conspic W/G tr, Fl (2) WG 6s 6m 7/5M, vis W280°-117°, G117°-280°; which leads 283° in transit with Sgeir Liath, Fl 3s 7m 8M. Chan Rk, 2ca to the S, is marked by Fl WR 6s 4m 6/4M. Close-in ldg lts 295°, both FG 11M on W framework trs. front 9m Or △ on Rubha Glas; rear, 457m from front, 15m Or ▽. Facilities: Bar, D, FW, P, ✉, R, V, Ferry to mainland.

HIE ⚓s are also located in the Outer Hebrides at:
L Rodel, Harris. AC 2642. 3 ⚓s at 57°44'·2N 06°57'·4W in Poll an Tigh-mhàil; enter from SW past jetties. No lts. ☎ (01851) 703773.
Kallin, Grimsay. AC 2904. 1 ⚓ at 57°28'·9N 07°12'·2W, NE of hbr. 3 chan lt buoys and 2 FR (vert) on hbr bkwtr. ☎ (01870) 602425.
L Carnan, S Uist. AC 2825. 2 ⚓s at 57°22'·15N 07°16'·4W ☎ (01870) 602425. App chan has lt buoys and ldg lts 222° to Sandwick quay; front Fl R 2s, rear Iso R 10s, both 5M, W ◇s on posts.
Acairseid Mhór, Eriskay. AC 2770. 3 ⚓s at 57°04'·0N 07°17'·4W on S side of inlet, opp pier, 2 FG (vert). Ldg lts 285°, both Oc R 6s 9/10m 4M. ☎ (01870) 602425.

ATLANTIC ISLAND

ST KILDA, Western Isles, 57°48'·30N 08°33'·00W. AC 2721, 2524. Tides at Village Bay, Hirta: HW –0510 on Dover; ML 1·9m; Duration 0615. See 10.8.7. A group of four isles and three stacks now taken over by the Army. ⚓ in Village Bay, SE-facing, in approx 5m about 1·5ca off the Army pier. If wind is between NE and SSW big swells enter the bay; good holding, but untenable if winds strong. Levenish Is (55m) is 1·5M E of Hirta with offlying rks. Ldg lts 270°, both Oc 5s 26/38m 3M. Call *Kilda Radio* VHF Ch 16 08 (HJ) for permission to land; ☎ (01870) 2384. Alternative ⚓ at Glen Bay on N side is only safe in S & E winds. Facilities: FW from wells near landings (courtesy of the Army).

AGENTS WANTED

If you are interested in becoming our agent for any of the following ports, please write to: The Editor, Edington House, Trent, Sherborne, Dorset DT9 4SR, England – and get your free copy of the Almanac annually. You do not have to live in a port to be the agent, but at least a fairly regular visitor.

Great Yarmouth	St Gilles-Croix-de-Vie
Port Ellen (Islay)	Les Sables d'Olonne
Maryport	Ile d'Oléron
Workington	River Seudre
Holyhead	Anglet/Bayonne
Lough Swilly	St Jean-de-Luz
St Peter Port, Guernsey	Hendaye
Diélette	Grandcamp-Maisy
Portbail	Port-en-Bessin
Iles Chausey	Courseulles
St Malo/Dinard	Ouistreham/Caen
Le Legue/St Brieuc	Emden
Tréguier	Dornumer-Accumersiel
Lampaul	Langeoog
L'Aberildut	Bremerhaven
Le Palais (Belle Ile)	Büsum
Morbihan/Vannes	

KINLOCHBERVIE   10-8-8

Highland 58°27'·28N 05°02'·70W   Rtg 1-3-2

CHARTS
AC 2503, 1785, 1954; OS 9

TIDES
–0400 Dover; ML 2·7; Duration 0610; Zone 0 (UT)

Standard Port ULLAPOOL (→)

Times				Height (metres)			
High Water		Low Water		MHWS	MHWN	MLWN	MLWS
0000	0600	0300	0900	5·2	3·9	2·1	0·7
1200	1800	1500	2100				
Differences LOCH BERVIE							
+0030	+0010	+0010	+0020	–0·3	–0·3	–0·2	0·0
LOCH LAXFORD							
+0015	+0015	+0005	+0005	–0·3	–0·4	–0·2	0·0
BADCALL BAY							
+0005	+0005	+0005	+0005	–0·7	–0·5	–0·5	+0·2
LOCH NEDD							
0000	0000	0000	0000	–0·3	–0·2	–0·2	0·0
LOCH INVER							
–0005	–0005	–0005	–0005	–0·2	0·0	0·0	+0·1

SHELTER
Very good in Kinlochbervie Hbr off the N shore of Loch Inchard. A useful passage port, only 14.5 track miles S of Cape Wrath. It is also a very busy FV port, but in NNE corner yachts AB on 18m long pontoon in 4m on SW side only; NE side is shoal/foul. If full, ‡ at Loch Clash, open to W; landing jetty in 2·7m. Other ‡s at: Camus Blair on S shore, 5ca SW of hbr ent, and up the loch at L Sheigra, Achriesgill Bay and 5ca short of the head of the loch.

NAVIGATION
WPT 58°27'·36N 05°05'·00W (at mouth of Loch Inchard), 280°/100° from/to hbr ent, 1·3M. The sides of the loch are clean, but keep to N side of Loch Inchard to clear a rk (3m depth) almost in mid-chan.

LIGHTS AND MARKS
From offshore in good vis Ceann Garbh, a conspic mountain 899m (6M inland), leads 110° toward ent of Loch Inchard. Rubha na Leacaig, Fl (2) 10s 30m 8M, marks N side of ent to loch. Creag Mhòr, Dir Oc lt WRG 2.8s 16m 9M, is on S shore of loch aligned 147°/327° with hbr ent chan; sectors G136·5°-146·5°, W146·°5-147·5°, R147·5°-157·5°. Ldg lts 327°into hbr, both Oc G 8s 16/26m 9M; front daymark is orange △ on white □; rear orange ▽ on white □. The 25m wide ent chan (and hbr) is dredged 4m and marked by 2 PHM bns, Fl R 4s and QR, and by a SHM bn, Fl G 4s.

RADIO TELEPHONE
VHF Ch **14** 16 HX. Ch 06 is used by FVs in the Minches.

TELEPHONE (Dial code 01971)
Hr Mr ☎ 521235, 📠 521718; MRSC (01851) 702013; ⌗ (0141) 887 9369 (H24); Marinecall 0891 500 464; Police 521222; Dr 502002.

FACILITIES
FW, D at FV quay, P (cans), Gas, CH, Sh, ME, ✉, Bar, V, R. Showers (Mission). In summer, bus to Inverness.

ANCHORAGES BETWEEN KINLOCHBERVIE AND ULLAPOOL

LOCH LAXFORD, Highland, 58°24'·80N 05°07'·10W. AC 2503. HW –0410 on Dover. ML 2·7m. See 10.8.8. Ent between Rubha Ruadh and Ardmore Pt, 1M ENE, clearly identified by 3 isolated mountains (N-S) Ceann Garbh, Ben Arkle and Ben Stack. The many ‡s in the loch include: Loch a'Chadh-fi, on N/NE sides of islet (John Ridgeway's Adventure School on Pt on W side of narrows has moorings); Bagh nah-Airde Beag, next bay to E, (beware rk 5ca off SE shore which covers at MHWS); Weaver's Bay on SW shore, 3M from ent (beware drying rk off NW Pt of ent); Bagh na Fionndalach Mor on SW shore (4-6m); Fanagmore Bay on SW shore (beware head of bay foul with old moorings). Beware many fish farming cages. Facilities: none, nearest stores at Scourie (5M).

LOCH INVER, Highland, 58°09'·00N 05°14'·70W. AC 2504. HW –0433 on Dover; ML 3·0m. See 10.8.8. Good shelter in all weathers at head of loch in busy fishing hbr on S side. Ent N or S of Soyea Is, Fl (2) 10s 34m 6M; beware rk drying 1·7m about 50m off Kirkaig Point (S side of ent). Approach in W sectors of Glas Leac lt, Fl WRG 3s 7m, W071°-078°, W103°-111°, (see 10.8.4); passing it to N or S. At the hbr there is a bkwtr and 2 piers, all pointing N: Aird Ghlas bkwtr has QG lt; both piers have 2FG (vert). There is a yacht pontoon in 5m between Aird Ghlas and the first pier; or ‡ at head of loch in 6m N of the E pier, or as Hr Mr directs: VHF Ch 09 16. ☎ (01571) 844247. Facilities: Gas, FW, P, D, V, ✉, Hotel.

8

ULLAPOOL

MEAN SPRING
AND NEAP CURVES

MEAN RANGES	
Springs	4.5m
Neaps	1.8m

Springs occur 1 day
after
New and Full Moon

ULLAPOOL   10·8·9

Highland 57°53´.72N 05°09´.30W   Rtg 2-4-2

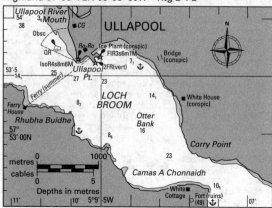

CHARTS
AC 2500, 2501, 2509, 1794; OS 19

TIDES
–0415 Dover; ML 3·0; Duration 0610; Zone 0 (UT)

Standard Port ULLAPOOL (⟶)

Times				Height (metres)			
High Water		Low Water		MHWS	MHWN	MLWN	MLWS
0000	0600	0300	0900	5·2	3·9	2·1	0·7
1200	1800	1500	2100				

Differences SUMMER ISLES (Tanera Mor)

–0005	–0005	–0010	–0010	–0·1	+0·1	0·0	+0·1

LOCH EWE (Mellon Charles)

–0010	–0010	–0010	–0010	–0·1	–0·1	–0·1	0·0

LOCH GAIRLOCH

–0020	–0020	–0010	–0010	0·0	+0·1	–0·3	–0·1

Ullapool is a Standard Port and detailed tidal predictions for each day of the year are given below.

SHELTER
Good in ⚓ E of pier; access at all tides. See Hr Mr for temp moorings. From Aug to Mar Ullapool is mainly a FV port and the pier is extremely congested. Loch Kanaird (N of ent to Loch Broom) has good ⚓ E of Isle Martin. Possible ⚓s 6ca S of Ullapool Pt, and beyond the narrows 3ca ESE of W cottage. The upper loch is squally in strong winds.

NAVIGATION
WPT L Broom ent 57°55´.80N 05°15´.00W, 309°/129° from/ to Ullapool Pt lt, 3.5M. N of Ullapool Pt extensive drying flats off the mouth of Ullapool R are marked by QR buoy. Beware fish pens and unlit buoys SE of narrows off W shore.

LIGHTS AND MARKS
Rhubha Cadail, N of L. Broom ent, Fl WRG 6s 11m 9/6M. Cailleach Hd, W of ent, Fl (2) 12s 60m 9M. Ullapool Pt Iso R 4s 8m 6M; grey mast, vis 258°-108°.

RADIO TELEPHONE
VHF Ch 14 16 12 (July-Nov: H24. Dec-June: HO).

TELEPHONE (Dial code 01854)
Hr Mr 612091/612165; MRSC (01851) 702013; ⌗ (0141) 887 9369; Marinecall 0891 500464; Police 612017; Dr 612015.

FACILITIES
Pier AB £5 for 1 or more nights, D, FW, CH; **Ullapool YC** Gas; **Services:** ME, El, Ⓔ, Sh, ACA. **Town** EC Tues (winter); P, Ⓞ, V, R, Bar, ⊠, Ⓑ, ⇌ (bus to Garve). Daily buses to Inverness (✈), ferries twice daily (summer) to Stornoway.

ADJACENT ANCHORAGES

SUMMER ISLES, High. 58°01´N 05°25´W. AC 2501, 2509. HW –0425 Dover; See 10.8.9; streams are weak and irregular. In the N apps to Loch Broom some 30 islands and rks, the main ones being Eilean Mullagrach, Isle Ristol, Glas-leac Mor, Tanera Beg, Eilean a' Char, Eilean Fada Mor. ⚓s: Isle Ristol, ⚓ to the S of drying causeway; close to slip is lt Fl G 3s. Tanera Beg, ⚓ in the chan to the E inside Eilean Fada Mor (beware bys, nets and drying rks). Tanera Mor on E side, ⚓ in bay (the "Cabbage Patch"); new pier but many moorings; or in NW, ⚓ close E of Eilean na Saille, but N of drying rk. Temp ⚓ at Badentarbat B for Achiltibuie on mainland. Facilities: V, R, Gas, FW, D (emerg) ☎ (01854) 622261.

LOCH EWE, Highland, 57°52´.00N 05°40´.00W. AC 3146, 2509. Tides: See 10.8.9; HW –0415 on Dover; ML 2·9m; Duration 0610. Shelter in all winds. Easy ent with no dangers in loch. Rhubha Reidh lt, Fl (4) 15s 37m 24M, W tr, is 4·5M W of ent. Loch approx 7M long with Isle Ewe and 2 small islets about 2M from ent in centre; can be passed on either side. Beware unlit buoys E side Isle Ewe. Excellent ⚓ in Loch Thurnaig to S. Aultbea Pier, partly derelict, to NE. Beware fish farms. Boor Rks on W shore about 7ca from loch hd. Fairway buoy SWM L Fl 10s; No 1 lt buoy Fl (3) G 10s; NATO fuelling jetty and dolphins, all Fl G 4s. Facilities: Dr, P, ⊠, R, V, Bar. S of Poolewe Bay (3.5m): **Inverewe Gdns** FW, D, L on pier; P (at garage), ⊠, R, Bar, V, Gas; **Aultbea** V.

LOCH GAIRLOCH, Highland, 57°43´.00N 05°45´.00W. AC 2528, 2210. HW –0440 on Dover. See 10.8.9. A wide loch facing W. Ent clear of dangers. Quite heavy seas enter in bad weather. Good shelter in Badachro, SW of Eilean Horrisdale on S side of loch or in Loch Shieldaig at SE end of the loch. Or ⚓ in approx 6m near Gairloch pier (NB: proposed marina at river mouth). Lts: Glas Eilean Fl WRG 6s 9m 6/4M, W080°-102°, R102°-296°, W296°-333°, G333°-080°. Pier hd, QR 9m. Hr Mr ☎ (01445) 712140. VHF Ch 16 (occas). Gairloch Pier: AB fees charged. Facilities: P, D, FW, Hotel, Gas, V.

SCOTLAND – ULLAPOOL

LAT 57°54′N   LONG 5°10′W

TIMES AND HEIGHTS OF HIGH AND LOW WATERS

YEAR **1998**

TIME ZONE (UT)
For Summer Time add ONE hour in non-shaded areas

8

JANUARY

	Time	m		Time	m
1 TH	0232 0827 1458 2056	0.9 5.4 0.8 5.0	**16** F	0305 0854 1539 2128	1.2 5.0 1.1 4.7
2 F	0315 0911 1543 2145	1.0 5.3 0.9 4.8	**17** SA	0340 0928 1615 2207	1.3 4.8 1.3 4.5
3 SA	0400 1000 1631 2240	1.2 5.1 1.0 4.6	**18** SU	0417 1004 1652 2249	1.5 4.6 1.5 4.3
4 SU	0450 1057 1723 2342	1.4 4.9 1.2 4.5	**19** M	0455 1047 1733 2340	1.7 4.4 1.8 4.1
5 M	0545 1202 1822	1.6 4.7 1.5	**20** TU	0538 1140 1820	2.0 4.1 2.0
6 TU	0053 0650 1315 1929	4.3 1.9 4.5 1.7	**21** W	0044 0628 1251 1919	3.9 2.2 4.0 2.2
7 W	0209 0805 1431 2046	4.3 2.0 4.5 1.7	**22** TH	0157 0733 1414 2037	3.9 2.4 3.9 2.2
8 TH	0322 0928 1542 2200	4.4 1.9 4.5 1.6	**23** F	0307 0858 1528 2154	4.0 2.4 4.0 2.1
9 F	0425 1037 1644 2300	4.6 1.7 4.7 1.5	**24** SA	0405 1013 1626 2251	4.2 2.1 4.2 1.8
10 SA	0517 1134 1736 2350	4.8 1.4 4.8 1.3	**25** SU	0452 1109 1713 2337	4.5 1.8 4.5 1.5
11 SU	0600 1223 1820	5.0 1.2 5.0	**26** M	0533 1155 1755	4.8 1.4 4.7
12 M O	0035 0637 1307 1859	5.1 5.1 1.1 5.0	**27** TU	0018 0611 1238 1834	1.2 5.1 1.1 5.0
13 TU	0116 0712 1348 1936	1.1 5.2 1.0 5.0	**28** W ●	0058 0650 1319 1914	1.0 5.4 0.8 5.2
14 W	0153 0746 1427 2013	1.1 5.2 0.9 5.0	**29** TH	0138 0729 1401 1956	0.8 5.5 0.5 5.2
15 TH	0229 0820 1503 2051	1.1 5.1 1.0 4.8	**30** F	0219 0810 1443 2038	0.6 5.6 0.4 5.2
			31 SA	0301 0852 1527 2124	0.6 5.5 0.5 5.1

FEBRUARY

	Time	m		Time	m
1 SU	0344 0938 1612 2214	0.7 5.3 0.6 4.9	**16** M	0348 0926 1616 2158	1.2 4.7 1.2 4.4
2 M	0431 1031 1700 2311	1.0 5.0 1.3 4.6	**17** TU	0422 1002 1650 2240	1.4 4.5 1.5 4.2
3 TU	0521 1132 1753	1.3 4.7 1.3	**18** W	0459 1043 1729 2334	1.7 4.2 1.8 4.0
4 W	0018 0619 1245 1854	4.3 1.6 4.4 1.6	**19** TH	0542 1138 1816	1.9 4.0 2.0
5 TH	0136 0730 1407 2011	4.2 1.9 4.2 1.9	**20** F	0045 0636 1300 1921	3.8 2.2 3.8 2.2
6 F	0300 0904 1530 2139	4.1 2.0 4.2 1.9	**21** SA	0210 0750 1437 2106	4.0 2.3 3.8 2.2
7 SA	0413 1027 1638 2248	4.3 1.8 4.4 1.7	**22** SU	0324 0933 1555 2223	4.0 2.2 4.0 1.9
8 SU	0510 1126 1730 2340	4.5 1.5 4.6 1.5	**23** M	0423 1044 1651 2315	4.3 1.8 4.3 1.6
9 M	0553 1214 1811	4.7 1.3 4.7	**24** TU	0509 1135 1735 2358	4.7 1.3 4.7 1.2
10 TU	0023 0627 1256 1845	1.3 4.9 1.1 4.8	**25** W	0551 1218 1816	5.1 0.9 5.0
11 W O	0102 0657 1333 1918	1.1 5.0 0.9 4.9	**26** TH ●	0039 0630 1301 1856	0.8 5.4 0.5 5.3
12 TH	0137 0727 1407 1950	1.0 5.1 0.8 4.9	**27** F	0120 0710 1343 1936	0.5 5.6 0.2 5.4
13 F	0210 0757 1439 2021	0.9 5.1 0.8 4.9	**28** SA	0202 0750 1425 2018	0.3 5.7 0.1 5.4
14 SA	0242 0825 1511 2052	0.9 5.0 0.9 4.8			
15 SU	0315 0854 1543 2123	1.0 4.9 1.0 4.6			

MARCH

	Time	m		Time	m
1 SU	0243 0832 1507 2101	0.3 5.7 0.2 5.3	**16** M	0249 0825 1512 2048	0.8 4.9 0.9 4.7
2 M	0327 0917 1551 2148	0.4 5.4 0.4 5.0	**17** TU	0321 0856 1543 2123	1.0 4.7 1.1 4.5
3 TU	0411 1008 1636 2241	0.7 5.1 0.8 4.7	**18** W	0353 0930 1616 2202	1.2 4.5 1.3 4.3
4 W	0459 1108 1726 2346	1.1 4.7 1.2 4.3	**19** TH	0429 1009 1652 2250	1.4 4.2 1.6 4.0
5 TH	0554 1222 1824	1.5 4.3 1.7	**20** F	0510 1059 1737 2357	1.7 3.9 1.9 3.8
6 F	0106 0703 1350 1939	4.1 1.9 4.0 2.0	**21** SA	0602 1217 1837	2.0 3.7 2.1
7 SA	0238 0844 1520 2119	4.0 2.0 4.0 2.1	**22** SU	0123 0710 1359 2010	3.8 2.1 3.7 2.2
8 SU	0359 1016 1629 2235	4.1 1.8 4.1 1.9	**23** M	0245 0850 1526 2152	3.9 2.1 3.9 2.0
9 M	0457 1115 1719 2327	4.3 1.6 4.3 1.6	**24** TU	0350 1016 1627 2249	4.2 1.7 4.2 1.6
10 TU	0540 1200 1757	4.5 1.3 4.5	**25** W	0442 1110 1714 2335	4.6 1.2 4.7 1.1
11 W	0008 0611 1239 1826	1.4 4.7 1.1 4.6	**26** TH	0527 1156 1756	5.0 0.8 5.0
12 TH	0044 0637 1313 1855	1.2 4.8 0.9 4.8	**27** F	0018 0609 1240 1836	0.7 5.4 0.4 5.3
13 F	0116 0705 1343 1924	1.0 4.9 0.8 4.8	**28** SA O	0101 0650 1322 1916	0.4 5.6 0.1 5.5
14 SA	0147 0732 1412 1952	0.9 5.0 0.7 4.9	**29** SU	0143 0731 1404 1957	0.2 5.7 0.0 5.5
15 SU	0218 0758 1442 2019	0.8 5.0 0.8 4.8	**30** M	0226 0814 1447 2039	0.2 5.6 0.1 5.3
			31 TU	0309 0900 1530 2125	0.3 5.4 0.4 5.1

APRIL

	Time	m		Time	m
1 W	0354 0951 1614 2216	0.6 5.0 0.8 4.7	**16** TH	0330 0909 1548 2137	1.1 4.4 1.2 4.4
2 TH	0441 1051 1702 2320	1.0 4.6 0.9 4.3	**17** F	0407 0951 1626 2225	1.3 4.2 1.5 4.1
3 F	0535 1204 1757	1.4 4.2 1.7	**18** SA	0450 1045 1711 2329	1.5 3.9 1.8 3.9
4 SA	0039 0643 1331 1911	4.0 1.8 3.9 2.1	**19** SU	0542 1201 1811	1.8 3.7 2.0
5 SU	0211 0818 1501 2048	3.9 2.0 3.9 2.1	**20** M	0050 0648 1333 1936	3.9 1.9 3.7 2.1
6 M	0334 0953 1610 2211	4.0 1.8 4.0 2.0	**21** TU	0208 0817 1457 2113	4.0 1.8 3.9 1.9
7 TU	0433 1053 1659 2304	4.1 1.6 4.2 1.7	**22** W	0316 0942 1602 2218	4.2 1.5 4.2 1.5
8 W	0515 1137 1734 2344	4.3 1.4 4.3 1.5	**23** TH	0413 1041 1652 2308	4.6 1.1 4.6 1.1
9 TH	0546 1214 1802	4.6 1.1 4.5	**24** F	0503 1131 1736 2355	4.9 0.7 5.0 0.8
10 F	0019 0612 1246 1830	1.3 4.7 1.0 4.7	**25** SA	0548 1217 1817	5.3 0.4 5.3
11 SA O	0051 0640 1315 1858	1.1 4.8 0.9 4.8	**26** SU ●	0040 0631 1301 1857	0.5 5.5 0.2 5.4
12 SU	0122 0707 1344 1925	0.8 4.8 0.8 4.9	**27** M	0125 0714 1344 1938	0.3 5.6 0.2 5.4
13 M	0153 0733 1413 1951	0.8 4.8 0.8 4.8	**28** TU	0209 0759 1427 2021	0.2 5.5 0.3 5.3
14 TU	0224 0801 1443 2022	0.8 4.8 0.9 4.7	**29** W	0254 0846 1510 2106	0.4 5.2 0.5 5.1
15 W	0256 0834 1515 2057	0.9 4.6 1.0 4.6	**30** TH	0339 0938 1554 2156	0.6 4.9 0.9 4.7

Chart Datum: 2·75 metres below Ordnance Datum (Newlyn)

SCOTLAND – ULLAPOOL

LAT 57°54′N　LONG 5°10′W

TIMES AND HEIGHTS OF HIGH AND LOW WATERS

YEAR **1998**

TIME ZONE (UT)
For Summer Time add ONE
hour in non-shaded areas

MAY

	Time	m		Time	m
1 F	0427 1037 1641 2257	1.0 4.5 1.3 4.4	**16** SA	0352 0945 1608 2210	1.2 4.2 1.4 4.3
2 SA	0520 1145 1734	1.3 4.2 1.8	**17** SU	0437 1041 1656 2311	1.3 4.0 1.6
3 SU	0010 0623 1302 1841	4.1 1.7 3.9 2.1	**18** M	0529 1150 1755	1.5 3.9 1.9
4 M	0132 0741 1425 2003	3.9 1.9 3.8 2.2	**19** TU	0022 0632 1308 1910	4.1 1.8 3.9 1.9
5 TU	0251 0906 1534 2125	3.9 1.9 3.9 2.1	**20** W	0135 0748 1425 2033	4.1 1.6 4.0 1.8
6 W	0352 1013 1624 2225	4.0 1.7 4.0 1.9	**21** TH	0243 0905 1533 2144	4.3 1.4 4.2 1.6
7 TH	0437 1101 1701 2310	4.1 1.5 4.2 1.7	**22** F	0345 1010 1629 2241	4.5 1.1 4.6 1.2
8 F	0512 1139 1733 2347	4.3 1.3 4.4 1.4	**23** SA	0439 1105 1717 2333	4.8 0.9 4.9 0.9
9 SA	0544 1213 1804	4.5 1.2 4.6	**24** SU	0529 1155 1800	5.1 0.6 5.1
10 SU O	0021 0615 1244 1833	1.2 4.6 1.0 4.7	**25** M ●	0022 0616 1242 1842	0.7 5.2 0.4 5.3
11 M O	0055 0644 1315 1901	1.1 4.7 0.9 4.8	**26** TU	0110 0701 1327 1923	0.5 5.3 0.4 5.3
12 TU	0128 0712 1347 1930	1.0 4.7 0.9 4.8	**27** W	0156 0747 1410 2005	0.4 5.2 0.5 5.2
13 W	0201 0743 1419 2003	0.9 4.7 0.9 4.8	**28** TH	0241 0835 1453 2049	0.5 5.1 0.8 5.0
14 TH	0236 0819 1452 2040	1.0 4.6 1.0 4.7	**29** F	0327 0925 1536 2137	0.7 4.8 1.0 4.8
15 F	0312 0859 1528 2121	1.0 4.4 1.2 4.5	**30** SA	0414 1018 1621 2231	0.9 4.5 1.3 4.5
			31 SU	0503 1117 1710 2333	1.2 4.2 1.7 4.2

JUNE

	Time	m		Time	m
1 M	0557 1220 1805	1.5 4.0 2.0	**16** TU	0516 1131 1738 2355	1.2 4.1 1.6 4.3
2 TU	0042 0656 1329 1910	4.0 1.7 3.8 2.1	**17** W	0614 1239 1844	1.3 4.0 1.7
3 W	0152 0803 1436 2021	3.9 1.9 3.8 2.2	**18** TH	0102 0718 1353 1956	4.3 1.4 4.1 1.7
4 TH	0255 0910 1534 2129	3.9 1.8 3.9 2.1	**19** F	0212 0829 1504 2110	4.3 1.4 4.2 1.6
5 F	0348 1009 1621 2224	4.0 1.7 4.1 1.9	**20** SA	0319 0940 1607 2218	4.4 1.3 4.4 1.4
6 SA	0434 1056 1701 2310	4.1 1.6 4.3 1.7	**21** SU	0421 1042 1700 2316	4.6 1.1 4.7 1.1
7 SU	0514 1137 1737 2350	4.2 1.4 4.5 1.5	**22** M	0516 1137 1747	4.8 0.9 4.9
8 M	0550 1214 1811	4.4 1.3 4.6	**23** TU	0009 0605 1227 1830	0.9 4.9 0.8 5.1
9 TU	0028 0623 1249 1841	1.3 4.5 1.1 4.8	**24** W ●	0058 0651 1312 1911	0.7 5.0 0.8 5.2
10 W O	0105 0655 1324 1913	1.1 4.6 1.0 4.8	**25** TH	0145 0736 1356 1951	0.6 5.0 0.8 5.1
11 TH	0141 0730 1359 1948	1.0 4.6 1.0 4.9	**26** F	0230 0820 1437 2032	0.6 4.9 0.9 5.0
12 F	0218 0809 1435 2026	0.9 4.6 1.0 4.8	**27** SA	0313 0905 1518 2114	0.7 4.8 1.0 4.8
13 SA	0257 0851 1513 2109	0.9 4.5 1.1 4.7	**28** SU	0355 0951 1558 2159	0.9 4.6 1.2 4.6
14 SU	0339 0938 1556 2156	1.0 4.4 1.2 4.6	**29** M	0437 1040 1641 2249	1.1 4.3 1.5 4.3
15 M	0425 1031 1643 2251	1.1 4.3 1.4 4.4	**30** TU	0521 1133 1726 2346	1.4 4.1 1.7 4.1

JULY

	Time	m		Time	m
1 W	0609 1231 1817	1.6 3.9 2.0	**16** TH	0550 1210 1816	1.1 4.2 1.5
2 TH	0050 0702 1335 1917	3.9 1.8 3.8 2.1	**17** F	0034 0649 1322 1923	4.4 1.3 4.1 1.7
3 F	0156 0803 1438 2024	3.8 1.9 3.8 2.2	**18** SA	0147 0757 1438 2042	4.3 1.5 4.1 1.7
4 SA	0258 0909 1537 2133	3.8 1.9 3.9 2.1	**19** SU	0301 0913 1550 2202	4.3 1.5 4.3 1.6
5 SU	0354 1011 1627 2232	3.9 1.8 4.1 1.9	**20** M	0410 1026 1649 2306	4.4 1.4 4.5 1.3
6 M	0443 1102 1710 2321	4.1 1.7 4.3 1.7	**21** TU	0509 1125 1739	4.5 1.3 4.7
7 TU	0525 1146 1747	4.2 1.5 4.5	**22** W	0000 0558 1215 1821	1.1 4.7 1.1 4.9
8 W	0003 0602 1227 1821	1.4 4.4 1.3 4.7	**23** TH ●	0049 0642 1300 1859	0.9 4.8 1.0 5.0
9 TH O	0043 0638 1304 1856	1.2 4.6 1.1 4.9	**24** F	0133 0722 1341 1934	0.7 4.9 0.9 5.1
10 F	0122 0715 1341 1932	1.0 4.7 1.0 5.0	**25** SA	0214 0800 1419 2010	0.7 4.9 0.9 5.0
11 SA	0201 0755 1419 2010	0.8 4.8 0.9 5.0	**26** SU	0252 0839 1455 2045	0.7 4.8 1.0 4.9
12 SU	0242 0837 1459 2051	0.7 4.8 0.9 5.0	**27** M	0329 0918 1532 2121	0.8 4.6 1.1 4.7
13 M	0324 0922 1541 2136	0.7 4.7 0.9 4.9	**28** TU	0405 0957 1608 2158	1.0 4.4 1.3 4.5
14 TU	0409 1011 1627 2227	0.7 4.5 1.1 4.7	**29** W	0442 1039 1647 2239	1.2 4.2 1.5 4.2
15 W	0457 1107 1718 2327	0.9 4.4 1.3 4.5	**30** TH	0522 1127 1728 2330	1.5 4.0 1.8 4.0
			31 F	0605 1227 1816	1.7 3.8 2.0

AUGUST

	Time	m		Time	m
1 SA	0039 0657 1339 1917	3.8 2.0 3.8 2.2	**16** SU	0129 0728 1418 2022	4.2 1.7 4.1 1.8
2 SU	0159 0805 1450 2036	3.7 2.1 3.8 2.3	**17** M	0252 0853 1538 2155	4.1 1.8 4.2 1.7
3 M	0312 0926 1552 2156	3.8 2.1 4.0 2.1	**18** TU	0406 1016 1642 2301	4.2 1.7 4.4 1.4
4 TU	0412 1032 1642 2255	3.9 1.9 4.2 1.8	**19** W	0505 1116 1731 2352	4.4 1.5 4.6 1.2
5 W	0500 1122 1723 2341	4.1 1.6 4.5 1.5	**20** TH	0552 1203 1811	4.6 1.3 4.8
6 TH	0541 1204 1800	4.4 1.4 4.8	**21** F	0037 0629 1245 1843	1.0 4.7 1.1 5.0
7 F	0022 0618 1244 1835	1.1 4.7 1.1 5.0	**22** SA ●	0117 0703 1322 1914	0.8 4.8 1.0 5.1
8 SA O	0102 0656 1322 1912	0.8 4.9 0.8 5.2	**23** SU	0153 0736 1356 1945	0.7 4.9 0.9 5.1
9 SU	0142 0735 1400 1950	0.6 5.0 0.7 5.3	**24** M	0226 0808 1430 2015	0.7 4.8 0.9 5.0
10 M	0222 0816 1441 2030	0.4 5.1 0.6 5.3	**25** TU	0258 0840 1503 2044	0.8 4.8 1.0 4.8
11 TU	0305 0859 1523 2113	0.4 5.0 0.6 5.2	**26** W	0330 0912 1536 2114	0.9 4.6 1.1 4.6
12 W	0348 0946 1607 2202	0.5 4.8 0.8 5.0	**27** TH	0403 0946 1610 2148	1.1 4.4 1.4 4.4
13 TH	0434 1039 1655 2300	0.7 4.6 1.1 4.7	**28** F	0438 1026 1647 2230	1.4 4.2 1.6 4.1
14 F	0524 1141 1750	1.0 4.4 1.4	**29** SA	0515 1118 1728 2326	1.7 4.0 1.9 3.9
15 SA	0010 0620 1256 1856	4.4 1.4 4.2 1.7	**30** SU	0600 1231 1821	2.0 3.8 2.2
			31 M	0050 0659 1359 1934	3.7 2.2 3.8 2.3

Chart Datum: 2·75 metres below Ordnance Datum (Newlyn)

SCOTLAND – ULLAPOOL

LAT 57°54′N   LONG 5°10′W

TIMES AND HEIGHTS OF HIGH AND LOW WATERS

YEAR **1998**

TIME ZONE (UT)
For Summer Time add ONE hour in non-shaded areas

SEPTEMBER

	Time	m		Time	m
1 TU	0227 0838 1513 2122	3.7 2.3 3.9 2.2	**16** W	0401 1007 1630 2252	4.2 1.9 4.4 1.5
2 W	0342 1004 1611 2230	3.8 2.1 4.2 1.9	**17** TH	0457 1104 1718 2340	4.4 1.7 4.6 1.3
3 TH	0436 1057 1656 2318	4.1 1.7 4.5 1.5	**18** F	0539 1148 1755	4.5 1.5 4.8
4 F	0518 1140 1734 2359	4.5 1.4 4.9 1.1	**19** SA	0019 0612 1226 1823	1.0 4.7 1.2 5.0
5 SA	0556 1220 1812	4.8 1.0 5.2	**20** SU	0055 0640 1259 1851	0.9 4.8 1.1 5.0
6 SU	0039 0634 1259 1849	0.7 5.1 0.7 5.5	**21** M	0127 0709 1331 1918	0.8 4.9 1.0 5.1
7 M	0119 0713 1339 1928	0.4 5.3 0.5 5.6	**22** TU	0156 0737 1402 1945	0.8 4.9 0.9 5.0
8 TU	0200 0753 1420 2008	0.2 5.4 0.4 5.6	**23** W	0225 0805 1434 2011	0.8 4.9 1.0 4.9
9 W	0242 0835 1502 2051	0.2 5.3 0.5 5.4	**24** TH	0256 0834 1506 2040	1.0 4.8 1.1 4.7
10 TH	0325 0920 1546 2140	0.4 5.1 0.7 5.1	**25** F	0327 0907 1539 2113	1.1 4.6 1.3 4.5
11 F	0410 1012 1634 2239	0.7 4.8 1.0 4.8	**26** SA	0400 0946 1613 2152	1.4 4.4 1.6 4.2
12 SA	0458 1115 1728 2353	1.1 4.5 1.4 4.4	**27** SU	0435 1034 1653 2244	1.7 4.1 1.9 3.9
13 SU	0554 1234 1835	1.6 4.2 1.8	**28** M	0517 1142 1743	2.0 3.9 2.2
14 M	0119 0703 1403 2010	4.1 1.9 4.1 2.0	**29** TU	0007 0613 1312 1851	3.7 2.3 3.8 2.3
15 TU	0247 0838 1526 2150	4.1 2.1 4.2 1.8	**30** W	0148 0743 1432 2042	3.7 2.4 4.0 2.3

OCTOBER

	Time	m		Time	m
1 TH	0310 0931 1535 2201	3.9 2.2 4.2 1.9	**16** F	0438 1043 1657 2317	4.4 1.9 4.6 1.4
2 F	0408 1028 1625 2251	4.2 1.8 4.5 1.4	**17** SA	0518 1125 1731 2355	4.5 1.7 4.8 1.2
3 SA	0453 1113 1707 2334	4.6 1.4 5.0 1.0	**18** SU	0548 1200 1759	4.7 1.4 4.9
4 SU	0533 1155 1748	5.0 1.0 5.4	**19** M	0027 0615 1233 1826	1.1 4.8 1.3 5.0
5 M	0015 0611 1236 1827	0.6 5.3 0.7 5.7	**20** TU	0057 0642 1304 1854	1.0 5.0 1.1 5.0
6 TU	0056 0651 1317 1907	0.3 5.5 0.5 5.8	**21** W	0126 0709 1336 1920	1.0 5.0 1.1 5.0
7 W	0137 0731 1400 1948	0.2 5.6 0.4 5.8	**22** TH	0155 0736 1407 1946	1.0 5.0 1.1 4.9
8 TH	0220 0812 1443 2033	0.2 5.5 0.4 5.5	**23** F	0226 0805 1440 2016	1.1 4.9 1.2 4.8
9 F	0303 0857 1528 2123	0.5 5.3 0.7 5.2	**24** SA	0257 0839 1513 2051	1.2 4.8 1.3 4.6
10 SA	0347 0948 1616 2224	0.8 5.0 1.0 4.8	**25** SU	0329 0918 1549 2131	1.4 4.6 1.6 4.3
11 SU	0435 1051 1710 2340	1.3 4.6 1.5 4.4	**26** M	0405 1006 1629 2225	1.7 4.3 1.8 4.0
12 M	0530 1213 1818	1.8 4.3 1.9	**27** TU	0447 1109 1718 2343	2.1 4.1 2.1 3.8
13 TU	0106 0640 1343 1953	4.1 2.1 4.2 2.0	**28** W	0543 1231 1824	2.3 4.0 2.2
14 W	0233 0815 1506 2131	4.1 2.3 4.2 1.9	**29** TH	0113 0702 1350 1956	3.8 2.4 4.1 2.2
15 TH	0344 0946 1609 2233	4.2 2.2 4.4 1.6	**30** F	0234 0818 1456 2123	4.0 2.3 4.3 1.9
			31 SA	0337 0953 1552 2219	4.3 1.9 4.7 1.4

NOVEMBER

	Time	m		Time	m
1 SU	0426 1044 1640 2306	4.7 1.5 5.1 1.0	**16** M	0519 1130 1732 2356	4.6 1.7 4.7 1.4
2 M	0510 1129 1724 2350	5.1 1.1 5.4 0.7	**17** TU	0549 1205 1803	4.8 1.5 4.8
3 TU	0551 1213 1807	5.4 0.8 5.7	**18** W	0027 0618 1239 1833	1.3 4.9 1.4 4.9
4 W	0033 0631 1258 1849	0.4 5.6 0.6 5.8	**19** TH	0058 0647 1312 1901	1.2 5.0 1.3 4.9
5 TH	0117 0712 1342 1933	0.4 5.7 0.5 5.7	**20** F	0129 0715 1345 1930	1.2 5.1 1.2 4.9
6 F	0200 0754 1427 2020	0.4 5.6 0.6 5.5	**21** SA	0201 0746 1419 2002	1.2 5.0 1.3 4.8
7 SA	0243 0839 1513 2112	0.6 5.4 0.8 5.2	**22** SU	0234 0822 1454 2039	1.3 4.9 1.3 4.6
8 SU	0328 0929 1602 2212	1.0 5.1 1.1 4.8	**23** M	0308 0901 1532 2122	1.4 4.8 1.5 4.4
9 M	0415 1029 1656 2322	1.4 4.8 1.5 4.5	**24** TU	0346 0947 1613 2215	1.6 4.6 1.6 4.2
10 TU	0508 1144 1800	1.8 4.5 1.8	**25** W	0429 1044 1702 2322	1.9 4.4 1.8 4.1
11 W	0041 0613 1308 1919	4.2 2.2 4.3 2.0	**26** TH	0522 1153 1802	2.1 4.3 2.0
12 TH	0201 0733 1429 2047	4.1 2.4 4.2 2.0	**27** F	0038 0630 1306 1916	4.0 2.2 4.3 2.0
13 F	0311 0900 1534 2155	4.2 2.3 4.3 1.9	**28** SA	0153 0755 1415 2037	4.1 2.2 4.4 1.8
14 SA	0407 1005 1623 2243	4.3 2.1 4.5 1.7	**29** SU	0301 0912 1517 2144	4.3 2.0 4.7 1.5
15 SU	0447 1052 1700 2322	4.4 1.9 4.6 1.5	**30** M	0359 1013 1613 2238	4.7 1.6 5.0 1.2

DECEMBER

	Time	m		Time	m
1 TU	0448 1105 1704 2328	5.0 1.3 5.2 0.9	**16** W	0523 1137 1740	4.6 1.8 4.6
2 W	0533 1154 1751	5.3 1.0 5.5	**17** TH	0000 0557 1215 1814	1.5 4.8 1.6 4.7
3 TH	0014 0616 1242 1837	0.7 5.5 0.8 5.6	**18** F	0035 0629 1252 1846	1.4 5.0 1.4 4.8
4 F	0100 0658 1328 1923	0.6 5.6 0.7 5.6	**19** SA	0109 0700 1327 1918	1.3 5.1 1.3 4.8
5 SA	0144 0741 1415 2011	0.7 5.6 0.7 5.4	**20** SU	0143 0732 1403 1952	1.2 5.1 1.2 4.8
6 SU	0228 0825 1501 2101	1.0 5.4 0.8 5.2	**21** M	0217 0808 1440 2030	1.2 5.1 1.2 4.7
7 M	0312 0912 1549 2155	1.1 5.2 1.1 4.9	**22** TU	0253 0847 1518 2113	1.3 5.0 1.2 4.6
8 TU	0357 1004 1639 2254	1.4 4.9 1.3 4.6	**23** W	0332 0930 1600 2201	1.4 4.9 1.3 4.5
9 W	0445 1105 1733 2359	1.7 4.6 1.7 4.3	**24** TH	0415 1019 1646 2257	1.6 4.7 1.4 4.3
10 TH	0539 1215 1834	2.1 4.4 1.9	**25** F	0504 1117 1739	1.8 4.6 1.6
11 F	0107 0642 1329 1943	4.1 2.3 4.2 2.1	**26** SA	0001 0602 1223 1841	4.2 1.9 4.5 1.7
12 SA	0216 0753 1437 2054	4.2 2.4 4.2 2.1	**27** SU	0112 0711 1334 1952	4.2 2.0 4.5 1.7
13 SU	0316 0906 1535 2155	4.1 2.3 4.4 2.0	**28** M	0224 0828 1444 2106	4.3 2.0 4.6 1.6
14 M	0406 1007 1622 2243	4.3 2.2 4.4 1.8	**29** TU	0331 0943 1550 2213	4.5 1.8 4.7 1.4
15 TU	0447 1056 1703 2323	4.4 2.0 4.5 1.7	**30** W	0430 1046 1649 2309	4.8 1.5 5.0 1.2
			31 TH	0521 1141 1741	5.1 1.2 5.2

Chart Datum: 2·75 metres below Ordnance Datum (Newlyn)

8

PORTREE   10-8-10

Skye (Highland) 57°24'·75N 06°11'·00W   Rtg 2-4-1

CHARTS
AC 2534, 2209; Imray C66; OS 23

TIDES
–0445 Dover; ML no data; Duration 0610; Zone 0 (UT)

Standard Port ULLAPOOL (←)

Times				Height (metres)			
High Water		Low Water		MHWS	MHWN	MLWN	MLWS
0000	0600	0300	0900	5·2	3·9	2·1	0·7
1200	1800	1500	2100				
Differences PORTREE (Skye)							
–0025	–0025	–0025	–0025	+0·1	–0·2	–0·2	0·0
SHIELDAIG (Loch Torridon)							
–0020	–0020	–0015	–0015	+0·4	+0·3	+0·1	0·0
LOCH A'BHRAIGE (Rona)							
–0020	0000	–0010	0000	–0·1	–0·1	–0·1	–0·2
PLOCKTON (Loch Carron)							
+0005	–0005	–0005	–0010	+0·5	+0·5	+0·5	+0·2
LOCH SNIZORT (Uig Bay, Skye)							
–0045	–0020	–0005	–0025	+0·1	–0·4	–0·2	0·0
LOCH DUNVEGAN (Skye)							
–0105	–0030	–0020	–0040	0·0	–0·1	0·0	0·0
LOCH HARPORT (Skye)							
–0115	–0035	–0020	–0100	–0·1	–0·1	0·0	+0·1
SOAY (Camus nan Gall)							
–0055	–0025	–0025	–0045	–0·4	–0·2	No data	
KYLE OF LOCHALSH							
–0040	–0020	–0005	–0025	+0·1	0·0	+0·1	+0·1
DORNIE BRIDGE (Loch Alsh)							
–0040	–0010	–0005	–0020	+0·1	–0·1	0·0	0·0
GLENELG BAY (Kyle Rhea)							
–0105	–0035	–0035	–0055	–0·4	–0·4	–0·9	–0·1
LOCH HOURN							
–0125	–0050	–0040	–0110	–0·2	–0·1	–0·1	+0·1

SHELTER
Secure in all but strong SW'lies, when Camas Bàn is more sheltered. In the N of the bay there are 8 HIE ⚓s for <15 tons.

NAVIGATION
WPT 57°24'·60N 06°10'·00W, 095°/275° from/to pier, 0·72M. From the S, avoid rks off An Tom Pt (1·5M to E, off chartlet).

LIGHTS AND MARKS
Only lts are a SHM buoy Fl G 5s marking Sgeir Mhór, 2 FR (vert) 6m 4M (occas) on the pier and a SPM buoy Fl Y 5s.

RADIO TELEPHONE
VHF Ch 16 12 (occas).

TELEPHONE (Dial code 01478)
Hr Mr ☎ 612926; Moorings 612341; MRSC (01631) 563720; ⌗ (0141) 887 9369; Marinecall 0891 500464; Police 612888; Dr 612013; Ⓗ 612704.

FACILITIES
Pier D (cans), L, FW. **Town** EC Wed; P, V, Gas, Gaz, Ⓞ, R, Bar, ✉, Ⓑ, ⇌ (bus/ferry to Kyle of Lochalsh).

ANCHORAGES AROUND OR NEAR SKYE

LOCH TORRIDON, Highland, 57°36'N 05°49'W. AC 2210. Tides, see 10.8.10. Three large lochs: ent to outer loch (Torridon) is 3M wide, with isolated Sgeir na Trian (2m) almost in mid-chan; ⚓s on SW side behind Eilean Mór and in L Beag. L Sheildaig is middle loch with good ⚓ between the Is and village. 1M to the N, a 2ca wide chan leads into Upper L Torridon; many fish cages and prone to squalls. Few facilities, except Shieldaig: FW, V, R, Bar, ✉, Garage.

LOCH A'BHRAIGE, Rona (Highland), 57°34'·63N 05°57'·87W. AC 2534, 2479. HW –0438 on Dover; ML 2·8m; Duration 0605. See 10.8.10. A good ⚓ in NW of the island, safe except in NNW winds. Beware rks on NE side up to 1ca off shore. Hbr in NE corner of loch head. Ldg lts 137°, see 10.8.4. Facilities: jetty, FW and a helipad, all owned by MOD (DRA). Before ent, call *Rona* VHF Ch 16. **Acarseid Mhor** is ⚓ on W of Rona. App S of Eilean Garbh marked by W arrow. SD sketch of rks at ent is necessary. FW (cans), showers. At **Churchton Bay**, SW tip of Raasay, there are 4 HIE ⚓s; ☎ (01478) 612341; Slip, showers, R.

LOCH DUNVEGAN, 4 HIE ⚓s off Stein, 57°30'·9N 06°34'·5W. 3 HIE ⚓s off Dunvegan, 57°26'·3N 06°35'·2W. Fuel, FW, R. ☎ (01478) 612341.

LOCH HARPORT, Skye (Highland), 57°20'·60N 06°25'·80W. AC 1795. HW –0447 (sp), –0527 (np) on Dover. See 10.8.10. On E side of Loch Bracadale, entered between Oronsay Is and Ardtreck Pt (W lt ho, Iso 4s 17m 9M). SW end of Oronsay has conspic rk pillar, called The Castle; keep ¼M off-shore here and off E coast of Oronsay which is joined to Ullinish Pt by drying reef. ⚓ Oronsay Is, N side of drying reef (4m), or on E side, but beware rk (dries) 0·5ca off N shore of Oronsay. Fiskavaig Bay 1M S of Ardtreck (7m); Loch Beag on N side of loch, exposed to W winds; Port na Long E of Ardtreck, sheltered except from E winds (beware fish farm); Carbost on SW shore. Facilities: EC Wed (Carbost); V (local shop), Bar, R, P (garage), ✉, FW. (Port na Long) Bar, FW, V (shop).

SOAY HARBOUR, Skye (Highland), 57°09'·50N 06°13'·40W. AC 2208. Tides see 10.8.10. Narrow inlet on NW side of Soay; enter from Soay Sound above half flood to clear bar, dries 0·6m. Appr on 135° from 5ca out to avoid reefs close each side of ent. Cross bar slightly E of mid-chan, altering 20° stbd for best water; ent is 15m wide between boulder spits. ⚓ in 3m mid-pool or shoal draft boats can enter inner pool. Good shelter and holding. Camas nan Gall (poor holding) has public ☎; no other facilities.

CROWLIN ISLANDS, Highland, 57°21'·08N 05°50'·59W. AC 2498, 2209. HW –0435 on Dover, –0020 on Ullapool; HW +0·3m on Ullapool. See 10.8.10. ⚓ between Eilean Meadhonach and Eilean Mor, appr from N, keep E of Eilean Beg. Excellent shelter except in strong N winds. There is an inner ⚓ with 3½m but ent chan dries. Eilean Beg lt ho Fl 6s 32m 6M, W tr. There are no facilities.

PLOCKTON
10-8-11

Highland 57°20′·54N 05°38′·40W   Rtg 3-4-1

CHARTS
AC 2528, 2209; Imray C66; OS 24, 33
TIDES
−0435 Dover; ML 3·5m; Duration 0600; See 10.8.10
SHELTER
Good, exposed only to N/NE'lies. ‡ in centre of bay in approx 3·5m or find a vacant mooring. Inner part of bay shoals and dries to the SW.
NAVIGATION
WPT 57°21′·41N 05°39′·36W; thence steer ENE between Sgeir Bhuidhe and Sgeir Golach (3·8m). When past the latter alter for Duncraig Castle 170°, between Bogha Dubh Sgeir (1·5m, PHM bn) and Hawk Rk (0·1m, E of Cat Is). A shorter appr is SE between a PHM bn (S of Sgeir Golach) and Cat Is. Beware Plockton Rks (3·1m) on E side of bay.
LIGHTS AND MARKS
No lts or buoys. Old lt ho (13m) on Cat Is is conspic, as is Duncraig Castle with white △ bn.
RADIO TELEPHONE
None.
TELEPHONE
Hr Mr ☎/⌂ (01599) 534167 at Kyle of Lochalsh, mobile 0802 367253; MRSC (01631) 563720; ⌗ (0141) 887 9369; Marinecall 0891 500 464; Police/Dr via Hr Mr.
FACILITIES
Village FW, M, L at 24m long pontoon, D (cans), CH, V, R, Bar, ✉, ≷, Gas, airstrip, (bus to Kyle of Lochalsh).

LOCH CARRON. Strome Narrows are no longer buoyed or lit. At head of loch are 3 Y ⚓s (max LOA 14m) in 3m off drying jetty at 57°23′·95N 05°29′·0W; call ☎ 01520 722321. Appr on 328° between Sgeir Chreagach and Sgeir Fhada.

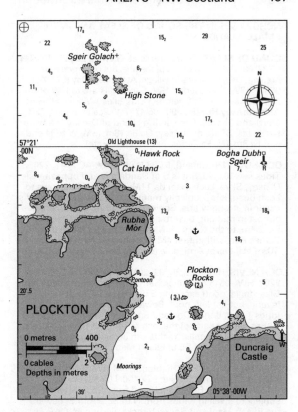

LOCH ALSH
10-8-12

Highland 57°16′·70N 05°42′·80W   Rtg 2-4-1

CHARTS
AC 2540, 2541; Imray C66; OS 33
TIDES
−0450 Dover; ML 3·0m; Duration 0555; See 10.8.10
SHELTER
At **Kyle (of Lochalsh)** AB on Railway Pier, with FVs, or on 40m pontoon planned for summer 97, close W of Railway Pier; or ‡ off the hotel there in 11m. Off **Kyleakin** 4 ⚓s, as shown, are free but subject to tidal stream. A pontoon was planned for late 97 on S side of hbr; up to 8 ⚓s in bay 3ca E of hbr are planned for March 1998. Safe ‡s, depending on winds, are (clockwise from Kyle): Avernish B, (2ca N of Racoon Rk) in 3m clear of power cables, open to SW; NW of Eilean Donnan Castle (conspic); in Ratagan B at head of L Duich in 7m; in Totaig B facing Loch Long ent in 3·5m; on S shore in Ardintoul B in 5·5m; at head of Loch na Béiste in 7m close inshore and W of fish cages.

NAVIGATION
WPT (from Inner Sound) 57°17′·00N 05°45′·70W, 303°/123° from/to bridge, 7½ca. Chan to bridge is marked by 2 PHM and 2 SHM lt buoys. Bridge to Skye, 30m clearance, is lit Oc 6s in centre of main span, Iso R 4s on S pier and Iso G4s on N pier. The secondary NE span is lit, but has only 4.5m clearance.
LIGHTS AND MARKS
Lts/marks as chartlet. Direction of buoyage is N in Kyle Rhea, thence E up Loch Alsh; but W through Kyle Akin and the bridge, ie SHMs are on N side of chan.
RADIO TELEPHONE
VHF Ch 11 16.
TELEPHONE (Dial code 01599)
Hr Mr ☎/⌂ 534167; MRSC (01631) 563720; ⌗ (0141) 887 9369; Marinecall 0891 500 464; Police, Dr, ⊞: via Hr Mr.
FACILITIES
Kyle of Lochalsh: AB, FW, D (Fish pier), P (cans), ME, Ⓔ, CH, ✉, Ⓑ, R, Bar, V, Gas, ≷ (useful railhead), Bus to Glasgow & Inverness; buses every ½hr to/from Kyleakin.
Kyleakin: AB, M, FW, V, R, Bar.

ANCHORAGES IN THE SOUND OF SLEAT AND IN THE SMALL ISLANDS

SOUND OF SLEAT: There are ⚓s at: **Glenelg Bay** (57°12'·58N 05°37'·88W) SW of pier out of the tide, but only moderate holding. Usual facilities in village. At **Sandaig Bay** (57°10'·00N 05°41'·43W), exposed to SW. Sandaig Is are to NW of the bay; beware rks off Sgeir nan Eun. Eilean Mór has lt Fl 6s. At **Isleornsay Hbr** (57°09'N 05°47'·7W) 2ca N of pier, 2FR (vert) and floodlit. Give drying N end of Ornsay Is a wide berth. Lts: SE tip of Ornsay, Oc 8s 18m 15M, W tr; N end, Fl R 6s 8m 4M. Facilities: FW, P, V, ✉, Hotel.

LOCH HOURN, Highland, 57°08'N 05°42'W. AC 2541, 2208. Tides see 10.8.10. Ent is S of Sandaig Is and opposite Isle Ornsay, Skye. Loch extends 11M inland via 4 narrows to Loch Beag; it is scenically magnificent, but violent squalls occur in strong winds. Sgeir Ulibhe, drying 2·1m, bn, lies almost in mid-ent; best to pass S of it to clear Clansman Rk, 2·1m, to the N. ⚓s on N shore at Eilean Ràrsaidh and Camas Bàn, within first 4M. For pilotage further E, consult SDs. Facilities at Arnisdale (Camas Bàn): FW, V, R, Bar, ✉.

LOCH NEVIS, Highland, 57°02'·20N 05°43'·34W. AC 2541, 2208. HW –0515 on Dover. See 10.8.13. ⚓ NE of Eilean na Glaschoille, good except in S winds; or 1M further E off Inverie, but holding poor. Beware rks Bogha cas Sruth (dries 1·8m), Bogha Don and Sgeirean Glasa both marked by bns. Upper parts of the loch are subject to very violent unpredictable squalls. Yachts can enter the inner loch with caution, and ⚓ N or SE of Eilean Maol. No facilities.

ARMADALE BAY, Skye (Highland), 4M NW of Mallaig. AC 2208. 6 HIE ⚓s in 2 trots at 57°04'·0N 05°53'·6W (☎ (01478) 612341). Bay is sheltered from SE to N winds but subject to swell in winds from N to SE. From S, beware the Eilean Maol and Sgorach rocks. Ferry pier, Oc R 6s 6m 6M, with conspic W shed. Facilities: FW at ferry pier or on charter (☎ 01471 844216) moorings from long hose on old pier; D (cans), V, Gas, showers at Ardvasar ¾ mile; P (cans), Gaz at ¼ mile; R, Bar, ferry to Mallaig for ⇌.

CANNA, The Small Islands, 57°03'·30N 06°29'·40W. AC 2208, 1796. HW –0457 (Sp), –0550 (Np) on Dover; HW –0035 and –0·4m on Ullapool; Duration 0605. Good holding and shelter, except in strong E'lies, in hbr between Canna and Sanday Is. Appr along Sanday shore, keeping N of Sgeir a' Phuirt, dries 4·6m. Ldg marks as in SDs. ⚓ in 3 - 4m W of Canna pier, off which beware drying rky patch. ⚓ Lt is advised due to FVs. Conspic W lt bn, Fl 6s 32m 9M, vis 152°-061°, at E end of Sanday Is. Magnetic anomaly off NE Canna. Facilities: FW only. Note: National Trust for Scotland runs island; please do not ditch rubbish.

RHUM, The Small Islands, 57°00'·08N 06°15'·70W. AC 2207, 2208. HW –0500 on Dover; –0035 and –0·3m on Ullapool; ML 2·4m; Duration 0600. Nature Conservancy Council owns Is. The mountains (809m) are unmistakeable. Landing is only allowed at L Scresort on E side; no dogs. Beware drying rks 1ca off N point of ent and almost 3ca off S point. The head of the loch dries 2ca out; ⚓ off slip on S side or further in, to NE of jetty. Hbr is open to E winds/ swell. Facilities: Hotel, ✉, FW, V, R, Bar, ferry to Mallaig.

EIGG HARBOUR, The Small Islands, 56°52'·64N 06°07'·60W. AC 2207. HW –0523 on Dover. See 10.8.13. Coming from N or E enter between Garbh Sgeir and Flod Sgeir (bn, ○ topmark), drying rks. An Sgùrr is a conspic 391m high peak/ ridge brg 290°/1·3M from pier. Most of hbr dries, but good ⚓ 1ca NE of Galmisdale Pt pier, except in NE winds when yachts should go through the narrows and ⚓ in South Bay in 6-8m; tide runs hard in the narrows. Also ⚓ in 2·5m at Poll nam Partan, about 2ca N of Flod Sgeir. SE point of Eilean Chathastail Fl 6s 24m 8M, vis 181°-shore, W tr. VHF Ch 08 *Eigg Hbr.* Hr Mr ☎ via (01687) 482428. FW, repairs. **Cleadale village** (2M to N) Bar, ✉, R, V, Gas.

MUCK, The Small Islands, 56°49'·80N 06°13'·33W. AC 2207. Tides approx as Eigg, see 10.8.13. Port Mór at the SE end is the main hbr, with a deep pool inside offlying rks, but exposed to S'lies. Appr with tree plantation bearing exactly 329°; this leads between Dubh Sgeir and Bogha Ruadh rks. ⚓ towards the NW side of inlet; NE side has drying rks. On N side of Is, Bagh a' Ghallanaich is ⚓ protected from S; entrance needs SDs and careful identification of marks. Few facilities.

MALLAIG   10-8-13
Highland 57°00'·48N 05°49'·40W   Rtg 1-2-2

CHARTS
AC 2541, 2208; Imray C65, C66; OS 40

TIDES
–0515 Dover; ML 2·9; Duration 0605; Zone 0 (UT)

Standard Port OBAN (→)

Times				Height (metres)			
High Water		Low Water		MHWS	MHWN	MLWN	MLWS
0000	0600	0100	0700	4·0	2·9	1·8	0·7
1200	1800	1300	1900				
Differences MALLAIG							
+0017	+0017	+0017	+0017	+1·0	+0·7	+0·3	+0·1
INVERIE BAY (Loch Nevis)							
+0030	+0020	+0035	+0020	+1·0	+0·9	+0·2	0·0
BAY OF LAIG (Eigg)							
+0015	+0030	+0040	+0005	+0·7	+0·6	–0·2	–0·2
LOCH MOIDART							
+0015	+0015	+0040	+0020	+0·8	+0·6	–0·2	–0·2

SHELTER
Good in SW'lies but open to N. Access H24. ⚓ in SE part of hbr or find a berth on Fish Pier. No ⚓s. Hbr is often full of FVs; also Skye ferry. WIP on new N bkwtr and FV basin.

NAVIGATION
WPT 57°00'·76N 05°49'·42W, 011°/191° from/to Steamer Pier lt, 540m, passing E of Sgeir Dhearg lt bn. The former W chan is now much narrower and no longer advised.

▲ No visitors moorings

LIGHTS AND MARKS
As chartlet & 10.8.4. Town lts may obscure Sgeir Dhearg lt. IPTS (3 FR vert at pierhd) are only for ferries, Easter-Oct.

RADIO TELEPHONE
Call: *Mallaig Hbr Radio* VHF Ch 09 16 (HO).

TELEPHONE (Dial code 01687)
Hr Mr 462154, ☎ 462172; MRSC (01631) 563720; ⌗ (0141) 887 9369; Marinecall 0891 500464; Police 462177.

FACILITIES
Hbr Slip, AB, M, P (cans), D (tanker), FW, ME, El, Sh, C (10 ton mobile), CH, Ⓔ, ACA; a busy FV hbr, but yacht berths may be provided at a later date near root of the Fish Pier. **Town** EC Wed; Dr 462202. V, R, Gas, Gaz, Bar, ✉, Ⓑ, ⇌.

ADJACENT ANCHORAGE

ARISAIG HARBOUR, (Loch nan Ceall), Highland, 56°53'·78N 05°54'·50W. AC 2207. HW–0515 on Dover; +0030 and +0·9m on Oban; ML 2·9m; Duration 0605. Ldg line 256° into loch is S point of Eigg and N point of Muck. There are many unmarked rks, but no lts. S Chan is winding, but marked by perches. ⚓ above Cave Rk, approx 1M within the ent, is well sheltered. Access HW –3 to +2. Call *Arisaig Hbr* VHF Ch 12 16, M. **Arisaig Marine** ☎ (01687) 450224, ☎ 450678, ⚓ ⚓s, C (10 ton), CH, D & FW at pier (HW), P (cans), El, ME, Sh, Slip. **Village** EC Thurs; FW at hotel, Bar, ✉, R, Gas, V, ⇌.

LOCH SUNART   10-8-14
Highland 56°39'·50N 06°00'·00W

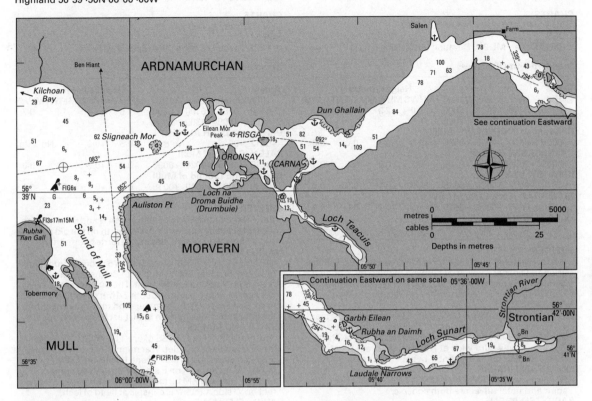

CHARTS
AC 2394, 2392, *2171*; Imray C65; OS 45, 47, 49

TIDES
Salen –0500 Dover; ML 2·0; Zone 0 (UT)

Standard Port OBAN (⟶)

Times				Height (metres)			
High Water		Low Water		MHWS	MHWN	MLWN	MLWS
0100	0700	0100	0800	4·0	2·9	1·8	0·7
1300	1900	1300	2000				
Differences SALEN (L Sunart)							
–0015	+0015	+0010	+0005	+0·6	+0·5	–0·1	–0·1
LOCH EATHARNA (Coll)							
+0025	+0010	+0015	+0025	+0·4	+0·3	No data	
GOTT BAY (Tiree)							
0000	+0010	+0005	+0010	0·0	+0·1	0·0	0·0

SHELTER
8 HIE Ⓐs at Kilchoan B (56°24'·5N 06°07'·3W); ☎ (01972)
510209. ‡s in Loch na Droma Buidhe (S of Oronsay)
sheltered in all winds; in Sailean Mór (N of Oronsay)
convenient and easy ent; between Oronsay and Carna; in
Loch Teacuis (very tricky ent); E of Carna; Salen Bay, with
Ⓐs; Garbh Eilean (NW of Rubha an Daimh), and E of sand
spit by Strontian R.

NAVIGATION
West WPT, 56°39'·70N 06°03'·00W, 263°/083° from/to
Creag nan Sgarbh (NW tip of Orinsay), 3·7M.
South WPT, 56°38'·00N 06°00'·65W, 1M S of Auliston Pt;
there are extensive rky reefs W of this pt. Chart 2394 and
detailed directions are needed to navigate the 17M long
loch, particularly in its upper reaches. Beware Ross Rk, S
of Risga; Broad Rk, E of Risga; Dun Ghallain Rk; shoals
extending 3ca NNW from Eilean mo Shlinneag off S
shore; drying rk 1ca W of Garbh Eilean and strong
streams at sp in Laudale Narrows.

LIGHTS AND MARKS
Unlit. Transits as on the chart: from W WPT, Risga on
with N tip of Oronsay at 083°; N pt of Carna on with top
of Risga 092°. From S WPT, Ben Hiant bearing 354°,
thence Eilean Mor Peak at 052°. Further up the loch, 339°
and 294°, as on chartlet, are useful. Many other transits
are shown on AC 2394.

RADIO TELEPHONE
None.

TELEPHONE (Dial code 01967)
MRSC (01631) 563720; ⌗ (0141) 887 9369; Marinecall 0891
500463; Dr 431231.

FACILITIES
SALEN
Services: FW, CH, Gas, Gaz, M, Diver, D by hose, limited V,
R, Bar, ME, El; **Acharacle** (2½M), P, V, ✉, Ⓑ (Tues/Wed,
mobile), ⇌ (bus to Loch Ailort/Ft William), ✈ (Oban).
STRONTIAN
FW, P, V, hotel, ✉, Gas, Gaz, Bar. Bus to Fort William.

ANCHORAGES IN COLL AND TIREE (Argyll and Bute)

ARINAGOUR, Loch Eatharna, Coll, 56°37'·00N 06°31'·20W.
AC 2474, 2171. HW –0530 on Dover; ML 1·4m; Duration
0600; see 10.8.14. Good shelter except with SE swell or
strong winds from ENE to SSW. Enter at SHM buoy, Fl G
6s, marking Bogha Mòr. Thence NW to Arinagour ferry
pier, 2 FR(vert) 10m. Beware McQuarrie's Rk (dries 2·9m)
1ca E of pier hd and unmarked drying rks further N on E
side of fairway. Ch and hotel are conspic ahead. Continue
N towards old stone pier; ‡ S of it or pick up a buoy. Six
HIE Ⓐs on W side of hbr, between the two piers. Also ‡ E
of Eilean Eatharna. Piermaster ☎ (01879) 230347; VHF Ch
31. Facilities: **HIE Trading Post** ☎ 230349, M, D, FW, Gas,
V, CH, R. **Village** ▣, FW, P, ✉, ferry to Oban (⇌).

GOTT BAY, Tiree, 56°30'·75N 06°48'·00W. AC 2474. Tides as
10.8.14; HW –0540 on Dover. Adequate shelter in calm
weather, but exposed in winds ENE to S. The bay, at NE
end of island, can be identified by conspic latticed tr at
Scarinish about 8ca SW of ent, with lt Fl 3s 11m 16M
close by (obscd over hbr). Appr on NW track, keeping to
SW side of bay which is obstructed on NE side by Soa Is
and drying rks. The ferry pier at S side of ent has FR ldg
lts 286½°. ‡ about 1ca NW of pier head in 3m on sand;
dinghy landing at pier. Facilities: P & D (cans), Gas, V, R,
Bar, ✉ at Scarinish (½M), ferry to Oban (⇌).

TOBERMORY   10-8-15

Mull (Argyll and Bute) 56°37'·60N 06°03'·15W   Rtg 2-4-1

CHARTS
AC 2474, *2390, 2171*; Imray C65; OS 47
TIDES
–0519 Dover; ML 2·4; Duration 0610; Zone 0 (UT)

Standard Port OBAN (→)

Times				Height (metres)			
High Water		Low Water		MHWS	MHWN	MLWN	MLWS
0100	0700	0100	0800	4·0	2·9	1·8	0·7
1300	1900	1300	2000				
Differences TOBERMORY (Mull)							
+0025	+0010	+0015	+0025	+0·4	+0·4	0·0	0·0
CARSAIG BAY (S Mull)							
–0015	–0005	–0030	+0020	+0·1	+0·2	0·0	–0·1
IONA (SW Mull)							
–0010	–0005	–0020	+0015	0·0	+0·1	–0·3	–0·2
BUNESSAN (Loch Lathaich, SW Mull)							
–0015	–0015	–0010	–0015	+0·3	+0·1	0·0	–0·1
ULVA SOUND (W Mull)							
–0010	–0015	0000	–0005	+0·4	+0·3	0·0	–0·1

SHELTER
Good, but some swell in strong N/NE winds. 8 Bu HIE ⚓s are S of Old Pier. ⚓ clear of fairway, marked by Y buoys; or in Aros Bay (clear of pier and fish farms); at SE end of The Doirlinn; or in restricted bay on W side of Calve Is.
NAVIGATION
WPT 56°38'·00N 06°02'·00W, 058°/238° from/to ferry pier, 1·1M. N ent is wide and clear of dangers. From SE beware Sgeir Calve 1·8m on NE side of Calve Is. S ent via The Doirlinn is only 80m wide at HW, and dries at LW; at HW±2 least depth is 2m. Enter between 2 bns on 300°.
LIGHTS AND MARKS
Rhuba nan Gall, Fl 3s 17m 15M, W tr is 1M N of ent. Ch spire and hotel turret are both conspic.
RADIO TELEPHONE
VHF Ch 16 12 (HO), M.
TELEPHONE (Dial code 01688)
Hr Mr 302017; MRSC (01631) 563720; Local CG 302200; Marinecall 0891 500463; Police 302016; Dr 302013.
FACILITIES
Ferry Pier, temp AB for P, D, FW £2; **Western Isles YC** ☎ 302207; **Services:** ME, CH, ACA, Gaz, Gas, Divers.
Town EC Wed (winter); FW, P, Dr, V, R, Bar, ⊠, Ⓑ, ◎, ⇌ (ferry to Oban), ✈ (grass strip; helipad on golf course).

SOUND OF MULL. 8M SE of Tobermory at **Salen Bay** (Mull, 56°31'·45N 05°56'·75W) are 8 HIE ⚓s. Beware drying rks 6ca E of the bay; ent on SE side. Land at jetty in SW corner. At **Craignure**, (Mull, 56°28'·37N 05°42'·25W) 9M SE, are 8 more HIE ⚓s, N of ferry pier; ldg lts 241°, both FR 10/12m. Facilities: V, Bar, ⊠, Gas, ferry to Oban. Tides, see 10.8.13. There are 2 Historic Wrecks at the SE end of the Sound: *Dartmouth* at 56°30'·19N 05°41'·95W on W side of Eilean Rubha an Ridire; and *Speedwell* on Duart Point at 56°27'·45N 05°39'·32W. See 10.0.3h.

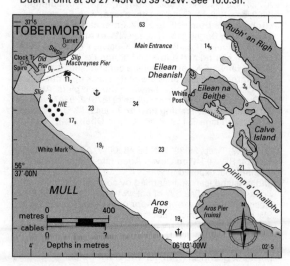

LOCH ALINE   10-8-16

Highland 56°32'·10N 05°46'·40W   Rtg 2-5-1

CHARTS
AC *2390*; Imray C65; OS 49
TIDES
–0523 Dover; Duration 0610; Zone 0 (UT)

Standard Port OBAN (→)

Times				Height (metres)			
High Water		Low Water		MHWS	MHWN	MLWN	MLWS
0100	0700	0100	0800	4·0	2·9	1·8	0·7
1300	1900	1300	2000				
Differences LOCH ALINE							
+0012	+0012	No data		+0·5	+0·3	No data	
SALEN (Sound of Mull)							
+0045	+0015	+0020	+0030	+0·2	+0·2	–0·1	0·0
CRAIGNURE (Sound of Mull)							
+0030	+0005	+0010	+0015	0·0	+0·1	–0·1	–0·1

SHELTER
Very good. ⚓s in SE end of loch and in N and E part of loch are restricted by fish farms. Temp berth on the old stone slip in the ent on W side, depth and ferries permitting.
NAVIGATION
WPT 56°31'·50N 05°46'·30W, 356°/176° from/to front ldg bn, 0·9M. Bns lead 356°, 100m W of Bogha Lurcain, drying rk off Bolorkle Pt on E side of ent. The buoyed ent is easy, but narrow with a bar (min depth 2·1m); stream runs 2½kn at sp. Beware coasters from the sand mine going to/from the jetty and ferries to/from Mull. Last 5ca of loch dries.
LIGHTS AND MARKS
Ardtornish Pt lt ho, 1M SSE of ent, Fl (2) WRG 10s 7m 8/5M. Lts and buoys as chartlet. War memorial cross (conspic, 9m high) stands on W side of ent. Ldg lts are FW 2/4m (H24). 1M up the loch on E side a Y bn with ● topmark marks a reef, and ½M further up similar bn marks a larger reef on W side. Clock tr is conspic at head of loch.
RADIO TELEPHONE
None.
TELEPHONE (Dial code 01967)
MRSC (01631) 563720; ⌗ (0141) 887 9369; Marinecall 0891 500463; Ⓗ (01631) 563727; Dr 421252.
FACILITIES
Village Gas, V, R, Bar, P, ⊠, (Ⓑ, ⇌, ✈ at Oban), Ferry to Fishnish Bay (Mull).

ANCHORAGES on WEST and SOUTH COASTS OF MULL		

(Anti-clockwise from the North. SDs essential)

TRESHNISH ISLES, 56°30'N 06°24'W. AC 2652. The main Is (N to S) are: Cairn na Burgh, Fladda, Lunga, Bac Mòr and Bac Beag. Tides run hard and isles are exposed to swell, but merit a visit in calm weather. Appr with caution on ldg lines as in CCC SDs; temp ⚓ off Lunga's N tip in 4m.

STAFFA, 56°25'·97N 06°20'·27W. AC 2652. Spectacular isle with Fingal's Cave, but same caveats as above. Very temp ⚓ off SE tip where there is landing; beware unmarked rks.

GOMETRA, 56°28'·86N 06°16'W. AC 2652. Tides as 10.8.15. The narrow inlet between Gometra and Ulva Is offers sheltered ⚓, except in S'lies. Appr on 020° between Staffa and Little Colonsay, or N of the former. Beware rks drying 3·2m, to stbd and 5ca S of ent. Inside, E side is cleaner.

LOCH NA KEAL, 56°27'N 06°11'W (ent). AC 2652. Tides in 10.8.15. Appr S of Geasgill Is and N of drying rks off **Inch Kenneth**; E of this Is and in **Sound of Ulva** are sheltered ⚓s, except in S'lies. Beware MacQuarrie's Rk, dries 0·8m.

LOCH LATHAICH, Mull, 56°19'·30N 06°15'·40W. AC 2617. HW –0545 on Dover; ML 2·4. See 10.8.15. Excellent shelter with easy access; good base for cruising W Mull. Eilean na Liathanaich (a group of islets) lie off the ent, marked by a W bn at the E end, Fl WR 6s 12m 8/6M, R088°-108°, W108°-088°. Keep to W side of loch and ⚓ off Bendoran BY in SW, or SE of Eilean Ban off the pier in approx 5m. Facilities: **Bendoran BY** ☎ (01681) 700435 AB, M, P (cans), D, FW, CH, ⬚, Slip, Sh. (Bunessan) Shop, ✉, Bar, R, FW.

SOUND OF IONA, 56°19'·46N 06°23'·05W. AC 2617. Tides see 10.8.15. From N, enter in mid-chan; from S keep clear of Torran Rks. Cathedral brg 012° closes the Iona shore past 2 SHM buoys and SCM buoy. Beware a bank 0·1m in mid-sound, between cathedral and Fionnphort; also tel cables and ferries. ⚓ S of ferry close in to Iona, or in Bull Hole. Consult SDs. Crowded in season; limited facilities.

TINKER'S HOLE, Ross of Mull, 56°17'·50N 06°23'·00W. AC 2617. Beware Torran Rks, reefs extending 5M S and SW of Erraid. Usual app from S, avoiding Rankin's Rks, dry 0·8m, and Rk, dries 2·3m, between Eilean nam Muc and Erraid. Popular ⚓ in mid-pool twixt Eilean Dubh and Erraid.

CARSAIG BAY, Ross of Mull, 56°19'·20N 05°59'·00W. Tides see 10.8.15. AC 2386. Temp, fair weather ⚓s to N of Gamhnach Mhòr, reef 2m high, or close into NW corner of bay. Landing at stone quay on NE side. No facilities.

LOCH SPELVE, Mull, 56°23'N 05°41'W. AC 2387. Tides as Oban. Landlocked water, prone to squalls off surrounding hills. Ent narrows to ½ca due to shoal S side and drying rk N side. CCC SDs give local ldg lines. ⚓s in SW and NW arms, clear of fish farms. Pier at Croggan; no facilities.

ANCHORAGES ALONG LOCH LINNHE (AC 2378, 2379, 2380)

LYNN OF LORN, 56°33'N 05°25'·2W: At NE end are ⚓s off **Port Appin**, clear of ferry and cables (beware Appin Rks); and in **Airds Bay**, open to SW. At NW tip of Lismore, **Port Ramsey** offers good ⚓s between the 3 main islets.

LOCH CRERAN, 56°32'·15N 05°25'·15W. Tides 10.8.17. Ent at Airds Pt, Dir lt 050°, Fl WRG 2s, W vis 041-058°. Chan turns 90° stbd and streams runs 4kn. Sgeir Callich, rky ridge juts out NE to SHM By, Fl G 3s; ⚓ W of it. ⚓s (max LOA 7m) off Barcaldine; also off Creagan Inn, ☎ (01631) 573250, 3 ⚓s max LOA 9m. Bridge has 12m clearance.

LOCH LEVEN, 56°41'·62N 05°12'W. Tides 10.8.17. Fair weather ⚓s in Ballachulish Bay at Kentallen B (deep), Onich and off St Brides on N shore. App bridge (17m clnce) on 114°; 4ca ENE of br are moorings and ⚓ at Poll an Dùnan, entered W of perch. Facilities at Ballachulish: Hotels, V, R, ✉, ⑧. Loch is navigable 7M to Kinlochleven.

CORRAN NARROWS, 56°43'·28N 05°14'·27W. AC 2372. Sp rate 6kn. Well buoyed; Corran Pt lt ho, Iso WRG 4s, and lt bn 5ca NE. ⚓ 5ca NW of Pt, off Camas Aiseig pier/slip.

FORT WILLIAM/CORPACH 10-8-17

Highland 56°49'·00N 05°07'·00W (off Fort William)

CHARTS
AC 2372, 2380; Imray C65; OS 41

TIDES
–0535 Dover; ML 2·3; Duration 0610; Zone 0 (UT)

Standard Port OBAN (⟶)

Times				Height (metres)			
High Water		Low Water		MHWS	MHWN	MLWN	MLWS
0100	0700	0100	0800	4·0	2·9	1·8	0·7
1300	1900	1300	2000				
Differences CORPACH							
0000	+0020	+0040	0000	0·0	0·0	–0·2	–0·2
LOCH EIL (Head)							
+0025	+0045	+0105	+0025		No data		No data
CORRAN NARROWS							
+0007	+0007	+0004	+0004	+0·4	+0·4	–0·1	0·0
LOCH LEVEN (Head)							
+0045	+0045	+0045	+0045		No data		No data
LOCH LINNHE (Port Appin)							
–0005	–0005	–0030	0000	+0·2	+0·2	+0·1	+0·1
LOCH CRERAN (Barcaldine Pier)							
+0010	+0020	+0040	+0015	+0·1	+0·1	0·0	+0·1
LOCH CRERAN (Head)							
+0015	+0025	+0120	+0020	–0·3	–0·3	–0·4	–0·3

SHELTER
Exposed to winds SW thro' N to NE. ⚓s off Fort William pier; in Camus na Gall; SSW of Eilean A Bhealaidh; and off Corpach Basin, where there is also a waiting pontoon; or inside the canal. The sea lock is normally available HW±4 during canal hrs. For Caledonian Canal see 10.8.18.

NAVIGATION
Corpach WPT 56°50'·30N 05°07'·00W, 135°/315° from/to lock ent, 0·30M. Beware McLean Rk, dries 0·3m, buoyed, 8ca N of Fort William. Lochy Flats dry 3ca off the E bank. In Annat Narrows at ent to Loch Eil streams reach 5kn.

LIGHTS AND MARKS
Iso WRG 4s lt is at N jetty of sea-lock ent, W310°-335°. A long pier/viaduct off Ft William is unlit.

RADIO TELEPHONE
Call: *Corpach Lock* VHF Ch 74 16 (during canal hours).

TELEPHONE (Dial code 01397)
Hr Mr 772249 (Corpach); MRSC (01631) 563720; ⌗ 702948; Marinecall 0891 500463; Police 702361; Dr 703136.

FACILITIES
FORT WILLIAM. **Pier** ☎ 703881, AB; **Services:** Slip, L, CH, ACA. **Town** EC Wed; P, ME, El, Sh, YC, V, R, Bar, Ⓗ, ✉, ⑧, ⇌.
CORPACH. **Corpach Basin** ☎ 772249, AB, L, FW; **Lochaber YC** ☎ 703576, M, FW, L, Slip; **Services:** ME, El, Sh, D (cans), M, CH, C, (18 ton), Slip, Divers. **Village** P, V, R, Bar, ✉, ⑧, ⇌.

CALEDONIAN CANAL   10-8-18

Highland   Rtg 3-2-1

CHARTS
AC 1791; OS 41, 34, 26

TIDES
Tidal differences: Corpach –0455 on Dover; See 10.8.14.
Clachnaharry: +0116 on Dover; See 10.7.16.

SHELTER
Corpach is at the SW ent of the Caledonian Canal, which is available for vessels up to 45m LOA, 10m beam, 4m draft and max mast ht 27·4m. Access from HW–4 to HW+4 (sp); H24 (nps); the sea locks at both ends do not open LW±2 at springs. For best shelter transit the sea lock and lie above the double lock. Numerous pontoons along the canal; cost is included in the canal dues. For Inverness see 10.7.16.

NAVIGATION
The 60M canal consists of 38M through 3 lochs, (Lochs Lochy, Oich and Ness), connected by 22M through canals. Loch Oich is part of a hydro-electric scheme which may vary the water level. The passage normally takes two full days, possibly longer in the summer; absolute minimum is 14 hrs. Speed limit is 5kn in the canal sections. There are 10 swing bridges; road tfc has priority at peak hrs. Do not pass bridges without the keeper's instructions.

LOCKS
There are 29 locks: 14 between Loch Linnhe (Corpach), via Lochs Lochy and Oich up to the summit (106′ above sea level); and 15 locks from the summit down via Loch Ness to Inverness. All locks are manned and operate early May to early Oct, 0800-1800LT daily. Contact canal office for reduced hrs in autumn, winter and spring; shut Christmas and New Year. The Sea locks are normally available HW±4 during canal hrs; they will open outside hrs for extra fees. Last lockings start ½ hr before the canal closes for the day. Dues, payable at Corpach, at 1997 rates, inc VAT: £7.00 per metre for 1 day; £11.55 for 3 days, plus special offers. For regulations and useful booklet *Skipper's Guide* apply: Canal Manager, Canal Office, Seaport Marina, Muirtown Wharf, Inverness IV3 5LS, ☎ (01463) 233140/☎ 710942.

LIGHTS & MARKS
See 10.8.17 and 10.7.16 for ent lts. Channel is marked by posts, cairns and unlit buoys, PHM on the NW side of the chan and SHM on the SE side.

BOAT SAFETY SCHEME
BWB, who operate the Caledonian & Crinan Canals, require a "nautical MOT" for craft based on these waterways; it is compulsory wef 1 January 1997. Transient/visiting vessels will be checked for apparent dangerous defects eg leaking gas or fuel, heat damaged electrical cables or taking in water. For details contact: Boat Safety Scheme, Willow Grange, Church Road, Watford WD1 3QA. ☎ 01923 226422; ☎ 226081.

RADIO TELEPHONE
Sea locks and main lock flights operate VHF Ch **74** (HO).

TELEPHONE
Corpach Sea Lock/Basin (01397) 772249; Canal Office, Inverness (01463) 233140; Clachnaharry Sea Lock (01463) 713896.

FACILITIES
For details see *Skipper's Guide* (using the maps).
– Corpach see 10.8.17.
– Banavie (Neptune's Staircase; one-way locking takes 1½ hrs) AC, 60m jetty, V, ✉.
– Gairlochy AB, R.
– NE end of Loch Lochy V, M, AB, R.
– Oich (Laggan) Bridge D, AB, R.
– Invergarry V, L, FW, AB.
– Fort Augustus AB, FW, D, P, jetty, ME, El, V, ✉, Dr, Bar.
– Urquhart B. (L. Ness) FW, AC, AB £6, 3m depth, V, Bar.
– Dochgarroch FW, AC, P, V.
At Inverness (10.7.16):
– Caley Marina (25+25 visitors) ☎ (01463) 236539, FW, CH, D, ME, El, Sh, AC, C (20 ton), ACA.
– Seaport (Muirtown) Marina (20 + 20 Ⓥ), £6, ☎ (01463) 239475, D, El, ME, Sh, FW, Gas, Gaz, ▣, C (40 ton), AC.

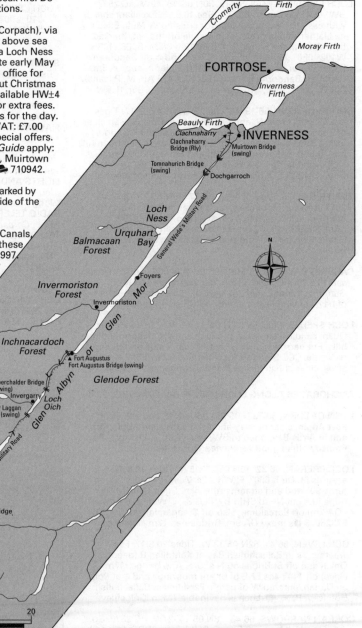

SCOTLAND – OBAN

LAT 56°25′N   LONG 5°29′W

TIMES AND HEIGHTS OF HIGH AND LOW WATERS

YEAR **1998**

TIME ZONE (UT)
For Summer Time add ONE hour in non-shaded areas

JANUARY

Day	Time	m	Day	Time	m
1 TH	0109 / 0713 / 1336 / 1924	0.8 / 4.1 / 0.9 / 3.9	**16** F	0147 / 0737 / 1425 / 1959	1.0 / 4.0 / 1.3 / 3.8
2 F	0151 / 0753 / 1422 / 2006	0.8 / 4.0 / 0.9 / 3.7	**17** SA	0224 / 0811 / 1501 / 2033	1.1 / 3.9 / 1.5 / 3.6
3 SA	0236 / 0838 / 1510 / 2051	0.9 / 3.9 / 1.1 / 3.5	**18** SU	0301 / 0845 / 1537 / 2109	1.3 / 3.7 / 1.7 / 3.5
4 SU	0326 / 0928 / 1604 / 2142	1.0 / 3.7 / 1.2 / 3.3	**19** M	0340 / 0921 / 1618 / 2148	1.5 / 3.5 / 1.9 / 3.3
5 M	0422 / 1027 / 1705 / 2244	1.2 / 3.5 / 1.4 / 3.1	**20** TU	0423 / 1000 / 1708 / 2236	1.7 / 3.3 / 2.0 / 3.1
6 TU	0528 / 1147 / 1813	1.3 / 3.3 / 1.5	**21** W	0512 / 1050 / 1807 / 2345	1.8 / 3.1 / 2.1 / 3.0
7 W	0005 / 0641 / 1327 / 1923	3.0 / 1.4 / 3.3 / 1.5	**22** TH	0610 / 1207 / 1916	1.9 / 3.0 / 2.1
8 TH	0143 / 0759 / 1442 / 2032	3.1 / 1.5 / 3.4 / 1.5	**23** F	0137 / 0714 / 1405 / 2026	3.0 / 1.9 / 3.1 / 1.9
9 F	0256 / 0913 / 1540 / 2133	3.3 / 1.4 / 3.5 / 1.3	**24** SA	0253 / 0823 / 1514 / 2126	3.1 / 1.8 / 3.2 / 1.7
10 SA	0349 / 1016 / 1627 / 2224	3.5 / 1.2 / 3.7 / 1.2	**25** SU	0344 / 0929 / 1603 / 2214	3.3 / 1.6 / 3.4 / 1.4
11 SU	0432 / 1107 / 1707 / 2309	3.7 / 1.1 / 3.8 / 1.0	**26** M	0428 / 1025 / 1645 / 2255	3.6 / 1.3 / 3.6 / 1.1
12 M ○	0511 / 1151 / 1743 / 2351	3.9 / 1.1 / 3.9 / 0.9	**27** TU	0509 / 1114 / 1723 / 2334	3.8 / 1.0 / 3.8 / 0.8
13 TU	0550 / 1233 / 1819	4.0 / 1.1 / 3.9	**28** W ●	0547 / 1158 / 1800	4.0 / 0.8 / 3.9
14 W	0031 / 0626 / 1312 / 1852	0.9 / 4.1 / 1.1 / 3.9	**29** TH	0014 / 0625 / 1241 / 1835	0.6 / 4.1 / 0.6 / 4.0
15 TH	0110 / 0702 / 1350 / 1926	0.9 / 4.1 / 1.2 / 3.9	**30** F	0056 / 0702 / 1324 / 1912	0.5 / 4.2 / 0.6 / 4.0
			31 SA	0138 / 0742 / 1407 / 1952	0.4 / 4.1 / 0.6 / 3.9

FEBRUARY

Day	Time	m	Day	Time	m
1 SU	0223 / 0823 / 1452 / 2034	0.5 / 4.0 / 0.7 / 3.7	**16** M	0230 / 0816 / 1459 / 2037	1.1 / 3.8 / 1.5 / 3.6
2 M	0310 / 0908 / 1541 / 2119	0.7 / 3.8 / 0.9 / 3.4	**17** TU	0302 / 0845 / 1528 / 2109	1.3 / 3.6 / 1.6 / 3.4
3 TU	0402 / 1000 / 1635 / 2212	0.9 / 3.5 / 1.2 / 3.2	**18** W	0336 / 0916 / 1605 / 2147	1.5 / 3.4 / 1.8 / 3.2
4 W	0502 / 1106 / 1737 / 2321	1.2 / 3.2 / 1.4 / 3.0	**19** TH	0418 / 0955 / 1701 / 2236	1.7 / 3.2 / 2.0 / 3.0
5 TH	0612 / 1253 / 1847	1.4 / 3.0 / 1.6	**20** F	0517 / 1049 / 1815 / 2355	1.9 / 3.0 / 2.0 / 2.9
6 F	0104 / 0733 / 1428 / 2002	2.9 / 1.5 / 3.1 / 1.6	**21** SA	0631 / 1242 / 1932	1.9 / 2.9 / 1.9
7 SA	0237 / 0907 / 1541 / 2115	3.0 / 1.5 / 3.2 / 1.5	**22** SU	0219 / 0749 / 1455 / 2047	3.0 / 1.8 / 3.0 / 1.7
8 SU	0342 / 1015 / 1628 / 2211	3.2 / 1.4 / 3.4 / 1.3	**23** M	0324 / 0906 / 1549 / 2147	3.3 / 1.6 / 3.3 / 1.4
9 M	0423 / 1104 / 1702 / 2257	3.5 / 1.2 / 3.6 / 1.1	**24** TU	0411 / 1010 / 1631 / 2234	3.5 / 1.2 / 3.5 / 1.0
10 TU	0500 / 1144 / 1733 / 2337	3.7 / 1.1 / 3.7 / 0.9	**25** W	0452 / 1100 / 1708 / 2317	3.8 / 0.9 / 3.7 / 0.7
11 W ○	0536 / 1221 / 1805	3.9 / 1.0 / 3.8	**26** TH ●	0531 / 1144 / 1744 / 2358	4.1 / 0.6 / 3.9 / 0.4
12 TH	0015 / 0611 / 1255 / 1836	0.8 / 4.0 / 1.0 / 3.9	**27** F	0609 / 1226 / 1820	4.2 / 0.4 / 4.0
13 F	0051 / 0644 / 1328 / 1907	0.8 / 4.0 / 1.1 / 3.9	**28** SA	0040 / 0647 / 1307 / 1856	0.2 / 4.3 / 0.3 / 4.0
14 SA	0126 / 0716 / 1400 / 1937	0.8 / 4.0 / 1.2 / 3.9			
15 SU	0159 / 0747 / 1430 / 2007	0.9 / 3.9 / 1.3 / 3.8			

MARCH

Day	Time	m	Day	Time	m
1 SU	0123 / 0725 / 1349 / 1934	0.2 / 4.2 / 0.3 / 3.9	**16** M	0132 / 0721 / 1359 / 1940	0.9 / 3.9 / 1.1 / 3.8
2 M	0207 / 0805 / 1431 / 2014	0.3 / 4.0 / 0.5 / 3.8	**17** TU	0200 / 0747 / 1423 / 2008	1.0 / 3.8 / 1.3 / 3.7
3 TU	0253 / 0847 / 1517 / 2056	0.5 / 3.8 / 0.7 / 3.5	**18** W	0227 / 0813 / 1443 / 2038	1.2 / 3.6 / 1.4 / 3.5
4 W	0343 / 0934 / 1607 / 2143	0.8 / 3.4 / 1.0 / 3.2	**19** TH	0256 / 0843 / 1512 / 2113	1.4 / 3.4 / 1.6 / 3.3
5 TH	0440 / 1033 / 1705 / 2245	1.1 / 3.1 / 1.3 / 3.0	**20** F	0334 / 0919 / 1558 / 2158	1.6 / 3.2 / 1.8 / 3.1
6 F	0547 / 1222 / 1813	1.4 / 2.8 / 1.5	**21** SA	0431 / 1010 / 1719 / 2305	1.8 / 3.0 / 1.9 / 2.9
7 SA	0030 / 0714 / 1419 / 1932	2.8 / 1.6 / 2.8 / 1.6	**22** SU	0557 / 1135 / 1847	1.9 / 2.8 / 1.9
8 SU	0220 / 0905 / 1542 / 2054	2.9 / 1.6 / 3.0 / 1.5	**23** M	0137 / 0724 / 1431 / 2007	2.9 / 1.8 / 2.9 / 1.7
9 M	0340 / 1009 / 1622 / 2155	3.1 / 1.4 / 3.2 / 1.3	**24** TU	0258 / 0846 / 1529 / 2116	3.2 / 1.5 / 3.1 / 1.3
10 TU	0408 / 1053 / 1646 / 2240	3.3 / 1.2 / 3.4 / 1.1	**25** W	0347 / 0950 / 1610 / 2209	3.5 / 1.1 / 3.4 / 0.9
11 W	0442 / 1129 / 1713 / 2318	3.6 / 1.1 / 3.6 / 0.9	**26** TH	0430 / 1040 / 1647 / 2256	3.8 / 0.8 / 3.7 / 0.6
12 TH	0516 / 1201 / 1744 / 2354	3.8 / 1.0 / 3.8 / 0.8	**27** F	0510 / 1124 / 1723 / 2340	4.1 / 0.5 / 3.9 / 0.3
13 F ○	0550 / 1231 / 1815	3.9 / 0.9 / 3.9	**28** SA ●	0549 / 1206 / 1759	4.3 / 0.2 / 4.0
14 SA	0028 / 0622 / 1301 / 1844	0.7 / 4.0 / 0.9 / 3.9	**29** SU	0023 / 0627 / 1247 / 1836	0.1 / 4.3 / 0.2 / 4.1
15 SU	0101 / 0652 / 1331 / 1912	0.8 / 4.0 / 1.0 / 3.9	**30** M	0107 / 0706 / 1328 / 1914	0.1 / 4.2 / 0.2 / 4.0
			31 TU	0151 / 0746 / 1410 / 1954	0.2 / 4.0 / 0.4 / 3.8

APRIL

Day	Time	m	Day	Time	m
1 W	0237 / 0827 / 1454 / 2035	0.4 / 3.7 / 0.6 / 3.6	**16** TH	0159 / 0749 / 1414 / 2014	1.2 / 3.6 / 1.3 / 3.5
2 TH	0326 / 0912 / 1543 / 2121	0.8 / 3.3 / 1.0 / 3.3	**17** F	0230 / 0820 / 1446 / 2050	1.3 / 3.4 / 1.4 / 3.4
3 F	0421 / 1007 / 1638 / 2218	1.1 / 3.0 / 1.2 / 3.0	**18** SA	0311 / 0859 / 1532 / 2137	1.5 / 3.2 / 1.6 / 3.2
4 SA	0527 / 1149 / 1742 / 2352	1.5 / 2.7 / 1.5 / 2.8	**19** SU	0409 / 0953 / 1641 / 2243	1.6 / 3.0 / 1.7 / 3.0
5 SU	0657 / 1355 / 1858	1.7 / 2.7 / 1.6	**20** M	0533 / 1115 / 1808	1.7 / 2.8 / 1.7
6 M	0151 / 0848 / 1516 / 2022	2.8 / 1.6 / 2.8 / 1.5	**21** TU	0037 / 0702 / 1346 / 1930	3.0 / 1.6 / 2.8 / 1.6
7 TU	0308 / 0949 / 1554 / 2127	3.0 / 1.5 / 3.0 / 1.4	**22** W	0222 / 0821 / 1457 / 2042	3.2 / 1.4 / 3.1 / 1.3
8 W	0342 / 1030 / 1617 / 2214	3.2 / 1.3 / 3.3 / 1.2	**23** TH	0318 / 0924 / 1543 / 2141	3.5 / 1.1 / 3.4 / 0.9
9 TH	0415 / 1104 / 1645 / 2252	3.4 / 1.1 / 3.5 / 1.0	**24** F	0403 / 1015 / 1621 / 2232	3.8 / 0.7 / 3.6 / 0.6
10 F	0450 / 1134 / 1716 / 2327	3.6 / 1.0 / 3.7 / 0.9	**25** SA	0446 / 1101 / 1659 / 2320	4.1 / 0.5 / 3.9 / 0.3
11 SA ○	0523 / 1203 / 1748	3.8 / 1.0 / 3.8	**26** SU ●	0527 / 1143 / 1738	4.2 / 0.3 / 4.0
12 SU	0000 / 0555 / 1231 / 1818	0.8 / 3.9 / 0.9 / 3.9	**27** M	0005 / 0607 / 1225 / 1816	0.2 / 4.2 / 0.2 / 4.1
13 M	0033 / 0626 / 1300 / 1846	0.8 / 3.9 / 1.0 / 3.9	**28** TU	0051 / 0647 / 1307 / 1856	0.2 / 4.1 / 0.3 / 4.0
14 TU	0104 / 0655 / 1328 / 1914	0.9 / 3.8 / 1.0 / 3.8	**29** W	0136 / 0728 / 1349 / 1937	0.3 / 3.9 / 0.4 / 3.9
15 W	0132 / 0722 / 1352 / 1943	1.0 / 3.7 / 1.2 / 3.7	**30** TH	0223 / 0809 / 1433 / 2018	0.6 / 3.6 / 0.7 / 3.6

8

Chart Datum: 2·10 metres below Ordnance Datum (Newlyn)

SCOTLAND – OBAN

LAT 56°25′N   LONG   5°29′W

TIMES AND HEIGHTS OF HIGH AND LOW WATERS

YEAR **1998**

TIME ZONE (UT)
For Summer Time add ONE hour in non-shaded areas

MAY

Date	Day	Time	m	Time	m	Time	m	Time	m
1	F	0311	0.9	0853	3.3	1520	0.9	2103	3.4
2	SA	0404	1.2	0945	3.0	1612	1.2	2155	3.1
3	SU	0506	1.5	1103	2.8	1711	1.4	2307	2.9
4	M	0627	1.7	1310	2.7	1817	1.6		
5	TU	0057	2.9	0808	1.7	1422	2.8	1932	1.6
6	W	0218	3.0	0913	1.6	1507	3.0	2043	1.5
7	TH	0305	3.1	0957	1.4	1540	3.2	2136	1.3
8	F	0342	3.3	1032	1.3	1612	3.4	2218	1.2
9	SA	0418	3.5	1102	1.2	1646	3.6	2254	1.1
10	SU	0454	3.7	1131	1.1	1719	3.7	2328	1.0
11	M O	0529	3.8	1200	1.0	1752	3.8		
12	TU	0002	0.9	0602	3.8	1230	1.0	1822	3.8
13	W	0037	1.0	0633	3.8	1300	1.0	1852	3.8
14	TH	0110	1.0	0702	3.7	1329	1.1	1924	3.7
15	F	0143	1.1	0733	3.6	1358	1.2	1958	3.6
16	SA	0219	1.2	0809	3.4	1435	1.3	2038	3.4
17	SU	0303	1.4	0853	3.2	1521	1.4	2127	3.3
18	M	0401	1.5	0948	3.0	1622	1.5	2230	3.2
19	TU	0516	1.5	1100	2.9	1737	1.5	2356	3.2
20	W	0636	1.5	1240	2.9	1855	1.4		
21	TH	0138	3.3	0751	1.5	1415	3.1	2008	1.3
22	F	0246	3.5	0855	1.1	1511	3.3	2113	1.0
23	SA	0338	3.7	0949	0.9	1556	3.6	2210	0.8
24	SU	0424	3.9	1037	0.6	1637	3.8	2301	0.6
25	M ●	0508	4.1	1122	0.5	1719	3.9	2349	0.5
26	TU	0550	4.1	1205	0.4	1800	4.0		
27	W	0036	0.5	0631	4.0	1248	0.5	1841	4.0
28	TH	0123	0.6	0713	3.8	1330	0.6	1922	3.9
29	F	0209	0.8	0754	3.6	1414	0.7	2003	3.7
30	SA	0256	1.0	0837	3.4	1459	1.0	2045	3.6
31	SU	0345	1.3	0923	3.1	1546	1.2	2131	3.3

JUNE

Date	Day	Time	m	Time	m	Time	m	Time	m
1	M	0440	1.5	1018	2.9	1637	1.4	2225	3.1
2	TU	0543	1.7	1144	2.8	1733	1.5	2334	3.0
3	W	0701	1.8	1318	2.8	1833	1.6		
4	TH	0102	2.9	0818	1.7	1415	2.9	1937	1.6
5	F	0213	3.0	0913	1.6	1459	3.1	2039	1.6
6	SA	0302	3.2	0954	1.5	1537	3.3	2131	1.4
7	SU	0345	3.3	1027	1.4	1615	3.4	2215	1.3
8	M	0426	3.5	1059	1.2	1652	3.6	2255	1.2
9	TU	0505	3.6	1131	1.1	1729	3.7	2335	1.1
10	W O	0542	3.7	1203	1.0	1804	3.8		
11	TH	0013	1.0	0616	3.7	1237	1.0	1837	3.8
12	F	0053	1.0	0649	3.7	1312	1.0	1911	3.8
13	SA	0132	1.0	0723	3.6	1347	1.0	1948	3.7
14	SU	0213	1.1	0802	3.5	1427	1.0	2030	3.6
15	M	0259	1.2	0847	3.3	1512	1.1	2118	3.5
16	TU	0353	1.3	0938	3.2	1607	1.2	2215	3.4
17	W	0456	1.3	1040	3.0	1711	1.3	2326	3.3
18	TH	0607	1.4	1157	3.0	1824	1.3		
19	F	0056	3.3	0718	1.3	1330	3.0	1938	1.3
20	SA	0217	3.4	0825	1.2	1442	3.2	2048	1.2
21	SU	0318	3.6	0924	1.0	1536	3.4	2151	1.0
22	M	0410	3.7	1016	0.9	1622	3.7	2247	0.9
23	TU	0457	3.8	1104	0.7	1706	3.8	2338	0.7
24	W ●	0540	3.9	1149	0.7	1747	3.9		
25	TH	0025	0.7	0621	3.9	1232	0.6	1828	4.0
26	F	0111	0.8	0701	3.8	1314	0.7	1908	3.9
27	SA	0155	0.9	0740	3.7	1355	0.8	1947	3.8
28	SU	0238	1.1	0818	3.5	1436	0.9	2025	3.7
29	M	0321	1.3	0857	3.3	1518	1.1	2105	3.5
30	TU	0406	1.5	0939	3.2	1602	1.3	2147	3.3

JULY

Date	Day	Time	m	Time	m	Time	m	Time	m
1	W	0454	1.7	1028	3.0	1649	1.5	2235	3.1
2	TH	0549	1.8	1134	2.9	1741	1.7	2337	3.0
3	F	0653	1.9	1301	2.9	1837	1.7		
4	SA	0058	3.0	0803	1.8	1411	3.0	1937	1.7
5	SU	0215	3.1	0905	1.7	1504	3.1	2038	1.7
6	M	0314	3.2	0952	1.5	1549	3.3	2135	1.5
7	TU	0402	3.4	1031	1.3	1631	3.5	2226	1.3
8	W	0446	3.5	1106	1.2	1711	3.7	2312	1.1
9	TH O	0527	3.6	1142	1.0	1749	3.8	2356	1.0
10	F	0604	3.7	1218	0.9	1826	3.9		
11	SA	0038	0.9	0638	3.7	1255	0.8	1901	3.9
12	SU	0121	0.8	0713	3.7	1334	0.7	1939	3.9
13	M	0203	0.8	0751	3.6	1415	0.7	2019	3.8
14	TU	0248	0.9	0833	3.5	1500	0.8	2104	3.7
15	W	0337	1.0	0920	3.3	1550	1.0	2156	3.5
16	TH	0433	1.2	1015	3.2	1649	1.1	2258	3.3
17	F	0537	1.3	1123	3.0	1757	1.3	2337	3.0
18	SA	0023	3.2	0646	1.4	1255	3.0	1912	1.4
19	SU	0157	3.2	0757	1.3	1424	3.1	2030	1.3
20	M	0309	3.3	0904	1.2	1528	3.3	2142	1.2
21	TU	0407	3.5	1002	1.1	1617	3.5	2241	1.1
22	W	0454	3.6	1051	0.9	1659	3.7	2331	1.0
23	TH ●	0535	3.7	1136	0.8	1738	3.9		
24	F	0016	0.9	0612	3.8	1218	0.7	1815	4.0
25	SA	0058	0.9	0647	3.8	1257	0.7	1852	4.0
26	SU	0137	1.0	0722	3.8	1335	0.8	1927	3.9
27	M	0215	1.1	0755	3.7	1412	0.9	2001	3.9
28	TU	0252	1.3	0827	3.6	1449	1.1	2035	3.7
29	W	0328	1.4	0902	3.4	1527	1.3	2110	3.5
30	TH	0408	1.6	0940	3.2	1608	1.5	2147	3.3
31	F	0454	1.8	1026	3.1	1655	1.7	2231	3.1

AUGUST

Date	Day	Time	m	Time	m	Time	m	Time	m
1	SA	0550	1.9	1131	2.9	1749	1.8	2333	3.0
2	SU	0657	1.9	1316	2.9	1851	1.9		
3	M	0126	2.9	0810	1.9	1437	3.0	1957	1.8
4	TU	0250	3.0	0917	1.7	1531	3.2	2105	1.7
5	W	0346	3.2	1006	1.4	1615	3.4	2206	1.4
6	TH	0432	3.4	1046	1.2	1656	3.7	2256	1.1
7	F	0513	3.6	1123	0.9	1735	3.9	2341	0.9
8	SA O	0550	3.8	1200	0.7	1812	4.0		
9	SU	0023	0.7	0623	3.8	1238	0.5	1848	4.1
10	M	0105	0.6	0657	3.9	1318	0.4	1924	4.1
11	TU	0147	0.5	0734	3.8	1400	0.5	2003	4.0
12	W	0230	0.6	0814	3.7	1444	0.6	2045	3.8
13	TH	0316	0.8	0857	3.5	1533	0.8	2133	3.6
14	F	0408	1.0	0948	3.2	1630	1.1	2230	3.3
15	SA	0508	1.2	1052	3.0	1736	1.3	2357	3.1
16	SU	0617	1.4	1231	2.9	1853	1.5		
17	M	0147	3.0	0732	1.5	1419	3.0	2023	1.5
18	TU	0310	3.1	0848	1.4	1532	3.2	2146	1.4
19	W	0409	3.3	0950	1.2	1616	3.4	2242	1.2
20	TH	0450	3.5	1039	1.0	1649	3.7	2325	1.1
21	F	0523	3.6	1121	0.9	1724	3.9		
22	SA ●	0003	1.0	0555	3.8	1201	0.7	1757	4.0
23	SU	0039	0.9	0627	3.9	1238	0.7	1831	4.0
24	M	0113	1.0	0658	3.9	1313	0.7	1903	4.0
25	TU	0146	1.0	0727	3.8	1346	0.9	1934	3.9
26	W	0219	1.2	0757	3.7	1418	1.0	2004	3.8
27	TH	0251	1.3	0827	3.6	1452	1.3	2034	3.6
28	F	0325	1.5	0900	3.4	1528	1.5	2104	3.4
29	SA	0404	1.7	0939	3.2	1611	1.7	2140	3.2
30	SU	0458	1.9	1028	3.0	1706	1.9	2227	3.0
31	M	0606	2.0	1203	2.9	1814	2.0		

Chart Datum: 2·10 metres below Ordnance Datum (Newlyn)

SCOTLAND – OBAN

LAT 56°25′N   LONG 5°29′W

TIMES AND HEIGHTS OF HIGH AND LOW WATERS

YEAR **1998**

TIME ZONE (UT)
For Summer Time add ONE hour in non-shaded areas

Chart Datum: 2·10 metres below Ordnance Datum (Newlyn)

SEPTEMBER

#	Time	m	#	Time	m
1 TU	0000 0723 1418 1929	2.8 2.0 3.0 1.9	**16** W	0312 0831 1541 2146	3.0 1.5 3.2 1.5
2 W	0237 0841 1515 2046	2.9 1.8 3.2 1.7	**17** TH	0405 0934 1606 2233	3.2 1.3 3.4 1.3
3 TH	0334 0940 1558 2151	3.2 1.5 3.5 1.4	**18** F	0434 1022 1630 2310	3.4 1.1 3.7 1.1
4 F	0417 1024 1638 2241	3.4 1.1 3.8 1.1	**19** SA	0500 1102 1701 2342	3.6 0.9 3.9 1.0
5 SA	0455 1102 1715 2324	3.7 0.8 4.0 0.7	**20** SU ●	0530 1139 1734	3.8 0.8 4.0
6 SU ○	0530 1140 1752	3.8 0.5 4.2	**21** M	0014 0600 1214 1805	1.0 3.9 0.8 4.1
7 M	0005 0602 1220 1827	0.5 4.0 0.3 4.3	**22** TU	0045 0630 1246 1835	1.0 4.0 0.8 4.1
8 TU	0045 0636 1300 1904	0.4 4.0 0.3 4.3	**23** W	0115 0658 1318 1905	1.0 4.0 0.9 4.0
9 W	0126 0713 1343 1942	0.4 4.0 0.3 4.1	**24** TH	0146 0727 1348 1933	1.1 3.9 1.1 3.9
10 TH	0208 0752 1428 2023	0.5 3.8 0.5 3.9	**25** F	0215 0756 1419 2000	1.3 3.8 1.3 3.7
11 F	0253 0834 1517 2108	0.7 3.6 0.8 3.6	**26** SA	0243 0827 1450 2028	1.5 3.6 1.5 3.5
12 SA	0343 0922 1613 2204	0.9 3.3 1.1 3.2	**27** SU	0313 0902 1528 2101	1.7 3.4 1.8 3.3
13 SU	0441 1024 1719 2335	1.2 3.1 1.4 2.9	**28** M	0357 0947 1624 2146	1.9 3.1 2.0 3.0
14 M	0549 1213 1840	1.5 2.9 1.6	**29** TU	0514 1056 1744 2301	2.0 3.0 2.1 2.8
15 TU	0142 0707 1421 2031	2.9 1.5 3.0 1.6	**30** W	0638 1351 1907	2.0 3.0 2.0

OCTOBER

#	Time	m	#	Time	m
1 TH	0219 0759 1452 2027	2.9 1.8 3.3 1.7	**16** F	0343 0908 1540 2211	3.1 1.4 3.4 1.4
2 F	0315 0905 1535 2130	3.1 1.5 3.6 1.4	**17** SA	0406 0956 1603 2245	3.3 1.2 3.6 1.3
3 SA	0355 0954 1613 2219	3.4 1.2 3.9 1.0	**18** SU	0431 1037 1634 2316	3.6 1.1 3.9 1.1
4 SU	0431 1037 1650 2302	3.7 0.8 4.2 0.7	**19** M	0501 1112 1706 2345	3.8 1.0 4.0 1.1
5 M ○	0504 1118 1727 2342	3.9 0.5 4.4 0.4	**20** TU ●	0532 1146 1737	3.9 0.9 4.1
6 TU	0538 1159 1804	4.1 0.3 4.4	**21** W	0013 0602 1219 1808	1.0 4.0 0.9 4.1
7 W	0022 0614 1242 1841	0.3 4.1 0.3 4.4	**22** TH	0044 0631 1250 1838	1.0 4.0 1.1 4.0
8 TH	0103 0651 1326 1920	0.3 4.1 0.3 4.2	**23** F	0115 0700 1321 1907	1.1 4.0 1.2 3.9
9 F	0145 0731 1412 2001	0.4 4.0 0.5 3.9	**24** SA	0144 0730 1351 1934	1.3 3.9 1.4 3.8
10 SA	0230 0813 1501 2046	0.7 3.7 0.8 3.6	**25** SU	0210 0801 1421 2003	1.4 3.7 1.6 3.6
11 SU	0319 0900 1557 2139	0.9 3.5 1.2 3.2	**26** M	0237 0921 1459 2038	1.6 3.5 1.8 3.3
12 M	0415 0959 1702 2306	1.2 3.2 1.5 2.9	**27** TU	0316 0921 1553 2124	1.8 3.3 1.9 3.1
13 TU	0520 1143 1827	1.5 3.0 1.7	**28** W	0421 1024 1715 2236	1.9 3.1 2.0 2.9
14 W	0127 0636 1408 2021	2.8 1.6 3.0 1.7	**29** TH	0548 1244 1841	2.0 3.1 2.0
15 TH	0255 0801 1524 2129	2.9 1.6 3.2 1.6	**30** F	0132 0709 1415 1959	2.9 1.8 3.3 1.7
			31 SA	0242 0822 1504 2101	3.1 1.6 3.6 1.4

NOVEMBER

#	Time	m	#	Time	m
1 SU	0326 0920 1545 2151	3.4 1.2 3.9 1.1	**16** M	0358 1005 1604 2246	3.5 1.3 3.7 1.3
2 M	0402 1010 1624 2236	3.7 0.9 4.2 0.8	**17** TU	0431 1043 1637 2315	3.7 1.2 3.8 1.2
3 TU	0437 1055 1703 2318	3.9 0.6 4.4 0.5	**18** W	0504 1117 1711 2344	3.9 1.2 4.0 1.2
4 W ○	0514 1140 1742 2359	4.1 0.5 4.4 0.4	**19** TH ●	0537 1150 1745	4.0 1.1 4.0
5 TH	0553 1225 1821	4.2 0.4 4.4	**20** F	0015 0608 1225 1817	1.1 4.0 1.2 4.0
6 F	0041 0633 1311 1901	0.4 4.2 0.5 4.2	**21** SA	0048 0640 1259 1847	1.2 3.9 1.3 3.9
7 SA	0124 0714 1358 1943	0.5 4.1 0.7 3.9	**22** SU	0119 0711 1332 1917	1.2 3.9 1.4 3.8
8 SU	0209 0757 1447 2028	0.7 3.9 1.0 3.6	**23** M	0148 0744 1405 1949	1.4 3.8 1.5 3.6
9 M	0258 0843 1541 2118	1.0 3.6 1.3 3.2	**24** TU	0219 0821 1444 2027	1.5 3.6 1.7 3.4
10 TU	0350 0937 1643 2226	1.2 3.3 1.6 3.0	**25** W	0258 0905 1535 2114	1.6 3.5 1.8 3.2
11 W	0450 1052 1801	1.5 3.1 1.8	**26** TH	0351 1002 1644 2217	1.7 3.4 1.9 3.1
12 TH	0043 0557 1307 1942	2.8 1.6 3.1 1.8	**27** F	0501 1120 1804 2343	1.8 3.3 1.9 3.0
13 F	0206 0714 1427 2054	2.9 1.7 3.2 1.7	**28** SA	0621 1316 1920	1.7 3.4 1.7
14 SA	0257 0826 1503 2139	3.1 1.6 3.3 1.6	**29** SU	0139 0737 1426 2025	3.1 1.6 3.6 1.5
15 SU	0328 0922 1532 2215	3.3 1.5 3.5 1.5	**30** M	0245 0845 1516 2121	3.3 1.3 3.8 1.2

DECEMBER

#	Time	m	#	Time	m
1 TU	0331 0943 1600 2210	3.6 1.1 4.1 0.9	**16** W	0402 1009 1612 2247	3.5 1.5 3.6 1.4
2 W	0413 1036 1643 2255	3.9 0.8 4.2 0.7	**17** TH	0439 1048 1650 2319	3.7 1.4 3.8 1.3
3 TH ○	0455 1124 1725 2339	4.1 0.7 4.3 0.6	**18** F ●	0516 1126 1727 2352	3.8 1.3 3.9 1.2
4 F	0537 1212 1806	4.2 0.6 4.3	**19** SA	0551 1203 1802	3.9 1.3 3.9
5 SA	0023 0618 1259 1848	0.6 4.2 0.7 4.1	**20** SU	0026 0625 1241 1835	1.2 4.0 1.2 3.9
6 SU	0107 0701 1346 1930	0.6 4.1 0.8 3.9	**21** M	0059 0658 1318 1906	1.1 3.9 1.3 3.8
7 M	0152 0743 1434 2012	0.7 4.0 1.1 3.7	**22** TU	0132 0732 1354 1940	1.2 3.9 1.3 3.7
8 TU	0237 0827 1523 2057	0.9 3.8 1.4 3.4	**23** W	0206 0809 1433 2018	1.2 3.8 1.4 3.6
9 W	0325 0914 1617 2148	1.2 3.5 1.6 3.1	**24** TH	0245 0851 1519 2103	1.3 3.7 1.5 3.4
10 TH	0417 1007 1718 2257	1.4 3.3 1.8 3.0	**25** F	0331 0941 1615 2155	1.4 3.5 1.6 3.2
11 F	0513 1117 1832	1.6 3.2 1.9	**26** SA	0429 1043 1723 2301	1.5 3.4 1.7 3.1
12 SA	0047 0614 1259 1953	2.9 1.7 3.1 1.9	**27** SU	0539 1205 1836	1.6 3.4 1.6
13 SU	0156 0722 1412 2055	3.0 1.7 3.2 1.8	**28** M	0025 0657 1343 1946	3.1 1.5 3.5 1.5
14 M	0244 0829 1456 2140	3.2 1.7 3.3 1.7	**29** TU	0158 0813 1452 2050	3.2 1.4 3.6 1.3
15 TU	0324 0925 1534 2215	3.3 1.6 3.5 1.6	**30** W	0306 0922 1546 2147	3.4 1.2 3.8 1.1
			31 TH	0357 1022 1633 2238	3.7 1.0 3.9 0.9

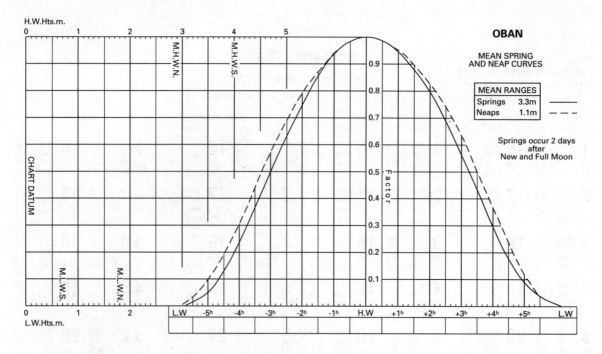

OBAN

MEAN SPRING
AND NEAP CURVES

MEAN RANGES	
Springs	3.3m
Neaps	1.1m

Springs occur 2 days
after
New and Full Moon

ADJACENT ANCHORAGES/HAVEN

DUNSTAFFNAGE BAY, Argyll & Bute, 56°27´·05N 05°25´·90W. Rtg 3-2-1. AC 2378, 2387. HW −0530 on Dover; see 10.8.19. Good shelter at marina pontoons, SE side of bay entered 'twixt Rubha Garbh and Eilean Mór; little room to ⚓, but 7 Y Øs available. No navigational hazards; W and SW sides of bay dry. Private pier on NW side has 2 FG (vert) 4m 2M. **Dunstaffnage Marina** ☎ (01631) 566555, 📠 567422, VHF Ch 80, AB £10.74, FW, Slip, BH (10 ton), SM, R, Bar; **Alba Yachts** ☎ 565630, VHF Ch M call *Alba*, ME, El, Sh, CH, Gas. Facilities: P & D (cans, ¾M), V (½M), Bus, ⇌ Oban (2M) & Connel (airstrip). In the bay 8ca to E, 37 Øs and landing pontoon are approved.

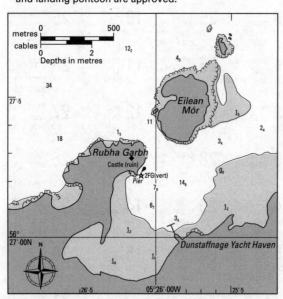

LOCH ETIVE, AC 2378 to Bonawe, thence AC 5076. Connel Bridge, 15m clrnce, and Falls of Lora can be physical and tidal barriers. HT cables at Bonawe have 13m clrnce. See CCC SDs.

OBAN   10-8-19

Argyll and Bute 56°25´·00N 05°29´·00W   Rtg 1-2-2

CHARTS
AC 1790, 2387, *2171*; Imray C65; OS 49
TIDES
−0530 Dover; ML 2·4; Duration 0610; Zone 0 (UT)

Standard Port OBAN (⟵)

Times				Height (metres)			
High Water		Low Water		MHWS	MHWN	MLWN	MLWS
0100	0700	0100	0800	4·0	2·9	1·8	0·7
1300	1900	1300	2000				
Differences DUNSTAFFNAGE BAY							
+0005	0000	0000	+0005	+0·1	+0·1	+0·1	+0·1
CONNEL							
+0020	+0005	+0010	+0015	−0·3	−0·2	−0·1	+0·1
BONAWE							
+0150	+0205	+0240	+0210	−2·0	−1·7	−1·3	−0·5

Oban is a Standard Port and tidal predictions for each day of the year are given above.

SHELTER
Good except in strong SW/NW winds, but Ardantrive Bay (20 Øs, some pontoon berths and water taxi 0800-2300) is sheltered from these winds. See chartlet for Øs. ⚓s off town, but in deep water. ⚓ or M off Brandystone and in Kerrera Sound at: Horseshoe Bay, Gallanachbeg (rk dries 0·3m) and Little Horseshoe Bay.
Dunstaffnage Bay, 3M NE: see facing column.
NAVIGATION
WPT 56°25´·80N 05°30´·00W, 306°/126° from/to Dunollie lt, 0·71M. Beware Sgeir Rathaid, buoyed, in middle of the bay; also CalMac ferries running to/from Railway Quay.
LIGHTS AND MARKS
N Spit of Kerrera Fl R 3s 9m 5M, W col, R bands. Dunollie Fl (2) WRG 6s 7m 5/4M; G351°-009°, W009°-047°, R047°-120°, W120°-138°, G138°-143°. N Pier 2FG (vert). S Quay 2FG (vert). Northern Lights Wharf Oc G 6s.
RADIO TELEPHONE
Call *North Pier* Ch 12 16 (0900-1700). For Railway Quay, call *CalMac* Ch 06 12 16. For Ardantrive Bay, call *Oban Yachts* Ch 80.
TELEPHONE (Dial code 01631)
Pier 562892; Marinecall 0891 500 463; ✆ 563079; MRSC 563720; Police 562213; Dr 563175.

OBAN *continued*

FACILITIES
N Pier ☎ 562892, L, FW, C (15 ton mobile) via Piermaster;
Rly Quay, L, Slip, D, FW, CH;
Services: BY, Slip, ACA, Gas, ME, EI, divers;
Oban Yachts (Ardantrive Bay) ☎ 565333, 📠 565888, AB
£12.24, M, D, FW, ME, Sh, C, CH, Slip, BH (16 ton), Gas.
Town EC Thurs; P, V, R, Bar, ✉, Ⓑ, 🄾, ≈, ✈.

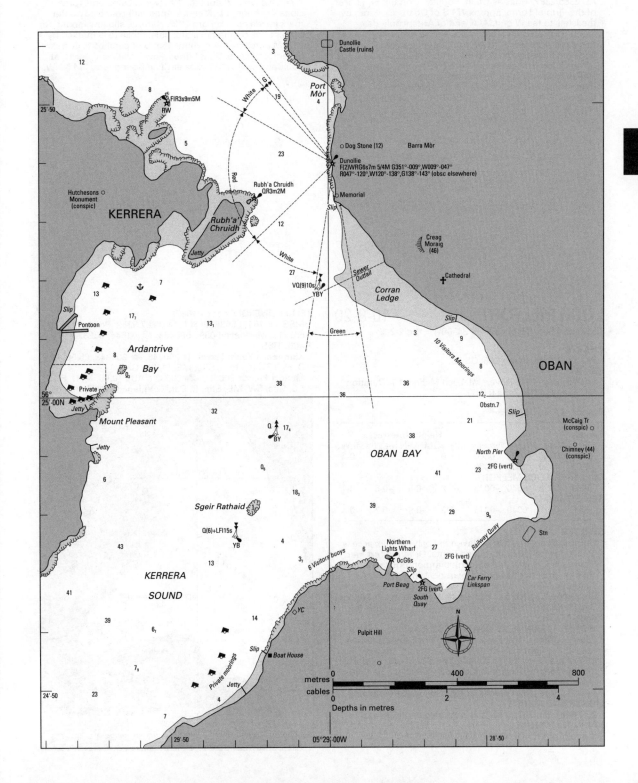

ANCHORAGES ON MAINLAND SHORE OF FIRTH OF LORN

LOCH FEOCHAN, Argyll and Bute, 56°21'.40N 05°29'.70W. AC 2387. HW = HW Oban; flood runs 4 hrs, ebb for 8 hrs. Caution: strong streams off Ardentallan Pt. Good shelter, 5M S of Oban and 1.5M SE of Kerrera. Best appr at local slack LW = LW Oban +0200. Narrow chan marked by 3 PHM buoys, 2 PHM perches on shore and 5 SHM buoys. ⌕ off pier, or moor/berth at **Ardoran Marine** ☎ (01631) 566123, ⚓ 566611 AB, M, D, FW, ME, Gas, Sh, Slip, CH, Showers, V. **Royal Highland YC**, Ardentallan Ho ☎ (01631) 563309.

PUILLADOBHRAIN, Argyll & Bute, 56°19'.48N 05°35'.15W. AC 2386/2387. Tides as Oban. Popular ⌕ on the SE shore of the Firth of Lorne, approx 7M S of Oban, sheltered by the islets to the W of it. At N end of Ardencaple Bay identify Eilean Dùin (18m) and steer SE keeping 1½ca off to clear a rk awash at its NE tip. Continue for 4ca between Eilean nam Beathach, with Orange drum on N tip, and Dun Horses rks drying 2.7m. Two W cairns on E side of Eilean nam Freumha lead approx 215° into the inner ⌕ in about 4m. Landing at head of inlet. Nearest facilities: Bar, P at Clachan Br (½M); ☎, ⊠ at Clachan Seil.

CUAN SOUND, Argyll & Bute, 56°15'.85N 05°37'.40W. AC 2326, 2386. Tides see 10.8.20 Seil Sound. Streams reach 6kn at sp; N-going makes at HW Oban +0420, S-going at HW Oban −2. The Sound is a useful doglegged short cut from Firth of Lorne to Lochs Melfort and Shuna, but needs care due to rks and tides. There are ⌕s at either end to await the tide. At the 90° dogleg, pass close N of Cleit Rk onto which the tide sets; it is marked by a Y △ perch. The chan is only ¾ca wide here due to rks off Seil. Overhead cables (35m) cross from Seil to Luing. There are ⌕s out of the tide to the S of Cleit Rk. No Its/facilities. See CCC SDs.

ARDINAMAR, Luing/Torsa, 56°14'.93N 05°36'.97W. AC 2326. HW −0555 on Dover; ML 1.7m; see 10.8.20 SEIL SOUND. A small cove and popular ⌕ between Luing and Torsa, close W of ent to L. Melfort. Appr with conspic W paint mark inside cove on brg 290°. Narrow, shallow (about 1m CD) ent has drying rks either side, those to N marked by 2 SHM perches. Keep about 15m S of perches to ⌕ in 2m in centre of cove; S part dries. Few facilities: V, ⊠, ☎, at Cullipool 1½M WNW. Gas at Cuan Sound ferry 2M NNW.

LOCH MELFORT   10-8-20

Argyll and Bute 56°14'.60N 05°34'.00W   Rtg 2-2-1

CHARTS
AC *2326, 2169*; Imray C65; OS 55

TIDES
Loch Shuna −0615 Dover; ML Loch Melfort 1.7; Duration Seil Sound 0615; Zone 0 (UT)

Standard Port OBAN (←—)

Times				Height (metres)			
High Water		Low Water		MHWS	MHWN	MLWN	MLWS
0100	0700	0100	0800	4.0	2.9	1.8	0.7
1300	1900	1300	2000				
Differences LOCH MELFORT							
−0055	−0025	−0040	−0035	−1.2	−0.8	−0.5	−0.1
SEIL SOUND							
−0035	−0015	−0040	−0015	−1.3	−0.9	−0.7	−0.3

SHELTER
Good at Kilmelford Yacht Haven in Loch na Cille; access at all tides for 3m draft, but no lights. Or at Melfort Pier (Fearnach Bay at N end of loch): pier/pontoons in 2m, but chan to inner hbr has only 1m; good ⌕ in N winds. ⌕s sheltered from S − W at: a bay with moorings ½M inside the ent on S shore, but beware rk drying 1.5m; in Kames Bay (1.5M further E) clear of moorings, rks and fish farm.

NAVIGATION
WPT 56°14'.00N 05°35'.00W, 210°/030° from/to summit Eilean Gamhna, 4ca. Pass either side of Eilean Gamhna. 8ca NE lies Campbell Rk (1.8m). A rk drying 1m lies 1½ca ESE of the FS on Eilean Coltair. The S side of L Melfort is mostly steep-to, except in Kames Bay. At Loch na Cille, beware drying reef ¾ca off NE shore (PHM perch), and rk near S shore (SHM perch); boats may obscure perches.

LIGHTS AND MARKS
2FR (vert) 6m 3M on Melfort pier; also depth gauge.

RADIO TELEPHONE
Kilmelford VHF Ch **80** M (HO). *Melfort Pier* Ch 12 16.

TELEPHONE (Dial code 01852)
MRSC (01631) 563720; ‡ (0141) 887 9369; Police (01631) 562213; Marinecall 0891 500463; Ⓗ (01546) 602323.

FACILITIES
Kilmelford Yacht Haven ☎ 200248, ⚓ 200343, £8.50, M, D, FW, BH (12 ton), Slip, ME, El, Sh, Gas;
Melfort Pier ☎ 200333, ⚓ 200329, AB £10.50, M, D, P, AC, Gas, FW, ME, Slip, R, Bar, Ⓞ. **Village** (¾M) V, Bar, ⊠.

CRAOBH MARINA (Loch Shuna)

Argyll & Bute 56°12'·81N 05°33'·47W Rtg 1-1-1   **10-8-21**

CHARTS
AC *2326, 2169*; Imray C65; OS 55

TIDES
HW Loch Shuna –0615 Dover; Seil Sound Duration 0615, ML 1·4; Zone 0 (UT). For tidal figures see 10.8.20.

SHELTER
Very good. Craobh (pronounced Croove) Marina (access H24) on SE shore of Loch Shuna is enclosed by N and S causeways between islets. The ent is between 2 bkwtrs on the N side. In the marina, a shoal area S of the E bkwtr is marked by PHM buoys. A pink perch in W corner of hbr marks a spit; elsewhere ample depth. There are ⚓s in Asknish Bay 1M to the N, and in the bays E of Eilean Arsa and at Bàgh an Tigh-Stòir, S of Craobh.

NAVIGATION
WPT 56°13'·02N 05°33'·50W, 353°/173° from/to ent, 2ca. Tidal streams in Loch Shuna are weak. Beware lobster pots in appr's and unmarked rks (dr 1·5m) 4ca NNE of ent. An unlit SHM buoy marks a rk (1m) 150m NNW of the W bkwtr. 1M N of marina, Eich Donna, an unmarked reef (dr 1·5m), lies between Eilean Creagach and Arduaine Pt.

LIGHTS AND MARKS
The W sector, 162°-183°, of Dir Lt, Iso WRG 5s 10m 5/3M, on E bkwtr hd leads 172° between the close-in rks above.

RADIO TELEPHONE
VHF Ch M, 80 (summer 0830-2000LT; winter 0830-1800).

TELEPHONE (Dial code 01852)
Hr Mr 500222; MRSC (01631) 563720; ⌗ (0141) 887 9369; Marinecall 0891 500463; Police (01546) 602222; Ⓗ (01546) 602323.

FACILITIES
Craobh Marina (200+50 Ⓥ) ☎ 500222, ⛴ 500252, £14.49, AC, D, FW, SM, BY, CH, Slip, BH (15 ton), C (12 ton), Gas, Gaz, ME, El, Sh, R, SC, Ⓔ, ◌, Divers. **Village** V, Bar, Ⓑ (Wed), ✉ (Kilmelford), ⇌ (Oban by bus), ✈ (Glasgow).

8

LOCH CRAIGNISH   10-8-22

Argyll and Bute 56°08'·00N 05°35'·00W   Rtg (Ardfern) 2-1-1

CHARTS
AC *2326, 2169*; Imray C63, C65; OS 55

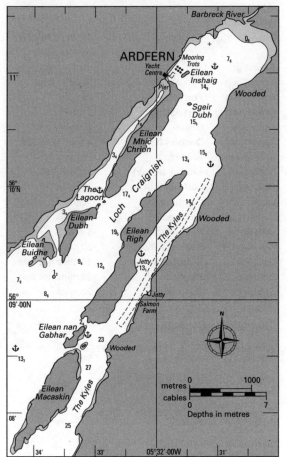

TIDES
+0600 Dover; ML (Loch Beag)1·2; Duration (Seil Sound) 0615; Zone 0 (UT)

Standard Port OBAN (⟵)

Times				Height (metres)			
High Water		Low Water		MHWS	MHWN	MLWN	MLWS
0100	0700	0100	0800	4·0	2·9	1·8	0·7
1300	1900	1300	2000				
Differences LOCH BEAG (Sound of Jura)							
–0110	–0045	–0035	–0045	–1·6	–1·2	–0·8	–0·4

Note: HW Ardfern is approx HW Oban –0045; times/heights much affected by local winds and barometric pressure

SHELTER
Good at Ardfern, 56°11'·0N 05°31'·8W, access H24; ⚓s at:
– Eilean nan Gabhar; appr from E chan and ⚓ E of island.
– Eilean Righ; midway up the E side of the island.
– Bàgh na Cille, NNE of Craignish Pt.
– Eilean Dubh in the "lagoon" between the Is and mainland. Beware squalls in E'lies, especially on E side of loch.

NAVIGATION
WPT 56°07'·60N 05°35'·30W (off chartlet) between Dorus Mór and Liath-sgier Mhòr. Beware: strong tidal streams (up to 8kn) in Dorus Mór; a reef extending 1ca SSW of the SE chain of islands; rk 1½ca SSW of Eilean Dubh; fish cages especially on E side of loch; a drying rk at N end of Ardfern ⚓ with a rk awash ¼ca E of it. (These 2 rks are ½ca S of the more S'ly of little islets close to mainland. The main fairway is free from hazards, except for Sgeir Dhubh, a rk 3½ca SSE of Ardfern, with a reef extending about ½ca all round. Ardfern is 1ca W of Eilean Inshaig.

LIGHTS AND MARKS
No lts.

RADIO TELEPHONE
Ardfern Yacht Centre VHF Ch 80 M (office hrs).

TELEPHONE (Dial code 01852)
Hr Mr (Yacht Centre) 500247/500636; MRSC (01631) 563720; Marinecall 0891 500 463; ⌗ (0141) 887 9369; Dr (01546) 602921; Ⓗ (01546) 602449.

FACILITIES
Ardfern Yacht Centre (87+20 visitors); ☎ 500247/500636, ⛴ 500624, AB £10.96, M, FW, AC, D, BH (20 ton), Slip, ME, El, Sh, ACA, C (12 ton), CH, Gas, Gaz.
Village R, V, Ⓑ (Wed), ✉ , ⇌ (Oban), ✈ (Glasgow).

SUBMARINE EXERCISE AREAS (SUBFACTS)   10-8-23

Areas N of Mull in which submarine activity is planned for the next 16 hrs are broadcast after the weather forecast at 0303, 0703, 1103, 1503, 1903, 2303UT by the following **Coast Radio Stations** (see also 6.5.1):
Lewis Ch 05; **Hebrides** 1866kHz; and **Skye** Ch 24.
Stornoway CG will pass details on request Ch 16.
Navtex broadcasts by **Portpatrick Radio** at 0930 & 2130UT include Subfacts and Gunfacts.
A Fisherman's Hotline ☎ (01374) 613097 deals with queries. FOSNI Ops, ☎ (01346) 674321 Ext 6100, may also assist. The areas are referred to not by numbers (as shown, for lack of space, on the chartlet below), but by the names listed below. For Areas 22 – 81 (S of Mull), see 10.9.23. Submarines on the surface and at periscope depth always listen on Ch 16. The former will comply strictly with IRPCS; the latter will not close to within 1500 yds of a FV without its express permission; see also 8.5.1 for general advice.

1	Tiumpan	14	Raasay
2	Minch North	15	Neist
3	Stoer	16	Bracadale
4	Shiant	17	Ushenish
5	Minch South	18	Hebrides North
6	Ewe	19	Canna
7	Troddax	20	Rhum
8	Rona West	21	Sleat
9	Rona North	22	Barra
10	Lochmaddy	23	Hebrides Central
11	Dunvegan	24	Hawes
12	Portree	25	Eigg
13	Rona South	26	Hebrides South

FERRIES ON THE WEST COAST OF SCOTLAND   10-8-24

The following is a brief summary of the many ferries plying between mainland and island harbours. It supplements the UK and Continental ferry services listed in 10.0.4, and may prove useful when cruise plans or crews change, often in remote places. It covers Area 8 (Stornoway to Oban) and Area 9 (Jura to the Clyde).
The major operator is Caledonian MacBrayne: Head Office, The Ferry Terminal, Gourock PA19 1QP; ☎ 0990-650000 for reservations, 🖂 (01475) 637607. Many routes are very short and not be pre-bookable; seasonal routes are *asterisked.

From	To	Time	Remarks
Area 8			
Ullapool	Stornoway	2¾ hrs	See 10.0.4
Kyles Scalpay	Scalpay (Lewis)	10 mins	Not Sun
Uig (Skye)	Tarbert (Harris)	1¾ hrs	Not Sun
Uig	Lochmaddy (N Uist)	1¾ hrs	
Tarbert	Lochmaddy	1¾ hrs	Not Sun
Oban/Mallaig	Castlebay/Lochboisdale	5 hrs/1hr 50m	
Sconser (Skye)	Raasay	15 mins	Not Sun
Mallaig*	Kyle of Lochalsh	2 hrs	Fri only
Mallaig*	Armadale (Skye)	30 mins	
Mallaig	Eigg-Muck-Rhum-Canna	Varies	Not Sun
Oban	Tobermory-Coll-Tiree	Varies	Not Sun
Tobermory	Kilchoan	35 mins	
Fionnphort	Iona	5 mins	
Lochaline	Fishnish (Mull)	15 mins	
Oban	Craignure (Mull)	40 mins	
Oban	Lismore	50 mins	Not Sun
Areas 8/9			
Oban	Colonsay	2h10m	M/W/Fri
Area 9			
Kennacraig	Port Askaig/Colonsay	Varies	Wed
Kennacraig	Port Ellen	2h 10m	
Kennacraig	Port Askaig	2 hrs	
Tayinloan	Gigha	20 mins	
Ardrossan*	Douglas (IoM)	8 hrs	Sat/Sun
Ardrossan	Brodick	55 mins	
Rothesay*	Brodick (Arran)	1h50m	Mon/Thur
Claonaig	Lochranza (Arran)	30 mins	
Largs	Cumbrae Slip	15 mins	
Tarbert (L Fyne)	Portavadie*	20 mins	
Colintraive	Rhubodach (Bute)	5 mins	
Wemyss Bay	Rothesay (Bute)	30 mins	
Gourock	Kilcreggan	10 mins	Not Sun
Gourock	Helensburgh	30 mins	Not Sun
Gourock	Dunoon	20 mins	

Other Operators/services

Western Ferries (Argyll Ltd), ☎ *0141 332 8766:*
Port Askaig   Feolin (Jura)   Short

Argyll & Bute Council ☎ *01631 562125:*
Seil   Luing   Short

D.J.Rodgers, ☎ *01878 720261:*
South Uist   Eriskay

W. Rusk, ☎ *01878 720233:*
South Uist   Barra

VOLVO PENTA SERVICE

Sales and service centres in area 9

STRATHCLYDE *J. N. MacDonald & Co Ltd*, 47-49 Byron Street, Glasgow G11 6LP Tel 0141-334 6171 **RENFREWSHIRE** *J. N. MacDonald & Co Ltd*, Units B & C, The Yacht Harbour, Inverkip, Greenock, PA16 0AS Tel (01475) 522450

Area 9

South-West Scotland
Crinan Canal to Mull of Galloway

VOLVO PENTA

9

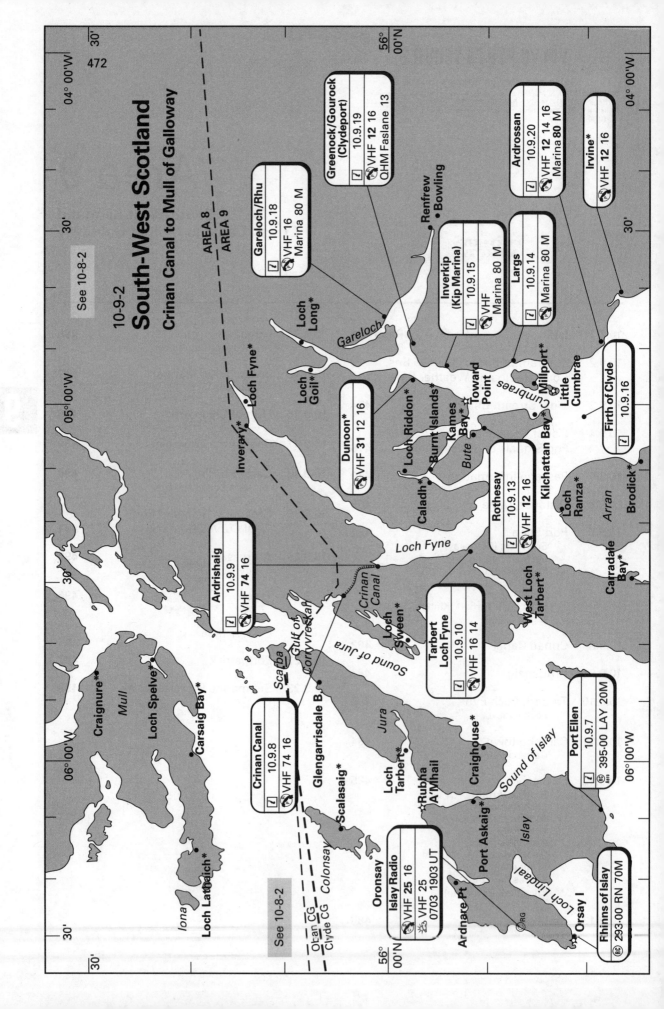

472

10-9-2
South-West Scotland
Crinan Canal to Mull of Galloway

See 10-8-2

AREA 8
AREA 9

Gareloch/Rhu
10.9.18
ℹ️ | 📻 VHF 16
Marina 80 M

Greenock/Gourock (Clydeport)
10.9.19
ℹ️ | 📻 VHF 12 16
QHM Faslane 13

Ardrossan
10.9.20
ℹ️ | 📻 VHF 12 14 16
Marina 80 M

Irvine*
📻 VHF 12 16

Inverkip (Kip Marina)
10.9.15
ℹ️ | 📻 VHF
Marina 80 M

Largs
10.9.14
ℹ️ | 📻 Marina 80 M

Firth of Clyde
10.9.16
ℹ️

Renfrew
Bowling

Loch Long*

Gareloch

Loch Goil*

Loch Fyne*

Inverary*

Dunoon*
📻 VHF 31 12 16

Loch Riddon*
Burnt Islands*
Kames Bay*
Caladh*

Bute
Toward Point
Cumbraes
Little Cumbrae
Millport*

Kilchattan Bay*

Rothesay
10.9.13
ℹ️ | 📻 VHF 12 16

Loch Ranza*
Arran
Brodick*

Ardrishaig
10.9.9
ℹ️ | 📻 VHF 74 16

Loch Fyne

Gulf of Corryvreckan

Scarba

Crinan Canal

Loch Sween*

Sound of Jura

Tarbert Loch Fyne
10.9.10
ℹ️ | 📻 VHF 16 14

West Loch Tarbert*

Carradale Bay*

Crinan Canal
10.9.8
ℹ️ | 📻 VHF 74 16

Glengarrisdale B.*

Jura

Scalasaig*

Loch Tarbert*

Rubha A'Mhail
☆

Craighouse*

Sound of Islay

Port Ellen
10.9.7
ℹ️ | 📻 395·00 LAY 20M

Islay Radio
📻 VHF 25 16
📡 VHF 25
0703 1903 UT

Oronsay

See 10-8-2

Oban CG
Clyde CG   Colonsay

Ardnave Pt

Port Askaig*

Islay

Loch Lindaal

Orsay I

Fhinns of Islay
293·00 RN 70M

Craignure**
Mull
Loch Spelve*
Carsaig Bay*

Iona

Loch Latoaich*

30'

06°00'W

05°00'W

04°00'W

56°00'N

56°00'N

30'

30'

30'

30'

Troon
10.9.21
ⓘ
🕮 VHF 14 16
Marina 80 M

Ayr*
🕮 VHF 14 16

Girvan*
🕮 VHF 12 16

Stranraer
🕮 VHF 14 16

Kirkcudbright
10.10.7
ⓘ
🕮 VHF 12 16

Lamlash
10.9.12
ⓘ

Campbeltown
10.9.11
ⓘ
🕮 VHF 12 14 16

Portpatrick
10.9.22
ⓘ

Portpatrick Radio
🕮 VHF 27 16
MF **1710** 1883

📻 VHF 27
MF 1883
0703 1903 UT

Variation
8°W (1998)

90
180
270
0

30'
04° 00'W

55°
00'N

30'

473

30'
05° 00'W

06° 00'W

30'

SEPARATION ZONE

For details
see Fig.10(7)3

NOTE: For summary of
navigational aids, etc. in
Northern Ireland, see 10-13-2.

55°
00'N

30'
06° 00'W

30'
05° 00'W

30'

04° 00'W

9

Holy
Island

Pladda ☆

Island Davaar ☆

Southend ☆

Sanda I.

Mull of
Kintyre ☆

Macrihanish ●

Fair
Head

Rathlin

Ailsa Craig ☆

Turnberry
Point ☆

Prestwick ●

Loch
Ryan*

Black Head ☆

Corsewall
Point ☆

Drummore ●

Crammag Head ☆

Mull of Galloway ☆

Clyde CG
Liverpool CG

Luce Bay

Port
William ●

Isle of Whithorn*

Garlieston*

Burrow Head

Wigtown Bay

Little Ross ●

Kirkcudbright

See 10-10-2

Key to Symbols

📻🕮   Coast Radio Station: VHF/MF frequencies

🕮📻   Port, VTS, or Marina Radio: VHF frequencies

🔘 ℞Ⓒ   Marine RDF beacon

Aero RDF beacon

ⓘ   See for harbour information/tidal data

📻   Weather information
(Frequencies/times of broadcasts)

🚁   SAR Helicopter base

☆   Selected Principal Lights

Light vessel/Light float/Lanby

Ⓞʀɢ   Emergency VHF DF

*   See Area Index

10-9-3   AREA 9 TIDAL STREAMS

5 Hours before HW Dover (0605 after HW Greenock)

4 Hours before HW Dover (0520 before HW Greenock)

3 Hours before HW Dover (0420 before HW Greenock)

2 Hours before HW Dover (0320 before HW Greenock)

1 Hour before HW Dover (0220 before HW Greenock)

HW Dover (0120 before HW Greenock)

Northward 10.8.3   Irish Sea 10.10.3   North Ireland 10.13.3

1 Hour after HW Dover (0020 before HW Greenock)

2 Hours after HW Dover (0040 after HW Greenock)

3 Hours after HW Dover (0140 after HW Greenock)

4 Hours after HW Dover (0240 after HW Greenock)

5 Hours after HW Dover (0340 after HW Greenock)

6 Hours after HW Dover (0440 after HW Greenock)

9

10.9.4 COASTAL LIGHTS, FOG SIGNALS AND WAYPOINTS

Abbreviations used below are given in 1.4.1. Principal lights are in **bold** print, places in CAPITALS, and light-vessels, light floats and Lanbys in *CAPITAL ITALICS*. Unless otherwise stated lights are white. m – elevation in metres; M – nominal range in miles. Fog signals are in *italics*. Useful waypoints are underlined – use those on land with care. All geographical positions should be assumed to be approximate. See 4.4.1. All positions are referenced to the OSGB 36 datum.

COLONSAY TO ISLAY

COLONSAY
Scalasaig, Rubha Dubh 56°04'·02N 06°10'·83W Fl (2) WR 10s 6m W8M, R5M; W bldg; vis R shore-230°, W230°-337°, R337°-354°.
Pier Hd Ldg Lts 262° FR 8/10m (occas).

SOUND OF ISLAY
Rhubh' a Mhàil (Ruvaal) 55°56'·20N 06°07'·35W Fl (3) WR 15s 45m **W24M, R21M**; W Tr; vis R075°-180°, W180°-075°.
Carragh an t'Struith 55°52'·3N 06°05'·7W Fl WG 3s 8m W9M, G6M, W Tr; vis W354°-078°, G078°-170°, W170°-185°.
Carraig Mòr 55°50'·4N 06°06'·0W Fl (2) WR 6s 7m W8M, R6M; W Tr; vis R shore-175°, W175°-347°, R347°-shore.
McArthur's Hd, S end 55°45'·85N 06°02'·80W Fl (2) WR 10s 39m W14M, R11M; W Tr; W in Sound of Islay from NE coast-159°, R159°-244°, W244°-E coast of Islay.
Eilean a Chùirn 55°40'·14N 06°01'·15W Fl (3) 18s 26m 8M; W Bn; obsc when brg more than 040°.
Otter Rock Lt By 55°33'·92N 06°07'·80W Q (6) + L Fl 15s; SCM.

PORT ELLEN
Port Ellen Lt By 55°37'·00N 06°12'·22W QG; SHM.
Carraig Fhada Fl WRG 3s 20m W8M, R6M, G6M; W ■ Tr; vis W shore-248°, G248°-311°, W311°-340°, R340°-shore.
Ro-Ro terminal 2 FG (vert) 7/6m 3M.

LOCH INDAAL
Bruichladdich Pier Hd 2 FR (vert) 6m 5M.
Rubh'an Dùin 55°44'·70N 06°22'·35W Fl (2) WR 7s 15m W13M, R12M; W Tr; vis W218°-249°, R249°-350°, W350°-036°.

Orsay Is, **Rhinns of Islay** 55°40'·38N 06°30'·70W Fl 5s 46m **24M**; W Tr; vis 256°-184°; RC.

JURA TO MULL OF KINTYRE

SOUND OF JURA/CRAIGHOUSE/LOCH SWEEN/GIGHA
Reisa an t-Struith, S end of Is 56°07'·78N 05°38'·84W Fl (2) 12s 12m 7M; W col.
Ruadh Sgeir 56°04'·32N 05°39'·69W Fl 6s 13m 8M; W ●Tr.
Skervuile 55°52'·47N 05°49'·80W Fl 15s 22m 9M; W Tr.
Eilean nan Gabhar 55°50'·05N 05°56'·15W Fl 5s 7m 8M; framework Tr; vis 225°-010°.
Na Cùiltean 55°48'·65N 05°54'·85W Fl 10s 9m 9M; col on W bldg.
Gamhna Gigha 55°43'·78N 05°41'·02W Fl (2) 6s 7m 5M.
Badh Rk Lt By 55°42'·30N 05°41'·18W Fl (2) G 12s; SHM.
Sgeir Nuadh Lt By 55°41'·78N 05°42'·00W Fl R 6s; PHM.
Sgeir Gigalum Lt By 55°39'·97N 05°42'·60W Fl G 6s; SHM.
Gigalum Rks Lt By 55°39'·20N 05°43'·62W Q (9) 15s; WCM.
Cathsgeir Lt By 55°39'·66N 05°47'·43W Q (9) 15s; WCM.
Caolas Gigalum Bn 55°39'·16N 05°44'·50W; NCM.

WEST LOCH TARBERT
Dunskeig Bay, N end Q (2) 10s 11m 8M.
Eileen Tráighe (off S side) 55°45'·40N 05°35'·70W Fl (2) R 5s 5m 3M; R post; Ra refl.

Corran Pt 55°46'·12N 05°34'·28W QG 3m 3M; G post.
Sgeir Mhein 55°47'·06N 05°32'·33W QR 3m 3M; R post.
Black Rocks 55°47'·91N 05°30'·07W QG 3M; G post.
Kennacraig Lt By 55°48'·67N 05°29'·10W QR; PHM.
Kennacraig ferry terminal 55°48'·42N 05°28'·94W 2 FG (vert) 7m 3M; silver post.

Mull of Kintyre 55°18'·6N 05°48'·1W Fl (2) 20s 91m **24M**; W Tr on W bldg; vis 347°-178°; *Horn Mo (N) 90s*.

CRINAN CANAL
E of lock ent 56°05'·48N 05°33'·30W Fl WG 3s 8m 4M; W Tr, R band; vis W shore-146°, G146°-shore.

ARDRISHAIG
Bkwtr Hd 56°00'·76N 05°26'·53W L Fl WRG 6s 9m 4M; W Tr; vis G287°-339°, W339°-350°, R350°-035°.
Sgeir Sgalag No. 49 By 56°00'·36N 05°26'·23W; SHM.
Gulnare Rk No. 48 Lt By 56°00'·18N 05°26'·24W Fl R 4s; PHM.

LOCH FYNE TO SANDA ISLAND

UPPER LOCH FYNE/INVERARY
'P' Lt By 56°00'·23N 05°21'·98W Fl R 3s; PHM.
Otter Spit 56°00'·63N 05°21'·03W Fl G 3s 7m 8M; G tank on pyramid.
Glas Eilean, S end 56°01'·10N 05°21'·10W Fl R 5s 12m 7M; R col on pedestal.
'Q' Lt By 56°00'·97N 05°20'·60W Fl R 3s; PHM.
Sgeir an Eirionnaich 56°06'·49N 05°13'·47W Fl WR 3s 7m 8M; B Tr on B ○ Tr, W stripes; vis R044°-087°, W087°-192°, R192°-210°, W210°-044°.
Furnace Wharf 56°09'·06N 05°10'·38W 2 FR (vert) 9m 5M.

EAST LOCH TARBERT
Madadh Maol, ent S side 55°52'·02N 05°24'·18W Fl R 2·5s 4m 3M; R col.
Eilean a'Choic, SE side QG 3m 2M; G col.

PORTAVADIE
Bkwtr 55°52'·52N 05°19'·16W 2 FG (vert) 6/4m 4M.

Sgat Mór (S end) 55°50'·85N 05°18'·42W Fl 3s 9m 12M; W ○ Tr.
No. 51 Lt By 55°45'·57N 05°19'·60W Fl R 4s; PHM.
Skipness range 55°46'·7N 05°19'·0W Iso R 8s 7m 10M; Y ◊ on bldg; vis 292·2°-312·2°. Oc (2) Y 10s **24M** when range in use (occas).

KILBRANNAN SOUND/CRANNAICH/CARRADALE BAY
Port Crannaich Bkwtr Hd 55°35'·7N 05°27'·8W Fl R 10s 5m 6M; vis 099°-279°.
Crubon Rk Lt By 55°34'·48N 05°27'·00W Fl (2) R 12s; PHM.
Otterard Lt By 55°27'·07N 05°31'·04W Q (3) 10s; ECM.
Smerby By 55°26'·89N 05°31'·92; PHM.

CAMPBELTOWN LOCH
Davaar N Pt 55°25'·69N 05°32'·37W Fl (2) 10s 37m **23M**; W Tr; vis 073°-330°; *Horn (2) 20s*.
'C' Lt By 55°25'·30N 05°34'·35W Fl (2) 6s; IDM.
Arranman's Barrels Lt By 55°19'·40N 05°32'·80W Fl (2) 12s; PHM.
Macosh Rk Lt By 55°17'·95N 05°36'·90W Fl R 6s; PHM.
Sanda Island, S side 55°16'·50N 05°34'·90W Fl 10s 50m **15M**; W Tr; Racon (T).
Patersons Rk Lt By 55°16'·90N 05°32'·40W Fl (3) R 18s; PHM.

KYLES OF BUTE TO RIVER CLYDE

KYLES OF BUTE/CALADH ·
Ardlamont Pt No. 47 Lt By 55°49'·59N 05°11'·68W Fl R 4s; PHM.

Carry Pt No. 46 Lt By 55°51'·42N 05°12'·17W Fl R 4s; PHM.

Rubha Ban Lt By 55°54'·95N 05°12'·33W Fl R 4s; PHM.

Burnt Is Lt By (NE of Eilean Fraoich) 55°55'·79N 05°10'·43W Fl G 3s; SHM.

Burnt Islands No. 42 Lt By (S of Eilean Buidhe) 55°55'·77N 05°10'·32W Fl R 2s; PHM.

Creyke Rk No. 45 By 55°55'·67N 05°10'·80W; PHM.

Beere Rk No. 44 By 55°55'·56N 05°10'·56W; SHM.

Wood Farm Rk No. 43 By 55°55'·43N 05°10'·25W; SHM.

Rubha Bodach Lt By 55°55'·39N 05°09'·53W Fl G; SHM.

Ardmaleish Pt No. 41 Lt By 55°53'·02N 05°04'·62W Q; NCM.

ROTHESAY
Front Pier, E end 55°50'·32N 05°03'·03W 2 FG (vert) 7m 5M.

Pier W end 2 FR (vert) 7m 5M.

Albert Pier near N end 2 FR (vert) 8m 5M.

FIRTH OF CLYDE
Ascog Patches No. 13 Lt Bn   55°49'·71N 05°00'·17W Fl (2) 10s 5m 5M; IDM.

Toward Pt 55°51'·73N 04°58'·73W Fl 10s 21m **22M**; W Tr.

No. 34 By 55°51'·43N 04°59'·03W; ECM.

Toward Bank No. 35 Lt By 55°51'·04N 04°59'·93W Fl G 3s; SHM.

Skelmorlie Lt By 55°51'·65N 04°56'·27W Iso 5s; SWM.

WEMYSS BAY/INVERKIP
Pier 55°52'·57N 04°53'·39W 2 FG (vert) 7/5m 5M.

No. 12 55°52'·96N 04°53'·70W Oc (2) Y 10s 5m 3M; SPM.

Inverkip oil jetty, S and N ends 2 FG (vert) 11m 2M.

'M' Lt By 55°53'·53N 04°54'·35W Fl G 5s; SHM.

Kip Lt By 55°54'·49N 04°52'·95W QG; SHM.

Cowal Lt By 55°56'·00N 04°54'·75W L Fl 10s; SWM.

Lunderston Bay No. 8 55°55'·5N 04°52'·9W Fl (4) Y 10s 5m 3M.

The Gantocks 55°56'·45N 04°55'·00W Fl R 6s 12m 6M; ● Tr.

DUNOON
Pier, S end and N end 2 FR (vert) 5m 6M.

Cloch Pt 55°56'·55N 04°52'·67W Fl 3s 24m 8M; W ● Tr, B band, W dwellings.

McInroy's Pt, Ro-Ro terminal 55°57'·09N 04°51'·20W 2 FG (vert) 5/3m 6M.

No. 5 55°56'·97N 04°51'·62W Oc (2) Y 10s 5m 3M; SPM.

HOLY LOCH
Hunter's Quay, Ro-Ro terminal 55°58'·27N 04°54'·42W 2 FR (vert) 6/4m 6M.

LOCH LONG/LOCH GOIL
Loch Long Lt By 55°59'·17N 04°52'·33W Oc 6s; SWM.

Baron's Pt No. 3 55°59'·2N 04°51'·0W Oc (2) Y 10s 5m 3M.

Ravenrock Pt 56°02'·17N 04°54'·32W Fl 4s 12m 10M; W Tr on W col. Dir Lt 204°, Dir WRG 9m (same Tr); vis R201·5°-203°, Al WR203°-203·5° (W phase incr with brg), F W203·5°-204·5°, Al WG204·5°-205° (G phase incr with brg), FG205°-206·5°.

Port Dornaige 56°03·76N 04°53'·60W Fl 6s 8m 11M; W col; vis 026°-206°.

Carraig nan Ron (Dog Rock) 56°06'·01N 04°51'·60W Fl 2s 7m 11M; W col.

The Perch, Ldg Lts 318° Front, 56°06'·90N 04°54'·20W Dir Fl WRG 3m 5M; vis G311°-317°, W317°-320°, R320°-322°. Same structure, Fl R 3s 3m 3M. Rear, 700m from front, F 7m 5M; vis 312°-322·5°.

Rubha Ardnahein 56°06'·20N 04°53'·50W Fl R 5s 3m 3M.

Finnart Oil Terminal, Cnap Pt 56°07'·41N 04°49'·88W Ldg Lts 031°. Front, Q 8m 10M; W col. Rear, 87m from front F 13m; R line on W Tr.

Ashton Lt By 55°58'·12N 04°50'·58W Iso 5s; SWM.

GOUROCK
Railway Pier Hd 55°57'·8N 04°49'·0W 2 FG (vert) 10/8m 3M; Gy Tr.

Kempock Pt No. 4 55°57'·72N 04°49'·27W Oc (2) Y 10s 6m 3M.

Whiteforeland Lt By 55°58'·12N 04°47'·20W L Fl 10s; SWM.

Rosneath Patch, S end 55°58'·52N 04°47'·37W Fl (2) 10s 5m 10M.

ROSNEATH/RHU NARROWS/GARELOCH
Ldg Lts 356°. **Front, No. 7N** 56°00'·06N 04°45'·28W Dir Lt 356°. Dir WRG 5m **W16M**, R13M, G13M; vis Al G/W 353°-355°, FW 355°-357°, Al W/R 357°-000° .

Dir Lt 115° WRG 3m **W16M**, R13M, G13M; vis Al WG 111°-114°; F 114°-116°, Al W/R 116°-119°; FR 119°-121°. Passing Lt Oc G 6s 3m 3M; vis 360°; G △ on G pile structure. Rear, Ardencaple Castle Centre 56°00'·55N 04°45'·35W 2 FG (vert) 26m 12M; Tr on Castle NW corner; vis 335°-020°.

No. 8N Lt Bn. Dir Lt 080° 55°59'·09N 04°44'·13W Dir WRG 3m; vis F & Al **W16M**, R13M, G13M; vis FG 075°-077·5°, AlWG077·5°-079·5°, FW079·5°-080·5°, Alt WR080·5°-082·5°, FR082·5°-085°. Dir Lt 138° WRG 3m F & Al; **W16M**, R13M, G13M; vis FG132°-134°, Al WG134°-137°, FW 137°-139°, Al WR139°-142°. Fl Y 3s 3m 3M; vis 360°; Y ✖ on Y pile structure..

Gareloch No. 1 Lt Bn 55°59'·12N 04°43'·81W VQ (4) Y 5s 9m; Y ✖ on Y structure.

Row Lt By 55°59'·85N 04°45'·05W Fl G 5s; SHM.

Cairndhu Lt By 56°00'·36N 04°45'·93W Fl G 2·5s; SHM.

Castle Pt 56°00'·20N 04°46'·43W Fl (2) R 10s 8m 6M; R mast.

Lt By 56°00'·62N 04°46'·47W Fl G 4s; SHM.

No. 3 N Lt Bn 56°00'·08N 04°46'·64W Dir Lt 149° WRG 9m **W16M**, R13M, G13M F & Al ; vis FG144°-145°, AlWG145°-148°, F148°-150°, Al WR150°-153°, FR153°-154°. Passing Lt Oc R 8s 9m 3M.

Rosneath DG Jetty 56°00'·40N 04°47'·43W 2 FR (vert) 5M; W col; vis 150°-330°.

Rhu SE Lt By 56°00'·65N 04°47'·09W Fl G 3s; SHM.

Rhu Pt 56°00'·96N 04°47'·12W Q (3) WRG 6s 9m W10M, R7M, G7M; vis G270°-000°, W000°-114°, R114°-188°.

Dir Lt 318° Dir WRG **W16M**, R13M,G13M; vis Al WG 315°-317°, F317°-319°, Al WR319°-321°, FR321°-325°.

Limekiln No. 2N Lt Bn 56°00'·67N 04°47'·64W Dir Lt 295° WRG 5m **W16M**, R13M, G13M F & Al; R ☐ on R Bn; vis AlWG291°-294°, F294°-296°, AlWR 296°-299°, FR299°-301°.

Rhu NE Lt By 56°01'·03N 04°47'·50W QG; SHM.

Rhu Spit Lt Bn 56°00'·85N 04°47'·27W Fl 3s 6m 6M.

Mambeg Dir Lt 331° 56°03'·77N 04°50'·39W Dir Q (4) WRG 8s 8m 14M; W I; vis G328·5°-330°, W330°-332°, R332°-333°; shown H24.

Faslane Base, Jetty, S elbow 56°03'·17N 04°49'·12W Fl G 5s 11m 5M.

Floating Barrier 56°03'·85N 04°49'·54W Fl Y 5s 3M.

Garelochhead, S Fuel Jetty 56°04'·23N 04°49'·62W 2 FG (vert) 10m 5M.

N Fuel Jetty, elbow 56°04'·35N 04°49'·66W Iso WRG 4s 10m 14M; vis G351°-356°, W356°-006°, R006°-011°.

GREENOCK
Anchorage Lts in line 196°. Front, 55°57'·6N 04°46'·5W FG 7m 12M; Y col. Rear, 32m from front, FG 9m 12M. Y col.

Lts in line 194·5°. Front, 55°57'·4N 04°45'·8W FG 18m. Rear, 360m from front, FG 33m.

Clydeport Container Terminal NW corner QG 8m 8M.
Victoria Hbr ent W side 2 FG 5m (vert).
Garvel Embankment, W end 55°56'·81N 04°43'·48W Oc G
10s 9m 4M.
E end, Maurice Clark Pt 55°56'·61N 04°42'·78W QG 7m 2M;
G Tr.

PORT GLASGOW
Beacon off ent 55°56'·25N 04°41'·18W FG 7m 9M; B&W
chequered Tr and cupola.
Steamboat Quay, W end FG 12m 12M; B&W chequered col;
vis 210°-290°. From here to Glasgow Lts on S bank are Fl G
and Lts on N bank are Fl R.

CLYDE TO MULL OF GALLOWAY

LARGS
Marina S Bkwtr Hd 55°46'·35N 04°51'·67W Oc G 10s 4m 4M.
W Bkwtr Hd Oc R 10s 4m 4M; R ■ on col.
Approach Lt By 55°46'·40N 04°51'·78W L Fl 10s; SWM.
Largs Pier Hd N end 2 FG (vert) 7/5m 5M (H24).

FAIRLIE
Hunterston Jetty, S end 55°45'·10N 04°52'·80W 2 FG (vert).
Pier N end 2 FG (vert) 7m 5M.
NATO Pier Hd 2 FG (vert) N and S ends.

MILLPORT, GREAT CUMBRAE
The Eileans, W end 55°44'·89N 04°55'·52W QG 5m 2M;
(shown 1/9-30/4.)

Ldg Lts 333°. Pier Hd front, 55°45'·04N 04°55'·78W FR 7m
5M. Rear, 137m from front, FR 9m 5M.

Mountstuart Lt By 55°48'·00N 04°57'·50W L Fl 10s; SWM.
Portachur Lt By 55°44'·35N 04°58'·44W Fl G 3s; SHM.
Runnaneun Pt (Rubha'n Eun) 55°43'·79N 05°00'·17W Fl R
6s 8m 12M; W Tr.

Little Cumbrae, Cumbrae Elbow 55°43'·27N 04°57'·95W
Fl 3s 31m **23M**; W Tr; vis 334°-210°. Shown by day when))⟩
operating.

ARDROSSAN
Approach Dir Lt 055° 55°38'·66N 04°49'·14W Dir F WRG
15m W14M, R11M, G11M; vis FG 050°-051·2°, Alt WG
051·2°-053·8°, W phase increasing with Brg; FW 053·8°-
056·2°; Alt WR 056·2°-058·8°. R phase increasing with brg;
FR 058·8°-060°. FR 13m 6M; vis 325°-145°.

N Bkwtr Hd Fl WR 2s 7m 5M; R gantry; vis R041°-126°,
W126°-041°.
Lighthouse Pier Hd 55°38'·47N 04°49'·50W Iso WG 4s 11m
9M; W Tr; vis W035°-317°, G317°-035°.
Eagle Rk Lt By 55°38'·22N 04°49'·62W Fl G 5s; SHM.

IRVINE
Ent N side 55°36'·21N 04°42'·01W Fl R 3s 6m 5M; R col.
S side Fl G 3s 6m 5M; G col.
Ldg Lts 051°. Front, 55°36'·41N 04°41'·50W FG 10m 5M.
Rear, 101m from front, FR 15m 5M; G masts, vis 019°-120°.

TROON
Troon Lt By 55°33'·07N 04°41'·28W Fl G 4s; SHM.
West Pier Hd 55°33'·07N 04°40'·95W Fl (2) WG 5s 11m 9M;
W Tr; vis G036°-090°, W090°-036°.
E Pier Hd Fl R 10s 6m 3M.

Lady I 55°31'·63N 04°43'·95W Fl (4) 30s 19m 8M; W Bn.

ARRAN/RANZA/LAMLASH/BRODICK
Hamilton Rk Lt By 55°32'·63N 05°04'·83W Fl R 6s; PHM.
Brodick Bay, Pier Hd 2 FR (vert) 9m 4M.
Pillar Rk Pt (Holy Island), 55°31'·05N 05°03'·57W Fl (2) 20s
38m **25M**; W ■ Tr.
Holy I SW end Fl G 3s 14m 10M; W Tr; vis 282°-147°.
Pladda 55°25'·50N 05°07'·07W Fl (3) 30s 40m **17M**; W Tr.

AYR
Bar Lt By 55°28'·12N 04°39'·38W Fl G 2s; SHM.
N Bkwtr Hd 55°28'·22N 04°38'·71W QR 9m 5M.
S Pier Hd Q 7m 7M; R Tr; vis 012°-161°. FG 5m 5M; same Tr;
vis 012°-082°.
Ldg Lts 098°. Front, 55°28'·16N 04°38'·31W FR 10m 5M;
R Tr. Rear, 130m from front Oc R 10s 18m 9M.

Turnberry Pt, near castle ruins 55°19'·55N 04°50'·60W
Fl 15s 29m **24M**; W Tr.
Ailsa Craig 55°15'·12N 05°06'·42W Fl 4s 18m **17M**; W Tr;
vis 145°-028°.

GIRVAN
N Groyne Hd 55°14'·71N 04°51'·64W Iso 4s 3m 4M.
S Pier Hd 2 FG (vert) 8m 4M; W Tr.
N Bkwtr Hd 55°14'·74N 04°51'·77W Fl (2) R 6s 7m 4M.

LOCH RYAN
Cairn Pt 54°58'·48N 05°01'·77W Fl (2) R 10s 14m 12M; W Tr.
Cairnryan 54°57'·77N 05°00'·92W Fl R 5s 5m 5M.
Forbes Shoal Lt By 54°59'·48N 05°02'·88W QR; PHM.
Loch Ryan W Lt By 54°59'·23N 05°03'·17W QG; SHM.

Stranraer No. 1 Bn 54°56'·69N 05°01'·30W Oc G 6s; SHM.
No. 3 Bn 54°55'·89N 05°01'·52W QG; SHM.
No. 5 54°55'·09N 05°01'·80W Fl G 3s; SHM.

STRANRAER
Ross Pier Hd 2 F Bu (vert).
E Pier Hd 54°54'·62N 05°01'·52W 2 FR (vert) 9m.
W Pier Hd 2 FG (vert) 8m 4M; Gy col.

Corsewall Pt 55°00'·43N 05°09'·50W Fl (5) 30s 34m **22M**;
W Tr; vis 027°-257°.
Killantringan, Black Hd 54°51'·71N 05°08'·75W Fl (2) 15s
49m **25M**; W Tr.

PORTPATRICK
Ldg Lts 050·5°. Front, 54°50'·50N 05°06'·95W FG (occas).
Rear, 68m from front, FG 8m (occas).

Crammag Hd 54°39'·90N 04°57'·80W Fl 10s 35m **18M**; W Tr.
Mull of Galloway, SE end 54°38'·05N 04°51'·35W Fl 20s
99m **28M**; W Tr; vis 182°-105°.

10.9.5 PASSAGE INFORMATION

Although conditions in the South-West of Scotland are in general less rugged than from Mull northwards, some of the remarks at the start of 10.8.5 are equally applicable to this area. Refer to the Admiralty *West Coast of Scotland Pilot*; to *Yachtsman's Pilot to the W Coast of Scotland, Clyde to Colonsay*, Imray/Lawrence, and to the Clyde Cruising Club's SDs. Submarines exercise throughout these waters; see 10.8.20 and 10.9.22 for information on active areas (Subfacts).

Some of the following more common Gaelic terms may help with navigation: *Acairseid*: anchorage. *Ailean*: meadow. *Aird, ard*: promontory. *Aisir, aisridh*: passage between rocks. *Beag*: little. *Beinn*: mountain. *Bo, boghar, bodha*: rock. *Cala*: harbour. *Camas*: channel, bay. *Caol*: strait. *Cladach*: shore, beach. *Creag*: cliff. *Cumhamn*: narrows. *Dubh, dhubh*: black. *Dun*: castle. *Eilean, eileanan*: island. *Garbh*: rough. *Geal, gheal*: white. *Glas, ghlas*: grey, green. *Inis*: island. *Kyle*: narrow strait. *Linn, Linne*: pool. *Mor, mhor*: large. *Mull*: promontory. *Rinn, roinn*: point. *Ruadh*: red, brown. *Rubha, rhu*: cape. *Sgeir*: rock. *Sruth*: current. *Strath*: river valley. *Tarbert*: isthmus. *Traigh*: beach. *Uig*: bay.

CORRYVRECKAN TO CRINAN (charts *2326*, 2343)

Between Scarba and Jura is the Gulf of Corryvreckan (chart 2343) which is best avoided, and should never be attempted by yachts except at slack water and in calm conditions. (In any event the Sound of Luing is always a safer and not much longer alternative). The Gulf has a least width of 6ca and is free of dangers, other than its very strong tides which, in conjunction with a very uneven bottom, cause extreme turbulence. This is particularly dangerous with strong W winds over a W-going (flood) tide which spews out several miles to seaward of the gulf, with overfalls extending 5M from the W of ent (The Great Race). Keep to the S side of the gulf to avoid the worst turbulence and the whirlpool known as The Hag, caused by depths of only 29m, as opposed to more than 100m in the fairway. The W-going stream in the gulf begins at HW Oban + 0410, and the E-going at HW Oban – 0210. Sp rate W-going is 8·5kn, and E-going about 6kn.

The range of tide at sp can vary nearly 2m between the E end of the gulf (1·5m) and the W end (3·4m), with HW ½ hr earlier at the E end. Slack water occurs at HW Oban +4 and –2½ and lasts almost 1 hr at nps, but only 15 mins at sps. On the W-going (flood) stream eddies form both sides of the gulf, but the one on the N (Scarba) shore is more important. Where this eddy meets the main stream off Camas nam Bairneach there is violent turbulence, with heavy overfalls extending W at the division of the eddy and the main stream. There are temp anchs with the wind in the right quarter in Bàgh Gleann a' Mhaoil in the SE corner of Scarba, and in Bàgh Gleann nam Muc at N end of Jura but the latter has rks in approaches E and SW of Eilean Beag.

SE of Corryvreckan is Loch Crinan, which leads to the Crinan Canal (10.9.8). Beware Black Rk, 2m high and 2ca N of the canal sea lock, and dangers extending 100m from the rk.

WEST OF JURA TO ISLAY (charts 2481, 2168)

The W coasts of Colonsay and Oronsay (chart *2169*) are fringed with dangers up to 2M offshore. The two islands are separated by a narrow chan which dries and has an overhead cable (10m). There are HIE ⚓s at Scalasaig; see 10.9.7.

The Sound of Islay presents no difficulty; hold to the Islay shore, where all dangers are close in. The N-going stream begins at HW Oban + 0440, and the S-going at HW Oban – 0140. The sp rates are 2·5kn at N entrance and 1·5kn at S entrance, but reaching 5kn in the narrows off Port Askaig.

There are anchs in the Sound, but mostly holding ground is poor. The best places are alongside at Port Askaig (10.9.7), or at anch off the distillery in Bunnahabhain B, 2·5M to N. There are overfalls off McArthur's Hd (Islay side of S entrance) during the S-going stream.

The N coast of Islay and Rhinns of Islay are very exposed. In the N there is anch SE of Nave Island at entrance to Loch Gruinart; beware Balach Rks which dry, just to N. To the SW off Orsay (lt), Frenchman's Rks and W Bank there is a race and overfalls which should be cleared by 3M. Here the NW-going stream begins at HW Oban + 0530, and the SE-going at HW Oban – 0040; sp rates are 6-8kn inshore, but decrease to 3kn 5M offshore. Loch Indaal gives some shelter; beware rks extending from Laggan Pt on E side of ent. Off the Mull of Oa there are further overfalls. Port Ellen, the main hbr on Islay, has HIE ⚓s; there are some dangers in approach, and it is exposed to S; see 10.9.7 and chart 2474.

SOUND OF JURA TO GIGHA (charts 2397, 2396, 2168)

From Crinan to Gigha the Sound of Jura is safe if a mid-chan course is held. Ruadh Sgeir (lt) are rky ledges in mid-fairway, about 3M W of Crinan. Loch Sween (chart 2397) can be approached N or SE of MacCormaig Islands, where there is an attractive anch on NE side of Eilean Mor, but exposed to NE. Coming from N beware Keills Rk and Danna Rk. Sgeirean a Mhain is a rk in fairway 1·5M NE of Castle Sween (conspic on SE shore). Anch at Tayvallich, near head of loch on W side. See 10.9.7.

W Loch Tarbert (chart 2477) is long and narrow, with good anchs lts near ent, but unmarked shoals. On entry give a berth of at least 2½ca to Eilean Traighe off N shore, E of Ardpatrick Pt. Dun Skeig, an isolated hill, is conspic on S shore. Good anch near head of loch, 1M by road from E Loch Tarbert, Loch Fyne; see 10.9.10.

On W side of Sound, near S end of Jura, are The Small Is (chart 2396) across the mouth of Loch na Mile. Beware Goat Rk (dries 0·3m) 1½ca off southernmost Is, Eilean nan Gabhar, behind which is good anch. Also possible to go alongside Craighouse Pier (HIE ⚓) (10.9.7). Another anch is in Lowlandman's B, about 3M to N, but exposed to S winds; Ninefoot Rks with depth of 2·4m and ECM lt buoy lie off ent. Skervuile (lt) is a reef to the E, in middle of the Sound.

S of W Loch Tarbert, and about 2M off the Kintyre shore, is Gigha Is (chart 2475 and 10.9.7). Good anchs on E side in Druimyeon B and Ardminish B (HIE ⚓s), respectively N and S of Ardminish Pt. Outer and Inner Red Rks (least depth 2m) lie 2M SW of N end of Gigha Is. Dangers extend 1M W off S end of Gigha Is. Gigalum Is and Cara Is are off the S end. Gigha Sound needs very careful pilotage, since there are several dangerous rks, some buoyed/lit, others not. The N-going stream begins at HW Oban + 0430, and S-going at HW Oban – 0155, sp rates 1·3kn.

MULL OF KINTYRE (charts 2126, 2199, 2798)

From Crinan to Mull of Kintyre is about 50M. This long peninsula much affects the tidal streams in North Chan. Off Mull of Kintyre (lt, fog sig) the N-going stream begins at HW Oban + 0400, and the S-going at HW Oban – 0225, sp rate 5kn. A strong race and overfalls exist S and SW of Mull of Kintyre, dangerous in strong S winds against S-going tide. Careful timing is needed, especially W-bound. The Traffic Separation Scheme in the North Channel, see Fig. 10 (7), is only 2M W of the Mull and may limit sea-room in the ITZ.

Sanda Sound separates Sanda Is (lt) and its rks and islets, from Kintyre. On the mainland shore beware Macosh Rks (dry, PHM lt buoy) forming part of Barley Ridges, 2ca offshore; Arranman Barrels, drying and submerged, marked by PHM lt buoy; and Blindman Rk (depth 2m) 1·3M N of Ru Stafnish, where 3 radio masts are 5ca inland. Sanda Is has Sheep Is 3ca to the N; Paterson's Rk (dries) is 1M E. There is anch in Sanda hbr on N side. In Sanda Sound the E-going stream begins at HW Greenock + 0340, and the W-going at HW Greenock – 0230, sp rates 5kn. Tide races extend W, N and NE from Sanda, and in strong S or SW winds the Sound is dangerous. In these conditions pass 2M S of Mull of Kintyre and Sanda and E of Paterson's Rk.

MULL OF KINTYRE TO UPPER LOCH FYNE
(charts *2126*, 2383, 2381, 2382).

Once E of Mull of Kintyre, tidal conditions and pilotage much improve. Campbeltown (10.9.11) is entered N of Island Davaar (lt, fog sig). 1·5M N of lt ho is Otterard Rk (depth 3·8m), with Long Rk (dries 1·1m) 5ca W of it; both are buoyed. E of Island Davaar tide runs 3kn at sp, and there are overfalls.

Kilbrannan Sound runs 21M from Island Davaar to Skipness Pt, where it joins Inchmarnock Water, Lower Loch Fyne and Bute Sound. There are few dangers apart from overfalls on Erins Bank, 10M S of Skipness, on S-going stream. Good anch in Carradale B (10.9.11), off Torrisdale Castle. There are overfalls off Carradale Pt on S-going stream.

Lower L. Fyne (chart 2381) is mainly clear of dangers to East L. Tarbert (10.9.10). On E shore beware rks off Ardlamont Pt; 4M to NW is Skate Is which is best passed to W. 3M S of Ardrishaig (10.9.9) beware Big Rk (depth 2·1m). Further N, at entrance to Loch Gilp (mostly dries) note shoals (least depth 1·5m) round Gulnare Rk, PHM lt buoy; also Duncuan Is with dangers extending SW to Sgeir Sgalag (depth 0·6m), buoyed.

Where Upper L. Fyne turns NE (The Narrows) it is partly obstructed by Otter Spit (dries 0·9m), extending 8ca WNW from E shore and marked by lt bn. The stream runs up to 2kn here. A buoyed/lit rk, depth less than 2m, lies about 7ca SW of Otter Spit bn. In Upper L. Fyne (chart 2382) off Minard Pt, the chan between rks and islands in the fairway is buoyed/lit. For Inveraray, see 10.9.10.

ARRAN, BUTE AND FIRTH OF CLYDE (charts 1906, 1907)

Bute Sound leads into Firth of Clyde, and is clear in fairway. Arran's mountains tend to cause squalls or calms, but it has good anchs at Lamlash (10.9.12), Brodick and Loch Ranza. Sannox Rock (depth 1·5m) is 2½ca off Arran coast 8M N of Lamlash (10.9.12). 1ca off W side of Inchmarnock is Tra na-h-uil, a rk drying 1·5m. In Inchmarnock Sound, Shearwater Rk (depth 0·9m) lies in centre of S entrance.

Kyles of Bute are attractive chan N of Bute from Inchmarnock Water to Firth of Clyde, and straightforward apart from Burnt Islands. Here it is best to take the north channel, narrow but well buoyed, passing S of Eilean Buidhe, and N of Eilean Fraoich and Eilean Mor. Care is needed, since sp stream may reach 5kn. Caladh Hbr is a beautiful anch 7ca NW of Burnt Is.

In contrast, the N lochs in Firth of Clyde are less attractive. Loch Goil is worth a visit but Loch Long is squally and has few anchs, while Gareloch (10.9.18) has little to attract cruising yachts other than Rhu marina. Navigation in Firth of Clyde is easy since tidal streams are weak, seldom exceeding 1kn and chans are well marked; but beware commercial and naval shipping and also unlit moorings, see 10.9.19. There are marinas on the mainland at Largs (10.9.14) and Inverkip (10.9.15). Rothesay hbr (10.9.13) on E Bute, and Kilchattan B (anch 6M to S) are both sheltered from SSE to WNW.

FIRTH OF CLYDE TO MULL OF GALLOWAY
(charts *2131*, *2126*, 2199, 2198)

Further S the coast is less inviting, with mostly commercial hbrs until reaching Ardrossan (10.9.20) and Troon (10.9.21), NW of which there are various dangers: beware Troon Rk (depth 5·6m, but sea can break), Lappock Rk (dries 0·6m, marked by bn), and Mill Rk (dries 0·4m, buoyed). Lady Isle (lt), shoal to NE, is 2M WSW of Troon.

There is a severe race off Bennane Hd (8M SSE of Ailsa Craig, conspic) when tide is running strongly. Loch Ryan offers little for yachtsmen but there is anch S of Kirkcolm Pt, inside the drying spit which runs in SE direction 1·5M from the point. There is also useful anch in Lady Bay, sheltered except from NE. Between Corsewall Pt and Mull of Galloway the S-going stream begins at HW Greenock + 0310, and the N-going at HW Greenock – 0250. Sp rate off Corsewall Pt is 2-3 kn, increasing to 5kn off and S of Black Hd. Portpatrick (10.9.22) is a useful passage hbr, but not in onshore winds. Races occur off Morroch B, Money Hd, Mull of Logan and SSE of Crammag Hd.

Mull of Galloway (lt) is S point of Scotland, a high (82m) headland and steep-to, but beware dangerous race extending nearly 3M to S. On E-going stream the race extends NNE into Luce B; on W-going stream it extends SW and W. Best to give the race a wide berth, or pass close inshore at slack water nps and calm weather.

See 10.10.5 for continuation eastward to Solway Firth and south into the Irish Sea. For notes on crossing the Irish Sea, see 10.13.5.

10.9.6   DISTANCE TABLE

Approximate distances in nautical miles are by the most direct route, whilst avoiding dangers and allowing for Traffic Separation Schemes. Places in *italics* are in adjoining areas; places in **bold** are in 10.0.5, Distances across the Irish Sea.

	1	2	3	4	5	6	7	8	9	10	11	12	13	14	15	16	17	18	19	20
1. *Loch Craignish*	**1**																			
2. **Port Ellen (Islay)**	42	**2**																		
3. Crinan	5	39	**3**																	
4. Ardrishaig	14	48	9	**4**																
5. East Loch Tarbert	24	58	19	10	**5**															
6. **Campbeltown**	55	47	50	39	31	**6**														
7. Mull of Kintyre	56	27	51	54	45	20	**7**													
8. Lamlash	48	61	43	34	25	24	34	**8**												
9. Largs	48	94	43	34	24	39	47	17	**9**											
10. Rothesay	49	95	44	35	25	43	48	23	9	**10**										
11. Kip Marina	53	85	48	39	28	50	58	25	10	8	**11**									
12. Greenock	59	90	54	45	36	53	63	31	16	14	6	**12**								
13. Rhu (Helensburgh)	62	94	57	48	37	59	67	33	19	17	9	4	**13**							
14. **Troon**	54	71	49	40	33	33	44	16	20	25	29	34	38	**14**						
15. Girvan	67	58	62	53	43	29	31	20	33	40	46	49	51	21	**15**					
16. Stranraer	89	62	84	75	65	34	35	39	56	63	69	65	74	44	23	**16**				
17. **Portpatrick**	88	63	83	74	66	39	36	44	61	67	68	77	77	49	28	23	**17**			
18. **Mull of Galloway**	104	78	99	90	82	56	52	60	78	82	84	93	93	65	62	39	16	**18**		
19. *Kirkcudbright*	136	111	131	122	114	88	84	92	110	114	116	124	125	97	94	71	48	32	**19**	
20. *Douglas (IoM)*	146	120	141	132	124	106	94	102	141	130	126	141	135	107	104	84	60	42	45	**20**

HARBOURS AND ANCHORAGES IN COLONSAY, JURA, ISLAY AND THE SOUND OF JURA

SCALASAIG, Colonsay, 56°04′·15N 06°10′·80W. AC 2474, 2169. HW +0542 on Dover; ML 2·2m. See 10·9·7. Conspic monument ½M SW of hbr. Beware group of rks N of pier hd marked by bn. 2 HIE Ⓥ berths on N side of pier, inner end approx 2·5m. Inner hbr to SW of pier is safe, but dries. Ldg lts 262°, both FR 8/10m on pier. Also ⚓ clear of cable in **Loch Staosnaig**; SW of Rubha Dubh lt, Fl (2) WR 10s 6m 8/5M; R shore-230°, W230°-337°, R337°-354°. Facilities: D, P, V (all at ✉), FW, Hotel ☎ (01951) 200316.

LOCH TARBERT, W Jura, 55°57′·70N 06°00′·00W. AC 2481, 2169. Tides as Rubha A'Mhàil (N tip of Islay). See 10.9.7. HW –0540 on Dover; ML 2·1m; Duration 0600. Excellent shelter inside the loch, but subject to squalls in strong winds; ⚓ outside in Glenbatrick Bay in approx 6m in S winds, or at Bagh Gleann Righ Mor in approx 2m in N winds. To enter inner loch via Cumhann Beag, there are four pairs of ldg marks (W stones) at approx 120°, 150°, 077°, and 188°, the latter astern, to be used in sequence; pilot book required. There are no facilities.

PORT ASKAIG, Islay, 55°50′·88N 06°06′·20W. AC 2481, 2168. HW +0610 on Dover; ML 1·2m. See 10·9·7. Hbr on W side of Sound of Islay. ⚓ close inshore in 4m or secure to ferry pier. Beware strong tide/eddies. ☆ FR at LB. Facilities: FW (hose on pier), Gas, P, R, Hotel, V, ✉, ferries to Jura and Kintyre. Other ⚓s in the Sound at: Bunnahabhain (2M N); Whitefarland Bay, Jura, opp Caol Ila distillery; NW of Am Fraoch Eilean (S tip of Jura); Aros Bay, N of Ardmore Pt.

CRAIGHOUSE, SE Jura, 55°50′·00N 05°56′·25W. AC 2396, 2481, 2168. HW +0600 on Dover; ML 0·5m; Duration 0640 np, 0530 sp. See 10·9·7. Good shelter, but squalls occur in W winds. Enter between lt bn on SW end of Eilean nan Gabhar, Fl 5s 7m 8M vis 225°-010°, and unlit bn close SW. There are 8 HIE ⚓s N of pier (☎ (01496) 810332), where yachts may berth alongside; or ⚓ in 5m in poor holding at the N end of Loch na Mile. Facilities: very limited, Bar, FW, ✉, R, V, Gas, P & D (cans). **Lowlandman's Bay** is 1M further N, with ECM buoy, Q (3) 10s, marking Nine Foot Rk (2·4m) off the ent. ⚓ to SW of conspic houses, off stone jetty.

LOCH SWEEN, Argyll and Bute, 55°55′·70N 05°41′·20W. AC 2397. HW +0550 on Dover; ML 1·5m; Duration 0610. See 10.9.8 Carsaig Bay. Off the ent to loch, **Eilean Mòr** (most SW'ly of MacCormaig Isles) has tiny ⚓ on N side in 3m; local transit marks keep clear of two rks, 0·6m and 0·9m. Inside the loch, beware Sgeirean a'Mhain, a rk in mid-chan to S of Taynish Is, 3M from ent. Good shelter in Loch a Bhealaich (⚓ outside **Tayvallich** in approx 7m on boulders) or enter inner hbr to ⚓ W of central reef. There are no lts. Facilities: Gas, Bar, ✉, FW (⚓ by ✉), R, V. Close to NE are ⚓s at **Caol Scotnish** and **Fairy Is**, the former obstructed by rks 3ca from ent.

WEST LOCH TARBERT, Argyll and Bute, (Kintyre), 55°45′N 05°36′W. AC 2477. Tides as Gigha Sound, 10.9.7. Good shelter. Ent is S of Eilean Traighe, Fl (2) R 5s, and NW of Dun Skeig, Q (2) 10s, where there is also conspic conical hill (142m). Loch is lit for 5M by 3 bns, QG, QR and QG in sequence, up to Kennacraig ferry pier, 2FG (vert). PHM buoy, QR, is 2½ca NW of pier. Caution: many drying rks and fish farms outside the fairway and near head of loch. ⚓s are NE of Eilean Traighe (beware weed & ferry wash); near Rhu Pt, possible ⚓s; NE of Eilean dà Gallagain, and at loch hd by pier (ru). Tarbert (10.9.10) is 1·5M walk/bus.

GIGHA ISLAND, Argyll and Bute, 55°40′·60N 05°44′·00W. AC 2475, 2168. HW +0600 on Dover; ML 0·9m; Duration 0530. See 10·9·7. Main ⚓ is **Ardminish Bay**: 12 HIE ⚓s in the centre. Reefs extend off both points, the S'ly reef marked by an unlit PHM buoy. Kiln Rk (dries 1·5m) is close NE of the old ferry jetty. **Druimyeon Bay** is more sheltered in E'lies, but care needed entering from S. ⚓s sheltered from winds in ( ): Port Mór (S-W), Bàgh na Dòirlinne (SE-S), W Tarbert Bay (NE). Caolas Gigalum (⚓ 50m SE of pier) is safe in all but NE-E winds. Beware many rks in Gigha Sound. Lts: Fl (2) 6s, on Gamhna Gigha (off NE tip), and WCM buoy Fl (9) 15s marks Gigalum Rks, at S end of Gigha. **Ardminish** ☎/⛽ (01583) 505254: FW, Gas, P & D (cans), ⛽, ✉, Bar, R, V.

PORT ELLEN   10·9·7
Islay (Argyll and Bute) 55°37′·30N 06°12′·20W   Rtg 3-4-2

CHARTS
AC 2474, 2168

TIDES
HW +0620 np, +0130 sp on Dover; ML 0·6. Sea level is much affected by the weather, rising by 1m in S/E gales; at nps the tide is sometimes diurnal and range negligible.

Standard Port OBAN (←—)

Times				Height (metres)			
High Water		Low Water		MHWS	MHWN	MLWN	MLWS
0100	0700	0100	0800	4·0	2·89	1·8	0·7
1300	1900	1300	2000				
Differences PORT ELLEN (S Islay)							
–0530	–0050	–0045	–0530	–3·1	–2·1	–1·3	–0·4
SCALASAIG (E Colonsay)							
–0020	–0005	–0015	+0005	–0·1	–0·2	–0·2	–0·2
GLENGARRISDALE BAY (N Jura)							
–0020	–0010	0000	0000	–0·4	–0·2	0·0	–0·2
CRAIGHOUSE (SE Jura)							
–0230	–0250	–0150	–0230	–3·0	–2·4	–1·3	–0·6
RUBHA A'MHÀIL (N Islay)							
–0020	0000	+0005	–0015	–0·3	–0·1	–0·3	–0·1
ARDNAVE POINT (NW Islay)							
–0035	+0010	0000	–0025	–0·4	–0·2	–0·3	–0·1
ORSAY ISLAND (SW Islay)							
–0110	–0110	–0040	–0040	–1·4	–0·6	–0·5	–0·2
BRUICHLADDICH (Islay, Loch Indaal)							
–0100	–0005	–0110	–0040	–1·7	–1·4	–0·4	+0·1
PORT ASKAIG (Sound of Islay)							
–0110	–0030	–0020	–0020	–1·9	–1·4	–0·8	–0·3
GIGHA SOUND (Sound of Jura)							
–0450	–0210	–0130	–0410	–2·5	–1·6	–1·0	–0·1
MACHRIHANISH							
–0520	–0350	–0340	–0540		Mean range 0·5 metres.		

SHELTER
Good shelter close S of pier and clear of ferries/FVs, but in S winds swell sets into the bay. 10 HIE ⚓s to W of Rubha Glas; adjacent rks are marked by 3 perches with reflective topmarks. Inner hbr dries. In W'lies ⚓ in Kilnaughton Bay, N of Carraig Fhada lt ho; or 4M ENE at Loch-an-t-Sàilein.

NAVIGATION
WPT 55°36′·70N 06°12′·00W, 146°/326° from/to Carraig Fhada lt ho, 0·63M. Beware Otter Rk 4M SE of hbr, and rks closer in on both sides of ent and in NE corner of bay.

LIGHTS AND MARKS
On W side 10 Radio masts (103m) and Carraig Fhada lt ho (conspic), Fl WRG 3s 20m 8/6M; W shore-248°, G248°-311°, W311°-340°, G340°-shore; keep in W sector until past the SHM buoy, QG. Ro-Ro pier shows 2 FG (vert).

RADIO TELEPHONE
None.

TELEPHONE (Dial code 01496)
Moorings 810332; ∰ 810337; MRCC (01475) 729988.

FACILITIES
Village Bar, FW, ✉, R, V, Gas.

CRINAN CANAL   10-9-8

Argyll and Bute 56°05'·50N 05°33'·31W   Crinan Rtg 3-3-1

CHARTS
AC 2320, *2326*; Imray C65; OS 55

TIDES
–0608 Dover; ML 2·1; Duration 0605; Zone 0 (UT)
HW Crinan is at HW Oban –0045

Standard Port OBAN (←—)

Times				Height (metres)			
High Water		Low Water		MHWS	MHWN	MLWN	MLWS
0100	0700	0100	0800	4·0	2·89	1·8	0·7
1300	1900	1300	2000				

Differences CARSAIG BAY (4·5M SSW of Loch Crinan)
–0105 –0040 –0050 –0050   –2·1   –1·6   –1·0   –0·4
Note: In the Sound of Jura, S of Loch Crinan, the rise of tide occurs mainly during the 3½hrs after LW; the fall during the 3½hrs after HW. At other times the changes in level are usually small and irregular.

SHELTER
Complete shelter in canal basin; yachts are welcome, but often many FVs lie there. Good shelter in Crinan Hbr to E of Eilean da Mheim, but full of moorings. Except in strong W/N winds, ⌕ E of the canal ent, clear of fairway. Berths may be reserved at Bellanoch Bay (see chartlet).

NAVIGATION
WPT 56°05'·70N 05°33'·57W, 326°/146° from/to Fl WG 3s lt, 0·27M. Beware Black Rock (2m high) and other rks in appr and near sector line 146° of dir Fl WG 3s lt. Off NW corner of chartlet, in the centre of Loch Crinan, a nearly rectangular area, 6ca by 6ca, is devoted to shellfish beds (⌕ prohib). SPM lt buoys mark each corner: Fl (4) Y 12s at the NE and NW corners, Fl Y 6s at the SW and SE corners; the latter being about 100m NE of Black Rk.

CANAL
Canal is 9M long and has 15 locks. Least transit time is 5 to 6 hrs, observing the 4kn speed limit. Entry at all tides. Sea locks open 0800-2100 daily in season, but only HW±3 in drought. Sea lock outer gates are left open after hours for yachts to shelter in the locks. All 7 bridges open. Max size: 26·5m LOA, 6m beam, 2·9m draught, mast ht 28·9m. Vessels NW-bound have right of way. Canal dues can be paid at Ardrishaig or Crinan sea locks. Total transit/lock fee in 1997 was £7.85/metre, inc VAT, for 3 days = £70.65 for 30'/9.14m LOA. Inland locks and bridges operate 0800-1800 daily; lock 14 and Crinan Bridge open 0800-2100 Fri-Sun (all times subject to change). Last locking 30 mins before close. For reduced hrs in autumn, winter and spring, contact canal office. Canal shut Xmas/New Year. If short-handed, helpers may be available via canal staff.

BOAT SAFETY SCHEME A "nautical MOT" for craft based on the canal is compulsory wef 1 Jan 1997. For details and applicability to visitors/transit craft see 10.8.18.

LIGHTS AND MARKS
Crinan Hotel is conspic W bldg. A conspic chy, 3ca SW of hotel, leads 187° into Crinan Hbr. E of sea-lock: Dir Fl WG 3s 8m 4M, vis W shore-146°, G146°-shore. Ent: 2 FG (vert) and 2FR (vert).

RADIO TELEPHONE
VHF Ch **74** (throughout the canal) 16.

TELEPHONE (Dial code 01546)
Sea lock 830285; Canal HQ 603210; MRCC (01475) 729988; ⌖ (0141) 887 9369 (H24); Marinecall 0891 500463; Police 602222; Dr 602921.

FACILITIES
Canal HQ ☎ 603210, M, L, FW; **Sea Basin** AB £14.85, D; **Services:** BY, Slip, ME, El, Sh, Gas, ACA, C (5 ton), ◎, CH, P (cans), V, R, Bar.
Village ⌖, Ⓑ (Ardrishaig), ⇌ (Oban), ✈ (Glasgow or Macrihanish). There is a wintering park, plus BY and CH, at Cairnbaan for yachts <10m LOA.

ARDRISHAIG   10-9-9

Argyll and Bute 56°00′·78N 05°26′·55W   Rtg 3-3-2

TARBERT, LOCH FYNE   10-9-10

Argyll and Bute 55°52′·05N 05°24′·15W   Rtg 2-2-2

CHARTS
AC 2381, *2131*; Imray C63; OS 62

TIDES
+0120 Dover; ML 1·9; Duration 0640; Zone 0 (UT)

Standard Port GREENOCK (→)

Times				Height (metres)			
High Water		Low Water		MHWS	MHWN	MLWN	MLWS
0000	0600	0000	0600	3·4	2·8	1·0	0·3
1200	1800	1200	1800				
Differences EAST LOCH TARBERT							
+0005	+0005	−0020	+0015	0·0	0·0	+0·1	−0·1

Contact Duty Sea lock keeper

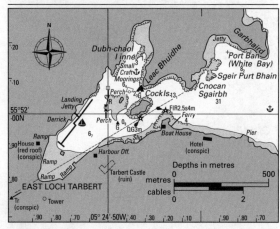

SHELTER
Very good in all weathers but gets crowded. Access H24. Visitors berth only on SE side of yacht pontoons in 5m. Note: also known as East Loch Tarbert.

NAVIGATION
WPT 55°52′·02N 05°22′·96W, 090°/270° from/to Fl R 2·5s lt, 0·70M. Ent is very narrow. Cock Isle divides the ent in half: Main hbr to the S, Buteman's Hole to the N, where ⸕s are fouled by heavy moorings and lost chains.

LIGHTS AND MARKS
Outer ldg lts 252° to S ent: Fl R 2·5s on with Cock Is lt QG. Inner ldg line 239°: same QG, G column, on with conspic ⊕ tr. Note: The W sector, 065°-078°, of Eilean na Beithe ☆, Fl WRG 3s 7m 5M (on E shore of Lower Loch Fyne), could be used to position for the initial appr to Tarbert.

RADIO TELEPHONE
Call VHF Ch 16; work Ch 14 (0900-1700LT).

TELEPHONE (Dial code 01880)
Hr Mr 820344, ⚓ 820719; MRCC (01475) 729988; ⌗ (0141) 887 9369 (H24); Marinecall 0891 500462; Police 820200; Ⓗ (01546) 602323.

FACILITIES
Yacht Berthing Facility 100 visitors, AB £8.55, FW, AC; **Old Quay** D, FW; **Tarbert YC** Slip, L; **Services:** SM, ▣, ACA, Sh, CH. **Town** EC Wed; P & D (cans), Gas, Gaz, L, V, R, Bar, ⊠, Ⓑ, ⇌ (bus to Glasgow), ✈ (Glasgow/Campbeltown).

CHARTS
AC 2381, *2131*; Imray C63; OS 55

TIDES
+0120 Dover; ML 1·9; Duration 0640; Zone 0 (UT)

Standard Port GREENOCK (→)

Times				Height (metres)			
High Water		Low Water		MHWS	MHWN	MLWN	MLWS
0000	0600	0000	0600	3·4	2·8	1·0	0·3
1200	1800	1200	1800				
Differences ARDRISHAIG							
+0006	+0006	−0015	+0020	0·0	0·0	+0·1	−0·1
INVERARAY							
+0011	+0011	+0034	+0034	−0·1	+0·1	−0·5	−0·2

SHELTER
Hbr is sheltered except from strong E'lies; do not berth on pier or ⸕ due to commercial vessels H24. Sea lock into the Crinan Canal is usually left open; access at all tides. Complete shelter in the canal basin, or beyond lock No 2; see 10.9.8. Also ⸕ 2ca N of hbr, off the W shore of L Gilp.

NAVIGATION
WPT No 48 PHM buoy, Fl R 4s, 56°00′·18N 05°26′·24W, 165°/345° from/to bkwtr lt, 0·61M. Dangerous drying rks to E of appr chan are marked by No 49 unlit SHM buoy.

LIGHTS AND MARKS
Conspic W Ho on with block of flats leads 315°between Nos 48 & 49 buoys. Bkwtr lt, L Fl WRG 6s, W339°-350°.

RADIO TELEPHONE
VHF Ch 74 16.

TELEPHONE (Dial code 01546)
Hr Mr 603210; MRCC (01475) 729988; ⌗ (0141) 887 9369 (H24); Marinecall 0891 500462; Police 603233; Dr 602921.

FACILITIES
Pier/Hbr ☎ 603210, AB, Slip, FW; **Sea Lock** ☎ 602458, AB £16.65; **Crinan Canal** AB, M, L, FW, R, Bar; see 10.9.8. **Services:** BY, ME, EI, Sh, CH, D (cans), Gas; C (20 ton) at Lochgilphead (2M). **Village** EC Wed; P & D (cans), V, R, Bar, ⊠, Ⓑ, ⇌ (bus to Oban), ✈ (Glasgow or Campbeltown).

ANCHORAGES IN LOCH FYNE

INVERARAY, Argyll and Bute, 56°13′·95N 05°04′·00W. AC 2382, *2131*. HW +0126 on Dover. See 10.9.9. For Upper Loch Fyne see 10.9.5. Beyond Otter Spit, are ⸕s on NW bank at Port Ann, Loch Gair and Minard Bay; and on SE bank at Otter Ferry, Strachur Bay (5 ⸕s off Creggans Inn, ☎ (01369) 860279) and St Catherine's.
Inveraray: beware An Oitir drying spit 2ca offshore, ½M S of pier. Some ⸕s or ⸕ SSW of pier in 4m or dry out NW of the pier. FW (on pier), ⊠, V, R, Bar, Gas, bus to Glasgow. In Lower L Fyne, 6M NNE of East Loch Tarbert there is a ⸕ at Kilfinan Bay, ☎ (01700) 821201.

CAMPBELTOWN   10-9-11
Argyll & Bute 55°25'·90N 05°32'·50W (Hbr ent) Rtg 1-2-1

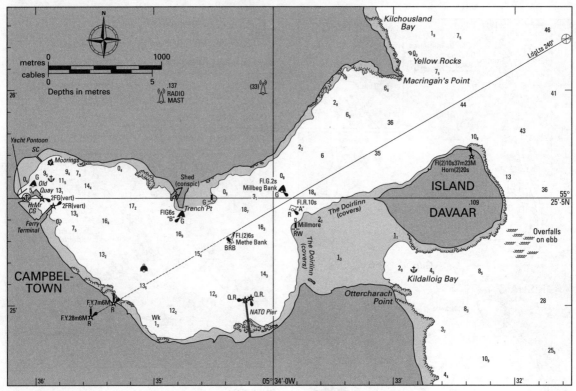

CHARTS
AC 1864, *2126*; Imray C63; OS 68

TIDES
+0125 Dover; ML 1·8; Duration 0630; Zone 0 (UT)

Standard Port GREENOCK (→)

Times				Height (metres)			
High Water		Low Water		MHWS	MHWN	MLWN	MLWS
0000	0600	0000	0600	3·4	2·8	1·0	0·3
1200	1800	1200	1800				
Differences CAMPBELTOWN							
−0025	−0005	−0015	+0005	−0·5	−0·3	+0·1	+0·2
CARRADALE BAY							
−0015	−0005	−0005	+0005	−0·3	−0·2	+0·1	+0·1
SOUTHEND, (Mull of Kintyre)							
−0030	−0010	+0005	+0035	−1·3	−1·2	−0·5	−0·2

SHELTER
Good, but gusts off the hills in strong SW'lies. Yacht pontoon (6+34 visitors) dredged 3·0m is close NW of Old Quay and gives excellent sheltered berthing. Yachts >12m LOA should pre-notify ETA to Berthing Master by ☎ (below). Excellent ⚓ and moorings NNE of the hbr. S of Island Davaar there is a temp ⚓ in Kildalloig Bay, but no access to the loch.

NAVIGATION
WPT 55°26'·24N 05°31'·55W, 060°/240° from/to first chan buoys, 1·4M. The ent is easily identified by radio masts N and NE of Trench Pt (conspic W bldg) and conspic lt ho on N tip of Island Davaar off which streams are strong (4kn sp). Caution: The Dhorlin, a bank drying 2·5m which covers at HW, is close S of the ldg line.

LIGHTS AND MARKS
Davaar Fl (2) 10s 37m 23M. Otterard Rk (3·8m depth, off chartlet, 1·5M NNE of Island Davaar), is marked by ECM buoy Q (3) 10s. Ldg lts 240°, both FY 7/28m 6M, are sodium vapour lts, H24.

RADIO TELEPHONE
VHF Ch 12 13 16 (Mon-Thur 0845-1645; Fri 0845-1600LT).

TELEPHONE (Dial code 01586)
Hr Mr 552552, ⛴ 554700, Yacht pontoon Berthing Master 554381, 554782 (night); MRCC (01475) 729988; ✉ 552261; Marinecall 0891 500462; Police 552253; Dr 552105.

FACILITIES
Yacht pontoon £9, FW, AC;
Old Quay ☎ 552552, D, FW, AB;
New Quay Slip, Ro-Ro ferry to Ballycastle (N Ireland);
Campbeltown SC Slip (dinghies), Bar, regular racing.
Town EC Wed; BY, ME, ACA, C (25 ton), CH, P, D, El, Ⓔ, Gas, Gaz, V (2 supermarkets), R, Bar, ✉, Ⓑ, Ⓞ, Ⓗ; Bus thrice daily to Glasgow, ✈ twice daily to Glasgow, ⇌ (nearest is Arrochar, 90 miles N by road). Car hire/taxi.
Almost an Island – Always a Welcome.

ADJACENT ANCHORAGE IN KILBRANNAN SOUND

CARRADALE BAY, Argyll and Bute, 55°34'·40N 05°28'·60W. AC *2131*, HW+0115 on Dover. ML 1·8m. See 10.9.11. Good ⚓ in 7m off Torrisdale Castle in SW corner of Carradale Bay. In N & E winds ⚓ in NE corner of bay, W of Carradale Pt. 3ca E of this Pt, a PHM buoy Fl (2) R 12s marks Cruban Rk. With S & SE winds a swell sets into bay, when good shelter can be found 1M N in **Carradale Harbour** (Port Crannaich); if full of FVs, ⚓ 100m N of Hbr. Bkwtr lt, Fl R 10s 5m 6M. Piermaster ☎ (01586) 431228. Facilities: FW on pier, D & P (cans), Gas, V, R, Bar, ✉.

LAMLASH 10-9-12

Isle of Arran, N Ayrshire 55°32'·00N 05°07'·00W   Rtg 1-2-1

CHARTS
AC 1864, 2220, *2131*; Imray C63; OS 69

TIDES
+0115 Dover; ML no data; Duration 0635; Zone 0 (UT)

Standard Port GREENOCK (→)

Times				Height (metres)			
High Water		Low Water		MHWS	MHWN	MLWN	MLWS
0000	0600	0000	0600	3·4	2·8	1·0	0·3
1200	1800	1200	1800				
Differences LAMLASH							
–0016	–0036	–0024	–0004	–0·2	–0·2	No data	
BRODICK BAY							
0000	0000	+0005	+0005	–0·2	–0·2	0·0	0·0
LOCH RANZA							
–0015	–0005	–0010	–0005	–0·4	–0·3	–0·1	0·0

SHELTER
Very good in all weathers. Lamlash is a natural hbr and anchorage sheltered as follows: ‡ off Lamlash except in E'lies; off Kingscross Point, good except in strong N/NW winds; off the Farm at NW of Holy Island in E'lies; or dry out against the Old Pier. See also Brodick 5M to the N, and Loch Ranza 14M to the N, both on facing page.

NAVIGATION
WPT 55°32'·63N 05°03'·00W, 090°/270° from/to N Chan buoy (Fl R 6s), 1·0M. Beware submarines which exercise frequently in this area (see 10.9.20), and also wreck of landing craft (charted) off farmhouse on Holy Is.

LIGHTS AND MARKS
Lts as on chartlet. There are two consecutive measured miles marked by poles north of Sannox, courses 322°/142° (about 12M N of Lamlash).

RADIO TELEPHONE
None.

TELEPHONE (Dial code 01770)
MRCC (01475) 729988; ⌗ (0141) 887 9369 (H24); Marinecall 0891 500462; Police 302573; ⊞ 600777.

FACILITIES
Lamlash Old Pier Slip, L, FW, CH, Sh (hull repairs);
Village EC Wed (Lamlash/Brodick); ME, P & D (cans), Bar, R, V, ⊠, ⇌ (bus to Brodick, ferry to Ardrossan), ✈ (Glasgow or Prestwick).

OTHER HARBOURS ON ARRAN

BRODICK, Arran, 55°35'·50N 05°08'·60W. AC 1864, 2220, *2131*. HW +0115 on Dover; ML 1·8m; Duration 0635. See 10.9.12. Shelter is good except in E winds. ‡ W of ferry pier in 3m; on NW side just below the Castle in 4·5m, or further N off Merkland Pt in 3-4m. Also 5 ⚓s: contact ☎ (01770) 302140. There are no navigational dangers but the bay is in a submarine exercise area; see 10.9.22. Only Its are 2FR (vert) 9/7m 4M on pier hd and Admiralty buoy, Fl Y 2s, 5ca N of pier. Facilities: EC Wed; Ⓑ, Bar, P and D (cans), FW (at pier hd), ME, ⊠, R, V. Ferry to Rothesay and Ardrossan.

LOCH RANZA, Arran, 55°42'·60N 05°17'·90W. AC 2221, 2383, *2131*. HW +0120 on Dover; ML 1·7m; Duration 0635. See 10.9.12. Good shelter, but swell enters loch with N winds. The 850m mountain 4M to S causes fierce squalls in the loch with S winds. Beware Screda Reef extending SW off Newton Pt. 5 ⚓s; call ☎ (01770) 302140. ‡ in 5m off castle (conspic); holding is suspect in soft mud. S shore dries. Facilities: Bar, FW at ferry slip, ⊠, R, V. Ferry to Claonaig.

HARBOURS AND ANCHORAGES AROUND BUTE
(Clockwise from Garroch Head, S tip of Bute)

ST NINIAN'S BAY, Bute, 55°48'·15N 05°07'·80W. AC 2383, 2221. Inchmarnock Is gives some shelter from the W, but Sound is exposed to S'lies. At S end, beware Shearwater Rk, 0·9m, almost in mid-sound. ‡ in about 7m, 2ca E of St Ninian's Pt; beware drying spit to S of this Pt. Or ‡ off E side of Inchmarnock, close abeam Midpark Farm.

WEST KYLE, Bute, 55°54'N 05°12'·7W. AC1906. Tides, see 10.9.13 (Tighnabruaich). On W bank PHM buoys, each Fl R 4s, mark Ardlamont Pt, Carry Pt and Rubha Ban; N of which are two Fl Y buoys (fish farms). ‡ close off Kames or Tighnabruaich, where space allows; or in Black Farland Bay (N of Rubha Dubh). There are 24 HIE ⚓s (4 groups of 6) on W side, linked to Kames Hotel ☎ (01700) 811489; Kyles of Bute Hotel 811350; Royal Hotel 811239; and Tighnabruaich Hotel 811615. Facilities: FW, D (cans), BY, V.

CALADH HARBOUR, Argyll & Bute, 55°56'·00N, 05°11'·67W. AC 1906. HW (Tighnabruaich) +0015 on Dover; ML 2·1m. See 10.9.13. Perfectly sheltered natural hbr on W side of ent to Loch Riddon. Enter Caladh Hbr to N or S of Eilean Dubh; keep to the middle of the S passage. When using the N ent, keep between R and G bns to clear a drying rk marked by perch. ‡ in the middle of hbr; land at a stone slip on SW side. No facilities/stores; see West Kyle above.

LOCH RIDDON, Argyll & Bute, 55°57'N 05°11'·6W. AC 1906. Tides, see 10.9.13. Water is deep for 1·3M N of Caladh and shore is steep-to; upper 1·5M of loch dries. ‡ on W side close N of Ormidale pier; on E side at Salthouse; off Eilean Dearg (One Tree Is); and at NW corner of Fearnoch Bay.

BURNT ISLANDS, Bute, 55°55'·76N 05°10'·33W. AC 1906. Tides, see 10.9.13. The three islands (Eilean Mor, Fraoich and Buidhe) straddle the East Kyle. There are 2 channels: North, between Buidhe and the other 2 islets, is narrow, short and marked by 2 SHM buoys (the NW'ly one is Fl G 3s), and one PHM buoy, Fl R 2s. South chan lies between Bute and Fraoich/Mor; it is unlit, but marked by one PHM and two SHM buoys. A SHM buoy, Fl G 3s, is off Rubha a' Bhodaich, 4ca ESE. Direction of buoyage is to SE. Sp streams reach 5kn in N Chan and 3kn in S Chan. ‡ in Wreck Bay, Balnakailly Bay or in the lee of Buidhe and Mor in W'lies; also W of Colintraive Pt, clear of ferry and cables. There are 4 ⚓s off the hotel, ☎ (01700) 84207.

KAMES BAY, Bute, 55°51'·7N 05°04'·75W. AC 1867, 1906. Tides as Rothesay. Deep water bay, but dries 2ca off head of loch and 1ca off NW shore. ‡ off Port Bannatyne (S shore) as space permits W of ruined jetty. Beware drying rks 1ca off Ardbeg Pt. No Its. Facilities: BY, FW, Gas, V, Bar, ⊠.

KILCHATTAN BAY, Bute, 55°45'N 05°01'·1W. AC 1907. Bay is deep, but dries 3ca off the W shore. Temp ‡s only in offshore winds: off the village on SW side, or on N side near Kerrytonlia Pt. ⚓s for hotel guests. Rubh' an Eun Lt, Fl R 6s, is 1·1M to SSE. Facilities: FW, V, ⊠, bus Rothesay.

9

ROTHESAY   10-9-13

Isle of Bute, Argyll & Bute 55°50'.32N 05°03'.01W   Rtg 2-3-1

CHARTS
AC 1867, 1906, 1907, *2131*; Imray C63; OS 63

TIDES
+0100 Dover; ML 1·9; Duration 0640; Zone 0 (UT)

Standard Port GREENOCK (→)

Times				Height (metres)			
High Water		Low Water		MHWS	MHWN	MLWN	MLWS
0000	0600	0000	0600	3·4	2·8	1·0	0·3
1200	1800	1200	1800				
Differences ROTHESAY BAY							
−0020	−0015	−0010	−0002	+0·2	+0·2	+0·2	+0·2
RUBHA A'BHODAICH (Burnt Is)							
−0020	−0010	−0007	−0007	−0·2	−0·1	+0·2	+0·2
TIGHNABRUAICH							
+0007	−0010	−0002	−0015	0·0	+0·2	+0·4	+0·5

SHELTER
Good on yacht pontoons in Outer Hbr (2m) and at W end inside the Front pier (2m). 40 ⌀s WNW of pier or good ⚓ in bay ¼M W, off Isle of Bute SC; except in strong N/NE'lies when Kyles of Bute or Kames Bay offer better shelter.

NAVIGATION
WPT 55°51'.00N 05°02'.69W, 014°/194° from/to Outer hbr ent, 0·69M. From E keep 1ca off Bogany Pt, and off Ardbeg Pt from N.

LIGHTS AND MARKS
Lts as chartlet, hard to see against shore lts. Conspic Ch spire leads 190° to outer hbr; at night beware large, unlit Admiralty buoy "MK" on this brg 5½ca from hbr. 3½ca N of hbr is Rothesay 'A' mooring buoy, Fl Y 2s.

RADIO TELEPHONE
VHF Ch 12 16 (1 May-30 Sept: 0600-2100; 1 Oct-30 Apl: 0600-1900 LT).

TELEPHONE (Dial code 01700)
Hr Mr 503842; Moorings 504750; MRCC (01475) 729988; ⊞ (0141) 887 9369 (H24); Marinecall 0891 500462; Police 502121; Dr 503985; Ⓗ 503938.

FACILITIES
Outer Hbr AB, AC, FW, Slip, D*, L, FW, ME, EI, CH; **Inner Hbr** L, FW, AB, Note: due to be dredged in slow time; **Front Pier (W)** FW, AC, R; **Albert Pier** D*, L, FW, C (4 ton mobile).
Town EC Wed; P, D, CH, V, R, Bar, ✉, Ⓑ, ⇌ (ferry to Wemyss Bay), ✈ (Glasgow).
*By arrangement (min 200 galls).

GREAT CUMBRAE ISLAND

MILLPORT, Great Cumbrae, N Ayrshire, 55°45'.00N 04°55'.75W. AC 1867, 1907. HW +0100 on Dover; ML 1·9m; Duration 0640. See 10.9.14. Good shelter, except in S'lies. Berth at pontoon N side of pier hd or ⚓ in approx 3m S of pier or E of the Eileans. 12 HIE ⌀s 1½ca SSE of pier; call ☎ (01475) 530741. Ldg marks: pier hd on with ⊞ twr 333°; or Ldg lts 333°, both FR 7/9m 5M, between the Spoig and the Eileans, QG. Unmarked, drying rk is close E of ldg line. Hr Mr ☎ (01475) 530826.
Town EC Wed; CH, Bar, Gas, D, P, FW, ✉, R, Slip, V.

LARGS   10-9-14

N Ayrshire 55°46'.40N 04°51'.77W   Rtg 2-1-2

CHARTS
AC 1867, 1907, *2131*; Imray C63; OS 63

TIDES
+0105 Dover; ML 1·9; Duration 0640; Zone 0 (UT)

Standard Port GREENOCK (→)

Times				Heights (metres)			
High Water		Low Water		MHWS	MHWN	MLWN	MLWS
0000	0600	0000	0600	3·4	2·8	1·0	0·3
1200	1800	1200	1800				
Differences MILLPORT							
−0005	−0025	−0025	−0005	0·0	−0·1	0·0	+0·1

SHELTER
Excellent in Yacht Haven (1·4M S of Largs Pier), access all tides (3·5m in ent & deep berths; 2·5m elsewhere). Largs Chan is sheltered from W'lies by Cumbrae Is, but open to winds from S or N. Temp'y ⚓ in 10m about ½ca N of pier.

NAVIGATION
WPT 55°46'.40N 04°51'.77W, SWM buoy, L Fl 10s, off yacht haven. From S beware Hunterston and Southannan sands and outfalls from Hunterston Power Stn (conspic). From S bkwtr to the NATO pier is a restricted, no ⚓ area.

LIGHTS AND MARKS
"Pencil" monument (12m) is conspic 4ca N of ent. Lts as on chartlet. Largs Pier, 2 FG (vert) when vessel expected.

RADIO TELEPHONE
Marina Ch **80** M (H24).

TELEPHONE (Dial code 01475)
Yacht Haven 675333; MRCC 729988; ⊞ (0141) 887 9369 (H24); Dr 673380; Ⓗ 733777; Marinecall 0891 500 462; Police 674651.

FACILITIES
Largs Yacht Haven (600, some Ⓥ) ☎ 675333, ⚓ 672245, £14.07, FW, D, P, AC, SM, BY, C (17 ton), BH (40 ton), ME, Divers, EI, Sh, Ⓒ, CH, ☐, Gas, Gaz, Slip (oooo00 H24), ⌑or, R;
Largs SC ☎ 520826; **Fairlie YC; Town** EC Wed; V, R, Bar, ✉, Ⓑ, ⇌, ✈ (Glasgow).

INVERKIP (KIP MARINA)   10-9-15

Inverclyde 55°54′·50N 04°53′·00W   Rtg 2-1-2

CHARTS
AC 1907, *2131*; Imray C63; OS 63

TIDES
+0110 Dover; ML 1·8; Duration 0640; Zone 0 (UT)

Standard Port GREENOCK (——>)

Times				Height (metres)			
High Water		Low Water		MHWS	MHWN	MLWN	MLWS
0000	0600	0000	0600	3·4	2·8	1·0	0·3
1200	1800	1200	1800				
Differences WEMYSS BAY							
–0005	–0005	–0005	–0005	0·0	0·0	+0·1	+0·1

SHELTER
Excellent. Chan and marina are dredged 3·5m; accessible at all tides. Inverkip Bay is exposed to SW/NW winds.

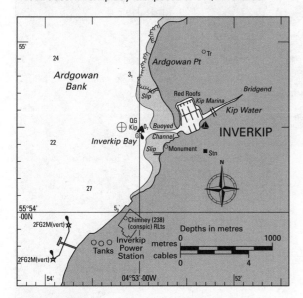

NAVIGATION
WPT 55°54′·48N 04°52′·95W, Kip SHM buoy, QG, at ent to buoyed chan; beware shifting bank to the N.

LIGHTS AND MARKS
Ent is ½M N of conspic chey (238m). SPM buoy marks sewer outfall off Ardgowan Pt. From Kip SHM buoy, 3 SHM and 3 PHM buoys mark 365m long appr chan.

RADIO TELEPHONE
VHF Ch **80** M (H24).

TELEPHONE (Dial code 01475)
Hr Mr 521485; MRCC 729988; ⌗ (0141) 887 9369 (H24); Marinecall 0891 500462; Police 521222; Dr 520248; ⊞ 33777.

FACILITIES
Kip Marina (700+40 Ⓥ), ☎ 521485, 🚤 521298, £13.90, AC, FW, D, P (cans), Sh, C, ME, El, Ⓔ, SM, CH, Diver, BH (40 ton), V, R, Bar, Ⓞ, Gas, Gaz, YC.
Town EC Wed; ✉, Ⓑ (Gourock), ⇌, ✈ (Glasgow).

ADJACENT ANCHORAGE

DUNOON, Argyll and Bute, 55°56′·70N 04°55′·20W. AC 1994, 1907, *2131*. Use Greenock tides. Temp ⚓ in West or East Bays (S and N of Dunoon Pt). The former is open to the S; the latter more shoal. Six HIE ⚓s (free) in each bay; call ☎ (01369) 703785. The Gantocks, drying rks 3ca SE of Dunoon Pt, have W ○ bn tr, Fl R 6s 12m 6M. 2FR (vert) on ferry pier. Facilities: P & D (cans), V, R, Bar, ✉, Gas, ferry to Gourock. 3 ⚓s off Inellan, 3·7M S of Dunoon, ☎ (01369) 830445.

FIRTH OF CLYDE AREA   10-9-16

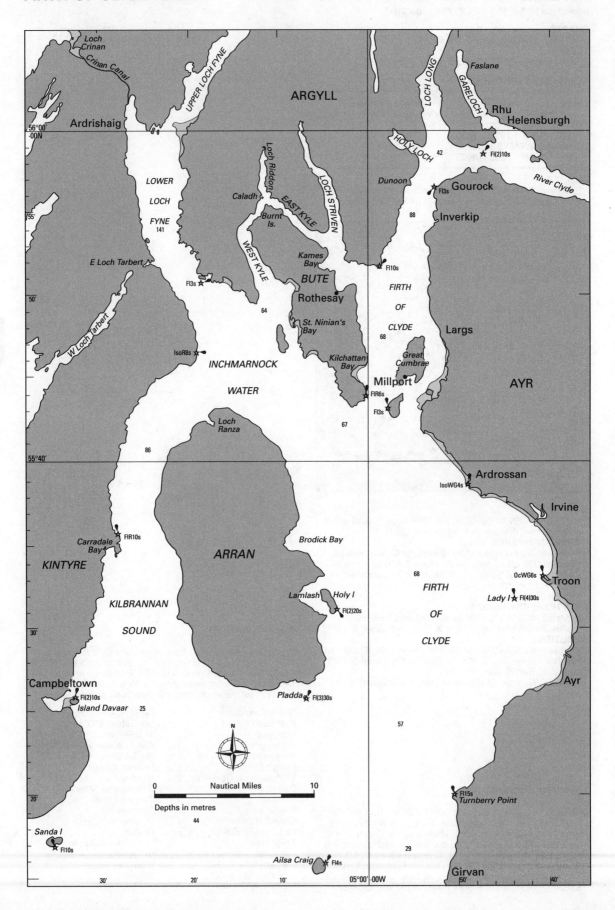

ARGYLL

Loch Crinan
Crinan Canal
UPPER LOCH FYNE
Ardrishaig
56°00'-00N

Faslane
LOCH LONG
GARELOCH
Rhu
Helensburgh
42   Fl(2)10s
HOLY LOCH
River Clyde

LOWER LOCH FYNE
141
55'

Loch Riddon
Caladh
Burnt Is.
EAST KYLE
LOCH STRIVEN
Dunoon   Fl3s   Gourock
88   Inverkip

E Loch Tarbert
50'
W Loch Tarbert
WEST KYLE
Kames Bay
BUTE
Rothesay
Fl3s
64
St. Ninian's Bay
FIRTH
OF
CLYDE
68   Largs

Fl10s

IsoR8s
INCHMARNOCK
WATER
Kilchattan Bay
67
Millport
FIR6s
Fl3s
Great Cumbrae

AYR

Loch Ranza
55°40'
86

Ardrossan
IsoWG4s
Irvine

Carradale Bay
FIR10s
KINTYRE
ARRAN
Brodick Bay
68
FIRTH
OF
CLYDE
OcWG6s   Troon
Lady I   Fl(4)30s

KILBRANNAN
SOUND
30'
Lamlash   Holy I
Fl(2)20s

Ayr

Campbeltown
Fl(2)10s
Island Davaar   25
Pladda   Fl(3)30s

57

N

0   Nautical Miles   10
Depths in metres
44

20'
Sanda I
Fl10s

29

Ailsa Craig   Fl4s
05°00'-00W   Girvan

Fl15s
Turnberry Point

30'   20'   10'   50'   40'

CLYDE AREA WAYPOINTS
10-9-17

Selected waypoints for use in the SW Scotland area are listed in alphabetical order below. Further waypoints for use in coastal waters are given in section 4 of each relevant area. All positions are referenced to the OSGB 36 datum.

AE Lt Buoy	55°51'·68N 05°02'·32W
Ailsa Craig Lt	55°15'·12N 05°06'·42W
Ardgowan Outfall By	55°54'·92N 04°53'·04W
Ardlamont Pt No. 47 Lt By	55°49'·59N 05°11'·68W
Ardmaleish No.41 Lt By	55°53'·02N 05°04'·62W
Ardmore No. 4 Lt By	55°58'·75N 04°48'·30W
Ardmore No. 5 Lt By	55°58'·67N 04°47'·43W
Ardmore No. 8 Lt By	55°58'·95N 04°46'·67W
Ardmore No.10 Lt By	55°59'·03N 04°45'·62W
Ardyne Lt By	55°52'·10N 05°03'·12W
Arranman's Barrels Lt By	55°19'·40N 05°32'·80W
Ascog Patches Lt Bn (No. 13)	55°49'·71N 05°00'·17W
Ashton Lt By	55°58'·12N 04°50'·58W
Ayr Bar Lt By	55°28'·12N 04°39'·38W
Beere Rk By	55°55'·56N 05°10'·56W
Big Rock Lt By	55°57'·89N 05°25'·27W
Burnt Islands No. 43 Lt By	55°55'·43N 05°10'·27W
Burnt Islands No. 44 Lt By	55°55'·56N 05°10'·57W
Cairndhu Lt By	56°00'·36N 04°45'·93W
Carry Pt No. 46 Lt By	55°51'·42N 05°12'·17W
Cowal Lt By	55°56'·00N 04°54'·75W
Creyke Rk By	55°55'·67N 05°10'·80W
Crubon Rk Lt By	55°34'·48N 05°27'·00W
Dunoon Bank Lt By	55°56'·65N 04°54'·08W
Eagle Rk Lt By	55°38'·22N 04°49'·62W
Eilean Buidhe Lt By	55°55'·77N 05°10'·32W
Eilean Fraoich Lt By	55°55'·78N 05°10'·43W
Fairlie Patch Lt By	55°45'·37N 04°52'·27W
Fullerton Rk Lt By	55°30'·65N 05°04'·50W
Gantock Bn	55°56'·57N 04°55'·05W
Green Isle Lt By	55°59'·40N 04°45'·47W
Gulnare Rk No. 48 Lt By	56°00'·18N 05°26'·24W
Hotel Lt By	56°00'·67N 04°47'·45W
Hun 1 Lt By	55°48'·12N 04°54'·14W
Hun 3 Lt By	55°47'·61N 04°53'·44W
Hun 5 Lt By	55°45'·87N 04°52'·45W
Hun 7 Lt By	55°44'·97N 04°53'·87W
Hun 8 Lt By	55°44'·79N 04°53'·64W
Hun 9 Lt By	55°44'·67N 04°54'·37W
Hun 10 Lt By	55°44'·16N 04°54'·79W
Hun 11 Lt By	55°43'·46N 04°55'·10W
Hun 12 Lt By	55°43'·46N 04°55'·57W
Hun 13 Lt By	55°42'·53N 04°55'·10W
Hun 14 Lt By	55°42'·53N 04°55'·56W
Ironotter Outfall Lt By	55°58'·37N 04°48'·33W
Iron Rk Ledges Lt By	55°26'·83N 05°18'·80W

Kilcreggan No. 1 Lt By	55°58'·68N 04°50'·20W
Kilcreggan No. 3 Lt By	55°59'·20N 04°51'·38W
Kilcreggan No. 3 Lt Bn	55°59'·18N 04°51'·03W
Kip Lt By	55°54'·49N 04°52'·95W
Lady Isle Lt	55°31'·63N 04°43'·95W
Lamlash N Chan Lt By	55°32'·65N 05°04'·85W
Lamlash S Chan Lt By	55°30'·66N 05°04'·50W
Largs Lt By	55°46'·40N 04°51'·78W
Loch Long Lt By	55°59'·17N 04°52'·33W
Macosh Rk Lt By	55°17'·95N 05°36'·90W
Methe Bank Lt By	55°25'·30N 05°34'·36W
Millbeg Bank Lt By	55°25'·53N 05°33'·93W
Mountstuart Lt By	55°48'·00N 04°57'·50W
Otterard Lt By	55°27'·07N 05°31'·04W
Outer St Nicholas Lt By	55°28'·11N 04°39'·37W
Outfall Lt By	55°43'·58N 04°54'·70W
Patersons Rk Lt By	55°16'·90N 05°32'·40W
Pillar Rk Lt Ho	55°31'·05N 05°03'·57W
Perch Rk By	55°59'·45N 04°45'·58W
Pladda Lt Ho	55°25'·50N 05°07'·07W
Portachur Lt By	55°44'·35N 04°58'·44W
"Q" Loch Fyne Narrows Lt By	56°00'·97N 05°20'·60W
Rhu NE Lt By	56°01'·03N 04°47'·50W
Rhu SE Lt By	56°00'·65N 04°47'·09W
Rosneath Patch Lt Bn	55°58'·52N 04°47'·37W
Rosneath Patch No. 27 Lt By	55°58'·31N 04°47'·19W
Row Lt By	55°59'·85N 04°45'·05W
Rubha Ban Lt By	55°54'·96N 05°12'·33W
Skelmorlie Bank Lt By	55°51'·64N 04°55'·84W
Skelmorlie 'A' Lt By	55°46'·50N 04°57'·70W
Skelmorlie 'B' Lt By	55°47'·13N 04°57'·47W
Skelmorlie 'C' Lt By	55°48'·11N 04°55'·23W
Skelmorlie 'D' Lt By	55°47'·85N 04°56'·22W
Skelmorlie 'F' Lt By	55°48'·63N 04°54'·90W
Skelmorlie 'G' Lt By	55°49'·00N 04°54'·15W
Skelmorlie 'H' Lt By	55°49'·00N 04°54'·63W
Skelmorlie 'J' Lt By	55°51'·53N 04°54'·63W
Skelmorlie 'L' Lt By	55°52'·38N 04°54'·42W
Skelmorlie 'M' Lt By	55°53'·53N 04°54'·35W
Skelmorlie 'N' Lt By	55°53'·80N 04°55'·10W
Skelmorlie 'O' Lt By	55°54'·55N 04°54'·47W
Skipness Pt No. 51 Lt By	55°45'·57N 05°19'·60W
Strone Lt By	55°58'·77N 04°53'·77W
Tann Spit (No. 38) By	55°44'·42N 04°57'·06W
Toward Bank Lt By No.35	55°51'·04N 04°59'·93W
Troon Lt By	55°33'·07N 04°41'·28W
Warden Bank Lt By	55°55'·78N 04°54'·48W
Wemyss Bay No. 12 Lt Bn	55°52'·96N 04°53'·70W
West Crinan Lt By	55°38'·47N 04°49'·82W
Whiteforeland Lt By	55°58'·12N 04°47'·20W
Wood Farm Rk By	55°55'·43N 05°10'·25W
7N Lt Bn	56°00'·06N 04°45'·28W
8N Lt Bn	55°59'·09N 04°44'·13W

9

GARELOCH/RHU   10-9-18

Argyll & Bute 56°00'·71N 04°46'·50W (Rhu marina)
Rtgs: Rhu 2-4-2; Sandpoint (W Dunbartonshire) 1-5-3

CHARTS
AC 2000, 1994, *2131*; Imray C63; OS 56, 63

TIDES
+0110 Dover; ML 1·9; Duration 0640; Zone 0 (UT). Tides at Helensburgh are the same as at Greenock

Standard Port GREENOCK (→)

Times				Height (metres)			
High Water		Low Water		MHWS	MHWN	MLWN	MLWS
0000	0600	0000	0600	3·4	2·8	1·0	0·3
1200	1800	1200	1800				
Differences ROSNEATH (Rhu pier)							
–0005	–0005	–0005	–0005	0·0	–0·1	0·0	0·0
FASLANE							
–0010	–0010	–0010	–0010	0·0	0·0	–0·1	–0·2
GARELOCHHEAD							
0000	0000	0000	0000	0·0	0·0	0·0	–0·1
COULPORT							
–0011	–0011	–0008	–0008	0·0	0·0	0·0	0·0
LOCHGOILHEAD							
+0015	0000	–0005	–0005	–0·2	–0·3	–0·3	–0·3
ARROCHAR							
–0005	–0005	–0005	–0005	0·0	0·0	–0·1	–0·1

NAVIGATION
WPT 55°59'·30N 04°45'·19W, 176°/356° from/to bn No 7, 1·3M. Beaches between Cairndhu Pt and Helensburgh Pier (dries almost to the head) are strewn with large boulders above/below MLWS. Gareloch ent is about 225m wide due to drying spit off Rhu Pt. Beware large unlit MoD buoys and barges off W shore of Gareloch; for Garelochhead keep to W shore until well clear of Faslane Base area.

LIGHTS AND MARKS
Ldg/dir lts into Gareloch 356°, 318°, 295°, 329° and 331°. Conspic ⊕ tr at Rhu. Gareloch Fuel Depot lt, Iso WRG 4s 10m 14M, G351°-356°, W356°-006°, R006°-011°, is clearly visible from the S. Many shore lts and an unlit floating boom make night sailing near the Base area inadvisable.

RADIO TELEPHONE
VHF Ch 16. Rhu Marina Ch **80** M (H24). See also 10.19.19.

TELEPHONE (Dial code 01436)
Marina 820652; Queen's Hr Mr 674321; MRCC (01475) 729014; ⌗ (0141) 887 9369 (H24); Marinecall 0891 500462; Police 672141; Ⓗ (01389) 754121; Dr 672277.

FACILITIES
Rhu Marina (200) ☎ 820652, ⚓ 821039, AB £13.91, D, M, FW, AC, BH (35 ton), CH, ME, El, Slip, M, C hire, Gas, Gaz; **Royal Northern and Clyde YC** ☎ 820322, L, R, Bar; **Helensburgh SC** ☎ 672778 Slip (dinghies) L, FW; **Helensburgh** (1M) EC Wed; all services, ⇌, ✈ (Glasgow). **Sandpoint**, at Dumbarton (20), ☎ (01389) 762396, ⚓ 732605, M, AC, FW, Slip, BH (10 ton), CH.

BYELAWS
Loch Long and Gareloch are classified as Dockyard Ports under the jurisdiction of the Queen's Harbour Master. Do not impede the passage of submarines/warships.

SHELTER
Rhu Marina is entered between low, floating wavebreaks on its S and W sides, not easy to find at night; caution cross-tides. On E/SE sides a rock bkwtr 1m above MHWS protects from strong SE'lies. At Rhu Hard keep clear of army craft. Helensburgh Pier is only a temp drying berth, rather exposed, used by occas steamers. ⚓ E of marina or in Rosneath Bay. There are moorings N of the narrows at Stroul B and at Clynder; N of Rhu Pt; and at the head of the loch. The Clyde Naval Base at Faslane is best avoided by yachts. See also Loch Long/Loch Goil.

Naval activity: Beware submarines from Faslane Base. See 10.9.23 for submarine activity (Subfacts) in the Clyde and offshore or call FOSNI Ops ☎ (01346) 674321 Ext 6100.
Protected Areas: Vessels are never allowed within 150m of naval shore installations at Faslane and Coulport.
Restricted Areas (Faslane, Rhu Chan and Coulport): These are closed to all vessels during submarine movements (see below and *W Coast of Scotland Pilot*, App 2). MoD Police patrols enforce areas which are shown on charts. The S limit of Faslane Restricted area is marked by two Or posts with X topmarks on Shandon foreshore. The W limit is marked by Iso WRG 4s, vis W356°-006°, at Gareloch Oil fuel depot N jetty. The following signals are shown when restrictions are in force:

1. Entrance to Gareloch
   by day : ⓡ ⓖ ⓖ (vert), supplemented by R flag with
   W diagonal bar.
   by night : ⓡ ⓖ ⓖ (vert).
2. Faslane and Coulport
   by day : 3 ⓖ (vert), supplemented by International
   Code pendant over pendant Nine.
   by night : 3 ⓖ (vert) in conspic position.

HOLY LOCH, Argyll & Bute, 55°58'·5N 04°54'·0W is no more
a restricted or protected area. There are some moorings
on the S side, and AB for about 4 boats on former USN
jetty. ⚓ not advised as the bottom is reported to be foul.

LOCH LONG/LOCH GOIL, Argyll and Bute, approx 56°00'N
04°52'·5W to 56°12'·00N 04°45'·00W. AC 3746. Tides: See
10·9·18 for differences. ML 1·7m; Duration 0645. **Shelter:**
Loch Long is about 15M long. Temp ⚓s (S→N) at Cove,
Blairmore (not in S'lies), Ardentinny, Portincaple,
Coilessan (about 1M S of Ardgartan Pt), and near head of
loch (Arrochar) on either shore.
In Loch Goil ⚓ at Swines Hole and off Carrick Castle (S of
the pier, in N'lies a swell builds). Avoid ⚓ near Douglas
Pier. The head of the loch is crowded with private/dinghy
moorings, and is either too steep-to or too shallow to ⚓.
Lights: Coulport Jetty, 2FG (vert) each end and two Fl G
12s on N jetty; Port Dornaige Fl 6s 8m 11M, vis 026°-206°;
Dog Rock (Carraig nan Ron) Fl 2s 11M; Finnart Oil
Terminal has FG lts and ldg lts 031° QW/FW on Cnap Pt.
Upper Loch Long is unlit.
Loch Goil ent is marked by 2 PHM buoys (Fl R 3s and
QR), a SHM buoy (QG) and ldg lts 318°: front (The Perch)
Dir FWRG and Fl R 3s; rear FW. Rubha Ardnahein Fl R5s.
Facilities: Loch Long (Cove), Cove SC, FW, Bar; V, FW
(pier); (Portincaple) shops, hotel, ✉, FW; (Ardentinny)
shop, V, R, hotel, M; (Blairmore) shops, ✉, Slip, FW;
(Arrochar) shops, hotel, FW, Gas, ✉.
Loch Goil (Carrick Castle) has ✉, shop, hotel;
(Lochgoilhead) has all stores, ✉, hotel, FW, Gas.

◩◩ Restricted Area-Max speed 7Kn
----- Southern limit of Dockyard Port

GREENOCK/GOUROCK   10-9-19
Inverclyde 55°58'·00N 04°49'·00W (As WPT)   Rtg 1-5-3

CHARTS
AC 1994, *2131*; Imray C63; OS 63
TIDES
+0122 Dover; ML 2·0; Duration 0640; Zone 0 (UT)

Standard Port GREENOCK (→)

Times				Height (metres)			
High Water		Low Water		MHWS	MHWN	MLWN	MLWS
0000	0600	0000	0600	3·4	2·8	1·0	0·3
1200	1800	1200	1800				
Differences PORT GLASGOW							
+0010	+0005	+0010	+0020	+0·2	+0·1	0·0	0·0
BOWLING							
+0020	+0010	+0030	+0055	+0·6	+0·5	+0·3	+0·1
RENFREW							
+0025	+0015	+0035	+0100	+0·9	+0·8	+0·5	+0·2
GLASGOW							
+0025	+0015	+0035	+0105	+1·3	+1·2	+0·6	+0·4

Greenock is a Standard Port and tidal predictions for each
day of the year are given below.

SHELTER
Gourock: good ⚓ in West Bay, but open to N/NE winds.
Greenock is a commercial port. Up-river, possible AB at
Dumbarton (McAlister's BY), Bowling Hbr and at Renfrew
Hbr, but the R Clyde is only suitable for laying-up/repairs.
Hbrs are controlled by Clyde Port Authority.

NAVIGATION
Gourock WPT 55°58'·00N 04°49'·00W, 000°/180° from/to
Kempock Pt lt, 0·22M. No navigational dangers, but much
shipping and ferries in the Clyde. Beware foul ground in
Gourock Bay. Cardwell Bay pier (lit) is disused.
LIGHTS AND MARKS
As chartlet. Note Ashton and Whiteforeland SWM buoys.
RADIO TELEPHONE
Call: *Clydeport Estuary Radio* VHF Ch 12 16 (H24). Info on
weather and traffic available on request.
TELEPHONE (Dial codes: Gourock/Greenock 01475;
Glasgow 0141)
General Mgr Marine 725775; Estuary Control 726221;
MRCC 729988; ☏ (0141) 308 3618; Police 724444;
Marinecall 0891 500462; Dr 634617.
FACILITIES
GOUROCK: **Royal Gourock YC** ☎ 632983 M, L, FW, ME, V,
R, Bar; **Services:** SM.
Town EC Wed; P, D, V, R, Bar, ✉, Ⓑ, ⇌, ✈ (Glasgow).
GREENOCK: All facilities, but small craft not particularly
encouraged. **Services:** AB, FW, AC, D, CH, Gas, ME, Sh,
El, Ⓔ, SM, C (45 ton).
GLASGOW (0141): Clyde Yacht Clubs Association is at 8 St
James St, Paisley, ☎ 887 8296. Clyde Cruising Club is at
Suite 408, Pentagon Centre, 36 Washington St, Glasgow
G3 8AZ, ☎ 221 2774, 🕿 221 2775. **Services:** ACA, CH.

TIME ZONE (UT)
For Summer Time add ONE hour in non-shaded areas

SCOTLAND – GREENOCK

LAT 55°57′N   LONG 4°46′W

TIMES AND HEIGHTS OF HIGH AND LOW WATERS

YEAR 1998

JANUARY

Day	Time / m	Time / m	Time / m	Time / m
1 TH	0155 3.4	0717 0.5	1415 3.7	1948 0.2
2 F	0240 3.4	0804 0.5	1456 3.7	2036 0.2
3 SA	0324 3.4	0853 0.5	1538 3.7	2127 0.3
4 SU	0410 3.3	0944 0.6	1624 3.6	2222 0.4
5 M	0500 3.2	1040 0.8	1715 3.4	2323 0.5
6 TU	0554 3.1	1143 0.9	1815 3.3	
7 W	0030 0.6	0656 3.1	1252 1.0	1933 3.1
8 TH	0139 0.6	0816 3.0	1405 1.0	2104 3.1
9 F	0244 0.6	0938 3.1	1514 0.8	2215 3.2
10 SA	0343 0.6	1038 3.3	1611 0.7	2313 3.3
11 SU	0434 0.5	1128 3.4	1659 0.5	
12 M ○	0004 3.4	0520 0.5	1212 3.6	1741 0.4
13 TU	0051 3.4	0603 0.5	1253 3.7	1821 0.4
14 W	0135 3.3	0644 0.5	1332 3.7	1859 0.4
15 TH	0213 3.3	0723 0.6	1409 3.7	1936 0.4
16 F	0249 3.3	0801 0.6	1445 3.7	2014 0.5
17 SA	0324 3.3	0839 0.7	1521 3.7	2052 0.6
18 SU	0400 3.2	0919 0.8	1557 3.6	2132 0.7
19 M	0438 3.2	1001 0.9	1635 3.5	2215 0.8
20 TU	0520 3.1	1049 1.0	1717 3.3	2306 0.9
21 W	0606 3.0	1145 1.1	1804 3.1	
22 TH	0004 1.0	0658 2.9	1252 1.2	1859 3.0
23 F	0112 1.1	0803 2.8	1405 1.2	2005 2.9
24 SA	0220 1.0	0925 2.9	1511 1.0	2121 2.9
25 SU	0319 0.9	1031 3.0	1602 0.8	2228 3.0
26 M	0408 0.7	1118 3.2	1646 0.5	2322 3.1
27 TU	0452 0.6	1159 3.4	1726 0.3	
28 W ●	0010 3.2	0534 0.4	1240 3.5	1806 0.1
29 TH	0057 3.3	0617 0.3	1321 3.6	1848 0.0
30 F	0143 3.3	0701 0.3	1403 3.7	1932 0.0
31 SA	0227 3.4	0747 0.3	1444 3.8	2018 0.0

FEBRUARY

Day	Time / m	Time / m	Time / m	Time / m
1 SU	0310 3.4	0834 0.3	1526 3.8	2106 0.1
2 M	0351 3.4	0923 0.4	1609 3.7	2158 0.2
3 TU	0435 3.3	1015 0.5	1654 3.5	2255 0.4
4 W	0521 3.2	1114 0.7	1746 3.3	
5 TH	0002 0.6	0614 3.1	1225 0.9	1849 3.1
6 F	0117 0.7	0720 3.0	1346 0.9	2041 2.9
7 SA	0229 0.8	0910 3.0	1502 0.8	2207 3.0
8 SU	0331 0.7	1021 3.1	1601 0.7	2306 3.1
9 M	0424 0.6	1113 3.3	1648 0.6	2356 3.2
10 TU	0509 0.5	1158 3.4	1730 0.4	
11 W ○	0041 3.2	0549 0.4	1239 3.5	1806 0.3
12 TH	0121 3.2	0626 0.4	1317 3.6	1840 0.3
13 F	0157 3.2	0701 0.4	1351 3.6	1913 0.4
14 SA	0228 3.2	0734 0.5	1424 3.6	1946 0.4
15 SU	0258 3.2	0808 0.5	1456 3.6	2020 0.5
16 M	0329 3.2	0843 0.5	1529 3.5	2055 0.5
17 TU	0401 3.2	0922 0.6	1604 3.4	2134 0.6
18 W	0437 3.1	1004 0.7	1643 3.3	2218 0.7
19 TH	0518 2.9	1054 0.9	1726 3.1	2310 0.9
20 F	0607 2.8	1153 1.0	1818 2.9	
21 SA	0011 1.0	0708 2.7	1304 1.1	1922 2.8
22 SU	0122 1.0	0827 2.7	1426 1.0	2041 2.8
23 M	0239 0.9	0951 2.9	1532 0.7	2202 2.9
24 TU	0342 0.7	1049 3.1	1622 0.4	2303 3.0
25 W	0431 0.5	1136 3.3	1705 0.1	2354 3.2
26 TH ●	0516 0.3	1219 3.5	1747 0.0	
27 F	0041 3.3	0558 0.2	1304 3.6	1828 -0.2
28 SA	0127 3.4	0642 0.1	1347 3.7	1912 -0.2

MARCH

Day	Time / m	Time / m	Time / m	Time / m
1 SU	0209 3.4	0726 0.1	1429 3.8	1956 -0.2
2 M	0249 3.5	0812 0.1	1511 3.8	2043 0.0
3 TU	0328 3.5	0859 0.2	1552 3.7	2133 0.2
4 W	0408 3.4	0949 0.4	1635 3.5	2228 0.4
5 TH	0452 3.3	1046 0.6	1723 3.2	2334 0.7
6 F	0541 3.1	1158 0.8	1821 2.9	
7 SA	0055 0.9	0641 2.9	1329 0.9	2022 2.7
8 SU	0212 0.9	0829 2.8	1445 0.8	2157 2.8
9 M	0315 0.8	1001 3.0	1543 0.6	2254 3.0
10 TU	0408 0.6	1054 3.2	1630 0.5	2340 3.1
11 W	0452 0.5	1139 3.3	1711 0.3	
12 TH	0022 3.1	0530 0.4	1220 3.4	1745 0.3
13 F ○	0100 3.1	0605 0.4	1256 3.4	1817 0.3
14 SA	0134 3.1	0636 0.3	1329 3.4	1846 0.3
15 SU	0203 3.1	0705 0.3	1359 3.4	1916 0.3
16 M	0229 3.2	0736 0.3	1429 3.4	1948 0.3
17 TU	0256 3.2	0810 0.3	1502 3.4	2023 0.4
18 W	0326 3.2	0848 0.4	1536 3.3	2101 0.4
19 TH	0400 3.1	0929 0.5	1614 3.2	2143 0.5
20 F	0437 3.0	1017 0.6	1655 3.0	2233 0.7
21 SA	0521 2.8	1114 0.8	1745 2.9	2333 0.9
22 SU	0621 2.7	1222 0.9	1849 2.7	
23 M	0042 1.0	0741 2.6	1342 0.8	2010 2.7
24 TU	0200 0.9	0912 2.8	1458 0.6	2137 2.8
25 W	0312 0.7	1019 3.0	1554 0.3	2243 3.0
26 TH	0408 0.4	1110 3.3	1640 0.0	2335 3.2
27 F	0454 0.2	1157 3.5	1723 -0.2	
28 SA ●	0021 3.3	0537 0.1	1243 3.6	1806 -0.3
29 SU	0106 3.4	0621 0.0	1328 3.7	1849 -0.2
30 M	0147 3.5	0705 -0.1	1412 3.8	1934 -0.2
31 TU	0226 3.6	0750 0.0	1454 3.8	2021 0.0

APRIL

Day	Time / m	Time / m	Time / m	Time / m
1 W	0305 3.6	0836 0.1	1536 3.6	2110 0.2
2 TH	0344 3.5	0926 0.3	1619 3.4	2203 0.5
3 F	0427 3.4	1022 0.5	1707 3.2	2309 0.8
4 SA	0515 3.2	1135 0.8	1805 2.9	
5 SU	0029 1.0	0613 3.0	1306 0.8	1951 2.7
6 M	0145 1.0	0734 2.8	1418 0.8	2136 2.8
7 TU	0249 0.9	0930 2.9	1516 0.6	2231 2.9
8 W	0343 0.7	1027 3.1	1604 0.5	2315 3.0
9 TH	0428 0.5	1112 3.2	1644 0.4	2355 3.1
10 F	0507 0.4	1153 3.2	1719 0.3	
11 SA ○	0032 3.1	0540 0.3	1229 3.2	1750 0.3
12 SU	0105 3.1	0609 0.3	1301 3.2	1818 0.3
13 M	0134 3.1	0638 0.3	1330 3.2	1847 0.3
14 TU	0159 3.2	0708 0.3	1401 3.2	1919 0.3
15 W	0225 3.2	0742 0.2	1435 3.3	1955 0.3
16 TH	0256 3.2	0820 0.3	1512 3.2	2035 0.4
17 F	0329 3.2	0902 0.3	1550 3.1	2119 0.5
18 SA	0405 3.0	0951 0.5	1633 3.0	2210 0.6
19 SU	0446 2.9	1049 0.6	1723 2.8	2308 0.8
20 M	0542 2.7	1156 0.7	1827 2.7	
21 TU	0015 0.9	0704 2.7	1311 0.6	1946 2.7
22 W	0129 0.8	0836 2.8	1424 0.4	2110 2.8
23 TH	0242 0.7	0948 3.0	1523 0.2	2218 3.0
24 F	0342 0.5	1043 3.2	1613 0.0	2311 3.2
25 SA	0431 0.2	1133 3.4	1659 -0.2	2359 3.3
26 SU ●	0517 0.1	1220 3.6	1743 -0.2	
27 M	0043 3.4	0600 0.0	1308 3.6	1828 -0.2
28 TU	0125 3.5	0645 -0.1	1354 3.7	1914 -0.1
29 W	0205 3.6	0730 0.0	1438 3.6	2001 0.1
30 TH	0244 3.6	0817 0.1	1521 3.5	2050 0.3

Chart Datum: 1·62 metres below Ordnance Datum (Newlyn)

SCOTLAND – GREENOCK

LAT 55°57'N   LONG 4°46'W

TIMES AND HEIGHTS OF HIGH AND LOW WATERS

YEAR 1998

TIME ZONE (UT)
For Summer Time add ONE hour in non-shaded areas

Chart Datum: 1·62 metres below Ordnance Datum (Newlyn)

MAY

Day	Time	m	Time	m	Time	m	Time	m
1 F	0324	3.6	0906	0.3	1606	3.3	2143	0.6
16 SA	0306	3.2	0843	0.3	1533	3.1	2103	0.4
2 SA	0406	3.5	1001	0.5	1655	3.1	2244	0.8
17 SU	0344	3.1	0934	0.3	1618	3.0	2154	0.5
3 SU	0454	3.3	1110	0.7	1753	2.9	2355	1.0
18 M	0426	3.0	1031	0.4	1710	2.9	2251	0.7
4 M	0550	3.0	1231	0.8	1907	2.7		
19 TU	0521	2.9	1137	0.5	1813	2.8	2354	0.7
5 TU	0107	1.0	0657	2.9	1342	0.8	2052	2.7
20 W	0636	2.8	1246	0.4	1924	2.8		
6 W	0213	1.0	0833	2.9	1440	0.7	2153	2.8
21 TH	0102	0.8	0802	2.9	1354	0.3	2040	2.8
7 TH	0310	0.8	0947	3.0	1529	0.5	2241	3.0
22 F	0212	0.7	0917	3.0	1454	0.1	2150	3.0
8 F	0358	0.6	1037	3.1	1612	0.4	2322	3.0
23 SA	0315	0.5	1018	3.2	1548	0.0	2247	3.1
9 SA	0438	0.5	1119	3.1	1649	0.4		
24 SU	0410	0.3	1110	3.3	1637	-0.1	2336	3.3
10 SU	0000	3.1	0513	0.4	1157	3.1	1721	0.4
25 M ●	0458	0.1	1200	3.5	1724	-0.1		
11 M ○	0035	3.1	0544	0.3	1229	3.1	1751	0.4
26 TU	0022	3.4	0543	0.0	1250	3.5	1810	0.0
12 TU	0104	3.1	0613	0.3	1300	3.1	1821	0.4
27 W	0105	3.5	0628	0.0	1313	3.5	1857	0.1
13 W	0131	3.2	0645	0.2	1334	3.1	1855	0.3
28 TH	0146	3.6	0714	0.0	1425	3.5	1945	0.2
14 TH	0159	3.2	0720	0.2	1412	3.1	1934	0.3
29 F	0227	3.6	0800	0.0	1510	3.4	2033	0.4
15 F	0231	3.3	0759	0.2	1451	3.1	2016	0.3
30 SA	0307	3.6	0848	0.3	1555	3.2	2123	0.6
31 SU	0349	3.5	0939	0.4	1642	3.1	2216	0.7

JUNE

Day	Time	m	Time	m	Time	m	Time	m
1 M	0434	3.4	1038	0.6	1733	2.9	2315	0.9
16 TU	0414	3.2	1015	0.3	1658	3.0	2234	0.5
2 TU	0524	3.2	1147	0.7	1830	2.8		
17 W	0506	3.1	1117	0.3	1754	2.9	2333	0.6
3 W	0020	1.0	0621	3.0	1257	0.8	1933	2.8
18 TH	0610	3.0	1222	0.3	1856	2.9		
4 TH	0127	1.0	0726	2.9	1358	0.7	2050	2.8
19 F	0036	0.7	0727	2.9	1327	0.3	2005	2.9
5 F	0228	0.9	0841	2.9	1450	0.7	2154	2.8
20 SA	0144	0.7	0848	3.0	1430	0.2	2120	2.9
6 SA	0322	0.8	0949	2.9	1536	0.6	2244	2.9
21 SU	0252	0.6	0956	3.1	1527	0.2	2224	3.1
7 SU	0407	0.6	1039	3.0	1617	0.5	2326	3.0
22 M	0352	0.4	1053	3.2	1620	0.1	2317	3.2
8 M	0446	0.5	1119	3.0	1653	0.5		
23 TU	0445	0.3	1146	3.3	1709	0.1		
9 TU	0003	3.1	0520	0.4	1155	3.0	1726	0.4
24 W ●	0004	3.4	0531	0.2	1238	3.3	1756	0.2
10 W ○	0036	3.1	0553	0.3	1231	3.0	1759	0.3
25 TH	0049	3.5	0616	0.1	1327	3.3	1843	0.3
11 TH	0106	3.2	0627	0.2	1310	3.1	1836	0.4
26 F	0131	3.5	0700	0.1	1414	3.3	1929	0.3
12 F	0138	3.3	0703	0.2	1352	3.1	1917	0.3
27 SA	0211	3.6	0743	0.2	1457	3.2	2014	0.4
13 SA	0213	3.3	0744	0.2	1435	3.1	2002	0.3
28 SU	0251	3.6	0827	0.3	1539	3.2	2059	0.5
14 SU	0251	3.3	0829	0.2	1520	3.1	2049	0.4
29 M	0331	3.5	0912	0.4	1622	3.1	2145	0.6
15 M	0330	3.3	0920	0.2	1607	3.0	2140	0.4
30 TU	0411	3.4	1000	0.6	1705	3.0	2232	0.8

JULY

Day	Time	m	Time	m	Time	m	Time	m
1 W	0454	3.3	1055	0.7	1751	2.9	2326	0.9
16 TH	0448	3.3	1053	0.2	1729	3.0	2309	0.5
2 TH	0541	3.1	1157	0.8	1840	2.8		
17 F	0543	3.1	1156	0.3	1823	3.0		
3 F	0027	1.0	0633	2.9	1305	0.9	1934	2.8
18 SA	0011	0.7	0651	3.0	1304	0.4	1925	2.9
4 SA	0135	1.0	0732	2.8	1405	0.8	2041	2.8
19 SU	0120	0.7	0820	2.9	1410	0.4	2049	2.9
5 SU	0240	0.9	0839	2.8	1458	0.8	2156	2.8
20 M	0234	0.7	0942	3.0	1513	0.4	2205	3.0
6 M	0334	0.8	0947	2.8	1544	0.7	2250	2.9
21 TU	0342	0.6	1045	3.1	1609	0.4	2302	3.2
7 TU	0419	0.6	1041	2.9	1626	0.6	2333	3.1
22 W	0437	0.4	1139	3.2	1700	0.3	2351	3.3
8 W	0459	0.5	1126	3.0	1703	0.5		
23 TH ●	0523	0.3	1230	3.2	1746	0.3		
9 TH ○	0009	3.2	0535	0.3	1208	3.0	1740	0.4
24 F	0035	3.4	0605	0.2	1318	3.2	1829	0.4
10 F	0045	3.2	0611	0.2	1252	3.1	1820	0.4
25 SA	0117	3.5	0645	0.2	1402	3.2	1911	0.4
11 SA	0120	3.3	0649	0.2	1337	3.1	1902	0.3
26 SU	0156	3.6	0724	0.2	1441	3.2	1951	0.4
12 SU	0158	3.4	0730	0.1	1422	3.2	1947	0.3
27 M	0233	3.6	0802	0.3	1517	3.2	2030	0.5
13 M	0238	3.4	0815	0.0	1507	3.1	2033	0.3
28 TU	0309	3.5	0841	0.4	1553	3.1	2109	0.6
14 TU	0318	3.4	0903	0.1	1552	3.1	2122	0.3
29 W	0345	3.5	0920	0.5	1630	3.1	2150	0.7
15 W	0401	3.4	0955	0.1	1639	3.1	2213	0.4
30 TH	0422	3.4	1003	0.7	1710	3.0	2234	0.8
31 F	0502	3.2	1053	0.8	1752	2.9	2326	0.9

AUGUST

Day	Time	m	Time	m	Time	m	Time	m
1 SA	0548	3.0	1151	0.9	1841	2.8		
16 SU	0618	3.0	1243	0.7	1847	3.0		
2 SU	0027	1.0	0642	2.8	1301	1.0	1937	2.7
17 M	0100	0.8	0755	2.8	1358	0.7	2014	2.9
3 M	0143	1.1	0746	2.8	1411	1.0	2050	2.8
18 TU	0226	0.8	0938	2.9	1504	0.7	2150	3.0
4 TU	0257	0.9	0859	2.8	1510	0.9	2210	2.9
19 W	0335	0.7	1042	3.1	1601	0.6	2249	3.2
5 W	0352	0.7	1010	2.9	1559	0.7	2302	3.0
20 TH	0428	0.5	1134	3.2	1649	0.5	2337	3.3
6 TH	0436	0.5	1104	3.0	1641	0.6	2344	3.2
21 F	0512	0.3	1221	3.2	1732	0.4		
7 F	0515	0.3	1151	3.1	1721	0.5		
22 SA ●	0021	3.4	0550	0.3	1305	3.2	1811	
8 SA ○	0023	3.3	0552	0.1	1237	3.1	1801	0.4
23 SU	0101	3.5	0626	0.3	1344	3.2	1848	0.4
9 SU	0102	3.4	0631	0.0	1322	3.2	1843	0.3
24 M	0137	3.5	0700	0.3	1418	3.2	1923	0.5
10 M	0143	3.5	0711	0.0	1407	3.2	1927	0.4
25 TU	0211	3.5	0733	0.4	1449	3.2	1957	0.5
11 TU	0223	3.6	0755	-0.1	1450	3.3	2012	0.2
26 W	0243	3.5	0806	0.5	1520	3.2	2032	0.5
12 W	0304	3.6	0841	0.0	1532	3.3	2100	0.3
27 TH	0316	3.5	0841	0.5	1552	3.2	2109	0.6
13 TH	0345	3.6	0931	0.1	1614	3.3	2149	0.4
28 F	0350	3.4	0918	0.6	1627	3.1	2150	0.7
14 F	0428	3.4	1026	0.3	1658	3.2	2244	0.5
29 SA	0427	3.3	1000	0.8	1707	3.0	2237	0.9
15 SA	0518	3.2	1130	0.5	1748	3.1	2346	0.7
30 SU	0509	3.1	1051	1.0	1753	2.9	2333	1.0
31 M	0601	2.9	1154	1.1	1850	2.8		

SCOTLAND – GREENOCK

LAT 55°57′N   LONG 4°46′W

TIMES AND HEIGHTS OF HIGH AND LOW WATERS

YEAR **1998**

TIME ZONE (UT)
For Summer Time add ONE hour in non-shaded areas

SEPTEMBER

Date	Day	Time	m	Time	m	Time	m	Time	m
1	TU	0041	1.1	0706	2.7	1310	1.2	1958	2.7
2	W	0212	1.0	0823	2.7	1430	1.1	2123	2.8
3	TH	0321	0.8	0944	2.9	1530	0.9	2230	3.0
4	F	0409	0.5	1046	3.0	1617	0.7	2317	3.2
5	SA	0450	0.3	1135	3.2	1659	0.5	2359	3.4
6 ○	SU	0529	0.1	1220	3.3	1739	0.3		
7	M	0041	3.5	0608	-0.1	1304	3.3	1820	0.3
8	TU	0124	3.6	0649	-0.1	1347	3.4	1904	0.2
9	W	0205	3.7	0731	-0.1	1427	3.5	1948	0.2
10	TH	0246	3.7	0817	0.0	1507	3.5	2035	0.3
11	F	0327	3.7	0905	0.2	1547	3.5	2124	0.4
12	SA	0409	3.5	0959	0.5	1629	3.4	2218	0.6
13	SU	0456	3.3	1104	0.8	1717	3.2	2323	0.8
14	M	0554	3.0	1225	1.0	1814	3.1		
15	TU	0048	1.0	0742	2.8	1344	1.0	1936	3.0
16	W	0215	0.9	0934	2.9	1450	0.9	2132	3.1
17	TH	0321	0.7	1034	3.1	1546	0.8	2231	3.3
18	F	0411	0.5	1121	3.2	1632	0.6	2319	3.4
19	SA	0453	0.4	1204	3.3	1713	0.5		
20 ●	SU	0001	3.5	0529	0.4	1244	3.3	1749	0.5
21	M	0039	3.5	0543	0.4	1319	3.3	1822	0.5
22	TU	0114	3.5	0632	0.4	1350	3.3	1853	0.5
23	W	0145	3.5	0702	0.5	1418	3.3	1924	0.5
24	TH	0215	3.5	0732	0.5	1446	3.3	1957	0.6
25	F	0247	3.5	0805	0.6	1516	3.3	2033	0.6
26	SA	0320	3.4	0841	0.7	1549	3.3	2113	0.7
27	SU	0357	3.3	0922	0.8	1626	3.2	2158	0.8
28	M	0438	3.1	1010	1.0	1710	3.0	2253	1.0
29	TU	0528	2.9	1111	1.2	1806	2.9	2359	1.1
30	W	0633	2.8	1223	1.3	1917	2.8		

OCTOBER

Date	Day	Time	m	Time	m	Time	m	Time	m
1	TH	0120	1.1	0753	2.8	1345	1.2	2041	2.9
2	F	0242	0.8	0918	2.9	1456	1.0	2154	3.1
3	SA	0337	0.5	1025	3.1	1548	0.8	2248	3.3
4	SU	0421	0.3	1114	3.3	1633	0.5	2334	3.5
5 ○	M	0503	0.1	1159	3.4	1716	0.4		
6	TU	0018	3.7	0543	-0.1	1242	3.5	1757	0.3
7	W	0103	3.8	0624	-0.1	1324	3.6	1840	0.2
8	TH	0146	3.8	0708	0.0	1404	3.7	1925	0.2
9	F	0229	3.8	0754	0.2	1443	3.7	2012	0.3
10	SA	0310	3.8	0842	0.4	1522	3.7	2101	0.5
11	SU	0353	3.6	0936	0.7	1605	3.6	2156	0.7
12	M	0441	3.3	1040	1.0	1652	3.4	2303	0.9
13	TU	0540	3.0	1203	1.2	1749	3.2		
14	W	0032	1.0	0727	2.8	1321	1.2	1904	3.1
15	TH	0152	1.0	0916	3.0	1426	1.1	2100	3.1
16	F	0254	0.8	1013	3.1	1521	1.0	2204	3.3
17	SA	0345	0.7	1058	3.3	1609	0.8	2253	3.4
18	SU	0427	0.5	1138	3.4	1650	0.6	2335	3.5
19	M	0504	0.5	1215	3.4	1725	0.6		
20 ●	TU	0013	3.5	0535	0.5	1250	3.4	1757	0.6
21	W	0047	3.5	0605	0.5	1320	3.4	1825	0.6
22	TH	0118	3.4	0633	0.6	1347	3.4	1855	0.6
23	F	0147	3.4	0703	0.6	1414	3.5	1927	0.6
24	SA	0220	3.4	0736	0.6	1444	3.5	2004	0.6
25	SU	0255	3.4	0813	0.7	1517	3.4	2044	0.7
26	M	0332	3.2	0855	0.8	1553	3.3	2130	0.8
27	TU	0414	3.2	0943	1.0	1634	3.2	2225	0.9
28	W	0502	3.0	1042	1.1	1726	3.0	2329	1.0
29	TH	0606	2.9	1151	1.3	1837	2.9		
30	F	0043	1.0	0724	2.8	1307	1.2	2000	3.0
31	SA	0158	0.8	0847	3.0	1418	1.1	2118	3.2

NOVEMBER

Date	Day	Time	m	Time	m	Time	m	Time	m
1	SU	0300	0.5	0956	3.2	1517	0.8	2217	3.4
2	M	0350	0.3	1049	3.4	1607	0.6	2308	3.6
3	TU	0435	0.1	1135	3.5	1653	0.4	2355	3.7
4 ○	W	0519	0.0	1218	3.6	1736	0.3		
5	TH	0042	3.8	0602	0.1	1301	3.8	1820	0.2
6	F	0128	3.8	0647	0.2	1342	3.8	1905	0.3
7	SA	0213	3.8	0734	0.3	1422	3.9	1953	0.3
8	SU	0257	3.7	0824	0.6	1503	3.9	2042	0.5
9	M	0342	3.6	0917	0.8	1546	3.8	2137	0.7
10	TU	0431	3.3	1018	1.1	1633	3.6	2241	0.9
11	W	0529	3.1	1131	1.2	1727	3.4		
12	TH	0000	1.0	0648	3.0	1245	1.3	1832	3.2
13	F	0116	1.0	0835	3.0	1351	1.3	2000	3.2
14	SA	0218	0.9	0938	3.0	1449	1.1	2123	3.2
15	SU	0311	0.8	1025	3.3	1539	0.9	2219	3.3
16	M	0356	0.7	1106	3.4	1622	0.8	2304	3.4
17	TU	0435	0.7	1144	3.4	1700	0.7	2343	3.4
18	W	0509	0.6	1220	3.5	1733	0.6		
19 ●	TH	0018	3.4	0539	0.7	1252	3.5	1803	0.6
20	F	0050	3.4	0608	0.7	1320	3.5	1832	0.6
21	SA	0121	3.4	0639	0.7	1348	3.5	1905	0.6
22	SU	0156	3.4	0714	0.7	1419	3.5	1942	0.6
23	M	0234	3.3	0753	0.7	1453	3.5	2023	0.6
24	TU	0313	3.3	0837	0.8	1530	3.4	2110	0.7
25	W	0356	3.2	0926	0.9	1610	3.3	2203	0.7
26	TH	0444	3.1	1021	1.0	1658	3.2	2305	0.8
27	F	0543	3.0	1125	1.1	1801	3.1		
28	SA	0012	0.8	0652	2.9	1234	1.1	1918	3.1
29	SU	0121	0.7	0808	3.0	1342	1.1	2039	3.2
30	M	0224	0.5	0921	3.1	1446	0.9	2147	3.3

DECEMBER

Date	Day	Time	m	Time	m	Time	m	Time	m
1	TU	0320	0.4	1021	3.3	1542	0.7	2244	3.5
2	W	0411	0.2	1111	3.5	1632	0.5	2335	3.6
3 ○	TH	0458	0.2	1157	3.7	1719	0.4		
4	F	0024	3.7	0544	0.2	1242	3.8	1804	0.3
5	SA	0114	3.7	0631	0.3	1324	3.9	1850	0.3
6	SU	0201	3.7	0719	0.5	1406	3.9	1937	0.3
7	M	0247	3.6	0808	0.6	1448	3.9	2026	0.5
8	TU	0332	3.5	0859	0.8	1530	3.9	2117	0.6
9	W	0420	3.4	0953	1.0	1615	3.7	2212	0.8
10	TH	0511	3.2	1052	1.2	1704	3.5	2317	0.9
11	F	0608	3.1	1159	1.3	1758	3.4		
12	SA	0029	1.0	0713	3.0	1307	1.3	1859	3.2
13	SU	0135	1.0	0833	3.0	1410	1.2	2012	3.1
14	M	0232	1.0	0939	3.1	1505	1.1	2130	3.1
15	TU	0321	0.9	1030	3.2	1553	0.9	2227	3.2
16	W	0405	0.8	1113	3.3	1635	0.8	2312	3.2
17	TH	0442	0.8	1152	3.4	1711	0.7	2350	3.2
18 ●	F	0516	0.7	1226	3.5	1744	0.6		
19	SA	0024	3.2	0548	0.7	1257	3.5	1816	0.6
20	SU	0059	3.3	0621	0.7	1327	3.5	1849	0.5
21	M	0137	3.3	0657	0.6	1400	3.6	1926	0.5
22	TU	0217	3.3	0738	0.6	1435	3.6	2008	0.4
23	W	0258	3.3	0822	0.7	1513	3.5	2053	0.5
24	TH	0341	3.2	0910	0.7	1554	3.4	2144	0.5
25	F	0427	3.2	1001	0.8	1638	3.3	2240	0.5
26	SA	0517	3.1	1059	0.9	1731	3.2	2342	0.6
27	SU	0615	3.0	1202	1.0	1836	3.2		
28	M	0047	0.6	0721	3.0	1309	1.0	1956	3.1
29	TU	0153	0.5	0840	3.1	1417	0.9	2118	3.2
30	W	0255	0.5	0953	3.2	1521	0.7	2224	3.3
31	TH	0351	0.4	1051	3.4	1617	0.6	2321	3.4

Chart Datum: 1·62 metres below Ordnance Datum (Newlyn)

H.W.Hts.m.

GREENOCK

MEAN SPRING
AND NEAP CURVES

MEAN RANGES	
Springs 3.1m	
Neaps 1.8m	

Springs occur 2 days
after
New and Full Moon.

ARDROSSAN

10-9-20

N Ayrshire 55°38'·50N 04°49'·54W   Rtg 2·2·2

CHARTS
AC 1866, 2491, 2221, *2126*; Imray C63; OS 63/70

TIDES
+0055 Dover; ML 1·9; Duration 0630; Zone 0 (UT)

Standard Port GREENOCK (←—)

Times				Height (metres)			
High Water		Low Water		MHWS	MHWN	MLWN	MLWS
0000	0600	0000	0600	3·4	2·8	1·0	0·3
1200	1800	1200	1800				
Differences ARDROSSAN							
–0020	–0010	–0010	–0010	–0·2	–0·2	+0·1	+0·1
IRVINE							
–0020	–0020	–0030	–0010	–0·3	–0·3	–0·1	0·0

SHELTER
Good in marina (formerly Eglinton Dock), access at all tides over sill, 5·2m least depth. But strong SW/NW winds cause heavy seas in the apprs and the hbr may be closed in SW gales. Ferries berth on both sides of Winton Pier.

NAVIGATION
WPT 55°38'·13N 04°50'·48W, 235°/055° from/to hbr ent, 0·65M. From the W/NW keep clear of low-lying Horse Isle (conspic W tower on its S end) ringed by drying ledges. The passage between Horse Isle and the mainland is obstructed by drying rks and should not be attempted. Be aware of following dangers: From the S/SE, Eagle Rk 3ca S of hbr ent, marked by SHM buoy, Fl G 5s. 3ca SE of Eagle Rk lies unmarked Campbell Rk (0·2m). W Crinan Rk (1·1m) is 300m W of hbr ent, marked by PHM buoy, Fl R 4s.

LIGHTS AND MARKS
Dir lt WRG 15m W14M, R/G11M (see 10.9.4); W sector leads 055° to hbr ent between lt ho and detached bkwtr. Lt ho al Iso WG 4s 11m 9M, G317°-035°, W elsewhere. On S end of detached bkwtr, Fl WR 2s 7m 5M, R041°-126°, W elsewhere. Tfc signals, shown from control twr at ent to marina:
3 F(R) lts (vert) = hbr and marina closed; no entry/exit for commercial and pleasure vessels.
3 F(G) lts (vert) = marina open, hbr closed; pleasure craft may enter/exit the marina, no commercial movements.
2 F(R) lts over 1 F(G) = hbr open, marina closed; commercial vessels may enter/exit subject to approval by Hbr Control on VHF. Pleasure craft must clear the approach channel, ferry turning area (between the detached bkwtr and Winton Pier) and the outer basin.

RADIO TELEPHONE
Marina VHF Ch **80** M. Ardrossan Hr Mr Ch 12 14 16 (H24).

TELEPHONE (Dial code 01294)
Marina 607077, 📠 607076; Hr Mr 63972; MRCC (01475) 729988; ▦ (0141) 887 9369 (H24); Marinecall 0891 500462; Police 468236; Dr 463838; Ⓗ (01563) 521133.

FACILITIES
Clyde Marina (250+50 visitors) ☎ 607077, 📠 607076, £12.69, access all tides. D, AC, FW, ME, EI, Ⓔ, CH, BH (20 ton). **Town** EC Wed; V, R, Bar, ◙, Gas, Gaz, ✉, Ⓑ, ⇌, ✈ (Prestwick/Glasgow). Ferries to Brodick (Arran) and Douglas (IOM).

9

HARBOUR BETWEEN ARDROSSAN AND TROON

IRVINE, N Ayrshire, 55°36'·17N 04°42'·00W. AC 1866, 2220, *2126*. HW +0055 on Dover. Tides: see 10.9.20. Good shelter once across the bar (0·5m CD); access approx HW ±3½ for 1·4m draft. Do not attempt ent in heavy onshore weather. The IB-B SPM buoy, Fl Y 3s, is 1·15M from hbr ent, close NW of ldg line. 5 blocks of flats and chys are conspic ENE of ent. Ldg lts 051°: front, FG 10m 5M; rear, FR 15m 5M. The ent groynes have bns, Fl R 3s and Fl G 3s; groynes inside the ent have unlit perches. W Pilot tr with mast is conspic 3ca inside ent. Berth 2ca beyond this on S side at visitors' quay (2·2m). ‡ prohib. VHF Ch 12 (0800-1600 Tues and Thurs; 0800-1300 Wed). Hr Mr ☎ (01294) 487000/278132. Facilities: **Quay** AB £5, FW, Slip, C (3 ton), Showers, SM. **Town** P & D (cans, 1·5km), Gas, V, R, ⇌, ✈ (Prestwick).

TROON   10-9-21

S Ayrshire 55°33'·10N 04°40'·90W   Rtg 2-1-2

CHARTS
AC 1866, 2220, *2126*; Imray C63; OS 70
TIDES
+0050 Dover; ML 1·9; Duration 0630; Zone 0 (UT)

Standard Port GREENOCK (←)

Times				Height (metres)			
High Water		Low Water		MHWS	MHWN	MLWN	MLWS
0000	0600	0000	0600	3·4	2·8	1·0	0·3
1200	1800	1200	1800				
Differences TROON							
−0025	−0025	−0020	−0020	−0·2	−0·2	0·0	0·0
AYR							
−0025	−0025	−0030	−0015	−0·4	−0·3	+0·1	+0·1
GIRVAN							
−0025	−0040	−0035	−0010	−0·3	−0·3	−0·1	0·0
LOCH RYAN (Stranraer)							
−0020	−0020	−0017	−0017	−0·4	−0·4	−0·4	−0·2

SHELTER
Complete in marina (2·4m at ent, 1·6m at SE end); speed limit 5kn. Strong SW/NW winds cause heavy seas in the apprs. Inside hbr, keep clear of Ailsa Shipyard.
NAVIGATION
WPT 55°33'·20N 04°42'·00W, 283°/103° from/to W pier lt, 0·61M. Appr in sector SW to NW. Beware Lady Isle, Fl (4) 30s 19m 8M, W bn, 2·2M SW; Troon Rock (5·6m, occas breaks) 1·1M W; Lappock Rock (0·6m, bn with G barrel topmark) 1·6M NNW; Mill Rock (0·4m) ½M NNE of hbr ent, marked by unlit PHM buoy.
LIGHTS AND MARKS
No ldg lts. Sheds (35m) at Ailsa Shipyard are conspic and floodlit at night. Ent sigs (not applicable to yachts): 2B ●s or 2F® lts (vert) = ent/exit prohib. W pier hd Fl (2) WG 5s 11m 9M, G036°-090°, W090°-036°. 14m SE of this lt there is a floodlit dolphin, W with dayglow patches. A SHM lt buoy, FG, marks the chan in the ent to marina.
RADIO TELEPHONE
Marina VHF Ch **80** M (H24).
TELEPHONE (Dial code 01292)
Hr Mr 315553; MRCC (01475) 729988; ⌗ 478548; Marinecall 0891 500 462; Police 313100; Dr 313593; ⊞ 610553.
FACILITIES
Troon Yacht Haven (marina: 250+50 visitors) ☎ 315553, ⚓ 312836, £12.97, access all tides. Ⓥ on pontoon A, first to stbd. AB for LOA 36m x 3m draft at end of pontoons. D, FW, ME, El, Ⓔ, CH, AC, Sh , SM (dly pick-up), BH (12 ton), C (2 ton), Slip, V, R, Bar, Ⓖ, Gas, Gaz; **Hbr Pier** FW, AB, V; **Troon Cruising Club** ☎ 311908; **Ailsa Shipyard** has all normal 'big ship' repair facilities.
Town EC Wed; ⊠, Ⓑ, ⇌, ✈ (Prestwick/Glasgow).

HARBOURS ON THE FIRTH OF CLYDE SOUTH OF TROON

AYR, S Ayrshire, 55°28'·22N 04°38'·71W. AC 1866, 2220, *2126*. HW +0050 on Dover; ML 1·8m. Duration 0630. See 10·9·21. Good shelter in the dock on S side of ent chan, which is open to W'lies. After heavy rains large amounts of debris may be washed down the R Ayr. From the W, hbr ent lies between conspic gasholder to the N and townhall spire to the S. Outer St Nicholas SHM buoy, Fl G 2s, warns of shoals and eponymous Rock (0·8m) 150m S of ent. Ldg lts 098°: front, by Pilot Stn, FR 10m 5M R tr, also tfc sigs; rear (130m from front), Oc R 10s 18m 9M. N bkwtr hd, QR 9m 5M. S pier hd, Q 7m 7M, vis 012°-161°, and FG 5m 5M, same structure, vis 012°-082°, over St Nicholas Rk. Tfc sigs (near front ldg lt): 2 B ●s (vert) or 2FR (vert) = hbr closed; 1 B ● (1 ® or 1 Ⓖ) = proceed with care. Hr Mr ☎ (01292) 281687; VHF Ch 14 16; ⌗ 478548; **Ayr Y & CC** at S dock, M. **Services**: Sh, ME, El, CH. **Town** EC Wed; Ⓑ, Bar, Gas, P & D, FW, ⊠, R, ⇌, V.

Continued opposite

GIRVAN, S Ayrshire, 55°14'·77N 04°51'·80W. AC 1866, 2199. HW +0043 on Dover; ML 1·8m; Duration 0630. See 10.9.21. Good shelter at inner hbr for 16 yachts on 60m pontoon (1·7m) beyond LB. Coasters and FVs berth on adjacent quay. No access LW±2 over bar 1·5m. Beware Girvan Patch, 1·7m, 4ca SW of ent, and Brest Rks, 3·5M N of hbr extending 6ca offshore. Ch spire (conspic) brg 104° leads between N bkwtr, Fl (2) R 6s 7m 4M, and S pier, 2 FG (vert) 8m 4M. Inner N groyne, Iso 4s 3m 4M. Tfc sigs at root of S pier: 2 B discs (hor), at night 2 Ⓡ (hor) = hbr shut. VHF Ch 12 16 (HO). Hr Mr ☎ (01465) 713048; FW, Slip. **Town** EC Wed; Ⓑ, ✉, V, R, ⇌, P & D (cans).

ANCHORAGES WITHIN LOCH RYAN

LOCH RYAN, Dumfries and Galloway, 55°01'·00N 05°05'·00W. AC 1403, 2198. HW (Stranraer) +0055 on Dover; ML 1·6m; Duration 0640. See 10.9.21. Very good shelter except in strong NW winds. Ent between Milleur Pt and Finnarts Pt. ⚓s in Lady Bay, 1·3M SSE of Milleur Pt, but exposed to heavy wash from fast catamaran ferries; in The Wig in 3m (avoid weed patches); or off Stranraer 3ca NW of W pier hd. Larger yachts berth on NE side of E pier, by arrangement with Hr Mr, VHF Ch 14 (H24) or ☎ (01776) 702460. Beware The Beef Barrel, rk 1m high 6ca SSE of Milleur Pt; the sand spit running 1·5M to SE from W shore opposite Cairn Pt lt ho Fl (2) R 10s 14m 12M. Lt at Cairnryan ferry terminal Fl R 5s 5m 5M. Lts at Stranraer: centre pier hd 2FBu (vert), E pier hd 2FR (vert), W pier hd 2 FG (vert) 8m 4M. Facilities (Stranraer): EC Wed; Ⓑ, Bar, D, FW, P, ✉, R, ⇌, V.

PORTPATRICK   10-9-22

Dumfries and Galloway 54°50'·42N 05°07'·11W   Rtg 3-4-2

CHARTS
AC 2198, *2724*; Imray C62; OS 82

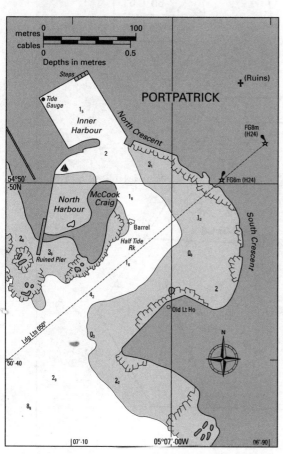

9

PORTPATRICK *continued*

TIDES
+0032 Dover; ML 2·1; Duration 0615; Zone 0 (UT)

Standard Port LIVERPOOL (→)

Times				Heights (metres)			
High Water		Low Water		MHWS	MHWN	MLWN	MLWS
0000	0600	0200	0800	9·3	7·4	2·9	0·9
1200	1800	1400	2000				
Differences PORTPATRICK							
+0018	+0026	0000	−0035	−5·5	−4·4	−2·0	−0·6

SHELTER
Good in Inner hbr, but ent is difficult in strong SW/NW winds. Beware cross tides off ent, up to 3kn at springs.
NAVIGATION
WPT 54°50'·00N 05°08'·00W, 235°/055° from/to ent, 0·70M. Ent to outer hbr by short narrow chan with hazards either side, including rky shelf covered at HW. Barrel buoy marks end of Half Tide Rk.
LIGHTS AND MARKS
Killantringan lt ho, Fl (2) 15s 49m 25M, is 1.6M NW of ent. Ldg lts 050°, FG (H24) 6/8m: Front on sea wall; rear on bldg; 2 vert orange stripes by day. Conspic features include: TV mast 1M NE, almost on ldg line; large hotel on cliffs about 1½ca NNW of hbr ent; Dunskey Castle (ru) 4ca SE of hbr.
RADIO TELEPHONE
None. Portpatrick Coast Radio Stn VHF Ch 27 16.
TELEPHONE (Dial code 01776)
Hr Mr 810355; MRSC (01475) 729988; ⊞ (0141) 887 9369 (H24); Marinecall 0891 500462; Police 810222; Ⓗ 702323.
FACILITIES
Hbr Slip (small craft), AB £6, M, FW, L. Note: Pontoons are planned in inner hbr, to be dredged approx 2·5m.
Village EC Thurs; P (cans), D (bulk tanker), Gas, V, R, Bar, ✉, Ⓑ (Stranraer), ⇌ (bus to Stranraer), ✈ (Carlisle).

SUBMARINE EXERCISE AREAS (SUBFACTS)

Those areas in which submarine activity is planned for the next 16 hrs are broadcast by Coast Radio Stations at the times and on the channels shown below. The areas are referred to not by numbers, but by names as listed on the previous page; see also 10.8.20 for areas to the N of Mull.

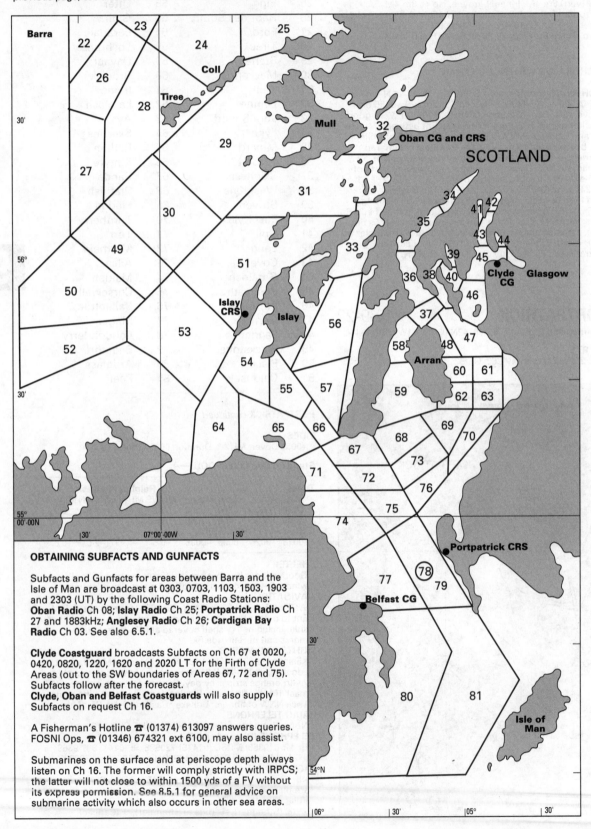

OBTAINING SUBFACTS AND GUNFACTS

Subfacts and Gunfacts for areas between Barra and the Isle of Man are broadcast at 0303, 0703, 1103, 1503, 1903 and 2303 (UT) by the following Coast Radio Stations: **Oban Radio** Ch 08; **Islay Radio** Ch 25; **Portpatrick Radio** Ch 27 and 1883kHz; **Anglesey Radio** Ch 26; **Cardigan Bay Radio** Ch 03. See also 6.5.1.

Clyde Coastguard broadcasts Subfacts on Ch 67 at 0020, 0420, 0820, 1220, 1620 and 2020 LT for the Firth of Clyde Areas (out to the SW boundaries of Areas 67, 72 and 75). Subfacts follow after the forecast.
Clyde, Oban and Belfast Coastguards will also supply Subfacts on request Ch 16.

A Fisherman's Hotline ☎ (01374) 613097 answers queries. FOSNI Ops, ☎ (01346) 674321 ext 6100, may also assist.

Submarines on the surface and at periscope depth always listen on Ch 16. The former will comply strictly with IRPCS; the latter will not close to within 1500 yds of a FV without its express permission. See 8.5.1 for general advice on submarine activity which also occurs in other sea areas.

VOLVO PENTA SERVICE

Sales and service centres in area 10

CUMBRIA *Waterhead Marine Ltd*, Ambleside, LA22 0EX Tel (015394) 32424
Shepherds (Windermere) Ltd, Bowness Bay, Windermere LA23 3HE
Tel (015394) 44031 **MERSEYSIDE** *James Troop & Co Ltd*, Pleasant Hill Street,
Liverpool L8 5SZ Tel 0151-709 0581 **GWYNEDD** *Abersoch Land & Sea*,
Abersoch, Pwllheli, Gwynedd LL53 7AH (01758) 713434 *Arfon Oceaneering*,
Victoria Dock Slipway, Balaclava Road, Caernarfon LL55 1TG Tel (01286)
676055

Area 10

North-West England, Isle of Man and North Wales
Mull of Galloway to Bardsey Island

VOLVO PENTA

10

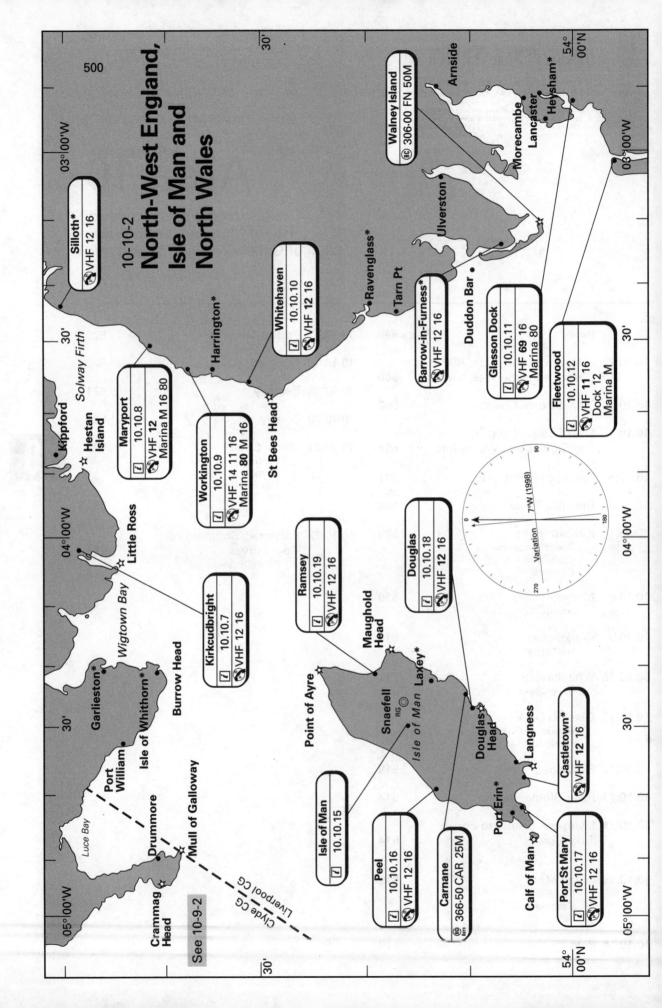

10-10-2 North-West England, Isle of Man and North Wales

500

Silloth*
VHF 12 16

Maryport 10.10.8
i VHF 12 Marina M 16 80

Workington 10.10.9
i VHF 14 11 16 Marina 80 M

Whitehaven 10.10.10
i VHF **12** 16

Harrington*

Ravenglass*

Tarn Pt

St Bees Head

Barrow-in-Furness* 10.10.11
VHF 12 16

Duddon Bar

Glasson Dock 10.10.11
i VHF 69 16 Marina 80

Fleetwood 10.10.12
i VHF **11** 16 Dock 12 Marina M

Walney Island
☉RC 306·00 FN 50M

Arnside

Heysham*

Morecambe

Lancaster

Ulverston

Kippford

Hestan Island

Solway Firth

Little Ross

Wigtown Bay

Kirkcudbright 10.10.7
i VHF 12 16

Garlieston*

Isle of Whithorn*

Burrow Head

Port William

Luce Bay

Drummore

Mull of Galloway

Crammag Head

See 10-9-2

Clyde CG
Liverpool CG

Ramsey 10.10.19
i VHF 12 16

Maughold Head

Point of Ayre

Snaefell
RG ◎

Isle of Man

Isle of Man 10.10.15
i

Laxey*

Douglas 10.10.18
i VHF 12 16

Douglas Head

Langness

Castletown* VHF 12 16

Peel 10.10.16
i VHF 12 16

Carnane
☉RC 366·50 CAR 25M

Port Erin*

Calf of Man

Port St Mary 10.10.17
i VHF 12 16

Variation 7°W (1998)

54° 00'N

Key to Symbols

📞 Coast Radio Station: VHF/MF frequencies
📞 Port, VTS, or Marina Radio: VHF frequencies
Ⓡᴄ Marine RDF beacon
Ⓡᴄ Aero RDF beacon
ⓘ See for harbour information/tidal data
📡 Weather information
   (Frequencies/times of broadcasts)
🚁 SAR Helicopter base
☆ Selected Principal Lights
🚩 Light vessel/Light float/Lanby
Ⓡɢ Emergency VHF DF
* See Area Index

Blackpool
Ⓡᴄ 420·00 BPL 15M

Warton
Ⓡᴄ 337·00 WTN 15M

River Ribble
Preston
ⓘ 10.10.13
📞 VHF Preston
Marina 80 14 16

Liverpool
ⓘ 10.10.14
📞 VHF
Port Ops 12
Ops/Radar 18
Bcsts 09
Marina M

Mostyn Quay
📞 VHF 14 16

Convy
ⓘ 10.10.20
📞 VHF 14 06 08
12 71
Marina 80 M

Liverpool CG
Holyhead CG

Anglesey Radio
📞 VHF 26 28 16
📡 VHF 26
0703 1903 UT

Menai Strait
ⓘ 10.10.21

Port Dinorwic*
📞 VHF Marina 80

Caernarfon*
📞 VHF 12 14 16

Point Lynas
Ⓡᴄ 304·00 PS 50M

For details
see Fig.10(7)1

Holyhead
ⓘ 10.10.22
📞 VHF 14 16

See 10-11-2

10

Blackpool
Warton
Formby
R Alt
Chester
Connah's Quay
Hilbre I
Colwyn Bay
Llandudno
Great Ormes Head Ⓡɢ
Trwyn-Du
Beaumaris*
Bangor*
Moelfre
Amlwch
Cemaes B
Skerries ☆
Anglesey
Valley
Port Trecastell
The Swellies*
Trefor
Treaddur Bay
South Stack ☆
Porth Dinllaen
Porth Ysgaden

SEPARATION ZONE

501

53° 00'N

03°00'W

30'

04°00'W

30'

05°00'W

30'

53° 00'N

05°00'W

30'

53° 00'N

10-10-3   AREA 10 TIDAL STREAMS

5 Hours before HW Dover (0515 before HW Liverpool)

4 Hours before HW Dover (0415 before HW Liverpool)

3 Hours before HW Dover (0315 before HW Liverpool)

2 Hours before HW Dover (0215 before HW Liverpool)

1 Hour before HW Dover (0115 before HW Liverpool)

HW Dover (0015 before HW Liverpool)

Northward 10.9.3   Southward 10.11.3   North Ireland 10.13.3   South Ireland 10.12.3

1 Hour after HW Dover (0045 after HW Liverpool)

2 Hours after HW Dover (0145 after HW Liverpool)

3 Hours after HW Dover (0245 after HW Liverpool)

4 Hours after HW Dover (0345 after HW Liverpool)

5 Hours after HW Dover (0445 after HW Liverpool)

6 Hours after HW Dover (0545 after HW Liverpool)

10.10.4 COASTAL LIGHTS, FOG SIGNALS AND WAYPOINTS

Abbreviations used below are given in 1.4.1. Principal lights are in **bold** print, places in CAPITALS, and light-vessels, light floats and Lanbys in *CAPITAL ITALICS*. Unless otherwise stated lights are white. m – elevation in metres; M – nominal range in miles. Fog signals are in *italics*. Useful waypoints are underlined – use those on land with care. All geographical positions should be assumed to be approximate. See 4.4.1. All positions are referenced to the OSGB 36 datum.

SOLWAY FIRTH TO BARROW-IN-FURNESS

ISLE OF WHITHORN/GARLIESTON
Port William Ldg Lts 105°. Front, Pier Hd 54°45'·65N 04°35'·10W Fl G 3s 7m 3M. Rear, 130m from front, FG 10m 2M.
Isle of Whithorn Hbr E Pier Hd 54°41'·8N 04°21'·7W QG 4m 5M; Gy col.
Ldg Lts 335°. Front, 54°42'·01N 04°22'·00W Oc R 8s 7m 7M; Or ◆. Rear, 35m from front, Oc R 8s 9m 7M; Or ◆, synch.
Garlieston Pier Hd 54°47'·30N 04°21'·70W 2 FR (vert) 8m 3M.

Little Ross 54°45'·93N 04°05'·02W Fl 5s 50m 12M; W Tr; obsc in Wigtown B when brg more than 103°.

KIRKCUDBRIGHT BAY/KIPPFORD
No. 1 Lifeboat House 54°47'·68N 04°03'·66W Fl 3s 7m 3M; vis G080°-037°, W037°-043°, R043°-080°.
No.12 Lt By 54°49'·13N 04°04'·76W Fl R 3s 3m.
Perch No.14 54°49'·25N 04°04'·76W Fl 3s 5m.
No. 22 Lt By 54°50'·08N 04°03'·93W Fl R 3s 2m.
Outfall 54°50'·18N 04°03'·76W Fl Y 5s 3m 2M; Y Tr.
Hestan I, E end 54°49'·90N 03°48'·40W Fl (2) 10s 42m 9M; W Tr.
Barnkirk Pt 54°58'·00N 03°15'·90W Fl 2s 18m 2M.

SILLOTH
Two Feet Bank By 54°42'·40N 03°44'·40W; WCM.
Solway Lt By 54°46'·80N 03°30'·05W Fl G; SHM.
Corner Lt By 54°48'·90N 03°29'·45W Fl G; SHM.
Lees Scar Lt Bn 54°51'·80N 03°24'·75W QG 11m 8M; W structure on piles; vis 005°-317°.
E Cote 54°52'·78N 03°22'·78W FG 15m 12M; vis 046°-058°.
Groyne Hd 54°52'·14N 03°23'·84W 2 FG (vert) 4m 4M; Fl Bu tfc signals close by.

MARYPORT
S Pier Hd 54°43'·06N 03°30'·56W Fl 1·5s 10m 6M.

WORKINGTON/HARRINGTON
N Workington By 54°40'·10N 03°38'·10W; NCM.
S Workington Lt By 54°37'·00N 03°38'·50W VQ (6) + L Fl 10s; SCM.
S Pier 54°39'·13N 03°34'·71W Fl 5s 11m 8M; R bldg; *Siren 20s*.
Ldg Lts 131·8°. Front, 54°38'·92N 03°34'·12W FR 10m 3M. Rear, 134m from front, FR 12m 3M; both on W pyramidal Tr, Or bands.

WHITEHAVEN
W Pier Hd 54°33'·16N 03°35'·84W Fl G 5s 16m 13M; W● Tr.
N Pier Hd 54°33'·17N 03°35'·67W 2 FR (vert) 8m 9M; W● Tr.

Saint Bees Hd 54°30'·80N 03°38'·15W Fl (2) 20s 102m **21M**; W ● Tr; obsc shore-340°.

RAVENGLASS
Blockhouse 54°20'·15N 03°25'·27W FG.
Selker Lt By 54°16'·13N 03°29'·50W Fl (3) G 10s; SHM; *Bell*.

BARROW-IN-FURNESS
Lightning Knoll Lt By 53°59'·83N 03°14'·20W L Fl 10s; SWM; *Bell*.
Sea 1 Lt By 53°59'·73N 03°11'·79W Fl G 2·5s; SHM.
Halfway Shoal Lt Bn 54°01'·48N 03°11'·79W Fl R 5s; QR 19m 10s; R&W checqered Bn; Racon (B).
Outer Bar Lt By 54°02'·00N 03°11'·05W Fl (4) R 10s; PHM.
Bar Lt By 54°02'·32N 03°10'·14W Fl (2) R 5s; PHM.
Isle of Walney 54°02'·92N 03°10'·65W Fl 15s 21m **23M**; stone Tr; obsc 122°-127° within 3M of shore; RC.
Walney Chan Ldg Lts 040·7°. No.1 Front, 54°03'·33N 03°08'·93W Q 7m 10M; Pile, Or daymark. No. 2 Rear, 0·61M from front, Iso 2s 13m 10M; Pile, Or daymark.
Haws Pt W Bn 54°02'·98N 03°10'·03W QR 8m 6M.
Rampside Sands Ldg Lts 005·1°. No. 3 Front, 54°04'·40N 03°09'·70W Q 7m10M; W● Tr. No. 4 Rear, 0·77M from front, Iso 2s 13m 6M; R col, W face.

BARROW TO RIVERS MERSEY AND DEE

MORECAMBE
Morecambe Lt By 53°52'·00N 03°24'·00W Q (9) 15s; WCM; *Whis*.
Lune Deep Lt By 53°55'·80N 03°11'·00W Q (6) + L Fl 15s; SCM; *Whis*; Racon.
Shell Wharf Lt By 53°55'·45N 03°08'·88W Fl G 2·5s; SHM.
King Scar Lt By 53°56'·95N 03°04'·30W Fl G 2·5s; SHM.
Sewer outfall 54°04'·33N 02°53'·74W Fl G 2s 4m 2M; Tr.
Lts in line about 090°. Front, 54°04'·40N 02°52'·52W FR 10m 2M; G mast. Rear, 140m from front, FR 14m 2M; G mast.

HEYSHAM
S Outfall 54°01'·73N 02°55'·73W Fl (2) G 10s 5m 2M.
N Outfall 54°01'·85N 02°55'·69W Fl G 5s 5m 2M; metal post.
S Bkwtr Hd 54°01'·90N 02°55'·64W 2 FG (vert) 9m 5M; W Tr; Ra refl; *Siren 30s*.
SW Quay Ldg Lts 102·2°. Front, 54°01'·90N 02°55'·13W both F Bu 11/14m 2M; Or & B ◆ on masts.
S Pier Hd 54°01'·90N 02°55'·35W Oc G 7·5s 9m 6M.

RIVER LUNE/GLASSON DOCK
R Lune No.1 Lt By 53°58'·62N 02°59'·99W Q (9) 15s; WCM.
Ldg Lts 083·7°. Front, Plover Scar 53°58'·87N 02°52'·88W Fl 2s 6m 6M; W Tr, B lantern. Rear, 854m from front, Cockersand Abbey F 18m 8M; R Tr (chan liable to change).
Crook Perch, No. 7 53°59'·45N 02°52'·28W Fl G 5s 3M; G ▲ on mast.
Bazil Perch, No.16 54°00'·19N 02°51'·58W Fl (3) R 10s 3M.
Glasson Quay 54°00'·02N 02°50·94W FG 1M.

FLEETWOOD
Fairway No. 1 Lt By 53°57'·56N 03°02'·25W Q; NCM; *Bell*.
Esplanade Ldg Lts 156°. Front, 53°55'·70N 03°00'·47W Fl G 2s 14m. Rear, 320m from front, Fl G 4s 28m. Both stone Trs. Vis on Ldg line only. (H24) (chan liable to change).
Steep Breast Perch 53°55'·73N 03°00'·49W Iso G 2s 3m 2M.
Knott End slip Hd 53°55'·72N 03°00'·02W 2 FR (vert) 3m 2M.

BLACKPOOL
N Pier Hd 53°49'·16N 03°03'·83W 2 FG (vert) 3M.
Central Pier Hd 53°48'·65N 03°03'·55W 2 FG (vert) 4M.
Obstn By 53°48'·45N 03°04'·22W; SHM.
S Pier Hd 53°47'·72N 03°03'·60W 2 FG (vert) 4M.
Blackpool Tr 53°48'·95N 03°03'·26W Aero FR 158m.

RIVER RIBBLE
Gut Lt By 53°41'·75N 03°08'·90W L Fl 10s; SWM.
Perches show Fl R on N side, and Fl G on S side of chan.
S side, 14·3M Perch 53°42'·75N 03°04'·85W Fl G 5s 6m 3M.
Southport Pier Hd 52°39'·35N 03°01'·25W 2 FG (vert) 6m 5M; W post; vis 033°-213°.
Jordan's Spit Lt By 53°35'·75N 03°19'·20W Q (9) 15s, WCM.

FT Lt By 53°34'·55N 03°13'·12W Q; NCM.
Spoil Ground Lt By 53°34'·25N 03°17'·30W Fl Y 3s; SPM.

RIVER MERSEY/LIVERPOOL
BAR Lt F 53°32'·00N 03°20'·90W Fl 5s 10m 12M; R structure on By; Racon (T); *Horn (2) 20s.*
Q1 Lt F 53°31'·00N 03°16'·62W VQ; NCM.
Q2 Lt F 53°31'·47N 03°14'·87W VQ R; PHM.
Q3 Lt By 53°30'·95N 03°15'·00W Fl G 3s; SHM.
Burbo Trs Lt By 53°30'·41N 03°17'·52W Fl (3) G 9s; SHM.
FORMBY Lt F 53°31'·10N 03°13'·45W Iso 4s 11m 6M; R hull, W stripes.
C4 Lt F 53°31'·82N 03°08'·42W Fl R 3s; PHM.
CROSBY Lt F 53°30'·72N 03°06'·21W Oc 5s 11m 8M; R hull, W stripes.
C14 Lt F 53°29'·91N 03°05'·27W Fl R 3s; PHM.
BRAZIL Lt F 53°26'·83N 03°02'·18W QG; SHM.
Seacombe Ferry N and S corners 53°24'·6N 03°00'·8W 3 FG 5m 5M; near N corner FY 8m 6M; *Bell (3) 20s .*
Birkenhead, Woodside Landing Stage N end 53°23'·7N 03°00'·4W 3 FG 5m 4M and S end 2 FG (vert) with *Bell (4) 15s.*
Cammell Laird slip, SE corner 53°23'·96N 03°00'·22W Fl (2) G 6s 5m 5M.
Pluckington Bk Lt By 53°22'·99N 02°59'·48W VQ (9) 10s; WCM.
Brombro Lt By 53°21'·81N 02°58'·59W Q (3) 10s; ECM.
Eastham Locks E Dn 53°19'·57N 02°56'·92W Fl (2) R 6s 5m 8M.
Garston NW Dn 53°20'·87N 02°54'·54W 2 FG (vert) 12m 9M; *Horn 11s.*

RIVER DEE
HE1 Lt By 53°26'·31N 03°18'·00W Q (9) 15s; WCM.
HE2 Lt By 53°25'·11N 03°13'·09W Q (3) 10s; ECM.
HE3 Lt By 53°24'·75N 03°12'·90W; SHM.
Hilbre I 53°22'·97N 03°13'·70W Fl R 3s 14m 5M; W Tr.
HE4 By 53°22'·30N 03°14'·20W; SHM.

MOSTYN/CONNAH'S QUAY
Mostyn Training Wall Hd 53°19'·52N 03°15'·62W 2 FR (vert) 10m 3M; B mast.
Mostyn Ldg Lts 215·7°. Front, 53°19'·18N 03°16'·15W FR 12m; W ♦ on B mast. Rear, 135m from front, FR 22m; W ♦ on B mast.
Flint Sands, N Training wall Hd 53°15'·05N 03°06'·40W Fl R 3s 4m 6M; Tr.
Connah's Quay, S Trg Wall Hd 53°13'·75N 03°04'·02W Fl G 5s 3m 6M.

WELSH CHANNEL
Bank Lt By 53°20'·31N 03°15'·96W Fl R 5s; PHM.
Mostyn Lt By 53°21'·00N 03°16'·40W Fl (4) G 15s; SHM.
NE Mostyn Lt By 53°21'·48N 03°17'·73W Fl (3) G 10s; SHM.
Air By 53°21'·83N 03°19'·20W SHM.
Dee Lt By 53°21'·97N 03°18'·78W Q (6) + L Fl 15s; SCM.
E Hoyle Lt By 53°22'·03N 03°21'·03'W Fl (4) R 15s; PHM.
Earwig Lt By 53°21'·37N 03°23'·50W Fl (2) G 5s; SHM.
S Hoyle Lt By 53°21'·40N 03°24'·78W Fl (3) R 10s; PHM.
Mid Hoyle By 53°22'·90N 03°19'·63W; PHM.
Hoyle Lt By 53°23'·14N 03°21'·30W QR; PHM.
NW Hoyle Lt By 53°23'·30N 03°23'·80W VQ; NCM.
N Hoyle Lt By 53°26'·67N 03°30'·50W VQ; NCM.

ISLE OF MAN
Point of Ayre 54°24'·95N 04°22'·03W Fl (4) 20s 32m **19M**; W Tr, two R bands; Racon (M); *Horn (3) 60s.*
Low Lt 54°25'·05N 04°21'·80W Fl 3s 10m 8M; R Tr, lower part W, on B Base; part obsc 335°-341°.

JURBY/PEEL
Cronk y Cliwe 54°22'·30N 04°31'·40W 2 Fl R 5s (vert); synch.
Orrisdale 54°19'·30N 04°34'·10W 2 Fl R 5s (vert); synch.
Peel Bkwtr Hd 54°13'·67N 04°41'·62W Oc 7s 11m 6M; W Tr;

Bell (4) 12s (occas).
Peel Groyne Hd 54°13'·55N 04°41'·60W Iso R 2s 4m.

PORT ERIN
Ldg Lts 099·1°. Front, 54°05'·23N 04°45'·49W FR 10m 5M; W Tr, R band. Rear, 39m from front, FR 19m 5M; W col, R band.
Raglan Pier Hd 54°05'·11N 04°45'·79W Oc G 5s 8m 5M.
Thousla Rk 54°03'·71N 04°47'·97W Fl R 3s 9m 4M.
Calf of Man W Pt 54°03'·20N 04°49'·70W Fl 15s 93m **26M**; W 8-sided Tr; vis 274°-190°; *Horn 45s.*
Chicken Rk 54°02'·30N 04°50'·20W Fl 5s 38m 13M;Tr; *Horn 60s.*

PORT ST MARY
The Carrick 54°04'·30N 04°42'·60W Q (2) 5s 6m 3M; IDM.
Alfred Pier Hd 54°04'·32N 04°43'·74W Oc R 10s 8m 6M; W Tr, R band.
Inner Pier Hd 54°04'·42N 04°44'·07W Oc R 3s 8m 5M.

CASTLETOWN/DERBY HAVEN
Lt By 54°03'·72N 04°38'·54W Fl R 3s; PHM; *Bell.*
New Pier Hd 54°04'·32N 04°38'·89W Oc R 15s 8m 5M.
Langness, Dreswick Pt 54°03'·28N 04°37'·45W Fl (2) 30s 23m 12M; W Tr.
Derby Haven, Bkwtr SW end 54°04'·57N 04°36'·98W Iso G 2s 5m 5M; W Tr, G band.

DOUGLAS
Douglas Hd 54°08'·58N 04°27'·88W Fl 10s 32m **24M**; W Tr; obsc brg more than 037°. FR Lts on radio masts 1 and 3M West.
No. 1 Lt By 54°09'·03N 04°27'·61W Q (3) G 5s; SHM.
Princess Alexandra Pier Hd 54°08'·85N 04°27'·80W Fl R 5s 16m 8M; R mast; *Whis (2) 40s.*
Ldg Lts 229·3°, Front, 54°08'·71N 04°28'·17W Oc 10s 9m 5M; W ▲ R border on mast. Rear, 62m from front, Oc 10s 12m 5M; W ▼ on R border; synch with front.
Victoria Pier Hd 54°08'·83N 04°28'·01W Oc G 8s 10m 3M; W col; vis 225°-327°; Intnl Port Tfc Signals.

LAXEY
Pier Hd 54°13'·45N 04°23'·20W Oc R 3s 7m 5M; W Tr, R band; obsc when brg less than 318°.
Bkwtr Hd 54°13'·50N 04°23'·30W Oc G 3s 7m; W Tr, G band.
Maughold Hd 54°17'·70N 04°18'·50W Fl (3) 30s 65m **21M**.
Bahama Lt By 54°20'·00N 04°08'·50W VQ (6) + L Fl 10s; SCM; *Bell.*

RAMSEY
Queens Pier Dn 54°19'·27N 04°21'·87W Fl R 5s.
S Pier Hd 54°19'·42N 04°22'·43W QR 8m 10M; W Tr, R band, B base.
N Pier Hd 54°19'·48N 04°22'·43W QG 9m 10M; W Tr, B base.
Whitestone Bk Lt By 54°24'·55N 04°20'·20W Q (9) 15s; WCM.
King William Bk Lt By 54°26'·00N 04°00'·00W Q (3) 10s; ECM.

WALES – NORTH COAST
Chester Flat Lt By 53°21'·65N 03°27'·40W Fl (2) R 5s; PHM.
Mid Patch Spit Lt By 53°21'·80N 03°31'·50W Fl R 5s; PHM.
N Rhyl Lt By 53°22'·75N 03°34'·50W Q; NCM.
W Constable Lt By 53°23'·13N 03°49'·17W Q (9) 15s; WCM.

RHYL/LLANDUDNO/CONWY
River Clwyd Bkwtr Hd 53°19'·50N 03°30'·30W QR 7m 2M.
Llanddulas, Llysfaen Jetty 53°17'·55N 03°39'·45W Fl G 10s.
Raynes Quarry Jetty Hd 53°17'·60N 03°40'·28W 2 FG (vert).
Llandudno Pier Hd 53°19'·90N 03°49'·40W 2 FG (vert) 8m 4M.

10

Great Ormes Hd Lt Ho 53°20'·55N 03°52'·10W (unlit).
Conwy Fairway By 53°17'·92N 03°55'·47W; SWM.
Conway R ent S side 53°17'·98N 03°50'·90W Fl WR 5s 5m
2M; vis W076°-088°, R088°-171°, W171°-319°, R319°-076°.

ANGLESEY
Pilot Station Pier 53°24'·90N 04°17'·20W 2 FR (vert).
Pt Lynas 53°24'·97N 04°17'·30W Oc 10s 39m **20M**; W
castellated Tr; vis 109°-315°; (H24). Fog Det Lt F 25m 16M
vis 211·8°-214·3°; RC; *Horn 45s*.

AMLWCH
Main Bkwtr 53°25'·01N 04°19'·80W Fl G 15s 11m 3M; W
mast; vis 141°-271°.
Inner Bkwtr 53°24'·98N 04°19'·85W 2 FR (vert) 12m 5M; W
mast; vis 164°-239°.
Inner Hbr 53°24'·94N 04°19'·90W F 9m 8M; W post; vis 233°-
257°.

Wylfa power station 53°25'·06N 04°29'·17W 2 FG (vert) 13m 6M.
Furlong By 53°25'·40N 04°30'·40W; SHM.
Archdeacon Rk By 53°26'·70N 04°30'·80W; NCM.
Victoria Bank By 53°25'·60N 04°31'·30W; NCM.
Coal Rk By 53°25'·90N 04°32'·72W; SCM.
Ethel Rk By 53°26'·63N 04°33'·60W; NCM.
W Mouse Bn 53°25'·03N 04°33'·20W; SWM.
The Skerries 53°25'·25N 04°36'·45W Fl (2) 10s 36m **22M**;
W ● Tr, R band; Racon (T). FR 26m **16M**; same Tr; vis 231°-
254°; *Horn (2) 20s*.
Langdon Lt By 53°22'·74N 04°38'·58W Q (9) 15s; WCM.
Bolivar Rk By 53°21'·50N 04°35'·23W; SHM.
Wk Lt By 53°20'·43N 04°36'·42W Fl (2) R 10s; PHM.
Clipera Lt By 53°20'·08N 04°36'·15W Fl (4) R 15s; PHM; *Bell*.

HOLYHEAD
Bkwtr Hd 53°19'·83N 04°37'·08W Fl (3) G 15s 21m 14M; W
■ Tr, B band; *Siren 20s*.
Old Hbr, Admiralty Pier Dn 53°18'·85N 04°37'·00W 2 FG
(vert) 8m 5M; *Horn 15s (occas)*.

S Stack 53°18'·39N 04°41'·91W Fl 10s 60m **27M**; (H24); W
● Tr; obsc to N by N Stack and part obsc in Penrhos bay.
Horn 30s. Fog Det Lt vis 145°-325°.
Llanddwyn I Lt 53°08'·00N 04°24'·70W Fl WR 2·5s 12m
W7M, R4M; W Tr; vis R280°-013°, W015°-120°.

MENAI STRAIT TO BARDSEY ISLAND
Trwyn-Du 53°18'·76N 04°02'·38W Fl 5s 19m 12M; W ●
castellated Tr, B bands; vis 101°-023°; *Bell (1) 30s*, sounded
continuously. FR on radio mast 2M SW.
Ten Feet Bank By 53°19'·45N 04°02'·66W; PHM.
Dinmor By 53°19'·33N 04°03'·20W; SHM.

BEAUMARIS/BANGOR
(Direction of buoyage NE to SW)
Perch Rk Bn 53°18'·73N 04°02'·09W; PHM.
B2 Lt By 53°18'·32N 04°02'·00W Fl (2) R 5s; PHM.

B1 Lt By 53°18'·12N 04°02'·23W Fl (2) G 10s; SHM.
B3 Lt By 53°17'·44N 04°02'·33W QG; SHM.
B8 By 53°16'·48N 04°04'·40W; PHM.
B5 Lt By 53°17'·77N 04°04'·83W Fl G 5s; SHM.
B6 Lt By 53°17'·14N 04°03'·42W Fl R 3s; PHM.
Beaumaris Pier 53°15'·67N 04°05'·33W F WG 5m 6M;
vis G212°-286°, W286°-014°, G014°-071°.
B10 Lt By 53°15'·59N 04°05'·15W Fl (2) R 10s; PHM.
B12 Lt By 53°15'·26N 04°05'·30W QR; PHM.
B7 Lt By 53°15'·05N 04°06'·03W Fl (2) G 5s; SHM.
Bangor By 53°14'·47N 04°07'·00W; PHM.
St George's Pier 53°13'·53N 04°09'·50W Fl G 10s.
E side of chan 53°13'·20N 04°09'·53W QR 4m; R mast; vis 064°-
222°. (0·1M E of Menai Suspension Bridge.)
Price's Pt 53°13'·10N 04°10'·44W Fl WR 2s 5m 3M; W Bn; vis
R059°-239°, W239°-259°.
Britannia tubular bridge, S chan Ldg Lts 231° E side. Front,
53°12'·90N 04°10'·97W FW. Rear, 45m from front, FW.
Centre span of bridge Iso 5s 27m 3M, one either side. SE end
of bridge, FR 21m 3M either side, NW end of bridge section
FG 21m 3M either side.

PORT DINORWIC
Port Dinorwic Lt By 53°11'·22N 04°13'·64W Fl R; PHM.
Pier Hd 53°11'·18N 04°12'·56W F WR 5m 2M; vis R225°-
357°, W357°-225°.
C9 By 53°10'·63N 04°13'·91W; SHM.
Channel By 53°10'·34N 04°15'·19W; SHM.
C14 By 53°10'·17N 04°15'·31W; PHM.
C11 By 53°09'·90N 04°15'·61W; SHM.
C13 By 53°09'·50N 04°15'·87W; SHM.

(Direction of buoyage SW to NE)

Change By 53°08'·80N 04°16'·67W; SCM.

CAERNARFON
Caernarfon N Pier Hd 53°08'·59N 04°16'·60W 2 FG (vert) 5m 2M.
C10 Lt By 53°07'·94N 04°18'·20W QR; PHM.
Abermenai Pt 53°07'·60N 04°19'·64W Fl WR 3·5s 6m 3M;
W mast; vis R065°-245°, W245°-065°.
Mussel Bk Lt By 53°07'·23N 04°20'·85W Fl (2) R 5s; PHM.
C6 Lt By 53°07'·07N 04°22'·25W Fl R 5s; PHM.
C5 By 53°07'·04N 04°22'·60W; SHM.
C4 Lt By 53°07'·21N 04°23'·06W QR; PHM.
C3 Lt By 53°07'·33N 04°23'·80W QG; SHM.
C1 Lt By 53°07'·18N 04°24'·37W Fl G 5s; SHM.
C2 Lt By 53°07'·28N 04°24'·42W Fl R 10s; PHM.
Poole Lt By 53°00'·00N 04°34'·00W Fl Y 6s; SPM (Apr-Oct).

PORTH DINLLÄEN
CG Stn 52°56'·80N 04°33'·81W FR when firing taking place
10M North.
Careg y Chwislen 52°56'·96N 04°33'·44W; IDM (unlit).

Bardsey I 52°44'·97N 04°47'·93W Fl (5) 15s 39m **26M**; W ■
Tr, R bands; obsc by Bardsey I 198°-250° and in Tremadoc B
when brg less than 260°; *Horn Mo (N) 45s*.

10.10.5 PASSAGE INFORMATION

For detailed directions covering these waters and harbours refer to the Admiralty Pilot *W Coast of England and Wales*; *A Cruising Guide to NW England & Wales* (Griffiths/Imray) and *Lundy and Irish Sea Pilot* (Taylor/Imray).

SCOTLAND – SW COAST

The Scares, two groups of rocks, lie at the mouth of Luce Bay which elsewhere is clear more than 3ca offshore; but the whole bay is occupied by a practice bombing range, marked by 12 DZ SPM lt buoys. Good anch at E Tarbert B to await the tide around the Mull of Galloway, or dry out alongside in shelter of Drummore. Off Burrow Hd there is a bad race in strong W winds with W-going tide. In Wigtown B the best anch is in Isle of Whithorn B, but exposed to S. It is also possible to dry out in Garlieston, see 10.10.7.

A tank firing range, between the E side of ent to Kirkcudbright Bay (10.10.7) and Abbey Hd, 4M to E, extends 14M offshore. If unable to avoid the area, cross it at N end close inshore. For information contact Range Control ☎ (01557) 323236 or call the Range safety boat "Gallovidian" on VHF Ch 16, 73. The range operates 0900-1600LT Mon-Fri, but weekend and night firing may also occur.

SOLWAY FIRTH (chart 1346)

Between Abbey Head and St Bees Head lies the Solway Firth, most of which is encumbered by shifting sandbanks. Off the entrances to the Firth, and in the approaches to Workington (10.10.9) beware shoals over which strong W winds raise a heavy sea. There are navigable, buoyed chans as far as Annan on the N shore, but buoys are laid primarily for the aid of Pilots. Local knowledge is required, particularly in the upper Firth, where streams run very strongly in the chans when the banks are dry, and less strongly over the banks when covered. In Powfoot chan for example the in-going stream begins at HW Liverpool – 0300, and the outgoing at HW Liverpool + 0100, sp rates up to 6kn. For Silloth and Maryport see 10.10.8; Workington and Harrington 10.10.9, Whitehaven and Ravenglass 10.10.10. South along the Cumbrian coast past St Bees Hd to Walney Is there are no dangers more than 2M offshore, but no shelter either.

BARROW TO CONWY (AC 2010, 1981, *1978*)

Ent to Barrow-in-Furness (10.10.11 and chart 3164) is about 1M S of Hilpsford Pt at S end of Walney Island where the lt ho (RC) is prominent. The stream sets across the narrow chan, which is well marked but shallow in patches. W winds cause rough sea in the ent. Moorings and anch off Piel and Roa Islands, but space is limited and stream runs hard on ebb. Coming from the S it is possible with sufficient rise of tide to cross the sands between Fleetwood and Barrow.

Lune Deep, 2M NW of Rossall Pt, is ent to Morecambe B (chart 2010), and gives access to the ferry/commercial port of Heysham, Glasson Dock (10.10.11), and Fleetwood (10.10.12); it is well buoyed. Streams run 3·5kn at sp. Most of Bay is encumbered with drying sands, intersected by chans which are subject to change. S of Morecambe B, beware shoals extending 3M W of Rossall Pt. Further S, R. Ribble (10.10.13) gives access via a long drying chan to the marina at Preston.

Queen's Chan and Crosby Chan (charts 1951 and *1978*) are entered E of the Bar Lanby. They are well buoyed, dredged and preserved by training banks, and give main access to R. Mersey and Liverpool (10.10.14). Keep clear of commercial shipping. From the N the old Formby chan is abandoned, but possible near HW. Towards HW and in moderate winds a yacht can cross the training bank (level of which varies between 2m and 3m above CD) E of Great Burbo Bank, if coming from the W. Rock Chan, parts of which dry and which is unmarked, may also be used but beware wrecks.

In good weather and at nps, the Dee Estuary (charts 1953, *1970*) is accessible for boats able to take the ground. But most of estuary dries and banks extend 6M seaward. Chans shift, and buoys are moved as required. Stream runs hard in chans when banks are dry. Main ent is Welsh Chan, but if coming from N, Hilbre Swash runs W of Hilbre Is (lit).

Sailing W from the Dee on the ebb, it is feasible to take the Inner Passage (buoyed) S of West Hoyle Spit, and this enjoys some protection from onshore winds at half tide or below. Rhyl is a tidal hbr, not accessible in strong onshore winds, but gives shelter for yachts able to take the ground. Abergele Road, Colwyn B and Llandudno B are possible anchs in settled weather and S winds. Conwy (10.10.20) offer good shelter in both marina and harbour.

Between Point of Ayr and Great Ormes Head the E-going stream begins at HW Liverpool + 0600, and the W-going at HW Liverpool – 0015, sp rates 3kn.

ISLE OF MAN (IOM) (charts 2094, 2696)

For general pilotage information, tidal streams and hbr details of IOM, see *IOM Sailing Directions*, *Tidal Streams and Anchorages*, published by the Manx Sailing and Cruising Club. For notes on crossing the Irish Sea, see 10.13.5.

There are four choices when rounding South of Isle of Man: a, In bad weather, or at night, keep S of Chicken Rk (lt, fog sig). b, In good conditions, take the chan between Chicken Rk and Calf of Man (lt, fog sig). c, Alternatively, with winds of Force 3 or less and a reliable engine capable of producing a speed of at least 5kn, by day only use Calf Sound between Calf of Man and IOM, passing W of Kitterland Island but E of Thousla Rock, which is marked by lt bn and is close to Calf of Man shore. d, There is also a minor chan, called Little Sound, E of Kitterland Is.

The stream runs strongly through Calf Sound, starting N-going at HW Liverpool – 0145, and S-going at HW Liverpool + 0345, sp rates 3·5kn. W of Calf of Man the stream runs N and S, but changes direction off Chicken Rk and runs W and E between Calf of Man and Langness Pt 6M to E. Overfalls extend E from Chicken Rk on E-going stream, which begins at HW Liverpool + 0610, and N from the rk on W-going stream, which begins at HW Liverpool.

Off Langness Pt (lt) the Skerranes (dry) extend 1ca SW, and tidal stream runs strongly, with eddies and a race. E side of Langness peninsula is foul ground, over which a dangerous sea can build in strong winds. Here the NE-going stream begins at HW Liverpool + 0545, and the SW-going at HW Liverpool – 0415, sp rates 2·25kn.

There is anch in Derby Haven, N of St Michael's Is, but exposed to E. From here to Douglas (10.10.18) and on to Maughold Hd (lt), there are no dangers more than 4ca offshore. Near the coast the SW-going stream runs for 9 hours and the NE-going for 3 hours, since an eddy forms during the second half of the main NE-going stream. Off Maughold Hd the NE-going stream begins at HW Liverpool + 0500, and the SW-going at HW Liverpool – 0415.

SE, E and NW of Pt of Ayre are dangerous banks, on which seas break in bad weather. These are Whitestone Bk (least depth 2·0m), Bahama Bk (1·5m, buoy), Ballacash Bk (2·7m), King William Bks (3·3m, buoy), and Strunakill Bk (6·7m).

The W coast of IOM has few pilotage hazards. A spit with depth of 1·4m runs 2ca offshore from Rue Pt. Jurby Rk (depth 2·7m) lies 3ca off Jurby Hd. Craig Rk (depth 4 m) and shoals lie 2·5M NNE of Peel (10.10.16).

MENAI STRAIT (10.10.19 and chart *1464*)

The main features of this narrow chan include: Puffin Is, seaward of NE end; Beaumaris; Garth Pt at Bangor, where NE end of Strait begins; Menai Suspension Bridge (30·5m); The Swellies, a narrow 1M stretch with strong tide and dangers mid-stream; Britannia Rail Bridge (27·4m), with cables close W at elevation of 22m; Port Dinorwic and Caernarfon (10.10.21); Abermenai Pt and Fort Belan, where narrows mark SW end of Strait; and Caernarfon Bar.

The following brief notes only cover very basic pilotage. For detailed directions see *W Coasts of England and Wales Pilot*, or *Cruising Anglesey and N Wales* (NW Venturers Yacht Club). The Swellies should be taken near local HW slack, and an understanding of tidal streams is essential. The tide is about 1 hour later, and sp range about 2·7m more, at NE end of Strait than at SW end. Levels differ most at about HW +1 (when level at NE end is more than 1·8m above level at SW end); and at about HW – 0445 (when level at NE end is more than 1·8m below level at SW end). Normally the stream runs as follows (times referred to HW Holyhead). HW – 0040 to HW + 0420: SW between Garth Pt and Abermenai Pt. HW + 0420 to HW + 0545: outwards from about The Swellies, ie NE towards Garth Pt and SW towards Abermenai Pt. HW + 0545 to HW – 0040: NE between Abermenai Pt and Garth Pt. Sp rates are generally about 3kn, but more in narrows, e.g. 5kn off Abermenai Pt, 6kn between the bridges, and 8kn at The Swellies. The timings and rates of streams may be affected by strong winds in either direction.

From NE, enter chan W of Puffin Island, taking first of ebb to rerach the Swellies at slack HW (HW Holyhead – 0100). Slack HW only lasts about 20 mins at sps, a little more at nps. Pass under centre of suspension bridge span, and steer to leave Platters (dry) on mainland shore to port and Swellies lt bn close to stbd. From Swellies lt bn to Britannia Bridge hold mainland shore, leaving bn on Price Pt to port, and Gored Goch and Gribbin Rk to stbd. Leave Britannia Rk (centre pier of bridge) to stbd. Thence to SW hold to buoyed chan near mainland shore. (Note: A Historic Wreck (see 10.0.3h) is 4ca SW of Britannia Bridge at 53°12'·77N 04°11'·72W). Port Dinorwic is useful to await right tidal conditions for onward passage in either direction.

Note that direction of lateral buoyage changes at Caernarfon.

Caernarfon Bar is impassable even in moderately strong winds against ebb, but narrows at Abermenai Pt demand a fair tide, or slackish water, since tide runs strongly here. Going seaward on first of ebb, when there is water over the banks, it may not be practicable to return to the Strait if conditions on the bar are bad. Then it is best to anch near Mussel Bank buoy and await slack water, before returning to Caernarfon (say). Leaving Abermenai Pt on last of ebb means banks to seaward are exposed and there is little water in chan or over bar.

Going NE'ward it is safe to reach the Swellies with last of flood, leaving Caernarfon about HW Holyhead – 0230. Do not leave too late, or full force of ebb will be met before reaching Bangor.

ANGLESEY TO BARDSEY ISLAND (AC *1977*, 1970, 1971)

On N coast of Anglesey, a race extends 5ca off Pt Lynas (lt, fog sig, RC) on E-going stream. Amlwch is a small hbr (partly dries) 1·5M W of Pt Lynas. A drying rk lies 100m offshore on W side of appr, which should not be attempted in strong onshore winds. From here to Carmel Hd beware E Mouse (and shoals to SE), Middle Mouse, Harry Furlong's Rks (dry), Victoria Bank (least depth 1·8m), Coal Rk (awash), and W Mouse (with dangers to W and SW). The outermost of these dangers is 2M offshore. There are overfalls and races at headlands and over many rks and shoals along this coast.

Between Carmel Hd and The Skerries (lt, fog sig, Racon) the NE-going stream begins at HW Holyhead + 0550, and the SW-going at HW Holyhead – 0010, sp rates 5kn. 1M NW of Skerries the stream turns 1½ hours later, and runs less strongly. Note: A Historic Wreck (*Mary*; see 10.0.3h) is on The Skerries. Simplest passage, or at night or in bad weather, is to pass 1M off Skerries, in the TSS ITZ, see Fig. 10(7). In good conditions by day and at slack water, Carmel Hd can be rounded close inshore; but beware short, steep, breaking seas here in even moderate winds against tide.

Holyhead (10.10.22) is a harbour of refuge, access H24 in all weathers, with new marina in New Harbour; beware fast ferries. Races also occur off N Stack and (more severe) off S Stack (lt, fog sig), up to 1·5M offshore on NNE-going stream which begins at HW Holyhead – 0605, sp rate 5kn. Races do not extend so far on SSW-going stream which begins at HW Holyhead + 0020, sp rate 5kn.

The W coast of Anglesey is rugged with rks, some drying, up to 1·5M offshore. There are races off Penrhyn Mawr and Rhoscolyn Hd. Pilot's Cove, E of Llanddwyn Is, is good anch while waiting right conditions for Menai Strait.

On the Lleyn Peninsula Porth Dinllaen (10.10.22) is good anch, but exposed to N and NE. Braich y Pwll is the steep, rky point at end of Lleyn Peninsula (chart 1971). About 1M N of it and up to 1M offshore lie The Tripods, a bank on which there are overfalls and a bad sea with wind against tide.

Bardsey Sound, 1·5M wide, can be used by day in moderate winds. Stream reaches 6kn at sp, and passage should be made at slack water, – 0015 HW or + 0035 LW Holyhead. Avoid Carreg Ddu on N side and Maen Bugail Rk (dries 4·1m) on S side of Sound, where there are dangerous races. If passing outside Bardsey Is (lt, fog sig) make a good offing to avoid overfalls which extend 1·5M W and 2·5M S of Island. Turbulence occurs over Bastram Shoal, Devil's Tail and Devil's Ridge, which lie SSE and E of Bardsey Is.

10.10.6   DISTANCE TABLE

Approximate distances in nautical miles are by the most direct route, whilst avoiding dangers and allowing for Traffic Separation Schemes. Places in *italics* are in adjoining areas; places in **bold** are in 10.0.6, Distances across the Irish Sea.

	1	2	3	4	5	6	7	8	9	10	11	12	13	14	15	16	17	18	19	20
1. *Portpatrick*	1																			
2. *Mull of Galloway*	16	2																		
3. **Kirkcudbright**	48	32	3																	
4. **Maryport**	65	49	26	4																
5. Workington	63	47	25	6	5															
6. Ravenglass	70	54	40	30	23	6														
7. **Point of Ayre**	38	22	28	37	31	34	7													
8. Peel	41	26	46	55	49	52	18	8												
9. **Port St Mary**	56	41	61	63	57	50	35	18	9											
10. Douglas	60	42	46	50	44	39	19	30	13	10										
11. Ramsey	44	28	34	41	35	34	6	24	27	15	11									
12. Glasson Dock	101	85	74	66	60	37	64	85	69	63	61	12								
13. **Fleetwood**	95	79	68	59	53	30	58	80	63	57	55	10	13							
14. **Liverpool**	118	102	97	89	83	60	80	86	76	70	77	52	46	14						
15. Conwy	111	95	95	92	86	58	72	72	57	59	68	62	56	46	15					
16. Beaumaris	109	93	94	95	89	72	71	73	58	58	70	66	60	49	12	16				
17. **Caernarfon**	117	103	104	105	99	82	81	73	68	68	80	76	70	59	22	10	17			
10. **Holyhead**	93	81	94	96	90	69	68	62	46	50	65	79	73	68	36	32	26	18		
19. Bardsey Island	127	113	129	129	123	114	107	94	80	88	98	107	101	90	53	41	31	43	19	
20. *Fishguard*	171	158	175	175	169	160	153	140	126	134	144	153	147	136	100	88	78	89	45	20

KIRKCUDBRIGHT   10-10-7

Dumfries and Galloway 54°50'·30N 04°03'·40W   Rtg 3-2-1

CHARTS
AC1344, 1346, 2094, *1826*; Imray C62; OS 84

TIDES
+0030 Dover; ML 4·1; Duration 0545; Zone 0 (UT)

Standard Port LIVERPOOL (⟶)

Times				Height (metres)			
High Water		Low Water		MHWS	MHWN	MLWN	MLWS
0000	0600	0200	0800	9·3	7·4	2·9	0·9
1200	1800	1400	2000				

Differences KIRKCUDBRIGHT BAY
+0015	+0015	+0010	+0000	−1·8	−1·5	−0·5	−0·1

DRUMMORE
+0030	+0040	+0015	+0020	−3·4	−2·5	−0·9	−0·3

PORT WILLIAM
+0030	+0030	+0025	0000	−2·9	−2·2	−0·8	No data

GARLIESTON
+0025	+0035	+0030	+0005	−2·3	−1·7	−0·5	No data

ISLE OF WHITHORN
+0020	+0025	+0025	+0005	−2·4	−2·0	−0·8	−0·2

HESTAN ISLET (Kippford)
+0025	+0025	+0020	+0025	−1·0	−1·1	−0·5	0·0

SOUTHERNESS POINT
+0030	+0030	+0030	+0010	−0·7	−0·7		No data

ANNAN WATERFOOT
+0050	+0105	+0220	+0310	−2·2	−2·6	−2·7	*

TORDUFF POINT
+0105	+0140	+0520	+0410	−4·1	−4·9		*Not below CD

REDKIRK
+0110	+0215	+0715	+0445	−5·5	−6·2		*Not below CD

Notes: At Annan Waterfoot, Torduff Pt and Redkirk the LW time differences are for the start of the rise, which at sp is very sudden. *At LW the tide does not usually fall below CD.

SHELTER
Very good at floating pontoon/jetty; and pile moorings in 1-3m; drying out on ⚓s or against town quay. The River Dee has many shoal patches of 0·3m or less and the chan shifts. Down-river there are good ⚓s behind Ross Is and ½ca N of Torrs Pt, except in S'lies which raise heavy swell.

NAVIGATION
WPT 54°45'·50N 04°04'·00W, 185°/005° from/to Torrs Pt, 1·4M. The Bar is 1ca N of Torrs Pt; access HW±3. Spring tides run up to 3-4kn. A firing range crosses the ent; call Range Safety Officer ☎ (01557) 323236 or VHF 16 73.

LIGHTS AND MARKS
Little Ross lt ho, W of ent, Fl 5s 50m 12M, (obscured in Wigtown bay when brg more than 103°). No 1 lt bn, Fl WRG 3s, is atop the LB shed (54°47'·70N); vis G080°-037°, W037°-043°, R043°-080°. The river is well lit/buoyed. There are Fl G lts on the mooring piles off the town.

RADIO TELEPHONE
VHF Ch 12 16 (0730-1700). *Range Control* Ch 16 73.

TELEPHONE (Dial code 01557)
Hr Mr 331135; ⌗ (0141) 887 9369; MRCC 0151-931 3341; Marinecall 0891 500 461; Police 330600; Dr 330755.

FACILITIES
Pontoon/jetty £5.50, AC, FW; **Town Quay** P (hose), D (road tanker), FW, El, C (15 ton) CH, ME. **KYC** ☎ 330963; **SC** ☎ 330032, Slip, M, FW; **Town** EC Thur; V, R, Bar, ⌧, Ⓑ, ⇌ (Dumfries 30M), ✈ (Glasgow 100M).

OTHER HARBOURS ON THE COAST OF DUMFRIES AND GALLOWAY

ISLE OF WHITHORN, Dumfries and Galloway, 54°41'·90N 04°21'·80W. AC 2094, *1826*. HW +0035 on Dover; ML 3·7m; Duration 0545. See 10.10.7. Shelter good but hbr dries, having approx 2·5m at HW±3. On W side of ent beware the Skerries, a ledge with pole/radar reflector. St Ninian's Tr (W ☐ tr) is conspic at E side of ent. E pier hd has QG 4m 5M; ldg lts 335°, both Oc R 8s 7/9m 7M, synch, Or masts and ◇. Hr Mr ☎ (01988) 500246; Facilities: AB on quay £3, Slip, P, D, FW, ME, Sh, CH, V, Bar, ⌧, VHF Ch 80 (occas).

Luce Bay Firing Range (D402/403) lies to the NW. For info on activity ☎ (01776) 888792.

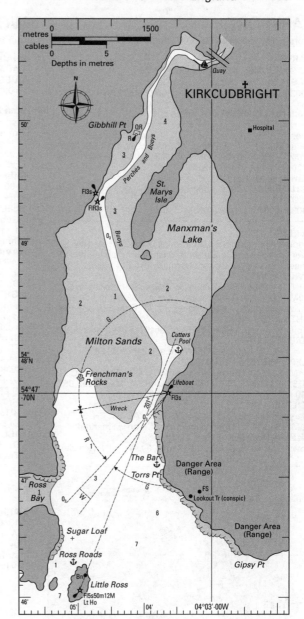

GARLIESTON, Dumfries and Galloway, 54°47'·35N 04°21'·75W. AC 2094, *1826*. HW +0035 on Dover; ML no data; Duration 0545. See 10.10.7. Hbr affords complete shelter but dries. Access (2m) HW±3. Pier hd lt 2FR (vert) 5m 3M. Beware rky outcrops in W side of bay marked by a perch. Hr Mr ☎ (01988) 600274. Facilities: M £3, FW, AC on quay, Slip. **Town**: V, ME, P, D.

KIPPFORD, Dumfries & Galloway, 54°52'·35N 03°48'·85W. AC 1346, *1826*. HW +0040 on Dover; ML 4·2m (Hestan Is). See 10.10.7. Good shelter on drying moorings/pontoons off Kippford, 2·75M up drying Urr Estuary from Hestan Is lt ho Fl (2) 10s 42m 9M. Access HW±2 via marked, unlit chan. CCC or Solway SDs (from Solway YC) are strongly advised. Beware Craig Roan on E side of ent. Temp ⚓s NE or W of Hestan Is to await tide. VHF: Ch M call *Kippford Startline* (YC) HW±2 in season. Ch 16 *Kippford Slipway* (Pilotage). Facilities: **Solway YC** (01556) 620249, AB, AC, FW, M; **Services**: AB £6, M, Slip, D (cans), CH, BY, ME. **Town** P, SM, V, ⌧, Bar, Slip

10

MARYPORT   10-10-8

Cumbria 54°43'.03N 03°30'.38W   Rtg 3-2-1

CHARTS
AC 2013, 1346, *1826*; Imray C62; OS 89

TIDES
+0038 Dover; ML no data; Duration 0550; Zone 0 (UT)

Standard Port LIVERPOOL (→)

Times				Height (metres)			
High Water		Low Water		MHWS	MHWN	MLWN	MLWS
0000	0600	0200	0800	9·3	7·4	2·9	0·9
1200	1800	1400	2000				
Differences MARYPORT							
+0017	+0032	+0020	+0005	−0·7	−0·8	−0·4	0·0
SILLOTH							
+0030	+0040	+0045	+0055	−0·1	−0·3	−0·6	−0·1

SHELTER
Good shelter in marina (Senhouse Dock), access HW ±3 over sill 1·75m; or in Elizabeth Basin (commercial) which dries, access HW±1½, (not normally used by yachts).

NAVIGATION
WPT 54°43'.08N 03°32'.39W, 270°/090° from/to S pier lt, 1·0M. 1·8m over bar between piers at ent at half tide and in river chan. Mud banks cover HW −2. Chan not buoyed.

LIGHTS AND MARKS
S pier Fl 1·5s 10m 6M. Fl G 5s on post 7ca SW marks outfall.

RADIO TELEPHONE
Port VHF Ch 12 (occas) 16. Marina (H24) Ch M 80 16.

TELEPHONE (Dial code 01900)
Hr Mr 817440; Hbr Authority 604351; CG 2238; MRSC (0151) 931 3341; ⌗ (01482) 782107 (H24); Marinecall 0891 500 461; Police 812601; Dr 815544; Ⓗ 812634.

FACILITIES
Maryport Marina (200) ☎ 813331, £8.81, AC, BY, CH, El, FW, ▣, ME, Slip, (P & D from Fisherman's Co-op via marina); **Elizabeth Dock** Slip (at HW), M, Sh, AB.
Town EC Wed; P, D, ME, V, R, Bar, ✉, Ⓑ, ⇌, ✈ (Newcastle).

MARYPORT

MINOR HARBOUR 10M NNE OF MARYPORT

SILLOTH, Cumbria, 54°52'.15N 03°23'.78W. AC 2013, 1346, *1826*. HW −0050 on Dover; ML no data; Duration 0520. See 10·10·8. Appr via English or Middle Chans, approx 8M long, requires local knowledge. Beware constantly shifting chans and banks. Yachts are not encouraged. ⌘ SW of ent in about 4m off Lees Scar, QG 11m 8M; exposed to SW winds. Outer hbr dries; lock into New Dock, which is mainly commercial. East Cote Dir lt 052° FG 15m 12M; vis 046°-058°, intens 052°. Ldg lts, both F, 115°. Groyne 2 FG (vert). Tfc sigs on mast at New Dock: no entry unless Y signal arm raised by day or Ω Bu lt by night, VHF Ch 16 12 (HW−2½ to HW+1½). Hr Mr ☎ (016973) 31358; ⌗ (01900) 604611. Facilities: EC Tues; FW, Ⓑ, Bar, ✉, R, V.

WORKINGTON   10-10-9

Cumbria 54°39'.02N 03°34'.30W   Rtg 2-4-3

CHARTS
AC 2013, 1346, *1826*; Imray C62; OS 89

TIDES
+0025 Dover; ML 4·5; Duration 0545; Zone 0 (UT)

Standard Port LIVERPOOL (→)

Times				Height (metres)			
High Water		Low Water		MHWS	MHWN	MLWN	MLWS
0000	0600	0200	0800	9·3	7·4	2·9	0·9
1200	1800	1400	2000				
Differences WORKINGTON							
+0020	+0020	+0020	+0010	−1·2	−1·1	−0·3	0·0

SHELTER
Good, but hbr dries. Berth where you can (free) or ⌘ in Turning Basin. Lock (HW±1½) into Dock 1·8m (for coasters). Inner tidal hbr is restricted by low (1·8m) fixed rly bridge.

NAVIGATION
WPT 54°39'.58N 03°35'.30W, 311°/131° from/to front ldg lt, 1·0M. In periods of heavy rain a strong freshet from R Derwent may be encountered in the hbr.

LIGHTS AND MARKS
Workington Bank, least depth 5·5m, is 2M W of hbr ent; it is marked by an unlit NCM buoy and a SCM buoy, VQ (6) + L Fl 10s, (see 10.10.4). A SHM buoy, Fl G 5s, 1·3M NW of hbr ent is a mark for English Chan. Ldg lts 132°, both FR 10/12m 3M, on W pyramidal trs with Y bands. Two sets of F Bu lts in line mark NE and SW edges of chan.

RADIO TELEPHONE
VHF Ch 11 14 16 (HW−2½ to HW+2).

TELEPHONE (Dial code 01900)
Hr Mr 602301; CG 2238; ⌗ (01482) 782107 (H24); MRSC (0151) 931 3341; Marinecall 0891 500 461; Police 812601; Dr 64866; Ⓗ 602244.

FACILITIES
Dock D, FW, ME, El; **Vanguard SC** ☎ 826886, M, FW.
Town EC Thurs; P, V, R, Bar, ✉, Ⓑ, ⇌, ✈ (Carlisle).

MINOR HARBOUR 2M SOUTH OF WORKINGTON

HARRINGTON, Cumbria, 54°36'.76N 03°34'.21W. AC 2013, 1346, *1826*. HW +0025 on Dover; Duration 0540; Use Diff's Workington 10.10.9. Good shelter in small hbr only used by local FVs and yachts; dries 3ca offshore. Ent difficult in strong W winds. Berth on N wall of inner hbr (free). Call ☎ (01946) 823741 Ext 148 for moorings. Limited facilities. **SC**.

AGENTS WANTED

If you are interested in becoming our agent for any of the following ports, please write to: The Editor, Edington House, Trent, Sherborne, Dorset DT9 4SR, England – and get your free copy of the Almanac annually. You do not have to live in a port to be the agent, but at least a fairly regular visitor.

Great Yarmouth	St Gilles-Croix-de-Vie
Port Ellen (Islay)	Les Sables d'Olonne
Maryport	Ile d'Oléron
Workington	River Seudre
Holyhead	Anglet/Bayonne
Lough Swilly	St Jean-de-Luz
St Peter Port, Guernsey	Hendaye
Diélette	Grandcamp-Maisy
Portbail	Port-en-Bessin
Iles Chausey	Courseulles
St Malo/Dinard	Ouistreham/Caen
Le Legue/St Brieuc	Emden
Tréguier	Dornumer-Accumersiel
Lampaul	Langeoog
L'Aberildut	Bremerhaven
Le Palais (Belle Ile)	Busum
Morbihan/Vannes	

WORKINGTON *continued*

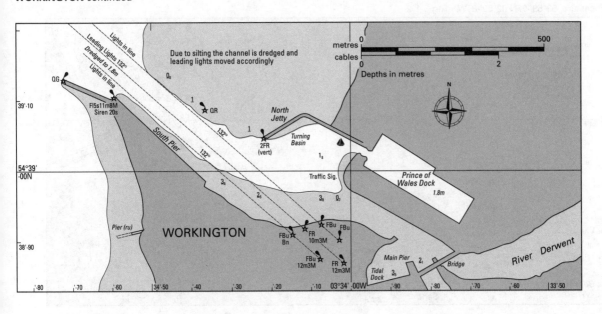

WHITEHAVEN   10-10-10

Cumbria 54°33'·17N 03°35'·74W   Rtg 2-3-2

CHARTS
AC 2013, 1346, *1826*; Imray C62; OS 89
TIDES
+0015 Dover; ML 4·5; Duration 0550; Zone 0 (UT)

Standard Port LIVERPOOL (→)

Times				Height (metres)			
High Water		Low Water		MHWS	MHWN	MLWN	MLWS
0000	0600	0200	0800	9·3	7·4	2·9	0·9
1200	1800	1400	2000				
Differences WHITEHAVEN							
+0005	+0015	+0010	+0005	−1·3	−1·1	−0·5	+0·1
TARN POINT (3M S of Ravenglass)							
+0005	+0005	+0010	0000	−1·0	−1·0	−0·4	0·0
DUDDON BAR (54°09'N 03°20'W)							
+0003	+0003	+0008	+0002	−0·8	−0·8	−0·3	0·0

SHELTER
Very good, entry safe in most weathers. A new marina in the Inner Hbr was due to complete in spring 1998 making Whitehaven one of the more accessible ports of refuge in NW England. Appr chan across the outer hbr is dredged to 1·0m above CD giving access approx 18 out of 24 hours. Sea lock (30m x 13·7m), with sill at CD, maintains 5·5m within inner hbr. Yacht pontoons will be in Inner Hbr. Queens Dock (from which the lock gates will be removed) and N Hbr remain for commercial and FV use. *Further details will be in the Supplements.*
NAVIGATION
WPT 54°33'·33N 03°36'·13W, 313°/133° from/to W pier hd, 4½ca. There are no hazards in the offing. Keep close to W pier when entering on the flood, due to strong E'ly set.
LIGHTS AND MARKS
Several tall chimneys are charted within 1·5M S of hbr. St Bees Head, Fl (2) 20s 102m 21M, is 2·7M SSW of hbr ent. W pier Fl G 5s 16m 13M; N pier 2 FR (vert) 8m 9M; Sea lock 2 FR (vert) 8m 2M, and 2 FG (vert) 8m 2M. SHM bn, Fl G 2·5s, 4½ca S of W pierhead marks sewer outfall.
RADIO TELEPHONE
Hr Mr VHF Ch 12 16 (as for access times).
TELEPHONE (Dial code 01946)
Hr Mr 692435, ⌂ 691135; ⌗ (01482) 782107 (H24); MRSC (0151) 931 3341; Marinecall 0891 500 461.
FACILITIES
Marina (100) ☎ 692435, AC, FW, D at N Hbr wall, Slip, **SC**. **Town** EC Wed, Market days Thurs, Sat; P (cans), Bar, Ⓑ, ⊠, R, V.

MINOR HARBOUR BETWEEN ST BEES HEAD AND MORECAMBE BAY

RAVENGLASS, Cumbria, 54°20'·80N 03°24'·87W. AC 1346, *1826*. HW +0020 on Dover; ML no data; Duration 0545. See 10.10.10 (Tarn Point). Large drying hbr, formed by estuaries of R Mite, Irt and Esk, has approx 2·5m in ent at HW−2. There is a FG lt (occas) on blockhouse at S side of ent. Local knowledge advised. From N beware Drigg Rk and from S Selker Rks, marked by SHM buoy Fl (3) G 10s, 5M SSW of ent. Firing range D406 is close S at Eskmeals (R flags flown and VHF Ch 13 when in use), ☎ (01229) 717631 Ext 245. **Village**: EC Wed; FW, Slip, Bar, V, ⊠.

GLASSON DOCK   10-10-11

Lancashire 53°59'·97N 02°50'·85W   Rtg 3-1-2

CHARTS
AC 1552, 2010, *1826*; Imray C62; OS 102, 97
TIDES
+0020 Dover; ML No data; Duration 0535; Zone 0 (UT)

Standard Port LIVERPOOL (→)

Times				Height (metres)			
High Water		Low Water		MHWS	MHWN	MLWN	MLWS
0000	0600	0200	0700	9·3	7·4	2·9	0·9
1200	1800	1400	1900				
Differences BARROW-IN-FURNESS (Ramsden Dock)							
+0015	+0015	+0015	+0015	0·0	−0·3	+0·1	+0·2
ULVERSTON							
+0020	+0040	No data		0·0	−0·1	No data	
ARNSIDE							
+0100	+0135	No data		+0·5	+0·2	No data	
MORECAMBE							
+0005	+0010	+0030	+0015	+0·2	0·0	0·0	+0·2
HEYSHAM							
+0005	+0005	+0015	0000	+0·1	0·0	0·0	+0·2
GLASSON DOCK							
+0020	+0030	+0220	+0240	−2·7	−3·0	No data	
LANCASTER							
+0110	+0030	No data		−5·0	−4·9	Dries out	

Note: At Glasson Dock LW time differences give the end of
a LW stand which lasts up to 2 hours at sp.

SHELTER
Very good in marina; also sheltered ⚓ in R Lune to await
sea lock, opens HW Liverpool −0045 to HW, into Glasson
Dock. Inner lock/swing bridge lead into BWB basin.
NAVIGATION
WPT 53°58'·40N 03°00'·00W (2ca S of R Lune No 1 WCM
By), 264°/084° from/to front ldg lt 084°, 4·2M. Leave WPT
at HW−2 via buoyed/lit chan. Plover Scar bn has a tide
gauge showing depth over the lock sill at Glasson Dock. ⚓
is prohib between Sutherland Pt and No 10 PHM lt buoy.
Beyond this a training wall, marked by PHM lt buoys/bn,
extends to lock ent. R Lune is navigable to Lancaster.
LIGHTS AND MARKS
Ldg lts (hard to see from WPT): Plover Scar, Fl 2s, on with
Cockersand, FW, leads 084° up to Nos 2 /3 buoys; thence
follow buoyed chan which shifts.
Tfc Sigs by day (night) at E side of lock:
1 ● (Ⓡ)   = lock manned, but shut
R flag (Ⓡ over Ⓦ)   = lock open, clear to enter
R flag over ● (2 Ⓡ vert)   = lock open, vessels leaving
RADIO TELEPHONE
VHF Ch 69 16 (HW−2 to HW+1). Marina Ch 80.
TELEPHONE (Dial code 01524)
Hr Mr 751724; MRSC 0151-931 3341; ⌗ (0161) 912 6977
(H24); Marinecall 0891 500 461; Police 791239; Ⓗ 765944.

FACILITIES
Marina (240+20 visitors) ☎ 751491, £7.50, Slip, D, FW, ME,
EI, Ⓔ, Sh, C, (50 ton), BH (50 ton), AC, CH;
Glasson Basin, M, AB; **Glasson SC** ☎ 751089 Slip, M, C;
Lune CC Access HW±2.
Town EC Lancaster Wed; P (cans), V, R, Bar, ✉, Ⓑ
(Lancaster), ⇌ (bus to Lancaster 4M), ✈ (Blackpool).

ADJACENT HARBOURS IN MORECAMBE BAY

BARROW-IN-FURNESS, Cumbria, 54°05'·63N 03°13'·36W.
AC 3164, 2010, *1826*. HW +0030 on Dover; See 10·10·11.
ML 5·0m; Duration 0530. Good shelter but open to SE'lies.
Drying moorings off Piel and Roa Islands or ⚓ clear of
fairway. Marks/lts: Walney Island lt ho (conspic stone tr),
Fl 15s 21m 23M (obsc 122°-127° within 3M of shore), RC.
From Lightning Knoll SWM buoy (L Fl 10s) ldg lts, front Q
7m 10M; rear (6ca from front), Iso 2s 13m 10M (lattice
structures) lead 041°/3·7M past Halfway Shoal bn, QR 16m
10M with RY chequers, Racon, to Bar buoy Fl (2) R 5s
(abeam Walney Island lt ho). Inner Chan ldg lts, front Q
9m 10M, rear Iso 2s 14m 6M, lead 006° past Piel Is with
least charted depth 1·7m. Piel Island has conspic ruined
castle, slip and moorings on E side. Roa Island, 5ca N,
has jetty at S end and moorings on E side; a causeway
joins it to mainland. Commercial docks, 3M NW at
Barrow, reached via buoyed/lit Walney Chan, dredged
3·5m, which must be kept clear. Hr Mr (Barrow) ☎
(01229) 822911, ⚓ 835822; VHF *Ramsden Dock* Ch 12 16
(H24). ⌗ (0161) 912 6977 (H24). Facilities: Piel Is, Bar; Roa,
Hotel, V. **Barrow** EC Thurs; SM, all needs.

HEYSHAM, Lancashire, 54°02'·00N 02°55'·88W. AC 1552,
2010, *1826*. HW +0015 on Dover; ML 5·1m; Duration 0545.
See 10·10·11. Good shelter, but yachts only normally
accepted without special reason. Beware ferries and 'rig'
supply ships. Ldg lts 102°, both F Bu 11/14m 2M, Y+B ◊
on masts. S jetty lt 2 FG (vert), Siren 30s. S pier hd, Oc G
7·5s 9m 6M. N pier hd, 2FR (vert) 11m, obsc from
seaward. Ent sigs: R flag or (Ⓡ) = no entry; no sig = no
dep; 2 R flags or 2 (Ⓡ) = no ent or dep. VHF Ch 14 74 16
(H24). Hr Mr ☎ (01524) 52070. Facilities: EC Wed
(Morecambe also); Bar, FW, R, V at Morecambe (2M).

FLEETWOOD   10-10-12
Lancashire 53°55'·48N 03°00'·07W   Rtg 1 (hbr) -2-2

CHARTS
AC 1552, 2010, *1826*; Imray C62; OS 102

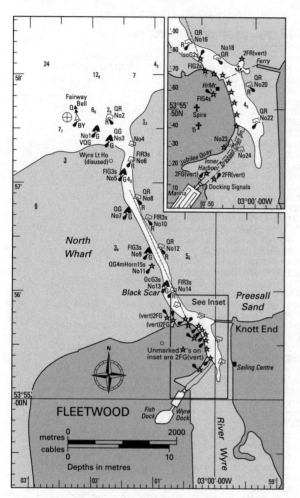

TIDES
+0015 Dover; ML 5.0; Duration 0530; Zone 0 (UT)

Standard Port LIVERPOOL (→)

Times				Height (metres)			
High Water		Low Water		MHWS	MHWN	MLWN	MLWS
0000	0600	0200	0700	9·3	7·4	2·9	0·9
1200	1800	1400	1900				
Differences WYRE LIGHTHOUSE							
−0010	−0010	+0005	0000	−0·1	−0·1		No data
FLEETWOOD							
0000	0000	+0005	0000	−0·1	−0·1	+0·1	+0·3
BLACKPOOL							
−0015	−0005	−0005	−0015	−0·4	−0·4	−0·1	+0·1

SHELTER
Very good in Wyre Dock Marina. Sheltered ⚓ off Knott End pier on E bank to await tide. Passage up-river to Skippool (5M) needs local knowledge and shoal draft; access HW±1 (if ht of tide is >8·0m).

NAVIGATION
WPT 53°57'·57N 03°02'·33W, Fairway NCM lt buoy, 285°/105° from/to No 1 SHM lt buoy, 5ca; here the appr chan turns SE then S. Caution: avoid ferries and dredgers turning in lower hbr, dredged 4·5m. Further up the hbr, Nos 23 SHM and 24 PHM buoys mark start of marina ent chan dredged to drying height of 3m, giving access HW±2 to lock. For best water keep 15m NW of the 300m long training wall (5 Y perches, △ topmarks).

LIGHTS AND MARKS
Chan is well buoyed/lit. Ldg lts, front Fl G 2s; rear Fl G 4s, 156° (only to be used between Nos 8 and 13 buoys). Lock sigs (only enter on instructions): 1 ● (1 ⓡ) = Gates open for entry; 2 ● (2 ⓡ) = open for departures.

RADIO TELEPHONE
Call *Fleetwood Hbr Control* Ch 11, when ferries under way. Call *Fleetwood Dock* Ch **12** 16, HW±2 for marina/Fish Dock.

TELEPHONE (Dial code 01253)
Hr Mr (ABP) 872323, 🕿 777549; MRSC (0151) 931 3341/3; ⌗ (0151) 922 9161 and (0161) 912 6977 (H24); Marinecall 0891 500 461; Police 876611; Dr 873312.

FACILITIES
Marina (210) ☎ 872323, 🕿 777549, £12.93, D, FW, AC, ⊙, C (25 ton), CH, SM, ACA, ME, El, Sh, Ⓔ, C (mobile 50 ton by arrangement).
Wardley's YC ☎ 700429, 1 Ⓥ.
Blackpool & Fleetwood YC (Skippool) ☎ 884205, AB, Slip, FW, Bar; **Town** EC Wed; P & D (cans), ME, El, Sh, CH, V, R, Bar, ✉, Ⓑ, �₊ (Poulton-le-Fylde or Blackpool), ✈ (Blackpool).

10

RIVER RIBBLE/PRESTON　10-10-13

Lancashire 53°43′·50N 03°00′·00W　Rtg 3-1-2

CHARTS
AC 1981, *1826*; Imray C62; OS 102

TIDES
+0013 Dover; ML No data; Duration 0520; Zone 0 (UT)

Standard Port LIVERPOOL (→)

Times				Height (metres)			
High Water		Low Water		MHWS	MHWN	MLWN	MLWS
0000	0600	0200	0700	9·3	7·4	2·9	0·9
1200	1800	1400	1900				

Differences PRESTON

| +0010 | +0010 | +0335 | +0310 | −4·0 | −4·1 | −2·8 | −0·8 |

LW time differences give the end of a LW stand lasting 3½ hrs.

SHELTER
Good in Preston marina (5m depth) 15M upriver. Lock in HW±1½, (no commercial tfc); lay-by berth outside No 1 Lock for 2m draft. Possible drying berths on the N bank at Lytham or Freckleton, or 2M up R Douglas access HW±1.

NAVIGATION
WPT Ⓐ 53°41′·75N 03°08′·90W, Gut SWM buoy, L Fl 10s. The seaward 2·5M of original lit chan has silted up; best water is now via South Gut chan (liable to shift), navigable HW±2. Not before HW Liverpool −2, leave WPT Ⓐ tracking 2M E to WPT Ⓑ 53°41′·80N 03°05′·50W, at the ent to S Gut chan. Thence the transit of 11½M perch, Fl (2) R 10s, with conspic W Dome leads 055° to a gap in the south training wall at WPT Ⓒ 53°43′·30N 03°01′·85W. Enter via the gap, leaving 11½M perch 100m to port. The river trends 080° between training walls, drying 3m, marked by perches, lit as below, but night appr not advised.
Note: The chartlet shows only the seaward end of the estuary. The rest of the long chan and the entrance to the marina on the N side of river are both straightforward.

LIGHTS AND MARKS
14½M perch, Fl G 5s, is the most seaward chan mark. Upriver from 11½M perch there is a PHM buoy and perch (off chartlet), both Fl R 5s. 4 SHM perches, Fl G 5s, lead to 5M perch, Fl (2) G 10s, marking mouth of unlit R Douglas. 3M and 2M perches are Fl G 5s; 1M perch is Fl G 10s. The Warton airfield beacon, Mo (WQ) G 9s, is N abeam 5M perch, Fl G 5s.

RADIO TELEPHONE
At Preston, for locks call *Riversway* Ch 16 14; Marina Ch **80**, both (HW−3 to +1½). Douglas BY Ch 16 when vessel due.

TELEPHONE (Dial code 01772)
Preston Locks 726711; ⌗ (0161) 912 6977; MRSC (0151) 9313341; Marinecall 0891 500461; Police 203203; Ⓗ 710408.

FACILITIES
Douglas BY, ☎/⤓ 812462, AB, C (7 ton), CH, D, FW, Sh, Slip, ME. **Preston Marina** (250) ☎ 733595, ⤓ 731881, £5, AC, FW, D, CH, ME, Sh, Gas, C (50 ton), R, V, ACA.
Ribble Cruising Club ☎ (01253) 739983. ACA at Southport.

LIVERPOOL　10-10-14

Merseyside 53°24′·20N 03°00′·20W (Liver Bldg)　Rtg 2-1-2

CHARTS
AC 3490, 1951, *1978, 1826*; Imray C62; OS 108

TIDES
+0015 Dover; ML 5·2; Duration 0535; Zone 0 (UT)

Standard Port LIVERPOOL (PRINCES PIER) (→)

Times				Height (metres)			
High Water		Low Water		MHWS	MHWN	MLWN	MLWS
0000	0600	0200	0700	9·3	7·4	2·9	0·9
1200	1800	1400	1900				

Differences SOUTHPORT

−0020	−0010	No data		−0·3	−0·3	No data	

FORMBY
| −0015 | −0010 | −0020 | −0020 | −0·3 | −0·1 | 0·0 | +0·1 |

GLADSTONE DOCK
| −0003 | −0003 | −0003 | −0003 | −0·1 | −0·1 | 0·0 | −0·1 |

EASTHAM (River Mersey)
| +0010 | +0010 | +0009 | +0009 | +0·3 | +0·1 | −0·1 | −0·3 |

HALE HEAD (River Mersey)
| +0030 | +0025 | No data | | −2·4 | −2·5 | No data | |

WIDNES (River Mersey)
| +0040 | +0045 | +0400 | +0345 | −4·2 | −4·4 | −2·5 | −0·3 |

FIDDLER'S FERRY (River Mersey)
| +0100 | +0115 | +0540 | +0450 | −5·9 | −6·3 | −2·4 | −0·4 |

HILBRE ISLAND (River Dee)
| −0015 | −0012 | −0010 | −0015 | −0·3 | −0·2 | +0·2 | +0·4 |

MOSTYN QUAY (River Dee)
| −0020 | −0015 | −0020 | −0020 | −0·8 | −0·7 | No data | |

CONNAH'S QUAY (River Dee)
| 0000 | +0015 | +0355 | +0340 | −4·6 | −4·4 | Dries out | |

CHESTER (River Dee)
| +0105 | +0105 | +0500 | +0500 | −5·3 | −5·4 | Dries out | |

COLWYN BAY
| −0035 | −0025 | No data | | −1·5 | −1·3 | No data | |

LLANDUDNO
| −0035 | −0025 | −0025 | −0035 | −1·9 | −1·5 | −0·5 | −0·2 |

NOTE: LW time differences at Connah's Quay give the end of a LW stand lasting about 3¾hrs at sp and 5hrs at nps. A bore occurs in the R Dee at Chester.

SHELTER
Good at marina in the Coburg and Brunswick docks. Ent is 1M S of Liver Bldg and abeam the Pluckington Bank WCM; access HW ±2 approx. Good shelter also in Canning and Albert Docks but access HW−2 to HW. ⚓ on the SW side of river but only in fair wx.

NAVIGATION
WPT Bar PHM Lt F 53°32′·00N 03°20′·90W, 280°/100° from/to Queen's Chan, 3M. From Bar Lt F to marina ent is 17M via Queen's and Crosby Chans. Wind against tide causes steep seas in outer reaches of Mersey. The whole area (R Dee, R Mersey to R Alt and N to Morecambe B) is littered with sandbanks. R Mersey is safe inside buoyed chan, but elsewhere local knowledge and great caution needed. For **R Dee**: WPT 53°26′·20N 03°16′·80W, Hilbre Swash HE2 PHM buoy, QR, (chan shifts).

LIVERPOOL

MEAN SPRING
AND NEAP CURVES

MEAN RANGES	
Springs 8.4m	———
Neaps 4.5m	- - -

Springs occur 2 days
after
New and Full Moon.

10

LIGHTS AND MARKS
The ent to R Mersey is at the Bar PHM lt F, Fl 5s 12m 21M, Horn (2) 20s, Racon. Queen's Chan and Crosby Chan are marked by Boat lt bns to port, normal buoys to stbd. Formby and Crosby lt Floats are mid-chan SWMs. See also 10.10.4. Both chans have training banks which cover. Conspic black control bldg at lock ent has 3 R/G lts (vert).

RADIO TELEPHONE
Call: *Mersey Radio* VHF Ch **12** 16 (H24). Radar Ch 18. Marina Ch M. Traffic movements, nav warnings and weather reports broadcast on Ch 09 at HW–3 and –2. Local nav and gale warnings are broadcast on receipt on Ch 12. Eastham Locks Ch 07 (H24). Manchester Ship Canal Ch 14.

TELEPHONE (Dial code 0151)
Port Ops 949 6134/5; MRSC 931 3341; ⌗ (0161) 912 6977; Marinecall 0891 500 461; Police 709 6010; Ⓗ 709 0141.

FACILITIES
Marina (300 + 50) ☎ 708 5228, (0600-2130 Mar–Oct), 🛥 709 8731. Ent via Brunswick Dock lock, min depth 3·5m. £10.57, D, P (½M), AC, FW, BH (60 ton), Slip, CH, SM, Bar, ▣, R, V; **Albert Dock** ☎ 236 6090, VHF Ch M when ent manned, AB, FW, AC;
Royal Mersey YC ☎ 645 3204, Slip, M, P, D, L, FW, R, Bar. **W Kirby SC** ☎ 625 5579, AB (at HW), Slip, M (in Dee Est), L, FW, C (30ton), Bar; **Hoylake SC** ☎ 632 2616, Slip, M, FW, Bar; **Services:** CH, SM, ME, EI, Sh, ACA, Ⓔ.
City EC Wed; ✉, Ⓑ, ⇌, ✈.
Note: Access to E Coast via Leeds & Liverpool Canal (BWB), ent at Stanley Dock. Max draft 1·0m, air draft 2·2m, beam 4·3m, LOA 18·3m. Liverpool to Goole 161M, 103 locks.

ADJACENT ANCHORAGE

RIVER ALT, Merseyside, 53°31'·40N 03°03'·72W. AC 1951, *1978*. HW –0008 on Dover; see 10·10·14. Good shelter but only for LOA <8·5m x 1·2m draft on a HW of at least 8m. Mersey E training wall can be crossed HW±2. Ent to chan (shifts frequently) is E of C14 PHM lt float, thence marked by locally-laid Y Fairway buoy and perches on the training wall. Unsafe to ⚓ in R Alt; pick up a free mooring off the SC and contact club. Local knowledge advised. Facilities very limited. **Blundellsands SC** ☎ (0151) 929 2101 (occas), Slip, L (at HW), FW, Bar.

ENGLAND – LIVERPOOL (ALFRED DOCK)

LAT 53°24′N   LONG   3°01′W

TIMES AND HEIGHTS OF HIGH AND LOW WATERS

YEAR **1998**

TIME ZONE (UT)
For Summer Time add ONE hour in non-shaded areas

JANUARY

Date	Day	Time	m	Time	m	Time	m	Time	m
1	TH	0034	9.3	0713	1.3	1256	9.6	1940	1.1
16	F	0109	9.0	0744	1.7	1325	9.2	2017	1.6
2	F	0119	9.3	0756	1.3	1341	9.6	2024	1.1
17	SA	0144	8.8	0813	1.9	1400	9.0	2047	1.9
3	SA	0205	9.2	0839	1.5	1428	9.5	2108	1.3
18	SU	0220	8.6	0842	2.1	1436	8.7	2117	2.2
4	SU	0254	9.0	0925	1.8	1518	9.2	2156	1.6
19	M	0258	8.3	0916	2.5	1516	8.4	2154	2.5
5	M	0346	8.6	1016	2.1	1613	8.8	2250	2.0
20	TU	0340	7.9	1001	2.8	1601	8.0	2242	2.9
6	TU	0447	8.3	1117	2.4	1716	8.5	2354	2.3
21	W	0431	7.5	1057	3.2	1655	7.6	2344	3.1
7	W	0556	8.0	1227	2.6	1827	8.3		
22	TH	0534	7.3	1205	3.3	1800	7.4		
8	TH	0108	2.4	0710	8.1	1348	2.5	1939	8.3
23	F	0054	3.1	0648	7.4	1317	3.2	1912	7.5
9	F	0228	2.2	0819	8.3	1506	2.2	2046	8.6
24	SA	0202	2.9	0758	7.7	1426	2.9	2020	7.8
10	SA	0335	1.9	0917	8.7	1608	1.8	2142	8.9
25	SU	0304	2.5	0856	8.2	1528	2.4	2116	8.3
11	SU	0429	1.6	1007	9.1	1659	1.5	2231	9.2
26	M	0359	2.0	0944	8.8	1622	1.9	2205	8.8
12	M	0515	1.4	1052	9.3	1746	1.2	O 2315	9.3
27	TU	0448	1.6	1029	9.2	1713	1.4	2251	9.2
13	TU	0556	1.3	1133	9.4	1828	1.2	2356	9.3
28	W	0534	1.2	1113	9.6	1800	1.0	● 2336	9.5
14	W	0635	1.4	1212	9.4	1908	1.2		
29	TH	0620	1.0	1157	9.9	1846	0.7		
15	TH	0033	9.2	0711	1.5	1249	9.4	1944	1.4
30	F	0021	9.7	0703	0.8	1242	10.0	1930	0.5
31	SA	0106	9.7	0746	0.8	1327	10.1	2012	0.6

FEBRUARY

Date	Day	Time	m	Time	m	Time	m	Time	m
1	SU	0151	9.7	0827	0.9	1413	9.9	2054	0.8
16	M	0151	8.8	0814	1.7	1408	8.9	2041	1.8
2	M	0236	9.4	0910	1.2	1500	9.6	2137	1.2
17	TU	0225	8.6	0845	2.0	1443	8.6	2113	2.2
3	TU	0324	9.0	0957	1.6	1550	9.1	2226	1.7
18	W	0302	8.3	0924	2.4	1522	8.2	2153	2.6
4	W	0418	8.4	1051	2.1	1648	8.5	2324	2.3
19	TH	0345	7.9	1012	2.8	1610	7.8	2248	3.0
5	TH	0523	7.9	1158	2.6	1759	8.0		
20	F	0441	7.5	1116	3.2	1711	7.4		
6	F	0035	2.7	0643	7.7	1322	2.7	1920	7.9
21	SA	0002	3.3	0550	7.3	1233	3.3	1822	7.3
7	SA	0203	2.7	0802	7.9	1454	2.5	2033	8.1
22	SU	0121	3.2	0709	7.4	1350	3.0	1940	7.5
8	SU	0323	2.4	0904	8.4	1559	2.0	2131	8.5
23	M	0233	2.7	0821	8.0	1501	2.4	2049	8.1
9	M	0420	2.0	0955	8.8	1651	1.6	2220	8.9
24	TU	0335	2.1	0919	8.6	1602	1.8	2144	8.7
10	TU	0504	1.7	1040	9.2	1734	1.3	2302	9.1
25	W	0429	1.5	1008	9.2	1655	1.1	2232	9.3
11	W	0544	1.5	1119	9.3	1813	1.2	O 2340	9.2
26	TH	0518	1.0	1101	9.8	1744	0.6	● 2318	9.7
12	TH	0619	1.4	1156	9.4	1849	1.2		
27	F	0604	0.6	1138	10.1	1830	0.2		
13	F	0014	9.2	0652	1.4	1230	9.4	1921	1.2
28	SA	0003	9.9	0648	0.3	1224	10.3	1913	0.1
14	SA	0047	9.1	0722	1.4	1302	9.3	1950	1.4
15	SU	0119	9.0	0747	1.6	1334	9.1	2015	1.6

MARCH

Date	Day	Time	m	Time	m	Time	m	Time	m
1	SU	0048	10.0	0731	0.2	1309	10.3	1955	0.1
16	M	0052	9.0	0722	1.3	1308	9.1	1943	1.4
2	M	0132	9.4	0812	0.4	1354	10.1	2035	0.4
17	TU	0123	8.9	0749	1.4	1340	8.9	2009	1.6
3	TU	0216	9.6	0854	0.7	1439	9.7	2116	0.9
18	W	0156	8.8	0820	1.7	1413	8.7	2040	1.9
4	W	0301	9.1	0938	1.3	1527	9.0	2202	1.6
19	TH	0230	8.5	0855	2.0	1450	8.3	2116	2.4
5	TH	0351	8.5	1031	1.9	1623	8.3	2257	2.3
20	F	0309	8.1	0937	2.5	1535	7.9	2202	2.8
6	F	0453	7.8	1135	2.5	1735	7.7		
21	SA	0400	7.7	1035	2.9	1634	7.4	2314	3.2
7	SA	0006	2.9	0617	7.5	1300	2.8	1902	7.5
22	SU	0509	7.3	1155	3.1	1747	7.2		
8	SU	0136	3.0	0741	7.6	1439	2.6	2017	7.7
23	M	0041	3.2	0628	7.4	1318	2.9	1907	7.4
9	M	0308	2.7	0846	8.1	1545	2.1	2115	8.2
24	TU	0201	2.8	0747	7.8	1434	2.3	2022	8.0
10	TU	0405	2.2	0937	8.6	1634	1.6	2202	8.6
25	W	0309	2.2	0851	8.5	1539	1.6	2120	8.7
11	W	0448	1.8	1021	9.0	1715	1.3	2242	8.9
26	TH	0406	1.5	0943	9.2	1634	0.9	2210	9.3
12	TH	0524	1.5	1059	9.2	1751	1.2	2318	9.1
27	F	0457	0.8	1031	9.8	1723	0.3	2256	9.8
13	F	0558	1.3	1134	9.3	1823	1.1	O 2351	9.1
28	SA	0544	0.3	1117	10.2	1809	0.0	● 2341	10.0
14	SA	0629	1.3	1206	9.2	1853	1.2		
29	SU	0629	0.0	1202	10.3	1852	-0.2		
15	SU	0021	9.1	0656	1.3	1237	9.2	1919	1.2
30	M	0025	10.1	0712	0.0	1248	10.3	1934	0.0
31	TU	0110	9.9	0755	0.2	1333	10.0	2014	0.4

APRIL

Date	Day	Time	m	Time	m	Time	m	Time	m
1	W	0154	9.6	0837	0.6	1419	9.5	2055	1.0
16	TH	0129	8.8	0759	1.5	1349	8.6	2014	1.8
2	TH	0238	9.1	0922	1.1	1506	8.8	2139	1.7
17	F	0204	8.6	0834	1.8	1427	8.4	2050	2.2
3	F	0326	8.5	1013	1.8	1600	8.1	2233	2.4
18	SA	0244	8.3	0915	2.2	1512	8.0	2134	2.6
4	SA	0426	7.8	1116	2.4	1710	7.5	2339	3.0
19	SU	0334	7.9	1010	2.6	1609	7.6	2240	3.0
5	SU	0548	7.4	1235	2.7	1837	7.2		
20	M	0440	7.6	1124	2.8	1720	7.4		
6	M	0100	3.2	0712	7.4	1408	2.6	1950	7.5
21	TU	0005	3.1	0556	7.6	1246	2.6	1838	7.5
7	TU	0234	2.9	0817	7.8	1517	2.2	2048	7.9
22	W	0127	2.8	0714	7.9	1403	2.2	1953	8.0
8	W	0335	2.4	0909	8.3	1606	1.8	2134	8.4
23	TH	0238	2.1	0820	8.6	1511	1.5	2053	8.7
9	TH	0419	2.0	0954	8.7	1646	1.5	2215	8.7
24	F	0339	1.4	0917	9.2	1608	0.8	2145	9.3
10	F	0456	1.7	1033	8.9	1720	1.3	2251	8.9
25	SA	0433	0.8	1007	9.7	1658	0.3	2232	9.7
11	SA	0529	1.4	1108	9.0	1751	1.2	O 2323	9.0
26	SU	0521	0.4	1054	10.0	1745	0.4	● 2318	9.9
12	SU	0600	1.3	1140	9.0	1820	1.2	2354	9.0
27	M	0608	0.1	1141	10.1	1829	0.0		
13	M	0629	1.2	1210	9.0	1847	1.2		
28	TU	0002	10.0	0653	0.1	1228	10.0	1911	0.2
14	TU	0024	9.0	0657	1.2	1242	8.9	1914	1.3
29	W	0048	9.8	0738	0.2	1314	9.7	1952	0.6
15	W	0056	8.9	0726	1.3	1314	8.8	1943	1.5
30	TH	0132	9.5	0822	0.6	1359	9.3	2034	1.1

Chart Datum: 4·93 metres below Ordnance Datum (Newlyn)

ENGLAND – LIVERPOOL (ALFRED DOCK)

LAT 53°24'N   LONG 3°01'W

TIMES AND HEIGHTS OF HIGH AND LOW WATERS

YEAR **1998**

TIME ZONE (UT)
For Summer Time add ONE hour in non-shaded areas

Chart Datum: 4·93 metres below Ordnance Datum (Newlyn)

MAY

Day	Time	m	Time	m	Time	m	Time	m
1 F	0217	9.0	0907	1.1	1446	8.7	2118	1.8
2 SA	0304	8.5	0957	1.7	1538	8.1	2208	2.4
3 SU	0359	7.9	1055	2.3	1641	7.5	2309	2.9
4 M	0511	7.5	1201	2.6	1758	7.2		
5 TU	0018	3.2	0630	7.4	1316	2.7	1910	7.3
6 W	0135	3.1	0737	7.6	1428	2.5	2010	7.7
7 TH	0246	2.7	0833	8.0	1523	2.1	2059	8.1
8 F	0337	2.3	0920	8.3	1606	1.8	2141	8.5
9 SA	0418	1.9	1001	8.6	1642	1.6	2218	8.7
10 SU	0453	1.6	1037	8.8	1714	1.4	2253	8.9
11 M ○	0527	1.5	1111	8.8	1746	1.3	2325	8.9
12 TU	0600	1.3	1144	8.8	1817	1.3	2358	8.9
13 W	0633	1.3	1217	8.8	1849	1.4		
14 TH	0031	8.9	0707	1.3	1253	8.8	1921	1.5
15 F	0107	8.8	0743	1.5	1330	8.7	1956	1.8
16 SA	0145	8.7	0821	1.7	1411	8.5	2034	2.1
17 SU	0228	8.5	0904	1.9	1457	8.2	2120	2.4
18 M	0319	8.2	0956	2.2	1552	7.9	2219	2.7
19 TU	0420	8.0	1101	2.4	1658	7.7	2333	2.8
20 W	0531	7.9	1214	2.3	1811	7.8		
21 TH	0050	2.6	0643	8.1	1329	2.1	1922	8.1
22 F	0204	2.2	0750	8.6	1440	1.6	2025	8.6
23 SA	0310	1.6	0850	9.1	1541	1.1	2120	9.1
24 SU	0407	1.1	0944	9.5	1634	0.7	2209	9.5
25 M ●	0459	0.6	1034	9.7	1722	0.4	2256	9.7
26 TU	0548	0.4	1122	9.8	1807	0.4	2342	9.7
27 W	0636	0.4	1209	9.7	1851	0.6		
28 TH	0027	9.6	0722	0.5	1256	9.5	1933	0.9
29 F	0112	9.3	0807	0.8	1341	9.1	2014	1.4
30 SA	0157	9.0	0852	1.2	1426	8.7	2056	1.9
31 SU	0242	8.6	0938	1.7	1513	8.2	2141	2.4

JUNE

Day	Time	m	Time	m	Time	m	Time	m
1 M	0330	8.2	1027	2.1	1604	7.7	2232	2.8
2 TU	0427	7.7	1121	2.5	1706	7.4	2331	3.1
3 W	0535	7.5	1220	2.7	1816	7.3		
4 TH	0035	3.2	0645	7.5	1323	2.7	1921	7.4
5 F	0140	3.0	0746	7.7	1423	2.5	2016	7.8
6 SA	0240	2.7	0839	8.0	1515	2.2	2103	8.2
7 SU	0331	2.3	0924	8.2	1558	1.9	2144	8.5
8 M	0414	2.0	1005	8.5	1637	1.7	2222	8.7
9 TU	0453	1.7	1042	8.6	1714	1.5	2258	8.9
10 W	0532	1.5	1119	8.7	1750	1.5	2334	9.0
11 TH	0612	1.4	1156	8.8	1828	1.5		
12 F	0011	9.0	0651	1.4	1235	8.8	1905	1.5
13 SA	0050	9.0	0732	1.4	1316	8.8	1944	1.6
14 SU	0132	9.0	0813	1.5	1359	8.7	2024	1.8
15 M	0217	8.9	0857	1.6	1445	8.6	2110	2.0
16 TU	0306	8.7	0945	1.8	1537	8.3	2203	2.3
17 W	0402	8.3	1041	2.0	1636	8.1	2306	2.4
18 TH	0506	8.3	1144	2.1	1743	8.0		
19 F	0015	2.4	0614	8.3	1254	2.1	1852	8.1
20 SA	0130	2.3	0722	8.5	1408	1.9	1959	8.5
21 SU	0242	1.9	0827	8.8	1515	1.5	2058	8.9
22 M	0346	1.5	0925	9.1	1612	1.2	2151	9.2
23 TU	0442	1.1	1018	9.3	1703	1.0	2240	9.4
24 W	0533	0.8	1107	9.4	1749	1.0	● 2326	9.5
25 TH	0622	0.8	1154	9.4	1833	1.0		
26 F	0011	9.4	0708	0.8	1240	9.3	1915	1.2
27 SA	0054	9.3	0752	1.0	1323	9.0	1954	1.5
28 SU	0136	9.1	0834	1.3	1404	8.8	2032	1.8
29 M	0217	8.8	0914	1.6	1444	8.4	2109	2.2
30 TU	0258	8.5	0954	2.0	1526	8.0	2148	2.6

JULY

Day	Time	m	Time	m	Time	m	Time	m
1 W	0343	8.1	1036	2.4	1613	7.7	2236	2.9
2 TH	0434	7.7	1125	2.7	1710	7.4	2335	3.1
3 F	0536	7.5	1222	2.9	1818	7.3		
4 SA	0039	3.2	0645	7.4	1323	2.8	1924	7.5
5 SU	0143	3.0	0750	7.6	1422	2.6	2021	7.8
6 M	0243	2.7	0845	7.9	1516	2.3	2110	8.2
7 TU	0336	2.3	0933	8.2	1603	2.0	2153	8.6
8 W	0424	1.9	1016	8.5	1647	1.7	● 2233	8.9
9 TH	0509	1.6	1056	8.7	1729	1.5	O 2313	9.1
10 F	0554	1.4	1137	8.9	1811	1.4	2353	9.2
11 SA	0638	1.2	1219	9.0	1852	1.4		
12 SU	0035	9.3	0721	1.1	1302	9.1	1933	1.3
13 M	0119	9.4	0804	1.1	1346	9.1	2015	1.4
14 TU	0204	9.3	0846	1.2	1431	9.0	2058	1.6
15 W	0251	9.2	0931	1.4	1519	8.8	2145	1.8
16 TH	0343	8.9	1020	1.6	1613	8.5	2241	2.1
17 F	0441	8.6	1117	2.0	1715	8.2	2346	2.4
18 SA	0547	8.3	1223	2.2	1825	8.0		
19 SU	0101	2.4	0658	8.2	1339	2.2	1937	8.2
20 M	0223	2.2	0810	8.4	1456	2.0	2043	8.5
21 TU	0333	1.8	0913	8.7	1558	1.7	2139	8.9
22 W	0432	1.4	1008	9.0	1651	1.4	2228	9.2
23 TH	0523	1.1	1056	9.2	1736	1.3	● 2313	9.4
24 F	0610	1.0	1141	9.2	1819	1.3	2355	9.4
25 SA	0654	1.0	1222	9.2	1858	1.3		
26 SU	0035	9.3	0733	1.1	1301	9.0	1933	1.5
27 M	0113	9.2	0810	1.3	1338	8.8	2005	1.7
28 TU	0149	9.0	0843	1.6	1413	8.6	2034	2.0
29 W	0225	8.7	0914	1.9	1449	8.3	2105	2.3
30 TH	0303	8.4	0947	2.3	1529	8.0	2144	2.7
31 F	0346	8.0	1029	2.6	1615	7.6	2236	3.0

AUGUST

Day	Time	m	Time	m	Time	m	Time	m
1 SA	0436	7.6	1124	3.0	1712	7.4	2343	3.3
2 SU	0538	7.3	1230	3.1	1822	7.3		
3 M	0055	3.2	0651	7.3	1337	3.0	1935	7.5
4 TU	0204	2.9	0803	7.5	1440	2.7	2036	8.0
5 W	0305	2.5	0902	8.0	1535	2.2	2126	8.5
6 TH	0400	2.0	0951	8.4	1625	1.8	2210	8.9
7 F	0450	1.6	1035	8.8	1711	1.5	2252	9.3
8 SA	0538	1.2	1118	9.1	1756	1.2	O 2334	9.6
9 SU	0624	0.9	1201	9.3	1839	1.0		
10 M	0017	9.7	0707	0.7	1245	9.4	1920	0.9
11 TU	0102	9.8	0750	0.6	1329	9.5	2001	1.0
12 W	0146	9.7	0831	0.7	1413	9.3	2043	1.1
13 TH	0232	9.5	0912	1.0	1459	9.1	2127	1.5
14 F	0321	9.1	0958	1.5	1549	8.6	2219	2.0
15 SA	0416	8.6	1052	2.0	1648	8.2	2323	2.4
16 SU	0523	8.1	1158	2.5	1801	7.8		
17 M	0042	2.7	0642	7.8	1319	2.7	1922	7.9
18 TU	0214	2.5	0801	8.0	1446	2.5	2033	8.2
19 W	0329	2.0	0905	8.4	1551	2.1	2129	8.7
20 TH	0425	1.6	0958	8.8	1642	1.7	2217	9.1
21 F	0513	1.2	1043	9.0	1724	1.5	2259	9.3
22 SA	0555	1.0	1124	9.1	1802	1.4	● 2338	9.4
23 SU	0633	1.0	1202	9.1	1837	1.4		
24 M	0013	9.3	0708	1.1	1236	9.0	1909	1.4
25 TU	0047	9.2	0740	1.3	1309	8.9	1937	1.6
26 W	0119	9.0	0808	1.5	1341	8.8	2002	1.8
27 TH	0152	8.8	0834	1.8	1414	8.6	2030	2.0
28 F	0227	8.5	0902	2.1	1450	8.3	2105	2.4
29 SA	0306	8.1	0939	2.6	1531	7.9	2150	2.8
30 SU	0352	7.7	1029	3.0	1622	7.5	2252	3.2
31 M	0449	7.3	1140	3.3	1727	7.3		

ENGLAND – LIVERPOOL (ALFRED DOCK)

LAT 53°24′N   LONG 3°01′W

TIMES AND HEIGHTS OF HIGH AND LOW WATERS

YEAR 1998

TIME ZONE (UT)
For Summer Time add ONE hour in non-shaded areas

Chart Datum: 4·93 metres below Ordnance Datum (Newlyn)

SEPTEMBER

Day		Water 1	Water 2	Water 3	Water 4
1	TU	0012 3.4	0600 7.1	1258 3.3	1844 7.3
16	W	0207 2.6	0750 7.8	1437 2.8	2018 8.1
2	W	0130 3.1	0720 7.3	1408 3.0	2000 7.8
17	TH	0319 2.1	0851 8.2	1540 2.3	2113 8.6
3	TH	0238 2.6	0832 7.8	1510 2.4	2058 8.4
18	F	0411 1.6	0941 8.7	1627 1.9	2159 9.0
4	F	0338 2.0	0926 8.4	1604 1.9	2145 9.0
19	SA	0455 1.2	1024 9.0	1706 1.6	2239 9.3
5	SA	0430 1.4	1013 8.9	1652 1.3	2229 9.5
20	SU	0533 1.1	1102 9.1	1741 1.4	● 2316 9.3
6	SU	0519 0.8	1056 9.4	1738 0.9	O 2313 9.9
21	M	0607 1.1	1136 9.1	1813 1.4	2348 9.3
7	M	0604 0.5	1140 9.6	1822 0.6	2356 10.1
22	TU	0639 1.1	1208 9.1	1842 1.4	
8	TU	0648 0.3	1223 9.8	1904 0.5	
23	W	0019 9.2	0707 1.3	1238 9.0	1908 1.5
9	W	0040 10.1	0730 0.3	1307 9.8	1945 0.6
24	TH	0050 9.0	0732 1.5	1309 8.9	1933 1.6
10	TH	0126 10.0	0811 0.5	1351 9.6	2026 0.8
25	F	0122 8.8	0757 1.7	1341 8.7	2001 1.8
11	F	0212 9.6	0852 0.9	1436 9.2	2110 1.3
26	SA	0155 8.6	0825 2.1	1416 8.4	2035 2.2
12	SA	0300 9.1	0936 1.5	1525 8.7	2201 1.9
27	SU	0232 8.2	0900 2.5	1454 8.1	2115 2.6
13	SU	0354 8.4	1029 2.2	1623 8.1	2305 2.5
28	M	0315 7.8	0944 3.0	1541 7.7	2210 3.1
14	M	0503 7.8	1136 2.8	1740 7.6	
29	TU	0411 7.3	1050 3.4	1644 7.3	2331 3.3
15	TU	0029 2.8	0630 7.5	1302 3.0	1908 7.7
30	W	0522 7.1	1217 3.5	1801 7.3	

OCTOBER

Day		Water 1	Water 2	Water 3	Water 4
1	TH	0056 3.2	0643 7.2	1336 3.1	1920 7.7
16	F	0255 2.2	0827 8.0	1516 2.5	2048 8.4
2	F	0210 2.6	0800 7.8	1443 2.5	2026 8.4
17	SA	0346 1.8	0916 8.5	1602 2.1	2134 8.8
3	SA	0313 1.9	0859 8.5	1540 1.8	2118 9.1
18	SU	0428 1.5	0958 8.8	1640 1.8	2214 9.1
4	SU	0407 1.2	0947 9.1	1630 1.2	2204 9.7
19	M	0503 1.3	1035 9.0	1713 1.6	2250 9.2
5	M	0456 0.6	1032 9.6	1717 0.7	O 2249 10.1
20	TU	0536 1.2	1108 9.1	1745 1.5	● 2322 9.2
6	TU	0542 0.2	1115 9.9	1802 0.4	2334 10.3
21	W	0606 1.3	1139 9.1	1814 1.4	2352 9.1
7	W	0626 0.1	1159 10.0	1845 0.3	
22	TH	0634 1.4	1209 9.0	1842 1.5	
8	TH	0019 10.2	0708 0.2	1244 9.9	1927 0.4
23	F	0022 9.0	0700 1.5	1241 8.9	1909 1.6
9	F	0105 10.0	0749 0.5	1329 9.7	2010 0.7
24	SA	0055 8.8	0727 1.7	1329 1.8	1939 1.8
10	SA	0151 9.6	0831 1.0	1414 9.2	2055 1.2
25	SU	0129 8.6	0758 2.0	1347 8.6	2013 2.1
11	SU	0240 9.0	0916 1.6	1503 8.7	2146 1.8
26	M	0206 8.3	0833 2.4	1426 8.3	2052 2.4
12	M	0335 8.3	1008 2.4	1600 8.1	2250 2.4
27	TU	0248 8.0	0914 2.9	1512 7.9	2142 2.8
13	TU	0444 7.7	1115 2.9	1718 7.6	
28	W	0342 7.6	1013 3.3	1612 7.6	2255 3.1
14	W	0012 2.8	0611 7.4	1238 3.2	1843 7.6
29	TH	0451 7.3	1136 3.4	1725 7.5	
15	TH	0145 2.6	0727 7.6	1412 3.0	1953 7.9
30	F	0018 3.0	0609 7.4	1258 3.2	1842 7.8
31	SA	0136 2.6	0725 7.8	1410 2.6	1951 8.4

NOVEMBER

Day		Water 1	Water 2	Water 3	Water 4
1	SU	0243 1.9	0828 8.5	1511 1.9	2048 9.1
16	M	0352 1.9	0927 8.6	1606 2.1	2144 8.7
2	M	0340 1.2	0919 9.2	1605 1.3	2138 9.7
17	TU	0429 1.7	1005 8.9	1642 1.9	2221 8.9
3	TU	0431 0.7	1006 9.7	1654 0.8	2226 10.1
18	W	0502 1.5	1039 9.0	1715 1.7	2255 9.0
4	W	0518 0.3	1052 10.0	1741 0.4	O 2312 10.2
19	TH	0533 1.5	1112 9.1	1746 1.6	● 2327 9.0
5	TH	0603 0.2	1137 10.1	1827 0.2	2359 10.2
20	F	0603 1.5	1144 9.1	1818 1.6	2359 8.9
6	F	0646 0.3	1222 10.0	1912 0.4	
21	SA	0634 1.6	1217 9.0	1850 1.6	
7	SA	0045 9.9	0729 0.6	1308 9.7	1956 0.7
22	SU	0032 8.8	0706 1.7	1251 8.9	1924 1.7
8	SU	0133 9.5	0812 1.1	1355 9.3	2043 1.2
23	M	0109 8.7	0739 2.0	1327 8.8	2000 1.9
9	M	0222 8.9	0857 1.8	1443 8.8	2134 1.8
24	TU	0147 8.5	0816 2.3	1407 8.6	2040 2.2
10	TU	0315 8.3	0948 2.4	1538 8.2	2232 2.3
25	W	0230 8.3	0858 2.6	1453 8.3	2128 2.5
11	W	0418 7.7	1048 3.0	1646 7.8	2341 2.7
26	TH	0321 7.9	0951 2.9	1549 8.1	2228 2.7
12	TH	0536 7.4	1158 3.3	1805 7.6	
27	F	0424 7.7	1059 3.1	1655 7.9	2340 2.7
13	F	0059 2.7	0650 7.5	1319 3.2	1915 7.8
28	SA	0536 7.6	1214 3.0	1806 8.1	
14	SA	0213 2.5	0752 7.9	1432 2.9	2013 8.1
29	SU	0055 2.5	0649 7.9	1329 2.7	1915 8.4
15	SU	0309 2.2	0843 8.2	1524 2.5	2102 8.5
30	M	0207 2.0	0755 8.5	1438 2.1	2018 9.0

DECEMBER

Day		Water 1	Water 2	Water 3	Water 4
1	TU	0311 1.5	0852 9.0	1539 1.5	2114 9.4
16	W	0350 2.1	0934 8.5	1606 2.3	2152 8.6
2	W	0406 1.0	0943 9.5	1632 1.0	2205 9.8
17	TH	0428 1.9	1012 8.8	1644 2.0	2229 8.7
3	TH	0456 0.7	1032 9.8	1723 0.7	O 2254 10.0
18	F	0503 1.7	1048 9.0	1721 1.8	● 2305 8.8
4	F	0543 0.5	1118 9.9	1811 0.6	2342 10.0
19	SA	0539 1.6	1123 9.1	1758 1.7	2340 8.9
5	SA	0628 0.6	1205 9.9	1859 0.6	
20	SU	0614 1.6	1158 9.1	1835 1.6	
6	SU	0030 9.8	0712 0.9	1251 9.7	1945 0.8
21	M	0016 8.9	0650 1.7	1235 9.1	1913 1.6
7	M	0118 9.4	0756 1.3	1338 9.4	2032 1.2
22	TU	0054 8.9	0727 1.8	1313 9.1	1952 1.7
8	TU	0205 9.0	0840 1.7	1424 9.0	2119 1.6
23	W	0134 8.8	0806 1.9	1354 9.0	2032 1.8
9	W	0253 8.5	0925 2.3	1512 8.6	2208 2.1
24	TH	0217 8.7	0847 2.2	1439 8.9	2116 2.0
10	TH	0344 8.0	1015 2.8	1606 8.1	2302 2.5
25	F	0304 8.4	0934 2.4	1529 8.7	2206 2.2
11	F	0445 7.6	1111 3.1	1710 7.7	
26	SA	0359 8.2	1030 2.6	1627 8.4	2306 2.4
12	SA	0001 2.8	0555 7.4	1215 3.3	1820 7.6
27	SU	0503 8.0	1134 2.7	1733 8.3	
13	SU	0107 2.9	0703 7.5	1322 3.3	1926 7.7
28	M	0014 2.4	0613 8.0	1247 2.7	1842 8.4
14	M	0211 2.7	0802 7.8	1428 3.0	2022 8.0
29	TU	0129 2.3	0724 8.2	1404 2.4	1951 8.7
15	TU	0305 2.4	0851 8.2	1522 2.6	2110 8.3
30	W	0242 1.9	0829 8.7	1516 1.9	2054 9.0
31	TH	0345 1.5	0926 9.2	1616 1.4	2151 9.4

ISLE OF MAN   10·10·15

CHARTS
AC 2696 (ports), 2094 (small scale). Irish Sea *1826, 1411*

The Isle of Man is one of the British Islands, set in the Irish Sea almost equidistant from England, Scotland and Ireland but it is not part of the UK. It has a large degree of self-government. The IOM comes under the same customs umbrella as the rest of the UK, but there are no formalities on landing from or returning to UK.

Harbours and anchorages. Manx hbrs are administered by the IOM Government and lights are maintained by the Commissioners of Northern Lighthouses in Scotland. Besides the four main hbrs given below, there are good ⚓s at Castletown in the SE, Laxey Bay in the E and Port Erin in the SW; see below. There are also good ⚓s in Derby Haven in the SE; this is a rather bleak area and the inner hbr dries. Most of the hbrs are on the E and S sides but a visit to the W coast with its characteristic cliffs is worth while. All IOM hbrs charge the same overnight berthing fee, ie £6.51 regardless of LOA; or £32.50 weekly fee allows use of all hbrs (1997 figures, inc VAT).

Passage information. Including Calf Sound, see 10·10·5.

R/T. If contact with local Hr Mrs cannot be established on VHF, vessels should call *Douglas Hbr Control* Ch 12 16 for urgent messages or other info.

Coastguard. Call Liverpool MRSC Ch 16 67; there is no loss of VHF coverage as the Snaefell (IoM) aerial is linked to Liverpool by land line.

Weather. Forecasts can be obtained from Manx Radio, see Table 7 (5); or direct from the forecaster at Ronaldsway Met Office ☎ 0696 888 200, (0700-2030LT). Recorded shipping forecast (updated 3 times daily) ☎ 0696 888 322; recorded general forecast ☎ 0696 888 320.

Directions. The *Isle of Man SDs, Tidal streams and Anchorages* by the Manx Sailing and Cruising Club in Ramsey, ☎ 01624-813494, are recommended.

Distances. See 10.10.6 for distances between ports in Area 10 and 10.0.6 for distances across the Irish Sea, North Channel and St George's Channel.

MINOR HARBOURS IN THE ISLE OF MAN

PORT ERIN, Isle of Man, 54°05'·30N 04°46'·27W. AC 2696, 2094. HW −0020 on Dover; ML 2·9m; Duration 0555. See 10·10·16. The bay has good ⚓ in 3-8m, but exposed to all W winds. Ldg lts, both FR 10/19m 5M, lead 099° into the bay. Beware the ruined bkwtr extending N from the SW corner, marked by an unlit SHM buoy. A small hbr on the S side dries 0·8m. Raglan Pier (E arm of hbr) Oc G 5s 8m 5M. Two ⚑s W of Raglan Pier; call Hr Mr Port St. Mary (VHF Ch 12). Facilities: EC Thurs; Bar, D, P, FW, R, Slip, V.

CASTLETOWN, Isle of Man, 54°03'·50N 04°38'·50W. AC 2696, 2094. HW +0025 on Dover; ML 3·4m; Duration 0555. See 10.10.17. Hbr dries (level sand). Access HW±2½. Berth in Outer Hbr or go via swing bridge (manually operated) into Inner Hbr below fixed bridge. ⚓ between Lheeah-rio Rks and pier in 3m; off Langness Pt; or in Derby Haven (dries). The bay gives good shelter except in SE to SW winds. Beware Lheeah-rio Rks in W of bay, marked by PHM Fl R 3s, Bell. Keep inside the race off Dreswick Pt, or give it a wide berth. Langness lt , on Dreswick Pt, Fl (2) 30s 23m 12M. S side of ent: New Pier Oc R 15s 8m 5M; then Irish Quay, Oc R 4s 5m 5M, vis 142°-322°. 150m NW is swing bridge marked by 2 FR (hor). N side of ent Oc G 4s 3m (W metal post on concrete column). VHF Ch 12 16 (when vessel due). Hr Mr ☎ 823549. Facilities: **Outer Hbr** Slip, L, C (20 ton) AB; **Irish Quay** AB, C, FW; **Inner Hbr** AB, C, FW; **Services:** P, D, Gas, ME. **Town** EC Thurs; Dr 823597.

LAXEY, Isle of Man, 54°13'·45N 04°23'·25W. AC 2094. HW +0025 on Dover, +0010 on Liverpool; HW ht −2·0m on Liverpool; ML 4·0m; Duration 0550. The bay gives good shelter in SW to N winds. The hbr dries 3·0m to rk and is only suitable for small yachts; access HW±3 for 1·5m draft. Beware rks on N side of the narrow ent. Keep close to pier after entering to avoid training wall to N. Pier hd lt Oc R 3s 7m 5M, obsc when brg <318°. Bkwtr hd lt Oc G 3s 7m. Facilities: FW, R, ✉, Ⓑ, Bar.

PEEL   10·10·16

Isle of Man 54°13'·60N 04°41'·61W   Rtg 3-3-1

CHARTS
AC 2696, 2094; Imray C62; Y70; OS 95

TIDES
+0005 Dover; ML 2·9; Duration 0545; Zone 0 (UT)

🔺 Report to HrMr

Standard Port LIVERPOOL (←—)

Times				Height (metres)			
High Water		Low Water		MHWS	MHWN	MLWN	MLWS
0000	0600	0200	0700	9·3	7·4	2·9	0·9
1200	1800	1400	1900				
Differences PEEL							
−0015	+0010	0000	−0010	−4·0	−3·2	−1·4	−0·4
PORT ERIN							
−0005	+0015	−0010	−0050	−4·1	−3·2	−1·3	−0·5

SHELTER
Good, except in strong NW to NE winds when ent should not be attempted. 3 R ⚑s off S groyne in about 2m. Fin keelers may be able to berth on N bkwtr in 5m. Hbr dries; very crowded Jun-Oct. Inner hbr dries approx 2·8m to flat sand; access HW±3, possible AB on W quay.

NAVIGATION
WPT 54°13'·96N 04°41'·36W, 020°/200° from/to groyne lt, 0·42M. When approaching, a rky coastline indicates that you are S of Peel; a sandy coastline means you are to the N. When close in, beware groyne on S side of hbr ent, submerged at half tide.

LIGHTS AND MARKS
Power stn chy (80m, grey with B top; R lts) at S end of inner hbr is conspic from W and N; chy brg 203° leads to hbr ent. Groyne lt and Clock Tr (conspic) in transit 200° are almost on same line. Peel Castle and 2 twrs are conspic on St Patrick's Isle to NW of hbr. No ldg lts. N bkwtr Oc 7s 11m 6M. Groyne Iso R 2s 4m. S pier hd Oc R 7s 8m 5M; vis 156°-249°. Castle jetty Oc G 7s 5m 4M.

RADIO TELEPHONE
VHF Ch 12 16 (when vessel expected; at other times call *Douglas Hbr Control* Ch 12).

TELEPHONE (Dial code 01624)
Hr Mr ☎/⊠ 842338; MRSC 0151-931 3341; ⌗ 674321; Weather 0696 888322; Marinecall 0891 500 461; Police 842208; Dr 843636.

FACILITIES
Outer & Inner Hbrs, AB £6.51 (see 10.10.15), M, Slip, FW, ME, El, Sh, C (30 ton mobile); **Peel Sailing and Cruising Club** ☎ 842390, P & D (cans), R, ◨, Bar; **Services:** Gas, BY, CH, ACA. **Town** EC Thurs; V, R, Bar, ✉, Ⓑ, ⇌ (bus to Douglas, ferry to Heysham & Liverpool), ✈ Ronaldsway.

PORT ST MARY   10-10-17
Isle of Man 54°04'·42N 04°43'·64W   Rtg 3-3-2

CHARTS
AC 2696, 2094; Imray C62; Y70; OS 95

TIDES
+0020 Dover; ML 3·2; Duration 0605; Zone 0 (UT)

Standard Port LIVERPOOL (←—)

Times				Height (metres)			
High Water		Low Water		MHWS	MHWN	MLWN	MLWS
0000	0600	0200	0700	9·3	7·4	2·9	0·9
1200	1800	1400	1900				
Differences PORT ST MARY							
+0005	+0015	–0010	–0030	–3·4	–2·7	–1·2	–0·3
CALF SOUND							
+0005	+0005	–0015	–0025	–3·2	–2·6	–0·9	–0·3

SHELTER
Very good except in E or SE winds. Inner hbr dries 2·4m on sand. ‡ S of Gansey Pt, but poor holding. 8 R ⚓s in same area.

NAVIGATION
WPT 54°04'·20N 04°43'·30W, 115°/295° from/to Alfred Pier lt, 0·30M. Rky outcrops to SE of pier to 2ca offshore. Beware lobster/crab pots, especially between Calf Island and Langness Pt.

LIGHTS AND MARKS
Alfred Pier, Oc R 10s 8m 6M. Inner pier, Oc R 3s 8m 5M; both lts on W trs + R band, in transit 295° lead clear S of The Carrick Rk, in centre of bay, which is marked by IDM bn, Q (2) 5s 6m 3M. A conspic TV mast (133m), 5ca WNW of hbr, in transit with Alfred Pier lt leads 290° towards the hbr and also clears The Carrick rock.

RADIO TELEPHONE
Call *Port St Mary Hbr* VHF Ch 12 16 (when vessel due or through Douglas Hbr Control Ch 12).

TELEPHONE (Dial code 01624)
Hr Mr 833206; MRSC 0151-931 3341; ⌗ 674321; Marinecall 0891 500 461; Police 822222; Dr 832281.

FACILITIES
Alfred Pier AB £6.51 (see 10.10.15), Slip, D (road tanker), L, FW, C (20 ton mobile);
Inner Hbr AB, Slip, D, L, FW; **Isle of Man YC** ☎ 832088, FW, Bar; **Services:** ME, CH, D, El, SM.
Town EC Thurs; CH, V, R, Bar, ✉, Ⓑ, ⇌ (bus to Douglas, ferry to Heysham), ✈ Ronaldsway.

DOUGLAS   10-10-18
Isle of Man 54°08'·86N 04°27'·89W   Rtg 2-4-1

CHARTS
AC 2696, 2094; Imray C62; Y70; OS 95

TIDES
+0009 Dover; ML 3·8; Duration 0600; Zone 0 (UT)

Standard Port LIVERPOOL (←—)

Times				Height (metres)			
High Water		Low Water		MHWS	MHWN	MLWN	MLWS
0000	0600	0200	0700	9·3	7·4	2·9	0·9
1200	0800	1400	1900				
Differences DOUGLAS							
–0004	–0004	–0022	–0032	–2·4	–2·0	–0·5	–0·1

SHELTER
Good except in NE winds. Very heavy seas run in during NE gales. Close NW of front ldg lt the Dept of Transport provides a B can ⚓, to which yachts should moor stern-to, bower ‡ laid out radially. About 6 yachts can raft up on small pontoon at inner end of Battery Pier; untenable in NE/E winds. Complete shelter, but very full in summer, at drying inner hbr W of swing bridge which opens 2300-0700 for shipping, and on request HW±3. Victoria and King Edward VIII piers are for commercial vessels/ferries.

NAVIGATION
WPT 54°09'·00N 04°27'·60W (abeam No 1 SHM buoy, Q (3) G 5s), 049°/229° from/to front ldg lt, 0·47M. Appr from NE of No 1 buoy (to avoid overfalls E of Princess Alexandra Pier) and await port entry sig, or call on VHF Ch 12. There is no bar. Keep clear of large vessels and ferries. Beware swing bridge and also concrete step at end of dredged area (◊ mark on King Edward Pier).

LIGHTS AND MARKS
Douglas Head Fl 10s 32m 24M. Ldg lts 229°, both Oc 10s 9/12m 5M, synch; front W △; rear W ▽, both on R border. IPTS Nos 2, 3 & 5 shown from mast on Victoria Pier. Dolphin at N end of Alexandra Pier 2FR (vert).

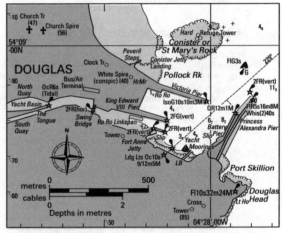

RADIO TELEPHONE
Douglas Hbr Control VHF Ch 12 16 (H24); also broadcasts nav warnings for IoM coastal waters on Ch 12 at 0133, 0533, 0733, 0933, 1333, 1733 and 2133; met & tidal info on request.

TELEPHONE (Dial code 01624)
Hr Mr 686628 (H24); MRSC 0151-931 3341; ⌗ 674321; Marinecall 0891 500 461; Police 631212; Ⓗ 642642.

FACILITIES
Outer Hbr AB £6.51 (see 10.10.15), M, FW at pontoon, P & D (cans) across the road from pontoon, ME, El, Sh, C (10, 5 ton), Slip;
Inner Hbr (N and S Quays) AB, M, AC, FW, ME, C, El, Sh, CH, Slip;
Douglas Bay YC (S side of inner hbr) ☎ 673965, Bar, Slip, L.
Services: P & D (cans), CH, ACA, El, Divers, Gas, Gaz, Kos.
Town EC Thurs; V, R, Bar, ✉, Ⓑ, ◎, Ferry to Heysham; also in summer to Belfast and Liverpool; ✈ Ronaldsway

RAMSEY   10-10-19

Isle of Man 54°19'·43N 04°22'·42W   Rtg 3-3-2

CHARTS
AC 2696, 2094; Imray C62; Y70; OS 95

TIDES
+0020 Dover; ML 4·2; Duration 0545; Zone 0 (UT)

Standard Port LIVERPOOL (⟵)

Times				Height (metres)			
High Water		Low Water		MHWS	MHWN	MLWN	MLWS
0000	0600	0200	0700	9·3	7·4	2·9	0·9
1200	1800	1400	1900				
Differences RAMSEY							
+0005	+0015	−0005	−0015	−1·7	−1·5	−0·6	+0·1

SHELTER
Very good except in strong NE/SE winds. Hbr dries 1·8m-6m. Access and ent only permitted HW −2½ to HW +2. Berth on Town quay (S side) or as directed by Hr Mr on entry. There are Y ⚓s SE of Queens Pier hd (summer only). Note: Landing on Queens Pier is prohibited.

NAVIGATION
WPT 54°19'·43N 04°21'·80W, 090°/270° from/to ent, 0·37M. The foreshore dries out 1ca to seaward of the pier hds.

LIGHTS AND MARKS
No ldg lts/marks. Relative to hbr ent, Pt of Ayre, Fl (4) 20s 32m 19M, is 5·5M N; Maughold Hd, Fl (3) 30s 65m 21M, is 3M SE; Albert Tr (□ stone tr 14m, on hill 130m) is conspic 7ca S; and Snaefell (617m) bears 220°/5M. The Iso G 4s, G SHM post, inside the hbr marks the S tip of Mooragh Bank; it is not visible from seaward. 2FR (hor) on each side mark the centre of swing bridge.

RADIO TELEPHONE
Ramsey Hbr VHF Ch **12** 16 (0830-1700LT and when a vessel is due); OT call *Douglas Hbr Control* Ch **12**.

TELEPHONE (Dial code 01624)
Hr Mr (non-resident) 812245; MRSC 0151-931 3341; ⌗ 674321; Marinecall 0891 500 461; Police 812234; Dr 813881; ⊞ 813254.

FACILITIES
Outer Hbr: E Quay ☎ 812245, AB (but mainly FVs), FW;
Town Quay (S side) AB £6.51 (see 10.10.15), AC, FW, C*;
Inner Hbr, W Quay AB, AC, FW, Slip (Grid); **N Quay** AB, FW;
Shipyard Quay Slip; **Old Hbr** AB, Slip, M;
Manx Sailing & Cruising Club ☎ 813494, Bar.
Services: P & D (cans) from garages; none located at hbr. Gas, ME, El, Ⓔ, Sh.
Town EC Wed; V, R, Gas, Gaz, Kos, Bar, ▢, ✉, Ⓑ, ⇌ (bus to Douglas, ferry to Heysham), ✈ Ronaldsway.
*Mobile cranes for hire from Douglas.

CONWY   10-10-20

Conwy 53°17'·25N 03°50'·00W (marina)   Rtg 3-2-1

CHARTS
AC *1978, 1977, 1826*; Imray C61; OS 115

TIDES
−0015 Dover; ML 4·3; Duration 0545; Zone 0 (UT)

Standard Port HOLYHEAD (⟶)

Times				Height (metres)			
High Water		Low Water		MHWS	MHWN	MLWN	MLWS
0000	0600	0500	1100	5·6	4·4	2·0	0·7
1200	1800	1700	2300				
Differences CONWY							
+0020	+0020	No data	+0050	+2·1	+1·6	+0·3	No data

NOTE: HW Conwy is approx HW Liverpool −0040 sp and −0020 nps.

SHELTER
Good, except in strong NW'lies. Marina is to stbd past the Narrows or berth on pontoon between marina and castle or ask Hr Mr for ⚓. 10kn speed limit above Perch lt.

NAVIGATION
WPT Fairway SWM By, 53°17'·95N 03°55'·54W, 291°/111° from/to No 2 PHM lt By, 0·90M. Access HW±2; if Conwy Sands (to N) are covered, there is enough water in chan for 2m draft boat. Chan is marked by 4 PHM buoys (No 2: Fl (2) R 10s; No 6: Fl (6) R 30s; No 8: Fl (8) R 30s) and 3 unlit SHM buoys, all with radar reflectors. After No 6 lt buoy, stand on for approx 20m to clear The Scabs (gravel patch, 0·1m depth); then alter 030° for No 8 buoy. Leave Perch lt approx 30m to stbd. Beware unlit moorings. Sp ebb reaches 5kn. The "Inshore Passage" (close SW of Gt Orme's Hd) is only advised with local knowledge.

LIGHTS AND MARKS
Ent chan is mainly within W sector of Perch lt, Fl WR 5s 5m 2M, vis W076°-088°, R088°-171°, W171°-319°, R319°-076°. Unlit PHM buoy at the Narrows, then marina bkwtr marked by Fl G lt; ent between SHM pile and PHM buoy.

RADIO TELEPHONE
Hr Mr Ch **14** 06 08 12 71 80 16 (Summer 09-1700LT every day; winter, same times Mon-Fri). Conwy Marina Ch 80 (H24). N Wales CA Ch **80** M. Conwy YC Ch M (water taxi).

TELEPHONE (Dial code 01492)
Hr Mr 596253; MRSC (01407) 762051; ⌗ (01407) 762714; Marinecall 0891 500 460; Police 2222; Dr 592424.

FACILITIES
Marina (420) ☎ 593000, ⬎ 572111, £13.98, AC, FW, D & P (0700-2359), BH (30 ton), CH, Gas, ▢, R, Bar;
Harbour ☎ 596253, Pontoon AB £7.00, Quay AB dries (12·3m max LOA; short stay for loading), M, D, FW;
Deganwy Dock (dries), AB, Slip, FW, C (mobile);
Conwy YC ☎ 583690, Slip, M, L, FW, R, Bar, water taxi;
N Wales Cruising Ass'n ☎ 593481, AB, M, FW, Bar.
Services: ME, Gas, Gaz, Sh, El, Ⓔ. **Town** EC Wed; P & D (cans), V, R, Bar, ✉, Ⓑ, ⇌, ✈ (Liverpool).

10

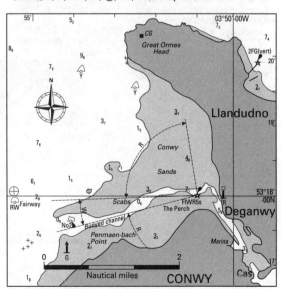

MENAI STRAIT 10-10-21

Gwynedd/Isle of Anglesey

CHARTS
AC 1464, Imray C61; OS 114, 115. NOTE: The definitive Pilot book is *Cruising Anglesey and the North Wales Coast* by R Morris, 5th edition 1995: North West Venturers YC

TIDES
Beaumaris –0025 Dover; ML Beaumaris 4·2; Duration 0540
Standard Port HOLYHEAD (→)

Times				Height (metres)			
High Water		Low Water		MHWS	MHWN	MLWN	MLWS
0000	0600	0500	1100	5·6	4·4	2·0	0·7
1200	1800	1700	2300				
Differences BEAUMARIS							
+0025	+0010	+0055	+0035	+2·0	+1·6	+0·5	+0·1
MENAI BRIDGE							
+0030	+0010	+0100	+0035	+1·7	+1·4	+0·3	0·0
PORT DINORWIC							
–0015	–0025	+0030	0000	0·0	0·0	0·0	+0·1
CAERNARFON							
–0030	–0030	+0015	–0005	–0·4	–0·4	–0·1	–0·1
FORT BELAN							
–0040	–0015	–0025	–0005	–1·0	–0·9	–0·2	–0·1
LLANDDWYN ISLAND							
–0115	–0055	–0030	–0020	–0·7	–0·5	–0·1	–0·1

Sketch showing the relationship of Caernarfon, Port Dinorwic, The Swellies, Bangor, and Beaumaris in the Menai Strait.

SOUTH WEST ENTRANCE
NAVIGATION
WPT 53°07'·60N 04°26'·00W, 270°/090° from/to Abermenai Pt, 3·8M. A dangerous sea can build in even a moderate breeze against tide, especially if a swell is running in the Irish Sea. Caernarfon Bar shifts often and unpredictably. See 10.10.5.

LIGHTS AND MARKS
Llanddwyn Is lt, Fl WR 2·5s 12m 7/4M, R280°-015°, W015°-120°. Abermenai Pt lt, Fl WR 3·5s; R065°-245°, W245°-065°.
Direction of buoyage changes at Caernarfon.

PORT DINORWIC 53°11'·22N 04°13'·62W

TELEPHONE (Dial code 01248)
Hr Mr 670441; MRSC (01407) 762051; Dr 670423.
FACILITIES
Port Dinorwic Marina (230 berths in fresh water). Call *Dinorwic Marina* VHF Ch **80** M (HO). **Tidal basin** dries at sp; lock opens HW±2. ☎ 671500, D, P (cans), AC, CH, SM; Pier hd F WR 5m 2M, vis R225°-357°, W357°-225°.
Services: SM, ME, El, Sh, Slip, C, CH. **Town** Ⓔ, ✉ (Bangor or Caernarfon), Ⓑ, ⇌ (Bangor), ✈ (Liverpool).
Note: Between Port Dinorwic and Caernarfon is **Plas Menai** ☎ 670964, the Sport Council for Wales Sailing and Sports Centre. *Menai Base* Ch **80** M. Day moorings only.

CAERNARFON 53°08'·50N 04°16'·75W   Rtg 3-1-1

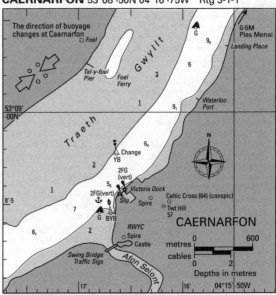

▲ Apply to HrMr

SHELTER
Good in Victoria Dock, access HW±2 via gates; pontoons at SW end in 2m. Or in river hbr (S of conspic castle), dries to mud/gravel, access HW±3 via swing bridge; for opening sound B (—···). ↓ off Foel Ferry, with local knowledge; or temp ↓ in fair holding off Abermenai Pt, sheltered from W'lies, but strong streams.
RADIO TELEPHONE
VHF Ch 14 16 (HJ).
TELEPHONE (Dial code 01286)
Hr Mr 672118; MRSC (01407) 762051; ⌗ (01407) 762714; Police 673333; Dr 672236; Ⓗ 384384.
FACILITIES
Dock £10.62 **River Hbr** £9.35, FW, Slip, C (2 ton), V, D at BY, ME, El, Ⓔ, Sh, CH; **Caernarfon SC** ☎ 672861, L, Bar; **Royal Welsh YC** ☎ 672599, Bar; **Town** P (cans), ✉, Ⓑ.

NORTH EAST ENTRANCE

NAVIGATION
WPT 53°19'·47N 04°03'·20W, 317°/137° from/to Perch Rk PHM bn, 1·0M. In N'ly gales seas break on Ten Foot Bank. In N Strait keep to buoyed chan, nearer Anglesey. Night pilotage not advised due to many unlit buoys/moorings.

LIGHTS AND MARKS
At NE end of Strait, Trwyn-Du lt, W tr/B bands, Fl 5s 19m 12M, vis 101°-023° (282°), Bell 30s. Conspic tr on Puffin Is. Chan is laterally buoyed, some lit. Beaumaris pier has FWG sectored lt (see 10.10.4). **Direction of buoyage changes at Caernarfon.**

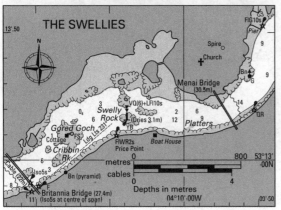

MENAI BRIDGE/BEAUMARIS 53°15'·65N 04°05'·30W

SHELTER
Reasonable off Beaumaris except from NE winds. ⚓ S of B10 PHM buoy or call YCs for mooring. At Menai Bridge, call Hr Mr VHF Ch 69 16 for mooring or temp'y berth on St George's Pier (S of which a marina is planned).

TELEPHONE (Dial code 01248)
Hr Mr Menai 712312; MRSC (01407) 762051; Marinecall 0891 500 460; ☏ (01407) 762714; Police (01407) 762323; Dr 810501.

FACILITIES
St George's Pier (Fl G 10s) L at all tides; **Royal Anglesey YC** ☎ 810295, Slip, M, L, R, Bar, P; **North Venturers YC** ☎ 810023, M, L, FW, water taxi at w/ends only; **Menai Bridge SC. Services:** Slip, P & D (cans), FW, ME, BH (20 ton), Sh, C (2 ton), CH, El, Ⓔ, Gas.
Both towns EC Wed; ⊠, Ⓑ, ⇌ (bus to Bangor), ✈ (Liverpool).

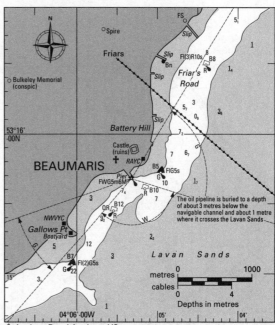

⚠ Apply to Royal Anglesey YC

BANGOR 53°14'·45N 04°07'·50W

SHELTER
Good, except in E'lies, at Dickies BY or Port Penrhyn dock (both dry; access HW±2).

RADIO TELEPHONE
Dickies VHF Ch 09 M 16, all year.

TELEPHONE (Dial code 01248)
Penrhyn Hr Mr 352525; MRSC (01407) 762051; ☏ (01407) 762714; Dr 362055.

FACILITIES
Services: Slip, D, P (cans), FW, ME, El, Sh, C, CH, Ⓔ, SM, BH (30 ton), Gas, Gaz, ACA; **Port Penrhyn**, Slip, AB, D. **Town** ⊠, Ⓑ, ⇌, ✈ (Chester).

THE SWELLIES 53°13'·13N 04°10'·38W

NAVIGATION
For pilotage notes, see 10.10.5. The passage should only be attempted at slack HW, which is −0200 HW Liverpool. The shallow rky narrows between the bridges are dangerous for yachts at other times, when the stream can reach 8kn. At slack HW there is 3m over The Platters and the outcrop off Price Pt, which can be ignored. For shoal-draft boats passage is also possible at slack LW nps, but there are depths of 0·5m close E of Britannia Bridge. The bridges and power cables have a least clearance of 22m at MHWS. Night passage is not recommended.

LIGHTS AND MARKS
SE side of chan QR 4m, R mast, vis 064°-222°. Price Pt, Fl WR 2s 5m 3M, W Bn, vis R059°-239°, W239°-259°. Britannia Bridge, E side, ldg lts 231°, both FW. Bridge lts, both sides: Centre span Iso 5s 27m 3M; S end, FR 21m 3M; N end, FG 21m 3M.

HOLYHEAD   10-10-22
Isle of Anglesey 53°19'·70N 04°37'·00W   Rtg 1-2-2

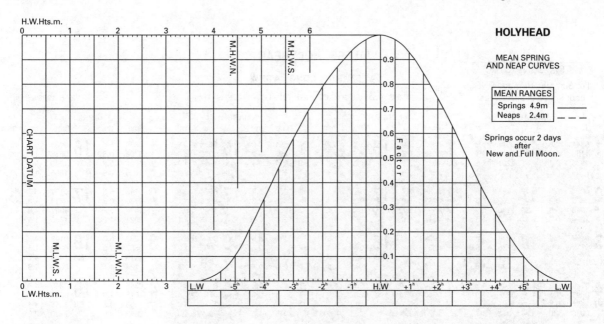

H.W.Hts.m.

HOLYHEAD

MEAN SPRING
AND NEAP CURVES

MEAN RANGES
| Springs | 4.9m |
| Neaps | 2.4m |

Springs occur 2 days
after
New and Full Moon.

L.W.Hts.m.

CHARTS
AC 2011, 1413, *1977*, 1970, *1826*; Imray C61; OS 114

TIDES
−0035 Dover; ML 3·2; Duration 0615; Zone 0 (UT)

Standard Port HOLYHEAD (→)

Times				Height (metres)			
High Water		Low Water		MHWS	MHWN	MLWN	MLWS
0000	0600	0500	1100	5·6	4·4	2·0	0·7
1200	1800	1700	2300				

Differences TRWYN DINMOR (W of Puffin Is)
| +0025 | +0015 | +0050 | +0035 | +1·9 | +1·5 | +0·5 | +0·2 |

MOELFRE (NE Anglesey)
| +0025 | +0020 | +0050 | +0035 | +1·9 | +1·4 | +0·5 | +0·2 |

AMLWCH (N Anglesey)
| +0020 | +0010 | +0035 | +0025 | +1·6 | +1·3 | +0·5 | +0·2 |

CEMAES BAY (N Anglesey)
| +0020 | +0025 | +0040 | +0035 | +1·0 | +0·7 | +0·3 | +0·1 |

TREARDDUR BAY (W Anglesey)
| −0045 | −0025 | −0015 | −0015 | −0·4 | −0·4 | 0·0 | +0·1 |

PORTH TRECASTELL (SW Anglesey)
| −0045 | −0025 | −0005 | −0015 | −0·6 | −0·6 | 0·0 | 0·0 |

TREFOR (Lleyn peninsula)
| −0115 | −0100 | −0030 | −0020 | −0·8 | −0·9 | −0·2 | −0·1 |

PORTH DINLLAEN (Lleyn peninsula)
| −0120 | −0105 | −0035 | −0025 | −1·0 | −1·0 | −0·2 | −0·2 |

PORTH YSGADEN (Lleyn peninsula)
| −0125 | −0110 | −0040 | −0035 | −1·1 | −1·0 | −0·1 | −0·1 |

BARDSEY ISLAND
| −0220 | −0240 | −0145 | −0140 | −1·2 | −1·2 | −0·5 | −0·1 |

Holyhead is a Standard Port and tidal predictions for each day of the year are given below.

SHELTER
Very good. ⚓ or moor off HSC (Ch M); or temp AB on bkwtr; or in Fish Dock (also D). Strong NE winds raise a slight sea.

NAVIGATION
WPT 53°20'·10N 04°37'·20W, 345°/165° from/to bkwtr lt ho, 0·28M. Beware very fast catamaran ferries in approaches. Yachts entering New Hbr should use the Small Craft Chan, parallel to and within 70m of the bkwtr; but beware shoal, drying 0·5m, which extends 35m SE of bkwtr head. Keep clear of the Aluminium Jetty (Ore terminal), Outer Platters (buoyed) and 8 large unlit mooring buoys at W end of New Hbr. No anchoring in fairways.
Ferries comply with a mini-TSS at the hbr ent by entering within 2½ca of bkwtr hd for the Ro-Ro terminal in New Hbr or the Inner Hbr; outbound ferries pass within 2½ca WSW of Clipera PHM buoy, Fl (4) R 15s. Yachts to keep clear.

LIGHTS AND MARKS
Ldg marks 165°, bkwtr lt ho on with chy (127m) R lts.
Tfc sigs from old lt ho at E end of Admty pier: Ⓡ = Ent to Inner hbr is impracticable. Ⓦ = Ent to Inner hbr is clear.

RADIO TELEPHONE
Call *Holyhead* VHF Ch 14 16 (H24) before entering and to monitor ferry traffic. Marina and Holyhead SC: Ch M.

TELEPHONE (Dial code 01407)
Port Control 606700; MRSC 762051; ☷ 762714; Marinecall 0891 500 460; Police 762323; Dr via MRSC.

FACILITIES
Holyhead SC (HSC) ☎ 762526, M, L, FW, Slip, launch, R (season only), Bar;
Fish Dock ☎ 760139 AB on pontoons, FW, D by hose.
Inner Hbr ☎ 762304, used by Stena HSS; not advised for yachts.
Services: BY, ACA, CH, ME, El, Sh, C (100 ton), BH, Slip, Ⓔ.
Town EC Tues; P, V, R, Bar, ▣, ✉, Ⓑ, ⇌, ✈ (Liverpool). Ferry/Fast Cat to Dun Laoghaire and Dublin.
Trearddur Bay (3M south) M (small craft only), L; **BY** ☎ 860501, D, FW, Sh, CH. **Village** P, V, R, Bar.

MINOR HARBOUR ON THE LLEYN PENINSULA

PORTH DINLLAEN, Gwynedd, 52°56'·66N 04°33'·59W. AC 1512, 1971. HW −0240 on Dover; ML 2·5m; Duration 0535. See 10.10.22. Shelter good in S to W winds but strong NNW to NNE winds cause heavy seas in the bay. Beware Carreg-y-Chad (1·8m) 0·75M SW of the point, and Carreg-y-Chwislen (dries, with unlit IDM Bn) 2ca ENE of the point. From N, Carn Fadryn (369m) brg 182° leads into the bay. Best ⚓ 1ca S of LB ho in approx 2m, or ⚓ 1½ca E of ruined jetty. Hr Mr ☎ (01758) 720295; CG ☎ 720204. Facilities: EC Wed; Bar, V by landing stage. At Morfa Nefyn (1M), Bar, P, R, V.

At last about tea-time, when land began to loom vaguely to port, to starboard, and also ahead, we realized that we were near the head of Cardigan Bay, two points off course and some forty miles from Holyhead. Currents, the compass, the helmsman, even the navigator, may be responsible for these anomalies. It is not, however, for the navigator to accept responsibility for them or to show surprise, or he may sap what confidence the crew have in him. Attack is the best form of defence. A few remarks about the impossibility of navigating the ship if it is not steered straight will restore his own confidence and subdue and mystify the crew.

Mostly Mischief: H.W.Tilman

With acknowledgements to the Executors of the estate of H.W.Tilman and to Hollis & Carter (Publishers 1966).

10

WALES – HOLYHEAD

LAT 53°19′N   LONG 4°37′W

TIMES AND HEIGHTS OF HIGH AND LOW WATERS

YEAR **1998**

TIME ZONE (UT)
For Summer Time add ONE hour in non-shaded areas

JANUARY

Day	Time	m	Time	m	Time	m	Time	m
1 TH	0541	0.8	1155	5.8	1808	0.7		
2 F	0021	5.5	0625	0.9	1240	5.8	1854	0.7
3 SA	0109	5.4	0712	1.0	1328	5.7	1943	0.9
4 SU	0200	5.2	0803	1.2	1421	5.5	2038	1.0
5 M	0257	5.0	0901	1.4	1519	5.3	2141	1.2
6 TU	0403	4.8	1009	1.6	1627	5.1	2250	1.4
7 W	0517	4.8	1123	1.7	1740	5.0		
8 TH	0001	1.5	0630	4.8	1235	1.6	1851	5.1
9 F	0109	1.4	0735	5.0	1341	1.5	1955	5.2
10 SA	0208	1.3	0830	5.2	1438	1.2	2051	5.3
11 SU	0300	1.2	0918	5.4	1528	1.0	2139	5.4
12 M O	0344	1.0	1001	5.6	1612	0.9	2222	5.5
13 TU	0425	1.0	1040	5.7	1653	0.8	2302	5.5
14 W	0503	1.0	1119	5.7	1732	0.8	2340	5.4
15 TH	0539	1.0	1155	5.6	1809	0.9		
16 F	0017	5.3	0614	1.1	1231	5.5	1845	1.1
17 SA	0053	5.2	0650	1.3	1306	5.4	1922	1.3
18 SU	0128	5.0	0726	1.5	1341	5.2	2000	1.5
19 M	0207	4.8	0806	1.8	1421	4.9	2043	1.7
20 TU	0252	4.6	0852	2.0	1508	4.7	2134	1.9
21 W	0347	4.4	0949	2.2	1607	4.5	2237	2.1
22 TH	0457	4.4	1100	2.3	1723	4.4	2348	2.1
23 F	0612	4.4	1216	2.2	1840	4.5		
24 SA	0055	2.0	0717	4.6	1322	2.0	1943	4.7
25 SU	0152	1.7	0810	4.9	1413	1.5	2034	4.9
26 M	0240	1.4	0854	5.2	1503	1.3	2118	5.2
27 TU	0323	1.1	0935	5.4	1546	0.9	2159	5.4
28 W ●	0404	0.8	1016	5.7	1627	0.6	2240	5.6
29 TH	0445	1.0	1057	5.9	1709	0.4	2322	5.7
30 F	0527	0.5	1139	6.0	1753	0.3		
31 SA	0006	5.7	0609	0.5	1224	6.0	1837	0.4

FEBRUARY

Day	Time	m	Time	m	Time	m	Time	m
1 SU	0051	5.6	0654	0.6	1311	5.9	1924	0.5
2 M	0139	5.4	0743	0.9	1400	5.7	2015	0.8
3 TU	0231	5.2	0837	1.2	1454	5.4	2112	1.2
4 W	0330	4.9	0940	1.5	1559	5.1	2220	1.5
5 TH	0443	4.7	1056	1.7	1716	4.8	2336	1.7
6 F	0605	4.7	1216	1.7	1838	4.8		
7 SA	0052	1.7	0721	4.8	1331	1.6	1951	4.9
8 SU	0159	1.6	0822	5.0	1432	1.4	2048	5.0
9 M	0252	1.4	0911	5.3	1521	1.1	2134	5.2
10 TU	0335	1.2	0951	5.4	1602	1.0	2212	5.3
11 W O	0412	1.1	1026	5.6	1638	0.9	2246	5.4
12 TH	0446	0.9	1100	5.6	1712	0.8	2319	5.4
13 F	0518	0.9	1133	5.6	1745	0.9	2350	5.3
14 SA	0550	1.0	1204	5.5	1816	0.9		
15 SU	0022	5.3	0621	1.1	1236	5.4	1848	1.1
16 M	0055	5.2	0654	1.2	1309	5.3	1922	1.3
17 TU	0129	5.0	0729	1.4	1343	5.1	1958	1.5
18 W	0207	4.8	0809	1.7	1423	4.8	2041	1.8
19 TH	0252	4.6	0857	1.9	1512	4.6	2135	2.0
20 F	0351	4.4	1001	2.2	1621	4.4	2248	2.2
21 SA	0511	4.3	1124	2.2	1753	4.3		
22 SU	0010	2.1	0634	4.5	1245	2.0	1912	4.5
23 M	0120	1.8	0739	4.8	1348	1.6	2011	4.8
24 TU	0215	1.5	0830	5.1	1440	1.2	2059	5.1
25 W	0302	1.1	0914	5.5	1525	0.8	2141	5.5
26 TH ●	0345	0.8	0955	5.8	1608	0.4	2222	5.7
27 F	0426	0.4	1037	6.0	1650	0.1	2303	5.8
28 SA	0508	0.2	1120	6.2	1733	0.0	2346	5.9

MARCH

Day	Time	m	Time	m	Time	m	Time	m
1 SU	0551	0.2	1205	6.2	1817	0.1		
2 M	0030	5.8	0635	0.3	1251	6.0	1902	0.4
3 TU	0116	5.5	0722	0.6	1339	5.7	1951	0.7
4 W	0205	5.2	0814	0.9	1432	5.3	2045	1.2
5 TH	0301	4.9	0916	1.3	1536	4.9	2151	1.6
6 F	0412	4.6	1033	1.7	1656	4.6	2311	1.9
7 SA	0539	4.5	1159	1.8	1826	4.5		
8 SU	0035	1.9	0703	4.7	1318	1.6	1944	4.7
9 M	0146	1.8	0808	4.9	1419	1.4	2039	4.9
10 TU	0239	1.5	0856	5.1	1506	1.2	2120	5.0
11 W	0320	1.3	0934	5.3	1544	1.0	2154	5.2
12 TH	0354	1.1	1006	5.4	1617	0.9	2224	5.3
13 F O	0425	1.0	1037	5.5	1648	0.8	2254	5.3
14 SA	0455	0.9	1107	5.5	1717	0.8	2323	5.4
15 SU	0524	0.9	1137	5.5	1747	0.9	2353	5.4
16 M	0555	0.9	1208	5.4	1817	1.0		
17 TU	0024	5.3	0626	1.1	1240	5.3	1848	1.1
18 W	0057	5.1	0659	1.2	1313	5.1	1922	1.4
19 TH	0132	5.0	0737	1.4	1350	4.9	2002	1.6
20 F	0213	4.8	0822	1.7	1435	4.6	2052	1.9
21 SA	0306	4.5	0921	1.9	1539	4.4	2200	2.1
22 SU	0421	4.4	1041	2.0	1711	4.3	2328	2.1
23 M	0551	4.4	1208	1.9	1841	4.4		
24 TU	0047	1.9	0704	4.7	1318	1.5	1945	4.8
25 W	0148	1.5	0801	5.1	1413	1.0	2035	5.2
26 TH	0237	1.1	0848	5.5	1501	0.6	2118	5.5
27 F	0322	0.6	0932	5.8	1544	0.2	2200	5.7
28 SA ●	0404	0.3	1015	6.1	1627	0.0	2242	5.9
29 SU	0447	0.1	1059	6.2	1711	0.0	2324	5.9
30 M	0530	0.1	1144	6.2	1755	0.1		
31 TU	0009	5.8	0615	0.2	1232	6.0	1840	0.4

APRIL

Day	Time	m	Time	m	Time	m	Time	m
1 W	0055	5.6	0703	0.5	1321	5.7	1928	0.8
2 TH	0143	5.3	0756	0.9	1414	5.2	2021	1.2
3 F	0237	5.0	0857	1.3	1516	4.8	2124	1.7
4 SA	0345	4.7	1011	1.6	1635	4.5	2243	2.0
5 SU	0509	4.5	1135	1.8	1805	4.4		
6 M	0008	2.1	0633	4.6	1253	1.7	1922	4.5
7 TU	0121	1.9	0741	4.8	1354	1.5	2016	4.7
8 W	0214	1.7	0829	5.0	1440	1.3	2056	4.9
9 TH	0255	1.4	0907	5.1	1518	1.1	2129	5.1
10 F	0329	1.2	0939	5.3	1550	1.0	2158	5.2
11 SA O	0400	1.0	1010	5.4	1619	0.9	2227	5.3
12 SU	0429	0.9	1040	5.4	1649	0.8	2256	5.4
13 M	0459	0.9	1111	5.4	1718	0.9	2326	5.4
14 TU	0529	0.9	1142	5.3	1749	1.0	2358	5.3
15 W	0602	1.0	1214	5.2	1821	1.1		
16 TH	0031	5.2	0636	1.1	1249	5.1	1855	1.3
17 F	0107	5.1	0714	1.3	1327	4.9	1935	1.5
18 SA	0148	4.9	0800	1.5	1414	4.7	2025	1.8
19 SU	0240	4.7	0857	1.7	1516	4.4	2130	2.0
20 M	0349	4.6	1012	1.8	1640	4.4	2253	2.0
21 TU	0513	4.6	1135	1.7	1808	4.5		
22 W	0013	1.8	0628	4.8	1246	1.3	1915	4.8
23 TH	0117	1.4	0729	5.1	1344	0.9	2008	5.2
24 F	0210	1.0	0820	5.5	1434	0.6	2053	5.5
25 SA	0257	0.6	0907	5.8	1520	0.3	2137	5.7
26 SU ●	0341	0.2	0952	6.0	1605	0.1	2220	5.9
27 M	0426	0.2	1039	6.1	1649	0.1	2304	5.9
28 TU	0512	0.1	1126	6.0	1734	0.2	2349	5.8
29 W	0559	0.3	1214	5.8	1820	0.5		
30 TH	0035	5.6	0647	0.5	1304	5.5	1908	0.9

Chart Datum: 3·05 metres below Ordnance Datum (Newlyn)

WALES – HOLYHEAD

LAT 53°19′N   LONG 4°37′W

TIMES AND HEIGHTS OF HIGH AND LOW WATERS   YEAR **1998**

TIME ZONE (UT)
For Summer Time add ONE hour in non-shaded areas

Chart Datum: 3·05 metres below Ordnance Datum (Newlyn)

MAY

Day	Time	m		Day	Time	m
1 F	0124 / 0740 / 1357 / 1959	5.4 / 0.8 / 5.1 / 1.3		**16** SA	0049 / 0659 / 1313 / 1918	5.2 / 1.1 / 4.9 / 1.4
2 SA	0216 / 0838 / 1456 / 2057	5.1 / 1.2 / 4.8 / 1.7		**17** SU	0133 / 0746 / 1402 / 2009	5.1 / 1.3 / 4.8 / 1.6
3 SU	0317 / 0945 / 1607 / 2208	4.8 / 1.5 / 4.5 / 2.0		**18** M	0225 / 0842 / 1502 / 2110	4.9 / 1.4 / 4.6 / 1.8
4 M	0430 / 1100 / 1727 / 2327	4.6 / 1.7 / 4.3 / 2.2		**19** TU	0328 / 0950 / 1616 / 2223	4.8 / 1.5 / 4.5 / 1.8
5 TU	0548 / 1213 / 1842	4.5 / 1.7 / 4.4		**20** W	0441 / 1105 / 1735 / 2339	4.8 / 1.4 / 4.6 / 1.7
6 W	0039 / 0657 / 1315 / 1938	2.1 / 4.6 / 1.6 / 4.6		**21** TH	0554 / 1214 / 1843	4.9 / 1.2 / 4.8
7 TH	0137 / 0750 / 1404 / 2021	1.9 / 4.8 / 1.4 / 4.8		**22** F	0045 / 0657 / 1315 / 1940	1.4 / 5.2 / 0.9 / 5.1
8 F	0222 / 0832 / 1444 / 2056	1.6 / 4.9 / 1.3 / 5.0		**23** SA	0142 / 0753 / 1409 / 2029	1.1 / 5.4 / 0.7 / 5.4
9 SA	0258 / 0907 / 1518 / 2128	1.4 / 5.1 / 1.1 / 5.2		**24** SU	0234 / 0844 / 1458 / 2116	0.8 / 5.6 / 0.5 / 5.6
10 SU	0331 / 0940 / 1549 / 2159	1.2 / 5.2 / 1.0 / 5.3		**25** M	0322 / 0933 / 1545 / 2201 ●	0.5 / 5.8 / 0.3 / 5.7
11 M O	0402 / 1013 / 1620 / 2229	1.1 / 5.3 / 1.0 / 5.4		**26** TU	0409 / 1022 / 1631 / 2246	0.4 / 5.9 / 0.4 / 5.8
12 TU	0434 / 1045 / 1652 / 2301	1.0 / 5.3 / 0.9 / 5.4		**27** W	0457 / 1110 / 1717 / 2332	0.3 / 5.8 / 0.5 / 5.8
13 W	0507 / 1119 / 1724 / 2335	1.0 / 5.3 / 1.0 / 5.4		**28** TH	0545 / 1159 / 1802	0.4 / 5.6 / 0.7
14 TH	0541 / 1154 / 1759	1.0 / 5.2 / 1.1		**29** F	0019 / 0633 / 1248 / 1848	5.6 / 0.6 / 5.4 / 1.0
15 F	0010 / 0618 / 1231 / 1836	5.3 / 1.0 / 5.1 / 1.2		**30** SA	0106 / 0722 / 1338 / 1936	5.4 / 0.9 / 5.1 / 1.3
				31 SU	0154 / 0815 / 1430 / 2027	5.2 / 1.2 / 4.8 / 1.6

JUNE

Day	Time	m		Day	Time	m
1 M	0246 / 0912 / 1528 / 2125	4.9 / 1.5 / 4.5 / 1.9		**16** TU	0211 / 0827 / 1446 / 2051	5.2 / 1.1 / 4.8 / 1.5
2 TU	0345 / 1015 / 1634 / 2233	4.7 / 1.7 / 4.4 / 2.1		**17** W	0308 / 0928 / 1550 / 2156	5.1 / 1.2 / 4.7 / 1.6
3 W	0451 / 1121 / 1743 / 2342	4.5 / 1.8 / 4.4 / 2.2		**18** TH	0413 / 1036 / 1702 / 2307	5.0 / 1.2 / 4.7 / 1.6
4 TH	0559 / 1223 / 1846	4.5 / 1.8 / 4.5		**19** F	0523 / 1144 / 1812	5.0 / 1.2 / 4.8
5 F	0046 / 0659 / 1318 / 1937	2.1 / 4.6 / 1.7 / 4.6		**20** SA	0016 / 0630 / 1249 / 1914	1.5 / 5.1 / 1.1 / 5.0
6 SA	0139 / 0750 / 1404 / 2019	1.9 / 4.7 / 1.5 / 4.8		**21** SU	0119 / 0731 / 1348 / 2010	1.2 / 5.3 / 0.9 / 5.2
7 SU	0222 / 0833 / 1443 / 2056	1.6 / 4.9 / 1.3 / 5.0		**22** M	0216 / 0828 / 1441 / 2100	1.0 / 5.4 / 0.8 / 5.4
8 M	0300 / 0911 / 1519 / 2131	1.4 / 5.0 / 1.2 / 5.2		**23** TU	0309 / 0920 / 1530 / 2147	0.8 / 5.5 / 0.7 / 5.6
9 TU	0336 / 0947 / 1554 / 2205	1.2 / 5.1 / 1.1 / 5.3		**24** W	0358 / 1010 / 1617 / 2233 ●	0.6 / 5.6 / 0.7 / 5.7
10 W O	0411 / 1023 / 1628 / 2239	1.1 / 5.2 / 1.0 / 5.4		**25** TH	0446 / 1058 / 1701 / 2318	0.5 / 5.6 / 0.7 / 5.7
11 TH	0447 / 1059 / 1704 / 2315	1.0 / 5.2 / 1.0 / 5.4		**26** F	0532 / 1144 / 1745	0.6 / 5.5 / 0.8
12 F	0525 / 1137 / 1741 / 2354	0.9 / 5.2 / 1.0 / 5.4		**27** SA	0002 / 0616 / 1229 / 1827	5.6 / 0.7 / 5.3 / 1.0
13 SA	0605 / 1217 / 1821	0.9 / 5.2 / 1.1		**28** SU	0045 / 0701 / 1313 / 1910	5.5 / 0.9 / 5.1 / 1.2
14 SU	0035 / 0647 / 1302 / 1905	5.4 / 1.0 / 5.1 / 1.2		**29** M	0128 / 0746 / 1357 / 1953	5.3 / 1.1 / 4.9 / 1.5
15 M	0121 / 0734 / 1350 / 1954	5.3 / 1.0 / 5.0 / 1.3		**30** TU	0211 / 0832 / 1443 / 2040	5.1 / 1.4 / 4.7 / 1.8

JULY

Day	Time	m		Day	Time	m
1 W	0257 / 0923 / 1534 / 2133	4.8 / 1.6 / 4.5 / 2.0		**16** TH	0246 / 0904 / 1524 / 2130	5.3 / 1.0 / 4.9 / 1.4
2 TH	0350 / 1020 / 1635 / 2236	4.6 / 1.8 / 4.4 / 2.2		**17** F	0347 / 1008 / 1632 / 2239	5.1 / 1.2 / 4.8 / 1.5
3 F	0453 / 1122 / 1742 / 2344	4.5 / 1.9 / 4.4 / 2.2		**18** SA	0456 / 1118 / 1745 / 2353	5.0 / 1.3 / 4.8 / 1.6
4 SA	0601 / 1224 / 1845	4.5 / 1.9 / 4.5		**19** SU	0610 / 1228 / 1856	5.0 / 1.3 / 4.9
5 SU	0048 / 0704 / 1320 / 1939	2.1 / 4.5 / 1.8 / 4.7		**20** M	0103 / 0719 / 1333 / 1957	1.4 / 5.0 / 1.3 / 5.1
6 M	0143 / 0758 / 1408 / 2024	1.9 / 4.7 / 1.6 / 4.9		**21** TU	0207 / 0821 / 1431 / 2051	1.2 / 5.2 / 1.1 / 5.3
7 TU	0230 / 0844 / 1451 / 2104	1.6 / 4.9 / 1.4 / 5.1		**22** W	0302 / 0915 / 1521 / 2138	1.0 / 5.3 / 1.0 / 5.5
8 W	0312 / 0925 / 1530 / 2142	1.4 / 5.0 / 1.2 / 5.3		**23** TH	0351 / 1002 / 1605 / 2221 ●	0.8 / 5.4 / 0.9 / 5.6
9 TH O	0351 / 1003 / 1607 / 2219	1.1 / 5.2 / 1.1 / 5.4		**24** F	0435 / 1046 / 1646 / 2302	0.7 / 5.4 / 0.9 / 5.7
10 F	0429 / 1041 / 1645 / 2257	0.9 / 5.3 / 0.9 / 5.6		**25** SA	0516 / 1126 / 1726 / 2341	0.7 / 5.4 / 0.9 / 5.6
11 SA	0509 / 1121 / 1725 / 2337	0.8 / 5.3 / 0.8 / 5.6		**26** SU	0556 / 1205 / 1803	0.7 / 5.3 / 1.0
12 SU	0550 / 1203 / 1806	0.7 / 5.3 / 0.8		**27** M	0019 / 0634 / 1243 / 1840	5.5 / 0.9 / 5.2 / 1.2
13 M	0020 / 0632 / 1247 / 1850	5.6 / 0.7 / 5.3 / 0.9		**28** TU	0056 / 0711 / 1320 / 1917	5.4 / 1.1 / 5.0 / 1.4
14 TU	0105 / 0718 / 1334 / 1937	5.6 / 0.7 / 5.2 / 1.0		**29** W	0133 / 0750 / 1358 / 1956	5.2 / 1.3 / 4.8 / 1.6
15 W	0153 / 0808 / 1425 / 2029	5.5 / 0.9 / 5.0 / 1.2		**30** TH	0211 / 0831 / 1440 / 2040	5.0 / 1.6 / 4.7 / 1.9
				31 F	0255 / 0918 / 1531 / 2133	4.7 / 1.8 / 4.5 / 2.1

AUGUST

Day	Time	m		Day	Time	m
1 SA	0349 / 1017 / 1634 / 2240	4.5 / 2.0 / 4.4 / 2.3		**16** SU	0436 / 1055 / 1723 / 2337	4.9 / 1.6 / 4.7 / 1.7
2 SU	0459 / 1125 / 1748 / 2355	4.4 / 2.1 / 4.4 / 2.2		**17** M	0558 / 1213 / 1842	4.8 / 1.7 / 4.8
3 M	0618 / 1234 / 1857	4.4 / 2.0 / 4.5		**18** TU	0055 / 0716 / 1325 / 1950	1.6 / 4.8 / 1.6 / 5.0
4 TU	0104 / 0726 / 1334 / 1952	2.0 / 4.5 / 1.8 / 4.8		**19** W	0203 / 0821 / 1425 / 2044	1.4 / 5.0 / 1.4 / 5.2
5 W	0201 / 0820 / 1424 / 2038	1.7 / 4.7 / 1.6 / 5.1		**20** TH	0257 / 0911 / 1512 / 2128	1.1 / 5.2 / 1.2 / 5.4
6 TH	0248 / 0904 / 1507 / 2119	1.4 / 5.0 / 1.3 / 5.3		**21** F	0342 / 0953 / 1553 / 2207	0.9 / 5.3 / 1.1 / 5.6
7 F	0330 / 0944 / 1547 / 2158	1.1 / 5.2 / 1.1 / 5.6		**22** SA	0421 / 1030 / 1629 / 2243 ●	0.8 / 5.4 / 1.0 / 5.7
8 SA O	0410 / 1023 / 1626 / 2237	0.8 / 5.4 / 0.8 / 5.8		**23** SU	0456 / 1104 / 1703 / 2317	0.8 / 5.4 / 0.9 / 5.6
9 SU	0450 / 1102 / 1706 / 2318	0.8 / 5.5 / 0.6 / 5.9		**24** M	0530 / 1137 / 1736 / 2351	0.8 / 5.4 / 1.0 / 5.6
10 M	0531 / 1144 / 1747	0.4 / 5.6 / 0.6		**25** TU	0603 / 1210 / 1809	0.9 / 5.3 / 1.1
11 TU	0000 / 0613 / 1227 / 1830	5.9 / 0.4 / 5.6 / 0.6		**26** W	0023 / 0636 / 1243 / 1842	5.4 / 1.1 / 5.2 / 1.3
12 W	0045 / 0658 / 1313 / 1916	5.9 / 0.5 / 5.4 / 0.8		**27** TH	0056 / 0709 / 1317 / 1917	5.3 / 1.3 / 5.0 / 1.5
13 TH	0132 / 0746 / 1402 / 2007	5.7 / 0.7 / 5.2 / 1.0		**28** F	0131 / 0746 / 1355 / 1957	5.1 / 1.5 / 4.8 / 1.7
14 F	0224 / 0839 / 1457 / 2105	5.5 / 1.0 / 5.0 / 1.3		**29** SA	0209 / 0827 / 1439 / 2043	4.8 / 1.8 / 4.6 / 2.0
15 SA	0323 / 0942 / 1604 / 2216	5.2 / 1.3 / 4.8 / 1.6		**30** SU	0257 / 0918 / 1535 / 2144	4.6 / 2.0 / 4.5 / 2.2
				31 M	0403 / 1027 / 1650 / 2305	4.3 / 2.2 / 4.4 / 2.3

10

WALES – HOLYHEAD

LAT 53°19′N   LONG 4°37′W

TIMES AND HEIGHTS OF HIGH AND LOW WATERS

YEAR 1998

TIME ZONE (UT)
For Summer Time add ONE hour in non-shaded areas

SEPTEMBER

Day	Time	m	Day	Time	m
1 TU	0532 / 1148 / 1813	4.3 / 2.2 / 4.5	16 W	0046 / 0713 / 1315 / 1939	1.7 / 4.7 / 1.8 / 5.0
2 W	0026 / 0654 / 1300 / 1919	2.1 / 4.4 / 2.0 / 4.7	17 TH	0153 / 0815 / 1414 / 2032	1.4 / 4.9 / 1.6 / 5.2
3 TH	0131 / 0755 / 1357 / 2011	1.8 / 4.7 / 1.7 / 5.1	18 F	0244 / 0901 / 1458 / 2113	1.2 / 5.1 / 1.4 / 5.4
4 F	0222 / 0841 / 1443 / 2054	1.4 / 5.0 / 1.3 / 5.4	19 SA	0325 / 0937 / 1535 / 2147	1.0 / 5.3 / 1.2 / 5.5
5 SA	0306 / 0922 / 1524 / 2134	1.0 / 5.3 / 0.9 / 5.7	20 SU ●	0400 / 1008 / 1608 / 2219	0.9 / 5.4 / 1.1 / 5.6
6 SU O	0347 / 1001 / 1604 / 2214	0.6 / 5.6 / 0.6 / 5.9	21 M	0432 / 1038 / 1639 / 2250	0.9 / 5.4 / 1.0 / 5.6
7 M	0427 / 1040 / 1644 / 2255	0.3 / 5.8 / 0.4 / 6.1	22 TU	0502 / 1108 / 1709 / 2321	0.9 / 5.4 / 1.0 / 5.6
8 TU	0508 / 1121 / 1725 / 2338	0.2 / 5.8 / 0.4 / 6.1	23 W	0532 / 1139 / 1740 / 2352	0.9 / 5.4 / 1.1 / 5.5
9 W	0551 / 1204 / 1809	0.2 / 5.8 / 0.4	24 TH	0602 / 1210 / 1811	1.1 / 5.3 / 1.2
10 TH	0023 / 0635 / 1250 / 1855	6.0 / 0.4 / 5.6 / 0.6	25 F	0024 / 0634 / 1243 / 1845	5.3 / 1.3 / 5.2 / 1.4
11 F	0111 / 0723 / 1338 / 1946	5.8 / 0.7 / 5.4 / 0.9	26 SA	0057 / 0707 / 1318 / 1922	5.1 / 1.5 / 5.0 / 1.6
12 SA	0203 / 0815 / 1432 / 2045	5.5 / 1.1 / 5.1 / 1.3	27 SU	0134 / 0746 / 1358 / 2006	4.9 / 1.7 / 4.8 / 1.9
13 SU	0304 / 0918 / 1540 / 2159	5.1 / 1.5 / 4.8 / 1.6	28 M	0218 / 0833 / 1450 / 2103	4.6 / 2.0 / 4.6 / 2.1
14 M	0421 / 1035 / 1704 / 2325	4.8 / 1.9 / 4.7 / 1.8	29 TU	0319 / 0938 / 1600 / 2220	4.4 / 2.3 / 4.5 / 2.2
15 TU	0551 / 1200 / 1829	4.6 / 2.0 / 4.8	30 W	0448 / 1103 / 1728 / 2347	4.3 / 2.3 / 4.5 / 2.1

OCTOBER

Day	Time	m	Day	Time	m
1 TH	0621 / 1224 / 1843	4.4 / 2.1 / 4.7	16 F	0131 / 0756 / 1352 / 2009	1.5 / 4.9 / 1.8 / 5.2
2 F	0058 / 0726 / 1326 / 1939	1.8 / 4.8 / 1.7 / 5.1	17 SA	0221 / 0839 / 1436 / 2049	1.3 / 5.1 / 1.6 / 5.3
3 SA	0153 / 0815 / 1415 / 2026	1.3 / 5.1 / 1.3 / 5.5	18 SU	0301 / 0913 / 1512 / 2122	1.2 / 5.2 / 1.4 / 5.4
4 SU	0239 / 0857 / 1458 / 2108	0.9 / 5.4 / 0.9 / 5.8	19 M	0334 / 0954 / 1544 / 2153	1.1 / 5.4 / 1.2 / 5.5
5 M O	0321 / 0937 / 1540 / 2150	0.5 / 5.7 / 0.6 / 6.1	20 TU ●	0404 / 1011 / 1613 / 2224	1.0 / 5.4 / 1.1 / 5.5
6 TU	0403 / 1017 / 1621 / 2232	0.2 / 5.9 / 0.3 / 6.2	21 W	0433 / 1041 / 1643 / 2254	1.0 / 5.5 / 1.1 / 5.5
7 W	0445 / 1058 / 1704 / 2317	0.1 / 6.0 / 0.3 / 6.3	22 TH	0503 / 1111 / 1714 / 2325	1.0 / 5.5 / 1.1 / 5.4
8 TH	0528 / 1142 / 1749	0.2 / 5.9 / 0.3	23 F	0533 / 1142 / 1746 / 2357	1.1 / 5.4 / 1.2 / 5.3
9 F	0003 / 0613 / 1228 / 1836	6.1 / 0.4 / 5.8 / 0.6	24 SA	0605 / 1214 / 1820	1.3 / 5.3 / 1.3
10 SA	0053 / 0701 / 1317 / 1928	5.8 / 0.8 / 5.5 / 0.9	25 SU	0031 / 0638 / 1250 / 1857	5.1 / 1.5 / 5.2 / 1.5
11 SU	0146 / 0754 / 1412 / 2029	5.4 / 1.2 / 5.2 / 1.3	26 M	0109 / 0717 / 1330 / 1940	4.9 / 1.7 / 5.0 / 1.7
12 M	0249 / 0856 / 1518 / 2143	5.0 / 1.7 / 4.9 / 1.6	27 TU	0153 / 0803 / 1419 / 2035	4.7 / 2.0 / 4.8 / 1.9
13 TU	0407 / 1013 / 1641 / 2307	4.7 / 2.0 / 4.7 / 1.8	28 W	0252 / 0904 / 1524 / 2146	4.5 / 2.2 / 4.6 / 2.0
14 W	0536 / 1138 / 1806	4.6 / 2.1 / 4.8	29 TH	0412 / 1023 / 1645 / 2308	4.4 / 2.3 / 4.6 / 1.9
15 TH	0026 / 0656 / 1254 / 1916	1.7 / 4.7 / 2.0 / 5.0	30 F	0542 / 1145 / 1803	4.5 / 2.1 / 4.9
			31 SA	0021 / 0651 / 1252 / 1905	1.6 / 4.8 / 1.8 / 5.1

NOVEMBER

Day	Time	m	Day	Time	m
1 SU	0120 / 0744 / 1345 / 1956	1.2 / 5.2 / 1.3 / 5.5	16 M	0229 / 0843 / 1444 / 2054	1.4 / 5.1 / 1.6 / 5.2
2 M	0210 / 0830 / 1432 / 2042	0.8 / 5.5 / 0.9 / 5.8	17 TU	0305 / 0915 / 1518 / 2127	1.3 / 5.3 / 1.4 / 5.3
3 TU	0255 / 0912 / 1516 / 2126	0.5 / 5.8 / 0.6 / 6.1	18 W	0337 / 0946 / 1549 / 2159	1.2 / 5.4 / 1.3 / 5.4
4 W O	0339 / 0954 / 1600 / 2212	0.3 / 5.9 / 0.4 / 6.2	19 TH ●	0407 / 1016 / 1620 / 2231	1.1 / 5.5 / 1.2 / 5.4
5 TH	0423 / 1038 / 1645 / 2258	0.2 / 6.0 / 0.3 / 6.2	20 F	0437 / 1047 / 1652 / 2303	1.1 / 5.5 / 1.2 / 5.4
6 F	0508 / 1123 / 1732 / 2347	0.3 / 6.0 / 0.4 / 6.0	21 SA	0509 / 1119 / 1726 / 2337	1.2 / 5.5 / 1.2 / 5.3
7 SA	0554 / 1209 / 1822	0.5 / 5.8 / 0.6	22 SU	0542 / 1153 / 1801	1.3 / 5.4 / 1.3
8 SU	0037 / 0642 / 1259 / 1914	5.7 / 0.9 / 5.6 / 0.9	23 M	0013 / 0617 / 1231 / 1840	5.2 / 1.4 / 5.3 / 1.4
9 M	0132 / 0734 / 1353 / 2013	5.4 / 1.3 / 5.3 / 1.2	24 TU	0052 / 0657 / 1312 / 1924	5.0 / 1.6 / 5.2 / 1.5
10 TU	0232 / 0833 / 1454 / 2121	5.0 / 1.7 / 5.0 / 1.6	25 W	0137 / 0743 / 1359 / 2016	4.9 / 1.8 / 5.0 / 1.6
11 W	0343 / 0943 / 1607 / 2236	4.7 / 2.1 / 4.8 / 1.7	26 TH	0232 / 0839 / 1458 / 2118	4.7 / 2.0 / 4.9 / 1.7
12 TH	0503 / 1102 / 1726 / 2351	4.5 / 2.2 / 4.8 / 1.8	27 F	0341 / 0948 / 1608 / 2231	4.6 / 2.1 / 4.8 / 1.7
13 F	0620 / 1216 / 1837	4.6 / 2.2 / 4.8	28 SA	0501 / 1105 / 1722 / 2343	4.6 / 2.0 / 4.9 / 1.5
14 SA	0055 / 0721 / 1318 / 1933	1.7 / 4.7 / 2.0 / 5.0	29 SU	0613 / 1214 / 1829	4.8 / 1.8 / 5.2
15 SU	0148 / 0807 / 1405 / 2017	1.6 / 4.9 / 1.8 / 5.1	30 M	0046 / 0713 / 1314 / 1926	1.2 / 5.1 / 1.4 / 5.4

DECEMBER

Day	Time	m	Day	Time	m
1 TU	0142 / 0804 / 1407 / 2018	0.9 / 5.4 / 1.1 / 5.7	16 W	0234 / 0847 / 1451 / 2102	1.5 / 5.1 / 1.6 / 5.1
2 W	0232 / 0851 / 1456 / 2107	0.7 / 5.7 / 0.8 / 5.9	17 TH	0310 / 0921 / 1527 / 2137	1.4 / 5.3 / 1.4 / 5.2
3 TH O	0320 / 0936 / 1544 / 2156	0.5 / 5.8 / 0.6 / 6.0	18 F ●	0344 / 0954 / 1601 / 2211	1.3 / 5.4 / 1.3 / 5.3
4 F	0406 / 1022 / 1632 / 2245	0.4 / 6.0 / 0.4 / 6.0	19 SA	0417 / 1027 / 1635 / 2246	1.2 / 5.5 / 1.2 / 5.3
5 SA	0452 / 1108 / 1720 / 2334	0.5 / 6.0 / 0.5 / 5.9	20 SU	0450 / 1101 / 1711 / 2321	1.2 / 5.6 / 1.1 / 5.3
6 SU	0539 / 1155 / 1809	0.7 / 5.9 / 0.6	21 M	0525 / 1137 / 1748 / 2358	1.2 / 5.6 / 1.1 / 5.3
7 M	0024 / 0625 / 1243 / 1900	5.6 / 1.0 / 5.7 / 0.8	22 TU	0602 / 1215 / 1827	1.2 / 5.5 / 1.1
8 TU	0115 / 0714 / 1333 / 1953	5.3 / 1.3 / 5.5 / 1.1	23 W	0039 / 0642 / 1257 / 1910	5.2 / 1.3 / 5.4 / 1.2
9 W	0208 / 0806 / 1426 / 2050	5.0 / 1.6 / 5.2 / 1.5	24 TH	0123 / 0727 / 1343 / 1958	5.1 / 1.4 / 5.3 / 1.3
10 TH	0307 / 0903 / 1524 / 2153	4.7 / 2.0 / 4.9 / 1.7	25 F	0213 / 0817 / 1435 / 2053	4.9 / 1.6 / 5.2 / 1.4
11 F	0412 / 1009 / 1631 / 2300	4.5 / 2.2 / 4.7 / 1.9	26 SA	0311 / 0917 / 1535 / 2157	4.8 / 1.7 / 5.1 / 1.5
12 SA	0523 / 1121 / 1740	4.5 / 2.3 / 4.7	27 SU	0420 / 1026 / 1644 / 2307	4.7 / 1.8 / 5.0 / 1.4
13 SU	0005 / 0629 / 1228 / 1844	1.9 / 4.5 / 2.2 / 4.7	28 M	0535 / 1139 / 1755	4.8 / 1.7 / 5.1
14 M	0104 / 0724 / 1325 / 1938	1.8 / 4.7 / 2.1 / 4.8	29 TU	0015 / 0643 / 1247 / 1901	1.3 / 5.0 / 1.5 / 5.3
15 TU	0152 / 0809 / 1412 / 2022	1.7 / 4.9 / 1.8 / 5.0	30 W	0118 / 0742 / 1348 / 2001	1.2 / 5.1 / 1.3 / 5.4
			31 TH	0215 / 0835 / 1443 / 2055	1.0 / 5.4 / 1.0 / 5.6

Chart Datum: 3·05 metres below Ordnance Datum (Newlyn)

VOLVO PENTA SERVICE

Sales and service centres in area 11

DYFED *Dale Sailing Co Ltd*, Brunel Quay, Neyland, Milford Haven SA73 1PY Tel (01646) 601636 **SOUTH GLAMORGAN** *John A. Sparks & Co. Ltd*, Ipswich Road, Cardiff, CF3 7AQ Tel (01222) 492788 *Wigmore - Wright Marine Services*, The Boatyard, Portway Marina, Penarth CF64 1BW (01222) 709983 **WEST MIDLANDS** *Marine Performance*, Upton Marina, Upton-on-Severn, Worcester WR8 0PB Tel (01684) 594540

Area 11

South Wales and Bristol Channel
Bardsey Island to Lands End

VOLVO PENTA

11

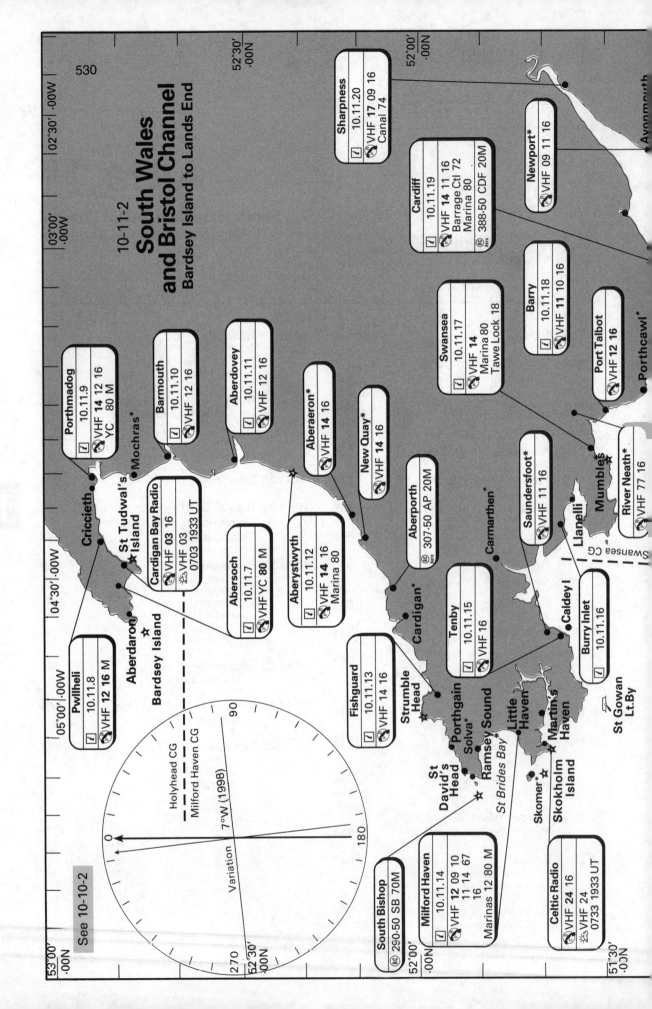

530

10-11-2
South Wales and Bristol Channel
Bardsey Island to Lands End

Sharpness 10.11.20
VHF 17 09 16
Canal 74

Cardiff 10.11.19
VHF **14** 11 16
Barrage Ctl 72
Marina 80
388·50 CDF 20M

Newport* VHF 09 11 16

Porthmadog 10.11.9
VHF **14** 12 16
YC 80 M

Barmouth 10.11.10
VHF 12 16

Aberdovey 10.11.11
VHF 12 16

Aberaeron* VHF **14** 16

New Quay* VHF **14** 16

Swansea 10.11.17
VHF **14**
Marina 80
Tawe Lock 18

Barry 10.11.18
VHF **11** 10 16

Port Talbot VHF 12 16

Cricieth

St Tudwal's Island

Mochras*

Cardigan Bay Radio
VHF 03 16
VHF 03
0703 1933 UT

Abersoch 10.11.7
VHF YC 80 M

Aberystwyth 10.11.12
VHF **14** 16
Marina 80

Aberporth
307·50 AP 20M

Carmarthen*

Saundersfoot* VHF 11 16

Mumbles

River Neath* VHF 77 16

Pwllheli 10.11.8
VHF **12** 16 M

Fishguard 10.11.13
VHF **14** 16

Strumble Head

Cardigan*

Tenby 10.11.15
VHF 16

Caldey I

Burry Inlet 10.11.16

Llanelli

Swansea CG

Aberdaron

Bardsey Island

Porthgain
Solva*

St David's Head

Ramsey Sound

Little Haven

St Brides Bay*

Martin's Haven

St Gowan Lt.By

See 10-10-2

Holyhead CG
Milford Haven CG

7°W (1998)

Variation

South Bishop
290·50 SB 70M

Milford Haven 10.11.14
VHF **12** 09 10
11 14 67
16
Marinas 12 80 M

Celtic Radio
VHF 24 16
VHF 24
0733 1933 UT

Skomer*

Skokholm Island

Avonmouth

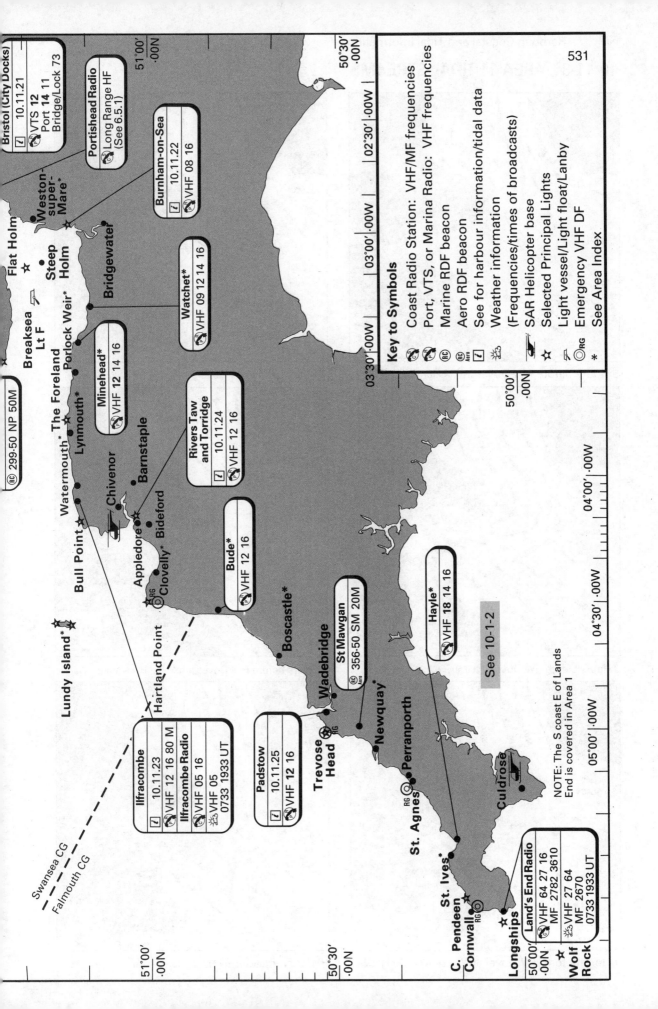

531

Key to Symbols

Coast Radio Station: VHF/MF frequencies
Port, VTS, or Marina Radio: VHF frequencies
(RC)	Marine RDF beacon
(RC) Aero	Aero RDF beacon
i	See for harbour information/tidal data
	Weather information (Frequencies/times of broadcasts)
	SAR Helicopter base
☆	Selected Principal Lights
	Light vessel/Light float/Lanby
(O)RG	Emergency VHF DF
*	See Area Index

Bristol (City Docks)
i VTS **12**
Port **14** 11 10.11.21
Bridge/Lock 73

Portishead Radio
Long Range HF
(See 6.5.1)

Burnham-on-Sea
i 10.11.22
VHF 08 16

Watchet*
VHF 09 12 14 16

Minehead*
VHF 12 14 16

Rivers Taw and Torridge
i 10.11.24
VHF 12 16

Bude*
VHF 12 16

St Mawgan
(RC) Aero 356·50 SM 20M

Hayle*
VHF 18 14 16

See 10-1-2

Ilfracombe
i 10.11.23
VHF 12 16 80 M
Ilfracombe Radio
VHF 05 16
VHF 05
0733 1933 UT

Padstow
i 10.11.25
VHF 12 16

Land's End Radio
VHF 64 27 16
MF 2782 3610
VHF 27 64
MF 2670
0733 1933 UT

NOTE: The S coast E of Lands
End is covered in Area 1

(RC) 299·50 NP 50M

Swansea CG
Falmouth CG

Weston-super-Mare*

Flat Holm
Steep Holm
Breaksea Lt F
Porlock Weir*
Bridgewater

Watermouth*
The Foreland
Lynmouth*

Bull Point
Chivenor
Barnstaple
Appledore
Bideford
Clovelly*

Lundy Island*

Hartland Point

Boscastle*

Wadebridge

Trevose Head

Newquay*
Perranporth

St. Agnes*

St. Ives*

C. Pendeen
Cornwall

Longships

Wolf Rock

Culdrose

51°00'.00N

51°00'.00N

50°30'.00N

50°30'.00N

50°00'.00N

50°30'.00N

50°00'.00N

05°00'.00W
04°30'.00W
04°00'.00W
03°30'.00W
03°00'.00W
02°30'.00W

10-11-3   AREA 11 TIDAL STREAMS

5 Hours before HW Dover (HW Milford Haven)

4 Hours before HW Dover (0100 after HW Milford Haven)

3 Hours before HW Dover (0200 after HW Milford Haven)

2 Hours before HW Dover (0300 after HW Milford Haven)

1 Hour before HW Dover (0400 after HW Milford Haven)

HW Dover (0500 after HW Milford Haven)

Southward 10.1.3   Northward   10.10.3   South Ireland 10.12.3

1 Hour after HW Dover (0600 after HW Milford Haven)

2 Hours after HW Dover (0525 before HW Milford Haven)

3 Hours after HW Dover (0425 before HW Milford Haven)

4 Hours after HW Dover (0325 before HW Milford Haven)

5 Hours after HW Dover (0225 before HW Milford Haven)

6 Hours after HW Dover (0125 before HW Milford Haven)

11

10.11.4 COASTAL LIGHTS, FOG SIGNALS AND WAYPOINTS

Abbreviations used below are given in 1.4.1. Principal lights are in **bold** print, places in CAPITALS, and light-vessels, light floats and Lanbys in *CAPITAL ITALICS*. Unless otherwise stated lights are white. m – elevation in metres; M – nominal range in miles. Fog signals are in *italics*. Useful waypoints are underlined – use those on land with care. All geographical positions should be assumed to be approximate. See 4.4.1. All positions are referenced to the OSGB 36 datum.

CARDIGAN BAY (see also 10.10.4)

Bardsey I 52°44'·97N 04°47'·93W Fl (5) 15s 39m **26M**; W ■ Tr, R bands; obsc by Bardsey I 198°-250° and in Tremadoc B when brg less than 260°; *Horn Mo(N) 45s.*
St Tudwal's, 52°47'·89N 04°28'·20W Fl WR 15s 46m W14, R10M; W ● Tr; vis W349°-169°, R169°-221°, W221°-243°, R243°-259°, W259°-293°, R293°-349°; obsc by East I 211°-231°.

PWLLHELI/PORTHMADOG/MOCHRAS LAGOON
Pwllheli App Lt By 52°53'·00N 04°23'·00W Iso 2s; SWM.
Training Arm Hd 52°53'·23N 04°23'·67W QG 3m 3M.
Sewer Outfall 52°53'·18N 04°23'·69W Fl R 2·5s.
Abererch By 52°53'·50N 04°23'·00W; SPM (Apr-Oct).
Butlins By 52°53'·00N 04°22'·00W; SPM (Apr-Oct).
West End By 52°52'·40N 04°25'·50W; SPM (Apr-Oct).
Porthmadog Fairway Lt By 52°52'·95N 04°11'·11W L Fl 10s; SWM.
Shell I, NE Corner 52°49'·53N 04°07'·64W Fl WRG 4s; vis G079°-124°, W124°-134°, R134°-179°; (Mar- Nov).

BARMOUTH
Diffuser Lt By 52°43'·17N 04°05'·31W Fl Y 5s; SPM.
Barmouth Outer Lt By 52°42'·90N 04°04'·90W L Fl 10s; SWM.
N Bank Y Perch 52°42'·81N 04°03'·67W QR 4m 5M.
Ynys y Brawd, SE end 52°42'·97N 04°03'·07W Fl R 5s 5M.
Sarn Badrig Causeway Lt By 52°41'·17N 04°25'·30W Q (9) 15s; WCM; *Bell.*
Sarn-y-Bwch. Bwch By 52°34'·80N 04°13'·50W; WCM.

ABERDOVEY
Aberdovey Outer By 52°31'·30N 04°05'·05W; L Fl 10s SWM.
Cynfelyn Patches, Patches By 52°25'·80N 04°16'·30W; WCM.

ABERYSTWYTH/ABERAERON/NEW QUAY
Aberystwyth S Bkwtr Hd 52°24'·39N 04°05'·46W Fl (2) WG 10s 12m 10M; B col; vis G030°-053°, W053°-210°.
Ldg Lts 135°. Front, 52°24'·35N 04°05'·32W FR 4m 5M. Rear, 52m from front, FR 7m 6M.
Aberaeron S Pier 52°14'·60N 04°15'·87W Fl (3) G 10s 11m 6M; vis 125°-200°.
N Pier Fl (4) WRG 15s 10m 6M; vis G050°-104°, W104°-178°, R178°-232°.
Carreg Ina By 52°13'·27N 04°20'·47W; NCM.
New Quay Pier Hd 52°12'·94N 04°21'·27W Fl WG 3s 12m W8M, G5M; G △; vis W135°-252°, G252°-295.

CARDIGAN
CG Bldg 52°06'·98N 04°41'·14W 2 FR (vert).
Channel Bn 52°06'·44N 04°41'·32W Fl (2) 5s; IDM.
Bridge, Iso Y 2s on upstream and downstream sides.

FISHGUARD
N Bkwtr Hd 52°00'·74N 04°58'·15W Fl G 4·5s 18m 13M; 8-sided Tr; *Bell (1) 8s.*
E Bkwtr Hd Fl R 3s 10m 5M.
Lts in line 282°. Front 52°00'·65N 04°59'·20W FG 77m 5M; W ◊ on W mast. Rear, 46m from front, FG 89m 5M; W ◊ on W mast.
Penanglas, 152m S of Pt, *Dia (2) 60s;* W obelisk.

Strumble Hd 52°01'·78N 05°04'·35W Fl (4) 15s 45m **26M**; W ● Tr; vis 038°-257°; (H24).

BISHOPS AND SMALLS

South Bishop 51°51'·15N 05°24'·65W Fl 5s 44m **19M**; W ● Tr; (H24); RC; *Horn (3) 45s.*
Brawdy. St Brides Bay. Research Area, seaward Lt Bys.
Lt By A1 51°49'·30N 05°20'·00W Fl (4) Y 20s; SPM.
Lt By B1 51°48'·30N 05°20'·00W Fl (4) Y 20s; SPM.

The Smalls 51°43'·25N 05°40'·15W Fl (3) 15s 36m **25M**; Graniten Tr, R lantern and R helideck supports; Racon (T); *Horn (2) 60s.* Same Tr, FR 33m 13M; vis 253°-285° over Hats and Barrels Rk; both Lts shown H24.

Skokholm I, SW end 51°41'·61N 05°17'·15W Fl 10s 54m **20M**; W 8-sided Tr; part obsc 226°-258°; (H24).

WALES – SOUTH COAST – BRISTOL CHANNEL

MILFORD HAVEN
St Ann's Hd 51°40'·85N 05°10'·35W Fl WR 5s 48m **W18M, R17**/14M; W 8-sided Tr; vis W233°-247°, R247°-285°, R (intens) 285°-314°, R314°-332°, W332°-124°, W129°-131°; *Horn (2) 60s.*
W Blockhouse Pt Ldg Lts 022·5°. Front, 51°41'·30N 05°09'·40W F 54m 13M; B stripe on W Tr; vis 004·5°-040·5°. By day 10M.
Watwick Pt Rear, 0·5M from front F 80m **15M**; vis 013·5°-031·5°. By day 10M.
W Blockhouse Pt 51°41'·26N 05°09'·40W Q WR 21m 9/7M; R lantern on W base.
Dale Fort 51°42'·13N 05°08'·93W Fl (2) WR 5s 20m W5M, R3M; vis R222°-276°, W276°-019°.
Great Castle Hd 51°42'·60N 05°07'·00W F WRG 27m W5M, R3M, G3M; W ■ Tr, B stripe; vis R243°-281°, G281°-299°, W299°-029°. Same Tr Ldg Lts 039·8° Oc 4s 27m **15M**; vis 031·2°-048·2°. **Rear**, 890m from front, **Little Castle Hd** 51°43'·02N 05°06'·52W Oc 8s 53m **15M**; vis 031·2°-048·2°.
St Anne's Hd Lt By 51°40'·23N 05°10'·43W Fl R 2·5s; PHM.
Mid Channel Rks Lt By 51°40'·16N 05°10'·08W Q (9) 15s; WCM.
Middle Chan Rks Lt Tr 51°40'·29N 05°09'·77W Fl (3) G 7s 18m 8M; B ● Tr, lantern.
Sheep Lt By 51°40'·03N 05°08'·23W QG; SHM.
Millbay Lt By 51°41'·02N 05°09'·38W Fl (2) R 5s; PHM.
W Chapel Lt By 51°40'·97N 05°08'·60W Fl G 10s; SHM.
E Chapel Lt By 51°40'·85N 05°08'·08W Fl R 5s; PHM.
Rat Lt By 51°40'·77N 05°07'·80W Fl G 5s; SHM.
Angle Lt By 51°41'·60N 05°08'·20W VQ; WCM.
Thorn Rock Lt By 51°41'·50N 05°07'·70W Q (9) 15s; WCM.
Dakotian Lt By 51°42'·13N 05°08'·22W Q (3) 10s; ECM.
Chapel Lt By 51°41'·63N 05°06'·80W Fl G 5s; SHM.
Stack Lt By 51°42'·00N 05°06'·46W Fl R 2·5s; PHM.
S Hook Lt By 51°41'·80N 05°06'·03W Q (6) +L Fl 15s; WCM.
Esso Lt By 51°41'·72N 05°05'·17W Q; NCM.
E Angle Lt By 51°41'·68N 05°04'·20W Fl (3) G 10s; SHM.
Turbot Bank Lt By 51°37'·40N 05°10'·00W VQ (9) 10s; WCM.
St Gowan Lt By 51°31'·90N 04°59'·70W Q (6) + L Fl 15s; Racon (T); *Whis;* SCM.
Caldey I 51°37'·86N 04°41'·00W Fl (3) WR 20s 65m W14M, R12M; W ● Tr; vis R173°-212°, W212°-088°, R088°- 102°.
Eel Pt By 51°38'·83N 04°42'·17W; SHM.
Giltar Spit By 51°39'·00N 04°42'·05W; PHM.
Spaniel By 51°38'·03N 04°39'·67W; ECM.
Woolhouse By 51°39'·32N 04°39'·62W; WCM.
North Highcliff By 51°39'·35N 04°40'·70W; NCM.

TENBY/SAUNDERSFOOT/CARMARTHEN BAY/BURRY INLET
Tenby Pier Hd 51°40'·37N 04°41'·81W FR 7m 7M.
Saundersfoot Pier Hd 51°42'·55N 04°41'·68W Fl R 5s 6m 7M.
DZ1 By 51°42'·02N 04°35'·90; SPM.

DZ2 Lt By 51°39'·75N 04°37'·45W Fl Y 2·5s; SPM.
DZ2 Lt By 51°39'·95N 04°37'·50W Fl Y 2·5s; SPM.
DZ3 By 51°37'·35N 04°37'·75W; SPM.
DZ7 Lt By 51°38'·05N 04°30'·05W Fl Y 10s; SPM.
DZ4 Lt By 51°35'·70N 04°30'·00W Fl Y 5s; SPM.
DZ8 By 51°41'·50N 04°24'·30W; SPM.
DZ6 By 51°38'·00N 04°24'·17W; SPM.
DZ5 Lt By 51°36'·30N 04°24'·17W Fl Y 2·5s; SPM.
Burry Port Barrel Post 51°40'·47N 04°14'·94W Fl R 3s 5M.
Burry Port Inlet 51°40'·60N 04°14'·98W Fl 5s 7m **15M**.
Llanell Ent N side Fl R 5s 2M
West Helwick (W HWK) Lt By 51°31'·37N 04°23'·58W
Q (9) 15s; Racon (T); *Whis*; WCM .
E Helwick Lt By 51°31'·77N 04°12'·60W VQ (3) 5s; *Bell;* ECM.

SWANSEA BAY/SWANSEA
Ledge Lt By 51°29'·90N 03°58'·70W VQ (6) + L Fl 10s; SCM.
Mixon Lt By 51°33'·10N 03°58'·70W Fl (2) R 5s; *Bell;* PHM.
Outer Spoil Gnd Lt By 51°32'·08N 03°55'·67W Fl Y 2·5s;
SPM.
Grounds Lt By 51°32'·78N 03°53'·40W VQ (3) 5s; ECM.

Mumbles 51°34'·00N 03°58'·20W Fl (4) 20s 35m **16M**; W Tr;
vis 331·5°-336·5°; *Horn (3) 60s.*
Railway Pier Hd 51°34'·19N 03°58'·36W 2 FR (vert) 11m 9M.
SW Inner Green Grounds Lt By 51°34'·04N 03°56'·95W
Q (6) + L Fl 15s; *Bell;* SCM.
Outer Fairway Lt By 51°35'·50N 03°56'·01W QG; *Bell;* SHM.
W Pier Hd 51°36'·47N 03°55'·67W Fl (2) R 10s 11m 9M; FR
Lts on radio mast 014° 1·3M.
Swansea Inner Fairway Lt By 51°36'·20N 03°55'·60W
Fl G 2·5s; *Bell;* SHM.
E Bkwtr Hd 51°36'·35N 03°55'·55W 2 FG (vert) 10m 6M;
W Tr; *Siren 30s.*
Lts in line 020°. Jetty Hd Front, 51°36'·51N 03°55'·43W
Oc G 4s 5m 2M. Rear, 260m from front, FG 6M.

SWANSEA BAY/RIVER NEATH/PORT TALBOT
Neath App Chan Lt By 51°35'·70N 03°52'·75W Fl G 5s; SHM.
Neath SE Training Wall, near S end 51°36'·30N 03°51'·89W
2 FG (vert) 6m 5M R mast.
Neath SE Training Wall Middle 51°36'·68N 03°51'·33W FG
6m 5M; R mast.
Neath SE Training Wall N End 51°37'·07N 03°50'·77W 3 FG
(vert) 6m 5M; R mast.
Cabenda Lt By 51°33'·43N 03°52'·25W VQ (6) + L Fl 10s; SCM.
P Talbot S Outer Lt By 51°33'·66N 03°51'·20W Fl G 5s; SHM.
P Talbot N Outer Lt By 51°33'·76N 03°51'·304W Fl R 5s;
PHM.
P Talbot N Inner Lt By 51°34'·20N 03°50'·18W Fl R 3s; PHM; *Horn.*
Ldg Lts 059·8° (occas). Front 51°34'·89N 03°48'·02W
Oc R 3s 12m 6M; Y & Or ◆ on Tr. Rear, 400m from front,
Oc R 6s 32m 6M; Y & Or ◆ on Tr.
N Bkwtr Hd 51°34'·73N 03°48'·93W Fl (4) R 10s 11m 3M.
S Bkwtr Hd 51°34'·43N 03°48'·95W Fl G 3s 11m 3M.

BRISTOL CHANNEL – EASTERN PART (NORTH SHORE)
Kenfig Lt By 51°29'·71N 03°46'·43W Q (3) 10s; ECM.
W Scarweather (W SCAR) Lt By 51°28'·28N 03°55'·50 Q (9)
15s; Racon (T); *Bell;* WCM.
S Scarweather (S SCAR) Lt By 51°27'·58N 03°51'·50W
Q (6) + L Fl 15s; SCM.
Hugo By 51°28'·72N 03°48'·30W; PHM.
E Scarweather By 51°28'·12N 03°46'·23W; ECM.

PORTHCAWL
Fairy By 51°27'·83N 03°42'·00W; WCM.
Tusker Lt By 51°26'·82N 03°40'·67W Fl (2) R 5s; PHM.

Porthcawl Bkwtr Hd 51°28'·33N 03°41'·95W F WRG 10m
W6M, R4M, G4M; W 6-sided Tr, B base; vis G302°-036°,
W036°-082°, R082°-122°.
W Nash Lt By 51°25'·95N 03°45'·88W VQ(9) 10s; WCM.
Middle Nash By 51°24'·80N 03°39'·34W; WCM.
E Nash Lt By 51°24'·03N 03°34'·03W Q (3) 10s; ECM.

Nash 51°24'·00N 03°33'·05W Fl (2) WR 10s 56m **W21M, R20/
17M**; W I Tr; vis R280°-290°, W290°-097°, R097°-100°, R (intens)
100°-104°, R104°-120°, W120°-128°; *Siren (2) 45s;* RC.

Saint Hilary 51° 27'·40N 03°24'·10W Aero QR 346m 11M;
radio mast; 4 FR (vert) on same mast 6M.
Breaksea Pt intake 51°22'·50N 03°24'·45W Fl R 11m; Tr.

Breaksea Lt By 51°19'·85N 03°19'·00W Fl 15s; Racon (T);
Horn (2) 30s;
Wenvoe 51°27'·50N 03°16'·80W Aero Q 365m 12M; radio
mast (H24).
Merkur Lt By 51°21'·85N 03°15'·90W Fl R 2·5s; PHM.
Welsh Water Barry W Lt By 51°22'·23N 03°16'·84W Fl R 5s;
PHM.

BARRY
W Bkwtr Hd 51°23'·43N 03°15'·43W Fl 2·5s 12m 10M.
E Bkwtr Hd 51°23'·50N 03°15'·37W QG 7m 8M.
Lavernock Spit Lt By 51°22'·99N 03°10'·74W VQ (6) + L Fl
10s; SCM.
One Fathom N Lt By 51°20'·91N 03°12'·08W Q; NCM.
Mackenzie Lt By 51°21'·72N 03°08'·15W QR; PHM.
Holm Middle Lt By 51°21'·69N 03°06'·64W Fl G 2·5s; SHM.
Wolves Lt By 51°23'·10N 03°08'·80W VQ; NCM.

Flat Holm, SE Pt 51°22'·52N 03°07'·05W Fl (3) WR 10s 50m
W15M, R13M; W ● Tr; vis R106°-140°, W140°-151°, R151°-
203°, W203°-106°; (H24).
Weston Lt By 51°22'·58N 03°05'·66W Fl (2) R 5s; PHM.
Monkstone Rock Lt 51°24'·87N 03°05'·92W Fl 5s 13m 12M;
R col on ● Tr.

CARDIFF AND PENARTH ROADS
Lavernock Outfall Lt By 51°23'·91N 03°09'·40W Fl Y 5s; SPM.
Ranie Lt By 51°24'·22N 03°09'·30W Fl (2) R 5s; PHM.
S Cardiff Lt By 51°24'·15N 03°08'·48W Q (6) + L Fl 15s; SCM; *Bell.*
Mid Cardiff Lt By 51°25'·57N 03°08'·00W Fl (3) G 10s; SHM.
Cardiff Spit By 51°25'·53N 03°06'·42W; PHM.
N Cardiff Lt By 51°27'·77N 03°05'·28W QG; SHM.

PENARTH/CARDIFF
Penarth Promenade Pier near Hd 51°26'·06N 03°09'·82W
2 FR (vert) 8/6m 3M; *Reed Mo(BA) 60s,* sounded 10 min
before a steamer expected.
Penarth Sailing Club pontoon 51°26'·80N 03°10'·50W Q.
Ldg Lts 349°. **Front**, 51°27'·67N 03°09'·55W F 4m **17M**.
Rear, 520m from front, F 24m **17M**.
Outer Wrach Lt By 51°26'·13N 03°09'·40W Q (9) 15s; WCM.
Inner Wrach Lt By 51°26'·67N 03°09'·55W Fl G 2·5s; SHM.
Queen Alexandra Dock ent S Jetty Hd 51°27'·06N 03°09'·50W
2 FG (vert); Tfc sigs; *Dia 60s.*
Tail Patch Lt By 51°23'·50N 03°03'·59W QG; SHM.
Hope Lt By 51°24'·82N 03°02'·60W Q (3) 10s; ECM.
NW Elbow Lt By 51°26'·48N 02°59'·61W VQ (9) 10s; WCM; *Bell.*
English and Welsh Grounds Lt By 51°26'·90N 03°00'·10W
L Fl 10s 7M; Racon (O); SWM; *Whis.*

NEWPORT DEEP
Newport Deep Lt By 51°29'·33N 02°59'·03W Fl (3) G 10s;
Bell; SHM.

RIVER USK/NEWPORT
East Usk 51°32'·38N 02°57'·93W Fl (2) WRG 10s 11m
W15M, R11M, G11M; W ● Tr; vis W284°-290°, R290°-017°,

W017°-037°, G037°-115°, W115°-120°. Also Oc WRG 10s 10m W11M, R9M, G9M; vis G018°-022°, W022°-024°, R024°-028°.
Alexandra Dock, S Lock W Pier Hd 51°32'·84N 02°59'·18W 2 FR (vert) 9m 6M; *Horn 60s.*
E Pier Hd 51°32'·93N 02°59'·03W 2 FG (vert) 9m 6M.
Julians Pill Ldg Lts about 057°. Common Front, 51°33'·28N 02°57'·85W FG 5m 4M. Rear, 61m from front, FG 8m 4M.
Ldg Lts 149°. Rear, 137m from common front, FG 9m 4M.
Birdport Jetty 51°33'·64N 02°58'·01W 2 FG (vert) 6m.
Dallimores Wharf 51°33'·85N 02°58'·51W 2 FG (vert).
Transporter Bridge, W side 2 FR (vert); 2 FY (vert) shown on transporter car.
E side 2 FG (vert). Centres of George Street and Newport Bridges marked by FY Lts.

BRISTOL CHANNEL – EASTERN PART (SOUTH SHORE)

BRISTOL DEEP
N Elbow Lt By 51°27'·12N 02°58'·10W QG; *Bell;* SHM.
S Mid Grounds Lt By 51°27'·66N 02°58'·34W VQ (6) + L Fl 10s; SCM.
E Mid Grounds Lt By 51°27'·95N 02°54'·00W Fl R 5s; PHM.
Clevedon Lt By 51°27'·40N 02°54'·84W VQ; NCM.
Welsh Hook Lt By 51°28'·49N 02°51'·78W Q (6) + L Fl 15s; *Bell;* SCM.
Avon Lt By 51°27'·90N 02°51'·65W Fl G 2·5s; SHM.
Clevedon Pier 51°26'·61N 02°51'·82W 2 FG (vert) 7m 3M.
Walton Bay, Old signal station 51°27'·86N 02°49'·71W Fl 2·5s 35m 2M.
Black Nore Pt 51°29'·05N 02°47'·95W Fl (2) 10s 11m **15M**; W ● Tr; obsc by Sand Pt when brg less than 049°; vis 044°-243°.
Newcome Lt By 51°29'·98N 02°46'·63W Fl (3) R 10s; PHM.
Firefly Lt By 51°29'·93N 02°45'·27W Fl (2) G 5s; SHM.
Outer Lt By 51°29'·97N 02°44'·71W IQ G 12s; SHM.
Middle Lt By 51°29'·90N 02°44'·13W Fl G 5s; SHM.
Inner Lt By 51°29'·83N 02°43'·78W Fl (3) G 15s; SHM.
Cockburn Lt By 51°30'·43N 02°44'·00W Fl R 2·5s; PHM.

Portishead Pt 51°29'·64N 02°46'·34W Q (3) 10s 9m **16M**; B Tr, W base; vis 060°-262°; *Horn 20s.*

PORTISHEAD
Pier Hd 51°29'·66N 02°45'·18W Iso G 2s 5m 3M; W col.
Lock E side 51°29'·54N 02°45'·33W 2 FR (vert) 7m 1M; Gy col; (occas.)
Lock W side 2 FG (vert) 7m 1M; Gy col; (occas.)

Seabank. Lts in line 086·8°. Front, 51°29'·99N 02°43'·66W IQ 13m 5M; vis 070·3°-103·3°, 076·8°-096·8°. Rear, 500m from front, IQ W 16m 5M; vis 070·3°-103·3°, 076·8°-096·8°. By day, both 1M.
Royal Portbury Dock Pier end 51°30'·13N 02°43'·64W L Fl G 15s 5m 6M; Gy pillar.
Pier corner 51°30'·10N 02°43'·77W Fl G 2s 7m 7M; Gy pillar; *Dia 30s,* sounded HW-4 to HW+3.
Knuckle Lts in line 099·6° 51°29'·92N 02°43'·60W Oc G 5s 6m 6M, rear, 165m from front, FG 13m 6M; vis 044°-134°.

AVONMOUTH
Royal Edward Dock N Pier Hd 51°30'·47N 02°43'·00W Fl 10s 15m 10M; ● Tr; vis 060°-228·5°.
King Road Ldg Lts 072·4°. N Pier Hd Front, 51°30'·47N 02°43'·00W Oc R 5s 5m 9M; W obelisk, R bands; vis 062°-082°. Rear, 546m from front, QR 15m 10M; B&W striped ● on Tr, Or bands; vis 066°-078°.
Oil Jetty Hd 51°30'·62N 02°42'·85W 2 FG (vert) 6m 2M.

RIVER AVON
S Pier Hd (see above)
Ldg Lts 127·2°. Front, 51°30'·05N 02°42'·47W FR 7m 3M;

W □, R stripes; vis 010°-160°. Rear. 142m from front FR 17m 3M; W ○, vis 048°-138°.
Monoliths 51°30'·23N 02°42'·68W Fl R 5s 5m 3M; W □, B stripes on W col; vis 317°-137°.
Saint George Ldg Lts 173·3°, 51°29'·73N 02°42'·58W both Oc G 5s 6/9m 1M, on Or cols; vis 158°-305°; synch.
Nelson Pt 51°29'·82N 02°42'·43W Fl R 3s 9m 3M; W mast.
Broad Pill 51°29'·6N 02°41'·8W QY 11m 1M; W Tr.
Avonmouth Bridge, NE end 51°29'·36N 02°41'·45W L Fl R 10s 5m 3M, SW end L Fl G 10s 5m 3M, showing up and downstream. From here to City Docks, Oc G Lts are shown on S bank, and R or Y Lts on N bank.

CUMBERLAND BASIN
Ent N side 51°26'·95N 02°37'·36W 2 FR (vert) 6m 1M; S side W end 2 FG (vert) 7m 1M;

AVON BRIDGE
N side 51°26'·79N 02°37'·34W FR 6m 1M on Bridge pier.
Centre of span Iso 5s 6m 1M.
S side FG 6m 1M on Bridge pier.

SEVERN ESTUARY

THE SHOOTS
Redcliffe Ldg Lts 012·9° Front 51°36'·35N 02°41'·23W F Bu 16m; vis 358°-028°. Rear, 320m from front, F Bu 33m 10M.
Lower Shoots Bn 51°33'·83N 02°41'·98W Q (9) 15s 6m 7M; WCM.
North Mixoms 51°34'·03N 02°42'·57W Fl (3) R 10s 6M; PHM.
Upper Shoots Bn 51°34'·20N 02°41'·79W (unlit); WCM.
Second Severn Crossing, Centre span, Q Bu 5M; Racon.
Old Man's Hd 51°34'·72N 02°41'·62W VQ (9) W 10s; WCM.
Lady Bench 51°34'·83N 02°42'·13W QR 6m 6M; PHM.
Charston Rk 51°35'·32N 02°41'·60W Fl 3s 5m 13/8M; W ● Tr, B stripe; vis (13M) 343°-043°, (8M) 043°-343°.
Chapel Rk 51°36'·40N 02°39'·13W Fl WRG 2·6s 6m W8M, R5M, G5M; B Tr, W lantern; vis W213°-284°, R284°-049°, W049°-051·5°, G051·5°-160°.

RIVER WYE
Wye Bridge 51°37'·03N 02°39'·54W 2F Bu (hor); centre of span.

SEVERN BRIDGE
West Tr 3 QR (hor) on upstream and downstream sides; *Horn (3) 45s;* obscured 040°-065°.
Centre of span 51°36'·57N 02°38'·32W Q Bu, each side.
E Tr 3 QG (hor) on upstream and downstream sides.
Aust 51°36'·13N 02°37'·91W 2 QG (vert) 11/5m 6M; power cable pylon.
Lyde Rk 51°36'·85N 02°38'·58W QR 5m 5M; B Tr, W lantern.
Sedbury 51°37'·75N 02°38'·93W 2 FR (vert) 10m 3M.
Slime Road Ldg Lts 210·4°. Front, 51°37'·21N 02°39'·00W F Bu 9m 5M. Rear, 91 m from front, F Bu 16m 5M; B Tr, Inward Rocks Ldg Lts 252·5°. Front, 51°39'·23N 02°37'·37W F 6m 6M; B Tr. Rear, 183m from front, F 13m 2M.
Counts Lt By 51°39'·45N 02°35'·74W Q; NCM.
Sheperdine Ldg Lts 070·4°. Front, 51°40'·03N 02°33'·22W F 8m 5M; B Tr, W lantern. Rear, 168m from front, F 13m 5M; B Tr, W lantern; *Bell (26) 60s.*
Ledges Lt By 51°39'·75N 02°34'·06W Fl (3) G 10s; SHM.
Narlwood Rks Ldg Lts 224·9°. Front, 51°39'·54N 02°34'·68W Fl 2s 5m 8M; Y Bn, B lantern. Rear, 198m from front Fl 2s 9m 8M; Y Bn, B lantern.
Hills Flats Lt By 51°40'·66N 02°32'·59W Fl G 4s; SHM.
Hayward Rk Lt By 51°41'·24N 02°31'·00W Q; NCM.
Conigre Ldg Lts 077·5°. Front, 51°41'·43N 02°29'·92W F Bu 21m 8M. Rear, 213m from front, F Bu 29m 8M.
Fishing House Ldg Lts 217·7°. Front, 51°40'·95N 02°30'·91W F 5m 2M; W hut and post. Rear, F 11m 2M; W hut and mast.

BERKELEY
Power Station Centre 51°41'·62N 02°29'·97W 3x2 FG (vert); *Siren (2) 30s.*
Bull Rk 51°41'·78N 02°29'·80W Oc (2) 6m 8M.
Berkeley Pill Ldg Lts 187·8°. Front, 51°41'·95N 02°29'·32W FG 5m 2M. Rear, 152m from front, FG 11m 2M; both B Trs, W lanterns.
Panthurst Pill 51°42'·56N 02°28'·93W F Bu 6m 1M; Y pillar.
Lydney Docks Pier Hd 51°42'·60N 02°30'·27W FW or R (tidal); *Gong* (tidal).

SHARPNESS DOCKS
S Pier Hd 51°42'·93N 02°29'·01W 2 FG (vert) 6m 3M; *Siren 20s.*
N Pier 2 FR (vert) 6m 3M.
Old ent, S side, 51°43'·49N 02°28'·82W; S*iren 5s* (tidal).

BRISTOL CHANNEL (SOUTH SHORE)

WESTON-SUPER-MARE
Pier Hd 51°20'·85N 02°59'·17W 2 FG (vert) 6m.
E Culver Lt By 51°17'·70N 03°14'·50W Q (3) 10s; ECM.
W Culver Lt By 51°16'·85N 03°19'·20W VQ (9) 10s; WCM.
Gore Lt By 51°13'·93N 03°09'·70W Iso 5s; *Bell;* SWM.

BURNHAM-ON-SEA/RIVER PARRETT
Ent 51°14'·86N 03°00'·26W Fl 7·5s 7m 12M; vis 074°-164°.
Dir Lt 076°. Dir F WRG 4m W12M, R10M, G10M; same Tr; vis G071°-075°, W075°-077°, R077°-081°.
Seafront Lts in line 112°, moved for changing chan, Front, 51°14'·38N 02°59'·86W FR 6m 3M W □, Or stripe on sea wall. Rear, FR 12m 3M; church Tr.
Brue Bn 51°13'·50N 03°00'·20W QR 4m 3M; W mast, R bands. (TE 1992).
Stert Reach 51°11'·32N 03°01'·90W Fl 3s 4m 7M; vis 187°-217°.
DZ No. 1 Lt By 51°15'·25N 03°09'·40W Fl Y 2·5s; SPM.

Hinkley Pt,intake 51°12'·90N 03°07'·96W 2 FG (vert) 7m 3M.
DZ No. 2 Lt By 51°13'·75N 03°17'·10W Fl Y 10s; SPM.
DZ No. 3 Lt By 51°15'·50N 03°14'·90W Fl Y 5s; SPM.

WATCHET
W Bkwtr Hd 51°11'·03N 03°19'·67W FG 9m 9M.
FR Lts on radio masts 1·6M SSW.
E Pier 51°10'·97N 03°19'·63W 2 FR (vert) 3M.

MINEHEAD/PORLOCK WEIR
Bkwtr Hd 51°12'·78N 03°28'·28W Fl (2) G 5s 4M; vis 127°-262°.
Sewer Outfall 51°12'·95N 03°28'·22W QG 6m 7M; SHM Bn.

Lynmouth Foreland 51°14'·70N 03°47'·15W Fl (4) 15s 67m **18M**; W ● Tr; vis 083°-275°; (H24).

LYNMOUTH/WATERMOUTH
River training arm 51°13'·88N 03°49'·77W 2 FR (vert) 6m 5M.
Harbour arm 51°13'·89N 03°49'·78W 2 FG (vert) 6m 5M.
Sand Ridge By 51°14'·98N 03°49'·70W; SHM.
Copperas Rock By 51°13'·77N 04°00'·50W; SHM.
Watermouth 51°12'·90N 04°04'·50W Oc WRG 5s 1m; W △; vis G149·5°-151·5°, W151·5°-154·5°, R154·5°-156·5°.

ILFRACOMBE
Lantern Hill 51°12'·63N 04°06'·72W Fl G 2·5s 39m 6M.
Promenade Pier N end 51°12'·66N 04°06'·60W 2 FG (vert).
Horseshoe Lt By 51°15'·00N 04°12'·85W Q; NCM.

Bull Point 51°11'·95N 04°12'·05W Fl (3) 10s 54m **25M**; W ● Tr, obscd shore-056°. Same Tr; FR 48m 12M; vis 058°-096°.
Morte Stone By 51°11'·30N 04°14'·85W; SHM.
Baggy Leap By 51°08'·90N 04°16'·90W; SHM.

BIDEFORD, RIVERS TAW AND TORRIDGE
Bideford Fairway Lt By 51°05'·23N 04°16'·17W L Fl 10s; *Bell;* SWM.
Bideford Bar By 51°04'·93N 04°14'·76W; SHM.
Instow Ldg Lts 118°. **Front**, 51°03'·59N 04°10'·60W Oc 6s 22m **15M**; vis 104·5°-131·5°. **Rear**, 427m from front, Oc 10s 38m **15M**; vis 103°-133°; (H24).
Crow Pt 51°03'·93N 04°11'·32W Fl R 5s 8m 4M; W Tr; vis 225°-045°.
Clovelly Hbr Quay Hd 50°59'·85N 04°23'·75W Fl G 5s 5m 5M.

LUNDY
Near North Pt 51°12'·07N 04°40'·57W Fl 15s 48m **17M**; W ● Tr; vis 009°-285°.
SE Pt 51°09'·70N 04°39'·30W Fl 5s 53m **15M**; W ● Tr; vis 170°-073°; *Horn 25s.*

Hartland Pt 51°01'·27N 04°31'·50W Fl (6) 15s 37m **25M**; (H24); W ● Tr; *Horn 60s.*

NORTH CORNWALL

BUDE
Compass Pt Tr 50°49'·70N 04°33'·35W.

PADSTOW
Stepper Pt 50°34'·11N 04°56'·63W L Fl 10s 12m 4M.
St Saviour's Pt 50°32'·72N 04°56'·00W L Fl G 10s 1M; G △.
N Quay Hd 50°32'·48N 04°56'·10W 2 FG (vert) 6m 2M.
Trevose Hd 50°32'·93N 05°02'·05W Fl R 7·5s 62m **21M**; W ● Tr. *Horn (2) 30s.*

NEWQUAY
N Pier Hd 50°25'·04N 05°05'·12W 2 FG (vert) 5m 2M.
S Pier Hd 50°25'·02N 05°05'·13W 2 FR (vert) 4m 2M; ● Tr.

The Stones Lt By 50°15'·60N 05°25'·40W Q; NCM.
Godrevy I 50°14'·50N 05°23'·95W Fl WR 10s 37m W12M, R9M; W 8-sided Tr; vis W022°-101°, R101°-145°, W145°-272°.

HAYLE
App Lt By 50°12'·25N 05°26'·45W Iso G 2s; SHM.
Lts in line 180°. Front, 50°11'·55N 05°26'·14W F 17m 4M.
Rear, 110m from front, F 23m 4M.
Carnew Weir 50°11'·40N 05°25'·97W Q.

ST IVES
E Pier Hd 50°12'·77N 05°28'·53W 2 FG (vert) 8m 5M; W ● Tr.
W Pier Hd 50°12'·74N 05°28'·67W 2 FR (vert) 5m 3M Gy col.

Pendeen 50°09'·80N 05°40'·20W Fl (4) 15s 59m **16M**; W ● Tr; vis 042°-240°; in B between Gurnard Hd and Pendeen it shows to coast; *Horn 20s.* For Lts further SW see 10.1.4.

11

10.11.5 PASSAGE INFORMATION

For directions on this coast refer to the Admiralty *W Coasts of England and Wales Pilot*. *A Cruising Guide to NW England & Wales* (Imray/Griffiths) covers as far S as Tenby; *Lundy and Irish Sea Pilot* (Imray/Taylor) continues to Land's End.

It is useful to know some Welsh words with navigational significance. *Aber*: estuary. *Afon*: river. *Bach, bychan, fach*: little. *Borth*: cove. *Bryn*: hill. *Careg, craig*: rock. *Coch, goch*: red. *Dinas*: fort. *Ddu*: black. *Fawr, Mawr*: big. *Ffrydiau*: tiderip. *Llwyd*: grey. *Moel*: bare conical hill. *Mor*: sea. *Morfa*: sandy shore. *Mynydd*: mountain. *Penrhyn*: headland. *Porth*: cove. *Ynys, Ynysoedd*: island(s).

CARDIGAN BAY (charts 1971, 1972, 1973)

Hbrs are mostly on a lee shore, and/or have bars which make them dangerous to approach in bad weather. Abersoch (10.11.7) and Pwllheli (10.11.8) offer best shelter from prevailing W'lies. There may be overfalls off Trwyn Cilan, SW of St Tudwal's Is (lit). In N part of bay there are three major dangers to coasting yachts, as described briefly below: St Patrick's Causeway (Sarn Badrig) runs 12M SW from Mochras Pt. It is mostly large loose stones, and dries (up to 1.5m) for much of its length. In strong winds the sea breaks heavily at all states of tide. The outer end is marked by a WCM lt buoy. At the inner end there is a chan about 5ca offshore, which can be taken with care at half tide.

Sarn-y-Bwch runs 4M WSW from Pen Bwch Pt. It is composed of rky boulders, drying in places close inshore and with least depth 0.3m over 1M offshore. There is a WCM buoy off W end. NW of Aberystwyth (10.11.12), Sarn Cynfelyn and Cynfelyn Patches extend a total of 6.5M offshore, with depths of 1.5m in places. A WCM buoy is at the outer end. Almost halfway along the bank is Main Channel, 3ca wide, running roughly N/S, but not marked.

A military firing area occupies much of Cardigan B. Beware targets and buoys, some unlit. Range activity is broadcast on VHF Ch 16, 0800-1600LT Mon-Fri or ☎ (01239) 813219.

If on passage N/S through St George's Chan (i.e. not bound for Cardigan B or Milford Haven) the easiest route, and always by night, is W of the Bishops and the Smalls, noting the TSS, Fig 10 (3) 1. If bound to/from Milford Haven or Cardigan Bay, passage inside both the Smalls and Grassholm is possible.

RAMSEY SOUND AND THE BISHOPS (chart 1482)

The Bishops and the Clerks are islets and rks 2.5M W and NW of Ramsey Is, a bird sanctuary SSW of St David's Hd. N Bishop is the N'ly of the group, 3ca ENE of which is Bell Rk (depth 1.9m). S Bishop (Lt, fog sig, RC) is 3M to the SSW.

Between S Bishop and Ramsey Is the dangers include Daufraich with offliers to the E and heavy overfalls; Llech Isaf and Llech Uchaf drying rks are further ENE. Carreg Rhoson and offliers are between Daufraich and N Bishop. There are navigable routes between most of these islets and rocks, but only by day in good vis and with local knowledge. The N/S route close W of Ramsey Island is said to be easier than Ramsey Sound (see below).

2M W of The Bishops the S-going stream begins at HW Milford Haven + 0400, and the N-going at HW Milford Haven – 0225, sp rates 2kn. Between The Bishops and Ramsey Is the SW-going stream begins at HW Milford Haven + 0330, and the NE-going at HW Milford Haven – 0255, sp rates 5kn.

Ramsey Sound should be taken at slack water. The S-going stream begins at HW Milford Haven + 0300, and the N-going at HW Milford Haven – 0325, sp rates 6kn at The Bitches, where chan is narrowest (2ca), decreasing N and S. The Bitches are rks extending 2ca from E side of Ramsey Is. Other dangers are: Gwahan and Carreg-gafeiliog, at N end of Sound, to W and E; Horse Rk (dries 0.9m) almost in mid-chan about 5ca NNE of The Bitches, with associated overfalls; Shoe Rk (dries 3m) at SE end of chan; and rks extending 5ca SSE from S end of Ramsey Is.

THE SMALLS TO MILFORD HAVEN (chart 1478)

St Brides B (10.11.13) provides anch in settled weather or offshore winds, but is a trap in westerlies. Solva is a little hbr with shelter for boats able to take the ground, or anch behind Black Rk (dries 3.6m) in the middle of the entrance.

The Smalls Lt, where there is a Historic Wreck (see 10.0.3h) is 13M W of the Welsh mainland (Wooltack Pt). 2M and 4M E of The Smalls are the Hats and Barrels, rky patches on which the sea breaks. 7M E of The Smalls is Grassholm Island with a race either end and strong tidal eddies so that it is advisable to pass about 1M off. The chan between Barrels and Grassholm is 2.5M wide, and here the S-going stream begins at HW Milford Haven + 0440, and the N-going at HW Milford Haven – 0135, sp rates 5kn. 5M of clear water lie between Grassholm and Skomer Is/Skokholm Is to the E. But Wildgoose Race, which forms W of Skomer and Skokholm is very dangerous, so keep 2M W of these two Islands.

To E of Skomer is Midland Is, and between here and Wooltack Pt is Jack Sound which is only 2ca wide and should not be attempted without chart 1482, detailed pilotage directions, and only at slack water nps; it is a testing passage. Dangers which must be identified include: The Crab Stones, E from Midland Is; The Cable, a drying rk on E side of chan; Tusker Rk, steep-to on its W side, off Wooltack Pt; The Black Stones; and The Anvil and other rks off Anvil Pt. In Jack Sound the S-going stream begins at HW Milford Haven + 0200, and the N-going at HW Milford Haven – 0425, sp rates 6kn.

MILFORD HAVEN TO MUMBLES HD (charts 1179, 1076)

Milford Haven (10.11.14) is a long natural, all-weather hbr with marinas beyond the oil terminals. 3M S of the ent, beware Turbot Bank (WCM lt buoy). Crow Rk (dries 5.5m) is 5ca SSE of Linney Hd, and The Toes are dangerous submerged rks close W and SE of Crow Rk. There is a passage inshore of these dangers. There are overfalls on St Gowan Shoals which extend 4M SW of St Govan's Hd, and the sea breaks on the shallow patches in bad weather. For firing areas from Linney Hd to Carmarthen Bay, see 10.11.14.

Caldey Is (Lt) lies S of Tenby (10.11.15). Off its NW pt is St Margaret's Is connected by a rky reef. Caldey Sound, between St Margaret's Is and Giltar Pt (chart 1482), is buoyed, but beware Eel Spit near W end of Caldey Is where there can be a nasty sea with wind against tide, and Woolhouse Rks (dry 3.6m) 1ca NE of Caldey Is. Saundersfoot hbr (dries) is 2M N of Tenby, with anch well sheltered from N and W but subject to swell. Streams are weak here. Carmarthen Bay has no offshore dangers for yachts, other than the extensive drying sands at head of B and on its E side off Burry Inlet (10.11.16).

S of Worms Head, Helwick Sands (buoyed at each end) extend 7M W from Port Eynon Pt; least depth of 1.3m is near their W end. Stream sets NE/SW across the sands. There is a narrow chan inshore, close to Port Eynon Pt. Between here and Mumbles Hd the stream runs roughly along coast, sp rates 3kn off Pts, but there are eddies in Port Eynon B and Oxwich B (both yacht anchs), and overfalls SSE of Oxwich Pt.

MUMBLES HEAD TO CARDIFF (charts 1165, 1182)

Off Mumbles Hd (Lt, fog sig) beware Mixon Shoal (dries 0.3m), marked by PHM buoy. In good conditions pass N of shoal, 1ca off Mumbles Hd. Anch N of Mumbles Hd, good holding but exposed to swell. At W side of Swansea Bay, Green Grounds, rky shoals, lie in appr's to Swansea (10.11.17).

Scarweather Sands, much of which dry (up to 3.3m) and where sea breaks heavily, extend 7M W from Porthcawl (10.11.17) and are well buoyed (chart 1161). There is a chan between the sands and coast to E, but beware Hugo Bank (dries 2.6m) and Kenfig Patches (0.5m) with overfalls up to 7ca offshore between Sker Pt and Porthcawl.

Nash Sands extend 7.5M WNW from Nash Pt. Depths vary and are least at inshore end (dries 3m), but Nash Passage, 1ca wide, runs close inshore between E Nash ECM buoy and rky ledge off Nash Pt. On E-going stream there are heavy overfalls off Nash Pt and at W end of Nash Sands. Between Nash Pt and Breaksea Pt the E-going stream begins at HW Avonmouth + 0535, and the W-going at HW Avonmouth – 0035, sp rates 3kn. Off Breaksea Pt there may be overfalls.

From Rhoose Pt to Lavernock Pt the coast is fringed with foul ground. Lavernock Spit extends 1·75M S of Lavernock Pt, and E of the spit is main chan to Cardiff (10.11.19); the other side of the chan being Cardiff Grounds, a bank drying 5·4m which lies parallel with the shore and about 1·5M from it.

SEVERN ESTUARY (charts 1176, 1166)

Near the centre of Bristol Chan, either side of the buoyed fairway are the islands of Flat Holm (Lt, fog sig) and Steep Holm. 7M SW of Flat Holm lies Culver Sand (0·9m), 3M in length, with W & ECM bys. Monkstone Rk (Lt, dries) is 2M NW of the buoyed chan to Avonmouth and Bristol (10.11.21). Extensive drying banks cover the N shore of the estuary, beyond Newport and the Severn bridges (chart 1176).

The range of tide in the Bristol Chan is exceptionally large, 12·2m sp and 6·0m np, and tidal streams are very powerful, particularly above Avonmouth. Between Flat Holm and Steep Holm the E-going stream begins at HW Avonmouth – 0610, sp 3kn, and the W-going at HW Avonmouth + 0015, sp 4kn.

The ent to the R. Avon is just to the S of Avonmouth S Pier Hd. Bristol City Docks lie some 6M up river. Approach the ent via King Road and the Newcombe and Cockburn lt buoys and thence via the Swash chan into the Avon. The ent dries at LW but the river is navigable at about half tide. Tidal streams are strong in the approaches to Avonmouth, up to 5kn at sp. The tide is also strong in the R. Avon which is best entered no earlier than HW Avonmouth – 0200.

From Avonmouth it is 16M to Sharpness which yachts should aim to reach at about HW Avonmouth. Spring streams can run 8kn at the Shoots, and 6kn at the Severn bridges (10.11.19). At the Shoots the flood begins at HW Avonmouth –0430 and the ebb at HW Avonmouth + 0045. The Severn Bore can usually be seen if Avonmouth range is 13·5m or more.

AVONMOUTH TO HARTLAND POINT (AC 1152, 1165)

From Avonmouth to Sand Pt, the part-drying English Grounds extend 3M off the S shore. Extensive mud flats fill the bays S to Burnham-on-Sea (10.11.22). Westward, the S shore of Bristol Chan is cleaner than N shore. But there is less shelter since hbrs such as Watchet (marina planned), Minehead, Porlock Weir and Watermouth dry out, see 10.11.22. In bad weather dangerous overfalls occur NW and NE of Foreland Pt. 5M to W there is a race off Highveer Pt. Between Ilfracombe (10.11.23) and Bull Pt the E-going stream begins at HW Milford Haven + 0540, and the W-going at HW Milford Haven – 0025, sp rates 3kn. Overfalls occur up to 1·5M N of Bull Pt and over Horseshoe Rks, which lie 3M N. There is a dangerous race off Morte Pt, 1·5M to W of Bull Pt.

Shelter is available under lee of Lundy Is (10.11.23); but avoid bad races to NE (White Horses), the NW (Hen and Chickens), and to SE; also overfalls over NW Bank. W of Lundy streams are moderate, but strong around the Is and much stronger towards Bristol Chan proper.

Proceeding WSW from Rivers Taw/Torridge (10.11.24), keep 3M off to avoid the race N of Hartland Pt (Lt, fog sig, conspic radome). There is shelter off Clovelly in S/SW winds.

HARTLAND POINT TO LAND'S END (charts 1156, 1149)

The N coast of Cornwall and SW approaches to Bristol Chan are very exposed. Yachts need to be sturdy and well equipped, since if bad weather develops no shelter may be at hand. Bude (10.11.25) dries, and is not approachable in W winds; only accessible in calm weather or offshore winds. Boscastle is a tiny hbr (dries) 3M NE of Tintagel Hd. Only approach in good weather or offshore winds; anch off or dry out alongside.

Padstow is a refuge, but in strong NW winds the sea breaks on bar and prevents entry. Off Trevose Hd (Lt) beware Quies Rks which extend 1M to W. From here S the coast is relatively clear to Godrevy Is, apart from Bawden Rks 1M N of St Agnes Hd. Newquay B (10.11.25) is good anch in offshore winds, and the hbr (dries) is sheltered but uncomfortable in N winds. Off Godrevy Is (Lt) are The Stones, drying rky shoals extending 1·5M offshore and marked by NCM lt buoy.

In St Ives Bay (chart 1168), Hayle (10.11.25) is a commercial port (dries); seas break heavily on bar at times, especially with a ground swell. Stream is strong, so enter just before HW. The bottom is mostly sand. St Ives (dries) (10.11.25) gives shelter from winds E to SW, but is very exposed to N; there is sometimes a heavy breaking sea if there is ground swell.

From St Ives to Land's End coast is rugged and exposed. There are overfalls SW of Pendeen Pt (Lt, fog sig). Vyneck Rks lie awash about 3ca NW of C Cornwall. The Brisons are two high rky islets 5ca SW of C Cornwall, with rky ledges inshore and to the S. The Longships (Lt, fog sig) group of rks is about 1M W of Land's End. The inshore passage (001° on Brisons) is about 4ca wide with unmarked drying rks on the W side; only to be considered in calm weather.

For Isles of Scilly and South Cornwall, see 10.1.5.

10.11.6   DISTANCE TABLE

Approximate distances in nautical miles are by the most direct route, whilst avoiding dangers and allowing for Traffic Separation Schemes. Places in *italics* are in adjoining areas; places in **bold** are in 10.0.7, Distances across the Irish Sea.

1.	*Bardsey Island*	**1**																		
2.	Abersoch	14	**2**																	
3.	**Pwllheli**	18	5	**3**																
4.	Barmouth	27	18	18	**4**															
5.	Aberdovey	31	26	25	14	**5**														
6.	Aberystwyth	33	30	30	20	10	**6**													
7.	**Fishguard**	45	54	58	56	47	40	**7**												
8.	South Bishop	60	70	74	74	67	61	25	**8**											
9.	**Milford Haven**	83	93	97	97	90	84	48	23	**9**										
10.	Tenby	106	116	120	120	113	107	71	46	28	**10**									
11.	**Swansea**	129	139	143	143	136	130	94	69	55	36	**11**								
12.	Barry	151	161	165	165	158	152	116	91	77	57	37	**12**							
13.	Cardiff	160	170	174	174	167	161	125	100	86	66	46	9	**13**						
14.	Sharpness	191	201	205	205	198	192	156	131	117	106	75	39	33	**14**					
15.	**Avonmouth**	174	184	188	188	181	175	139	114	100	89	58	22	20	18	**15**				
16.	Burnham-on-Sea	168	178	182	182	175	169	133	108	94	70	48	18	53	50	33	**16**			
17.	Ilfracombe	127	137	141	141	134	128	92	67	53	35	25	35	44	74	57	45	**17**		
18.	Lundy Island	110	120	124	124	117	111	75	50	38	30	37	54	63	95	78	66	22	**18**	
19.	**Padstow**	141	151	155	155	148	142	106	81	70	70	76	88	97	127	110	98	55	39	**19**
20.	*Longships*	168	178	182	182	175	169	133	108	105	110	120	130	139	169	152	140	95	82	50	**20**

11

ABERSOCH   10-11-7

Gwynedd 52°49'·29N 04°29'·20W (⚓)   Rtg 3-3-2

CHARTS
AC 1512, 1971, *1410*; Imray C61; OS 123
TIDES
–0315 Dover; ML 2·5; Duration 0520; Zone 0 (UT)

Standard Port MILFORD HAVEN (→)

Times				Height (metres)			
High Water		Low Water		MHWS	MHWN	MLWN	MLWS
0100	0800	0100	0700	7·0	5·2	2·5	0·7
1300	2000	1300	1900				
Differences ST TUDWAL'S ROADS							
+0155	+0145	+0240	+0310	–2·2	–1·9	–0·7	–0·2
ABERDARON							
+0210	+0200	+0240	+0310	–2·4	–1·9	–0·6	–0·2

SHELTER
There are few moorings for visitors. Apply to Hr Mr or SC. ⚓ in St Tudwal's Roads clear of moored yachts; sheltered from SSE through S to NE.
NAVIGATION
WPT 52°48'·50N 04°26'·06W, 113°/293° from/to YC jetty, 2·4M. There are no navigational dangers, but steer well clear of the drying rks to the E of East Island; a PHM buoy is 2ca E of these rks (just off chartlet). St Tudwal's islands themselves are fairly steep-to, except at N ends. St Tudwal's Sound is clear of dangers.
LIGHTS AND MARKS
The only lt is on St Tudwal's West Island, Fl WR 15s 46m 14/10M (see chartlet and 10.11.4).
RADIO TELEPHONE
S Caernarfon YC Ch 80 M.
TELEPHONE (Dial code 01758)
Hr Mr 812684; MRSC (01407) 762051; ⌗ (01407) 762714; Marinecall 0891 500 460; Police 2022; Dr 612535.
FACILITIES
S. Caernarvonshire YC ☎ 812338, Slip, M, L, FW, R, Bar (May-Sept), D; **Abersoch Power Boat Club** ☎ 812027.
Services: BY, Slip, ME, El, Sh, ACA, CH, P, C (12 ton).
Town EC Wed; CH, V, R, Bar, ✉, ⑧, ⇌ (Pwllheli), ✈ (Chester).

PWLLHELI   10-11-8

Gwynedd 52°53'·21N 04°23'·68W   Rtg 1-1-1

CHARTS
AC 1512, 1971, *1410*; Imray C61; OS 123
TIDES
–0315 Dover; ML 2·6; Duration 0510; Zone 0 (UT)

Standard Port MILFORD HAVEN (→)

Times				Height (metres)			
High Water		Low Water		MHWS	MHWN	MLWN	MLWS
0100	0800	0100	0700	7·0	5·2	2·5	0·7
1300	2000	1300	1900				
Differences PWLLHELI							
+0210	+0150	+0245	+0320	–2·0	–1·8	–0·6	–0·2
CRICCIETH							
+0210	+0155	+0255	+0320	–2·0	–1·8	–0·7	–0·3

SHELTER
Good in hbr & marina. Visitors must first report to marina. Pile berths on S side of chan. No ⚓ in hbr; 4kn speed limit. Drying moorings in inner hbr (SW and NW bights).
NAVIGATION
WPT 52°53'·00N 04°23'·00W, SWM lt buoy, Iso 2s, 119°/ 299° from/to QG lt at head of Training Arm, 0·47M. Ent is safe in most winds, but in strong E to SW winds sea breaks on offshore shoals. Bar and hbr chan are dredged to at least 1·0m; 3 tide gauges. Max tidal stream 2kn.
LIGHTS AND MARKS
No ldg lts/marks, but ent chan well marked (see chartlet). Gimblet Rock (30m) is conspic conical rock 3ca SW of ent.
RADIO TELEPHONE
Hr Mr: VHF Ch 12 16 (0900-1715). Marina: Ch 80 M H24.
TELEPHONE (Dial code 01758)
Hr Mr 704081; MRSC (01407) 762051; CG 701589; ⌗ (01407) 762714; Marinecall 0891 500 460; Police 701177; Dr 612535.

FACILITIES
Marina (400) ☎ 701219 (H24), ⚓ 701443, £10.74, FW, P, D, AC, BH (40 ton), C, Slip, ▣; **Marina Club** ☎ 612271, Slip, FW; **Hbr Authority** Slip, M, L, FW, AB; **South Caernarvonshire YC** ☎ 812338; **Pwllheli SC** ☎ 612219; **Services:** BY, Slip, L, FW, ME, Gas, Sh, CH, ACA, D, C (14 ton), El, Ⓔ, SM.
Town EC Thurs; V, R, Bar, ✉, ⑧, ⇌, ✈ (Chester).

ADJACENT HARBOUR

MOCHRAS, Gwynedd, 52°49'·55N 04°07'·70W. AC 1512, 1971. HW –0245 on Dover. Small yacht hbr on SE side of Shell Is. Mochras lagoon dries. Bar, about 2ca seaward. Entry advised HW±2. Tide runs strongly in the narrows on the ebb; at sp beware severe eddies inside ent. Ent between Shell Is (lt Fl WRG 4s; G079°-124°, W124°-134°, R134°-179°; shown mid Mar-Nov) and sea wall. 3 grey posts, R topmarks, mark N side of chan. Shifting chan, marked by posts & buoys, runs NE to Pensarn, where permanent moorings limit space. To S, buoyed chan runs to Shell Is Yacht Hbr ☎ (0134120) 450 with facilities: M, FW, Slip, R, Bar, shwrs. Pensarn: drying AB, ⇌.

PORTHMADOG   10-11-9

Gwynedd 52°55'·30N 04°07'·70W   Rtg 5-2-1

CHARTS
AC 1512, 1971, *1410*; Imray C61; OS 124

TIDES
−0247 Dover; ML no data; Duration 0455; Zone 0 (UT)

Standard Port MILFORD HAVEN (—→)

Times				Height (metres)			
High Water		Low Water		MHWS	MHWN	MLWN	MLWS
0100	0800	0100	0700	7·0	5·2	2·5	0·7
1300	2000	1300	1900				
Differences PORTHMADOG							
+0235	+0210	No data		−1·9	−1·8		No data

SHELTER
Inner hbr (N of Cei Ballast): Good all year round; visitors' drying AB adjacent Madoc YC or afloat rafted on moored yachts off YC. (Greaves Wharf is obstructed by dinghies and salmon nets). Outer hbr: Summer only and exposed to S winds. Speed limit 6kn in hbr upstream of No 11 By.

NAVIGATION
WPT Fairway SWM buoy, 52°52'·95N 04°11'·11W, 240°/060° from/to conspic white Ho at W side of ent, 2M; chan shifts and may divide. Bar changes frequently, but is near to No 3 and 4 buoys; dries approx 0·3m. Latest info from Hr Mr on request. Advise entering HW±1½. In SW'lies, waves are steep-sided and close, especially on the ebb.

LIGHTS AND MARKS
Fairway buoy RW, L Fl 10s. Chan marker buoys (14) have R/G reflective top marks and numbers in W reflective tape. Moel-y-Gest is conspic hill (259m) approx 1M WNW of hbr. Harlech Castle (ru) is about 3M SE of appr chan.

RADIO TELEPHONE
Hr Mr Ch 14 12 16 (0900-1715 and when vessel due). Madoc YC: Ch **80** M 16.

TELEPHONE (Dial code 01766)
Hr Mr 512927, mobile (0374) 631844; MRSC (01407) 762051; Pilot 514939, Home 75684; Hbr Authority Gwynedd Council (01758) 613131; ⌗ (01407) 762714; Marinecall 0891 500 460; Police 512226; Dr 512239.

FACILITIES
Hbr (265 berths) ☎ 512927, £4.47, D, FW, C, Slip; **Madoc YC** ☎ 512976, AB, M, FW, Bar; **Porthmadog and Transfynydd SC** ☎ 513546, AB, M, FW, Slip; **Services:** CH, ACA, Sh, D, P (45 gall drums), C (3½ ton), M, BY, El, Pilot.
Town EC Wed; ⌧, Ⓑ, ⇌, ✈ (Chester).

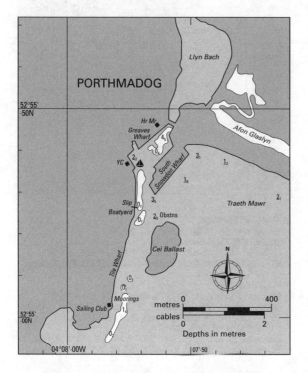

BARMOUTH   10-11-10

Gwynedd 52°42'·95N 04°03'·00W   Rtg 4-4-1

CHARTS
AC 1484, 1971, *1410*; Imray C61; OS 124

TIDES
−0305 Dover; ML 2·6; Duration 0515; Zone 0 (UT)

Standard Port MILFORD HAVEN (—→)

Times				Height (metres)			
High Water		Low Water		MHWS	MHWN	MLWN	MLWS
0100	0800	0100	0700	7·0	5·2	2·5	0·7
1300	2000	1300	1900				
Differences BARMOUTH							
+0215	+0205	+0310	+0320	−2·0	−1·7	−0·7	0·0

SHELTER
Good. Entry HW±2½ safe, but impossible with strong SW'lies. Exposed ⚓ W of Barmouth Outer buoy in 6 to 10m. In hbr there are 3 ⚓s; secure as directed by Hr Mr, because of submarine cables and strong tidal streams. A ❻ berth is marked at W end of quay, dries at half-tide. The estuary and river (Afon Mawddach) are tidal and can be navigated for about 7M above railway bridge (clearance approx 5·5m); but chan is not buoyed, and sandbanks move constantly - local knowledge essential.

NAVIGATION
WPT, Barmouth Outer SWM buoy, L Fl 10s, 52°42'·90N 04°04'·90W, 277°/097° from/to Y perch lt, QR, 0·75M. Appr from SW between St Patrick's Causeway (Sarn Badrig) and Sarn-y-Bwch (see 10·11·5). Barmouth can be identified by Cader Idris, a mountain 890m high, 5M ESE. Fegla Fawr, a rounded hill, lies on S side of hbr. The Bar, 0·75M W of Penrhyn Pt, with min depth 0·3m is subject to considerable change. Chan is marked by the Bar SHM buoy and 2 PHM buoys, all unlit and moved as necessary. Spring ebb runs 3 - 5kn.
Note: A Historic Wreck (see 10.0.3h) is at 52°46'·73N 04°07'·53W, 4·5M NNW of Barmouth Outer SWM buoy.

LIGHTS AND MARKS
Y perch, QR 4m 5M, R framework tr, marks S end of stony ledge extending 3ca SW from Ynys y Brawd across N Bank. Ynys y Brawd groyne, SE end, marked by bn with lt, Fl R 5s 5M. NW end of rly bridge 2 FR (hor).

RADIO TELEPHONE
Call *Barmouth Hbr* VHF Ch **12** 16 (Apl-Sept 0900-2200LT; Oct-Mar 0900-1600LT); wind and sea state are available.

TELEPHONE (Dial code 01341)
Hr Mr 280671; MRSC (01407) 762051; ⌗ (01407) 762714; Marinecall 0891 500460; Police 280222; Dr 280521.

FACILITIES
Quay £6.50, M (contact Hr Mr in advance if deep water ⚓ required), D, FW, El, AC, Slip; **Merioneth YC** ☎ 280000; **Services:** CH, ACA.
Town EC Wed; P, D, V, R, Bar, ⌧, Ⓑ, ⇌, ✈ (Chester), Ferry across to Penrhyn Pt.

11

ABERDOVEY   10-11-11

Gwynedd 52°32'·55N 04°02'·65W (Jetty)   Rtg 4-4-1

CHARTS
AC 1484, 1972, *1410*; Imray C61; OS 135
TIDES
−0320 Dover; ML 2·6; Duration 0535; Zone 0 (UT)

Standard Port MILFORD HAVEN (→)

Times				Height (metres)			
High Water		Low Water		MHWS	MHWN	MLWN	MLWS
0100	0800	0100	0700	7·0	5·2	2·5	0·7
1300	2000	1300	1900				
Differences ABERDOVEY							
+0215	+0200	+0230	+0305	−2·0	−1·7	−0·5	0·0

SHELTER
Good except in strong W/SW winds. Berth on jetty; to the E there is heavy silting.
NAVIGATION
WPT Aberdovey Outer SWM buoy, L Fl 10s, 52°31'·30N 04°05'·05W, 230°/050° from/to Bar buoy, 6ca. Bar (0·7m) and chan constantly shift and are hazardous below half-tide; buoys moved accordingly. Visitors should call Hr Mr on VHF before entering or ☎ the Pilot. Submarine cables (prohib ⚓s) marked by bns with R ◇ topmarks.
LIGHTS AND MARKS
No daymarks. 4 SHM buoys (Bar Fl G 5s, S Spit Fl G 9s, Inner Fl G 7s and No 4 unlit) mark chan to jetty.
RADIO TELEPHONE
Call *Aberdovey Hbr* VHF Ch 12 16.
TELEPHONE (Dial code 01654)
Hr Mr 767626; MRSC (01646) 690909; Pilot 767247; ✽ (01407) 762714 Ext 262; Marinecall 0891 500 460; Police 767222; Dr 710414; Ⓗ 710411.
FACILITIES
Jetty AB £6.50, M, FW; **Wharf** Slip, AB, L, FW, C; **Dovey YC** ☎ (01827) 286514, Bar, Slip, L, FW; **Services:** BY, ME, El, Sh, CH, ACA, Ⓔ. **Town** EC Wed (winter only); P & D (cans), ME, El, CH, V, R, Bar, ⊠, Ⓑ, ⇌, ✈ (Chester).

OTHER HARBOURS IN SOUTH CARDIGAN BAY

ABERAERON, Ceredigion, 52°14'·60N 04°15'·87W. AC 1484, 1972, *1410*. HW −0325 on Dover; +0140 and −1·9m on Milford Haven; ML 2·7m; Duration 0540. A small, popular drying hbr at the mouth of the R Aeron; access HW±1½. Short drying piers extend each side of river ent. In strong NW'lies there is little shelter. AB £2.50 on NW wall. Foul ground with depths of 1·5m extend 3ca offshore to SW of Aberaeron. Beware Carreg Gloyn (0·3m) 4ca WSW of hbr, and Sarn Cadwgan (1·8m) shoals 5ca N of the hbr ent. Lts: N pier Fl (4) WRG 15s 10m 6M, G050°-104°, W104°-178°, R178°-232°. S pier Fl (3) G 10s 11m 6M, vis 050°-243°. VHF 14 16. Hr Mr ☎ (01545) 571645; **YC** ☎ 570077.

NEW QUAY, Ceredigion, 52°12'·90N 04°21'·15W. AC 1484, 1972, *1410*. HW −0335 on Dover; Duration 0540; see 10.11.12. Good shelter in offshore winds, but untenable in NW'lies. On E side of bay Carreg Ina, rks drying 1·3m, are marked by NCM buoy. 2 Y bns indicate a sewer outfall extending 7ca NNW from Ina Pt. The hbr (dries 1·6m) is protected by a pier with lt, Fl WG 3s 12m 8/5M; W135°-252°, G252°-295°. Groyne extends 80m SSE of pierhd to a SHM bn; close ENE of which is a ECM bn, Q (3) 10s. ⚓s are 1ca E of pier; £2.50. VHF Ch 12 16 80. Hr Mr ☎ (01545) 560368. CG ☎ 560212; Dr ☎ 560203; YC ☎ 560516; Facilities: D (from fishermen). **Town** FW, P (3M), ⊠, R, Bar.

ABERYSTWYTH   10-11-12

Ceredigion 52°24'·40N 04°05'·40W Rtg 3-2-1

CHARTS
AC 1484, 1972, *1410*; Imray C61; OS 135
TIDES
−0330 Dover; ML 2·7; Duration 0540; Zone 0 (UT)

Standard Port MILFORD HAVEN (→)

Times				Height (metres)			
High Water		Low Water		MHWS	MHWN	MLWN	MLWS
0100	0800	0100	0700	7·0	5·2	2·5	0·7
1300	2000	1300	1900				
Differences ABERYSTWYTH							
+0145	+0130	+0210	+0245	−2·0	−1·7	−0·7	0·0
NEW QUAY							
+0150	+0125	+0155	+0230	−2·1	−1·8	−0·6	−0·1
ABERPORTH							
+0135	+0120	+0150	+0220	−2·1	−1·8	−0·6	−0·1

SHELTER
Good, in marina (2·3m) on E side of chan; or dry against Town Quay. Access approx HW±3 (HW±2 for strangers). The Bar, close off S pier hd, has 0·7m least depth. E edge of inner hbr chan 0·3m is defined by WCM beacon.
NAVIGATION
WPT 52°24'·81N 04°06'·15W, 313°/133° from/to ent, 0·6M. Approach dangerous in strong on-shore winds. From N, beware Castle Rks, within R sector 141°-175° of N bkwtr lt, QWR 9m 2M; also rks drying 0·5m W of N bkwtr and boulders below S pier hd. Turn 90° port inside narrow ent.
LIGHTS AND MARKS
N bkwtr hd ≠ 140° Wellington Mon't (on top Pendinas, conspic hill 120m high) clears to S of Castle Rks. Ldg lts 133°, both FR on Ystwyth Bridge, white daymarks. WCM bn on with Y daymark leads 100° across bar into hbr ent.

RADIO TELEPHONE
Hr Mr VHF Ch 14 16. Marina Ch 80 16.
TELEPHONE (Dial code 01970)
Hr Mr 611433; Marina 611422; MRSC (01646) 690909; ✽ (01222) 763880 (H24); Marinecall 0891 500460; Police 612791; Dr 624855.
FACILITIES
Marina (Y Lanfa), ☎ 611422, ⛽ 624122, (88 + 12 Ⓥ), £9.23, access HW±2, AC, FW, D, Slip, BH (10 ton), C (max 15 ton by arrangement); **Town Quay** AB £3.75, C (3 ton), L, FW; **YC** ☎ 612907, Slip, M, Bar;
Services: Fl, CH, D, Ⓔ, ME, Sh, M, Slip, C (25 ton), Gas.
Town P (cans), CH, V, R, Bar, ◎, ⊠, Ⓑ, ⇌, ✈ (Swansea).

FISHGUARD   10-11-13
Pembrokeshire 52°00'·10N 04°58'·33W
Commercial Hbr Rtg 1-3-3; Lower Hbr Rtg 4-5-1

CHARTS
AC 1484, 1973, *1410, 1178*; Imray C61/60; OS 157
TIDES
−0400 Dover; ML 2·6; Duration 0550; Zone 0 (UT)

Standard Port MILFORD HAVEN (→)

Times				Height (metres)			
High Water		Low Water		MHWS	MHWN	MLWN	MLWS
0100	0800	0100	0700	7·0	5·2	2·5	0·7
1300	2000	1300	1900				
Differences FISHGUARD							
+0115	+0100	+0110	+0135	−2·2	−1·8	−0·5	+0·1
PORT CARDIGAN							
+0140	+0120	+0220	+0130	−2·3	−1·8	−0·5	0·0
CARDIGAN (Town)							
+0220	+0150	No data		−2·2	−1·6	No data	
PORTHGAIN							
+0055	+0045	+0045	+0100	−2·5	−1·8	−0·6	0·0
RAMSEY SOUND							
+0030	+0030	+0030	+0030	−1·9	−1·3	−0·3	0·0
SOLVA							
+0015	+0010	+0035	+0015	−1·5	−1·0	−0·2	0·0
LITTLE HAVEN							
+0010	+0010	+0025	+0015	−1·1	−0·8	−0·2	0·0
MARTIN'S HAVEN							
+0010	+0010	+0015	+0015	−0·8	−0·5	+0·1	+0·1

SHELTER
Good, except in strong NW/NE winds. Access H24 to
Goodwick (upper, commercial) hbr with only 2 ♥ berths;
no ⚓, except SW of ferry quay. Lower Town (Fishguard)
dries 3·2m; access HW±1, limited AB. Good holding in
most of the bay; ⚓ off Saddle Pt in 2m or as shown.
Strong S'lies funnel down the hbr.
NAVIGATION
WPT 52°01'·00N 04°57'·50W, 057°/237° from/to N bkwtr lt,
0·48m. Beware large swell, especially in N winds. Keep
clear of ferries and high-speed SeaCat manoeuvring.
LIGHTS AND MARKS
Strumble Hd lt, Fl (4) 15s 45m 26M, is approx 4M WNW of
hbr. N bkwtr Fl G 4·5s 18m 13M, Bell 8s. E bkwtr Fl R 3s 10m
5M. Ldg lts 282° (to ferry berths), both FG; W ◊ on masts.
RADIO TELEPHONE
Hr Mr Ch 14 16. Goodwick Marine Ch M (occas).
TELEPHONE (Dial code 01348)
Commercial Hbr Supervisor 872881; Hr Mr (Lower hbr)
874616/873231; MRSC (01646) 690909; ⌗ (01222) 763880
(H24); Marinecall 0891 500 460; Police 873073; Dr 872802.
FACILITIES
Goodwick Hbr AB £10; **Lower Town, Fishguard**, M (free
o'night) via Hr Mr; **Fishguard Bay YC** ☎ 872866, FW, Bar;
Services: BY, Sh, ME, ACA, Slip, CH, El.
Town EC Wed; P & D (cans), V, R, Gas, Bar, ⊠, ▣, Ⓑ, ⇌,
✈ (Cardiff), Ferry–Rosslare.

MINOR HARBOUR, 12M NE of Fishguard

PORT CARDIGAN, Ceredigion, 52°07'·00N 04°42'·00W. AC
1484, 1973. HW −0405 on Dover; ML 2·4m; Duration 0500;
See above. Shelter is good, but ent dangerous in strong N/
NW winds. Large scale chart (1484) and local advice essential.
Bar has 0·3m or less; breakers form esp on sp ebb. ⚓ near
Hotel (conspic) on E side of ent by 2 FR (vert). Chan is close
to E side; IDM bn, Fl (2) 5s, should be left to stbd. From Pen-
yr-Ergyd to Bryn-Du chan is unmarked and shifts constantly.
⚓ in pools off Pen-yr-Ergyd or near St Dogmaels. Possible
⚓s off Teifi Boating Club. Hr Mr ☎ as Aberaeron or New
Quay. Facilities: **Moorings**: at Gwbert (drying) ☎ (01239)
612832, at Netpool (afloat) ☎ 612166; **Teifi BC** Hon Sec ☎
612361 FW, Bar; **Services**: ME, Sh.
Town EC Wed; Ⓑ, V, CH, P, D, FW, ME, Bar, R, ⇌.

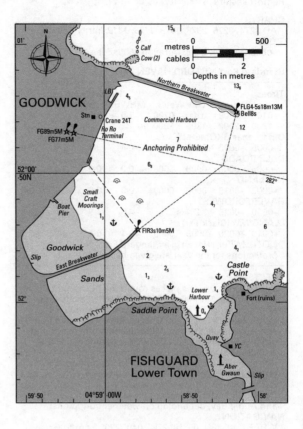

ADJACENT HARBOURS IN ST BRIDES BAY

SOLVA, Pembrokeshire, 51°52'00N 05°11'·60W. AC *1478*.
HW −0450 on Dover; ML 3·2m; Duration 0555. See 10.11.13.
Good shelter for small boats that can take the ground;
access HW±3. Avoid in strong S winds. Black Scar, Green
Scar and The Mare are rks 5ca S. Ent via SSE side; best
water near Black Rk in centre of ent. Beware stone spit at
Trwyn Caws on W just inside ent. There are 9 R ⚓s and
some drying moorings available; or ⚓ behind the rk in
approx 3m. Small craft can go up to the quay. Facilities
limited; stores in village. FW on quay. Hr Mr (01437)
720153, M, CH. **Solva Boat Owners Assn** ☎ 721489.

ST BRIDES BAY, Pembrokeshire, 51°49'00N 05°10'·00W.
AC *1478*. HW (Little Haven) −0450 on Dover; ML 3·2m;
Duration 0555. See 10.11.13. Keep at least 100m offshore
1/9-28/2 to avoid disturbing seals, and ditto nesting sea
birds 1/3-31/7. Many good ⚓s, especially between Little
Haven and Borough Head in S or E winds or between
Solva and Dinas Fawr in N or E winds. In W'lies boats
should shelter in Solva (above), Skomer (below) or
Pendinas Bach. For apprs from the N or S see 10·11·5.
Facilities: (Little Haven) CH, V, R, Bar, FW (cans).

SKOMER, Pembrokeshire, 51°44'·40N 05°16'·70W. AC
2878, *1478*. HW −0455 Dover. See 10.11.14. The island is
a National Nature Reserve (fee payable to Warden on
landing) and also a Marine Nature Reserve, extending to
Marloes Peninsula. Keep at least 100m offshore 1/9-28/2
to avoid disturbing seals and ditto nesting sea birds 1/3-
31/7. There is a 5kn speed limit within 100m of the island.
⚓ in N or S Haven. Enter N Haven close to W shore, and
land on W side of bay on beach or at steps. In N Haven
pick up ⚓s provided or ⚓ to seaward of them. No access
to the island from S Haven. For Jack Sound see 10·11·5.
There are no lts, marks or facilities. For info, Marine
Conservation Officer ☎ (01646) 636736.

11

MILFORD HAVEN   10-11-14

Pembrokeshire 51°40'·10N 05°08'·10W. Rtg 1-1-2

CHARTS
AC 3274, 3275, *2878, 1478, 1178, 1410*; Imray C60; OS 157

TIDES
–0500 Dover; ML 3·8; Duration 0605; Zone 0 (UT)

Standard Port MILFORD HAVEN (→)

Times				Height (metres)			
High Water		Low Water		MHWS	MHWN	MLWN	MLWS
0100	0800	0100	0700	7·0	5·2	2·5	0·7
1300	2000	1300	1900				
Differences SKOMER IS							
–0005	–0005	+0005	+0005	–0·4	–0·1	0·0	0·0
DALE ROADS							
–0005	–0005	–0008	–0008	0·0	0·0	0·0	–0·1
NEYLAND							
+0002	+0010	0000	0000	0·0	0·0	0·0	0·0
HAVERFORDWEST							
+0010	+0025	Dries		–4·8	–4·9	Dries out	
LLANGWM (Black Tar)							
+0010	+0020	+0005	0000	+0·1	+0·1	0·0	–0·1

NOTE: Milford Haven is a Standard Port and all tidal predictions for the year are given below.

SHELTER
Very good in various places round the hbr, especially in Milford Dock Marina and Neyland Yacht Haven. Call Milford Haven Sig Stn to ascertain most suitable ⚓ or berth. ⚓s in Dale Bay; off Chapel Bay and Angle Pt on S shore; off Scotch Bay by Milford, above the town; and others above Pembroke Dock. Free pontoons include: Dale Bay (all year); waiting pontoons off Milford Dock and Hobbs Pt (Pembroke Dock); and drying pontoons (May-Oct) at Dale Beach, Gelliswick, Hazelbeach, Neyland and Burton; mainly intended for tenders. It is possible to take the ground safely at inshore areas of Dale, Sandy Haven and Angle Bay, depending on weather conditions.

NAVIGATION
WPT 51°40'·18N, 05°10'·22W, 040°/220° from/to Great Castle Hd ldg lt, 3·18M. The tide sets strongly across the ent to the Haven particularly at sp. In bad weather avoid passing over Mid Chan Rks and St Ann's Hd shoal, where a confused sea and swell will be found. Give St Ann's Head a wide berth especially on the ebb, when East Chan by Sheep Island is better. Beware large tankers entering and leaving the haven and ferries moving at high speed in lower Haven. Caution: Only 15m clearance below cables between Thorn Is and Thorn Pt.

NOTE: Milford Haven Port Authority has a jetty, Sig Stn and offices near Hubberston Pt. Their launches have G hulls and W upperworks with 'Harbourmaster' in white letters and fly a Pilot flag (HOTEL) or a Bu flag while on patrol. Their instructions must be obeyed. No vessel may operate within 100 metres of any terminal or any tanker whether at ⚓ or under way.

River Cleddau is navigable to Picton Pt, 6M, at junction of West and East arms, at all tides for boats of moderate draught. Clearance under Cleddau Bridge above Neyland is 37m; and 25m under power cable 1M upstream. Chan to Haverfordwest has 2m at HW and clearances of only 6m below cables and bridge; only feasible for shoal draft/lifting keel and unmasted craft.

LIGHTS AND MARKS
St Ann's Hd Fl WR 5s 48m 18/14M, Horn (2) 60s. Middle Chan Rks Fl (3) G 7s 18m 8M; B tr, steel lantern. Ldg lts (for W chan) 040°: Front Oc 4s 27m 15M; rear Oc 8s 53m 15M; both vis 031°-048° (H24).

Milford Dock ldg lts 348°, both FG, with W ○ daymarks. Dock entry sigs on E side of lock: 2 FG (vert) = gates open, vessels may enter. Exit sigs are given via VHF Ch12. VHF is normally used for ent/exit by day and night.

RADIO TELEPHONE
Port Authority call: *Milford Haven Radio* (Port Sig Stn), VHF Ch **12** 11 14 16 (H24); 09 10 67. *Milford Haven Patrol* launches, Ch 11 12 (H24). To enter Milford Docks call *Milford Pierhead* Ch 09 **12** 14 16 (HW–2 to HW); then an additional call to *Milford Marina* Ch M, M2, 80. Neyland Yacht Haven Ch **80** M. Lawrenny Yacht Stn Ch M.

Broadcasts: Local forecasts on Ch 12 14 at approx 0300, 0900, 1500 and 2100UT. Nav warnings on Ch 14 follow these forecasts. Gale warnings issued on receipt Ch 12.

Shipping movements on Ch 12, 0800–0830, 2000–2030LT and on request. Tide hts and winds on request.

TELEPHONE (Dial code 01646)
Port Authority 693091, 🛥 690179; Lock 692275/1; Sig Stn 692342; MRSC 690909; ⌗ (01222) 763880 (H24); Marinecall 0891 500 459; Police (Milford Haven) 692351, (Pembroke) 682121, (Neyland) 600221; Ⓗ Haverfordwest (01437) 764545; Dr 600314.

FACILITIES
Marinas/ Berthing (from seaward):
Dale YC ☎ 636362, Sh, CH, V, FW, M, P (Dale, cans), R (Dale), Slip (Dale), Gas, Gaz.
Milford Haven Port Authority Jetty ☎ 692342 (occas use by visitors with approval from Hr Mr), AB, FW.
Milford Dock Marina (230) ☎ 692271/2, 🛥 692274; £10. VHF Ch 12. Lock ent/exit HW–3, free flow HW –2 to HW, exit HW+1¾, ent HW+2½; FW, D, AC, CH, El, ME, Sh, SM, Ⓔ, Gas, Gaz, V, R, Ⓖ, C (various).
Neyland Yacht Haven (410+40 visitors) ☎ 601601, 🛥 600713, £10.46, FW, D, AC, CH, Ⓔ, Gas, Gaz, Ⓖ, C (20 ton), SM, SC, ME, El, Sh, R, V; Access lower basin H24, upper basin HW±3½ (sill + gauge);
Lawrenny Yacht Station (100) ☎ 651367, AB, FW, M, BY, CH, D, P, Sh, C (20 ton), ME, Slip, Ⓖ, Bar, R, V , ⊠ in village.
Services: All marine services are available in the Haven; check with Hr Mr, marinas or YC/SC. Rudder's Boatyard, small but useful, is just upstream of Burton Pt.
Yacht Clubs: Dale YC ☎ 636362; Pembrokeshire YC ☎ 692799; Neyland YC ☎ 600267; Pembroke YC ☎ 684403; Pembroke Haven YC ☎ 651959; Lawrenny YC ☎ 651212.
Towns: Milford Haven, EC Thurs; ⊠, Ⓑ, ⇌. Pembroke Dock, EC Wed; ⊠, Ⓑ, ⇌, Ⓗ. Neyland, EC Wed; ⊠, Ⓑ. Haverfordwest, EC Thurs; ⊠, Ⓗ, Ⓑ, ⇌, ✈ (Swansea or Cardiff); also a small airfield (Withybush) near Haverfordwest. Ferry: Pembroke Dock–Rosslare.

FIRING RANGES to the South and South East:

Castlemartin Range Danger Area extends 12M WNW from Linney Hd, thence in an anti-clockwise arc to a point 12M S of St Govan's Hd. The exact Danger Area operative on any one day depends on the ranges/ammunition used; it is primarily a tank range. When firing is in progress R flags are flown (Fl R lts at night) along the coast from Freshwater West to Linney Hd to St Govan's Hd. Yachts are requested to keep clear of ranges when active. Firing takes place on weekdays 0900 -1630, exceptionally to 1700. Night firing takes place on Mon to Thurs, up to 2359, depending on the hours of darkness. In Jan/Feb only small arms are usually fired and the danger area is reduced.
Days/times of firing are published locally and can be obtained by VHF from *Castlemartin Control Tower* Ch 16; Range safety launches Ch 16 or 12; and Milford Haven CG Ch 16. Also from the Range Office ☎ 661321 ext 4336, 4285, 4287.

Manorbier Range (further E at Old Castle Head) partly overlaps Castlemartin Range. It is small arms only and seldom, if ever, interferes with passage through Caldey Sound. Info ☎ (01834) 871282, 🛥 871283.

Pendine Range (between Tenby and Burry Inlet) is a MOD range for testing explosive devices. It is usually possible to steer the rhumb line course from Tenby to Worms Hd without interference. Info ☎ (01994) 453243. Broadcasts on VHF Ch 16, 73 at 0900 and 1400LT. Range active 0800-1615.

Pembrey Range (approx 5M NW of Burry Inlet) is used for bombing practice by the RAF. Info ☎ (01554) 891224.

MILFORD HAVEN *continued*

WALES – MILFORD HAVEN

LAT 51°42′N   LONG 5°03′W

TIMES AND HEIGHTS OF HIGH AND LOW WATERS

YEAR **1998**

TIME ZONE (UT)
For Summer Time add ONE hour in non-shaded areas

JANUARY

Day	Time	m		Day	Time	m
1 TH	0146 / 0749 / 1411 / 2011	0.8 / 7.1 / 0.7 / 6.9		**16** F	0217 / 0821 / 1441 / 2040	1.1 / 6.6 / 1.2 / 6.4
2 F	0229 / 0832 / 1454 / 2055	0.8 / 7.1 / 0.8 / 6.8		**17** SA	0250 / 0855 / 1513 / 2114	1.3 / 6.4 / 1.4 / 6.1
3 SA	0312 / 0918 / 1540 / 2142	1.0 / 6.9 / 0.9 / 6.6		**18** SU	0322 / 0928 / 1546 / 2149	1.5 / 6.2 / 1.6 / 5.9
4 SU	0359 / 1007 / 1629 / 2233	1.2 / 6.7 / 1.2 / 6.3		**19** M	0357 / 1004 / 1622 / 2227	1.8 / 5.9 / 1.9 / 5.6
5 M	0451 / 1102 / 1725 / 2332	1.5 / 6.4 / 1.5 / 6.0		**20** TU	0437 / 1046 / 1707 / 2314	2.1 / 5.6 / 2.2 / 5.3
6 TU	0552 / 1204 / 1830	1.8 / 6.1 / 1.8		**21** W	0528 / 1138 / 1804	2.4 / 5.3 / 2.5
7 W	0039 / 0704 / 1314 / 1943	5.8 / 1.9 / 5.9 / 1.9		**22** TH	0016 / 0636 / 1247 / 1921	5.1 / 2.6 / 5.2 / 2.6
8 TH	0153 / 0822 / 1428 / 2057	5.7 / 1.9 / 5.9 / 1.8		**23** F	0134 / 0800 / 1405 / 2041	5.1 / 2.5 / 5.2 / 2.4
9 F	0306 / 0934 / 1537 / 2202	5.9 / 1.7 / 6.1 / 1.6		**24** SA	0249 / 0913 / 1515 / 2144	5.3 / 2.3 / 5.5 / 2.1
10 SA	0409 / 1036 / 1636 / 2258	6.2 / 1.4 / 6.3 / 1.3		**25** SU	0349 / 1011 / 1612 / 2236	5.7 / 1.8 / 5.9 / 1.6
11 SU	0503 / 1128 / 1728 / 2345	6.5 / 1.2 / 6.5 / 1.1		**26** M	0439 / 1101 / 1701 / 2323	6.2 / 1.4 / 6.3 / 1.2
12 M O	0550 / 1214 / 1813	6.7 / 1.0 / 6.6		**27** TU	0525 / 1147 / 1747	6.7 / 1.0 / 6.7
13 TU	0028 / 0632 / 1256 / 1853	1.0 / 6.8 / 0.9 / 6.7		**28** W ●	0007 / 0652 / 1232 / 1831	0.8 / 7.0 / 0.6 / 7.0
14 W	0107 / 0711 / 1333 / 1931	0.9 / 6.8 / 0.9 / 6.7		**29** TH	0051 / 0652 / 1315 / 1914	0.6 / 7.3 / 0.4 / 7.2
15 TH	0143 / 0747 / 1408 / 2006	0.9 / 6.8 / 1.0 / 6.5		**30** F	0134 / 0735 / 1358 / 1958	0.5 / 7.4 / 0.2 / 7.3
				31 SA	0216 / 0819 / 1441 / 2041	0.4 / 7.4 / 0.3 / 7.2

FEBRUARY

Day	Time	m		Day	Time	m
1 SU	0259 / 0903 / 1525 / 2126	0.5 / 7.3 / 0.5 / 6.9		**16** M	0254 / 0858 / 1514 / 2115	1.2 / 6.4 / 1.3 / 6.1
2 M	0343 / 0949 / 1609 / 2212	0.8 / 7.0 / 0.9 / 6.5		**17** TU	0325 / 0929 / 1547 / 2147	1.4 / 6.2 / 1.6 / 5.9
3 TU	0430 / 1038 / 1658 / 2304	1.2 / 6.5 / 1.3 / 6.1		**18** W	0359 / 1003 / 1620 / 2225	1.8 / 5.8 / 2.0 / 5.6
4 W	0523 / 1135 / 1756	1.6 / 6.1 / 1.7		**19** TH	0440 / 1045 / 1705 / 2314	2.1 / 5.5 / 2.3 / 5.2
5 TH	0006 / 0631 / 1243 / 1910	5.7 / 2.0 / 5.7 / 2.1		**20** F	0535 / 1142 / 1810	2.4 / 5.2 / 2.6
6 F	0122 / 0756 / 1402 / 2033	5.5 / 2.1 / 5.5 / 2.1		**21** SA	0026 / 0656 / 1304 / 1943	5.0 / 2.6 / 5.0 / 2.6
7 SA	0245 / 0919 / 1522 / 2148	5.5 / 2.0 / 5.6 / 1.9		**22** SU	0156 / 0829 / 1432 / 2107	5.1 / 2.4 / 5.2 / 2.3
8 SU	0356 / 1026 / 1626 / 2246	5.8 / 1.7 / 5.9 / 1.6		**23** M	0314 / 0940 / 1543 / 2209	5.5 / 2.0 / 5.7 / 1.7
9 M	0452 / 1119 / 1716 / 2334	6.2 / 1.4 / 6.2 / 1.3		**24** TU	0413 / 1036 / 1638 / 2300	6.1 / 1.4 / 6.2 / 1.2
10 TU	0538 / 1202 / 1759	6.5 / 1.1 / 6.5		**25** W	0503 / 1125 / 1727 / 2347	6.6 / 0.9 / 6.7 / 0.7
11 W O	0014 / 0617 / 1240 / 1836	1.0 / 6.7 / 0.9 / 6.6		**26** TH ●	0549 / 1212 / 1813	7.1 / 0.4 / 7.2
12 TH	0050 / 0653 / 1314 / 1911	0.8 / 6.8 / 0.9 / 6.7		**27** F	0032 / 0633 / 1257 / 1856	0.3 / 7.5 / 0.1 / 7.4
13 F	0123 / 0726 / 1346 / 1943	0.9 / 6.8 / 0.9 / 6.6		**28** SA	0117 / 0717 / 1341 / 1940	0.1 / 7.7 / -0.1 / 7.5
14 SA	0154 / 0757 / 1415 / 2014	0.9 / 6.7 / 0.9 / 6.5				
15 SU	0224 / 0828 / 1445 / 2044	1.0 / 6.6 / 1.1 / 6.4				

MARCH

Day	Time	m		Day	Time	m
1 SU	0159 / 0801 / 1423 / 2022	0.0 / 7.7 / 0.0 / 7.4		**16** M	0158 / 0800 / 1416 / 2015	0.8 / 6.7 / 1.0 / 6.5
2 M	0242 / 0844 / 1505 / 2105	0.2 / 7.5 / 0.3 / 7.1		**17** TU	0227 / 0829 / 1445 / 2044	1.0 / 6.5 / 1.2 / 6.3
3 TU	0324 / 0928 / 1547 / 2149	0.5 / 7.1 / 0.7 / 6.7		**18** W	0258 / 0859 / 1514 / 2115	1.2 / 6.3 / 1.5 / 6.1
4 W	0408 / 1015 / 1632 / 2237	1.0 / 6.6 / 1.3 / 6.2		**19** TH	0330 / 0931 / 1546 / 2150	1.6 / 6.0 / 1.8 / 5.8
5 TH	0457 / 1107 / 1725 / 2335	1.5 / 6.0 / 1.8 / 5.7		**20** F	0407 / 1009 / 1625 / 2234	1.9 / 5.6 / 2.1 / 5.5
6 F	0602 / 1213 / 1837	2.0 / 5.5 / 2.2		**21** SA	0456 / 1101 / 1722 / 2338	2.2 / 5.3 / 2.4 / 5.2
7 SA	0050 / 0731 / 1337 / 2009	5.3 / 2.3 / 5.2 / 2.3		**22** SU	0609 / 1216 / 1850	2.5 / 5.1 / 2.6
8 SU	0223 / 0903 / 1505 / 2131	5.3 / 2.2 / 5.3 / 2.1		**23** M	0109 / 0746 / 1352 / 2028	5.1 / 2.4 / 5.2 / 2.3
9 M	0340 / 1012 / 1610 / 2231	5.6 / 1.8 / 5.7 / 1.7		**24** TU	0236 / 0906 / 1512 / 2138	5.6 / 1.9 / 5.6 / 1.8
10 TU	0435 / 1103 / 1659 / 2316	6.0 / 1.4 / 6.1 / 1.4		**25** W	0343 / 1008 / 1612 / 2234	6.1 / 1.3 / 6.2 / 1.2
11 W	0518 / 1143 / 1739 / 2353	6.3 / 1.2 / 6.4 / 1.1		**26** TH	0436 / 1100 / 1703 / 2323	6.7 / 0.8 / 6.8 / 0.6
12 TH	0556 / 1217 / 1814	6.6 / 1.0 / 6.5		**27** F	0525 / 1149 / 1750	7.2 / 0.3 / 7.3
13 F O	0027 / 0629 / 1249 / 1846	0.9 / 6.7 / 0.8 / 6.7		**28** SA ●	0010 / 0611 / 1235 / 1834	0.2 / 7.6 / 0.0 / 7.5
14 SA	0059 / 0701 / 1319 / 1917	0.8 / 6.8 / 0.8 / 6.7		**29** SU	0056 / 0656 / 1319 / 1918	0.0 / 7.7 / -0.2 / 7.6
15 SU	0128 / 0731 / 1348 / 1946	0.8 / 6.8 / 0.8 / 6.6		**30** M	0140 / 0803 / 1402 / 2001	-0.1 / 7.7 / -0.1 / 7.5
				31 TU	0222 / 0824 / 1444 / 2044	0.1 / 7.5 / 0.3 / 7.2

APRIL

Day	Time	m		Day	Time	m
1 W	0305 / 0907 / 1525 / 2127	0.5 / 7.0 / 0.7 / 6.7		**16** TH	0235 / 0834 / 1450 / 2051	1.2 / 6.3 / 1.4 / 6.2
2 TH	0348 / 0953 / 1608 / 2213	1.0 / 6.4 / 1.3 / 6.2		**17** F	0309 / 0908 / 1523 / 2127	1.4 / 6.1 / 1.7 / 6.0
3 F	0436 / 1043 / 1658 / 2308	1.5 / 5.9 / 1.9 / 5.7		**18** SA	0346 / 0947 / 1602 / 2212	1.7 / 5.8 / 2.0 / 5.7
4 SA	0537 / 1145 / 1806	2.1 / 5.3 / 2.3		**19** SU	0435 / 1038 / 1657 / 2313	2.0 / 5.5 / 2.3 / 5.4
5 SU	0020 / 0703 / 1308 / 1937	5.3 / 2.3 / 5.1 / 2.5		**20** M	0542 / 1150 / 1817	2.2 / 5.2 / 2.4
6 M	0151 / 0835 / 1437 / 2101	5.2 / 2.3 / 5.2 / 2.3		**21** TU	0035 / 0709 / 1319 / 1950	5.4 / 2.2 / 5.3 / 2.2
7 TU	0311 / 0944 / 1543 / 2202	5.5 / 1.9 / 5.5 / 1.9		**22** W	0200 / 0831 / 1439 / 2104	5.6 / 1.8 / 5.7 / 1.7
8 W	0407 / 1034 / 1631 / 2247	5.8 / 1.6 / 5.9 / 1.5		**23** TH	0310 / 0936 / 1543 / 2204	6.1 / 1.3 / 6.2 / 1.2
9 TH	0450 / 1114 / 1711 / 2325	6.2 / 1.3 / 6.2 / 1.2		**24** F	0408 / 1032 / 1637 / 2257	6.7 / 0.8 / 6.8 / 0.7
10 F	0528 / 1148 / 1746 / 2359	6.4 / 1.1 / 6.5 / 1.0		**25** SA	0500 / 1123 / 1726 / 2347	7.1 / 0.3 / 7.2 / 0.3
11 SA O	0602 / 1219 / 1819	6.6 / 0.9 / 6.6		**26** SU ●	0548 / 1211 / 1812	7.4 / 0.1 / 7.4
12 SU	0030 / 0633 / 1250 / 1849	0.9 / 6.7 / 0.8 / 6.7		**27** M	0034 / 0634 / 1257 / 1856	0.1 / 7.6 / 0.0 / 7.5
13 M	0102 / 0703 / 1320 / 1919	0.8 / 6.7 / 0.9 / 6.7		**28** TU	0119 / 0719 / 1340 / 1940	0.1 / 7.5 / 0.1 / 7.4
14 TU	0132 / 0733 / 1349 / 1949	0.8 / 6.7 / 0.9 / 6.6		**29** W	0204 / 0804 / 1423 / 2023	0.2 / 7.2 / 0.4 / 7.1
15 W	0203 / 0803 / 1419 / 2019	1.0 / 6.5 / 1.1 / 6.5		**30** TH	0247 / 0848 / 1505 / 2107	0.6 / 6.8 / 0.8 / 6.7

Chart Datum: 3·71 metres below Ordnance Datum (Newlyn)

WALES – MILFORD HAVEN

LAT 51°42′N   LONG 5°03′W

TIMES AND HEIGHTS OF HIGH AND LOW WATERS   YEAR **1998**

TIME ZONE (UT)
For Summer Time add ONE hour in non-shaded areas

MAY

Day	Time	m	Time	m	Time	m	Time	m
1 F	0331	1.0	0933	6.3	1547	1.4	2152	6.2
2 SA	0417	1.5	1021	5.8	1634	1.9	2244	5.7
3 SU	0513	2.0	1118	5.3	1734	2.3	2347	5.4
4 M	0627	2.3	1230	5.1	1854	2.5		
5 TU	0105	5.2	0750	2.3	1352	5.1	2015	2.4
6 W	0225	5.4	0859	2.1	1502	5.4	2119	2.1
7 TH	0326	5.7	0953	1.8	1554	5.7	2209	1.8
8 F	0414	6.0	1036	1.5	1637	6.0	2250	1.5
9 SA	0454	6.2	1113	1.3	1714	6.3	2327	1.2
10 SU	0530	6.4	1147	1.1	1748	6.5		
11 M O	0002	1.1	0603	6.5	1221	1.0	1821	6.6
12 TU	0036	1.0	0636	6.6	1253	1.0	1853	6.7
13 W	0109	0.9	0708	6.6	1325	1.0	1925	6.6
14 TH	0143	1.0	0741	6.5	1358	1.1	1959	6.5
15 F	0218	1.1	0815	6.4	1432	1.3	2034	6.4
16 SA	0254	1.3	0853	6.2	1509	1.5	2114	6.2
17 SU	0335	1.5	0935	5.9	1551	1.8	2200	6.0
18 M	0424	1.7	1027	5.7	1645	2.0	2259	5.8
19 TU	0526	1.9	1133	5.5	1755	2.1		
20 W	0011	5.7	0640	1.9	1251	5.5	1916	2.0
21 TH	0128	5.8	0757	1.7	1407	5.8	2030	1.7
22 F	0238	6.2	0904	1.3	1513	6.2	2135	1.3
23 SA	0340	6.6	1004	0.9	1610	6.6	2232	0.9
24 SU	0435	6.9	1058	0.6	1702	7.0	2324	0.6
25 M ●	0526	7.1	1148	0.4	1751	7.2		
26 TU	0014	0.4	0615	7.2	1236	0.3	1837	7.2
27 W	0102	0.3	0701	7.2	1321	0.4	1922	7.2
28 TH	0147	0.5	0747	7.0	1404	0.6	2006	7.0
29 F	0231	0.7	0831	6.7	1446	1.0	2049	6.6
30 SA	0314	1.1	0914	6.3	1527	1.4	2132	6.3
31 SU	0358	1.5	0959	5.9	1611	1.8	2218	5.9

JUNE

Day	Time	m	Time	m	Time	m	Time	m
1 M	0445	1.9	1048	5.5	1700	2.1	2311	5.6
2 TU	0542	2.2	1146	5.2	1802	2.4		
3 W	0014	5.3	0650	2.3	1255	5.1	1915	2.4
4 TH	0125	5.3	0725	2.2	1406	5.2	2024	2.3
5 F	0233	5.4	0901	2.1	1507	5.5	2122	2.0
6 SA	0329	5.7	0952	1.8	1557	5.8	2211	1.8
7 SU	0416	5.9	1036	1.6	1640	6.1	2254	1.5
8 M	0457	6.2	1115	1.4	1718	6.3	2333	1.3
9 TU	0535	6.3	1152	1.2	1755	6.5		
10 W O	0011	1.1	0611	6.5	1229	1.1	1830	6.6
11 TH	0048	1.0	0647	6.5	1305	1.0	1906	6.7
12 F	0126	1.0	0724	6.5	1342	1.1	1943	6.7
13 SA	0204	1.0	0802	6.5	1420	1.1	2023	6.6
14 SU	0244	1.1	0843	6.4	1500	1.3	2105	6.5
15 M	0327	1.2	0927	6.2	1544	1.4	2152	6.3
16 TU	0415	1.4	1018	6.0	1635	1.6	2246	6.2
17 W	0510	1.6	1116	5.9	1736	1.8	2349	6.0
18 TH	0614	1.7	1224	5.8	1846	1.8		
19 F	0058	6.0	0725	1.6	1336	5.8	1959	1.7
20 SA	0208	6.1	0835	1.5	1445	6.1	2108	1.5
21 SU	0314	6.3	0939	1.3	1547	6.3	2211	1.2
22 M	0415	6.5	1037	1.0	1644	6.6	2307	0.9
23 TU	0510	6.7	1130	0.8	1735	6.8	2359	0.7
24 W ●	0600	6.8	1218	0.7	1823	7.0		
25 TH	0047	0.7	0647	6.9	1304	0.7	1907	7.0
26 F	0132	0.7	0731	6.8	1347	0.8	1949	6.9
27 SA	0215	0.8	0813	6.6	1427	1.0	2030	6.7
28 SU	0255	1.1	0853	6.3	1506	1.3	2110	6.4
29 M	0334	1.4	0933	6.0	1543	1.6	2150	6.1
30 TU	0412	1.7	1014	5.7	1623	1.9	2233	5.8

JULY

Day	Time	m	Time	m	Time	m	Time	m
1 W	0455	2.0	1100	5.4	1710	2.2	2322	5.5
2 TH	0547	2.2	1155	5.2	1808	2.4		
3 F	0021	5.3	0650	2.4	1301	5.1	1919	2.4
4 SA	0130	5.3	0801	2.3	1411	5.2	2030	2.3
5 SU	0238	5.4	0905	2.2	1513	5.5	2130	2.1
6 M	0336	5.6	0958	1.9	1605	5.8	2221	1.8
7 TU	0425	5.9	1045	1.6	1649	6.1	2306	1.5
8 W	0508	6.2	1127	1.4	1730	6.4	2348	1.2
9 TH O	0549	6.4	1207	1.2	1810	6.6		
10 F	0029	1.0	0629	6.6	1247	1.0	1849	6.8
11 SA	0110	0.9	0709	6.7	1327	0.9	1929	6.9
12 SU	0151	0.8	0750	6.8	1408	0.9	2011	7.0
13 M	0233	0.8	0832	6.7	1449	0.9	2054	6.9
14 TU	0316	0.9	0916	6.6	1533	1.1	2140	6.7
15 W	0401	1.1	1003	6.4	1620	1.3	2229	6.5
16 TH	0451	1.3	1056	6.1	1714	1.6	2326	6.2
17 F	0548	1.6	1157	5.9	1818	1.8		
18 SA	0031	6.0	0655	1.7	1307	5.8	1932	1.9
19 SU	0142	5.9	0810	1.8	1421	5.8	2049	1.8
20 M	0255	6.0	0921	1.6	1531	6.0	2158	1.6
21 TU	0402	6.2	1024	1.4	1632	6.3	2258	1.3
22 W	0459	6.4	1118	1.2	1724	6.6	2349	1.0
23 TH ●	0550	6.6	1206	1.0	1811	6.8		
24 F	0035	0.9	0634	6.7	1249	0.9	1853	6.8
25 SA	0117	0.8	0715	6.7	1328	0.8	1932	6.8
26 SU	0155	0.9	0753	6.6	1405	1.0	2008	6.7
27 M	0231	1.0	0828	6.4	1440	1.2	2043	6.5
28 TU	0304	1.2	0903	6.2	1513	1.4	2118	6.3
29 W	0337	1.5	0938	6.0	1546	1.7	2153	6.0
30 TH	0411	1.8	1015	5.7	1624	2.0	2233	5.7
31 F	0451	2.1	1059	5.4	1710	2.3	2321	5.4

AUGUST

Day	Time	m	Time	m	Time	m	Time	m
1 SA	0543	2.4	1155	5.2	1812	2.5		
2 SU	0023	5.2	0652	2.6	1308	5.1	1932	2.6
3 M	0140	5.1	0814	2.5	1426	5.2	2050	2.4
4 TU	0254	5.3	0923	2.2	1531	5.6	2151	2.1
5 W	0354	5.7	1017	1.9	1622	6.0	2241	1.6
6 TH	0444	6.1	1103	1.5	1707	6.4	2327	1.2
7 F	0528	6.4	1146	1.1	1749	6.8		
8 SA	0010	0.9	0610	6.8	1229	0.8	1831	7.1
9 SU	0053	0.6	0652	7.0	1311	0.6	1913	7.3
10 M	0135	0.4	0734	7.1	1353	0.5	1955	7.4
11 TU	0217	0.4	0817	7.1	1434	0.6	2038	7.3
12 W	0259	0.5	0900	7.0	1517	0.8	2122	7.1
13 TH	0343	0.8	0944	6.7	1602	1.1	2209	6.7
14 F	0429	1.2	1034	6.3	1652	1.5	2302	6.3
15 SA	0522	1.6	1131	5.9	1753	1.9		
16 SU	0005	5.9	0628	2.0	1241	5.6	1912	2.1
17 M	0121	5.6	0750	2.1	1403	5.6	2038	2.1
18 TU	0243	5.6	0910	2.0	1521	5.8	2153	1.8
19 W	0355	5.9	1016	1.7	1624	6.1	2252	1.5
20 TH	0451	6.2	1109	1.4	1714	6.5	2340	1.2
21 F	0537	6.5	1153	1.1	1757	6.7		
22 SA ●	0021	1.0	0617	6.6	1232	1.0	1835	6.8
23 SU	0058	0.9	0654	6.7	1307	0.9	1910	6.9
24 M	0131	0.9	0728	6.7	1340	0.9	1943	6.8
25 TU	0202	1.0	0800	6.6	1411	1.1	2014	6.7
26 W	0232	1.1	0831	6.4	1441	1.2	2045	6.5
27 TH	0301	1.4	0902	6.2	1512	1.5	2116	6.2
28 F	0332	1.7	0935	5.9	1545	1.8	2150	5.9
29 SA	0406	2.0	1011	5.6	1625	2.2	2229	5.5
30 SU	0449	2.4	1057	5.3	1717	2.5	2322	5.2
31 M	0549	2.7	1204	5.0	1834	2.7		

11

Chart Datum: 3·71 metres below Ordnance Datum (Newlyn)

WALES – MILFORD HAVEN

LAT 51°42'N   LONG 5°03'W

TIMES AND HEIGHTS OF HIGH AND LOW WATERS

YEAR **1998**

TIME ZONE (UT)
For Summer Time add ONE hour in non-shaded areas

SEPTEMBER

Day	Time/m	Time/m	Time/m	Time/m
1 TU	0040 5.0	0719 2.8	1335 5.1	2009 2.6
2 W	0212 5.1	0847 2.5	1456 5.4	2121 2.2
3 TH	0324 5.5	0949 2.0	1554 5.9	2216 1.7
4 F	0419 6.1	1039 1.5	1642 6.5	2304 1.2
5 SA	0505 6.6	1124 1.0	1726 7.0	2348 0.7
6 SU O	0549 7.0	1208 0.6	1810 7.4	
7 M	0032 0.4	0632 7.3	1251 0.4	1852 7.6
8 TU	0115 0.2	0714 7.5	1334 0.3	1935 7.7
9 W	0158 0.2	0757 7.4	1416 0.3	2018 7.5
10 TH	0240 0.4	0839 7.2	1458 0.6	2102 7.2
11 F	0322 0.7	0923 6.9	1542 1.0	2148 6.8
12 SA	0406 1.2	1011 6.4	1631 1.5	2240 6.2
13 SU	0458 1.8	1107 5.9	1732 2.0	2342 5.7
14 M	0605 2.2	1218 5.5	1857 2.3	
15 TU	0102 5.4	0735 2.4	1348 5.4	2031 2.3
16 W	0233 5.4	0808 2.2	1511 5.7	2146 1.9
17 TH	0344 5.7	1005 1.9	1611 6.1	2241 1.6
18 F	0437 6.1	1054 1.5	1658 6.4	2324 1.2
19 SA	0519 6.4	1134 1.2	1737 6.7	
20 SU ●	0000 1.0	0556 6.6	1210 1.0	1812 6.8
21 M	0033 0.9	0630 6.7	1242 0.9	1844 6.9
22 TU	0103 0.9	0701 6.8	1312 1.0	1915 6.9
23 W	0132 1.0	0731 6.7	1342 1.0	1945 6.8
24 TH	0201 1.1	0801 6.6	1412 1.2	2014 6.6
25 F	0229 1.3	0830 6.4	1442 1.4	2044 6.3
26 SA	0259 1.6	0901 6.1	1514 1.7	2115 6.0
27 SU	0330 1.9	0934 5.8	1551 2.1	2152 5.7
28 M	0408 2.3	1016 5.5	1638 2.3	2239 5.3
29 TU	0501 2.6	1116 5.2	1748 2.7	2350 5.0
30 W	0626 2.8	1245 5.1	1927 2.7	

OCTOBER

Day	Time/m	Time/m	Time/m	Time/m
1 TH	0128 5.1	0808 2.6	1416 5.4	2048 2.3
2 F	0251 5.5	0917 2.1	1522 6.0	2147 1.7
3 SA	0350 6.1	1011 1.5	1614 6.6	2237 1.1
4 SU	0440 6.7	1059 1.0	1701 7.1	2324 0.6
5 M O	0525 7.2	1144 0.5	1746 7.6	
6 TU	0009 0.2	0609 7.5	1229 0.2	1830 7.8
7 W	0053 0.1	0653 7.7	1313 0.1	1914 7.8
8 TH	0136 0.1	0736 7.6	1357 0.2	1958 7.6
9 F	0219 0.3	0819 7.4	1440 0.5	2042 7.2
10 SA	0301 0.8	0903 6.9	1525 1.0	2129 6.7
11 SU	0346 1.3	0950 6.4	1614 1.6	2220 6.1
12 M	0436 1.9	1045 5.9	1715 2.1	2321 5.5
13 TU	0542 2.3	1155 5.5	1840 2.4	
14 W	0041 5.2	0713 2.5	1324 5.4	2013 2.4
15 TH	0212 5.3	0839 2.4	1447 5.6	2125 2.0
16 F	0322 5.6	0943 2.0	1547 6.0	2217 1.7
17 SA	0413 6.0	1030 1.6	1633 6.3	2258 1.4
18 SU	0454 6.3	1109 1.4	1711 6.6	2333 1.2
19 M	0530 6.6	1143 1.2	1746 6.7	
20 TU ●	0004 1.0	0603 6.7	1215 1.0	1817 6.8
21 W	0035 1.0	0634 6.8	1246 1.0	1848 6.8
22 TH	0104 1.0	0704 6.8	1316 1.0	1918 6.8
23 F	0133 1.1	0734 6.7	1347 1.2	1947 6.6
24 SA	0203 1.3	0804 6.5	1418 1.4	2018 6.4
25 SU	0233 1.5	0835 6.3	1452 1.7	2050 6.1
26 M	0305 1.9	0909 6.0	1528 2.0	2127 5.8
27 TU	0342 2.2	0951 5.7	1614 2.3	2214 5.5
28 W	0433 2.5	1047 5.4	1718 2.5	2320 5.2
29 TH	0549 2.7	1207 5.3	1845 2.5	
30 F	0049 5.2	0724 2.5	1335 5.5	2009 2.2
31 SA	0214 5.6	0841 2.1	1446 6.0	2113 1.7

NOVEMBER

Day	Time/m	Time/m	Time/m	Time/m
1 SU	0318 6.1	0940 1.5	1543 6.6	2208 1.1
2 M	0412 6.7	1032 1.0	1634 7.1	2258 0.6
3 TU	0501 7.2	1121 0.6	1722 7.5	2345 0.3
4 W O	0547 7.5	1208 0.3	1809 7.7	
5 TH	0031 0.1	0632 7.6	1254 0.2	1855 7.7
6 F	0116 0.2	0716 7.6	1339 0.3	1940 7.5
7 SA	0200 0.4	0801 7.3	1425 0.6	2026 7.1
8 SU	0244 0.8	0846 7.0	1510 1.0	2112 6.6
9 M	0328 1.3	0932 6.5	1559 1.5	2202 6.1
10 TU	0417 1.9	1025 6.0	1656 2.0	2259 5.6
11 W	0517 2.3	1127 5.6	1809 2.4	
12 TH	0008 5.2	0635 2.6	1244 5.4	1933 2.4
13 F	0130 5.2	0758 2.5	1405 5.5	2045 2.2
14 SA	0244 5.4	0904 2.2	1509 5.8	2140 1.9
15 SU	0339 5.8	0956 1.9	1559 6.1	2224 1.6
16 M	0423 6.1	1037 1.6	1640 6.3	2301 1.4
17 TU	0501 6.4	1114 1.4	1717 6.5	2335 1.2
18 W	0536 6.6	1149 1.2	1751 6.6	
19 TH ●	0008 1.1	0609 6.7	1222 1.1	1824 6.7
20 F	0040 1.1	0640 6.7	1255 1.1	1855 6.7
21 SA	0111 1.1	0712 6.7	1328 1.2	1927 6.6
22 SU	0143 1.3	0744 6.6	1402 1.5	2000 6.4
23 M	0216 1.4	0818 6.4	1437 1.5	2035 6.2
24 TU	0251 1.7	0855 6.2	1516 1.7	2114 6.0
25 W	0330 1.9	0938 6.0	1601 2.0	2201 5.7
26 TH	0419 2.2	1031 5.8	1658 2.1	2301 5.5
27 F	0523 2.3	1138 5.7	1809 2.2	
28 SA	0016 5.5	0642 2.3	1255 5.8	1927 2.0
29 SU	0135 5.7	0801 2.0	1408 6.1	2037 1.7
30 M	0244 6.1	0901 1.6	1512 6.5	2138 1.2

DECEMBER

Day	Time/m	Time/m	Time/m	Time/m
1 TU	0344 6.5	1006 1.2	1609 6.9	2233 0.9
2 W	0437 6.9	1059 0.8	1702 7.2	2324 0.6
3 TH O	0527 7.2	1150 0.5	1752 7.4	
4 F	0013 0.4	0614 7.4	1239 0.4	1839 7.4
5 SA	0100 0.4	0701 7.4	1326 0.4	1926 7.2
6 SU	0144 0.6	0746 7.2	1412 0.6	2012 7.0
7 M	0228 0.9	0831 6.9	1457 1.0	2057 6.6
8 TU	0312 1.3	0915 6.6	1543 1.4	2142 6.1
9 W	0356 1.7	1002 6.2	1631 1.8	2231 5.7
10 TH	0445 2.1	1054 5.8	1726 2.2	2327 5.4
11 F	0544 2.4	1154 5.5	1833 2.4	
12 SA	0033 5.2	0656 2.5	1304 5.4	1944 2.4
13 SU	0146 5.2	0808 2.5	1416 5.5	2049 2.2
14 M	0252 5.4	0910 2.2	1516 5.7	2142 2.0
15 TU	0346 5.8	1001 1.9	1606 5.9	2227 1.7
16 W	0430 6.1	1045 1.7	1648 6.2	2307 1.5
17 TH	0510 6.3	1124 1.4	1727 6.4	2344 1.3
18 F ●	0546 6.5	1201 1.3	1803 6.5	
19 SA	0019 1.2	0621 6.6	1237 1.1	1837 6.6
20 SU	0054 1.2	0655 6.7	1313 1.1	1912 6.6
21 M	0128 1.2	0730 6.7	1349 1.1	1947 6.5
22 TU	0204 1.2	0806 6.7	1427 1.2	2025 6.4
23 W	0241 1.3	0845 6.6	1506 1.3	2105 6.3
24 TH	0321 1.5	0927 6.4	1549 1.5	2150 6.1
25 F	0406 1.7	1016 6.2	1639 1.7	2242 5.9
26 SA	0501 1.9	1113 6.1	1738 1.8	2345 5.8
27 SU	0607 2.0	1220 6.0	1847 1.9	
28 M	0057 5.7	0722 2.0	1333 6.0	2001 1.8
29 TU	0211 5.9	0836 1.8	1443 6.2	2111 1.5
30 W	0318 6.2	0944 1.4	1548 6.5	2213 1.2
31 TH	0419 6.6	1044 1.1	1646 6.7	2308 0.9

Chart Datum: 3·71 metres below Ordnance Datum (Newlyn)

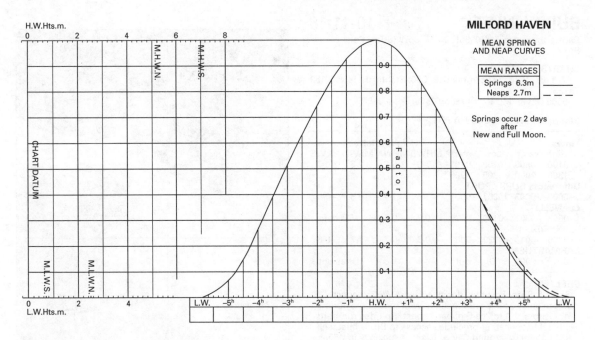

MILFORD HAVEN

MEAN SPRING
AND NEAP CURVES

MEAN RANGES
Springs 6.3m ———
Neaps 2.7m - - - -

Springs occur 2 days
after
New and Full Moon.

TENBY   10-11-15

Pembrokeshire 51·40'·40N 04°41'·85W   Rtg 3-4-1

CHARTS
AC 1482, 1076, *1179*; Imray C60; Stanfords 14; OS 158

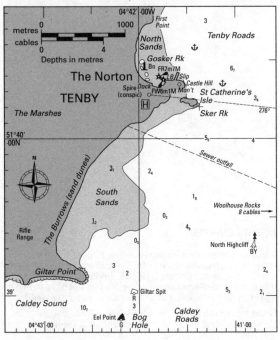

TIDES
–0510 Dover; ML 4·5; Duration 0610; Zone 0 (UT)

Standard Port MILFORD HAVEN (←—)

Times				Height (metres)			
High Water		Low Water		MHWS	MHWN	MLWN	MLWS
0100	0800	0100	0700	7·0	5·2	2·5	0·7
1300	2000	1300	1900				
Differences TENBY							
–0015	–0010	–0015	–0020	+1·4	+1·1	+0·5	+0·2
STACKPOLE QUAY (7M W of Caldey Island)							
–0005	+0025	–0010	–0010	+0·9	+0·7	+0·2	+0·3

SHELTER
Good, but hbr dries up to 5m; access HW±2½. Sheltered ⚓s, depending on wind direction, to NE in Tenby Roads, in Lydstep Haven (2·5M SW), and around Caldey Island as follows: Priory Bay (shallow, to the N), Jone's Bay (NE), Drinkim Bay (E) or Sandtop Bay (W). Also at Saundersfoot about 2M to the N; see below.

NAVIGATION
WPT 51°40'·00N 04°38'·00W, 099°/279° from/to monument on Castle Hill, 2·2M. The ⊕ WPT (off chartlet) is 2ca W of DZ2 SPM buoy, Fl Y 2·5s. Beware Woolhouse Rks (3·6m) 1·5M SExE of the hbr, marked by unlit SCM buoy; and Sker Rk (1m high) closer in off St Catherine's Island (28m). From the W, Caldey Sound is navigable with care by day between Eel Pt SHM and Giltar Spit PHM unlit buoys. Approaching Tenby Roads, keep outside the line of mooring buoys. For adjacent Firing ranges, see 10.11.14.

LIGHTS AND MARKS
Church spire and N side of St Catherine's Is in line at 276°. FR 7m 7M on pier hd. Inside hbr, FW 6m 1M marks landing PHM beacon (unlit) marks outcrop from Gosker Rk on beach close N of hbr ent. Hbr is floodlit.

RADIO TELEPHONE
VHF Ch 16 80 (listening during HO).

TELEPHONE (Dial code 01834)
Hr Mr 842717 (end May-end Sept), Mobile 0831 185917; MRSC (01646) 690909; ⧈ (01222) 763880 (H24); Marinecall 0891 500459; Police 842303; Dr 844161; Ⓗ 842040.

FACILITIES
Hbr ☎/📞 842717, Slip (up to 4·2m), L, AB, Sh, FW; **Tenby YC** ☎ 842762;
Town EC Wed; P & D (cans), ▣, CH, V, R, Bar, Gas, ✉, Ⓑ, ⇌, ✈ (Swansea); and a small airfield at Haverfordwest).

ADJACENT HARBOUR

SAUNDERSFOOT, Pembrokeshire, 51°42'·58N 04°41'·68W. AC 1482, 1076, *1179*. HW –0510 on Dover; ML 4·4m; Duration 0605. See 10.11.15. A half-tide hbr with good shelter, but there may be a surge in prolonged E winds. On appr, beware buoys marking restricted area (power boats, etc) between Coppett Hall Pt and Perry's Pt. AB may be available (see Hr Mr), or moorings in the middle. Pier hd lt Fl R 5s 6m 7M on stone cupola. VHF: Hr Mr 11 16. Hr Mr ☎/📞 (01834) 812094/(Home 813782). Facilities: CH, FW (on SW wall), Slip, P & D (cans), ME, BH.
Town EC Wed; V, R, Bar, ✉, Ⓑ, ⇌ (Tenby/Saundersfoot).

BURRY INLET   10-11-16

Carmarthenshire 51°40'·50N 04°14'·85W (Burry Port)
Rtg 4-4-3

CHARTS
AC 1167, 1076, *1179*; Imray C59, C60; Stanfords 14; OS 159

TIDES
–0500 Dover; ML 4·7; Duration 0555; Zohe 0 (UT)

Standard Port MILFORD HAVEN (←—)

Times				Height (metres)			
High Water		Low Water		MHWS	MHWN	MLWN	MLWS
0100	0800	0100	0700	7·0	5·2	2·5	0·7
1300	2000	1300	1900				
Differences BURRY PORT							
+0003	+0003	+0007	+0007	+1·6	+1·4	+0·5	+0·4
LLANELLI							
–0003	–0003	+0150	+0020	+0·8	+0·6	No data	
FERRYSIDE							
0000	–0010	+0220	0000	–0·3	–0·7	–1·7	–0·6
CARMARTHEN							
+0010	0000	Dries out		–4·4	–4·8	Dries out	

SHELTER
Good in Burry Port hbr (dries); access HW±2. Inspect before entry as it is entirely filled with moorings, none for visitors. ‡ 1 to 2ca E of barrel post. Sp tides run hard. Note: If bad weather precludes access to Burry Inlet, see 10.11.15 for ‡s around Caldey Island, especially in W'lies.

NAVIGATION
WPT DZ5 SPM buoy, Fl Y 2·5s, 51°36'·35N 04°24'·30W, 267°/087° from/to Burry Holms 3·3M; thence 4·5M to Burry Port. Carmarthen Bar, extending from the R Towy ent SE to Burry Holms, should not be attempted in W winds >F5 nor at night. Best entry is close NW of Burry Holms at HW–2; thence track 018° with Worms Hd on a stern transit (198°) between Burry Holms and Limekiln Pt. When Whiteford lt ho (disused) bears about 082°, alter approx 050° into deeper water for St Mary's spire and the barrel post. Chan is not buoyed/lit and is liable to shift. Before appr, check Firing range activity (10.11.14).

LIGHTS AND MARKS
Whiteford lt ho is conspic, but no longer lit. Barrel post, Fl R 3s 5M, is 1½ca S of conspic Old lt ho, W tr, R top, Fl 5s 7m 15M, and FS on W bkwtr.

RADIO TELEPHONE
None.

TELEPHONE (Dial code 01554)
Superintendent 758181; MRCC (01792) 366534; ☎ (01222) 763880 (H24); Pendine Range (01994) 453243 Ext 240; Marinecall 0891 500459; Police 772222; Dr 832240.

FACILITIES
Outer Hbr W pier and Basin ☎ 833342, Slip, M, L, CH; **E Pier** Slip; **Burry Port YC** Bar;
Services: D, ME, El, Sh, C, Gas.
Town EC Tues; P, D, V, R, Bar, ✉, Ⓑ, ⇌, ✈ (Cardiff).

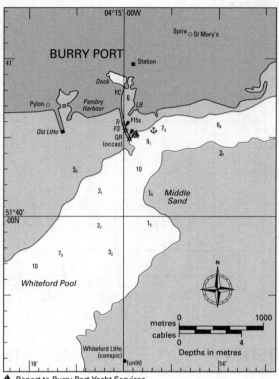

▲ Report to Burry Port Yacht Services

ADJACENT HARBOUR
CARMARTHEN, Carmarthenshire, 51°46'·25N 04°22'·45W. AC 1076, *1179*. HW –0455 on Dover. See 10.11.16. R Towy dries out, except for river water; access HW±2. Beware Carmarthen Bar off mouth of R Towy and Taf. Local knowledge or a pilot are essential. Chan into rivers shifts frequently and is not buoyed. Six electric cables, min clearance 15m, cross between the mouth and the fixed rly bridge in Carmarthen. Visitors berths at R Towy YC at Ferryside (9M below Carmarthen), access HW±3 (liable to dry). Facilities: **R Towy YC** ☎ (01207) 267366, Bar, FW, M
Town Usual facilities, Ⓑ, Bar, Gas, ✉, V, ⇌, ✈ (Cardiff).

SWANSEA   10-11-17

Swansea 51°36'·40N 03°55'·60W. Rtg 2-1-2

CHARTS
AC 1161, *1165, 1179*; Imray C59; Stanfords 14; OS 159

TIDES
−0500 Dover; ML 5·2; Duration 0620; Zone 0 (UT)

Standard Port MILFORD HAVEN (←)

Times				Height (metres)			
High Water		Low Water		MHWS	MHWN	MLWN	MLWS
0100	0800	0100	0700	7·0	5·2	2·5	0·7
1300	2000	1300	1900				
Differences SWANSEA							
+0004	+0006	−0006	−0003	+2·6	+2·1	+0·7	+0·3
MUMBLES							
+0005	+0010	−0020	−0015	+2·3	+1·7	+0·6	+0·2
PORT TALBOT							
+0003	+0003	−0013	−0007	+2·7	+2·2	+1·0	+0·3
PORTHCAWL							
0000	0000	0000	−0015	+2·9	+2·3	+0·8	+0·3

SHELTER
Very good in marina; enter via R Tawe Barrage lock, which operates on request HW±4½ (co-ordinated with the marina lock), 0700-2200BST; out of season, 0700-1900UT, but to 2200 at w/ends. Locks are closed when ht of tide falls to 1·5m above CD, usually at MLWS. At sp, yachts should not enter river until LW+2. Two large Or holding buoys below barrage in mid-stream; also, at W side of barrage lock, a landing pontoon (dries, foul ground). No Ⓥ berths at SY & SAC pontoons close N of marina ent.

NAVIGATION
WPT SHM By, QG, Bell, 51°35'·50N 03°56'·06W, 200°/020° from/to E bkwtr lt, 0·92M. In Swansea Bay tidal streams flow anti-clockwise for 9½ hrs (Swansea HW −3½ to +6), with at times a race off Mumbles Hd. From HW−6 to −3 the stream reverses, setting N past Mumbles Hd towards Swansea. Keep seaward of Mixon Shoal. When N of SW Inner Green Grounds (SWIGG) SCM lt buoy, Q (6)+L Fl 15s, keep to W of dredged chan and clear of commercial ships. Yachts must motor in hbr and appr, max speed 4kn.

LIGHTS AND MARKS
Mumbles Hd, Fl (4) 20s 35m 16M, is 3M SSW of hbr ent. A conspic TV mast (R lts) NNE of hbr is almost aligned with the fairway. Ldg lts 020°: front Oc G 4s 5m 2M; rear FG 6M; these mark E side of chan dredged 3m. From E, keep well seaward of the inner fairway buoy (SHM, Fl G 2·5s).

Port Traffic sigs are conspic at W side of ent to King's Dock; there are 9 lts, Ⓡ or Ⓖ, arranged in a 3 x 3 frame. Yachts arriving must obey the middle lt in left column:
Ⓡ = Do not enter the river; hold SW of W Pier.
Ⓖ = Yachts may enter the river, keeping to mid-chan, then to W of holding buoys.
Lock Master will advise on tfc movements Ch 18.
Lock sigs for barrage and marina locks alike are:
2Ⓡ = Lock closed. Do not proceed
Ⓡ = Wait
Ⓖ = Enter with caution
Ⓡ
Ⓖ } = Free flow operating; proceed with caution
Barrage lock lit by 2FR/FG (vert) to seaward.

RADIO TELEPHONE
Call *Swansea Docks Radio* VHF Ch14 (H24). For barrage, call *Tawe Lock* Ch 18. For marina call *Swansea Marina* Ch 80.

TELEPHONE (Dial code 01792)
Hr Mr 650855 Ext 260; Barrage 456014; MRCC 366534; Police 456999; ℍ 652373/4 and (01222) 763880 (H24); Marinecall 0891 500 459; Ⓗ 205666; Dr 653452; DVLA (for SSR) 783355.

FACILITIES
Swansea Marina (350+50 visitors) ☎ 470310, 🖷 463948, £10.69, D (no P), AC, FW, C (1 ton), BH (18 ton), Gas, Gaz, CH, ME, El, Ⓔ, Sh, Ⓞ, Bar, R;
Swansea Yacht & Sub Aqua Club ☎ 654863, M, L, (no visitors' berths); FW, C (5 ton static), R, Bar;
Services: ME, SM, ACA, CH, El, Ⓔ, Sh.
City ME, El, Sh, CH, V, R, Bar, ✉, Ⓑ, ⇌, ✈.

ADJACENT HARBOURS AND ANCHORAGES

MUMBLES, 51°34'·2N 03°58'·2W. Good ⚓ in W'lies 5ca N of Mumbles Hd lt ho. **Bristol Chan YC** ☎ (01792) 366000, Slip, M; **Mumbles YC** ☎ 369321, Slip, M, L, FW, C (hire).

R. NEATH, 51°37'·85N 03°49'·9W. **Monkstone Marina**, on W bank just S of bridge, has about 1m. Ent over bar HW±2½ via 1·5M chan, marked/lit training wall. Facilities: AB, M, D, FW, Slip, BH (15 ton), R, Bar, Visitors welcome; **Monkstone C & SC**, ☎ (01792) 812229; VHF Ch M (occas).

PORTHCAWL, Bridgend, 51°28'·45N 03°41'·95W. AC 1169, *1165*. HW −0500 on Dover; ML 5·3m. See 10·11·17. A tiny drying hbr (access HW±2) protected by bkwtr running SE from Porthcawl Pt. Beware rk ledge (dries) W of bkwtr. Porthcawl lt ho, W 6-sided tr with B base, F WRG 10m 6/4M, vis G302°-036°, W036°-082°, R082°-122°; in line 094° with St Hilary radio mast (QR & FR) leads through Shord chan. Tidal streams can reach 6kn at sp off end of bkwtr. ⚓ approx 3ca SSE of lt ho. Hr Mr ☎ (01656) 782756, 3 Ⓥs; Facilities: **Porthcawl Hbr B C** ☎ 782342. **Town** FC Wed; P & D (cans), CH, V, R, Bar, ✉, Ⓑ, ⇌ (Bridgend), ✈ (Cardiff).

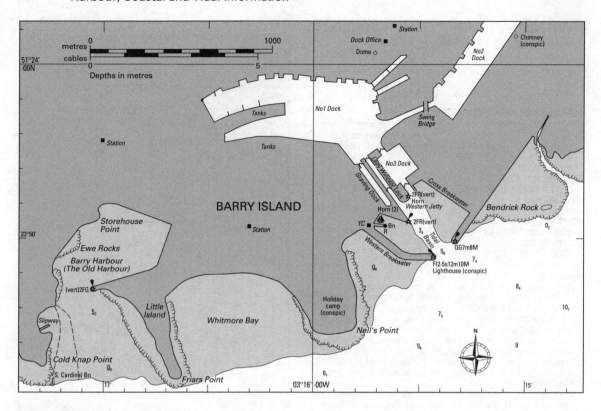

BARRY

10-11-18

Vale of Glamorgan 51°23'·45N 03°15'·37W   Rtg 2-2-2

CHARTS
AC 1182, *1152, 1179*; Imray C59; Stanfords 14; OS 171

TIDES
−0423 Dover; ML 6·1; Duration 0630; Zone 0 (UT)

Standard Port BRISTOL (AVONMOUTH) (→)

Times				Height (metres)			
High Water		Low Water		MHWS	MHWN	MLWN	MLWS
0600	1100	0300	0800	13·2	9·8	3·8	1·0
1800	2300	1500	2000				
Differences BARRY							
−0030	−0015	−0125	−0030	−1·8	−1·3	+0·2	0·0
FLAT HOLM							
−0015	−0015	−0045	−0045	−1·3	−1·1	−0·2	+0·2
STEEP HOLM							
−0020	−0020	−0050	−0050	−1·6	−1·2	−0·2	−0·2

SHELTER
Good, but in strong E/SE winds avoid Barry; No 1 Dock is no longer available to pleasure craft. Access HW±3 to the Outer hbr. No AB; pick up a mooring (free) and see YC. The Old Hbr to W of Barry Island dries and is not used.

NAVIGATION
WPT 51°23'·00N 03°15'·00W, 152°/332° from/to ent, 0·53M. Beware heavy merchant traffic. Approaching from E keep well out from the shore. Strong tidal stream across ent.

LIGHTS AND MARKS
Welsh Water Barry West PHM buoy, Fl R 5s, and Merkur PHM buoy, Fl R 2·5s, lie respectively 217°/1·5M and 191°/1·65M from hbr ent. A SPM buoy, Fl Y 5s, 6ca E of hbr ent marks sewer outfall. W bkwtr Fl 2·5s 10M. E bkwtr QG 8M.

RADIO TELEPHONE
Call: *Barry Radio* VHF Ch **11** 10 16 (HW−4 to HW+3). Tidal info available on request.

TELEPHONE (Dial code 01446)
Hr Mr 700754; MRCC (01792) 366534; ⌗ (01222) 763880 (H24); Marinecall 0891 500 459; Police 734451; Dr 739543.

FACILITIES
Barry YC (130) ☎ 735511, access HW±3½, Slip, M, Bar, FW; **Services:** Slip, D, FW, Gas, ME, El, Sh, CH, SM.
Town EC Wed; P (cans, 1M away), D, CH, V, Ⓡ, Bar, ✉, Ⓑ, ⇌, ✈ (Cardiff).

THE SEVERN BRIDGES

The Second Severn Crossing (37m cl'nce), from 51°34'·88N 02°43'·80W to 51°34'·14N 02°39'·82W, is 3M downriver of the Severn Bridge and 4M above Avonmouth. Going upriver, pass both bridges at about HW Avonmouth −1¾ (see also 10.11.20); max sp stream is 8kn at The Shoots and 6kn at the Severn Bridge, setting across the channel when the banks are covered. Redcliffe F Bu ldg lts in transit 013° with Charston Rock lt, Fl 3s, W ○ tr, B stripe, lead through the Shoots, a narrow passage twixt English Stones (6·2m) and rocky ledges (5·1m) off the Welsh shore. 5ca S of the Second Crossing, chan is marked by Lower Shoots WCM bn, Q (9) 15s 6m 7M, and Mixoms PHM bn, Fl (3) R 10s 6m 6M. 4ca N of the Second Crossing, leave the 013° transit before passing Old Man's Hd WCM bn, VQ (9) 10s 6m 7M and Lady Bench PHM bn, QR 6m 6M. From abeam Charston Rk, keep Chapel Rk, Fl WRG 2·6s, brg 050° until E tr of Severn Bridge bears 068°; which brg maintain until Lyde Rk, QR, bears about 355°, when alter 010° to transit the bridge (36·6m cl'nce) close to rks drying 1m. These brief directions, the strong streams and shifting banks underline the need for locally acquired knowledge together with AC 1166.

CARDIFF (Penarth)   10-11-19
Vale of Glamorgan 51°27'·10N 03°09'·55W   Rtg 3-2-1

CHARTS
AC 1182, *1176, 1179*; Imray C59; Stanfords 14; OS 171

TIDES
–0425 Dover; ML 6·4; Duration 0610; Zone 0 (UT)

Standard Port BRISTOL (AVONMOUTH) (→)

Times				Height (metres)			
High Water		Low Water		MHWS	MHWN	MLWN	MLWS
0600	1100	0300	0800	13·2	9·8	3·8	1·0
1800	2300	1500	2000				
Differences CARDIFF							
–0015	–0015	–0100	–0030	–1·0	–0·6	+0·1	0·0
NEWPORT							
–0020	–0010	0000	–0020	–1·1	–1·0	–0·6	–0·7

Note: At Newport the ht of LW does not normally fall below MLWS. Tidal hts are based on a minimum river flow; max flow may raise ht of LW by as much as 0·3m. HW Chepstow is 20 mins after HW Avonmouth.

SHELTER
Very good in marina (open H24). Access approx HW±3¾, via lock with sill 3·5m above CD. Depth gauge on outer wall shows ht of water above sill. Waiting ⚓ off Penarth seafront in W'lies; in E'lies cramped ⚓ off Alexandra Dock ent in 2m. See NAV below for temp'y restrictions.

NAVIGATION
WPT 51°24'·00N 03°08'·73W (2½ca SW of S Cardiff SCM lt buoy), 169°/349° from/to barrage locks, 2·9M. The outer appr's from W or SW are via Breaksea lt float and N of One Fathom Bank. Keep S of Lavernock Spit (SCM lt buoy) and NW of Flat Holm and Wolves drying rk (NCM lt buoy). From NE, drying ledges and shoals extend >1M offshore. From E, appr via Monkstone lt ho and S Cardiff SCM lt buoy. On the ldg line 349°, Ranny Spit (dries) is 3½ca to the W, and Cardiff Grounds same distance to the E. The Wrach Chan is buoyed/lit and dredged 1·2m; it passes 1½ca off Penarth Head. Do not impede merchant shipping, which can be heavy.

CARDIFF BAY BARRAGE
Timescale: Construction of a barrage and locks, which will close off Cardiff Bay but allow access to Penarth marina and to the commercial docks, is due to finish by the end of 1998. The completed barrage/locks are shown above. By the end of 1997, 2 of 3 new locks were due to be in use, allowing interim access arrangements to cease. (These arrangements, as shown on a temporary chartlet printed in Supplement 2/97, are repeated below under Pilotage in case of delay).

The marina lock will continue to operate HW±3¾ until the gap in the barrage is closed in late 1998; it will then stay open, since access through 2 of the 3 barrage locks is expected to be H24. *When known, details of procedures at the new locks will be published in the Supplement(s).*

Pilotage: Until 1998 temporary access remains as before, ie proceed 349° up Wrach Chan to Inner Wrach SHM buoy, Fl G 2·5s (51°26'·72N 03°09'·57W). Request bridge opening to *Bridge Control* Ch 72, and tell *Penarth Marina* Ch 80 your ETA. The bridge opens HW±4 at every H and H+30 for 10 minutes; longer at weekends. Appr chan to the bridge on 280° is marked by BBC No 1 PHM buoy, Fl R 6s (51°26'·92N 03°09'·73W), and 3 unlit buoys. Bridge tfc lts (vert) are: Ⓖ Ⓖ Ⓦ = proceed; Ⓡ Ⓡ Ⓡ = wait, bridge down/lowering. Yachts may wait alongside holding barges. The cill below the bridge is 2·8m above CD. From the bridge proceed SSW via buoyed/unlit chan to marina.

Note: The chartlet below depicts the Barrage, associated locks and approach to Penarth marina as they are expected to be in late 1998. A new chartlet will be published in the 1999 Almanac based on the latest hydrographic survey.

LIGHTS AND MARKS
Ldg lts 349°, both FW 3/24m 20M. Marina lock sigs: Ⓖ = enter lock. Ⓡ = Keep clear, lock in use. Ⓡ Ⓡ = Keep clear; fast freeflow in progress, or no water.

RADIO TELEPHONE
Port VHF Ch **14** 11 16 (HW–4 to HW+3). *Barrage Control* Ch 72. Penarth marina Ch 80.

TELEPHONE (Dial code 01222)
Hr Mr 471311; Marina 705021; MRCC (01792) 366534; ⌗ (01222) 763880 (H24); Marinecall 0891 500 459; Weather Centre 397020; Police 373934; Dr 415258.

FACILITIES
Penarth Marina (350 + 50 visitors; max draft 3m), ☎ 705021, 🛥 712170, £12.74, FW, AC, P, D, El, ME, Sh, C, CH, BY, Gas, Ⓙ, R;
Penarth YC ☎ 708196, Slip, FW, Bar; **Cardiff YC** ☎ 387697, Slip, M, FW, L (floating pontoon), Bar;
Penarth MB & SC ☎ 226575, M, L, C, FW, Bar, Slip;
Services: D, SM, Sh, C (20 ton), CH, ACA, ME, El, Ⓔ, BY, Slip, BH (10 ton), Gas.
City EC Wed; P, D, ME, El, V, R, Bar, ✉, Ⓑ, ⇌, ✈.

ADJACENT HARBOUR

NEWPORT, Newport, 51°32'·95N 02°59'·13W. AC *1176, 1152, 1179*. HW –0425 on Dover; ML 6·0m; Duration 0620. See 10·11·19. A commercial port controlled by ABP, but a safe shelter for yachts. Enter R Usk over bar (approx 0·5m) E of West Usk buoy, QR Bell) and follow buoyed and lit chan to S Lock ent; turn NE (ldg lts 057°) for yacht moorings on S side between power stn pier and YC. Beware overhead cables in Julian's Pill, clearance 3·8m. East Usk lt ho Fl (2) WRG 10s 11m 15/11M, W284°–290°, R290°–017°, W017°–037°, G037°–115°, W115°–120°. Ldg lts 057°, both FG. Alexandra Dock, S lock W pier head 2 FR (vert) 9/7m 6M. E pier head 2 FG (vert) 9/7m 6M. Port VHF Ch 09 11 16 (HW ±4). There is also a VTS, not compulsory for yachts; call *Newport Pier Head* VHF Ch 69, 71, 16, HW±4. Hr Mr (ABP) ☎ (01633) 244411. ⌗ ☎ 273709; Facilities: **Newport and Uskmouth SC** Bar, M; **Services:** CH, El, ME, Sh, Ⓔ. **Town** EC Thurs; all facilities.

11

AVONMOUTH

MEAN SPRING
AND NEAP CURVES

MEAN RANGES
Springs 12.2m
Neaps 6.0m

Springs occur 2 days
after
New and Full Moon.

SHARPNESS   10-11-20

Gloucestershire 51°43'·00N 02°29'·00W   Rtg 3-3-2

CHARTS
AC 1166, Imray C59; Stanfords 14; OS 162

TIDES
−0315 Dover; Duration 0415; Zone 0 (UT). Note: The tidal
regime is irregular and deviates from Avonmouth curve.

Standard Port BRISTOL (AVONMOUTH) (→)

Times				Height (metres)			
High Water		Low Water		MHWS	MHWN	MLWN	MLWS
0000	0600	0000	0700	13·2	9·8	3·8	1·0
1200	1800	1200	1900				
Differences SUDBROOK (Second Severn Bridge)							
+0010	+0010	+0025	+0015	+0·2	+0·1	−0·1	+0·1
BEACHLEY/AUST (Severn Bridge)							
+0010	+0015	+0040	+0025	−0·2	−0·2	−0·5	−0·3
NARLWOOD ROCKS							
+0025	+0025	+0120	+0100	−1·9	−2·0	−2·3	−0·8
SHARPNESS DOCK							
+0035	+0050	+0305	+0245	−3·9	−4·2	−3·3	−0·4

SHELTER
Very good. The lock into Commercial Docks opens HW −2
to HW, but prompt arrival is not advised due to lack of water;
the flood starts to make much later in the upper river. Pass 2
swing bridges for marina or Gloucester & Sharpness Canal.

NAVIGATION
WPT 51°42'·80N 02°29'·20W, 208°/028° from/to ent, 2ca.
Leave King Road, Avonmouth (17M downriver) not before
HW Sharpness −3, to be off hbr ent about HW −½. Stem
strong flood S of F Bu lt; beware cross tide. Low-powered
craft arriving any earlier may be unable to stem the tide.
The fairway between King Road and Sharpness ent is
defined as a narrow chan (Rule 9 of IRPCS). Small craft
shall not impede the passage of commercial vessels.

LIGHTS AND MARKS
Berkeley Power Stn is conspic 1·5M S of lock. Lts as chartlet,
but night passage not advised without local knowledge/pilot.

RADIO TELEPHONE
Call: Sharpness Pierhead VHF Ch **17** 16 (HW −6 to +2) for lock.
Gloucester & Sharpness Canal Ch 74 for bridges; no locks.

TELEPHONE (Dial code 01453)
Pierhead 511968 (HW−6 to HW+2); Hr Mr 811644 (HO);
⌗ (01222) 763880 (H24); Marinecall 0891 500 459; MRCC
(01792) 366534; Police 810477; Ⓗ 810777.

FACILITIES
Sharpness Marine (100+15) ☎ 811476, £4, D, AC, FW, Sh,
CH, Gas; **Services:** ME, El, C. **Town** EC Sat; V, R, Bar, ✉, Ⓑ
(Berkeley), ⇌ (Stonehouse), ✈ (Bristol). ACA, Gloucester.

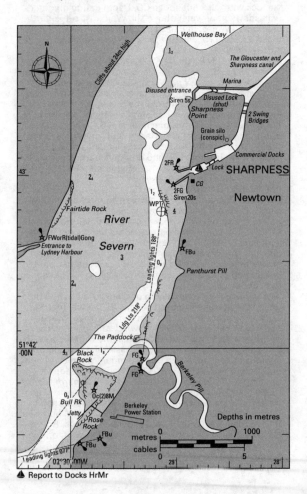

▲ Report to Docks HrMr

TIME ZONE (UT)
For Summer Time add ONE hour in non-shaded areas

ENGLAND – PORT OF BRISTOL (AVONMOUTH)

LAT 51°30′N   LONG   2°44′W

TIMES AND HEIGHTS OF HIGH AND LOW WATERS

YEAR 1998

JANUARY

Day	Time	m	Time	m
1 TH	0315	1.4	1540	1.3
	2113	13.2		
16 F	0347	1.5	0921	12.8
	1605	1.9	2141	12.4
2 F	0353	1.5	0932	13.3
	1617	1.3	2156	13.1
17 SA	0410	1.8	0952	12.4
	1625	2.2	2209	12.0
3 SA	0428	1.6	1015	13.1
	1654	1.5	2239	12.7
18 SU	0431	2.1	1021	11.9
	1646	2.3	2239	11.5
4 SU	0504	1.8	1100	12.7
	1734	1.8	2325	12.2
19 M	0457	2.3	1052	11.4
	1714	2.5	2311	11.0
5 M	0546	2.2	1151	12.1
	1819	2.2		
20 TU	0531	2.6	1127	10.8
	1752	2.9	2351	10.5
6 TU	0017	11.6	0635	2.7
	1252	11.4	1914	2.7
21 W	0615	3.1	1213	10.3
	1841	3.4		
7 W	0123	11.0	0741	3.2
	1409	11.1	2036	3.1
22 TH	0045	10.0	0716	3.6
	1320	9.9	1950	3.7
8 TH	0245	10.8	0922	3.3
	1526	11.1	2203	3.0
23 F	0201	9.8	0835	3.7
	1443	10.0	2112	3.7
9 F	0358	11.1	1040	2.9
	1632	11.6	2310	2.4
24 SA	0326	10.2	0953	3.4
	1559	10.6	2230	3.2
10 SA	0500	11.8	1142	2.3
	1730	12.1		
25 SU	0434	11.0	1103	2.7
	1702	11.4	2337	2.5
11 SU	0008	1.8	0553	12.4
	1237	1.7	1821	12.6
26 M	0530	11.9	1205	2.1
	1756	12.2		
12 M ○	0101	1.4	0642	13.0
	1328	1.3	1908	13.0
27 TU	0036	1.9	0620	12.7
	1303	1.6	1845	12.8
13 TU	0150	1.1	0726	13.2
	1417	1.2	1952	13.1
28 W	0131	1.5	0707	13.4
	1358	1.2	1932	13.4
14 W	0235	1.0	0808	13.3
	1501	1.3	2033	13.0
29 TH	0223	1.0	0753	13.8
	1449	0.9	2018	13.7
15 TH	0315	1.2	0847	13.1
	1538	1.5	2109	12.7
30 F	0309	1.0	0838	14.0
	1534	0.7	2102	13.9
31 SA	0350	0.9	0921	14.1
	1613	0.7	2144	13.8

FEBRUARY

Day	Time	m	Time	m
1 SU	0426	1.0	1003	13.9
	1648	0.9	2225	13.5
16 M	0412	1.8	0955	12.2
	1620	2.1	2210	11.9
2 M	0459	1.2	1046	13.4
	1721	1.3	2307	12.9
17 TU	0430	1.9	1021	11.8
	1642	2.1	2237	11.5
3 TU	0532	1.7	1130	12.6
	1757	1.9	2352	12.0
18 W	0459	2.1	1050	11.3
	1714	2.4	2310	11.1
4 W	0610	2.3	1222	11.6
	1840	2.6		
19 TH	0535	2.5	1129	10.8
	1754	2.9	2355	10.5
5 TH	0047	11.1	0700	3.1
	1332	10.8	1938	3.3
20 F	0623	3.2	1223	10.2
	1848	3.5		
6 F	0208	10.4	0820	3.8
	1459	10.5	2124	3.6
21 SA	0057	10.0	0732	3.7
	1337	9.8	2009	3.9
7 SA	0331	10.4	1015	3.6
	1611	10.8	2245	3.2
22 SU	0222	9.9	0907	3.7
	1512	10.1	2149	3.6
8 SU	0439	11.0	1122	2.8
	1712	11.4	2346	2.4
23 M	0356	10.6	1030	3.1
	1633	11.0	2308	2.8
9 M	0537	11.8	1217	2.1
	1805	12.1		
24 TU	0504	11.6	1142	2.7
	1735	12.0		
10 TU	0039	1.7	0625	12.5
	1308	1.5	1852	12.7
25 W	0014	2.1	0559	12.7
	1244	1.5	1826	13.0
11 W ○	0129	1.2	0710	13.0
	1356	1.2	1934	13.0
26 TH ●	0113	1.4	0649	13.5
	1342	1.0	1915	13.7
12 TH	0215	0.9	0750	13.2
	1441	1.1	2013	13.0
27 F	0207	0.9	0736	14.2
	1434	0.5	2001	14.2
13 F	0257	1.0	0827	13.2
	1519	1.3	2047	12.8
28 SA	0256	0.5	0822	14.5
	1520	0.2	2045	14.4
14 SA	0331	1.2	0859	12.9
	1549	1.6	2117	12.6
15 SU	0356	1.6	0928	12.6
	1608	1.9	2144	12.3

MARCH

Day	Time	m	Time	m
1 SU	0338	0.4	0905	14.6
	1600	0.2	2127	14.3
16 M	0336	1.4	0902	12.6
	1548	1.8	2117	12.4
2 M	0414	0.5	0947	14.3
	1633	0.5	2207	13.9
17 TU	0352	1.7	0928	12.3
	1555	2.0	2141	12.1
3 TU	0445	1.0	1027	13.7
	1702	1.1	2246	13.2
18 W	0405	1.7	0953	12.0
	1614	1.9	2207	11.8
4 W	0513	1.4	1108	12.7
	1731	1.8	2326	12.1
19 TH	0432	1.8	1022	11.6
	1644	2.1	2240	11.4
5 TH	0545	2.2	1153	11.6
	1808	2.6		
20 F	0505	2.2	1101	11.1
	1720	2.5	2324	10.8
6 F	0013	11.0	0628	3.1
	1256	10.4	1858	3.5
21 SA	0547	2.8	1151	10.5
	1807	3.2		
7 SA	0130	10.1	0732	3.9
	1433	9.9	2025	4.1
22 SU	0020	10.2	0645	3.4
	1258	10.0	1914	3.8
8 SU	0307	9.9	0948	4.0
	1550	10.2	2220	3.6
23 M	0137	9.9	0819	3.7
	1428	10.0	2108	3.8
9 M	0417	10.5	1100	3.1
	1652	11.0	2322	2.7
24 TU	0317	10.4	1001	3.2
	1605	10.8	2242	3.0
10 TU	0515	11.4	1154	2.2
	1744	11.8		
25 W	0438	11.5	1119	2.2
	1712	12.0	2352	2.0
11 W	0015	1.8	0604	12.3
	1244	1.5	1829	12.5
26 TH	0537	12.6	1223	1.4
	1806	13.1		
12 TH	0104	1.2	0647	12.9
	1331	1.1	1910	12.9
27 F	0051	1.3	0628	13.6
	1320	0.7	1854	13.9
13 F ○	0150	0.8	0726	13.1
	1415	0.9	1947	13.0
28 SA ●	0146	0.6	0716	14.3
	1412	0.2	1940	14.4
14 SA	0232	0.8	0801	13.1
	1455	1.1	2020	12.9
29 SU	0235	0.1	0801	14.7
	1459	0.0	2024	14.6
15 SU	0309	1.0	0833	12.9
	1527	1.4	2050	12.7
30 M	0319	0.1	0845	14.7
	1539	0.1	2106	14.5
31 TU	0356	0.3	0927	14.4
	1613	0.5	2146	14.0

APRIL

Day	Time	m	Time	m
1 W	0427	0.8	1007	13.7
	1641	1.1	2224	13.1
16 TH	0345	1.7	0930	12.0
	1552	1.9	2144	12.0
2 TH	0454	1.4	1047	12.6
	1707	1.8	2302	12.1
17 F	0411	1.7	1002	11.8
	1622	1.9	2220	11.7
3 F	0523	2.2	1128	11.4
	1741	2.7	2345	10.9
18 SA	0445	1.9	1042	11.4
	1658	2.3	2303	11.2
4 SA	0603	3.1	1224	10.2
	1829	3.6		
19 SU	0526	2.4	1131	10.8
	1744	2.9	2359	10.6
5 SU	0055	9.9	0703	3.9
	1404	9.6	1943	4.2
20 M	0621	3.0	1235	10.3
	1846	3.5		
6 M	0238	9.7	0850	4.2
	1522	9.9	2144	3.9
21 TU	0111	10.2	0744	3.4
	1358	10.2	2028	3.7
7 TU	0348	10.3	1029	3.3
	1622	10.7	2252	2.9
22 W	0243	10.5	0932	3.0
	1533	10.8	2214	2.9
8 W	0445	11.1	1124	2.4
	1715	11.5	2344	2.0
23 TH	0408	11.5	1053	2.2
	1644	11.9	2325	2.0
9 TH	0534	12.0	1213	1.6
	1800	12.3		
24 F	0511	12.6	1157	1.3
	1740	13.0		
10 F	0032	1.3	0617	12.6
	1259	1.2	1839	12.7
25 SA	0025	1.2	0604	13.5
	1254	0.7	1830	13.8
11 SA ○	0118	0.9	0655	12.9
	1343	1.0	1916	12.9
26 SU ●	0120	0.6	0653	14.2
	1346	0.2	1916	14.3
12 SU	0201	0.9	0731	12.9
	1424	1.1	1950	12.9
27 M	0210	0.2	0739	14.5
	1434	0.1	2001	14.5
13 M	0240	1.1	0805	12.7
	1459	1.4	2021	12.7
28 TU	0255	0.2	0825	14.4
	1516	0.2	2044	14.3
14 TU	0311	1.4	0836	12.5
	1523	1.8	2050	12.4
29 W	0335	0.4	0908	14.1
	1552	0.6	2125	13.8
15 W	0331	1.6	0904	12.3
	1533	1.9	2116	12.2
30 TH	0409	0.9	0949	13.4
	1621	1.2	2204	13.0

11

Chart Datum: 6·50 metres below Ordnance Datum (Newlyn)

TIME ZONE (UT)
For Summer Time add ONE hour in non-shaded areas

ENGLAND – PORT OF BRISTOL (AVONMOUTH)

LAT 51°30′N LONG 2°44′W

TIMES AND HEIGHTS OF HIGH AND LOW WATERS

YEAR **1998**

MAY

Date	Time	m	Date	Time	m
1 F	0438 / 1028 / 1648 / 2242	1.5 / 12.4 / 1.9 / 12.0	**16** SA	0401 / 0951 / 1611 / 2208	1.7 / 11.9 / 1.9 / 11.9
2 SA	0507 / 1109 / 1721 / 2324	2.3 / 11.4 / 2.6 / 11.0	**17** SU	0436 / 1032 / 1648 / 2252	1.8 / 11.6 / 2.1 / 11.5
3 SU	0545 / 1158 / 1805	3.0 / 10.3 / 3.4	**18** M	0518 / 1121 / 1733 / 2346	2.2 / 11.2 / 2.6 / 11.0
4 M	0024 / 0638 / 1319 / 1909	10.1 / 3.6 / 9.7 / 3.9	**19** TU	0612 / 1220 / 1832	2.6 / 10.8 / 3.1
5 TU	0159 / 0751 / 1442 / 2031	9.8 / 3.9 / 9.9 / 3.9	**20** W	0053 / 0724 / 1334 / 1958	10.7 / 2.9 / 10.6 / 3.3
6 W	0309 / 0927 / 1544 / 2202	10.1 / 3.6 / 10.4 / 3.2	**21** TH	0216 / 0900 / 1459 / 2142	10.9 / 2.8 / 11.0 / 2.8
7 TH	0406 / 1041 / 1636 / 2303	10.8 / 2.8 / 11.1 / 2.4	**22** F	0336 / 1022 / 1613 / 2256	11.5 / 2.2 / 11.8 / 2.1
8 F	0456 / 1133 / 1723 / 2354	11.5 / 2.0 / 11.8 / 1.7	**23** SA	0443 / 1128 / 1713 / 2357	12.3 / 1.5 / 12.6 / 1.4
9 SA	0541 / 1221 / 1804	12.1 / 1.5 / 12.4	**24** SU	0539 / 1226 / 1806	13.1 / 0.9 / 13.4
10 SU	0041 / 0621 / 1307 / 1842	1.3 / 12.4 / 1.3 / 12.6	**25** M ●	0053 / 0630 / 1320 / 1854	0.8 / 13.7 / 0.5 / 13.8
11 M O	0126 / 0659 / 1350 / 1919	1.2 / 12.5 / 1.3 / 12.7	**26** TU	0145 / 0718 / 1409 / 1940	0.5 / 13.9 / 0.4 / 14.0
12 TU	0207 / 0736 / 1428 / 1953	1.2 / 12.5 / 1.5 / 12.6	**27** W	0233 / 0805 / 1454 / 2024	0.5 / 13.9 / 0.5 / 13.9
13 W	0243 / 0810 / 1458 / 2026	1.4 / 12.4 / 1.7 / 12.5	**28** TH	0317 / 0850 / 1534 / 2107	0.7 / 13.6 / 0.8 / 13.5
14 TH	0311 / 0843 / 1518 / 2057	1.6 / 12.2 / 1.8 / 12.3	**29** F	0355 / 0932 / 1606 / 2147	1.1 / 13.0 / 1.3 / 12.8
15 F	0333 / 0915 / 1540 / 2130	1.7 / 12.1 / 1.9 / 12.1	**30** SA	0426 / 1012 / 1634 / 2225	1.7 / 12.1 / 1.9 / 12.1
			31 SU	0454 / 1051 / 1704 / 2304	2.2 / 11.5 / 2.4 / 11.3

JUNE

Date	Time	m	Date	Time	m
1 M	0528 / 1132 / 1743 / 2352	2.7 / 10.7 / 2.9 / 10.5	**16** TU	0517 / 1113 / 1730 / 2336	1.9 / 11.8 / 2.2 / 11.7
2 TU	0613 / 1226 / 1835	3.2 / 10.1 / 3.4	**17** W	0606 / 1207 / 1823	2.2 / 11.4 / 2.6
3 W	0059 / 0709 / 1339 / 1939	10.0 / 3.5 / 9.8 / 3.6	**18** TH	0036 / 0706 / 1311 / 1931	11.3 / 2.5 / 11.0 / 2.9
4 TH	0215 / 0815 / 1450 / 2049	10.0 / 3.5 / 10.0 / 3.4	**19** F	0149 / 0825 / 1427 / 2106	11.1 / 2.6 / 11.0 / 2.9
5 F	0317 / 0925 / 1548 / 2200	10.4 / 3.1 / 10.6 / 2.9	**20** SA	0307 / 0950 / 1543 / 2227	11.4 / 2.4 / 11.4 / 2.4
6 SA	0411 / 1036 / 1640 / 2305	10.9 / 2.6 / 11.2 / 2.3	**21** SU	0416 / 1100 / 1647 / 2332	11.9 / 1.9 / 12.1 / 1.8
7 SU	0500 / 1135 / 1726 / 2359	11.5 / 2.1 / 11.8 / 1.8	**22** M	0516 / 1201 / 1744	12.4 / 1.4 / 12.7
8 M	0545 / 1226 / 1809	11.9 / 1.7 / 12.3	**23** TU	0030 / 0610 / 1256 / 1834	1.3 / 12.9 / 1.0 / 13.2
9 TU	0048 / 0627 / 1314 / 1849	1.5 / 12.2 / 1.5 / 12.5	**24** W ●	0124 / 0700 / 1348 / 1922	1.0 / 13.2 / 0.8 / 13.5
10 W O	0134 / 0708 / 1357 / 1928	1.4 / 12.3 / 1.5 / 12.6	**25** TH	0214 / 0748 / 1436 / 2007	0.9 / 13.3 / 0.8 / 13.5
11 TH	0217 / 0748 / 1436 / 2006	1.4 / 12.4 / 1.6 / 12.6	**26** F	0301 / 0834 / 1519 / 2051	1.0 / 13.2 / 1.0 / 13.3
12 F	0255 / 0827 / 1509 / 2043	1.5 / 12.4 / 1.7 / 12.6	**27** SA	0342 / 0916 / 1555 / 2131	1.2 / 12.8 / 1.3 / 12.8
13 SA	0328 / 0905 / 1538 / 2121	1.6 / 12.3 / 1.8 / 12.5	**28** SU	0416 / 0955 / 1623 / 2207	1.7 / 12.4 / 1.8 / 12.3
14 SU	0400 / 0945 / 1609 / 2201	1.6 / 12.3 / 1.8 / 12.3	**29** M	0442 / 1030 / 1649 / 2242	2.1 / 11.8 / 2.1 / 11.7
15 M	0436 / 1027 / 1647 / 2246	1.7 / 12.1 / 1.9 / 12.1	**30** TU	0509 / 1104 / 1720 / 2319	2.4 / 11.2 / 2.5 / 11.1

JULY

Date	Time	m	Date	Time	m
1 W	0543 / 1143 / 1800	2.7 / 10.7 / 2.8	**16** TH	0556 / 1150 / 1809	1.8 / 11.9 / 2.2
2 TH	0004 / 0627 / 1233 / 1851	10.5 / 3.0 / 10.2 / 3.2	**17** F	0016 / 0644 / 1246 / 1903	11.7 / 2.2 / 11.3 / 2.8
3 F	0104 / 0723 / 1338 / 1954	10.1 / 3.3 / 9.9 / 3.4	**18** SA	0123 / 0747 / 1357 / 2025	11.2 / 2.7 / 10.9 / 3.2
4 SA	0214 / 0827 / 1449 / 2103	10.0 / 3.3 / 10.1 / 3.3	**19** SU	0241 / 0918 / 1516 / 2202	11.0 / 2.9 / 10.9 / 3.0
5 SU	0319 / 0936 / 1553 / 2212	10.3 / 3.1 / 10.6 / 2.9	**20** M	0355 / 1036 / 1626 / 2312	11.2 / 2.6 / 11.4 / 2.5
6 M	0418 / 1045 / 1648 / 2316	10.8 / 2.7 / 11.2 / 2.3	**21** TU	0459 / 1139 / 1726	11.7 / 2.0 / 12.0
7 TU	0511 / 1146 / 1738	11.4 / 2.2 / 11.9	**22** W	0011 / 0555 / 1237 / 1818	1.8 / 12.3 / 1.5 / 12.7
8 W	0013 / 0559 / 1241 / 1824	1.8 / 11.9 / 1.8 / 12.4	**23** TH ●	0106 / 0646 / 1329 / 1907	1.3 / 12.7 / 1.1 / 13.1
9 TH O	0105 / 0645 / 1331 / 1907	1.6 / 12.3 / 1.6 / 12.7	**24** F	0158 / 0733 / 1419 / 1952	1.1 / 13.0 / 0.9 / 13.3
10 F	0155 / 0729 / 1418 / 1950	1.4 / 12.5 / 1.5 / 12.9	**25** SA	0246 / 0818 / 1503 / 2034	1.0 / 13.0 / 0.9 / 13.2
11 SA	0242 / 0813 / 1502 / 2031	1.4 / 12.7 / 1.5 / 13.0	**26** SU	0328 / 0858 / 1541 / 2112	1.1 / 12.8 / 1.2 / 13.0
12 SU	0325 / 0855 / 1539 / 2113	1.3 / 12.8 / 1.5 / 13.0	**27** M	0403 / 0933 / 1610 / 2145	1.5 / 12.5 / 1.6 / 12.6
13 M	0403 / 0937 / 1623 / 2154	1.3 / 12.8 / 1.6 / 13.0	**28** TU	0427 / 1004 / 1632 / 2215	1.9 / 12.1 / 1.9 / 12.1
14 TU	0439 / 1019 / 1648 / 2237	1.5 / 12.7 / 1.6 / 12.7	**29** W	0447 / 1034 / 1654 / 2245	2.2 / 11.6 / 2.1 / 11.5
15 W	0515 / 1102 / 1725 / 2323	1.5 / 12.4 / 1.8 / 12.3	**30** TH	0511 / 1105 / 1724 / 2318	2.4 / 11.1 / 2.4 / 10.9
			31 F	0544 / 1142 / 1803	2.7 / 10.6 / 2.9

AUGUST

Date	Time	m	Date	Time	m
1 SA	0000 / 0627 / 1232 / 1857	10.3 / 3.1 / 10.0 / 3.4	**16** SU	0055 / 0710 / 1329 / 1942	10.9 / 3.0 / 10.6 / 3.6
2 SU	0101 / 0729 / 1342 / 2011	9.8 / 3.5 / 9.8 / 3.7	**17** M	0220 / 0843 / 1456 / 2142	10.4 / 3.5 / 10.4 / 3.7
3 M	0222 / 0846 / 1504 / 2128	9.8 / 3.6 / 10.0 / 3.5	**18** TU	0339 / 1016 / 1609 / 2257	10.5 / 3.0 / 10.8 / 3.0
4 TU	0337 / 1003 / 1613 / 2240	10.2 / 3.2 / 10.7 / 2.8	**19** W	0445 / 1122 / 1711 / 2356	11.1 / 2.5 / 11.6 / 2.1
5 W	0441 / 1112 / 1711 / 2344	10.9 / 2.6 / 11.5 / 2.2	**20** TH	0541 / 1218 / 1804	11.9 / 1.7 / 12.4
6 TH	0535 / 1213 / 1801	11.7 / 2.1 / 12.3	**21** F	0048 / 0631 / 1310 / 1850	1.4 / 12.5 / 1.2 / 13.0
7 F	0042 / 0624 / 1310 / 1848	1.7 / 12.4 / 1.7 / 12.9	**22** SA ●	0139 / 0716 / 1359 / 1933	1.0 / 12.9 / 0.8 / 13.3
8 SA O	0137 / 0712 / 1403 / 1933	1.3 / 12.9 / 1.4 / 13.3	**23** SU	0225 / 0757 / 1443 / 2013	0.8 / 13.1 / 0.8 / 13.3
9 SU	0229 / 0757 / 1452 / 2017	1.1 / 13.2 / 1.2 / 13.6	**24** M	0308 / 0835 / 1522 / 2048	0.9 / 13.0 / 1.0 / 13.1
10 M	0316 / 0841 / 1534 / 2100	0.9 / 13.4 / 1.1 / 13.7	**25** TU	0343 / 0907 / 1552 / 2119	1.3 / 12.7 / 1.4 / 12.7
11 TU	0357 / 0924 / 1611 / 2142	0.8 / 13.4 / 1.1 / 13.6	**26** W	0408 / 0936 / 1612 / 2146	1.8 / 12.3 / 1.8 / 12.2
12 W	0433 / 1005 / 1643 / 2223	0.9 / 13.3 / 1.2 / 13.3	**27** TH	0422 / 1002 / 1627 / 2212	2.1 / 11.9 / 2.0 / 11.7
13 TH	0505 / 1045 / 1714 / 2306	1.2 / 12.9 / 1.6 / 12.7	**28** F	0436 / 1029 / 1650 / 2239	2.3 / 11.4 / 2.2 / 11.2
14 F	0538 / 1129 / 1750 / 2354	1.6 / 12.2 / 2.1 / 11.8	**29** SA	0502 / 1058 / 1722 / 2312	2.5 / 10.9 / 2.7 / 10.6
15 SA	0617 / 1219 / 1835	2.3 / 11.3 / 2.9	**30** SU	0538 / 1138 / 1804	2.9 / 10.3 / 3.3
			31 M	0000 / 0627 / 1236 / 1908	10.0 / 3.6 / 9.7 / 3.9

Chart Datum: 6·50 metres below Ordnance Datum (Newlyn)

TIME ZONE (UT)
For Summer Time add ONE hour in non-shaded areas

ENGLAND – PORT OF BRISTOL (AVONMOUTH)

LAT 51°30'N   LONG 2°44'W

TIMES AND HEIGHTS OF HIGH AND LOW WATERS   YEAR 1998

SEPTEMBER

Day	Time	m	Time	m	Time	m	Time	m
1 TU	0113	9.5	0745	4.0	1406	9.6	2045	4.0
16 W	0324	10.1	0959	3.7	1553	10.5	2241	3.2
2 W	0255	9.7	0925	3.8	1540	10.2	2209	3.3
17 TH	0428	10.8	1103	2.7	1653	11.4	2336	2.2
3 TH	0414	10.6	1044	3.1	1646	11.3	2321	2.4
18 F	0523	11.7	1156	1.8	1744	12.3		
4 F	0514	11.6	1151	2.3	1740	12.3		
19 SA	0026	1.4	0610	12.5	1246	1.1	1829	13.0
5 SA	0022	1.7	0605	12.5	1250	1.6	1828	13.2
20 SU ●	0114	0.9	0652	13.0	1333	0.8	1910	13.3
6 SU O	0119	1.1	0652	13.3	1345	1.2	1914	13.8
21 M	0159	0.7	0731	13.2	1417	0.7	1947	13.3
7 M	0212	0.8	0738	13.7	1435	0.9	1959	14.2
22 TU	0241	0.8	0806	13.0	1456	0.9	2020	13.1
8 TU	0300	0.5	0822	14.0	1519	0.7	2042	14.3
23 W	0317	1.2	0838	12.8	1529	1.3	2051	12.7
9 W	0342	0.4	0905	14.0	1557	0.7	2124	14.1
24 TH	0343	1.7	0906	12.4	1549	1.8	2118	12.3
10 TH	0417	0.6	0945	13.7	1630	1.0	2205	13.7
25 F	0355	2.1	0931	12.0	1600	2.1	2142	11.8
11 F	0447	1.1	1025	13.2	1658	1.5	2246	12.8
26 SA	0405	2.2	0955	11.6	1620	2.2	2206	11.4
12 SA	0516	1.7	1106	12.3	1729	2.2	2330	11.8
27 SU	0429	2.4	1024	11.1	1649	2.5	2240	10.9
13 SU	0550	2.5	1153	11.2	1808	3.1		
28 M	0502	2.7	1103	10.6	1727	3.1	2325	10.2
14 M	0028	10.6	0636	3.4	1303	10.2	1908	3.9
29 TU	0544	3.4	1155	9.9	1819	3.8		
15 TU	0203	9.9	0802	4.1	1440	10.0	2127	4.1
30 W	0028	9.6	0646	4.1	1311	9.5	1951	4.2

OCTOBER

Day	Time	m	Time	m	Time	m	Time	m
1 TH	0203	9.5	0840	4.2	1502	10.0	2138	3.6
16 F	0403	10.7	1036	3.0	1626	11.3	2309	2.5
2 F	0345	10.4	1017	3.4	1618	11.1	2257	2.6
17 SA	0456	11.6	1128	2.0	1717	12.1	2357	1.6
3 SA	0449	11.5	1127	2.4	1715	12.3		
18 SU	0542	12.4	1216	1.3	1801	12.8		
4 SU	0000	1.7	0542	12.7	1227	1.6	1805	13.3
19 M	0043	1.1	0623	12.9	1302	0.9	1841	13.1
5 M O	0056	1.0	0630	13.5	1321	1.0	1852	14.1
20 TU ●	0128	0.8	0701	13.1	1346	0.8	1917	13.2
6 TU	0148	0.5	0715	14.1	1412	0.6	1937	14.5
21 W	0209	0.9	0736	13.0	1426	1.0	1951	13.0
7 W	0236	0.3	0800	14.4	1457	0.5	2021	14.6
22 TH	0246	1.3	0808	12.8	1500	1.4	2023	12.6
8 TH	0319	0.3	0842	14.3	1537	0.5	2104	14.3
23 F	0315	1.7	0838	12.4	1525	1.8	2051	12.3
9 F	0355	0.6	0924	14.0	1611	0.9	2146	13.8
24 SA	0330	2.1	0852	12.1	1538	2.1	2117	11.9
10 SA	0427	1.1	1004	13.3	1641	1.5	2227	12.8
25 SU	0341	2.2	0929	11.8	1557	2.2	2144	11.6
11 SU	0455	1.8	1045	12.3	1710	2.3	2310	11.7
26 M	0406	2.3	1000	11.4	1628	2.4	2219	11.1
12 M	0526	2.7	1130	11.2	1748	3.2		
27 TU	0439	2.6	1041	10.9	1705	2.8	2304	10.6
13 TU	0005	10.5	0610	3.6	1240	10.1	1844	4.1
28 W	0520	3.1	1131	10.3	1754	3.4		
14 W	0141	9.7	0723	4.3	1419	9.9	2058	4.3
29 TH	0003	10.0	0615	3.7	1240	9.9	1906	3.9
15 TH	0301	9.9	0932	4.0	1528	10.4	2215	3.5
30 F	0123	9.8	0743	4.1	1414	10.1	2058	3.7
31 SA	0305	10.3	0942	3.5	1543	11.0	2225	2.8

NOVEMBER

Day	Time	m	Time	m	Time	m	Time	m
1 SU	0419	11.5	1057	2.6	1646	12.2	2331	1.8
16 M	0509	11.9	1140	1.9	1728	12.2		
2 M	0515	12.6	1158	1.7	1739	13.2		
17 TU	0008	1.6	0551	12.5	1227	1.4	1808	12.6
3 TU	0028	1.1	0605	13.5	1253	1.0	1828	14.0
18 W	0052	1.3	0629	12.8	1311	1.2	1847	12.8
4 W O	0121	0.5	0651	14.1	1345	0.6	1915	14.4
19 TH ●	0135	1.2	0705	12.9	1353	1.2	1923	12.7
5 TH	0209	0.3	0737	14.4	1432	0.5	2000	14.5
20 F	0214	1.4	0740	12.7	1430	1.5	1958	12.5
6 F	0254	0.3	0821	14.4	1515	0.6	2045	14.3
21 SA	0247	1.7	0813	12.5	1501	1.8	2030	12.3
7 SA	0334	0.6	0904	14.0	1553	1.0	2128	13.7
22 SU	0310	2.0	0843	12.3	1523	2.0	2100	12.0
8 SU	0408	1.2	0946	13.3	1626	1.6	2211	12.8
23 M	0327	2.2	0913	12.0	1545	2.1	2132	11.8
9 M	0438	1.9	1027	12.4	1657	2.3	2254	11.7
24 TU	0353	2.2	0947	11.7	1616	2.2	2209	11.5
10 TU	0509	2.6	1112	11.3	1733	3.1	2344	10.7
25 W	0427	2.4	1028	11.4	1655	2.5	2253	11.1
11 W	0550	3.4	1212	10.4	1822	3.8		
26 TH	0508	2.7	1117	11.0	1742	2.9	2347	10.7
12 TH	0102	9.9	0649	4.0	1344	10.0	1935	4.2
27 F	0600	3.2	1218	10.6	1844	3.3		
13 F	0225	9.8	0817	4.2	1454	10.3	2128	3.8
28 SA	0054	10.4	0709	3.6	1335	10.6	2010	3.4
14 SA	0327	10.4	0953	3.5	1551	10.9	2230	3.0
29 SU	0218	10.6	0853	3.5	1502	11.1	2146	2.9
15 SU	0421	11.1	1051	2.8	1642	11.6	2321	2.2
30 M	0341	11.3	1022	2.8	1614	11.9	2259	2.1

DECEMBER

Day	Time	m	Time	m	Time	m	Time	m
1 TU	0446	12.2	1128	2.0	1713	12.8	2359	1.4
16 W	0515	11.7	1145	2.1	1735	11.9		
2 W	0540	13.1	1226	1.3	1806	13.6		
17 TH	0012	1.9	0557	12.2	1234	1.7	1816	12.3
3 TH	0053	0.9	0629	13.8	1320	0.9	1854	14.0
18 F ●	0059	1.6	0637	12.6	1319	1.5	1857	12.4
4 F	0145	0.6	0716	14.1	1410	0.7	1942	14.1
19 SA	0142	1.6	0716	12.7	1402	1.7	1936	12.5
5 SA	0232	0.5	0802	14.1	1457	0.7	2029	14.0
20 SU	0222	1.7	0753	12.6	1441	1.7	2013	12.4
6 SU	0316	0.7	0847	13.9	1539	1.0	2114	13.5
21 M	0256	1.9	0829	12.5	1514	1.9	2049	12.3
7 M	0354	1.2	0931	13.3	1615	1.6	2156	12.9
22 TU	0323	2.0	0903	12.4	1543	1.9	2125	12.2
8 TU	0425	1.8	1012	12.6	1647	2.2	2237	12.0
23 W	0350	2.1	0940	12.3	1614	2.0	2203	12.1
9 W	0455	2.4	1054	11.8	1718	2.7	2319	11.2
24 TH	0424	2.1	1021	12.1	1651	2.1	2245	11.8
10 TH	0530	2.9	1140	11.0	1757	3.2		
25 F	0503	2.3	1106	11.8	1734	2.3	2333	11.5
11 F	0009	10.4	0616	3.5	1243	10.3	1848	3.7
26 SA	0549	2.6	1159	11.4	1825	2.7		
12 SA	0122	9.9	0715	3.8	1400	10.1	1951	3.8
27 SU	0029	11.1	0644	3.0	1304	11.1	1929	3.0
13 SU	0236	10.0	0824	3.8	1505	10.4	2104	3.6
28 M	0139	10.8	0759	3.3	1423	11.1	2100	3.0
14 M	0336	10.8	0940	3.4	1600	10.9	2222	3.1
29 TU	0302	11.0	0943	3.1	1542	11.5	2226	2.6
15 TU	0428	11.1	1050	2.7	1649	11.4	2322	2.5
30 W	0416	11.6	1101	2.5	1649	12.1	2333	2.0
31 TH	0517	12.4	1203	1.8	1746	12.8		

11

Chart Datum: 6·50 metres below Ordnance Datum (Newlyn)

BRISTOL (CITY DOCKS)   10-11-21
City of Bristol 51°26'·92N 02°37'·36W   Rtg 3-1-1

CHARTS
AC 1859, *1176, 1179*; Imray C59; Stanfords 14; OS 172
TIDES
–0410 on Dover; ML 7·0; Duration 0620; Zone 0 (UT)

Standard Port BRISTOL (AVONMOUTH) (←)

Times				Height (metres)			
High Water		Low Water		MHWS	MHWN	MLWN	MLWS
0200	0800	0300	0800	13·2	9·8	3·8	1·0
1400	2000	1500	2000				

Differences CUMBERLAND BASIN (Ent)

+0010	+0010	Dries out		–2·9	–3·0	Dries out

NOTE: The Port of Bristol (Avonmouth) is a Standard Port and tidal predictions for each day are given above.

SHELTER
Excellent in Harbour and marina. For R Avon, Cumberland Basin & Bristol Hbr refer to *Bristol Harbour: Info for Boat Owners*, (from Hr Mr). Pill Creek has drying moorings.

NAVIGATION
Avonmouth WPT 51°30'·42N 02°43'·25W, 307°/127° from/ to front ldg lt, 0·61M. The chan from Flatholm is buoyed. See R/T below for compliance with VTS and reporting. Avonmouth, Royal Portbury and Portishead Docks are prohib to yachts, except in emergency. Tidal stream across ent can run at >5kn. Best to reach ent lock into Cumberland Basin by HW (approx 7M upriver from WPT); waiting pontoon (dries). Ent lock opens at HW–2½, –1½ and –¼hr for arrivals; departing craft lock out approx 15 mins after these times. Swing bridge opens in unison with lock, but not during road tfc rush hrs 0800-0900 and 1700-1800 Mon-Fri. Inner (Junction) lock is always open, except if ht of HW >9·5m ('stopgate' tide) when it closes.
LIGHTS AND MARKS
R Avon ent is abeam S pier lt Oc RG 30s, vis R294°-036°, G036°-194°. Ldg lts 127° both FR. St George ldg lts 173°, both Oc G 5s synch, Or daymarks. Above Pill Creek SHM lts are Oc G 5s, and PHM are mostly FY.
Ent sigs to Bristol Hbr are on E bank, 1½ and 2½ca beyond Clifton Suspension Bridge: Ⓖ = continue with caution; Ⓡ = stop and await orders.
Bridges: Prince St and Redcliffe bridges are manned 0600-2230 summer, 0900-1645 winter. Other bridges HW–3 to +1. Pre-notify Bridgemaster ☎ 9299338, or sound ·—·(R).
RADIO TELEPHONE
Yachts bound to/from Bristol should call *Avonmouth Radio* VHF Ch **12** 09 at English and Welsh Grounds SWM buoy and at Welsh Hook PHM buoy; comply with any VTS orders. On entering R Avon call again, low power, stating that you are bound for City Docks. (If no radio fitted, sig Avonmouth Sig Stn with Flag R or flash morse R (·—·). The sig stn will reply by light or loud hailer). Keep well clear of large vessels.
At Black Rks (0·8M to run) call *City Docks Radio* Ch **14** 11 (HW–3 to HW+1) for locking instructions.
For berths, call *Bristol Hbr* Ch **73** 16 (HO), and/or Bristol Marina Ch **80** M. Prince St bridge, Netham lock Ch 73.
TELEPHONE (Dial code 0117)
Hr Mr 9264797; Dock Master, Cumberland Basin 9273633; Prince St & Redcliffe Bridges 9299338; Netham Lock 9776590; ⌗ (01222) 763880 (H24); MRCC (01792) 366534; Weather 9279298; Marinecall 0891 500 459; Police 9277777; Ⓗ 9230000.
FACILITIES
Portishead CC (Pill Creek), M; **Bristol Hbr** ☎ 9264797, AB £7.33; gridiron outside Cumberland Basin;
Bristol Marina (150, inc visitors) ☎ 9265730, £7.15, D, FW, El, ME, Sh, AC, SM, Slip, C, BH (30 ton), access HW–3 to +1;
Baltic Wharf Leisure Centre ☎ 9297608, Slip, L, Bar;
Cabot Cruising Club ☎ 9268318, M, L, FW, AB, Bar;
Portavon Marina ☎ 9861626, Slip, M, FW, ME, Sh, CH, R;
Services: C (8 ton), FW, ME, El, Sh, CH, Ⓔ, ACA, P, D.
City EC Wed/Sat; all facilities, ✉, Ⓑ, ⇌, ✈.

BURNHAM-ON-SEA   10-11-22

Somerset 51°14'·20N 03°00'·25W

CHARTS
AC *1152, 1179*; Imray C59; Stanfords 14; OS 182

TIDES
−0435 Dover; ML 5·4; Duration 0620; Zone 0 (UT)

Standard Port BRISTOL (AVONMOUTH) (←—)

Times				Height (metres)			
High Water		Low Water		MHWS	MHWN	MLWN	MLWS
0200	0800	0300	0800	13·2	9·8	3·8	1·0
1400	2000	1500	2000				
Differences BURNHAM							
−0020	−0025	−0030	0000	−2·3	−1·9	−1·4	−1·1
WESTON-SUPER-MARE							
−0020	−0030	−0130	−0030	−1·2	−1·0	−0·8	−0·2
BRIDGWATER							
−0015	−0030	+0305	+0455	−8·6	−8·1	Dries out	
WATCHET							
−0035	−0050	−0145	−0040	−1·9	−1·5	+0·1	+0·1
MINEHEAD							
−0037	−0052	−0155	−0045	−2·6	−1·9	−0·2	0·0
PORLOCK BAY							
−0045	−0055	−0205	−0050	−3·0	−2·2	−0·1	−0·1
LYNMOUTH							
−0055	−0115	No data		−3·6	−2·7	No data	

SHELTER
Ent is very choppy in strong winds, especially from SW to W and from N to NE. ‡ in 4m about 40m E of No 1 buoy or S of town jetty or, for best shelter, ⚓ in R. Brue (dries).

NAVIGATION
WPT 51°13'·35N 03°10'·00W, 256°/076° from/to Low lt, 6·2M. Enter HW −3 to HW; not advised at night. From 0·5M S of Gore SWM buoy appr on 076° in W sector of Low lt ho, Fl 7·5s and Dir FWRG. Approx 1·3M past No 1 PHM buoy QR, steer on ldg line/lts 112°; thence alter 180° into river chan. Beware unmarked fishing stakes outside appr chan.

LIGHTS AND MARKS
Low lt ho Fl 7·5s & F G071°-075°, W075°-077°, R077°-081°. Ldg marks/lts 112° (moved as chan shifts): front, Or stripe on W □ on sea wall; rear, ⊕ tr; both FR 6/12m 3M.

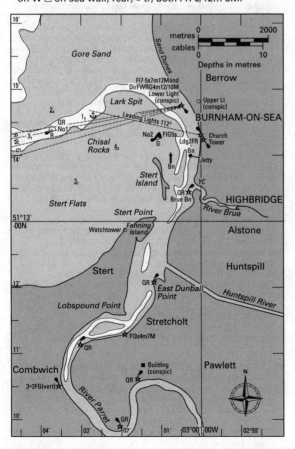

RADIO TELEPHONE
Hr Mr and Pilot VHF Ch 08 16 (when vessel expected).

TELEPHONE (Dial code 01278)
Hr Mr and Pilot 782180, ☎ 788861; MRCC (01792) 366534; ⌗ (01222) 763880 (H24); Marinecall 0891 500 459; Police 782288; ⊞ 782262.

FACILITIES
Burnham-on-Sea SC ☎ 792911, M, few drying ⚓s in River Brue, L, Slip, Bar; **Jetty** Slip;
Services: ME, El, Sh, ACA (Bridgwater).
Town EC Wed; Gas, ⊠, Ⓑ, ⇌ (Highbridge), ✈ (Bristol).
Note: No access to Bridgwater marina from sea/R Parrett.

OTHER HARBOURS ON S SHORE OF BRISTOL CHANNEL

WESTON-SUPER-MARE, North Somerset, 51°21'·00N 02°59'·20W. AC *1152, 1176, 1179*. HW −0435 on Dover; ML 6·1m; Duration 0655. See 10·11·22. Shelter is good except in S winds, in Knightstone Hbr (dries) at N end of bay; access HW±2. Causeway at ent marked by bn. Grand Pier hd 2 FG (vert) 6/5m. Or ‡ in good weather in R Axe (dries), entry HW±2. Facilities: **Weston Bay YC** ☎ 620772, FW, Bar, VHF Ch **80; Services:** AB, CH, El, D, BH (10 ton), Slip, ME, Sh. **Town** EC Mon; Bar, Ⓑ, FW, P, ⊠, R, ⇌, V.

WATCHET, Somerset, 51°11'·00N 03°19'·64W. AC 1160, *1152, 1179*. HW −0450 on Dover; ML 5·9m; Duration 0655. See 10·11·22. Culver Sand is approx 6M NNE. 2 radio masts (R lts) brg 210°/1·6M from ent are conspic approach marks. Good shelter in semi-commercial hbr, dries 6·5m; access approx HW±2½. The ent has about 6m at MHWS. Rks/mud dry ½M to seaward. Beware tidal streams round W pier hd. Yachts berth on W pier; hd FG 9m 9M on Red (R) tr. E pier hd 2 FR (vert) 3M. VHF Ch 16 09 12 14 (from HW−2). On W bkwtr hd B ● (Fl G at night) and on E pier 2 FR (vert) = at least 2·4m on flood or 3m on ebb. Hr Mr ☎ (01984) 631264; ⌗ ☎ (01446) 420241; Facilities: **Watchet Boat Owners Assn. Town** EC Wed; FW, D, P, Slip, CH, V, R, Bar. A new marina may be completed end '98/early '99.

MINEHEAD, Somerset, 51°12'·76N 03°28'·29W. AC 1160, *1165, 1179*. HW −0450 on Dover. ML 5·7m. See 10.11.22. Small hbr, dries 7·5m; access HW±2. Good shelter within pier curving E and then SE, over which seas may break in gales at MHWS; exposed to E'lies. Best appr from N or NW; beware The Gables, shingle bank (dries 3·7m) about 5ca ENE of pier. Keep E of a sewer outfall which passes ½ca E of pierhd and extends 1¾ca NNE of it; outfall is protected by rk covering, drying 2·8m and N end marked by SHM bn QG 6m 7M. There are 8 R ⚓s at hbr ent just seaward of 3 posts or dry out against pier. Hbr gets very crowded. Holiday camp is conspic 6ca SE. Pierhd lt Fl (2) G 5s 4M, vis 127°-262°. VHF Ch 16 12 14 (occas). Hr Mr ☎ (01643) 702566; Facilities: **Hbr** FW, Slip. **Town** EC Wed; D, P, El, Gas, ME, Sh, R, Bar, V, ⊠, Ⓑ, ⇌ (Taunton).

PORLOCK WEIR, Somerset, 51°13'·14N 03°37'·57W. AC 1160, *1165, 1179*. HW −0500 on Dover; ML 5·6m. See 10·11·22. Access HW±1½. Ent chan (250°), about 15m wide marked by withies (3 PHM and 1 SHM), between shingle bank/wood pilings to stbd and sunken wooden wall to port is difficult in any seas. A small pool (1m) just inside ent is for shoal draft boats; others dry out on pebble banks. Or turn 90° stbd, via gates (usually open), into inner drying dock with good shelter. No lts. Hr Mr ☎ (01643) 863277. **Porlock Weir SC** ☎ 862028. Facilities: FW and limited V.

LYNMOUTH, Devon, 51°14'·13N 03°49'·72W. AC 1160, *1165,*. HW−0515 on Dover. See 10.11.22. Tiny hbr, dries approx 5m; access HW±1, but only in settled offshore weather. Appr from Sand Ridge SHM buoy, 1·6M W of Foreland Pt and 9ca N of hbr ent. The narrow appr chan between drying boulder ledges is marked by 7 unlit posts. Hbr ent is between piers, 2FR/FG lts, on W side of river course. Berth on E pier, which covers at MHWS. Resort facilities.

WATERMOUTH, Devon, 51°13'·00N 04°04'·60W. AC *1165, 1179*. HW −0525 on Dover; ML 4·9m; Duration 0625. Use 10.11.23. Good shelter in drying hbr, but heavy surge runs in strong NW winds. Access HW±3 at sp; only as far as inner bkwtr at np. Dir lt 153° Oc WRG 5s 1m, vis W151·5°-154·5°, W △ on structure, 1½ca inside ent on S shore. Bkwtr, covered at half tide, has Fl G 5s 2M. Eight Y ⚓s with B handles. Hr Mr ☎ (01271) 865422. Facilities: **Hbr** D (cans), FW (cans), CH, C (12 ton), Slip; **YC** ☎ 865048, Bar.

ILFRACOMBE   10-11-23

Devon 51°12'·62N 04°06'·58W   Rtg 3-4-2

CHARTS
AC 1160, *1165,* 1179; Imray C59; Stanfords 14; OS 180

TIDES
–0525 Dover; ML 5·0; Duration 0625; Zone 0 (UT)

Standard Port MILFORD HAVEN (←—)

Times				Height (metres)			
High Water		Low Water		MHWS	MHWN	MLWN	MLWS
0100	0700	0100	0700	7·0	5·2	2·5	0·7
1300	1900	1300	1900				
Differences ILFRACOMBE							
–0030	–0015	–0035	–0055	+2·2	+1·7	+0·5	0·0
LUNDY ISLAND							
–0030	–0030	–0020	–0040	+1·0	+0·7	+0·2	+0·1

SHELTER
Good except in NE/E winds. SW gales can cause surge in hbrs, which dry. 12 ⚓s in outer hbr; or ⚓ clear of pier and LB Slip. Possible AB on quays in inner hbr, access HW±3.

NAVIGATION
WPT 51°13'·20N 04°06'·60W, 000°/180° from/to pier hd, 0·55M. From E, beware Copperas Rks (4M to E), (SHM buoy) and tiderips on Buggy Pit, 7ca NE of ent. On entry keep toward Promenade Pier to clear drying ledges and lobster keep-pots obstructing hbr ent on SE side.

LIGHTS AND MARKS
No ldg marks/lts. Lantern Hill lt, Fl G 2·5s 39m 6M, on small conspic chapel. Promenade Pier has three 2FG (vert), shown 1/9-30/4. Inner bkwtr 2 FG (vert).

RADIO TELEPHONE
Call: *Ilfracombe Hbr* VHF Ch 12 16 (Apl-Oct 0800-2000 when manned; Nov-Mar occas). Ch **80** M (occas).

TELEPHONE (Dial code 01271)
Hr Mr 862108; MRCC (01792) 366534; ⌗ (01222) 763880 (H24); Marinecall 0891 500 459; Police 863633; Dr 863119.

FACILITIES
Hbr M, D (cans), FW, CH, Slip, ME, EI, Sh; **Ilfracombe YC**
☎ 863969, M, ⬛, Bar, C (35 ton, as arranged); **Town** EC Thurs, V, R, Bar, ✉, Ⓑ, ⇌ (bus to Barnstaple), ✈ (Exeter).

LUNDY ISLAND, Devon, 51°09'·80N 04°39'·20W. AC *1164, 1179.* HW –0530 on Dover; ML 4·3m; Duration 0605. See above. Shelter good in lee of island's high ground (145m). In SSW to NW winds, usual ⚓ is close inshore to NW of SE Pt and Rat Is, clear of ferry. In N'lies ⚓ in The Rattles, small bay on S side. In E'lies Jenny's Cove is safe if no W'ly swell. Beware bad tide races, esp on E-going flood, off the N and SE tips of the Is; and to the SW on the W-going ebb. A violent race forms over Stanley Bank 3M NE of the N tip. Waters off the Is are a Marine Nature Reserve. Lts: NW Pt, Fl 15s 48m 17M, vis 009°-285°, W ○ tr. On SE Pt, Fl 5s 53m 15M, vis 170°-073°, W ○ tr, horn 25s. Two Historic Wrecks (see 10.0.3h) lie on the E side of the island, at 51°11'N 04°39'·1W, and 4ca further E. Facilities: Landing by the ⚓ off SE end of Island; £2 per head landing fee. **Lundy Co Landmark Trust** ☎ (01271) 870870, CH, Gas, bar and hotel.

RIVERS TAW & TORRIDGE

Devon 51°04'·34N 04°12'·81W   Rtg 3-5-1   10-11-24

CHARTS
AC 1160, *1164,* 1179; Imray C58; Stanfords 14; OS 180

TIDES
–0525 (Appledore) Dover; ML 3·6; Duration 0600; Zone 0 (UT)

Standard Port MILFORD HAVEN (←—)

Times				Height (metres)			
High Water		Low Water		MHWS	MHWN	MLWN	MLWS
0100	0700	0100	0700	7·0	5·2	2·5	0·7
1300	1900	1300	1900				
Differences APPLEDORE							
–0020	–0025	+0015	–0045	+0·5	0·0	–0·9	–0·5
YELLAND MARSH (R Taw)							
–0010	–0015	+0100	–0015	+0·1	–0·4	–1·2	–0·6
FREMINGTON (R Taw)							
–0010	–0015	+0030	–0030	–1·1	–1·8	–2·2	–0·5
BARNSTAPLE (R Taw)							
0000	–0015	–0155	–0245	–2·9	–3·8	–2·2	–0·4
BIDEFORD (R Torridge)							
–0020	–0025	0000	0000	–1·1	–1·6	–2·5	–0·7
CLOVELLY							
–0030	–0030	–0020	–0040	+1·3	+1·1	+0·2	+0·2

SHELTER
Very well protected, but ent in strong on-shore winds is dangerous. Yachts can ⚓ or pick up buoy in Appledore Pool, N of Skern Pt where sp stream can reach 5kn. The quay at Bideford dries to soft mud; used by coasters.

NAVIGATION
WPT 51°05'·40N 04°16'·04W (abeam Fairway buoy, off chartlet), 298°/118° from/to Bar buoy, 0·9M. Bar and sands constantly shift and buoys are moved occasionally to comply. Advice on bar, where there are depths of 0·1 and 0·4m, from Pilot VHF Ch 12 or Swansea CG. Estuary dries; access is only feasible from HW–2 to HW. Once tide is ebbing, breakers quickly form between Bar buoy (unlit NCM) and Middle Ridge SHM buoy. 2M passage to Bideford is not difficult. If going 7M up to Barnstaple, take a pilot (from Appledore) or seek local knowledge.

LIGHTS AND MARKS
Entry at night is NOT advised. Apart from jetties etc, only lts are Bideford Fairway buoy L Fl 10s, Outer Pulley buoy Fl G 2·5s, Crow Pt Fl R 5s, and the two ldg marks; these are W trs, lit H24; front Oc 6s, rear Oc 10s. The ldg line 118° is only valid as far as Outer Pulley buoy after which the chan deviates to stbd toward Pulley unlit SHM buoy, Grey Sand Hill and Appledore. The Torridge is unlit, other than a QY on Bideford bridge showing the preferred chan.

RADIO TELEPHONE
Two Rivers Port/Pilots VHF Ch 12 16 (Listens from HW–2).

TELEPHONE (Dial codes: Bideford/Appledore 01237; Instow/Barnstaple 01271;)
Hr Mr Bideford 476711 Ext 317 or 477928; Barnstaple call Amenities Officer 388327; Pilot (Appledore) 473806; MRCC (01792) 366534; ⌗ (01222) 763880 (H24); Marinecall 0891 500 459; Police (Bideford) 476896; Dr (Appledore) 474994, (Bideford) 471071/476363, (Barnstaple) 75221/473443.

FACILITIES
APPLEDORE: (01237) is a free port; no authority can charge for use of public facilities eg slips at town quay and AB.
Services: CH, EI, Ⓔ, BY, C (70 tons), Slip, ME, Sh.
BIDEFORD: AB (few/not encouraged; call Capt V. Harris ☎ 474569), V, R, Gas, Bar.
INSTOW: **N. Devon YC** FW ☎ 860367, Slip, R, Bar;
Services: AB £5, D, ME, M, Ⓔ, C (4 ton). **Town** R, FW, Bar.
BARNSTAPLE: AB (see Hr Mr), V, Bar, Gas. FW: limited facilities; P & D: small quantities in cans. Bulk D (min 500 ltrs/110 galls) by bowser, see Hr Mr.
Towns: EC Barnstaple & Bideford = Wed; ✉ (all four), Ⓑ (Barnstaple, Bideford), ⇌ (Barnstaple), ✈ (Exeter).

CLOVELLY, Devon, 51°00'·15N 04°23'·70W. Rtg 5-4-1. AC *1164.* Tides see above. HW –0524 on Dover. Tiny drying hbr 5M E of Hartland Pt has some AB £5 on pier, access only near HW; better to ⚓ off in 5m, sheltered from S/SW winds. Useful to await the tide around Hartland Pt or into Bideford. Lt Fl G 5s 5m 5M on hbr wall. Hr Mr ☎ (01237) 431237 (Red Lion). Facilities: Slip, FW, ✉, limited V.

RIVERS TAW & TORRIDGE *continued*

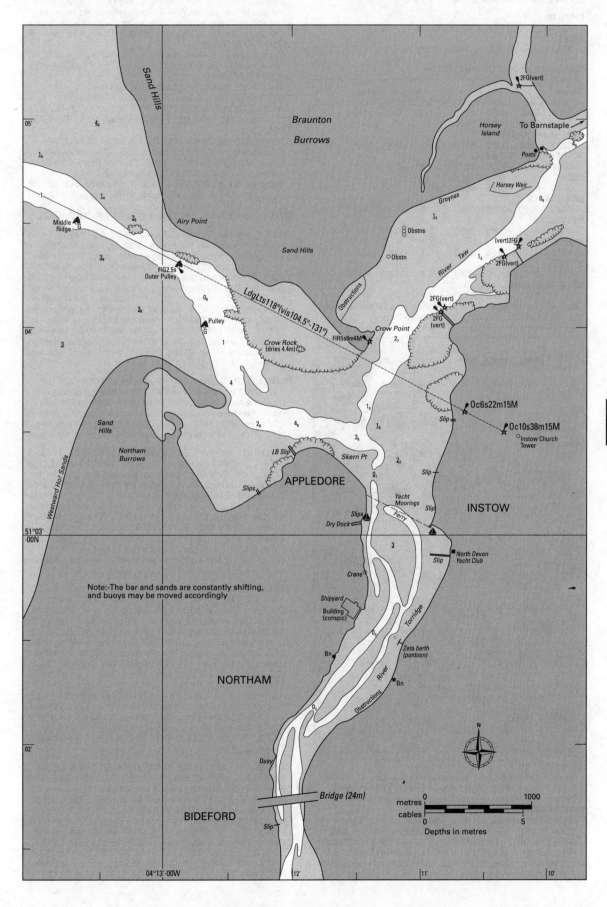

Sand Hills

Braunton

Burrows

Horsey Island

To Barnstaple

2FG(vert)

Posts

Horsey Weir

0_9

4_8

1_8

1_4

1

3_6

Middle Ridge G

Airy Point

Sand Hills

Groynes

1_3

Obstns

River   Taw

Obstn

1_5

(vert)2FG

2FG(vert)

3_8

3_8

FlG2.5s Outer Pulley

0_9

LdgLts118°(vis104.5°-131°)

Obstructions

2FG(vert)

2FG (vert)

3_6

Pulley G

1

Crow Rock (dries 4.4m)

Crow Point

FlR5s8m4M

2_7

4

1_8

Oc6s22m15M

Slip

2_6

4_8

3_9

1_8

Oc10s38m15M

Instow Church Tower

Sand Hills

Northam Burrows

LB Slip

Skern Pt

2_2

Slip

0_1

APPLEDORE

Westward Ho! Sands

Slips

Yacht Moorings

Ferry

INSTOW

Slip

Slips

Dry Dock

Slip

3

North Devon Yacht Club

Slip

Crane

Note:-The bar and sands are constantly shifting, and buoys may be moved accordingly

Shipyard

Building (conspic)

0_3

Torridge

River

Zeta berth (pontoon)

Bn

NORTHAM

Bn

0_3

Obstructions

N

Quay

Bridge (24m)

metres   1000

cables

BIDEFORD

Slip

Depths in metres

0_2

11

PADSTOW   10-11-25

Cornwall 50°32'·48N 04°56'·10W. Rtg 3-3-1

CHARTS
AC 1168, 1156; Imray C58; Stanfords 13; OS 200
TIDES
–0550 Dover; ML 4·0; Duration 0600; Zone 0 (UT)

Standard Port MILFORD HAVEN (⟵)

Times				Height (metres)			
High Water		Low Water		MHWS	MHWN	MLWN	MLWS
0100	0700	0100	0700	7·0	5·2	2·5	0·7
1300	1900	1300	1900				
Differences PADSTOW							
–0055	–0050	–0040	–0050	+0·3	+0·4	+0·1	+0·1
WADEBRIDGE (R Camel)							
–0052	–0052	+0235	+0245	–3·8	–3·8	–2·5	–0·4
BUDE							
–0040	–0040	–0035	–0045	+0·7	+0·6		No data
BOSCASTLE							
–0045	–0010	–0110	–0100	+0·3	+0·4	+0·2	+0·2
NEWQUAY							
–0100	–0110	–0105	–0050	0·0	+0·1	0·0	–0·1
PERRANPORTH							
–0100	–0110	–0110	–0050	–0·1	0·0	0·0	+0·1
ST IVES							
–0050	–0115	–0105	–0040	–0·4	–0·3	–0·1	+0·1
CAPE CORNWALL							
–0130	–0145	–0120	–0120	–1·0	–0·9	–0·5	–0·1

Note: At Wadebridge LW time differences give the start of the rise, following a LW stand of about 5 hours.

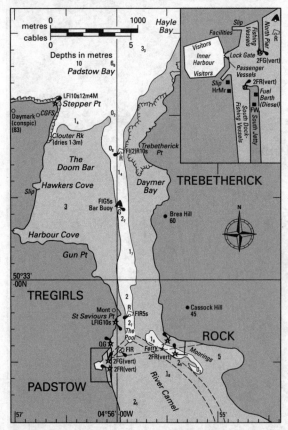

SHELTER
Good in inner hbr 3m+, access HW±2 via lock; or HW±4½ moor in the Pool or ‡ just down-stream in 1·5m LWS. Drying moorings available for small vessels on passage.
NAVIGATION
WPT 50°35'·00N 04°58'·50W, 305°/125° from/to Stepper Pt, 1·5M. From S, beware Quies Rks, Gulland Rk, The Hen, Gurley Rk and Chimney Rks and a wreck 5ca W of Stepper Pt (all off the chartlet). From N, keep well off Newland Is and its offlying reef. Identify the first 2 chan buoys before entry. With strong onshore winds or heavy ground swell,

seas can break on Doom Bar and in adjacent chan. Final appr S of St Saviour's Pt runs close to W shore. Allow ample rise of tide. Do not enter LW±1½; least depth on the bar is 0·5m at MLWS. Shifting sandbanks in estuary require local knowledge, care and a rising tide; ditto the drying R Camel to Wadebridge (4M). Consult Hr Mr (VHF).
LIGHTS AND MARKS
Conspic stone tr (83m daymark), 3ca W of Stepper Pt, L Fl 10s 12m 4M, marks the ent. Lock ent has 2 FG/FR (vert).
RADIO TELEPHONE
VHF Ch 12 16 (Mon-Fri 0800–1700 and HW±2).
TELEPHONE (Dial codes 01841; 01208 = Wadebridge)
Hr Mr 532239; MRCC (01326) 317575; ⌗ 0345 231110 (H24); Marinecall 0891 500 458; Police (01566) 774211; Dr 532346.
FACILITIES
Hbr ☎ 532239, 🚣 533346, Mobile (0379) 338531, AB £11.30, Slip, M, FW, El, C (60 ton), D, ME, ▢, showers, V, R, Bar; Rock SC ☎ (01208) 862431, Slip; Ferry 1 (to Rock, summer only) ☎ (01326) 317575 or VHF Ch 12 16; Services: BY, C, ME, CH, Slip, L, Sh. Town EC Wed; ▢, P, ✉, Ⓑ, ⇌ (bus to Bodmin Road), ✈ (Newquay/Plymouth).

OTHER HARBOURS ON THE N COAST OF CORNWALL

BUDE, Cornwall, 50°49'·90N 04°33'·30W. AC 1156. HW –0540 on Dover. Duration 0605. See 10·11·25. Limited shelter in drying hbr, access for average yacht HW±2. Yachts can, by prior arrangement, lock into quiet canal berth (5·5m over CD required), but lock fees are high (£86 (HO); £125 outside HO; £167 Sun), and gates will only open if there is no swell. Conspic W radar dish aerials 3·3M N of hbr. Outer ldg marks 075°, front W spar with Y ◊ topmark, rear W flagstaff; hold this line until inner ldg marks in line at 131°, front W pile, rear W spar, both with Y △ topmarks. There are no lts. VHF Ch 16 12 (when vessel expected). Facilities: Hr Mr ☎ (01288) 353111; very limited facilities; Town EC Thurs; Ⓑ, Bar, ✉, R, V, Gas.

BOSCASTLE, Cornwall, 50°41'·45N 04°42·10W. AC 1156. HW –0543 on Dover; see 10·11·25. A tiny, picturesque hbr, almost a land-locked cleft in the cliffs. Access HW±2, but not in onshore winds when swell causes surge inside. An E'ly appr, S of Meachard Rk (37m high, 2ca NW of hbr), is best. 2 short bkwtrs at ent; moor bows-on to drying S quay.

NEWQUAY, Cornwall, 50°25'·03N 05°05'·12W. AC 1168, 1149. HW –0604 on Dover; ML 3·7m; see 10·11·25. Ent to drying hbr ('The Gap') between two walls, is 23m wide. Beware Old Dane Rk and Listrey Rk outside hbr towards Towan Hd. Swell causes a surge in the hbr. Enter HW±2 but not in strong onshore winds. Berth as directed by Hr Mr. Lts: N pier 2 FG (vert) 2M; S pier 2 FR (vert) 2M. VHF Ch16 14. Hr Mr ☎ (01637) 872809. Facilities: Gas, Gaz, CH. Town EC Wed (winter only); FW, Slip, D, V, R, Bar. Note: Shoal draft boats can dry out in Gannel Creek, close S of Newquay, but only in settled weather. Beware causeway bridge about half way up the creek.

HAYLE, Cornwall, 50°11'·74N 05°26'·10W (Chan ent). Rtg 5.5.3. AC 1168, 1149. HW –0605 on Dover; ML 3·6m; Duration 0555. See 10·11·25. Drying hbr gives very good shelter, but in ground swell dangerous seas break on the bar, drying 2·7m; approx 4m at ent @ MHWS. Cross the bar in good weather HW±1, but hbr is not recommended for yachts. Charted aids do not necessarily indicate best water. Ldg lts, both FW 17/23m 4M, 180°. A PHM lt buoy, Fl (2) R 5s, and a SHM lt buoy, Iso G 2s, are about 8ca N of the front ldg lt. Training wall on W side of ent chan is marked by 4 perches (FG lts). The hbr is divided by long central island (about 700m long, with lt bn Q at NW end) which should be left to stbd. Follow the SE arm of hbr to Hayle; the S arm leads to Lelant Quay. VHF Ch 18 16 (0900-1700). Hr Mr ☎ (01736) 754043, AB £6. Facilities: EC Thurs; Ⓑ, Bar, FW, ⇌, R, V, P & D (cans).

ST IVES, Cornwall, 50°12'·76N 05°28'·60W. Rtg 3-4-1. AC 1168, 1149. HW –0610 on Dover; ML 3·6m; Duration 0555. See 10·11·25. Shelter is good except in on-shore winds when heavy swell builds up. 7 Øs available, £8. Drying hbr with approx 4·5m at MHWS. Alternative ‡ in 3m between the hbr and Porthminster Pt to S. From the NW beware Hoe Rk off St Ives Hd, and from SE The Carracks. Keep E of SHM buoy about 1½ ca ENE of E pier. Lts: E pier hd 2 FG (vert) 8m 5M. W pier hd 2 FR (vert) 5m 3M. VHF Ch 12 16. Hr Mr ☎ (01736) 795018. Facilities: E Pier FW. Town EC Thurs; Gas, Gaz, Ⓑ, ▢, Bar, ✉, R, V, ⇌.

VOLVO PENTA SERVICE

Sales and service centres in area 12
Republic of Ireland COUNTY DUBLIN *Western Marine Ltd*, Bulloch Harbour, Dalkey, Dublin Tel 00 353 1 2800321 **COUNTY CORK** *Kilmacsimon Boatyard Ltd*, Kilmacsimon Quay, Bandon Tel 00 353 21 775134 **COUNTY CLARE** *Derg Marine*, Kilaloe Tel 00 353 61 376364

Area 12

South Ireland
Malahide, south to Liscanor Bay

VOLVO PENTA

12

564

See 10·13·2

10°W   9°W

Cashel Bay

Malin CG
Valentia CG

Galway

Galway Bay

Eeragh Island ☆

Inishmore • **Kilronan**

Aran Islands

Black Head ☆

Inisheer 🪨

Ennis
Ⓡ 352·00 ENS 80M

53° N

See Area 13

Liscanor Bay

Loop Head
Ⓡ 311·50 LP 50M

Kilrush
ⓘ 10.12.31
VHF **12** 16
Marina 80 M

Limerick
VHF 12 13 16

Shannon Radio
VHF **28** 24 67 16
VHF 28 every
3 h from 0103 LT

Shannon Estuary
ⓘ 10.12.30

Foynes
VHF 12 13 16
Ⓡ 395·00 FOY 50M

Kerry Head

Dingle
ⓘ 10.12.29

Little Samphire Island ☆

Cork Harbour
ⓘ 10.12.19
VHF 12 14 16
Marinas M

Cork Radio
VHF 26 67 16
VHF 26 every
3 h from 0103 LT

Brandon Bay* •

Tralee Bay*

Smerwick Harbour*

Ventry*

Inishtearaght ☆

Dingle Bay

Valentia Radio
VHF 24 28 67 16
MF **1752** 1746
VHF 24 every
3 h from 0103 LT
MF 1752
0833 2033 UT

Kinsale
ⓘ 10.12.20
VHF 06 14 16
Marinas M 16

52° N

Port Magee*

Kenmare River
ⓘ 10.12.28

Old Head of Kinsale
Ⓡ 288·00 OH 50M

Oyster Haven*

☆

Great Skellig ☆

Kenmare River

Glengarriff* •

Adrigole*

Bantry* •

Bantry Bay
ⓘ 10.12.27
VHF **14** 10 11 16

Courtmacsherry
ⓘ 10.12.21

Lawrence's Cove*

Castletown*

☆ **Lonehort Hbr***

Bantry Bay

Schull
ⓘ 10.12.25

Bull Rock ☆

Sheep Head

Roaring Water Bay*

Galley Head

Barlogue Creek*

Glandore
ⓘ 10.12.22

Bantry Radio
VHF **23** 67 85 16
VHF 23 every
3 h from 0103 LT

Crookhaven
ⓘ 10.12.26

C. Clear

Castle Haven
ⓘ 10.12.23

Fastnet ☆ **Cape Clear***

Mizen Head
Ⓡ 300·00 MZ 100M

Baltimore
ⓘ 10.12.24
VHF 09 16

For details
see Fig 10(3)2

10°W   9°W

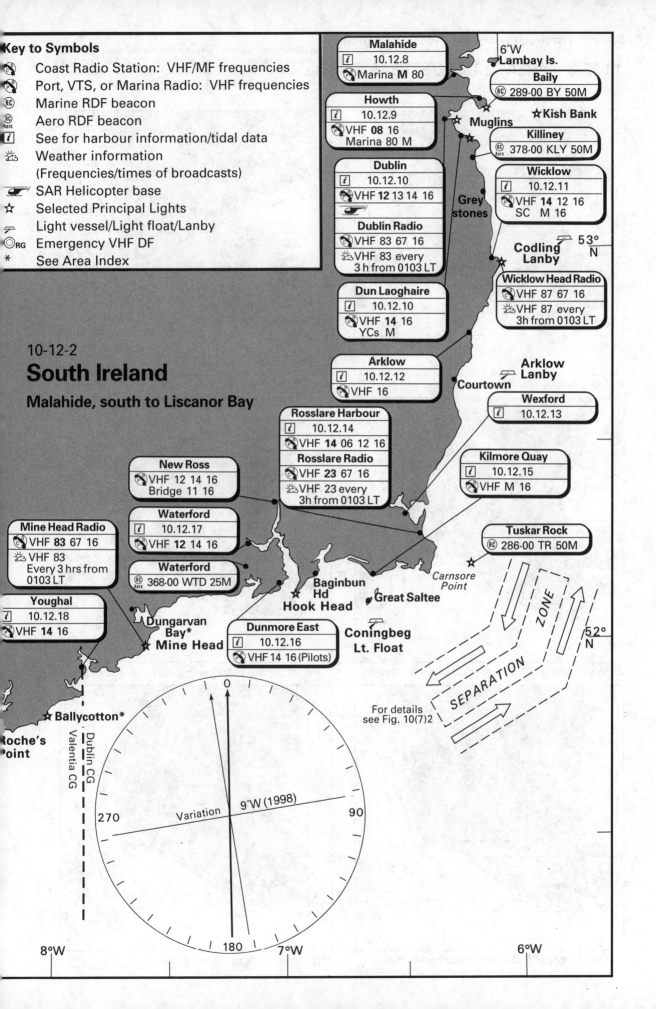

Key to Symbols

📞 Coast Radio Station: VHF/MF frequencies
📞 Port, VTS, or Marina Radio: VHF frequencies
RC Marine RDF beacon
RC Aero Aero RDF beacon
ℹ️ See for harbour information/tidal data
🌊 Weather information (Frequencies/times of broadcasts)
🚁 SAR Helicopter base
☆ Selected Principal Lights
⚓ Light vessel/Light float/Lanby
◯RG Emergency VHF DF
* See Area Index

10-12-2
South Ireland

Malahide, south to Liscanor Bay

Malahide
ℹ️ 10.12.8
📞 Marina **M** 80

Howth
ℹ️ 10.12.9
📞 VHF **08** 16
Marina 80 M

Dublin
ℹ️ 10.12.10
📞 VHF **12** 13 14 16
🚁

Dublin Radio
📞 VHF 83 67 16
🌊 VHF 83 every 3 h from 0103 LT

Dun Laoghaire
ℹ️ 10.12.10
📞 VHF **14** 16
YCs M

Arklow
ℹ️ 10.12.12
📞 VHF 16

6°W
Lambay Is.

Baily
RC 289·00 BY 50M

☆ Muglins
☆ Kish Bank

Killiney
RC Aero 378·00 KLY 50M

Wicklow
ℹ️ 10.12.11
📞 VHF **14** 12 16
SC M 16

Grey stones

Codling Lanby
⚓ 53° N

Wicklow Head Radio
📞 VHF 87 67 16
🌊 VHF 87 every 3h from 0103 LT

Arklow Lanby
⚓
Courtown

Wexford
ℹ️ 10.12.13

Rosslare Harbour
ℹ️ 10.12.14
📞 VHF **14** 06 12 16

Rosslare Radio
📞 VHF **23** 67 16
🌊 VHF 23 every 3h from 0103 LT

New Ross
📞 VHF 12 14 16
Bridge 11 16

Kilmore Quay
ℹ️ 10.12.15
📞 VHF M 16

Waterford
ℹ️ 10.12.17
📞 VHF **12** 14 16

Waterford
RC Aero 368·00 WTD 25M

Tuskar Rock
RC 286·00 TR 50M

Mine Head Radio
📞 VHF **83** 67 16
🌊 VHF 83 Every 3 hrs from 0103 LT

Baginbun Hd
☆ Hook Head

Great Saltee

Carnsore Point

Youghal
ℹ️ 10.12.18
📞 VHF **14** 16

Dungarvan Bay*
☆ Mine Head

Dunmore East
ℹ️ 10.12.16
📞 VHF 14 16 (Pilots)

Coningbeg Lt. Float

ZONE

For details see Fig. 10(7)2

SEPARATION

☆ Ballycotton*

Roche's Point

Valentia CG
Dublin CG

52° N

0

270 — Variation 9°W (1998) — 90

180

8°W   7°W   6°W

10-12-3   AREA 12 TIDAL STREAMS

The tidal arrows (with no rates shown) off the S and W coasts of Ireland are printed by kind permission of the Irish Cruising Club, to whom the Editors are indebted. They have been found accurate, but should be used with caution.

5 Hours before HW Dover (0530 before HW Dublin)

4 Hours before HW Dover (0430 before HW Dublin)

3 Hours before HW Dover (0330 before HW Dublin)

2 Hours before HW Dover (0230 before HW Dublin)

1 Hour before HW Dover (0130 before HW Dublin)

HW Dover (0030 before HW Dublin)

The tidal arrows (with no rates shown) off the S and W coasts of Ireland are printed by kind permission of the Irish Cruising Club, to whom the Editors are indebted. They have been found accurate, but should be used with caution.

1 Hour after HW Dover (0030 after HW Dublin)

2 Hours after HW Dover (0130 after HW Dublin)

3 Hours after HW Dover (0230 after HW Dublin)

4 Hours after HW Dover (0330 after HW Dublin)

5 Hours after HW Dover (0430 after HW Dublin)

6 Hours after HW Dover (0530 after HW Dublin)

12

10.12.4 COASTAL LIGHTS, FOG SIGNALS AND WAYPOINTS

Abbreviations used below are given in 1.4.1. Principal lights are in **bold** print, places in CAPITALS, and light-vessels, light floats and Lanbys in *CAPITAL ITALICS*. Unless otherwise stated lights are white. m – elevation in metres; M – nominal range in miles. Fog signals are in *italics*. Useful waypoints are underlined – use those on land with care. All geographical positions should be assumed to be approximate. See 4.4.1. All positions are referenced to the Ordnance Survey of Ireland datum.

IRELAND – EAST COAST
LAMBAY ISLAND TO TUSKAR ROCK

MALAHIDE/LAMBAY ISLAND
Taylor Rks By 53°30'·00N 06°01'·75W; SHM.
Burren Rks Bn 53°29'·34N 06°02'·40W; SHM.

Dublin Airport 53°25'·75N 06°14'·65W Aero Al Fl WG 4s 95m.

HOWTH
S Rowan Lt By 53°23'·80N 06°03'·89W QG; SHM.
Howth Lt By 53°23'·72N 06°03'·58W Fl G 5s; SHM.
Rowan Rks Lt By 53°23'·87N 06°03'·20W Q (3) 10s; ECM.
E Pier Hd 53°23'·64N 06°03'·97W Fl (2) WR 7·5s 13m W12M, R9M; W Tr; vis W256°-295°, R295°-256°.

Baily 53°21'·68N 06°03'·08W Fl 15s 41m **26M**; Tr; RC; Racon (K).
Rosbeg E Lt By 53°21'·00N 06°03'·39W Q (3) 10s; ECM.
Rosbeg S Lt By 53°20'·37N 06°04'·27W Q (6) + L Fl 15s; SCM.
Dublin Bay Lt By 53°19'·90N 06°04'·58W Mo (A) 10s; Racon (M); SWM.

PORT OF DUBLIN
Great S Wall Hd, **Poolbeg** 53°20'·52N 06°09'·02W Oc (2) R 20s 20m **15M**; R ● Tr; *Horn (2) 60s.*
N Bull Wall Hd, **N Bull** 53°20'·67N 06°08'·92W Fl (3) G 10s 15m **15M**; G ● Tr.
N Bank 53°20'·68N 06°10'·53W Oc G 8s 10m **16M**; G ■ Tr.

DUN LAOGHAIRE
E Bkwtr Hd 53°18'·13N 06°07'·57W Fl (2) R 10s 16m **17M**; Tr, R lantern; *Horn 30s* (or *Bell (1) 6s*).
W Bkwtr Hd 53°18'·17N 06°07'·82W Fl (3) G 7·5s 11m 7M; Tr, G lantern; vis 188°-062°.

N Burford Lt By 53°20'·05N 06°01'·44W Q; *Whis;* SWM.
S Burford Lt By 53°18'·05N 06°01'·21W VQ (6) + L Fl 10s; *Whis;* SWM.
Muglins 53°16'·53N 06°04'·52W Fl 5s 14m 8M; W Tr, R band.
Bennett Bank Lt By 53°20'·15N 05°55'·05W Q (6) + L Fl 15s; *Whis;* SCM.
N Kish Lt By 53°18'·54N 05°56'·38W VQ; NCM.
Kish Bank 53°18'·68N 05°55'·38W Fl (2) 20s 29m **22M**; W Tr, R band; Racon (T); *Horn (2) 30s.*
E Kish Lt By 53°14'·33N 05°53'·50W Fl (2) R 10s; PHM.
E Codling Lt By 53°08'·52N 05°47'·05W Fl (4) R 10s; PHM.
W Codling Lt By 53°06'·95N 05°54'·45W Fl G 10s; SHM.
S Codling Lt By 53°04'·72N 05°49'·70W VQ (6) + L Fl 10s; SCM.
Greystones Lt By 53°08'·38N 06°02'·44W Fl Y 5s; SPM.
Moulditch Bk Lt By 53°08'·40N 06°01'·16W Fl R 10s; PHM.
Breaches Shoal Lt By 53°05'·65N 05°59'·75W Fl (2) R 6s; PHM.
India N Lt By 53°03'·15N 05°53'·40W Q; NCM.
India S Lt By 53°00'·34N 05°53'·25W Q (6) + L Fl 15s; SCM.
CODLING LANBY 53°03'·00N 05°40'·70W Fl 4s 12m **15M**; tubular structure on By; Racon (G); *Horn 20s.*

WICKLOW
Wicklow Lt By 52°59'·55N 06°01'·23W; Fl (4) Y 10s; SPM.
E Pier Hd 52°58'·98N 06°02'·01W Fl WR 5s 11m 6M; W Tr, R base and cupola; vis R136°-293°, W293°-136°.

Wicklow Hd 52°57'·93N 05°59'·83W Fl (3) 15s 37m **23M**; W Tr.
Horseshoe Lt By 52°56'·60N 05°59'·25W Fl R 3s; PHM.
N Arklow Lt By 52°53'·84N 05°55'·15W Q; *Whis;* SCM.
No. 2 Arklow Lt By 52°50'·20N 05°54'·50W Fl R 6s; PHM.

ARKLOW
S Pier Hd 52°47'·59N 06°08'·16W Fl WR 6s 11m 13M; Tr; vis R shore-223°, W223°-350°; R350°-shore.
N Pier Hd 52°47'·61N 06°08'·23W L Fl G 7s 7m 10M.
Roadstone Jetty Hd 52°46'·68N 05°59'·30W Oc R 10s 9m 9M.
No. 1 Arklow Lt By 52°44'·30N 05°55'·96W Fl (3) R 10s; PHM.
S Arklow Lt By 52°40'·80N 05°59'·15W VQ (6) + L Fl 10s; SCM.
ARKLOW LANBY 52°39'·50N 05°58'·10W Fl (2) 12s 12m **15M**; tubular structure on By; Racon (O); *Horn Mo (A) 30s.*
No. 2 Glassgorman Lt By 52°44'·50N 06°05'·30W Fl (4) R 10s; PHM.
No. 1 Glassgorman Lt By 52°39'·06N 06°07'·40W Fl (2) R 6s; PHM.
N Blackwater Lt By 52°32'·20N 06°09'·50W Q; NCM.
E Blackwater Lt By 52°28'·00N 06°08'·00W Q (3) 10s; *Horn (3) 20s;* SCM.
SE Blackwater Lt By 52°25'·62N 06°09'·70W Fl R 10s; PHM.
S Blackwater Lt By 52°22'·74N 06°12'·80W Q (6) + L Fl 15s; *Whis;* SCM.
No. 4 Rusk By 52°31'·05N 06°10'·75W; PHM.
W Blackwater By 52°25'·83N 06°13'·20W; SHM.

WEXFORD
N Training Wall Bn 52°20'·18N 06°26'·78W.
N Long Lt By 52°21'·42N 06°16'·90W Q; *Whis;* NCM.
West Long Lt By 52°18'·16N 06°17'·90W QG; SHM.
Lucifer Lt By 52°17'·00N 06°12'·61W VQ (3) 5s; ECM.

ROSSLARE
Pier Hd 52°15'·42N 06°20'·23W Oc WRG 5s 15m W13M, R10M, G10M; R Tr; vis G098°-188°, W188°-208°, R208°-246°, G246°-283°, W283°-286°, R286°-320°.
W Holdens Lt By 52°15'·75N 06°18'·68W Fl (3) G 10s; SHM.
S Long Lt By 52°14'·82N 06°15'·58W VQ (6) + L Fl 10s; SCM; *Whis.*
Splaugh Lt By 52°14'·35N 06°16'·70W Fl R 6s; PHM.
Tuskar 52°12'·17N 06°12'·40W Q (2) 7·5s 33m **24M**; W Tr; RC; Racon (T); *Horn (4) 45s.*

TUSKAR ROCK TO OLD HEAD OF KINSALE

S Rock Lt By 52°10'·80N 06°12'·80W Q (6) + L Fl 15s; SCM.

Fundale Lt By 52°10'·66N 06°20'·20W Fl (2) R 10s; PHM.

CARNA
Pier Hd 52°11'·89N 06°20'·80W Fl R 3s 6m 4M.
Barrels Lt By 52°08'·30N 06°22'·00W Q (3) 10s; *Whis;* ECM.

KILMORE
Bkwtr Hd 52°10'·25N 06°35'·10W Q RG 6m 5M; vis R269°-354°, G354°-003°, R003°-077°.
CONINGBEG Lt F 52°02'·38N 06°39'·44W Fl (3) 30s 12m **24M**; R hull, and Tr, Racon (M); *Horn (3) 60s.*

WATERFORD
Hook Hd 52°07'·30N 06°55'·80W Fl 3s 46m **23M**; W Tr, two B bands; Racon (K).
Duncannon Dir lt 002°. 52°13'·21N 06°56'·19W Oc WRG 4s 13m W11M, R8M, G8M; W Tr on fort; vis G358°-001·7°, W001·7°-002·2°, R002·2°-006°. Same Tr, Oc WR 4s 13m W9M, R7M; vis R119°-149°, W149°-172°.
Duncannon Bar Lt By 52°11'·27N 06°55'·90W Fl G 2s; SHM.
Duncannon Bar Lt By 52°11'·27N 06°56'·23W Fl R 2s; PHM.
Duncannon Spit Lt By 52°12'·67N 06°56'·00W Fl (2) G 5s; Cl IM.
Passage Pt 52°14'·23N 06°57'·70W Fl WR 5s 7m W6M, R5M; R pile structure; vis W shore-127°, R127°-302°.

Cheek Pt 52°16'·11N 06°59'·30W Q WR 6m 5M; W mast; vis W007°-289°, R289°-007°.

Sheagh 52°16'·29N 06°59'·38W Fl R 3s 29m 3M; Gy Tr; vis 090°-318°.

Kilmokea 52°16'·48N 06°58'·85W Fl 5s.

R. Barrow Railway Bridge 2 FR (Hor); tfc sigs.

Snowhill Pt Ldg Lts 255°. Front, 52°16'·37N 07°00'·85W Fl WR 2·5s 5m 3M; vis W222°-020°, R020°-057°, W057°-107°. Rear, Flour Mill, 750m from front, Q 12m 5M.

Queen's Chan Ldg Lts 098°. Front, 52°15'·30N 07°02'·32W QR 8m 5M; B Tr, W band; vis 030°-210°. Rear, 550m from front, Q 15m 5M; W mast.

Giles Quay 52°15'·47N 07°04'·15W Fl 3s 9m; vis 255°-086°.

Cove 52°15'·02N 07°05'·10W Fl WRG 6s 6m 2M; W Tr; vis R111°-161°, G161°-234°, W234°-111°.

Smelting Ho Pt 52°15'·13N 07°05'·20W Q 8m 3M; W mast.

Ballycar 52°15'·06N 07°05'·42W Fl RG 3s 5m; vis G127°-212°, R212°-284°.

DUNMORE EAST

Dunmore East, E Pier Hd 52°08'·91N 06°59'·32W Fl WR 8s 13m **W17M**, R13M; Gy Tr, vis W225°-310°, R310°-004°.

E Bkwtr extn 52°08'·96N 06°59'·32W Fl R 2s 6m 4M; vis 000°-310°.

DUNGARVAN

Ballinacourty Pt 52°04'·67N 07°33'·13W Fl (2) WRG 10s 16m W10M, R8M, G8M; W Tr; vis G245°-274°, W274°-302°, R302°-325°, W325°-117°.

Helvick Lt By 52°03'·59N 07°32'·20W Q (3) 10s; ECM.

Mine Hd 51°59'·50N 07°35'·20W Fl (4) 20s 87m **28M**; W Tr, B band; vis 228°-052°.

YOUGHAL

Bar Rocks By 51°54'·83N 07°50'·00W; SCM.

Blackball Ledge By 51°55'·32N 07°48'·48W; PHM.

W side of ent 51°56'·55N 07°50'·48W Fl WR 2·5s 24m **W17M**, R13M; W Tr; vis W183°-273°, R273°-295°, W295°-307°, R307°-351°, W351°-003°.

BALLYCOTTON

Ballycotton 51°49'·50N 07°59'·10W Fl WR 10s 59m **W21M, R17M**; B Tr, within W walls, B lantern; vis W238°-048°, R048°-238°; Horn (4) 90s.

Smiths Lt By 51°48'·60N 08°00'·66W Fl (3) R 10s; PHM.

Pollock Rk Lt By 51°46'·20N 08°07'·80W Fl R 6s; PHM.

CORK

Daunt Rk Lt By 51°43'·50N 08°17'·60W Fl (2) R 6s; PHM.

Cork Lt By 51°42'·90N 08°15'·55W L Fl 10s; Whis; Racon (T); SWM.

Fort Davis Ldg Lts 354·1°. Front, 51°48'·79N 08°15'·77W Oc 5s 29m 10M; Or □. Dir Lt WRG; vis FG351·5°-352·25°, AIWG352·25°-353°, FW353°-355°, AIWR355°-355·75°, FR355·75°-356·5°. Rear, Dognose Quay, 203m from front, Oc 5s 37m 10M; Or □, synch with front.

Roche's Pt 51°47'·57N 08°15'·24W Fl WR 3s 30m **W20M, R16M**; vis Rshore-292°, W292°-016°, R016°-033°, W(unintens) 033°-159°, R159°-shore.

Outer Hbr Lt By E2 51°47'·50N 08°15'·62W Fl R 2·5s; PHM.

Chicago Knoll Lt By E1 51°47'·66N 08°15'·50W Fl G 5s; SHM.

The Sound Lt By E4 51°47'·91N 08°15'·72W Q; NCM.

White Bay Ldg Lts 034·6°. Front, 51°48'·51N 08°15'·18W Oc R 5s 11m 5M; W hut. Rear, 113m from front, Oc R 5s 21m 5M; W hut; synch with front.

Curraghbinney Ldg Lts 252°. Front, 51°48'·63N 08°17'·56W F 10m 3M; W ◊ on col. Rear, 61m from front, F 15m 3M; W ◊ on col; vis 229·5°-274·5°.

Spit Bank Pile 51°50'·70N 08°16'·41W Iso WR 4s 10m W10M, R7M; W house on R piles; vis R087°-196°, W196°-221°, R221°-358°.

East Ferry Marina, E Passage 51°51'·90N 08°12'·75W 2 FR (vert) at N and S ends.

Power Lt By 51°45'·57N 08°06'·62W Q (6) + L Fl 15s; SCM.

KINSALE/OYSTER HAVEN

Bulman Lt By 51°40'·11N 08°29'·70W Q (6) + L Fl 15s; SCM; Bell.

Charle's Fort 51°41'·72N 08°29'·94W Fl WRG 5s 18m W8M, R5M, G6M; vis G348°-358°, W358°-004°, R004°-168°; H24.

IRELAND – SOUTH COAST
OLD HEAD OF KINSALE TO MIZEN HEAD

Old Hd of Kinsale, S point 51°36'·26N 08°31'·98W Fl (2) 10s 72m **25M**; B Tr, two W bands; RC; Horn (3) 45s.

COURTMACSHERRY

Black Tom By 51°36'·39N 08°37'·00W; SHM.

Wood Pt (Land Pt) 51°38'·3N 08°41'·0W Fl (2) WR 5s 15m 5M; vis W315°-332°, R332°-315°.

Galley Hd summit 51°31'·78N 08°57'·14W Fl (5) 20s 53m **23M**; W Tr; vis 256°-065°.

GLANDORE

Glandore Harbour SW Lt Bn 51°33'·12N 09°06'·60W Fl (2+1) G 10s 4M; GRG.

Sunk Rk Lt By 51°33'·50N 09°06'·80W Q; NCM.

CASTLE HAVEN

Reen Pt 51°30'·95N 09°10'·46W Fl WRG 10s 9m W5M, R3M, G3M; W Tr; vis Gshore-338°, W338°-001°, R001°-shore.

Kowloon Bridge Lt By 51°27'·55N 09°13'·71W Q (6) + L Fl 15s; SCM.

BALTIMORE

Barrack Pt 51°28'·33N 09°23'·65W Fl (2) WR 6s 40m W6M, R3M; vis R168°-294°, W294°-038°.

Loo Rk Lt By 51°28'·42N 09°23'·42W Fl G 3s; SHM.

Fastnet, W end 51°23'·33N 09°36'·14W Fl 5s 49m **27M**; Gy Tr; Racon (G); Horn (4) 60s.

Copper Pt Long Island, E end 51°30'·22N 09°32'·02W Q (3) 10s 16m 8M; W ● Tr.

Amelia Rk Lt By 51°29'·95N 09°31'·42W Fl G 3s; SHM.

SCHULL

Ldg Lts 346° Front, 51°31'·64N 09°32'·39W Oc 5s 5m 11M, W mast. Rear, 91m from front, Oc 5s 8m 11M; W mast.

CROOKHAVEN

Rock Island Pt 51°28'·57N 09°42'·23W L Fl WR 8s 20m W13M, R11M; W Tr; vis W over Long Island B to 281°, R281°-340°; inside harbour R281°-348°, W348° towards N shore.

Mizen Hd 51°26'·97N 09°49'·18W Iso 4s 55m **15M**; vis 313°-133°; RC; Racon (T).

IRELAND – WEST COAST
MIZEN HEAD TO DINGLE BAY

Sheep's Hd 51°32'·57N 09°50'·89W Fl (3) WR 15s 83m **W18M, R15M**; W bldg; vis R007°-017°, W017°-212°.

BANTRY BAY/CASTLETOWN BEARHAVEN/WHIDDY ISLE/BANTRY/GLENGARIFF

Roancarrigmore 51°39'·17N 09°44'·79W Fl WR 3s 18m **W18M**, R14M; W ● Tr, B band; vis W312°-050°, R050°-122°, R(unintens) 122°-242°, R242°-312°. Reserve Lt W8M, R6M obsc 140°-220°.

Whiddy Island W clearing Lt 51°41'·01N 09°31'·81W Oc 2s 22m 3M; vis 073°-106°.

12

W ent, **Ardnakinna Pt** 51°37'·08N 09°55'·06W Fl (2) WR 10s 62m **W17M**, R14M; W ● Tr; vis R319°-348°, W348°-066°, R066°-shore.
FR on radio mast 3·45M 295°.
Castletown Dir Lt 024° 51°38'·78N 09°54'·05W Dir Oc WRG 5s 4m W14M, R11M, G11M; W hut, R stripe; vis G020·5°-024°, W024°-024·5°, R024·5°-027·5°.
Perch Rk 51°38'·82N 09°54'·43W QG 4m 1M; G col.
Castletown Ldg Lts 010°. Front, 51°39'·14N 09°54'·37W Oc 3s 4m 1M; W col, R stripe; vis 005°-015°. Rear, 80m from front, Oc 3s 7m 1M; W with R stripe; vis 005°-015°.

Bull Rock 51°35'·50N 10°18'·02W Fl 15s 83m **21M**; W Tr; vis 220°-186°.

KENMARE RIVER/DARRYNANE/BALLYCROVANE
Ballycrovane Hbr 51°42'·63N 09° 57'·53W Fl R 3s.
Darrynane Ldg Lts 034°. Front, 51°45'·90N 10°09'·20W Oc 3s 10m 4M. Rear, Oc 3s 16m 4M.

Skelligs Rk 51°46'·09N 10°32'·45W Fl (3) 10s 53m **27M**; W Tr; vis 262°-115°; part obsc within 6M 110°-115°.

VALENTIA/PORTMAGEE
Fort (Cromwell) Pt 51°56'·00N 10°19'·25W Fl WR 2s 16m **W17M, R15M**; W Tr; vis R304°-351°, W102°-304°; obsc from seaward by Doulus Hd when brg more than 180°.
FR Lts on radio masts on Geokaun hill 1·20M WSW.
Harbour Rk Lt 51°55'·79N 10°18'·91W Q (3) 10s 4m 5M; vis 080°-040°; ECM.
Ldg Lts 141°. Front, 51°55'·49N 10°18'·39W Oc WRG 4s 25m W11M, R8M, G8M; W Tr, R stripe; vis G134°-140°, W140°-142°, R142°-148°. Rear, 122m from front, Oc 4s 43m 5M; vis 133°-233° synch with front.

DINGLE BAY TO LOOP HEAD

DINGLE BAY/VENTRY/DINGLE
Dingle, NE side of ent 52°07'·28N 10°15'·48W Fl G 3s 20m 6M.
Pier Hd 52°08'·21N 10°16'·49W.
Ldg Lts 182°. Front 52°07'·40N 10°16'·53W, rear 100m from front, both Oc 3s.

Inishtearaght, W end Blasket Islands 52°04'·51N 10°39'·66W Fl (2) 20s 84m **27M**; W Tr; vis 318°-221°; Racon (O).

BRANDON BAY
Brandon Pier Hd 52°16'·05N 10°09'·58W 2 FG (vert) 5m 4M.

TRALEE BAY
Little Samphire I 52°16'·23N 09°52'·88W Fl WRG 5s 27m **W16M**, R13M; G13M; Bu ● Tr; vis R262°-275°, R280°-090°, G090°-140°, W140°-152°, R152°-172°.
Gt Samphire I 52°16'·13N 09°51'·78W QR 15m 3M; vis 242°-097°.
Fenit Hbr Pier Hd 52°16'·22N 09°51'·51W 2 FR (vert) 12m 3M; vis 148°-058°.

RIVER SHANNON

Ballybunnion Lt By 52°32'·50N 09°46'·90W VQ; NCM: Racon.
Kilcredaune Hd 52°34'·79N 09°42'·58W Fl 6s 41m 13M; W Tr; obsc 224°-247° by hill within 1M.
Kilcredaune Lt By 52°34'·42N 09°41'·17W Fl (2+1) R 10s; PHM.
Tail of Beal Lt By 52°34'·37N 09°40'·71W Q (9) 15s; WCM.
Carrigaholt Lt By 52°34'·90N 09°40'·47W Fl (2) R 6s; PHM.
Beal Spit Lt By 52°34'·80N 09°39'·94W VQ (9) 10s; WCM.
Beal Bar Lt By 52°35'·16N 09°39'·19W Q; NCM.

Doonaha Lt By 52°35'·47N 09°38'·46W Fl (3) R 10s; PHM.
Letter Pt Lt By 52°35'·42N 09°35'·85W Fl R 7s; PHM.
Asdee Lt By 52°35'·07N 09°34'·51W Fl R 5s; PHM.
Rineanna Lt By 52°35'·57N 09°31'·20W QR; PHM.
Carrig Lt By 52°35'·59N 09°29'·72W Fl G 3s; SHM.
Scattery I, Rineana Pt 52°36'·32N 09°31'·03W Fl (2) 7·5s 15m 10M; W Tr; vis 208°-092° (H24).

KILRUSH
Marina Ent Chan Ldg Lts 355°. Front, 52°37'·93N 09°30'·26W Oc 3s. Rear, 75m from front, Oc 3s.
Tarbert I N Pt 52°35'·50N 09°21'·79W Iso WR 4s 18m W14M, R10M; W ● Tr; vis W069°-277°, R277°-287°, W287°-339°.
Tarbert (Ballyhoolahan Pt) Ldg Lts 128·2°. Front, 52°34'·32N 09°18'·75W Iso 2s 13m 3M; △ on W Tr; vis 123·2°-133·2°. Rear, 400m from front, Iso 5s 18m 3M; G stripe on W Bn.
Garraunbaun Pt 51°35'·59N 09°13'·90W Fl (3) WR 10s 16m W8M, R5M; W ■ col, vis R shore-072°, W072°-242°, R242°-shore.
Rinealon Pt 52°37'·10N 09°09'·77W Fl 2·5s 4m 7M; B col, W bands; vis 234°-088°.

FOYNES
W Chan Ldg Lts 107·6° (may be moved for changes in chan).
Front, Barneen Pt 52°36'·89N 09°06'·55W Iso WRG 4s 3m W4M, R3M, G3M; B △ with W stripe on W col with B bands; vis W273·2°-038·2°, R038·2°-094·2°, G094·2°-104·2°, W104·2°-108·2°, R108·2°-114·2°. Rear, E Jetty, 540m from front, Oc 4s 16m 10M; Or △ on post.
Colleen Pt No. 3 52°36'·89N 09°06'·81W QG 2m 2M; W col, B bands.
Hunts (Weir) Pt No. 4 52°37'·01N 09°06'·96W VQ (4) R 10s 2m 2M; W col, B bands.

Beeves Rk 52°39'·00N 09°01'·30W Fl WR 5s 12m W12M, R9M; vis W064·5°-091°, R091°-238°, W238°-265°, W(unintens) 265°-064·5°.
Shannon Airport 52°41'·71N 08°55'·66W Aero Al Fl WG 7·5s 40m.
Dernish I Pier Hd, 2 FR (vert) 4m 2M each end.
E Bkwtr Hd 52°40'·82N 08°54'·80W QR 3m 1M.
Conor Rock 52°40'·91N 08°54'·20W Fl R 4s 6m 6M; W Tr; vis 228°-093°.
N Channel Ldg Lts 093°. Front, Tradree Rk 52°40'·99N 08°49'·82W Fl R 2s 6m 5M; W Trs; vis 246°-110°. Rear 0·65M from front, Iso 6s 14m 5M; W Tr, R bands; vis 327°-190°.
Bird Rock 52°40'·93N 08°50'·22W QG 6m 5M; W Tr.
Grass I 52°40'·41N 08°48'·40W Fl G 2s 6m 4M; W col, B bands.
Laheen's Rk 52°40'·32N 08°48'·10W QR 4m 5M.
S side Spilling Rk 52°40'·0N 08°47'·1W Fl G 5s 5m 5M.
N side, Ldg Lts 061°. Front, 52°40'·69N 08°45'·23W, Crawford Rk 490m from rear, Fl R 3s 6m 5M. Crawford No. 2, Common Rear, 52°40'·83N 08°44'·84W Iso 6s 10m 5M.
Ldg Lts 302·1°. Flagstaff Rk, 670m from rear, Fl R 2s 7m 5M.
The Whelps 52°40'·67N 08°45'·05W Fl G 3s 5m 5M; W pile.
Ldg Lts 106·5°. Meelick Rk, Front 52°40'·23N 08°42'·31W Iso 4s 6m 3M. Meelick No. 2, rear 275m from front Iso 6s 9m 5M; both W pile structures.
Ldg Lts 146°, Braemar Pt, Front 52°39'·16N 08°41'·89W Iso 4s 5m 5M. Rear, Braemar No. 2, 122m from front, Iso 6s 6m 4M; both W pile structures.
N side Clonmacken Pt 52°39'·50N 08°40'·64W Fl R 3s 7m 4M.
E side Spillane's Tr 52°39'·33N 08°39'·67W Fl 3s 11m 6M; turret on Tr.

LIMERICK DOCK
Lts in line 098·5°. Front, 52°39'·48N 08°38'·76W. Rear, 100m from front; both F; R ◊ on cols; occas.

Loop Head 52°33'·65N 09°55'·90W Fl (4) 20s 84m **23M**; RC.

10.12.5 PASSAGE INFORMATION

For all Irish waters the Sailing Directions published by the Irish Cruising Club are strongly recommended, and particularly on the W coast, where other information is scarce. They are published in two volumes: *E and N coasts of Ireland* which runs anti-clockwise from Carnsore Pt to Bloody Foreland, and *S and W coasts of Ireland* which goes clockwise. For notes on crossing the Irish Sea, see 10.13.5; and for Distances across it see 10.0.6.

MALAHIDE TO TUSKAR ROCK (charts 1468, 1787)

Malahide (10.12.8), 4M from both Lambay Is and Howth, can be entered in most weather via a chan dredged (allegedly in 1996) through drying sandbanks. Ireland's Eye, a rky island which rises steeply to a height of 99m, lies about 7½ca N of Howth (10.12.9) with reefs running SE and SW from Thulla Rk at its SE end. Ben of Howth, on N side of Dublin Bay, is steep-to, with no dangers more than 1ca offshore.

Rosbeg Bank lies on the N side of Dublin Bay. Burford Bank, on which the sea breaks in E gales, and Kish Bank lie offshore in the approaches. The N-going stream begins at HW Dublin – 0600, and the S-going at HW Dublin, sp rates 3kn.

From Dublin (10.12.10) to Carnsore Pt the shallow offshore banks cause dangerous overfalls and dictate the route which is sheltered from the W winds. Tidal streams run mainly N and S, but the N-going flood sets across the banks on the inside, and the S-going ebb sets across them on the outside. As a cruising area, hbr facilities are starting to improve (1996).

Leaving Dublin Bay, yachts normally use Dalkey Sound, but with a foul tide or light wind it is better to use Muglins Sound. Muglins (lt) is steep-to except for a rk about 1ca WSW of the lt. Beware Leac Buidhe (dries) 1ca E of Clare Rk. The inshore passage is best as far as Wicklow (10.12.11).

Thereafter yachts may either route offshore, passing east of Arklow Bank and its Lanby to fetch Tuskar Rock or Greenore Pt. Or keep inshore of Arklow Bank, avoiding Glassgorman Banks; through the Rusk Channel, inside Blackwater and Lucifer Banks, to round Carnsore Pt NW of Tuskar Rock. Arklow (10.12.12) is safe in offshore winds; Wexford (10.12.13) has a difficult entrance. Rosslare (10.12.14) lacks yacht facilities, but provides good shelter to wait out a SW'ly blow.

TUSKAR ROCK TO OLD HEAD OF KINSALE (chart 2049)

Dangerous rks lie up to 2ca NW and 6½ca SSW of Tuskar Rk and there can be a dangerous race off Carnsore Pt. In bad weather or poor visibility, use the Inshore Traffic Zone of the Tuskar Rock TSS, Fig. 10 (7), passing to seaward of Tuskar Rk (lt, RC), the Barrels ECM lt buoy and Coningbeg lt float.

If taking the inshore passage from Greenore Pt, stay inside The Bailies to pass 2ca off Carnsore Pt. Watch for lobster pots in this area. Steer WSW to pass N of Black Rk and the Bohurs, S of which are extensive overfalls. The little hbr of Kilmore Quay (10.12.15) has been rebuilt with a new marina, but beware rks and shoals in the approaches.

Saltee Sound (chart 2740) is a safe passage, least width 3ca, between Great and Little Saltee, conspic islands to S and N. Sebber Bridge extends 7½ca N from the NE point of Great Saltee and Jackeen Rk is 1M NW of the S end of Little Saltee, so care is needed through the sound, where the stream runs 3·5 kn at sp. There are several rks S of the Saltees, but yachts may pass between Coningbeg Rk and the lt float. There are no obstructions on a direct course for a point 1M S of Hook Head, to avoid the overfalls and Tower Race, which at times extend about 1M S of the Head.

Dunmore East (10.12.16 and chart 2046) is a useful passage port at the mouth of Waterford Hbr (10.12.17). To the W, beware salmon nets and Falskirt, a dangerous rk off Swines Pt. There are few offlying rks from Tramore Bay to Ballinacourty

Pt on the N side of Dungarvan Bay (10.12.18 and chart 2017). Helvick is a small sheltered hbr approached along the S shore of the bay, keeping S of Helvick Rk (ECM lt buoy) and other dangers to the N.

Mine Hd (lt) has two dangerous rks, The Rogue about 2½ca E and The Longship 1M SW. To the W, there is a submerged rk 100m SE of Ram Hd. Here the W-going stream starts at HW Cobh + 0230, and the E-going at HW Cobh –0215, sp rates 1·5 kn. For Youghal, see 10.12.18. Pass 1ca S of Capel Island. The sound is not recommended.

The N side of Ballycotton B is foul up to 5ca offshore. Ballycotton Hbr (10.12.18) is small and crowded, but usually there is sheltered anch outside. Sound Rk and Small Is lie between the mainland and Ballycotton Is (lt, fog sig). From Ballycotton to Cork keep at least 5ca off for dangers including The Smiths (PHM lt buoy) 1·5M WSW of Ballycotton Island. Pass between Hawk Rk, close off Power Hd, and Pollock Rk (PHM lt buoy) 1.25M SE.

Near the easy entrance and excellent shelter of Cork Harbour (10.12.19 and chart 1777), Ringabella Bay offers temp anch in good weather. 7ca SE of Robert's Hd is Daunt Rk (3·5m) on which seas break in bad weather; marked by SHM lt buoy. Little Sovereign on with Reanies Hd 241° leads inshore of it. The Sovereigns are large rks off Oyster Haven, a good hbr but prone to swell in S'lies. The ent is clear except for Harbour Rk which must be passed on its W side, see 10.12.20. Bulman Rk (SCM lt buoy) is 4ca S of Preghane Pt at the ent to Kinsale's fine harbour (10.12.20).

Old Head of Kinsale (lt, fog sig, RC) is quite steep-to, but a race extends 1M to SW on W-going stream, and to SE on E-going stream. There is an inshore passage in light weather, but in strong winds keep 2M off.

OLD HEAD OF KINSALE TO MIZEN HEAD (chart 2424)

From Cork to Mizen Hd there are many natural hbrs. Only the best are mentioned here. Offshore the stream seldom exceeds 1·5kn, but it is stronger off headlands causing races and overfalls with wind against tide. Prolonged W winds increase the rate/duration of the E-going stream, and strong E winds have a similar effect on the W-going stream.

In the middle of Courtmacsherry Bay are several dangers, from E to W: Blueboy Rk, Barrel Rk (with Inner Barrels closer inshore), and Black Tom; Horse Rk is off Barry's Pt at the W side of the bay. These must be avoided going to or from Courtmacsherry, where the bar breaks in strong S/SE winds, but the river carries 2·5m; see 10.12.21. Beware Cotton Rk and Shoonta Rk close E of Seven Heads, off which rks extend 50m. Clonakilty B has little to offer. Keep at least 5ca off Galley Hd to clear Dhulic Rk, and further off in fresh winds. Offshore the W-going stream makes at HW Cobh + 0200, and the E-going at HW Cobh – 0420, sp rates 1·5 kn.

Across Glandore Bay there are good anchs off Glandore (10.12.22), or off Union Hall. Sailing W from Glandore, pass outside or inside High Is and Low Is, but if inside beware Belly Rk (awash) about 3ca S of Rabbit Is. On passage Toe Head has foul ground 100m S, and 7½ca S is a group of rks called the Stags. Castle Haven (10.12.23), a sheltered and attractive hbr, is entered between Reen Pt (lt) and Battery Pt. Baltimore (10.12.24) is 10M further W.

Fastnet Rk (lt, fog sig) is nearly 4M WSW of C Clear; 2½ca NE of it is an outlying rk. An E/W TSS, Fig 10(3), lies between 2 and 8M SSE of the Fastnet. Long Island Bay can be entered from C Clear or through Gascanane Sound, between Clear Is and Sherkin Is. Carrigmore Rks lie in the middle of this chan, with Gascanane Rk 1ca W of them. The chan between Carrigmore Rks and Badger Island is best. If bound for Crookhaven, beware Bullig Reef, N of Clear Is.

Schull (10.12.25) is N of Long Island, inside which passage can be made W'ward to Crookhaven (10.12.26). This is a well sheltered hbr, accessible at all states of tide, entered between

Rock Is lt Ho and Alderman Rks, ENE of Streek Hd. Anch off the village.

Off Mizen Hd the W-going stream starts at HW Cobh + 0120, and the E-going at HW Cobh – 0500. The sp rate is 4 kn, which with wind against tide forms a dangerous race, sometimes reaching to Brow Hd or Three Castle Hd , with broken water right to the shore.

THE WEST COAST

This coast offers wonderful cruising, although exposed to the Atlantic and any swell offshore; but this diminishes mid-summer. In bad weather however the sea breaks dangerously on shoals with quite substantial depths. There is usually a refuge close by, but if caught out in deteriorating weather and poor vis, a stranger may need to make an offing until conditions improve, so a stout yacht and good crew are required. Even in mid-summer at least one gale may be meet in a two-week cruise. Fog is less frequent than in the Irish Sea. Listen regularly to the Radio Telefis Eireann forecasts; see Table 7(2).

Tidal streams are weak, except round headlands. There are few lights, so inshore navigation is unwise after dark. Coastal navigation is feasible at night in good visibility. Keep a good watch for drift nets off the coast, and for lobster pots in inshore waters. Stores, fuel and water are not readily available.

MIZZEN HEAD TO DINGLE BAY (chart 2423)

At S end of Dunmanus Bay Three Castle Hd has rks 1ca W, and sea can break on S Bullig 4ca off Hd. Dunmanus B (chart 2552) has three hbrs: Dunmanus, Kitchen Cove and Dunbeacon. Carbery, Cold and Furze Is lie in middle of B, and it is best to keep N of them. Sheep's Hd (lt) is at the S end of Bantry Bay (10.12.27; charts 1838, 1840) which has excellent hbrs, notably Glengariff and Castletown. There are few dangers offshore, except around Bear and Whiddy Islands. Off Blackball Hd at W entrance to Bantry B there can be a nasty race, particularly on W-going stream against the wind. Keep 3ca off Crow Is to clear dangers.

Dursey Island is steep-to except for rk 7½ca NE of Dursey Hd and Lea Rk (1·4m)1½ca SW . The Bull (lt, fog sig) and two rks W of it lie 2·5M WNW of Dursey Hd. The Cow is midway between The Bull and Dursey Hd, with clear water each side. Calf and Heifer Rks are 7½ca SW of Dursey Hd, where there is often broken water. 2M W of The Bull the stream turns NW at HW Cobh + 0150, and SE at HW Cobh – 0420. Dursey Sound (chart 2495) is a good short cut, but the stream runs 4kn at sp; W-going starts at HW Cobh + 0135, and E-going at HW Cobh – 0450. Flag Rk lies almost awash in mid-chan at the narrows, which are crossed by cables 25m above MHWS. Hold very close to the Island shore. Beware wind changes in the sound, and broken water at N entrance.

Kenmare R. (chart 2495 and 10.12.28) has attractive hbrs and anchs, but its shores are rky, with no lights. The best places are Sneem, Kilmakilloge and Ardgroom. Off Lamb's Head, Two Headed Island is steep-to; further W is Moylaun Is with a rk 300m SW of it. Little Hog (or Deenish) Island is rky 1·5M to W, followed by Great Hog (or Scariff) Is which has a rk close N, and a reef extending 2ca W.

Darrynane is an attractive, sheltered hbr NNW of Lamb Hd. The entrance has ldg lts and marks, but is narrow and dangerous in bad weather. Ballinskelligs Bay has an anch N of Horse Is, which has two rks close off E end. Centre of bay is a prohib anch (cables reported).

Rough water is met between Bolus Hd and Bray Hd with fresh onshore winds or swell. The SW end of Puffin Island is steep-to, but the sound to the E is rky and not advised. Great Skellig (lit) is 6M, and Little Skellig 5M WSW of Puffin Is. Lemon Rk lies between Puffin Is and Little Skellig. Here the stream turns N at HW Cobh + 0500, and S at HW Cobh – 0110. There is a rk 3ca SW of Great Skellig. When very calm it is possible to go alongside at Blind Man's Cove on NE side of Great Skellig, where there are interesting ruins.

DINGLE BAY TO LISCANOR BAY (chart 2254)

Dingle Bay (charts 2789, 2790) is wide and deep, with few dangers around its shores. Dingle (10.12.29) has a small marina. The best anchs are at Portmagee and Ventry. At the NW ent to the bay, 2·5M SSW of Slea Hd, is Wild Bank (or Three Fathom Pinnacle), a shallow patch with overfalls. 3M SW of Wild Bank is Barrack Rk, which breaks in strong winds.

The Blasket Islands are very exposed, with strong tides and overfalls, but worth a visit in settled weather (chart 2790). Great Blasket and Inishvickillane each have anch and landing on their NE side. Inishtearaght is the most W'ly Is (lt), but further W lie Tearaght Rks, and 3M S are Little Foze and Gt Foze Rks. Blasket Sound is the most convenient N-S route, 1M wide, and easy in daylight and reasonable weather with fair wind or tide; extensive rks and shoals form its W side. The N-going stream starts at HW Galway + 0430, and the S-going at HW Galway – 0155, with sp rate 3 kn.

Between Blasket Sound and Sybil Pt there is a race in W or NW winds with N-going tide, and often a nasty sea. Sybil Pt has steep cliffs, and offlying rks extend 3½ca.

Smerwick hbr, entered between Duncapple Is and the E Sister is sheltered, except from NW or N winds. From here the scenery is spectacular to Brandon Bay on the W side of which there is an anch, but exposed to N winds and to swell.

There is no lt from Inishtearaght to Loop Hd, apart from Little Samphire Is in Tralee B, where Fenit hbr provides the only secure refuge until entering the Shannon Estuary. The coast from Loop Hd to Liscanor Bay has no safe anchs, and no lts. Take care not to be set inshore, although there are few offlying dangers except near Mutton Is and in Liscanor Bay.

THE SHANNON ESTUARY (charts 1819, 1547, 1548, 1549)

The estuary and lower reaches of the Shannon (10.12.31), are tidal for 50M, from its mouth between Loop Hd and Kerry Hd up to Limerick Dock, some 15M beyond the junction with R. Fergus. The tides and streams are those of a deep-water inlet, with roughly equal durations of rise and fall, and equal rates of flood and ebb streams. In the entrance the flood stream begins at HW Galway – 0555, and the ebb at HW Galway + 0015.

There are several anchs available for yachts on passage up or down the coast. Kilbaha Bay (chart 1819) is about 3M E of Loop Hd, and is convenient in good weather or in N winds, but exposed to SE and any swell. Carrigaholt B (chart 1547), entered about 1M N of Kilcredaun Pt, is well sheltered from W winds and has little tidal stream. In N winds there is anch SE of Querrin Pt (chart 1547), 4·5M further up river on N shore. At Kilrush (10.12.30) there is a marina and anchs E of Scattery Is and N of Hog Is. Note that there are overfalls 0·75M S of Scattery Is with W winds and ebb tide.

Off Kilcredaun Pt the ebb reaches 4kn at sp, and in strong winds between S and NW a bad race forms. This can be mostly avoided by keeping near the N shore, which is free from offlying dangers, thereby cheating the worst of the tide. When leaving the Shannon in strong W winds, aim to pass Kilcredaun Pt at slack water, and again keep near the N shore. Loop Hd (lt, RC) marks the N side of Shannon est, and should be passed 3ca off. Here the stream runs SW from HW Galway + 0300, and NE from HW Galway – 0300.

Above the junction with R. Fergus (chart 1540) the tidal characteristics become more like those of most rivers, ie the flood stream is stronger than the ebb, but it runs for a shorter time. In the Shannon the stream is much affected by the wind. S and W winds increase the rate and duration of the flood stream, and reduce the ebb. Strong N or E winds have the opposite effect. Prolonged or heavy rain increases the rate and duration of the ebb. The Shannon is the longest river in Ireland, rising at Lough Allen 100M above Limerick, thence 50M to the sea.

10.12.6   DISTANCE TABLE

Approximate distances in nautical miles are by the most direct route, whilst avoiding dangers and allowing for Traffic Separation Schemes. Places in *italics* are in adjoining areas; places in **bold** are in 10.0.6, Distances across the Irish Sea.

		1	2	3	4	5	6	7	8	9	10	11	12	13	14	15	16	17	18	19	20
1.	*Carlingford Lough*	1																			
2.	**Howth**	39	2																		
3.	**Dun Laoghaire**	48	8	3																	
4.	**Wicklow**	63	25	21	4																
5.	**Arklow**	75	37	36	15	5															
6.	**Tuskar Rock**	113	73	70	52	37	6														
7.	**Rosslare**	108	70	66	47	34	8	7													
8.	**Dunmore East**	139	101	102	84	69	32	32	8												
9.	**Youghal**	172	134	133	115	100	63	65	34	9											
10.	**Crosshaven**	192	154	155	137	122	85	85	59	25	10										
11.	Kinsale	202	164	168	150	135	98	95	69	35	17	11									
12.	**Baltimore**	239	201	196	177	164	128	132	102	70	54	42	12								
13.	**Fastnet Rock**	250	212	207	189	174	137	144	112	78	60	49	10	13							
14.	Bantry	281	243	241	223	208	171	174	146	112	94	83	42	34	14						
15.	Darrynane	283	245	240	221	208	172	176	146	114	98	86	44	39	38	15					
16.	Valentia	295	257	252	242	227	184	188	165	131	113	102	56	48	55	16	16				
17.	Dingle	308	270	265	246	233	197	201	171	139	123	111	69	61	63	29	13	17			
18.	Kilrush	361	323	318	299	286	250	254	224	192	176	164	122	114	116	82	66	64	18		
19.	*Galway*	366	362	357	339	324	287	291	262	228	210	199	159	150	155	119	103	101	76	19	
20.	*Slyne Head*	317	351	346	328	313	276	283	251	217	199	188	153	139	144	113	97	95	75	49	20

SPECIAL NOTES FOR IRELAND   10.12.7

ORDNANCE SURVEY map numbers refer to the Irish OS maps, scale 1:50,000 or 1¼ inch to 1 mile, which cover the whole island, including Ulster, in 89 sheets.

IRISH CUSTOMS: First port of call should preferably be at Customs posts in one of the following hbrs: Dublin, Dun Laoghaire, Waterford, New Ross, Cork, Ringaskiddy, Bantry, Foynes, Limerick, Galway, Sligo and Killybegs. Yachts may, in fact, make their first call anywhere and if no Customs officer arrives within a reasonable time, the skipper should inform the nearest Garda (Police) station of the yacht's arrival. Only non-EC members should fly flag Q or show Ⓡ over Ⓦ lts on arrival. Passports are not required by UK citizens.

IRISH MARINE EMERGENCY SERVICE (IMES): SAR ops in the Republic are controlled by MRSCs at Dublin, Malin Head and Valentia; and coordinated by Dublin MRCC, ☎ (01) 6620922/3. MRSC ☎ No(s), as shown in each port, should normally be used, but in emergency dial 999 and ask for *Marine Rescue*.
Dublin MRCC communicates/relays to vessels via the Coast Radio Stns at Dublin, Wicklow, Rosslare, Minehead, Cork, Bantry, Valentia, Shannon, Malin, Glenhead, Belmullet and Clifden (see 6.3.16 for VHF channels). The IMES can call on IMES helicopters, based at Dublin, Shannon and Finner (Donegal), the RNLI, Coast & Cliff Rescue Service, Irish Air Corps helicopters and search aircraft, Irish naval vessels, civil aircraft, the Irish lighthouse service and the Garda Siochana. The IMES liaises with UK and France and acts as a clearing house for all messages received during any rescue operation within 100M of the Irish coast.

COAST AND CLIFF RESCUE SERVICE: This is part of the IMES and comprises about 50 stations manned by volunteers, who are trained in first aid and equipped with inflatables, breeches buoys, cliff ladders etc. Their ☎ numbers (the Leader's residence) are given, where appropriate, under each port.

WEATHER: Weather bulletins (comprising gale warnings and a 24 hrs forecast for the Irish Sea and Irish waters up to 30M offshore) are broadcast by RTE Radio 1 at: 0602, 1253, 1823 (Sat, Sun, Hols), 1824 (Mon-Fri) and 2355, all LT; see Table 7(2).

TELEPHONE: To call the Irish Republic from the UK, dial 00 -353, then the area code (given in UK ☎ directories and below) minus the initial 0, followed by the ☎ number.
To call UK from the Irish Republic: dial 00-44, followed by the area code minus the initial 0, then the number.

SALMON DRIFT NETS are everywhere along the S and W coasts, off headlands and islands during the summer and especially May-Jul. They may be 1½ to 3M long and are hard to see. FVs may give warnings on VHF Ch 16, 06, 08.

LIQUIFIED PETROLEUM GAS: In Eire LPG is supplied by Kosan, a sister company of Calor Gas Ltd, but the bottles have different connections, and the smallest bottle is taller than the normal Calor one fitted in most yachts. Calor Gas bottles can be filled in most larger towns. Camping Gaz is widely available. The abbreviation Kos indicates where Kosan gas is available.

INFORMATION: The Irish Cruising Club publishes 2 highly recommended books of Sailing Directions, one for the S and W coasts of Ireland, the other for the N and E coasts. They are distributed by Imray and are available in good UK bookshops and chandleries. For further info about the Republic of Ireland, write to: Irish Yachting Association, 3 Park Road, Dun Laoghaire, Co Dublin ☎ (01) 2800239 or to Irish Tourist Board, 150 New Bond Street, London W1Y 0AQ ☎ (0171) 493 3201.

CURRENCY in the Republic of Ireland is the Punt (£IR), divided into 100p. Cash is most readily obtained via Euro or Travellers' cheques.

ACCESS BY AIR: There are airports in Eire at Dublin, Waterford, Cork, Kerry, Shannon, Galway, Connaught, Sligo and Donegal/Carrickfin. See also Ferries in 10.0.4.

GAELIC: As in Scotland (see 10.8.5), it helps to understand some of the commoner words for navigational features (courtesy of the Irish Cruising Club):
Ail, alt: cliff, height. *Ath:* ford. *Bal, Bally:* town. *Barra:* sandbank. *Bel, beal:* river mouth, strait. *Beg:* little. *Ben, bin, binna:* hill. *Bo:* (Cow), sunken rock. *Boy, bwee:* yellow. *Bullig:* shoal, rounded rock, breaker. *Bun:* end, river mouth. *Caher:* fort. *Camus:* bay, river bend. *Carrick, carrig:* rock. *Cuan, coon:* harbour. *Derg, dearg:* red. *Drum:* hill, ridge. *Duff, dubh:* black. *Dun, doon:* fort. *Ennis:* island. *Fad, fadda:* long. *Fan:* slope. *Fin:* white. *Freagh, free:* heather. *Glas, glass:* green. *Gorm:* blue. *Gub:* point of land. *Hassans:* swift current. *Inish, innis, illaun:* island. *Inver:* river mouth. *Keal, keel:* narrow place, sound. *Kill:* church. *Kin, ken:* head, promontory. *Knock:* hill. *Lahan:* broad. *Lea:* grey. *Lenan:* weed-covered rock. *Long, luing:* ship. *Maan:* middle. *Maol, mwee:* bare. *More, mor:* big. *Rannagh, rin, rush:* point. *Roan:* seal. *Roe, ruadh:* red. *Scrow, scrah, scraw:* boggy, grass sward. *Slieve:* mountain. *Stag, stac:* high rock. *Togher:* causeway. *Tra, traw:* strand. *Turlin:* boulder beach. *Vad, bad:* boat.

NORTHERN IRELAND:
Belfast CG (MRSC) is at Bangor, Co Down, ☎ (01247) 463933, ☏ 465886.
HM Customs (▦) should be contacted on ☎ (01232) 358250 at the following ports, if a local Customs Officer is not available: Belfast, Warrenpoint, Kilkeel, Ardglass, Portavogie, Larne, Londonderry, Coleraine.
Northern Ireland's main airport is Belfast (Aldergrove).

12

MALAHIDE   10-12-8

Dublin 53°27'·20N 06°08'·90W   Rtg 3-2-2

CHARTS
AC 633, 1468; Imray C61, C62; Irish OS 50

TIDES
+0030 Dover; ML 2·4; Duration 0615; Zone 0 (UT)

Standard Port DUBLIN (NORTH WALL) (→)

Times				Height (metres)			
High Water		Low Water		MHWS	MHWN	MLWN	MLWS
0000	0700	0000	0500	4·1	3·4	1·5	0·7
1200	1900	1200	1700				
Differences MALAHIDE							
–0019	–0013	+0014	+0006	+0·1	+0·1	0·0	0·0

SHELTER
Good in new marina, dredged approx 3·2m. Or safe ⌕ about 3ca E of conspic Grand Hotel. Caution: crowded moorings.
Note: Consult the marina or the Supplement(s) to this Almanac for latest details of buoys/lts and the alignment and depths of the dredged chan from the bar to the marina (see also under NAVIGATION).

LIGHTS AND MARKS
Outer appr with ch spire on 266° just open N of conspic Grand Hotel. The chan across the Bar to the marina was planned to be marked by 2 PHM lt buoys QR and 1 SHM lt buoy QG.

RADIO TELEPHONE
Marina Ch **M** (H24) 80. MYC, call *Yacht Base* Ch M (occas).

TELEPHONE (Dial code 01)
Marina 8454129, ☎ 8454255; MRCC 6620922/3; ⌗ 8746571; Police 845 0216; Dr 845 1953; Ⓗ 837 7755.

FACILITIES
Marina (150, increasing to 300 berths) ☎ 8454129, ☎ 8454255, £IR 11.88, FW, AC, D, P, Gas, BH (30 ton), BY, R, Bar, Ice, Ⓒ;
Malahide YC ☎ 8450216, Slip, Scrubbing posts for <10m LOA; **Services:** Ⓔ, Sh, Kos.
Town Ⓞ, ✉, Ⓑ, ⇌, ✈ (Dublin).

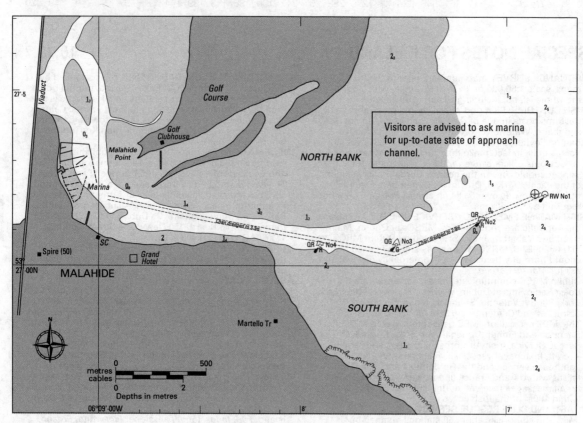

Visitors are advised to ask marina for up-to-date state of approach channel.

NAVIGATION
WPT 53°27'·20N 06°06'·80W, SWM lt buoy, 082°/262° from/to Grand Hotel, 1·2M. WPT is approx 2ca E of the Bar, which was planned to be dredged to 2·9m. The appr chan across drying sandbanks was planned to be dredged to 3·3m. Do not attempt entry in thick weather or HN, nor in strong onshore winds. The flood reaches 3kn sp, and the ebb 3½kn. Speed limit 4kn in fairway and marina. *The 1996 and 1997 Almanacs and their Supplements have repeatedly stressed the need to obtain up-to-date information by ☎ or VHF from the marina as to the latest state of dredging, depths and buoyage BEFORE even considering an approach. Dredging of the bar and approach channel up to the marina has been much delayed and an accurate timescale remains uncertain. The final alignment, depths and buoyage of this chan, as depicted by pecked lines and associated captions on the chartlet, may yet be different.*

HOWTH   10-12-9

Dublin 53°23'·60N 06°04'·00W   Rtg 1-2-1

CHARTS
AC 1415, 1468; Imray C61, C62; Irish OS 50
TIDES
+0025 Dover; ML 2·4; Duration 0625; Zone 0 (UT)

Standard Port DUBLIN (NORTH WALL) (→)

Times				Height (metres)			
High Water		Low Water		MHWS	MHWN	MLWN	MLWS
0000	0700	0000	0500	4·1	3·4	1·5	0·7
1200	1900	1200	1700				
Differences HOWTH							
–0005	–0015	–0005	+0005	0·0	0·0	–0·3	0·0

SHELTER
Good, available at all tides and in almost any conditions. After a severe ENE'ly storm, expect a dangerous scend in the app chan. Marina dredged to 3m. No ent to FV basin for yachts. Caution: many moorings in E part of outer hbr. Inside the inner hbr keep strictly to chan to avoid drying shoals on either side and a substantial wavebreak. 4kn speed limit. There is a fair weather ⚓ in 2-3m at Carrigeen Bay, SW side of Irelnd's Eye.
NAVIGATION
WPT Howth SHM buoy, Fl G 5s, 53°23'·72N 06°03'·53W, 071°/251° from/to E pier lt, 0·27M. Beware Casana Rk 4ca S of the Nose of Howth, where Puck's Rks extend about 50m off it. Ireland's Eye is 0·6M N of hbr, with the Rowan Rks SE and SW from Thulla, marked by Rowan Rks ECM, and S Rowan SHM lt buoys.

The usual appr is S of Ireland's Eye; to the W of which Howth Sound has 2·4m min depth. Between the Nose and the hbr, watch out for lobster pots. Beware rks off both pier hds. Give way to FVs (constrained by draft) in the Sound and hbr entrance.
LIGHTS AND MARKS
E pier lt, Fl (2) WR 7·5s 13m 12/9M; W 256°–295°, R elsewhere. W sector leads safely to NE pierhead which should be rounded 50m off. Ent to FV Basin has QR and Fl G 3s. The chan to marina is unlit, but marked by R and G floating perches with W reflective tops; these are reported to be difficult to discern at night.
Baily Lt Ho, Fl 15s 41m 26M, is 1·5M S of Nose of Howth.
RADIO TELEPHONE
Hr Mr VHF Ch 16 08 (Mon-Fri 0700–2300LT; Sat/Sun occas). Marina Ch M 80 (H24).
TELEPHONE (Dial code 01)
Hr Mr 832 2252; MRCC 6620922/3; ⌗ 8746571; Police 832 2806; Dr 832 3191; Ⓗ 837 7755.
FACILITIES
Howth YC Marina (300 inc Ⓥ) ☎ 839 2777, ⏢ 839 2430, £IR10.50, D (H24), P (cans), FW, Slip, C (7 ton), AC, ◙;
Howth YC ☎ 832 2141, Scrubbing posts <20m LOA, R (☎ 839 2100), Bar, ◙;
Services: Gas, Kos, ME, SM, CH, EI, Ⓔ.
Town EC Sat; P & D (cans), ✉, Ⓑ, ◙, ⇌, ✈ (Dublin).

HOWTH

DUBLIN/DUN LAOGHAIRE 10-12-10

Dun Laoghaire (Port ent) 53°18'·16N 06°07'·68W
Rtgs: 1-2-1 (Dun Laoghaire); 1-4-3 (Dublin)

CHARTS

AC 1447, 1415, 1468; Imray C61, C62; Irish OS 50

TIDES

+0042 Dover; ML 2·4; Duration 0640; Zone 0 (UT)

Standard Port DUBLIN (NORTH WALL) (→)

Times				Height (metres)			
High Water		Low Water		MHWS	MHWN	MLWN	MLWS
0000	0700	0000	0500	4·1	3·4	1·5	0·7
1200	1900	1200	1700				

Differences DUBLIN BAR and DUN LAOGHAIRE
| –0006 | –0001 | –0002 | –0003 | 0·0 | 0·0 | 0·0 | +0·1 |

GREYSTONES (53°09'N 06°04'W)
| –0008 | –0008 | –0008 | –0008 | –0·5 | –0·4 | | No data |

Dublin is a Standard Port; daily predictions are overleaf.

SHELTER

Dun Laoghaire, one of the main yachting centres for Dublin, is accessible H24, but is open to NE swell and ⚓ holding is poor. No ⚓ in areas marked 'moorings' and in fairways. All YCs have pontoons, but only for fuel/stores/ water. Yachts may find AB on the inshore side of Traders Wharf (priority to FVs). In bad conditions, unless YCs can offer sheltered moorings (the best option), yachts should go to **Howth** (7·5M NNE).

Dublin Port is a commercial port which, due to security risks and lift-bridge/road tfc delays, does not encourage yachts, unless too big for Dun Laoghaire. For clearance to enter call *Dublin Port Radio* Ch 12. Do not impede large vessels and avoid the TSS and fairway which start at Dublin Bay SWM lt buoy, Mo (A) 10s, 2·75M ESE of Dublin Port (see NAVIGATION). Expect to berth at the inner end of S Quay, near Poolbeg YC (see FACILITIES).

NAVIGATION

WPT 53°18'·40N 06°07'·00W, 060°/240° from/to ent, 0·47M. Keep clear of the many coasters and ferries, not least the HSS catamarans (41kn), which turn off St Michael's Pier. Beware drying rks approx 10m off the E Pierhead. **TSS**: Dublin Bay SWM buoy (53°19'·90N 06°04'·58W, 2·5M NE of Dun Laoghaire) is the centre of a circular TSS, radius 2·3ca. Ships bound to/from Dublin Port follow this TSS in an anti-clockwise direction; yachts to keep clear. Two more TSS, to the N and S of Burford Bank, are intended for 1997, together with a VTS and commercial ⚓ berths.

LIGHTS AND MARKS

There are no ldg lts/marks. On W Pier 2 △ bns in transit define the E edge of the triangular anchorage. Close to ☆ Q on St Michael's Pier, a ☆ QY = Ferries under way; small craft keep clear of No 1 Fairway (which extends 600m to seaward of the pier heads). Other lts as chartlet.

RADIO TELEPHONE

Call *Dun Laoghaire Hbr* VHF Ch **14** 16 (H24). YCs Ch M. At Dublin: call *Dublin Port Radio* Ch **12** 13 14 16 (H24). Lifting bridge (call *Eastlink*) Ch 12 13. Poolbeg YC Ch 12 16. Dublin Coast Radio Stn 16 67 83.

TELEPHONE (Dial code 01)

Hr Mr Dun Laoghaire 2801130; Hr Mr Dublin 8555507; MRCC 6620922/3; Coast/Cliff Rescue Service 2803900; ⌗ 2803992; Weather 1550 123855; Police (Dun Laoghaire) 2801285, (Dublin) 6778141; Dr 2859244; Ⓗ 2806901.

FACILITIES

No overnight charges at Dun Laoghaire.
Yacht Clubs: National YC ☎ 2805725, Slip, M, L, C (7 ton), FW, D, R, Bar; **Royal St. George YC** ☎ 2801811, Slip, M, D, L, FW, C (5 ton), R, Bar; **Royal Irish YC** ☎ 2809452, Slip, M, D, L, FW, C (5 ton), R, Bar; **Dun Laoghaire Motor YC** ☎ 2801371, Slip, FW, AB, Bar; V within ½M of all YCs. At Dublin: **Poolbeg YC** ☎ 6604681, M, AB only for 20ft max LOA, Slip, Bar, FW. **Services** FW, C (5 ton), AB, SM, CH, ACA, Sh, Ⓔ, El, Gas. **City** All needs, ⇌, ✈.

Sketch showing relative positions of Dublin Docks and Dun Laoghaire

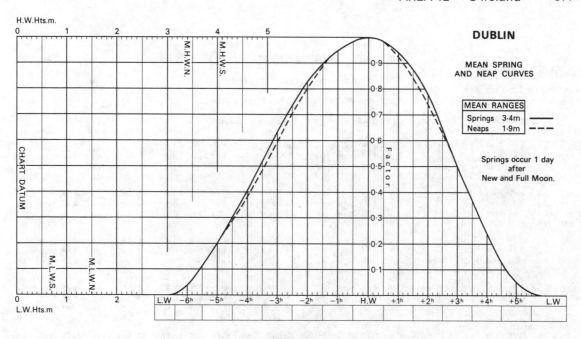

H.W.Hts.m.

DUBLIN

**MEAN SPRING
AND NEAP CURVES**

MEAN RANGES	
Springs	3·4m
Neaps	1·9m

Springs occur 1 day
after
New and Full Moon.

06°07'·80W

Two Bns

Fl(3)G7·5s11m7M

Fl(2)R10s16m17M
Horn30s

Yacht
Moorings

Fairway No 2

Fairway
No 1

Anchorage

Anemometer

Boyd Obelisk

Yacht
Moorings

West Pier

2FR(vert)

Yacht Moorings

White

Q6m3M
andQY
HrMr

St Michael's Pier

Inner
Moorings
Harbour

Hand
Cranes

Slip

Traders Wharf

Old Quay

Steps

Old Harbour
Moorings

Turret

Irish Lights
Depot

Slip

Fl R3s9m1M

Bandstand

East Pier

Dun Laoghaire
Motor Yacht Club

Royal Irish
Yacht Club

Car Ferry
Terminal

Carlisle Pier

Moorings

East
Pier
Berth

DUN LAOGHAIRE

Railway
Stn.

Royal
St George
Yacht
Club

Moorings

Clock Tower
(disused)

Clock
Tower

St Michael's
Hosp

National
Yacht Club

Slip

Boat
Ho

Spire
St Michael's
Church

Spire
Mariners
Church

06°08'·00W

metres
cables

500

2

Depths in metres

07'·5

IRELAND – DUBLIN (NORTH WALL)

LAT 53°21′N   LONG   6°13′W

TIMES AND HEIGHTS OF HIGH AND LOW WATERS

YEAR **1998**

TIME ZONE (UT)
For Summer Time add ONE hour in non-shaded areas

JANUARY

Day	Time	m	Day	Time	m
1 TH	0053 / 0624 / 1307 / 1853	4.0 / 0.7 / 4.3 / 0.5	16 F	0130 / 0709 / 1348 / 1943	3.8 / 0.9 / 4.0 / 0.7
2 F	0140 / 0710 / 1355 / 1943	4.0 / 0.8 / 4.3 / 0.6	17 SA	0209 / 0747 / 1427 / 2024	3.7 / 1.0 / 3.9 / 0.9
3 SA	0230 / 0801 / 1446 / 2037	4.0 / 0.9 / 4.2 / 0.6	18 SU	0250 / 0828 / 1509 / 2107	3.6 / 1.1 / 3.8 / 1.0
4 SU	0325 / 0858 / 1540 / 2135	3.9 / 1.0 / 4.1 / 0.8	19 M	0335 / 0914 / 1554 / 2153	3.5 / 1.3 / 3.6 / 1.2
5 M	0424 / 1000 / 1638 / 2238	3.8 / 1.1 / 4.0 / 0.9	20 TU	0425 / 1007 / 1644 / 2245	3.4 / 1.5 / 3.5 / 1.3
6 TU	0530 / 1107 / 1743 / 2346	3.7 / 1.2 / 3.9 / 1.0	21 W	0524 / 1109 / 1746 / 2344	3.3 / 1.6 / 3.3 / 1.4
7 W	0641 / 1218 / 1855	3.7 / 1.3 / 3.8	22 TH	0635 / 1215 / 1859	3.3 / 1.7 / 3.3
8 TH	0058 / 0750 / 1329 / 2007	1.1 / 3.7 / 1.3 / 3.8	23 F	0046 / 0740 / 1320 / 2005	1.5 / 3.3 / 1.6 / 3.3
9 F	0208 / 0854 / 1435 / 2114	1.1 / 3.8 / 1.2 / 3.8	24 SA	0148 / 0836 / 1418 / 2101	1.4 / 3.5 / 1.4 / 3.5
10 SA	0308 / 0952 / 1533 / 2213	1.0 / 3.9 / 1.0 / 3.9	25 SU	0242 / 0924 / 1507 / 2149	1.3 / 3.7 / 1.2 / 3.6
11 SU	0400 / 1043 / 1623 / 2304	0.9 / 4.0 / 0.8 / 3.9	26 M	0327 / 1006 / 1550 / 2232	1.0 / 3.9 / 0.9 / 3.8
12 M O	0444 / 1126 / 1707 / 2346	0.9 / 4.1 / 0.7 / 3.9	27 TU	0407 / 1045 / 1630 / 2312	0.8 / 4.1 / 0.7 / 4.0
13 TU	0523 / 1203 / 1748	0.8 / 4.1 / 0.7	28 W ●	0446 / 1124 / 1710 / 2353	0.6 / 4.2 / 0.5 / 4.1
14 W	0021 / 0558 / 1237 / 1826	3.9 / 0.8 / 4.1 / 0.6	29 TH	0526 / 1205 / 1752	0.5 / 4.2 / 0.3
15 TH	0054 / 0633 / 1311 / 1904	3.8 / 0.9 / 4.1 / 0.7	30 F	0035 / 0607 / 1248 / 1836	4.1 / 0.5 / 4.4 / 0.3
			31 SA	0120 / 0652 / 1335 / 1924	4.1 / 0.5 / 4.4 / 0.3

FEBRUARY

Day	Time	m	Day	Time	m
1 SU	0207 / 0741 / 1424 / 2015	4.1 / 0.6 / 4.3 / 0.4	16 M	0211 / 0748 / 1433 / 2020	3.7 / 0.9 / 3.8 / 0.9
2 M	0259 / 0834 / 1517 / 2110	4.0 / 0.7 / 4.2 / 0.6	17 TU	0250 / 0825 / 1514 / 2058	3.6 / 1.0 / 3.7 / 1.0
3 TU	0355 / 0933 / 1614 / 2209	3.8 / 0.9 / 4.0 / 0.8	18 W	0333 / 0908 / 1559 / 2142	3.5 / 1.2 / 3.5 / 1.2
4 W	0458 / 1038 / 1720 / 2315	3.7 / 1.1 / 3.8 / 1.1	19 TH	0423 / 0958 / 1651 / 2237	3.4 / 1.4 / 3.3 / 1.4
5 TH	0611 / 1150 / 1836	3.6 / 1.2 / 3.7	20 F	0522 / 1106 / 1758 / 2350	3.2 / 1.5 / 3.2 / 1.5
6 F	0029 / 0725 / 1307 / 1952	1.2 / 3.6 / 1.3 / 3.6	21 SA	0638 / 1228 / 1920	3.2 / 1.5 / 3.2
7 SA	0149 / 0834 / 1422 / 2104	1.3 / 3.7 / 1.2 / 3.6	22 SU	0104 / 0752 / 1339 / 2029	1.5 / 3.3 / 1.4 / 3.3
8 SU	0257 / 0937 / 1524 / 2206	1.2 / 3.8 / 1.0 / 3.7	23 M	0209 / 0850 / 1438 / 2124	1.3 / 3.5 / 1.1 / 3.5
9 M	0349 / 1031 / 1613 / 2257	1.1 / 3.9 / 0.9 / 3.7	24 TU	0303 / 0939 / 1527 / 2211	1.0 / 3.8 / 0.8 / 3.8
10 TU	0432 / 1115 / 1655 / 2337	0.9 / 4.0 / 0.7 / 3.8	25 W	0347 / 1023 / 1610 / 2252	0.8 / 4.0 / 0.5 / 4.0
11 W	0509 / 1151 / 1732	0.8 / 4.0 / 0.6	26 TH O	0428 / 1104 / 1652 / 2333	0.5 / 4.2 / 0.4 / 4.1
12 TH	0006 / 0542 / 1220 / 1806	3.8 / 0.8 / 4.0 / 0.6	27 F	0508 / 1145 / 1733	0.3 / 4.4 / 0.1
13 F	0032 / 0613 / 1248 / 1840	3.8 / 0.8 / 4.0 / 0.6	28 SA	0014 / 0549 / 1228 / 1816	4.2 / 0.2 / 4.4 / 0.0
14 SA	0101 / 0644 / 1320 / 1913	3.7 / 0.8 / 4.0 / 0.7			
15 SU	0135 / 0715 / 1355 / 1946	3.7 / 0.8 / 3.9 / 0.8			

MARCH

Day	Time	m	Day	Time	m
1 SU	0057 / 0633 / 1314 / 1902	4.2 / 0.2 / 4.4 / 0.1	16 M	0103 / 0645 / 1326 / 1908	3.8 / 0.7 / 3.8 / 0.7
2 M	0143 / 0720 / 1403 / 1951	4.1 / 0.3 / 4.3 / 0.3	17 TU	0137 / 0715 / 1403 / 1941	3.7 / 0.8 / 3.8 / 0.8
3 TU	0232 / 0812 / 1455 / 2044	4.0 / 0.5 / 4.1 / 0.6	18 W	0215 / 0751 / 1443 / 2019	3.7 / 0.8 / 3.7 / 0.9
4 W	0325 / 0910 / 1553 / 2142	3.8 / 0.7 / 3.9 / 0.9	19 TH	0258 / 0833 / 1528 / 2102	3.6 / 1.0 / 3.5 / 1.1
5 TH	0428 / 1014 / 1701 / 2245	3.7 / 1.0 / 3.7 / 1.2	20 F	0345 / 0921 / 1618 / 2154	3.4 / 1.1 / 3.3 / 1.3
6 F	0542 / 1124 / 1819 / 2359	3.5 / 1.2 / 3.5 / 1.4	21 SA	0439 / 1018 / 1720 / 2302	3.3 / 1.2 / 3.2 / 1.4
7 SA	0659 / 1245 / 1937	3.5 / 1.2 / 3.4	22 SU	0547 / 1144 / 1839	3.2 / 1.4 / 3.2
8 SU	0127 / 0812 / 1406 / 2051	1.4 / 3.5 / 1.2 / 3.5	23 M	0025 / 0707 / 1304 / 1956	1.5 / 3.3 / 1.2 / 3.3
9 M	0241 / 0919 / 1508 / 2154	1.3 / 3.7 / 1.0 / 3.6	24 TU	0138 / 0815 / 1410 / 2057	1.3 / 3.7 / 1.0 / 3.5
10 TU	0333 / 1013 / 1555 / 2242	1.2 / 3.8 / 0.8 / 3.6	25 W	0237 / 0911 / 1503 / 2147	1.0 / 3.7 / 0.6 / 3.8
11 W	0414 / 1057 / 1635 / 2319	1.0 / 3.9 / 0.7 / 3.7	26 TH	0325 / 0958 / 1549 / 2230	0.8 / 4.0 / 0.3 / 4.0
12 TH	0450 / 1131 / 1710 / 2345	0.8 / 3.9 / 0.6 / 3.7	27 F	0408 / 1042 / 1632 / 2312	0.4 / 4.2 / 0.1 / 4.1
13 F O	0522 / 1158 / 1742	0.8 / 3.9 / 0.6	28 SA ●	0449 / 1125 / 1714 / 2352	0.2 / 4.3 / 0.0 / 4.1
14 SA	0007 / 0551 / 1225 / 1812	3.7 / 0.7 / 3.9 / 0.6	29 SU	0531 / 1209 / 1757	0.1 / 4.4 / 0.0
15 SU	0033 / 0618 / 1253 / 1840	3.7 / 0.7 / 3.9 / 0.7	30 M	0034 / 0614 / 1255 / 1841	4.2 / 0.1 / 4.4 / 0.1
			31 TU	0119 / 0702 / 1345 / 1929	4.1 / 0.2 / 4.2 / 0.3

APRIL

Day	Time	m	Day	Time	m
1 W	0208 / 0754 / 1438 / 2021	4.0 / 0.4 / 4.0 / 0.6	16 TH	0148 / 0726 / 1419 / 1950	3.8 / 0.8 / 3.7 / 0.9
2 TH	0300 / 0851 / 1536 / 2117	3.8 / 0.6 / 3.8 / 0.9	17 F	0231 / 0809 / 1505 / 2036	3.7 / 0.9 / 3.5 / 1.0
3 F	0401 / 0953 / 1644 / 2218	3.7 / 0.8 / 3.6 / 1.2	18 SA	0319 / 0900 / 1556 / 2129	3.6 / 1.0 / 3.4 / 1.2
4 SA	0514 / 1101 / 1759 / 2328	3.5 / 1.0 / 3.4 / 1.4	19 SU	0412 / 1001 / 1656 / 2234	3.4 / 1.1 / 3.3 / 1.3
5 SU	0630 / 1218 / 1915	3.4 / 1.2 / 3.3	20 M	0515 / 1116 / 1808 / 2351	3.4 / 1.2 / 3.3 / 1.4
6 M	0053 / 0743 / 1339 / 2028	1.5 / 3.5 / 1.1 / 3.4	21 TU	0629 / 1233 / 1924	3.4 / 1.1 / 3.4
7 TU	0212 / 0850 / 1441 / 2130	1.4 / 3.6 / 1.0 / 3.5	22 W	0105 / 0739 / 1341 / 2027	1.3 / 3.5 / 0.8 / 3.5
8 W	0307 / 0946 / 1529 / 2216	1.2 / 3.7 / 0.9 / 3.6	23 TH	0207 / 0840 / 1438 / 2121	1.0 / 3.8 / 0.6 / 3.8
9 TH	0349 / 1029 / 1608 / 2251	1.0 / 3.8 / 0.7 / 3.6	24 F	0300 / 0933 / 1527 / 2207	0.7 / 4.0 / 0.3 / 4.0
10 F	0425 / 1104 / 1643 / 2317	0.9 / 3.8 / 0.7 / 3.7	25 SA	0346 / 1021 / 1612 / 2251	0.5 / 4.2 / 0.1 / 4.1
11 SA O	0457 / 1133 / 1714 / 2341	0.8 / 3.8 / 0.7 / 3.7	26 SU ●	0431 / 1107 / 1656 / 2333	0.3 / 4.3 / 0.1 / 4.2
12 SU	0527 / 1200 / 1743	0.7 / 3.8 / 0.7	27 M	0514 / 1153 / 1739	0.2 / 4.3 / 0.1
13 M	0005 / 0552 / 1228 / 1808	3.8 / 0.7 / 3.8 / 0.7	28 TU	0016 / 0559 / 1241 / 1823	4.2 / 0.2 / 4.3 / 0.2
14 TU	0034 / 0617 / 1300 / 1836	3.8 / 0.7 / 3.8 / 0.7	29 W	0100 / 0647 / 1330 / 1909	4.1 / 0.2 / 4.1 / 0.4
15 W	0108 / 0648 / 1338 / 1910	3.8 / 0.7 / 3.7 / 0.8	30 TH	0148 / 0739 / 1423 / 2000	4.0 / 0.4 / 4.0 / 0.7

Chart Datum: 0·20 metres above Ordnance Datum (Dublin)

IRELAND – DUBLIN (NORTH WALL)

LAT 53°21′N   LONG 6°13′W

TIMES AND HEIGHTS OF HIGH AND LOW WATERS   YEAR **1998**

TIME ZONE (UT)
For Summer Time add ONE hour in non-shaded areas

MAY

Time	m		Time	m
1 F 0240 / 0835 / 1520 / 2054	3.9 / 0.6 / 3.8 / 1.0	**16** SA 0210 / 0753 / 1446 / 2016	3.8 / 0.8 / 3.6 / 1.0	
2 SA 0338 / 0934 / 1623 / 2152	3.7 / 0.8 / 3.5 / 1.2	**17** SU 0259 / 0846 / 1538 / 2111	3.7 / 0.9 / 3.6 / 1.1	
3 SU 0445 / 1036 / 1732 / 2255	3.6 / 0.8 / 3.4 / 1.4	**18** M 0352 / 0946 / 1636 / 2213	3.7 / 1.0 / 3.5 / 1.2	
4 M 0557 / 1145 / 1842	3.5 / 1.1 / 3.3	**19** TU 0452 / 1054 / 1742 / 2322	3.6 / 1.0 / 3.4 / 1.3	
5 TU 0008 / 0706 / 1259 / 1950	1.5 / 3.5 / 1.1 / 3.3	**20** W 0558 / 1205 / 1852	3.6 / 0.9 / 3.5	
6 W 0127 / 0811 / 1404 / 2050	1.5 / 3.5 / 1.1 / 3.4	**21** TH 0032 / 0707 / 1313 / 1956	1.2 / 3.7 / 0.8 / 3.6	
7 TH 0229 / 0906 / 1455 / 2136	1.3 / 3.6 / 1.0 / 3.5	**22** F 0137 / 0810 / 1412 / 2054	1.0 / 3.8 / 0.6 / 3.8	
8 F 0316 / 0952 / 1536 / 2213	1.2 / 3.7 / 0.9 / 3.6	**23** SA 0234 / 0909 / 1506 / 2146	0.8 / 4.0 / 0.5 / 4.0	
9 SA 0354 / 1030 / 1612 / 2245	1.0 / 3.7 / 0.8 / 3.7	**24** SU 0326 / 1002 / 1555 / 2233	0.6 / 4.1 / 0.3 / 4.1	
10 SU 0428 / 1104 / 1643 / 2313	0.9 / 3.8 / 0.8 / 3.7	**25** M 0414 / 1052 / 1640 / ●2318	0.5 / 4.2 / 0.3 / 4.1	
11 M O 0459 / 1134 / 1712 / 2339	0.9 / 3.8 / 0.8 / 3.8	**26** TU 0501 / 1141 / 1724	0.4 / 4.2 / 0.3	
12 TU 0526 / 1204 / 1739	0.8 / 3.8 / 0.8	**27** W 0001 / 0547 / 1228 / 1807	4.2 / 0.3 / 4.2 / 0.4	
13 W 0008 / 0553 / 1238 / 1809	3.8 / 0.8 / 3.8 / 0.8	**28** TH 0045 / 0635 / 1316 / 1852	4.1 / 0.4 / 4.0 / 0.6	
14 TH 0044 / 0626 / 1316 / 1845	3.9 / 0.8 / 3.7 / 0.8	**29** F 0131 / 0725 / 1406 / 1939	4.1 / 0.5 / 3.9 / 0.8	
15 F 0125 / 0706 / 1359 / 1928	3.9 / 0.8 / 3.7 / 0.9	**30** SA 0220 / 0817 / 1459 / 2030	4.0 / 0.6 / 3.7 / 1.0	
		31 SU 0314 / 0912 / 1555 / 2124	3.8 / 0.8 / 3.6 / 1.2	

JUNE

Time	m		Time	m
1 M 0413 / 1009 / 1656 / 2221	3.7 / 0.9 / 3.4 / 1.4	**16** TU 0333 / 0930 / 1616 / 2150	3.9 / 0.8 / 3.7 / 1.1	
2 TU 0517 / 1108 / 1800 / 2323	3.6 / 1.1 / 3.3 / 1.5	**17** W 0430 / 1033 / 1717 / 2254	3.9 / 0.8 / 3.6 / 1.2	
3 W 0623 / 1210 / 1902	3.5 / 1.1 / 3.3	**18** TH 0532 / 1139 / 1823	3.8 / 0.9 / 3.6	
4 TH 0029 / 0724 / 1314 / 1959	1.5 / 3.5 / 1.2 / 3.4	**19** F 0001 / 0638 / 1245 / 1929	1.2 / 3.8 / 0.8 / 3.7	
5 F 0137 / 0821 / 1411 / 2049	1.5 / 3.5 / 1.1 / 3.5	**20** SA 0108 / 0746 / 1349 / 2031	1.1 / 3.8 / 0.8 / 3.8	
6 SA 0233 / 0911 / 1457 / 2133	1.3 / 3.6 / 1.1 / 3.6	**21** SU 0211 / 0850 / 1447 / 2128	1.0 / 3.9 / 0.7 / 3.9	
7 SU 0318 / 0954 / 1537 / 2211	1.2 / 3.7 / 1.0 / 3.7	**22** M 0310 / 0949 / 1541 / 2220	0.8 / 4.0 / 0.6 / 4.0	
8 M 0356 / 1033 / 1611 / 2244	1.1 / 3.7 / 0.9 / 3.8	**23** TU 0403 / 1043 / 1629 / 2306	0.7 / 4.1 / 0.6 / 4.1	
9 TU 0429 / 1108 / 1642 / 2314	1.0 / 3.7 / 0.9 / 3.9	**24** W 0452 / 1132 / 1713 / ●2349	0.6 / 4.1 / 0.6 / 4.1	
10 W 0459 / 1142 / 1713 / O2346	0.9 / 3.8 / 0.8 / 3.9	**25** TH 0538 / 1217 / 1754	0.5 / 4.0 / 0.5	
11 TH 0531 / 1217 / 1747	0.8 / 3.8 / 0.8	**26** F 0030 / 0623 / 1301 / 1835	4.1 / 0.5 / 3.9 / 0.8	
12 F 0023 / 0607 / 1257 / 1825	4.0 / 0.8 / 3.8 / 0.8	**27** SA 0112 / 0709 / 1345 / 1917	4.1 / 0.6 / 3.8 / 0.8	
13 SA 0105 / 0650 / 1341 / 1909	4.0 / 0.7 / 3.8 / 0.9	**28** SU 0156 / 0756 / 1431 / 2002	4.0 / 0.6 / 3.7 / 1.0	
14 SU 0151 / 0738 / 1429 / 1957	4.0 / 0.7 / 3.8 / 0.9	**29** M 0243 / 0845 / 1519 / 2051	3.9 / 0.8 / 3.6 / 1.1	
15 M 0240 / 0831 / 1520 / 2051	4.0 / 0.8 / 3.7 / 1.0	**30** TU 0333 / 0935 / 1611 / 2143	3.8 / 0.9 / 3.5 / 1.3	

JULY

Time	m		Time	m
1 W 0428 / 1028 / 1708 / 2240	3.6 / 1.1 / 3.4 / 1.4	**16** TH 0406 / 1008 / 1650 / 2227	4.0 / 0.8 / 3.7 / 1.1	
2 TH 0530 / 1122 / 1809 / 2339	3.5 / 1.2 / 3.3 / 1.5	**17** F 0507 / 1112 / 1755 / 2334	3.9 / 0.9 / 3.7 / 1.2	
3 F 0635 / 1220 / 1909	3.4 / 1.3 / 3.3	**18** SA 0616 / 1219 / 1905	3.8 / 1.0 / 3.6	
4 SA 0041 / 0735 / 1318 / 2004	1.5 / 3.4 / 1.3 / 3.4	**19** SU 0044 / 0729 / 1328 / 2013	1.2 / 3.8 / 1.0 / 3.7	
5 SU 0143 / 0830 / 1413 / 2054	1.5 / 3.5 / 1.3 / 3.5	**20** M 0155 / 0839 / 1433 / 2115	1.1 / 3.8 / 1.0 / 3.8	
6 M 0237 / 0920 / 1500 / 2138	1.4 / 3.5 / 1.2 / 3.7	**21** TU 0259 / 0943 / 1530 / 2211	1.0 / 3.9 / 0.9 / 3.9	
7 TU 0322 / 1004 / 1541 / 2216	1.2 / 3.6 / 1.0 / 3.8	**22** W 0356 / 1038 / 1619 / 2258	0.8 / 3.9 / 0.8 / 4.0	
8 W 0400 / 1044 / 1616 / 2251	1.1 / 3.7 / 0.9 / 3.9	**23** TH 0444 / 1126 / 1701 / ●2339	0.7 / 3.9 / 0.8 / 4.1	
9 TH 0435 / 1120 / 1651 / O2325	0.9 / 3.8 / 0.9 / 4.0	**24** F 0528 / 1207 / 1740	0.6 / 3.9 / 0.8	
10 F 0511 / 1158 / 1727	0.8 / 3.9 / 0.7	**25** SA 0015 / 0609 / 1243 / 1816	4.1 / 0.6 / 3.8 / 0.8	
11 SA 0003 / 0549 / 1238 / 1806	4.1 / 0.7 / 3.9 / 0.7	**26** SU 0050 / 0649 / 1318 / 1853	4.1 / 0.6 / 3.8 / 0.8	
12 SU 0045 / 0632 / 1321 / 1849	4.2 / 0.6 / 3.9 / 0.7	**27** M 0128 / 0729 / 1357 / 1932	4.0 / 0.7 / 3.7 / 0.9	
13 M 0130 / 0719 / 1408 / 1937	4.2 / 0.6 / 3.9 / 0.8	**28** TU 0208 / 0812 / 1438 / 2014	3.9 / 0.8 / 3.6 / 1.0	
14 TU 0219 / 0812 / 1458 / 2029	4.2 / 0.6 / 3.9 / 0.9	**29** W 0251 / 0856 / 1521 / 2100	3.8 / 0.9 / 3.5 / 1.2	
15 W 0310 / 0908 / 1551 / 2126	4.1 / 0.7 / 3.8 / 1.0	**30** TH 0337 / 0944 / 1609 / 2151	3.7 / 1.1 / 3.4 / 1.3	
		31 F 0428 / 1034 / 1704 / 2248	3.5 / 1.2 / 3.3 / 1.5	

AUGUST

Time	m		Time	m
1 SA 0532 / 1130 / 1811 / 2351	3.4 / 1.4 / 3.3 / 1.6	**16** SU 0558 / 1155 / 1845	3.7 / 1.2 / 3.6	
2 SU 0646 / 1229 / 1918	3.3 / 1.4 / 3.3	**17** M 0025 / 0718 / 1310 / 1957	1.3 / 3.6 / 1.2 / 3.7	
3 M 0056 / 0752 / 1329 / 2016	1.6 / 3.3 / 1.4 / 3.4	**18** TU 0144 / 0833 / 1421 / 2103	1.2 / 3.7 / 1.2 / 3.8	
4 TU 0158 / 0849 / 1425 / 2106	1.5 / 3.4 / 1.3 / 3.6	**19** W 0253 / 0938 / 1520 / 2201	1.1 / 3.7 / 1.1 / 3.9	
5 W 0251 / 0938 / 1512 / 2149	1.3 / 3.5 / 1.1 / 3.8	**20** TH 0348 / 1033 / 1607 / 2249	0.9 / 3.8 / 1.0 / 4.0	
6 TH 0335 / 1021 / 1552 / 2227	1.0 / 3.7 / 0.9 / 4.0	**21** F 0434 / 1118 / 1647 / 2327	0.7 / 3.8 / 0.9 / 4.1	
7 F 0413 / 1100 / 1629 / 2304	0.8 / 3.9 / 0.8 / 4.1	**22** SA 0513 / 1154 / 1723 / ●2357	0.6 / 3.8 / 0.8 / 4.1	
8 SA 0451 / 1137 / 1707 / O2342	0.6 / 4.0 / 0.6 / 4.2	**23** SU 0550 / 1221 / 1756	0.6 / 3.8 / 0.8	
9 SU 0530 / 1217 / 1746	0.4 / 4.0 / 0.5	**24** M 0026 / 0624 / 1250 / 1828	4.1 / 0.6 / 3.8 / 0.8	
10 M 0022 / 0612 / 1259 / 1828	4.3 / 0.3 / 4.1 / 0.5	**25** TU 0059 / 0659 / 1323 / 1901	4.0 / 0.7 / 3.7 / 0.9	
11 TU 0107 / 0658 / 1344 / 1914	4.3 / 0.3 / 4.0 / 0.6	**26** W 0134 / 0734 / 1359 / 1936	3.9 / 0.8 / 3.7 / 0.9	
12 W 0154 / 0748 / 1433 / 2004	4.3 / 0.4 / 4.0 / 0.7	**27** TH 0213 / 0812 / 1438 / 2014	3.8 / 0.9 / 3.6 / 1.1	
13 TH 0245 / 0842 / 1525 / 2100	4.2 / 0.6 / 3.9 / 0.8	**28** F 0255 / 0852 / 1520 / 2057	3.7 / 1.0 / 3.5 / 1.2	
14 F 0341 / 0941 / 1622 / 2202	4.1 / 0.8 / 3.8 / 1.0	**29** SA 0341 / 0939 / 1608 / 2147	3.5 / 1.2 / 3.4 / 1.4	
15 SA 0443 / 1045 / 1729 / 2310	3.9 / 1.0 / 3.6 / 1.2	**30** SU 0435 / 1035 / 1705 / 2255	3.4 / 1.4 / 3.3 / 1.6	
		31 M 0547 / 1142 / 1820	3.2 / 1.5 / 3.3	

12

Chart Datum: 0·20 metres above Ordnance Datum (Dublin)

IRELAND – DUBLIN (NORTH WALL)

LAT 53°21′N LONG 6°13′W

TIMES AND HEIGHTS OF HIGH AND LOW WATERS

YEAR **1998**

TIME ZONE (UT)
For Summer Time add ONE hour in non-shaded areas

SEPTEMBER

Day	Time	m	Day	Time	m
1 TU	0012 / 0712 / 1250 / 1935	1.6 / 3.2 / 1.5 / 3.3	16 W	0133 / 0824 / 1407 / 2048	1.2 / 3.6 / 1.4 / 3.8
2 W	0122 / 0819 / 1353 / 2034	1.5 / 3.3 / 1.4 / 3.5	17 TH	0241 / 0929 / 1505 / 2146	1.1 / 3.7 / 1.2 / 3.9
3 TH	0223 / 0913 / 1446 / 2121	1.3 / 3.5 / 1.2 / 3.8	18 F	0334 / 1022 / 1550 / 2233	0.9 / 3.8 / 1.1 / 4.0
4 F	0311 / 0958 / 1529 / 2203	1.0 / 3.7 / 0.9 / 4.0	19 SA	0416 / 1103 / 1629 / 2310	0.7 / 3.8 / 0.9 / 4.1
5 SA	0352 / 1038 / 1608 / 2241	0.6 / 3.9 / 0.7 / 4.2	20 SU	0453 / 1135 / 1703 / 2338 ●	0.7 / 3.8 / 0.8 / 4.0
6 SU O	0430 / 1116 / 1646 / 2320	0.4 / 4.1 / 0.5 / 4.4	21 M	0527 / 1158 / 1734	0.6 / 3.8 / 0.8
7 M	0510 / 1154 / 1726	0.2 / 4.2 / 0.3	22 TU	0003 / 0557 / 1223 / 1804	4.0 / 0.6 / 3.8 / 0.8
8 TU	0000 / 0550 / 1235 / 1807	4.4 / 0.1 / 4.2 / 0.3	23 W	0033 / 0627 / 1253 / 1833	4.0 / 0.7 / 3.8 / 0.8
9 W	0043 / 0635 / 1319 / 1852	4.5 / 0.2 / 4.2 / 0.4	24 TH	0106 / 0657 / 1326 / 1903	3.9 / 0.9 / 3.8 / 0.9
10 TH	0130 / 0722 / 1406 / 1942	4.4 / 0.3 / 4.1 / 0.5	25 F	0142 / 0729 / 1404 / 1938	3.8 / 0.9 / 3.8 / 1.0
11 F	0222 / 0816 / 1458 / 2038	4.2 / 0.6 / 3.9 / 0.8	26 SA	0223 / 0806 / 1445 / 2018	3.7 / 1.0 / 3.7 / 1.1
12 SA	0318 / 0914 / 1556 / 2141	4.0 / 0.9 / 3.8 / 1.0	27 SU	0308 / 0850 / 1531 / 2106	3.6 / 1.2 / 3.5 / 1.3
13 SU	0424 / 1019 / 1706 / 2251	3.8 / 1.1 / 3.6 / 1.2	28 M	0359 / 0943 / 1623 / 2206	3.4 / 1.4 / 3.4 / 1.5
14 M	0546 / 1131 / 1824	3.6 / 1.3 / 3.6	29 TU	0503 / 1054 / 1728 / 2328	3.2 / 1.6 / 3.3 / 1.5
15 TU	0009 / 0708 / 1252 / 1939	1.3 / 3.5 / 1.4 / 3.6	30 W	0630 / 1212 / 1848	3.2 / 1.6 / 3.3

OCTOBER

Day	Time	m	Day	Time	m
1 TH	0047 / 0747 / 1321 / 1956	1.4 / 3.3 / 1.5 / 3.5	16 F	0219 / 0909 / 1441 / 2121	1.1 / 3.7 / 1.3 / 3.9
2 F	0153 / 0845 / 1418 / 2050	1.2 / 3.5 / 1.2 / 3.8	17 SA	0310 / 1000 / 1527 / 2208	0.9 / 3.8 / 1.2 / 4.0
3 SA	0245 / 0932 / 1505 / 2136	0.9 / 3.8 / 0.9 / 4.0	18 SU	0352 / 1039 / 1606 / 2246	0.8 / 3.8 / 1.0 / 4.0
4 SU	0329 / 1014 / 1546 / 2217	0.5 / 3.9 / 0.6 / 4.3	19 M	0428 / 1109 / 1641 / 2315	0.7 / 3.9 / 0.9 / 4.0
5 M	0409 / 1053 / 1626 / 2258 O	0.3 / 4.2 / 0.4 / 4.4	20 TU	0501 / 1134 / 1712 / 2342 ●	0.7 / 3.9 / 0.9 / 4.0
6 TU	0449 / 1132 / 1706 / 2339	0.1 / 4.3 / 0.3 / 4.5	21 W	0531 / 1159 / 1742	0.7 / 3.9 / 0.9
7 W	0530 / 1212 / 1748	0.1 / 4.3 / 0.3	22 TH	0010 / 0558 / 1227 / 1809	3.9 / 0.8 / 3.9 / 0.9
8 TH	0023 / 0613 / 1256 / 1833	4.5 / 0.2 / 4.3 / 0.3	23 F	0042 / 0625 / 1259 / 1838	3.9 / 0.9 / 3.9 / 0.9
9 F	0111 / 0700 / 1344 / 1924	4.4 / 0.4 / 4.2 / 0.5	24 SA	0118 / 0656 / 1336 / 1912	3.8 / 0.9 / 3.9 / 1.0
10 SA	0203 / 0752 / 1436 / 2020	4.2 / 0.7 / 4.0 / 0.7	25 SU	0158 / 0733 / 1417 / 1953	3.7 / 1.1 / 3.8 / 1.1
11 SU	0302 / 0850 / 1534 / 2123	4.0 / 1.0 / 3.9 / 0.9	26 M	0243 / 0817 / 1503 / 2040	3.6 / 1.2 / 3.7 / 1.2
12 M	0411 / 0954 / 1644 / 2231	3.7 / 1.3 / 3.7 / 1.1	27 TU	0334 / 0954 / 1554 / 2138	3.5 / 1.4 / 3.6 / 1.3
13 TU	0531 / 1104 / 1800 / 2348	3.5 / 1.5 / 3.6 / 1.3	28 W	0435 / 1015 / 1653 / 2250	3.3 / 1.6 / 3.5 / 1.4
14 W	0650 / 1225 / 1914	3.5 / 1.6 / 3.7	29 TH	0550 / 1133 / 1803	3.3 / 1.6 / 3.5
15 TH	0111 / 0707 / 1343 / 2023	1.2 / 3.5 / 1.5 / 3.8	30 F	0010 / 0707 / 1246 / 1913	1.3 / 3.4 / 1.5 / 3.6
			31 SA	0119 / 0810 / 1346 / 2014	1.1 / 3.6 / 1.3 / 3.8

NOVEMBER

Day	Time	m	Day	Time	m
1 SU	0215 / 0902 / 1437 / 2106	0.8 / 3.8 / 1.0 / 4.0	16 M	0323 / 1005 / 1541 / 2215	1.0 / 3.8 / 1.2 / 3.9
2 M	0304 / 0948 / 1523 / 2153	0.5 / 4.1 / 0.7 / 4.3	17 TU	0401 / 1038 / 1617 / 2250	0.9 / 3.9 / 1.1 / 3.9
3 TU	0348 / 1030 / 1606 / 2238	0.3 / 4.2 / 0.5 / 4.4	18 W	0434 / 1108 / 1650 / 2321	0.9 / 3.9 / 1.0 / 3.9
4 W O	0430 / 1112 / 1649 / 2323	0.2 / 4.3 / 0.3 / 4.5	19 TH	0504 / 1136 / 1721 / 2351 ●	0.9 / 4.0 / 1.0 / 3.9
5 TH	0512 / 1154 / 1733	0.2 / 4.4 / 0.3	20 F	0532 / 1204 / 1749	0.9 / 4.0 / 1.0
6 F	0009 / 0555 / 1238 / 1819	4.4 / 0.3 / 4.3 / 0.3	21 SA	0022 / 0558 / 1235 / 1817	3.9 / 0.9 / 4.0 / 1.0
7 SA	0058 / 0642 / 1326 / 1910	4.3 / 0.5 / 4.2 / 0.5	22 SU	0058 / 0630 / 1313 / 1852	3.8 / 1.0 / 4.0 / 1.0
8 SU	0151 / 0732 / 1418 / 2005	4.1 / 0.8 / 4.1 / 0.7	23 M	0138 / 0709 / 1355 / 1933	3.8 / 1.1 / 3.9 / 1.0
9 M	0249 / 0827 / 1515 / 2105	3.9 / 1.0 / 4.0 / 0.9	24 TU	0224 / 0753 / 1441 / 2021	3.7 / 1.2 / 3.8 / 1.1
10 TU	0356 / 0928 / 1620 / 2209	3.7 / 1.3 / 3.8 / 1.1	25 W	0314 / 0845 / 1530 / 2116	3.6 / 1.3 / 3.8 / 1.2
11 W	0508 / 1034 / 1730 / 2318	3.5 / 1.5 / 3.7 / 1.2	26 TH	0411 / 0945 / 1625 / 2220	3.5 / 1.5 / 3.7 / 1.2
12 TH	0621 / 1147 / 1840	3.5 / 1.6 / 3.7	27 F	0515 / 1054 / 1727 / 2331	3.5 / 1.5 / 3.7 / 1.2
13 F	0034 / 0731 / 1305 / 1946	1.2 / 3.5 / 1.6 / 3.7	28 SA	0625 / 1205 / 1833	3.5 / 1.5 / 3.7
14 SA	0144 / 0834 / 1409 / 2045	1.1 / 3.6 / 1.5 / 3.8	29 SU	0041 / 0732 / 1311 / 1937	1.1 / 3.7 / 1.3 / 3.8
15 SU	0239 / 0925 / 1459 / 2135	1.1 / 3.7 / 1.3 / 3.9	30 M	0144 / 0830 / 1409 / 2036	0.9 / 3.8 / 1.1 / 4.0

DECEMBER

Day	Time	m	Day	Time	m
1 TU	0239 / 0922 / 1501 / 2131	0.7 / 4.0 / 0.9 / 4.2	16 W	0331 / 1004 / 1552 / 2222	1.1 / 3.8 / 1.2 / 3.8
2 W	0329 / 1010 / 1550 / 2223	0.5 / 4.2 / 0.6 / 4.3	17 TH	0407 / 1040 / 1628 / 2259	1.1 / 3.9 / 1.1 / 3.8
3 TH	0415 / 1056 / 1637 / 2312 O	0.4 / 4.3 / 0.5 / 4.3	18 F	0439 / 1113 / 1659 / 2332 ●	1.0 / 4.0 / 1.1 / 3.8
4 F	0459 / 1140 / 1723	0.4 / 4.3 / 0.4	19 SA	0508 / 1143 / 1729	1.0 / 4.0 / 1.0
5 SA	0000 / 0542 / 1225 / 1810	4.3 / 0.5 / 4.3 / 0.4	20 SU	0004 / 0537 / 1215 / 1759	3.8 / 1.0 / 4.0 / 0.9
6 SU	0049 / 0627 / 1312 / 1859	4.2 / 0.6 / 4.3 / 0.5	21 M	0040 / 0610 / 1252 / 1834	3.8 / 1.0 / 4.1 / 0.9
7 M	0139 / 0714 / 1401 / 1950	4.1 / 0.8 / 4.2 / 0.6	22 TU	0120 / 0649 / 1334 / 1916	3.8 / 1.0 / 4.0 / 0.9
8 TU	0233 / 0805 / 1454 / 2044	3.9 / 1.0 / 4.1 / 0.8	23 W	0204 / 0732 / 1419 / 2003	3.8 / 1.0 / 4.0 / 0.9
9 W	0331 / 0900 / 1551 / 2141	3.7 / 1.3 / 3.9 / 1.0	24 TH	0252 / 0822 / 1508 / 2054	3.8 / 1.1 / 4.0 / 0.9
10 TH	0434 / 0959 / 1652 / 2241	3.6 / 1.5 / 3.8 / 1.1	25 F	0345 / 0917 / 1559 / 2151	3.7 / 1.2 / 3.9 / 1.0
11 F	0539 / 1103 / 1757 / 2345	3.5 / 1.6 / 3.7 / 1.2	26 SA	0443 / 1018 / 1656 / 2255	3.6 / 1.3 / 3.9 / 1.0
12 SA	0644 / 1212 / 1900	3.4 / 1.6 / 3.6	27 SU	0547 / 1126 / 1758	3.6 / 1.3 / 3.8
13 SU	0054 / 0744 / 1323 / 2000	1.3 / 3.5 / 1.6 / 3.6	28 M	0004 / 0654 / 1236 / 1905	1.0 / 3.7 / 1.3 / 3.8
14 M	0158 / 0838 / 1424 / 2054	1.3 / 3.6 / 1.5 / 3.7	29 TU	0113 / 0800 / 1342 / 2012	0.9 / 3.8 / 1.2 / 3.9
15 TU	0249 / 0924 / 1512 / 2141	1.2 / 3.7 / 1.4 / 3.7	30 W	0217 / 0900 / 1443 / 2116	0.9 / 3.9 / 1.0 / 4.0
			31 TH	0314 / 0955 / 1538 / 2213	0.8 / 4.1 / 0.8 / 4.1

Chart Datum: 0·20 metres above Ordnance Datum (Dublin)

WICKLOW   10-12-11

Wicklow 52°58'·98N 06°02'·70W   Rtg 1-4-1

CHARTS
AC 633, 1468; Imray C61; Irish OS 56

TIDES
−0010 Dover; ML 1·7; Duration 0640; Zone 0 (UT)

Standard Port DUBLIN (NORTH WALL) (←—)

Times				Height (metres)			
High Water		Low Water		MHWS	MHWN	MLWN	MLWS
0000	0700	0000	0500	4·1	3·4	1·5	0·7
1200	1900	1200	1700				
Differences WICKLOW							
−0019	−0019	−0024	−0026	−1·4	−1·1	−0·4	0·0

SHELTER
Very safe, and access H24. Outer hbr is open to NE winds which cause a swell. Moorings in NW of hbr belong to YC. Berths on E Pier (2·5m) are convenient and now well fendered; W pier is not recommended. Inner hbr (river) gives excellent shelter in 2·5m on New Quay (S), which is used by FVs. Packet Quay (N) is for ships (2·5m), but may be used if none due. ⚓ in hbr is restricted by ships' turning circle and foul ground. A rk, 5m NNW of Packet Quay point, should be avoided by at least 10m at LWS.

NAVIGATION
WPT 52°59'·20N 06°01'·80W, 040°/220° from/to ent, 0·27M. Appr presents no difficulty; keep in the R sector of the E pier lt to avoid Planet Rk and Pogeen Rk.

LIGHTS AND MARKS
No ldg marks/lts; lts are as on the chartlet. ☆ Fl WG 10s on W Packet Quay head is vis G076°-256°, W256°-076°.

RADIO TELEPHONE
VHF Ch 12, **14**, 16. Wicklow SC Ch M 16.

TELEPHONE (Dial code 0404)
Hr Mr 67455; MRCC (01) 6620922; Coast/Cliff Rescue Service 67310; ⌗ 67222; Police 67107; Dr 67381.

FACILITIES
East Pier L, AB £IR5.50, plus good deals for longer stay; **New (S) Quay**, P & D (cans; bulk: see Hr Mr), L, FW, AB; **Wicklow SC ☎** 67526, Slip (HW), M, L, FW, Bar; **Services:** M, ME, El, C, Sh, AB, Kos, Gaz.
Town EC Thurs; CH, V, R, Bar, ⊠, Ⓑ, ⇌, ✈ (Dublin).

ARKLOW   10-12-12

Wicklow 52°47'·60N 06°08'·20W   Rtg 2-2-2

CHARTS
AC 633, 1468; Imray C61; Irish OS 62

TIDES
−0150 Dover; ML 1·0; Duration 0640; Zone 0 (UT)

Standard Port DUBLIN (NORTH WALL) (←—)

Times				Height (metres)			
High Water		Low Water		MHWS	MHWN	MLWN	MLWS
0000	0700	0000	0500	4·1	3·4	1·5	0·7
1200	1900	1200	1700				
Differences ARKLOW (Note small Range)							
−0315	−0201	−0140	−0134	−2·7	−2·2	−0·6	−0·1
COURTOWN							
−0328	−0242	−0158	−0138	−2·8	−2·4	−0·5	0·0

SHELTER
Good, access H24; but ent unsafe in strong NE to SE onshore winds, when seas break across the bar. Ent is difficult without power, due to blanking by piers. Night entry, see below. Once in Dock (3m), berth on SE wall in perfect shelter, but amidst FVs. One ⚓ in river off slipway and one AB for Ⓥ (1.4m) at YC quay, but Caution: keep to N side of river, due to obstructions up-river of Dock ent; take local advice. Good ⚓ in bay; avoid whelk pots. **Arklow Rock Hbr**, 1M S of Arklow, offers emergency ⚓ during SE winds off Roadstone Jetty (Oc R 10s 9m 9M). 2ca S of jetty a mole (QY) extends ENE for 3ca. Best ⚓ in 4m between jetty and mole, neither suitable for AB.

NAVIGATION
WPT 52°47'·60N 06°07'·50W, 090°/270° from/to ent, 0·40M. No navigational dangers, but beware ebb setting SE across hbr ent. The ent to the dock is 13·5m wide.

LIGHTS AND MARKS
No ldg lts/marks. 2 conspic factory chy's 2·5ca NW of piers. N pier L Fl G 7s 7m 10M, vis shore–287°. S pier Fl WR 6s 11m 13M; vis R shore–223°, W223°–350°, R350°–shore. **Caution:** The pier head lts are very difficult to see due to powerful orange flood lts near the root of both piers shining E/ENE onto the piers (to assist pilotage of departing commercial vessels). Best advice to visitors is to approach from the N in the R sector of the S pier lt, or enter by day.

RADIO TELEPHONE
VHF Ch 16 (HJ).

TELEPHONE (Dial code 0402)
Hr Mr 32426; MRCC (01) 6620922/3; Coast/Cliff Rescue Service 32430; RNLI 32001; ⌗ 32497; Police 2101; Dr 32421.

FACILITIES
Dock ☎ 32426, AB £9.75 for 1 week, FW, ME, El, C (1 ton), D (hose, as arranged), BH, Slip; **Arklow YC** (on NE bank, 2·6ca up-river of Dock) quay/jetty, M;
Services: BY, M, FW, ME, El, Sh, C (5 ton mobile), Kos.
Town EC Wed; CH, V, R, P & D (cans), Bar, ⊠, Ⓑ, ⇌, ✈ (Dublin).

12

WEXFORD   10-12-13
Wexford 52°20'·10N 06°27'·00W   Rtg 3-3-1

CHARTS
AC 1772, 1787; Imray C61; Irish OS 77

TIDES
–0450 Dover; ML 1·3; Duration 0630; Zone 0 (UT)

Standard Port COBH (→)

Times				Height (metres)			
High Water		Low Water		MHWS	MHWN	MLWN	MLWS
0500	1100	0500	1100	4·1	3·2	1·3	0·4
1700	2300	1700	2300				
Differences WEXFORD							
+0126	+0126	+0118	+0108	–2·1	–1·7	–0·3	+0·1

SHELTER
Safe sheltered ⚓ off town quays in 2·3m, but difficult ent; access approx HW±2. Do not attempt in strong E/S winds, when seas break on the bar. No commercial users, other than FVs. Some ⚓s are provided by WHBC, close N of Ballast Bank. Note: WIP 1996-1999 on new waterfront, to include a small marina.

NAVIGATION
WPT 52°20'·55N 06°20'·15W, Bar buoy, Iso Y, (pillar-shape, dayglow orange) about 8ca ESE of The Raven Pt. The Bar partly dries and shifts. Hbr Board has ceased to function, so in summer about 20 dayglow orange buoys are locally laid to mark the chan which has only 1m in places. The following directions are subject to considerable annual change: After 3rd PHM buoy, N of ruins (awash at HW), head NW. About ¼M off, keep along shore for approx 1M. After passing two W posts, head SW towards conspic chy, SE end of town. Turn stbd when 1ca off training wall. Within the trng walls, Ballast Bank (small islet) can be passed either side. There are no pilots; it is recommended that first-time visitors should seek **local advice from Mr J Sherwood ☎ 22875 (home 22713)**.

LIGHTS AND MARKS
Ldg marks and tracks on chartlet should be treated with great caution. Channel buoys are re-laid annually using a depth sounder to find best water.

RADIO TELEPHONE
Wexford Hbr BC VHF Ch 16 occas.

TELEPHONE (Dial code 053)
Hr Mr 33114; MRSC (01) 6620922/3; ⌗ 33116; Police 22333; Dr 31154; Ⓗ 42233.

FACILITIES
Wexford Quays AB (free), Slip, P, D, FW, ME, El, V, CH; **Wexford Hbr Boat Club** ☎ 22039, Slip, C (5 ton), Bar; **Town** ✉, Ⓑ, ⇌, ✈ (Waterford).

AGENTS WANTED

If you are interested in becoming our agent for any of the following ports, please write to: The Editor, Edington House, Trent, Sherborne, Dorset DT9 4SR, England – and get your free copy of the Almanac annually. You do not have to live in a port to be the agent, but at least a fairly regular visitor.

Great Yarmouth	St Gilles-Croix-de-Vie
Port Ellen (Islay)	Les Sables d'Olonne
Maryport	Ile d'Oléron
Workington	River Seudre
Holyhead	Anglet/Bayonne
Lough Swilly	St Jean-de-Luz
St Peter Port, Guernsey	Hendaye
Diélette	Grandcamp-Maisy
Portbail	Port-en-Bessin
Iles Chausey	Courseulles
St Malo/Dinard	Ouistreham/Caen
Le Legue/St Brieuc	Emden
Tréguier	Dornumer-Accumersiel
Lampaul	Langeoog
L'Aberildut	Bremerhaven
Le Palais (Belle Ile)	Büsum
Morbihan/Vannes	

ROSSLARE HARBOUR   10-12-14

Dublin 52°15'·30N 06°20'·90W   Rtg 2-4-2

CHARTS
AC 1772, 1787; Imray C61; Irish OS 77

TIDES
–0510 Dover; ML 1·1; Duration 0640; Zone 0 (UT)

Standard Port COBH (→)

Times				Height (metres)			
High Water		Low Water		MHWS	MHWN	MLWN	MLWS
0500	1100	0500	1100	4·1	3·2	1·3	0·4
1700	2300	1700	2300				
Differences ROSSLARE HARBOUR							
+0055	+0043	+0022	+0002	−2·2	−1·8	−0·5	−0·1

SHELTER
Useful passage shelter from SW'lies, but few facilities for yachts. Rosslare is a busy port with 160 ferry/high-speed catamaran (41kn) movements per week. In winds from WNW-NNE it is often uncomfortable and, if these winds freshen, dangerous; leave at once, via S Shear.
Yachts may berth on E wall of marshalling area (⏢ on the chartlet, 3·7m), or ⚓ approx 0·5M W of hbr. Small craft hbr has 1m max at LW, bottom is reported foul; mainly used by local fishermen.

NAVIGATION
WPT 52°14'·70N 06°15·60W, (abeam S Long SCM buoy, VQ (6)+L Fl 10s), 105°/285° from/to bkwtr lt, 2·92M. Main appr from E, S and W is via S Shear, buoyed/lit chan to S of Holden's Bed, a shoal of varying depth; the tide sets across the chan. From S, beware rks off Greenore Pt, and overfalls here and over The Baillies. From the N, appr via N Shear. The Tuskar TSS, Fig 10(7), is approx 8M ESE of the hbr.

LIGHTS AND MARKS
Water tr (R lt, 35m) is conspic 0·8M SSE of hbr ent.
Tuskar Rk, Q (2) 7·5s 33m 28M, is 5·8M SE of hbr ent.
Bkwtr lt, Oc WRG 5s 15m 13/10M, shows G098°-188° over Rosslare B; W188°-208° through N Shear; R208°-246° over N part of Holdens Bed and Long Bank; G246°-283° over S part of Holdens Bed; W283°-286° over S Shear, and R286°-320° over rks/shoals off Greenore Pt.
The Oc 3s 11/13m 3M ldg lts lead 146° to ferry berths. At N corner of marshalling area, Oc WR 1·7s 7m 4M, is vis Rshore-152°, W152°-205° (unintens 200°-205°), R205°-shore. Note: powerful floodlights in the port make identification of navigational lights difficult.

RADIO TELEPHONE
Call: *Rosslare Hbr* VHF Ch **12** (H24) before entering hbr.

TELEPHONE (Dial code 053)
Hr Mr 33864/33162; MRCC (01) 6620922/3; LB Lookout Stn 33205; ⌗ 33116; Police 22333; Dr 31154; Ⓗ 42233.

FACILITIES
Pier ☎ 33114, No fee, M, P, D, L, FW, ME, C, Divers;
Services: Kos, BY, ME, Sh, El, Slip, C. (Marina planned)
Town EC Thurs; V, R, Bar, ✉, Ⓑ, ⇌, ✈ (Dublin). Ferries to Fishguard, Pembroke Dock, Cherbourg, Le Havre and Roscoff.

12

ROSSLARE HARBOUR

KILMORE QUAY   10-12-15

Wexford 52°10'·25N 06°35'·15W   Rtg 2-3-1

CHARTS
AC 2740, 2049; Imray C61, C57; Irish OS 77

TIDES
−0535 Dover; ML No data; Duration 0605; Zone 0 (UT)

Standard Port COBH (→)

Times				Height (metres)			
High Water		Low Water		MHWS	MHWN	MLWN	MLWS
0500	1100	0500	1100	4·1	3·2	1·3	0·4
1700	2300	1700	2300				
Differences BAGINBUN HEAD							
+0003	+0003	−0008	−0008	−0·2	−0·1	+0·2	+0·2
GREAT SALTEE							
+0019	+0009	−0004	+0006	−0·3	−0·4	No data	
CARNSORE POINT							
+0029	+0019	−0002	+0008	−1·1	−1·0	No data	

SHELTER
Excellent in marina (3·0m depth), but hbr ent is exposed to SE'lies. FVs berth on W quay and E quay to the S of the marina.

NAVIGATION
WPT 52°09'·46N 06°35'·10W, 179°/359° from/to bkwtr lt, 0·75M. From the E, best appr initially is via Saltee Sound, thence N to WPT. Caution: In bad weather seas break on the Bohurs and The Bore, rks 2M E of Saltee Islands. Beware Goose Rk (2·6m) close W of Little Saltee and Murroch's Rk (2·1m) 6ca NW of Little Saltee.
St Patrick's Bridge, close S of the WPT, is used by FVs, but is narrow and carries only 2·4m. A PHM buoy, Fl R 6s 2M, and a SHM buoy, Fl G 6s 2M, are laid (Apr to mid-Sep) about 9ca S of hbr ent to mark this E/W passage; general direction of buoyage is E.
From the W, appr is clear but keep at least 5ca off Forlorn Pt to avoid Forlorn Rk (1·5m).
In the near appr, at night track 359° in G sector (354°-003°) of QRG lt. By day this lt (W post) in transit with conspic ✠ spire leads 354° to hbr ent, but be aware that this track is on E edge of G sector with shingle banks drying 0·6m close to stbd.
See below for proposed ldg lts/marks.

LIGHTS AND MARKS
W Quay lt QRG 7m 5M, R269°-354°, G354°-003°(9°), R003°-077°. Ldg lts approx 007°, both Oc 4s, were expected to be installed June 1997 on the shore close NNE of the hbr; by day W bns with R vert stripe. Two 20m high flood lt pylons on the E quay are conspic. A disused lt ship at the inner end of W quay is a museum; its lt housing is of no navigational significance. Ballyteige Castle (AC 2740) is hard to see and of no navigational use. Great (57m) and Little (35m) Saltee Islands lie respectively about 3M and 1·7M to SSW and S of hbr, separated by Saltee Sound.

RADIO TELEPHONE
VHF Ch M 16 (occas).

TELEPHONE (Dial code 053)
Hr Mr 29955; ⌗ 33741; MRCC (01) 6620922/3; Emergency/Dr/Police 999.

FACILITIES
Marina (35+20 Ⓥ) ☎/🗄 29955, £10, AC, FW, Slip, LB; **Village** Gaz, CH, ME, El, D (cans), P (cans) is 3M away, R, Bar, V, ✉, Ⓗ (Wexford 15M).

DUNMORE EAST 10-12-16

Waterford 52°08'·95N 06°59'·37W Rtg 2-3-1

CHARTS
AC 2046, 2049; Imray C61, C57; Irish OS 76
TIDES
–0535 Dover; ML 2·4; Duration 0605; Zone 0 (UT)

Standard Port COBH (→)

Times				Height (metres)			
High Water		Low Water		MHWS	MHWN	MLWN	MLWS
0500	1100	0500	1100	4·1	3·2	1·3	0·4
1700	2300	1700	2300				
Differences DUNMORE EAST							
+0008	+0003	0000	0000	+0·1	+0·1	+0·2	0·0

SHELTER
Very good, except in NE/SE winds. A useful passage port, but primarily a busy FV hbr, where yachts are scarcely tolerated; possible AB on W Wharf, clear of ice berth. Craft stay afloat in 2 - 3·4m at all times. No ⚓s, but ⚓ N of the hbr. (Marina plans are subject to delay).
NAVIGATION
WPT (see also 10·12·17) 52°08'·00N, 06°58'·00W, 137°/317° from/to bkwtr lt, 1·2M. There are no navigational dangers, but clear Hook Hd and Tower Race by 1·5M min; then alter course for hbr in R sector of E pier lt ho. From W, beware Falskirt Rk; by night steer for Hook Hd until in R sector of E pier lt, then alter to N. Enter under power.
LIGHTS AND MARKS
E Pier lt ho Fl WR8s 13m 17/13M, W225°-310°, R310°-004°. E bkwtr hd Fl R2s 6m 4M, vis 000°-310°. W wharf Fl G 2s 6m 4M, vis 165°–246°.
RADIO TELEPHONE
VHF Ch 14 16 (Pilot Station).
TELEPHONE (Dial code 051)
Hr Mr 83166; Pilot 83119; ⌗ 75391; MRCC (01) 6620922/3; Coast Life Saving Service 83115; Dr 83194.
FACILITIES
Hbr ☎ 83166, BH (230 ton), D, FW (on E pier); **Waterford Hbr SC** ☎ 83389, R, Bar; **Services:** Kos, CH. **Village** D, P (cans), Slip, R, Bar, V, ⑧, ✉, ≈ (Waterford), ✈ (Dublin).

WATERFORD 10-12-17

Waterford 52°15'·50N 07°06'·00W Rtg 1-3-2

CHARTS
AC 2046, 2049; Imray C57; Irish OS 76
TIDES
–0520 Dover; ML 2·4; Duration 0605; Zone 0 (UT)

Standard Port COBH (→)

Times				Height (metres)			
High Water		Low Water		MHWS	MHWN	MLWN	MLWS
0500	1100	0500	1100	4·1	3·2	1·3	0·4
1700	2300	1700	2300				
Differences WATERFORD							
+0057	+0057	+0046	+0046	+0·4	+0·3	–0·1	+0·1
CHEEK POINT							
+0022	+0020	+0020	+0020	+0·3	+0·2	+0·2	+0·1
KILMOKEA POINT							
+0026	+0022	+0020	+0020	+0·2	+0·1	+0·1	+0·1
NEW ROSS							
+0100	+0030	+0055	+0130	+0·3	+0·4	+0·3	+0·4

SHELTER
Very good, with many excellent ⚓s: 9M up the estuary, off the quays just W of Cheek Pt where 4 groynes marked by SPM lt buoys, extend into the river; about 3M further W, on S side of R Suir in Kings Chan which should only be entered W of Little Is; in Waterford on a pontoon S bank, close downstream of clock tr; up the R Barrow near Marsh Pt (about 2M S of New Ross) and 0·5M S of New Ross fixed bridge.
Note: the rly swing bridge at the ent to R Barrow opens at its W end. Call bridge-keeper VHF Ch 16 or ☎ 88137.

Continued

See 10-12-16

WATERFORD *Continued*

NAVIGATION
WPT 52°06'·50N 06°56'·50W, 182°/002° from/to Dir lt at Duncannon, 6·7M. From the W do not confuse Waterford ent with Tramore Bay; beware Falskirt Rk (2ca off Swine Hd). From the E, keep clear of Brecaun reef (2M NE of Hook Hd). Give Tower Race a wide berth; overfalls extend about 1·5M S of Hook Hd.

LIGHTS AND MARKS
The ent to R Suir lies between Dunmore East L Fl WR 8s 13m 16/12M; vis W225°–310°, R310°–004°; and Hook Hd, Fl 3s 46m 23M, W tr with 2 B bands. Duncannon Dir lt Oc WRG 4s 13m 11/8M, G358°–001·7°, W001·7°–002·2°, R002·2°–006°, leads 002° up-river via well-buoyed lit chan. On same structure is lt, Oc WR 4s 13m 9/7M, R119°–149°, W149°–172°. The R Barrow is also well lit/marked up to New Ross.

RADIO TELEPHONE
Waterford and New Ross VHF Ch 12 14 16.

TELEPHONE (Dial code 051)
Hr Mr Waterford 74499/New Ross 21303; MRCC (01) 6620922/3; ⌗ 75391; Police 74888; Dr 83194; ⊞ 75429.

FACILITIES
Services: BY (Ballyhack), ME, El, Sh, C.
Town EC Thurs; AB, M, FW, P, D, Gaz, V, R, Bar, ⇌, ✈.

MINOR HARBOUR 15M ENE of YOUGHAL

DUNGARVAN BAY, Waterford, 52°05'·15N 07°36'·70W. Rtg 3-4-3. AC 2017. HW –0540 on Dover; Duration 0600. See below. A large bay, drying to the W, entered between Helvick Hd to the S and Ballynacourty Pt to the N. Appr in W sector (274°–302°) of Ballynacourty Pt Dir lt, Fl (2) WRG 10s 16m 12/9M, G245°–274°, W274°–302°, R302°–325°, W325°–117°. This sector clears Carricknamoan islet to the N, and Carrickapane Rk and Helvick Rk (ECM buoy Q (3) 10s) to the SW. The Gainers, an extensive unmarked rky patch (dries 0·8m), are 2 to 5ca NNW of Helvick New Pier. ⚓ in approx 4m off Helvick hbr, or head W to Dungarvan town hbr not later than HW+3½, via buoyed chan.
Note that due to the chan having shifted N'ward, in Sept 1996 both sets of ldg lts were temp'y extinguished, ie Ballynacourty ldg lts 083°/263°, both Oc 5s 9/12m 2M on W columns with B bands, 46m apart; and Dungarvan ldg lts 298°, both FR 8/9m 2M. See NM 386(P)/97; AC 2017 corrections awaited at time of going to press. Beware salmon nets. Facilities at Dungarvan: EC Thurs; AB, no dues, Bar, ⑧, D (cans), P (on quay), ✉, R, V, Kos.

YOUGHAL   10-12-18

Cork 51°56'·54N 07°50'·20W   Rtg 3-2-2

CHARTS
AC 2071, 2049; Imray C57; Irish OS 81, 82

TIDES
–0556 Dover; ML 2·1; Duration 0555; Zone 0 (UT)

metres
cables
Depths in metres

No special visitors berths

Standard Port COBH (→)

Times				Height (metres)			
High Water		Low Water		MHWS	MHWN	MLWN	MLWS
0500	1100	0500	1100	4·1	3·2	1·3	0·4
1700	2300	1700	2300				
Differences YOUGHAL							
0000	+0010	+0010	0000	–0·2	–0·1	–0·1	–0·1
DUNGARVAN HARBOUR							
+0004	+0012	+0007	–0001	0·0	+0·1	–0·2	0·0
BALLYCOTTON							
–0011	+0001	+0003	–0009	0·0	0·0	–0·1	0·0

SHELTER
Good, but strong S winds cause a swell inside the hbr. ⚓s as on chartlet; no dues. Caution strong tidal streams.

NAVIGATION
WPT, East Bar, 51°55'·62N 07°48'·00W, 122°/302° from/to Fl WR 2·5s lt, 1·8M. Beware Blackball Ledge (PHM buoy) and Bar Rks (SCM buoy), both outside hbr ent in R sector of lt ho. From W, appr via West Bar (1·7m) is shorter; E Bar has 2·0m. In winds E to SSW >F6 both Bars are likely to have dangerous seas. Beware salmon nets May-July.

LIGHTS AND MARKS
W of ent, Fl WR 2·5s 24m 17/14M, W tr (15m), has two W sectors ldg over the bars (see 10.12.4). Convent tr on with the town hall at 175° leads clear W of Red Bank up-river. Conspic water tr approx 0·65M WNW of clock tr.

RADIO TELEPHONE
VHF Ch 14 16 HW±3.

TELEPHONE (Dial code 024)
Hr Mr 92820; MRCC (01) 6620922/3; Coast/Cliff Rescue Service 93252; ⌗ (021) 968783; Police 92200; Dr 92702.

FACILITIES
Services: ME, El, Sh, CH, L, FW (see Hr Mr), Slip. **Town** P & D (cans), V, R, Bar, ✉, ⑧, ⇌ (Cork/Waterford), ✈ (Cork).

MINOR HARBOUR 10M SOUTHWEST of YOUGHAL

BALLYCOTTON, Cork, 51°49'·70N 08°00'·19W. AC 2424. HW –0555 on Dover; ML no data; Duration 0550. See above. Small, N-facing hbr at W end of bay; suffers from scend in strong SE winds. 3m in ent and about 1·5m against piers. Many FVs alongside piers, on which yachts should berth, rather than ⚓ in hbr, which is foul with old ground tackle. Outside hbr, good ⚓ in offshore winds in 6m NE of bkwtr, protected by Ballycotton Is. Lt ho Fl WR 10s 59m 21/17M, B tr in W walls; W238°–048°, R048°–238°; Horn (4) 90s. Facilities: FW on pier. **Village** Bar, ✉, R, V, LB, Kos.

IRELAND – COBH

LAT 51°51′N   LONG 8°18′W

TIMES AND HEIGHTS OF HIGH AND LOW WATERS

YEAR **1998**

TIME ZONE (UT)
For Summer Time add ONE hour in non-shaded areas

JANUARY

Day	Time	m	Time	m	Time	m	Time	m
1 TH	0105	0.5	0703	4.2	1328	0.6	1918	4.1
16 F	0140	0.7	0734	4.1	1403	0.8	1945	3.9
2 F	0149	0.5	0747	4.2	1412	0.6	2003	4.0
17 SA	0214	0.8	0809	4.0	1437	0.9	2020	3.8
3 SA	0235	0.6	0834	4.1	1459	0.7	2051	3.9
18 SU	0249	0.9	0845	3.8	1513	1.0	2057	3.7
4 SU	0325	0.7	0924	4.0	1549	0.8	2142	3.8
19 M	0328	1.0	0923	3.7	1554	1.2	2139	3.6
5 M	0418	0.8	1017	3.9	1644	1.0	2238	3.7
20 TU	0412	1.2	1006	3.6	1641	1.3	2226	3.5
6 TU	0517	1.0	1116	3.7	1747	1.1	2341	3.6
21 W	0505	1.3	1056	3.5	1739	1.4	2323	3.4
7 W	0625	1.0	1223	3.6	1858	1.1		
22 TH	0609	1.4	1156	3.4	1846	1.4		
8 TH	0051	3.6	0738	1.0	1334	3.6	2011	1.0
23 F	0030	3.4	0717	1.4	1306	3.4	1953	1.4
9 F	0205	3.6	0851	0.9	1442	3.7	2119	0.9
24 SA	0143	3.4	0822	1.3	1417	3.5	2055	1.2
10 SA	0314	3.8	0955	0.8	1543	3.8	2218	0.8
25 SU	0250	3.6	0923	1.1	1519	3.7	2151	1.0
11 SU	0412	3.9	1050	0.7	1636	4.0	2308	0.6
26 M	0347	3.8	1018	0.8	1612	3.8	2241	0.7
12 M ○	0502	4.1	1136	0.6	1722	4.1	2351	0.5
27 TU	0437	4.0	1106	0.6	1659	4.1	2327	0.5
13 TU	0545	4.2	1217	0.5	1802	4.1		
28 W ●	0523	4.2	1150	0.5	1742	4.1		
14 W	0030	0.5	0623	4.2	1255	0.6	1838	4.1
29 TH	0009	0.4	0606	4.3	1233	0.3	1824	4.2
15 TH	0106	0.6	0659	4.1	1329	0.7	1912	4.0
30 F	0051	0.3	0649	4.3	1315	0.3	1906	4.2
31 SA	0134	0.3	0733	4.3	1358	0.3	1950	4.2

FEBRUARY

Day	Time	m	Time	m	Time	m	Time	m
1 SU	0219	0.3	0818	4.2	1442	0.4	2035	4.1
16 M	0214	0.8	0812	3.9	1437	0.9	2025	3.8
2 M	0306	0.4	0904	4.1	1529	0.6	2121	3.9
17 TU	0249	0.9	0846	3.8	1512	1.0	2102	3.7
3 TU	0355	0.5	0953	3.9	1619	0.8	2212	3.7
18 W	0328	1.0	0924	3.7	1553	1.2	2144	3.6
4 W	0449	0.8	1047	3.7	1715	1.0	2309	3.6
19 TH	0414	1.2	1009	3.5	1643	1.3	2234	3.5
5 TH	0552	1.0	1150	3.5	1823	1.1		
20 F	0514	1.3	1104	3.4	1750	1.4	2338	3.3
6 F	0020	3.4	0707	1.1	1306	3.4	1943	1.2
21 SA	0627	1.4	1212	3.3	1907	1.4		
7 SA	0142	3.4	0830	1.1	1422	3.4	2102	1.0
22 SU	0054	3.3	0742	1.3	1331	3.3	2019	1.3
8 SU	0257	3.5	0942	0.9	1528	3.6	2207	0.8
23 M	0212	3.5	0851	1.1	1446	3.5	2122	1.0
9 M	0358	3.8	1039	0.7	1622	3.8	2258	0.7
24 TU	0319	3.7	0952	0.8	1548	3.7	2218	0.7
10 TU	0447	4.0	1124	0.6	1638	4.0	2339	0.5
25 W	0414	4.0	1045	0.5	1638	4.0	2306	0.4
11 W ○	0529	4.1	1203	0.5	1746	4.0		
26 TH ●	0502	4.2	1131	0.3	1724	4.1	2350	0.2
12 TH	0014	0.5	0605	4.3	1236	0.5	1820	4.1
27 F	0547	4.3	1215	0.1	1807	4.3		
13 F	0045	0.5	0639	4.1	1306	0.6	1851	4.0
28 SA	0033	0.1	0630	4.4	1257	0.1	1849	4.3
14 SA	0114	0.6	0710	4.1	1335	0.7	1921	4.0
15 SU	0143	0.7	0741	4.0	1405	0.8	1952	3.9

MARCH

Day	Time	m	Time	m	Time	m	Time	m
1 SU	0117	0.0	0713	4.3	1340	0.1	1931	4.2
16 M	0113	0.6	0712	4.0	1334	0.7	1925	3.9
2 M	0200	0.1	0757	4.3	1423	0.2	2014	4.1
17 TU	0143	0.7	0741	3.9	1405	0.8	1956	3.9
3 TU	0246	0.2	0842	4.1	1508	0.4	2059	4.0
18 W	0217	0.8	0813	3.8	1439	0.9	2030	3.8
4 W	0333	0.4	0928	3.9	1555	0.6	2146	3.7
19 TH	0255	0.9	0849	3.7	1517	1.0	2110	3.7
5 TH	0425	0.7	1019	3.6	1648	0.9	2241	3.5
20 F	0339	1.1	0932	3.6	1603	1.2	2158	3.5
6 F	0525	0.9	1121	3.3	1753	1.1	2351	3.3
21 SA	0434	1.2	1026	3.4	1705	1.3	2259	3.4
7 SA	0639	1.1	1239	3.2	1915	1.2		
22 SU	0545	1.3	1133	3.2	1825	1.4		
8 SU	0119	3.2	0808	1.1	1401	3.2	2044	1.1
23 M	0014	3.3	0704	1.3	1253	3.2	1942	1.2
9 M	0239	3.4	0925	0.9	1509	3.4	2152	0.9
24 TU	0136	3.4	0818	1.1	1413	3.4	2051	1.0
10 TU	0339	3.6	1022	0.7	1603	3.7	2242	0.6
25 W	0248	3.6	0923	0.8	1519	3.7	2150	0.6
11 W	0427	3.8	1106	0.6	1647	3.8	2322	0.6
26 TH	0346	3.9	1019	0.4	1613	3.9	2242	0.4
12 TH	0507	4.0	1143	0.5	1725	4.0	2355	0.5
27 F	0437	4.2	1108	0.2	1701	4.1	2329	0.1
13 F ○	0543	4.1	1214	0.5	1759	4.0		
28 SA ●	0524	4.3	1153	0.0	1745	4.2		
14 SA	0022	0.5	0615	4.1	1241	0.5	1828	4.0
29 SU	0013	-0.1	0608	4.4	1237	-0.1	1828	4.3
15 SU	0047	0.5	0644	4.0	1306	0.6	1856	4.0
30 M	0058	-0.1	0652	4.3	1320	0.0	1911	4.3
31 TU	0142	0.0	0736	4.2	1404	0.1	1954	4.2

APRIL

Day	Time	m	Time	m	Time	m	Time	m
1 W	0227	0.1	0820	4.0	1449	0.3	2038	4.0
16 TH	0152	0.7	0746	3.8	1414	0.8	2006	3.8
2 TH	0315	0.4	0906	3.8	1536	0.5	2125	3.7
17 F	0231	0.8	0824	3.7	1454	0.9	2046	3.7
3 F	0405	0.6	0956	3.5	1628	0.8	2218	3.5
18 SA	0316	1.0	0908	3.6	1540	1.1	2134	3.6
4 SA	0503	0.9	1055	3.3	1731	1.0	2326	3.2
19 SU	0410	1.1	1001	3.4	1640	1.2	2233	3.5
5 SU	0614	1.1	1212	3.1	1849	1.1		
20 M	0516	1.2	1107	3.3	1753	1.2	2346	3.4
6 M	0054	3.2	0739	1.1	1335	3.1	2015	1.1
21 TU	0632	1.2	1223	3.3	1910	1.1		
7 TU	0211	3.3	0856	0.9	1442	3.3	2123	0.9
22 W	0104	3.5	0745	1.0	1340	3.4	2019	0.9
8 W	0310	3.5	0952	0.8	1536	3.5	2214	0.7
23 TH	0216	3.7	0852	0.7	1447	3.7	2121	0.6
9 TH	0358	3.7	1037	0.6	1620	3.7	2254	0.6
24 F	0317	3.9	0950	0.4	1545	3.9	2216	0.3
10 F	0439	3.9	1115	0.5	1732	3.9	2327	0.6
25 SA	0411	4.1	1043	0.2	1636	4.1	2307	0.1
11 SA ○	0516	3.9	1145	0.5	1732	3.9	2354	0.5
26 SU ●	0500	4.3	1132	0.0	1723	4.3	2354	0.0
12 SU	0548	4.0	1212	0.5	1803	4.0		
27 M	0547	4.3	1217	0.0	1809	4.3		
13 M	0018	0.5	0616	3.9	1238	0.6	1830	3.9
28 TU	0040	0.0	0632	4.3	1303	0.0	1852	4.3
14 TU	0046	0.6	0644	3.9	1306	0.6	1859	3.9
29 W	0126	0.0	0716	4.2	1347	0.1	1936	4.1
15 W	0117	0.6	0713	3.9	1339	0.7	1931	3.9
30 TH	0211	0.2	0801	4.0	1433	0.3	2020	4.0

12

Chart Datum: 0·13 metres above Ordnance Datum (Dublin)

IRELAND – COBH

LAT 51°51′N   LONG 8°18′W

TIMES AND HEIGHTS OF HIGH AND LOW WATERS

YEAR **1998**

TIME ZONE (UT)
For Summer Time add ONE hour in non-shaded areas

MAY

Date	Time / m (four readings per day)
1 F	0258 0.4 · 0846 3.8 · 1520 0.5 · 2107 3.7
2 SA	0348 0.6 · 0934 3.5 · 1611 0.7 · 2158 3.5
3 SU	0443 0.9 · 1030 3.3 · 1710 1.0 · 2300 3.3
4 M	0547 1.0 · 1138 3.1 · 1818 1.1
5 TU	0018 3.2 · 0700 1.1 · 1256 3.1 · 1932 1.1
6 W	0133 3.3 · 0810 1.0 · 1403 3.3 · 2038 1.0
7 TH	0232 3.4 · 0908 0.9 · 1458 3.4 · 2132 0.8
8 F	0321 3.6 · 0956 0.7 · 1544 3.6 · 2215 0.7
9 SA	0405 3.7 · 1037 0.7 · 1625 3.8 · 2251 0.6
10 SU	0444 3.8 · 1111 0.6 · 1702 3.9 · 2322 0.6
11 M O	0518 3.9 · 1141 0.6 · 1735 3.9 · 2351 0.6
12 TU	0550 3.9 · 1211 0.6 · 1806 3.9
13 W	0021 0.6 · 0619 3.9 · 1244 0.6 · 1837 3.9
14 TH	0056 0.6 · 0651 3.9 · 1319 0.7 · 1911 3.9
15 F	0134 0.7 · 0726 3.8 · 1358 0.8 · 1949 3.9
16 SA	0215 0.8 · 0807 3.8 · 1440 0.8 · 2032 3.8
17 SU	0302 0.9 · 0853 3.7 · 1528 0.9 · 2120 3.7
18 M	0354 1.0 · 0947 3.5 · 1624 1.0 · 2218 3.6
19 TU	0455 1.0 · 1048 3.5 · 1730 1.1 · 2324 3.5
20 W	0604 1.0 · 1157 3.4 · 1841 1.0
21 TH	0036 3.6 · 0715 0.9 · 1309 3.5 · 1949 0.8
22 F	0146 3.7 · 0822 0.7 · 1416 3.7 · 2053 0.6
23 SA	0249 3.9 · 0923 0.5 · 1517 3.9 · 2152 0.4
24 SU	0346 4.0 · 1020 0.3 · 1612 4.1 · 2246 0.2
25 M ●	0439 4.1 · 1112 0.2 · 1703 4.2 · 2337 0.1
26 TU	0528 4.2 · 1200 0.1 · 1751 4.2
27 W	0024 0.1 · 0614 4.2 · 1247 0.1 · 1836 4.2
28 TH	0110 0.2 · 0659 4.1 · 1332 0.2 · 1920 4.1
29 F	0156 0.3 · 0743 4.0 · 1417 0.4 · 2003 4.0
30 SA	0241 0.5 · 0827 3.8 · 1503 0.5 · 2048 3.8
31 SU	0329 0.7 · 0912 3.6 · 1551 0.7 · 2135 3.6

JUNE

Date	Time / m (four readings per day)
1 M	0419 0.9 · 1001 3.4 · 1643 0.9 · 2228 3.4
2 TU	0514 1.0 · 1056 3.3 · 1741 1.1 · 2331 3.3
3 W	0615 1.1 · 1201 3.2 · 1843 1.1
4 TH	0039 3.3 · 0716 1.1 · 1309 3.2 · 1943 1.1
5 F	0143 3.3 · 0814 1.0 · 1409 3.4 · 2038 1.0
6 SA	0237 3.5 · 0906 0.9 · 1500 3.5 · 2127 0.9
7 SU	0325 3.6 · 0952 0.8 · 1546 3.7 · 2210 0.8
8 M	0408 3.7 · 1034 0.7 · 1628 3.8 · 2249 0.7
9 TU	0448 3.8 · 1112 0.7 · 1707 3.9 · 2325 0.6
10 W O	0524 3.9 · 1149 0.6 · 1744 3.9
11 TH	0002 0.6 · 0559 3.9 · 1226 0.6 · 1820 4.0
12 F	0040 0.6 · 0635 3.9 · 1304 0.6 · 1857 4.0
13 SA	0120 0.6 · 0713 3.9 · 1345 0.6 · 1937 4.0
14 SU	0203 0.7 · 0756 3.8 · 1429 0.7 · 2021 3.9
15 M	0249 0.7 · 0843 3.8 · 1517 0.8 · 2110 3.8
16 TU	0340 0.8 · 0934 3.7 · 1609 0.8 · 2204 3.8
17 W	0435 0.9 · 1031 3.6 · 1707 0.9 · 2303 3.7
18 TH	0538 0.9 · 1133 3.6 · 1813 0.9
19 F	0009 3.7 · 0645 0.9 · 1240 3.6 · 1920 0.8
20 SA	0117 3.7 · 0753 0.8 · 1347 3.7 · 2027 0.7
21 SU	0223 3.8 · 0858 0.7 · 1452 3.8 · 2131 0.6
22 M	0324 3.9 · 0959 0.5 · 1552 3.9 · 2229 0.4
23 TU	0421 4.0 · 1055 0.4 · 1647 4.1 · 2322 0.3
24 W ●	0512 4.1 · 1145 0.3 · 1736 4.1
25 TH	0010 0.3 · 0559 4.1 · 1232 0.3 · 1821 4.1
26 F	0055 0.3 · 0643 4.0 · 1315 0.3 · 1903 4.1
27 SA	0138 0.4 · 0724 3.9 · 1358 0.4 · 1944 4.0
28 SU	0220 0.5 · 0805 3.8 · 1440 0.6 · 2025 3.8
29 M	0302 0.7 · 0845 3.7 · 1522 0.7 · 2107 3.7
30 TU	0346 0.9 · 0927 3.5 · 1607 0.9 · 2151 3.5

JULY

Date	Time / m (four readings per day)
1 W	0432 1.0 · 1012 3.4 · 1654 1.0 · 2239 3.4
2 TH	0524 1.1 · 1104 3.3 · 1748 1.1 · 2335 3.3
3 F	0620 1.2 · 1204 3.3 · 1846 1.2
4 SA	0039 3.3 · 0719 1.2 · 1309 3.3 · 1944 1.1
5 SU	0143 3.4 · 0816 1.1 · 1411 3.4 · 2039 1.1
6 M	0241 3.5 · 0910 1.0 · 1506 3.6 · 2131 0.9
7 TU	0332 3.6 · 1000 0.8 · 1556 3.7 · 2219 0.8
8 W	0419 3.7 · 1046 0.7 · 1641 3.9 · 2303 0.7
9 TH O	0501 3.8 · 1128 0.6 · 1723 4.0 · 2344 0.6
10 F	0541 3.9 · 1208 0.5 · 1804 4.0
11 SA	0024 0.5 · 0620 4.0 · 1249 0.5 · 1843 4.1
12 SU	0106 0.5 · 0701 4.0 · 1330 0.5 · 1925 4.1
13 M	0149 0.5 · 0744 3.9 · 1414 0.5 · 2009 4.0
14 TU	0234 0.6 · 0830 3.9 · 1500 0.6 · 2056 4.0
15 W	0322 0.6 · 0918 3.8 · 1549 0.6 · 2146 3.9
16 TH	0413 0.7 · 1010 3.7 · 1643 0.7 · 2240 3.8
17 F	0510 0.8 · 1107 3.6 · 1743 0.8 · 2341 3.6
18 SA	0615 0.9 · 1211 3.6 · 1852 0.9
19 SU	0050 3.6 · 0726 0.9 · 1322 3.6 · 2004 0.8
20 M	0200 3.6 · 0838 0.8 · 1433 3.6 · 2115 0.8
21 TU	0307 3.7 · 0945 0.7 · 1538 3.8 · 2217 0.6
22 W	0407 3.8 · 1043 0.5 · 1635 3.9 · 2311 0.5
23 TH ●	0459 3.9 · 1132 0.4 · 1723 4.0 · 2357 0.4
24 F	0544 4.0 · 1216 0.4 · 1806 4.1
25 SA	0038 0.4 · 0625 4.0 · 1256 0.4 · 1845 4.1
26 SU	0116 0.5 · 0703 3.9 · 1334 0.5 · 1921 4.0
27 M	0153 0.6 · 0739 3.9 · 1410 0.6 · 1957 3.9
28 TU	0229 0.7 · 0814 3.8 · 1446 0.7 · 2034 3.8
29 W	0306 0.8 · 0851 3.7 · 1523 0.9 · 2111 3.7
30 TH	0345 1.0 · 0918 3.6 · 1602 1.0 · 2152 3.5
31 F	0428 1.1 · 1015 3.5 · 1649 1.1 · 2238 3.4

AUGUST

Date	Time / m (four readings per day)
1 SA	0521 1.2 · 1106 3.3 · 1746 1.3 · 2333 3.3
2 SU	0623 1.3 · 1208 3.3 · 1851 1.3
3 M	0040 3.3 · 0729 1.3 · 1320 3.3 · 1955 1.2
4 TU	0153 3.4 · 0831 1.2 · 1428 3.4 · 2056 1.1
5 W	0257 3.5 · 0929 1.0 · 1527 3.6 · 2152 0.9
6 TH	0352 3.7 · 1021 0.8 · 1617 3.8 · 2241 0.7
7 F	0439 3.8 · 1106 0.6 · 1702 4.0 · 2325 0.5
8 SA O	0522 4.0 · 1148 0.4 · 1745 4.1
9 SU	0007 0.4 · 0603 4.0 · 1230 0.3 · 1825 4.2
10 M	0048 0.3 · 0644 4.1 · 1311 0.3 · 1907 4.2
11 TU	0131 0.3 · 0727 4.1 · 1354 0.3 · 1951 4.2
12 W	0215 0.4 · 0811 4.0 · 1440 0.4 · 2036 4.1
13 TH	0301 0.5 · 0857 3.9 · 1527 0.5 · 2123 3.9
14 F	0350 0.6 · 0947 3.8 · 1618 0.7 · 2215 3.7
15 SA	0443 0.8 · 1041 3.6 · 1716 0.8 · 2314 3.6
16 SU	0546 1.0 · 1145 3.5 · 1825 1.0
17 M	0025 3.4 · 0701 1.0 · 1303 3.4 · 1945 1.0
18 TU	0143 3.4 · 0823 1.0 · 1422 3.5 · 2104 0.9
19 W	0254 3.5 · 0935 0.8 · 1529 3.7 · 2209 0.7
20 TH	0354 3.7 · 1033 0.6 · 1623 3.9 · 2300 0.6
21 F	0444 3.9 · 1120 0.5 · 1708 4.0 · 2342 0.5
22 SA ●	0527 4.0 · 1200 0.4 · 1748 4.1
23 SU	0019 0.4 · 0605 4.0 · 1234 0.4 · 1823 4.1
24 M	0052 0.5 · 0639 4.0 · 1305 0.5 · 1855 4.0
25 TU	0122 0.6 · 0710 3.9 · 1335 0.6 · 1927 3.9
26 W	0152 0.7 · 0742 3.8 · 1405 0.7 · 1958 3.9
27 TH	0223 0.8 · 0815 3.8 · 1438 0.8 · 2032 3.8
28 F	0258 1.0 · 0851 3.7 · 1514 1.0 · 2108 3.7
29 SA	0338 1.1 · 0932 3.5 · 1556 1.1 · 2150 3.5
30 SU	0425 1.3 · 1019 3.4 · 1650 1.3 · 2241 3.4
31 M	0528 1.4 · 1118 3.3 · 1759 1.4 · 2346 3.3

Chart Datum: 0·13 metres above Ordnance Datum (Dublin)

IRELAND – COBH

LAT 51°51′N   LONG 8°18′W

TIMES AND HEIGHTS OF HIGH AND LOW WATERS   YEAR **1998**

TIME ZONE (UT)
For Summer Time add ONE hour in non-shaded areas

SEPTEMBER

Day	Time	m	Day	Time	m
1 TU	0643 / 1232 / 1915	1.4 / 3.2 / 1.4	**16** W	0129 / 0812 / 1411 / 2054	3.3 / 1.1 / 3.4 / 1.0
2 W	0104 / 0755 / 1351 / 2023	3.3 / 1.3 / 3.4 / 1.2	**17** TH	0241 / 0925 / 1515 / 2156	3.4 / 0.9 / 3.6 / 0.8
3 TH	0222 / 0858 / 1457 / 2124	3.4 / 1.0 / 3.6 / 0.9	**18** F	0338 / 1019 / 1606 / 2243	3.7 / 0.6 / 3.8 / 0.6
4 F	0324 / 0954 / 1551 / 2216	3.6 / 0.8 / 3.9 / 0.6	**19** SA	0426 / 1103 / 1648 / 2323	3.9 / 0.5 / 4.0 / 0.5
5 SA	0414 / 1042 / 1638 / 2303	3.9 / 0.5 / 4.1 / 0.4	**20** SU	0506 / 1139 / 1725 / ● 2356	4.0 / 0.4 / 4.1 / 0.5
6 SU	0459 / 1126 / 1722 / O 2346	4.1 / 0.3 / 4.2 / 0.2	**21** M	0542 / 1209 / 1759	4.0 / 0.5 / 4.1
7 M	0542 / 1208 / 1804	4.2 / 0.2 / 4.3	**22** TU	0024 / 0613 / 1236 / 1828	0.5 / 4.0 / 0.5 / 4.0
8 TU	0027 / 0623 / 1250 / 1846	0.2 / 4.2 / 0.1 / 4.3	**23** W	0049 / 0642 / 1301 / 1856	0.6 / 4.0 / 0.6 / 4.0
9 W	0110 / 0706 / 1333 / 1929	0.2 / 4.2 / 0.2 / 4.3	**24** TH	0116 / 0711 / 1328 / 1924	0.7 / 3.9 / 0.7 / 3.9
10 TH	0154 / 0750 / 1418 / 2013	0.2 / 4.1 / 0.3 / 4.1	**25** F	0146 / 0742 / 1400 / 1955	0.8 / 3.8 / 0.9 / 3.8
11 F	0239 / 0835 / 1505 / 2100	0.4 / 4.0 / 0.4 / 3.9	**26** SA	0220 / 0816 / 1436 / 2030	1.0 / 3.8 / 1.0 / 3.7
12 SA	0328 / 0924 / 1556 / 2151	0.6 / 3.8 / 0.6 / 3.7	**27** SU	0258 / 0855 / 1518 / 2112	1.1 / 3.6 / 1.2 / 3.6
13 SU	0421 / 1018 / 1653 / 2249	0.8 / 3.6 / 0.9 / 3.5	**28** M	0344 / 0942 / 1609 / 2202	1.3 / 3.5 / 1.3 / 3.4
14 M	0524 / 1124 / 1803	1.0 / 3.4 / 1.1	**29** TU	0444 / 1040 / 1716 / 2305	1.4 / 3.4 / 1.4 / 3.3
15 TU	0004 / 0642 / 1249 / 1931	3.3 / 1.1 / 3.3 / 1.1	**30** W	0601 / 1152 / 1836	1.4 / 3.3 / 1.4

OCTOBER

Day	Time	m	Day	Time	m
1 TH	0023 / 0718 / 1313 / 1950	3.3 / 1.3 / 3.4 / 1.2	**16** F	0219 / 0902 / 1451 / 2131	3.4 / 0.9 / 3.6 / 0.9
2 F	0145 / 0826 / 1425 / 2054	3.4 / 1.1 / 3.6 / 1.0	**17** SA	0315 / 0955 / 1540 / 2217	3.6 / 0.7 / 3.8 / 0.7
3 SA	0252 / 0924 / 1522 / 2149	3.7 / 0.8 / 3.9 / 0.6	**18** SU	0401 / 1038 / 1622 / 2256	3.8 / 0.6 / 4.0 / 0.6
4 SU	0346 / 1015 / 1611 / 2238	3.9 / 0.5 / 4.1 / 0.4	**19** M	0440 / 1113 / 1659 / 2328	4.0 / 0.6 / 4.1 / 0.6
5 M	0433 / 1102 / 1657 / O 2323	4.1 / 0.3 / 4.3 / 0.2	**20** TU	0516 / 1142 / 1732 / ● 2355	4.0 / 0.6 / 4.1 / 0.6
6 TU	0518 / 1146 / 1741	4.3 / 0.1 / 4.4	**21** W	0547 / 1206 / 1801	4.0 / 0.6 / 4.1
7 W	0006 / 0601 / 1231 / 1824	0.1 / 4.3 / 0.1 / 4.4	**22** TH	0019 / 0615 / 1231 / 1827	0.7 / 4.0 / 0.7 / 4.1
8 TH	0050 / 0645 / 1315 / 1908	0.1 / 4.3 / 0.1 / 4.3	**23** F	0046 / 0644 / 1300 / 1855	0.8 / 4.0 / 0.8 / 4.0
9 F	0135 / 0729 / 1400 / 1953	0.2 / 4.2 / 0.2 / 4.2	**24** SA	0117 / 0715 / 1333 / 1926	0.8 / 3.9 / 0.9 / 3.9
10 SA	0221 / 0815 / 1448 / 2039	0.4 / 4.0 / 0.4 / 3.9	**25** SU	0152 / 0749 / 1410 / 2001	1.0 / 3.9 / 1.0 / 3.8
11 SU	0310 / 0904 / 1538 / 2129	0.6 / 3.8 / 0.7 / 3.7	**26** M	0231 / 0829 / 1453 / 2043	1.1 / 3.8 / 1.2 / 3.7
12 M	0403 / 0959 / 1636 / 2228	0.8 / 3.6 / 1.0 / 3.4	**27** TU	0317 / 0915 / 1543 / 2134	1.2 / 3.6 / 1.3 / 3.6
13 TU	0506 / 1105 / 1745 / 2342	1.1 / 3.4 / 1.2 / 3.2	**28** W	0415 / 1012 / 1646 / 2236	1.4 / 3.5 / 1.4 / 3.4
14 W	0624 / 1230 / 1913	1.3 / 3.3 / 1.2	**29** TH	0527 / 1121 / 1802 / 2350	1.4 / 3.4 / 1.4 / 3.4
15 TH	0107 / 0753 / 1350 / 2032	3.2 / 1.1 / 3.4 / 1.1	**30** F	0643 / 1238 / 1917	1.3 / 3.5 / 1.3
			31 SA	0108 / 0753 / 1350 / 2023	3.5 / 1.1 / 3.7 / 1.0

NOVEMBER

Day	Time	m	Day	Time	m
1 SU	0218 / 0854 / 1451 / 2121	3.7 / 0.8 / 3.9 / 0.7	**16** M	0328 / 1002 / 1549 / 2222	3.7 / 0.8 / 3.9 / 0.8
2 M	0316 / 0949 / 1544 / 2213	4.0 / 0.5 / 4.2 / 0.4	**17** TU	0409 / 1040 / 1629 / 2256	3.9 / 0.8 / 4.0 / 0.8
3 TU	0407 / 1040 / 1633 / 2302	4.2 / 0.3 / 4.3 / 0.3	**18** W	0447 / 1112 / 1704 / 2326	4.0 / 0.7 / 4.0 / 0.7
4 W	0456 / 1128 / 1720 / O 2348	4.3 / 0.2 / 4.4 / 0.2	**19** TH	0521 / 1140 / 1735 / ● 2354	4.1 / 0.8 / 4.0 / 0.7
5 TH	0542 / 1214 / 1806	4.4 / 0.1 / 4.4	**20** F	0552 / 1208 / 1804	4.1 / 0.8 / 4.0
6 F	0033 / 0627 / 1300 / 1850	0.2 / 4.4 / 0.2 / 4.3	**21** SA	0024 / 0623 / 1240 / 1833	0.8 / 4.1 / 0.9 / 4.0
7 SA	0119 / 0713 / 1346 / 1935	0.2 / 4.3 / 0.3 / 4.2	**22** SU	0057 / 0656 / 1315 / 1906	0.8 / 4.0 / 0.9 / 4.0
8 SU	0206 / 0759 / 1434 / 2021	0.4 / 4.1 / 0.5 / 4.0	**23** M	0134 / 0731 / 1354 / 1943	0.9 / 4.0 / 1.0 / 3.9
9 M	0255 / 0848 / 1524 / 2110	0.6 / 3.9 / 0.8 / 3.7	**24** TU	0215 / 0812 / 1438 / 2026	1.0 / 3.9 / 1.1 / 3.8
10 TU	0347 / 0941 / 1619 / 2205	0.8 / 3.7 / 1.0 / 3.5	**25** W	0302 / 0858 / 1527 / 2116	1.1 / 3.8 / 1.2 / 3.7
11 W	0447 / 1043 / 1724 / 2312	1.1 / 3.4 / 1.2 / 3.3	**26** TH	0356 / 0953 / 1624 / 2214	1.2 / 3.7 / 1.3 / 3.6
12 TH	0557 / 1158 / 1839	1.2 / 3.3 / 1.3	**27** F	0459 / 1058 / 1731 / 2321	1.3 / 3.6 / 1.3 / 3.5
13 F	0031 / 0715 / 1314 / 1953	3.2 / 1.2 / 3.4 / 1.2	**28** SA	0609 / 1205 / 1843	1.3 / 3.6 / 1.2
14 SA	0143 / 0823 / 1415 / 2052	3.4 / 1.1 / 3.5 / 1.1	**29** SU	0033 / 0719 / 1315 / 1951	3.6 / 1.1 / 3.8 / 1.0
15 SU	0240 / 0918 / 1506 / 2141	3.6 / 0.9 / 3.7 / 0.9	**30** M	0143 / 0825 / 1419 / 2054	3.7 / 0.9 / 3.9 / 0.8

DECEMBER

Day	Time	m	Day	Time	m
1 TU	0246 / 0925 / 1517 / 2151	3.9 / 0.7 / 4.1 / 0.6	**16** W	0334 / 1003 / 1556 / 2223	3.8 / 1.0 / 3.8 / 0.9
2 W	0343 / 1020 / 1611 / 2244	4.1 / 0.5 / 4.2 / 0.4	**17** TH	0417 / 1042 / 1637 / 2300	3.9 / 0.9 / 3.9 / 0.8
3 TH	0437 / 1112 / 1702 / O 2333	4.3 / 0.3 / 4.3 / 0.3	**18** F	0456 / 1118 / 1713 / ● 2334	4.0 / 0.8 / 4.0 / 0.8
4 F	0527 / 1201 / 1750	4.4 / 0.3 / 4.3	**19** SA	0533 / 1152 / 1747	4.1 / 0.8 / 4.0
5 SA	0020 / 0614 / 1248 / 1835	0.3 / 4.4 / 0.3 / 4.3	**20** SU	0008 / 0607 / 1227 / 1819	0.8 / 4.1 / 0.8 / 4.0
6 SU	0106 / 0659 / 1334 / 1920	0.3 / 4.3 / 0.4 / 4.2	**21** M	0044 / 0643 / 1304 / 1853	0.8 / 4.1 / 0.8 / 4.0
7 M	0152 / 0745 / 1420 / 2005	0.4 / 4.2 / 0.6 / 4.0	**22** TU	0121 / 0720 / 1343 / 1931	0.8 / 4.1 / 0.9 / 4.0
8 TU	0239 / 0831 / 1508 / 2050	0.6 / 4.0 / 0.8 / 3.8	**23** W	0203 / 0800 / 1426 / 2014	0.9 / 4.0 / 0.9 / 3.9
9 W	0328 / 0920 / 1558 / 2138	0.8 / 3.8 / 1.0 / 3.6	**24** TH	0248 / 0845 / 1512 / 2101	0.9 / 4.0 / 1.0 / 3.8
10 TH	0420 / 1012 / 1652 / 2232	1.0 / 3.6 / 1.2 / 3.4	**25** F	0338 / 0935 / 1603 / 2154	1.0 / 3.9 / 1.1 / 3.7
11 F	0519 / 1112 / 1753 / 2336	1.2 / 3.4 / 1.3 / 3.3	**26** SA	0433 / 1031 / 1701 / 2253	1.1 / 3.8 / 1.2 / 3.7
12 SA	0623 / 1219 / 1859	1.2 / 3.4 / 1.3	**27** SU	0536 / 1133 / 1807 / 2359	1.1 / 3.7 / 1.2 / 3.6
13 SU	0047 / 0728 / 1325 / 1959	3.3 / 1.2 / 3.4 / 1.3	**28** M	0645 / 1241 / 1918	1.1 / 3.7 / 1.1
14 M	0151 / 0826 / 1422 / 2054	3.4 / 1.2 / 3.6 / 1.1	**29** TU	0109 / 0754 / 1349 / 2026	3.7 / 1.0 / 3.8 / 1.0
15 TU	0246 / 0918 / 1511 / 2141	3.6 / 1.1 / 3.7 / 1.0	**30** W	0218 / 0902 / 1454 / 2130	3.8 / 0.9 / 3.9 / 0.8
			31 TH	0323 / 1005 / 1554 / 2229	4.0 / 0.7 / 4.0 / 0.6

12

Chart Datum: 0·13 metres above Ordnance Datum (Dublin)

COBH

MEAN SPRING
AND NEAP CURVES

MEAN RANGES	
Springs	3·7m ———
Neaps	1·9m – – –

Springs occur 2 days
after
New and Full Moon

CORK HARBOUR   10-12-19

Cork 51°47'·50N 08°15'·54W   Rtg 1-1-1

CHARTS
AC 1773, 1777, 1765; Imray C56, C57; Irish OS 81, 87
TIDES
−0523 Dover; ML 2·3; Duration 0555; Zone 0 (UT)

Standard Port COBH (←——)

Times				Height (metres)			
High Water		Low Water		MHWS	MHWN	MLWN	MLWS
0500	1100	0500	1100	4·1	3·2	1·3	0·4
1700	2300	1700	2300				
Differences RINGASKIDDY							
+0005	+0020	+0007	+0013	+0·1	+0·1	+0·1	+0·1
MARINO POINT							
0000	+0010	0000	+0010	+0·1	+0·1	0·0	0·0
CORK CITY							
+0005	+0010	+0020	+0010	+0·4	+0·4	+0·3	+0·2
ROBERTS COVE (approx 4M SW of Roche's Point)							
−0005	−0005	−0005	−0005	−0·1	0·0	0·0	+0·1

NOTE: Cobh is a Standard Port. Daily predictions are above.

SHELTER
Very good in all conditions, esp in Crosshaven and East
Passage. There are 3 main marinas at Crosshaven (see
Facilities), plus a small private marina and several ⚓s
further up the Owenboy River, in particular at Drake's
Pool. There is also a marina at E Ferry in E Passage at the
E end of Great Island. Cobh and Cork City are ferry/
commercial ports; before proceeding up river contact
Port Operations for advice on possible yacht berths.
NAVIGATION
WPT 51°46'·00N, 08°15'·30W, 174°/354° from/to front ldg
lt, 2·8M. There are no navigational dangers for yachts. It
is one of the safest hbrs to enter in the world, being deep
and well marked. Tidal streams run about 1½kn in ent at
sp, but more between the forts. Main chan up to Cork is
buoyed.
Ent to Owenboy River carries at least of 2·5m at LWS,
and the chan is buoyed. Head for Cage buoy (C1), Fl G
10s to pick up the ldg lts 252°.

LIGHTS AND MARKS
The hammerhead water tr S of Crosshaven is a very
conspic mark, 24·5m high.
Ldg lts, two sets, both below Fort Davis on E shore:
(a) Oc 5s, 29/37m 10M lead 354° E of Hbr Rks. At the
front ldg lt is also a Dir lt WRG 354°, sectors: FG 351·5°-
352·75° (0·75°), AIWG352·25°-353° (0·75°), FW353°-355°
(2°), AIWR355°-355·75° (0·75°), FR355·75°-356·5° (0·75°).
(b) Oc R 5s, 11/21m 5M, lead 034° W of Hbr Rks.
Ldg lts, FW 10/15m 3M, with W ◇ day marks, lead 252° to
Crosshaven; lts are now easier to see and chan carries
3m LWS. 6 extra buoys are laid during Race weeks.
RADIO TELEPHONE
Call: *Cork Hbr Radio* (Port Ops) VHF Ch 12 14 16 (H24);
Crosshaven BY Ch M (Mon– Fri: 0830– 1700LT). Royal
Cork YC Marina Ch M (1000– 2359LT). East Ferry Marina
Ch M 80 (0800– 2200LT).
TELEPHONE (Dial code 021)
Hr Mr 273125; Port Operations 811380; MRCC (01)
6620922/3; Coast/Cliff Rescue Service 831448; ⌗ 271322;
Recorded Weather 964600; Police 831222; Dr 831716;
Ⓗ + Emergency 546400.
FACILITIES
Royal Cork YC Marina (90 + 15 visitors) ☎ 831023, ⛽
831586, £12, AC, FW, P (cans), Bar, R, Slip;
Crosshaven BY Marina (100 + 20 visitors) ☎ 831161, ⛽
831603, £10, AC, BH (40 ton), C (1·5 tons), M, Ⓔ, CH, D, P,
EI, FW, Gas, Gaz, ME, Sh, Slip (100 tons);
Salve Marine (28 + 12 visitors) ☎ 831145, ⛽ 831747, AB
£10, M, FW, AC, BY, EI, ME, C, CH, D, P (cans), Slip;
East Ferry Marina (85 + 15 visitors) ☎ 811342, £10, D, AC,
FW, Bar, R, Slip; access all tides, max draft 5·5m.
Services: EI, ME, Slip, SM, ACA, CH, BY, Ⓔ. **Crosshaven
Village** Bar, Dr, L, ✉, R, V, ⊙, YC, Gas, Gaz.
Cork City All facilities. Ferries (to UK and France), ⇌, ✈.

KINSALE 10-12-20

Cork 51°40'·80N 08°30'·00W   Rtg 1-1-1

CHARTS
AC 2053, 1765; Imray C56; Irish OS 87

TIDES
−0600 Dover; ML 2·2; Duration 0600; Zone 0 (UT)

Standard Port COBH (←—)

Times				Height (metres)			
High Water		Low Water		MHWS	MHWN	MLWN	MLWS
0500	1100	0500	1100	4·1	3·2	1·3	0·4
1700	2300	1700	2300				
Differences KINSALE							
−0019	−0005	−0009	−0023	−0·2	0·0	+0·1	+0·2

SHELTER
Excellent, except in very strong SE winds. Access H24 in all weathers/tides. Small marina at Kinsale BY, opposite Money Pt. Marinas at Kinsale YC and Castlepark; NNW of latter is FV pontoon and no ‡ area. Hbr speed limit 6kn.

NAVIGATION
WPT 51°40'·00N 08°30'·00W, 181°/001° from/to Charles's Fort lt, 1·7M. Beware: Bulman Rk (0·9m; SCM lt buoy) 4ca S of Preghane Pt; and Farmer Rk (0·6m) ¾ca off W bank.

LIGHTS AND MARKS
Charles's Fort Dir 001°, Fl WRG 5s 18m 9/6M, vis G348°-358°, W358°-004°, R004°-168° (H24). Chan is marked by PHM lt buoys. Both marinas lit as on chartlet.

RADIO TELEPHONE
VHF Ch 06 **14** 16. Kinsale and Castlepark márinas M 16.

TELEPHONE (Dial code 021)
Hr Mr 772503 (HO), 773047 (OT); MRCC (01) 6620922/3; Coast/Cliff Rescue Service 772133; ⋕ 968783; Police 772302; Dr 772253, 772717; ℍ 546400.

FACILITIES
Kinsale BY, ☎ 775134, �‌ 775405. AB (3m), M, D, FW, ME, Sh, El, C. **Kinsale YC Marina** (170 + 50 Ⓥ; 10m depth), ☎ 772196, ⛴ 774455, £11, M, FW, AC, D, P, Slip, C, R, Bar; **Castlepark Marina** (70+20 Ⓥ) ☎ 774959, �‌ 774958, £11, 10m, FW, AC, M, Slip, Bar, El, ▢; ferry (3 mins) to town. **Services**: D, ME, El, Ⓔ, C (35 ton), CH, Gas, Gaz, SM. **Town** EC Thurs; P, D, V, R, Bar, ✉, Ⓑ, ⇌ , ✈ (bus to Cork).

MINOR HARBOUR 2M EAST OF KINSALE

OYSTER HAVEN, Cork, 51°41'·20N 08°26'·90W. Rtg 3-5-2. AC 2053, 1765. HW −0600 on Dover; ML 2·2m; Duration 0600. See 10.12.20. Good shelter but subject to swell in S winds. Enter 0·5M N of Big Sovereign, a steep islet divided into two. Keep to S of Little Sovereign on E side of ent. There is foul ground off Ballymacus Pt on W side, and off Kinure Pt on E side. Pass W of Hbr Rk (0·9m) off Ferry Pt, the only danger within hbr. ‡ NNW of Ferry Pt in 4–6m on soft mud/weed. NW arm shoals suddenly about 5ca NW of Ferry Pt. Also ‡ up N arm of hbr in 3m off the W shore. Weed in higher reaches may foul ‡. No lts, marks or radio telephone. Coast/Cliff Rescue Service ☎ (021) 770711. Facilities at Kinsale. See 10·12·20.

COURTMACSHERRY 10-12-21

Cork 51°38'·22N 08°40'·90W   Rtg 3-3-1

CHARTS
AC 2081, 2092; Imray C56; Irish OS 87

TIDES
HW −0610 on Dover; Duration 0545; Zone 0 (UT)

Standard Port COBH (←—)

Times				Height (metres)			
High Water		Low Water		MHWS	MHWN	MLWN	MLWS
0500	1100	0500	1100	4·1	3·2	1·3	0·4
1700	2300	1700	2300				
Differences COURTMACSHERRY							
−0029	−0007	+0005	−0017	−0·4	−0·3	−0·2	−0·1

SHELTER
Good shelter up-river, but in strong S/SE winds seas break on the bar (2·3m), when ent must not be attempted. Berth on pontoon/jetty or dry out against the quay. ‡ NE of Ferry Pt in about 2·5m or N of the quay. Weed.may foul ‡; best to moor fore/aft.

NAVIGATION
WPT, 51°37'·50N 08°40'·17W, 144°/324° from/to Wood Pt, 0·8M. Appr in the W sector of Wood Pt lt, between Black Tom and Horse Rk (dries 3·6m); the latter is 3-4½ca E of Barry Pt on the W shore. Black Tom (2·3m), with unlit SHM buoy 5ca SSE, is close NE of the appr. Beware other hazards further to NE: In centre of bay, Barrel Rk (dries 2·6m), has unlit SCM perch (no topmark). To NNW and E of it are Inner Barrels (0·5m) and Blueboy Rk. The river is entered between Wood Pt and a SHM buoy 2ċa NE, Fl G 3s. Chan (2m) is marked by 4 unlit SHM spar buoys; keep about ½ − ¾ca off the S shore and close N of moorings.

LIGHTS AND MARKS
Wood Pt Fl (2) WR 5s 15m 5M, W315°-332° (17°), R332°-315° (343°). Old Hd of Kinsale, Fl (2) 10s 72m 25M, RC.

RADIO TELEPHONE
None.

TELEPHONE (023)
Hr Mr/RNLI 46311/46199; Dr 46142; Police 46122; Coast Rescue Service ☎ 40110.

FACILITIES
Quay AB, FW, D, L, Slip, LB. **Village** ✉, Bar, R, ✈ (Cork).

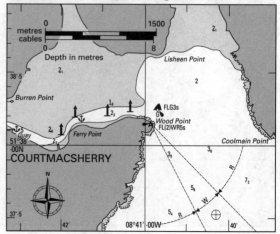

GLANDORE   10-12-22

Cork, 51°33'·70N 09°07'·20W

CHARTS
AC 2092; Imray C56; Irish OS 89
TIDES
Approx as for 10·12·23 Castletownshend. Zone 0 (UT)
SHELTER
Excellent. ‡ 1½ca SW of Glandore Pier in 2m or 1ca NE of the New pier at Unionhall in 3m.
NAVIGATION
WPT 51°32'·35N 09°05'·10W, 309°/129° from/to Outer Dangers 1·2M. Approach between Adam Is and Goat's Hd, thence keep E of Eve Is and W of the chain of rks: Outer, Middle and Inner Dangers and Sunk Rk. Before altering W for Unionhall, stand on to clear mudbank 1ca off S shore.
LIGHTS AND MARKS
Galley Hd, Fl (5) 20s, is 5M E of the ent. Outer Dangers are marked by a preferred-chan-to-port bn (GRG), Fl (2+1) G 10s, and a PHM bn (not on chartlet); Middle and Inner Dangers by 2 SHM bns; and Sunk Rk by a NCM lt buoy, Q.
RADIO TELEPHONE
None.
TELEPHONE (Dial code 028)
No Hr Mr; Police 48162; Dr 21488; Coast Rescue ☎ 33115.
FACILITIES
FW at both piers; **Glandore** CH, YC, ⊠, R, V, Bar, Kos.
Unionhall D, P, ME, Gas, ⊠, R, Bar, V.

CASTLE HAVEN   10-12-23

Cork 51°30'·90N 09°10'·70W

CHARTS
AC 2129, 2092; Imray C56; Irish OS 88, 89
TIDES
+0605 Dover; ML 2·2; Duration 0605; Zone 0 (UT)

Standard Port COBH (←—)

Times				Height (metres)			
High Water		Low Water		MHWS	MHWN	MLWN	MLWS
0500	1100	0500	1100	4·1	3·2	1·3	0·4
1700	2300	1700	2300				
Differences CASTLETOWNSHEND							
−0020	−0030	−0020	−0050	−0·4	−0·2	+0·1	+0·3
CLONAKILTY BAY							
−0033	−0011	−0019	−0041	−0·3	−0·2		No data

SHELTER
Excellent ‡ protected from all weathers and available at all tides, H24, although the outer part of hbr is subject to swell in S winds. ‡ in midstream SE of Castletownshend slip; N of Cat Island, or upstream as depth permits.
NAVIGATION
WPT 51°29'·00N, 09°10'·00W, 171°/351° from/to Reen Pt lt, 2M. Enter between Horse Is and Skiddy Is both of which have foul ground all round. Black Rk lies off the SE side of Horse Is and is steep-to along its S side. Inside Horse Is, Flea Sound is a narrow boat chan, obstructed by rks. Colonel Rk (0·5m) lies close to the E shore, 2ca N of Reen Pt. A submarine cable runs E/W across the hbr from the slip close N of Reen Pier to the slip at Castletownshend.
LIGHTS AND MARKS
Reen Pt lt, Fl WRG 10s 9m 5/3M; W tr; vis G shore– 338°, W338°– 001°, R001°– shore. A ruined tr stands on E end of Horse Is.
RADIO TELEPHONE
None.
TELEPHONE (Dial code 028)
MRCC (01) 6620922/3; Coast/Cliff Rescue Service 21039; ⌗ Bantry (027) 50061; Police 36144; Dr 21488; Ⓗ 21677.
FACILITIES
Reen Pier L, FW; **SC** ☎ 36100. **Castletownshend Village** Slip, Bar, R, V, FW, ⊠, Ⓑ (Skibbereen), ⇌ , ✈ (Cork).

ANCHORAGE W OF TOE HEAD

BARLOGE CREEK, Cork, 51°29'·57N 09°17'·58W. AC 2129. Tides approx as Castletownshend. A narrow creek, well-sheltered except from S/SE winds. Appr with Gokane Pt brg 120°. Enter W of Bullock Is, keeping to the W side to clear rks S of the island. ‡ W of the Is in 3m. No facilities.

BALTIMORE   10-12-24

Cork 51°28'·30N 09°23'·40W

CHARTS
AC 3725, 2129; Imray C56; Irish OS 88
TIDES
–0605 Dover; ML 2·1; Duration 0610; Zone 0 (UT)

Standard Port COBH (⟵)

Times				Height (metres)			
High Water		Low Water		MHWS	MHWN	MLWN	MLWS
0500	1100	0500	1100	4·1	3·2	1·3	0·4
1700	2300	1700	2300				
Differences BALTIMORE							
–0025	–0005	–0010	–0050	–0·6	–0·3	+0·1	+0·2

SHELTER
Excellent; access H24. Hbr, partly drying, is between N
and S piers. The marina (20 berths) is a large water barge
at the end of the S pier. Possible AB on N side of N pier
for FW. ⚓ N or W of N pier, or in Church Strand Bay
beyond LB slip in 2 to 3m. In strong W'ly winds ⚓ off
ruined castle on Sherkin Is (off chartlet), 1ca N of ferry
and submarine cable. A similar water barge/marina is
close S on Sherkin Is at the jetty below ruined abbey.
NAVIGATION
WPT 51°27'·80N 09°23'·42W, 180°/000° from/to Loo Rk
SHM Fl G 3s, 0·62M. Beware Lousy Rks (SCM bn) and
Wallis Rk (PHM buoy, QR) in the middle of the bay. Hbr
can also be entered from the N via The Sound, but this is
tricky and not recommended; ICC SDs essential. R Ilen is
navigable on the flood for at least 4M above The Sound.
LIGHTS AND MARKS
Ent easily identified by conspic W tr (Lot's Wife) to stbd
on Beacon Pt and Barrack Pt lt ho, Fl (2) WR 6s, to port.
RADIO TELEPHONE
VHF Ch 09 16.
TELEPHONE (Dial code 028)
Hr Mr 20132; MRCC (01) 6620922/3; Coast/Cliff Rescue
Service 20125; ✚ (027) 50061; Police 20102; Dr 21488;
Ⓗ 21677.
FACILITIES
Marina (20 inc visitors) ☎ (021) 774959, ⚓ (021) 774958,
(May-Sept), Slip, AB, FW; **Baltimore SC** ☎/⚓ 20426, Bar,
showers, visitors welcome; **Glenans Irish Sailing School**
☎ (01) 6611481. **Services:** P & D, BY, ME, El, CH, V, Gas,
Gaz, Kos, Sh, ACA;
Village EC None; P, Bar, ✉, ⇌ (bus to Cork), ✈ (Cork).

ADJACENT ANCHORAGES

HORSESHOE HARBOUR, 51°28'·20N 09°23'·86W. Small unlit
hbr on Sherkin Is, 3ca WSW of ent to Baltimore. Keep to
the W at narrow ent. ⚓ in about 5m in centre of cove.

CLEAR ISLAND, NORTH HARBOUR, 51°26'·60N 09°30'·20W.
AC 2129. Tides approx as Schull, 10.12.25. A tiny, partly
drying inlet on N coast of Clear Is, exposed to N'ly swell.
There are rks either side of the outer appr 196°. Inside the
narrow (30m), rky ent keep to the E. ⚓ fore & aft on E side
in about 1·5m or berth at inner end of pier. Few facilities.

ROARING WATER BAY
Long Island Bay, entered between Cape Clear and Mizen
Hd, extends NE into Roaring Water Bay (AC 2129). The
Fastnet Rk, Fl 5s 49m 28M, Horn (4) 60s, is 4M to
seaward. Safest appr, S of Schull, is via Carthy's Sound
(51°30'N 09°30'W), but beware Toorane Rks, Anima Rk and outlying
rks off many of the islands. Shelter in various winds at ⚓s
clockwise from Horse Island: 3ca E and 7ca NE of E tip of
Horse Is; in Ballydehob B 2m; Poulgorm B 2m; 5ca ENE
of Mannin Is in 4m; 2ca SE of Carrigvalish Rks in 6m.
Rincolisky Cas (ru) is conspic on S side of bay. The
narrow chan E of Hare Is and N of Sherkin Is has two ⚓s;
it also leads via The Sound into Baltimore hbr. Local
advice is useful. There are temp fair weather ⚓s in the
Carthy's Islands. Rossbrin Cove, 2·5M E of Schull, is a
safe ⚓, but many local moorings; no access from E of
Horse Is due to drying Horse Ridge. No facilities at most
of the above ⚓s.

SCHULL   10-12-25
Cork 51°30'·80N 09°32'·00W

CHARTS
AC 2129, 2184; Imray C56; Irish OS 88
TIDES
+0610 Dover; ML 1·8; Duration 0610; Zone 0 (UT)

Standard Port COBH (←—)

Times				Height (metres)			
High Water		Low Water		MHWS	MHWN	MLWN	MLWS
0500	1100	0500	1100	4·1	3·2	1·3	0·4
1700	2300	1700	2300				
Differences SCHULL							
−0040	−0015	−0015	−0110	−0·9	−0·6	−0·2	0·0

SHELTER
Good, except in strong S/SE winds when best shelter is N
of Long Island. Schull Hbr access H24. ⚓ in 3m clear of
fairway, 1ca SE of pier, usually lit by street lts all night.
NAVIGATION
WPT 51°29'·60N 09°31'·60W, 166°/346° from/to front ldg
lt, 2·1M. In mid-chan between Schull Pt and Coosheen Pt,
keep E of Bull Rk (dries 1·8m) marked by a R iron perch.
LIGHTS AND MARKS
Ldg lts, Oc 5s 5/8m 11M, lead 346° between Long Is Pt, Q
(3) 10s 16m 8M, W ○ tr, and Amelia Rk SHM buoy Fl G 3s;
thence E of Bull Rk and toward head of bay. By day 2 W
radomes conspic on Mt Gabriel (2M N of Schull) lead 355°
with Long Is Pt lt ho in transit.
RADIO TELEPHONE
None.
TELEPHONE (Dial code 028)
Hr Mr 28136; MRCC (01) 6620922/3; Coast/Cliff Rescue
Service 35117; ⌗ (027) 50061; Police 28111; Dr 28311;
Ⓗ (027) 50133.

⚓ Report to Hr Mr

FACILITIES
Schull Pier Slip, M, D, L, FW, AC, AB; **Sailing Club** ☎
28286; **Services:** Kos, BY, M, Sh, Slip, CH.
Village EC Tues; P, ME, El, Sh, V, R, Bar, ⊠, Ⓑ, ⇌ (bus to
Cork), ✈, car ferry (Cork).

CROOKHAVEN   10-12-26
Cork 51°28'·50N 09°42'·00W

CHARTS
AC 2184; Imray C56; Irish OS 88
TIDES
+0550 Dover; ML 1·8; Duration 0610; Zone 0 (UT)

Standard Port COBH (←—)

Times				Height (metres)			
High Water		Low Water		MHWS	MHWN	MLWN	MLWS
0500	1100	0500	1100	4·1	3·2	1·3	0·4
1700	2300	1700	2300				
Differences CROOKHAVEN							
−0057	−0033	−0048	−0112	−0·8	−0·6	−0·4	−0·1
DUNMANUS HARBOUR							
−0107	−0031	−0044	−0120	−0·7	−0·6	−0·2	0·0
DUNBEACON HARBOUR							
−0057	−0025	−0032	−0104	−0·8	−0·7	−0·3	−0·1

SHELTER
Excellent, but holding is poor, especially in strong SW'lies.
⚓s in middle of bay in 3m; off W tip of Rock Is, and E of
Granny Is; last two are far from the village. Beware weed.
A pontoon for 10-12 yachts was intended for summer 97.
NAVIGATION
WPT 51°28'·50N 09°40'·50W, 094°/274° from/to Rock Is lt
ho, 1M. Ent between this lt and NCM bn on Black Horse
Rks (3½ca ESE). From S, keep 1ca E of Alderman Rks and
½ca off Black Horse Rks bn. Passage between Streek Hd
and Alderman Rks is not advised. Inside the bay the
shores are steep to.
LIGHTS AND MARKS
Lt ho on Rock Is (conspic W tr) L Fl WR 8s 20m 13/11M;
vis outside hbr: W over Long Is Bay–281°, R281°–340°; vis
inside hbr: R 281°–348°, W348°–N shore.
RADIO TELEPHONE
None.
TELEPHONE (Dial code 028)
MRCC (01) 6620922/3; Coast/Cliff Rescue Service Goleen
35318; ⌗ (027) 50061; Dr 35148.
FACILITIES
Village Sh, ME, V, Kos, Ⓑ (Bantry), ⊠, ⇌ and ✈ (Cork).

ADJACENT HARBOURS

GOLEEN (Kireal-coegea), Cork, 51°29'·65N 09°42'·21W.
AC 2184. Tides as Crookhaven. A narrow inlet 6ca N of
Spanish Pt; good shelter in fair weather, except from SE.
2 churches are easily seen, but ent not visible until close.
Keep to S side of ent and ⚓ fore-and-aft just below quay,
where AB also possible. Facilities: P, V, Bar.

DUNMANUS BAY, Cork. AC 2552. Tides see 10.12.26.
Appr between Three Castle Hd and Sheep's Hd, Fl (3)
WR 15s 83m 18/15M; no other lts. Ent to **Dunmanus Hbr**,
51°32'·70N 09°39'·86W, is 1ca wide; breakers both sides.
⚓ in 4m centre of B. **Kitchen Cove**, 51°35'·50N 09°38'·05W,
is the best of the 3 hbrs; enter W of Owens Is and ⚓ 1ca
NNW of it or 2ca further N in 3m. Exposed to S, but good
holding. Quay at Ahakista village: V, R, Bar. **Dunbeacon
Hbr**, 51°36'·35N 09°33'·60W, is shallow and rock-girt. ⚓ E
or SE of Mannion Is. At Durrus (1¼M): Fuel (cans), R, Bar.

12

BANTRY BAY   10-12-27

Cork 51°34'N 09°57'W

CHARTS

AC 1838, 1840, 2552; Imray C56; Irish OS 84, 85, 88

TIDES

+0600 Dover; ML 1·8; Duration 0610; Zone 0 (UT)

Standard Port COBH (←)

Times				Height (metres)			
High Water		Low Water		MHWS	MHWN	MLWN	MLWS
0500	1100	0500	1100	4·1	3·2	1·3	0·4
1700	2300	1700	2300				
Differences BANTRY							
–0045	–0025	–0040	–0105	–0·9	–0·8	–0·2	0·0
CASTLETOWN (Bearhaven)							
–0048	–0012	–0025	–0101	–0·9	–0·6	–0·1	0·0
BLACK BALL HARBOUR							
–0115	–0035	–0047	–0127	–0·7	–0·6	–0·1	+0·1

SHELTER/NAVIGATION

Bantry Bay extends 20M ENE from Sheep's Hd, Fl (3) WR 15s 83m 18/15M. Access is easy, but the B is exposed to W'lies. The shore is clean everywhere except off Bear Is and Whiddy Is. Some of the many well sheltered ‡s on the N shore are detailed on this page. The S shore has few ‡s. See also chartlet 10.12.28.

CASTLETOWN, 51°38'·80N 09°54'·45W. AC 1840. Sheltered ‡ in 2·4m NW of Dinish Is, to E of 010° ldg line; also at **Dunboy B**, W of Piper Sound (open to E). Lts: At W ent, Ardnakinna Pt, Fl (2) WR 10s 62m 17/14M. At E ent to

Bearhaven: Roancarrigmore, Fl WR 3s 18m 18/14M. Appr W of Bear Is on 024° Dir lt, Oc WRG 5s 4m 14/11M (W024°–024·5°); thence inner ldg lts 010°, both Oc 3s 4/7m 1M, vis 005°-015°, via ent chan which narrows to 50m abeam Perch Rk lt bn, QG. Beware Walter Scott Rk (2·7m), SCM buoy, Q (6) + L Fl 15s, and Carrigaglos (0·6m high) S of Dinish Is. VHF Ch 08 16. Hr Mr ☎ (027) 70220, ☎ 70329. Facilities: FW & D on quay; BH on Dinish Is. **Town** El, ME, Sh, P (cans), Bar, ⑧, ✉, V, R, Kos.

HARBOURS AT EAST END OF BEAR ISLAND

LAWRENCE'S COVE, 51°38'·28N 09°49'·28W AC 1840. Good shelter on N side of Bear Island, open only to the N. ‡ in 4m to W of Turk Is or, closer in, to NW of rky ridge off E shore. New marina on S side of cove has E/W pontoon 50m long (about 2.4m at LW). ☎/⊜ 027 75044, mobile ☎ 087 506429; VHF Ch 16. AB (£10), FW, AC, D, R. At Rerrin village: BY, Slip, V, R, Bar, ✉; Glenans sailing school.

LONEHORT HARBOUR, 51°38'·12N 09°47'·80W. AC 1840. At E tip of Bear Is, good shelter but keep S at ent to clear unmarked rks; then turn ENE to ‡ in 2·7m at E end of cove.

ADRIGOLE, 51°40'·51N 09°43'·22W. AC 1840.1M SSW of ent beware Doucallia Rk, dries 1·2m. Beyond the 2ca wide ent, keep E of Orthons Is (rks on W side). ‡s to suit wind direction: off pier on E shore 4m; N or NW of Orthons Is. Good shelter, but squally in W/N gales. Drumlave (½M E): V.

HARBOURS AT THE HEAD OF THE BAY

GLENGARIFF, 51°44'·20N 09°31'·90W. AC 1838. Tides as Bantry. Beautiful ‡ S of Bark Is in 7-10m; or to NE in 3m. Better for yachts than Bantry hbr. Ent between Big Pt and Gun Pt. No lts/marks. Keep 1ca E of rks off Garinish Island (Illnacullen) and Ship Is; beware marine farms. Rky chan W of Garinish, with HT cable 15m clearance, should not be attempted. Facilities: **Village** FW, Bar, D, P, ✉, R, V, Kos.

BANTRY, 51°40'·85N 09°27'·85W. AC 1838. Beware Gerane Rks 1M W of Whiddy Is lt, Oc 2s 22m 3M, vis 073°-106°. Appr via the buoyed/lit N chan (10m) to E of Horse and Chapel Is; keep 2ca off all islands to clear unlit mussel rafts. The S chan, fair weather only, has a bar 2m; ldg marks 091°, front RW post, FW lt; rear W post, FR lt. VHF Ch 14 11 16 (H24). Hr Mr (027) 505205; ✆ 50061; Police 50045; Dr 50405; ⊞ 50133. MRCC (01) 6620922. Facilities: **Pier** L, FW; **Bantry Bay SC** ☎ 50081 Slip, L; **Town** EC Wed; P & D (cans), Kos, ME, CH, V, R, Bar, ✉, ⑧, bus to Cork.

KENMARE RIVER   10-12-28

Kerry 51°45'.00N 10°00'.00W   Rtg 1-5-2

CHARTS

AC 2495; Imray C56; Irish OS 84

TIDES

+0515 Dover; Duration Dunkerron 0620; West Cove 0610.
Zone 0 (UT)

Standard Port COBH (◄—)

Times				Height (metres)			
High Water		Low Water		MHWS	MHWN	MLWN	MLWS
0500	1100	0500	1100	4·1	3·2	1·3	0·4
1700	2300	1700	2300				

Differences BALLYCROVANE HARBOUR (Coulagh Bay)
−0116	−0036	−0053	−0133	−0·6	−0·5	−0·1	0·0

DUNKERRON HARBOUR
−0117	−0027	−0050	−0140	−0·2	−0·3	+0·1	0·0

WEST COVE (51°46'N 10°03'W)
−0113	−0033	−0049	−0129	−0·6	−0·5	−0·1	0·0

BALLINSKELLIGS BAY
−0119	−0039	−0054	−0134	−0·5	−0·5	−0·1	0·0

VALENTIA HARBOUR (Knights Town)
−0118	−0038	−0056	−0136	−0·6	−0·4	−0·1	0·0

SHELTER

Garnish Bay: is only good in settled weather and W'ly winds. ⚓ either W or 1ca S of the Carrigduff concrete bn.
Ballycrovane: in NE of Coulagh B is a good ⚓, but open to W'ly swell which breaks on submerged rks in SE. N and E shores are foul. ⚓ ½ca NE of Bird Is.
Cleanderry: Ent NE of Illaunbweeheen (Yellow Is) is only 7m wide and rky. ⚓ ENE of inner hbr.
Ardgroom: excellent shelter, but intricate ent over rky bar. Appr with B bn brg 135°; then 2 W bns (front on Black Rk, rear ashore) lead 099° through bar. Alter 206° as two bns astern come in transit. When clear, steer WNW to ⚓ ½ca E of Reenavade pier; power needed. Beware fish farms.
Kilmakilloge: is a safe ⚓ in all winds. Beware mussel beds and rky shoals. On appr steer W of Spanish Is, but pass N of it. Ldg lts 041°, both Iso Y 8s, for Bunaw Hbr (access only near HW; AB for shoal draft). ⚓ 2ca E of Spanish Is; 2ca W of Carrigwee bn; S of Eskadawer Pt; or Collorus Hbr.
Ormond's Hbr: gives good shelter, but beware rk 2½ca ENE of Hog Is. ⚓ in S half of bay.

Kenmare: Good shelter. Access only near HW. 2 W piles in line astern mark max depth to the quay (AB) on N side of river, just below town.
Dunkerron Hbr: Ent between Cod Rks and The Boar to ⚓ 1ca NW of Fox Is in 3·2m; land at Templenoe pier. 4ca E of Reen Pt behind pier, AB (£IR6) at floating jetty in 1·5m.
Sneem: enter between Sherky Is and Rossdohan Is. Hotel conspic NE of hbr. ⚓ NE of Garinish Is, but uncomfortable when considerable swell passes each side of Sherky Is.
Darrynane: 1½M NW of Lamb's Hd, is appr'd from the S between Deenish and Moylaun Islands, but not with high SW swell. Enter with care on the ldg marks/lts 034°, 2 W bns, both Oc 3s 10/16m 4M. Safe ⚓ (3m) NE of Lamb's Is. Other ⚓s include Lehid Hbr, R Blackwater, Coongar Hbr and W Cove.

NAVIGATION

WPT 51°40'.00N 10°17'.20W, 245°/065° from/to 0.5M S of Sherky Island 15·6M. At night, an appr into the river is possible, but close appr to hbrs or ⚓s is not advised. From SW, keep NW of The Bull and Dursey Is. From SE, Dursey Sound is possible in fair wx but narrow (beware Flag Rk 0·3m) and with cable car, 21m clearance. To clear dangerous rks off Coulagh Bay, keep twr on Dursey Is well open of Cod's Head 220°. From NW, there are 3 deep chans off Lamb's Head: between Scarriff Is and Deenish Is which is clear; between Deenish and Moylaun Is which has rky shoals; and between Moylaun and Two Headed Is which is clear and 4½ca wide. Up-river from Sneem Hbr, keep N of Maiden Rk, dries 0·5m, and Church Rks; also Lackeen Rks. Beware salmon nets Jun -Sep. See 10.12.5.

LIGHTS AND MARKS

On Dursey Is: Old Watch Twr (conspic) 250m. Eagle Hill (Cod's Hd) 216m. The few lights are as on chartlet.

RADIO TELEPHONE

None.

TELEPHONE (Dial code 064)

MRCC (01) 6620922/3; Coast/Cliff Rescue Service (Waterville) (066) 74320; ✠ Bantry (027) 50061; Ⓗ 41088.

FACILITIES

ARDGROOM (Pallas Hbr): D & P (cans), V, R, Bar, Kos, ✉ at Ardgroom village (2M SSW of Reenavade pier).
KILMAKILLOGE: **Bunaw Pier**, AB, V, Bar; 2M to D, Kos, ✉.
KENMARE: AB. **Town** D & P (cans), Kos, Gaz, R, V, Bar, Ⓗ, ✉, Ⓑ, ⇌ (bus to Killarney), ✈ (Cork or Killarney).
SNEEM: L at Hotel Parknasilla & Oysterbed Ho pier (FW).
Town (2M from hbr), P & D (cans), R, Bar, ✉, Slip, V, Kos.

ANCHORAGES ON S SIDE OF ENTRANCE TO DINGLE BAY

PORTMAGEE, Kerry, 51°53'·20N 10°22'·29W. AC 2125. HW +0550 on Dover; ML 2·0m; Duration 0610; See 10·12·28 under VALENTIA HBR. A safe ⚓ 2·5M E of Bray Hd in Portmagee Sound between the mainland and Valentia Is. The ent to the Sound often has bad seas„ but dangers are visible. Care required E of Reencaheragh Pt (S side) due rks either side. Deepest water is N of mid-chan. ⚓ off the pier in 5m, opposite Skelling Heritage Centre (well worth a visit). AB on pier is not recommended due to strong tides. Facilities: ⚓, FW, V, R, Bar, Kos. 1ca E of pier, road bridge centre span opens, as pre-arranged with ☎ (066) 77174 or call *Valentia Radio* VHF Ch 24, 28; giving access to Valentia Hbr (Knight's Town) via intricate chan with 1·5m.

VALENTIA HARBOUR, Kerry, 51°56'·20N 10°19'·31W. AC 2125. Tides at 10.12.28. Main ent is at NE end of Valentia Is, between Fort Pt and Beginish Is. Easy access except in strong NW winds. Fort Pt lt, Fl WR 2s 16m 17/15M, W102°-304°, R304°-351°, obsc'd from seaward when E of Doulus Head. Ldg lts 141°: Front Dir Oc WRG 4s 25m 11/8M, W sector 140°-142°; rear, Oc 4s 43m 5M, synch. Beware Hbr Rk, 2·6m, 3ca SE of Fort Pt and 100m SW of ldg line; marked by ECM bn Q (3) 10s. Good shelter in ⚓s at: Glanleam B, 6ca S of Fort Pt in 4m; 1ca NW of LB slip in 2·5m (beware The Foot, spit drying 1·2m, marked by ECM buoy, Q (3) 5s); off the ferry pier at Knight's Town (E end of the island) in 4m; in bay on the S side of Beginish Is in 3m. Moorings via Hr Mr ☎ (066) 76124. Facilities (Knightstown): BY, Sh, ME, Gas, Fuel (cans), Kos, some V, R, Bar, ⊠. Ferry/bus to Cahersiveen (2½M) for all normal shops; EC Thurs.

DINGLE   10-12-29

Kerry 52°07'·14N 10°15'·48W   Rtg 1-1-1

CHARTS
AC 2790, 2789; Imray C55, 56; Irish OS 70
TIDES
+0540 Dover; ML 2·1m; Duration 0605; Zone 0 (UT)

Standard Port COBH (⟵)

Times				Height (metres)			
High Water		Low Water		MHWS	MHWN	MLWN	MLWS
0500	1100	0500	1100	4·1	3·2	1·3	0·4
1700	2300	1700	2300				
Differences DINGLE							
–0111	–0041	–0049	–0119	–0·1	0·0	+0·3	+0·4
SMERWICK HARBOUR							
–0107	–0027	–0041	–0121	–0·3	–0·4	No data	
FENIT PIER (Tralee Bay)							
–0057	–0017	–0029	–0109	+0·5	+0·2	+0·3	+0·1

SHELTER
Excellent at marina (5m depth) in landlocked hbr. A busy fishing port. There is ⚓ 7ca S of pier, clear of dredged chan and semi-submerged store pots.

NAVIGATION
WPT 52°06'·20N 10° 15'·48W, 180°/360° from/to lt Fl G 3s, 1·06M. Easy ent H24. Beware Crow Rk (dries 3·7m), 0·8M SW of Reenbeg Pt; and rky ledge SW of Black Pt. Note: Castlemaine Hbr, approx 15M E at the head of Dingle Bay, largely dries and should not be attempted.
LIGHTS AND MARKS
Eask Twr (195m, with fingerpost pointing E) is conspic 0·85M WSW of ent. Lt tr, Fl G 3s 20m 6M, on NE side of ent. Ent chan, dredged 2·6m, is marked by 4 SHM lt buoys and 3 PHM lt buoys, as chartlet. Ldg lts, both Oc 3s, (◊ daymarks) lead from astern 182° to hbr bkwtrs.
RADIO TELEPHONE
Ch M, 14 (occas). Valentia Radio (Ch 24 28) has good VHF cover and will relay urgent messages to Dingle.
TELEPHONE (Dial code 066)
Hr Mr 51629; MRCC (01) 6620922/3; ‖ 21480; Dr 51341; Ⓗ 51455; Police 51522. NB: 999 best for all emergencies.
FACILITIES
Marina (60 + 20 visitors) ☎/⚓ 51629, £10, AC, FW, D, C (hire). **Town** EC Thurs; P (cans), Kos, ME, Ⓔ, SM, ⊠, R, Bar, V, Ⓑ, ⇌ Tralee (by bus), ✈ (Kerry/Farranfore 30M).

ANCHORAGE CLOSE WEST OF DINGLE BAY

VENTRY Kerry, 52°06'·70N 10°20'·30W. AC 2790, 2789. HW +0540 on Dover; ML 2·1m; Duration 0605; See 10·12·29. Ent is 2M W of conspic Eask Tr. A pleasant hbr with easy ent 1M wide and good holding on hard sand; sheltered from SW to N winds, but open to swell from the SE, and in fresh W'lies prone to sharp squalls. Beware Reenvare Rks 1ca SE of Parkmore Pt; also a rky ridge 2·9m, on which seas break, extends 2·5ca SSE of Ballymore Pt. ⚓ off Ventry Strand in approx 4m (⊕ brg W, the village NE) or in 3m S side of bay, 1ca N of pier. On N side a new pier, almost dries, gives access to Ventry village. No lts. Facilities: L, P, Slip, V, Kos, Bar, R, ⊠.

ANCHORAGES BETWEEN THE BLASKETS AND KERRY HD

SMERWICK HARBOUR, Kerry, 52°13'·00N 10°24'·00W. AC 2789. Tides 10.12.29. Adequate shelter in this 1M wide bay, except from NW'ly when considerable swell runs in. Ent between East Sister (150m hill) and Dunacapple Is to the NE. ⚓s at: the W side close N or S of the Boat Hr in 3-10m; to the S, off Carrigveen Pt in 2·5m; or in N'lies at the bay in NE corner inside 10m line. Facilities: Ballynagall village on E side has pier (0·5m) and limited V, Bar, Bus.

BRANDON BAY, Kerry, 52°16'·10N 10°09'·92W. AC 2739. Tides as Fenit 10.12.29. A 4M wide bay, very exposed to the N, but in moderate SW-W winds there is safe ⚓ in 6m close E of drying Brandon Pier, 2FG (vert). Cloghane Inlet in SW of Bay is not advised. Facilities at Brandon: limited V, P (1M), ⊠, R, Bar, bus.

TRALEE BAY, Kerry, 52°18'·00N 09°56'·00W. AC 2739. HW –0612 on Dover; ML 2·6m; Duration 0605. See 10·12·29. Enter the bay passing 3M N of Magharee Islands. Pick up the W sector (W140°–152°) of Little Samphire Is lt, Fl WRG 5s 17m 16/13M; see 10.12.4 for sectors. Approach between Magharee Is and Mucklaghmore (30m high).   *Continued*

FENIT HARBOUR, 52°16'·20N 09°51'·61W, is in SE corner of Tralee Bay (see above). Appr on 146° to Little Samphire Island lt, Fl WRG 5s 17m 16/13M, thence 7ca E to the new marina. Good shelter, but may be exposed to E/NE'lies. Samphire Is has 3 conspic fuel tanks and lt QR 15m 3M vis 242°–097°. Fenit Pier head 2 FR (vert) 12m 3M, vis 148°–058°. For ⚓s call *Neptune* (Tralee SC) VHF Ch 14 16, or ⚓ N of the pier hd in 4m on good holding. Hr Mr ☎/📠 (066) 36231; ⌗ ☎ 36115.
Marina (114 inc Ⓥ; max LOA 15m), £10, FW, AC, D, Ⓞ;
Village Slip, C, P (cans), ME, V, Bar, R, ✉.

SHANNON ESTUARY   10-12-30

Clare (N); Kerry and Limerick (S) 52°35'·00N 09°40'·00W

CHARTS
AC 1819, 1547, 1548, 1549, 1540; L. Derg 5080; L. Ree 5078. Imray C55. OS 63, 64. The ICC's *Sailing Directions for S & W Ireland* and/or Admiralty *Irish Coast Pilot* are essential.

TIDES

HW at	HW Galway	HW Dover
Kilbaha & Carrigaholt	–0015	+0605
Tarbert	+0035	–0530
Foynes	+0050	–0515
Limerick	+0130	–0435

At Limerick strong S-W winds increase the height and delay the times of HW; strong N-E winds do the opposite.

SHELTER
The Shannon Estuary is 50M long, (Loop Hd to Limerick). For boats on passage N/S the nearest ⚓ is Kilbaha Bay, 3M inside Loop Hd; it has ⚓s sheltered in winds from W to NE, but is exposed to swell and holding is poor.

6M further E, Carrigaholt Bay has ⚓s and good shelter from W'lies; ⚓ just N of the new quay, out of the tide. Kilrush marina (10.12.31) with all facilities is 7M further E. From Kilconly and Kilcredaun Pts in the W to the R Fergus ent (about 25M) there are ⚓s or ⚓s, protected from all but E winds, at Tarbert Is, Glin, Labashadee, Killadysert and among the islands in the Fergus mouth. The best ⚓ in the estuary is at Foynes on the S bank, with also a pontoon off the YC. There are drying quays at Ballylongford Creek (Saleen), Knock and Clarecastle (S of Ennis, off chartlet). Yachts may enter Limerick Dock, but this is a commercial port with usual problems; major improvements planned.

NAVIGATION
WPT 52°32'·50N 09°46'·90W, Ballybunnion NCM By VQ, 244°/064° from/to Tail of Beal Bar buoy WCM, Q (9) 15s, 4·2M. For notes on ent and tidal streams see 10·12·5. The ebb can reach 4kn. The lower estuary between Kerry and Loop Heads is 9M wide, narrowing to 2M off Kilcredaun Pt. Here the chan is well buoyed in mid-stream and then follows the Kerry shore, S of Scattery Is. From Tarbert Is to Foynes Is the river narrows to less than 1M in places, before widening where the R Fergus joins from the N, abeam Shannon airport.
Above this point the buoyed chan narrows and becomes shallower although there is a minimum of 2m at LWS. AC 1540 is essential for the final 15M stretch to Limerick.

RIVER SHANNON
The Shannon, the longest navigable river in the UK or Ireland, is managed by Limerick Hbr Commissioners up to Limerick. Up-stream it effectively becomes an inland waterway; progress is restricted by locks and bridges. Info on navigation and facilities can be obtained from the Office of Public Works, Shannon Navigation Branch, Athlone, Co Westmeath; or Inland Waterways Assoc'n of Ireland, Kingston Ho, Ballinteer, Dublin 4, ☎ 01-983392; also from Tourist Offices and inland marinas.

LIGHTS AND MARKS
Principal lts are listed in 10·12·4. There are QW (vert) aero hazard lts on tall chimneys at Money Pt power station 3M ESE of Kilrush. 2 chys at Tarbert Is are conspic (R lts).

RADIO TELEPHONE
Foynes Ch 12 13 16 (occas). Limerick Ch 12 13 16 (HO).

FACILITIES
Marine facilities are available at several communities on the Shannon; P & D (cans), FW, V, M can be found at many villages. ⚓s are being laid at Labasheeda, Glin Pier (pontoon) and Foynes. E of Aughanish Is on S shore, R Deal is navigable 3M to Askeaton. Ent, marked by RW bn, is 8ca SE of Beeves Rk with 1m in buoyed chan. BY at Massey's Pier ☎ 061-392198, 📠 392344, ⚓s, FW, C, CH, AC, D, Slip. At the two major hbrs facilities include:
Foynes Slip, L, AB, P & D (cans), FW, ✉, Ⓑ, Dr, V, R, Bar;
Foynes YC ☎ (069) 65261, Bar, R.
Limerick: Hbr Commission ☎ (061) 315377; ⌗ ☎ 415366.
City Slip, AB, L, FW, P & D (cans), Kos, Gas, Gaz, ME, El, Dr, Ⓗ, ✉, all usual city amenities, ⇌, ✈ (Shannon).

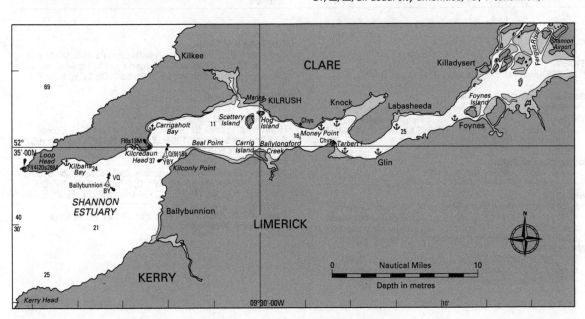

KILRUSH   10-12-31

Clare 52°37'·90N 09°29'·70W   Rtg 1-1-1

CHARTS
AC 1547, 1819; Imray C55; Irish OS 63
TIDES
−0555 Dover; ML 2·6; Duration 0610; Zone 0 (UT)

Standard Port GALWAY (→)

Times				Height (metres)			
High Water		Low Water		MHWS	MHWN	MLWN	MLWS
1000	0500	0000	0600	5·1	3·9	2·0	0·6
2200	1700	1200	1800				
Differences KILRUSH							
−0006	+0027	+0057	−0016	−0·1	−0·2	−0·3	−0·1

SHELTER
Excellent in Kilrush Creek Marina (2·7m), access via lock H24. Close to the E, Cappagh hbr partly dries, but is well sheltered except in SE winds; pier is constantly used by Shannon pilot boats and tugs. Day ⚓ in lee of Scattery Is.
NAVIGATION
WPT 52°37'·00N 09°32'·10W, 242°/062° from/to SWM buoy, 1·33M. See also 10·12·30. From seaward usual appr is N of Scattery Is (conspic Round Twr, 26m); beware Baurnahard Spit and Carrigillaun to the N. Coming down-river between Hog Is and mainland, beware Wolf Rk.

LIGHTS AND MARKS
Ldg marks 055° White Ho on with Glynn's Mill. SWM By L Fl 10s (52°37'·6N 09°30'·2W) marks ent to buoyed chan (dredged 2·5m), with ldg lts 355°, both Oc 3s, to lock. Fl G 3s 2M, S side of lock.
RADIO TELEPHONE
VHF Ch 12 16. Marina Ch 80.
TELEPHONE (Dial code 065)
Hr Mr 51327; Lock 52155; MRCC (01) 6620922/3; Coast/ Cliff Rescue Service 51004; ☰ (061) 415366; Weather (061) 62677; Police 51017; Dr (065) 51581.
FACILITIES
Marina (120+50) ☎ 52072, mobile 087-2313870, ⛽ 51692, £9.10, £2.50 for <6hrs, AC, FW, D, P (cans), Slip, BY, CH, Gas, Gaz, Kos, BH (45 ton), C (26 ton), ME, El, ◎, V;
Cappagh, Slip, AB, L, FW, P, V.
Town EC Thurs; El, CH, V, R, Bar, Dr, ✉, Ⓑ, ⇌ (bus to Limerick), ✈ (Shannon).

VOLVO PENTA SERVICE

Sales and service centres in area 13
Northern Ireland *Robert Craig & Sons Ltd*, 15-21 Great Georges Street,
Belfast BT15 1BW Tel (01232) 232971

Area 13

North Ireland
Lambay Island, north to Liscanor Bay

VOLVO PENTA

13

North Ireland

Lambay Island, north to Liscanor Bay

Tory Island
(RC) 313·00 TY 100M

Fanad Head

Horn Head

Bloody Foreland

Mulroy Bay

Sheep Haven

Gweedore /
Bunbeg*

Aranmore

Burtonport*

Lough Swilly
(i) 10.13.16

Boylagh Bay

Glen Head Radio
📞 VHF 24 67 16
☼ VHF 24 every
3h from 0103 LT

Teelin Harbour*

Rathlin O'Birne

Donegal

St John's Point

Killybegs
(i) 10.13.17
📞 VHF 16

Mullaghmore

Donegal Bay

Finner Camp
🚁

Eagle Island
(RC) 307·00 GL 100M

Portnafrankagh*
Ballyglass

Broadhaven*

Killala Bay

**Ballysaddare
Bay**

Killala*

Frenchport*

Belmullet Radio
📞 VHF 83 67 16
☼ VHF 83 every
3h from 0103 LT

Sligo
(RC Aero) 384·00 SLG 25M

Sligo
(i) 10.13.18
📞 VHF 12 14 16

**Black
Rock**
54°00'
·00N

**Blacksod
Bay**

Achill I.

Achill Head

Achillbeg I.

Clare I. *Clew Bay*

Inishturk

Inishraher

**Westport
and Clew Bay**
(i) 10.13.19

Inishbofin

Killary*

Inishark

Ballynakill*

Clivden Radio
📞 VHF 26 67 16
☼ VHF 26 every
3 hr from 0103 LT

Clifden Bay

**Slyne
Head**

Malin CG
Valentia CG

Rossaveel
📞 VHF 12 14 16

Galway Hbr*

Galway Bay

Galway Bay
(i) 10.13.20
📞 VHF 12 16

Eeragh Island
Inishmore

Kilronan

Black Head

Aran Islands

Inisheer
Liscanor Bay

Variation 10°W (1998)

Key to Symbols

📞 Coast Radio Station: VHF/MF frequencies
📞 Port, VTS, or Marina Radio: VHF frequencies
(RC) Marine RDF beacon
(RC Aero) Aero RDF beacon
(i) See for harbour information/tidal data
☼ Weather information
(Frequencies/times of broadcasts)
🚁 SAR Helicopter base
☆ Selected Principal Lights
🚩 Light vessel/Light float/Lanby
(O)RG Emergency VHF DF
* See Area Index

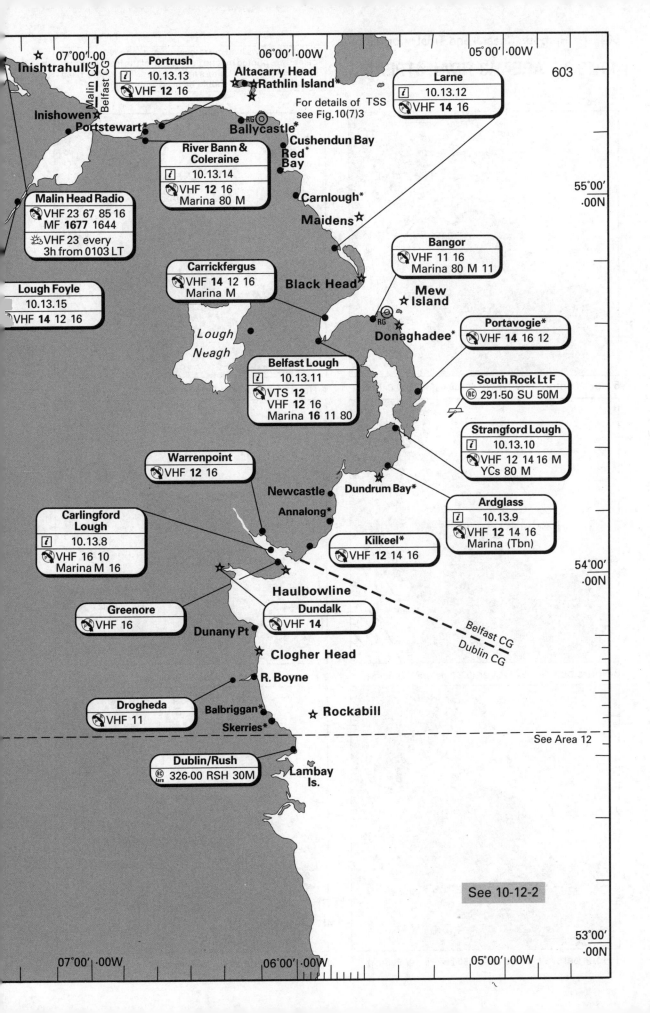

☆ Inishtrahull

Portrush
ⓘ 10.13.13
📻 VHF **12** 16

☆ Altacarry Head
☆ Rathlin Island*

For details of TSS
see Fig.10(7)3

Larne
ⓘ 10.13.12
📻 VHF **14** 16

603

Inishowen ☆
Portstewart*

Ballycastle*

Cushendun Bay
Red*
Bay

River Bann & Coleraine
ⓘ 10.13.14
📻 VHF **12** 16
Marina 80 M

● Carnlough*
Maidens ☆

55°00'
·00N

Malin Head Radio
📻 VHF 23 67 85 16
MF **1677** 1644
☼ VHF 23 every
3h from 0103 LT

Bangor
📻 VHF 11 16
Marina 80 M 11

Lough Foyle
10.13.15
📻 VHF **14** 12 16

Carrickfergus
📻 VHF **14** 12 16
Marina M

Black Head ☆

Mew
☆ **Island**

Portavogie*
📻 VHF **14** 16 12

Donaghadee*

Lough

Neagh

South Rock Lt F
Ⓡ 291·50 SU 50M

Belfast Lough
ⓘ 10.13.11
📻 VTS **12**
VHF **12** 16
Marina **16** 11 80

Strangford Lough
ⓘ 10.13.10
📻 VHF 12 14 16 M
YCs 80 M

Warrenpoint
📻 VHF **12** 16

Newcastle
Annalong*

Dundrum Bay* ☆

Ardglass
ⓘ 10.13.9
📻 VHF **12** 14 16
Marina (Tbn)

Carlingford Lough
ⓘ 10.13.8
📻 VHF **16** 10
Marina M 16

Kilkeel*
📻 VHF **12** 14 16

54°00'
·00N

Haulbowline

Belfast CG
Dublin CG

Greenore
📻 VHF 16

Dunany Pt

Dundalk
📻 VHF **14**

☆ Clogher Head

R. Boyne

Drogheda
📻 VHF 11

Balbriggan*

Skerries*

☆ **Rockabill**

See Area 12

Dublin/Rush
Ⓡ 326·00 RSH 30M
Aero

**Lambay
Is.**

See 10-12-2

53°00'
·00N

07°00'·00W   06°00'·00W   05°00'·00W

10-13-3   AREA 13 TIDAL STREAMS

The tidal arrows (with no rates shown) off the NW coast of Ireland are printed by kind permission of the Irish Cruising Club, to whom the Editors are indebted. They have been found accurate, but should be used with caution.

5 Hours before HW Dover (0450 before HW Belfast)

4 Hours before HW Dover (0350 before HW Belfast)

3 Hours before HW Dover (0250 before HW Belfast)

2 Hours before HW Dover (0150 before HW Belfast)

1 Hour before HW Dover (0050 before HW Belfast)

HW Dover (0010 after HW Belfast)

The tidal arrows (with no rates shown) off the NW coast of Ireland are printed by kind permission of the Irish Cruising Club, to whom the Editors are indebted. They have been found accurate, but should be used with caution.

Southward 10.12.3   North Irish Sea 10.10.3
SW Scotland 10.9.3

1 Hour after HW Dover (0110 after HW Belfast)

2 Hours after HW Dover (0210 after HW Belfast)

3 Hours after HW Dover (0310 after HW Belfast)

4 Hours after HW Dover (0410 after HW Belfast)

5 Hours after HW Dover (0510 after HW Belfast)

6 Hours after HW Dover (0610 after HW Belfast)

10.13.4 COASTAL LIGHTS, FOG SIGNALS AND WAYPOINTS

Abbreviations used below are given in 1.4.1. Principal lights are in **bold** print, places in CAPITALS, and light-vessels, light floats and Lanbys in *CAPITAL ITALICS*. Unless otherwise stated lights are white. m – elevation in metres; M – nominal range in miles. Fog signals are in *italics*. Useful waypoints are underlined – use those on land with care. All geographical positions should be assumed to be approximate. See 4.4.1. All positions are referenced to Ordnance Survey of Ireland for South Ireland and OSGB 36 for North Ireland.

LAMBAY ISLAND TO DONAGHADEE

Rockabill 53°35'·80N 06°00'·20W Fl WR 12s 45m **W22M, R18M**; W Tr, B band; vis W178°-329°, R329°-178°; *Horn (4) 60s*. Also shown by day when ຈ) is operating.
Skerries Bay Pier Hd 53°35'·08N 06°06'·43W Oc R 6s 7m 7M; W col; vis 103°-154°.
Balbriggan 53°36'·75N 06°10'·75W Fl (3) WRG 20s 12m W13M, R10M, G10M; W Tr; vis G159°-193°, W193°-288°, R288°-305°.

DROGHEDA

Lts in line about 248°. **Front,** 53°43'·14N 06°14'·80W Oc 12s 8m **15M**; Tr, W lantern; vis 203°-293°. **Rear,** 85m from front, Oc 12s 12m **17M**; Tr; vis 246°-252°.
North Light 53°43'·43N 06°15'·20W Fl R 4s 7m **15M**; Tr, W lantern; vis 282°-288°; tfc sigs.
Aleria Lt Bn 53°43'·34N 06°14'·27W QG 11m 3M; G Bn.
Lyons Lt Bn 53°43'·24N 06°41'·20W R 5s 2m. Above this Pt Lts on stbd hand when ent are G, and on port hand R.
Dunany Lt By 53°53'·55N 06°09'·40W Fl R 3s; PHM.

DUNDALK

Giles Quay 53°59'·04N 06°14'·35W Fl G 3s;vis 030°-210°.
N training wall Hd, **Pile Lt** 53°58'·54N 06°17'·68W Fl WR 15s 10m **W21M, R18M**; W Ho; vis W124°-151°, R151°-284°, W284°-313°, R313°-124°. Oc G 5s 8m; same Tr; vis 325·5°-328·5°; Fog Det Lt VQ 7m, vis when brg 358°; *Horn (3) 60s*.
No. 2 Bn 53°58'·33N 06°17'·73W Fl (2) R 5s 4m 3M; 2 in R □.
No. 8 Bn 53°59'·30N 06°18'·91W Fl R 3s; R pile. Above this Pt Lts on stbd hand when ent are QG, and on port hand QR.
Imogene Lt By 53°57'·02N 06°06'·95W Fl (2) R 10s; PHM.
Carlingford Lt By 53°58'·75N 06°01'·06W L Fl 10s; *Whis;* SWM.

CARLINGFORD LOUGH/NEWRY RIVER

Hellyhunter Lt By 54°00'·34N 06°01'·99W Q (6) + L Fl 15s; *Whis;* Racon (K); SCM.
Haulbowline 54°01'·18N 06°04'·68W Fl (3) 10s 32m **17M**; Gy Tr; reserve Lt 15M; Fog Det Lt VQ 26m; vis 330°.
Turning Lt FR 21m 9M; same Tr; vis 196°-208°; *Horn 30s*.
Ldg Lts 310·4° Front, 54°01'·78N 06°05'·37W Oc 3s 7m 11M; R △ on Tr; vis 295°-325°. Rear, 457m from front, Oc 3s 12m 11M; R ▽ on Tr; vis 295°-325°; both H24.
Greenore Pier Hd 54°02'·06N 06°07'·91W Fl R 7·5s 10m 5M.
Carlingford Quay Hd 54°02'·59N 06°11'·01W Fl 3s 5m 2M.
Newry River Ldg Lts 310·4°. Front, 54°06'·37N 06°16'·46W. Rear, 274m from front. Both Iso 4s 5/15m 2M; stone cols.
Warren Pt Bkwtr Hd 54°05'·78N 06°15'·20W Fl G 3s 6m 3M.

KILKEEL

Pier Hd 54°03'·45N 05°59'·27W Fl WR 2s 8m 8M; vis R296°-313°, W313°-017°.
Meeney's Pier Hd Fl G 3s 6m 2M.

ANNALONG

E Bkwtr Hd 54°06'·50N 05°53'·65W Oc WRG 5s 8m 9M; Tr; vis G204°-249°, W249°-309°, R309°-024°.

DUNDRUM BAY

St John's Pt 54°13'·60N 05°39'·23W Q (2) 7·5s 37m **25M**; B ● Tr, Y bands; H24 when ຈ) operating.
Auxiliary Lt Fl WR 3s 14m **W15M**, R11M; same Tr; vis W064°-078°, R078°-shore; Fog Det Lt VQ 14m vis 270°; *Horn (2) 60s*.
Dundrum Hbr FR on W side of chan outside Hbr and 3 FR on W side of chan inside Hbr when local vessels expected. FR on flagstaffs S and E of ent when firing takes place.
DZ East By 54°13'·50N 05°46'·16W; SPM.
DZ Middle By 54°13'·00N 05°48'·50W; SPM.
DZ West By 54°13'·34N 05°50'·00W; SPM.

ARDGLASS

Inner Pier Hd 54°15'·78N 05°36'·28W Iso WRG 4s 10m W8M, R7M, G5M; Tr; vis G shore-308°, W308°-314°, R314°-shore.
Outer Pier Hd 54°15'·62N 05°36'·07W Fl R 3s 10m 5M.

STRANGFORD LOUGH

Strangford Lt By 54°18'·63N 05°28'·62W L Fl 10s;*Whis;* SWM.
Bar Pladdy Lt By 54°19'·33N 05°30'·43W Q (6) + L Fl 15s; SCM.
Angus Rk 54°19'·83N 05°31'·48W Fl R 5s 15m 6M shown H24.
Dogtail Pt Ldg Lts 341° Front, 54°20'·78N 05°31'·78W Oc (4) 10s 2m 5M. Rear, Gowlands Rk, 0·8M from front, Oc (2) 10s 6m 5M.
Salt Rk 56°21'·41N 05°32'·60W Fl R 3s 8m 3M.
Swan I 54°22'·37N 05°33'·10W Fl (2) WR 6s 5m; W col; vis W115°-334°, R334°-115°.
Church Pt Bn 54°22'·59N 05°33'·35W Fl (4) R 10s.
Portaferry Pier Hd 54°22'·81N 05°32'·94W Oc WR 10s 9m W9M, R6M; Or mast; vis W335°-005°, R005°-017°, W017°-128°.
Killyleagh Town Rk Bn 54°23'·61N 05°38'·47W Q 4M; PHM.
Limestone Rk 54°25'·13N 05°36'·04W QR 3m 3M.
Butter Plady Lt By 54°22'·44N 05°25'·66W Q (3) 10s; ECM.

SOUTH ROCK Lt F 54°24'·48N 05°21'·94W Fl (3) R 30s 12m **20M**; R hull and Lt Tr, W Mast; RC; Racon (T); *Horn (3) 45s*.

PORTAVOGIE/BALLYWATER/DONAGHADEE

Plough Rk Lt By 54°27'·39N 05°25'·04W Fl (2) R 10s; PHM.
S Pier Hd 54°27'·44N 05°26'·08W, Iso WRG 5s 9m 9M; ■ Tr; vis G shore-258°, W258°-275°, R275°-348°.
Skulmartin Lt By 54°31'·83N 05°24'·83W L Fl 10s; *Whis;* SWM.
Ballywalter, Bkwtr Hd 54°32'·67N 05°28'·75W Fl WRG 1·5s 5m 9M; vis G240°-267°, W267°-277°, R277°-314°. Unreliable.
Donaghadee, S Pier Hd 54°38'·70N 05°31'·80W Iso WR 4s 17m **W18M**, R14M; W Tr; vis W shore-326°, R326°-shore; *Siren 12s*.

DONAGHADEE TO RATHLIN ISLAND

Governor Rks Lt By 54°39'·36N 05°31'·93W Fl R 3s; PHM.
Deputy Reefs Lt By 54°39'·51N 05°31'·88W Fl G 2s; SHM.
Foreland Spit Lt By 54°39'·64N 05°32'·25W Fl R 6s; PHM.
Ninion Bushes By 54°41'·07N 05°30'·40W; PHM.

BELFAST LOUGH

Mew I NE end 54°41'·91N 05°30'·73W Fl (4) 30s 37m **24M**; B Tr, W band; Racon (O).
S Briggs Lt By 54°41'·19N 05°35'·66W Fl (2) R 10s; PHM.

BANGOR

N Pier Hd 54°40'·02N 05°40'·30W Iso R 12s 9m14M.
Dir Lt 105°. 54°39'·98N 05°40'·09W Dir Oc 10s WRG 1M; vis G093°-104·8°, W104·8°-105·2°, R105·2°-117°.
Marina ent 54°39'·97N 05°40'·22W Fl G 3s 5m 1M.

Belfast No. 1 Chan Lt By 54°41'·67N 05°46'·30W I QG; *Bell*; SHM.
Cloghan Jetty Lt By 54°44'·10N 05°41'·52W QG; SHM.
Kilroot power station intake 54°43'·20N 05°45'·82W Oc G 4s; 2 QR on chy 500m N.

CARRICKFERGUS
E Pier Hd 54°42'·63N 05°48'·30W Fl G 7·5s 5m 4M; G col.
Marina E Bkwtr Hd 54°42'·71N 05°48'·63W QG 8m 3M; G ● pillar.
W Bkwtr QR 7m 3M; R ● pillar.
Pier Hd 54°42'·58N 05°48'·71W F WRG 5m 3M; vis G308°-317·5°, W317·5°-322·5°, R322·5°-332°.
Black Hd 54°45'·99N 05°41'·27W Fl 3s 45m **27M**; W 8-sided Tr; RC.
N Hunter Rk Lt By 54°53'·04N 05°45'·05W Q; NCM.
S Hunter Rk Lt By 54°52'·69N 05°45'·22W Q (6) + L Fl 15s.

LARNE
Barr Pt 54°51'·50N 05°46'·73W; *Horn 30s*. Fog Det Lt VQ.
No. 1 Lt By 54°51'·62N 05°47'·53W Q (3) 10s; ECM.
No. 3 Lt By 54°51'·27N 05°47'·56W Fl (2) G 6s; SHM.
Chaine Tr 54°51'·27N 05°47'·82W Iso WR 5s 23m **16M**; Gy Tr; vis W230°-240°, R240°-shore.
Larne No. 2 Lt Bn 54°51'·07N 05°47'·47W Fl R 3s.
Ent Ldg Lts 184°, No. 11 Front, 54°49'·59N 05°47'·74W Oc 4s 6m 12M; W ◊ with R stripe on R pile structure; vis 179°-189°.
No. 12 Rear, 610m from front, Oc 4s 14m 12M; W ◊ with R stripe on R ● Tr; synch with front, vis 179°-189°.
Maidens 54°55'·73N 05°43'·60W Fl (3) 20s 29m **24M**; W Tr, B band; Racon (M). Auxiliary Lt Fl R 5s 15m 8M; same Tr; vis 142°-182° over Russel and Highland Rks.

CARNLOUGH/RED BAY
Carnlough Hbr N Pier 54°59'·58N 05°59'·20W Fl G 3s 4m 5M; W col, B bands.
Red Bay Pier 55°03'·92N 06°03'·12W Fl 3s 10m 5M.

RATHLIN ISLAND TO INISHTRAHULL

RATHLIN ISLAND
Rue Pt 55°15'·53N 06°11'·40W Fl (2) 5s 16m 14M; W 8-sided Tr, B bands.
Drake Lt By 55°17'·00N 06°12'·41W Q (6) + L Fl 15s; SCM.
Altacarry Hd Rathlin E 55°18'·06N 06°10'·23W Fl (4) 20s 74m **26M**; W Tr, B band; vis 110°-006° and 036°-058°; Racon (O).
Rathlin W 0·5M NE of Bull Pt 55°18'·05N 06°16'·75W Fl R 5s 62m **22M**; W Tr, lantern at base; vis 015°-225°; H24.
Manor House 55°17'·56N 06°11'·64W Oc WRG 4s 5M; vis G020°-023°, W023°-026°, R026°-029°.

PORTRUSH
N Pier Hd 55°12'·35N 06°39'·52W Fl R 3s 6m 3M; vis 220°-160°.
Portstewart Pt 55°11'·32N 06°43'·20W Oc R 10s 21m 5M; R ■ hut; vis 040°-220°.

RIVER BANN/COLERAINE
Ldg Lts 165°. Front, 55°09'·95N 06°46'·17W Oc 5s 6m 2M; W Tr. Rear, 245m from front, Oc 5s 14m 2M; W ■ Tr. R. marked by Fl G on stbd hand, and Fl R on port.
W Mole 56°10'·32N 06°46'·40W Fl G 5s 4m 2M; Gy mast; vis 170°-000°.
Lough Foyle Lt By 55°15'·32N 06°52'·55W L Fl 10s; *Whis*; SWM;
Tuns Lt By 55°14'·00N 06°53'·49W Fl R 3s; PHM.

Inishowen 55°13'·56N 06°55'·69W Fl (2) WRG 10s 28m **W18M**, R14M, G14M; W Tr, 2 B bands; vis G197°-211°, W211°-249°, R249°-000°; *Horn (2) 30s*. Fog Det Lt VQ 16m vis 270°.

LOUGH FOYLE
Greencastle Ldg Lts 032°. Front, 55°12'·20N 06°58'·90W Fl 3s 11m 2M; Or ◊ on mast. Rear, 50m from front, Fl 3s 13m 2M; Or ◊ on mast. F WR 10m; vis R072°-082°, W082°-072°. F WR 5m; vis R037°-052°, W052°-037°.
Warren Pt Lt Bn Tr 55°12'·58N 06°57'·06W Fl 1·5s 9m 10M; W ● Tr, G abutment; vis 232°-061°.
Magilligan Pt 55°11'·74N 06°57'·97W QR 7m 10M; R structure. FR, 700m SE, when firing taking place.
McKinney's Bk 55°10'·92N 07°00'·50W Fl R 5s 6m 4M; R pile structure.
Moville 55°11'·00N 07°02'·06W Fl WR 2·5s 11m 4M; W house on G piles vis W240°-064°, R064°-240°.
Above this point the chal to R.Foyle is marked by Lts Fl G, when entering, on stbd hand, and Fl R on port hand. G Lts are shown from W structures on G or B piles; R Lts from W structures on R piles.
Kilderry 55°04'·09N 07°13'·95W Fl G 2s 6m 3M; W structure.
Muff 55°03'·63N 07°14'·21W Fl G 2s 5m 3M; G structure.
Coneyburrow 55°03'·32N 07°14'·42W Fl G 2·5s 5m 3M.
Faughan 55°03'·12N 07°14'·42W Fl R 4s 5m 3M.
Culmore Pt 55°02'·78N 07°15'·20W Q 6m 3M; G ● Tr.
Culmore Bay 55°02'·72N 07°15'·65W Fl G 5s 4m 2M.
Ballynagard 55°02'·28N 07°16'·37W Fl 3s 6m 3M; W lantern on G ● house.
Otter Bank 55°01'·95N 07°16'·65W Fl R 4s 6m 3M; W structure on R ● Tr.
Brook Hall 55°01'·70N 07°17'·07W QG 6m 3M; W structure on G base.
Mountjoy 55°01'·25N 07°17'·49W QR 5m 3M; W lantern on R piles.
Inishtrahull 55°25'·85N 07°14'·58W Fl (3) 15s 59m **25M**; W Tr; Racon (T).

INISHTRAHULL TO BLOODY FORELAND

LOUGH SWILLY/BUNCRANA/RATHMULLAN
Fanad Hd 55°16'·57N 07°37'·86W Fl (5) WR 20s 39m **W18M**, R14M; W Tr; vis R100°-110°, W110°-313°, R313°-345°, W345°-100°. FR on radio mast 3·08M 200°.
Swilly More Lt By 55°15'·11N 07°35'·74W Fl G 3s; SHM.
Dunree 55°11'·88N 07°33'·20W Fl (2) WR 5s 46m W12M, R9M; vis R320°-328°, W328°-183°, R183°-196°.
Colpagh Lt By 55°10'·42N 07°31'·50W; Fl R 6s; PHM.
White Strand Rks Lt By 55°09'·06N 07°29'·90W Fl R 10s; PHM.
Buncrana Pier near Hd 55°07'·61N 07°29'·82W Iso WR 4s 8m W14M, R11M; vis R shore-052° over Inch spit, W052°-139°, R139°-shore over White Strand Rk.
Rathmullan Pier Hd 55°05'·70N 07°31'·66W Fl G 3s 5M; vis 206°-345°.

MULROY BAY
Limeburner Lt By 55°18'·54N 07°48'·35W Q Fl; NCM; *Whis*.
Ravedy I 55°15'·15N 07°46'·80W Fl 3s 9m 3M; Tr; vis 177°-357°.
Dundooan Rks 55°13'·14N 07°47'·91W QG 4m 1M; G Tr.
Crannoge Pt 55°12'·29N 07°48'·37W Fl G 5s 5m 2M; G Tr.

SHEEPHAVEN
Downies Bay Pier Hd 55°11'·36N 07°50'·42W Fl R 3s 5m 2M; vis 283° through N till obsc by Downies Pt.
Portnablahy Ldg Lts 125·3°. Front 55°10'·80N 07°55'·60W Oc 6s 7m 2M; B col, W bands. Rear, 81m from front, Oc 6s 12m 2M; B col, W bands.
Tory I NW Pt 55°16'·35N 08°14'·92W Fl (4) 30s 40m **27M**; B Tr, W band; vis 302°-277°; RC; Racon (M); H24.

13

Inishbofin Pier 55°10'·1N 08°10·5W Fl 8s 3m 3M; part obsc.
Ballyness Hbr. Ldg Lts 119·5°. Front, 55°09'·0N 08°06'·9W
Iso 4s 25m 1M. Rear, 61m from front, Iso 4s 26m 1M.
Bloody Foreland 55°09'·51N 08°16'·98W Fl WG 7·5s 14m
W6M, G4M; vis W062°-232°, G232°-062°.

BLOODY FORELAND TO RATHLIN O'BIRNE

Glassagh. Ldg Lts 137·4°. Front, 55°06'·85N 08°18'·90W Oc 8s
12m 3M. Rear, 46m from front, Oc 8s 17m 3M, synch with front.
Inishsirrer, NW end 55°07'·41N 08°20'·89W Fl 3·7s 20m 4M;
W ■ Tr vis 083°-263°.

BUNBEG/MULLAGHDOO/OWEY SOUND
Gola I Ldg Lts 171·2°. Front, 55°05'·12N 08°21'·02W Oc 3s
9m 2M; W Bn, B band. Rear, 86m from front, Oc 3s 13m 2M;
B Bn, W band; synch with front.
Bo I E Pt 55°04'·78N 08°20'·08W Fl G 3s 3m; G Bn.
Inishinny No. 1 55°04'·48N 08°19'·78W QG 3m 1M; ■ col.

Inishcoole No. 4 55°03'·98N 08°18'·88W QR 4m 2M; R ■ col
on base.
Yellow Rks No. 6 55°03'·67N 08°18'·90W QR 3m 1M; ■ col
with steps; Neon.
Cruit I. Owey Sound Ldg Lts 068·3°. Front, 55°03'·07N
08°25'·79W Oc 10s. Rear, 107m from front, Oc 10s.
Rinnalea Pt 55°02'·60N 08°23'·67W Fl 7·5s 19m 9M; ■ Tr;
vis 132°-167°.

Aranmore, Rinrawros Pt 55°00'·90N 08°33'·60W Fl (2) 20s
71m **29M**; W Tr; obsc by land about 234°-007° and about
013°. Auxiliary Lt Fl R 3s 61m 13M, same Tr; vis 203°-234°.

NORTH SOUND OF ARAN/RUTLAND NORTH CHANNEL
Ldg Lts 186°. Front, 54°58'·94N 08°29'·22W Oc 8s 8m 3M;
B Bn, W band. Rear, 395m from front, Oc 8s 17m 3M; B Bn.
Ballagh Rks 54°59'·96N 08°28'·80W Fl 2·5s 13m 5M; W
structure, B band.
Black Rks 54°59'·43N 08°29'·59W Fl R 3s 3m 1M; R col.
Inishcoo Ldg Lts 119·3°. Front, 54°59'·12N 08°27'·70W Iso
6s 6m 1M; W Bn, B band. Rear, 248m from front, Iso 6s 11m
1M; B Bn, Y band.
Carrickatine No. 2 Bn 54°59'·26N 08°28'·06W QR 6m 1M;
R Bn with steps; Neon.
Rutland I Ldg Lts 137·6°. Front, 54°58'·97N 08°27'·63W Oc
6s 8m 1M; W Bn, B band. Rear, 330m from front, Oc 6s 14m
1M; B Bn, Y band.

BURTONPORT
Ldg Lts 068·1°. Front 54°58'·96N 08°26'·36W FG 17m 1M; Gy
Bn, W band. Rear, 355m from front, FG 23m 1M; Gy Bn,
Y band.

SOUTH SOUND OF ARAN/RUTLAND SOUTH CHANNEL
Illancrone I 54°56'·28N 08°28'·53W Fl 5s 7m 6M; W ■ Tr.
Wyon Pt 54°56'·50N 08°27'·50W Fl (2) WRG 10s 8m W6M,
R3M; W ■ Tr; vis G shore-021°, W021°-042°, R042°-121°,
W121°-150°, R 150°-shore.
Turk Rks 54°57'·30N 08°28'·15W Fl G 5s 6m 2M; G ■ Tr.
Aileen Reef 54°58'·18N 08°28'·78W QR 6m 1M. R ■ Bn.
Leac na bhFear 54°82'·1N 08°29'·2W Q (2) 5s 4m 2M.
Carrickbealatroha, Upper 54°58'·64N 08°28'·58W Fl 5s 3m
2M; W ■ brickwork Tr.
Corren's Rk 54°58'·12N 08°26'·68W Fl R 3s 4m 2M; R ■ Tr.
Teige's Rk 54°58'·61N 08°26'·75W Fl 3s 4m 2M; W ● Tr, ■
base.
Dawros Hd 54°49'·60N 08°33'·60W L Fl 10s 39m 4M; W■col.
Dawros Bay 54°49'·3N 08°32'W Fl (2) 10s 5m 3M.
Rathlin O'Birne, W side 54°39'·80N 08°49'·90W Fl WR 15s
35m **W18M, R14M**; W Tr; vis R195°-307°, W307°-195°;
Racon (O).

RATHLIN O'BIRNE TO EAGLE ISLAND

DONEGAL BAY, TEELIN/KILLYBEGS
Teelin Hbr 54°37'·32N 08°37'·72W Fl R 10s; R structure.
St John's Pt 54°34'·15N 08°27'·60W Fl 6s 30m 14M; W Tr.
Bullockmore Lt By 54°33'·98N 08°30'·10W Qk Fl (9) 15s;
WCM.
Rotten I 54°36'·87N 08°26'·39W Fl WR 4s 20m **W15M**,
R11M; W Tr; vis W255°-008°, R008°-039°, W039°-208°.
New Landing Dir Lt 338°. 54°38'·13N 08°26'·33W Dir WRG;
vis G328°°-334°, Al WG334°-336°, W336°-340°, Al WR340°-
342°, R342°-348°.
Killybegs Outer Lt By 54°37'·92N 08°26'·09W V Q (6) + L Fl 10s;
SCM.
Black Rk Jetty 54°38'·03N 08°26'·55W Fl RG 5s; Gy col; vis
R254°-204°, G204°-254°.
Finner Camp 54°29'·70N 08°13'·90W Aero Q WRG 67m.

SLIGO
Wheat Rk Lt By 54°18'·82N 08°39'·02W Q (6) + LFl 15s; SCM.
Black Rock 54°18'·45N 08°37'·03W Fl 5s 24m 13M; W Tr, B
band. Auxiliary Lt Fl R 3s 12m 5M; same Tr; vis 107°-130°
over Wheat and Seal rks.
Lower Rosses, N of Pt (Cullaun Bwee) 54°19'·71N 08°34'·36W
Fl (2) WRG 10s 8m W10M, R8M, G8M; W hut on piles; vis G
over Bungar bank-066°, W066°-070°, R070° over Drumcliff
bar; shown H24.
Ldg Lts 125°. Front, Metal Man 54°18'·23N 08°34'·51W Fl 4s
3m 7M. Rear, Oyster I, 365m from front, Oc 4s 13m 10M.
Both shown H24.

KILLALA
Inishcrone Pier Root 54°13'·20N 09°05'·74W Fl WRG 1·5s
8m 2M; vis W098°-116°, G116°-136°, R136°-187°.
Ldg Lts 230°. Rinnaun Pt, Front No. 1, 54°13'·53N 09°12'·21W
Oc 10s 7m 5M; ■ Tr. Rear, 150m from front, No. 2 Oc 10s 12m
5M; ■ Tr.
Dir Lt 215°, Inch I, 54°13'·29N 09°12'·25W Fl WRG 2s 6m
3M; ■ Tr; vis G205°-213°, W213°-217°, R217°-225°.
Ldg Lts 196°. Kilroe, Front, 54°12'·62N 09°12'·28W Oc 4s 5m
2M; ■ Tr. Rear, 120m from front, Oc 4s 10m 2M; ■ Tr.
Ldg Lts 236°. Pier, Front, 54°13'·01N 09°12'·80W Iso 2s 5m
2M; W ◊ on Tr. Rear, 200m from front, Iso 2s 7m 2M; W ◊ on
pole.
Killala Bay. Bone Rk, NE end 54°15'·80N 09°11'·20W Q 7m;
NCM.

BROAD HAVEN BAY
Gubacashel Pt 54°16'·05N 09°53'·28W Iso WR 4s 27m W12M,
R9M; W Tr; vis W shore (S side of bay)-355°, R355°-shore.
Ballyglass 54°15'·28N 09°53'·38W Fl G 3s.
Eagle I, W end 54°17'·02N 10°05'·51W Fl (3) 10s 67m **23M**;
W Tr; RC. Shown H24.

EAGLE ISLAND TO SLYNE HEAD

Black Rk 54°04'·00N 10°19'·20W Fl WR 12s 86m **W22M**,
R16M; W Tr; vis W276°-212°, R212°-276°.

BLACKSOD BAY
Blacksod Lt By 54°05'·88N 10°02'·96W Q (3) 10s, ECM.
Blacksod Pier Root 54°05'·91N 10°03'·60W Fl (2) WR 7·5s
13m W12M, R9M; W Tr on dwelling; vis R189°-210°, W210°-
018°.
Achill I Ridge Pt 54°01'·80N 09°58'·50W Fl 5s 21m 5M.

ACHILL SOUND
Achill Sound 53°56'·06N 09°55'·21W QR; R Bn.
Ldg Lts 330° Whitestone Pt, Front and rear both Oc 4s 5/6m;
W ◊, B stripe.
Saulia Pier 53°57'·03N 09°55'·53W Fl G 3s 12m.

Achillbeg E Lt Bn 53°52'·12N 09°56'·50W Fl R 2s 5m; R ■ Tr.
Carrigin-a-tShrutha 53°52'·29N 09°56'·70W Q (2) R 5s; R Bn.

Achill I Ldg Lts 310° Purteen 53°57'·79N 10°05'·92W (PA)
Oc 8s 5m. Rear, 46m from front Oc 8s 6m.

CLEW BAY/WESTPORT
Achillbeg I S Pt 53°51'·50N 09°56'·80W Fl WR 5s 56m
W18M, **R18M**, **R15M**; W ● Tr on ■ building; vis R262°-281°,
W281°-342°, R342°-060°, W060°-092°, R(intens) 092°-099°,
W099°-118°.
Clare I, E Pier 53°48'·00N 09°57'·00W Fl R 3s 5m 3M.
Cloghcormick By 53°50'·55N 09°43'·15W; WCM.
Dorinish Lt By 53°49'·47N 09°40'·45W Fl G 3s; SHM.
Inishgort S Pt 53°49'·60N 09°40'·20W L Fl 10s 11m 10M; W
Tr. Shown H24.
Westport Appr 53°47'·97N 09°34'·30W Fl 3s; G box on
conical Bn.
Roonagh Quay Ldg Lts 144°. Front 53°45'·80N 09°54'·20W.
Rear, 54m from front, both Iso 10s 9/15m.

INISHBOFIN/CLIFDEN BAY
Inishlyon Lyon Hd 53°36'·70N 10°09'·50W Fl WR 7·5s 13m
W7M, R4M; W post; vis W036°-058°, R058°-184°, W184°-
325°, R325°-036°.
Gun Rk 53°36'·58N 10°13'·18W Fl (2) 6s 8m 4M; W col; vis
296°-253°.

Cleggan Pt 53°34'·50N 10°07'·70W Fl (3) WRG 15s 20m
W6M, R3M, G3M; W col on W hut; vis W shore-091°, R091°-
124°, G124°-221°.
Carrickrana Rks Bn 53°29'·20N 10°09'·50W; large W Bn.
Slyne Hd, N Tr, Illaunamid 53°23'·98N 10°14'·02W Fl (2) 15s
35m **24M**; B Tr.

SLYNE HEAD TO BLACK HEAD
Inishnee 53°22'·75N 09°54'·40W Fl (2) WRG 10s 9m W5M,
R3M, G3M; W col on W ■ base; vis G314°-017°, W017°-030°,
R030°-080°, W080°-194°.
Croaghnakeela Is 53°19'·40N 09°58'·11W Fl 3·7s 7m 5M; W
col; vis 034°-045°, 218°-286°, 311°-325°.

GALWAY BAY/INISHMORE
Eeragh, Rock Is 53°08'·90N 09°51'·34W Fl 15s 35m **23M**; W
Tr, two B bands; vis 297°-262°.
Straw Is 53°07'·05N 09°37'·80W Fl (2) 5s 11m **15M**; W Tr.
Ldg Lts 192°. Front, 53°06'·25N 09°39'·70W Oc 5s 6m 3M;
W col on W ■ base; vis 142°-197°. Rear, 43m from front,
Oc 5s 8m 2M; W col on W ■ base; vis 142°-197°.

Killeany Lt By 53°07'·25N 09°38'·19W Fl G 3s; SHM.
Kilronan Pier Hd 53°07'·10N 09°39'·95W Fl WG 1·5s 5m 3M;
W col; vis G240°-326°, W326°-000°.

KIGGAUL BAY
Kiggaul Bay 53°14'·01N 09°43'·00W Fl WR 3s 5m W5M, R3M;
vis W329°-359°, R359°-059°, part obsc by W shore of bay.

CASHLA BAY/SPIDDLE
Ent W side 53°14'·23N 09°35'·14W Fl (3) WR 10s 8m W6M,
R3M; W col on concrete structure; vis W216°-000°, R000°-
069°.
Cannon Rk Lt By 53°14'·05N 09°34'·29W Fl G 5s; SHM.
Lion Pt Dir Lt 53°15'·83N 09°33'·93W Dir Iso WRG 4s 6m
W8M, R6M, G6M; W ■ Tr on col; vis G357·5°-008·5°,
W008·5°-011·5°, R011·5°-017·5°.
Rossaveel Pier Ldg Lts 116° Front, 53°15'·98N 09°33'·36W
Oc 3s 7m 3M; W mast. Rear, 90m from front, Oc 3s 8m 3M;
W mast.
Spiddle Pier Hd 53°14'·42N 09°18'·50W Fl WRG 3·5s 11m
W6M, R4M, G4M; Y col; vis G102°-282°, W282°-024°, R024°-
066°.

GALWAY
Margaretta Shoal Lt By 53°13'·67N 09°05'·95W Fl G 3s;
SHM; *Whis*.
Black Rock Lt By 53°13'·99N 09°06'·51W Fl R 3s; PHM.
Tawin Shoals Lt By 53°14'·29N 09°04'·22W Fl (3) G 10s; SHM.
Mutton Is Lt By 53°15'·06N 09°02'·89W Fl (2)R 6s; PHM.
Peter Rk By 53°15'·15N 09°01'·07W; SCM.
Leverets 53°15'·32N 09°01'·87W Q WRG 9m 10M; B ● Tr,
W bands; vis G015°-058°, W058°-065°, R065°-103°, G103°-
143·5°, W143·5°-146·5°, R146·5°-015°.
Rinmore 53°16'·11N 09°01'·93W Iso WRG 4s 7m 5M; W ■
Tr; vis G359°-008°, W008°-018°, R018°-027°.
Nimmo's Pier Hd 53°15'·99N 09°02'·77W Iso Y 6s 7m 6M.
Approach chan Ldg Lts 325°. Front, 53°16'·12N 09°02'·80W
Fl R 1·5s 12m 7M; R ◆, Y diagonal stripes on mast; vis 315°-
345°. Rear, 310m from front, Oc R 10s 19m 7M; R ◆, Y
diagonal stripes on framework Tr; vis 315°-345°.
Black Hd 53°09'·25N 09°15'·78W Fl WR 5s 20m W11M,
R8M, W ■ Tr; vis 045°-268°, R268°-276°.

Inisheer 53°02'·77N 09°31'·59W Iso WR 12s 34m **W20M,
R16M**; cis 225°-231°, W231°-245°, R245°-269°, W280°-218°;
Racon (K).

13

10.13.5   PASSAGE INFORMATION

For all Irish waters the Sailing Directions published by the Irish Cruising Club are strongly recommended, and particularly on the N and W coasts, where other information is scarce. They are published in 2 volumes: *E and N coasts of Ireland* which runs anti-clockwise from Carnsore Pt to Bloody Foreland, and *S and W coasts of Ireland* which goes clockwise.

CROSSING THE IRISH SEA (charts 1123, 1121, 1411)

Passages across the Irish Sea can range from the fairly long haul from Land's End to Cork (140M), to the relatively short hop from Mull of Kintyre to Torr Pt (11M). But such distances are deceptive, because the average cruising yacht needs to depart from and arrive at a reasonably secure hbr; also in the North Chan strong tidal streams can cause heavy overfalls. So each passage needs to be treated on its merits. See 10.0.6 for distances across the Irish Sea.

Many yachts use the Land's End/Cork route on their way to (and from) the delightful cruising ground along the S coast of Ireland, see 10.12.5. Penzance Bay, or one of the Scilly Is anchs, make a convenient place from which to leave, with good lights to assist departure.

Although the Celtic Sea is exposed to the Atlantic, there are no dangers on passage and the tidal streams are weak. A landfall between Ballycotton and Old Hd of Kinsale (RC) (both have good lights) presents no offlying dangers, and in poor vis decreasing soundings indicate approach to land. There is a likelihood, outward bound under sail, that the boat will be on the wind – a possible benefit on the return passage. If however the wind serves, and if it is intended to cruise along the southern coast, a landfall at the Fastnet with arrival at (say) Baltimore will place the yacht more to windward, for little extra distance.

From Land's End the other likely destination is Dun Laoghaire. A stop at (say) Milford Haven enables the skipper to select the best time for passing the Smalls or Bishops (see 10.11.5) and roughly divides the total passage into two equal parts. From S Bishop onwards there are the options of making the short crossing to Tuskar Rk and going N inside the banks (theoretically a good idea in strong W winds), or of keeping to seaward. But in bad weather the area off Tuskar is best avoided; apart from the Traffic Separation Scheme, the tide is strong at sp and the sea can be very rough.

The ferry route Holyhead/Dun Laoghaire is another typical crossing, and is relatively straightforward with easy landfalls either end. The tide runs hard round Anglesey at sp, so departure just before slack water minimises the set N or S. Beware also the TSS off The Skerries, see Fig. 10(3).

The Isle of Man (10.10.5) is a good centre for cruising in the Irish Sea, and its hbrs provide convenient staging points whether bound N/S or E/W.

CROSSING TO SCOTLAND (charts 2198, 2199, 2724)

Between Scotland and Northern Ireland there are several possible routes, but much depends on weather and tide. Time of departure must take full advantage of the stream, and avoid tide races and overfalls (see 10.9.5). Conditions can change quickly, so a flexible plan is needed.

From Belfast Lough ent, the passage distance to Mull of Kintyre is about 35M and, with a departure at HW Dover (also local HW) providing at least 6hrs of N-going tides, fair winds make it possible to get past the Mull or Sanda Is on one tide. But to be more confident of reaching Port Ellen or Gigha Is a departure from Carnlough or Red Bay at HW makes a shorter passage with better stream advantage. The inshore side of the TSS (Fig. 10(4)) coincides with the outer limit of the race S and SW off the Mull of Kintyre; this occurs between HW Dover + 0430 and + 0610 when a local S-going stream opposes the main N-going stream.
For information on submarine hazards see 10.9.22.

LAMBAY ISLAND TO FAIR HEAD (AC 44, 2093, 2198/9)

The coast is fairly steep-to except in larger bays, particularly Dundalk. Streams offshore run up to 2·5kn as far as Rockabill, but are weaker further N until approaching Belfast Lough. Lambay Island is private, and steep-to except on W side, where there can be overfalls. Skerries Islands (Colt, Shenick's and St Patrick's) are 1M E and SE of Red Island, to E of Skerries hbr. Shenick's Island is connected to shore at LW. Pass between Colt and St Patrick's Islands, but the latter has offliers 3ca to S. Rockabill, two steep-to rks with lt ho, is 2·5M E of St Patrick's Island.

Going NE from Carlingford Lough (10.13.8), after rounding Hellyhunter By, there are no offshore dangers until Strangford Lough (10.13.10). For Ardglass, see 10.13.9. N of Strangford keep 5ca off Ballyquintin Pt. 3M to NE is Butter Pladdy Rks; keep to E of these. 2M further N is South Rk, with disused lt ho, part of group of rks to be avoided in poor vis or bad weather by closing South Rk lt float. In good vis pass inshore of South Rk, between it and North Rks (chart 2156).

Three routes lead into Belfast Lough (10.13.11): E of Mew Is, but beware Ram Race (to the N on the ebb, and the S on the flood); Copeland Sound, between Mew Is and Copeland Is, is passable but not recommended; Donaghadee Sound is buoyed and a good short cut for yachts. Here the stream runs SSE from HW Belfast + 0530 and NW from HW Belfast – 0030, 4·5kn max. An eddy extends S to Ballyferris Pt, and about 1M offshore. For Donaghadee, see 10.13.11 and chart 3709.

N from Belfast Lough, Black Hd is clean. Pass E of Muck Is, which is steep-to. Hunter Rk (0·8m), 2·5M NE of Larne, is marked by N & S cardinals. 2M further N are the Maidens, two dangerous groups of rks extending 2·5M N/S; E Maiden is lit.

The very small hbr of Carnlough (10.13.12) provides shelter for small yachts, but should not be approached in strong onshore winds. Other anchs in offshore winds are at Red Bay (10.13.12) 5M further N, and in Cushendun B, 5M NNW of Garron Pt. All provide useful anch on passage to/from the Clyde or Western Is. Fair Hd is a bold 190m headland, steep-to all round, but with extensive overfalls in Rathlin Sound.

FAIR HEAD TO BLOODY FORELAND (chart 2723)

This is a good cruising area, under the lee of land in SW'lies, but very exposed to NW or N. Beware fishing boats and nets in many places and the North Channel TSS, see Fig. 10(4).

A fair tide is essential through Rathlin Sound where the stream runs 6kn at sp, and causes dangerous overfalls. The main stream runs NW from HW Galway – 0600 for 5hrs, and SE from HW Galway + 0100 for 4hrs. A W-going eddy runs from Fair Hd close inshore towards Carrickmannanon Rk from HW Galway + 0100, and an E-going eddy runs from HW Galway – 0500 to – 0100. The worst overfalls in the chan are from HW Galway – 0500 to – 0300, and it is best to enter W-bound at the end of this period, on the last of fair tide. Keep seaward of Carrickmannanon Rk and Sheep Is. There is a hbr in Church Bay, on the W side of Rathlin Is.

Proceeding to Portrush (10.13.13), use Skerries Sound in good weather. Enter Lough Foyle by either the North Chan W of The Tuns, or S chan passing 2ca N of Magilligan Pt and allowing for set towards The Tuns on the ebb (up to 3·5kn).

Tor Rks, Inishtrahull and Garvan Isles lie NE and E of Malin Hd. In bad weather it is best to pass at least 3M N of Tor Rks. Inishtrahull is lit and about 1M long; rks extend N about 3ca into Tor Sound. Inishtrahull Sound, between Inishtrahull and Garvan Isles, is exposed; tidal stream up to 4kn sp can raise a dangerous sea with no warning. Stream also sets hard through Garvan Isles, S of which Garvan Sound can be passed safely in daylight avoiding two sunken rks, one 1½ca NE of Rossnabarton, and the other 5ca NW. The main stream runs W for only 3hrs, from HW Galway – 0500 to – 0200. W of Malin Hd a W-going eddy starts at HW Galway + 0400, and an E-going one at HW Galway – 0300.

Note that direction of buoyage changes off Malin Head.

From Malin Head SW to Dunaff Head, at ent to Lough Swilly (10.13.16), keep 5ca offshore. Trawbreaga Lough (AC 2697) gives shelter, but is shallow, and sea can break on bar; only approach when no swell, and at half flood. Ent to L Swilly is clear except for Swilly Rks off the W shore, SSE of Fanad Hd.

W from Lough Swilly the coast is very foul. Beware Limeburner Rk (2m), 6·8M WNW of Fanad Hd. Mulroy Bay (10.13.16) has good anchs but needs accurate pilotage, as in *ICC SDs.*

Between Mulroy B and Sheephaven there is inshore passage S of Frenchman's Rk, and between Guill Rks and Carnabollion, safe in good weather; otherwise keep 1M offshore. Sheep Haven B (10.13.16) is easy to enter between Rinnafaghla Pt and Horn Hd, and has good anchs except in strong NW or N winds. Beware Wherryman Rks, dry 1·5m, 1ca off E shore.

Between Horn Hd and Bloody Foreland (chart 2752) are three low-lying islands: Inishbeg, Inishdooey and Inishbofin. The latter is almost part of the mainland; it has a temp anch on S side and a more sheltered anch on NE side in Toberglassan B. 6M offshore is Tory Is (lt, fog sig, RC) with rks for 5ca off SW side. Temp anch in good weather in Camusmore B. In Tory Sound the stream runs W from HW Galway + 0230, and E from HW Galway – 0530, sp rates 2kn.

BLOODY FORELAND TO EAGLE ISLAND (chart 2725)

Off low-lying Bloody Foreland (lt) there is often heavy swell. The coast and islands 15M SW to Aran Is give good cruising (chart 1883). An inshore passage avoids offlying dangers: Buniver and Brinlack shoals, which can break; Bullogconnell 1M NW of Gola Is; and Stag Rks 2M NNW of Owey Is. Anchs include Bunbeg and Gweedore hbr, and Cruit B which has easier access. Behind Aran Is are several good anchs. Use N ent, since S one is shallow (chart 2792). Rutland N Chan is main appr to Burtonport (10.13.16).

Boylagh B has shoals and rks N of Roaninish Is. Connell Rk (0·3m) is 1M N of Church Pool, a good anch, best approached from Dawros Hd 4·5M to W. On S side of Glen B a temp anch (but not in W or NW winds) is just E of Rinmeasa Pt. Rathlin O'Birne Is has steps E side; anch SE of them 100m offshore. Sound is 5ca wide; hold Is side to clear rks off Malin Beg Hd.

In Donegal B (chart 2702) beware uncharted rks W of Teelin, a good natural hbr but exposed to S/SW swell. Killybegs (10.13.17) has better shelter and is always accessible. Good shelter with fair access in Donegal Hbr (chart 2715). Good anch or ⚓ via YC at Mullaghmore in fair weather; sea state is calm with winds from SE through S to NW. Inishmurray is worth a visit in good weather, anch off S side. There are shoals close E and NE of the Is, and Bomore Rks 1·5M to N. Keep well clear of coast S to Sligo (10.13.18) in onshore winds, and watch for lobster pots.

Killala B has temp anch 1M S of Kilcummin Hd, on W side. Proceeding to Killala beware St Patrick's Rks. Ent has ldg lts and marks, but bar is dangerous in strong NE winds.

The coast W to Broadhaven is inhospitable. Only Belderg and Portacloy give a little shelter. Stag Rks are steep-to and high. Broadhaven (chart 2703) is good anch and refuge, but in N/ NW gales sea can break in ent. In approaches beware Slugga Rk on E side with offlier, and Monastery Rk (0·3m) on S side.

EAGLE ISLAND TO SLYNE HEAD (chart 2420)

This coast has many inlets, some sheltered. Streams are weak offshore. There are few lights. Keep 5ca off Erris Hd, and further in bad weather. Unless calm, keep seaward of Eagle Is (lt, RC) where there is race to N. Frenchport (chart 2703) is good temp anch except in strong W winds. Inishkea Is (chart 2704) can be visited in good weather; anch N or S of Rusheen Is. On passage keep 5ca W of Inishkea to avoid bad seas if wind over tide. The sound off Mullet Peninsula is

clear, but for Pluddany Rk 6ca E of Inishkea N.
Blacksod B (chart 2704 and 10.13.19) has easy ent (possible at night) and good shelter. In the approaches Black Rk (lt) has rks up to 1·25M SW. From N, in good weather, there is chan between Duvillaun Beg and Gaghta Is, but in W gales beware breakers 1M SE of Duvillaun More.

Rough water is likely off impressive Achill Hd. Achill Sound (chart 2667) is restricted by cables 11m high at swing bridge. Anchs each end of Sound, but the stream runs strongly.

Clare Is has Two Fathom Rk (3·4m) 5ca off NW coast, and Calliaghcrom Rk 5ca to the N; anch on NE side. In Clew Bay Newport and Westport (AC 2667, 2057 and 10.13.19) need detailed pilotage directions. S of Clare Is beware Meemore Shoal 1·5M W of Roonagh Hd. 2M further W is the isolated rk Mweelaun. The islands of Caher, Ballybeg, Inishturk (with anch on E side) and Inishdalla have few hidden dangers, but the coast to the E must be given a berth of 1·5M even in calm weather; in strong winds seas break much further offshore.

Killary B (chart 2706) and Little Killary both have good anchs in magnificent scenery. Consult sailing directions, and only approach in reasonable weather and good vis.

Ballynakill Hbr (chart 2706), easily entered either side of Freaghillaun South, has excellent shelter; Tully mountain is conspic to N. Beware Mullaghadrina and Ship Rk in N chan. Anch in Fahy, Derryinver or Barnaderg B. There is anch on S side of Inishbofin (lt), but difficult access/exit in strong SW wind or swell (10.13.19). Rks and breakers exist E of Inishbofin and S of Inishshark; see chart 2707 for clearing lines. Lecky Rks lie 1M SSE of Davillaun. Carrickmahoy is a very dangerous rk (1·9m) between Inishbofin and Cleggan Pt.

Cleggan B is moderate anch, open to NW but easy access. High Is Sound is usual coasting route, not Friar Is Sound or Aughrus Passage. Clifden B (chart 2708) has offlying dangers with breakers; enter 3ca S of Carrickrana Bn and anch off Drinagh Pt, in Clifden Hbr or Ardbear B; see 10.13.19.

Slyne Hd (lt) marks SW end of Rks and Is's stretching 2M WSW from coast. Here the stream turns N at HW Galway – 0320, and S at HW Galway + 0300. It runs 3kn at sp, and in bad weather causes a dangerous race. The sea may break on Barret Shoals, 3M NW of Slyne Hd.

SLYNE HEAD TO LISCANNOR BAY (chart 2173)

The Connemara coast (charts 2709, 2096) and Aran Islands (chart 3339) give excellent cruising in good vis. But there are many rks, and few navigational marks. Between Slyne Head and Roundstone B are many offlying dangers. If coasting, keep well seaward of Skerd Rks. A conspic twr (24m) on Golan Head is a key feature. Going E the better hbrs are Roundstone B, Cashel B, Killeany B, Greatman B and Cashla B. Kilronan (Killeany B) on Inishmore is only reasonable hbr in Aran Islands, but is exposed in E winds. Disused lt ho on centre of island is conspic.

Normal approach to Galway B is through N Sound or S Sound. N Sound is 4M wide from Eagle Rk and other dangers off Lettermullan shore, to banks on S side which break in strong winds. S Sound is 3M wide, with no dangers except Finnis Rk (0·4m) 5ca SE of Inisheer. The other channels are Gregory Sound, 1M wide between Inishmore and Inishmaan, and Foul Sound between Inishmaan and Inisheer. The latter has one danger, Pipe Rk and the reef inshore of it, extending 3ca NW of Inisheer.

The N side of Galway Bay is exposed, with no shelter. Galway (10.13.20) is a commercial port, with possible marina plans. 3M SE, New Hbr (chart 1984) is a more pleasant anch with moorings off Galway Bay SC. Westward to Black Hd there are many bays and inlets, often poorly marked, but providing shelter and exploration. The coast SW to Liscannor Bay is devoid of shelter. O'Brien's Twr is conspic just N of the 199m high Cliffs of Moher.

13

10.13.6   DISTANCE TABLE

Approximate distances in nautical miles are by the most direct route, whilst avoiding dangers and allowing for Traffic Separation Schemes. Places in *italics* are in adjoining areas; places in **bold** are in 10.0.6, Distances across the Irish Sea.

1.	*Dun Laoghaire*	**1**																		
2.	**Carlingford Lough**	50	**2**																	
3.	**Strangford Lough**	71	36	**3**																
4.	**Bangor**	96	61	34	**4**															
5.	**Carrickfergus**	101	66	39	6	**5**														
6.	**Larne**	108	73	45	16	16	**6**													
7.	**Carnlough**	118	78	50	25	26	11	**7**												
8.	Altacarry Head	135	102	74	45	45	31	21	**8**											
9.	**Portrush**	150	115	87	58	60	48	35	19	**9**										
10.	**Lough Foyle**	157	121	92	72	73	55	47	30	11	**10**									
11.	L Swilly (Fahan)	200	166	138	109	104	96	81	65	48	42	**11**								
12.	**Tory Island**	209	174	146	117	113	105	90	74	57	51	35	**12**							
13.	Burtonport	218	182	153	130	130	116	108	90	74	68	49	18	**13**						
14.	Killybegs	267	232	204	175	171	163	148	132	115	109	93	58	43	**14**					
15.	Sligo	281	246	218	189	179	177	156	146	123	117	107	72	51	30	**15**				
16.	Eagle Island	297	262	234	205	198	193	175	162	147	136	123	88	72	62	59	**16**			
17.	Westport	337	323	295	266	249	240	226	207	193	187	168	137	120	108	100	57	**17**		
18.	Slyne Head	352	317	289	260	257	248	234	217	201	195	178	143	128	117	114	55	44	**18**	
19.	Galway	348	366	338	309	307	297	284	266	253	245	227	192	178	166	163	104	94	49	**19**
20.	*Kilrush*	318	361	364	335	332	323	309	291	276	270	251	220	203	191	183	142	119	75	76	**20**

10.13.7   Special Notes for Ireland: see 10.12.7

MINOR HARBOURS AND ANCHORAGES TO THE NORTH WEST OF LAMBAY ISLAND

SKERRIES, Dublin, 53°35'·1N 06°06'·66W. AC 633. Tides as Balbriggan, 10.13.8. E & SE of Red Island (a peninsula) lie Colt, Shenick's and St Patrick's Islands, the latter foul to S and SW. Inshore passage between Colt and St Patrick's Is uses transit/brg as on chart to clear dangers. Good shelter and holding in 3m at Skerries Bay, W of Red Is. Appr from E or NE outside PHM buoy, Fl R 10s, off Red Is. ⚓ WNW of pier, Oc R 6s 7m 7M, vis 103°-154°; clear of moorings. Most facilities; Skerries SC ☎ 1-849 1233. Rockabill Lt, Fl WR 12s 45m 23/19M, is conspic 2·4M ExN of St Patrick's Is.

BALBRIGGAN, Dublin, 53°36'·8N 06°10'·7W. AC 1468, 44. Tides see 10.13.8. Good shelter in small hbr, dries about 0·9m, access approx HW ±2. Appr on SW, to open the outer hbr which is entered on SE; thence to inner hbr and AB on SE quay. Beware shoaling on both sides of outer hbr. Lt, Fl (3) WRG 20s 12m 13/10M, conspic W tr on E bkwtr head, vis G159°-193°, W193°-288°, R288°-305°. Facilities: FW, D, Gas, Slip, BH (9 ton), R, Bar, V. EC Thurs.

CARLINGFORD LOUGH   10-13-8

Louth/Down 54°01'·25N 06°04'·30W. Rtg (Warrenpoint) 2-3-2

CHARTS
AC 2800, 44; Imray C62; Irish OS 29, 36

TIDES
Cranfield Pt +0025 and Warrenpoint +0035 Dover; ML 2·9; Duration Cranfield Pt 0615, Warrenpoint 0540; Zone 0 (UT)

Standard Port DUBLIN (NORTH WALL) (⟵)

Times				Height (metres)			
High Water		Low Water		MHWS	MHWN	MLWN	MLWS
0000	0700	0000	0500	4·1	3·4	1·5	0·7
1200	1900	1200	1700				
Differences CRANFIELD POINT							
−0027	−0011	+0017	−0007	+0·7	+0·9	+0·3	+0·2
WARRENPOINT							
−0020	−0010	+0040	+0040	+1·0	+0·9	+0·1	+0·2
NEWRY (VICTORIA LOCK)							
−0010	−0010	+0040	Dries	+1·1	+1·0	+0·1	Dries
KILKEEL							
+0010	+0010	0000	0000	+1·8	+1·4	+0·8	+0·3
NEWCASTLE							
+0025	+0035	+0020	+0040	+1·6	+1·1	+0·4	+0·1
DUNDALK (SOLDIERS POINT)							
−0010	−0010	0000	+0045	+1·0	+0·8	+0·1	−0·1
DUNANY POINT							
−0028	−0018	−0008	−0006	+0·7	+0·9	No data	
RIVER BOYNE BAR							
−0025	−0015	+0110	0000	+0·4	+0·3	No data	
BALBRIGGAN							
−0021	−0015	+0010	+0002	+0·3	+0·2	No data	

SHELTER
Good. Options clockwise from ent include: ‡ at Greenore Pt, between SW end of quay and bkwtr, in 3m clear of commercial tfc. Carlingford Hbr (dries 2·2m), AB at piers. Carlingford Marina (pontoons: 1·4m; max depth 3·5m), protected on S side by sunken barges; appr from NE to clear the tail of Carlingford Bank (dries). Nos 18 and 23 buoys, on 012° astern, lead to marina. ‡ off Greer's Quay in 2m. Warrenpoint has pontoons on NW side of bkwtr (Fl G 3s); access dredged 1·1m. Caution: much shipping in narrow chan dredged 5·4m, outside which the head of the lough is shallow. ‡s off Rostrevor Quay, Killowen Pt (YC) and off derelict pier at Greencastle Pt (beware rks).

NAVIGATION
WPT 54°00'·23N 06°02'·20W, (abeam Hellyhunter SCM lt buoy) 131°/311° from/to first chan buoys, 1·1M. The main chan is Carlingford Cut (6·3m), about 3ca SW of Cranfield Pt, and passing 2ca NE of Haulbowline lt ho. Drying rks and shoals obstruct most of the ent. The lough becomes choppy in S winds and the ent is impassable in on-shore winds. Tides run up to 5kn off Greenore Pt and entry is impracticable against the ebb. Beware sudden squalls and waterspouts. Note: The NE bank is Ulster, SW bank is the Republic of Ireland. Yachts may be stopped by Naval vessels.

LIGHTS AND MARKS
Haulbowline Fl (3) 10s 32m 19M; granite tr; also turning lt FR 21m 9M, vis 196°-208°, horn 30s. Ldg lts 310°26': both Oc 3s 7/12m 11M, vis 295°-325°; R △ front, ▽ rear, on framework trs. Greenore Pier Fl R 7·5s 10m 5M. Newry R: Ldg lts 310°, both Iso 4s 5/15m 2M, stone columns.

RADIO TELEPHONE
Greenore (*Ferry Greenore*) Ch 12 16 (HJ). Carlingford marina Ch M 16. Warrenpoint Ch 12 16 (H24); call Ch 12 at By No. 23 to enter dredged chan. Dundalk Ch 14 16 (HW±3).

TELEPHONE
(Dial code Greenore/Carlingford 042; Warrenpoint 016937). Hr Mr Warrenpoint 73381; MRCC (01) 6620922/3 or (01247) 463933; ⌗ (01232) 358250; Irish ⌗, Dundalk (042) 34114; Marinecall 0891 500 465; Dr (042) 73110; ⊞ Newry 65511, (042) 34701; Police (042) 73102, (016937) 722222.

FACILITIES
Carlingford Marina (50 + 30 ❂s), ☎/🕾 73492, £9.10, AC, D, FW, P, C, CH, Divers, Slip. **Hbr** AB, Slip; **Village** V, R, Bar, ✉. **Carlingford YC** ☎ 38604, Slip, Bar, M, V, FW; **Dundalk SC** FW, Slip; **Services:** ME, El, Sh, Kos, Gas. **Warrenpoint** EC Wed; AB, M (but no access at LW), FW, P, D, ✉ (also at Rostrevor, Carlingford), ⑬ (also Dundalk), ⇶ (Dundalk, Newry), ✈ (Dublin).

MINOR HARBOURS BETWEEN CARLINGFORD LOUGH AND ST. JOHN'S POINT

KILKEEL, Down, 54°03'·47N 05°59'·26W. AC 2800, 44. HW +0015 on Dover; ML 2·9m; Duration 0620. See 10.13.8. Inner basin is completely sheltered, but gets crowded by FVs; depth off quays approx 1m. Secure in inner basin and see Hr Mr. There are drying banks both sides of ent chan and SW gales cause a sandbank right across ent. This is dredged or slowly eroded in E winds. S bkwtr lt Fl WR 2s 8m 8M, R296°-313°, W313°-017°, storm sigs. Meeney's pier (N bkwtr) Fl G 3s 6m 2M. VHF Ch 12 14 16 (Mon-Fri: 0900-2000). Hr Mr ☎ (016937) 62287; ⌗ (01232) 358250 or 62158; Facilities: FW on quay, BY (between fish market and dock), El, ME, Sh, Slip. **Town** (¾M) EC Thurs; Bar, ✉, R, V, Gas, ◌.

ANNALONG HBR, Down, 54°06'·50N 05°53'·65W. AC 44. Tides as Kilkeel, see 10.13.8. Excellent shelter in small drying hbr, approx 2m from HW±3. Appr in W sector of S bkwtr lt, Oc WRG 5s 8m 9M, vis G204°-249°, W249°-309°, R309°-024°. Hug N side of the bkwtr to avoid rky shore to stbd. 40m beyond a spur on N side, turn hard port into the basin; berth as available. Caution: many warps are rigged across hbr. Surge gate at hbr ent may be closed in SE winds. Facilities: V, Bar, ✉.

DUNDRUM BAY, Down. AC 44. Tides see 10.13.8. This 8M wide bay to the W of St John's Pt is shoal to 5ca offshore and unsafe in onshore winds. The small drying hbr at **Newcastle** (54°11'·8N 05°53'·0W) is for occas use in fair wx. Hr Mr ☎ (013967) 22106. **Dundrum Hbr** (54°14'·2N 05°49'·4W) provides ‡ in 2m for shoal draft; the bar carries about 0·3m. A steep sea can run at the bar in onshore winds. HW Dundrum is approx that of HW Liverpool; see also 10.13.8. ICC SDs are essential for the 1M long, buoyed appr chan. 3 unlit DZ buoys offshore are part of the Ballykinler firing range, 2M E of hbr; R flag/lts indicate range active.

13

AGENTS WANTED

If you are interested in becoming our agent for any of the following ports, please write to: The Editor, Edington House, Trent, Sherborne, Dorset DT9 4SR, England – and get your free copy of the Almanac annually. You do not have to live in a port to be the agent, but at least a fairly regular visitor.

Great Yarmouth	St Gilles-Croix-de-Vie
Port Ellen (Islay)	Les Sables d'Olonne
Maryport	Ile d'Oléron
Workington	River Seudre
Holyhead	Anglet/Bayonne
Lough Swilly	St Jean-de-Luz
St Peter Port, Guernsey	Hendaye
Diélette	Grandcamp-Maisy
Portbail	Port-en-Bessin
Iles Chausey	Courseulles
St Malo/Dinard	Ouistreham/Caen
Le Legue/St Brieuc	Emden
Tréguier	Dornumer-Accumersiel
Lampaul	Langeoog
L'Aberildut	Bremerhaven
Le Palais (Belle Ile)	Büsum
Morbihan/Vannes	

ARDGLASS   10-13-9

Down 54°15′·63N 05°35′·96W   Rtg 1-3-2

CHARTS
AC 633, 2093; Imray C62; Irish OS 21

TIDES
HW +0025 Dover; ML 3·0; Duration 0620; Zone 0 (UT)

Standard Port BELFAST (→)

Times				Height (metres)			
High Water		Low Water		MHWS	MHWN	MLWN	MLWS
0100	0700	0000	0600	3·5	3·0	1·1	0·4
1300	1900	1200	1800				
Differences ARDGLASS							
+0010	+0015	+0005	+0010	+1·7	+1·2	+0·6	+0·3

SHELTER
Good, except in strong E/S winds. Yachts berth on SW side of hbr in Phennick Cove Boatpark (marina), depths 1·0m to 2·8m. The busy fishing port is in South Hbr, with quays (2·1m) on inside of extended S bkwtr. At NW end of hbr, old drying N Dock is used by FVs. If Boatpark full, ⚓ clear of FVs in S Hbr.

NAVIGATION
WPT 54°15′·30N 05°35′·32W, 311°/131° from/to hbr ent, 5ca. Appr 311° in W sector of WRG Dir lt. Depth in chan 2·4m. Beyond the new inner bkwtr and a PHM buoy, turn via ldg lts WNW then SW towards marina, passing an unlit SHM buoy and PHM perches on S side.

LIGHTS AND MARKS
Dir lt, 311°, conspic W tr at inner hbr, Iso WRG 4s 10m 8/7/5M, G shore-308°, W308°-314°, R314° -shore. S bkwtr Fl R 3s 10m 5M. On NE side of ent, SHM bn Fl G 5s 10m 4M. W roof of shed on S bkwtr is conspic. Two sets of ldg lts were intended in spring 1997, lt characteristics unknown. The first set to lead approx 285° and the second approx 230°, assisting the turn into the marina. If entering S Hbr, avoid Churn Rk, unlit SCM bn.

RADIO TELEPHONE
Hbr VHF Ch 12 14 16. Marina Ch 37.

TELEPHONE (Dial code 01396)
Hr Mr 841291; MRSC (01247) 463933; ⌗ (01232) 358250; Marinecall 0891 500 465; Police 841202; Dr 841242.

FACILITIES
Boatpark (55, inc 20 visitors), £11, AC, FW, P & D (cans). **Town** Bar, ✉, R, V, Gas.

MINOR HARBOUR BETWEEN STRANGFORD AND BELFAST LOUGHS

PORTAVOGIE, Down, 54°27′·45N 05°26′·08W. Rtg 3-4-3. AC 2156. HW +0016 on Dover; ML 2·6m; Duration 0620. See 10·13·10. Good shelter, but hbr so full of FVs as to risk damage; best only for overnight or emergency. Entrance dangerous in strong onshore winds. Beware Plough Rks to SE marked by PHM buoy, Fl (2) R 10s, and McCammon Rks to NE of ent. Keep in W sector of outer bkwtr lt, Iso WRG 5s 9m 9M, G shore-258°, W258°-275°, R275°-348°. Inner bkwtr 2 FG (vert) 6m 4M. VHF Ch 12 14 16 (Mon-Fri: 0900-1700LT). Hr Mr ☎ (012477) 71470. Facilities: Slip, FW (on central quay) Sh, ME, El. **Town** EC Thurs; CH, D & P (cans), ✉, R, Gas, V. No licenced premises.

STRANGFORD LOUGH   10-13-10

Down 54°19′·33N 05°30′·85W   Rtg (Narrows) 3-4-1

CHARTS
AC 2159, 2156; Imray C62; Irish OS 21

TIDES
Killard Pt 0000, Strangford Quay +0200 Dover; ML 2·0; Duration 0610; Zone 0 (UT)

Standard Port BELFAST (→)

Times				Height (metres)			
High Water		Low Water		MHWS	MHWN	MLWN	MLWS
0100	0700	0000	0600	3·5	3·0	1·1	0·4
1300	1900	1200	1800				
Differences STRANGFORD							
+0147	+0157	+0148	+0208	+0·1	+0·1	−0·2	0·0
KILLARD POINT							
+0011	+0021	+0005	+0025	+1·0	+0·8	+0·1	+0·1
QUOILE BARRIER							
+0150	+0200	+0150	+0300	+0·2	+0·2	−0·3	−0·1
KILLYLEAGH							
+0157	+0207	+0211	+0231	+0·3	+0·3	No data	
KILLOUGH HARBOUR							
0000	+0020	No data		+1·8	+1·6	No data	
SOUTH ROCK							
+0023	+0023	+0025	+0025	+1·0	+0·8	+0·1	+0·1
PORTAVOGIE							
+0010	+0020	+0010	+0020	+1·2	+0·9	+0·3	+0·2

SHELTER
Excellent, largest inlet on E coast. Good ⚓s in the Narrows at Cross Roads; in Strangford Creek (NW of Swan Island, which is marked by 3 lt bns to S, E and N); in Audley Rds and Ballyhenry Bay. 3 🛟s at Strangford; AB on piers depends on state of tide. Portaferry has a small marina. Many good ⚓s and some 🛟s up the lough, by villages and YCs; dues, if applicable, are seldom collected.

NAVIGATION
WPT Strangford Fairway SWM buoy, L Fl 10s, Whis, 54°18′·62N 05°28′·62W, 126°/306° from/to Angus Rk lt tr, 2·05M. Visitors should use the E Chan. Beware overfalls in the SE apprs and at the bar, which can be dangerous when ebb from narrows is running against strong E to SSW winds. During flood the bar presents no special problem, but preferably enter on the young flood or when tide in the narrows is slack. Strong (up to 7kn at sp) tidal streams flow through the Narrows. Tidal flow in narrows, and hence the overfalls, relates to HW Strangford Quay (+0200 Dover) not to Killard Pt (0000). Beware St Patricks Rk, Bar Pladdy and Pladdy Lug; also car ferry plying from Strangford, S and E of Swan Is, to Portaferry. Swan Island, seen as grassy mound at HW, is edged with rks and a reef extends 32m E ending at W bn, Fl (2) WR 6s.
Further up the lough, AC 2156 is essential; pladdies are drying patches, often un-marked.

LIGHTS AND MARKS
See chartlet. Ent identified by Fairway buoy (SWM), W tr on Angus Rk, Pladdy Lug bn (W), Bar Pladdy SCM lt buoy and St Patrick's Rock perch. From NE, St Patrick's Rock perch on with Guns Island obelisk 224° clears Quintin Rk.

RADIO TELEPHONE
Strangford FerryTerminal Ch 12 14 16 M (Mon-Fri 0900-1700LT). In Strangford Lough most YCs and Seaquip Ch 80 M. Killyleagh Port VHF Ch 12 16 (occas).

TELEPHONE (Dial code 01396, or as shown)
Hr Mr 881637; MRSC (01247) 463933; ⌗ (01232) 358250; Marinecall 0891 500 465; Police 615011; Medical Clinic 313016; Casualty 613311.

FACILITIES
STRANGFORD: AB £10, 3 🛟s SE of Swan Is, FW, CH, El, Ⓔ, Sh, D (cans), Gas, V, R, Bar, ✉.
PORTAFERRY: Boatpark £10, Gas, Gaz, P & D (cans), V, R, Bar, ✉, Ⓑ.
QUOILE RIVER: **Quoile YC** ☎ 612266. AB, M, Slip, FW.
KILLYLEAGH: M, P & D (cans), L, C (mobile), CH, V, Gas, Gaz, Kos, R, Ⓑ, Bar, ✉; **Killyleagh YC** marina planned; N of village, **East Down YC** ☎ 828375.
RINGHADDY QUAY: CC, M, AB drying, FW, Slip.
SKETRICK ISLAND: To the SW in White Rk B, **Strangford Lough YC**, ☎ (01238) 541202, L, AB, FW, BY, CH, R, Bar. To the NW, **Down CC**, FW, D, Bar.
KIRCUBBIN: Gas, P & D (cans).

STRANGFORD LOUGH continued

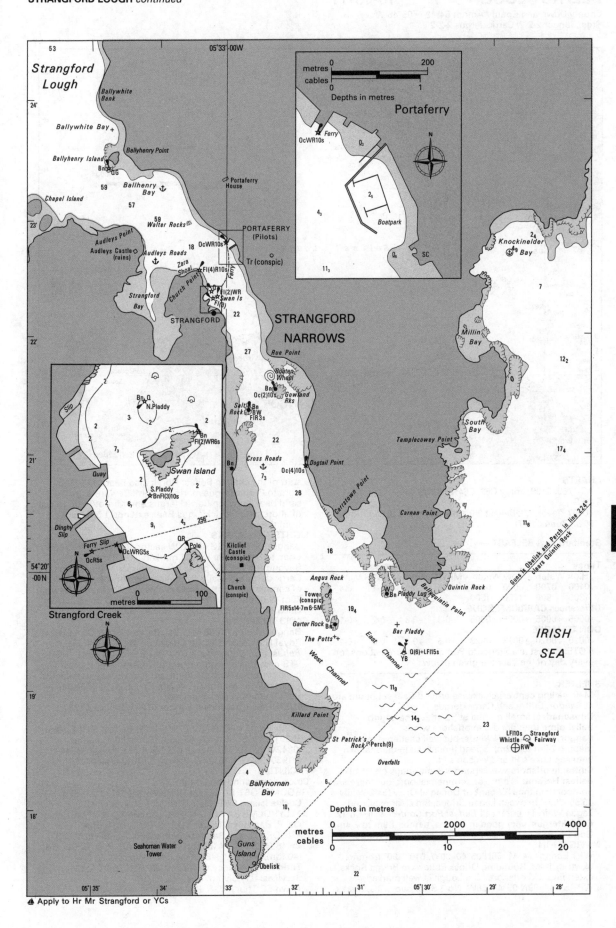

53

Strangford Lough

24'

Ballywhite Bank

Ballywhite Bay +

Ballyhenry Point

Ballyhenry Island

Bn QG

59

Chapel Island

57

Ballhenry Bay

59

Walter Rocks

23'

Audleys Point

Audleys Castle (ruins)

Audleys Roads

18

Zara Shoal

Church Point

Strangford Bay

22'

Strangford Bay

Fl(4)R10s

OcWR10s

Portaferry House

Portaferry

PORTAFERRY (Pilots)

Tr (conspic)

Fl(2)WR
Swan Is
Fl(8)

STRANGFORD

22

05°33'·00W

Portaferry

metres
cables

Depths in metres

0   200
0   1

N

Ferry
OcWR10s

Q₃

2₅

4₃

Boatpark

Q₆

11₃

SC

Knockinelder Bay

4₉

7

24

Millin Bay

8₁

STRANGFORD NARROWS

27

Rue Point

Routen Wheel

Bn Oc(2)10s

Gowland Rks

Salt Rocks

Bn BW
Fl R3s

22

Cross Roads

Bn

Dogtail Point
Oc(4)10s

7₃

26

16

South Bay

Templecowey Point

122

17₄

Carrstown Point

Carnan Point

11₆

Angus Rock

Tower (conspic)
Fl R5s14·7m6·5M

19₄

Garter Rock
Bn

The Potts ++

Kilclief Castle (conspic)

+ Church (conspic)

W
Bn Pladdy Lug

Ballyquintin Point

Quintin Rock

+ Bar Pladdy
Q(6)+LFl15s
YB

East Channel

West Channel

Killard Point

14₃

St Patrick's Rock Perch(9)

Overfalls

4

Ballyhornan Bay

10₁

6₈

11₉

23

LFl10s
Whistle

Strangford Fairway

RW

IRISH SEA

Guns Is to Obelisk and Perch in line 224°
clears Quintin Rock

13

Strangford Creek (inset)

Bn Q
N.Pladdy

Slip

2   3   2   2

2   7₃   2

Bn Fl(2)WR6s

Swan Island

Quay

S.Pladdy
BnFl(3)10s

6₇

2

Dinghy Slip

9₁   4₃   256°

Ferry Slip
OcWRG5s
OcR5s

QR
Pole

2

2

N

metres   0   100

54°20'·00 N

Seahornan Water Tower

Guns Island

Obelisk

22

Depths in metres

metres   0   2000   4000
cables   0   10   20

05° 35'   34'   33'   32'   31'   05° 30'   29'   28'

BELFAST LOUGH   10-13-11

County Down and County Antrim 54°42'N 05°45'W
Rtgs: Bangor 2-2-2; Carrickfergus 2-2-2

CHARTS
AC 1753, 2198; Imray C62, C64; Irish OS 15

TIDES
+0007 Dover; ML Belfast 2·0, Carrickfergus 1·8; Duration 0620; Zone 0 (UT)

Standard Port BELFAST (→)

Times				Height (metres)			
High Water		Low Water		MHWS	MHWN	MLWN	MLWS
0100	0700	0000	0600	3·5	3·0	1·1	0·4
1300	900	1200	1800				
Differences CARRICKFERGUS							
+0005	+0005	+0005	+0005	−0·3	−0·3	−0·2	−0·1
DONAGHADEE							
+0020	+0020	+0023	+0023	+0·5	+0·4	0·0	+0·1

NOTE: Belfast is a Standard Port and tidal predictions for every day of the year are given below.

SHELTER
Main sailing centres, clockwise around Belfast Lough, are at Bangor, Cultra and Carrickfergus.
Donaghadee: small marina at SE ent to the Lough.
Ballyholme Bay: good ⚓ in offshore winds.
Bangor: exposed to N winds, but well sheltered in marina (depths 2·9m to 2·2m). Speed limits: 4kn in marina, 8kn between Luke's Pt and Wilson's Pt.
Cultra: in offshore winds good ⚓ & moorings off RNoIYC.
Belfast Harbour is a major commercial port, but there are pontoons on the NW bank at Donegall Quay (54°36'·16N 05°55'·20W) between Lagan Bridge, 8m clearance, and Lagan Weir. To enter call *Belfast Port Control* VHF Ch **12**.
Carrickfergus: very good in marina, depths 1·9m to 2·4m. Good ⚓ SSE of Carrickfergus Pier, except in E winds.

NAVIGATION
WPT Bangor 54°41'·00N 05°40'·00W, 010°/190° from/to bkwtr lt, 1·0M. Rounding Orlock Pt beware Briggs Rocks extending ¾M offshore. The Lough is well marked.
WPT 54°41'·69N 05°46'·28W, No 1 SHM buoy, QG, marks

start of the chan to Belfast Hbr. It also bears 123°/303ᶜ from/to Carrickfergus marina, 1.65M. Beware a drying sand bank between Carrickfergus and Kilroot Pt up to 4ca offshore; and Carrickfergus Bank extends 1·5M SSW from the hbr.

LIGHTS AND MARKS
Bangor Dir Oc WRG 10s lt; W sector 105° leads into ent. Chan to Belfast Hbr is well marked/lit by buoys and bns. Beyond No 12 PHM bn it is dangerous to leave the chan. Carrickfergus is easily recognised by conspic castle to E of commercial port; marina is close W. On marina bkwtr, 30m W of the ☆ QR 7m 3M, a Dir lt, F WRG 5m 3M, (H24), G308°-317½°, W317½°-322½°, R322½°-332°, leads 320°.

RADIO TELEPHONE
Bangor Marina Ch **80** M (H24); Bangor Hr Mr Ch 11 (H24). Royal N of Ireland YC (at Cultra) Ch **16**; 11 (H24) 80. *Belfast Port Control* (at Milewater Basin) Ch **12** 16 (H24); VTS provides info on request to vessels in port area. The greater part of Belfast Lough is under radar surveillance. Carrickfergus Marina Ch M. Hbr Ch 12 14 16 (HW−3 to HW+1, when vessel expected).

TELEPHONE (Dial codes: Bangor 01247; Belfast 01232; Carrickfergus 01960)
Hr Mr Bangor (01247) 453297; Hr Mr Belfast 553011/📞 553017; MRSC (01247) 463933; ℻ 358250; Weather (08494) 22339; Marinecall 0891 500 465; Police 558411, (01960) 362021, (01247) 454444; Dr (01247)468521.

FACILITIES
Clockwise around the Lough:
GROOMSPORT BAY (01247): Hr Mr ☎ 464733, M, Slip, FW; **Cockle Island Boat Club**, Slip, M, FW, L, R.
BALLYHOLME BAY (01247): **Ballyholme YC** ☎ 271467, two ⚓s, R, Bar; **Royal Ulster YC** ☎ 270568, M, R, Bar.
BANGOR (01247): **Bangor Marina** (560 + 40 Ⓥ) ☎ 453297, 📞 453450, £12.74 (£3 for 4 hrs); FW, AC, P, D, C, CH, BH (40 ton), ME, El, Ⓔ, Sh, Gas, Gaz, Slip, SM, V, Ⓘ; **Todd Chart Agency** ☎ 466640, 📞 471070 ACA, CH.
Services: BY, Diving, Gas, ME, El, Sh.
Town EC Thurs; V, R, Bar, ✉, Ⓑ, ⇌, ✈ (Belfast).

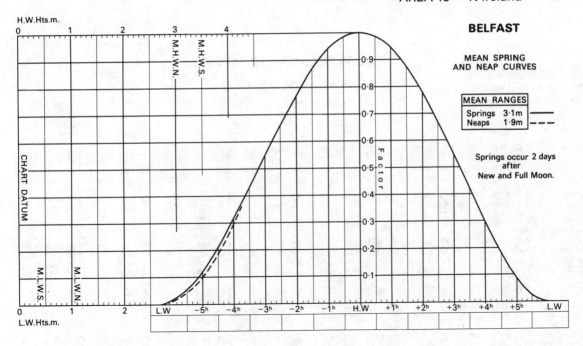

BELFAST

MEAN SPRING
AND NEAP CURVES

MEAN RANGES	
Springs	3·1m
Neaps	1·9m

Springs occur 2 days
after
New and Full Moon.

13

CULTRA (01232): **Royal North of Ireland YC,** ☎ 428041, M, L, AB, FW, Slip, P (½M), D, R, Bar.
Services: ME, EI, Sh; **Town** P, CH, V, R, Bar, ✉, Ⓑ, ⇝, ✈.
BELFAST (01232): River manager ☎ 315304, AB, P, D, FW, ME, EI, Sh, CH, C (200 ton), SM, Gas. **City** EC Wed; all facilities, ⇝, ✈.
CARRICKFERGUS (01960): **Marina** (270+30 Ⓥ) ☎ 366666, £13.50, AC, BH (30 ton), CH, D, EI, FW, Sh; **Carrick SC** ☎ 351402, M, L, FW, C, AB; **Services:** Gas, Rigging, ME, EI, Sh, Ⓔ. **Town** EC Wed; V, R, Ⓑ, ✉, ⇝, ✈ (Belfast).

MINOR HARBOUR AT SE ENTRANCE TO BELFAST LOUGH

DONAGHADEE, Down, 54°38′·71N 05°31′·85W. Rtg 4-4-1. AC 3709, 1753. HW +0025 on Dover; see 10.13.11; ML no data; Duration 0615. Excellent shelter and basic facilities in tiny marina, access HW±4 over sill; covers approx 1.1m at half tide. Appr on about 275° on ldg marks, orange △s to tricky ent with sharp 90° port turn into marina (pilots available). Appr in strong winds or at night not advised. 3ca to the N, the Old Hbr is small and very full; scend often sets in. Beware rky reef with less than 2m extends 1·5ca ENE from S pier hd. Max depth in hbr is approx 2·5m, dries at SW end; best berth alongside SE quay. S pier lt, Iso WR 4s 17m 18/14M, W shore–326°, R326°–shore. Hr Mr ☎ (01247) 882377. Police 882526. Facilities: **Copelands Marina** ☎ 882184; VHF Ch **16** 11 80; AB for 6 Ⓥ, FW, D, AC, C (20 ton). **Old Hbr** AB £4.
Town Bar, D, P, Gas, ✉, R, V, Ⓑ, ⇝ (Bangor), ✈ (Belfast).

NORTHERN IRELAND – BELFAST

LAT 54°36′N   LONG 5°55′W

TIMES AND HEIGHTS OF HIGH AND LOW WATERS

YEAR **1998**

TIME ZONE (UT)
For Summer Time add ONE hour in non-shaded areas

JANUARY

Day	Time	m		Day	Time	m
1 TH	0020 / 0622 / 1241 / 1855	3.4 / 0.7 / 3.6 / 0.5		**16** F	0116 / 0705 / 1333 / 1922	3.2 / 0.9 / 3.7 / 0.5
2 F	0106 / 0706 / 1325 / 1939	3.4 / 0.7 / 3.6 / 0.5		**17** SA	0153 / 0739 / 1412 / 1958	3.1 / 0.9 / 3.6 / 0.7
3 SA	0156 / 0753 / 1413 / 2028	3.4 / 0.7 / 3.6 / 0.5		**18** SU	0232 / 0817 / 1451 / 2039	3.1 / 0.9 / 3.5 / 0.8
4 SU	0249 / 0844 / 1505 / 2122	3.3 / 0.8 / 3.5 / 0.6		**19** M	0314 / 0900 / 1533 / 2123	3.0 / 1.0 / 3.4 / 0.8
5 M	0346 / 0939 / 1603 / 2223	3.2 / 0.9 / 3.5 / 0.7		**20** TU	0359 / 0948 / 1618 / 2213	3.0 / 1.1 / 3.3 / 1.0
6 TU	0446 / 1042 / 1706 / 2333	3.2 / 1.0 / 3.4 / 0.8		**21** W	0448 / 1043 / 1708 / 2310	2.9 / 1.2 / 3.1 / 1.1
7 W	0552 / 1155 / 1817	3.1 / 1.1 / 3.3		**22** TH	0544 / 1154 / 1806	2.9 / 1.3 / 3.0
8 TH	0047 / 0706 / 1313 / 1934	0.9 / 3.2 / 1.1 / 3.3		**23** F	0023 / 0647 / 1313 / 1910	1.1 / 2.9 / 1.3 / 3.0
9 F	0155 / 0814 / 1419 / 2041	0.8 / 3.3 / 1.0 / 3.3		**24** SA	0135 / 0758 / 1415 / 2015	1.1 / 3.0 / 1.1 / 3.1
10 SA	0253 / 0911 / 1518 / 2138	0.8 / 3.4 / 0.9 / 3.4		**25** SU	0232 / 0900 / 1507 / 2113	1.0 / 3.1 / 1.0 / 3.2
11 SU	0346 / 1002 / 1610 / 2229	0.8 / 3.5 / 0.8 / 3.4		**26** M	0321 / 0947 / 1554 / 2200	0.8 / 3.3 / 0.8 / 3.3
12 M O	0434 / 1049 / 1658 / 2315	0.7 / 3.6 / 0.7 / 3.4		**27** TU	0405 / 1028 / 1638 / 2242	0.7 / 3.4 / 0.6 / 3.4
13 TU	0518 / 1133 / 1741 / 2358	0.8 / 3.7 / 0.7 / 3.3		**28** W ●	0447 / 1107 / 1719 / 2323	0.6 / 3.6 / 0.5 / 3.4
14 W	0558 / 1215 / 1818	0.8 / 3.7 / 0.7		**29** TH	0528 / 1146 / 1800	0.6 / 3.6 / 0.4
15 TH	0038 / 0633 / 1255 / 1849	3.3 / 0.8 / 3.7 / 0.7		**30** F	0006 / 0609 / 1228 / 1841	3.5 / 0.5 / 3.7 / 0.3
				31 SA	0051 / 0651 / 1312 / 1924	3.5 / 0.5 / 3.7 / 0.3

FEBRUARY

Day	Time	m		Day	Time	m
1 SU	0139 / 0737 / 1400 / 2011	3.4 / 0.6 / 3.7 / 0.4		**16** M	0156 / 0746 / 1417 / 2005	3.1 / 0.8 / 3.5 / 0.7
2 M	0229 / 0825 / 1451 / 2102	3.4 / 0.6 / 3.6 / 0.5		**17** TU	0230 / 0824 / 1453 / 2044	3.1 / 0.8 / 3.4 / 0.7
3 TU	0323 / 0918 / 1546 / 2200	3.3 / 0.7 / 3.5 / 0.7		**18** W	0308 / 0907 / 1534 / 2128	3.1 / 0.9 / 3.3 / 0.9
4 W	0420 / 1019 / 1647 / 2310	3.2 / 0.9 / 3.3 / 0.8		**19** TH	0353 / 0956 / 1622 / 2219	3.0 / 1.1 / 3.1 / 1.0
5 TH	0524 / 1133 / 1757	3.1 / 1.0 / 3.2		**20** F	0449 / 1057 / 1722 / 2323	2.9 / 1.2 / 3.0 / 1.1
6 F	0026 / 0642 / 1253 / 1921	0.9 / 3.1 / 1.0 / 3.1		**21** SA	0555 / 1231 / 1830	2.9 / 1.3 / 2.9
7 SA	0138 / 0757 / 1405 / 2032	1.0 / 3.2 / 1.0 / 3.2		**22** SU	0055 / 0709 / 1348 / 1940	1.2 / 2.9 / 1.1 / 3.0
8 SU	0241 / 0857 / 1509 / 2130	0.9 / 3.3 / 0.9 / 3.2		**23** M	0207 / 0822 / 1446 / 2046	1.1 / 3.1 / 0.9 / 3.1
9 M	0335 / 0949 / 1603 / 2220	0.8 / 3.4 / 0.7 / 3.3		**24** TU	0301 / 0918 / 1535 / 2138	0.9 / 3.3 / 0.7 / 3.3
10 TU	0423 / 1035 / 1649 / 2304	0.8 / 3.6 / 0.7 / 3.3		**25** W	0348 / 1003 / 1620 / 2223	0.7 / 3.4 / 0.5 / 3.4
11 W O	0505 / 1118 / 1729 / 2344	0.8 / 3.6 / 0.6 / 3.2		**26** TH ●	0430 / 1044 / 1702 / 2306	0.6 / 3.6 / 0.4 / 3.5
12 TH	0542 / 1157 / 1801	0.8 / 3.6 / 0.7		**27** F	0511 / 1127 / 1743 / 2349	0.5 / 3.7 / 0.2 / 3.5
13 F	0019 / 0612 / 1234 / 1827	3.2 / 0.8 / 3.6 / 0.7		**28** SA	0552 / 1210 / 1824	0.4 / 3.8 / 0.2
14 SA	0052 / 0640 / 1309 / 1856	3.2 / 0.8 / 3.6 / 0.7				
15 SU	0123 / 0711 / 1343 / 1929	3.1 / 0.8 / 3.6 / 0.7				

MARCH

Day	Time	m		Day	Time	m
1 SU	0034 / 0634 / 1257 / 1906	3.5 / 0.4 / 3.8 / 0.2		**16** M	0051 / 0645 / 1310 / 1900	3.2 / 0.7 / 3.5 / 0.7
2 M	0121 / 0718 / 1345 / 1951	3.4 / 0.4 / 3.7 / 0.3		**17** TU	0118 / 0717 / 1341 / 1933	3.2 / 0.7 / 3.4 / 0.7
3 TU	0210 / 0806 / 1437 / 2041	3.4 / 0.5 / 3.6 / 0.5		**18** W	0149 / 0753 / 1416 / 2009	3.2 / 0.7 / 3.4 / 0.7
4 W	0301 / 0858 / 1532 / 2138	3.3 / 0.6 / 3.5 / 0.7		**19** TH	0225 / 0833 / 1457 / 2051	3.2 / 0.8 / 3.3 / 0.8
5 TH	0357 / 0959 / 1631 / 2247	3.2 / 0.8 / 3.3 / 0.9		**20** F	0307 / 0919 / 1547 / 2140	3.1 / 1.0 / 3.1 / 1.0
6 F	0459 / 1114 / 1742	3.1 / 0.9 / 3.1		**21** SA	0359 / 1017 / 1649 / 2240	3.0 / 1.1 / 3.0 / 1.1
7 SA	0004 / 0617 / 1234 / 1908	1.0 / 3.0 / 1.0 / 3.0		**22** SU	0507 / 1139 / 1758 / 2358	2.9 / 1.2 / 2.9 / 1.2
8 SU	0118 / 0735 / 1350 / 2019	1.0 / 3.1 / 0.9 / 3.0		**23** M	0626 / 1319 / 1909	2.9 / 1.1 / 3.0
9 M	0225 / 0838 / 1457 / 2116	1.0 / 3.2 / 0.8 / 3.1		**24** TU	0138 / 0742 / 1421 / 2017	1.1 / 3.0 / 0.8 / 3.1
10 TU	0321 / 0930 / 1550 / 2204	0.9 / 3.4 / 0.7 / 3.2		**25** W	0238 / 0844 / 1513 / 2113	0.9 / 3.3 / 0.6 / 3.3
11 W	0407 / 1016 / 1633 / 2246	0.8 / 3.5 / 0.6 / 3.2		**26** TH	0327 / 0934 / 1558 / 2200	0.7 / 3.5 / 0.4 / 3.5
12 TH	0447 / 1057 / 1708 / 2324	0.7 / 3.5 / 0.6 / 3.2		**27** F	0411 / 1019 / 1641 / 2245	0.6 / 3.6 / 0.2 / 3.6
13 F O	0520 / 1134 / 1736 / 2356	0.7 / 3.5 / 0.6 / 3.2		**28** SA ●	0452 / 1104 / 1722 / 2330	0.4 / 3.7 / 0.2 / 3.6
14 SA	0549 / 1208 / 1803	0.7 / 3.5 / 0.7		**29** SU	0533 / 1151 / 1804	0.4 / 3.8 / 0.2
15 SU	0025 / 0616 / 1240 / 1830	3.2 / 0.7 / 3.5 / 0.7		**30** M	0016 / 0616 / 1240 / 1846	3.6 / 0.3 / 3.8 / 0.2
				31 TU	0103 / 0700 / 1330 / 1932	3.6 / 0.3 / 3.7 / 0.3

APRIL

Day	Time	m		Day	Time	m
1 W	0152 / 0748 / 1422 / 2022	3.5 / 0.4 / 3.6 / 0.5		**16** TH	0119 / 0726 / 1346 / 1940	3.3 / 0.7 / 3.3 / 0.7
2 TH	0242 / 0840 / 1517 / 2119	3.4 / 0.5 / 3.4 / 0.7		**17** F	0156 / 0806 / 1430 / 2023	3.3 / 0.8 / 3.3 / 0.8
3 F	0335 / 0942 / 1616 / 2225	3.3 / 0.7 / 3.2 / 0.9		**18** SA	0239 / 0853 / 1523 / 2113	3.3 / 0.8 / 3.2 / 0.9
4 SA	0434 / 1055 / 1724 / 2337	3.2 / 0.8 / 3.0 / 1.1		**19** SU	0330 / 0951 / 1625 / 2212	3.2 / 1.0 / 3.0 / 1.1
5 SU	0545 / 1209 / 1848	3.1 / 0.9 / 2.9		**20** M	0433 / 1103 / 1732 / 2321	3.1 / 1.0 / 3.0 / 1.2
6 M	0048 / 0705 / 1323 / 1958	1.1 / 3.1 / 0.9 / 3.0		**21** TU	0550 / 1243 / 1841	3.0 / 0.9 / 3.0
7 TU	0157 / 0810 / 1431 / 2054	1.0 / 3.2 / 0.8 / 3.0		**22** W	0054 / 0706 / 1351 / 1947	1.1 / 3.1 / 0.7 / 3.2
8 W	0255 / 0903 / 1523 / 2140	0.9 / 3.3 / 0.7 / 3.1		**23** TH	0208 / 0811 / 1445 / 2045	1.0 / 3.3 / 0.5 / 3.3
9 TH	0342 / 0949 / 1603 / 2221	0.8 / 3.4 / 0.6 / 3.2		**24** F	0301 / 0906 / 1533 / 2135	0.8 / 3.5 / 0.3 / 3.5
10 F	0420 / 1029 / 1636 / 2257	0.8 / 3.4 / 0.6 / 3.2		**25** SA	0348 / 0955 / 1617 / 2223	0.6 / 3.6 / 0.2 / 3.6
11 SA O	0453 / 1106 / 1705 / 2328	0.7 / 3.4 / 0.6 / 3.2		**26** SU ●	0432 / 1043 / 1700 / 2310	0.5 / 3.7 / 0.2 / 3.7
12 SU	0523 / 1138 / 1734 / 2354	0.7 / 3.4 / 0.7 / 3.2		**27** M	0515 / 1132 / 1744 / 2357	0.4 / 3.7 / 0.2 / 3.7
13 M	0552 / 1206 / 1803	0.7 / 3.4 / 0.7		**28** TU	0559 / 1222 / 1829	0.3 / 3.7 / 0.3
14 TU	0018 / 0621 / 1236 / 1832	3.2 / 0.7 / 3.4 / 0.7		**29** W	0045 / 0645 / 1313 / 1915	3.7 / 0.3 / 3.6 / 0.4
15 W	0046 / 0652 / 1308 / 1903	3.3 / 0.7 / 3.4 / 0.7		**30** TH	0134 / 0732 / 1405 / 2004	3.6 / 0.4 / 3.5 / 0.6

Chart Datum: 2·01 metres below Ordnance Datum (Belfast)

NORTHERN IRELAND – BELFAST

LAT 54°36′N   LONG 5°55′W

TIMES AND HEIGHTS OF HIGH AND LOW WATERS

YEAR **1998**

TIME ZONE (UT)
For Summer Time add ONE hour in non-shaded areas

MAY

#	Time	m	#	Time	m
1 F	0223 0824 1459 2059	3.5 0.5 3.3 0.8	**16** SA	0136 0749 1410 2004	3.4 0.7 3.3 0.8
2 SA	0313 0924 1555 2201	3.4 0.6 3.1 0.9	**17** SU	0220 0836 1505 2055	3.4 0.7 3.2 0.9
3 SU	0407 1032 1658 2306	3.3 0.7 3.0 1.1	**18** M	0311 0933 1605 2152	3.3 0.8 3.1 1.0
4 M	0508 1139 1815	3.2 0.8 2.9	**19** TU	0411 1039 1708 2255	3.2 0.8 3.1 1.1
5 TU	0011 0619 1245 1926	1.1 3.1 0.8 2.9	**20** W	0521 1200 1813	3.2 0.8 3.1
6 W	0115 0732 1347 2022	1.1 3.1 0.8 3.0	**21** TH	0009 0633 1316 1917	1.1 3.2 0.7 3.2
7 TH	0214 0829 1440 2108	1.0 3.2 0.7 3.1	**22** F	0130 0741 1415 2017	1.0 3.3 0.6 3.3
8 F	0304 0916 1521 2148	0.9 3.3 0.7 3.1	**23** SA	0232 0841 1506 2111	0.8 3.5 0.4 3.5
9 SA	0345 0956 1557 2223	0.8 3.3 0.7 3.2	**24** SU	0325 0934 1554 2201	0.7 3.6 0.4 3.6
10 SU	0421 1032 1631 2255	0.8 3.3 0.7 3.2	**25** M ●	0413 1024 1640 2250	0.6 3.7 0.4 3.7
11 M O	0455 1104 1704 2323	0.7 3.3 0.7 3.3	**26** TU	0500 1115 1726 2339	0.5 3.7 0.4 3.7
12 TU	0527 1134 1735 2350	0.7 3.3 0.7 3.3	**27** W	0546 1205 1812	0.4 3.6 0.5
13 W	0600 1205 1807	0.7 3.3 0.7	**28** TH	0027 0631 1256 1858	3.7 0.4 3.5 0.6
14 TH	0021 0632 1242 1841	3.4 0.7 3.3 0.7	**29** F	0115 0718 1346 1946	3.7 0.4 3.4 0.7
15 F	0056 0708 1323 1920	3.4 0.7 3.3 0.7	**30** SA	0202 0806 1437 2036	3.6 0.5 3.3 0.8
			31 SU	0250 0859 1528 2130	3.5 0.6 3.1 0.9

JUNE

#	Time	m	#	Time	m
1 M	0339 0959 1621 2228	3.4 0.7 3.0 1.0	**16** TU	0255 0916 1543 2133	3.5 0.7 3.2 0.9
2 TU	0431 1100 1719 2328	3.3 0.8 2.9 1.1	**17** W	0352 1016 1643 2232	3.4 0.7 3.2 1.0
3 W	0527 1200 1828	3.2 0.9 2.9	**18** TH	0455 1126 1744 2338	3.3 0.9 3.2 1.0
4 TH	0028 0630 1259 1934	1.1 3.1 0.9 2.9	**19** F	0604 1241 1848	3.3 0.7 3.2
5 F	0126 0738 1352 2025	1.1 3.1 0.8 3.0	**20** SA	0055 0715 1347 1952	1.0 3.3 0.7 3.3
6 SA	0219 0833 1438 2108	1.0 3.2 0.8 3.1	**21** SU	0207 0826 1444 2050	0.9 3.4 0.6 3.4
7 SU	0306 0919 1519 2146	0.9 3.2 0.7 3.2	**22** M	0306 0918 1536 2143	0.8 3.5 0.5 3.6
8 M	0347 0959 1558 2222	0.8 3.3 0.7 3.3	**23** TU	0358 1011 1624 2233	0.7 3.6 0.5 3.6
9 TU	0426 1035 1635 2256	0.8 3.3 0.7 3.3	**24** W ●	0448 1102 1712 2322	0.6 3.5 0.6 3.7
10 W O	0504 1108 1711 2328	0.7 3.3 0.7 3.4	**25** TH	0535 1151 1758	0.5 3.5 0.6
11 TH	0540 1143 1747	0.7 3.3 0.7	**26** F	0009 0620 1239 1841	3.7 0.5 3.4 0.7
12 F	0001 0617 1222 1824	3.4 0.6 3.3 0.7	**27** SA	0056 0702 1325 1924	3.7 0.5 3.3 0.7
13 SA	0038 0655 1305 1905	3.5 0.6 3.3 0.7	**28** SU	0140 0743 1411 2006	3.7 0.6 3.2 0.8
14 SU	0120 0736 1353 1950	3.5 0.6 3.3 0.8	**29** M	0224 0826 1457 2050	3.6 0.6 3.1 0.9
15 M	0205 0823 1446 2040	3.5 0.6 3.3 0.8	**30** TU	0309 0912 1543 2137	3.5 0.7 3.0 1.0

JULY

#	Time	m	#	Time	m
1 W	0356 1003 1630 2229	3.4 0.8 3.0 1.1	**16** TH	0331 0951 1616 2208	3.5 0.6 3.2 0.9
2 TH	0445 1101 1721 2329	3.3 0.9 2.9 1.2	**17** F	0431 1057 1716 2312	3.4 0.7 3.2 1.0
3 F	0538 1203 1817	3.1 1.0 2.9	**18** SA	0538 1213 1821	3.3 0.8 3.2
4 SA	0034 0637 1303 1919	1.2 3.1 1.0 3.0	**19** SU	0031 0653 1326 1931	1.0 3.3 0.8 3.2
5 SU	0135 0741 1357 2020	1.1 3.1 0.9 3.1	**20** M	0148 0807 1428 2034	1.0 3.3 0.8 3.4
6 M	0229 0840 1445 2109	1.0 3.1 0.9 3.2	**21** TU	0252 0909 1522 2129	0.9 3.4 0.7 3.5
7 TU	0317 0929 1529 2153	0.9 3.2 0.8 3.3	**22** W	0349 1003 1612 2220	0.7 3.4 0.7 3.6
8 W	0401 1011 1610 2231	0.8 3.3 0.7 3.4	**23** TH ●	0440 1052 1659 2307	0.6 3.4 0.7 3.7
9 TH O	0442 1049 1650 2307	0.7 3.3 0.7 3.5	**24** F	0526 1138 1743 2352	0.6 3.4 0.7 3.7
10 F	0522 1125 1730 2342	0.6 3.4 0.7 3.5	**25** SA	0608 1221 1823	0.6 3.3 0.8
11 SA	0602 1204 1809	0.5 3.4 0.7	**26** SU	0034 0643 1303 1858	3.7 0.6 3.3 0.8
12 SU	0020 0640 1247 1850	3.6 0.5 3.4 0.7	**27** M	0116 0715 1343 1931	3.7 0.6 3.2 0.9
13 M	0102 0721 1334 1934	3.6 0.5 3.4 0.7	**28** TU	0156 0749 1422 2008	3.6 0.7 3.1 0.9
14 TU	0148 0806 1425 2021	3.6 0.5 3.3 0.7	**29** W	0237 0827 1503 2049	3.5 0.7 3.1 0.9
15 W	0237 0855 1519 2112	3.6 0.5 3.3 0.8	**30** TH	0319 0910 1547 2135	3.4 0.8 3.1 1.0
			31 F	0403 0958 1634 2227	3.3 0.9 3.0 1.1

AUGUST

#	Time	m	#	Time	m
1 SA	0452 1054 1725 2332	3.1 1.0 3.0 1.2	**16** SU	0518 1150 1756	3.2 1.0 3.2
2 SU	0548 1205 1824	3.0 1.1 3.0	**17** M	0012 0639 1309 1913	1.1 3.1 1.0 3.2
3 M	0049 0652 1317 1930	1.3 3.0 1.1 3.0	**18** TU	0133 0759 1415 2021	1.0 3.1 1.0 3.3
4 TU	0156 0802 1415 2034	1.2 3.0 1.1 3.1	**19** W	0243 0902 1511 2117	0.9 3.2 0.9 3.4
5 W	0251 0903 1505 2125	1.1 3.1 0.9 3.3	**20** TH	0342 0955 1601 2206	0.8 3.3 0.8 3.6
6 TH	0339 0950 1549 2207	0.8 3.3 0.8 3.4	**21** F	0431 1042 1646 2251	0.6 3.3 0.8 3.6
7 F	0423 1031 1631 2244	0.6 3.4 0.7 3.5	**22** SA ●	0515 1124 1726 2333	0.6 3.3 0.8 3.7
8 SA O	0504 1108 1711 2320	0.5 3.4 0.6 3.6	**23** SU	0552 1203 1801	0.6 3.3 0.8
9 SU	0543 1146 1751	0.4 3.5 0.6	**24** M	0012 0620 1239 1830	3.7 0.6 3.2 0.8
10 M	0000 0622 1228 1831	3.7 0.4 3.5 0.6	**25** TU	0049 0645 1312 1859	3.6 0.7 3.2 0.9
11 TU	0043 0702 1313 1914	3.6 0.4 3.5 0.6	**26** W	0125 0715 1345 1933	3.6 0.7 3.2 0.9
12 W	0128 0745 1401 1959	3.7 0.4 3.4 0.7	**27** TH	0201 0750 1420 2010	3.5 0.7 3.2 0.9
13 TH	0217 0832 1453 2049	3.6 0.5 3.4 0.7	**28** F	0237 0827 1459 2052	3.4 0.8 3.2 1.0
14 F	0311 0926 1549 2144	3.5 0.7 3.3 0.9	**29** SA	0317 0910 1543 2139	3.3 0.9 3.1 1.1
15 SA	0410 1030 1648 2249	3.4 0.8 3.2 1.0	**30** SU	0405 0959 1634 2236	3.2 1.1 3.0 1.2
			31 M	0502 1100 1734 2359	3.0 1.2 3.0 1.3

13

Chart Datum: 2·01 metres below Ordnance Datum (Belfast)

NORTHERN IRELAND – BELFAST

LAT 54°36′N   LONG 5°55′W

TIMES AND HEIGHTS OF HIGH AND LOW WATERS

YEAR **1998**

TIME ZONE (UT)
For Summer Time add ONE hour in non-shaded areas

SEPTEMBER

Day	Time m	Day	Time m
1 TU	0609 2.9 / 1231 1.3 / 1842 3.0	**16** W	0117 1.0 / 0749 3.1 / 1400 1.1 / 2004 3.3
2 W	0124 1.2 / 0723 2.9 / 1347 1.2 / 1953 3.1	**17** TH	0232 0.9 / 0851 3.2 / 1458 1.0 / 2100 3.4
3 TH	0226 1.0 / 0834 3.1 / 1442 1.0 / 2052 3.3	**18** F	0330 0.7 / 0941 3.3 / 1547 0.9 / 2148 3.5
4 F	0317 0.8 / 0926 3.3 / 1529 0.8 / 2138 3.4	**19** SA	0417 0.7 / 1025 3.3 / 1630 0.7 / 2231 3.6
5 SA	0401 0.6 / 1008 3.4 / 1610 0.7 / 2218 3.6	**20** SU	0456 0.6 / 1105 3.3 / 1706 0.8 / 2311 3.6 ●
6 SU	0442 0.4 / 1047 3.5 / 1650 0.6 / 2257 3.7 O	**21** M	0527 0.7 / 1140 3.3 / 1737 0.8 / 2347 3.6
7 M	0521 0.3 / 1126 3.6 / 1729 0.6 / 2338 3.7	**22** TU	0551 0.7 / 1212 3.3 / 1803 0.9
8 TU	0600 0.3 / 1207 3.6 / 1809 0.5	**23** W	0020 3.5 / 0615 0.8 / 1240 3.3 / 1830 0.9
9 W	0021 3.8 / 0639 0.3 / 1252 3.6 / 1851 0.5	**24** TH	0052 3.5 / 0643 0.8 / 1307 3.3 / 1901 0.9
10 TH	0109 3.7 / 0722 0.4 / 1339 3.5 / 1937 0.6	**25** F	0123 3.5 / 0714 0.8 / 1338 3.3 / 1935 0.9
11 F	0159 3.6 / 0809 0.5 / 1429 3.4 / 2026 0.7	**26** SA	0157 3.4 / 0749 0.8 / 1413 3.3 / 2014 0.9
12 SA	0253 3.5 / 0902 0.7 / 1524 3.3 / 2122 0.8	**27** SU	0235 3.3 / 0829 0.9 / 1454 3.2 / 2059 1.0
13 SU	0354 3.3 / 1008 0.9 / 1624 3.2 / 2231 1.0	**28** M	0323 3.2 / 0916 1.1 / 1544 3.1 / 2153 1.2
14 M	0504 3.1 / 1130 1.1 / 1734 3.2 / 2354 1.0	**29** TU	0423 3.0 / 1013 1.2 / 1645 3.0 / 2302 1.3
15 TU	0629 3.0 / 1249 1.1 / 1855 3.2	**30** W	0533 2.9 / 1125 1.3 / 1757 3.0

OCTOBER

Day	Time m	Day	Time m
1 TH	0046 1.2 / 0645 2.9 / 1311 1.3 / 1910 3.1	**16** F	0206 0.9 / 0830 3.1 / 1435 1.1 / 2036 3.3
2 F	0155 1.0 / 0758 3.1 / 1415 1.1 / 2015 3.3	**17** SA	0306 0.8 / 0919 3.2 / 1525 0.9 / 2125 3.4
3 SA	0249 0.8 / 0855 3.3 / 1504 0.9 / 2106 3.5	**18** SU	0350 0.7 / 1002 3.3 / 1606 0.9 / 2208 3.5
4 SU	0335 0.6 / 0941 3.5 / 1547 0.7 / 2150 3.6	**19** M	0425 0.7 / 1040 3.3 / 1640 0.8 / 2246 3.5
5 M	0416 0.4 / 1022 3.6 / 1626 0.6 / 2233 3.7 O	**20** TU	0453 0.7 / 1114 3.3 / 1709 0.8 / 2320 3.5 ●
6 TU	0455 0.3 / 1104 3.7 / 1706 0.5 / 2317 3.8	**21** W	0519 0.8 / 1144 3.3 / 1737 0.9 / 2350 3.5
7 W	0535 0.3 / 1147 3.7 / 1747 0.5	**22** TH	0546 0.8 / 1208 3.3 / 1805 0.9
8 TH	0003 3.8 / 0616 0.3 / 1232 3.7 / 1830 0.5	**23** F	0018 3.4 / 0613 0.8 / 1234 3.4 / 1834 0.8
9 F	0053 3.7 / 0700 0.5 / 1320 3.6 / 1917 0.5	**24** SA	0050 3.4 / 0642 0.8 / 1305 3.4 / 1907 0.8
10 SA	0145 3.6 / 0749 0.6 / 1409 3.5 / 2007 0.6	**25** SU	0125 3.4 / 0717 0.9 / 1340 3.4 / 1945 0.9
11 SU	0240 3.5 / 0844 0.8 / 1503 3.4 / 2105 0.7	**26** M	0205 3.3 / 0758 0.9 / 1420 3.3 / 2030 0.9
12 M	0341 3.3 / 0950 1.0 / 1601 3.3 / 2214 0.9	**27** TU	0253 3.2 / 0857 1.1 / 1507 3.3 / 2122 1.0
13 TU	0450 3.1 / 1107 1.2 / 1709 3.2 / 2332 1.0	**28** W	0353 3.1 / 0943 1.2 / 1605 3.2 / 2226 1.1
14 W	0613 3.0 / 1222 1.2 / 1828 3.2	**29** TH	0502 3.0 / 1048 1.3 / 1715 3.1 / 2347 1.1
15 TH	0050 1.0 / 0730 3.1 / 1334 1.2 / 1939 3.2	**30** F	0612 3.0 / 1208 1.3 / 1830 3.1
		31 SA	0114 1.0 / 0720 3.1 / 1336 1.2 / 1938 3.3

NOVEMBER

Day	Time m	Day	Time m
1 SU	0214 0.8 / 0821 3.3 / 1432 1.0 / 2035 3.5	**16** M	0306 0.8 / 0934 3.2 / 1532 1.0 / 2140 3.4
2 M	0303 0.6 / 0912 3.5 / 1519 0.8 / 2125 3.6	**17** TU	0343 0.8 / 1012 3.3 / 1608 0.9 / 2219 3.4
3 TU	0347 0.4 / 0958 3.6 / 1602 0.7 / 2212 3.7	**18** W	0415 0.8 / 1047 3.3 / 1640 0.9 / 2253 3.4
4 W	0429 0.4 / 1043 3.7 / 1644 0.7 / 2259 3.8 O	**19** TH	0447 0.8 / 1117 3.4 / 1711 0.9 / 2323 3.4 ●
5 TH	0512 0.4 / 1129 3.8 / 1728 0.5 / 2349 3.8	**20** F	0518 0.9 / 1143 3.4 / 1742 0.9 / 2352 3.4
6 F	0556 0.5 / 1216 3.7 / 1814 0.5	**21** SA	0548 0.9 / 1211 3.4 / 1814 0.5
7 SA	0040 3.7 / 0642 0.6 / 1304 3.7 / 1901 0.5	**22** SU	0024 3.4 / 0619 0.9 / 1243 3.5 / 1847 0.7
8 SU	0133 3.6 / 0732 0.7 / 1353 3.6 / 1951 0.5	**23** M	0102 3.3 / 0655 0.9 / 1318 3.5 / 1926 0.8
9 M	0227 3.4 / 0827 0.9 / 1445 3.5 / 2048 0.7	**24** TU	0144 3.3 / 0737 0.9 / 1359 3.4 / 2010 0.8
10 TU	0325 3.2 / 0930 1.0 / 1540 3.4 / 2154 0.8	**25** W	0232 3.2 / 0826 1.0 / 1445 3.4 / 2101 0.8
11 W	0429 3.1 / 1039 1.2 / 1640 3.3 / 2303 0.9	**26** TH	0329 3.2 / 0920 1.1 / 1538 3.3 / 2200 0.9
12 TH	0545 3.0 / 1147 1.2 / 1749 3.2	**27** F	0432 3.1 / 1021 1.2 / 1641 3.2 / 2306 1.0
13 F	0012 0.9 / 0700 3.0 / 1253 1.2 / 1903 3.2	**28** SA	0537 3.1 / 1127 1.2 / 1752 3.2
14 SA	0119 0.9 / 0801 3.0 / 1355 1.1 / 2005 3.2	**29** SU	0022 0.9 / 0644 3.2 / 1244 1.2 / 1902 3.3
15 SU	0220 0.9 / 0851 3.1 / 1449 1.0 / 2056 3.3	**30** M	0134 0.8 / 0748 3.3 / 1356 1.1 / 2006 3.4

DECEMBER

Day	Time m	Day	Time m
1 TU	0231 0.7 / 0845 3.4 / 1452 0.8 / 2103 3.6	**16** W	0303 0.9 / 0942 3.2 / 1534 1.0 / 2150 3.3
2 W	0321 0.6 / 0936 3.6 / 1541 0.7 / 2155 3.6	**17** TH	0342 0.9 / 1019 3.3 / 1612 0.9 / 2228 3.3
3 TH	0408 0.5 / 1025 3.7 / 1628 0.6 / 2246 3.7 O	**18** F	0419 0.5 / 1054 3.4 / 1648 0.9 / 2302 3.3 ●
4 F	0454 0.5 / 1113 3.8 / 1715 0.5 / 2337 3.7	**19** SA	0455 0.8 / 1125 3.4 / 1724 0.8 / 2333 3.3
5 SA	0541 0.6 / 1202 3.8 / 1801 0.5	**20** SU	0530 0.8 / 1154 3.5 / 1759 0.8
6 SU	0028 3.6 / 0628 0.7 / 1250 3.8 / 1848 0.5	**21** M	0005 3.3 / 0604 0.8 / 1226 3.5 / 1835 0.7
7 M	0120 3.5 / 0717 0.8 / 1338 3.7 / 1937 0.6	**22** TU	0043 3.3 / 0642 0.8 / 1302 3.5 / 1913 0.7
8 TU	0211 3.4 / 0808 0.9 / 1427 3.7 / 2028 0.6	**23** W	0125 3.3 / 0723 0.8 / 1343 3.5 / 1955 0.7
9 W	0304 3.2 / 0903 1.0 / 1517 3.6 / 2125 0.7	**24** TH	0212 3.3 / 0809 0.9 / 1428 3.5 / 2043 0.7
10 TH	0358 3.1 / 1004 1.1 / 1609 3.4 / 2227 0.8	**25** F	0305 3.2 / 0900 0.9 / 1518 3.4 / 2136 0.8
11 F	0458 3.0 / 1106 1.2 / 1704 3.3 / 2329 0.9	**26** SA	0402 3.2 / 0955 1.0 / 1615 3.4 / 2236 0.8
12 SA	0611 2.9 / 1206 1.2 / 1807 3.2	**27** SU	0503 3.1 / 1055 1.1 / 1720 3.3 / 2344 0.9
13 SU	0029 1.0 / 0720 2.9 / 1306 1.2 / 1918 3.1	**28** M	0608 3.1 / 1205 1.1 / 1830 3.3
14 M	0128 0.9 / 0815 3.0 / 1403 1.1 / 2019 3.2	**29** TU	0100 0.9 / 0717 3.2 / 1326 1.1 / 1941 3.3
15 TU	0219 1.0 / 0901 3.1 / 1452 1.1 / 2108 3.2	**30** W	0207 0.8 / 0822 3.3 / 1432 1.0 / 2046 3.4
		31 TH	0304 0.7 / 0919 3.5 / 1528 0.8 / 2143 3.5

Chart Datum: 2·01 metres below Ordnance Datum (Belfast)

LARNE   10-13-12

Antrim 54°51'·20N 05°47'·50W   Rtg 1-4-2

CHARTS

AC 1237, 2198; Imray C62, C64; Irish OS 9

TIDES

0000 Dover; ML 1·6; Duration 0620; Zone 0 (UT)

Standard Port BELFAST (⟵)

Times				Height (metres)			
High Water		Low Water		MHWS	MHWN	MLWN	MLWS
0100	0700	0000	0600	3·5	3·0	1·1	0·4
1300	1900	1200	1800				
Differences LARNE							
+0005	0000	+0010	–0005	–0·7	–0·5	–0·3	0·0
RED BAY							
+0022	–0010	+0007	–0017	–1·9	–1·5	–0·8	–0·2
CUSHENDUN BAY							
+0010	–0030	0000	–0025	–1·7	–1·5	–0·6	–0·2

SHELTER

Secure shelter in Larne Lough or ‡ overnight outside hbr in Brown's Bay (E of Barr Pt) in 2–4m. Hbr can be entered H24 in any conditions. Larne is a busy commercial and ferry port; W side is commercial until Curran Pt where there are two YCs with congested moorings. ‡ S of Ballylumford Power Stn. No AB available for visitors. Yachts should not berth on any commercial quays, inc Castle Quay, without Hr Mr's express permission.

Boat Hbr (0·6m) 2ca S of Ferris Pt only for shoal draft craft. Note: Work continues (started 1993) to extend the harbour southward and will eventually result in E Antrim BC moving to Curran Point, with fewer moorings.

NAVIGATION

WPT 54°51'·70N 05°47'·47W, 004°/184° from/to front ldg lt, 2·1M. Beware Hunter Rk 2M NE of hbr ent. Magnetic abnomalies exist near Hunter Rk and between it and the mainland. Inside the narrow ent, the recommended chan is close to the E shore. Tide in the ent runs at up to 3½kn.

LIGHTS AND MARKS

Ldg lts 184°, Oc 4s 6/14m 12M, synch and vis 179°-189°; W ◇ with R stripes. Chaine Tr and fairway lts as chartlet. Note: Many shore lts on W side of ent may be mistaken for nav lts.

RADIO TELEPHONE

VHF Ch 14 16 *Larne Harbour*. Traffic, weather and tidal info available on Ch 14.

TELEPHONE (Dial code 01574)

Hr Mr 279221; MRSC (01247) 463933; Pilot 273785; ☰ (01232) 358250; Marinecall 0891 500 465; Police 272266; Dr 275331.

FACILITIES

Pier ☎ 279221, M, L, FW, C (32 ton); **E Antrim Boat Club** ☎ 277204, Visitors should pre-contact Sec'y for advice on moorings; Slip, L, V, FW, Bar; **Services:** D, Gas, Sh, El. **Town** EC Tues; P & D (delivered, tidal), CH, V, R, Bar Ⓑ, ⇌, Ferry to Cairnryan, ✈ (Belfast City and Belfas Aldergrove).

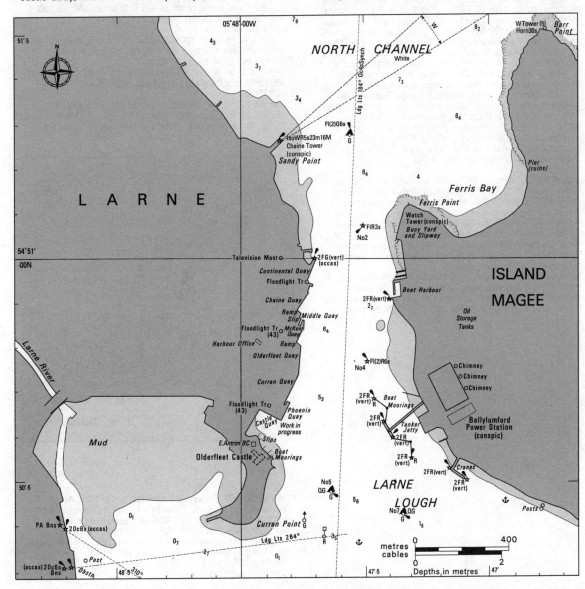

MINOR HARBOURS AND ANCHORAGES BETWEEN LARNE AND PORTRUSH

CARNLOUGH HARBOUR, Antrim, 54°59´·87N 05°59´·20W. AC 2198. HW +0006 on Dover, +0005 on Belfast; HW –1·6m on Belfast; ML no data; Duration 0625. Good shelter except in SE gales; do not ent in onshore winds >F6. Ldg marks 310°, R ▲s on B/W posts. Small hbr used by yachts and small FVs; visitors welcome. Ent and hbr dredged 2m every May. Beware fish farms in the bay marked by lt buoys (unreliable); also beware rks which cover at HW on either side of ent. N pier lt, Fl G 3s 4m 5M; S pier Fl R 3s 6m 5M. Hr Mr ☎ (01574) 272677. Facilities: **Quay** AB £6, AC (see Hr Mr), FW, Slip. **Town** P & D (cans), Gas, Gaz, ⊠, R, V, Bar.

RED BAY, Antrim, 55°03´·91N 06°03´·13W. AC 2199. HW +0006 on Dover; ML 1·1m; Duration 0625. See 10·13·12. Good holding, but open to E winds. Beware rks, 2 ruined piers W of Garron Pt and fish farms, marked by lt Bys, on S side of bay, approx ½M from shore. Glenariff pier has lt Fl 3s 10m 5M. In S and E winds ‡ 2ca off W stone arch near hd of bay in approx 3·5m; in N or W winds ‡ S of small pier in 2 – 5m, ½M NE of Waterfoot village. Facilities: **Cushendall** (1M N of pier) Bar, D & P (cans), ⊠, R, V, Gas; **Services**: CH, El, Slip. **Waterfoot** Bar, R, ⊠.

RATHLIN ISLAND, Antrim, 55°17´·52N 06°11´·60W. AC 2798. HW sp –0445, nps –0200 on Dover. Small hbr in NE corner of Church Bay, sheltered from winds NW through E to SSE. Beware sp streams up to 6kn in Rathlin Sound and the North Channel TSS, Fig 10(7), 2M to the N and E of the Is. A wreck, marked on its SE side by a SCM buoy, Q(6)+L Fl 15s, is 1M SW of hbr. When clear, appr on NNE to the new W and S piers which form an outer hbr. The W sector of Manor House pier dir lt leads 024·5° to inner hbr ent via chan dredged 2·5m. ‡ outside hbr, close W of Sheephouse pier in about 5m; or within the outer hbr on N side in about 1·2m clear of chan. Lts: Rue Point (S tip), Fl (2) 5s 16m 14M, W 8-sided tr, B bands. Rathlin East (Altacarry Head), Fl (4) 20s 74m 26M, vis 110°–006°, 036°–058°, W tr, B band, Racon. Rathlin West, Fl R 5s 62m 22M, vis 015°–225°, shown by day in reduced vis, W tr, lantern at base; also Fog Det Lt VQ, 69m, vis 119°. Manor House pier, Oc WRG 4s 5M, G020°–023°, W023°–026°, R026°–029°. Church Bay R, Bar, V, ⊠.

BALLYCASTLE, Antrim, 55°12´·50N 06°14´·30W. AC 2798. Tides as for Rathlin Is (above); ML 0·8m. A fair weather ‡ on S side of Rathlin Sound, clear of strong tidal streams, but liable to sudden swell. ‡ off the old pier in 5m, well sheltered from winds ENE to W; or berth on hd of pier (2·7m), clear of FVs and Rathlin ferry. Facilities: AB, FW, L, Slip. CG ☎ (012657) 62226; Ⓗ 62666. New ferry pier is operational; additional yacht facilities, if/when available, will be in the Supplements.
Services: P & D (cans), Gas. **Town** EC Wed; R, Bar, V, ⊠, Ⓑ. Ferry to/from Campbeltown (10.9.11, Mull of Kintyre). Note: A Historic Wreck (*Girona*; see 10.0.3h) is at Lacada Point, 55°14´·85N 06°30´·05W, 6M ENE of Portrush.

PORTRUSH   10-13-13

Antrim 55°12´·34N 06°39´·49W   Rtg 3-2-1

CHARTS
AC 49, 2499, 2798; Imray C64; Irish OS 4
TIDES
–0410 Dover; ML 1·1; Duration 0610; Zone 0 (UT)

Standard Port BELFAST (←—)

Times				Height (metres)			
High Water		Low Water		MHWS	MHWN	MLWN	MLWS
0100	0700	0000	0600	3·5	3·0	1·1	0·4
1300	1900	1200	1800				
Differences PORTRUSH							
–0433		–0433		–1·6	–1·6	–0·3	0·0

SHELTER
Good in hbr, except in strong NW/N winds. Berth on N pier or on pontoon at NE end of it and see Hr Mr. A ⚓ may be available, but very congested in season. ‡ on E side of Ramore Hd in Skerries Roads 1ca S of Large Skerrie gives good shelter in most conditions, but open to NW sea/swell.
NAVIGATION
WPT 55°13´·00N 06°41´·00W, 308°/128° from/to N pier lt, 1·1M. Ent with on-shore winds >F 4 is difficult. Beware submerged bkwtr projecting 20m SW from N pier. Depth is 2·8m in hbr entrance.
LIGHTS AND MARKS
Ldg lts 028° (occas, for LB use) both FR 6/8m 1M; R △ on metal bn and metal mast. N pier Fl R 3s 6m 3M; vis 220°-160°. S pier Fl G 3s 6m 3M; vis 220°-100°.
RADIO TELEPHONE
VHF Ch 12 16 (0900-1700LT, Mon-Fri; extended evening hrs June-Sept; Sat-Sun: 0900–1700, June-Sept only).
TELEPHONE (Dial code 01265)
Hr Mr 822307; MRSC (01247) 463933; ⌗ 44803; Marinecall 0891 500 465; Police 822721; Dr 823767; Ⓗ 44177.
FACILITIES
Hbr AB £7, D, FW, M, Slip, Gas, El, Ⓔ; **Portrush YC** ☎ 823932, Bar; **Town** EC Wed; V, R, Bar, ◻, D & P (cans), ⊠, Ⓑ, ⇌, ✈ (Belfast). Giant's Causeway is 10M ENE.

PORTSTEWART, Antrim, 55°11´·21N 06°43´·21W. AC 49. Tides as for Portrush. A tiny hbr 1·1ca S of Portstewart Pt lt, Oc R 10s 21m 5M, vis 040°–220°, obscd in final appr. A temp, fair weather berth (£9) at S end of inner basin in 0·8 – 1·7m; the very narrow ent is open to SW wind and swell. Beware salmon nets and rks close to S bkwtr.
Facilities: EC Thurs; FW, Gas, D (tanker), Slip, Bar, V, R, convenient shops.

RIVER BANN   10-13-14

Londonderry/Antrim 55°10'·32N 06°46'·35W   Rtg 3-2-2

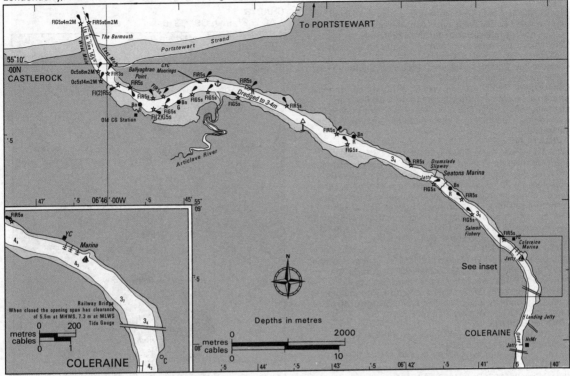

CHARTS
AC 2499, 2798, 2723; Imray C64; Irish OS 4
TIDES
–0345 Dover (Coleraine); ML 1·1; Duration 0540; Zone 0 (UT)

Standard Port BELFAST (←—)

Times				Height (metres)			
High Water		Low Water		MHWS	MHWN	MLWN	MLWS
0100	0700	0000	0600	3·5	3·0	1·1	0·4
1300	1900	1200	1800				
Differences COLERAINE							
–0403		–0403		–1·3	–1·2	–0·2	0·0

SHELTER
Good, once inside the river ent (The Barmouth) between 2 training walls, extending 2ca N from the beaches. Do not try to enter in strong on-shore winds or when swell breaks on the pierheads. If in doubt call *Coleraine Hbr Radio* or ring Hr Mr. ⚓ upstream of old CG stn, or berth at Seaton's or Coleraine marinas, 3½M & 4½M from ent, on NE bank.
NAVIGATION
WPT 55°11'·00N, 06°46'·65W, 345°/165° from/to ent, 0·72M. Appr from E of N to bring ldg lts into line at bkwtr ends. The sand bar is constantly moving but ent is dredged to approx 3·5m. Beware salmon nets across the width of the river at 2M or 4M above ent, May to July. Also beware commercial traffic.
LIGHTS AND MARKS
Ldg lts 165°, both Oc 5s 6/14m 2M, front on W pyramidal metal tr; rear W □ tr. Portstewart Pt, Oc R 10s, is 2M ENE.
RADIO TELEPHONE
Coleraine Hbr Radio Ch 12 (Mon-Fri: HO and when vessel due). Coleraine Marina Ch M.
TELEPHONE (Dial code 01265)
Hr Mr 42012; ‡‡ (01232) 358250 or 44803; MRSC (01247) 463933; Marinecall 0891 500 465; Rly Bridge 42403; Police 44122; Ⓗ 44177; Dr 44831.
FACILITIES
Seatons Marina ☎ 832086, £10.00, BH (12 ton), CH, Slip. **Coleraine Hbr** ☎ 42012, BH (35 ton); **Coleraine (Borough Council) Marina** (45+15 visitors), ☎ 44768, £9, Slip, D, FW, R, BH (15 ton), AC; **Coleraine YC** ☎ 44503, Bar, M; **Services:** Gas, Kos, El, Ⓔ. **Town** EC Thurs; P & D (cans), V, R, ✉, Ⓑ, ⇌, ✈ (Belfast).

LOUGH FOYLE   10-13-15

13

Londonderry (to SE)/Donegal (to NW) 55°14'N 06°54W

CHARTS
AC 2499, 2798, 2723; Imray C64; Irish OS 3, 4, 7
TIDES
Warren Point –0430 Dover
Moville) –0350 Dover
Moville) –0055 Londonderry
Moville) –0400 Belfast
Culmore Point –0025 Londonderry
Londonderry –0300 Dover
ML 1·6; Duration 0615; Zone 0 (UT)

Standard Port GALWAY (—→)

Times				Height (metres)			
High Water		Low Water		MHWS	MHWN	MLWN	MLWS
0200	0900	0200	0800	5·1	3·9	2·0	0·6
1400	2100	1400	2000				
Differences LONDONDERRY							
+0254	+0319	+0322	+0321	–2·4	–1·8	–0·8	–0·1
INISHTRAHULL							
+0100	+0100	+0115	+0200	–1·8	–1·4	–0·4	–0·2
PORTMORE							
+0120	+0120	+0135	+0135	–1·3	–1·1	–0·4	–0·1
TRAWBREAGA BAY							
+0115	+0059	+0109	+0125	–1·1	–0·8	No data	

SHELTER
The SE side of the Lough is low lying and shallow. The NW rises steeply and has several village hbrs between the ent and Londonderry (often referred to as Derry). **Greencastle**: a busy fishing hbr, open to swell in winds SW to E. Only advised for yachts in emergency.

LOUGH FOYLE continued

Moville: the pier, with 1·5m at the end, is near the village (shops closed all day Wed), but is considerably damaged. ⚓ outside hbr is exposed; inside for shoal draft only.

Carrickarory: pier/quay is condemned as unsafe. ⚓ in bay is sheltered in winds from SW to NNW.

Culmore Bay: Complete shelter; ⚓ 1½ca W of Culmore Pt in pleasant cove, 4M from Londonderry.

Londonderry: Rarely used by yachts, although commercial operations have been transferred to new facilities at Lisahally (55°02'·6N 07°15'·6W). AB on non-commercial quay below Guildhall or ⚓ close below Craigavon Bridge clearance 1·7m.

NAVIGATION
WPT Tuns PHM buoy, Fl R 3s, 55°14'·01N 06°53'·38W, 055°/235° from/to Warren Pt lt, 2·5M. The Tuns bank lies 3M NE of Magilligan Pt. The main or N Chan, ¾M wide, runs NW of The Tuns; a lesser chan, min depth 4m, runs 3ca off shore around NE side of Magilligan Pt. Beware commercial traffic. Foyle Bridge at Rosses Pt has 32m clearance. In June and July the chan is at times obstructed by salmon nets at night. N Chan tides reach 3½kn, and up in the river the ebb runs up to 6kn.

LIGHTS AND MARKS
Inishowen Fl (2) WRG 10s 28m 18/14M; W tr, two B bands; vis G197°–211°, W211°–249°, R249°–000°; Horn (2) 30s. Warren Pt Fl 1·5s 9m 10M; W tr, G abutment; vis 232°–061°. Magilligan Pt QR 7m 4M; R structure. The main chan up to Londonderry is very well lit. Foyle Bridge centre FW each side; VQG on W pier; VQR on E pier.

RADIO TELEPHONE
VHF Ch **14** 12 16 (H24). Traffic and nav info Ch 14.

TELEPHONE (Dial code 01504)
Hr Mr (at Lisahally) 860555, ☎ 861168; MRSC (01247) 463933; ⌗ 261937 or (01232) 358250; Marinecall 0891 500 465; Police 261893; Dr 264868; Ⓗ 45171.

FACILITIES (Londonderry)
Hbr Mr ☎ 860555, M, FW; **Prehen Boat Club** ☎ 43405. **City** P & D (cans), ME, El, V, R, Bar, ⊠, Ⓑ, ⇌, ✈.

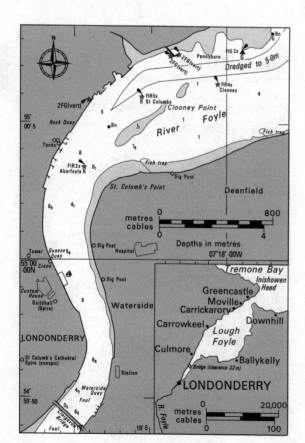

LOUGH SWILLY   10-13-16
Donegal 55°17'N 07°34'W

CHARTS
AC 2697; Irish OS 2, 3, 6

TIDES
–0500 Dover; ML 2·3; Duration 0605; Zone 0 (UT)

Standard Port GALWAY (→)

Times				Height (metres)			
High Water		Low Water		MHWS	MHWN	MLWN	MLWS
0200	0900	0200	0800	5·1	3·9	2·0	0·6
1400	2100	1400	2000				
Differences FANAD HEAD							
+0115	+0040	+0125	+0120	–1·1	–0·9	–0·5	–0·1
RATHMULLAN							
+0125	+0050	+0126	+0118	–0·8	–0·7	–0·1	–0·1
MULROY BAY (BAR)							
+0108	+0052	+0102	+0118	–1·2	–1·0	No data	
SHEEP HAVEN (DOWNIES BAY)							
+0057	+0043	+0053	+0107	–1·1	–0·9	No data	

SHELTER
Ent easy, but beware downdrafts on E side. ⚓s N of Inch Is may suffer from swell. ⚓ in Port Salon B (off chartlet to NW), except in E'lies; off Macamish Pt sheltered from SE to N; Rathmullan Road N of pier, where yacht pontoon lies N/S in 3·6m MLWS; Fahan Creek, ent at HW–1.

NAVIGATION
WPT 55°17'·50N 07°34'·50W, 352°/172° from/to Dunree Hd lt, 5·7M. Main chan is well lit/buoyed. Beware Swilly More Rks, Kinnegar Spit, Colpagh Rks off E shore, Kinnegar Strand, Inch Flats and fish farms. Fahan Creek is buoyed.

LIGHTS AND MARKS
Fanad Hd lt, Fl (5) WR 20s 39m 18/14M; touching Dunree Hd lt, Fl (2) WR 5s 46m 12/9M, leads 151° into the Lough. Thence Ballygreen Pt and Hawk's Nest in line at 202°.

RADIO TELEPHONE
None.

TELEPHONE (Dial code 074)
Hr Mr 58177; MRCC (01) 6620922/3; ⌗ 21935; Police 58113; Dr 58135; Pier Hotel, Rathmullan pontoon 58178.

FACILITIES
RATHMULLAN: Pier AB (£10), AC, C (5 ton), FW, L, M, Slip; **Services:** CH, M, ▣, R, Bar. **Town** EC Wed; D & P (cans), Kos, Bar, R, V, ⊠, Ⓑ, ⇌, ✈ (bus to Londonderry). **RAMELTON:** AB, L. **Town** Bar, P & D (cans), FW, Kos, R, V, ⊠. **FAHAN:** AB on pontoon, Slip, FW, L, R; **L Swilly YC** ☎ 60189, M, Bar; **Services:** (1M SE), Kos, V, P & D (cans).

OTHER HARBOURS AND ANCHORAGES IN DONEGAL

MULROY BAY, Donegal, 55°15′·30N 07°46′·30W. AC 2699; HW (bar) −0455 on Dover. See 10.13.16. Beware Limeburner Rk, (marked by NCM buoy, Q, whis) 3M N of ent and the bar which is dangerous in swell or onshore winds. Ent at half flood (not HN); chan lies between Bar Rks and Sessiagh Rks, thence through First, Second and Third Narrows (with strong tides) to Broad Water. HW at the head of the lough is 2¼ hrs later than at the bar. ‡s: Close SW of Ravedy Is (Fl 3s 9m 3M); Fanny's Bay (2m), excellent; Rosnakill Bay (3·5m) in SE side; Cranford Bay; Milford Port (3 to 4m). Beware power cable 6m, over Moross chan, barring North Water to masted boats. Facilities: **Milford Port** AB, FW, V; **Fanny's Bay** ✉, Shop at Downings village (1M), hotel at Rosepenna (¾M).

SHEEP HAVEN, Donegal, 55°11′·00N 07°51′·00W. AC 2699. HW −0515 on Dover. See 10.13.16. Bay is 4M wide with many ‡ s, easily accessible in daylight, but exposed to N winds. Beware rks for 3ca off Rinnafaghla Pt; also Wherryman Rks, which dry, 1ca off E shore 2¼M S of Rinnafaghla Pt. ‡ in Downies (or Downings) Bay to SW of pier; in Pollcormick Inlet close W in 3m; in Ards Bay for excellent shelter, but beware the bar in strong winds. Lts: Portnablahy ldg lts 125°, both Oc 6s 7/12m 2M, B col, W bands; Downies pier hd, Fl R 3s 5m 2M, R post. Facilities: (Downies) EC Wed; V, FW, P (cans 300m), R, Bar; (Portnablahy Bay) V, P (cans), R, Bar.

GWEEDORE HBR/BUNBEG, Donegal, 55°03′·75N 08°18′·87W. AC 1883. Tides see 10.13.17. Gweedore hbr, the estuary of the R Gweedore, has sheltered ‡s or temp AB at Bunbeg Quay, usually full of FVs. Apprs via Gola N or S Sounds are not simple especially in poor visibility. N Sound is easier with ldg lts 171°, both Oc 3s 9/13m 2M, B/W bns, on the SE tip of Gola Is. (There are also ‡s on the S and E sides of Gola Is). E of Bo Is the bar 0·4m has a Fl G 3s and the chan, lying E of Inishinny Is and W of Inishcoole, is marked by a QG and 3 QR. A QG marks ent to Bunbeg. Night ent not advised. Facilities: FW, D at quay; V, ✉, Ⓑ, Bar at village ½M.

BURTONPORT, Donegal, 54°58′·93N 08°26′·60W. AC 2792, 1879. HW −0525 on Dover; ML 2·0m; Duration 0605. See 10.13.17. Normal ent via N Chan. Hbr very full, no space to ‡; berth on local boat at pier or go to Rutland Hbr or Aran Is. Ent safe in all weathers except NW gales. Ldg marks/lts: N Chan ldg lts on Inishcoo 119°, both Iso 6s 6/11m 1M; front W bn, B band; rear B bn, Y band. Rutland Is ldg lts 138°, both Oc 6s 8/14m 1M; front W bn, B band; rear B bn, Y band. Burtonport ldg lts 068°, both FG 17/23m 1M; front Gy bn, W band; rear Gy bn, Y band. Hr Mr ☎ (075) 42258 (43170 home), ⛝ (074) 41205; VHF Ch 06, 12, **14**, 16. Facilities: D (just inside pier), FW (root of pier), P (½M inland). **Village** Bar, ✉, R, V, Kos.

TEELIN HARBOUR, Donegal, 54°37′·50N 08°37′·87W. AC 2792. Tides as for Killybegs (below). A possible passage ‡, being mid-way between Rathlin O'Birne and Killybegs. But the hbr is open to S'ly swell and prone to squalls in NW winds. Ent, 1ca wide, is close E of Teelin Pt lt, Fl R 10s, which is hard to see by day. ‡ on W side in 3m to N of pier, or on E side near derelict pier. Many moorings and, in the NE, mussel rafts. Facilities: possible FW, D, V at Carrick, 3M inland.

KILLYBEGS   10-13-17

Donegal 54°36′·90N 08°26′·80W   Rtg 1-3-3

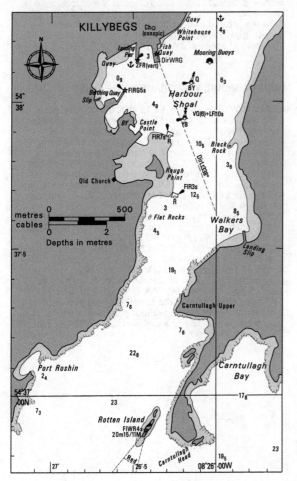

CHARTS
AC 2792, 2702; Irish OS 10

TIDES
−0520 Dover; ML 2·2; Duration 0620; Zone 0 (UT)

Standard Port GALWAY (→)

Times				Height (metres)			
High Water		Low Water		MHWS	MHWN	MLWN	MLWS
0600	1100	0000	0700	5·1	3·9	2·0	0·6
1800	2300	1200	1900				
Differences KILLYBEGS							
+0040	+0050	+0055	+0035	−1·0	−0·9	−0·5	0·0
GWEEDORE HARBOUR							
+0048	+0100	+0055	+0107	−1·3	−1·0	−0·5	−0·1
BURTONPORT							
+0042	+0055	+0115	+0055	−1·2	−1·0	−0·6	−0·1
DONEGAL HARBOUR (SALTHILL QUAY)							
+0038	+0050	+0052	+0104	−1·2	−0·9	No data	

SHELTER
Secure natural hbr, but some swell in SSW winds. A busy major FV port, H24 access. ‡ about 2½ca NE of the Pier, off blue shed (Gallagher Bros) in 3m, clear of FV wash. Or **Bruckless Hbr**, about 2M E at the head of McSwyne's Bay, is a pleasant ‡ in 1·8m, sheltered from all except SW winds. Ent on 038° between rks; ICC SDs are essential.

NAVIGATION
WPT 54°36′·00N 08°27′·00W, 202°/022° from/to Rotten Is lt, 0·94M. From W, beware Manister Rk (covers at HW; dries at LW) off Fintragh B. Keep mid chan until off Rough Pt, then follow the Dir lt or Y ◊ ldg marks 338° into hbr.

LIGHTS AND MARKS
Rotten Is lt, Fl WR 4s 20m 15/11M, W tr, vis W255°–008°, R008°–039°, W039°–208°. Dir lt 338°, F W and Al WG/WR; W sector 336°-340° (see 10.13.4). Harbour Shoal is marked by a SCM and NCM lt buoy.

RADIO TELEPHONE
Hr Mr VHF Ch 16 **14**; essential to request a berth.

TELEPHONE (Dial code 073)
Hr Mr 31032; MRCC (01) 6620922/3; Bundoran Inshore Rescue ☎ (072) 41713; ∦ 31070; Police 31002; Dr 31148 (Surgery).

FACILITIES
Landing Pier ☎ 31032, AB (free), M, D & P (cans), FW, ME, El, CH, Slip, V, R, Bar; **Berthing Quay** AB, M, Slip, D; **Services:** Sh, C (12 ton), ME, El, Sh, Kos, Ⓔ. **Town** EC Wed; ✉, Ⓑ, ⇌ (bus to Sligo), ✈ (Strandhill).

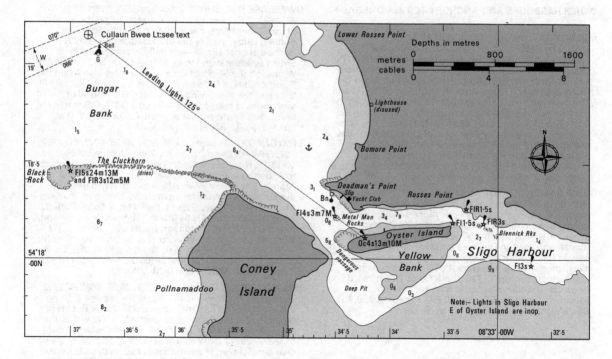

SLIGO   10-13-18

Sligo 54°18'·30N 08°34'·70W   Rtg 3-4-1

CHARTS
AC 2852, 2767; Imray C54; Irish OS 16, 25
TIDES
−0511 Dover; ML 2·3; Duration 0620; Zone 0 (UT)

Standard Port GALWAY (→)

Times				Height (metres)			
High Water		Low Water		MHWS	MHWN	MLWN	MLWS
0600	1100	0000	0700	5·1	3·9	2·0	0·6
1800	2300	1200	1900				
Differences SLIGO HARBOUR (Oyster Is)							
+0043	+0055	+0042	+0054	−1·0	−0·9	−0·5	−0·1
MULLAGHMORE							
+0036	+0048	+0047	+0059	−1·4	−1·0	−0·4	−0·2
BALLYSADARE BAY (Culleenamore)							
+0059	+0111	+0111	+0123	−1·2	−0·9	No data	
KILLALA BAY (Inishcrone)							
+0035	+0055	+0030	+0050	−1·3	−1·2	−0·7	−0·2

SHELTER
The lower hbr is fairly exposed; ⚓ along N side of Oyster Is, or proceed 4M (not at night) up to the shelter of Sligo town; 2nd berth below bridge for yachts.
NAVIGATION
WPT 54°19'·15N 08°36'·77W, 305°/125° from/to front ldg lt, 1·6M. The passage between Oyster Is and Coney Island is marked 'Dangerous'. Pass N of Oyster Is leaving Blennick Rks to port. Passage up to Sligo town between training walls. Some perches are in bad repair. Pilots at Raghly Pt and Rosses Pt. Chan up to quays dredged 1·6m.
LIGHTS AND MARKS
Cullaun Bwee Dir lt (off chartlet), Fl (2) WRG 10s 8m10/8M (H24), W sector 066°-070°. Ldg lts (H24) lead 125° into ent: front, Fl 4s 3m 7M, Metal Man Rks (statue of a man on a twr); rear, Oyster Is lt ho, Oc 4s 13m 10M. Lts up-channel are inop.
RADIO TELEPHONE
Pilots VHF Ch 12 16.
TELEPHONE (Dial code 071)
Hbr Office 61197; MRCC (01) 6620922/3; ⌗ 61064; Police 42031; Dr 42886; Ⓗ 71111.
FACILITIES
Deepwater Pier AB, P & D (in cans), L, FW, ME, El, Sh, CH, C (15 ton); **Sligo YC** ☎ 77168, ⚓s, FW, Bar, Slip.
Services: Slip, D, ME, El, Sh, SM, Gas;
Town V, R, Bar, ⊠, Ⓑ, ⇌ Irish Rail ☎ 69888, Bus ☎ 60066, ✈ (Strandhill) ☎ 68280.

MINOR HARBOUR ON S SIDE OF DONEGAL BAY

MULLAGHMORE 54°27'·90N 08°26'·80W. AC 2702. Tides see 10.13.18. Fair weather ⚓ in 2-3m off hbr ent, sheltered by Mullaghmore Head, except from N/NE winds. For ⚓s near hbr ent; call Rodney Lomax at BY, ☎/⇰ 071 66124, mobile ☎ 088 2727358. Keep close to N pier to avoid a rk drying 1m, ⅔ of the way across the ent toward the S pier. Take the ground or dry out against the piers inside hbr, access approx HW±2 when least depth is 2m. VHF Ch 16 18 (occas). Facilities: BY, Sh, D (cans), V, R, Bar.

MINOR HARBOUR/ANCHORAGE TO THE WEST

KILLALA BAY, Sligo/Mayo, 54°13'·02N 09°12'·80W. AC 2715. Tides, see 10.13.18. The bay, which is exposed to the N and NE, is entered between Lenadoon Pt and Kilcummin Hd, 6M to the W. Carrickpatrick ECM buoy, Q (3) 10s, in mid-bay marks St Patrick's Rks to the W. Thence, if bound for Killala hbr, make good Killala SHM buoy, Fl G 6s, 7½ca to the SSW. The Round Tr and cathedral spire at Killala are conspic. Four sets of ldg bns/ lts lead via a narrow chan between sand dunes and over the bar (0·3m) as follows:
1. 230°, Rinnaun Pt lts Oc 10s 7/12m 5M, ☐ concrete trs.
2. 215°, Inch ls, ☐ concrete trs; the rear has Dir lt Fl WRG 2s, G205°-213°, W213°-217°, R217°-225°.
3. 196°, Kilroe lts Oc 4s 5/10m 2M, W ☐ trs, which lead to ⚓ in Bartragh Pool, 6ca NE of Killala hbr; thence
4. 236°, Pier lts Iso 2s 5/7m 2M, W ◊ daymarks, lead via narrow, dredged chan to pier where AB is possible in about 1·5m. Facilities: FW, P & D (cans), V in town ½M, EC Thurs. Other hbrs in the bay: R Moy leading to Ballina should not be attempted without pilot/local knowledge. Inishcrone in the SE has a pier and lt, Fl WRG 1·5s 8m 2M; see 10.13.4.

WESTPORT (CLEW BAY)   10-13-19

Mayo 53°47'·85N 09°35'·40W   Rtg 4-4-1

CHARTS
AC 2057, 2667; Imray C54; Irish OS 30, 31

TIDES
–0545 Dover; ML 2·5; Duration 0610; Zone 0 (UT)

Standard Port GALWAY (→)

Times				Height (metres)			
High Water		Low Water		MHWS	MHWN	MLWN	MLWS
0600	1100	0000	0700	5·1	3·9	2·0	0·6
1800	2300	1200	1900				
Differences INISHRAHER							
+0030	+0012	+0058	+0026	–0·6	–0·5	–0·3	–0·1
BROADHAVEN							
+0040	+0050	+0040	+0050	–1·4	–1·1	–0·4	–0·1
BLACKSOD QUAY							
+0025	+0035	+0040	+0040	–1·2	–1·0	–0·6	–0·2
BLACKSOD BAY (BULL'S MOUTH)							
+0101	+0057	+0109	+0105	–1·5	–1·0	–0·6	–0·1
CLARE ISLAND							
+0019	+0013	+0029	+0023	–1·0	–0·7	–0·4	–0·1
KILLARY HARBOUR							
+0021	+0015	+0035	+0029	–1·0	–0·8	–0·4	–0·1
INISHBOFIN HARBOUR							
+0013	+0009	+0021	+0017	–1·0	–0·8	–0·4	–0·1
CLIFDEN BAY							
+0005	+0005	+0016	+0016	–0·7	–0·5	No data	
SLYNE HEAD							
+0002	+0002	+0010	+0010	–0·7	–0·5	No data	

SHELTER
Secure ⚓s amongst the islands at all tides, as follows: E of Inishlyre in about 2m; E of Collan More as narrow ent off Rosmoney Pt; and 2ca NE of Dorinish More, good holding in lee of Dorinish Bar (dries). Or go up to Westport Quay HW±1½, to dry out on S side. Newport Hbr (dries) can be reached above mid-flood with careful pilotage (AC 2667); dry out against N quay or ⚓ at E end of Rabbit Is.

NAVIGATION
WPT 53°49'·20N 09°42'·10W, 251°/071° from/to Inishgort lt ho, 1·2M. Contact Tom Gibbons (Inishlyre Is) ☎ (098) 26381 for pilotage advice. Beware of Monkellys Rks (PHM buoy) and the Spit (G perch).

LIGHTS AND MARKS
Westport B entered via Inishgort lt, L Fl 10s 11m 10M (H24), and a series of ldg lines, but not advised at night. Final appr line 080° towards lt bn, Fl 3s. Chan from Westport Bay to Westport Quay, 1½M approx, is marked by bns.

RADIO TELEPHONE
None.

TELEPHONE (Dial code 098)
MRCC (01) 6620922/3; ⌗ (094) 21131; Police 25555; ⊞ (094) 21733.

FACILITIES
Quays M, AB free, Slip, V, R, Bar; **Mayo SC** ☎ 26160 L, Slip, Bar, at Rosmoney (safe for leaving boat); **Glénans Irish SC** ☎ 26046 on Collan More Is; **Services**: Kos, El, (Ⓔ); **Town** EC Wed; P & D (cans), ✉, Ⓑ, ≽, ✈ (Galway/Knock).

OTHER ANCHORAGES FROM EAGLE IS TO SLYNE HEAD

BROAD HAVEN, Mayo, 54°16'·00N 09°53'·20W. AC 2703. See 10.13.19 for tides; ML 1·9m. A safe refuge in all but N'lies. Easy appr across Broad Haven Bay to the ent between Brandy Pt and Gubacashel Pt, Iso WR 4s27m 12/9M, W tr. 7ca S of this lt is Ballyglas Fl G 3s on W side. ⚓ close N or S of Ballyglas which has pier (2m); or in E'lies ⚓ 3ca S of Inver Pt out of the tide. Further S, the inlet narrows off Barrett Pt then turns W to Belmullet. Facilities: V, ✉.

PORTNAFRANKAGH Mayo, 54°14'·95N 10°06'·00W. AC 2703. Tides approx as Broad Haven. A safe passage ⚓, close to the coastal route, but swell enters in all winds. Appr toward Port Pt, thence keep to the N side for better water; middle and S side break in onshore winds. ⚓ in 4–5m on S side, close inshore. L and slip at new pier. Unlit, but Eagle Is lt, Fl (3) 10s 67m 26M H24, W tr, is 2M N. No facilities; Belmullet 4M, V.

BLACKSOD BAY, Mayo, 54°05'·00N 10°02'·00W. AC 2704. HW – 0525 on Dover; ML 2·2m; Duration 0610. See 10.13.19. Safe ⚓ with no hidden dangers, access day or night. Good ⚓s NW of Blacksod Quay (3m); at Elly B (1·8m); Elly Hbr; Saleen B; N of Claggan Pt. Beware drying rk 3·5ca SSE of Ardmore Pt. Lts: Blacksod Pt, Fl (2) WR 7·5s 13m 9M, R189°-210°, W210°-018°. ECM buoy Q (3) 10s. Blacksod pier hd, 2 FR (vert) 6m 3M. No facilities, but supplies, inc P & D (cans), at Belmullet 2·5M N.

KILLARY HARBOUR, Mayo/Galway, 53°37'·83N 09°54'·00W. AC 2706. Tides 10.13.19. A spectacular 7M long inlet, narrow and deep. Appr in good vis to identify ldg marks. Doonee Is and Inishbarna bns lead 099° to ent. (Lat/Long above is 4ca W of Doonee Is on the ldg line). Caution fish farms, some with Fl Y lts. ⚓s off Dernasliggaun, Bundorragha and Leenaun at head of inlet. (Village: V, Bar, hotel). Enter Little Killary Bay 4ca S of Doonee. Rks at ent do not cover. Good ⚓ in 3m at hd of bay.

BALLYNAKILL, Galway, 53°34'·95N 10°03'·00W. AC 2706. Tides as Inishbofin/Killary. Easy appr between Cleggan Pt, Fl (3) WRG 15s and Rinvyle Pt. Usual ent N of Freaghillaun South Is, E of which is good passage ⚓ in 7m. Further E, Carrigeen and Ardagh Rks lie in mid-chan. Keep N for ⚓ in Derryinver B. S chan leads to ⚓s off Ross Pt; S of Roeillaun; or, inside bar dries 0·2m, in complete shelter at Fahy B. No facilities.

INISHBOFIN, Mayo, 53°36'·60N 10°13'·20W. AC 2707, 1820. HW –0555 on Dover; ML 1·9m. See 10.13.19. Very safe hbr once inside narrow ent. 2 conspic W trs lead 032°. ⚓ between new pier and Port Is. Old pier to the E dries. Gun Rock, Fl (2) 6s 8m 4M, vis 296°-253°. Facilities: FW, R, Bar, V, Hotel ☎ (095) 45803.

CLIFDEN BAY, Galway, 53°29'·40N 10°05'·90W. AC 2708, 1820. HW –0600 on Dover; Duration 0610. Tides see 10.13.19. The high W bn on Carrickrana Rks, 2·8M WSW of Fishing Pt, must be identified before entering. Ldg marks 080°: W bn at Fishing Pt on with Clifden Castle. Beware bar at ent by Fishing Pt and another SE of creek going up to Clifden; also Doolick Rks, Coghan Rks and rks off Errislannon Pt. ⚓ between Larner Rks and Drinagh Pt; dry out against Clifden Quay (beware ruined training wall); or ⚓ in Ardbear Bay SE of Yellow Slate Rks in 3·4m. Keep clear of fish farms. Facilities: **Town** EC Thurs; Bar, Ⓑ, CH, D, P, ✉, R, V, Kos, FW, V, R, Dr, ⊞. Bus to Galway.

13

GALWAY BAY
10-13-20

Galway 53°12'N 09°08'W

CHARTS
AC 1903, 1984, 3339, 2173; Imray C55; Irish OS 45, 46, 51
TIDES
−0555 Dover; ML 2·9; Duration 0620; Zone 0 (UT)

Standard Port GALWAY (→)

Times				Height (metres)			
High Water		Low Water		MHWS	MHWN	MLWN	MLWS
0600	1100	0000	0700	5·1	3·9	2·0	0·6
1800	2300	1200	1900				
Differences KILKIERAN COVE							
+0005	+0005	+0016	+0016	−0·3	−0·2	−0·1	0·0
ROUNDSTONE BAY							
+0003	+0003	+0008	+0008	−0·7	−0·5	−0·3	−0·1
KILLEANY BAY (Aran Islands)							
−0008	−0008	+0003	+0003	−0·4	−0·3	−0·2	−0·1
LISCANNOR							
−0003	−0007	+0006	+0002	−0·4	−0·3	No data	

NOTE: Galway is a Standard Port and tidal predictions for each day of the year are given below.

SHELTER
Galway Bay is sheltered from large swells by Aran Is, but seas get up in the 20M from Aran Is to Galway. Beware salmon drift nets in the apps to many bays. The better ⚓s clock-wise from Slyne Head and around Galway Bay are:
Bunowen B: Easy ent NE of Split Rk. ⚓ below conspic Doon Hill in 3-4m. Good shelter in W to NE winds; unsafe in S'ly.
Roundstone B: (Off chartlet). Safe shelter/access, except in SE'ly. ⚓ in 2m off N quay; other ⚓s E'ward in Cashel B.
Kilkieran B: A long (14M), sheltered bay with many ⚓s to suit wind conditions. Easy ent alongside Golam Tr (conspic).
Kiggaul B: Easy ent, H24; ⚓ close W/NW of Fl WR 3s 5/3M. Depth 3 to 4m; exposed to S/SE winds.
Greatman B: Beware English Rk (dries 1·2m), Keeraun Shoal (breaks in heavy weather), Arkeena Rk, Trabaan Rk, Rin Rks and Chapel Rks. ⚓ off Natawny Quay or go alongside at Maumeen Quay.
Cashla B: Easiest hbr on this coast; ent in all weather. ⚓ off Sruthan pier. Rossaveel, opposite, is busy fish and ferry hbr.
Note: There is no safe hbr from Cashla to Galway (20M).
Bays between Galway and Black Hd have rks and shoals, but give excellent shelter. Kinvarra B, Aughinish B, South B and Ballyvaghan B are the main ones. Enter Kinvarra B with caution on the flood; beware rks. Berth in small drying hbr. Ballvaghan B, entered either side of Illaunloo Rk, leads to two piers (both dry) or ⚓ close NE in pool (3m). Best access HW±2..

Aran Islands: The only reasonable shelter is on Inishmore at Killeany Bay, but very crowded with FVs and exposed to E/NE winds. ⚓ S of Kilronan pier, or off Trawmore Strand; or in good weather at Portmurvy.
NAVIGATION
Enter the Bay by one of four Sounds:
(1) N Sound between Inishmore and Golam Tr (conspic), 4½M wide, is easiest but beware Brocklinmore Bank in heavy weather.
(2) Gregory Sound between Inishmore and Inishmaan, is free of dangers, but give Straw Is a berth of 2 to 3ca.
(3) Foul Sound between Inishmaan and Inisheer; only danger is Pipe Rk (dries) at end of reef extending 3ca NW of Inisheer.
(4) S Sound between Inisheer and mainland. Only danger Finnis Rk (dries 0·4m) 4½ca SE of E point of Inisheer (marked by ECM buoy Q (3) 10s). From S, beware Kilstiffin Rks off Liscanor B.
LIGHTS AND MARKS
Roundstone B: Croaghnakeela Is Fl 3·7s 7m 5M. Inishnee lt Fl (2) WRG 10s 9m 5/3M has W sector 017°-030°.
Kiggaul B: Fl WR 3s 5m 5/3M, W329°-359°, R359°-059°.
Cashla B: Killeen Pt Fl (3) WR 10s 6/3M; Lion Pt Dir (010°) Iso WRG 4s 8/6M, W008·5°-011·5°. Rossaveel ldg lts 116°, Oc 3s.
Black Hd lt Fl WR 5s 20m 11/8M H24, vis W045°-268°, R268°-276° covers Illanloo Rk.
Aran Islands:
Inishmore: Eeragh Island (Rk Is) Fl 15s 35m 23M, W tr, B bands. Killeany B: Straw Is, Fl (2) 5s 11m 17M. Kilronan pier Fl WG 1·5s. Ldg lts 192° both Oc 5s for Killeany hbr.
Inisheer: Iso WR 12s 34m 20/16M, Racon, vis W225°-245° (partially obscd 225°-231° beyond 7M), R245°-269° covers Finnis Rk, W269°-115°; obscd 115°-225°.
FACILITIES
BUNOWEN B: No facilities.
ROUNDSTONE B: V, FW, Bar, ✉, Bus to Galway.
KILKIERAN B: Bar, ☎, P, V, Bus to Galway.
KIGGAUL B: Bar (no ☎), shop at Lettermullen (1M).
GREATMAN B: Maumeen V, P (1M), Bar.
CASHLA B: **Carraroe** (1M SW) V, Hotel, ☎; **Rossaveel** Hr Mr ☎ 091-72109, FW, D, ME; **Costelloe** (1½M E), Hotel, ✉, Gge.
KILRONAN: (Killeany B, Inishmore) V, D, FW, ✉, Ferry to Galway, ✈ to Galway from airstrip on beach.

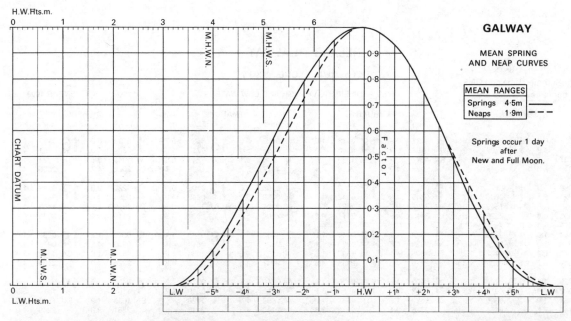

GALWAY

MEAN SPRING
AND NEAP CURVES

MEAN RANGES	
Springs	4·5m
Neaps	1·9m

Springs occur 1 day
after
New and Full Moon.

GALWAY HARBOUR 53°16'·07N 09°02'·74W Rtg 2-3-1

SHELTER
Very good in Galway hbr, being protected from SW by Mutton Island. Dock gates open HW–2 to HW, when min depth is 6m. Enter Galway dock and secure in SW corner of basin, or ask Hr Mr for waiting berth on lead-in pier. It is dangerous to lie in the 'Layby' (a dredged cut NE of New pier) when wind is SE or S; if strong from these points, seas sweep round the pierhead.
Note: Marina in Canal basin is under active discussion. New Harbour (2·5M ESE and home of Galway Bay SC) is nearest safe ⚓ to Galway.

NAVIGATION
Galway WPT 53°14'·80N 09°03'·40W, 241°/061° from/to Leverets lt, 1·1M.

LIGHTS AND MARKS
Leverets Q WRG 9m 10M; B tr, W bands; G015°-058°, W058°-065°, R065°-103°, G103°-143°, W143°-146°, R146°-015°.
Rinmore Iso WRG 4s 7m 5M; W □ tr ; G359°-008°, W008°-018°, R018°-027°.

Appr chan ldg lts 325°: front Fl R 1·5s, rear Oc R 10s; both R ◊ with Y diagonal stripes on masts, vis 315°-345°.
Note: Below the front ldg lt an experimental Dir lt (FW 325°) has the following characteristics and sectors: FG 322¼°-323¾°, Al GW 3s 323¾°-324¾°, FW 324¾°-325¼°, Al RW 3s 325¼°-326¼°, FR 326¼°-331¼°, Fl R 3s 331¼°-332¼°.

RADIO TELEPHONE
Call Hr Mr Galway VHF Ch 12 16 (HW–2½ to HW+1).

TELEPHONE (Dial code 091)
Hr Mr 561874, ⛴ 563738; MRCC (01) 6620922; Coast/Cliff Rescue Service (099) 61107; Police 563161; Dr 562453.

FACILITIES
Dock AB £IR5 (see Hr Mr), FW, El, ME, Sh, C (35 ton), CH, LB, PV, SM, V, R, Bar; Galway YC M, Slip, FW, C, CH, Bar; Galway Bay SC ☎ 794527, M, CH, Bar;
Town EC Mon; P, D, ACA, Gas, Gaz, Kos, V, R, Bar, ✉, Ⓑ, ⇌, ✈ Carnmore (6M to the E of Galway City).

IRELAND – GALWAY

LAT 53°16′N   LONG   9°03′W

TIMES AND HEIGHTS OF HIGH AND LOW WATERS

YEAR 1998

TIME ZONE (UT)
For Summer Time add ONE hour in non-shaded areas

JANUARY

Day	Time	m	Day	Time	m
1 TH	0013 / 0645 / 1237 / 1910	0.8 / 5.2 / 0.5 / 5.0	**16** F	0046 / 0722 / 1312 / 1945	1.0 / 4.9 / 0.8 / 4.6
2 F	0056 / 0728 / 1320 / 1955	0.8 / 5.1 / 0.5 / 4.8	**17** SA	0124 / 0800 / 1349 / 2026	1.1 / 4.7 / 1.0 / 4.5
3 SA	0141 / 0813 / 1405 / 2044	1.0 / 5.0 / 0.7 / 4.7	**18** SU	0203 / 0838 / 1427 / 2108	1.3 / 4.5 / 1.2 / 4.3
4 SU	0229 / 0904 / 1454 / 2142	1.2 / 4.8 / 1.0 / 4.5	**19** M	0244 / 0917 / 1509 / 2154	1.6 / 4.3 / 1.5 / 4.1
5 M	0325 / 1003 / 1551 / 2247	1.5 / 4.6 / 1.3 / 4.3	**20** TU	0331 / 0959 / 1556 / 2243	1.8 / 4.1 / 1.7 / 3.9
6 TU	0433 / 1109 / 1659 / 2355	1.7 / 4.4 / 1.5 / 4.3	**21** W	0430 / 1047 / 1657 / 2336	2.0 / 3.9 / 1.9 / 3.8
7 W	0555 / 1218 / 1825	1.7 / 4.4 / 1.6	**22** TH	0545 / 1141 / 1820	2.1 / 3.7 / 2.0
8 TH	0105 / 0712 / 1330 / 1941	4.3 / 1.6 / 4.4 / 1.5	**23** F	0038 / 0700 / 1250 / 1933	3.8 / 2.1 / 3.7 / 1.9
9 F	0211 / 0814 / 1434 / 2038	4.5 / 1.4 / 4.5 / 1.3	**24** SA	0151 / 0803 / 1421 / 2030	3.9 / 1.8 / 3.9 / 1.6
10 SA	0306 / 0906 / 1528 / 2125	4.7 / 1.2 / 4.7 / 1.2	**25** SU	0250 / 0854 / 1519 / 2117	4.2 / 1.5 / 4.1 / 1.3
11 SU	0354 / 0953 / 1616 / 2208	4.9 / 1.0 / 4.8 / 1.0	**26** M	0337 / 0940 / 1604 / 2159	4.5 / 1.1 / 4.4 / 1.0
12 M O	0439 / 1037 / 1702 / 2249	5.0 / 0.8 / 4.9 / 0.9	**27** TU	0421 / 1022 / 1647 / 2240	4.8 / 0.8 / 4.7 / 0.7
13 TU	0522 / 1118 / 1745 / 2329	5.0 / 0.7 / 4.9 / 0.9	**28** W ●	0504 / 1102 / 1730 / 2320	5.0 / 0.4 / 5.0 / 0.5
14 W	0604 / 1158 / 1826	5.0 / 0.7 / 4.9	**29** TH	0548 / 1143 / 1812	5.2 / 0.2 / 5.1
15 TH	0008 / 0643 / 1236 / 1906	0.9 / 5.0 / 0.7 / 4.8	**30** F	0001 / 0630 / 1224 / 1854	0.4 / 5.3 / 0.1 / 5.1
			31 SA	0043 / 0713 / 1305 / 1937	0.4 / 5.3 / 0.1 / 5.0

FEBRUARY

Day	Time	m	Day	Time	m
1 SU	0126 / 0757 / 1347 / 2023	0.5 / 5.2 / 0.3 / 4.8	**16** M	0133 / 0810 / 1353 / 2033	1.0 / 4.6 / 1.0 / 4.4
2 M	0212 / 0845 / 1433 / 2115	0.8 / 4.9 / 0.7 / 4.5	**17** TU	0208 / 0843 / 1427 / 2111	1.3 / 4.3 / 1.3 / 4.2
3 TU	0302 / 0930 / 1525 / 2216	1.1 / 4.6 / 1.1 / 4.3	**18** W	0246 / 0920 / 1505 / 2155	1.5 / 4.1 / 1.6 / 4.0
4 W	0403 / 1043 / 1627 / 2325	1.5 / 4.3 / 1.5 / 4.1	**19** TH	0330 / 1006 / 1551 / 2246	1.8 / 3.9 / 1.8 / 3.8
5 TH	0520 / 1153 / 1749	1.7 / 4.1 / 1.7	**20** F	0426 / 1101 / 1652 / 2343	2.0 / 3.7 / 2.0 / 3.7
6 F	0041 / 0645 / 1310 / 1920	4.0 / 1.7 / 4.1 / 1.7	**21** SA	0604 / 1204 / 1857	2.1 / 3.6 / 2.0
7 SA	0156 / 0759 / 1422 / 2026	4.2 / 1.6 / 4.2 / 1.5	**22** SU	0052 / 0733 / 1330 / 2007	3.8 / 1.9 / 3.7 / 1.8
8 SU	0256 / 0856 / 1519 / 2114	4.4 / 1.3 / 4.4 / 1.3	**23** M	0216 / 0832 / 1456 / 2058	4.0 / 1.5 / 4.0 / 1.4
9 M	0345 / 0942 / 1606 / 2155	4.6 / 1.1 / 4.6 / 1.1	**24** TU	0314 / 0920 / 1545 / 2142	4.3 / 1.1 / 4.4 / 1.0
10 TU	0428 / 1023 / 1649 / 2235	4.7 / 0.9 / 4.7 / 0.9	**25** W	0401 / 1003 / 1629 / 2223	4.7 / 0.6 / 4.8 / 0.6
11 W O	0510 / 1102 / 1729 / 2312	4.9 / 0.7 / 4.8 / 0.8	**26** TH ●	0446 / 1044 / 1711 / 2304	5.0 / 0.2 / 5.0 / 0.3
12 TH	0549 / 1139 / 1807 / 2349	4.9 / 0.6 / 4.8 / 0.7	**27** F	0530 / 1125 / 1754 / 2345	5.3 / 0.0 / 5.2 / 0.1
13 F	0626 / 1213 / 1845	4.9 / 0.6 / 4.8	**28** SA	0613 / 1205 / 1836	5.4 / -0.2 / 5.3
14 SA	0024 / 0702 / 1247 / 1921	0.8 / 4.9 / 0.7 / 4.7			
15 SU	0058 / 0737 / 1319 / 1957	0.9 / 4.7 / 0.8 / 4.6			

MARCH

Day	Time	m	Day	Time	m
1 SU	0026 / 0656 / 1246 / 1917	0.0 / 5.4 / -0.1 / 5.2	**16** M	0032 / 0712 / 1249 / 1928	0.7 / 4.7 / 0.8 / 4.7
2 M	0108 / 0739 / 1327 / 2000	0.2 / 5.3 / 0.2 / 5.0	**17** TU	0105 / 0743 / 1320 / 2001	0.9 / 4.6 / 0.9 / 4.5
3 TU	0152 / 0824 / 1411 / 2047	0.5 / 5.0 / 0.6 / 4.6	**18** W	0138 / 0814 / 1353 / 2035	1.1 / 4.4 / 1.2 / 4.3
4 W	0240 / 0915 / 1459 / 2143	0.9 / 4.6 / 1.0 / 4.3	**19** TH	0214 / 0849 / 1429 / 2116	1.3 / 4.2 / 1.5 / 4.1
5 TH	0337 / 1017 / 1559 / 2255	1.3 / 4.2 / 1.5 / 4.0	**20** F	0256 / 0934 / 1513 / 2208	1.6 / 3.9 / 1.8 / 3.9
6 F	0452 / 1130 / 1721	1.6 / 3.9 / 1.8	**21** SA	0347 / 1031 / 1610 / 2307	1.8 / 3.8 / 2.0 / 3.8
7 SA	0017 / 0618 / 1252 / 1856	3.9 / 1.7 / 3.9 / 1.9	**22** SU	0456 / 1135 / 1753	2.0 / 3.7 / 2.1
8 SU	0137 / 0741 / 1408 / 2010	3.9 / 1.6 / 4.0 / 1.7	**23** M	0013 / 0700 / 1253 / 1941	3.8 / 1.9 / 3.7 / 1.8
9 M	0240 / 0843 / 1505 / 2058	4.2 / 1.4 / 4.2 / 1.4	**24** TU	0136 / 0805 / 1428 / 2034	4.0 / 1.5 / 4.0 / 1.4
10 TU	0329 / 0926 / 1550 / 2137	4.4 / 1.1 / 4.4 / 1.2	**25** W	0247 / 0856 / 1522 / 2119	4.3 / 1.0 / 4.5 / 0.9
11 W	0411 / 1003 / 1630 / 2215	4.6 / 0.9 / 4.6 / 0.9	**26** TH	0338 / 0940 / 1606 / 2202	4.7 / 0.6 / 4.9 / 0.5
12 TH	0451 / 1040 / 1708 / 2251	4.7 / 0.7 / 4.8 / 0.7	**27** F	0424 / 1022 / 1648 / 2243	5.1 / 0.2 / 5.2 / 0.2
13 F O	0529 / 1115 / 1745 / 2326	4.8 / 0.6 / 4.8 / 0.7	**28** SA ●	0508 / 1102 / 1731 / 2324	5.4 / -0.1 / 5.4 / 0.0
14 SA	0605 / 1147 / 1820	4.9 / 0.6 / 4.8	**29** SU	0553 / 1143 / 1813	5.5 / -0.2 / 5.4
15 SU	0000 / 0639 / 1219 / 1854	0.7 / 4.8 / 0.6 / 4.8	**30** M	0006 / 0636 / 1225 / 1855	-0.1 / 5.5 / -0.1 / 5.3
			31 TU	0049 / 0719 / 1306 / 1937	0.1 / 5.3 / 0.2 / 5.1

APRIL

Day	Time	m	Day	Time	m
1 W	0133 / 0804 / 1349 / 2022	0.3 / 5.0 / 0.6 / 4.7	**16** TH	0112 / 0751 / 1324 / 2006	1.0 / 4.4 / 1.2 / 4.2
2 TH	0220 / 0854 / 1436 / 2115	0.8 / 4.6 / 1.1 / 4.4	**17** F	0149 / 0827 / 1403 / 2046	1.5 / 4.2 / 1.5 / 4.2
3 F	0316 / 0953 / 1534 / 2225	1.2 / 4.2 / 1.6 / 4.0	**18** SA	0233 / 0912 / 1448 / 2139	1.5 / 4.1 / 1.7 / 4.1
4 SA	0428 / 1107 / 1655 / 2351	1.6 / 3.9 / 1.9 / 3.8	**19** SU	0324 / 1010 / 1545 / 2240	1.7 / 3.9 / 2.0 / 4.0
5 SU	0550 / 1228 / 1824	1.7 / 3.8 / 2.0	**20** M	0429 / 1114 / 1705 / 2346	1.8 / 3.8 / 2.1 / 4.0
6 M	0111 / 0708 / 1345 / 1940	3.9 / 1.7 / 3.9 / 1.8	**21** TU	0615 / 1226 / 1908	1.8 / 3.9 / 1.9
7 TU	0215 / 0815 / 1443 / 2033	4.1 / 1.5 / 4.2 / 1.6	**22** W	0100 / 0733 / 1351 / 2006	4.1 / 1.4 / 4.2 / 1.4
8 W	0305 / 0900 / 1527 / 2113	4.3 / 1.2 / 4.4 / 1.3	**23** TH	0214 / 0827 / 1452 / 2054	4.4 / 1.0 / 4.6 / 1.0
9 TH	0348 / 0937 / 1606 / 2150	4.5 / 1.0 / 4.6 / 1.0	**24** F	0310 / 0914 / 1539 / 2138	4.8 / 0.6 / 4.9 / 0.6
10 F	0427 / 1013 / 1643 / 2226	4.6 / 0.8 / 4.7 / 0.8	**25** SA	0359 / 0957 / 1623 / 2221	5.1 / 0.3 / 5.2 / 0.3
11 SA O	0504 / 1047 / 1718 / 2301	4.7 / 0.7 / 4.8 / 0.7	**26** SU ●	0445 / 1039 / 1707 / 2303	5.4 / 0.1 / 5.4 / 0.1
12 SU	0539 / 1119 / 1750 / 2334	4.8 / 0.7 / 4.9 / 0.7	**27** M	0531 / 1121 / 1750 / 2347	5.5 / 0.1 / 5.5 / 0.0
13 M	0613 / 1150 / 1826	4.8 / 0.7 / 4.8	**28** TU	0617 / 1203 / 1834	5.4 / 0.2 / 5.4
14 TU	0006 / 0646 / 1220 / 1859	0.8 / 4.7 / 0.9 / 4.7	**29** W	0031 / 0701 / 1246 / 1916	0.2 / 5.3 / 0.4 / 5.2
15 W	0038 / 0718 / 1251 / 1932	0.9 / 4.6 / 1.0 / 4.6	**30** TH	0116 / 0746 / 1329 / 2002	0.4 / 5.0 / 0.8 / 4.8

Chart Datum: 0·20 metres below Ordnance Datum (Dublin)

IRELAND – GALWAY

LAT 53°16′N   LONG 9°03′W

TIMES AND HEIGHTS OF HIGH AND LOW WATERS

YEAR **1998**

TIME ZONE (UT)
For Summer Time add ONE hour in non-shaded areas

MAY

	Time	m		Time	m
1 F	0203 0835 1415 2052	0.8 4.6 1.2 4.5	**16** SA	0132 0810 1344 2026	1.1 4.4 1.4 4.4
2 SA	0257 0931 1511 2156	1.2 4.2 1.6 4.1	**17** SU	0216 0856 1431 2118	1.3 4.2 1.6 4.3
3 SU	0403 1038 1625 2317	1.5 4.0 1.9 3.9	**18** M	0308 0952 1528 2219	1.4 4.1 1.8 4.2
4 M	0517 1154 1746	1.7 3.8 2.0	**19** TU	0409 1054 1641 2323	1.6 4.0 1.9 4.2
5 TU	0034 0626 1308 1856	3.9 1.7 3.9 1.9	**20** W	0526 1201 1827	1.6 4.1 1.8
6 W	0140 0730 1410 1955	4.0 1.6 4.1 1.7	**21** TH	0031 0653 1315 1934	4.3 1.4 4.3 1.5
7 TH	0234 0823 1457 2041	4.1 1.4 4.3 1.5	**22** F	0142 0756 1421 2027	4.5 1.1 4.6 1.1
8 F	0318 0905 1537 2121	4.3 1.2 4.5 1.2	**23** SA	0243 0847 1513 2114	4.8 0.8 4.9 0.7
9 SA	0358 0942 1614 2158	4.5 1.1 4.6 1.0	**24** SU	0335 0933 1559 2159	5.0 0.6 5.2 0.5
10 SU O	0435 1017 1648 2234	4.6 0.9 4.8 0.9	**25** M ●	0423 1017 1644 2244	5.2 0.4 5.3 0.3
11 M O	0511 1051 1723 2309	4.6 0.9 4.8 0.8	**26** TU	0511 1101 1729 2329	5.3 0.4 5.4 0.3
12 TU	0546 1122 1757 2342	4.7 0.9 4.8 0.8	**27** W	0558 1144 1814	5.3 0.5 5.3
13 W	0621 1153 1832	4.6 1.0 4.8	**28** TH	0014 0644 1227 1859	0.3 5.1 0.6 5.1
14 TH	0015 0655 1227 1907	0.9 4.6 1.0 4.7	**29** F	0100 0729 1311 1944	0.5 4.9 0.9 4.9
15 F	0052 0731 1303 1944	1.0 4.5 1.2 4.6	**30** SA	0146 0816 1355 2032	0.8 4.6 1.2 4.6
			31 SU	0235 0907 1446 2128	1.1 4.3 1.6 4.3

JUNE

	Time	m		Time	m
1 M	0332 1004 1547 2233	1.4 4.1 1.8 4.0	**16** TU	0252 0933 1512 2158	1.1 4.3 1.5 4.4
2 TU	0436 1108 1700 2342	1.6 3.9 2.0 3.9	**17** W	0348 1032 1617 2301	1.3 4.2 1.7 4.3
3 W	0541 1214 1809	1.7 3.9 2.0	**18** TH	0454 1136 1740	1.4 4.2 1.7
4 TH	0049 0641 1321 1911	3.9 1.7 3.9 1.9	**19** F	0007 0610 1245 1902	4.4 1.4 4.3 1.5
5 F	0151 0738 1417 2004	3.9 1.6 4.1 1.7	**20** SA	0116 0725 1353 2003	4.5 1.3 4.5 1.2
6 SA	0242 0827 1502 2050	4.0 1.5 4.3 1.4	**21** SU	0220 0823 1451 2055	4.6 1.1 4.8 0.9
7 SU	0326 0910 1541 2130	4.2 1.3 4.5 1.2	**22** M	0315 0913 1540 2143	4.8 0.9 5.0 0.7
8 M	0405 0948 1617 2208	4.3 1.2 4.6 1.0	**23** TU	0406 0959 1627 2229	5.0 0.8 5.1 0.5
9 TU	0442 1024 1653 2245	4.4 1.1 4.7 0.9	**24** W ●	0455 1044 1713 2314	5.0 0.7 5.2 0.5
10 W O	0520 1059 1729 2321	4.5 1.0 4.8 0.8	**25** TH	0542 1127 1758 2359	5.0 0.7 5.1 0.5
11 TH	0557 1133 1807 2358	4.6 1.0 4.8 0.8	**26** F	0628 1210 1843	5.0 0.7 5.0
12 F	0635 1209 1846	4.6 1.0 4.8	**27** SA	0043 0712 1252 1926	0.5 4.8 0.9 4.9
13 SA	0036 0714 1249 1926	0.8 4.6 1.0 4.8	**28** SU	0126 0756 1333 2010	0.7 4.6 1.1 4.6
14 SU	0118 0755 1331 2009	0.8 4.5 1.2 4.6	**29** M	0209 0841 1416 2057	0.9 4.4 1.4 4.4
15 M	0202 0840 1418 2059	0.9 4.4 1.3 4.5	**30** TU	0255 0928 1505 2148	1.2 4.2 1.6 4.1

JULY

	Time	m		Time	m
1 W	0347 1020 1604 2244	1.4 4.0 1.8 3.9	**16** TH	0325 1006 1551 2238	1.0 4.3 1.5 4.4
2 TH	0446 1115 1713 2342	1.6 3.9 2.0 3.8	**17** F	0425 1109 1704 2344	1.3 4.2 1.6 4.3
3 F	0548 1214 1822	1.4 3.8 2.0	**18** SA	0536 1218 1832	1.4 4.2 1.6
4 SA	0048 0650 1320 1923	3.7 1.8 3.9 1.8	**19** SU	0053 0657 1331 1945	4.3 1.3 4.3 1.4
5 SU	0155 0748 1419 2017	3.8 1.7 4.0 1.6	**20** M	0202 0804 1436 2042	4.4 1.3 4.5 1.1
6 M	0250 0838 1507 2103	3.9 1.5 4.2 1.4	**21** TU	0302 0858 1529 2131	4.5 1.2 4.7 0.9
7 TU	0335 0922 1547 2145	4.1 1.3 4.4 1.1	**22** W	0354 0945 1616 2216	4.7 1.0 4.9 0.7
8 W	0416 1002 1626 2225	4.3 1.1 4.6 0.9	**23** TH ●	0442 1029 1701 2300	4.8 0.9 5.0 0.6
9 TH O	0456 1041 1705 2304	4.5 1.0 4.8 0.7	**24** F	0528 1111 1744 2342	4.8 0.8 5.0 0.5
10 F	0537 1118 1746 2343	4.6 0.8 4.9 0.5	**25** SA	0611 1151 1826	4.8 0.8 5.0
11 SA	0617 1156 1827	4.7 0.7 5.0	**26** SU	0022 0652 1230 1906	0.5 4.8 0.8 4.9
12 SU	0022 0657 1236 1908	0.5 4.8 0.7 5.0	**27** M	0101 0732 1307 1946	0.6 4.7 0.9 4.7
13 M	0103 0738 1318 1951	0.5 4.8 0.8 4.9	**28** TU	0138 0812 1346 2026	0.8 4.5 1.1 4.5
14 TU	0146 0822 1402 2039	0.6 4.6 1.0 4.7	**29** W	0217 0853 1426 2107	1.0 4.3 1.4 4.2
15 W	0233 0910 1452 2135	0.8 4.5 1.2 4.5	**30** TH	0300 0936 1510 2152	1.3 4.1 1.7 4.0
			31 F	0348 1021 1606 2241	1.6 3.9 1.9 3.8

AUGUST

	Time	m		Time	m
1 SA	0447 1154 1723 2336	1.8 4.0 2.0 3.6	**16** SU	0509 1154 1807	1.6 4.1 1.7
2 SU	0559 1207 1843	1.9 3.8 2.0	**17** M	0036 0636 1315 1933	4.1 1.7 4.1 1.5
3 M	0046 0710 1322 1947	3.6 1.9 3.8 1.8	**18** TU	0150 0750 1426 2034	4.2 1.6 4.3 1.3
4 TU	0212 0810 1432 2039	3.7 1.7 4.0 1.5	**19** W	0252 0845 1519 2120	4.4 1.4 4.6 1.0
5 W	0309 0859 1521 2124	3.9 1.5 4.3 1.2	**20** TH	0343 0930 1605 2202	4.5 1.2 4.8 0.8
6 TH	0354 0942 1603 2206	4.2 1.2 4.6 0.8	**21** F	0428 1012 1647 2242	4.7 1.0 4.9 0.6
7 F	0436 1023 1644 2246	4.5 0.9 4.8 0.5	**22** SA ●	0510 1051 1727 2320	4.8 0.8 5.0 0.5
8 SA O	0516 1102 1726 2325	4.7 0.6 5.0 0.3	**23** SU	0551 1129 1806 2357	4.8 0.7 5.0 0.5
9 SU	0557 1141 1808	4.9 0.5 5.2	**24** M	0629 1205 1843	4.8 0.7 4.9
10 M	0004 0637 1220 1849	0.1 5.0 0.4 5.2	**25** TU	0032 0706 1240 1919	0.6 4.8 0.8 4.8
11 TU	0045 0718 1301 1931	0.1 5.0 0.4 5.1	**26** W	0106 0743 1315 1955	0.8 4.7 1.0 4.6
12 W	0126 0759 1344 2017	0.3 4.9 0.6 4.9	**27** TH	0141 0819 1350 2030	1.0 4.5 1.2 4.3
13 TH	0211 0844 1430 2109	0.6 4.6 1.0 4.6	**28** F	0217 0856 1427 2109	1.3 4.3 1.5 4.1
14 F	0300 0937 1525 2212	0.9 4.4 1.3 4.3	**29** SA	0255 0936 1508 2156	1.6 4.1 1.8 3.8
15 SA	0357 1040 1635 2322	1.3 4.2 1.6 4.1	**30** SU	0341 1023 1603 2251	1.9 3.9 2.0 3.7
			31 M	0447 1117 1755 2353	2.1 3.8 2.1 3.6

13

Chart Datum: 0·20 metres below Ordnance Datum (Dublin)

TIME ZONE (UT)
For Summer Time add ONE hour in non-shaded areas

IRELAND – GALWAY

LAT 53°16′N LONG 9°03′W

TIMES AND HEIGHTS OF HIGH AND LOW WATERS

YEAR **1998**

SEPTEMBER

Day	Time	m	Time	m	Time	m	Time	m
1 TU	0638	2.1	1219	3.8	1919	1.9		
16 W	0138	4.1	0733	1.8	1412	4.2	2025	1.4
2 W	0121	3.6	0745	1.9	1348	3.9	2016	1.6
17 TH	0239	4.3	0828	1.5	1504	4.5	2107	1.1
3 TH	0244	3.9	0836	1.6	1455	4.2	2102	1.2
18 F	0327	4.6	0912	1.3	1548	4.7	2143	0.9
4 F	0331	4.3	0921	1.2	1541	4.6	2143	0.8
19 SA	0409	4.7	0951	1.1	1628	4.9	2219	0.7
5 SA	0412	4.6	1002	0.8	1622	4.9	2223	0.4
20 SU ●	0449	4.9	1029	0.9	1707	5.0	2255	0.6
6 SU O	0453	4.9	1041	0.5	1704	5.2	2302	0.1
21 M	0526	4.9	1105	0.8	1743	5.0	2329	0.6
7 M	0534	5.1	1120	0.3	1746	5.4	2342	0.0
22 TU	0603	4.9	1139	0.8	1818	4.9		
8 TU	0614	5.2	1200	0.2	1828	5.4		
23 W	0002	0.7	0638	4.9	1212	0.8	1852	4.8
9 W	0022	0.0	0654	5.2	1241	0.2	1910	5.3
24 TH	0034	0.9	0713	4.8	1245	1.0	1925	4.7
10 TH	0104	0.2	0735	5.1	1323	0.4	1955	5.1
25 F	0106	1.1	0747	4.6	1318	1.2	1958	4.4
11 F	0147	0.5	0818	4.8	1409	0.8	2045	4.7
26 SA	0139	1.4	0821	4.4	1352	1.4	2034	4.2
12 SA	0235	1.0	0908	4.5	1501	1.3	2147	4.3
27 SU	0215	1.7	0859	4.2	1432	1.7	2121	4.0
13 SU	0332	1.5	1011	4.2	1609	1.6	2301	4.1
28 M	0257	2.0	0946	4.0	1520	2.0	2218	3.8
14 M	0447	1.8	1132	4.0	1745	1.8		
29 TU	0352	2.2	1041	3.9	1627	2.2	2321	3.7
15 TU	0020	4.0	0619	1.9	1300	4.0	1921	1.7
30 W	0604	2.3	1142	3.9	1846	2.1		

OCTOBER

Day	Time	m	Time	m	Time	m	Time	m
1 TH	0034	3.8	0717	2.1	1254	4.0	1947	1.7
16 F	0218	4.4	0805	1.7	1442	4.5	2044	1.3
2 F	0208	4.0	0810	1.7	1419	4.3	2035	1.3
17 SA	0305	4.6	0849	1.5	1526	4.7	2119	1.1
3 SA	0302	4.4	0856	1.3	1512	4.7	2118	0.8
18 SU	0345	4.8	0928	1.2	1605	4.8	2154	0.9
4 SU	0344	4.8	0937	0.8	1557	5.1	2158	0.4
19 M	0423	4.9	1005	1.0	1642	4.9	2228	0.9
5 M O	0425	5.1	1018	0.5	1640	5.4	2238	0.1
20 TU ●	0459	5.0	1040	0.9	1718	5.0	2301	0.9
6 TU	0507	5.4	1058	0.2	1723	5.6	2318	0.0
21 W	0535	5.0	1114	0.9	1752	4.9	2332	0.9
7 W	0548	5.5	1139	0.1	1806	5.6	2359	0.1
22 TH	0609	5.0	1146	0.9	1825	4.8		
8 TH	0630	5.5	1221	0.2	1850	5.5		
23 F	0003	1.1	0643	4.9	1218	1.1	1858	4.7
9 F	0041	0.3	0712	5.3	1304	0.4	1935	5.2
24 SA	0034	1.2	0717	4.7	1251	1.2	1932	4.5
10 SA	0125	0.7	0755	5.0	1350	0.8	2025	4.8
25 SU	0108	1.5	0751	4.6	1327	1.4	2009	4.3
11 SU	0213	1.1	0844	4.6	1441	1.2	2125	4.4
26 M	0145	1.7	0829	4.4	1407	1.6	2054	4.1
12 M	0309	1.6	0940	4.3	1548	1.7	2240	4.1
27 TU	0229	2.0	0915	4.2	1455	1.9	2151	4.0
13 TU	0427	2.0	1109	4.0	1719	1.9		
28 W	0323	2.2	1011	4.1	1555	2.0	2255	3.9
14 W	0001	4.0	0556	2.1	1236	4.0	1855	1.8
29 TH	0441	2.3	1112	4.1	1738	2.0		
15 TH	0117	4.1	0708	2.0	1348	4.2	2004	1.6
30 F	0002	4.0	0642	2.1	1219	4.2	1910	1.7
31 SA	0120	4.2	0739	1.8	1335	4.4	2004	1.3

NOVEMBER

Day	Time	m	Time	m	Time	m	Time	m
1 SU	0225	4.6	0828	1.4	1439	4.8	2049	0.9
16 M	0318	4.7	0902	1.5	1539	4.6	2126	1.2
2 M	0313	5.0	0912	0.9	1529	5.2	2132	0.6
17 TU	0355	4.8	0940	1.3	1616	4.7	2201	1.1
3 TU	0357	5.3	0954	0.6	1615	5.5	2213	0.3
18 W	0431	4.9	1016	1.1	1651	4.8	2234	1.1
4 W O	0440	5.5	1036	0.3	1701	5.6	2255	0.2
19 TH ●	0506	4.9	1050	1.1	1726	4.9	2306	1.1
5 TH	0524	5.6	1119	0.2	1746	5.6	2337	0.3
20 F	0541	5.0	1124	1.1	1800	4.8	2337	1.2
6 F	0608	5.6	1203	0.3	1832	5.5		
21 SA	0617	4.9	1157	1.1	1835	4.7		
7 SA	0021	0.5	0652	5.4	1248	0.5	1919	5.2
22 SU	0010	1.3	0652	4.8	1232	1.2	1911	4.6
8 SU	0106	0.8	0737	5.1	1334	0.8	2008	4.9
23 M	0046	1.4	0728	4.7	1309	1.3	1950	4.5
9 M	0154	1.3	0826	4.8	1424	1.2	2105	4.5
24 TU	0126	1.6	0807	4.6	1351	1.4	2034	4.3
10 TU	0249	1.7	0923	4.4	1525	1.6	2214	4.2
25 W	0211	1.8	0851	4.5	1438	1.6	2128	4.2
11 W	0359	2.0	1038	4.2	1644	1.8	2330	4.1
26 TH	0303	2.0	0945	4.4	1533	1.7	2229	4.1
12 TH	0521	2.2	1159	4.1	1807	1.8		
27 F	0410	2.2	1045	4.3	1642	1.8	2334	4.2
13 F	0043	4.1	0631	2.1	1311	4.1	1919	1.7
28 SA	0544	2.1	1149	4.4	1813	1.7		
14 SA	0146	4.3	0731	1.9	1411	4.3	2011	1.6
29 SU	0041	4.3	0702	1.9	1259	4.5	1927	1.4
15 SU	0236	4.5	0820	1.7	1458	4.5	2051	1.4
30 M	0149	4.6	0758	1.5	1407	4.8	2021	1.1

DECEMBER

Day	Time	m	Time	m	Time	m	Time	m
1 TU	0244	4.9	0848	1.1	1504	5.1	2108	0.8
16 W	0326	4.5	0915	1.5	1549	4.4	2135	1.4
2 W	0333	5.2	0933	0.8	1554	5.3	2152	0.6
17 TH	0403	4.7	0954	1.3	1626	4.5	2211	1.3
3 TH O	0419	5.4	1018	0.5	1642	5.4	2235	0.5
18 F ●	0440	4.8	1031	1.2	1703	4.6	2246	1.2
4 F	0505	5.5	1103	0.4	1730	5.5	2320	0.5
19 SA	0517	4.9	1107	1.0	1739	4.7	2320	1.1
5 SA	0551	5.5	1148	0.4	1817	5.4		
20 SU	0554	4.9	1143	1.0	1817	4.7	2356	1.2
6 SU	0005	0.7	0637	5.4	1234	0.5	1904	5.2
21 M	0632	4.9	1218	0.9	1855	4.7		
7 M	0050	0.9	0722	5.2	1319	0.7	1952	4.9
22 TU	0033	1.2	0710	4.9	1257	0.9	1933	4.6
8 TU	0136	1.2	0809	4.9	1406	1.0	2044	4.6
23 W	0113	1.3	0749	4.8	1337	1.0	2016	4.5
9 W	0226	1.6	0901	4.6	1458	1.4	2143	4.3
24 TH	0157	1.5	0832	4.7	1422	1.2	2105	4.4
10 TH	0324	1.9	1001	4.3	1600	1.7	2248	4.1
25 F	0246	1.6	0921	4.6	1513	1.3	2202	4.3
11 F	0434	2.1	1108	4.1	1712	1.8	2354	4.0
26 SA	0344	1.8	1019	4.5	1611	1.5	2304	4.2
12 SA	0544	2.1	1217	4.0	1822	1.9		
27 SU	0453	1.9	1122	4.4	1720	1.6		
13 SU	0058	4.1	0647	2.1	1325	4.0	1925	1.8
28 M	0010	4.3	0616	1.8	1230	4.4	1843	1.5
14 M	0157	4.2	0744	1.9	1422	4.1	2016	1.6
29 TU	0118	4.5	0729	1.6	1341	4.6	1954	1.3
15 TU	0245	4.4	0832	1.7	1509	4.3	2058	1.5
30 W	0221	4.7	0827	1.3	1444	4.8	2048	1.1
31 TH	0315	5.0	0918	1.0	1539	5.0	2136	0.9

Chart Datum: 0·20 metres below Ordnance Datum (Dublin)

VOLVO PENTA SERVICE

Sales and service centres in area 14
Channel Islands **GUERNSEY** *Chicks Marine Ltd,* Collings Road, St. Peter Port
GY1 1FL Tel (01481) 723716/724536 **JERSEY** *D. K. Collins Marine Ltd,*
South Pier, St. Helier, JE2 3NB Tel (01534) 32415

VOLVO PENTA

Area 14

Channel Islands
Alderney to Jersey

14

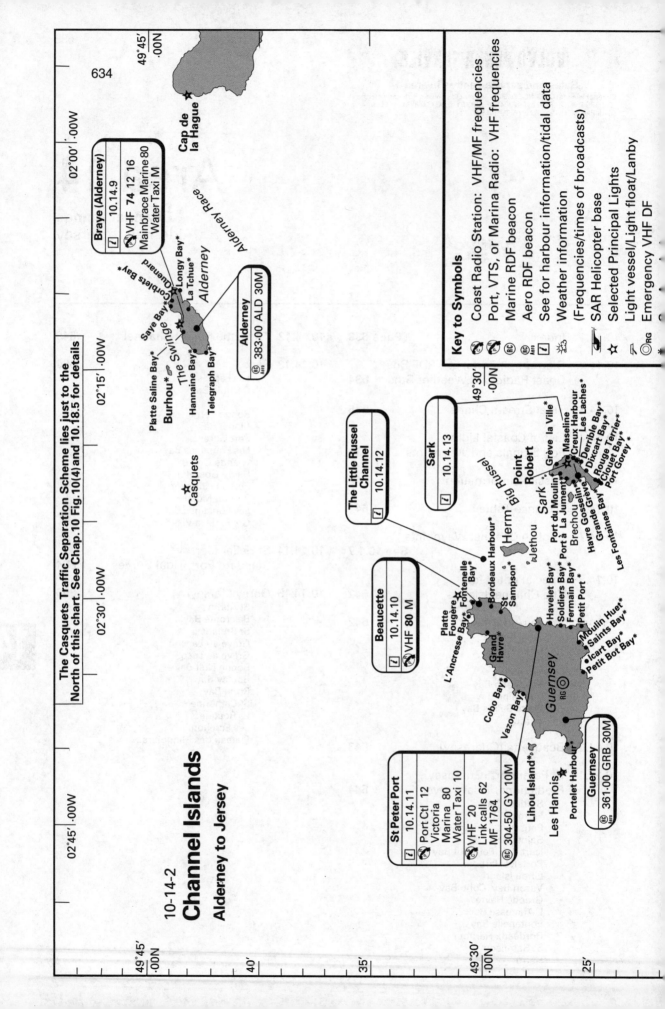

10-14-2

Channel Islands

Alderney to Jersey

634

The Casquets Traffic Separation Scheme lies just to the
North of this chart. See Chap.10 Fig.10(4) and 10.18.5 for details

Cap de la Hague

Braye (Alderney)

ℹ 10.14.9

📡 VHF 74 12 16
Mainbrace Marine 80
Water Taxi M

Corblets Bay*
Quenard
Longy Bay*
La Tchue*
Save Bay*
Platte Saline Bay*
Burhou*
The Swinge
Hannaine Bay*
Telegraph Bay*

Alderney

Alderney Race

Alderney

◎ 383·00 ALD 30M
RC Aero

Casquets ☆

The Little Russel Channel

ℹ 10.14.12

Sark

ℹ 10.14.13

Grève la Ville*
Maseline
Creux Harbour
Les Laches*
Derrible Bay*
Dixcart Bay*
Rouge Terrier*
Clouet Bay*
Port Gorey*

Point Robert ☆

Port du Moulin*
Port à La Jument*
Brechou
Havre Gosselin*
Grande Grève*
Grande Bay*
Les Fontaines Bay*

Sark

Herm
Big Russel
Jethou

Beaucette

ℹ 10.14.10

📡 VHF 80 M

Platte Fougère*
Fontenelle Bay*
Bordeaux Harbour*
St Sampson*

St Peter Port

ℹ 10.14.11

📡 Port Ctl 12
Victoria
Marina 80
Water Taxi 10

📡 VHF 20
Link calls 62
MF 1764

◎ 304·50 GY 10M
RC

L'Ancresse Bay*
Grand Havre*
Cobo Bay*
Vazon Bay*

Havelet Bay*
Soldiers Bay*
Fermain Bay*
Petit Port*
Moulin Huet*
Saints Bay*
Icart Bay*
Petit Bot Bay*

Guernsey
RG ◎

Lihou Island*◎
Les Hanois
Portelet Harbour*

Guernsey

◎ 361·00 GRB 30M
RC Aero

Key to Symbols

📡📡	Coast Radio Station: VHF/MF frequencies
📡📡	Port, VTS, or Marina Radio: VHF frequencies
◉ RC	Marine RDF beacon
◉ RC Aero	Aero RDF beacon
ℹ	See for harbour information/tidal data
📶	Weather information (Frequencies/times of broadcasts)
🚁	SAR Helicopter base
☆	Selected Principal Lights
◎ RG	Light vessel/Light float/Lanby
✳	Emergency VHF DF

Les Ecrehou*

49°15'
·00N

Gorey
10.14.15
ⓘ
☎ VHF 74

St Catherine
Bay*

Bouley Bay*

Bonne Nuit Bay*

Rozel Bay*

St Helier
10.14.14
ⓘ
☎ VHF 14

La Rocque*

Sorel Point
☆

Grève de Lecq*

Jersey

Belcroute
Bay*

Grosnez Point
☆

St Aubin

St
Brelade*

Grève au Lançon

Jersey West
Ⓡ 329·00 JW 25M
Aero

La Corbière
Ⓡ 295·50 CB 20M

Jersey Radio
☎ VHF 25 82
MF 1659
🔊 VHF 25 82
MF 1659
0645 0745 0845 LT
1245 1845 2245 UT
Ⓡ RG

See 10-15-2

Plateau des Minquiers*

635

See 10-16-2

Roches Douvres
Ⓡ 308·00 RD 70M

Plateau des
Roches Douvres
☆

90

4°30'W (1998)

O

180

Variation

270

Plateau de
Barnouic
☆

See 10-16-2

20'

49°15'
·00N

10'

05'

49°00'
·00N

55'

02°45'·00W   02°30'·00W   02°15'·00W   02°00'W   55'   50'
25'   ·20'   35'   40'   05'   10'   02°00'·00W   49°00'·00N

10-14-3   AREA 14 TIDAL STREAMS

5 Hours before HW Dover (HW St Helier)

4 Hours before HW Dover (0100 after HW St Helier)

3 Hours before HW Dover (0200 after HW St Helier)

2 Hours before HW Dover (0300 after HW St Helier)

1 Hour before HW Dover (0400 after HW St Helier)

HW Dover (0500 after HW St Helier)

Westward 10.16.3   Southward 10.15.3   Northward 10.2.3   Eastward 10.19.3

1 Hour after HW Dover (0600 after HW St Helier)

2 Hours after HW Dover (0530 before HW St Helier)

3 Hours after HW Dover (0430 before HW St Helier)

4 Hours after HW Dover (0330 before HW St Helier)

5 Hours after HW Dover (0230 before HW St Helier)

6 Hours after HW Dover (0130 before HW St Helier)

14

10.14.4 COASTAL LIGHTS, FOG SIGNALS AND WAYPOINTS

Abbreviations used below are given in 1.4.1. Principal lights are in **bold** print, places in CAPITALS, and light-vessels , light floats and Lanbys in *CAPITAL ITALICS*. Unless otherwise stated lights are white. m – elevation in metres; M – nominal range in miles. Fog signals are in *italics*. Useful waypoints are underlined – use those on land with care. All geographical positions should be assumed to be approximate. See 4.4.1. All positions are referenced to the ED 50 datum.

NOTE: For English Channel Waypoints see 10.1.7.

MID-CHANNEL MARKS

CHANNEL Lt F 49°54'·42N 02°53'·67W Fl 15s 12m **25M**; R hull with Lt Tr amidships; Racon (O); *Horn (1) 20s.*
E Channel Lt By 49°58'·67N 02°28'·87W Fl Y 5s; Racon (T); *Whis.*
EC 1 Lt By 50°05'·90N 01°48'·35W Fl Y 2·5s; Racon (T); *Whis.*
EC 2 Lt By 50°12'·10N 01°12'·40W Fl (4) Y 15s; Racon (T) ; *Whis.*
EC 3 Lt By 50°18'·30N 00°36'·10W Fl Y 5s; Racon (T); *Whis.*

THE CASQUETS AND ALDERNEY

Casquets 49°43'·38N 02°22'·55W Fl (5) 30s 37m **24M**; W Tr, the highest and NW of three; Racon (T); *Horn (2) 60s*; H24.

ALDERNEY
Alderney (Quenard Pt) 49°43'·81N 02°09'·77W Fl (4) 15s 37m **28M**; W ● Tr, B band; vis 085°-027°; *Siren (4) 60s.*
Château à L'Étoc Pt 49°44'·00N 02°10'·55W Iso WR 4s 20m W10M, R7M; W col; vis R071·1°-111·1°, W111·1°-151·1°; in line 111·1° with main Lt.
Ldg Bns 142°. Front, 49°43'·96N 02°10'·89W; W Bn, O topmark. Rear, 720m from front, BW Bn, △ topmark.

BRAYE
Ldg Lts 215°. **Front**, elbow of old pier, 49°43'·46N 02°11'·83W Q 8m **17M**; vis 210°-220°. **Rear**, 335m from front, Q 17m **18M**; vis 210°-220°. Both metal posts on W cols.
Bkwtr Hd 49°43'·87N 02°11'·59W L Fl 10s 7m 5M.
No. 1 Lt By 49°43'·78N 02°11'·63W QG; SHM.
Lt By 49°43'·63N 02°11'·90W Q (2) G 5S; SHM.
No. 2 Lt By 49°43'·66N 02°11'·67W QR; PHM.
Lt By 49°43'·60N 02°11'·85W Q (2) R 5S; PHM.
Braye Jetty Hd 49°43'·59N 02°11'·92W 2 FR (vert) 8m 5M.

APPROACHES TO GUERNSEY

LITTLE RUSSEL CHANNEL

Platte Fougère 49°30'·88N 02°29'·05W Fl WR 10s 15m **16M**; W 8-sided Tr, B band; vis W155°-085°, R085°-155°; Racon (P); *Horn 45s.*
Tautenay Lt Bn 49°30'·17N 02°26'·74W Q (3) WR 6s 7m W7M, R6M; B and W Bn; vis W050°-215°, R215°-050°.
Roustel Lt Bn Tr 49°29'·28N 02°28'·71W Q 8m 7M; Lantern on B & W chequered Tr.
Platte Lt Bn 49°29'·15N 02°29'·50W Fl WR 3s 6m W7M, R5M; G Tr; vis R024°-219°, W219°-024°.
Brehon Lt Bn 49°28'·34N 02°29'·20W Iso 4s 19m 9M; Bn on ● Tr.

BIG RUSSEL
Noire Pute 49°28'·27N 02°24'·93W Fl (2) WR 15s 8m 6M; vis W220°-040°, R040°-220°.
Fourquies Lt By 49°27'·40N 02°26'·40W Q; NCM.
Lower Heads Lt By 49°25'·91N 02°28'·48W Q (6) + L Fl 15s; SCM; *Bell .*

GUERNSEY

BEAUCETTE MARINA/BORDEAUX HARBOUR
Petite Canupe Lt Bn 49°30'·25N 02°29'·05W Q (6) + L Fl 15s; SCM.
Beaucette Ldg Lts 276°. Front 49°30'·25N 02°30'·13W FR; W board with R stripe. Rear, 185m from front, FR; R board with W stripe.
Bordeaux Hbr Bkwtr Hd 49°29'·38N 02°30'·30W; post.

ST SAMPSON
Ldg Lts 286°. Front Crocq Pier Hd 49°28'·97N 02°30'·66W FR 11m 5M; vis 250°-340°; Tfc sigs. Rear, 390m from front, FG 13m; clock Tr.
N Pier Hd 49°28'·98N 02°30'·62W FG 3m 5M; vis 230°-340°.
2 FR (vert) on chimneys (conspic) 300m NNW.

ST PETER PORT
Ldg Lts 220°. **Front**, Castle Bkwtr Hd 49°27'·36N 02°31'·34W Al WR 10s 14m **16M**; dark ● Tr, W on NE side; vis 187°-007°; RC (synch with)))); *Horn 15s.* Rear, Belvedere, Oc 10s 61m 14M; W ■ with Y stripe on W Tr; vis 179°-269°; both intens 217°-223°.
Reffée Lt By 49°27'·80N 02°31'·18W VQ (6) + L Fl 10s; SCM.
Queen Elizabeth II Marina 49°27'·79N 02°31'·78W. Dir Lt 270°. Dir Oc WRG 3s 5m 6M; vis G258°-268°, W268°-272°, R272°-282°.
Queen Elizabeth II Marina app Lt By 49°27'·78N 02°31'·66W QR; PHM.
White Rock Pier Hd 49°27'·43N 02°31'·60W Oc G 5s 11m 14M; ● stone Tr; intens 174°-354°; Tfc sigs.
Victoria Marina Ldg Lts 265°. Front, S Pier Hd, 49°27'·38N 02°31'·95W Oc R 5s 10m 14M; W framework Tr. Rear, 160m from front, Iso R 2s 22m 3M; vis 260°-270°.
Albert Dock Fish Quay Hd 49°27'·30N 02°31'·39W FR.

HAVELET BAY
Oyster Rk Bn 49°27'·15N 02°31'·38W; Y Bn 'O'.
Oyster Rk Lt By 49°27'·10N 02°31'·39W QG; SHM.
Moulinet Lt By 49°27'·03N 02°31'·46W QR; PHM.
Moulinet Bn 49°27'·01N 02°31'·49W; Y Bn 'M'.

SOLDIERS BAY
Anfré Bn 49°26'·52N 02°31'·40W; Y Bn 'A'.

St Martin's Pt 49°25'·37N 02°31'·61W Fl (3) WR 10s 15m 14M; flat-roofed, W bldg; vis R185°-191°, W191°-011°, R011°-081°. *Horn (3) 30s.*
Longue Pierre Bn 49°25'·42N 02°31'·39W; Y Bn.

Les Hanois 49°26'·16N 02°42'·06W Fl (2) 13s 33m **20M**; Gy ●Tr, B lantern, helicopter platform; vis 294°-237°; *Horn (2) 60s median brg 095°.* 4 FR on masts 1·27M ESE.

PORTELET HARBOUR
Portelet Hbr Bkwtr Bn 49°26'·22N 02°39'·74W.

COBO BAY/GRAND HAVRE
Grosse Rk Bn 49°29'·07N 02°36'·11W 11m; B Bn.
Rousse Pt Bkwtr Bn 49°29'·98N 02°32'·97W; B Bn.

HERM

Alligande Lt Bn 49°27'·91N 02°28'·69W Fl (3) G 5s; Orange 'A' on B mast; Ra refl.
Épec Lt Bn 49°28'·04N 02°27'·81W Fl G 3s; Black 'E' on G mast.
Vermerette Lt Bn 49°28'·18N 02°27'·67W Fl (2) Y 5s; Orange 'V' on Bn.
Percée Pass, Gate Rk 49°27'·94N 02°27'·44W Q (9) 15s; WCM.

SARK

Courbée du Nez 49°27'·15N 02°22'·08W Fl (4) WR 15s 14m 8M; vis W057°-230°, R230°-057°.
Founiais Bn 49°26'·08N 02°20'·28W; SPM; Topmark 'F'.

GRÈVE LA VILLE/MASELINE

Pt Robert 49°26'·20N 02°20'·70W Fl 15s 65m **20M**; W 8-sided Tr; vis 138°-353°; *Horn (2) 30s.*

Blanchard Lt By 49°25'·43N 02°17'·33W Q (3) 10s; ECM; *Bell.*

JERSEY

Desormes Lt By 49°19'·00N 02°17'·90W Q (9) 15s; WCM.
Grosnez Pt 49°15'·55N 02°14'·75W Fl (2) WR 15s 50m **W19M, R17M**; W hut; vis W081°-188°, R188°-241°.

La Corbière 49°10'·85N 02°14'·90W Iso WR 10s 36m **W18M, R16M**; ● stone Tr; vis W shore-294°, R294°-328°, W328°-148°, R148°-shore; RC; *Horn Mo (C) 60s.*

WESTERN PASSAGE/ST BRELADE

Ldg Lts 082°. Front, La Grève d'Azette 49°10'·21N 02°05'·00W Oc 5s 23m 14M; vis 034°-129°. Rear, Mont Ubé 1M from front, Oc R 5s 46m 12M; vis 250°-095°; Racon (T).
Noirmont Pt 49°09'·97N 02°09'·94W Fl (4) 12s 18m 13M; B Tr, W band.
Passage Rk Lt By 49°09'·59N 02°12'·18W VQ; NCM.
Les Fours Lt By 49°09'·65N 02°10'·08W Q; NCM.
Ruaudière Rk Lt By 49°09'·80N 02°08'·51W Fl G 3s; SHM; *Bell.*
Diamond Rk Lt By 49°10'·18N 02°08'·56W Fl (2) R 6s; PHM.

SAINT AUBIN

North Pier Hd 49°11'·27N 02°09'·95W Iso R 4s 12m 10M; and Dir Lt 254° Dir F WRG 5m, vis G248°-253°, W253°-255°, R255°-260°.
Fort Pier Hd 49°11'·18N 02°09'·52W Fl R 4s 8m 1M.

ST HELIER

Red and Green Passage (Small Roads) Ldg Lts 022·7°. Front, Elizabeth East Berth Dn 49°10'·69N 02°06'·86W Oc G 5s 10m 11M; R stripe on framework Tr. Rear, Albert Pier elbow, 230m from front, Oc R 5s 18m 12M; R stripe on framework Tr; synch with front.
E Rock Lt By 49°10'·02N 02°07'·20W QG; SHM.
Platte Rock Lt Bn 49°10'·22N 02°07'·27W Fl R 1·5s 6m 5M; R metal col.
Ldg Lts 078°. Front, 49°10'·68N 02°06'·58W FG. Rear, 80m from front, FG; both on W cols.
Victoria Pier Hd 49°10'·63N 02°06'·80W; *Bell*; Tfc sigs.

EASTERN PASSAGE/VIOLET CHANNEL/LA ROCQUE

Hinguette Lt By 49°09'·39N 02°07'·22W Fl (4) R 15s; PHM.
Demie de Pas Lt Bn Tr 49°09'·07N 02°06'·05W Mo (D) WR 12s 11m W14M, R10M; B Tr, Y top; vis R130°-303°, W303°-130°; *Horn (3) 60s.*
Icho Tr 49°08'·95N 02°02'·81W (conspic)
Canger Rock Lt By 49°07'·41N 02°00'·30W Q (9) 15s; WCM.
Frouquier Aubert Lt By 49°06'·14N 01°58'·78W Q (6) + L Fl 15s; SCM.
Violet Lt By 49°07'·87N 01°57'·05W L Fl 10s; SWM.
Petite Anquette 49°08'·52N 01°56'·21W; W Bn.
Grand Anquette 49°08'·38N 01°54'·11W; W Bn.

GOREY

Ldg Lts 298°. Front, Pier Hd 49°11'·86N 02°01'·25W Oc RG 5s 8m 12M; W framework Tr; vis R304°-352°, G352°-304°.
Rear, 490m from front, Oc R 5s 24m 8M.
Inner Road Lt By 49°11'·55N 02°00'·25W QG; SHM.

ST CATHERINE BAY/ROZEL BAY

Verclut Bkwtr Hd 49°13'·39N 02°00'·57W Fl 1·5s 18m 13M; framework Tr.
La Coupe Pt Turret 49°13'·98N 02°01'·70W.
Rozel Bay Dir Lt 245° 49°14'·27N 02°02'·68W Dir F WRG 11m 5M; vis G240°-244°, W244°-246°, R246°-250°.

BONNE NUIT BAY TO GRÈVE AU LANCON

Bonne Nuit Bay Ldg Lts 223°. Front, Pier Hd 49°15'·17N 02°07'·08W FG 7m 6M. Rear, 170m from front, FG 34m 6M.
Sorel Pt 49°15'·64N 02°09'·45W L Fl WR 7·5s 50m **15M**; B & W chequered ● Tr; vis W095°-112°, R112°-173°, W173°-230°, R230°-269°, W269°-273°.

OFFLYING ISLANDS

LES ÉCREHOU

Écrevière Lt By 49°15'·32N 01°52'·00W Q (6) + L Fl 15s; SCM.
Mâitre I Bn 49°17'·14N 01°55'·52W.

PLATEAU DES MINQUIERS

NW Minquiers Lt By 48°59'·70N 02°20'·50W Q; NCM; *Bell.*
SW Minquiers Lt By 48°54'·40N 02°19'·30W Q (9) 15s; WCM; *Whis.*
S Minquiers Lt By 48°53'·15N 02°10'·00W Q (6) + L Fl 15s; SCM.
SE Minquiers Lt By 48°53'·50N 02°00'·00W Q (3) 10s; ECM; *Bell.*
NE Minquiers Lt By 49°00'·90N 01°55'·20W VQ (3) 5s; ECM; *Bell.*
N Minquiers Lt By 49°01'·70N 02°00'·50W Q; NCM.
Demi de Vascelin By 49°00'·08N 02°05'·10W; SHM; (unlit.)

14

10.14.5   PASSAGE INFORMATION

Current Pilots for this popular area include: *Shell Channel Pilot* (Imray/Cunliffe); *Normandy and CI Pilot* (Adlard Coles/Brackenbury); *Brittany and CI Cruising Guide* (Adlard Coles/Jefferson); *N Brittany and CI Cruising* (YM/Cumberlidge).

CHANNEL ISLANDS – GENERAL (chart *2669*)

In an otherwise delightful cruising area, the main problems around the Channel Islands include fog and thick weather, the very big tidal range, strong tidal streams, overfalls and steep seas which get up very quickly. The shoreline is generally rugged with sandy bays and many offlying rks. It is important to use large scale charts, and recognised leading marks (of which there are plenty) when entering or leaving many of the hbrs and anchs. Several passages are marked by bns/perches identified by an alphabetical letter(s) in lieu of topmark.

From the N, note the Casquets TSS and ITZ – see Fig. 10 (4). Soundings of Hurd Deep can help navigation. The powerful lights at the Casquets, Alderney (Quenard Pt), Cap de la Hague, Cap Levi and Barfleur greatly assist a night or dawn landfall. By day Alderney is relatively low and conspic. Sark is often seen before Guernsey which slopes down from S to N. Jersey is low-lying in the SE. The islands are fringed by many rky dangers. In bad visibility it is prudent to stay in hbr.

It is important to appreciate that over a 12 hour period tidal streams broadly rotate anti-clockwise around the Islands, particularly in open water and in wider chans (see 10.14.3). The E-going (flood) stream is of less duration than the W-going, but is stronger. The islands lie across the main direction of the streams, so eddies are common along the shores. The range of tide is most in Jersey (9·6m sp, 4·1m np), and least in Alderney (5·3m sp, 2·2m np). Streams run hard through the chans and around headlands and need to be worked carefully; neaps are easier, particularly for a first visit. Strong W'lies cause a heavy sea, usually worst from local HW – 3 to + 3.

Apart from the main hbrs described in Area 14, there are many attractive minor hbrs and anchs, see Index. In the very nature of islands a lee can usually be found somewhere. Boats which can take the ground are best able to explore the quieter hbrs. Be careful to avoid lobster pots and oyster beds.

THE CASQUETS AND ORTAC ROCK (chart *60*)

Casquets lt ho (fog sig) is conspic on the largest island of this group of rks 5·5M W of Braye, Alderney (10.14.9). Off-lying dangers extend 4ca W and WSW (The Ledge and Noire Roque) and 4ca E (Pte Colotte). The tide runs very hard round and between these various obstructions. A shallow bank, on which are situated Fourquie and l'Equêt rks (dry), lies from 5ca to 1M E of Casquets, and should not be approached. Ortac rk (24m) is 3·5M E of Casquets. Ortac Chan runs N/S 5ca W of Ortac; here the stream begins to run NE at HW St Helier – 0230, and SW at HW St Helier + 0355, with sp rates up to 5½kn (7kn reported). Ortac Chan should not be used in bad weather due to tremendous overfalls; these also occur over Eight-fathom Ledge (8½ca W of Casquets), and over the Banks SW, SSW and SSE of the Casquets. An Historic Wreck lies about 300m E of Casquets lt ho (see 10.0.3g).

ALDERNEY AND THE SWINGE (chart *60*)

See 10.14.9 for Braye Harbour (chart *2845*) and approaches, together with pleasant bays and anchs around the island, offering shelter from different wind/sea directions.

The Swinge lies between Burhou with its bordering rks, and the NW coast of Alderney. It can be a dangerous chan, and should only be used in reasonable vis and fair weather. On N side of the Swinge the main dangers are Boues des Kaines, almost awash at LW about 7½ca ESE of Ortac, and North Rk 2½ca SE of Burhou. On S side of the Swinge beware Barsier Rk (dries) 3½ca NNW of Fort Clonque, and Corbet Rk (0·5m high), with drying outliers, 5ca N of Fort Clonque.

The SW-going stream begins at HW St Helier + 0340, and the NE stream at HW St Helier – 0245, sp rates 7-8kn. On the NE-going stream, beware the very strong northerly set in vicinity of Ortac. The tide runs very hard, and in strong or gale force winds from S or W there are very heavy overfalls on the SW-going stream between Ortac and Les Etacs (off W end of Alderney). In strong E winds, on the NE-going stream, overfalls occur between Burhou and Braye breakwater. These overfalls can mostly be avoided by choosing the best time and route (see below), but due to the uneven bottom and strong tides broken water may be met even in calm conditions.

The best time to pass SW through the Swinge is at about HW St Helier +0400, when the SW-going stream starts; hold to the SE side of the chan. But after HW St Helier +0500, to clear the worst of the overfalls keep close to Burhou and Ortac, avoiding North Rk and Boues des Kaines.

Heading NE at about HW St Helier –0200, Great Nannel in transit with E end of Burhou clears Pierre au Vraic to the E, but passes close W of Les Etacs. On this transit, when Roque Tourgis fort is abeam, alter slightly to stbd to pass 1ca NW of Corbet Rk; keep near SE side of chan.

Pierre au Vraic (dries 1·2m) is an isolated, unmarked rock 1·8M S of Ortac and 1·8M WSW of Les Étacs, almost in the fairway to/from the Swinge. On a fair tide from Guernsey it will be well covered, but it is a serious hazard if leaving the Swinge on a SW-going Spring tide close to LW (HW Dover to HW Dover +4). See AC 60 for clearing bearings.

THE ALDERNEY RACE (chart *3653*)

The Alderney Race, so called due to very strong tidal streams, runs NE/SW between Alderney and Cap de la Hague. The fairway, approx 4M wide, is bounded by Race Rk and Alderney S Banks to the NW, and to the SE by rky banks 4M WSW of Cap de la Hague, Milieu and Banc de la Schôle (least depth 2·7m). These dangers which cause breaking seas and heavy overfalls should be carefully avoided. In bad weather and strong wind-against-tide conditions the seas break in all parts of the Race and passage is not recommended. Conditions are exacerbated at sp tides.

In mid-chan the NE-going stream starts at HW St Helier – 0210 (HWD + 0530) and the SW stream at HW St Helier +0430 (HWD), sp rates both 5·5kn. Times at which streams turn do not vary much for various places, but the rates do; for example, 1M W of C de la Hague the sp rates are 7-8kn.

To obtain optimum conditions, timing is of the essence. As a rule of thumb the Race should be entered on the first of the fair tide so as to avoid the peak tidal streams with attendant overfalls/breaking seas.

Thus, bound SW, arrive off C de la Hague at about HW St Helier +0430 (HW Dover) when the stream will be slack, whilst just starting to run SW off Alderney. A yacht leaving Cherbourg at HW Dover –0300 will achieve the above timing by utilising the inshore W-going tidal eddy.

Conversely, NE bound, leave St Peter Port at approx local HW −0425 (HW Dover+3) with a foul tide so as to pass Banc de la Schôle as the first of the fair tide starts to make. A later departure should achieve a faster passage, but with potentially less favourable conditions in the Race. On the NE stream the worst overfalls are on the French side.

APPROACHES TO GUERNSEY (charts *808, 3654*)

From the N/NE, The Little Russel Chan (chartlet at 10.14.12) between Guernsey and Herm gives the most convenient access to Beaucette Marina (10.14.10) and St Peter Port (10.14.11 and chart *3140*). With lts on Platte Fougère, Tautenay, Roustel, Platte and Bréhon, plus the ldg lts (220°) for St Peter Port, the Little Russel can be navigated day or night in reasonable vis, even at LW. But it needs care, due to rks which fringe the chan and appr, and the strong tide which also sets across the ent. In mid chan, S of Platte and NW of Bréhon, the NE-going stream begins at HW St Peter Port −0245, and the SW stream at HW St Peter Port +0330, sp rates both 5·25kn which can raise a very steep sea with wind against tide.

The Big Russel is wider and easier; in bad weather or poor vis it may be a better approach to St Peter Port, via Lower Heads SCM lt buoy. From the NW, Doyle Passage, which is aligned 146°/326° off Beaucette, should only be used with local knowledge by day. From S or W, the natural route is around St Martin's Pt.

Minor hbrs and anchs around Guernsey are briefly described after the St Peter Port tidal predictions (10.14.11). In onshore winds keep well clear of Guernsey's W coast, where in bad weather the sea breaks on dangers up to 4M offshore.

HERM AND JETHOU (charts *807, 808*).

Herm (10.14.11) and Jethou (private) are reached from Little Russel via any of 7 passages all of which require reasonable vis and care with tidal streams; Alligande pass is most direct from St Peter Port. The appr from the Big Russel is more open and leads easily to pleasant ⚓s at Belvoir Bay and Shell Bay.

SARK (10.14.12 and chart *808*)

La Maseline and Creux on the E coast are the only proper hbrs, the former much used by ferries. Elsewhere around the island, whatever the wind direction, a sheltered anch can usually be found in a lee, although swell may intrude. On the NW coast, Port à La Jument and Port du Moulin in Banquette Bay offer some shelter from S and E winds. Fontaines Bay and La Grève de la Ville offer different degrees of protection on the NE coast. Derrible B, Dixcart B and Rouge Terrier are good anchs on the SE coast. Port Gorey, Les Fontaines B, La Grande Grève and Havre Gosselin are all on the W coast; the last named is crowded in season due to easy access from Guernsey. Tidal streams around Sark need careful study, especially returning from the E side towards Guernsey.

JERSEY (charts *3655*, 1136, *1137*, 1138)

To N and NE of Jersey, Les Pierres de Lecq, Les Dirouilles and Les Ecrehou are groups of drying rks, 2-4M offshore. On the N coast several bays (10.14.15) offer anchs sheltered in offshore winds. Coming from N, a convenient landfall is Desormes WCM buoy, 4M NNW of Grosnez Pt (conspic lookout tr). In St Ouen B on the W coast, which has drying rks almost 1M offshore, there are no good anchorages except NW of La Rocco tr which is sheltered in offshore winds.

Rounding the SW tip, to clear offlying dangers by 1M, keep the top of La Corbière lt ho (conspic) level with or below the clifftops behind (FR lt). The 'CB' RDF bn at the lt ho provides distance off in conjunction with the fog horn; see Table 4 (1). Coded wind info is also transmitted; see 7.2.15. Along the S coast the NW and W Passages (buoyed) lead E past Noirmont Pt toward St Helier (10.14.14). St Brelade and St Aubin Bays (10.14.15) provide some shelter from W'lies.

SE of Jersey the Violet Bank extends 2M off La Rocque Pt with rky plateaux 1M further to seaward. The Violet Channel (chart 1138), although buoyed is best avoided in bad weather, wind-over-tide or poor vis. From St Helier make good Canger Rk WCM buoy, thence track 078° for 2·2M to Violet SWM lt buoy. Turn N to pick up the charted ldg lines toward Gorey (10.14.15; dries) or St Catherine Bay, both popular hbrs. The safe width of Violet Chan is only 5ca in places. Beware Decca problems due to being in baseline extension area. Anquette Chan leads NE from Violet buoy between the Petite and Grande Anquette bns, towards France. The E coast of Jersey is sheltered from W'lies, but requires careful pilotage.

Les Minquiers (10.14.15), 10-18M S of St Helier, should only be entered with extreme caution and in ideal weather.

14

10.14.6   DISTANCE TABLE

Approximate distances in nautical miles are by the most direct route, whilst avoiding dangers and allowing for Traffic Separation Schemes. Places in *italics* are in adjoining areas; places in **bold** are in 10.0.5, Cross-Channel Distances.

	1	2	3	4	5	6	7	8	9	10	11	12	13	14	15	16	17	18	19	20
1. *Cherbourg*	1																			
2. *Cap de la Hague*	14	2																		
3. *Carteret*	41	23	3																	
4. *Granville*	75	61	38	4																
5. **St Malo**	87	73	38	23	5															
6. Casquets	31	17	32	63	70	6														
7. **Braye (Alderney)**	23	9	26	66	73	8	7													
8. Beaucette	39	25	34	59	58	15	19	8												
9. **St Peter Port**	42	28	31	55	54	18	23	4	9											
10. Les Hanois	49	35	37	58	56	23	29	14	10	10										
11. Creux (Sark)	37	23	23	50	52	18	22	11	10	16	11									
12. **St Helier**	59	45	28	30	38	43	46	33	29	32	24	12								
13. Gorey (Jersey)	47	33	16	29	38	36	35	32	29	35	20	13	13							
14. Dahouet	88	74	62	44	28	70	72	62	58	57	53	41	47	14						
15. **St Quay-Portrieux**	88	74	64	54	35	71	73	55	56	48	51	46	52	12	15					
16. Paimpol	91	77	65	56	42	67	70	54	50	45	50	45	53	24	24	16				
17. *Lézardrieux*	88	74	68	54	49	65	68	52	48	42	38	47	55	33	21	14	17			
18. *Tréguier*	94	80	72	72	60	66	72	56	52	42	58	53	63	58	46	29	22	18		
19. **Roscoff**	117	103	95	96	84	87	94	77	73	63	79	80	93	71	59	58	54	41	19	
20. **L'Aberwrac'h**	145	131	126	128	116	115	122	107	103	93	109	110	123	103	91	88	84	72	32	20

SPECIAL NOTES FOR THE CHANNEL ISLANDS   10-14-8

The Channel Islands (Jersey, Guernsey, Alderney, Sark and other smaller islands) lie, not in the Channel, but in the Bay of St. Malo. Alderney is part of the Bailiwick of Guernsey and the States of Alderney have seats in the States of Guernsey. Brecqhou belongs to Sark which, along with Herm and Jethou, is part of Guernsey.

History The Islands were originally part of Normandy and therefore French; the eastern ends of Jersey & Alderney are only 15 and 8·5 miles respectively from France. They could not be thought of as British until, at the earliest, the 13th century, after King John lost mainland Normandy. The French call them Les Iles Anglo-Normandes (Jersey, Guernesey, Aurigny et Sercq).

Customs The Islands are British but are not part of the UK nor of the EU. They are self-governing, with their own laws and customs regulations. British yachts entering Channel Island ports will be required to complete the local Customs declaration form and may have to produce the vessel's registration documents; they will also be subject to customs formalities on return to UK. Yachts going to France need the normal documents (passports etc) and British yachts returning to the Channel Islands from France, must, like all French yachts, wear the Q flag. (It is advisable to do so when arriving from UK, but not mandatory, except in Alderney). All Channel Islands have reciprocal medical arrangements with UK.

Ports of Entry are Braye, Beaucette, St Sampson, St Peter Port, St Helier and Gorey.

SAR operations are directed by the Hr Mrs of St Peter Port (for the N area) and St Helier (for the S area), via St Peter Port and Jersey Radio respectively. Major incidents are co-ordinated with CROSSMA Joburg and Falmouth MRCC. Unlike the UK there are no CGs, but there are LBs at Braye, St Peter Port, St Helier and St Catherines (Jersey).

Casquets TSS/ITZ is under radar surveillance by Jobourg Traffic (10.15.9). Portland CG provides radio cover Ch **69** 16. See also diagrams in Fig 10 (4) and 10.15.2.

Telephones All CI telephones are part of the UK BT system.

Radio Telephone VHF Link calls to the UK made by British yachtsmen through St Peter Port or Jersey Radio will incur handling charges by British Telecom at the rate for foreign calls (see 6.4.10).

Courtesy Flags Further to 6·3·6, many yachts fly a courtesy flag in Channel Island ports as a mark of politeness but it is not de rigueur. The local flags are:
Jersey W flag with R diagonal cross, with the Jersey Royal Arms (three lions passant with gold crown above) in the canton.
Guernsey R ensign with Duke William's cross in the fly. Vessels owned by Guernsey residents may wear this ensign.
Sark The English (St George's) flag with the Normandy arms in the canton.
Alderney The English (St George's) flag and in the centre a G disc charged with a gold lion.
Herm The English (St George's) flag, and in the canton the Arms of Herm (three cowled monks on a gold diagonal stripe between blue triangles containing a silver dolphin).

Cars can be hired in Jersey, Guernsey and Alderney. All cars are forbidden in Sark.

Animals The rules regarding animals are as strict as they are in UK. Landing of animals from boats is permitted only from UK, Ireland, Isle of Man or other Channel Isles, but not if the boat has visited France. Unless expressly permitted by a Revenue Officer, no vessel may lie alongside a pontoon or quay with an animal on board.

Currency is interchangeable with UK currency except in coin. Using CI notes on return to UK is not always popular! Postage stamps, issued by Jersey, Guernsey and Alderney must be used in the appropriate island. There is only one class of post; it is cheaper than UK.

BRAYE (Alderney)   10-14-9
Alderney 49°43'·83N 02°11'·42W   Rtg 1-4-1

CHARTS
AC *2845, 60, 3653, 2669*; SHOM 6934, 7158; ECM 1014; Imray C33A; Stanfords 7, 16
TIDES
–0400 Dover; ML 3·5; Duration 0545; Zone 0 (UT)

Standard Port ST HELIER (→)

Times				Height (metres)			
High Water		Low Water		MHWS	MHWN	MLWN	MLWS
0300	0900	0200	0900	11·0	8·1	4·0	1·4
1500	2100	1400	2100				
Differences BRAYE							
+0050	+0040	+0025	+0105	–4·8	–3·4	–1·5	–0·5

SHELTER
Good in Braye Hbr, except in strong N/NE winds. 80 Y ⚓s lie parallel to the Admiralty bkwtr and near Fort Albert. Orange buoys are for locals. No landing on Admiralty bkwtr; at its NE end beware submerged extension. ⚓ in hbr is good on sand, but only fair on rock or weed patches; keep clear of the fairway and jetty due to steamer traffic. Hbr speed limit 4kn. Access to inner hbr HW±2 for D, FW.
NAVIGATION
WPT 49°44'·32N 02°10'·90W, 035°/215° from/to front ldg lt 215°, 1·05M. The main hazards are strong tidal streams and the many rocks encircling Alderney. The safest appr is from the NE. Take the Swinge and the Race at/near slack water to avoid the dangerous overfalls in certain wind and tide conditions (see 10.14.5). In the Swinge calmest area is often near Corbet Rk, bn 'C'. At mid-flood (NE-going) a strong eddy flows SW past the hbr ent. On the S side of the island during the ebb, a strong NE-going eddy runs close inshore of Coque Lihou. Give Brinchetais Ledge (E end) a wide berth to avoid heavy overfalls. An Historic Wreck is 5ca N of Quenard Pt lt ho (see 10.0.3h).
LIGHTS AND MARKS
From NW, N side of Ft Albert and end of Admiralty bkwtr 115° clear the Nannels. Iso WR 4s at Chateau à l'Etoc Pt, E of the hbr, vis R071°-111°, W111°-151°, in line 111° with Quenard Pt lt ho, Fl (4) 15s, clears sunken ruins of bkwtr. Ldg lts, both Q vis 210°-220°, lead 215° into hbr; front 8m 17M; rear 17m 18M. The Admty bkwtr hd has a lt, L Fl 10s 7m 5M. By day, St Anne's church spire on with W bn at Douglas Quay leads 210° to fairway which is marked by a QR and QG buoy and an inner pair of Q (2) R 5s and Q (2) G 5s buoys. End of steamer quay has 2 FR (vert) lts.
RADIO TELEPHONE
Call: *Alderney Radio* VHF Ch **74** 16 (12) (Apr to Sept, 0800 -1800, daily; Oct 0800-1700 daily; Nov to Mar, 0800-1700, Mon-Fri: all LT). Note: In fog/limited vis radar assistance to small craft is available from Hr Mr during above hrs. Outside these hrs call St Peter Port. For the Casquets TSS see Cherbourg (10.15·9). Mainbrayce Marine Ch 80 M (Apr-mid Sept: 0800-2000LT). Water taxi call *Mainbrayce* Ch M, 0800-2359.
TELEPHONE (Dial code 01481)
Hr Mr & ⌗ 822620, ☎ 823699; Marinecall 0891 500 432; Police 822731; Dr 822077; ⊞ 822822; ⓥ Info 822994 (H24).
FACILITIES
Hbr ⚓ (£10 for <12m LOA, £12 for >12m); **Jetty** , FW, C, ◻; **Sapper Slip**, FW; **Alderney SC** ☎ 822758, Bar; **Services**: Slip, FW, ME, El, Ⓔ, Gas, SM, Sh, CH, ACA, P (cans), D (Mainbrayce, inner hbr HW±2). **Town** EC Wed; V, R, Bar, ✉, Ⓑ, ✈ to Guernsey, Jersey, Dinard, Southampton and Cherbourg. Ferry: via Guernsey – Poole.

ANCHORAGES AROUND ALDERNEY

There are several ⚓s, all picturesque but only safe in off-shore winds. None provide any facilities; clockwise from BRAYE:
SAYE BAY, Small sandy bay adjacent to Braye.
CORBLET BAY, A clear bay in NE corner of the island.
LONGY BAY, Wide sandy bay with good holding in sand. ⚓ between Essex Castle and Raz Is to await fair tide in the Race.
LA TCHUE, Good holding in small bay surrounded by cliffs.
TELEGRAPH BAY, Pleasant sandy bay on SW tip of the island.
HANNAINE BAY, A good place to wait for the flood tide.
PLATTE SALINE BAY, Good shelter from E winds.
BURHOU, ⚓ in bay in SW of the islands, below half tide.

BEAUCETTE   10-14-10

Guernsey (Channel Islands) 49°30'.25N 02°30'.12W

CHARTS

AC *808, 807, 3654*; SHOM 6903, 6904, 7159; ECM 1014;
Imray C33A; Stanfords 16

TIDES

−0450 Dover; ML 5·0; Duration 0550; Zone 0 (UT)
To find depth of water over the sill:
1. Look up predicted time and height of HW St Peter Port.
2. Enter table below on the line for height of HW.
3. Extract depth (m) of water for time before/after HW.

Ht (m) of HW St Peter Port	Depth of Water in metres over the Sill (dries 2·37 m)						
	HW	±1hr	±2hrs	±2½hrs	±3hrs	±3½hrs	±4hrs
6·20	3·85	3·67	3·30	3·03	2·75	2·47	2·20
·60	4·25	4·00	3·50	3·13	"	2·37	2·00
7·00	4·65	4·34	3·70	3·23	"	2·27	1·80
·40	5·05	4·67	3·90	3·33	"	2·17	1·60
·80	5·45	5·00	4·10	3·43	"	2·07	1·40
8·20	5·85	5·34	4·30	3·53	"	1·97	1·20
·60	6·25	5·67	4·50	3·63	"	1·87	1·00
9·00	6·65	6·00	4·70	3·73	"	1·77	0·80
·40	7·05	6·34	4·90	3·83	"	1·67	0·60
·80	7·45	6·67	5·20	3·93	"	1·57	0·40

SHELTER

Excellent, but access times over sill as above table; entry
not advised in strong onshore winds or heavy swell. 8 Y
waiting buoys are outside (water taxi, Ch 80) and tidal
depth gauges outside & inside the 18m wide ent chan.

NAVIGATION

WPT 49°30'·15N 02°28'·85W, 097°/277° from/to ent, 8½ca.
Appr from Little Russel to mid-way between Platte Fougère
lt tr (W with B band, 25m) and Roustel lt tr (BW chequered).
Pick up the unlit fairway buoy, ldg marks/lts and four
pairs of unlit lateral buoys. Beware cross tides setting on
to Petite Canupe Rocks (SCM lt bn) to the N, and rocks
and drying areas to the S of the approach channel.

LIGHTS AND MARKS

Petite Canupe SCM bn, Q (6) + L Fl 15s, close S of which is
an unlit fairway SWM buoy, signed to Beaucette, and on
the ldg line. Ldg lts/marks 277°: Front FR, R arrow on W
background on stbd side of ent; rear FR, W arrow on R
background, on roof of bldg, with windsock.

RADIO TELEPHONE

VHF Ch 80 (0700-2200 and at tide times) M 16.

TELEPHONE (Dial code 01481)

Hr Mr 45000, mobile (04481) 102302; ⌗ 45000; Marinecall
0891 500 432; Police 725111; St John Ambulance 725211.

FACILITIES

Marina (140+50 visitors; pre-booking advised), ☎ 45000,
🎩 47071, £13.71, D, FW, AC, Gas, Gaz, Slip, BH (16 ton),
ME, El, C (12.5 ton), Bar, R, V, ▣, Marine management.
Town EC Thurs; ✉, ⓑ (St Sampson), ✈ (Guernsey). Ferry:
St Peter Port – Poole.

14

ST. PETER PORT

MEAN SPRING
AND NEAP CURVES

MEAN RANGES	
Springs 7.8m.	——
Neaps 3.4m	– – –

Springs occur 2 days
after
New and Full Moon.

ST PETER PORT   10-14-11
Guernsey 49°27'·41N 02°31'·45W   Rtg 1-1-1

CHARTS
AC 3140, *808, 807, 3654*; SHOM 6903, 6904, 7159;
ECM 1014; Imray C33A; Stanfords 16
TIDES
−0439 Dover; ML 5·2; Duration 0550; Zone 0 (UT)
NOTE: Although not a Standard Port, predicted times and
hts of HW/LW for each day of the year are shown below.

SHELTER
Good, especially in Victoria Marina which has a sill 4·4m
above CD. Storm gates are fitted (usually open), with a
fixed vert pillar in mid-entrance, and gauge giving depth
over sill. Access approx HW±2½ according to draft; the
Table under 10.14.10 also applies to St Peter Port if 2m is
deducted from the given Depth over sill. R/G tfc lts control
ent/exit. Appr via buoyed/lit chan along S side of hbr.
Marina boat will direct yachts to waiting pontoon or Y ⚓s
to E of marina ent. Local moorings are in centre of hbr,
with a secondary fairway N of them. ⚓ prohib. Queen
Elizabeth II and Albert marinas are for local boats only.
Havelet Bay: Enter between Oyster Rk and Moulinet Rk,
marked by SHM By QG and PHM By QR, with unlit SHM
and PHM buoy approx 100m further inshore. Crowded ⚓
in summer; no ⚓s. Landing slip close W of Castle Cornet.
Note: Other hbrs and ⚓s around Guernsey, Herm and
Sark are listed after the St Peter Port tidal predictions.
NAVIGATION
WPT 49°27'·88N 02°30'·70W, 040°/220° from/to front ldg lt,
0·68M. Offlying dangers, big tidal range and strong tidal
streams demand careful navigation. Easiest appr from N
is via Big Russel between Herm and Sark, passing S of
Lower Hds SCM lt buoy. The Little Russel is slightly more
direct, but needs care especially in poor visibility; see
10.14.5 and 10.14.12 chartlet. From W and S of Guernsey,
give Les Hanois a wide berth. Beware ferries and
shipping. Hbr speed limits: 6kn from outer pier heads to
line from New Jetty to Castle Cornet; 4kn W of that line.

LIGHTS AND MARKS
Appr ldg lts 220°: Front, Castle bkwtr hd Al WR 10s 14m
16M (vis 187°-007°) Horn 15s*; rear, Belvedere Oc 10s
61m 14M, intens 217°-223°. By day, White patch at Castle
Cornet in line 223° with Belvedere Ho (conspic). *This
horn and 'GY' RDF bn give distance off; see Table 4 (1).
Inner ldg lts 265°: Front, Oc R 5s; rear, Iso R 2s, vis 260°-
270° (10°). This ldg line is for the use of ferries berthing at
New Jetty. It extends through moorings in The Pool, so
must not be used by yachts which should appr to Victoria
marina via the buoyed/lit S channel (dashed line).
Traffic Signals on White Rock pierhead:
Ⓡ (vis from seaward)   = No ent
Ⓡ (vis from landward)   = No exit (also shown from SW
corner of New Pier).
These sigs do not apply to boats, <15m LOA, under
power and keeping clear of the fairways.
RADIO TELEPHONE
Call: *Victoria Marina* VHF Ch 80. Water taxi Ch 10 (0800-
2359LT). For St Peter Port as a whole call *Port Control* Ch
12 (H24). If difficulty experienced in raising *Port Control*
on VHF, messages may be sent via St Peter Port Radio on
VHF Ch 20 or MF; see 6·5·1. Link calls Ch 62 via St Peter
Port Radio. St Sampson Ch 12 (H24).
TELEPHONE (Dial code 01481)
Hr Mr 720229, ☎ 714177; Marina 725987; ⌗ 726911; CG
Sig Stn 720085; Weather 37766/64033; Recorded forecast
for CI (06966) 0022; Marinecall 0891 500 432; Dr 725211
(St Johns Ambulance); Police 725111.
FACILITIES
Victoria Marina (400, all visitors) ☎ 725987, £12 (£1 extra
in Aug); FW, AC, Slip, ⬚, R, Max LOA/draft = 12·8m/1·8m,
Max stay 14 days; **N Pier** ☎ 720085, C (32, 20 & 7 ton), AB;
Castle Pier P, D, approx HW±3, 0730-1730 Mon-Sat, 0730-
1200 Sun; (also fuel pontoon at QE II marina). **Royal Chan
Is YC** ☎ 723154 Bar; **Guernsey YC** ☎ 722838; **Services:**
CH, Gas, Gaz, ACA, ME, El, SM, BY, Ⓔ.
Town EC Thurs; P, D, V, CH, R, ⬚, Bar, ✉, Ⓑ. Ferry to
Poole, Cherbourg, St. Malo; Hydrofoil/catamaran to Sark,
Poole, Jersey, St Malo; ✈ (Guernsey Airport).

ST. PETER PORT *continued*

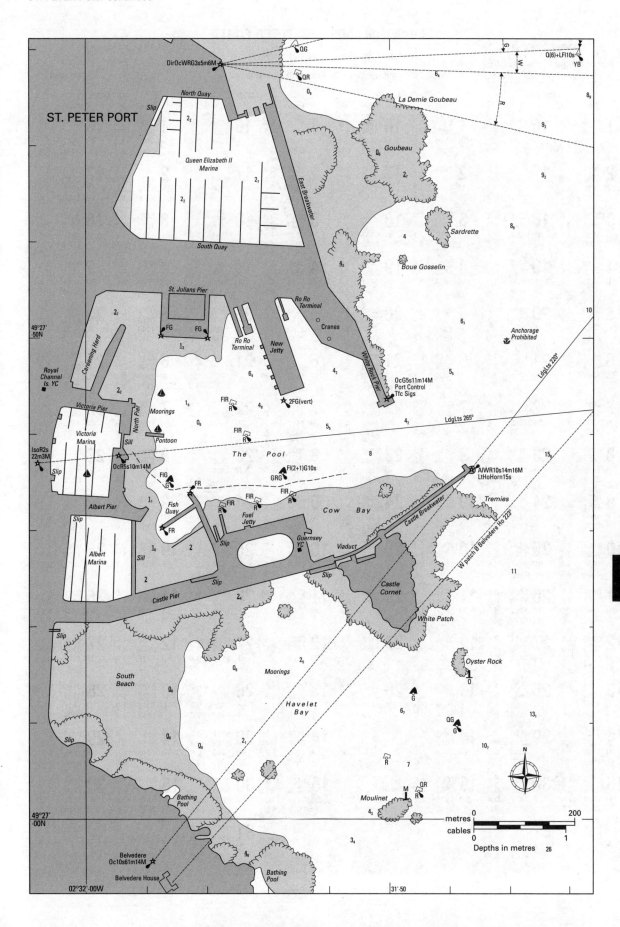

ST. PETER PORT

QG

DirOcWRG3s5m6M

QR

0₉

North Quay

Slip

2₂

Queen Elizabeth II
Marina

2₇

2₂

South Quay

East Breakwater

G

W

Q(6)+LFl10s

YB

6₄

8₉

La Demie Goubeau

0₆

Goubeau

2₇

9₂

9₂

4

Sardrette

8₉

Boue Gosselin

4₃

St. Julians Pier

2₇

FG   FG

1₃

Ro Ro
Terminal

Ro Ro
Terminal

New
Jetty

6₄

Cranes

4₂

White Rock Pier

OcG5s11m14M
Port Control
Tfc Sigs

5₅

6₇

Anchorage
Prohibited

10

49°27'
.50N

Careening Hard

2₇

2₂

North Pier

Moorings

1₆

FlR

4₈

2FG(vert)

0₅

LdgLts 265°

4₂

LdgLts 220°

Royal
Channel
Is. YC

Victoria Pier

Sill

Pontoon

FlR

5₅

8

15₅

Victoria
Marina

The   Pool

IsoR2s
22m3M

Slip

OcR5s10m14M

FlG
G

FR

Fish
Quay

1₁

GRG

Fl(2+1)G10s

FlR   FlR   FlR

Cow   Bay

AlWR10s14m16M
LtHoHorn15s

Castle Breakwater

Tremies

Albert Pier

Slip

Sill

1₆

FlR

Fuel
Jetty

2

Guernsey
YC

Viaduct

W patch ∅ Belvedere Ho 223°

Albert
Marina

2

Slip

Slip

Castle Pier

2₄

Slip

Castle
Cornet

11

White Patch

Slip

2₅

Oyster Rock

0

South
Beach

0₆

0₆

Moorings

Havelet
Bay

6₇

G

13₁

QG
G

Slip

0₆

0₉

2₁

10₇

R

7

N

Moulinet

M   QR
R

4₃

metres   0   200

cables   0   1

Depths in metres   26

Bathing
Pool

4₄

3₄

49°27'
.00N

Belvedere
Oc10s61m14M

Belvedere House

Bathing
Pool

02°32'.00W

31'.50

14

TIME ZONE (UT)
For Summer Time add ONE hour in non-shaded areas

CHANNEL ISLANDS – ST. PETER PORT

LAT 49°27'N   LONG 2°31'W

TIMES AND HEIGHTS OF HIGH AND LOW WATERS

YEAR 1998

JANUARY

Day	Time	m	Time	m
1 TH	0209 / 0809 / 1437 / 2033	1.3 / 9.3 / 1.1 / 9.1	**16** F 0246 / 0839 / 1510 / 2101	1.7 / 8.9 / 1.7 / 8.5
2 F	0251 / 0851 / 1519 / 2115	1.4 / 9.2 / 1.2 / 8.9	**17** SA 0316 / 0911 / 1540 / 2132	2.0 / 8.6 / 2.1 / 8.2
3 SA	0334 / 0935 / 1603 / 2200	1.6 / 9.0 / 1.5 / 8.6	**18** SU 0345 / 0943 / 1608 / 2204	2.4 / 8.2 / 2.5 / 7.8
4 SU	0419 / 1022 / 1650 / 2249	2.0 / 8.6 / 1.9 / 8.2	**19** M 0415 / 1016 / 1639 / 2238	2.8 / 7.8 / 2.9 / 7.4
5 M	0510 / 1116 / 1744 / 2346	2.4 / 8.2 / 2.4 / 7.8	**20** TU 0450 / 1054 / 1716 / 2319	3.2 / 7.3 / 3.3 / 7.0
6 TU	0612 / 1219 / 1849	2.8 / 7.8 / 2.7	**21** W 0536 / 1143 / 1808	3.6 / 7.0 / 3.6
7 W	0055 / 0729 / 1335 / 2007	7.5 / 3.0 / 7.6 / 2.9	**22** TH 0017 / 0647 / 1252 / 1928	6.8 / 3.8 / 6.8 / 3.7
8 TH	0215 / 0853 / 1453 / 2123	7.5 / 2.9 / 7.6 / 2.7	**23** F 0139 / 0813 / 1414 / 2046	6.8 / 3.7 / 6.8 / 3.6
9 F	0328 / 1001 / 1600 / 2227	7.8 / 2.6 / 7.9 / 2.4	**24** SA 0257 / 0923 / 1526 / 2152	7.0 / 3.3 / 7.1 / 3.1
10 SA	0427 / 1059 / 1657 / 2321	8.2 / 2.2 / 8.2 / 2.1	**25** SU 0400 / 1024 / 1627 / 2249	7.5 / 2.8 / 7.6 / 2.6
11 SU	0519 / 1151 / 1748	8.6 / 1.8 / 8.5	**26** M 0454 / 1118 / 1721 / 2341	8.1 / 2.2 / 8.1 / 2.0
12 M ○	0010 / 0606 / 1239 / 1834	1.8 / 8.9 / 1.5 / 8.8	**27** TU 0544 / 1209 / 1810	8.6 / 1.6 / 8.6
13 TU	0056 / 0649 / 1322 / 1916	1.6 / 9.1 / 1.4 / 8.9	**28** W ● 0030 / 0630 / 1258 / 1856	1.5 / 9.1 / 1.1 / 9.1
14 W	0136 / 0729 / 1402 / 1955	1.5 / 9.2 / 1.3 / 8.9	**29** TH 0117 / 0715 / 1344 / 1940	1.0 / 9.5 / 0.7 / 9.4
15 TH	0213 / 0806 / 1438 / 2029	1.5 / 9.1 / 1.4 / 8.8	**30** F 0201 / 0758 / 1427 / 2022	0.8 / 9.8 / 0.5 / 9.5
			31 SA 0243 / 0840 / 1509 / 2103	0.7 / 9.8 / 0.6 / 9.4

FEBRUARY

Day	Time / m	Day	Time / m
1 SU	0324 / 0922 / 1550 / 2145 — 0.9 / 9.5 / 0.9 / 9.1	**16** M	0317 / 0914 / 1536 / 2131 — 1.9 / 8.5 / 2.1 / 8.2
2 M	0406 / 1006 / 1632 / 2228 — 1.3 / 9.1 / 1.4 / 8.6	**17** TU	0343 / 0943 / 1601 / 2159 — 2.3 / 8.1 / 2.5 / 7.8
3 TU	0451 / 1053 / 1718 / 2317 — 1.9 / 8.4 / 2.1 / 8.0	**18** W	0412 / 1014 / 1631 / 2232 — 2.8 / 7.7 / 3.0 / 7.4
4 W	0543 / 1148 / 1814 — 2.6 / 7.8 / 2.7	**19** TH	0448 / 1054 / 1711 / 2317 — 3.2 / 7.2 / 3.4 / 7.0
5 TH	0018 / 0650 / 1301 / 1927 — 7.4 / 3.1 / 7.3 / 3.2	**20** F	0540 / 1150 / 1810 — 3.6 / 6.8 / 3.7
6 F	0140 / 0823 / 1431 / 2059 — 7.1 / 3.3 / 7.1 / 3.2	**21** SA	0025 / 0703 / 1313 / 1947 — 6.7 / 3.8 / 6.7 / 3.8
7 SA	0308 / 0946 / 1547 / 2213 — 7.3 / 3.0 / 7.4 / 2.9	**22** SU	0200 / 0843 / 1447 / 2117 — 6.8 / 3.5 / 6.9 / 3.4
8 SU	0414 / 1048 / 1646 / 2310 — 7.7 / 2.6 / 7.8 / 2.5	**23** M	0325 / 0955 / 1600 / 2224 — 7.2 / 2.9 / 7.4 / 2.8
9 M	0507 / 1140 / 1736 / 2358 — 8.1 / 2.1 / 8.2 / 2.0	**24** TU	0429 / 1056 / 1700 / 2321 — 7.9 / 2.2 / 8.0 / 2.1
10 TU	0553 / 1225 / 1820 — 8.6 / 1.7 / 8.6	**25** W	0523 / 1151 / 1752 — 8.6 / 1.5 / 8.7
11 W ○	0041 / 0634 / 1307 / 1859 — 1.7 / 8.9 / 1.4 / 8.8	**26** TH ●	0013 / 0612 / 1241 / 1839 — 1.4 / 9.3 / 0.8 / 9.3
12 TH	0120 / 0712 / 1343 / 1935 — 1.4 / 9.1 / 1.3 / 9.0	**27** F	0102 / 0658 / 1327 / 1924 — 0.8 / 9.8 / 0.3 / 9.7
13 F	0154 / 0746 / 1416 / 2007 — 1.3 / 9.2 / 1.3 / 9.0	**28** SA	0147 / 0742 / 1411 / 2006 — 0.4 / 10.1 / 0.1 / 10.0
14 SA	0224 / 0817 / 1445 / 2037 — 1.4 / 9.1 / 1.4 / 8.8		
15 SU	0251 / 0846 / 1511 / 2105 — 1.6 / 8.9 / 1.7 / 8.5		

MARCH

Day	Time / m	Day	Time / m
1 SU	0229 / 0824 / 1452 / 2046 — 0.2 / 10.2 / 0.1 / 9.9	**16** M	0225 / 0820 / 1441 / 2037 — 1.4 / 9.0 / 1.5 / 8.8
2 M	0309 / 0905 / 1532 / 2126 — 0.4 / 9.9 / 0.5 / 9.5	**17** TU	0250 / 0847 / 1506 / 2102 — 1.7 / 8.7 / 1.9 / 8.4
3 TU	0349 / 0947 / 1611 / 2206 — 0.9 / 9.3 / 1.1 / 8.9	**18** W	0316 / 0914 / 1531 / 2128 — 2.0 / 8.3 / 2.3 / 8.1
4 W	0430 / 1030 / 1653 / 2250 — 1.6 / 8.6 / 1.9 / 8.1	**19** TH	0344 / 0944 / 1559 / 2159 — 2.5 / 7.9 / 2.7 / 7.7
5 TH	0517 / 1120 / 1743 / 2344 — 2.4 / 7.7 / 2.8 / 7.4	**20** F	0418 / 1022 / 1637 / 2242 — 2.9 / 7.4 / 3.2 / 7.2
6 F	0619 / 1228 / 1851 — 3.1 / 7.0 / 3.4	**21** SA	0505 / 1115 / 1731 / 2345 — 3.3 / 7.0 / 3.6 / 6.9
7 SA	0104 / 0751 / 1410 / 2032 — 6.9 / 3.5 / 6.7 / 3.6	**22** SU	0617 / 1232 / 1855 — 3.6 / 6.7 / 3.8
8 SU	0247 / 0931 / 1533 / 2158 — 6.9 / 3.3 / 7.0 / 3.3	**23** M	0113 / 0805 / 1409 / 2042 — 6.8 / 3.5 / 6.8 / 3.5
9 M	0358 / 1034 / 1631 / 2254 — 7.3 / 2.8 / 7.5 / 2.8	**24** TU	0249 / 0928 / 1533 / 2158 — 7.2 / 2.9 / 7.4 / 2.8
10 TU	0450 / 1123 / 1718 / 2340 — 7.9 / 2.3 / 8.0 / 2.2	**25** W	0402 / 1032 / 1636 / 2259 — 7.9 / 2.2 / 8.1 / 2.1
11 W	0534 / 1205 / 1759 — 8.4 / 1.8 / 8.5	**26** TH	0459 / 1128 / 1729 / 2352 — 8.6 / 1.4 / 8.8 / 1.3
12 TH	0020 / 0613 / 1244 / 1836 — 1.8 / 8.8 / 1.5 / 8.8	**27** F	0550 / 1218 / 1817 — 9.3 / 0.7 / 9.5
13 F ○	0057 / 0649 / 1319 / 1910 — 1.5 / 9.0 / 1.3 / 9.0	**28** SA ●	0041 / 0637 / 1306 / 1902 — 0.7 / 9.9 / 0.2 / 9.9
14 SA	0129 / 0722 / 1349 / 1942 — 1.3 / 9.2 / 1.2 / 9.1	**29** SU	0127 / 0722 / 1350 / 1945 — 0.2 / 10.2 / 0.0 / 10.1
15 SU	0158 / 0752 / 1416 / 2010 — 1.3 / 9.1 / 1.3 / 9.0	**30** M	0210 / 0805 / 1432 / 2025 — 0.1 / 10.2 / 0.0 / 10.1
		31 TU	0251 / 0846 / 1511 / 2105 — 0.3 / 9.9 / 0.4 / 9.7

APRIL

Day	Time / m	Day	Time / m
1 W	0331 / 0927 / 1550 / 2144 — 0.8 / 9.3 / 1.1 / 9.0	**16** TH	0253 / 0851 / 1507 / 2104 — 1.9 / 8.4 / 2.2 / 8.3
2 TH	0412 / 1009 / 1630 / 2226 — 1.5 / 8.5 / 2.0 / 8.2	**17** F	0323 / 0923 / 1538 / 2138 — 2.2 / 8.0 / 2.6 / 7.9
3 F	0456 / 1057 / 1717 / 2316 — 2.3 / 7.7 / 2.8 / 7.5	**18** SA	0359 / 1003 / 1617 / 2222 — 2.7 / 7.6 / 3.0 / 7.5
4 SA	0554 / 1200 / 1820 — 3.1 / 6.9 / 3.5	**19** SU	0447 / 1057 / 1711 / 2324 — 3.1 / 7.2 / 3.4 / 7.2
5 SU	0028 / 0716 / 1340 / 1953 — 6.9 / 3.5 / 6.6 / 3.8	**20** M	0555 / 1210 / 1828 — 3.3 / 6.9 / 3.6
6 M	0214 / 0903 / 1508 / 2130 — 6.7 / 3.4 / 6.8 / 3.5	**21** TU	0044 / 0730 / 1337 / 2008 — 7.1 / 3.3 / 7.0 / 3.4
7 TU	0330 / 1008 / 1606 / 2227 — 7.1 / 3.0 / 7.3 / 3.0	**22** W	0214 / 0857 / 1502 / 2129 — 7.4 / 2.8 / 7.5 / 2.8
8 W	0423 / 1056 / 1651 / 2312 — 7.6 / 2.5 / 7.8 / 2.5	**23** TH	0331 / 1004 / 1607 / 2232 — 8.0 / 2.1 / 8.2 / 2.1
9 TH	0506 / 1137 / 1730 / 2351 — 8.1 / 2.0 / 8.3 / 2.0	**24** F	0431 / 1101 / 1702 / 2327 — 8.6 / 1.4 / 8.9 / 1.4
10 F	0545 / 1214 / 1807 — 8.5 / 1.7 / 8.7	**25** SA	0525 / 1153 / 1752 — 9.3 / 0.8 / 9.4
11 SA ○	0027 / 0620 / 1248 / 1840 — 1.6 / 8.8 / 1.4 / 8.9	**26** SU ●	0017 / 0614 / 1242 / 1838 — 0.9 / 9.7 / 0.4 / 9.9
12 SU	0059 / 0653 / 1318 / 1912 — 1.4 / 9.0 / 1.3 / 9.0	**27** M	0105 / 0700 / 1327 / 1922 — 0.4 / 10.0 / 0.2 / 10.0
13 M	0129 / 0725 / 1346 / 1942 — 1.3 / 9.0 / 1.3 / 9.0	**28** TU	0150 / 0745 / 1411 / 2004 — 0.2 / 10.0 / 0.3 / 10.0
14 TU	0157 / 0755 / 1413 / 2010 — 1.4 / 8.9 / 1.5 / 8.8	**29** W	0233 / 0828 / 1452 / 2045 — 0.4 / 9.7 / 0.7 / 9.6
15 W	0225 / 0823 / 1440 / 2036 — 1.6 / 8.7 / 1.8 / 8.6	**30** TH	0314 / 0909 / 1531 / 2124 — 0.8 / 9.2 / 1.3 / 9.0

Chart Datum: 5·06 metres below Ordnance Datum (Local)

CHANNEL ISLANDS – ST. PETER PORT

LAT 49°27'N   LONG 2°31'W

TIMES AND HEIGHTS OF HIGH AND LOW WATERS

YEAR **1998**

TIME ZONE (UT)
For Summer Time add ONE hour in non-shaded areas

Chart Datum: 5·06 metres below Ordnance Datum (Local)

MAY

Day	Time m	Time m	Time m	Time m
1 F	0355 1.5	0951 8.5	1611 2.0	2205 8.3
2 SA	0439 2.3	1037 7.7	1656 2.8	2252 7.6
3 SU	0532 3.0	1133 7.0	1753 3.5	2353 7.0
4 M	0639 3.4	1252 6.7	1906 3.8	
5 TU	0118 6.8	0807 3.5	1423 6.7	2037 3.7
6 W	0244 6.9	0924 3.2	1526 7.1	2145 3.3
7 TH	0343 7.3	1016 2.8	1613 7.6	2233 2.8
8 F	0428 7.8	1058 2.4	1654 8.0	2314 2.4
9 SA	0509 8.1	1136 2.0	1731 8.4	2350 2.0
10 SU	0546 8.5	1211 1.8	1808 8.7	
11 M O	0025 1.7	0622 8.7	1244 1.6	1842 8.9
12 TU	0059 1.5	0657 8.8	1316 1.5	1915 8.9
13 W	0131 1.5	0730 8.7	1348 1.6	1945 8.8
14 TH	0204 1.5	0802 8.6	1419 1.8	2016 8.7
15 F	0236 1.7	0835 8.4	1451 2.0	2049 8.4
16 SA	0311 2.0	0911 8.1	1526 2.4	2127 8.1
17 SU	0350 2.4	0954 7.8	1608 2.7	2213 7.8
18 M	0439 2.7	1047 7.5	1701 3.1	2311 7.5
19 TU	0542 2.9	1152 7.3	1811 3.3	
20 W	0022 7.4	0701 2.9	1309 7.3	1935 3.1
21 TH	0142 7.6	0824 2.6	1428 7.7	2057 2.7
22 F	0259 8.0	0934 2.2	1536 8.2	2204 2.1
23 SA	0403 8.5	1033 1.6	1634 8.7	2301 1.6
24 SU	0459 9.0	1127 1.2	1726 9.2	2354 1.1
25 M ●	0551 9.3	1218 0.8	1815 9.5	
26 TU	0043 0.7	0640 9.6	1306 0.7	1900 9.7
27 W	0131 0.6	0727 9.6	1351 0.7	1944 9.7
28 TH	0215 0.7	0811 9.4	1434 1.0	2026 9.4
29 F	0258 1.0	0853 9.0	1514 1.5	2106 9.0
30 SA	0339 1.5	0935 8.5	1554 2.0	2146 8.4
31 SU	0421 2.1	1017 7.9	1635 2.7	2228 7.8

JUNE

Day	Time m	Time m	Time m	Time m
1 M	0507 2.7	1105 7.3	1723 3.2	2318 7.3
2 TU	0601 3.2	1202 6.9	1820 3.6	
3 W	0020 6.9	0703 3.5	1312 6.8	1926 3.7
4 TH	0133 6.8	0812 3.4	1424 6.9	2036 3.6
5 F	0243 7.0	0915 3.2	1522 7.2	2137 3.2
6 SA	0339 7.3	1007 2.9	1610 7.6	2226 2.8
7 SU	0427 7.7	1051 2.5	1653 8.0	2309 2.4
8 M	0510 8.0	1132 2.2	1734 8.3	2350 2.0
9 TU	0552 8.3	1211 1.9	1813 8.6	
10 W O	0030 1.7	0631 8.5	1250 1.7	1850 8.8
11 TH	0109 1.6	0709 8.6	1327 1.6	1925 8.8
12 F	0147 1.5	0747 8.6	1404 1.7	2001 8.8
13 SA	0225 1.5	0824 8.6	1441 1.8	2039 8.7
14 SU	0303 1.7	0904 8.4	1520 2.0	2119 8.5
15 M	0345 1.9	0947 8.2	1603 2.3	2205 8.2
16 TU	0433 2.2	1036 7.9	1653 2.6	2258 8.0
17 W	0528 2.5	1134 7.7	1753 2.9	
18 TH	0001 7.8	0634 2.6	1241 7.6	1905 2.9
19 F	0113 7.7	0750 2.6	1355 7.7	2026 2.7
20 SA	0229 7.9	0904 2.4	1507 8.0	2138 2.4
21 SU	0338 8.2	1007 2.0	1609 8.4	2239 1.9
22 M	0438 8.5	1106 1.7	1705 8.8	2334 1.5
23 TU	0533 8.9	1159 1.4	1756 9.1	
24 W ●	0026 1.2	0624 9.1	1249 1.2	1843 9.3
25 TH	0115 1.0	0712 9.2	1335 1.1	1928 9.4
26 F	0200 1.0	0756 9.1	1418 1.2	2010 9.3
27 SA	0242 1.2	0838 8.9	1458 1.5	2049 9.0
28 SU	0322 1.5	0916 8.6	1535 1.9	2125 8.6
29 M	0359 2.0	0954 8.1	1611 2.4	2202 8.1
30 TU	0437 2.5	1032 7.7	1648 2.9	2242 7.7

JULY

Day	Time m	Time m	Time m	Time m
1 W	0518 3.0	1116 7.3	1732 3.3	2328 7.2
2 TH	0607 3.4	1209 7.0	1827 3.6	
3 F	0026 6.9	0707 3.6	1313 6.8	1932 3.7
4 SA	0136 6.8	0811 3.5	1421 6.9	2037 3.6
5 SU	0244 7.0	0912 3.3	1522 7.2	2138 3.2
6 M	0343 7.3	1007 3.0	1615 7.6	2231 2.8
7 TU	0436 7.6	1057 2.6	1702 8.0	2319 2.3
8 W	0523 8.0	1143 2.2	1746 8.4	
9 TH O	0005 1.9	0608 8.4	1228 1.8	1828 8.7
10 F	0050 1.6	0652 8.6	1311 1.6	1909 9.0
11 SA	0133 1.3	0733 8.8	1352 1.4	1949 9.1
12 SU	0215 1.2	0814 8.9	1433 1.4	2030 9.2
13 M	0256 1.2	0855 8.9	1513 1.5	2111 9.0
14 TU	0338 1.4	0937 8.7	1555 1.8	2154 8.8
15 W	0421 1.7	1022 8.4	1640 2.1	2242 8.4
16 TH	0510 2.1	1113 8.0	1733 2.5	2338 8.0
17 F	0608 2.5	1213 7.7	1837 2.9	
18 SA	0045 7.7	0719 2.8	1326 7.6	1956 3.0
19 SU	0204 7.6	0839 2.8	1444 7.7	2118 2.8
20 M	0321 7.8	0950 2.5	1552 8.0	2225 2.4
21 TU	0425 8.1	1051 2.2	1651 8.4	2322 2.0
22 W	0522 8.4	1145 1.8	1743 8.8	
23 TH ●	0013 1.6	0612 8.8	1235 1.6	1829 9.1
24 F	0101 1.3	0658 9.0	1320 1.4	1913 9.3
25 SA	0145 1.2	0741 9.1	1401 1.3	1953 9.3
26 SU	0224 1.3	0819 9.0	1438 1.5	2029 9.1
27 M	0300 1.5	0853 8.8	1511 1.7	2102 8.9
28 TU	0332 1.8	0926 8.4	1542 2.1	2133 8.5
29 W	0402 2.3	0958 8.0	1611 2.6	2205 8.0
30 TH	0432 2.8	1031 7.6	1643 3.1	2241 7.5
31 F	0506 3.2	1110 7.2	1722 3.5	2324 7.1

AUGUST

Day	Time m	Time m	Time m	Time m
1 SA	0554 3.6	1202 6.9	1821 3.8	
2 SU	0024 6.8	0707 3.8	1315 6.7	1942 3.9
3 M	0146 6.7	0824 3.7	1433 6.9	2056 3.6
4 TU	0302 7.0	0930 3.4	1559 7.3	2159 3.1
5 W	0405 7.4	1027 2.9	1634 7.8	2254 2.6
6 TH	0459 7.9	1120 2.4	1724 8.3	2345 2.0
7 F	0549 8.4	1209 1.9	1810 8.9	
8 SA O	0033 1.5	0635 8.8	1256 1.4	1853 9.3
9 SU	0119 1.0	0718 9.2	1339 1.1	1936 9.6
10 M	0202 0.8	0800 9.4	1421 0.9	2017 9.7
11 TU	0244 0.7	0841 9.4	1502 1.0	2058 9.6
12 W	0324 0.9	0921 9.2	1542 1.3	2139 9.3
13 TH	0405 1.4	1004 8.8	1624 1.8	2224 8.7
14 F	0450 1.9	1050 8.3	1712 2.4	2315 8.1
15 SA	0543 2.6	1146 7.7	1811 2.9	
16 SU	0019 7.5	0651 3.1	1300 7.4	1932 3.3
17 M	0146 7.3	0820 3.2	1428 7.3	2107 3.2
18 TU	0313 7.4	0941 3.0	1543 7.7	2218 2.8
19 W	0419 7.8	1043 2.6	1642 8.1	2314 2.3
20 TH	0513 8.3	1135 2.1	1731 8.6	
21 F	0002 1.8	0559 8.7	1222 1.7	1815 9.0
22 SA ●	0046 1.5	0642 9.0	1303 1.5	1856 9.3
23 SU	0126 1.3	0720 9.1	1341 1.4	1932 9.4
24 M	0202 1.3	0755 9.1	1414 1.4	2005 9.3
25 TU	0233 1.5	0826 9.0	1444 1.6	2035 9.1
26 W	0300 1.8	0855 8.7	1510 1.9	2103 8.7
27 TH	0325 2.2	0923 8.3	1536 2.4	2131 8.3
28 F	0350 2.6	0950 7.9	1602 2.9	2200 7.8
29 SA	0416 3.1	1021 7.4	1634 3.3	2235 7.3
30 SU	0452 3.6	1102 7.0	1719 3.7	2326 6.9
31 M	0548 3.9	1205 6.7	1834 4.0	

14

CHANNEL ISLANDS – ST. PETER PORT

LAT 49°27'N   LONG 2°31'W

TIMES AND HEIGHTS OF HIGH AND LOW WATERS

YEAR **1998**

TIME ZONE (UT)
For Summer Time add ONE hour in non-shaded areas

SEPTEMBER

Day	Time	m	Time	m	Time	m	Time	m
1 TU	0044	6.7	0732	4.0	1339	6.7	2017	3.9
16 W	0306	7.2	0933	3.3	1533	7.5	2210	3.0
2 W	0222	6.8	0857	3.7	1504	7.1	2131	3.4
17 TH	0409	7.7	1032	2.8	1628	8.0	2301	2.4
3 TH	0338	7.3	1002	3.1	1608	7.7	2231	2.7
18 F	0458	8.2	1120	2.3	1714	8.5	2345	2.0
4 F	0437	7.9	1058	2.5	1701	8.4	2325	2.0
19 SA	0540	8.7	1202	1.9	1756	8.9		
5 SA	0528	8.6	1149	1.8	1749	9.1		
20 SU ●	0025	1.6	0619	9.0	1241	1.6	1833	9.2
6 SU O	0014	1.3	0614	9.1	1237	1.2	1834	9.6
21 M	0102	1.4	0654	9.2	1316	1.4	1907	9.3
7 M	0101	0.8	0659	9.6	1322	0.8	1918	10.0
22 TU	0134	1.4	0727	9.2	1347	1.4	1938	9.3
8 TU	0144	0.5	0741	9.9	1405	0.6	2000	10.2
23 W	0202	1.5	0756	9.1	1414	1.6	2007	9.1
9 W	0226	0.4	0822	9.9	1446	0.6	2041	10.0
24 TH	0227	1.7	0824	8.9	1439	1.9	2034	8.8
10 TH	0306	0.7	0903	9.6	1526	1.0	2122	9.6
25 F	0251	2.1	0850	8.5	1505	2.2	2100	8.4
11 F	0346	1.2	0944	9.1	1607	1.6	2204	8.9
26 SA	0315	2.6	0915	8.1	1531	2.7	2128	8.0
12 SA	0429	1.9	1028	8.5	1652	2.3	2253	8.1
27 SU	0341	3.0	0944	7.7	1601	3.2	2201	7.5
13 SU	0519	2.7	1122	7.7	1750	3.1	2357	7.4
28 M	0415	3.5	1023	7.2	1643	3.6	2249	7.0
14 M	0627	3.4	1236	7.2	1914	3.5		
29 TU	0506	3.9	1123	6.9	1749	4.0		
15 TU	0132	7.0	0805	3.6	1416	7.1	2100	3.5
30 W	0003	6.7	0631	4.2	1251	6.8	1937	3.9

OCTOBER

Day	Time	m	Time	m	Time	m	Time	m
1 TH	0143	6.8	0825	3.9	1426	7.1	2102	3.4
16 F	0347	7.6	1010	3.1	1604	7.8	2237	2.7
2 F	0309	7.3	0936	3.2	1538	7.8	2206	2.7
17 SA	0434	8.1	1056	2.5	1649	8.3	2319	2.2
3 SA	0411	8.0	1034	2.5	1634	8.5	2301	1.9
18 SU	0514	8.5	1136	2.1	1729	8.7	2357	1.9
4 SU	0503	8.8	1126	1.7	1724	9.2	2351	1.2
19 M	0550	8.9	1212	1.8	1805	9.0		
5 M O	0550	9.4	1215	1.1	1812	9.8		
20 TU ●	0031	1.7	0624	9.1	1246	1.6	1838	9.1
6 TU	0038	0.7	0635	9.9	1302	0.6	1856	10.2
21 W	0102	1.6	0656	9.2	1316	1.5	1910	9.2
7 W	0123	0.4	0719	10.1	1346	0.4	1940	10.3
22 TH	0130	1.6	0726	9.1	1345	1.6	1939	9.0
8 TH	0205	0.4	0801	10.1	1428	0.5	2022	10.1
23 F	0156	1.8	0755	8.9	1412	1.8	2008	8.8
9 F	0247	0.6	0842	9.8	1509	0.9	2104	9.6
24 SA	0223	2.1	0821	8.6	1440	2.2	2036	8.5
10 SA	0327	1.2	0924	9.3	1551	1.5	2147	8.9
25 SU	0249	2.6	0848	8.3	1508	2.6	2105	8.1
11 SU	0409	2.1	1008	8.6	1636	2.3	2235	8.1
26 M	0317	2.9	0920	7.9	1541	3.0	2141	7.7
12 M	0459	2.9	1100	7.8	1733	3.1	2337	7.3
27 TU	0353	3.3	1000	7.5	1623	3.4	2229	7.2
13 TU	0605	3.6	1212	7.2	1853	3.6		
28 W	0443	3.8	1059	7.1	1725	3.7	2338	6.9
14 W	0113	6.9	0742	3.9	1353	7.0	2039	3.6
29 TH	0559	4.0	1217	7.0	1857	3.7		
15 TH	0247	7.1	0913	3.6	1510	7.4	2148	3.1
30 F	0105	7.0	0746	3.8	1346	7.3	2029	3.3
31 SA	0233	7.4	0906	3.2	1503	7.8	2136	2.6

NOVEMBER

Day	Time	m	Time	m	Time	m	Time	m
1 SU	0340	8.1	1007	2.5	1604	8.5	2233	1.9
16 M	0440	8.2	1103	2.5	1655	8.3	2323	2.3
2 M	0434	8.8	1101	1.8	1658	9.2	2325	1.3
17 TU	0517	8.5	1140	2.1	1733	8.5	2357	2.0
3 TU	0524	9.4	1151	1.2	1747	9.7		
18 W	0552	8.8	1214	1.9	1808	8.7		
4 W O	0014	0.8	0611	9.9	1240	0.7	1834	10.0
19 TH ●	0029	1.8	0626	9.0	1247	1.7	1842	8.8
5 TH	0101	0.5	0656	10.1	1326	0.5	1920	10.1
20 F	0100	1.8	0659	9.0	1319	1.7	1915	8.8
6 F	0145	0.5	0740	10.1	1410	0.6	2005	9.9
21 SA	0131	1.8	0730	8.9	1350	1.8	1947	8.7
7 SA	0228	0.8	0823	9.8	1454	0.9	2048	9.5
22 SU	0201	2.0	0801	8.7	1422	2.0	2019	8.5
8 SU	0310	1.3	0906	9.3	1537	1.5	2132	8.8
23 M	0232	2.3	0832	8.5	1455	2.3	2052	8.2
9 M	0353	2.0	0950	8.7	1623	2.2	2219	8.1
24 TU	0305	2.6	0907	8.1	1531	2.6	2130	7.9
10 TU	0441	2.8	1040	7.9	1716	2.9	2315	7.4
25 W	0343	3.0	0950	7.8	1615	3.0	2218	7.5
11 W	0540	3.5	1142	7.3	1823	3.4		
26 TH	0432	3.4	1044	7.5	1711	3.2	2319	7.3
12 TH	0033	6.9	0658	3.9	1306	7.2	1951	3.6
27 F	0537	3.6	1151	7.4	1823	3.3		
13 F	0207	6.9	0831	3.8	1429	7.1	2108	3.4
28 SA	0031	7.3	0702	3.6	1309	7.5	1947	3.1
14 SA	0312	7.3	0935	3.4	1528	7.5	2202	3.0
29 SU	0153	7.5	0828	3.2	1426	7.8	2102	2.6
15 SU	0400	7.7	1022	2.9	1615	7.9	2245	2.6
30 M	0305	8.0	0937	2.6	1533	8.3	2204	2.1

DECEMBER

Day	Time	m	Time	m	Time	m	Time	m
1 TU	0405	8.6	1035	2.0	1632	8.9	2300	1.6
16 W	0441	8.0	1103	2.6	1659	8.0	2321	2.4
2 W	0459	9.1	1128	1.4	1725	9.3	2351	1.2
17 TH	0521	8.4	1142	2.2	1739	8.3	2359	2.1
3 TH O	0549	9.6	1219	1.0	1816	9.6		
18 F ●	0600	8.6	1219	2.0	1819	8.5		
4 F	0040	0.9	0637	9.8	1309	0.8	1904	9.7
19 SA	0035	1.9	0636	8.8	1257	1.8	1856	8.6
5 SA	0128	0.8	0723	9.9	1356	0.7	1950	9.6
20 SU	0111	1.8	0712	8.8	1334	1.7	1933	8.6
6 SU	0213	1.0	0807	9.7	1441	0.9	2035	9.3
21 M	0147	1.8	0747	8.8	1411	1.7	2008	8.6
7 M	0256	1.4	0851	9.3	1524	1.4	2118	8.8
22 TU	0222	1.9	0822	8.7	1448	1.8	2044	8.4
8 TU	0338	1.8	0933	8.8	1608	1.9	2201	8.2
23 W	0259	2.1	0900	8.5	1526	2.1	2123	8.1
9 W	0422	2.5	1017	8.2	1653	2.6	2248	7.6
24 TH	0338	2.4	0942	8.3	1608	2.3	2207	8.0
10 TH	0510	3.2	1107	7.6	1745	3.1	2343	7.1
25 F	0423	2.7	1030	8.0	1656	2.6	2259	7.7
11 F	0607	3.6	1206	7.2	1845	3.5		
26 SA	0517	3.0	1127	7.8	1755	2.8		
12 SA	0052	6.9	0715	3.8	1319	7.0	1955	3.6
27 SU	0000	7.5	0624	3.2	1235	7.6	1905	2.9
13 SU	0210	6.9	0831	3.7	1431	7.0	2105	3.4
28 M	0113	7.5	0746	3.1	1351	7.7	2025	2.8
14 M	0311	7.2	0933	3.4	1529	7.3	2159	3.1
29 TU	0231	7.8	0906	2.8	1505	8.0	2137	2.4
15 TU	0359	7.6	1021	3.0	1616	7.6	2242	2.8
30 W	0339	8.2	1012	2.3	1610	8.3	2238	2.0
31 TH	0439	8.6	1110	1.8	1708	8.7	2334	1.6

Chart Datum: 5·06 metres below Ordnance Datum (Local)

ANCHORAGES AROUND GUERNSEY, HERM AND SARK

GUERNSEY

⚓s, clockwise from St. Peter Port:

SOLDIERS BAY, Quiet ⚓, sandy bottom, no facilities.

FERMAIN BAY, Popular with tourists. Good shelter from SW/NW. Café.

PETIT PORT BAY } S coast bays with sandy bottoms.
MOULIN HUET BAY } Sheltered from N and E winds.
SAINTS BAY } All tourist attractions with usual
PETIT BOT BAY } amenities. (Last is part of Icart B).

PORTELET HARBOUR, ⚓ on sandy bottom; shelter from E/S. Beware of fish farm. Best not to dry out against drying stone quay. Hotel, café/toilets. Bus to St. Peter Port.

LIHOU ISLAND, Privately owned, but visitors are welcome. ⚓ off NE corner. Sheltered from E'lies.

VAZON BAY, Large sandy beach with long surf line. Beware surfers and bathers. Facilities: Hotel/Timeshare complex, bus to St. Peter Port.

COBO BAY, Sandy beach with many local moorings. Facilities: Hotel, bar, D, L, P, ✉, R, V. Bus to St. Peter Port.

GRAND HAVRE, Very popular, many local moorings. ⚓ to W of Hommet de Greve, sheltered from S'lies. Stone slip; very busy in summer; lying alongside not recommended. Facilities: Hotel/Bar. Bus to St. Peter Port.

L'ANCRESSE BAY, Sandy bay, good shelter from S/SW.

FONTENELLE BAY, Good shelter from S, but many rks.

BORDEAUX HARBOUR, Small drying hbr full of local moorings. Facilities: Café. Bus to St. Peter Port.

ST SAMPSON HARBOUR, Hbr dries. Official port of entry. Good shelter but the disadvantages of a commercial hbr. Ldg lts 286°: Front, FR 3m 5M, on S pier hd, vis 230°-340°; rear, FG 13m, 390m from front, on clocktower. Lt on Crocq pier hd, FR 11m 5M, vis 250°-340°, and tfc sigs. N pier hd FG 3m 5M, vis 230°-340°. VHF Ch 12 (H24). Facilities: See Hr Mr for AB, C, FW. No yacht facilities. **Services:** Slip, ME, El, Sh, C. Bus to St Peter Port.

HERM ISLAND

Herm hbr has ldg lts, both FW (occas) and W drums at 078°. Dry out on sandy beach, or alongside bkwtr; 6 Red mooring buoys. Hbr very congested in summer; used by ferries above half tide. Facilities: Island Admin ☎ 722377; Hotel/bar. Alternatively use Rosiére steps to the S; or ⚓ in the bight to W of Rosiére steps. Speed limit is 6kn. Other ⚓s are on the E coast in Belvoir and Shell bays.
Note: JETHOU, CREVICHON and GRANDE FAUCONNIERE islands are private and landing is forbidden.

SARK (See overleaf)

All moorings are private; use in emergency only. ⚓s (clockwise from Creux) are unlit but safe in settled weather and offshore winds; in other conditions they can be uncomfortable:

DERRIBLE BAY. Good shelter and good holding on sand.

DIXCART BAY. Sandy and sheltered; good holding. 2 hotels.

ROUGE TERRIER (Little Sark). Sandy with cliff path to hotel.

CLOUET BAY, (good departure point for l'Etac). ⚓ at LW, but near HW swell is unpleasant .

PORT GOREY. Remains of quay exists but ⚓ in bay; heavy swell near HW.

LES FONTAINES BAY. SW-facing small bay.

LA GRANDE GREVE. Big sandy bay with small drying rk in centre. Exposed to SW'lies. Many steps to cliff-top Pub.

HAVRE GOSSELIN. A safe small ⚓, exposed to SW winds. Crowded in summer. Landing, plus many steps.

BRECQHOU ISLAND. Strictly private; landing prohib.

PORT À LA JUMENT. Shingle bay with good holding.

PORT DU MOULIN. Shingle bay.

LES FONTAINES BAY. Exposed to NE winds.

GREVE DE LA VILLE. Sand and shingle close into stone steps with access to village at cliff top.

LITTLE RUSSEL CHANNEL   10-14-12

See 10.14.5

SARK   10-14-13

Sark 49°25'·87N 02°20'·35W. Rtgs: Creux 4-5-1; Maseline 3-5-3

CHARTS
AC *808*; SHOM 6904; ECM 1014; Imray C33A; Stanfords 16

TIDES
−0450 Dover; ML 4·9; Duration 0550; Zone 0 (UT)

Standard Port ST HELIER (→)

Times				Height (metres)			
High Water		Low Water		MHWS	MHWN	MLWN	MLWS
0300	0900	0200	0900	11·0	8·1	4·0	1·4
1500	2100	1400	2100				
Differences SARK (MASELINE PIER)							
+0005	+0015	+0005	+0010	−2·1	−1·5	−0·6	−0·3

SHELTER
Many ⚓s (see overleaf) sheltered in various winds, but may be disturbed, except in settled weather. Only hbrs are Creux, access approx HW±2 in fair weather, where yachts dry out bow to quay, stern to ⚓, keeping clear of the pier; and Maseline, a busy ferry hbr with no yacht berths; ask Hr Mr's approval to stay here (other than to land people).

NAVIGATION
Creux WPT 49°25'·30N 02°20'·30W, 164°/344° from/to ent, 0·57M. Beware large tidal range, strong streams and many lobster pots. Sark is fringed by rks, but the centres of the bays are mainly clear of dangers.

LIGHTS AND MARKS
From S, Pinnacle Rk on with E edge of Grand Moie 001°; or Creux tunnel on with Pt Robert lt ho 344°.

RADIO TELEPHONE
VHF Ch 13, summer months only.

TELEPHONE (Dial code 01481)
Hr Mr 832323; ⌗ (Guernsey) 726911; Marinecall 0891 500 432; Police (Guernsey) 725111; Dr 832045.

FACILITIES
Maseline ☎ 832070 (kiosk), M (free), C (3 ton); Ferries to Guernsey; Condor catamaran to Jersey and St Malo.
Creux ☎ 832025 (kiosk), Slip, M (free), L, FW, C (1 ton); Tractor up steep hill to **Village** P & D (cans), Gas, Gaz, Kos, V, R, Bar, ✉, Ⓑ.

CHANNEL ISLANDS – ST. HELIER

LAT 49°11′N LONG 2°07′W

TIMES AND HEIGHTS OF HIGH AND LOW WATERS

YEAR **1998**

TIME ZONE (UT)
For Summer Time add ONE hour in non-shaded areas

JANUARY

Day	Time	m	Time	m	Time	m	Time	m		Day	Time	m	Time	m	Time	m	Time	m
1 TH	0225	1.6	0802	11.1	1453	1.4	2026	10.9		16 F	0300	2.0	0836	10.6	1521	2.0	2057	10.2
2 F	0306	1.7	0844	11.0	1535	1.5	2109	10.6		17 SA	0328	2.3	0906	10.2	1548	2.4	2127	9.8
3 SA	0348	1.9	0928	10.7	1617	1.8	2155	10.3		18 SU	0355	2.7	0936	9.7	1615	2.8	2156	9.3
4 SU	0432	2.3	1016	10.2	1703	2.2	2244	9.8		19 M	0424	3.1	1006	9.2	1645	3.2	2228	8.8
5 M	0522	2.7	1110	9.7	1755	2.6	2341	9.4		20 TU	0459	3.6	1041	8.7	1723	3.7	2308	8.4
6 TU	0621	3.1	1214	9.3	1858	3.0			21 W	0547	4.0	1129	8.3	1816	4.0		
7 W	0051	9.0	0732	3.4	1329	9.0	2011	3.2		22 TH	0008	8.0	0655	4.2	1242	8.0	1931	4.2
8 TH	0210	8.9	0851	3.4	1447	9.0	2127	3.1		23 F	0134	8.0	0818	4.2	1412	8.1	2055	4.0
9 F	0324	9.2	1005	3.2	1557	9.3	2234	2.8		24 SA	0257	8.4	0932	3.7	1526	8.5	2205	3.5
10 SA	0426	9.6	1109	2.6	1656	9.7	2333	2.4		25 SU	0400	9.0	1036	3.1	1626	9.2	2303	2.9
11 SU	0519	10.1	1205	2.2	1747	10.2			26 M	0453	9.7	1131	2.5	1718	9.8	2356	2.3
12 M O	0024	2.0	0605	10.6	1255	1.8	1832	10.5		27 TU	0542	10.4	1223	1.8	1806	10.5		
13 TU	0111	1.8	0647	10.9	1339	1.6	1913	10.7		28 W ●	0045	1.7	0627	11.0	1313	1.3	1851	11.0
14 W	0152	1.7	0727	11.0	1418	1.6	1951	10.7		29 TH	0132	1.3	0711	11.4	1400	0.9	1935	11.3
15 TH	0228	1.7	0802	10.9	1452	1.7	2025	10.5		30 F	0217	1.0	0754	11.6	1444	0.7	2017	11.4
										31 SA	0300	1.0	0836	11.6	1526	0.8	2059	11.3

FEBRUARY

Day	Time	m	Time	m	Time	m	Time	m		Day	Time	m	Time	m	Time	m	Time	m
1 SU	0340	1.1	0918	11.4	1606	1.0	2140	10.9		16 M	0332	2.1	0909	10.1	1548	2.3	2125	9.8
2 M	0421	1.5	1000	10.9	1646	1.6	2223	10.4		17 TU	0357	2.5	0934	9.6	1613	2.7	2150	9.3
3 TU	0503	2.1	1046	10.2	1731	2.2	2311	9.6		18 W	0425	3.0	1002	9.2	1644	3.2	2223	8.8
4 W	0553	2.8	1141	9.4	1824	3.0			19 TH	0502	3.5	1041	8.6	1726	3.7	2309	8.4
5 TH	0010	8.9	0656	3.4	1252	8.7	1934	3.5		20 F	0556	3.9	1139	8.1	1828	4.1		
6 F	0133	8.5	0819	3.7	1420	8.4	2058	3.7		21 SA	0020	8.0	0719	4.1	1307	7.9	1958	4.1
7 SA	0300	8.6	0947	3.5	1541	8.7	2216	3.4		22 SU	0203	8.0	0851	3.9	1448	8.1	2127	3.7
8 SU	0410	9.0	1056	3.0	1644	9.2	2318	2.8		23 M	0329	8.6	1006	3.2	1601	8.8	2236	3.0
9 M	0505	9.6	1151	2.5	1734	9.7			24 TU	0431	9.4	1108	2.4	1659	9.6	2334	2.2
10 TU	0009	2.3	0551	10.2	1239	2.0	1817	10.2		25 W	0524	10.2	1203	1.6	1750	10.4		
11 W O	0053	1.9	0631	10.6	1320	1.7	1855	10.5		26 TH ●	0027	1.5	0611	11.0	1255	0.9	1836	11.1
12 TH	0133	1.7	0708	10.9	1357	1.5	1931	10.7		27 F	0117	0.9	0657	11.6	1343	0.4	1920	11.6
13 F	0208	1.5	0743	10.9	1430	1.5	2003	10.7		28 SA	0203	0.4	0740	12.0	1428	0.1	2002	11.9
14 SA	0238	1.6	0814	10.8	1458	1.6	2033	10.5										
15 SU	0306	1.8	0843	10.5	1524	1.9	2100	10.2										

MARCH

Day	Time	m	Time	m	Time	m	Time	m		Day	Time	m	Time	m	Time	m	Time	m
1 SU	0246	0.3	0821	12.1	1509	0.1	2041	11.8		16 M	0242	1.5	0818	10.6	1458	1.6	2032	10.4
2 M	0326	0.5	0901	11.8	1548	0.5	2120	11.4		17 TU	0308	1.8	0843	10.2	1522	2.0	2056	10.0
3 TU	0404	1.0	0941	11.2	1626	1.2	2200	10.7		18 W	0333	2.1	0906	9.8	1545	2.4	2120	9.6
4 W	0443	1.7	1023	10.3	1706	2.1	2242	9.8		19 TH	0359	2.6	0934	9.4	1614	2.8	2152	9.2
5 TH	0527	2.6	1112	9.3	1754	3.0	2335	8.9		20 F	0432	3.0	1011	8.8	1652	3.3	2234	8.6
6 F	0625	3.1	1219	8.4	1901	3.8			21 SA	0519	3.5	1104	8.3	1747	3.8	2338	8.1
7 SA	0054	8.2	0749	3.9	1355	8.2	2031	4.0		22 SU	0633	3.9	1226	7.9	1912	4.0		
8 SU	0235	8.1	0928	3.8	1525	8.2	2157	3.7		23 M	0115	7.9	0811	3.7	1412	8.0	2050	3.7
9 M	0351	8.6	1039	3.2	1628	8.8	2259	3.1		24 TU	0255	8.4	0935	3.1	1535	8.7	2207	3.0
10 TU	0446	9.3	1132	2.6	1715	9.4	2348	2.5		25 W	0405	9.2	1042	2.3	1636	9.6	2309	2.1
11 W	0530	9.9	1215	2.1	1755	10.0			26 TH	0501	10.2	1140	1.4	1729	10.5		
12 TH	0030	2.0	0608	10.4	1255	1.7	1831	10.4		27 F	0005	1.3	0551	11.0	1233	0.7	1815	11.3
13 F	0108	1.6	0644	10.7	1330	1.4	1905	10.7		28 SA	0056	0.6	0637	11.7	1321	0.1	1859	11.8
14 SA	0142	1.4	0718	10.8	1402	1.3	1937	10.7		29 SU	0144	0.1	0720	12.1	1407	-0.2	1941	12.1
15 SU	0213	1.4	0748	10.8	1432	1.4	2006	10.6		30 M	0227	0.0	0802	12.2	1448	-0.1	2021	12.0
										31 TU	0308	0.2	0842	11.8	1528	0.4	2059	11.5

APRIL

Day	Time	m	Time	m	Time	m	Time	m		Day	Time	m	Time	m	Time	m	Time	m
1 W	0347	0.7	0922	11.2	1605	1.1	2137	10.8		16 TH	0312	1.9	0844	9.9	1523	2.2	2057	9.8
2 TH	0425	1.6	1003	10.2	1644	2.1	2219	9.8		17 F	0340	2.3	0914	9.5	1552	2.7	2130	9.4
3 F	0506	2.5	1050	9.2	1729	3.1	2308	8.9		18 SA	0413	2.7	0954	9.0	1630	3.1	2214	8.9
4 SA	0600	3.4	1153	8.3	1832	3.9			19 SU	0459	3.2	1047	8.4	1724	3.5	2316	8.4
5 SU	0021	8.1	0719	4.0	1327	7.8	2000	4.2		20 M	0607	3.5	1205	8.1	1843	3.8		
6 M	0201	7.9	0900	3.9	1458	8.0	2129	3.9		21 TU	0045	8.1	0738	3.4	1340	8.2	2017	3.5
7 TU	0320	8.3	1011	3.4	1600	8.6	2231	3.3		22 W	0220	8.5	0902	2.9	1504	8.8	2136	2.9
8 W	0416	8.9	1101	2.8	1646	9.2	2318	2.7		23 TH	0334	9.2	1012	2.2	1608	9.6	2241	2.0
9 TH	0500	9.5	1143	2.3	1725	9.8	2359	2.2		24 F	0434	10.1	1112	1.4	1703	10.4	2339	1.3
10 F	0539	10.0	1222	1.9	1801	10.2			25 SA	0527	10.9	1206	0.7	1752	11.2		
11 SA O	0036	1.8	0615	10.4	1258	1.6	1835	10.5		26 SU ●	0032	0.6	0615	11.5	1257	0.3	1837	11.7
12 SU	0112	1.5	0650	10.6	1331	1.4	1907	10.6		27 M	0122	0.2	0700	11.8	1344	0.0	1919	11.9
13 M	0145	1.4	0722	10.6	1403	1.4	1937	10.6		28 TU	0208	0.1	0743	11.9	1428	0.1	2000	11.8
14 TU	0217	1.5	0752	10.5	1431	1.6	2004	10.4		29 W	0250	0.3	0824	11.6	1508	0.6	2039	11.4
15 W	0245	1.6	0818	10.2	1457	1.9	2030	10.2		30 TH	0330	0.8	0905	10.9	1547	1.3	2118	10.7

14

Chart Datum: 5·88 metres below Ordnance Datum (Local)

CHANNEL ISLANDS – ST. HELIER

LAT 49°11′N   LONG 2°07′W

TIMES AND HEIGHTS OF HIGH AND LOW WATERS   YEAR 1998

TIME ZONE (UT)
For Summer Time add ONE hour in non-shaded areas

MAY

Day	Time	m	Day	Time	m
1 F	0409 / 0946 / 1626 / 2159	1.6 / 10.1 / 2.2 / 9.8	16 SA	0328 / 0904 / 1540 / 2119	2.1 / 9.7 / 2.5 / 9.7
2 SA	0449 / 1032 / 1708 / 2246	2.5 / 9.2 / 3.1 / 8.9	17 SU	0404 / 0947 / 1620 / 2206	2.5 / 9.2 / 2.9 / 9.2
3 SU	0538 / 1129 / 1804 / 2349	3.3 / 8.4 / 3.8 / 8.2	18 M	0451 / 1041 / 1714 / 2306	2.8 / 8.8 / 3.2 / 8.8
4 M	0644 / 1246 / 1918	3.8 / 7.9 / 4.2	19 TU	0554 / 1150 / 1825	3.0 / 8.5 / 3.4
5 TU	0112 / 0809 / 1412 / 2040	7.9 / 3.9 / 7.9 / 4.0	20 W	0023 / 0711 / 1311 / 1947	8.6 / 3.0 / 8.5 / 3.3
6 W	0233 / 0924 / 1517 / 2146	8.1 / 3.6 / 8.3 / 3.6	21 TH	0146 / 0829 / 1430 / 2104	8.8 / 2.7 / 8.9 / 2.8
7 TH	0333 / 1018 / 1606 / 2236	8.6 / 3.2 / 8.9 / 3.1	22 F	0300 / 0940 / 1538 / 2212	9.3 / 2.2 / 9.6 / 2.2
8 F	0421 / 1102 / 1648 / 2319	9.1 / 2.7 / 9.4 / 2.5	23 SA	0405 / 1043 / 1636 / 2313	9.9 / 1.7 / 10.2 / 1.6
9 SA	0504 / 1143 / 1726 / 2359	9.6 / 2.3 / 9.9 / 2.1	24 SU	0502 / 1141 / 1728	10.5 / 1.2 / 10.9
10 SU	0543 / 1221 / 1802	10.0 / 1.9 / 10.2	25 M	0009 / 0553 / 1234 / 1815 ●	1.0 / 11.0 / 0.8 / 11.3
11 M O	0038 / 0619 / 1259 / 1836	1.8 / 10.2 / 1.7 / 10.5	26 TU	0102 / 0641 / 1324 / 1900	0.7 / 11.3 / 0.6 / 11.5
12 TU	0116 / 0654 / 1334 / 1909	1.6 / 10.4 / 1.7 / 10.5	27 W	0150 / 0726 / 1410 / 1942	0.6 / 11.4 / 0.7 / 11.5
13 W	0151 / 0727 / 1406 / 1940	1.6 / 10.4 / 1.7 / 10.5	28 TH	0235 / 0809 / 1452 / 2023	0.7 / 11.2 / 1.0 / 11.2
14 TH	0224 / 0757 / 1436 / 2010	1.7 / 10.2 / 1.9 / 10.3	29 F	0317 / 0850 / 1532 / 2102	1.1 / 10.7 / 1.6 / 10.6
15 F	0256 / 0829 / 1506 / 2042	1.9 / 10.0 / 2.2 / 10.0	30 SA	0355 / 0931 / 1609 / 2142	1.7 / 10.1 / 2.3 / 9.9
			31 SU	0433 / 1014 / 1647 / 2224	2.4 / 9.3 / 3.0 / 9.2

JUNE

Day	Time	m	Day	Time	m
1 M	0513 / 1101 / 1731 / 2314	3.1 / 8.7 / 3.6 / 8.6	16 TU	0448 / 1034 / 1707 / 2256	2.3 / 9.4 / 2.8 / 9.4
2 TU	0602 / 1157 / 1826	3.6 / 8.2 / 4.0	17 W	0542 / 1133 / 1807	2.6 / 9.1 / 3.0
3 W	0017 / 0702 / 1308 / 1932	8.1 / 3.9 / 8.0 / 4.1	18 TH	0000 / 0646 / 1241 / 1918	9.1 / 2.7 / 8.9 / 3.1
4 TH	0130 / 0810 / 1419 / 2039	8.0 / 3.9 / 8.1 / 3.9	19 F	0113 / 0757 / 1356 / 2033	9.0 / 2.7 / 9.0 / 2.9
5 F	0238 / 0915 / 1517 / 2140	8.2 / 3.6 / 8.5 / 3.5	20 SA	0228 / 0909 / 1508 / 2144	9.2 / 2.5 / 9.3 / 2.5
6 SA	0335 / 1010 / 1606 / 2232	8.6 / 3.2 / 9.0 / 2.8	21 SU	0338 / 1016 / 1612 / 2250	9.5 / 2.2 / 9.8 / 2.1
7 SU	0424 / 1059 / 1649 / 2319	9.1 / 2.8 / 9.5 / 2.6	22 M	0441 / 1118 / 1708 / 2350	10.0 / 1.8 / 10.3 / 1.7
8 M	0508 / 1144 / 1729	9.5 / 2.4 / 9.9	23 TU	0536 / 1214 / 1758	10.4 / 1.5 / 10.8
9 TU	0004 / 0549 / 1227 / 1807	2.2 / 9.9 / 2.1 / 10.3	24 W	0045 / 0626 / 1307 / 1844 ●	1.3 / 10.7 / 1.3 / 11.1
10 W O	0047 / 0628 / 1307 / 1844	1.9 / 10.2 / 1.9 / 10.5	25 TH	0136 / 0712 / 1354 / 1928	1.1 / 10.9 / 1.2 / 11.2
11 TH	0128 / 0705 / 1345 / 1920	1.7 / 10.3 / 1.8 / 10.6	26 F	0221 / 0755 / 1437 / 2008	1.1 / 10.9 / 1.3 / 11.0
12 F	0207 / 0742 / 1421 / 1956	1.7 / 10.3 / 1.9 / 10.5	27 SA	0302 / 0836 / 1515 / 2046	1.3 / 10.6 / 1.7 / 10.7
13 SA	0245 / 0819 / 1457 / 2034	1.7 / 10.2 / 2.0 / 10.4	28 SU	0339 / 0914 / 1550 / 2123	1.7 / 10.2 / 2.2 / 10.2
14 SU	0322 / 0859 / 1535 / 2115	1.9 / 10.0 / 2.2 / 10.1	29 M	0412 / 0950 / 1622 / 2159	2.3 / 9.7 / 2.7 / 9.6
15 M	0402 / 0943 / 1617 / 2201	2.1 / 9.7 / 2.5 / 9.8	30 TU	0444 / 1027 / 1655 / 2237	2.8 / 9.1 / 3.2 / 9.0

JULY

Day	Time	m	Day	Time	m
1 W	0519 / 1108 / 1736 / 2323	3.3 / 8.6 / 3.7 / 8.5	16 TH	0526 / 1111 / 1747 / 2336	2.2 / 9.6 / 2.7 / 9.5
2 TH	0603 / 1159 / 1829	3.7 / 8.2 / 4.0	17 F	0621 / 1210 / 1850	2.6 / 9.2 / 3.0
3 F	0020 / 0700 / 1304 / 1934	8.1 / 4.0 / 8.0 / 4.1	18 SA	0042 / 0726 / 1323 / 2003	9.1 / 2.9 / 8.9 / 3.2
4 SA	0130 / 0808 / 1416 / 2042	8.0 / 4.0 / 8.2 / 3.9	19 SU	0159 / 0841 / 1442 / 2122	8.9 / 3.0 / 9.0 / 3.1
5 SU	0240 / 0916 / 1519 / 2146	8.2 / 3.7 / 8.5 / 3.5	20 M	0318 / 0955 / 1553 / 2234	9.0 / 2.8 / 9.3 / 2.7
6 M	0341 / 1016 / 1612 / 2242	8.6 / 3.3 / 9.1 / 3.0	21 TU	0426 / 1101 / 1653 / 2337	9.4 / 2.5 / 9.8 / 2.2
7 TU	0434 / 1109 / 1659 / 2334	9.1 / 2.8 / 9.6 / 2.5	22 W	0524 / 1200 / 1745	9.9 / 2.1 / 10.4
8 W	0522 / 1158 / 1743	9.6 / 2.4 / 10.1	23 TH	0032 / 0614 / 1252 / 1831 ●	1.8 / 10.3 / 1.7 / 10.8
9 TH O	0022 / 0605 / 1244 / 1825	2.1 / 10.1 / 2.1 / 10.5	24 F	0121 / 0658 / 1338 / 1913	1.5 / 10.6 / 1.5 / 11.0
10 F	0108 / 0648 / 1327 / 1906	1.8 / 10.4 / 1.8 / 10.8	25 SA	0205 / 0739 / 1419 / 1951	1.4 / 10.7 / 1.5 / 11.0
11 SA	0153 / 0730 / 1410 / 1946	1.5 / 10.6 / 1.7 / 10.9	26 SU	0243 / 0817 / 1454 / 2027	1.4 / 10.7 / 1.6 / 10.8
12 SU	0235 / 0811 / 1450 / 2027	1.4 / 10.6 / 1.6 / 10.9	27 M	0316 / 0851 / 1525 / 2059	1.7 / 10.4 / 1.9 / 10.5
13 M	0317 / 0852 / 1530 / 2108	1.4 / 10.6 / 1.7 / 10.7	28 TU	0345 / 0922 / 1553 / 2130	2.0 / 10.0 / 2.3 / 10.0
14 TU	0357 / 0935 / 1612 / 2152	1.8 / 10.3 / 1.9 / 10.4	29 W	0411 / 0952 / 1620 / 2201	2.5 / 9.5 / 2.8 / 9.4
15 W	0439 / 1020 / 1656 / 2241	1.8 / 10.0 / 2.3 / 10.0	30 TH	0438 / 1023 / 1650 / 2234	3.0 / 9.0 / 3.3 / 8.9
			31 F	0509 / 1100 / 1730 / 2315	3.4 / 8.5 / 3.7 / 8.4

AUGUST

Day	Time	m	Day	Time	m
1 SA	0555 / 1151 / 1829	3.9 / 8.1 / 4.1	16 SU	0013 / 0657 / 1253 / 1938	8.9 / 3.3 / 8.7 / 3.6
2 SU	0018 / 0701 / 1308 / 1948	8.0 / 4.1 / 7.9 / 4.2	17 M	0136 / 0818 / 1422 / 2108	8.5 / 3.6 / 8.6 / 3.6
3 M	0143 / 0824 / 1431 / 2105	7.9 / 4.1 / 8.2 / 3.9	18 TU	0306 / 0941 / 1540 / 2226	8.5 / 3.4 / 8.9 / 3.1
4 TU	0301 / 0938 / 1538 / 2211	8.3 / 3.7 / 8.7 / 3.4	19 W	0417 / 1050 / 1641 / 2326	9.0 / 2.9 / 9.5 / 2.5
5 W	0404 / 1039 / 1633 / 2308	8.8 / 3.1 / 9.3 / 2.7	20 TH	0513 / 1146 / 1731	9.6 / 2.4 / 10.1
6 TH	0458 / 1133 / 1722	9.4 / 2.6 / 10.0	21 F	0017 / 0558 / 1235 / 1814	2.0 / 10.1 / 2.0 / 10.6
7 F	0000 / 0546 / 1223 / 1807	2.1 / 10.0 / 2.0 / 10.6	22 SA	0102 / 0640 / 1317 / 1853 ●	1.6 / 10.5 / 1.6 / 10.9
8 SA O	0050 / 0632 / 1311 / 1851	1.6 / 10.6 / 1.6 / 11.1	23 SU	0142 / 0717 / 1355 / 1929	1.4 / 10.7 / 1.5 / 11.0
9 SU	0137 / 0715 / 1356 / 1934	1.2 / 10.9 / 1.3 / 11.4	24 M	0217 / 0752 / 1428 / 2002	1.4 / 10.8 / 1.5 / 11.0
10 M	0222 / 0757 / 1439 / 2015	0.9 / 11.2 / 1.1 / 11.5	25 TU	0247 / 0823 / 1457 / 2032	1.6 / 10.6 / 1.7 / 10.7
11 TU	0304 / 0838 / 1519 / 2055	0.9 / 11.2 / 1.1 / 11.4	26 W	0314 / 0851 / 1523 / 2100	1.8 / 10.3 / 2.0 / 10.2
12 W	0344 / 0919 / 1559 / 2137	1.0 / 10.9 / 1.4 / 11.0	27 TH	0337 / 0917 / 1547 / 2126	2.2 / 9.8 / 2.5 / 9.7
13 TH	0423 / 1000 / 1639 / 2220	1.4 / 10.5 / 1.9 / 10.4	28 F	0400 / 0942 / 1613 / 2151	2.7 / 9.3 / 3.0 / 9.2
14 F	0505 / 1046 / 1725 / 2310	2.0 / 9.9 / 2.5 / 9.6	29 SA	0427 / 1010 / 1647 / 2224	3.2 / 8.8 / 3.5 / 8.6
15 SA	0554 / 1140 / 1822	2.7 / 9.2 / 3.1	30 SU	0505 / 1051 / 1735 / 2315	3.7 / 8.3 / 4.0 / 8.1
			31 M	0601 / 1158 / 1850	4.2 / 7.9 / 4.3

Chart Datum: 5·88 metres below Ordnance Datum (Local)

CHANNEL ISLANDS – ST. HELIER

LAT 49°11′N   LONG   2°07′W

TIMES AND HEIGHTS OF HIGH AND LOW WATERS   YEAR **1998**

TIME ZONE (UT)
For Summer Time add ONE hour in non-shaded areas

SEPTEMBER

Day	Time	m	Time	m	Time	m	Time	m
1 TU	0043	7.7	0728	4.3	1344	7.9	2026	4.2
2 W	0226	8.0	0902	4.0	1507	8.4	2143	3.5
3 TH	0338	8.6	1012	3.3	1609	9.2	2245	2.8
4 F	0436	9.4	1109	2.6	1701	10.0	2339	2.0
5 SA	0526	10.1	1202	1.9	1748	10.7		
6 SU	0029	1.3	0612	10.8	1251	1.3	1833	11.4
7 M	0117	0.8	0656	11.3	1338	0.8	1915	11.8
8 TU	0202	0.5	0738	11.6	1421	0.6	1957	11.9
9 W	0244	0.4	0818	11.7	1502	0.7	2037	11.8
10 TH	0324	0.7	0858	11.4	1541	1.0	2117	11.3
11 F	0402	1.2	0938	10.8	1620	1.7	2159	10.5
12 SA	0442	2.0	1020	10.0	1702	2.5	2247	9.6
13 SU	0528	2.9	1112	9.1	1757	3.2	2349	8.7
14 M	0632	3.7	1226	8.4	1917	3.9		
15 TU	0119	8.1	0800	4.1	1405	8.3	2059	3.9
16 W	0256	8.3	0930	3.8	1525	8.7	2216	3.3
17 TH	0405	8.8	1037	3.2	1624	9.3	2311	2.7
18 F	0455	9.5	1128	2.6	1710	10.0	2356	2.1
19 SA	0537	10.1	1212	2.1	1751	10.5		
20 SU	0036	1.7	0614	10.5	1251	1.7	1827	10.8
21 M	0113	1.5	0649	10.8	1327	1.5	1902	11.0
22 TU	0146	1.5	0721	10.8	1359	1.5	1934	10.9
23 W	0216	1.6	0752	10.7	1428	1.6	2004	10.7
24 TH	0242	1.8	0819	10.4	1454	1.9	2030	10.3
25 F	0305	2.2	0844	10.0	1518	2.3	2053	9.9
26 SA	0328	2.6	0906	9.6	1544	2.8	2117	9.4
27 SU	0354	3.1	0933	9.1	1615	3.3	2149	8.8
28 M	0430	3.6	1011	8.6	1658	3.8	2236	8.2
29 TU	0521	4.1	1110	8.0	1804	4.2	2356	7.7
30 W	0640	4.4	1254	7.8	1945	4.2		

OCTOBER

Day	Time	m	Time	m	Time	m	Time	m
1 TH	0150	7.8	0825	4.2	1435	8.3	2113	3.6
2 F	0311	8.5	0943	3.4	1541	9.1	2218	2.8
3 SA	0411	9.4	1044	2.6	1636	10.0	2314	1.9
4 SU	0502	10.2	1137	1.8	1725	10.8		
5 M	0005	1.2	0548	11.0	1228	1.1	1810	11.5
6 TU	0053	0.6	0633	11.6	1316	0.6	1854	12.0
7 W	0139	0.3	0715	11.9	1401	0.4	1936	12.1
8 TH	0222	0.3	0756	11.9	1443	0.5	2016	11.9
9 F	0302	0.6	0835	11.6	1523	0.9	2057	11.4
10 SA	0341	1.3	0915	11.0	1602	1.6	2139	10.5
11 SU	0421	2.1	0958	10.1	1644	2.5	2227	9.5
12 M	0506	3.1	1049	9.1	1737	3.4	2329	8.6
13 TU	0609	3.9	1203	8.4	1857	4.0		
14 W	0100	8.0	0740	4.3	1340	8.2	2040	4.0
15 TH	0236	8.2	0911	4.0	1501	8.5	2154	3.5
16 F	0341	8.7	1014	3.4	1558	9.1	2246	2.9
17 SA	0428	9.3	1102	2.8	1643	9.7	2328	2.4
18 SU	0508	9.9	1143	2.3	1722	10.2		
19 M	0005	2.0	0543	10.4	1221	2.0	1758	10.6
20 TU	0041	1.8	0618	10.6	1255	1.7	1832	10.8
21 W	0114	1.7	0650	10.8	1328	1.6	1905	10.8
22 TH	0145	1.7	0721	10.7	1359	1.7	1936	10.6
23 F	0213	1.9	0749	10.5	1428	1.9	2003	10.3
24 SA	0238	2.2	0814	10.2	1454	2.3	2027	9.9
25 SU	0302	2.6	0838	9.8	1521	2.7	2053	9.5
26 M	0330	3.0	0907	9.4	1553	3.1	2127	
27 TU	0405	3.5	0946	8.8	1634	3.6	2215	8.4
28 W	0454	4.0	1043	8.3	1735	3.9	2328	3.8
29 TH	0607	4.3	1213	8.0	1904	4.0		
30 F	0111	8.0	0745	4.2	1356	8.3	2036	3.5
31 SA	0237	8.6	0910	3.5	1508	9.1	2147	2.8

NOVEMBER

Day	Time	m	Time	m	Time	m	Time	m
1 SU	0341	9.4	1014	2.6	1607	9.9	2245	2.0
2 M	0435	10.3	1111	1.8	1659	10.7	2338	1.3
3 TU	0523	11.0	1203	1.2	1747	11.4		
4 W	0028	0.7	0609	11.6	1253	0.7	1832	11.8
5 TH	0116	0.5	0653	11.9	1340	0.5	1916	12.0
6 F	0201	0.5	0735	11.9	1425	0.6	1958	11.8
7 SA	0243	0.8	0816	11.6	1507	1.0	2041	11.3
8 SU	0324	1.4	0857	11.0	1548	1.7	2124	10.5
9 M	0405	2.3	0940	10.2	1630	2.5	2211	9.6
10 TU	0449	3.1	1030	9.3	1720	3.3	2308	8.7
11 W	0545	3.9	1135	8.5	1827	4.0		
12 TH	0025	8.1	0702	4.3	1259	8.2	1956	4.1
13 F	0154	8.1	0829	4.3	1418	8.4	2113	3.8
14 SA	0302	8.5	0936	3.8	1519	8.8	2208	3.4
15 SU	0352	9.0	1026	3.3	1607	9.3	2252	2.9
16 M	0433	9.5	1108	2.8	1648	9.8	2330	2.5
17 TU	0511	10.0	1146	2.4	1727	10.1		
18 W	0007	2.2	0546	10.4	1223	2.1	1803	10.4
19 TH	0042	2.0	0620	10.6	1259	1.9	1838	10.5
20 F	0116	2.0	0653	10.6	1333	1.9	1911	10.5
21 SA	0148	2.1	0723	10.5	1406	2.0	1941	10.3
22 SU	0217	2.3	0752	10.3	1437	2.2	2010	10.1
23 M	0245	2.5	0821	10.0	1508	2.5	2041	9.7
24 TU	0316	2.9	0854	9.7	1542	2.9	2118	9.3
25 W	0353	3.2	0935	9.2	1624	3.2	2206	8.9
26 TH	0441	3.6	1030	8.8	1719	3.5	2310	8.5
27 F	0545	3.9	1144	8.5	1832	3.6		
28 SA	0032	8.4	0707	3.8	1312	8.6	1955	3.4
29 SU	0156	8.6	0831	3.4	1430	9.1	2110	2.9
30 M	0307	9.3	0942	2.8	1535	9.7	2215	2.2

DECEMBER

Day	Time	m	Time	m	Time	m	Time	m
1 TU	0406	10.0	1044	2.1	1633	10.4	2312	1.6
2 W	0500	10.7	1140	1.5	1725	11.0		
3 TH	0005	1.2	0548	11.3	1234	1.1	1814	11.4
4 F	0056	0.9	0635	11.6	1324	0.8	1900	11.6
5 SA	0144	0.9	0719	11.7	1411	0.9	1945	11.5
6 SU	0229	1.1	0802	11.5	1456	1.1	2028	11.1
7 M	0311	1.5	0844	11.0	1537	1.7	2111	10.5
8 TU	0351	2.2	0926	10.4	1618	2.3	2155	9.8
9 W	0431	2.9	1010	9.7	1659	3.0	2242	9.1
10 TH	0515	3.6	1100	9.0	1746	3.7	2338	8.5
11 F	0609	4.1	1202	8.4	1846	4.1		
12 SA	0047	8.1	0716	4.4	1316	8.2	1958	4.2
13 SU	0203	8.2	0828	4.3	1425	8.3	2108	4.0
14 M	0304	8.5	0932	3.9	1523	8.7	2203	3.6
15 TU	0354	9.0	1019	3.4	1612	9.1	2250	3.2
16 W	0437	9.5	1109	3.0	1655	9.6	2332	2.7
17 TH	0517	9.9	1151	2.5	1736	10.0		
18 F	0012	2.4	0554	10.3	1232	2.2	1814	10.2
19 SA	0051	2.2	0630	10.5	1312	2.0	1850	10.4
20 SU	0128	2.1	0705	10.6	1350	2.0	1926	10.4
21 M	0203	2.2	0739	10.5	1427	2.2	2000	10.3
22 TU	0237	2.3	0814	10.4	1502	2.2	2036	10.1
23 W	0311	2.5	0850	10.2	1539	2.4	2115	9.8
24 TH	0349	2.7	0932	9.8	1619	2.6	2159	9.5
25 F	0433	3.0	1020	9.5	1707	2.9	2252	9.1
26 SA	0527	3.3	1119	9.2	1805	3.1	2356	8.9
27 SU	0634	3.5	1231	9.0	1915	3.2		
28 M	0112	8.8	0751	3.4	1349	9.0	2031	3.0
29 TU	0231	9.1	0909	3.1	1504	9.3	2144	2.7
30 W	0340	9.6	1019	2.6	1611	9.8	2249	2.2
31 TH	0440	10.2	1122	2.1	1710	10.3	2348	1.8

14

Chart Datum: 5·88 metres below Ordnance Datum (Local)

ST HELIER   10-14-14

Jersey (Channel Is) 49°10'·63N 02°06'·90W   Rtg 1-2-2

CHARTS
AC *3278, 1137, 3655*; SHOM 6938, 7160, 7161; ECM 534, 1014; Imray C33B; Stanfords 16

TIDES
−0455 Dover; ML 6·1; Duration 0545; Zone 0 (UT)
NOTE: St Helier is a Standard Port and the tidal predictions for each day of the year are shown above.

SHELTER
Excellent in original **St Helier marina**, access HW±3 over sill (CD+3·6m); hinged gate rises 1·4m above sill to retain 5m. A waiting pontoon is to W of marina ent, near LB. Depths in marina vary from 2·8m at ent to 2·1m at N end. Ⓥ berths at pontoons E, F & G; (yachts >12m LOA or >2·1m draft, use N side of pontoon A; check with staff). New marina, known as **West of Albert marina**, is mainly intended for local boats; access HW±3 over sill/flap gate; max LOA 20m, drafts 2.1 to 3.5m.

H.W.Hts.m.

ST. HELIER

MEAN SPRING
AND NEAP CURVES

MEAN RANGES
Springs 9·6m
Neaps 4·1m

Springs occur 2 days
after
New and Full Moon.

Good shelter in **La Collette waiting basin**, depth 1·8m; access H24. Caution: Ent narrow at LWS; keep close to W side; PHM buoys mark shoal on E side. Waiting berths on pontoon D and W side of C. FVs berth on W side of basin. No ⚓ in St Helier Rds due to shipping & fish storage boxes. Note: For other hbrs and ⚓s around Jersey, see 10.14.15.

NAVIGATION
WPT 49°10'·01N 02°07'·30W, 203°/023° from/to front ldg lt, 0·74M. This WPT is common to all eight appr chans:
(1) W Passage (082°); beware race off Noirmont Pt, HW to HW +4.
(1A) NW Passage (095°, much used by yachts) passes 6ca S of La Corbière lt ho to join W Passage abm Noirmont Pt.
(2) Danger Rk Passage (044°) unlit; and
(3) Red and Green Passage (023°); both lead past rky, drying shoals (the latter over Fairway Rk 1·2m) and need precision and good vis.
(4) Middle Passage (339°) unlit, for St Aubin Bay.
(5) S Passage (341°) is clear but unlit. Alternatively, Demie de Pas on 350° with power stn chy is easier to see D/N.
(6) E Passage, 290° from Canger Rk WCM By, Q (9) 15s, passes S of Demie de Pas, B tr/Y top, Mo (D) WR 12s (at night stay in W sector); thence 314°.
(7) Violet Passage around SE tip of Jersey, see 10.14.15.
Caution: very large tidal range, and many offlying reefs. Entering hbr, note Oyster Rk (W bn; R 'O' topmark) to W of Red and Green (R & G) Passage; and to the E, Dog's Nest Rk (W bn with globe topmark). Speed limit 10kn N of Platte Rk, and 5kn N of La Collette.

LIGHTS AND MARKS
Power stn chy (95m, floodlit) and W concave roofs of Fort Regent are conspic, close E of R & G ldg line.
W Passage ldg lts: Front Oc 5s 23m 14M; rear Oc R 5s 46m 12M and Dog's Nest bn (unlit) lead 082°, N of Les Fours, NCM Q, and Ruaudière, SHM Fl G 3s, buoys, to a position close to E Rock, SHM buoy QG, where course is altered to pick up the **Red & Green Passage** ldg lts 023°: Front Oc G 5s; rear Oc R 5s, synch; (now easier to see against town lts) Daymarks are red dayglow patches on front dolphin and rear lt twr. Nos 2 and 4 PHM buoys (both QR) mark the fairway N of Platte Rk (Fl R 1·5s). Outer pier hds and dolphin are painted white and floodlit. Inner ldg lts 078°, both FG on W columns; not for yachts.

Entry Signals (at Port Control stn and marina)
Ⓖ lt (Oc , F or Fl)   = Enter, no exit
Ⓡ lt (Oc , F or Fl)   = Leave, no entry
Ⓡ and Ⓖ lts together = No exit/entry
Q Ⓨ lts on Port Control Stn indicate that power-driven craft < 25m LOA may enter/dep against the displayed sigs (keeping to stbd at ent and well clear of ferries). Note: Entry sigs are repeated at marina ent, where a large digital tide gauge shows depth over sill.

RADIO TELEPHONE
Monitor *St Helier Port Control* VHF Ch 14 (H24) for ferry movements. No marina VHF, but call *Port Control* if necessary. If unable to pass messages to *Port Control*, these can be relayed via *Jersey Radio* CRS, Ch **82** 25 16 (H24) or ☎ 41121. Jersey Radio broadcasts forecasts on Ch 25, 82 at 0645, 0745, 0845LT; & at 1245, 1845, 2245UT.

TELEPHONE (Dial code 01534)
Hr Mr 885588, ⚓ 885599; Marina 885508; ⌗ 30232; Jersey Weather Centre *(06966) 7777; Recorded forecast *(06966) 0011 for Jersey and 0022 for CI; Marinecall 0891 500 432; Police 612612; Dr 835742 and 853178; Ⓗ 59000. *(06966) is a dialling code within the CI for info services.

FACILITIES
St Helier Marina (180+200 visitors), ☎ 885508, £12.00, FW, AC, CH, ME, El, Sh, Grid, Gas, Gaz, ▣, V, Kos;
West of Albert Marina (589; few Ⓥ), ☎ 885508, £12.00, FW, AC, D & P (?).
La Collette Yacht Basin (130) ☎ 885529; (holding basin H24 when marina is inaccessible, plus a few visitors berths for up to 24 hrs), FW, AC, BH (18 ton), Slip;
Hbrs Dept ☎ 885588, FW, C (various, max 32 ton), Slip, Grids, BH (18 ton), AC; **St Helier YC** ☎ 832229, R, Bar;
S Pier (below YC) P & D (Access approx HW±3), FW.
Royal Channel Islands YC, at St Aubin: see overleaf.
Services: SM, CH, Sh, ME, El, Ⓔ, Gas. **Town** EC Thurs; P, D, CH, V, R, Bar, ✉, Ⓑ, ✈. Ro Ro Ferry: Guernsey, St Malo, Poole. Fast ferries (Mar-Nov): St Malo, Granville, Poole, Sark, Guernsey.

14

GOREY   10-14-15

Jersey 49°11'·84N 02°01'·28W   Rtg 3-4-1

CHARTS
AC 1138, *3655*; SHOM 6939, 7157, 7160; ECM 534, 1014;
Imray C33A; Stanfords 16

TIDES
−0454 Dover; ML 6·0; Duration 0545; Zone 0 (UT)

Standard Port ST HELIER (←—)

Times				Height (metres)			
High Water		Low Water		MHWS	MHWN	MLWN	MLWS
0300	0900	0200	0900	11·0	8·1	4·0	1·4
1500	2100	1400	2100				
Differences ST. CATHERINE BAY							
0000	+0010	+0010	+0010	0·0	−0·1	0·0	+0·1
BOULEY BAY							
+0002	+0002	+0004	+0004	−0·3	−0·3	−0·1	−0·1
LES ECREHOU							
+0005	+0009	+0011	+0009	+0·1	+0·5	−0·1	0·0
LES MINQUIERS							
−0014	−0018	−0001	−0008	+0·5	+0·6	+0·1	−0·1

SHELTER
Good in the hbr (dries completely), except in S/SE winds.
Access HW±3. There are 12 drying 🅰s 150m W of pier hd.
⚓ about 1½ca E of pier hd or in deeper water in the Roads;
also in St Catherine Bay to the N, except in S/SE winds.

NAVIGATION
WPT 49°10'·50N 01°57'·33W, 118°/298° from/to front ldg lt,
2·9M. Note the very large tidal range. On appr, keep well
outside all local bns until the ldg marks are identified, but
beware Banc du Chateau (0·4m), 1M offshore to N of 298°
ldg line; and Azicot Rk (dries 2·2m) just S of 298° ldg line,
2ca from ent.
From/to St Helier the Violet Chan skirts Violet Bank, but
requires good vis and can be very rough in strong E'lies.

LIGHTS AND MARKS
(1) Ldg lts 298°: front, Gorey pier lt, Oc RG 5s 8m 12M, W
    framework tr, vis R304°-352°, G352°-304°; rear, 490m
    from front, Oc R 5s 24m 8M, W □ with Or border.
(2) Front ldg lt on with church spire 304° leads over Road
    Rk (3·3m), and Azicot Rk (2·2m).
(3) Front ldg lt on with Fort William 250° leads close to Les
    Arch bn (B/W with A topmark) and Pacquet Rk (0·3m).

RADIO TELEPHONE
Gorey Hbr Ch 74 (HW±3 Apr-Oct only).

TELEPHONE (Dial code 01534)
Hr Mr 853616; ⌗ 30232; Marinecall 0891 500 432; for Dr
contact Hr Mr, or Hr Mr St Helier 885588.

FACILITIES
Hbr M, AB £6, P, D, FW, C (7 ton), ME, El, Sh, Gas.
Town EC Thurs; P, CH, V, R, Bar, ✉, Ⓑ, bus to St Helier.
Ferry (Mar-Nov) to Portbail, Carteret.

OTHER HARBOURS AND ANCHORAGES AROUND JERSEY

Of the many ⚓s around the island, the following are the
main ones, clockwise from St Helier:
ST AUBIN, Quiet ⚓ with off-shore winds in bay (mostly
dries) or yachts can dry out alongside N quay; access HW
±1. From seaward Middle Passage leads 339°, Mon Plaisir
Ho in transit with tr at St Aubin Fort. Final appr is N of St
Aubin Fort, via fairway in W sector of N pier head dir lt
254°, F WRG 5m, G248°-253°, W253°-255°, R255°-260°;
and, same structure, Iso R 4s 12m 10M. St Aubin Fort
pier head Fl R 4s 8m 1M. Facilities: AB, FW on N quay,
Slip, C (1 and 5 ton), Grid; **Royal Channel Islands YC**,
☎ 41023, Bar, R, M, Slip; **Services:** Sh, D, CH, BY, Gas, El,
ME, SM, Sh.
    Town Bar, D, FW, ◫, P, R, V, buses to St. Helier.
BELCROUTE BAY, N of Noirmont Pt. Excellent shelter from
W to SW winds, but dries 3·5m and many moorings; or
⚓ further off in 2·4m, landing by dinghy.
PORTELET BAY, W of Noirmont Pt. Good ⚓ in N'lies, either
side of Janvrin Tr.
ST BRELADE BAY, Small stone jetty in NW corner; local
moorings in Bouilly Port. A quiet ⚓ is in Beau Port. Good
shelter from N and W, but open to SW'ly swell. Beware
many rks, especially Fournier Rk (0·9m) in centre.
A very popular sandy tourist beach with various hotels.
GREVE AU LANCON (PLEMONT), A wide sandy bay E of
Grosnez Pt, Fl (2) WR 15s, which covers at HW. Suitable
for day visits on calm days. Exposed to swell. Beware
discontinued submarine cables.
GREVE de LECQ, Ldg line 202°: ○ W tr in line with white ho
with grey roof. Ruins extend E from present pier. Pub,
and bus to St. Helier. Exposed to swell.
BONNE NUIT BAY, Ldg lts 223°, both FG 7/34m 6M.
Conspic TV mast (232m) is ½M W of the bay. Avoid
Cheval Rk (dries 10·1m) close SE of ldg line. Hbr dries to
sand and shingle. Many local boat moorings. Hotel.
BOULEY BAY, Good ⚓. ML 5·8m. Rky bottom close to pier.
Local boat moorings. Hotel.
ROZEL BAY, Dir lt 245° F WRG, 11m 5M, G240°-244°,
W244°-246°, R246°-250°; W sector leads between pier
heads and bn. Hbr dries to sand and shingle. Local boat
moorings. Shops and pubs, bus to St Helier.
ST CATHERINE BAY, Many local moorings to S of Verclut
bkwtr, Fl 1·5s 18m 13M. ML 6·0m. Beware St Catherine
Bank, rocky plateau 3·3m in centre of bay. Landing on
slip at root of bkwtr. Dinghy SC, RNLI ILB Station, café.
LA ROCQUE, Small pier, local boat moorings, sandy
beach. Not suitable for visitors without good local
knowledge. No facilities.

OFFLYING ISLANDS

LES ECREHOU, 49°17'·45N 01°55'·50W. 5M NE of Rozel, has
about a dozen cottages. ML 6·2m. Arrive at about ½ tide
ebbing; see 10.14.15. Appr with Bigorne Rk on 022°; when
SE of Ile Maitre alter to 330° for FS on Marmotière Is.
Beware of strong and eddying tidal streams 4 - 8kn. Pick
up a buoy close SE of Marmotière or ⚓ in a pool 4ca
WSW of Marmotière (with FS and houses); other islands
are Maitre Ile (one house), Blanche and 5 other small
islands. Local knowledge or a detailed pilotage book is
essential. No lts.

PLATEAU des MINQUIERS, 48°58'·10N 02°03'·63W. About
12M S of Jersey (AC 3656, SHOM 7161) and ringed by six
cardinal light buoys. See 10.14.15 for tides. ML 6·4m.
Beware of strong and eddying tidal streams. Appr by day
in good vis from Demi de Vascelin SHM buoy on 161°,
Jetée des Fontaines RW bn in transit with FS on Maîtresse
Ile. Further transits skirt the W side of the islet to ⚓ due S
of it; safe only in settled weather and light winds. Maîtresse
Ile has about a dozen cottages. Land at the slipway NW
of the States of Jersey mooring buoy. Without local
knowledge, a detailed pilotage book is essential.

VOLVO PENTA SERVICE

Sales and service centres in area 15

France *Volvo Penta France* , 55 Avenue des Champs Pierreux, 92757 Cedex
Tel +33 1 55175457, Fax +33 1 55175261

**VOLVO
PENTA**

Area 15

Central North France
Pointe de Barfleur to
St. Quay-Portrieux

15

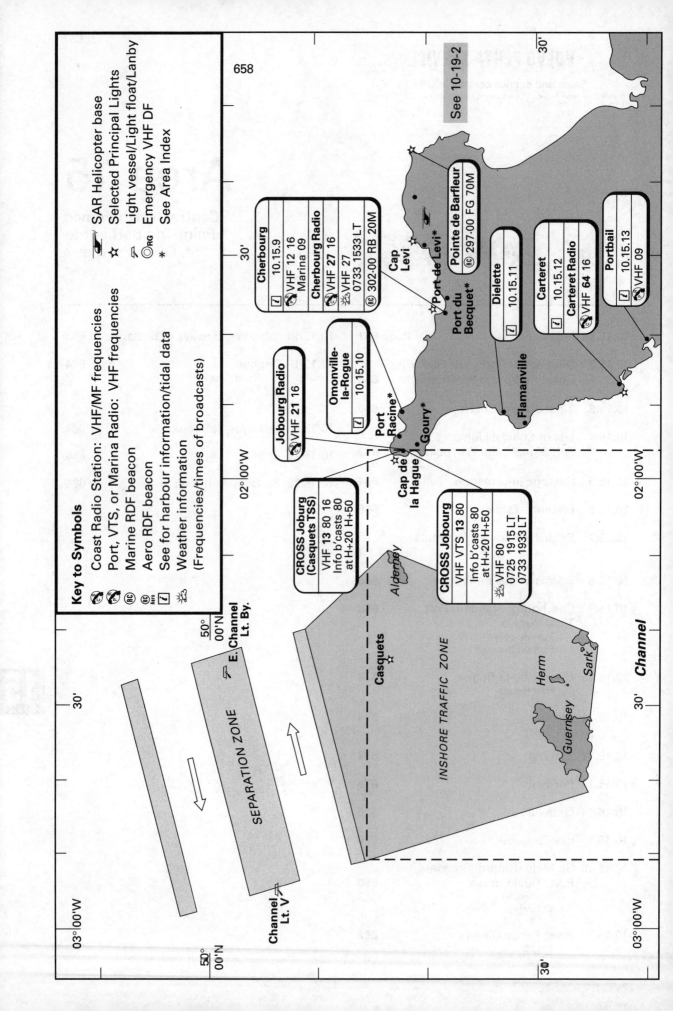

Key to Symbols

	Coast Radio Station: VHF/MF frequencies
	Port, VTS, or Marina Radio: VHF frequencies
RC	Marine RDF beacon
RC Aero	Aero RDF beacon
i	See for harbour information/tidal data
	Weather information (Frequencies/times of broadcasts)

	SAR Helicopter base
☆	Selected Principal Lights
	Light vessel/Light float/Lanby
☉RG	Emergency VHF DF
*	See Area Index

658

See 10-19-2

Cherbourg
10.15.9
i | VHF 12 16 Marina 09
Cherbourg Radio
VHF 27 16
VHF 27 0733 1533 LT
RC 302·00 RB 20M

Pointe de Barfleur
RC 297·00 FG 70M

Dielette
10.15.11
i

Carteret
10.15.12
i
Carteret Radio
VHF 64 16

Portbail
10.15.13
i | VHF 09

Jobourg Radio
VHF 21 16

Omonville-la-Rogue
10.15.10
i

CROSS Joburg (Casquets TSS)
VHF 13 80 16
Info b'casts 80 at H+20 H+50

CROSS Joburg
VHF VTS 13 80
Info b'casts 80 at H+20 H+50
VHF 80 0725 1915 LT 0733 1933 LT

Cap Levi

Port de Levi*

Port du Becquet*

Flamanville

Cap de la Hague

Port Racine*

Goury*

Channel Lt. V.

E. Channel Lt. By.

SEPARATION ZONE

INSHORE TRAFFIC ZONE

Alderney

Casquets

Guernsey

Herm

Sark

Channel

03°00'W

30'

02°00'W

30'

03°00'W

50° 00'N

30'

50° 00'N

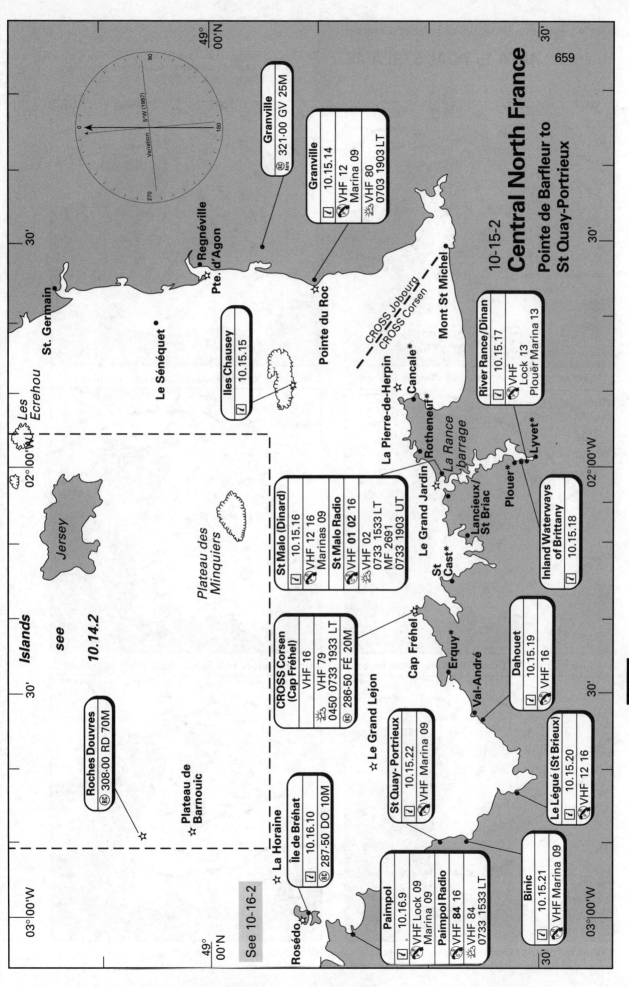

659

Central North France

10-15-2

Pointe de Barfleur to St Quay-Portrieux

15

03°00'W · 30' · Islands · see · 10.14.2 · 30' · 02°00'W · 30' · 02°00'W · 30' · 03°00'W

49°00'N · 30' · 49°00'N

90 · 5°W (1997) · Variation · 0 · 180 · 270

See 10-16-2

Granville
Ⓡ𝐂 Aero 321·00 GV 25M

Granville
10.15.14
ℹ VHF 12 Marina 09
⚓ VHF 80 0703 1903 LT

Iles Chausey
10.15.15
ℹ

St Germain

Regnéville

Pte. d'Agon

Le Sénéquet

Pointe du Roc ☆

CROSS Jobourg
CROSS Corsen

Mont St Michel

La Pierre-de-Herpin

Cancale*

Rothéneuf*

Le Grand Jardin ☆

St Malo (Dinard)
10.15.16
ℹ VHF 12 16 Marinas 09
St Malo Radio
⚓ VHF 01 02 16
⚓ VHF 02 0733 1533 LT MF 2691 0733 1903 UT

La Rance barrage

Lancieux/ St Briac

St Cast*

Plouer*

Lyvet*

River Rance/Dinan
10.15.17
ℹ VHF Lock 13 Plouër Marina 13

Inland Waterways of Brittany
10.15.18
ℹ

Dahouet
10.15.19
ℹ ⚓ VHF 16

Erquy*

Val-André

Le Légué (St Brieux)
10.15.20
ℹ ⚓ VHF 12 16

Les Écrehou
02°00'W

Jersey

Roches Douvres
Ⓡ𝐂 308·00 RD 70M

Plateau des Minquiers

Plateau de Barnouic

La Horaine ☆

☆ Le Grand Lejon

Cap Fréhel ☆

CROSS Corsen (Cap Fréhel)
VHF 16
⚓ VHF 79 0450 0733 1933 LT
Ⓡ𝐂 286·50 FÉ 20M

St Quay-Portrieux
10.15.22
ℹ ⚓ VHF Marina 09

Île de Bréhat
10.16.10
ℹ Ⓡ𝐂 287·50 DO 10M

Rosédo ☆

Paimpol
10.16.9
ℹ VHF Lock 09 Marina 09
Paimpol Radio
⚓ VHF 84 16
⚓ VHF 84 0733 1533 LT

Binic
10.15.21
ℹ ⚓ VHF Marina 09

10-15-3   AREA 15 TIDAL STREAMS

Due to very strong tidal stream rates, eddies may occur. Where possible these are shown, but in many areas there is insufficient information or the eddies are unstable.

5 Hours before HW Dover (0006 after HW St Malo)

4 Hours before HW Dover (0106 after HW St Malo)

3 Hours before HW Dover (0206 after HW St Malo)

2 Hours before HW Dover (0306 after HW St Malo)

1 Hour before HW Dover (0406 after HW St Malo)

HW Dover (0506 after HW St Malo)

Westward 10.16.3   Channel Islands 10.14.3   Eastward 10.19.3   Northward 10.2.3

1 Hour after HW Dover (0554 before HW St Malo)

2 Hours after HW Dover (0454 before HW St Malo)

3 Hours after HW Dover (0354 before HW St Malo)

4 Hours after HW Dover (0254 before HW St Malo)

5 Hours after HW Dover (0154 before HW St Malo)

6 Hours after HW Dover (0054 before HW St Malo)

15

10.15.4 COASTAL LIGHTS, FOG SIGNALS AND WAYPOINTS

Abbreviations used below are given in 1.4.1. Principal lights are in **bold** print, places in CAPITALS, and light-vessels, light floats and Lanbys in *CAPITAL ITALICS.* Unless otherwise stated lights are white. m – elevation in metres; M – nominal range in miles. Fog signals are in *italics*. Useful waypoints are underlined – use those on land with care. All geographical positions should be assumed to be approximate. See 4.4.1. All positions are referenced to the ED 50 datum.

NOTE: For English Channel Waypoints see 10.1.7.

POINTE DE BARFLEUR TO CAP DE LA HAGUE

Pte de Barfleur-Gatteville 49°41'·83N 01°15'·87W Fl (2) 10s 72m **29M**; Gy Tr, B top; obsc when brg less than 088°; RC; *Horn (2) 60s.*
Les Équets Lt By 49°43'·68N 01°18'·28W Q 8m 3M; NCM.
Basse du Rénier Lt By 49°44'·90N 01°22'·10W VQ 8m 4M; NCM; *Whis.*
La Pierre Noire Lt By 49°43'·57N 01°28'·98W Q (9) 15s 8m 4M; WCM.
Anse de Vicq Ldg Lts 158°. Front, 49°42'·26N 01°23'·88W FR 8m 7M; ▲ on W pylon, R top. Rear, 403m from front, FR 14m 7M; ▲ on W pylon, R top.

PORT DE LÉVI/LE BECQUET

Cap Lévi 49°41'·80N 01°28'·40W Fl R 5s 36m **22M**; Gy ■ Tr; W top.
Port de Lévi 49°41'·30N 01°28'·27W F RG 7m,R7M, G7M; vis G050°-109°, R109°-140°.
Le Becquet Ldg Lts 186·5°. Front, 49°39'·30N 01°32'·80W Dir Oc (2+1) 12s 8m 10M; W 8-sided Tr; intens 183°-190°. Rear, 49m from front, Dir Oc (2+1) R 12s 13m 7M; W 8-sided Tr, R top; synch with front, intens 183°-190°.

CHERBOURG PASSE DE L'EST TO MARINA

Fort des Flamands 49°39'·16N 01°35'·53W Dir Q WRG 13m W12M, R10M, G10M; vis G173·5°-176°, W176°-183°, R183°-193°.
Fort de l'Est 49°40'·33N 01°35'·93W Iso WG 4s 19m W12M, G9M; W pylon, G top; vis W008°-229°, G229°-008°.
La Truite Lt By 49°40'·39N 01°35'·39W Fl (4) R 15s; PHM.
Forte d'Île Pelée Oc (2) WR 6s 19m W10M, R7M; W & R pedestal on fort; vis W055°-120°, R120°-055°.
Digue du Homet 49°39'·53N 01°36'·88W FG 10m 8M; W pylon, G top on blockhouse; *Horn (2+1) 60s.*
Gare Maritime, NW corner QR 6m 6M; W col, R lantern.
Marina Môle Hd 49°38'·93N 01°37'·07W Oc (2) G 6s 7m 6M; G pylon.

CHERBOURG PASSE DE L'OUEST

CH1 Lt By 49°43'·30N 01°42'·10W L Fl 10s 8m 4M; SWM; *Whis*; Ra refl.
Passe de l'Ouest Ldg Lts 140·3° and 142·2°. **Front**, two Lts at root of Digue du Homet Dir Q (2 hor) 5m **17M**; W ▲ on parapet; 63m apart; intens 137·3°-143·3° and 139·2°-145·2°. Rear, Gare Maritime 0·99M from front Dir Q 35m **19M**; Gy pylon with W ▲ on building; intens 140°-142·5°.
Fort de l'Ouest 49°40'·50N 01°38'·87W Fl (3) WR 15s 19m **W24M, R20M**; Gy Tr, R top, on fort; vis W122°-355°, R355°-122°; RC; *Horn (3) 60s.*
Digue de Querqueville Hd 49°40'·36N 01°39'·72W Fl (4) WG 15s 8m W6M, G4M; W col, G top; vis W120°-290°, G290°-120°.
Le Tenarde Lt By 49°48'·78N 01°37'·67W VQ; NCM.
Ldg Lts 124·3°. Front, Digue du Homet Hd FG 10m 8M. Rear, 0·75M from front, Terre-plein de Mielles, Iso G 4s 16m 7M; W col, B bands; both intens 114·3°-134·3°.

OMONVILLE-LA-ROGUE/PORT RACINE

Omonville-la-Rogue 49°42'·33N 01°50'·10W Iso WRG 4s 13m W10M, R7M, G7M; W pylon; vis G180°-252°, W252°-262°, R262°-287°.
Port Racine Bkwtr Hd (unlit) 49°42'·78N 01°53'·70W.
Basse Bréfort Lt By 49°43'·70N 01°51'·05W VQ 8m 4M; NCM; *Whis.*
La Plate Lt Bn Tr 49°44'·02N 01°55'·65W Fl (2+1) WR 10s 11m W9M, R6M; Y 8-sided Tr, with B top; vis W115°-272°, R272°-115°; NCM.

CAP DE LA HAGUE TO ST MALO

Cap de la Hague (Gros du Raz) 49°43'·37N 01° 57'·19W Fl 5s 48m **23M**; Gy Tr, W top; *Horn 30s.*
La Foraine By 49°42'·95N 01°58'·40W; WCM; (occasionally submerged.)

GOURY/DIÉLETTE

Goury Ldg Lts 065·2°. Front, 49°42'·95N 01°56'·55W QR 5m 7M; R □ on W □ on pier. Rear, 116m from front, Q 11m 7M; W pylon on hut.
Diélette W Bkwtr Dir Lt 125·4°. Front, Jetée Ouest 49°33'·23N 01°51'·73W Iso WRG 4s 12m W10M, R7M, G7M; W Tr, G top; vis G070°-135°, W135°-145°, R145°-180°, and Fl G 4s 6m 2M; vis 115°-358°.
Flamanville Lt By 49°32'·62N 01°53'·93W Q (9) 15s; WCM.

CARTERET/PORTBAIL

Cap de Carteret 49°22'·46N 01°48'·35W Fl (2+1) 15s 81m **26M**; Gy Tr, G top; *Horn (3) 60s.*
Trois-Grunes Lt By 49°21'·88N 01°55'·12W Q (9) 15s; WCM.
Carteret Jetée Ouest Hd 49°22'·20N 01°47'·40W Oc R 4s 7m 7M; W col, R top.
Carteret Training wall Hd 49°22'·24N 01°47'·23W Fl G 2·5s 4m 2M; W mast, G top.
PB By 49°18'·47N 01°44'·60W; SWM.
Portbail Ldg Lts 042°. Front, La Caillourie 49°19'·79N 01°42'·40W Q 14m 10M; W pylon, R top. Rear, 870m from front, Oc 4s 20m 10M; belfry.
Portbail Training wall Hd Q (2) R 5s 5m 1M; W mast, R top.

REGNÉVILLE

La Catheue Lt By 48°57'·95N 01°42'·00W Q (6) + L Fl 15s; SCM.
Pte d'Agon 49°00'·25N 01°34'·60W Oc (2) WR 6s 12m W10M, R7M; W Tr, R top, W dwelling; vis R063°-110°, W110°-063°.
Dir Lt 028° 49°00'·77N 01°33'·28W Dir Oc WRG 4s 9m W12M, R9M, G9M; House; vis G024°-027°, W027°-029°, R029°-033°.

PASSAGE DE LA DÉROUTE

Écrévière Lt By 49°15'·33N 01°52'·08W Q (6) + L Fl 15s; SCM; *Bell.*
Bas Jourdan Lt By 49°06'·90N 01°44'·07W Q (3) 10s; ECM; *Whis.*
Le Sénéquet 49°05'·54N 01°39'·65W Fl (3) WR 12s 18m W13M, R10M; W Tr; vis R083·5°-116·5°, W116·5°-083·5°.
Basse le Marié Lt By 49°01'·89N 01°48'·76W Q (9) 15s; WCM.
Les Ardentes Lt By 48°57'·84N 01°51'·53W Q (3) 10s; ECM.
NE Minquiers Lt By 49°00'·90N 01°55'·20W VQ (3) 5s; ECM; *Bell.*
SE Minquiers Lt By 48°53'·50N 02°00'·00W Q (3) 10s; ECM; *Bell.*
S Minquiers Lt By 48°53'·15N 02°10'·00W Q (6) + L Fl 15s; SCM.

ÎLES CHAUSEY

La Petite Entrée Bn 48°54'·60N 01°49'·48W; WCM.
Le Pignon 48°53'·52N 01°43'·40 W Oc (2) WR 6s 10m W11M, R8M; B Tr, Y band; vis R005°-150°, W150°-005°.
Basse du Founet By 48°53'·34N 01°42'·22W; ECM.
Grande Île (Pte de la Tour) 48°52'·25N 01°49'·27W Fl 5s 39m **23M**; Gy ■ Tr; *Horn 30s.*
Channel Lt By 48°52'·18N 01°49'·00W Fl G 2s; SHM.

La Crabière Est Lt Bn Tr 48°52'·52N 01°49'·30W Oc WRG 4s 5m W9M, R6M, G6M; B Tr, Y top; vis W079°-291°, G291°-329°, W329°-335°, R335°-079°.

Anvers Wk Lt By 48°53'·90N 01°40'·84W Q (3) 10s; ECM.
Le Videcoq Lt By 48°49'·70N 01°42'·02W VQ (9) 10s; WCM.

GRANVILLE
Tourelle Fourchie 48°50'·21N 01°36'·92W; PHM; *Horn (4) 60s.*
Pointe du Roc 48°50'·11N 01°36'·70W Fl (4) 15s 49m **23M**; Gy Tr, R top.
Le Loup Lt Bn 48°49'·63N 01°36'·17W Fl (2) 6s 8m 11M; IDM.
Hérel Marina Hd 48°49'·96N 01°35'·82W Fl R 4s 12m 8M; W ● Tr, R top; *Horn (2) 40s.*
Commercial Port Jetée Ouest Hd 48°49'·92N 01°36'·16W Iso R 4s 12m 6M; R pylon.

CANCALE/ROTHENEUF
La Pierre-de-Herpin 48°43'·83N 01°48'·83W Oc (2) 6s 20m **17M**; W Tr, B top and base; *Siren Mo (N) 60s.*
Cancale Jetty Hd 48°40'·16N 01°51'·04W Oc (3) G 12s 12m 7M; W pylon, G top, G hut; obsc when brg less than 223°.
Rothneuf Entrance Bn 48°41'·42N 01°57'·61W; SHM; (unlit.)

ST MALO TO ST QUAY PORTRIEUX

APPROACHES TO ST MALO
La Plate Lt Bn Tr 48°40'·85N 02°01'·83W Fl WRG 4s 11m, W11M, R7M, G7M; vis W140°-203°, R203°-210°, W210°-225°, G225°-140°.
Brunel Lt By 48°40'·88N 02°05'·26W Q (9) 15s; WCM; *Bell.*

CHENAL DE LA PETITE PORTE/RADE DE ST MALO
Ldg Lts 130°. Front, **Le Grand Jardin** 48°40'·27N 02°04'·90W Fl (2) R 10s 24m **15M**; Gy Tr, R top; RC. Rear, **La Balue**, 4·08M from front, Dir FG 69m **24M**; Gy ■ Tr; intens 128·2°-129·7°.
Bassé NE Lt By 48°42'·51N 02°09'·34W Q; NCM; *Bell.*
Fairway Lt By 48°41'·42N 02°07'·21W L Fl 10s; SWM; *Whis.*
Les Courtis Lt Bn 48°40'·52N 02°05'·72W Fl (3) G 12s 14m 8M.

CHENAL DE LA GRANDE PORTE
Ldg Lts 089·1°. **Front, Le Grand Jardin** Fl (2) R 10s 24m **15M**. Rear, **Rochebonne** 4·2M from front 48°40'·32N 01°58'·61W Dir FR 40m **24M**; Gy ■ Tr, R top; intens 088·2°-089·7°.
Le Sou Lt By 48°40'·15N 02°05'·24W VQ (3) 5s; ECM; *Bell.*
No. 1 Lt By 48°40'·24N 02°05'·97W Fl G 4s; SHM; *Whis.*
No. 2 Lt By 48°40'·27N 02°07'·48W Fl (3) R 12s; PHM; *Whis.*
Banchenou Lt By 48°40'·52N 02°11'·42W Fl (5) 20s; SHM.
Ldg Lts 128·7°. Front, **Les Bas-Sablons** 48°38'·22N 02°01'·23W Dir FG 20m **22M**; W ■ Tr, B top; intens 127·5°-130·5°. Common rear, **La Balue**, 0·9M from front Dir FG 69m **25M**; Gy ■ Tr; intens 128·2°-129·7°.
Basse du Buron No. 12 Lt By 48°39'·46N 02°03'·44W L Fl R 10s; PHM.
Le Buron Lt Bn 48°39'·38N 02°03'·60W Fl (2) 6s 15m 8M; G Tr.
Plateau Rance Nord 48°38'·71N 02°02'·27W VQ; NCM.
Plateau Rance Sud 48°38'·52N 02°02'·23W Q (6) + L Fl 15s; SCM.

ST MALO
Ldg Lts 070·7°. Écluse du Naye Front, 48°38'·64N 02°01'·46W FR 7m 3M. Rear, FR 23m 8M vis 030°-120°.
La Grenouille Lt By 48°38'·44N 01°01'·92W Fl (4) G 15s; SHM.
Môle des Noires Hd 48°38'·58N 02°01'·85W Fl R 5s 11m 13M; W Tr, R top; obsc 155°-159°, 171°-178°, and when brg more than 192°; *Horn (2) 20s.*
Bas-Sablons Marina Môle Hd 48°38'·48N 02°01'·63W Fl G 4s 7m 5M; Gy mast.

LA RANCE
La Jument Lt Bn Tr 48°37'·50N 02°01'·68W Fl (5) G 20s 6m 3M; G Tr, SHM.
Tidal barrage, NW wall Fl G 4s 6m 5M, G pylon, vis 191°-291°.
NE dolphin Fl (2) R 6s 6m 5M; vis 040°-200°.

ST BRIAC/ST CAST
Embouchure du Fremur. Dir Lt 125° 48°37'·1N 02°08'·2W Dir Iso WRG 4s 10m W13M, R11M, G11M; W mast on hut, vis G121·5°-124·5°, W124·5°-125·5°, R125·5°-129·5°.
St Cast Môle Hd 48°38'·47N 02°14'·50W Iso WG 4s 11m W11M, G8M; G and W structure; vis W204°-217°, G217°-233°, W233°-245°, G245°-204°.

Cap Fréhel 48°41'·10N 02°19'·07W Fl (2) 10s 85m **29M**; Brown ■ Tr, G lantern; *Horn (2) 60s*; RC.

CHENAL D'ERQUY/ERQUY/VAL-ANDRÉ
Les Justières Lt By 48°40'·66N 02°26'·43W Q (6) + L Fl 15s; SCM.
Basses du Courant Lt By 48°39'·29N 02°29'·08W VQ (6) + L Fl 10s; SCM.
Erquy S Môle Hd 48°38'·13N 02°28'·60W Oc (2+1) WRG 12s 11m W11M, R8M, G8M; W Tr, R top; vis R055°-081°, W081°-094°, G094°-111°, W111°-120°, R120°-134°.
Erquy Inner Jetty Hd 48°38'·16N 02°28'·31W Fl R 2·5s 10m 3M; R and W Tr.
Val-Andre Jetty Hd 48°35'·89N 02°33'·24W.

PORT DE DAHOUET
La Dahouet By 48°35'·28N 02°35'·28W; NCM.
La Petite-Muette 48°34'·91N 02°34'·21W Fl WRG 4s 10m W9M, R6M, G6M; ▲ on G & W Tr; vis G055°-114°, W114°-146°, R146°-196°. Fl (2) G 6s; vis 156°-286° 240m SE.

BAIE DE SAINT BRIEUC
Grand Léjon 48°44'·95N 02°39'·90W Fl (5) WR 20s 17m **W18M**, R14M; R Tr, W bands; vis R015°-058°, W058°-283°, R283°-350°, W350°-015°.
Le Rohein Lt Bn Tr 48°38'·88N 02°37'·68W VQ (9) WRG 10s 13m W10M, R7M, G7M; WCM; vis R072°-105°, W105°-180°, G180°-193°, W193°-237°, G237°-282°, W282°-301°. G301°-330°, W330°-072°.

LE LÉGUÉ (St Brieuc)
Le Légué Lt By 48°34'·38N 02°41'·07W Mo (A)10s; SWM; *Whis.*
Pointe à l'Aigle Jetty 48°32'·15N 02°43'·05W VQ G 13m 8M; W Tr, G top; vis 160°-070°.
Custom House Jetty 48°31'·96N 02°43'·34W Iso G 4s 6m 8M, W cols, G top.

BINIC
Binic, Môle de Penthièvre Hd 48°36'·13N 02°48'·84W Oc (3) 12s 12m 11M; W Tr, G gallery; unintens 020°-110°.

SAINT-QUAY-PORTRIEUX
Caffa Lt By 48°37'·89N 02°43'·00W Q (3) 10s; ECM.
La Roselière Lt By 48°37'·51N 02°46'·31W VQ (9) 10s; WCM.
Elbow 48°39'·05N 02°49'·01W Dir Iso WRG 4s **W15M**, R11M, G11M; vis 159°-179°, G179°-316°, W316°-320·5°, R320·5°-159°; Reserve Lt ranges 12/9M.
Île Harbour Roches de Saint-Quay 48°40'·05N 02°48'·42W Oc (2) WRG 6s 16m W10M, R8M, G8M; W Tr and dwelling, R top; vis R011°-133°, G133°-270°, R270°-306°, G306°-358°, W358°-011°.
NE Môle Hd 48°38'·90N 02°48'·84W Fl (3) G 12s 2M; G Tr.
Herflux Dir Lt 130° 48°39'·13N 02°47'·87W Dir Fl (2) WRG 6s W8M, R6M, G6M; vis G115°-125°, W125°-135°, R135°-145°; SCM.

15

10.15.5 PASSAGE INFORMATION

Current Pilots for this area include: *Shell Channel Pilot* (Imray/Cunliffe); *Normandy and CI Pilot* (Adlard Coles/Brackenbury) as far W as St Malo; *Brittany and CI Cruising Guide* (Adlard Coles/Jefferson); *N Brittany and CI Cruising* (YM/Cumberlidge); *N Brittany Pilot* (Imray/RCC) W'ward from St Malo; *Admiralty Channel Pilot*. Charts *2669* and *1106* cover the whole area. For French Glossary see 1.4.2.

Off the French coastline between Pte de Barfleur and Cap Lévi rky shoals extend up to 2·5M seaward. From C. Lévi around C. de la Hague and S to C. de Flamanville the coast is cleaner with few dangers extending more than 1M offshore. Southward to Mont St Michel and W to St Malo the coast changes to extensive offshore shoals, sand dunes studded with rks and a series of drying hbrs. From St Malo to St Quay-Portrieux the coast is characterised by deep bays (often drying), a few rugged headlands and many offlying rks.

The sea areas around this coast, including the Channel Islands, are dominated by powerful tidal streams with an anti-clockwise rotational pattern and a very large tidal range. Across the top of the Cotentin Peninsula and between C. de la Hague and Alderney the main English Channel tidal streams are rectilinear E/W. Neap tides are best, particularly for a first visit, and tidal streams need to be worked carefully. Boats which can take the ground have an advantage for exploring the shallower hbrs. Be careful to avoid lobster pots, and oyster and mussel beds in some rivers and bays.

CROSSING FROM UK TO CHERBOURG OR ALDERNEY

The popular cross-Channel route from hbrs between Portland and Chichester to those on the Cotentin peninsula or in the Channel Islands is normally straightforward in summer, but can never be taken for granted. Review the planning guidelines in 10.3.5, especially at the start of the season. Cross-Channel distances are in 10.0.5 and waypoints in 10.1.7. Note any tidal constraints shown under the departure hbr itself. Other local factors to be considered include:
Portland & Weymouth: the Portland Race and Shambles Bank both require a wide berth. Check the tidal streams for possible wind-over-tide conditions.
Poole: leave hbr on the ebb, but at springs with a S/SE wind beware short steep seas in the Swash Channel; off Handfast, Peveril and Anvil Pts overfalls occur with wind against tide.
From **Solent ports** decide whether to leave via the Needles or east of the IOW. The former usually requires a fair tide through Hurst Narrows (HW Portsmouth –1 to +4½), which in turn will dictate your ETD from hbr. The latter has no tidal gate, but is longer and may give a less favourable slant if the wind is in the SW; in W'lies it offers better shelter in the lee of the IOW. In practice the nearer exit may prove to be the obvious choice.
On passage the greatest hazard is likely to be crossing the shipping lanes, especially if fog/poor vis are forecast when it may be safest not to sail. Whether crossing at the Casquets TSS, or further up-Channel, is almost academic; the risk of collision with another ship is the same.
Finally, review destination(s) and possible hbrs of refuge:
Braye (Alderney), whilst accessible at all times, presents a slight risk, especially at springs, of being swept past Alderney on a W-going tide. The yacht may then clew up in Guernsey, having unwittingly negotiated the Swinge or the Alderney Race. The moral is to plan and monitor track so as to approach from well up-tide. (For Guernsey, Sark & Jersey see 10.14.5).
French ports on the W side of the Cotentin (Diélette to Granville) are tidally constrained and exposed to the W; they are however in a lee with anticyclonic Easterlies.

Cherbourg is accessible at all times. On closing the coast especially at springs, a very large drift angle may be needed to maintain track. To the E, **Barfleur** dries; **St Vaast** is a safe anch, whilst awaiting lock opening (see Area 19).

POINTE DE BARFLEUR TO CAP DE LA HAGUE (AC *1106*)

The N coast of the Cotentin Peninsula runs E/W for 26M, mostly bordered by rks which extend 2·5M offshore from Pte de Barfleur to C. Lévi, and 1M offshore between Pte de Jardeheu and C. de la Hague. Tidal streams reach 5kn at sp, and raise a steep sea with wind against tide.

Pte de Barfleur has dangers up to 2M offshore, and a race, in which the sea breaks heavily, extends 3-4M NE and E from the lt ho. In bad weather, particularly with winds from NW or SE against the tide, it is necessary to keep at least 6M to seaward to avoid the worst effects; in calmer conditions the Pte can be rounded close inshore. The inner passage between Pte de Barfleur and C. Lévi, keeping S of three cardinal buoys, is not recommended without local knowledge except in good weather and visibility when the transits shown on chart *1106* can be used. Tidal streams run strongly with considerable local variations.

Off C. Lévi a race develops with wind against tide, and extends nearly 2M to N. Port Lévi and Port de Becquet are two small drying hbrs E of Cherbourg. Off Cherbourg (10.15.9) the stream is E-going from about HW – 0430 and W-going from HW + 0230.

Close inshore between Cherbourg and C. de la Hague a back eddy runs W. As an alternative to Omonville (10.15.10) there is anch in Anse de St Martin, about 2M E of C. de la Hague, open to N, but useful to await the tide in the Alderney Race.

THE ALDERNEY RACE (chart *3653*)

The Alderney Race, so called due to very strong tidal streams, runs SW/NE between C. de la Hague and Alderney. The fairway, approx 4M wide, is bounded by Race Rk and Alderney S Banks to the NW, and to the SE by rky banks 4M WSW of C. de la Hague, Milieu and Banc de la Schôle (least depth 2·7m). These dangers which cause breaking seas and heavy overfalls should be carefully avoided. In bad weather and strong wind-against-tide conditions the seas break in all parts of the Race and passage is not recommended. Conditions are exacerbated at sp tides.
In mid-chan the the SW-going stream starts at HW St Helier + 0430 (HW Dover) and the NE-going stream at HW St Helier –0210 (HW Dover + 0530), sp rates both 5·5kn. The times at which the stream turns do not vary much for various places, but the rates do; for example, 1M W of C. de la Hague the sp rates reach 7 to 8kn.

To obtain optimum conditions, timing is of the essence. As a rule of thumb the Race should be entered on the first of the fair tide so as to avoid the peak tidal stream with attendant overfalls/seas.

Thus, bound SW, arrive off C. de la Hague at around HW St Helier + 0430 (HW Dover) when the stream will be slack, whilst just starting to run SW off Alderney. A yacht leaving Cherbourg at HW Dover – 0300 will achieve the above timing by utilising the inshore W-going tidal eddy.

Conversely, NE bound, leave St Peter Port, say, at approx local HW St Helier – 0430 (HWD+3) with a foul tide so as to pass Banc de la Schôle as the first of the fair tide starts to make. A later departure should achieve a faster passage, but with potentially less favourable conditions in the Race. On the NE stream the worst overfalls are on the French side.

CAP DE LA HAGUE TO ST MALO
(charts *3659*, 3656, *3655*, *3653*)

The Jobourg radar surveillance station (CROSS) and atomic energy station Chy (R lts) are conspic about 3-4M SE of Gros du Raz (lt, fog sig), off C de la Hague. 5M S of C de la Hague beware Les Huquets de Jobourg, an extensive bank of drying and submerged rks, and Les Huquets de Vauville (dry) close SE of them.

The W coast of the Cotentin Peninsula is exposed, and is mostly rky and inhospitable; along much of this coast S of Carteret there is little depth of water, so that a nasty sea can build. The drying hbrs/non-tidal marinas* at Goury, Dielette* (10.15.11), Carteret* (10.15.12) and Portbail (10.15.13) are more readily accessible if cruising from S to N on the tide, since all hbrs are restricted by drying approaches.

The two main chans from/to the Alderney Race are Déroute de Terre and, further offshore, Passage de la Déroute. Neither chan are well marked in places, and are not advised at night. The former leads between Plateau des Trois Grunes and Carteret, between Basses de Portbail and Bancs Félés, between Le Sénéquet lt tr and Basse Jourdan, and E of Îles Chausey toward Pte du Roc, off Granville (10.15.14). The S end of this chan, E of Îles Chausey, is very shallow; for detailed directions see *Channel Pilot*.

The Passage de la Déroute passes W of Plateau des Trois Grunes, between Basses de Taillepied and Les Écrehou, between Chaussée de Boeufs and Plateau de l'Arconie, E and SE of Les Minquiers and Les Ardentes, and W of Îles Chausey (10.15.15).

To the S of Granville is the drying expanse of B du Mont St Michel. Proceeding W, the drying hbr of Cancale (10.15.16) with many oyster beds and a fair weather anch SE of Île des Rimains, lies 4M S of Pte du Grouin, off which the many dangers are marked by La Pierre-de-Herpin (lt, fog sig). The large drying inlet of Rothéneuf, with anch off in good weather, is 4M E of St Malo (10.15.16 and chart 2700).

ST MALO TO L'OST PIC (charts *3674*, *3659*)

In the apprs to St Malo (chart 2700) are many islets, rks and shoals, between which are several chans that can be used in good vis. Tidal streams reach 4kn at sp, and can set across chans. From E and N, with sufficient rise of tide and good vis,

Chenal de la Bigne, Chenal des Petits Pointus or Chenal de la Grande Conchée can be used, but they all pass over or near to drying patches. From the W and NW, Chenal de la Grande Porte and Chenal de la Petite Porte are the easiest routes and are well marked/lit. Chenal du Décollé is a shallow, demanding inshore route from the W, and no shorter than Chenal de la Grande Porte.

By passing through the lock at W end of the R. Rance barrage (10.15.17) it is possible to cruise up river to Dinan, via the lock at Châtelier (SHOM chart 4233). At Dinan is ent to Canal d'Ille et Rance to Biscay (10.15.18).

6M NW of St Malo beware Le Vieux-Banc (dries). Here the E-going stream begins at HW St Helier – 0555, and the W-going at HW St Helier – 0015, sp rates 2·5kn. There are W-going eddies very close inshore on the E-going stream. Between St Malo and C. Fréhel is St Cast hbr (10.15.19), and there are anchs S of Île Agot in the apprs to the drying hbr of St Briac, in B de l'Arguenon and B de la Fresnaye. From C. Fréhel to C. d'Erquy there are no worthwhile hbrs.
About 3ca off Cap d'Erquy, and inshore of the various rky patches close to seaward Chenal d'Erquy runs WSW/ENE into the E side of the B de St Brieuc. Erquy is a pleasant, drying hbr, but often crowded with fishing boats. The Plateau du Rohein (lt), at W end of a long ridge, is 6M W of C. d'Erquy. There are several rky shoals within the B itself, some extending nearly 2M offshore.

To seaward of Bay de St Brieuc is Grand Léjon (lt), a rky shoal 9M NE of St Quay-Portrieux. Rks extend 2½ca W and 8ca NNE of the lt ho. Petit Léjon (dries) lies 3·5M SSE of lt ho. From the N/NW, keep W of these dangers via a chan 3-4M wide which gives access to the shallow, partly drying S end of the Bay and the hbrs of Val André, Dahouet (10.15.19), Le Légué/St Brieux (10.15.20), and Binic (10.15.21). On the W side of Bay de St Brieuc, Roches de St Quay and offlying patches extend 4M E from St Quay-Portrieux (10.15.22) which can only be approached from NW or SE.

To the N and NE of L'Ost-Pic extensive offshore shoals guard the approaches to Paimpol (10.16.9), Ile de Bréhat and the Trieux river. Further N, the Plateau de Barnouic and Plateau des Roches Douvres (lt, fog sig, RC) should be avoided. Here the E-going stream begins at about HW St Malo – 0400 and the W-going at about HW St Malo +0100 with Sp rates exceeding 4kn.

15

10.15.6 DISTANCE TABLE
Approximate distances in nautical miles are by the most direct route, whilst avoiding dangers and allowing for Traffic Separation Schemes. Places in *italics* are in adjoining areas; places in **bold** are in 10.0.5, Cross-Channel Distances.

	1	2	3	4	5	6	7	8	9	10	11	12	13	14	15	16	17	18	19	20
1. *Calais*	1																			
2. *Barfleur*	148	2																		
3. **Cherbourg**	160	20	3																	
4. Omonville	163	27	10	4																
5. Cap de la Hague	167	32	18	6	5															
6. *Braye (Alderney)*	172	41	25	15	9	6														
7. ***St Peter Port***	193	60	44	34	28	23	7													
8. *Creux (Sark)*	190	55	37	29	23	22	10	8												
9. ***St Helier***	213	77	64	51	45	46	29	24	9											
10. Carteret	192	55	41	29	23	28	31	23	26	10										
11. Portbail	196	59	49	33	27	32	35	27	25	5	11									
12. Iles Chausey	222	87	69	61	55	58	48	43	25	33	30	12								
13. Granville	227	93	75	67	61	66	55	50	30	38	35	9	13							
14. Dinan	250	117	102	91	85	85	66	64	50	62	59	29	35	14						
15. **St Malo**	238	105	90	79	73	73	54	52	38	50	47	17	23	12	15					
16. Dahouet	240	106	88	80	74	72	54	52	41	60	59	37	45	41	29	16				
17. Le Légué/St Brieux	244	110	96	86	78	76	57	56	46	69	69	41	49	45	33	8	17			
18. Binic	244	115	95	84	78	75	56	55	46	70	70	43	51	45	33	10	8	18		
19. **St Quay-Portrieux**	244	106	88	80	74	73	56	51	46	64	64	47	54	47	35	11	7	4	19	
20. *Lézardrieux*	238	106	88	80	74	68	48	38	47	68	71	53	54	61	49	33	32	30	21	20

SPECIAL NOTES FOR FRANCE
(Areas 15 to 19)   10-15-8

Some minor differences in the information for French hbrs are: Instead of 'County' the 'Département' is given. French Standard Time is –0100 (i.e. 1300 Standard Time in France is 1200UT), DST not having been taken into account (see 9·1·2.)
For details of documentation apply to the French Tourist Office, 178 Piccadilly, London, W1V 0AL; ☎ 0171-629 2869, 📠 0171-493 6594, Info 0891 244123.

AFFAIRES MARITIMES
In every French port there is a representative of the central government, L'Administration Maritime, known as Affaires Maritimes. This organisation watches over all maritime activities (commercial, fishing, pleasure) and helps them develop harmoniously. Information on navigation and other maritime issues can be supplied by a local representative whose ☎ is given under each port. The Head Office is: Ministère Chargé de la Mer, Bureau de la Navigation de Plaisance, 3 Place Fontenoy, 75007 Paris, ☎ 01·44·49·80·00.

CHARTS
Two types of French chart are shown: SHOM as issued by the *Service Hydrographique et Oceanographique de la Marine*, the French Navy's Hydrographic Service; ECM *Éditions Cartographiques Maritimes* are charts for sea and river navigation. Notes: Under 'Facilities', SHOM means a chart agent. Any new edition of a SHOM chart receives a new, different chart number. SHOM charts refer elevations of lights, bridges etc to Mean Level (ML), not to MHWS as on Admiralty charts.

TIDAL COEFFICIENTS
See 10.16.24 for Coefficients based on Brest, together with explanatory notes and French tidal terms.

MÉTÉO (Weather)
The BQR (*Bulletin Quotidien des Renseignements*) is a very informative daily bulletin displayed in Hr Mr Offices and YC's. Some weather terms are in the Glossary 1.4.2. For each French port, under **TELEPHONE**, Météo is the ☎ of a local Met Office. Auto gives the ☎ for recorded Inshore and Coastal forecasts; dial 08.36.68.08.dd (dd is the Département No, shown under each port). To select the Inshore (*rivage*) or Coastal (*côte;* out to 20M offshore) bulletin, say "STOP" as your choice is spoken.
Inshore bulletins are 5 day forecasts, also containing local info on tides, signals, sea temperature, surf conditions, etc. Coastal bulletins (for 5 areas from the Belgian to Spanish borders) contain strong wind/gale warnings, general synopsis, 24hrs forecast and outlook.
For recorded Offshore bulletins for Channel/N. Sea, Atlantic or Mediterranean, Figs 7(7) & (8), dial ☎ 08.36.68.08.08. To select desired offshore area say "STOP" as it is named. Offshore bulletins contain strong wind/gale warnings, the general synopsis and forecast, and the 5 day outlook.

SAFETY AT SEA
CROSS (Centres Régionaux Opérationnel de Surveillance et de Sauvetage) equate to CG MRCCs; a Sous-CROSS is an MRSC. See map at Fig 6(3). CROSS primarily monitors Distress and Safety calls on VHF Ch 16 and 2182 kHz H24. All CROSS stations coordinate SAR operations on VHF Ch's 15, 67, **68** and 73. Geographic cover is as follows:
1.   *CROSS Gris Nez*: Belgian border to Cap d'Antifer.
      ☎ 03.21.87.21.87. Broadcasts Ch 79 (see Calais).
2.   *CROSS Jobourg*: Cap d'Antifer to Mont St Michel.
      ☎ 02.33.52.72.13. Broadcasts Ch 80 (see Cherbourg).
3.   *CROSS Corsen*: Mont St Michel to Pte Penmarc'h.
      ☎ 02.98.89.31.31. Broadcasts Ch 79 (see Brest).
4.   *CROSS Etel*: Pte Penmarc'h to Spanish border.
      ☎ 02.97.55.35.35. Broadcasts Ch 80.
4A.   *Sous-CROSS Soulac*: 46°20'N to Spanish border.
      ☎ 05.56.73.31.31. Broadcasts Ch 79. Soulac, near
      Pte de Grave, is subsidiary to Etel; hrs 0700-2200.
Other CROSS tasks include:
VHF broadcasts of urgent nav & weather info – see Tables 5(5) and 6(2) for times and VHF channels;
Marine and fishery surveillance Ch 13.
Note: CROSS does not accept public correspondence (eg link calls) which is the task of Coast Radio Stations.

CROSS can be contacted by radiotelephone, by ☎, through Coast Radio stations, via the Semaphore system as shown below, or via the National Gendarmerie or Affaires Maritimes.
Call Naval 'Semaphore' (ie Signal) stations on Ch 16 (working Ch 10) or by ☎ as follows:

* Dunkerque	03·28·66·86·18	Ouessant Creach	02·98·48·80·49
Boulogne	03·21·31·32·10	St-Mathieu	02·98·89·01·59
Ault	03·22·60·47·33	Portzic (Ch 8)	02·98·22·90·01
Dieppe	02·35·84·23·82	Toulinguet	02·98·27·90·02
Fecamp	02·35·28·00·91	Cap-de-la-Chevre	02·98·27·09·55
* La Heve	02·35·46·07·81	* Pointe-du-Raz	02·98·70·66·57
Le Havre (Ch 12)	02·35·21·74·39	* Penmarch	02·98·58·61·00
Villerville	02·31·88·11·13	Beg Meil	02·98·94·98·92
* Port-en-Bessin	02·31·21·81·51	Port-Louis	02·97·82·52·10
St-Vaast	02·33·54·44·50	Etel	02·97·55·35·59
* Barfleur	02·33·54·04·37	Beg Melen (Groix)	02·97·86·80·13
Levy	02·33·54·31·17	Taillefer (Belle-Ile)	02·97·31·83·18
Le Homet	02·33·92·60·08	Talut (Belle-Ile)	02·97·31·85·07
La Hague	02·33·52·71·07	St-Julien	02·97·50·09·35
Carteret	02·33·53·85·08	Piriac-sur-Mer	02·40·23·59·87
Le Roc	02·33·50·05·85	* Chemoulin	02·40·91·99·00
Le Grouin	02·99·89·60·12	St-Sauveur (Yeu)	02·51·58·31·01
St-Cast	02·96·41·85·30	Les Baleines (Ré)	05·46·29·42·06
* StQuay-Portrieux	02·96·70·42·18	Chassiron(Oléron)	05·46·47·85·43
Brehat	02·96·20·00·12	* La Coubre	05·46·22·41·73
* Ploumanach	02·96·91·46·51	Pointe-de-Grave	05·56·09·60·03
Batz	02·98·61·76·06	Cap Ferret	05·56·60·60·03
* Brignogan	02·98·83·50·84	* Socoa	05·59·47·18·54
Ouessant Stiff	02·98·48·81·50		

* H24. Remainder sunrise to sunset.

Although the lifeboat service SNSM (Société Nationale de Sauvetage en Mer) comes under CROSS, it is best to contact local lifeboat stns direct, ☎ as listed under SNSM. Notes: There are strict penalties for infringing the IRPCS. Speed under power is limited in France to 5kn, when within 300m of the shore.

MEDICAL
Doctors and/or hospital ☎ are given for each port. Also, the Services d'Aide Médicale Urgente (SAMU), which liaises closely with CROSS, can be contacted as follows:

NORD (Lille)	03.20·54·22·22
PAS-DE-CALAIS (Arras)	03.21·71·51·51
SOMME (Amiens)	03.22·44·33·33
SEINE-MARITIME (Le Havre)	02.35·47·15·15
CALVADOS (Caen)	02.31·44·88·88
CÔTES D'ARMOR (Saint Brieuc)	02.96·94·28·95
FINISTERE (Brest)	02.98·46·11·33
MORBIHAN (Vannes)	02.97·54·22·11
LOIRE-ATLANTIQUE (Nantes)	02.40·08·37·77
VENDEE (La Roche-sur-Yon)	02.51·44·62·15
CHARENTE-MARITIME (La Rochelle)	05.46·27·32·15
GIRONDE (Bordeaux)	05.56·96·70·70
LANDES (Mont-de-Marsan)	05.58·75·44·44
PYRÉNÉES-ATLANTIQUE (Bayonne)	05.59·63·33·33

PUBLIC HOLIDAYS
New Year's Day, Easter Sunday and Monday, Labour Day (1 May), Ascension Day, Armistice Day 1945 (8 May), Whit Sunday and Monday, National (Bastille) Day (14 July), Feast of the Assumption (15 Aug), All Saints' Day (1 Nov), Remembrance Day (11 Nov), Christmas Day.

FRENCH GLOSSARY: see 1.4.2.

FACILITIES.
At some marinas fuel can only be obtained/paid for by using a French credit card (of the smart variety) in a slot machine. If not in possession of such a card, it may be possible to persuade a Frenchman to use his card on your behalf and to reimburse him in cash.
The cost shown for a visitor's overnight berth is unavoidably the previous year's figure (as in similar publications). It is based on high season rates and is calculated on LOA, although beam may be taken into account at some ports. Low season rates and concessions can much reduce costs. The fee usually includes electricity, but rarely showers which average around FF10-12.

TELEPHONES

☎ Nos contain 10 digits, the first 2 digits being Zone codes (01 to 05), as appropriate to location. The two digit prefix for each port is shown after the sub-heading **TELEPHONE**. Mobile ☎ Nos are prefixed 06. Info Nos, eg the recorded weather (Auto) are prefixed 08. The ringing tone is long, equal on/off tones (slower than UK engaged tone). Rapid pips mean the call is being connected. Engaged tone is like that in UK. A recorded message means ☎ No unobtainable. To telephone France from UK, dial 00 33, followed by the 9 digit number, ie omitting the 0 from the Zone code prefix. To telephone UK from France dial 00 44 followed by the Area Code (omitting the first 0) and the number.
Emergencies: Dial 18 for Fire, 17 Police, 15 Ambulance; or 112 as used in all EC countries.
Phonecards for public 'phones may be bought at the PTT or at many cafés and tabacs. Cheap rates are 2130-0800 Mon-Sat; all day Sun.

SIGNALS

Standard sets of Traffic, Storm Warning and Tidal signals apply in all French ports unless otherwise stated.

Traffic Signals

Day		Night	
Full Code	Simplified Code	Full Code	Simplified Code
● ▲ ●	or **R** Flag	Ⓡ Ⓦ Ⓡ	or Ⓡ	NO ENTRY
▼ ▲ ●	**R** Flag or over **G** Flag	Ⓖ Ⓦ Ⓡ	or Ⓖ Ⓡ	NO ENT/DEP
▼ ▲ ▼	or **G** Flag	Ⓖ Ⓦ Ⓖ	or Ⓖ	NO DEP
● ● ●	**R** **R** Balls **R**	Ⓡ Ⓡ Ⓡ		EMERGENCY NO ENTRY
INTERNATIONAL CODE SIGNAL		Ⓖ Ⓖ Ⓖ		PORT OPEN

A Black Flag indicates a shipping casualty in the area. Flag 'P' sometimes indicates that lock or dock gates are open.

Storm Signals (International System)

Day	Night	
▲	Ⓡ Ⓡ	N.W. gale
▲	Ⓡ Ⓦ	N.E. gale
▼	Ⓦ Ⓦ	S.W. gale
▼	Ⓦ Ⓡ	S.E. gale
●	Ⓦ Ⓖ	Strong wind (force 6-7)
✚	Ⓡ Ⓖ Ⓡ	Hurricane (force 12) any direction
▬ }	colour of flags is variable	Wind veering
▬ }		Wind backing

In France, Ⓦ Lts, Q or IQ, by day only, indicate forecast wind >F6, as follows: Q = within 3 hrs; IQ = within 6 hrs.

Tidal Signals

There are two sets of signals, one showing the state of the tide and the other showing the height of tide.

a.   State of the tide is shown by:

	Day		Night
High Water . . .	⊠	W Flag B Cross	Ⓦ Ⓦ
Tide falling . . .	▼		Ⓦ / Ⓦ
Low Water . . .	▷	Bu Flag	Ⓖ Ⓖ
Tide rising . . .	▲		Ⓖ / Ⓦ

b.   The height of tide signals show the height above CD by adding together the values of the various shapes. Day: ▼ = 0·2m; ■ = 1·0m; ● = 5·0m. Night: Ⓖ = 0·2m; Ⓡ = 1·0m; Ⓦ = 5·0m. The three different shapes are shown horizontally, with ▼s to the left of ■s and ●s to the right, viewed from seaward. Lights are disposed similarly.
    The following examples will help to explain:

TOLLS AND QUALIFICATIONS ON INLAND WATERWAYS

Tolls are due on waterways managed by Voies Navigable de France (VNF), ie those E of a line Rouen to Arles; also the Canal Latéral à la Garonne, Canal du Midi and R. Loire. See also 10.15.18 and 10.18.23.
In 1997 licences were available for either one year, 30 days (not necessarily consecutive) or 16 consecutive days. The rates, were based on 5 categories of boat area, ie LOA x Beam (m) = m², as follows in French francs:

	<12m²	12-25m²	25-40m²	40-60m²	>60m²
1 Year	459	663	1327	2144	2654
30 days	265	475	837	1301	1613
16 days	102	204	306	408	510

Licence stickers (*vignettes*) must be visibly displayed stbd side forward; they are obtainable in person or by post from VNF offices at Le Havre, Rouen, Calais and Dunkerque and at larger centres on the canals; or from: Librairie VNF, 18 Quai d'Austerlitz, 75013 Paris; ☎ 01.45.84.85.69.
Detailed brochure from: French National Tourist Office, 178 Piccadilly, London W1V 0AL; ☎ 0171 629 2869, 🖷 0171 493 6594; Info 0891 244123.
or: VNF Head Office, 175 Rue Ludovic Boutleux, BP 820, 62408 Bethune, France. ☎ 03.21.63.24.22; 🖷 03.21.63.24.42.
    Helmsmen of craft <15m LOA and not capable of >20 kph (11kn) must have a Helmsman's Overseas Certificate of Competence or International Certificate of Competence, plus a copy of the French CEVNI rules. For larger, faster craft the requirements are under review.
    Foreign vessels >25m LOA must get permission to navigate or ⚓ in French inland waters and must keep watch on Ch 16 or other nominated frequency.

15

CHERBOURG   10-15-9
Manche 49°39'·00N 01°37'·03W (Marina ent)   Rtg 1-1-2

CHERBOURG *continued*

CHARTS
AC 2602, *1106, 2669*; SHOM 7086, 7092, 6737; ECM 528, 1014; Imray C32, C33A; Stanfords 7, 16
TIDES
−0308 Dover; ML 3·8; Duration 0535; Zone −0100

Cherbourg is a Standard Port and tidal predictions for every day of the year are given below.

SHELTER
Excellent; hbr accessible in all tides and weather. Visitors berth on pontoons M, N, P & Q, on S side of Chantereyne Marina. There is also a small craft ⚓ N of marina bkwtr. Lock into Bassin à Flot (HW±1) is normally for commercial vessels only.
NAVIGATION
WPT **Passe de l'Ouest** 49°41'·10N 01°39'·80W, 321°/141° from/to W ent, 0·85M. Note: CH1 SWM spar buoy, L Fl 10s, bears 323° from Fort de l'Ouest 3·5M.
WPT **Passe de l'Est** 49°41'·00N 01°35'·70W, 000°/180° from/to E ent, 0·65M. For coastal features from Cap de la Hague to Pte de Barfleur see 10·15·5.
There are 3 ents:
(1) Passe de l'Ouest (W ent) is the easiest. Rks extend about 80m from each bkwtr. From W, the white sector of Fort de l'Ouest lt (bearing more than 122° by day) keeps clear of offlying dangers E of Cap de la Hague.
(2) Passe de l'Est (E ent) carries 6m. Keep to W side of chan (but at least 80m off Fort de l'Est) to avoid dangers W of Ile Pelée marked by PHM buoy, Fl (4) R 15s, and by 2 unlit bn trs on N side which must be given a wide berth.
(3) Passe Collignon is a shallow (2m) chan, 93m wide, through Digue de l'Est (covers), near the shore. Not recommended except in good conditions and near HW.
LIGHTS AND MARKS
There are 3 powerful lts near Cherbourg:
(1) To the E, Cap Levi, Fl R 5s 36m 22M; and further E,
(2) Pte de Barfleur, Fl (2) 10s 72m 29M;
(3) To the W, Cap de la Hague, Fl 5s 48m 23M;
Further W, the lts of Alderney (Quenard Pt, Fl (4) 15s 37m 28M) and Casquets, Fl (5) 30s 37m 24M, can often be seen. See 10.14.4, 10.15.4 and 10.19.4 for details.
Fort de l'Ouest lt, at W end of Digue Centrale, Fl (3) WR 15s 19m 24/20M, vis W122°-355°, R355°-122°, RC, Reed (3) 60s. Close SSW is PHM buoy, Fl R 4s, marking shoal.
Passe de l'Ouest ldg lts 140·5°: Gare Maritime lt, Dir Q 35m 21M, in line with centre of 2Q (hor) 5m 15M at base of Digue du Homet. Grande Rade ldg lts 124°: Front FG 10m 9M, W pylon, G top, on blockhouse; rear, 0·75M from front, Iso G 4s 16m 12M, W column, B bands, W top, intens 114°-134°.
Passe de l'Est is covered by W sector (176°-183°) of Dir lt, Q WRG 13m 12/10M, at Fort des Flamands.
Inside Petite Rade steer 200° for marina ent, QR and Oc (2) G 6s. Shore lights may be confusing and mask nav lts.
RADIO TELEPHONE
Marina: call *Chantereyne* Ch 09 (0800-2300LT).
Cherbourg commercial port: call *Le Homet* Ch 12 16.
Jobourg Traffic Ch **13** 16 (H24) provides radar surveillance of the Casquets TSS/ITZ (see Fig 10 (4) and 10.15.2) and from Mont St Michel to Cap d'Antifer. Radar assistance is available on request, Ch 80, to vessels in the sector from due W to due N, out to 35M, from Jobourg Centre at 49°41'N 01°54'·5W. Jobourg also broadcasts traffic, nav and weather info in English and French on Ch 80 at H+20 & H+50; and at H+05 & H+35, when visibility < 2M.
TELEPHONE (Prefix ☎ nos with zone code 02)
Hr Mr (Port) 33·44·00·13; Hr Mr (Marina) 33·87·65·70; Aff Mar 33·23·36·12; CROSS 33·52·72·13; ⌗ 33·44·16·00; Météo 33·53·53·44; Auto 08.36.68.08.50; Police 33·44·20·22; ⊞ 33·52·61·45; Dr 33·53·05·68; Brit Consul 01·33·44·20·13.
FACILITIES
Port de Plaisance ☎ 33.87.65.70, 🛥 33.53.21.12, access H24, (900+300 visitors), FF100, Slip, AC, FW, ME, El, Sh, BH (30 ton), CH, P & D (0800-1200; 1400-1900);
YC de Cherbourg ☎ 33·53·02·83, FW, R, Bar;
Services: ME, El, Ⓔ, Sh, CH, M, SM, SHOM.
City P, D, Gaz, V, R, Bar, ✉, ⊙, Ⓑ, ⇌, ✈ (☎ 33.22.91.32).
Ferry: Portsmouth, Southampton, Poole; Weymouth (summer only).

MINOR HARBOURS TO THE EAST OF CHERBOURG

PORT DU BECQUET, Manche, 49°39'·30N 01°32'·80W. AC *1106*; SHOM 7092. Tides as 10·15·9. Shelter is good except in winds from N to E when a strong scend occurs. Secure to S of jetty (which lies E/W). Ldg lts 186·5°: Front Dir Oc (2+1) 12s 8m 10M, W 8-sided tr, intens 183·5°-190·5°; rear, 48m from front, Dir Oc (2+1) R 12s 13m 7M, synch, also in W 8-sided tr. Facilities: very few; all facilities at Cherbourg 2·5M.

PORT DE LÉVI, Manche, 49°41'·30 N 01°28'·30W. AC *1106*; SHOM 7092, 5609; HW −0310 on Dover (UT); +0024 on Cherbourg. HW ht +0·2m on Cherbourg. Shelter good except in winds SW to N. Secure on NE side below white wall. Lt is F RG 7m 7M, G050°-109°, R109°-140°. Keep in G sector. By day keep the white wall and lt between the white marks on each pier hd. Beware lobster pots. Facilities: None. Fermanville (1·5M) has V, R, Bar.

FOR CONTINUATION EASTWARD, SEE AREA 19

Plus ça change ...

There are few things in this world that produce a greater sense of satisfaction than to sail your own boat across the sea and into a foreign port. She may be only ten tons, but you have most of the rights – as well as the responsibilities – inherent in captaining the largest ship afloat, including (bureaucracy be praised!) the right to take tobacco and liquor 'out of bond', in other words free of Customs Duty. To visit Monsieur Henri Ryst's ship-chandling office and see hard liquor, like Scotch and gin, listed at less than a quarter of the price ashore, cognac at a third, cigarettes at a fifth – it is enough to raise the morale of even the tiredest Scotsman; and then to have Monsieur Ryst apologise for not delivering until five p.m. – because he has to victual the Queen Mary! And finally the moment when all those beautiful bottles are collected in the dinghy and taken back to the ship to be stored lovingly away against the day they will be drunk, the crew all lending a willing hand amongst a litter of paper and straw.

It is for this that one puts in to Cherbourg ...... Why else, when close-by are such attractive little ports as Omonville-la-Rogue?

Harvest of Journeys: Hammond Innes/William Collins Sons & Co Ltd, 1960.

15

AGENTS WANTED

If you are interested in becoming our agent for any of the following ports, please write to: The Editor, Edington House, Trent, Sherborne, Dorset DT9 4SR, England – and get your free copy of the Almanac annually. You do not have to live in a port to be the agent, but at least a fairly regular visitor.

Great Yarmouth	St Gilles-Croix-de-Vie
Port Ellen (Islay)	Les Sables d'Olonne
Maryport	Ile d'Oléron
Workington	River Seudre
Holyhead	Anglet/Bayonne
Lough Swilly	St Jean-de-Luz
St Peter Port, Guernsey	Hendaye
Diélette	Grandcamp-Maisy
Portbail	Port-en-Bessin
Iles Chausey	Courseulles
St Malo/Dinard	Ouistreham/Caen
Le Legue/St Brieuc	Emden
Tréguier	Dornumer-Accumersiel
Lampaul	Langeoog
L'Aberildut	Bremerhaven
Le Palais (Belle Ile)	Büsum
Morbihan/Vannes	

<table>
<tr><td>

TIME ZONE –0100
(French Standard Time)
Subtract 1 hour for UT

For French Summer Time add
ONE hour in non-shaded areas

</td><td>

FRANCE – CHERBOURG

LAT 49°39′N   LONG   1°38′W

TIMES AND HEIGHTS OF HIGH AND LOW WATERS

YEAR **1998**

</td></tr>
</table>

JANUARY

Time	m	Time	m
1 0454 1.2 / 1026 6.5 / TH 1718 1.0 / 2253 6.3		**16** 0527 1.5 / 1056 6.2 / F 1747 1.4 / 2321 5.9	
2 0537 1.3 / 1110 6.4 / F 1802 1.1 / 2338 6.1		**17** 0600 1.7 / 1129 6.0 / SA 1820 1.6 / 2353 5.7	
3 0622 1.5 / 1155 6.2 / SA 1847 1.2		**18** 0633 1.8 / 1201 5.7 / SU 1852 1.9	
4 0024 5.9 / 0710 1.7 / SU 1243 6.0 / 1936 1.5		**19** 0026 5.4 / 0708 2.2 / M 1235 5.4 / 1928 2.1	
5 0115 5.7 / 0804 1.9 / M 1337 5.7 / 2032 1.8		**20** 0103 5.2 / 0748 2.4 / TU 1315 5.1 / 2010 2.4	
6 0214 5.5 / 0907 2.2 / TU 1442 5.5 / 2137 2.0		**21** 0151 5.0 / 0838 2.7 / W 1408 4.9 / 2106 2.6	
7 0325 5.3 / 1019 2.4 / W 1557 5.4 / 2251 2.1		**22** 0254 4.8 / 0944 2.8 / TH 1519 4.7 / 2220 2.7	
8 0441 5.4 / 1136 2.2 / TH 1713 5.4		**23** 0413 4.9 / 1103 2.7 / F 1643 4.8 / 2338 2.6	
9 0005 2.0 / 0549 5.6 / F 1245 1.9 / 1820 5.6		**24** 0527 5.1 / 1215 2.4 / SA 1756 5.1	
10 0110 1.9 / 0649 5.8 / SA 1344 1.7 / 1919 5.8		**25** 0044 2.3 / 0627 5.4 / SU 1315 2.1 / 1854 5.4	
11 0205 1.7 / 0742 6.0 / SU 1435 1.4 / 2011 6.0		**26** 0139 1.9 / 0717 5.8 / M 1406 1.6 / 1944 5.8	
12 0254 1.5 / 0828 6.2 / M 1521 1.3 / O 2056 6.1		**27** 0228 1.6 / 0804 6.1 / TU 1453 1.3 / 2030 6.1	
13 0337 1.4 / 0909 6.3 / TU 1601 1.2 / 2135 6.2		**28** 0314 1.3 / 0849 6.4 / W 1539 0.9 / ● 2115 6.3	
14 0416 1.4 / 0946 6.3 / W 1639 1.2 / 2212 6.1		**29** 0359 1.0 / 0933 6.6 / TH 1623 0.7 / 2159 6.5	
15 0452 1.4 / 1022 6.3 / TH 1714 1.2 / 2247 6.1		**30** 0443 0.9 / 1017 6.7 / F 1707 0.6 / 2243 6.5	
		31 0527 0.9 / 1101 6.7 / SA 1750 0.6 / 2326 6.4	

FEBRUARY

Time	m	Time	m
1 0611 1.0 / 1144 6.5 / SU 1833 0.8		**16** 0604 1.6 / 1131 5.9 / M 1821 1.6 / 2351 5.7	
2 0009 6.2 / 0655 1.3 / M 1228 6.3 / 1918 1.2		**17** 0635 1.8 / 1200 5.6 / TU 1851 1.9	
3 0053 5.9 / 0744 1.6 / TU 1315 5.9 / 2008 1.6		**18** 0021 5.4 / 0708 2.1 / W 1233 5.3 / 1926 2.2	
4 0143 5.6 / 0839 2.0 / W 1412 5.5 / 2106 2.0		**19** 0058 5.2 / 0722 2.4 / TH 1315 5.0 / 2011 2.5	
5 0247 5.3 / 0948 2.3 / TH 1526 5.2 / 2220 2.3		**20** 0149 4.9 / 0844 2.6 / F 1417 4.7 / 2116 2.7	
6 0408 5.1 / 1110 2.4 / F 1652 5.1 / 2344 2.4		**21** 0305 4.7 / 1002 2.7 / SA 1547 4.6 / 2244 2.7	
7 0529 5.2 / 1228 2.2 / SA 1809 5.3		**22** 0438 4.8 / 1130 2.5 / SU 1721 4.9	
8 0057 2.2 / 0637 5.5 / SU 1333 1.9 / 1912 5.5		**23** 0007 2.5 / 0555 5.2 / M 1243 2.1 / 1829 5.3	
9 0155 1.9 / 0731 5.8 / M 1425 1.6 / 2002 5.8		**24** 0112 2.0 / 0653 5.6 / TU 1341 1.6 / 1923 5.7	
10 0243 1.7 / 0816 6.0 / TU 1508 1.4 / 2043 6.0		**25** 0207 1.6 / 0744 6.1 / W 1433 1.2 / 2012 6.1	
11 0324 1.5 / 0855 6.2 / W 1546 1.2 / 2119 6.1		**26** 0256 1.2 / 0832 6.4 / TH 1520 0.8 / ● 2059 6.4	
12 0400 1.4 / 0930 6.3 / TH 1621 1.1 / 2153 6.1		**27** 0343 0.8 / 0918 6.7 / F 1606 0.5 / 2144 6.7	
13 0434 1.3 / 1003 6.3 / F 1653 1.1 / 2224 6.1		**28** 0428 0.6 / 1003 6.9 / SA 1650 0.3 / 2228 6.7	
14 0505 1.3 / 1034 6.2 / SA 1723 1.2 / 2254 6.0			
15 0535 1.4 / 1103 6.1 / SU 1752 1.4 / 2323 5.9			

MARCH

Time	m	Time	m
1 0511 0.6 / 1047 6.9 / SU 1733 0.4 / 2310 6.6		**16** 0509 1.3 / 1037 6.1 / M 1724 1.3 / 2253 6.0	
2 0554 0.7 / 1129 6.7 / M 1815 0.7 / 2350 6.4		**17** 0537 1.4 / 1104 6.0 / TU 1752 1.5 / 2321 5.8	
3 0637 1.0 / 1211 6.4 / TU 1858 1.1		**18** 0606 1.6 / 1133 5.7 / W 1821 1.7 / 2349 5.6	
4 0030 6.1 / 0722 1.4 / W 1254 5.9 / 1943 1.6		**19** 0638 1.8 / 1204 5.5 / TH 1854 2.0	
5 0115 5.6 / 0813 1.9 / TH 1345 5.4 / 2038 2.2		**20** 0022 5.3 / 0716 2.1 / F 1242 5.1 / 1936 2.4	
6 0212 5.1 / 0918 2.3 / F 1458 5.0 / 2151 2.6		**21** 0106 5.0 / 0807 2.5 / SA 1337 4.8 / 2035 2.6	
7 0335 4.9 / 1044 2.5 / SA 1633 4.9 / 2323 2.6		**22** 0214 4.8 / 0918 2.6 / SU 1504 4.6 / 2201 2.8	
8 0507 5.0 / 1210 2.3 / SU 1758 5.0		**23** 0353 4.8 / 1049 2.5 / M 1647 4.8 / 2333 2.5	
9 0042 2.4 / 0621 5.1 / M 1317 2.0 / 1859 5.3		**24** 0521 5.1 / 1210 2.1 / TU 1802 5.2	
10 0141 2.1 / 0718 5.6 / TU 1408 1.7 / 1945 5.7		**25** 0045 2.1 / 0626 5.5 / W 1314 1.6 / 1859 5.7	
11 0227 1.8 / 0758 5.9 / W 1450 1.5 / 2023 5.9		**26** 0143 1.6 / 0720 6.0 / TH 1408 1.1 / 1950 6.2	
12 0306 1.5 / 0835 6.1 / TH 1526 1.3 / 2058 6.0		**27** 0235 1.1 / 0811 6.4 / F 1458 0.7 / 2038 6.5	
13 0340 1.4 / 0909 6.2 / F 1558 1.2 / O 2129 6.1		**28** 0323 0.7 / 0859 6.8 / SA 1545 0.4 / ● 2124 6.7	
14 0411 1.3 / 0940 6.2 / SA 1628 1.1 / 2159 6.1		**29** 0409 0.5 / 0945 6.9 / SU 1630 0.3 / 2208 6.8	
15 0441 1.2 / 1010 6.2 / SU 1657 1.2 / 2227 6.1		**30** 0453 0.4 / 1029 6.9 / M 1712 0.4 / 2249 6.7	
		31 0535 0.6 / 1111 6.7 / TU 1754 0.7 / 2329 6.5	

APRIL

Time	m	Time	m
1 0618 0.9 / 1152 6.3 / W 1836 1.2		**16** 0544 1.5 / 1113 5.8 / TH 1757 1.7 / 2328 5.7	
2 0008 6.1 / 0701 1.3 / TH 1234 5.9 / 1921 1.7		**17** 0617 1.6 / 1147 5.5 / F 1831 1.9	
3 0050 5.6 / 0750 1.8 / F 1324 5.3 / 2013 2.3		**18** 0002 5.5 / 0656 1.9 / SA 1227 5.2 / 1915 2.3	
4 0144 5.2 / 0851 2.3 / SA 1433 4.9 / 2123 2.7		**19** 0046 5.2 / 0746 2.2 / SU 1321 5.0 / 2013 2.5	
5 0302 4.9 / 1013 2.5 / SU 1608 4.8 / 2254 2.8		**20** 0149 4.9 / 0853 2.4 / M 1439 4.8 / 2134 2.6	
6 0435 4.8 / 1138 2.4 / M 1733 4.9		**21** 0317 4.9 / 1017 2.3 / TU 1615 4.9 / 2302 2.5	
7 0013 2.5 / 0551 5.1 / TU 1246 2.2 / 1832 5.2		**22** 0447 5.1 / 1137 2.0 / W 1732 5.3	
8 0113 2.2 / 0646 5.4 / W 1338 1.9 / 1916 5.5		**23** 0015 2.0 / 0555 5.5 / TH 1244 1.6 / 1831 5.7	
9 0200 1.9 / 0729 5.7 / TH 1420 1.6 / 1954 5.8		**24** 0116 1.6 / 0653 6.0 / F 1341 1.1 / 1924 6.2	
10 0239 1.6 / 0807 5.9 / F 1457 1.4 / 2029 6.0		**25** 0211 1.1 / 0746 6.4 / SA 1433 0.8 / 2013 6.5	
11 0313 1.5 / 0842 6.0 / SA 1530 1.3 / O 2101 6.1		**26** 0301 0.8 / 0836 6.7 / SU 1522 0.5 / ● 2100 6.7	
12 0344 1.3 / 0914 6.1 / SU 1600 1.2 / 2131 6.1		**27** 0348 0.6 / 0924 6.8 / M 1608 0.5 / 2145 6.7	
13 0414 1.3 / 0944 6.1 / M 1629 1.2 / 2159 6.1		**28** 0433 0.5 / 1009 6.8 / TU 1651 0.6 / 2228 6.7	
14 0444 1.3 / 1012 6.1 / TU 1658 1.3 / 2227 6.0		**29** 0516 0.5 / 1053 6.6 / W 1734 0.9 / 2308 6.4	
15 0513 1.3 / 1042 6.0 / W 1727 1.5 / 2256 5.9		**30** 0559 0.9 / 1134 6.2 / TH 1816 1.3 / 2348 6.1	

Chart Datum: 3·33 metres below Lallemand System (Mean Sea Level, Marseilles)

TIME ZONE –0100
(French Standard Time)
Subtract 1 hour for UT
For French Summer Time add ONE hour in non-shaded areas

FRANCE – CHERBOURG

LAT 49°39′N   LONG   1°38′W

TIMES AND HEIGHTS OF HIGH AND LOW WATERS   YEAR 1998

MAY

Day	Time	m		Day	Time	m
1 F	0643	1.3		16 SA	0603	1.5
	1217	5.8			1139	5.6
	1901	1.8			1818	1.9
					2354	5.6
2 SA	0030	5.7		17 SU	0645	1.7
	0729	1.8			1222	5.4
	1305	5.3			1904	2.1
	1951	2.3				
3 SU	0120	5.3		18 M	0040	5.4
	0824	2.2			0735	1.9
	1407	5.0			1314	5.2
	2054	2.6			2002	2.3
4 M	0227	4.9		19 TU	0138	5.2
	0934	2.4			0837	2.1
	1528	4.8			1422	5.0
	2212	2.7			2114	2.4
5 TU	0349	4.8		20 W	0252	5.1
	1051	2.5			0950	2.1
	1647	4.9			1544	5.1
	2327	2.6			2233	2.3
6 W	0503	4.9		21 TH	0413	5.2
	1159	2.3			1106	1.9
	1749	5.1			1700	5.4
					2346	2.0
7 TH	0029	2.4		22 F	0524	5.5
	0602	5.2			1214	1.6
	1255	2.0			1802	5.7
	1837	5.4				
8 F	0120	2.1		23 SA	0049	1.6
	0651	5.4			0625	5.9
	1341	1.8			1314	1.2
	1918	5.6			1857	6.1
9 SA	0203	1.8		24 SU	0146	1.2
	0733	5.6			0722	6.2
	1421	1.6			1409	1.0
	1956	5.8			1949	6.4
10 SU	0241	1.6		25 M ●	0239	1.0
	0812	5.8			0815	6.4
	1457	1.5			1500	0.8
	2031	6.0			2038	6.5
11 M O	0315	1.5		26 TU	0329	0.8
	0847	5.9			0905	6.5
	1530	1.4			1547	0.8
	2103	6.0			2125	6.6
12 TU	0347	1.3		27 W	0415	0.7
	0919	6.0			0952	6.5
	1602	1.4			1632	0.9
	2134	6.1			2208	6.5
13 W	0420	1.3		28 TH	0459	0.8
	0951	6.0			1036	6.3
	1634	1.4			1716	1.1
	2205	6.1			2250	6.4
14 TH	0453	1.3		29 F	0542	1.0
	1024	5.9			1118	6.1
	1706	1.5			1758	1.4
	2238	6.0			2330	6.1
15 F	0527	1.4		30 SA	0625	1.3
	1100	5.8			1201	5.8
	1740	1.6			1841	1.8
	2315	5.8				
				31 SU	0012	5.8
					0708	1.7
					1245	5.4
					1927	2.1

JUNE

Day	Time	m		Day	Time	m
1 M	0057	5.4		16 TU	0034	5.7
	0756	2.0			0726	1.6
	1336	5.1			1306	5.5
	2020	2.4			1952	2.0
2 TU	0151	5.1		17 W	0127	5.5
	0851	2.3			0821	1.7
	1438	4.9			1403	5.3
	2123	2.6			2055	2.2
3 W	0255	4.9		18 TH	0229	5.4
	0956	2.4			0925	1.8
	1547	4.9			1513	5.3
	2232	2.6			2206	2.2
4 TH	0405	4.9		19 F	0342	5.4
	1036	2.4			1036	1.8
	1653	5.0			1626	5.4
	2337	2.5			2318	2.0
5 F	0510	5.0		20 SA	0454	5.5
	1204	2.3			1145	1.7
	1750	5.2			1734	5.6
6 SA	0034	2.3		21 SU	0024	1.7
	0607	5.1			0601	5.7
	1257	2.1			1250	1.5
	1838	5.4			1834	5.9
7 SU	0123	2.0		22 M	0126	1.5
	0656	5.4			0702	5.9
	1342	1.9			1348	1.3
	1921	5.7			1930	6.1
8 M	0206	1.8		23 TU	0221	1.2
	0740	5.6			0759	6.1
	1423	1.7			1442	1.2
	2000	5.8			2021	6.3
9 TU	0245	1.6		24 W	0313	1.0
	0820	5.7			0851	6.2
	1500	1.6			1531	1.1
	2036	6.0			2108 ●	6.4
10 W	0322	1.4		25 TH	0400	0.9
	0857	5.9			0937	6.2
	1537	1.4			1616	1.2
	2112 O	6.1			2152	6.4
11 TH	0359	1.3		26 F	0444	1.0
	0933	5.9			1021	6.2
	1614	1.4			1659	1.3
	2147	6.1			2233	6.3
12 F	0437	1.2		27 SA	0525	1.1
	1010	6.0			1102	6.1
	1651	1.4			1740	1.4
	2225	6.1			2312	6.1
13 SA	0515	1.2		28 SU	0605	1.3
	1050	5.9			1141	5.9
	1730	1.5			1819	1.7
	2305	6.0			2351	5.9
14 SU	0555	1.3		29 M	0644	1.5
	1132	5.8			1220	5.6
	1811	1.7			1859	1.9
	2348	5.9				
15 M	0638	1.4		30 TU	0031	5.6
	1216	5.6			0723	1.8
	1858	1.8			1301	5.4
					1941	2.2

JULY

Day	Time	m		Day	Time	m
1 W	0112	5.3		16 TH	0111	5.8
	0806	2.1			0803	1.5
	1347	5.1			1341	5.6
	2030	2.5			2033	1.9
2 TH	0200	5.1		17 F	0206	5.6
	0857	2.3			0900	1.8
	1442	4.9			1442	5.4
	2129	2.6			2139	2.1
3 F	0259	4.9		18 SA	0314	5.3
	0959	2.5			1008	1.9
	1547	4.9			1556	5.3
	2236	2.6			2253	2.1
4 SA	0408	4.8		19 SU	0431	5.3
	1106	2.5			1122	2.0
	1654	5.0			1711	5.4
	2343	2.5				
5 SU	0517	4.9		20 M	0006	1.9
	1209	2.4			0545	5.5
	1754	5.2			1232	1.9
					1818	5.7
6 M	0041	2.3		21 TU	0111	1.7
	0618	5.1			0651	5.7
	1304	2.2			1335	1.7
	1845	5.4			1917	5.9
7 TU	0131	2.0		22 W	0209	1.4
	0710	5.4			0750	5.9
	1351	1.9			1429	1.5
	1931	5.7			2009	6.1
8 W	0217	1.7		23 TH	0301	1.2
	0755	5.6			0840	6.0
	1434	1.7			1518	1.4
	2012	5.9			2055 ●	6.3
9 TH	0259	1.5		24 F	0346	1.1
	0837	5.8			0925	6.1
	1516	1.5			1602	1.3
	2052 O	6.1			2137	6.3
10 F	0341	1.3		25 SA	0428	1.1
	0917	6.0			1005	6.1
	1557	1.4			1642	1.3
	2132	6.2			2215	6.3
11 SA	0422	1.1		26 SU	0506	1.1
	0958	6.1			1041	6.1
	1638	1.3			1719	1.4
	2213	6.3			2251	6.2
12 SU	0503	1.0		27 M	0542	1.2
	1039	6.1			1117	6.0
	1720	1.3			1754	1.5
	2255	6.3			2326	6.0
13 M	0545	1.0		28 TU	0615	1.4
	1122	6.1			1150	5.8
	1802	1.3			1827	1.8
	2339	6.2			2359	5.8
14 TU	0627	1.1		29 W	0648	1.7
	1205	6.0			1224	5.6
	1847	1.5			1902	2.0
15 W	0023	6.0		30 TH	0033	5.5
	0713	1.3			0723	2.0
	1251	5.8			1258	5.3
	1937	1.7			1941	2.3
				31 F	0110	5.2
					0803	2.3
					1340	5.1
					2028	2.5

AUGUST

Day	Time	m		Day	Time	m
1 SA	0156	4.9		16 SU	0250	5.3
	0854	2.5			0943	2.2
	1435	4.9			1527	5.2
	2130	2.7			2233	2.3
2 SU	0300	4.7		17 M	0414	5.1
	1002	2.7			1105	2.3
	1549	4.8			1653	5.2
	2246	2.7			2353	2.2
3 M	0423	4.7		18 TU	0537	5.2
	1119	2.7			1222	2.2
	1709	4.9			1807	5.5
	2359	2.5				
4 TU	0542	4.9		19 W	0102	1.9
	1227	2.4			0646	5.5
	1812	5.2			1327	2.0
					1908	5.8
5 W	0059	2.2		20 TH	0200	1.6
	0642	5.2			0742	5.8
	1322	2.1			1420	1.7
	1904	5.6			1958	6.0
6 TH	0150	1.8		21 F	0249	1.4
	0732	5.5			0828	6.0
	1411	1.8			1505	1.5
	1950	5.9			2040	6.2
7 F	0237	1.5		22 SA	0331	1.2
	0817	5.9			0908	6.1
	1456	1.5			1545	1.4
	2033	6.2			2118 ●	6.3
8 SA	0321	1.1		23 SU	0408	1.1
	0900	6.1			0943	6.2
	1540	1.2			1620	1.3
	2116 O	6.4			2153	6.3
9 SU	0405	0.9		24 M	0442	1.1
	0943	6.3			1016	6.2
	1623	1.1			1654	1.3
	2159	6.5			2225	6.3
10 M	0447	0.7		25 TU	0514	1.2
	1025	6.4			1047	6.1
	1705	1.0			1725	1.4
	2242	6.6			2256	6.1
11 TU	0529	0.7		26 W	0544	1.4
	1107	6.4			1117	5.9
	1748	1.0			1754	1.6
	2325	6.5			2325	5.9
12 W	0611	0.8		27 TH	0613	1.6
	1149	6.3			1145	5.7
	1831	1.2			1825	1.9
					2354	5.6
13 TH	0008	6.3		28 F	0642	1.9
	0655	1.1			1214	5.5
	1231	6.0			1858	2.1
	1918	1.5				
14 F	0053	6.0		29 SA	0025	5.3
	0742	1.4			0716	2.2
	1317	5.7			1248	5.2
	2010	1.8			1937	2.4
15 SA	0144	5.6		30 SU	0105	5.0
	0836	1.8			0758	2.6
	1413	5.4			1334	4.9
	2114	2.1			2030	2.7
				31 M	0202	4.7
					0859	2.8
					1444	4.7
					2146	2.8

15

Chart Datum: 3·33 metres below Lallemand System (Mean Sea Level, Marseilles)

TIME ZONE –0100
(French Standard Time)
Subtract 1 hour for UT
For French Summer Time add ONE hour in non-shaded areas

FRANCE – CHERBOURG

LAT 49°39′N   LONG 1°38′W

TIMES AND HEIGHTS OF HIGH AND LOW WATERS   YEAR **1998**

SEPTEMBER

Day	Time	m	Day	Time	m
1 TU	0328 / 1026 / 1619 / 2316	4.6 / 2.9 / 4.8 / 2.7	**16** W	0532 / 1213 / 1756	5.1 / 2.4 / 5.3
2 W	0506 / 1151 / 1739	4.8 / 2.7 / 5.1	**17** TH	0051 / 0638 / 1315 / 1902	2.0 / 5.4 / 2.1 / 5.7
3 TH	0027 / 0615 / 1254 / 1837	2.3 / 5.1 / 2.2 / 5.5	**18** F	0145 / 0727 / 1405 / 1940	1.7 / 5.7 / 1.8 / 6.0
4 F	0123 / 0707 / 1347 / 1926	1.9 / 5.6 / 1.8 / 5.9	**19** SA	0230 / 0808 / 1446 / 2019	1.5 / 6.0 / 1.6 / 6.2
5 SA	0212 / 0754 / 1434 / 2011	1.4 / 6.0 / 1.4 / 6.3	**20** SU	0309 / 0844 / 1522 / ●2054	1.3 / 6.2 / 1.4 / 6.3
6 SU	0259 / 0839 / 1520 / O2056	1.0 / 6.3 / 1.1 / 6.6	**21** M	0343 / 0916 / 1555 / 2127	1.2 / 6.2 / 1.4 / 6.3
7 M	0343 / 0922 / 1604 / 2140	0.7 / 6.5 / 0.8 / 6.8	**22** TU	0415 / 1016 / 1626 / 2157	1.2 / 6.2 / 1.4 / 6.3
8 TU	0426 / 1005 / 1646 / 2224	0.5 / 6.7 / 0.7 / 6.8	**23** W	0444 / 1016 / 1655 / 2225	1.3 / 6.2 / 1.4 / 6.2
9 W	0509 / 1047 / 1729 / 2306	0.5 / 6.6 / 0.8 / 6.7	**24** TH	0512 / 1042 / 1724 / 2252	1.4 / 6.0 / 1.6 / 6.0
10 TH	0551 / 1128 / 1812 / 2348	0.7 / 6.5 / 1.0 / 6.5	**25** F	0540 / 1108 / 1752 / 2319	1.6 / 5.9 / 1.8 / 5.7
11 F	0633 / 1209 / 1857	1.0 / 6.2 / 1.4	**26** SA	0608 / 1136 / 1823 / 2349	1.9 / 5.6 / 2.0 / 5.5
12 SA	0032 / 0719 / 1252 / 1947	6.1 / 1.5 / 5.8 / 1.8	**27** SU	0638 / 1207 / 1858	2.2 / 5.4 / 2.3
13 SU	0122 / 0812 / 1345 / 2051	5.6 / 2.1 / 5.4 / 2.2	**28** M	0026 / 0717 / 1249 / 1946	5.1 / 2.5 / 5.1 / 2.6
14 M	0230 / 0922 / 1502 / 2215	5.2 / 2.5 / 5.1 / 2.4	**29** TU	0119 / 0812 / 1353 / 2055	4.8 / 2.8 / 4.8 / 2.8
15 TU	0403 / 1052 / 1637 / 2342	5.0 / 2.6 / 5.1 / 2.3	**30** W	0243 / 0937 / 1529 / 2230	4.6 / 3.0 / 4.7 / 2.7

OCTOBER

Day	Time	m	Day	Time	m
1 TH	0429 / 1114 / 1702 / 2352	4.7 / 2.8 / 5.0 / 2.4	**16** F	0027 / 0614 / 1252 / 1836	2.2 / 5.4 / 2.3 / 5.5
2 F	0545 / 1225 / 1806	5.1 / 2.3 / 5.5	**17** SA	0120 / 0700 / 1340 / 1912	1.9 / 5.7 / 2.0 / 5.8
3 SA	0053 / 0639 / 1320 / 1858	1.9 / 5.6 / 1.8 / 5.9	**18** SU	0203 / 0738 / 1420 / 1951	1.6 / 5.9 / 1.7 / 6.0
4 SU	0145 / 0727 / 1410 / 1946	1.4 / 6.1 / 1.4 / 6.4	**19** M	0240 / 0813 / 1455 / 2026	1.5 / 6.1 / 1.5 / 6.2
5 M	0233 / 0813 / 1456 / O2032	0.9 / 6.5 / 1.0 / 6.7	**20** TU	0314 / 0846 / 1528 / ●2059	1.4 / 6.2 / 1.5 / 6.2
6 TU	0319 / 0858 / 1541 / 2118	0.6 / 6.7 / 0.7 / 6.9	**21** W	0345 / 0916 / 1558 / 2129	1.4 / 6.2 / 1.4 / 6.2
7 W	0403 / 0942 / 1625 / 2202	0.5 / 6.8 / 0.6 / 7.0	**22** TH	0414 / 0944 / 1627 / 2156	1.4 / 6.2 / 1.4 / 6.1
8 TH	0446 / 1024 / 1708 / 2246	0.5 / 6.8 / 0.7 / 6.8	**23** F	0443 / 1011 / 1657 / 2224	1.5 / 6.1 / 1.5 / 6.0
9 F	0529 / 1105 / 1752 / 2329	0.8 / 6.6 / 0.9 / 6.5	**24** SA	0511 / 1038 / 1726 / 2253	1.7 / 6.0 / 1.7 / 5.8
10 SA	0612 / 1146 / 1837	1.2 / 6.3 / 1.3	**25** SU	0540 / 1108 / 1757 / 2326	1.9 / 5.8 / 1.9 / 5.6
11 SU	0013 / 0658 / 1229 / 1926	6.1 / 1.7 / 5.9 / 1.8	**26** M	0612 / 1141 / 1833	2.2 / 5.5 / 2.1
12 M	0103 / 0750 / 1321 / 2028	5.5 / 2.2 / 5.4 / 2.3	**27** TU	0051 / 0651 / 1222 / 1919	5.3 / 2.5 / 5.3 / 2.4
13 TU	0211 / 0900 / 1436 / 2152	5.1 / 2.7 / 5.1 / 2.5	**28** W	0055 / 0744 / 1321 / 2022	5.0 / 2.7 / 5.0 / 2.6
14 W	0345 / 1032 / 1611 / 2319	4.9 / 2.8 / 5.0 / 2.5	**29** TH	0211 / 0901 / 1447 / 2147	4.8 / 2.9 / 4.9 / 2.6
15 TH	0513 / 1152 / 1730	5.0 / 2.6 / 5.1	**30** F	0347 / 1033 / 1619 / 2312	4.8 / 2.8 / 5.0 / 2.3
			31 SA	0507 / 1150 / 1729	5.2 / 2.4 / 5.5

NOVEMBER

Day	Time	m	Day	Time	m
1 SU	0019 / 0606 / 1250 / 1825	1.9 / 5.7 / 1.9 / 5.9	**16** M	0127 / 0702 / 1347 / 1917	1.9 / 5.8 / 1.9 / 5.8
2 M	0115 / 0656 / 1343 / 1917	1.4 / 6.1 / 1.4 / 6.4	**17** TU	0207 / 0740 / 1425 / 1955	1.7 / 6.0 / 1.7 / 5.9
3 TU	0206 / 0745 / 1432 / 2006	1.0 / 6.5 / 1.0 / 6.7	**18** W	0243 / 0815 / 1459 / 2030	1.6 / 6.1 / 1.6 / 6.0
4 W	0254 / 0831 / 1519 / O2054	0.7 / 6.7 / 0.8 / 6.9	**19** TH	0315 / 0847 / 1532 / ●2103	1.5 / 6.2 / 1.5 / 6.1
5 TH	0340 / 0917 / 1605 / 2141	0.6 / 6.9 / 0.7 / 6.9	**20** F	0347 / 0917 / 1603 / 2133	1.5 / 6.2 / 1.5 / 6.1
6 F	0425 / 1001 / 1649 / 2226	0.7 / 6.8 / 0.7 / 6.7	**21** SA	0418 / 0946 / 1635 / 2203	1.6 / 6.2 / 1.5 / 6.0
7 SA	0509 / 1043 / 1734 / 2311	0.9 / 6.6 / 1.0 / 6.4	**22** SU	0449 / 1017 / 1708 / 2237	1.7 / 6.1 / 1.6 / 5.9
8 SU	0553 / 1125 / 1819 / 2356	1.3 / 6.3 / 1.3 / 6.0	**23** M	0522 / 1051 / 1741 / 2313	1.8 / 5.9 / 1.7 / 5.7
9 M	0639 / 1209 / 1907	1.8 / 5.9 / 1.8	**24** TU	0556 / 1128 / 1819 / 2354	2.0 / 5.7 / 1.9 / 5.5
10 TU	0045 / 0730 / 1259 / 2004	5.6 / 2.3 / 5.5 / 2.2	**25** W	0637 / 1210 / 1904	2.3 / 5.5 / 2.1
11 W	0147 / 0833 / 1404 / 2116	5.2 / 2.7 / 5.1 / 2.5	**26** TH	0043 / 0728 / 1304 / 2001	5.2 / 2.5 / 5.3 / 2.3
12 TH	0307 / 0953 / 1526 / 2236	4.9 / 2.8 / 5.0 / 2.6	**27** F	0146 / 0835 / 1414 / 2112	5.1 / 2.6 / 5.1 / 2.4
13 F	0427 / 1111 / 1643 / 2345	5.0 / 2.7 / 5.1 / 2.4	**28** SA	0306 / 0955 / 1535 / 2231	5.0 / 2.6 / 5.2 / 2.2
14 SA	0532 / 1213 / 1745	5.2 / 2.5 / 5.3	**29** SU	0425 / 1112 / 1650 / 2343	5.3 / 2.3 / 5.4 / 1.9
15 SU	0041 / 0621 / 1304 / 1835	2.2 / 5.5 / 2.2 / 5.5	**30** M	0530 / 1219 / 1753	5.6 / 1.9 / 5.8

DECEMBER

Day	Time	m	Day	Time	m
1 TU	0044 / 0627 / 1317 / 1850	1.5 / 6.0 / 1.5 / 6.2	**16** W	0131 / 0706 / 1354 / 1925	2.1 / 5.7 / 2.0 / 5.6
2 W	0140 / 0719 / 1410 / 1944	1.2 / 6.4 / 1.2 / 6.5	**17** TH	0212 / 0745 / 1432 / 2005	1.9 / 5.9 / 1.8 / 5.8
3 TH	0232 / 0809 / 1500 / O2035	1.0 / 6.6 / 0.9 / 6.7	**18** F	0249 / 0821 / 1508 / ●2041	1.7 / 6.0 / 1.6 / 5.9
4 F	0321 / 0856 / 1548 / 2124	0.9 / 6.7 / 0.8 / 6.7	**19** SA	0324 / 0855 / 1543 / 2115	1.6 / 6.1 / 1.5 / 6.0
5 SA	0407 / 0942 / 1634 / 2210	0.9 / 6.7 / 0.8 / 6.6	**20** SU	0359 / 0928 / 1619 / 2149	1.6 / 6.2 / 1.4 / 6.0
6 SU	0453 / 1026 / 1719 / 2255	1.1 / 6.6 / 1.0 / 6.4	**21** M	0434 / 1003 / 1655 / 2226	1.6 / 6.2 / 1.4 / 6.0
7 M	0537 / 1108 / 1803 / 2340	1.4 / 6.4 / 1.3 / 6.0	**22** TU	0510 / 1040 / 1732 / 2305	1.6 / 6.1 / 1.4 / 5.9
8 TU	0621 / 1151 / 1848	1.7 / 6.0 / 1.6	**23** W	0547 / 1120 / 1811 / 2346	1.8 / 6.0 / 1.5 / 5.7
9 W	0026 / 0707 / 1236 / 1935	5.7 / 2.1 / 5.7 / 2.0	**24** TH	0629 / 1202 / 1854	1.9 / 5.8 / 1.7
10 TH	0116 / 0758 / 1328 / 2030	5.3 / 2.5 / 5.3 / 2.4	**25** F	0031 / 0716 / 1250 / 1944	5.5 / 2.1 / 5.6 / 1.9
11 F	0215 / 0859 / 1430 / 2134	5.1 / 2.7 / 5.1 / 2.6	**26** SA	0124 / 0812 / 1346 / 2043	5.4 / 2.3 / 5.4 / 2.0
12 SA	0324 / 1009 / 1540 / 2245	5.0 / 2.8 / 4.9 / 2.6	**27** SU	0227 / 0919 / 1455 / 2151	5.3 / 2.4 / 5.3 / 2.1
13 SU	0432 / 1118 / 1649 / 2349	5.0 / 2.7 / 5.0 / 2.5	**28** M	0341 / 1034 / 1612 / 2306	5.3 / 2.3 / 5.4 / 2.0
14 M	0532 / 1219 / 1750	5.2 / 2.5 / 5.2	**29** TU	0455 / 1148 / 1724	5.5 / 2.1 / 5.6
15 TU	0044 / 0622 / 1310 / 1841	2.3 / 5.4 / 2.2 / 5.4	**30** W	0016 / 0600 / 1254 / 1829	1.8 / 5.8 / 1.7 / 5.9
			31 TH	0119 / 0659 / 1352 / 1928	1.5 / 6.1 / 1.4 / 6.1

Chart Datum: 3·33 metres below Lallemand System (Mean Sea Level, Marseilles)

CHERBOURG

MEAN SPRING
AND NEAP CURVES

MEAN RANGES	
Springs	5.3m
Neaps	2.5m

Springs occur 2 days
after
New and Full Moon.

OMONVILLE-LA-ROGUE 10-15-10

Manche 49°42'.34N 01°49'.78W Rtg 3-4-2

CHARTS
AC *1106, 2669*; SHOM 5636, 6737, 7158; ECM 528, 1014;
Imray C33A; Stanfords 7, 16
TIDES
−0330 Dover; ML 3·6; Duration 0545; Zone −0100

Standard Port CHERBOURG (←)

Times				Height (metres)			
High Water		Low Water		MHWS	MHWN	MLWN	MLWS
0300	1000	0400	1000	6·4	5·0	2·5	1·1
1500	2200	1600	2200				
Differences OMONVILLE							
−0025	−0030	−0022	−0022	−0·3	−0·2	−0·2	−0·1
GOURY							
−0100	−0040	−0105	−0120	+1·7	+1·6	+1·0	+0·3

SHELTER
Good, except in strong winds from N to SE. There are 4
W conical ⚓s or ⚓ S of bkwtr; beware rks off outer end.
NAVIGATION
WPT 49°42'·50N 01°48'·60W, 075°/255° from/to Omonville
lt, 1·0M. Ent is 100m wide, between rks extending N from
Omonville Fort, and running ESE from bkwtr marked by
Le Tunard, G bn tr. From W or N, keep clear of Basse

Bréfort (depth 1m, marked by NCM buoy, VQ) 0·6M N of
Pte de Jardeheu. Appr on 195° transit (below), passing
100m E of Le Tunard and into W sector of lt before
turning stbd 290° for old Custom Ho and moorings. From
E, appr on 255° transit in W sector of lt, until S of Le
Tunard.
To ENE of port is a military firing area; when active, a R
flag is flown from the bkwtr head.
LIGHTS AND MARKS
Omonville lt, Iso WRG 4s 13m 11/8M, on W framework tr
with R top, vis G180°-252°, W252°-262°, R262°-287°. Lt in
transit 255° with ✠ steeple, 650m beyond, leads S of Le
Tunard. From N, Le Tunard leads 195° in transit with fort.
Street lts adequately illuminate the hbr area.
RADIO TELEPHONE
None. For Casquets TSS see Cherbourg (10·15·9).
TELEPHONE (Prefix ☎ nos with zone code 02)
Aff Mar Cherbourg 33·53·21·76; ⌗ Cherbourg 33·53·05·60;
CROSS 33·52·72·13; 33·52·71·33; Météo 33·22·91·77; Auto
08.36.68.08.50; Police 33·52·72·02; Dr 33·53·08·69; Brit
Consul 01·33·44·20·13.
FACILITIES
Jetty M, L, FW, AB, V, R, Bar. **Village** V, Gaz, R, Bar,
nearest fuel (cans) at Beaumont-Hague 5km, ✉, Ⓑ, ⇌
(bus to Cherbourg), ✈. Ferry: See Cherbourg.

15

ADJACENT HARBOUR

PORT RACINE, Manche, 49°42'·78N 01°53'·70W. AC *1106,
3653;* SHOM 5636. Tides as 10.15.10. Port Racine (said to
be the smallest hbr in France) is in the SW corner of Anse
de St. Martin. This bay, 2M E of Cap de la Hague, has ⚓s
sheltered from all but onshore winds. From N, appr with
conspic chy (279m) at atomic stn brg 175°; or from NE via
Basse Bréfort NCM buoy, VQ, on with St Germain des
Vaux spire brg 240°. Both lines clear La Parmentière rks
awash in centre of bay and Les Herbeuses and Le Grun
Rks to W and E respectively. ⚓ or moor off the hbr which
is obstructed by lines; only accessible by dinghy. R is
only facility.

DIÉLETTE   10-15-11

Manche, 49°33'·30'N 01°51'·80'W   Rtg 3-2-2

CHARTS
AC *3653*; SHOM 7133, 7158; ECM 528, 1014; Imray C33A;
Stanfords 16
TIDES
HW −0430 on Dover (UT); ML 5·2m

Standard Port ST-MALO (→)

Times				Height (metres)			
High Water		Low Water		MHWS	MHWN	MLWN	MLWS
0100	0800	0300	0800	12·2	9·2	4·3	1·6
1300	2000	1500	2000				
Differences FLAMANVILLE							
+0050	+0050	+0025	+0045	−2·7	−1·8	−1·1	−0·5

SHELTER
Good in marina, but do not attempt entry in strong W'lies.
Ent dredged to CD, NE part of outer hbr to 2m; access
H24 for 1·5m draft if coeff <80. W side of outer hbr dries
approx 5m (local moorings). Marina (1·5-2·5m) in SE
corner is entered over a sill 4·0m above CD; access about
HW±3 for 1·5m draft, waiting pontoon outside.
NAVIGATION
WPT 49°33'·55N 01°52'·15W, 320°/140° from/to W bkwtr lt,
0·40M. Appr is exposed to W'ly winds/swell. Caution: rky
reef dries close NE of appr; cross tides at hbr ent. Prohib
area from hbr to C de Flamanville extends 5ca offshore.
LIGHTS AND MARKS
Power stn chys (72m) are conspic 1·2M to SW. Dir lt 140°,
Iso WRG 4s 12m 10/7M, W tr/G top at hd of West bkwtr,
vis G070°-135°, W135°-145° (10°), R145°-180°; on same tr is
a lower lt, Fl G 4s 6m 2M. N bkwtr hd, Fl R 4s 8m 5M, W
mast/R top. Spur, close SE at ent to new basin, is Fl (2) R
6s 6m 1M.
RADIO TELEPHONE
VHF Ch 09, 0830-2000LT.
TELEPHONE (Prefix ☎ nos with zone code 02)
Hr Mr 33.53.68.78, ⚓ 33.53.68.79; Aff Mar 33.23.36.13;
Météo 08·36·68·12·34; CROSS 33.52.72.13; ⌗ 33.23.34.00;
SNSM 33.04.93.17; YC ☎ 33·20·14·08.
FACILITIES
Marina (410) FF124, AC, FW, Fuel, Slip, C (10ton); **Village**,
V, Bar, R. Also facilities at Flamanville (1·3M). Ferry to CI.

MINOR HARBOUR CLOSE SOUTH OF CAP DE LA HAGUE

GOURY, Manche, 49°43'·00N 01°56·70'W. AC *1106, 3653*;
SHOM 7133 (essential large scale chart) , 5636, 7158. HW
−0410 on Dover (UT); ML 5·1m. See 10.15.10. For visitors,
appr at slack water nps with no swell and good vis; a fair
wx hbr only, dries to flat sand/mud. Cap de la Hague lt, Fl
5s, is 0·5M NW of hbr; La Foraine WCM buoy is 1·1M to
the W. Ldg lts: Front QR 4m 7M, on bkwtr hd; rear (110m
from front), Q 10m 12M, intens 057°-075°, lead 065°
between Charlin to S and Les Grois to N. By day, W patch
with R ■ at end of bkwtr on with W pylon of rear ldg lt,
065°. ⚓ W of the 2 LB slips in 1·7m or dry out on the NE
side of the bkwtr. Facilities: R, Bar at Auderville (0·5M).

CARTERET   10-15-12

Manche 49°22'·20N 01°47'·38W   Rtg 3-2-2

CHARTS
AC *3655, 2669*; SHOM 7133, 7157, 7158; ECM 1014; Imray
C33A; Stanfords 16
TIDES
−0440 Dover; ML 5·9; Duration 0545; Zone −0100

Standard Port ST-MALO (→)

Times				Height (metres)			
High Water		Low Water		MHWS	MHWN	MLWN	MLWS
0100	0800	0300	0800	12·2	9·2	4·3	1·6
1300	2000	1500	2000				
Differences CARTERET							
+0035	+0025	+0020	+0035	−1·6	−1·1	−0·6	−0·3

SHELTER
Good in non-tidal marina (sill is 4m above CD; lifting gate
retains 2·3m within); access HW−2½ to +3 for 1·5m draft. ⓥ
berths on far side of the most E'ly pontoon (F). If too late
on the tide for the marina, possible waiting berths on W
Jetty (clear of ferry) where a 1·5m draft boat can stay
afloat for 6 hrs np, 9hrs sp. The tiny Port des Américains
and drying basin, close W of marina, have up to 5m at HW.
NAVIGATION
WPT 49°21'·18N 01°47'·50W (off chartlet), 189°/009° from/
to W Jetty lt, 1M. From N/NW, keep well off shore on appr
to avoid rks 1M N of Cap de Carteret extending about 1M
from coast. From W, about 4M off shore, beware Trois
Grune Rks (dry 1·6m) marked by WCM buoy, Q (9) 15s.

Appr dries ½M offshore and is exposed to fresh W/SW
winds which can make ent rough. There are no safe ⚓s off
shore. Best appr at HW−2 to avoid max tidal stream, 4½kn
sp. Bar, at right angles to W Jetty, dries 4m; the chan dries
progressively to firm sand, and is dredged to drying hts of
4m and 4.5m just W of the marina. Best water is toward
the W quays and outside of bend. The E bkwtr and head of
W bkwtr both partly cover at springs. No ⚓ in river.
LIGHTS AND MARKS
Cap de Carteret, Fl (2+1) 15s 81m 26M, grey tr, G top,
Horn (3) 60s, and conspic Sig Stn are 8ca WxN of the ent.
W Jetty, Oc R 4s 6m 8M, W col, R top; E bkwtr, Fl G 2·5s,
W mast G top. These lts in transit lead about 009° to ent.
The bend in the chan is marked by a PHM and SHM bn,
respectively Fl (2) R 6s & Fl (2) G 6s. Marina sill is marked
by a PHM and SHM lt bn, respectively Fl (3) R 12s & Fl (3)
G 12s, plus Y poles.
RADIO TELEPHONE
VHF Ch 16 64. Marina Ch 09.
TELEPHONE (Prefix ☎ nos with zone code 02)
Hr Mr 33.44.00.13; CROSS 33.52.72.13; ⌗ 33.04.90.08;
Météo 33.22.91.77; Auto 08.36.68.08.50; Police 33.53.80.17;
Ⓗ (Valognes) 33·40·14·39; Brit Consul 01·33·44·20·13.
FACILITIES
Port de Plaisance "Le Port des Iles" ☎ 33.04.70.84, ⚓
33040837, (260 + 60 visitors), FF109, AC, FW, CH, Fuel;
West Jetty AB free for 6 hrs, then at 50% of marina rate,
Slip, FW, R, Bar;
Cercle Nautique de Barneville-Carteret ☎ 33.53.88.29,
Slip, M, Bar.
Town ME, P & D (cans), V, Gaz, R, Bar, ✉, Ⓑ (Barneville),
⇌ (Valognes), ✈ (Cherbourg). Ferry: Cherbourg, Jersey.

CARTERET *continued*

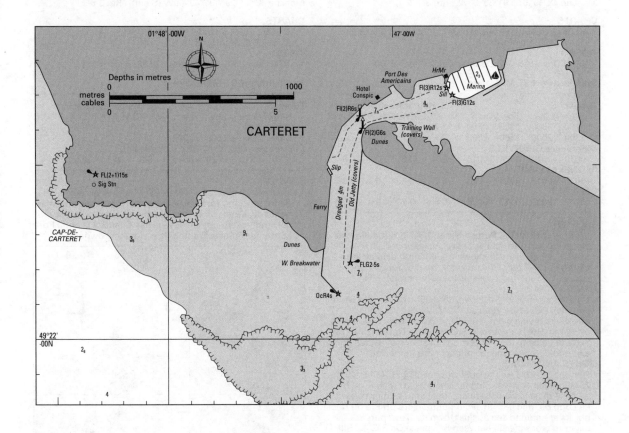

PORTBAIL　　　　　　　　10-15-13

Manche 49°19'·46N 01°42'·85W　Rtg 3-4-2

CHARTS
AC *3655, 2669*; SHOM 7133, 7157; ECM 1014; Imray C33A;
Stanfords 16

TIDES
HW −0440 on Dover (UT); ML 6·3m; Duration 0545

Standard Port ST-MALO (→)

Times				Height (metres)			
High Water		Low Water		MHWS	MHWN	MLWN	MLWS
0100	0800	0300	0800	12·2	9·2	4·3	1·6
1300	2000	1500	2000				
Differences PORTBAIL							
+0035	+0030	+0030	+0035	−0·8	−0·5	−0·3	−0·1
ST GERMAIN-SUR-AY							
+0030	+0030	+0040	+0040	−0·7	−0·4	−0·1	0·0
LE SÉNÉQUET							
+0020	+0020	+0028	+0028	−0·3	−0·2	0·0	0·0

SHELTER
Good. Hbr dries 7·0m, but access HW±½ at np, HW±2½ at
sp for 1m draft. Drying basin to E of jetty: visitors berth on
pontoon parallel with NW side of basin or moor on first
line of buoys parallel to jetty. Portbail is 4M SE of Carteret.

NAVIGATION
WPT 49°18'·30N 01°44'·49W (off chartlet, abeam "PB" SWM
buoy), 222°/042° from/to chan buoys, 1·4M. Beware very
strong tide over bar. Ldg line crosses sand banks (drying
about 8ca offshore) to a pair of unlit PHM/SHM buoys.
Thence via chan dredged 5·2m; on port side a training wall
(covers at HW) is marked by R spar bns, the first Q (2) R 5s.

LIGHTS AND MARKS
A Water Tr (43m) is conspic 6ca NNW of ent. Ldg lts 042°:
Front (La Caillourie) QW 14m 10M, W pylon, R top; rear,
870m from front, Oc 4s 20m 10M (church spire). Training
wall hd, Q (2) R 5s 5m 2M.

RADIO TELEPHONE
VHF Ch 09.

TELEPHONE (Prefix ☎ nos with zone code 02)
Hr Mr ☎ 33·04·83·48 (15 Jun-31 Aug).

FACILITIES
Quay FF50, FW, D, P, AC, C (5 ton); **Cercle Nautique de
Portbail-Denneville** ☎ 33·04·86·15, Bar, R; **YC de Portbail**
☎ 33·04·83·48, AB, C, Slip; **Services:** Sh, ME, El.
Town (½M by causeway) Bar, ⑧, ✉, R, V, ⇌ (Valognes).

GRANVILLE   10-15-14

Manche 48°49'·97N 01°35'·88W   Rtg 3-1-2

CHARTS
AC 3672, 3656, *3659*; SHOM 7341, 7156; ECM 534, 535;
Imray C33B; Stanfords 16

TIDES
−0510 Dover; ML 7·1; Duration 0525; Zone −0100

Standard Port ST-MALO (→)

Times				Height (metres)			
High Water		Low Water		MHWS	MHWN	MLWN	MLWS
0100	0800	0300	0800	12·2	9·2	4·3	1·6
1300	2000	1500	2000				
Differences GRANVILLE							
+0010	+0010	+0025	+0015	+0·7	+0·6	+0·2	−0·1
REGNÉVILLE-SUR-MER							
+0018	+0018	+0028	+0028	−0·2	−0·1	0·0	0·0
CANCALE							
−0002	−0002	+0012	+0006	+0·8	+0·7	+0·3	+0·1

SHELTER
Good in the marina, Port de Hérel, 1·5–2·5m. Caution: at
ent sharp turn restricts visibility. Access over sill HW −2½
to +3½. Depth over sill shown on lit digital display atop S
bkwtr: eg 76=7·6m; 00 = no entry; hard to read in bright
sun. The Avant Port (dries) is for commercial/ FVs.

NAVIGATION
WPT 48°49'·40N 01°37'·00W, 235°/055° from/to S bkwtr lt
(Fl R 4s), 0·95M. Le Videcoq WCM, VQ (9) 10s Whis,
marks rks drying 0·8m, 3¼M W of Pte du Roc. Beware rks
off Pte du Roc, La Fourchie and Banc de Tombelaine, 1M
SSW of Le Loup lt. Appr is rough in strong W winds. Ent/
exit under power; speed limit 4kn, 2kn in marina.

LIGHTS AND MARKS
Hbr ent is 0·6M E of Pte du Roc (conspic), Fl (4) 15s 49m
23M, grey tr, R top. No ldg lts, but S bkwtr lt, Fl R 4s, on
with TV mast leads 055° to ent. Best appr at night is with
Le Loup bearing 085° to avoid pot markers off Pte du Roc;
hbr lts are hard to see against town lts. Turn port at
bkwtr to cross the sill between R/G piles, Oc R/G 4s. Sill
of bathing pool to stbd is marked by 5 R piles, lit Fl Bu 4s.

RADIO TELEPHONE
Port VHF Ch 12 16 (HW±1½). Marina Ch 09, H24 in season.

TELEPHONE (Prefix ☎ nos with zone code 02)
Hr Mr (Hérel) 33·50·20·06; Hr Mr (Port) 33·50·17·75; Aff
Mar 33·50·00·59; CROSS 33·52·72·13; SNSM 33·61·26·51;
⌗ 33·50·19·90; Météo 33·22·91·77; Auto 08.36.68.08.50;

Police 33·50·01·00; Dr 33·50·00·07; Hosp 33·90·74·75;
Brit Consul 01·33·44·20·13.

FACILITIES
Hérel Marina (850+150 visitors) ☎ 33·50·20·06, FF115,
Slip, P, D, FW, ME, AC, BH (12 ton), C (10 ton), CH, Gaz, R,
▣, V, Bar, SM, El, Sh; **YC de Granville** ☎ 33·50·04·25, L, M,
BH, D, P, CH, ▣, Slip FW, AB, Bar;
Services: CH, M, ME, El, Ⓔ, Sh, SHOM, SM.
Town P, D, ME, V, Gaz, R, Bar, ✉, Ⓑ, ⇌, ✈ (Dinard).
Ferry: UK via Jersey or Cherbourg.

ILES CHAUSEY   10-15-15

Manche 48°52'·20N 01°49'·00W (S ent)   Rtg 3-5-1

CHARTS
AC 3656, *3659*; SHOM 7134, 7156, 7155; ECM 534, 535;
Imray C33B; Stanfords 16

TIDES
−0500 Dover; ML 7·4; Duration 0530; Zone −0100

Standard Port ST-MALO (→)

Times				Height (metres)			
High Water		Low Water		MHWS	MHWN	MLWN	MLWS
0100	0800	0300	0800	12·2	9·2	4·3	1·6
1300	2000	1500	2000				
Differences ILES CHAUSEY (Grande Ile)							
+0010	+0010	+0020	+0015	+0·8	+0·7	+0·5	+0·4

SHELTER
Good except in strong NW or SE winds. W ⚓s available
free for mooring fore-and-aft. Hbr very crowded summer
weekends. When ⚓ing, note the big tidal range, although
tidal streams are not excessive. Iles Chausey is not a Port
of Entry for France. Grande Ile is privately owned.

NAVIGATION
WPT 48°51'·50N 01°48'·48W, 152°/332° from/to La Crabière
lt, 1·2M. The easier route into the Sound is from the S,
but beware rks E and S of Pte de la Tour (conspic). The
route from N requires sufficient ht of tide; SHOM 7134 or
detailed SDs for transits, and local knowledge is advised.
Dangerous wk reported N of La Petite Entrée (off chartlet).

LIGHTS AND MARKS
Pte de la Tour, Fl 5s 39m 23M, Horn 30s. La Crabière, Oc
WRG 4s 5m 9/6M, B tr, Y top; sectors see 10.15.4. From N,
L'Enseigne bn tr (19m) on with Pte de la Tour lt ho leads
156°. From S, La Crabière on with L'Enseigne leads 332°.

RADIO TELEPHONE
None.

TELEPHONE (Prefix ☎ nos with zone code 02)
Police 33·52·72·02; CROSS 33·52·72·13; Auto 08.36.68.08.50.

FACILITIES
R. Tourelle L. **Village** FW, Gaz, V (limited), R, Bar. See
also Granville. Ferry to UK via Granville and Jersey.

TIME ZONE –0100
(French Standard Time)
Subtract 1 hour for UT

For French Summer Time add
ONE hour in non-shaded areas

FRANCE – ST. MALO

LAT 48°38′N   LONG   2°02′W

TIMES AND HEIGHTS OF HIGH AND LOW WATERS

YEAR 1998

JANUARY

	Time	m		Time	m
1 TH	0313 0836 1540 2101	1.9 12.2 1.7 11.9	**16** F	0344 0905 1606 2128	2.2 11.7 2.4 11.3
2 F	0355 0919 1623 2145	1.9 12.1 1.8 11.8	**17** SA	0415 0936 1634 2158	2.6 11.4 2.8 10.9
3 SA	0437 1004 1706 2231	2.2 11.8 2.0 11.4	**18** SU	0443 1006 1701 2229	3.0 10.9 3.3 10.4
4 SU	0520 1051 1751 2320	2.6 11.3 2.5 10.8	**19** M	0511 1038 1730 2303	3.5 10.3 3.8 9.9
5 M	0609 1145 1841	3.1 10.7 3.0	**20** TU	0545 1116 1808 2347	4.0 9.7 4.2 9.3
6 TU	0016 0706 1248 1942	10.3 3.5 10.2 3.4	**21** W	0632 1207 1901	4.5 9.2 4.7
7 W	0123 0819 1404 2057	9.9 3.8 10.0 3.6	**22** TH	0051 0735 1324 2013	8.9 4.9 8.8 4.9
8 TH	0241 0942 1522 2217	9.9 3.7 10.1 3.5	**23** F	0219 0855 1454 2136	8.8 4.9 8.8 4.7
9 F	0356 1058 1631 2326	10.2 3.4 10.4 3.1	**24** SA	0339 1013 1607 2247	9.2 4.5 9.3 4.2
10 SA	0500 1201 1730	10.7 2.9 10.8	**25** SU	0440 1118 1704 2346	9.8 3.8 10.0 3.5
11 SU	0024 0553 1255 1820	2.7 11.2 2.5 11.2	**26** M	0530 1215 1753	10.6 3.1 10.7
12 M ○	0114 0639 1341 1905	2.4 11.6 2.2 11.5	**27** TU	0041 0616 1309 1840	2.8 11.3 2.4 11.4
13 TU	0157 0720 1423 1945	2.2 11.8 2.0 11.6	**28** W ●	0133 0701 1401 1926	2.2 12.0 1.8 12.0
14 W	0235 0757 1500 2021	2.1 11.9 2.0 11.7	**29** TH	0222 0745 1449 2010	1.7 12.5 1.3 12.4
15 TH	0311 0832 1535 2056	2.1 11.9 2.1 11.6	**30** F	0309 0829 1535 2054	1.3 12.8 1.0 12.6
			31 SA	0352 0912 1617 2137	1.2 12.9 1.0 12.5

FEBRUARY

	Time	m		Time	m
1 SU	0432 0955 1657 2219	1.4 12.6 1.4 12.1	**16** M	0418 0940 1633 2158	2.5 11.3 2.8 10.9
2 M	0512 1039 1737 2301	1.9 12.0 2.0 11.5	**17** TU	0443 1007 1657 2226	2.9 10.8 3.3 10.4
3 TU	0554 1124 1820 2348	2.5 11.2 2.7 10.7	**18** W	0511 1037 1728 2258	3.5 10.1 3.8 9.7
4 W	0642 1218 1912	3.3 10.3 3.5	**19** TH	0547 1114 1809 2342	4.1 9.4 4.4 9.1
5 TH	0046 0746 1329 2020	9.9 4.0 9.6 4.1	**20** F	0637 1210 1907	4.6 8.8 4.9
6 F	0204 0912 1457 2147	9.4 4.2 9.4 4.2	**21** SA	0056 0748 1349 2031	8.6 5.0 8.5 5.0
7 SA	0333 1038 1617 2306	9.5 3.9 9.7 3.8	**22** SU	0244 0922 1529 2202	8.7 4.8 8.9 4.6
8 SU	0446 1146 1719	10.1 3.4 10.3	**23** M	0405 1043 1638 2315	9.3 4.0 9.7 3.7
9 M	0009 0540 1241 1808	3.3 10.7 2.8 10.8	**24** TU	0505 1150 1733	10.3 3.1 10.7
10 TU	0059 0625 1327 1851	2.8 11.2 2.4 11.3	**25** W	0018 0557 1250 1823	2.8 11.3 2.2 11.6
11 W ○	0142 0705 1408 1929	2.4 11.6 2.1 11.6	**26** TH ●	0117 0646 1346 1911	2.0 12.2 1.3 12.4
12 TH	0220 0741 1443 2003	2.1 11.9 1.9 11.8	**27** F	0210 0732 1437 1956	1.2 12.9 0.7 12.9
13 F	0254 0814 1515 2035	1.9 12.0 1.9 11.8	**28** SA	0258 0817 1523 2040	0.7 13.3 0.4 13.2
14 SA	0325 0844 1544 2104	1.9 11.9 2.0 11.6			
15 SU	0353 0913 1610 2132	2.1 11.7 2.3 11.4			

MARCH

	Time	m		Time	m
1 SU	0341 0900 1604 2121	0.6 13.4 0.5 13.1	**16** M	0328 0848 1543 2104	1.9 11.8 2.1 11.6
2 M	0421 0941 1642 2200	0.8 13.0 0.9 12.6	**17** TU	0353 0914 1607 2129	2.1 11.4 2.4 11.2
3 TU	0459 1021 1719 2239	1.4 12.3 1.7 11.8	**18** W	0418 0941 1631 2155	2.5 11.0 2.9 10.7
4 W	0536 1102 1756 2320	2.3 11.3 2.7 10.8	**19** TH	0446 1009 1659 2224	3.0 10.3 3.5 10.1
5 TH	0618 1150 1841	3.2 10.2 3.7	**20** F	0518 1041 1734 2300	3.6 9.6 4.1 9.4
6 F	0011 0714 1255 1944	9.8 4.1 9.3 4.4	**21** SA	0601 1127 1825 2357	4.3 8.9 4.6 8.7
7 SA	0127 0838 1432 2116	9.1 4.6 8.9 4.7	**22** SU	0704 1252 1942	4.7 8.4 4.9
8 SU	0309 1013 1603 2242	9.0 4.3 9.2 4.2	**23** M	0145 0836 1450 2120	8.5 4.7 8.7 4.6
9 M	0429 1126 1704 2347	9.6 3.7 9.9 3.5	**24** TU	0328 1009 1609 2244	9.1 4.0 9.6 3.7
10 TU	0523 1221 1750	10.4 3.0 10.6	**25** W	0438 1123 1709 2354	10.2 3.0 10.7 2.7
11 W	0038 0606 1307 1830	2.9 11.0 2.5 11.2	**26** TH	0535 1228 1802	11.3 1.9 11.7
12 TH	0121 0644 1346 1907	2.4 11.5 2.1 11.6	**27** F	0056 0626 1326 1851	1.7 12.3 1.0 12.6
13 F ○	0158 0720 1421 1940	2.1 11.8 1.9 11.8	**28** SA ●	0151 0714 1418 1937	0.9 13.1 0.4 13.2
14 SA	0231 0752 1451 2011	1.9 11.9 1.8 11.8	**29** SU	0241 0759 1504 2020	0.4 13.5 0.1 13.4
15 SU	0301 0821 1518 2038	1.8 11.9 1.9 11.8	**30** M	0325 0842 1545 2100	0.3 13.5 0.3 13.2
			31 TU	0405 0923 1623 2139	0.6 13.1 0.9 12.6

APRIL

	Time	m		Time	m
1 W	0441 1002 1657 2216	1.2 12.2 1.7 11.8	**16** TH	0358 0919 1609 2132	2.2 11.0 2.6 10.9
2 TH	0517 1041 1732 2255	2.2 11.2 2.8 10.8	**17** F	0427 0950 1638 2202	2.7 10.5 3.2 10.3
3 F	0555 1125 1812 2341	3.2 10.1 3.8 9.8	**18** SA	0500 1025 1714 2240	3.3 9.8 3.7 9.7
4 SA	0645 1225 1910	4.1 9.1 4.6	**19** SU	0542 1112 1802 2336	3.8 9.2 4.3 9.1
5 SU	0051 0801 1359 2037	9.0 4.6 8.6 4.8	**20** M	0641 1230 1914	4.2 8.8 4.5
6 M	0233 0935 1534 2205	8.8 4.5 9.0 4.4	**21** TU	0110 0806 1413 2047	8.8 4.2 8.9 4.3
7 TU	0357 1050 1636 2311	9.3 3.9 9.7 3.7	**22** W	0250 0937 1536 2213	9.3 3.7 9.7 3.5
8 W	0453 1147 1722	10.0 3.2 10.4	**23** TH	0406 1054 1640 2326	10.2 2.7 10.7 2.5
9 TH	0004 0537 1234 1801	3.1 10.7 2.6 11.0	**24** F	0507 1201 1736	11.3 1.8 11.7
10 F ○	0049 0616 1315 1838	2.6 11.2 2.3 11.4	**25** SA	0031 0601 1301 1826	1.6 12.2 1.2 12.5
11 SA ○	0129 0652 1351 1912	2.2 11.5 2.0 11.7	**26** SU ●	0128 0651 1354 1913	0.9 12.9 0.5 13.0
12 SU	0203 0726 1422 1942	2.0 11.7 1.9 11.8	**27** M	0219 0738 1441 1957	0.5 13.2 0.3 13.1
13 M	0233 0756 1450 2010	1.9 11.7 1.9 11.7	**28** TU	0304 0822 1523 2038	0.4 13.1 0.6 13.0
14 TU	0302 0824 1516 2037	1.8 11.6 2.0 11.6	**29** W	0345 0903 1600 2116	0.7 12.7 1.1 12.5
15 W	0329 0851 1542 2103	2.0 11.4 2.2 11.4	**30** TH	0422 0943 1635 2154	1.3 12.0 1.9 11.7

15

Chart Datum: 6·29 metres below Lallemand System (Mean Sea Level, Marseilles)

TIME ZONE –0100
(French Standard Time)
Subtract 1 hour for UT
For French Summer Time add ONE hour in non-shaded areas

FRANCE – ST. MALO

LAT 48°38′N   LONG 2°02′W

TIMES AND HEIGHTS OF HIGH AND LOW WATERS

YEAR **1998**

MAY

Date	Day	Time	m	Time	m	Time	m	Time	m
1	F	0459	2.2	1022	11.0	1710	2.8	2233	10.8
2	SA	0536	3.1	1104	10.1	1748	3.7	2316	9.9
3	SU	0620	3.9	1157	9.2	1839	4.4		
4	M	0015	9.2	0722	4.4	1313	8.8	1952	4.7
5	TU	0139	8.8	0842	4.5	1441	8.9	2113	4.5
6	W	0304	9.1	0957	4.1	1551	9.4	2222	4.0
7	TH	0408	9.7	1059	3.5	1642	10.1	2319	3.4
8	F	0458	10.3	1152	3.0	1725	10.7		
9	SA	0009	2.9	0542	10.8	1237	2.6	1804	11.1
10	SU	0052	2.5	0621	11.1	1316	2.3	1840	11.4
11 O	M	0130	2.3	0657	11.3	1350	2.2	1913	11.5
12	TU	0204	2.1	0730	11.4	1421	2.1	1944	11.6
13	W	0236	2.0	0801	11.4	1451	2.0	2013	11.6
14	TH	0309	2.0	0832	11.3	1522	2.2	2043	11.4
15	F	0341	2.1	0905	11.0	1553	2.5	2116	11.1
16	SA	0415	2.4	0941	10.6	1626	2.9	2152	10.6
17	SU	0452	2.9	1021	10.1	1704	3.3	2235	10.1
18	M	0536	3.8	1112	9.6	1753	3.8	2332	9.6
19	TU	0632	3.6	1220	9.3	1858	4.0		
20	W	0050	9.4	0745	3.7	1341	9.4	2020	3.9
21	TH	0216	9.7	0907	3.3	1501	9.9	2143	3.3
22	F	0333	10.3	1025	2.7	1609	10.7	2258	2.6
23	SA	0439	11.1	1134	2.0	1708	11.5		
24	SU	0005	1.8	0536	11.8	1235	1.4	1801	12.1
25 ●	M	0104	1.3	0629	12.3	1329	1.0	1850	12.5
26	TU	0156	1.0	0717	12.5	1417	0.9	1934	12.7
27	W	0242	0.9	0802	12.5	1500	1.1	2016	12.6
28	TH	0325	1.1	0845	12.2	1538	1.4	2056	12.2
29	F	0404	1.5	0925	11.7	1615	2.0	2134	11.7
30	SA	0441	2.2	1005	11.0	1650	2.7	2213	11.0
31	SU	0517	2.9	1045	10.3	1726	3.4	2253	10.2

JUNE

Date	Day	Time	m	Time	m	Time	m	Time	m
1	M	0555	3.6	1130	9.6	1808	4.1	2340	9.6
2	TU	0643	4.1	1225	9.1	1904	4.5		
3	W	0041	9.1	0746	4.4	1335	9.0	2014	4.5
4	TH	0156	9.0	0857	4.3	1449	9.2	2125	4.3
5	F	0310	9.3	1004	3.9	1552	9.6	2229	3.9
6	SA	0412	9.8	1104	3.5	1644	10.2	2325	3.4
7	SU	0504	10.2	1155	3.1	1729	10.7		
8	M	0013	3.0	0549	10.6	1239	2.8	1809	11.0
9	TU	0056	2.7	0629	10.9	1318	2.5	1846	11.3
10 O	W	0136	2.4	0707	11.1	1355	2.3	1920	11.5
11	TH	0214	2.1	0742	11.2	1431	2.2	1954	11.6
12	F	0252	2.0	0818	11.3	1507	2.1	2029	11.6
13	SA	0330	2.0	0855	11.2	1543	2.3	2107	11.5
14	SU	0409	2.1	0936	11.1	1620	2.5	2148	11.2
15	M	0449	2.4	1020	10.7	1701	2.8	2233	10.7
16	TU	0533	2.7	1108	10.4	1748	3.2	2326	10.3
17	W	0624	3.0	1205	10.0	1845	3.5		
18	TH	0030	10.0	0726	3.2	1312	9.9	1955	3.6
19	F	0145	10.0	0838	3.2	1426	10.0	2115	3.4
20	SA	0302	10.3	0955	2.9	1538	10.5	2233	2.9
21	SU	0412	10.7	1108	2.5	1642	11.0	2342	2.3
22	M	0514	11.2	1211	2.0	1739	11.6		
23	TU	0042	1.9	0610	11.6	1306	1.7	1830	11.9
24 ●	W	0135	1.6	0701	11.9	1355	1.6	1917	12.1
25	TH	0223	1.4	0747	11.9	1439	1.6	1959	12.2
26	F	0306	1.5	0829	11.9	1519	1.7	2039	12.1
27	SA	0346	1.7	0909	11.6	1556	2.0	2116	11.8
28	SU	0422	2.1	0947	11.2	1630	2.5	2152	11.3
29	M	0456	2.6	1023	10.7	1703	3.1	2228	10.7
30	TU	0528	3.2	1056	10.1	1736	3.6	2305	10.1

JULY

Date	Day	Time	m	Time	m	Time	m	Time	m
1	W	0603	3.8	1140	9.6	1816	4.1	2349	9.6
2	TH	0649	4.2	1232	9.3	1910	4.5		
3	F	0048	9.2	0751	4.4	1339	9.1	2020	4.6
4	SA	0203	9.0	0904	4.4	1454	9.2	2134	4.4
5	SU	0321	9.2	1013	4.1	1600	9.6	2240	4.0
6	M	0425	9.6	1113	3.7	1654	10.1	2336	3.5
7	TU	0518	10.1	1203	3.3	1740	10.6		
8	W	0025	3.0	0603	10.6	1249	2.9	1822	11.1
9 O	TH	0111	2.6	0645	10.9	1332	2.5	1901	11.4
10	F	0155	2.2	0726	11.3	1414	2.2	1940	11.7
11	SA	0239	1.9	0806	11.5	1456	2.0	2019	11.9
12	SU	0322	1.7	0847	11.7	1537	1.9	2100	12.0
13	M	0404	1.6	0929	11.7	1616	2.0	2142	11.9
14	TU	0445	1.8	1012	11.5	1657	2.2	2226	11.5
15	W	0526	2.1	1056	11.1	1739	2.6	2313	11.0
16	TH	0612	2.5	1146	10.6	1829	3.1		
17	F	0008	10.5	0705	3.0	1244	10.2	1930	3.5
18	SA	0117	10.1	0811	3.4	1354	10.0	2049	3.6
19	SU	0235	9.9	0930	3.4	1511	10.0	2213	3.4
20	M	0352	10.2	1047	3.1	1623	10.5	2325	2.9
21	TU	0500	10.6	1153	2.7	1724	11.0		
22	W	0027	2.5	0558	11.0	1250	2.4	1817	11.5
23 ●	TH	0120	2.1	0648	11.4	1339	2.1	1903	11.8
24	F	0207	1.8	0733	11.6	1422	1.9	1944	12.0
25	SA	0249	1.7	0813	11.8	1501	1.8	2021	12.0
26	SU	0326	1.7	0850	11.7	1536	1.9	2056	11.9
27	M	0401	2.0	0924	11.5	1608	2.2	2128	11.6
28	TU	0431	2.4	0956	11.1	1637	2.7	2159	11.1
29	W	0458	2.9	1026	10.6	1703	3.2	2229	10.5
30	TH	0524	3.5	1058	10.1	1733	3.8	2303	9.9
31	F	0557	4.0	1136	9.5	1813	4.3	2347	9.3

AUGUST

Date	Day	Time	m	Time	m	Time	m	Time	m
1	SA	0645	4.5	1232	9.0	1911	4.7		
2	SU	0055	8.8	0754	4.8	1352	8.8	2030	4.9
3	M	0227	8.7	0917	4.8	1516	9.0	2153	4.6
4	TU	0350	9.1	1030	4.4	1622	9.6	2300	4.0
5	W	0450	9.7	1129	3.8	1714	10.2	2356	3.3
6	TH	0540	10.3	1222	3.1	1800	10.9		
7	F	0047	2.7	0625	11.0	1312	2.5	1843	11.6
8 O	SA	0138	2.1	0709	11.6	1400	2.0	1925	12.1
9	SU	0226	1.5	0752	12.0	1446	1.6	2007	12.5
10	M	0312	1.2	0834	12.3	1529	1.3	2049	12.7
11	TU	0354	1.1	0916	12.4	1609	1.4	2131	12.6
12	W	0434	1.2	0957	12.2	1648	1.7	2213	12.1
13	TH	0514	1.7	1039	11.7	1727	2.2	2256	11.4
14	F	0555	2.3	1123	11.0	1811	2.9	2345	10.6
15	SA	0642	3.1	1215	10.2	1907	3.6		
16	SU	0049	9.8	0744	3.8	1325	9.6	2026	4.1
17	M	0213	9.4	0908	4.0	1451	9.5	2158	3.9
18	TU	0342	9.6	1032	3.8	1612	9.9	2314	3.4
19	W	0452	10.1	1140	3.2	1714	10.6		
20	TH	0015	2.8	0547	10.7	1236	2.7	1804	11.2
21	F	0107	2.3	0634	11.3	1323	2.3	1847	11.7
22 ●	SA	0151	2.0	0714	11.6	1404	2.0	1925	12.0
23	SU	0229	1.8	0751	11.8	1440	1.9	2000	12.1
24	M	0303	1.8	0825	11.8	1513	1.8	2032	12.0
25	TU	0334	1.9	0856	11.7	1542	2.0	2101	11.8
26	W	0401	2.2	0924	11.4	1608	2.4	2128	11.4
27	TH	0425	2.7	0950	11.0	1632	2.9	2155	10.8
28	F	0447	3.2	1017	10.4	1657	3.4	2222	10.2
29	SA	0514	3.8	1048	9.8	1730	4.0	2257	9.5
30	SU	0552	4.4	1129	9.1	1816	4.6	2348	8.7
31	M	0648	5.0	1240	8.5	1924	5.1		

Chart Datum: 0·20 metres below Lallemand System (Mean Sea Level, Marseilles)

TIME ZONE –0100
(French Standard Time)
Subtract 1 hour for UT

For French Summer Time add ONE hour in non-shaded areas

FRANCE – ST. MALO

LAT 48°38′N   LONG 2°02′W

TIMES AND HEIGHTS OF HIGH AND LOW WATERS

YEAR **1998**

SEPTEMBER

Date	Day	Time	m	Time	m	Time	m	Time	m
1	TU	0126	8.3	0812	5.2	1429	8.5	2100	5.0
16	W	0334	9.2	1016	4.2	1600	9.6	2301	3.7
2	W	0316	8.6	0946	4.8	1551	9.1	2224	4.4
17	TH	0442	9.9	1123	3.5	1659	10.4	2359	3.0
3	TH	0424	9.4	1056	4.1	1648	9.9	2327	3.5
18	F	0531	10.6	1216	2.9	1745	11.0		
4	F	0516	10.3	1155	3.2	1736	10.9		
19	SA	0046	2.5	0613	11.2	1301	2.4	1825	11.6
5	SA	0024	2.5	0603	11.2	1250	2.4	1822	11.8
20	SU ●	0128	2.1	0650	11.6	1340	2.1	1901	11.9
6	SU O	0118	1.7	0648	12.0	1342	1.6	1907	12.5
21	M	0204	1.9	0724	11.8	1415	1.9	1935	12.0
7	M	0209	1.1	0733	12.6	1431	1.1	1951	13.0
22	TU	0236	1.8	0756	11.9	1446	1.9	2005	12.0
8	TU	0256	0.7	0816	12.9	1515	0.8	2033	13.2
23	W	0304	1.9	0825	11.8	1514	2.0	2033	11.8
9	W	0339	0.6	0857	12.9	1556	0.9	2114	13.0
24	TH	0330	2.1	0851	11.6	1540	2.3	2058	11.4
10	TH	0418	0.9	0937	12.6	1634	1.3	2155	12.4
25	F	0353	2.5	0916	11.2	1604	2.7	2124	11.0
11	F	0456	1.5	1017	11.9	1712	2.0	2236	11.5
26	SA	0416	3.0	0941	10.7	1630	3.2	2150	10.3
12	SA	0534	2.4	1058	11.1	1752	2.9	2322	10.5
27	SU	0441	3.6	1009	10.0	1700	3.8	2220	9.6
13	SU	0618	3.4	1148	10.1	1844	3.8		
28	M	0514	4.3	1042	9.3	1740	4.4	2301	8.8
14	M	0023	9.5	0718	4.2	1257	9.3	2004	4.4
29	TU	0602	4.9	1136	8.6	1838	5.0		
15	TU	0156	8.9	0848	4.5	1434	9.1	2144	4.3
30	W	0019	8.2	0716	5.2	1330	8.3	2008	5.1

OCTOBER

Date	Day	Time	m	Time	m	Time	m	Time	m
1	TH	0235	8.4	0858	5.0	1512	8.8	2145	4.4
16	F	0420	9.6	1053	3.8	1633	10.1	2329	3.3
2	F	0352	9.2	1021	4.2	1616	9.8	2256	3.4
17	SA	0506	10.4	1145	3.1	1717	10.8		
3	SA	0447	10.3	1125	3.1	1709	10.9	2357	2.4
18	SU	0016	2.7	0545	11.0	1230	2.6	1757	11.3
4	SU	0537	11.3	1225	2.2	1758	12.0		
19	M	0057	2.3	0621	11.5	1310	2.0	1833	11.6
5	M	0054	1.5	0624	12.3	1320	1.4	1845	12.8
20	TU ●	0133	2.1	0655	11.7	1345	2.1	1907	11.8
6	TU O	0147	0.8	0709	12.9	1411	0.8	1930	13.3
21	W	0204	2.0	0726	11.8	1417	2.1	1937	11.8
7	W	0235	0.4	0753	13.2	1457	0.6	2013	13.4
22	TH	0233	2.0	0754	11.8	1446	2.1	2005	11.6
8	TH	0319	0.4	0835	13.2	1539	0.7	2055	13.1
23	F	0259	2.2	0821	11.6	1513	2.2	2032	11.4
9	F	0358	0.9	0915	12.8	1618	1.2	2135	12.4
24	SA	0325	2.4	0847	11.3	1541	2.5	2059	11.0
10	SA	0435	1.6	0954	12.0	1655	2.0	2216	11.4
25	SU	0351	2.9	0914	10.9	1609	3.0	2128	10.5
11	SU	0513	2.6	1035	11.1	1735	3.0	2301	10.3
26	M	0418	3.4	0943	10.3	1641	3.5	2200	9.9
12	M	0555	3.6	1123	10.0	1825	4.0	2359	9.3
27	TU	0451	4.0	1016	9.6	1719	4.1	2241	9.1
13	TU	0653	4.5	1230	9.2	1939	4.6		
28	W	0535	4.6	1107	8.9	1813	4.6	2349	8.5
14	W	0132	8.7	0819	4.8	1408	8.9	2116	4.6
29	TH	0642	4.9	1237	8.6	1931	4.7		
15	TH	0315	8.9	0947	4.5	1534	9.4	2232	4.0
30	F	0142	8.5	0814	4.8	1424	8.9	2103	4.2
31	SA	0311	9.2	0942	4.1	1538	9.8	2221	3.3

NOVEMBER

Date	Day	Time	m	Time	m	Time	m	Time	m
1	SU	0413	10.3	1054	3.1	1637	10.9	2327	2.3
16	M	0510	10.6	1152	3.1	1723	10.8		
2	M	0507	11.4	1157	2.1	1730	11.9		
17	TU	0019	2.8	0548	11.1	1235	2.7	1802	11.2
3	TU	0027	1.4	0557	12.3	1255	1.4	1820	12.7
18	W	0059	2.5	0624	11.4	1314	2.5	1838	11.4
4	W O	0122	0.8	0644	12.9	1348	0.9	1907	13.1
19	TH ●	0133	2.3	0701	11.6	1348	2.4	1911	11.4
5	TH	0211	0.6	0729	13.2	1436	0.7	1952	13.2
20	F	0204	2.3	0728	11.6	1420	2.3	1942	11.4
6	F	0256	0.6	0812	13.1	1520	0.8	2036	12.9
21	SA	0233	2.5	0756	11.6	1451	2.3	2012	11.3
7	SA	0337	1.1	0854	12.7	1601	1.3	2117	12.2
22	SU	0303	2.5	0826	11.4	1523	2.5	2043	11.0
8	SU	0415	1.8	0934	12.0	1640	2.1	2159	11.3
23	M	0333	2.7	0857	11.1	1556	2.8	2116	10.7
9	M	0453	2.7	1015	11.1	1720	3.0	2243	10.3
24	TU	0405	3.1	0931	10.7	1631	3.2	2154	10.2
10	TU	0534	3.6	1101	10.2	1806	3.9	2337	9.4
25	W	0440	3.6	1010	10.1	1711	3.6	2238	9.6
11	W	0626	4.4	1200	9.4	1906	4.5		
26	TH	0524	4.1	1059	9.6	1801	4.0	2337	9.2
12	TH	0051	8.8	0737	4.8	1320	9.0	2026	4.7
27	F	0623	4.4	1210	9.2	1906	4.1		
13	F	0224	8.8	0858	4.7	1445	9.1	2141	4.3
28	SA	0058	9.1	0740	4.4	1337	9.3	2025	3.9
14	SA	0338	9.3	1006	4.2	1551	9.6	2243	3.8
29	SU	0224	9.5	0904	4.0	1457	9.9	2144	3.3
15	SU	0429	10.0	1103	3.6	1640	10.3	2334	3.2
30	M	0336	10.2	1021	3.2	1604	10.8	2257	2.5

DECEMBER

Date	Day	Time	m	Time	m	Time	m	Time	m
1	TU	0437	11.1	1130	2.4	1703	11.6		
16	W	0515	10.6	1200	3.3	1732	10.6		
2	W	0000	1.8	0531	11.9	1231	1.7	1757	12.2
17	TH	0025	3.1	0555	11.0	1244	3.0	1813	10.9
3	TH O	0058	1.3	0622	12.5	1326	1.2	1847	12.6
18	F ●	0104	2.8	0632	11.3	1323	2.7	1850	11.1
4	F	0149	1.1	0709	12.8	1417	1.1	1935	12.7
19	SA	0140	2.6	0707	11.4	1359	2.5	1925	11.2
5	SA	0236	1.1	0754	12.8	1502	1.1	2020	12.5
20	SU	0214	2.5	0739	11.5	1435	2.4	1959	11.3
6	SU	0318	1.4	0836	12.5	1545	1.5	2103	12.0
21	M	0248	2.5	0813	11.6	1512	2.3	2034	11.2
7	M	0358	1.9	0917	12.0	1625	2.1	2145	11.4
22	TU	0323	2.5	0848	11.5	1549	2.4	2111	11.1
8	TU	0437	2.6	0958	11.4	1704	2.8	2227	10.6
23	W	0359	2.7	0926	11.2	1626	2.6	2151	10.8
9	W	0515	3.3	1040	10.6	1744	3.5	2311	9.9
24	TH	0437	3.0	1007	10.8	1706	2.9	2234	10.4
10	TH	0557	4.0	1126	9.8	1829	4.2		
25	F	0519	3.4	1053	10.4	1752	3.3	2324	10.0
11	F	0004	9.3	0649	4.6	1223	9.3	1926	4.6
26	SA	0609	3.7	1149	10.0	1845	3.5		
12	SA	0110	8.9	0754	4.8	1334	9.0	2034	4.6
27	SU	0026	9.7	0712	3.9	1300	9.8	1951	3.6
13	SU	0228	9.0	0905	4.6	1450	9.2	2144	4.3
28	M	0140	9.7	0827	3.9	1419	10.0	2108	3.4
14	M	0337	9.6	1011	4.2	1555	9.6	2246	3.9
29	TU	0258	10.1	0951	3.5	1534	10.4	2227	3.0
15	TU	0430	10.0	1110	3.6	1647	10.1	2339	3.4
30	W	0409	10.7	1106	2.9	1641	11.0	2337	2.5
31	TH	0510	11.3	1211	2.2	1740	11.6		

15

Chart Datum: 6·29 metres below Lallemand System (Mean Sea Level, Marseilles)

ST MALO/DINARD   10-15-16

Ille et Vilaine 48°38'·35N 02°01'·80W Rtgs: (Vauban) 3-4-1;
(Sablons) 3-3-1

CHARTS

AC 2700, *3659, 2669*; SHOM 7130, 7155, 7156, 6966; ECM
535; Imray C33B; Stanfords 16

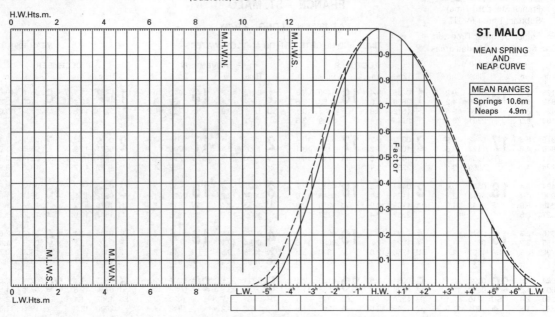

ST. MALO

MEAN SPRING
AND
NEAP CURVE

MEAN RANGES
Springs 10.6m
Neaps 4.9m

ST MALO/DINARD *continued*

TIDES
−0506 Dover; ML 6·8; Duration 0535; Zone −0100
Saint-Malo is a Standard Port and the tidal predictions for each day of the year are given above.

SHELTER
Two options: (1) Lock into the Bassin Vauban, min depth 6m. Excellent shelter near the walled city. Bassin Duguay -Trouin, via bridge, is better for long stay. No ⚓ in basins; 3kn speed limit. Outside the lock are 3 waiting buoys N of appr chan; keep clear of vedette and Condor berths. See next column for lock times and signals.
(2) Good shelter nearer St Servan in Bas Sablons marina, entered over sill 2m above CD. Ⓥ berths are 32-66 (even side) and 43-75 (odd side) on Pontoon A, and 92-102 and 91-101 on Pontoon B. N end of pontoon 'A' is exposed to NW winds. Caution: marina ent is only 40m wide, close S of ferry pier extending W from N corner of Bas-Sablons basin and beyond marina bkwtr, Fl G 4s 7m 5M. Two W waiting buoys outside. Depth of water over sill is shown on a digital gauge atop the bkwtr, visible only from seaward; inside, a conventional gauge at base of bkwtr shows depths <3m.
At **Dinard** there is a yacht ⚓ and moorings, reached by a beaconed chan, all dredged 2m, but virtually filled by local boats. (Marina planned).

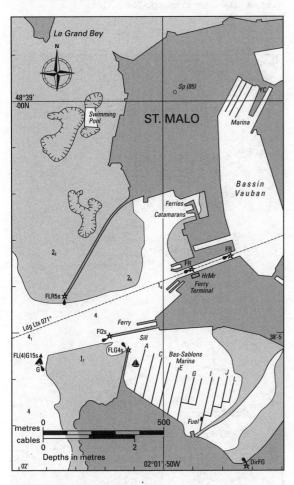

NAVIGATION
WPT Fairway SWM buoy, L Fl 10s Whis, 48°41′·42N 02°07′·20W, 307°/127° from/to Grand Jardin lt, 1·9M. Care is needed due to many dangerous rks around the appr chans, plus strong tidal streams. The 3 main chans are:
1. Petite Porte (130°/129°); best from N or NW and at night.
2. Grande Porte (089°/129°); from the W.
These 2 chans meet at Le Grand Jardin lt and continue 129°.
3. La Grande Conchée (182°); most direct from N.
The first two are well lit. In fresh W'lies it can be quite rough in the vicinity of Le Grand Jardin.

LIGHTS AND MARKS
Chenal de la Petite Porte: Ldg lts 130°, front, Le Grand Jardin, Fl (2) R 10s 24m 15M, grey tr; rear, La Balue, FG 69m 25M.
Chenal de la Grande Porte: Ldg lts 089°, front, Le Grand Jardin; rear, Rochebonne, FR 40m 24M, (off chartlet) 4·2M from front; leads into Chenal de la Petite Porte.
Inner ldg lts 129° from Le Grand Jardin lt ho: Front, Les Bas Sablons, FG 20m 16M; rear, La Balue (as above).
La Plate lt, Fl WRG 4s 11m 9/6M, W140°-203°, R203°-210°, W210°-225°, G225°-140°.
St Malo lock: Ldg lts, 2 FR, 071° into lock. Lock opens HW −2½ for first arrivals; first deps at HW−2. From HW− 1½ to about HW, both lock gates are usually open for freeflow; beware strong set. A complete lock cycle of arr/ dep lasts about 1hr. Last arr at HW+1½; last dep at HW+2.
Lock sigs:

Ⓖ
Ⓦ } No ent to lock without instructions
Ⓖ

Ⓖ
Ⓖ } Boats may enter lock
Ⓖ

Ⓡ
Ⓡ } No ent. Keep 200m from gates
Ⓡ

Ⓨ alongside the top lt shows that both gates are open; instructions are the same, but beware current.
2 Ⓡ over Ⓖ = all movements prohib, except departure of large ships.

RADIO TELEPHONE
Call: *St Malo Port* or *Grand Jardin* VHF Ch **12** 16 (H24).
Port Vauban and Les Bas Sablons marinas Ch 09.

TELEPHONE (Prefix ☎ nos with zone code 02)
ST MALO: Hr Mr 99·81·62·86; Hr Mr (Sablons) 99·81·71·34; Hr Mr (Vauban) 99·56·51·91; Aff Mar 99·56·87·00; CROSS 98·89·31·31; SNSM 98·89·31·31; ▦ 99·81·65·90; Météo 99·46·10·46; Auto 08.36.68.08.35; Police 99·81·52·30; Ⓗ 99·56·56·19; Brit Consul 99·46·26·64.
DINARD: Hr Mr 99·46·65·55; ▦ 99·46·12·42; Météo 99·46·10·46; Auto 08.36.68.08.35; Ⓗ 99·46·18·68.

FACILITIES
ST MALO: **Bassin Vauban** (250 + 100 Ⓥ) ☎ 99·56·51·91, FF91.50, FW, AC, C (1 ton); **Société Nautique de la Baie de St. Malo** ☎ 99·40·84·42, Bar (visitors welcome).
ST SERVAN: **Marina Les Bas-Sablons** (1216 + 64 visitors on Pontoon A, berths 43-75 and 32-64) ☎ 99·81·71·34, 🚤 99.81.91.81, FF93.50, Slip, C, AC, FW, CH, BH (10 ton), Gaz, R, YC, Bar, P & D at Pontoon I; Note: Fuel may only be paid for by French credit card.
Services: El, Ⓔ, ME, CH, Sh, C, BY, SM, SHOM.
Town Slip, P, Gaz, D, ME, El, Sh, C, V, R, Bar, ⊠, Ⓑ, ⇌, ✈ (Dinard). Ferry: Portsmouth, Poole or Jersey.
DINARD: **Port de Dinard** ☎ 99·46·65·55, Slip, ⚓, M FF83, P, D, L, FW, temp AB; **YC de Dinard** ☎ 99·46·14·32, Bar;
Services: ME, El, Ⓔ, Sh, M, SM.
Town P, D, ME, El, CH, V, Gaz, R, Bar, ⊠, Ⓑ, ⇌, ✈.

OTHER HARBOURS EAST OF ST MALO

CANCALE, Ille-et-Vilaine, 48°40′·10N 01°51′·10W. AC *3659*; SHOM 7131, 7155. HW −0510 on Dover (UT); ML 7·2m; Duration 0535. See 10.15.14. A drying hbr just inside Bay of Mont St Michel, 1M SW of Pte de la Chaine. Area dries to about 1M off-shore; ⚓ off Pte de la Chaine in deep water. Drying berths usually available in La Houle, the hbr in Cancale. Exposed to winds SW to SE. Jetty hd lt Oc (3) G 12s 12m 8M, obsc when brg < 223°. Facilities: **Quay** D, P, C (1·5 ton), FW; **Services:** El, M, ME, Sh; **Club Nautique de Cancale** ☎ 02·99·89·90·22.
Town (famous for oysters), Ⓑ, Bar, D, P, ⊠, R, V.

ROTHENEUF, Ille-et-Vilaine, 48°41′·42N 01°57′·56W. AC 2700, *3659*; SHOM 7131, 7155. HW −0510 on Dover (UT); Tides as for St. Malo; ML 7·0m; Duration 0540. Complete shelter in hbr which dries completely. ⚓ outside in 4m just N of spar bn marking ent. Rks on both sides of ent which is less than 170m wide. Safest to enter when rks uncovered. Ldg line at 163°, W side of Pte Benard and old converted windmill. There are no lts. Facilities: FW, Slip.
Village Bar, D, P, R, V.

15

RIVER RANCE/DINAN   10-15-17

Ille-et-Vilaine 48°37'·10N 02°01'·62W (Barrage)   Rtg 3-3-1

CHARTS
AC 2700, *3659*; SHOM 4233, 7130; Imray C33B; Stanfords 16

TIDES
Standard Port ST MALO (⟵) Zone −0100

Water levels up-river from the Rance hydro-electric tidal barrage are artificially maintained by sluice gates. From 0700 – 2100LT, 4m above CD is guaranteed, whilst from 0800 – 2000LT, during a specified 4 hour period, 8·5m above CD will be maintained.

Outside these hours levels may, exceptionally, drop by as much as 1·4m in 10 minutes. A French language pamphlet, issued by Électricité de France is available from Hr Mrs at St Malo and Bas Sablons; it is essential for a detailed understanding of the barrage and water level schedule (also published daily in *Ouest-France*). A visit to the barrage display (on site) may be instructive.

SHELTER
Good shelter up-river dependent on wind direction. The principal ⚓s/moorings on the E bank are at St Suliac and Mordreuc, and on the W bank at La Richardais, La Jouvente, Le Minihic and La Pommeraie. See below for marinas at Plouër, Lyvet (E bank, above the Chatelier lock) and Dinan.

NAVIGATION
From St Malo/Dinard, appr the lock at the W end of the barrage between a prohib area to port, marked by PHM buoys and wire cables, and Pointe de La Jument to stbd. Waiting dolphins either side of the lock.

Lock opening by day on the hour, every hour provided the level is at least 4m above CD; from 2030 – 0430 opening is on request. Yachts should arrive at H −20 mins, ideally HW −3. The lifting road-bridge across the lock opens between H and H +15. Boats leaving the lock have priority. Up-river of the lock a further prohib area to port is marked as above.

The 3M chan to St Suliac has min depth of 2m; the next 6M to the Chatelier lock partially dries. The suspension bridge at Port St. Hubert has 23m clearance, with a road bridge alongside it; whilst a railway viaduct 1M above Mordreuc has 19m clearance.

The Chatelier lock and swing bridge operate 0800-2000LT, provided there is at least 8·5m rise of tide. The final 3M to Dinan is canalised with min depth of approx 1·2m (check with lock-keeper). Dinan gives access to the Ille et Rance Canal and River Vilaine to Biscay (see 10.15.15).

LIGHTS AND MARKS
Approaching the barrage from seaward:
Pte de la Jument bn tr, Fl (5) G20s 6m 4M; PHM Prohib Area buoy opposite, Fl R 4s.
NW side of lock, Fl G 4s, with G △ on W background.
First dolphin, Fl R (2) 6s, with R □ on W background.
Approaching from Dinan:
PHM, Oc R 4s, at S end of Prohib Area.
Last dolphin, Oc R (2) 6s, with R □ on W background.
SE side of lock, Iso G4s, G △ on W background.
Lock entry sigs:
1 ▼ or Ⓡ = Passage permitted sea to river.
1 ● or Ⓖ = Passage permitted river to sea.
▼ & ● together or Ⓡ & Ⓖ = No entry to lock.
Additional sigs on the barrage to the E of the lock show the direction of flow through the turbines.
The chan up-river is partly buoyed and marked by stakes.

RADIO TELEPHONE
Barrage lock: VHF Ch 13.

TELEPHONE (Prefix ☎ nos with zone code 02)
Water levels/navigation 99·46·14·46; Barrage/lock info 99·46·21·87; Hr Mr (Richardais) 99·46·24·20; Hr Mr (Plouër) 96·86·83·15; Chatelier lock 96·39·55·66; Hr Mr (Lyvet) 96·83·35·57; Hr Mr (Dinan) 96·39·04·47; (Météo 99·46·10·46; Auto 08.36.68.08.35; Aff Mar 96·39·56·44; Police 99·81·52·30; Brit Consul 99·46·26·64.

FACILITIES
St. Suliac Slip, M, Bar, R, V, Divers (Convoimer); **Mordreuc** Slip, L, M, Bar, R, P, V; **La Richardais** CH, El, ME, Sh. **Villages**: Bar, D, P, ✉, R, V, Ⓑ; **La Jouvente** AB, Bar, R; **Le Minihic** M, L, Slip, ME, El, Sh; **La Pommeraie** M, L, SC, R.

MARINAS ON THE RIVER RANCE

PLOUËR, Côtes d'Armor, 49°32'·00N 01°58'·00W. Rtg 3-3-2. Marina is on the W bank of the R Rance, 6M above the barrage and 0·5M above the two St Hubert bridges. Access approx HW±3, when tide is 8m above CD, giving at least 1·5m water above rising gate. Approach on about 285°, ent in line with Plouër church spire. Unlit PHM and SHM perches are 30m from ent at S end of bkwtr. Ent is marked by FR and FG lts which are lit, by day or night, whenever access is available. Depth gauge (hard to read) has W flood-light. Facilities: **Marina** (240+ visitors on pontoon B) ☎ 02·96·86·83·15. VHF Ch 09. AB FF38-72, Slip, AC, FW, BY, R, Bar, limited V.

LYVET, Hr Mr ☎ 02·96·83·35·57; **Marina** (175 berths) AC, FW, R, Bar, limited V. Immediately upstream of Chatelier lock, on the E bank.

DINAN, Hr Mr ☎ 02·96·39·56·44; **Marina** AC, FW, P, D, C for masts, R, Bar. Berths line the W bank of the river, with finger pontoons close to the Port. Low bridge beyond Port has 2·5m headroom, giving access to the Ille et Rance canal. **Town** (75m above water level) V, R, ✉, Ⓑ, ⇌, ✈ (Dinard).

Ille et Rance canal (see opposite): On the Breton canals the tolls charged elsewhere in France (see 10.15.8) are not envisaged. A certificate of competence is not required, unless LOA >15m or speed >20kph/11kn.

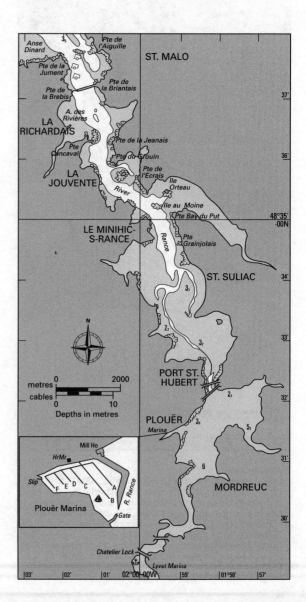

INLAND WATERWAYS OF BRITTANY

NAVIGATION

Canals and rivers across and within Brittany enable boats of limited water and air drafts to go from the Channel to the Bay of Biscay avoiding the passage around Finistere. Dinan to Arzal takes about 5 days. Distances, number of locks, boat size and speed limits are summarised opposite.

LOCKS

From Apr to Sept locks are worked 7 days a week 0800-1930LT, closing for lunch 1230-1330 approx. All locks are attended, but a fair measure of self-help is the order of the day. In Jul/Aug, in order to conserve water, locks may open on the hour only (and at H+30 if traffic demands).

ACCESS

For prior estimate of max draught possible, write: Equipement, Ille et Vilaine, 1 Avenue de Mail, 35000 Rennes. (☎ 02·99.59.20.60; 🖅 02·99.54.03.99); or obtain recorded information update on ☎ 99.59.11.12. For latest info on the Ille et Rance Canal/R Vilaine, contact: Rennes ☎ 02·99.59.20.60 or Redon ☎ 02·99.71.03.78. For the Lorient-Nantes Canal, contact: Nantes ☎ 02·40.71.02.00; Hennebont ☎ 02·97.85.15.15; Lorient ☎ 02·97.21.21.54; Pontivy ☎ 02·97.25.55.21. Closures *(Chômages)* for maintenance are scheduled in late autumn and in winter each Wednesday (approx first week in November to last week in March).

INFORMATION

For maps and guide books write (with SAE) to: Comité des Canaux Bretons, Service de Documentation du Comité, 12 rue de Jemmapes, 44000 Nantes (☎ 02·40.47.42.94). *Inland Waterways of France:* D Edwards-May (Imray) and the ECM Carte-Guide No 12 are recommended.

TOLLS may be due on the R Loire only; see 10.15.8 for rates.

SUMMARY	Length km	No of locks	Max draft m	Max air draft m	Max LOA m	Max beam m	Speed limit kn
St MALO-ARZAL (Ille et Rance Canal and La Vilaine)							
R Rance-Dinan	29·0	1	1·3	19	25	–	5·4
Ille et Rance Canal							
Dinan-Rennes	79·0	48	1·2	2·5	25	4·5	4·3
Rennes-Redon	89·0	13	1·2	3·2/2·6*	25	4·5	4·3
Redon-Arzal	42·0	1	1·3				
*Depending on water level							
LORIENT - NANTES (See 10.17.14)							
Canal du Blavet							
Lorient-Pontivy	70	28	1·4	2·6	25	4·6	4·3
Nantes-Brest Canal							
	184·3	106	–	3	25	4·6	4·3
Pontivy-Rohan			0·8 (possible closure)				
Rohan-Josselin			1·0				
Josselin-Redon			1·4				
Redon-Quiheix			1·1				
L'Erdre River	27·6	1	1·4	3·8	400	6·2	13·5
R Loire, above Nantes (10.17.26), may be navigable to Angers.							
R L'AULNE (See 10.16.28)							
Brest-Chateaulin	42	1	3·0	N/A	25	–	–
Chateaulin-Carhaix							
	72	33	1·1	2·5	25	4·6	4·3

15

DAHOUET   10-15-19

Côte d'Armor 48°34′·85N 02°34′·30W   Rtg 3-2-2

CHARTS
AC *3674*, 2669; SHOM 7310, 7154, 6966; ECM 536; Imray C33B, C34; Stanfords 16
TIDES
−0520 Dover; ML 6·3; Duration 0550; Zone −0100

Standard Port ST-MALO (←—)

Times				Height (metres)			
High Water		Low Water		MHWS	MHWN	MLWN	MLWS
0100	0800	0300	0800	12·2	9·2	4·3	1·6
1300	2000	1500	2000				
Differences DAHOUET							
−0006	−0006	−0020	−0015	−0·9	−0·6	−0·3	−0·3
ERQUY							
−0005	0000	−0018	−0012	−0·6	−0·4	−0·1	−0·1
SAINT CAST							
−0002	−0002	−0005	−0005	−0·2	−0·1	−0·1	−0·1

SHELTER
Good, but ent (dries 4m) unsafe in fresh NW winds; a bar may form after strong NW'lies. Outer hbr (FVs) dries 5·5m; access HW±2. Marina, min depth 2·5m, accessible over sill 5·5m above CD.
NAVIGATION
WPT 48°35′·28N 02°35′·28W, unlit NCM By, 297°/117° from/to La Petite Muette SHM lt tr, 0·8M; appr in W sector (see 10.15.20 chartlet) until close in. Hbr ent is a narrow break in the cliffs. Pick up 148° transit of 2 W bns, leaving these to port and Petite Muette to stbd. The W ent, S of Petite Muette is dangerous. There are rks W and SW of the ent.
LIGHTS AND MARKS
The wide beach at Val André and the W chapel at hbr ent are both conspic; see also 10.15.20 for other conspic marks in the bay. Appr is marked by G/W lt tr, La Petite Muette, Fl WRG 4s 10m 9/6M, G055°-114°, W114°-146°, R146°-196°. Stone pagoda is seen NE of ent. SHM bn, Fl (2) G 6s, vis 156°-286°, marks the narrow ent abeam the 2 W ldg bns. Sill ent has PHM and SHM perches.
RADIO TELEPHONE
VHF Ch 09 16.
TELEPHONE (Prefix ☎ nos with zone code 02)
Hr Mr 96·72·82·85; Météo 36·65·02·22; ☷ 96·74·75·32; Aff Mar 96·72·31·42; CROSS 98·89·31·31; Auto 08·36·68·08·22; Ⓗ 96·45·23·28; Brit Consul 99·46·26·64; Police 96·72·22·18.
FACILITIES
Marina (318+20) ☎ 96·72·82·85, FF87, FW, AC, BH (10 ton), Slip, C (14 ton); **Quay** P, D, C (4 ton); **YC du Val-André** ☎ 96·72·95·28;
Services: CH, El, ME, Sh. **Town**, V, R, Bar, ≥ (Lamballe), ✈ (St. Brieuc). Ferry: St. Malo-Portsmouth.

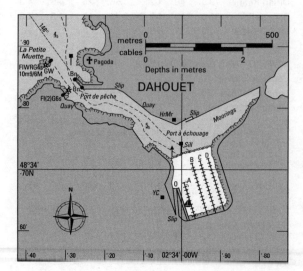

OTHER HARBOURS BETWEEN ST MALO AND DAHOUET

SAINT CAST, Côte d'Armor, 48°38′·45N 02°14′·51W. AC *3659*, 2669; SHOM 5646, 7155. HW −0515 on Dover (UT); ML 6·8m; Duration 0550. See 10·15·19. Good shelter from SW to N winds; ⚓ available in 1·8m. Beware Les Bourdinots (dry 2m) with ECM ¾M NE of Pte de St Cast, and La Feuillade (IDM bn) and Bec Rond (R bn) off hbr. Mole hd, Iso WG 4s 11m 11/8M; appr in either W sector (see 10.15.4). Hr Mr ☎ 02·96·41·88·34; SNSM ☎ 02·96·41·88·34; Facilities: YC ☎ 02·96·41·91·77. **Town** CH, El, ME, Sh, Ⓑ, Bar, D, P, ✉, R, V.

ERQUY, Côte d'Armor, 48°38′·10N 02°28′·60W. AC 3672, *3674*, 2669; SHOM 7310, 7154. HW −0515 on Dover (UT); ML 6·5m; Duration 0550. See 10·15·19. Sheltered from E, but exposed to SW/W winds. Hbr dries and is usually full of FVs. Beware Plateau des Portes d'Erquy (dry) about 2M to W. From S, beware rks off Pte de la Houssaye. Mole hd lt Oc (3+1) WRG 12s 11m 11/8M; appr in either W sector (see 10.15.4). Inner jetty hd Fl R 2·5s 10m 3M. Hr Mr and ☷ ☎ 02·96·72·19·32; **Cercle de la Voile d'Erquy** ☎ 02·96·72·32·40; Facilities: **Quay** C (3·5 ton), D, FW, P; **Town** CH, El, ME, Sh, R, V, Bar.

VAL-ANDRÉ, Côte d'Armor, 48°35′·88N 02°33′·24W. AC *3674*, 2669; SHOM 7310, 7154. HW −0520 on Dover (UT); ML 6·1m; Duration 0550. Tides as 10.15.19. Small drying hbr exposed to S/SW winds; access HW±3. From the E beware Le Verdelet, and Platier des Trois Têtes from the W. Berth on the quay, ask YC for mooring off Le Piegu or ⚓ off. Facilities: Hr Mr ☎ 02·96·72·83·20, FW, Slip; **YC du Val-André** ☎ 02·96·72·21·68; **Town** CH, El, ME, Sh, Bar, R, V.

LE LÉGUÉ (ST BRIEUC)   10-15-20

Côte d'Armor 48°31′·95N 02°43′·30W   Rtg 3-1-3

CHARTS
AC *3674*, 2669; SHOM 7128, 7154, 6966; ECM 536; Imray C34, C33B; Stanfords 16
TIDES
−0520 Dover; ML 6·5; Duration 0550; Zone −0100

Standard Port ST-MALO (←—)

Times				Height (metres)			
High Water		Low Water		MHWS	MHWN	MLWN	MLWS
0100	0800	0300	0800	12·2	9·2	4·3	1·6
1300	2000	1500	2000				
Differences LE LÉGUÉ							
+0005	+0005	−0013	−0003	−0·7	−0·3	−0·2	−0·2

SHELTER
Very good in Le Légué (the port for St Brieuc), especially in the wet basin. Yachts use Bassin No 2 (min 3m) near viaduct. Lock opens HW −2 to HW+1 sp; HW ±1 nps. The lock sill is 5·0m above CD. Yachts can wait against Le Quai Gilette (N bank), but soft mud slopes very steeply to chan.
NAVIGATION
WPT 48°34′·39N 02°41′·09W, Le Légué SWM buoy, Fl Mo (A) 10s, Whis, 030°/210° from/to Pte de l'Aigle lt, 2·6M. Appr via buoyed chan (with some gaps); not advised in strong N/NE winds. The area dries E/SE of conspic Pte du Roselier; see 10·18·5. Keep close to Pte à l'Aigle to avoid Les Galettes Rks.
LIGHTS AND MARKS
Conspic marks: Rohein tr, from N, and Le Verdelet ls from E (beware Plateau des Jaunes). No ldg lines; 2 lts on the NW bank of the river de Gouet ent: Pte de l'Aigle, QG 13m 8M, vis 160°-070°, W tr G top. Jetée de la Douane (W columns with G top), Iso G 4s 6m 8M.
RADIO TELEPHONE
Call: *Légué Port* VHF Ch 12 16 (approx HW−2 to +1½).
TELEPHONE (Prefix ☎ nos with zone code 02)
Hr Mr 96·33·35·41; Aff Mar 96·61·22·61; CROSS 98·89·31·31; Météo 99·46·10·46 and VHF Ch 13; Auto 08·36·68·08·22; SNSM 96·88·35·47; ☷ 96·33·33·03; Police 96·94·52·25; Dr St Brieuc 96·61·49·07; Brit Consul 99·46·26·64.
FACILITIES
Quai (100+20 visitors), AB FF61, C (30 ton), P & D (cans on quai or tanker); **Services:** Sh, ME, El, CH, SM, Ⓔ, El, CH. **Town (St Brieuc)** P & D (cans), FW, Gaz, V, R, Bar, ✉, Ⓑ, ≥ ✈. Ferry: St Malo.

LE LÉGUÉ/ST BRIEUC *continued*

BINIC   10-15-21

Côte d'Armor 48°36′·12N 02°48′·90W   Rtg 4-3-2

CHARTS
AC *3674*, 2669; SHOM 7128, 7154, 6966; ECM 536; Imray C33B; Stanfords 16

TIDES
–0525 Dover; ML 6·3; Duration 0550; Zone –0100

Standard Port ST-MALO (←)

Times				Height (metres)			
High Water		Low Water		MHWS	MHWN	MLWN	MLWS
0100	0800	0300	0800	12·2	9·2	4·3	1·6
1300	2000	1500	2000				
Differences BINIC							
–0003	–0003	–0025	–0010	–0·8	–0·6	–0·3	–0·3

SHELTER
Good, especially in Bassin à Flot/marina (1·5-3m). Easy access HW±3 by day/night to Avant Port (dries), except in E winds. Lock opens, in working hrs, approx HW–1 to HW near sp, if tide reaches 9·5m; no opening near nps, when gate may be closed for 4 or 5 days.

NAVIGATION
WPT 48°37′·00N 02°42′·00W, 078°/258° from/to ent, 4·7M. Best appr from E, from Baie de St Brieuc (see 10-18-5) keeping E of Caffa ECM, from which ent bears 246°; or from N through Rade de Portrieux. Ent between moles dries 4·2m.

LIGHTS AND MARKS
Ldg line 275°, N mole hd lt tr, Oc (3) 12s 12m 12M, W tr, G gallery, on with church spire.
Gate and sliding bridge sigs on mast N of gate:
By day: St Andrew's Cross, B on W flag = Gate open
By night: Ⓦ and Ⓡ (hor) = No entry
Ⓦ and Ⓖ (hor) = No exit
Ⓡ and Ⓖ (hor) = No exit/entry

RADIO TELEPHONE
VHF Ch 09.

TELEPHONE (Prefix ☎ nos with zone code 02)
Hr Mr 96·73·61·86, ☏ 96.73.72.38; Aff Mar 96·70·42·27; SNSM 96.73.74.41; CROSS 98·89·31·31; ⌗ 96·74·75·32; Météo 99·46·10·46; Auto 08·36·68·08·22; Police 96·73·60·32; Dr 96·42·61·05; Ⓗ 96.94.31.71; Brit Consul 99·46·26·64.

FACILITIES
Bassin (540+60), AB FF71.20, FW, AC, C (20 ton), Slip;
Club Nautique de Binic ☎ 96·73·31·67;
Services: CH, ME, EI, Ⓔ, Sh, SM, SHOM.
Town P, V, Gaz, ◙, R, Bar, ✉, Ⓑ, ⇌ (bus to St Brieu), ✈ (St Brieuc). Ferry: St Malo.

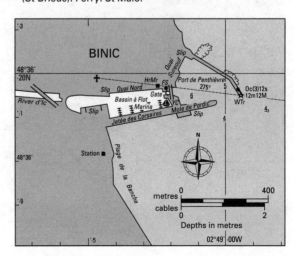

15

ST QUAY-PORTRIEUX   10-15-22

Côte d'Armor 48°38'·90N 02°48'·88W   Rtg 2-2-2

CHARTS
AC 3672, *3674*, 2669, *2668*; SHOM 7128, 7154, 6966; ECM
536, 537; Imray C33B, C34; Stanfords 16, 17

TIDES
−0520 Dover; ML 6·3; Duration 0550; Zone −0100

Standard Port ST-MALO (←)

Times				Height (metres)			
High Water		Low Water		MHWS	MHWN	MLWN	MLWS
0100	0800	0300	0800	12·2	9·2	4·3	1·6
1300	2000	1500	2000				
Differences ST QUAY-PORTRIEUX							
−0005	0000	−0020	−0010	−1·0	−0·6	−0·3	−0·2

SHELTER
Excellent in the marina (3·5m). Yachts may also dry out in
the Old Hbr. ⚓ in the Rade de Portrieux is good but
affected by winds from N to SE.

NAVIGATION
WPT 48°41'·00N 02°49'·60W, 349°/169° from/to NE mole
elbow, 2·0M. Portrieux lies inside the Roches de St Quay,
the chan between being about ½M wide. To NE lie the rky
Ile Harbour and to the E Rochers Déan. Due N beware the
Moulières de Portrieux, unlit ECM bn tr. From E and SE
appr via Caffa ECM Q (3) 10s and La Roselière WCM VQ
(9) 10s (both off chartlet).

LIGHTS AND MARKS
At night, from the N, White sectors of 4 Dir lts lead safely
to the marina in sequence 169°, 130°, 185° (astern), 318°
(see chartlet and below):
(1) NE mole elbow, Dir Iso WRG 4s 15/11M, **W159°-179°**,
G179°-316°, W316°-320·5°, R320·5°-159°.
(2) Herflux Dir lt, Fl (2) WRG 6s 8/6M, vis G115°-125°,
W125°-135°, R135°-145°; on Rochers Déan.
(3) Ile Harbour Dir lt, Oc (2) WRG 6s 16m 11/8M, vis R011°
-133°, G133°-270°, R270°-306°, G306°-358°, **W358°-011°**.
(4) NE mole elbow, as (1) above, **W316°-320·5°**.

RADIO TELEPHONE
VHF Ch 09 (0830-1230; 1330-1830LT. H24 in season).

TELEPHONE (Prefix ☎ nos with zone code 02)
Marina 96·70·81·30; Hr Mr (Old Hbr) 96·70·95·31; Aff Mar
96·70·42·27; CROSS 98·89·31·31; SNSM 96·70·52·04;
96·33·33·03; Météo 99·46·10·46; Auto 08.36.68.08.22;
Police 96·70·61·24; Dr 96·70·41·31; Brit Consul 99·46·26·64.

FACILITIES
Marina (900+100 visitors) ☎ 96·70·81·30, 🚢 96·70·81·31,
FF130, D, P, FW, BH, AC, C (5 ton);
Old Hbr (500+8 visitors) AB FF60, M, P, D, L, FW, Sh, Slip,
C (1·5 ton), ME, El, Ⓔ, Sh, CH, R, Bar;
Cercle de la Voile de Portrieux ☎ 96·70·41·76, M, FW, C (1
ton), Bar;
Town V, Gaz, R, Bar, ✉, Ⓑ, ⇌ (bus to St Brieuc), ✈ (St
Brieuc/Armor). Ferry: St Malo–Poole, Portsmouth.

VOLVO PENTA SERVICE

Sales and service centres in area 16
Names and addresses of Volvo Penta dealers in
this area are available from:
France *Volvo Penta France* , 55 Avenue des Champs Pierreux, 92757 Cedex
Tel +33 1 55175457, Fax +33 1 55175261

VOLVO PENTA

Area 16

North Brittany
Paimpol to Raz de Sein

16

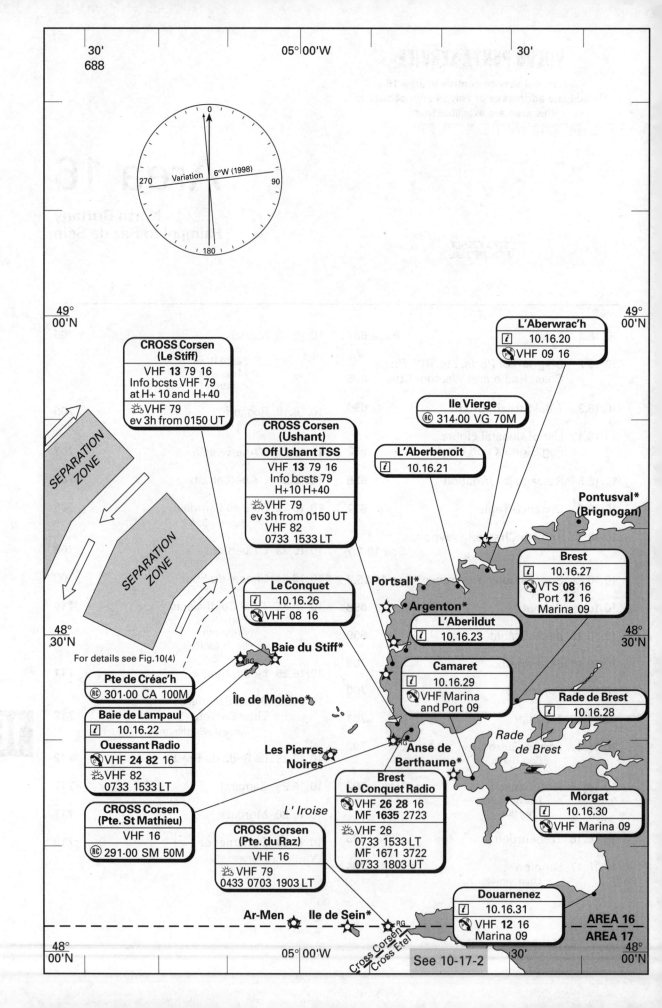

30'
688

05° 00'W

30'

Variation 6°W (1998)

49°
00'N

**CROSS Corsen
(Le Stiff)**
VHF **13** 79 16
Info bcsts VHF 79
at H+ 10 and H+40
VHF 79
ev 3h from 0150 UT

**CROSS Corsen
(Ushant)**
Off Ushant TSS
VHF **13** 79 16
Info bcsts 79
H+10 H+40
VHF 79
ev 3h from 0150 UT
VHF 82
0733 1533 LT

L'Aberwrac'h
ⓘ 10.16.20
VHF 09 16

49°
00'N

Ile Vierge
ⓇⒸ 314·00 VG 70M

L'Aberbenoit
ⓘ 10.16.21

**Pontusval*
(Brignogan)**

Brest
ⓘ 10.16.27
VTS **08** 16
Port **12** 16
Marina 09

SEPARATION
ZONE

SEPARATION
ZONE

Le Conquet
ⓘ 10.16.26
VHF 08 16

Portsall*

Argenton*

L'Aberildut
ⓘ 10.16.23

48°
30'N

For details see Fig.10(4)

Pte de Créac'h
ⓇⒸ 301·00 CA 100M

Baie du Stiff*
RG

Camaret
ⓘ 10.16.29
VHF Marina
and Port 09

Rade de Brest
ⓘ 10.16.28

48°
30'N

Baie de Lampaul
ⓘ 10.16.22
Ouessant Radio
VHF **24 82** 16
VHF 82
0733 1533 LT

Île de Molène*

**Les Pierres
Noires**

**Anse de
Berthaume***

Rade
de Brest

L' Iroise

Morgat
ⓘ 10.16.30
VHF Marina 09

**CROSS Corsen
(Pte. St Mathieu)**
VHF 16
ⓇⒸ 291·00 SM 50M

**CROSS Corsen
(Pte. du Raz)**
VHF 16
VHF 79
0433 0703 1903 LT

**Brest
Le Conquet Radio**
VHF **26 28** 16
MF **1635** 2723
VHF 26
0733 1533 LT
MF 1671 3722
0733 1803 UT

Ar-Men

Ile de Sein*

RG

Cross Corsen
Cross Etel

Douarnenez
ⓘ 10.16.31
VHF **12** 16
Marina 09

AREA 16

AREA 17

48°
00'N

05° 00'W

30'

See 10-17-2

48°
00'N

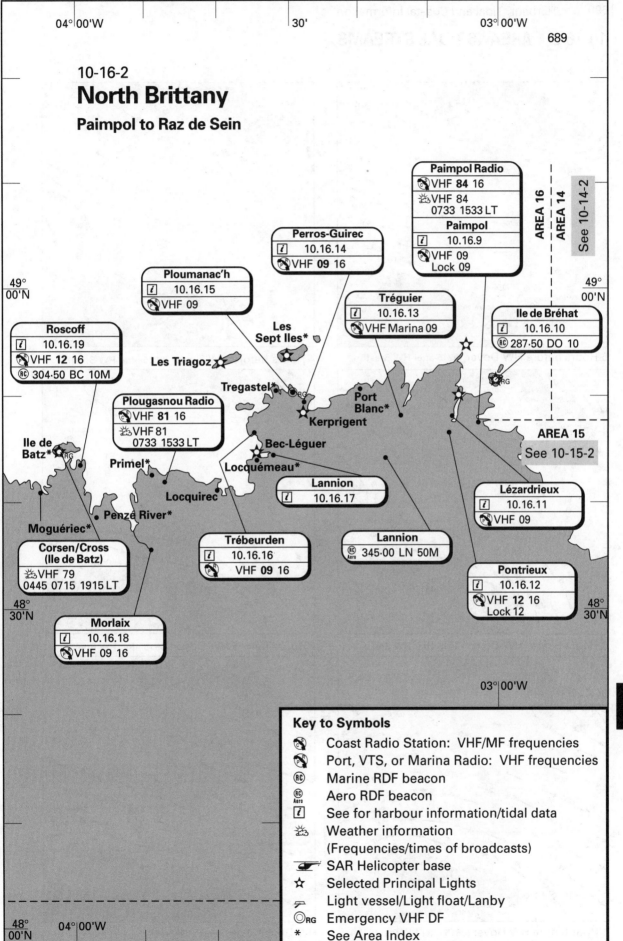

10-16-2

North Brittany

Paimpol to Raz de Sein

Paimpol Radio
📻 VHF **84** 16
🌦 VHF 84
0733 1533 LT

Paimpol
ℹ️ 10.16.9
📻 VHF 09
Lock 09

AREA 16

AREA 14

See 10-14-2

Perros-Guirec
ℹ️ 10.16.14
📻 VHF **09** 16

Ploumanac'h
ℹ️ 10.16.15
📻 VHF 09

Tréguier
ℹ️ 10.16.13
📻 VHF Marina 09

Ile de Bréhat
ℹ️ 10.16.10
🔘 287·50 DO 10

Les
Sept Iles*

Roscoff
ℹ️ 10.16.19
📻 VHF **12** 16
🔘 304·50 BC 10M

Les Triagoz✶

Tregastel*

Port
Blanc*

Kerprigent

Plougasnou Radio
📻 VHF **81** 16
🌦 VHF 81
0733 1533 LT

Ile de
Batz*

Bec-Léguer

Primel*

Locquémeau*

Locquirec

Lannion
ℹ️ 10.16.17

Lézardrieux
ℹ️ 10.16.11
📻 VHF 09

AREA 15

See 10-15-2

Penzé River*

Moguériec*

**Corsen/Cross
(Ile de Batz)**
🌦 VHF 79
0445 0715 1915 LT

Trébeurden
ℹ️ 10.16.16
VHF **09** 16

Lannion
🔘 345·00 LN 50M

Pontrieux
ℹ️ 10.16.12
📻 VHF **12** 16
Lock 12

Morlaix
ℹ️ 10.16.18
📻 VHF 09 16

03° 00'W

16

Key to Symbols

📻	Coast Radio Station: VHF/MF frequencies
📻	Port, VTS, or Marina Radio: VHF frequencies
🔘	Marine RDF beacon
🔘 Aero	Aero RDF beacon
ℹ️	See for harbour information/tidal data
🌦	Weather information (Frequencies/times of broadcasts)
🚁	SAR Helicopter base
✶	Selected Principal Lights
⚓	Light vessel/Light float/Lanby
◎RG	Emergency VHF DF
*	See Area Index

10-16-3   AREA 16 TIDAL STREAMS

5 Hours before HW Dover (0215 after HW Brest)

4 Hours before HW Dover (0315 after HW Brest)

3 Hours before HW Dover (0415 after HW Brest)

2 Hours before HW Dover (0515 after HW Brest)

1 Hour before HW Dover (0615 after HW Brest)

HW Dover (0510 before HW Brest)

Southward 10.17.3   Eastward 10.15.3   Northward 10.1.3

1 Hour after HW Dover (0410 before HW Brest)

2 Hours after HW Dover (0310 before HW Brest)

3 Hours after HW Dover (0210 before HW Brest)

4 Hours after HW Dover (0110 before HW Brest)

5 Hours after HW Dover (0010 before HW Brest)

6 Hours after HW Dover (0050 after HW Brest)

16

10.16.4 COASTAL LIGHTS, FOG SIGNALS AND WAYPOINTS

Abbreviations used below are given in 1.4.1. Principal lights are in **bold** print, places in CAPITALS, and light-vessels, light floats and Lanbys in *CAPITAL ITALICS*. Unless otherwise stated lights are white. m – elevation in metres; M – nominal range in miles. Fog signals are in *italics*. Useful waypoints are underlined – use those on land with care. All geographical positions should be assumed to be approximate. See 4.4.1. All positions are referenced to the ED 50 datum.

NOTE: For English Channel Waypoints see 10.1.7.

OFFSHORE MARKS

Roches Douvres 49°06'·35N 02°48'·65W Fl 5s 60m **28M**; pink Tr on dwelling with G roof; RC; RG; *Siren 60s*.
Barnouic Lt Tr 49°01'·70N 02°48'·33W VQ (3) 5s 15m 7M; ECM.
Roche Gautier Lt By 49°00'·49N 02°52'·92W VQ (9) 10s; WCM; *Whis*.

PAIMPOL TO ÎLE DE BRÉHAT

PAIMPOL
Les Calemarguiers By 48°47'·04N 02°54'·77W; ECM.
L'Ost Pic Lt Tr 48°46'·82N 02°56'·33W Oc WR 4s 20m W11M, R8M; 2 W Trs, R tops; vis W105°-116°, R116°-221°, W221°-253°, R253°-291°, W291°-329°; obsc by islets near Bréhat when brg less than 162°.
Les Charpentiers Bn 48°47'·95N 02°55'·92W; ECM.
La Gueule By 48°47'·48N 02°57'·25W; PHM.
La Jument Bn 48°47'·41N 02°57'·88W; PHM.

Pte de Porz-Don 48°47'·53N 03°01'·47W Oc (2) WR 6s 13m **W15M**, R11M; W house; vis W269°-272°, R272°-279°.
Ldg Lts 262·2°. Kernoa, front, 48°47'·26N 03°02'·37W FR 5m 7M; W & R hut. Rear, 370m from front, Dir FR 12m 14M; W pylon, R top; intens 260·2°-264·2°.

CHENAL DU DENOU/CHENAL DE BRÉHAT
Roc'h Denou Bn 48°47'·90N 02°57'·96W; W Bn.
Roc'h Denou Vihan Bn 48°48'·50N 02°57'·87W; SHM.
La Petite Moisie Bn 48°48'·65N 02°57'·60W; PHM.
Cain Ar Monse By 48°50'·22N 02°56'·73W; NCM.
Roche Guarine By 48°51'·69N 02°57'·54W; ECM.

CHENAL DU FERLAS
Le Ar Serive By 48°50'·04N 02°58'·68W; SCM.
Cadenenou By 48°49'·87N 02°58'·97W; NCM.
Les Piliers Bn 48°49'·83N 02°59'·91W; NCM.
Réceveur Bihan Bn 48°49'·76N 03°01'·87W; SCM.
Roche Quinonec Dir Lt 257·3°, 48°49'·43N 03°03'·58W Dir Q WRG 12m W10M, R8M, G8M; Gy Tr; vis G254°-257°, W257°-257·7°, R257·7°-260·7°.
Rompa Bn 48°49'·64N 02°02'·67W; IDM.
Kermouster, Embouchure du Trieux Dir Lt 271°, 48°49'·62N 03°05'·11W Dir Fl WRG 2s 16m W10M, R8M, G8M; W col; vis G267°-270°, W270°-272°, R272°-274°.

ÎLE DE BRÉHAT
Men-Marc'h By 48°52'·23N 02°51'·71W; ECM.
Nord Horaine By 48°54'·48N 02°55'·08W; NCM.
La Horaine 48°53'·57N 02°55'·15W Fl (3) 12s 13m 11M; Gy 8-sided Tr on B hut.

Rosédo 48°51'·51N 03°00'·21W Fl 5s 29m **20M**; W Tr; RC.
Le Paon 48°51'·98N 02°59'·08W F WRG 22m W11M, R8M, G8M; Y Tr; vis W033°-078°, G078°-181°, W181°-196°, R196°-307°, W307°-316°, R316°-348°.
Men-Joliguet 48°50'·18N 03°00'·12W Iso WRG 4s 6m W13M, R10M, G10M; WCM Bn Tr; vis R255°-279°, W279°-283°, G283°-175°.

LÉZARDRIEUX TO TRÉGUIER

LE TRIEUX RIVER, LÉZARDRIEUX/PONTRIEUX
Les Echaudés 48°53'·42N 02°57'·26W; PHM.
Les Sirlots By 48°53'·00N 02°59'·48W; SHM; *Whis*.
Vieille du Tréou Bn Tr 48°52'·05N 03°01'·00W; SHM.
Gosrod Bn 48°51'·48N 03°01'·14W; PHM.
Men Grenn Lt Bn Tr 48°51'·27N 03°03'·84W Q (9) 15s 7m 7M; WCM.
Ldg Lts 224·7°. Front, **La Croix** 48°50'·28N 03°03'·16W Dir Oc 4s 15m **19M**; two Gy ● Trs joined, W on NE side, R tops; intens 215°-235°. Rear **Bodic**, 2·1M from front Dir Q 55m **22M**; W house with G gable; intens 221°-229°.
Coatmer Ldg Lts 218·7°. Front, 48°48'·32N 03°05'·67W F RG 16m R9M, G9M; W gable; vis R200°-250°, G250°-053°. Rear, 660m from front, FR 50m 9M; W gable; vis 197°-242°.
Les Perdrix Lt Tr 48°47'·80N 03°05'·71W Fl (2) WG 6s 5m W6M, G3M; G Tr; vis G165°-197°, W197°-202·5°, G202·5°-040°.
3 F Bu Lts mark Marina pontoons, 750m SSW.

LE TRIEUX RIVER TO TRÉGUIER RIVER
An Ogejou Bihan Bn 48°53'·44N 03°01'·83W; ECM.
La Moisie Bn 48°53'·89N 03°02'·15W; ECM.
Les Héaux de Bréhat 48°54'·57N 03°05'·10W Oc (3) WRG 12s 48m **W15M**, R11M, G11M; Gy ● Tr; vis R227°-247°, W247°-270°, G270°-302°, W302°-227°.
Basse des Héaux Bn 48°54'·13N 03°05'·20W; SHM.
Pont de la Gaîne Bn 48°53'·20N 03°07'·26W; PHM.

TRÉGUIER RIVER
La Jument des Héaux Lt By 48°55'·41N 03°07'·95W VQ; NCM; *Bell*.
Grande Passe Ldg Lts 137°. Front, Port de la Chaîne 48°51'·61N 03°07'·80W Oc 4s 12m 11M; W house. Rear, **St Antoine**, 0·75M from front, Dir Oc R 4s 34m **15M**; R&W house; intens 134°-140°.
Basse Crublent Lt By 48°54'·35N 03°11'·07W Fl (2) R 6s; PHM; *Whis*.
Le Corbeau By 48°53'·42N 03°10'·20W; PHM.
Pierre à l'Anglais By 48°53'·30N 03°10'·38W; SHM.
Petit Pen ar Guézec By 48°52'·58N 03°09'·34W; SHM.
La Corne Lt Tr 48°51'·40N 03°10'·53W Fl (3) WRG 12s 14m W11M, R8M, G8M; W Tr, R base; vis W052°-059°, R059°-173°, G173°-213°, W213°-220°, R220°-052°.

TRÉGUIER TO TRÉBEURDEN

PORT-BLANC
Le Voleur Lt Tr 48°50'·27N 03°18'·44W Fl WRG 4s 17m W14M, R11M, G11M; W Tr; vis G140°-148°, W148°-152°, R152°-160°.

PERROS-GUIREC
Basse Guazer By 48°51'·65N 03°20'·89W; PHM.
Passe de l'Est Ldg Lts 224·5°. Front, **Le Colombier** 48°47'·93N 03°26'·58W Dir Oc (4) 12s 28m **15M**; W house; intens 214·5°-234·5°. Rear, **Kerprigent**, 1·5M from front, Dir Q 79m **21M**; W Tr; intens 221°-228°.
Pierre à Jean Rouzic By 48°49'·61N 03°24'·11W; SHM.
Pierre du Chenal Bn 48°49'·35N 03°24'·59W; IDM.
Passe de l'Ouest. Kerjean Dir Lt 143·6° 48°47'·85N 03°23'·31W Dir Oc (2+1) WRG 12s 78m **W15M**, R12M, G12M; W Tr, B top; vis G133·7°-143·2°, W143·2°-144·8°, R144·8°-154·3°.
Roc'h Hu de Perros Bn 48°48'·88N 03°24'·87W; PHM.
Jetée Est (Linkin) Hd 48°48'·26N 03°26'·23W Fl (2) G 6s 4m 9M; W pile, G top.
Roche Bernard Bn 48°49'·50N 03°25'·38W; SHM.
La Fronde By 48°49'·93N 03°25'·90W; SHM.
Bilzic Bn 48°50'·27N 03°25'·65W; PHM.
La Horaine Bn 48°49'·95N 03°27'·18W; NCM.
Les Couillons de Tomé By 48°50'·95N 03°25'·60W; WCM.

PLOUMANAC'H

Men-Ruz 48°50'·32N 03°28'·90W Oc WR 4s 26m W12M, R9M; pink ■ Tr; vis W226°-242°, R242°-226°; obsc by Pte de Trégastel when brg less than 080°, and part obsc by Les Sept-Îles 156°-207°, and by Île Tomé 264°-278°.

LES SEPT-ÎLES

Île-aux-Moines 48°52'·78N 03°29'·33W Fl (3) 15s 59m **24M**; Gy Tr and dwelling; obsc by Îlot Rouzic and E end of Île Bono 237°-241°, and in Baie de Lannion when brg less than 039°.
Les Dervinis By 48°52'·41N 03°27'·23W; SCM.

TRÉGASTEL

Île Dhu Bn 48°50'·43N 03°31'·13W; PHM.
Le Taureau Bn 48°50'·47N 03°31'·51W; SHM.

Les Triagoz 48°52'·35N 03°38'·73W Oc (2) WR 6s 31m W14M, R11M; Gy ■ Tr, R lantern; vis W010°-339°, R339°-010°; obsc in places 258°-268° by Les Sept-Îles.
Bar ar Gall Lt By 48°49'·80N 03°36'·00W VQ (9) 10s; WCM.
Le Crapaud Lt By 48°46'·65N 03°40'·40W Q (9) 15s; WCM.

TRÉBEURDEN

Ar Gouredec Lt By 48°46'·49N 03°36'·40W VQ (6) + L Fl 10s; SCM.
Lt By 48°46'·54N 03°35'·89W Fl (2) R 6s; PHM.
Pt de Lan Kerellec 48°46'·80N 03°34'·98W Iso WRG 4s; W8M, R5M, G5M; vis G058°-064°, W064°-069°, R069°-130°.

TRÉBEURDEN TO ROSCOFF

LÉGUER RIVER, LANNION

Kinierbel By 48°44'·20N 03°34'·95W; SHM; *Bell.*
Beg-Léguer 48°44'·40N 03°32'·83W Oc (4) WRG 12s 60m W12M, R9M, G9M; W face of W house, R lantern; vis G007°-084°, W084°-098°, R098°-129°.

LOCQUÉMEAU

Ldg Lts 121°. Front, 48°43'·48N 03°34'·40W FR 21m 6M; W pylon, R top; vis 068°-228°. Rear, 484m from front Oc (2+1) R 12s 39m 7M; W gabled house; vis 016°-232°.
Locquémeau By 48°43'·94N 03°35'·73W; SHM; *Whis.*

PRIMEL

Ldg Lts 152°. Front, 48°42'·52N 03°49'·10W FR 35m 6M; W ■, R stripe on pylon; vis 134°-168°. Rear, 172m from front, FR 56m 6M; W ■, R stripe.
Jetty Hd 48°42'·82N 03°49'·53W Fl G 4s 6m 7M.
Méloine By 48°45'·65N 03°50'·55W; WCM; *Whis.*

BAIE DE MORLAIX

Chenal du Tréguier Ldg Lts 190·5°. Front, Île Noire 48°40'·41N 03°52'·44W Oc (2) WRG 6s 15m W11M, R8M, G8M; W ■ Tr, R top; vis G051°-135°, R135°-211°, W211°-051°; obsc in places. Common Rear, **La Lande** 48°38'·26N 03°53'·04W Fl 5s 85m **23M**; W ■ Tr, B top; obsc by Pte Annelouesten when brg more than 204°.
La Pierre Noire Bn 48°41'·71N 03°53'·97W; SHM.
La Chambre Bn 48°40'·80N 03°52'·41W; SHM.
Grande Chenal Ldg Lts 176·4°. Front, **Île Louet** 48°40'·47N 03°53'·24W Oc (3) WG 12s 17m **W15M**, G10M; W ■ Tr, B top; vis W305°-244°, G244°-305°, vis 139°-223° from offshore, except when obsc by Is. Common Rear, **La Lande** above.
Pot de Fer By 48°44'·29N 03°53'·93W; ECM.
Vieille Bn 48°42'·66N 03°54'·03W; SHM.
Stolvezen By 48°42'·71N 03°53'·32W; PHM.
La Noire Bn 48°42'·61N 03°52'·11W; SHM.
Ricard Bn 48°41'·60N 03°53'·40W; SHM.
Barre de-Flot No. 1 By 48°40'·24N 05°52'·86W; SHM.
Marine farm prohib area Lt By 48°43'·00N 03°54'·10W VQ (6) + L Fl 10s; SCM.

BLOSCON/ROSCOFF

Le Menk Lt Bn Tr 48°43'·35N 03°56'·60W Q (9) WR 15s 6m W5M, R3M; vis W160°-188°; WCM.
Bloscon Jetty Hd 48°43'·27N 03°57'·59W Fl WG 4s 9m W10M, G7M; W Tr, G top, vis W206°-216°, G216°-206°; RC. In fog Fl 2s.
Ar Pourven Lt By 48°43'·10N 03°57'·61W Q; NCM.
Astan Lt By 48°44'·95N 03°57'·55W VQ (3) 5s 9m 6M; ECM; *Whis*; Ra refl.
Basse de Bloscon Lt By 48°43'·77N 03°57'·48W VQ; NCM.
Ar-Chaden Lt Bn 48°43'·99N 03°58'·15W Q (6) + L Fl WR 15s 14m W8M, R6M; vis R262°-289·5°, W289·5°-293°, R293°-326°, W326°-110°; SCM.
Men-Guen-Bras Lt Bn 48°43'·81N 03°57'·95W Q WRG 14m W9M, R6M, G6M; vis W068°-073°, R073°-197°, W197°-257°, G257°-068°; NCM.
Roscoff Ldg Lts 209°. Front, N Môle 48°43'·62N 03°58'·57W Oc (2+1) G 12s 7m 7M; W col, G top; vis 078°-318°. **Rear**, 430m from front, Oc (2+1) 12s 24m **15M**; Gy ■ Tr, W on NE side; vis 062°-242°.
Jetty Hd 48°43'·98N 03°58'·87W F Vi; W & Purple **l**.

ÎLE DE BATZ TO ÎLE VIERGE

ÎLE DE BATZ

Lt Ho 48°44'·78N 04°01'·55W Fl (4) 25s 69m **23M**; Gy Tr; auxiliary Lt FR 65m 7M; same Tr; vis 024°-059°.

CANAL DE L'ÎLE DE BATZ

Perroch Bn 48°44'·17N 03°59'·62W; NCM.
Île aux Moutons Ldg stage 48°44'·31N 04°00'·34W VQ (6) + L Fl 10s 3m 7M; SCM.
L'Oignon Bn 48°44'·10N 04°01'·27W; NCM.
Basse Plate Bn 48°44'·32N 04°02'·44W; NCM.

MOGUÉRIEC.

Ldg Lts 162°. Front, Jetty Hd 48°41'·40N 04°04'·40W Iso WG 4s 9m W11M, G6M; W Tr, G top; vis W158°-166°, G166°-158°. Rear, 440m from front, FG 22m 7M; W Col, G top; vis 142°-182°.

PONTUSVAL

Pointe de Pontusval By 48°41'·51N 04°19'·12W; ECM.
Ar Peich By 48°40'·95N 04°19'·08W; SHM.
An Neudenn Bn 48°40'·72N 04°19'·01W; PHM.
Pte de Beg-Pol 48°40'·73N 04°20'·70W Oc (3) WR 12s 16m W10M, R7M; W ■ Tr, B top, W dwelling; vis W shore-056°, R056°-096°, W096°-shore. QY and FR Lts on towers 2·4M S.

Aman-ar-Ross Lt By 48°41'·94N 04°26'·96W Q 9m 7M; NCM; *Whis.*
Barr Ar-Skoaz By 48°38'·29N 04°29'·99W; PHM.
Lizen Ven Ouest Lt By 48°40'·55N 04°33'·68W VQ (9) 10s 8m 5M; WCM; *Whis.*
Île-Vierge 48°38'·38N 04°33'·97W Fl 5s 77m **27M**; Gy Tr; vis 337°-325°; RC; *Horn 60s.*

ÎLE VIERGE TO LE FOUR

L'ABERWRAC'H

Libenter Lt By 48°37'·57N 04°38'·35W Q (9) 15s 8m 6M; Ra refl; WCM; *Whis.*
Ldg Lts 100·1° Front, Île Wrac'h 48°36'·95N 04°34'·47W QR 20m 7M; W ■ Tr, Or top, dwelling. Rear, Lanvaon 1·63M from front, Dir Q 55m 12M; W ■ Tr, Or ▲ on top; intens 090°-110°.
Trepied By 48°37'·35N 04°37'·47W; PHM.
Grand Pot de Beurre Bn 48°37'·27N 04°36'·39W; PHM.
Petit Pot de Beurre Bn 48°37'·18N 04°36'·13W; ECM.
Basse de la Croix Lt By 48°36'·98N 04°35'·90W Fl (3) G 12s; SHM.

16

Breac'h Ver Lt Tr 48°36'·70N 04°35'·30W Fl G 2·5s 6m 3M; ▲ on Tr; SHM.
Dir Lt 128°, N Bkwtr 48°35'·95N 04°33'·72W Dir Oc (2) WRG 6s 5m W13M, R11M, G11M; vis G125·7°-127·2°, W127·2°-128·7°, R128·7°-130·2°.

L'ABER BENOÎT
Petite Fourche By 48°37'·05N 04°38'·67W; WCM.
Rusven Ouest By 48°36'·15N 04°39'·34W.
Rusven Est By 48°36'·37N 04°38'·53W; SHM.
Basse de Chenal 48°35'·87N 04°38'·44W; SWM.
Poul Orvil By 48°35'·58N 04°38'·20W; WCM.
La Jument Bn 48°35'·19N 04°37'·30W; PHM.
Le Chien Bn 48°34'·73N 04°36'·80W; IDM.

Le Relec By 48°36'·05N 04°40'·76W; ECM.
Corn-Carhai 48°35'·25N 04°43'·86W Fl (3) 12s 19m 9M; W 8-sided Tr, B top.
Basse Paupian By 48°35'·38N 04°46'·16W; WCM.
Grande Basse de Portsall Lt By 48°36'·78N 04°46'·05W VQ (9) 10s 9m 4M; Ra refl; WCM; Whis.

PORTSALL/ARGENTON
Bosven Arval Bn 48°33'·88N 04°44'·18W; W Bn.
Men ar Pic Bn 48°33'·72N 04°43'·93W; G Bn.
Portsall 48°33'·89N 04°42'·18W Oc (4) WRG 12s 9m W13M, R10M, G10M; W col, R top; vis G058°-084°, W084°- 088°, R088°-058°.
Île Dolvez Front Ldg Mark 086° 48°31'·32N 04°46'·13W; W Bn.

Le Four 48°31'·45N 04°48'·23W Fl (5) 15s 28m **18M**; Gy ● Tr; Horn (3+2) 60s.

Le Taureau Bn 48°31'·51N 04°47'·26W; WCM.

CHENAL DU FOUR

L'ABER-ILDUT
L'Aber-Ildut 48°28'·32N 04°45'·47W Dir Oc (2) WR 6s 12m **W25M, R20M**; W bldgs; vis W081°-085°, R085°-087°.

Ldg Lts 158·5°. Front, **Kermorvan** 48°21'·80N 04°47'·31W Fl 5s 20m **22M**. Rear, **Pte de St Mathieu** Fl 15s 56m **29M**; Dir F 54m **28M**; same Tr; intens 157·5°-159·5° (see above).
Les Plâtresses 48°26'·35N 04°50'·85W Fl RG 4s 17m 6M; W Tr; vis R343°-153°, G153°-333°.
La Valbelle Lt By 48°26'·55N 04°49'·90W Fl (2) R 6s 8m 5M; PHM; Whis.
SE Plâtresses By 48°26'·03N 04°50'·43W; SHM.
Le Tendoc By 48°25'·73N 04°49'·36W; PHM.
Saint Paul Lt By 48°24'·93N 04°49'·08W Oc (2) R 9s; PHM.
Taboga By 48°23'·88N 04°47'·99W; IDM.

Pte de Corsen 48°24'·95N 04°47'·52W Dir Q WRG 33m W12M, R8M, G8M; W hut; vis R008°-012°, W012°-015°, G015°-021°.
Kermorvan 48°21'·80N 04°47'·31W Fl 5s 20m **22M**; W □ Tr; obsc by Pte de St Mathieu when brg less than 341°.
Rouget Lt By 48°22'·10N 04°48'·79W Fl G 4s; SHM; Whis.
La Grande Vinotière Lt Tr 48°22'·00N 04°48'·33W L Fl R 10s 15m 5M; R 8-sided Tr.

LE CONQUET
Môle Sainte Barbe 48°21'·64N 04°46'·94W Oc G 4s 5m 6M.

Bas des Renards By 48°21'·05N 04°47'·50W; IDM.
Lochrist 48°20'·63N 04°45'·73W Dir Oc (3) 12s 49m **22M**; W 8-sided Tr, R top; intens 135°-140°.
Tournant et Lochrist Lt By 48°20'·70N 04°48'·03W Iso R 4s; PHM.
Ar C'hristian Braz Bn 48°20'·75N 04°50'·10W; ECM.
Ldg Lts 007°. Front, **Kermorvan** 48°21'·80N 04°47'·31W Fl 5s 20m **22M**. Rear, **Trézien** 48°25'·48N 04°46'·65W Dir Oc (2) 6s 84m **20M**; Gy Tr, W on S side; intens 003°-011°.

Pte de St Mathieu 48°19'·85N 04°46'·17W Fl 15s 56m **29M**; W Tr, R top. Dir F 54m **28M**; same Tr; intens 157·5°-159·5°; RC. 54m 291° from St Mathieu Q WRG 26m, W14M, R11M, G11M; W Tr; vis G085°-107°, W107°-116°, R116°-134°.
La Fourmi By 48°19'·31N 04°47'·88W; SHM.
Les Vieux-Moines 48°19'·40N 04°46'·55W Fl R 4s 16m 5M; R 8-sided Tr; vis 280°-133°; PHM.

CHENAL DE LA HELLE

Ldg Lt 137·9°. Front, **Kermorvan** 48°21'·80N 04°47'·31W Fl 5s 20m **22M**. Rear, **Lochrist** 48°20·63N 04°45'·73W Dir Oc (3) 12s 49m **22M** (see above).
Luronne By 48°26'·67N 04°53'·70W; WCM; Bell.
Ldg Lts 293·5°. Front, Le Faix Lt Tr 48°25'·78N 04°53'·82W VQ; 16m 8M; NCM. Rear, **Le Stiff** 48°28'·60N 05°03'·10W Fl (2) R 20s 85m **24M** (see below).
Ldg Lt 142·5° for Chenal de La Helle. Front, **Kermorvan** 48°21'·80N 04°47'·31W Fl 5s 20m **22M** (see above). Rear, two W Bns 48°20'·17N 04°45'·44W.
Pourceaux Lt By 48°24'·07N 04°51'·22W Q; NCM.
S. Pierre By 48°23'·15N 04°49'·00W; SHM.

OUESSANT AND ÎLE DE MOLÈNE

Men-Korn Lt Bn Tr 48°27'·95N 05°01'·22W VQ (3) WR 5s 21m W8M, R8M; vis W145°-040°, R040°-145°; ECM.
Le Stiff 48°28'·60N 05°03'·10W Fl (2) R 20s 85m **24M**; two adjoining W Trs.
Gorle Vihan Bn 48°28'·40N 05°02'·50W; IDM.
Port du Stiff, Môle Est Hd 48°28'·18N 05°03'·16W Dir Q WRG 11m W10M, R7M, G7M; W Tr, G top; vis G251°-254°, W254°-264°, R264°-267°.

OUESSANT SW LANBY 48°31'·20N 05°49'·10W Fl 4s 10m **20M**; RC; Racon (M).
NE Lt By 48°45'·90N 05°11'·60W L Fl 10s 9m 8M; Whis; Racon.
Créac'h 48°27'·62N 05°07'·72W Fl (2) 10s 70m **32M**; W Tr, B bands; obsc 247°-255°; Racon (C), RC; RG; Horn (2) 120s.
Nividic Lt Tr 48°26'·80N 05°08'·95W VQ (9) 10s 28m 9M; W 8-sided Tr, R bands; obsc by Ouessant 225°-290°. Helicopter platform.
La Jument 48°25'·40N 05°07'·95W Fl (3) R 15s 36m **22M**; Gy 8-sided Tr, R Top; vis 241°-199°; Horn (3) 60s.
Men ar Froud Bn 48°26'·70N 05°03'·57W; SCM.

Kéréon (Men-Tensel) 48°26'·30N 05°01'·45W Oc (2+1) WR 24s 38m **W17M,** R7M; Gy Tr; vis W019°-248°, R248°-019°; Horn (2+1) 120s.
Pierres-Vertes Lt By 48°22'·26N 05°04'·68W VQ (9) 10s 9m 5M; WCM; Whis; Ra refl.

ÎLE DE MOLÈNE
Les Trois-Pierres 48°24'·75N 04°56'·75W Iso WRG 4s 15m W9M, R6M, G6M; W col; vis G070°-147°, W147°-185°, R185°-191°, G191°-197°, W197°-213°, R213°-070°.
Molène, Old Môle Hd Dir Lt 191° 48°23'·91N 04°57'·18W Dir Fl (3) WRG 12s 6m W9M, R7M, G7M; vis G183°-190°, W190°-192°, R192°-203°. Chenal des Laz Dir Lt 261°, Dir Fl (2) WRG 6s 9m W9M, R7M, G7M; same structure; vis G252·5°-259·5°, W259·5°-262·5°, R262·5°-269·5°.

L'IROISE/BREST AND APPROACHES

Pierres Noires By 48°18'·54N 04°58'·18W; SCM; Bell.
Les Pierres Noires 48°18'·73N 04°54'·80W Fl R 5s 27m **19M**; W Tr, R top; Horn (2) 60s.
Basse Royale Lt By 48°17'·52N 04°49'·52W Q (6) + L Fl 15s; SCM.
Vandrée Lt By 48°15'·30N 04°48'·17W VQ (9) 10s; Whis; WCM.

La Parquette 48°15'·96N 04°44'·25W Fl RG 4s 17m R6M, G6M; W 8-sided Tr, B diagonal stripes; vis R244°-285°, G285°-244°.

GOULET DE BREST
Roc du Charles Martel Lt By 48°18'·90N 04°42'·10W Fl (4) R; PHM; *Whis*.
Swansea Vale Lt By 48°18'·27N 04°38'·75W Fl (2) 6s; *Whis*; IDM.

CAMARET
Môle Nord Hd 48°16'·92N 04°35'·20W Iso WG 4s 7m W12M, G9M; W pylon, G top; vis W135°-182°, G182°-027°.
Môle Sud Hd 48°16'·69N 04°35'·25W Fl (2) R 6s 9m 5M; R pylon.

Pointe du Toulinguet 48°16'·88N 04°37'·64W Oc (3) WR 12s 49m **W15M**, R11M; W ■ Tr on bldg; vis W shore-028°, R028°-090°, W090°-shore.
Pte du Petit-Minou 48°20'·26N 04°36'·80W Fl (2) WR 6s 32m **W19M, R15M**; Gy Tr, R top; vis Rshore-252°, W252°-260°, R260°-307°, W(unintens) 307°-015°,W015°-065·5°, W070·5°-shore. Same structure, Ldg Lts 068°. **Front**, Dir Q 30m **23M,** intens 067·3°-068·8°. **Rear, Pte du Portzic**, Dir Q 56m **22M**; intens 065°-071°
Fillettes Lt By 48°19'·81N 04°35'·58W VQ (9); WCM; *Whis*.
Kerviniou Lt By 48°19'·81N 04°35'·20W Fl (2) 6s; PHM.
Roche Mengam 48°20'·40N 04°34'·48W Fl (3) WR 12s 10m W11M, R8M, R Tr, B bands; vis R034°-054°, W054°-034°.
Pte du Portzic 48°21'·55N 04°31'·96W Oc (2) WR 12s 56m **W19M, R15M**; Gy Tr; vis R219°-259°, W259°-338°, R338°-000°, W000°-065·5°, W070·5°-219°. Same structure Dir Q (6) + L Fl 15s 54m **23M**; intens 045°-050°.

BREST
Pénoupèle Lt By 48°28'·51N 04°30'·43W Fl (3) R 12s; PHM.
Port Militaire, Jetée Sud Hd 48°22'·17N 04°29'·37W QR 10m 5M; W Tr, R top; vis 094°-048°.
Jetée Est Hd 48°22'·22N 04°29'·12W QG 10m 8M; W Tr, G top; vis 299°-163°.
Ldg Lts 344°. Front, 48°22'·85N 04°29'·53W VQ WRG; 24m; W10M, R5M, G5M; vis G 334°-342°, W342°-346°, R346°-024°. Rear,118m from front, Dir VQ 32m 10M.
La Penfeld Ldg Lts 314° Front 48°22'·93N 04°29'·85W   Dir Iso R 5s 9m 10M. Rear, 17m from front, Dir Iso R 5s 16m 12M; both intens 309°-319°.
Port de Commerce Jetée du Sud W Hd 48°22'·66N 04°29'·02W Fl G 4s 10m 6M; vis 022°-257°.
Port de Commerce Jeteé du Sud E Hd 48°22'·76N 04°28'·39W Oc (2) R 6s 8m 5M; W pylon, R top; vis 018°-301°.

R2 Lt By 48°22'·07N 04°28'·66W Fl (2) R 6s; PHM.
R1 Lt By 48°21'·80N 04°28'·22W Fl G 4s; SHM.
R4 Lt By 48°22'·28N 04°27'·91W Fl R 10s; PHM.
Lt Bn 48°22'·74N 04°26'·45W Fl (4) R 15s; R □ on pile.
Moulin Blanc Lt By 48°22'·85N 04°25'·90W Fl (3) R 12s; PHM.

LE MOULIN BLANC
MB1 Lt By 48°23'·29N 04°25'·66W Fl G 2s; SHM.

L'IROISE/BAIE DE DOUARNENEZ
Basse Du Lis Lt By 48°13'·05N 04°44'·46W Q (6) + L Fl 15s 9m 6M; SCM HFP; *Whis*.
Le Chevreau By 48°13'·35N 04°36'·85W; WCM.
Le Bouc Lt By 48°11'·58N 04°37'·29W Q (9) 15s; WCM; *Whis*.
Basse Vieille Lt By 48°08'·30N 04°35'·68W Fl (2) 6s 8m 7M; IDM HFP; *Whis*; Ra refl.

MORGAT
Pointe de Morgat 48°13'·24N 04°29'·72W Oc (4) WRG 12s 77m **W15M**, R11M, G10M; W ■ Tr, R top, W dwelling; vis W shore-281°, G281°-301°, W301°-021°, R021°-043°; obsc by Pte du Rostudel when brg more than 027°.
Mole Hd 48°13'·57N 04°29'·92W Oc (2) WR 6s 8m W9M, R6M; W&R framework Tr; vis Wshore-257°, R257°-shore.
Marina ent through wavebreak pontoons marked by Fl G 4s to stbd and Fl R 4s to port.

DOUARNENEZ
Épi de Biron Hd 48°06'·15N 04°20'·38W QG 7m 6M; W col, G top.
Île Tristan 48°06'·20N 04°20'·17W Oc (3) WR 12s 35m W13M, R10M; Gy Tr, W band, B top; vis W shore-138°, R138°-153°, W153°-shore; obsc by Pte de Leidé when brg less than 111°.
Bassin Nord, N Mole E Hd 48°06'·02N 04°19'·20W Iso G 4s 9m 4M; W & G pylon.
S Mole N Hd Oc (2) R 6s 6m 6M; W&R pylon.
Elbow, Môle de Rosmeur Hd 48°05'·86N 04°19'·15W Oc G 4s 6m 6M; W pylon, G top; vis 170°-097°.

Pointe du Millier 48°05'·99N 04°27'·85W Oc (2) WRG 6s 34m **W16M**, R12M, G11M; W house; vis G080°-087°, W087°-113°, R113°-120°, W120°-129°, G129°-148°, W148°-251°, R251°-258°; part obsc 255·5°-081·5°.
Basse Jaune By 48°05'·25N 04°42'·35W; IDM.
Tévennec 48°04'·34N 04°47'·65W Q WR 28m W10M, R7M; W Tr; viz W090°-345°, R345°-090°. Dir Fl 4s 24m 12M; same Tr intens 324°-332°.

16

10.16.5   PASSAGE INFORMATION

NORTH BRITTANY (charts 2643 *2644 2668*)

Refer to *North Brittany Pilot* (Imray/RCC); Admiralty *Channel Pilot* (NP 27); *North Brittany and CI Cruising* (YM/Cumberlidge); *Brittany and CI Cruising Guide* (Adlard Coles/Jefferson), and *Shell Channel Pilot* (Imray/Cunliffe). For French Glossary see 1.4.2, and 10.17.5 for Breton words with navigational value.

Good landfall marks must be carefully identified before closing this rock-strewn coast. Closer inshore the tidal streams and currents vary, and overfalls are best avoided. In rough weather, low visibility (fog and summer haze are frequent) or if uncertain of position, it may be prudent to lie off and wait for conditions to improve; there are few safe havens. A high degree of planning is needed to achieve safe pilotage. In the W of the area the size of Atlantic swells can much reduce the range at which objects, especially floating marks, are seen.

PAIMPOL TO PLOUMANAC'H (AC 3670)

In the offing, between 11M and 18M NNE of Île de Bréhat, are Plateau de Barnouic (lit) and Plateau des Roches Douvres (lt, fog sig, RC), both with drying and submerged rks, to be given a wide berth particularly in poor vis.

Approaching from the SE, keep to seaward of the three ECM buoys off L'Ost-Pic or enter B de Paimpol (10.16.9) from a point about 1M E of the most N'ly ECM (Les Charpentiers). The Ferlas chan (AC 3673) runs S of Île de Bréhat (10.16.10), and is useful if entering/leaving R. Trieux from/to the E. It is well marked and not difficult, but best taken at half tide due to unmarked rks in chan almost awash at or near LW.

For the many yachts approaching from Guernsey, Les Héaux-de-Bréhat lt ho is a conspic landfall day/night for either Tréguier or Lézardrieux. Closer in or from the E, La Horaine (lt bn) is the best landfall for the latter. It marks the Plateaux de la horaine and des Échaudés and other rks to the SE. In poor visibility it should be closed with caution and left at least 7ca to the SE, as the flood stream sets strongly onto it. The Grand Chenal is the main, lit chan into R. de trieux for Lézardrieux (10.16.11) and up-river to Pontrieux (10.16.12). From NW the unlit Chenal de La Moisie leads SSE to join the Grand Chenal at Île de Bréhat (10.16.10).

Between Lézardrieux and Tréguier (10.16.13) the Passage de la Gaine is a useful inshore route, avoiding a detour round Les Heaux. It is unlit and needs good vis, but if taken at above half tide, presents no problem in fair weather. The Grande Passe into R. de Tréguier is well lit, but ldg marks are less easy to see by day. The NE Passage should be used with caution.

Between Basse Crublent lt buoy and Port Blanc unmarked rks extend 2M offshore. Port Blanc (AC 3672) can be difficult to identify by day. Perros-Guirec (10.16.14) is approached either side of Ile Tomé from NE or NW via well lit/marked chans (AC 3672). Ploumanac'h (10.16.15) can only be entered by day.

LES SEPT ÎLES TO BAIE DE MORLAIX (AC 3669)

Les Sept Îles (10.16.16 and AC 3670) consist of five main islands and several islets, through which the tide runs strongly. Île aux Moines is lit, and all the islands are bird sanctuaries. Further W, Plateau des Triagoz has offlying dangers WSW and NE of the lt, where the sea breaks heavily. Here the stream turns ENE at HW Brest – 0325, and WSW at HW Brest +0245, sp rates both 3·8kn.

Trégastel Ste Anne (10.16.16) is a small anchorage W of Ploumanac'h. To the SW the coast as far as Trébeurden (10.16.16) is not easily approached due to many offlying rks. The radome NE of Trébeurden is conspic. Further S in the B de Lannion is Locquémeau and anchs near the mouth of the drying R. Léguier up to Lannion (10.16.17). Primel (10.16.18), at the E ent to Baie de Morlaix, provides a good deep anch. To the N is the drying Plateau de la Méloine.

The B de Morlaix (10.16.18 and AC 2745) is bestrewn with drying rks and shoals, all marked. Careful pilotage and adequate visibility are needed to negotiate any of the chans which are narrow in parts. The Grand Chenal passes close E of Île Ricard with Île Louet and La Lande (both lit) in transit 176°; abeam Calhic bn tr alter to port to transit between Château du Taureau (conspic) and Île Louet. Continue SSE for the river up to Morlaix. The anchorage NE of Carantec is reached from Chenal Ouest de Ricard.

ÎLE DE BATZ TO LE FOUR (charts 3668, 3669)

N of Île de Batz the E-going stream begins at HW Brest – 0435, and the W-going stream at HW Brest +0105, sp rates 3·8kn. Approaching Roscoff (10.16.19) from NE, leave Basse Astan ECM lt buoy to stbd steering with Men Guen Bras NCM lt bn in transit 213° with Chapelle St Barbe to round Ar Chaden for Roscoff hbr (dries); or transit W via Canal de L'Île de Batz.

In daylight and above half tide Canal de L'Île de Batz is a useful short cut between the island and the mainland. From near Ar Chaden steer 275° for the Vi bn at end of the conspic Roscoff ferry pier. Pass 30m N of this bn, and at this point alter to 300° for Run Oan SCM. Thence steer 283°, leaving Perroch NCM bn 100m to port. When clear of this rky, drying shoal alter to 270°, leaving Por Kernock hbr bkwtrs well to stbd and aiming midway between L'Oignon NCM and La Croix SCM. When these are abeam steer 281° for Basse Plate NCM bn; thence West into open waters.

Proceeding W from Île de Batz toward Le Four there are many off-lying dangers, in places 3M offshore. Swell may break on shoals even further to seaward. The tide runs strongly, and in poor vis or bad weather it is a coast to avoid. But in good conditions this is an admirable cruising ground with delightful hbrs such as Moguériec and Pontusval (10.16.18), L'Aberwrac'h (10.16.20), L'Aberbenoit (10.16.21), Portsall and Argenton (10.16.25). N of L'Aberwrac'h is Île Vierge lt ho, reputedly the tallest in the world, and a conspic landmark. Off Le Libenter, at N side of L'Aberwrac'h ent, the E-going stream starts at HW Brest – 0500, sp rate 3·8kn, and the W-going stream at HW Brest + 0110.

W of L'Aberwrac'h is an inshore chan leading past Portsall to Le Four (lt bn). This is a sheltered short-cut, but must only be used by day and in good visibility. AC 1432 or SHOM 5772 and full directions, as in *North Brittany Pilot*, are needed.

OUESSANT (USHANT) (chart 2694)

Île Ouessant lies 10M off NW Brittany. It is a rky island, with dangers extending 5ca to NE, 7½ca to SE, 1·5M to SW and 1M to NW; here Chaussée de Keller is a dangerous chain of drying and submerged rks running 1M W of Île de Keller and into the ITZ. Apart from Lampaul (10.16.22) the only other anch is B du Stiff which gives some shelter in moderate winds between S and NW. Tidal streams are strong close to the island, and in chans between it and mainland. Off Pte de Créac'h (lt, fog sig, RC) the stream turns NNE at HW Brest – 0550, and SSW at HW Brest + 0045, sp rate 5·5kn.

The route outside Ouessant TSS, Fig 10(4), has little to commend it. Unless bound to/from Spain/Portugal it adds much to the distance and is exposed to sea and swell. Yachts should route Ouessant via the ITZ or the inshore channels. Besides being an important landfall, Ouessant in thick weather is an unhealthy area, and it is prudent to stay in harbour until the vis improves. But in fair weather and reasonable visibility the pilotage in the chans between it and the mainland is not very demanding. They are well buoyed and marked (see 10.16.24), but the tide runs hard in places, causing overfalls when wind against wind >Force 5.

The three main chans between the island and mainland are: The Chenal du Four, inshore and most direct and popular; Chenal de la Helle, an alternative to N part of Chenal du Four (partly used for access to Île Molène), is not so direct but better in bad weather. Passage du Fromveur, close SE of Ouessant, is easiest but longer and can become extremely rough; tidal streams may exceed 8kn.

CHENAL DU FOUR (10.16.24 and AC 3345, 2694)

It is imperative to work the tides to best advantage through this passage: 1M W of Le Four the S-going stream begins at HW Brest + 0130; the N-going stream at HW Brest – 0545, sp rates 3·6kn. Further S, off Pte de Corsen, the stream is weaker, max 2·3kn at sp. The tide runs strongest at S end of Chenal du Four, off Le Conquet. Here the S-going stream starts at HW Brest + 0015, max 5kn; the N-going stream begins at HW Brest – 0550, 5·2kn max at sp. Wind-over-tide effects may be considerable.

Yachts are less rigidly tied to transits/dir lts than large ships and the following pilotage sequence can be used day or night, buoy-hopping as necessary if transits are obscured:
From 1·2M W of Le Four, track 180° (04°50'W: clear of Les Liniou reef to port) for 5M to Valbelle PHM lt buoy. Here pick up the transit 158·5°of Pte de Kermorvan on with Pte St Mathieu. Maintain this transit until Pte de Corsen lt bears 012° astern; then alter 192° to pass between La Grande Vinotière lt bn and Roche du Rouget lt buoy. Stand on until Le Faix lt bn is on with Grand Courleau bn 325° astern; alter 145° to maintain this track for 2·3M when open water will be reached with Vieux-Moines lt bn 4ca abeam to port.

Double check all lt/marks; do not confuse St Mathieu with Lochrist. L'Aberildut (10.16.23), 3·5M SSE of Le Four, and Le Conquet (10.16.26), 3ca SE of Pte de Kermorvan are the only ports off the Chenal du Four; but in offshore winds anch can be found in Anse de Porsmoguer and Anse des Blancs-Sablons, both between Corsen and Kermorvan.

Homeward-bound, or along the N coast of France, enter the S end of Chenal du Four at LW Brest; a fair tide can then be carried through the chan and NE past Île Vierge. The reverse sequence of pilotage is followed.

CHENAL DE LA HELLE (10.16.24 and AC 3345, 2694)

At N end of Chenal de la Helle the ENE stream starts at HW Brest – 0520 (sp rate 2·8kn), and the SW stream at HW Brest – 0045 (sp rate 3·8kn). The Ch de la Helle converges at a 20° angle with the Ch du Four. From the N, steer SW from Le Four towards Ile de Molène lt to pick up the 138° transit of Pte de Kermorvan and Lochrist close to Luronne unlit WCM buoy. Maintain this transit until Le Faix lt bn and Le Stiff lt ho are in transit 293° astern; steer 113° for 8ca until Pte de Kermorvan is on with 2 W bns (Pignons de Kéravel) at 142°. This transit avoids Basse St Pierre (4·7m) and intercepts the Ch du Four 7ca N of Grande Vinotière.

APPROACHES TO BREST (charts 798, 3427, 3428)

The outer approaches lie between Chaussée des Pierres Noires and Pte St Mathieu to the N and Pte du Toulinguet to the S. From the W steer on the 068° transit of Petit Minhou and Portzic on the N shore. From the S steer NNE toward Petit Minhou to pick up the transit, but beware rks 7M W and SW of Pte du Toulinguet. Yachts <25m LOA are exempt from VTM, but should monitor VHF Ch 08 or 16.

Abeam Petit Minhou lt ho the Goulet (Narrows) de Brest narrows to 1M; there are well-marked drying rks almost in mid-stream. A course of 075° through the Passe Nord leaves Roc Mengam lt bn 2ca to stbd. Tidal streams attain 4·5kn in the Goulet. In Passe Sud there is a useful back-eddy close inshore which runs ENE during the ebb. Once beyond Pte du Portzic a buoyed chan leads ENE past the Naval and commercial hbrs to the Moulin Blanc marina (10.16.27). The Rade de Brest (10.16.28) opens to the S and E.

L'IROISE/BAIE DE DOUARNENEZ (charts 3427, 798)

L'Iroise is the area between Chaussée des Pierres Noires and Chaussée de Sein; the B de Douarnenez lies further E. On the NE side of L'Iroise (chart 3427) a chain of rks extends 7M W from Pte du Toulinguet. There are several chans through these rks, of which the simplest for Brest (10.16.27) and Camaret (10.15.29) is the 3ca wide Chenal du Toulinguet which runs NNW between La Louve bn tr (1ca W of Pte du Toulinguet) on E side and Le Pohen rk on the W side. Here the N-going stream begins at HW Brest – 0550, and the S-going at HW Brest + 0015, sp rates 2·75kn. 2·5M NW of C. de la Chèvre is Le Chévreau (dries), with La Chèvre 5ca to NE of it (1·25M WSW of Pte de Dinan). 7M W of Pte de Dinan lies Basse du Lis, rky shoals with depth of 2·4m.

The B de Douarnenez is entered between C. de la Chèvre and Raz de Sein. Off C. de la Chèvre various dangers, on which the sea breaks, extend SW for 2·25M to Basse Vieille (dries), lt buoy. Morgat (10.16.30) lies 4M NNE of C. de la Chèvre. Beware group of drying rks, including La Pierre-Profonde and Le Taureau close SSW of Les Verrès (rk 9m high), which lies nearly 2·5M ESE of Morgat.

Approaching Douarnenez (10.16.31) beware Basse Veur and Basse Neuve. The S shore of the B is clear of dangers more than 2ca offshore, except for Duellou Rk (4m high) 5ca offshore, and other rks 1M eastward. Further W beware Basse Jaune, an isolated rk (dries) about 1M N of Pte du Van.

10.16.6   DISTANCE TABLE

Approximate distances in nautical miles are by the most direct route, whilst avoiding dangers and allowing for Traffic Separation Schemes. Places in *italics* are in adjoining areas; places in **bold** are in 10.0.5, Cross-Channel Distances.

	1	2	3	4	5	6	7	8	9	10	11	12	13	14	15	16	17	18	19	20
1. *St Quay-Portrieux*	1																			
2. Paimpol	24	2																		
3. Bréhat (Port Clos)	15	8	3																	
4. **Lézardrieux**	21	14	6	4																
5. **Tréguier**	46	29	22	22	5															
6. Perros-Guirec	37	35	28	28	21	6														
7. Ploumanac'h	40	33	27	29	25	6	7													
8. Trébeurden	48	44	38	40	32	17	11	8												
9. **Lannion**	52	48	42	44	33	21	15	6	9											
10. Morlaix	67	64	58	60	46	36	30	23	24	10										
11. **Roscoff**	59	58	52	54	41	28	22	17	19	12	11									
12. **L'Aberwrac'h**	91	88	82	84	72	60	54	49	51	48	32	12								
13. L'Aberbenoit	92	89	83	85	76	61	55	50	52	45	33	7	13							
14. Lampaul	114	110	104	106	98	83	77	72	74	67	55	29	28	14						
15. **Le Conquet**	114	110	104	106	98	83	77	72	71	68	55	29	23	17	15					
16. Brest (marina)	125	119	114	114	107	92	86	83	87	79	67	42	41	31	18	16				
17. Camaret	124	120	114	116	98	93	87	82	81	78	65	39	33	27	13	10	17			
18. Morgat	134	130	124	126	118	103	97	92	91	88	75	49	43	37	20	24	16	18		
19. Douarnenez	139	135	129	131	123	108	102	97	96	93	80	54	48	42	25	29	21	11	19	
20. *Audierne*	144	139	133	135	128	113	108	102	101	98	86	55	53	40	30	34	28	27	30	20

10.16.7 English Channel Waypoints: See 10.1.7   **10.16.8** Special Notes for France: See 10.15.8

PAIMPOL   10-16-9

Côte d'Armor 48°47'·06N 03°02'·47W   Rtg 3-3-2

CHARTS
AC 3673, 3670, *2668*; SHOM 7127, 831, 7154; ECM 537; Imray C34; Stanfords 17

TIDES
Dover –0525; ML 6·1; Duration 0600; Zone –0100

Standard Port ST MALO (⟵)

Times				Height (metres)			
High Water		Low Water		MHWS	MHWN	MLWN	MLWS
0100	0800	0300	0800	12·2	9·2	4·3	1·6
1300	2000	1500	2000				
Differences PAIMPOL							
–0005	–0010	–0035	–0025	–1·4	–0·8	–0·5	–0·2

SHELTER
Good shelter from all winds in hbr, but few ⚓s as most of the Anse de Paimpol dries, including the appr chan to hbr. Lock opens HW ±2 when height of HW <10m; HW ±2½ when HW >10m. Visitors' berths at pontoon A, Basin No 2, min depth 3·8m. Larger yachts berth in Basin No 1.

NAVIGATION
WPT 48°47'·88N 02°54'·50W, 080°/260° from/to summit of Pte Brividic 4·7M. Chenal de la Jument is the normal appr from the E. After La Jument PHM bn tr, either ⚓ to await the tide; or alter 262° for unlit bns/buoys marking final 1M of chan. The drying rks (El Paimpol, El Bras and Ar Fav) are close N of the ldg line. An alternative appr from Ile de Bréhat at HW+2 lies E of Les Piliers NCM bn tr, thence S past Pte de la Trinité; or appr from further E via Chenal du Denou 193°. Bearing in mind the large tidal range, there is enough water in the bay from half-flood for most craft.

LIGHTS AND MARKS
4M E is L'Ost-Pic lt, Oc WR 4s 20m 11/8M, conspic □ W tr. Pte de Porz-Don, Oc (2) WR 6s 13m 15/11M, vis W269°-272°, R272°-279°, is 7ca ENE of hbr ent. W sector leads 270° to the inner ldg lts 262°. A conspic tr (52m) is 3ca W of Porz -Don.
Outer ldg marks 260° for Chenal de la Jument: Paimpol ⌖ spire on with the summit (27m) of Pte Brividic.
Inner ldg lts 262°: front, Jetée de Kernoa, FR 5m 7M; rear, Dir FR 12m 14M, intens 260°-264°.

RADIO TELEPHONE
VHF Ch 09 (0800-1200LT and lock opening hrs).

TELEPHONE (Prefix ☎ nos with zone code 02)
Hr Mr 96.20.47.65; Port Mgr 96·20·80·77; ⌗ 96·20·81·87; Aff Mar 96·20·84·30; CROSS 98·89·31·31;
Auto 08·36·68.08.22; Police 96·20·80·17; Ⓗ 96·20·86·02; Dr 96·20·80·04; Brit Consul 99·46·26·64.

FACILITIES
Basin No 2 (marina 280+20 visitors), FF98.50, FW, AC, D (quay), P (cans), ME, El; **Basin No 1** C (6 and 4 ton); **Quai de Kernoa** P, ME; **Quai neuf** Slip, M, FW, AB; **Services:** Sh, CH, SHOM, Ⓔ.
Town P, CH, V, R, Bar, Gaz, Ⓞ, ✉, Ⓑ, ⇌, ✈ Dinard, Brest, Rennes. Ferry: Roscoff, St Malo.

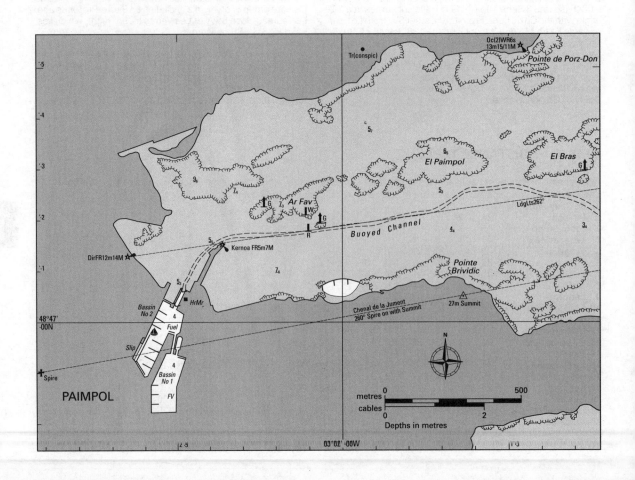

ILE DE BRÉHAT   10-16-10

Côte d'Armor 48°51'·00N 03°00'·00W   Rtg 2-4-1

CHARTS
AC 3673, 3670, *2668*; SHOM 7127, 831, 832; ECM 537;
Imray C34; Stanfords 17

TIDES
–0525 Dover; ML 5·8; Duration 0605; Zone –0100

Standard Port ST MALO (←)

Times				Height (metres)			
High Water		Low Water		MHWS	MHWN	MLWN	MLWS
0100	0800	0300	0800	12·2	9·2	4·3	1·6
1300	2000	1500	2000				
Differences LES HEAUX DE BRÉHAT							
–0018	–0017	–0050	–0050	–2·4	–1·6	–0·7	–0·3
ILE DE BRÉHAT							
–0008	–0013	–0040	–0037	–1·8	–1·2	–0·5	–0·3

SHELTER
Port Clos: drying main hbr; good shelter, but busy with
vedettes. No AB; ♄ clear of fairway. (Due to cables across
the Ferlas Chan, ♄ is prohib to the SW of Port Clos).
Port de la Corderie: hbr dries; get well out of strong tides.
Good shelter, except in W winds.
E of Le Bourg there are free drying private ⚓s near ♄.
La Chambre: ♄ in upper reaches just S of the 丁 area. Slip
can be floodlit by pressing button on lamp post at top of
slip.
Guerzido in the Chenal de Ferlas is good holding, partly
out of the strong tides. There are ⚓s or ♄ E of Men Allan
and close to the buoys of the boat barrier.

NAVIGATION
WPT Ferlas chan 48°49'·45N 02°55'·00W, 098°/278° from/to
La Croix lt, 5·5M. See also 10·16·10. On appr, beware La
Horaine, Men Marc'h and C'hign Bras closer in.

LIGHTS AND MARKS
For the three principal lts on Ile de Bréhat, see 10.16.4.

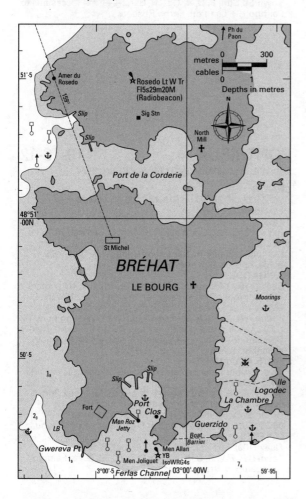

RADIO TELEPHONE
Sémaphore de Bréhat VHF Ch 16 10, Day only.
TELEPHONE (Prefix ☎ Nos with zone code 02)
Hr Mr none; CROSS 98·89·31·31; SNSM 96·20·00·14;
Auto 08·36·68.08.22; ⌗ 96·20·81·87; Police 96·20·80·17;
Dr 96·20·00·99; Brit Consul 99·46·26·64.

FACILITIES
Hbrs M, FW, P from fuel barge at Port Clos, Slip, full
access at HW; **CN de Bréhat**, FW, Bar; **Services:** ME.
Village V, Gaz, Bar, ✉, Ⓑ (Paimpol), ⇌ (ferry to Pte de
l'Arcouest, bus to Paimpol), ✈ (Dinard, Brest, Rennes to
London). Ferry: Plymouth-Roscoff. No cars on island.

---

*A Breton fishing-smack was working nets close to the
rocks. We sailed up to her and hailed:*
Où sommes nous? *The dripping men on board answered in
a chorus that came to us like the barking of sea lions. At
length we made out:* Les Roches Douvres.
*Now there was a flurry of charts and Sailing Directions.
Where was the nearest anchorage? (With us in such
circumstances the nearest is always the best). A place called
Lézardrieux situated some distance up the tidal Rivière de
Pontrieux, of whose dangers the Sailing Directions write in a
tone even more tartly warning than usual. Lézardrieux it
would have to be.*
*Fate is a strange bird. The night before I had ordered my
charts, Mr Adlard Coles had climbed down our ladder to have
a look at us. He happened to mention the anchorage at
Lézardrieux. So I had ordered a full-scale chart of the Pontrieux
River. On the chart the river looked small, but in the darkness
(and we were entering at approximately high water) it proved
to be vast.*
*A sea writhed and in places boiled on the bar, but we
buffeted through it. I had been so obsessed with navigation
and so keen to get somewhere as quickly as possible that it
had not occurred to me to reduce sail. Sailing at that speed
with breakers audible and sometimes visible on either hand
was too much for me, and I got down the mainsail. The engine
started at the first touch of the button.*
*We passed beacons, buoys, a cluster of wind-flattened
islands, and then entered the land between the hills. Leading
lights guided us up the main channel. A bend, more leading
lights, and the swell had changed to a ripple. The patent log
showed ninety-five miles for the day's run. We dropped
anchor in eight fathoms at the top of the last reach before the
village.*

A White boat from England (George Millar/Heinemann 1951)

AGENTS WANTED

If you are interested in becoming our agent for any of the
following ports, please write to: The Editor, Edington House,
Trent, Sherborne, Dorset DT9 4SR, England – and get your
free copy of the Almanac annually. You do not have to live in
a port to be the agent, but at least a fairly regular visitor.

Great Yarmouth	St Gilles-Croix-de-Vie
Port Ellen (Islay)	Les Sables d'Olonne
Maryport	Ile d'Oléron
Workington	River Seudre
Holyhead	Anglet/Bayonne
Lough Swilly	St Jean-de-Luz
St Peter Port, Guernsey	Hendaye
Diélette	Grandcamp-Maisy
Portbail	Port-en-Bessin
Iles Chausey	Courseulles
St Malo/Dinard	Ouistreham/Caen
Le Legue/St Brieuc	Emden
Tréguier	Dornumer-Accumersiel
Lampaul	Langeoog
L'Aberildut	Bremerhaven
Le Palais (Belle Ile)	Büsum
Morbihan/Vannes	

16

LÉZARDRIEUX   10-16-11

Côte d'Armor 48°47'·41N 03°05'·83W   Rtg 1-1-1

CHARTS
AC 3673, 3670, *2668*; SHOM 7126, 7127, 831, 7152; ECM 537; Imray C34; Stanfords 17

TIDES
−0510 Dover; ML 5·9; Duration 0610; Zone −0100

Standard Port ST MALO (←—)

Times				Height (metres)			
High Water		Low Water		MHWS	MHWN	MLWN	MLWS
0100	0800	0300	0800	12·2	9·2	4·3	1·6
1300	2000	1500	2000				
Differences LÉZARDRIEUX							
−0010	−0010	−0047	−0037	−1·7	−1·2	−0·6	−0·3

SHELTER
Very good in all weathers. The Trieux River and marina pontoons are accessible H24. Very close SW, a marina extension (247 berths) has some Ⓥ berths (2·4m inside). Access over sill 4·9m above CD, with automatic flap. As sill covers on the flood to 6·15m CD, flap automatically drops to give 1·25m clearance. A depth gauge shows water over sill. IPTS in use. Multi-hulls and boats >12·5m LOA should moor on ⓥs in the stream, rather than berth on pontoons. Yachts can go about 12km up river (bridge clearance 17m) to lock in at Pontrieux (10·16·11).

NAVIGATION
WPT 48°55'·00N 02°56'·20W, 045°/225° from/to front ldg lt 225° (La Croix), 6·7M. Roches Douvres and Barnouic are dangers in the outer apps; closer in, are the Plateau de la Horaine and rky shoals to the W. Off river ent beware strong cross streams. The 3 well-marked ent chans are:
Ferlas Chan from the E, running S of Ile de Bréhat;
Grand Chenal, main chan from NE, best for strangers;
and Moisie, unlit from the NW, which also connects with Passe de la Gaine from/to Tréguier (10.16.13).

LIGHTS AND MARKS
Offshore lts: Roches Douvres, Fl 5s 60m 28M, pink tr.
Barnouic ECM bn tr, VQ (3) 5s 15m 9M.
Les Héaux de Bréhat, Oc (3) WRG 12s 48m 17/12M, gy tr.
Pte du Paon and Rosédo, on Bréhat, see 10.16.4 and .12.
The ldg marks/lts for the ent chans are:
(1) Ferlas chan:
  W sector of Men Joliguet lt bn tr 271° (see 10.16.25).
  W sector of Roche Quinonec Dir Q WRG 257°.
  W sector of Kermouster Dir Fl WRG 2s leads 271° to join Coatmer ldg line.
(2) Grand Chenal ldg lts 225°: Front, La Croix Oc 4s 15m 19M; two grey trs joined, W on NE side with R tops, intens 215°-235°; rear, Bodic (2·1M from front) Q 55m 22M (intens 221°-229°).
(3) Moisie chan: Amer du Rosédo W obelisk on 159° with St Michael's chapel (both conspic on Ile de Bréhat).
Within the Trieux river:
(4) Coatmer ldg lts 219°: front F RG 16m 9/9M, vis R200°-250°, G250°-053°; rear, 660m from front, FR 50m 9M.
(5) W sector 200° of Les Perdrix G tr, Fl (2) WG 6s.
Beware, at night, the unlit Roc'h Donan 2½ca S of Perdrix. The only lts beyond Perdrix are F Bu lts at the outboard ends of the 3 'old' marina pontoons, and a Fl R 4s and Fl G 4s buoy 50 - 100m E of the ent to new marina; also unlit perches: PHM/SHM at ent; 1 ECM 50m NE of ent, and 5 Y SPM marking the limits of the marina.

RADIO TELEPHONE
VHF Ch 09 (0730-2200 Jul/Aug. 0800-1200 and 1400-1800 rest of year).

TELEPHONE (Prefix ☎ Nos with zone code 02)
Hr Mr 96·20·14·22; Aff Mar at Paimpol 96·20·84·30; CROSS 98·89·31·31; ☷ at Paimpol 96·20·81·87; Auto 08·36·68·08·22; Police 96·20·10·17; Dr 96·20·10·30; Brit Consul 99·46·26·64.

FACILITIES
Marina (477; visitors as directed by Hr Mr), ☎ 96·20·14·22, FF90, Slip, P, D, FW, AC, ME, EI, CH, SM, Sh, C (6 ton), Gaz, R, Ⓘ, Bar;
YC de Trieux ☎ 96·20·10·39. **Services:** Divers, Ⓔ;
Town EC Sun; P, D, V, Gaz, R, Bar, ⊠, Ⓑ, ⇌ (occas bus to Paimpol), ✈ Lannion. Ferry: Roscoff.

PONTRIEUX   10-16-12

Côte d'Armor 48°42'·80N 03°08'·90W   Rtg 3-4-1

CHARTS
ECM 537; AC 3673 and SHOM 7126 downstream of Lézardrieux

TIDES
HW at Pontrieux Lock is at HW ST MALO. See also 10·16·11.

SHELTER
Complete shelter in 2-4m depth alongside Quay (SE bank), approx 1km above lock.

NAVIGATION
See 10·16·11 for approach up to Lézardrieux. Not before HW −3, proceed via suspension bridge (17m clearance) 6M up-river, keeping to high, rky bank on bends. Lock opens HW −2 (−1 at weekends) to HW+1. Waiting buoy (½ tide) close E and slip with FW and AC on the bend. Below Château de la Roche Jagu there is also a waiting buoy available HW±3.

LIGHTS AND MARKS
River is unlit (beware sand dredgers at night); few marks.

RADIO TELEPHONE
Lock VHF Ch 12, HW −2 to +1. ☎ link to Pontrieux Port.

TELEPHONE (Prefix ☎ Nos with zone code 02)
Hr Mr ☎/⟱ 96·95·34·87; Lock 96·95·60·70; Auto 08.36.68.08.22. There is a ☎ at the Château Roche Jagu.

FACILITIES
Quay (100) AB FF72, FW, AC, C (6 ton), R, Bar.
Town Bar, FW, R, Slip, V, Gaz, P, D, Ⓑ, ⊠, Ⓘ, ⇌ Paimpol/Guingamp, ✈ Brest, Rennes & Dinard.

LIGHTS AND MARKS

Important marks: La Corne WR lt tr, Fl (3) WRG 12s 11/8M; 6ca to the N is Men Noblance WB bn tr on SE corner of Ile d'Er; and 4ca SW is Skeiviec W bn tr. The spire of Tréguier cathedral is 4·6M SSW of La Corne, but may be obscured by high wooded banks when entering the river estuary in the vicinity of Pen ar Guézec.

Ldg lts/marks for the appr chans:
(1) For Grande Passe 137°: front, Port de la Chaine, Oc 4s 12m 12M, white ho; rear, St Antoine Dir Oc R 4s 34m 15M, RW ho. At Pen ar Guézec unlit SHM buoy steer 216° in the W sector of La Corne lt.
Note: The ldg marks are very hard to identify by day. From Basse Crublent PHM buoy the Pleubian spire and water tower offer a clear transit 154° towards the Pierre à l'Anglais and Le Corbeau lateral buoys.
(2) For Passe de la Gaine 242°: Men Noblance bn tr, W with horiz B band, on with rear mark (W wall with B vert stripe) below the skyline and just right of conspic Plougrescant ✠. Hold this transit exactly to stay in narrow, marked chan; but marks hard to see from afar, especially against a low sun or in poor visibility.
(3) Passe du Nord-Est, for direct appr to La Corne having cleared W of La Jument NCM By and adjacent rky shoals: Tréguier cathedral spire and Skeiviec at 207°.

RADIO TELEPHONE

Marina Ch 09 (In season: Mon-Sat 0800-1200, 1330-2100; Sun 0800-1000, 1600-1800. Out of season: Sun/Mon closed; Tue-Sat 0800-1200, 1330-1700. All LT).

TELEPHONE (Prefix ☎ Nos with zone code 02)

Hr Mr 96·92·42·37; Aff Mar 96·92·30·38; CROSS 96·54·11·11; ⌗ 96·92·31·44; Auto 08·36·68.08.22; Police 96·92·32·17; Dr 96·92·32·14; Ⓗ 96·92·30·72; Brit Consul 99·46·26·64.

FACILITIES

Marina (200+130 visitors), ☎ 96·92·42·37, 🕿 96.92.29.25 (indicate for Port de Plaisance), FF80, Slip, FW, ME, C (8 ton), D (on most N'ly pontoon HW±1), CH, El, Sh, AC, Bar, R, Gaz, ▣;

Club Nautique du Trégor ☎ 96·92·42·37, excellent facilities, open all year. **Services:** M, CH;

Town EC Mon; Market Wed, P, FW, CH, V, Gaz, R, Bar, ✉, Ⓑ, V (small supermarket just E of cathedral delivers to boats), 🚍 (bus to Paimpol and Perros-Guirec), ✈ (St Brieuc, Lannion). Ferry: Roscoff.

PONTRIEUX
03°10'·00W

TRÉGUIER   10-16-13

Côte d'Armor 48°47'·27N 03°13'·18W   Rtg 1-2-1

CHARTS

AC 3672, 3670, *2668*; SHOM 7126, 7152; ECM 537; Imray C34; Stanfords 17

TIDES

−0540 Dover; ML 5·7; Duration 0600; Zone −0100
Standard Port ST MALO (←)

Times				Height (metres)			
High Water		Low Water		MHWS	MHWN	MLWN	MLWS
0100	0800	0300	0800	12·2	9·2	4·3	1·6
1300	2000	1500	2000				
Differences TRÉGUIER							
−0005	−0010	−0055	−0040	−2·3	−1·5	−0·7	−0·3
PORT-BÉNI							
−0017	−0022	−0100	−0045	−2·4	−1·5	−0·6	−0·2

SHELTER

Good in marina; always berth head to tide which runs hard through the pontoons. Possible ⚓s, keeping clear of the chan: 7ca SW of La Corne lt tr, but exposed to N'lies; N and S of La Roche Jaune village; in pool 1ca NE of No 10 buoy (1M N of marina).

NAVIGATION

WPT 48°55'·25N 03°13'·00W, 317°/137° from/to front ldg lt, 5M (Grande Passe). There are three ent chans:
(1) Grande Passe: well marked/lit, but marks are hard to see by day. Caution: strong tidal streams across the chan.
(2) Passe de la Gaine: well marked, navigable with care by day in good vis. Unlit short cut to/from Lézardrieux.
(3) Passe du Nord-Est: unlit, dangerous with winds from W and NW as sea breaks across the chan.
Within the R Jaudy it is important to heed chan buoys/bns. Speed limit is 6kn above La Roche Jaune.

MINOR HARBOUR, approx 8M ENE of PERROS-GUIREC

PORT BLANC, Côte d'Armor, 48°50′·60N 03°18′·80W, AC 3672, 3670; SHOM 7125, 7152. HW −0545 on Dover (UT); HW−0040 and ht −2·0m on St Malo; ML 5·3m; Duration 0600. Good natural hbr (known as Port Bago), but open to winds between NW and NNE. Appr on 150° toward Le Voleur Dir lt, Fl WRG 4s 17m 14/11M, G140°-148°, W148°-152°, R152°-160°. Note: the former rear ldg mark is reported ruined/obsc'd. The most conspic daymark is a 16m high W obelisk on Ile du Chateau Neuf, to stbd of appr chan; a less obvious W tr is to port on Ile St Gildas. There are 30 W 🛥s in the pool or yachts can ⚓ off or dry out alongside quays, 1·3m. Facilities: AB FF30, FW, AC, C (16 ton), Slip; **Services:** CH, El, ME, Sh. **Town** Bar, R, V.

PERROS-GUIREC   10-16-14

Côte d'Armor 48° 48′·23N 03° 26′·12W   Rtg 3-2-2

CHARTS
    AC 3672, 3670, *2668*; SHOM 7125, 7152; ECM 537, 538; Imray C34; Stanfords 17
TIDES
    −0550 Dover; ML 5·4; Duration 0605; Zone −0100

Standard Port ST MALO (←——)

Times				Height (metres)			
High Water		Low Water		MHWS	MHWN	MLWN	MLWS
0100	0800	0300	0800	12·2	9·2	4·3	1·6
1300	2000	1500	2000				
Differences PERROS-GUIREC							
−0030	−0040	−0115	−0055	−2·9	−1·8	−0·9	−0·3

SHELTER
    Very good in marina (2·5m). Enter via 6m wide gate, which is opened when rise of tide reaches 7m (there is no lock). Sill under gate is 3·5m above CD, giving 3·5m water inside gateway on first opening. Gate opening times depend mainly on tidal Coefficient (10.16.25), ie: Coeff >70, approx HW±1½; Coeff 60-70, HW±1; Coeff 50-60, HW−1 to +½; Coeff 40-50, HW−½ to HW. Caution: at Coeff <40, gate may not open for up to 4 days (neaped). Gate may open up to 30 mins ahead of published times, depending on weather, but does not close early. Retaining wall is marked by R & W poles. ⚓ prohib in basin. Drying moorings 1ca E of Jetée du Linkin. Off Pte du Chateau in approx 3m good holding and safe ⚓, except in NE'lies, plus 2 W 🛥s.
NAVIGATION
    WPT 48°52′·40N 03°20′·00W, 045°/225° from/to front ldg lt (Le Colombier), 6·4M. Beware Ile Tomé in the ent to Anse de Perros; rks extend 7ca off the W side and 6ca E of the N side. Explosive dumping ground is 8ca NNE of the island.

PERROS-GUIREC *continued*

LIGHTS AND MARKS
    From NE: Ldg lts 225°: front Le Colombier Dir Oc (4) 12s 28m 18M, intens 220°-230°; rear Kerprigent (1·5M from front) Q 79m 22M, intens 221°-228°.
    Passe de l'Ouest: Kerjean Dir lt 144° Oc (2+1) WRG 12s 78m 15/13M, vis G134°-143°, W143°-144°, R144°-154°.
    Gate sigs (flags/lts): Ⓖ over Ⓡ = closed;
    Ⓖ = open, priority to enter; Ⓡ = open, priority to leave.
RADIO TELEPHONE
    VHF Ch 09 16.
TELEPHONE (Prefix ☎ Nos with zone code 02)
    Hr Mr 96.23.37.82, 🚁 96.23.37.19; Basin gate 96.23.19.03; Aff Mar 96.23.13.78; ⌗ 96.23.18.12; CROSS 98.89.31.31; SNSM 96.20.00.45; Auto 08.36.68.08.22; Police 96.23.20.17; Dr 96.23.20.01; Brit Consul 99.46.26.64.
FACILITIES
    Marina (600+50 visitors) ☎ 96·23·19·03, FF105, P, D, FW, ME, AC, El, Sh, C (7 ton), CH, V, R, SM, Gas, Gaz, Kos, Ⓩ; **Services:** Ⓔ, SHOM; **Town** CH, V, Gaz, R, Bar, ✉, Ⓑ, ⇄ (Lannion), ✈ (Morlaix/Lannion). Ferry: Roscoff.

PLOUMANAC'H   10-16-15

Côte d'Armor 48° 50′·35N 03° 29′·14W   Rtg 3-4-1

CHARTS
    AC 3669, 3670, *2668*; SHOM 7125, 7152; ECM 537, 538; Imray C34; Stanfords 17
TIDES
    −0550 Dover; ML 5·5; Duration 0605; Zone −0100

Standard Port ST MALO (←——)

Times				Height (metres)			
High Water		Low Water		MHWS	MHWN	MLWN	MLWS
0100	0800	0300	0800	12·2	9·2	4·3	1·6
1300	2000	1500	2000				
Differences PLOUMANAC'H							
−0023	−0033	−0112	−0053	−2·9	−1·8	−0·7	−0·2

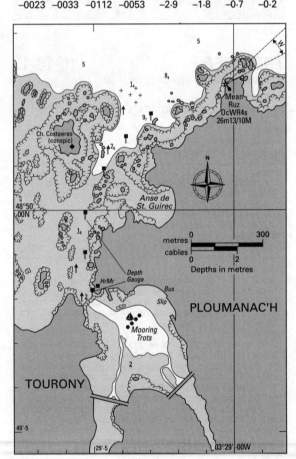

PLOUMANAC'H *continued*

SHELTER
Good; ⚓s are first line of dumbell buoys. A sill, drying 2·55m, retains at least 1·8m within. Depth gauges are on the 4th (unreliable) and the last PHM stakes. If the concrete base of the 3rd SHM stake is covered, depth over sill is >1·2m. Inside the sill, for best water keep to port and appr moorings from N. FV moorings to stbd of ent. SE and SW sides of hbr are very shallow.

NAVIGATION
WPT 48°51'·50N 03°29'·00W, 008°/188°, 1·25M from/to ent between Mean Ruz lt ho and Chateau Costaeres (conspic). Ent is difficult in strong NW'lies. From/to NW, beware An Dreuzinier, unmarked rks (drying 1·4m), 100m N and NE of No 1 SHM stake; not a problem with sufficient rise of tide, but near LW keep very close W of a line through the first two PHM stakes. Chan is marked by unlit stakes.

LIGHTS AND MARKS
Mean Ruz lt ho, Oc WR 4s, to E with adjacent sig stn, conspic.

RADIO TELEPHONE
VHF Ch 09.

TELEPHONE (Prefix ☎ Nos with zone code 02)
Hr Mr 96.91.44.31 or 96.23.37.82; SNSM 96.20.00.45; Auto 08.36.68.08.22; Dr 96.91.42.00; ME 96.23.31.40.

FACILITIES
Port de Plaisance (230 + 50 Ⓥ) M, FF100; **Quai Bellevue** FW, AC, L, Slip, P & D cans; Bus to Lannion & Perros; **YC Société Nautique de Perros Guirec**. Ferry: See Roscoff.

ADJACENT HARBOUR AND ANCHORAGES

LES SEPT ILES, Côte d'Armor, 48° 52'·80N 03°29'·10W, AC 3669, 3670; SHOM 7152. HW−0550 on Dover (UT); +0005 on Brest. HW ht −1·8m on Brest. ML 5·2m. Use 10.16.15 differences. All 7 islands form a bird sanctuary. Main ⚓ between Île aux Moines and Ile Bono. Landing on latter is prohib. ⚓ due E of jetty; below the Old Fort, or close to S side of Ile Bono. Île aux Moines lt ho, grey tr, Fl (3) 15s 59m 24M, obsc 237°-241° and in Baie de Lannion when brg < 039°. No facilities.

TRÉGASTEL, Côte d'Armor, 48°50'·10N 03°31'·20W, AC 3669, 3670; SHOM 7152. HW −0550 on Dover (UT); +0005 and −1·8m on Brest HW; ML 5·1m; Duration 0605. Use 10·16·15 differences. Good ⚓ in 2m, but exposed to winds from W to N. Ent, 2ca W of La Pierre Pendue (conspic rk), is marked by PHM bn on Ile Dhu and SHM buoy off Le Taureau, rk drying 4·5m (bn destroyed). Turreted house, conspic, brg approx 165° leads between Ile Dhu and Le Taureau. Thence after 2 more PHM and 1 SHM bns, turn E to the ⚓ or Orange ⚓s S of Ile Ronde. Facilities: Slip; **Club Nautique de Trégastel** ☎ 02·96·23·45·05; **Town** (Ste Anne, 0·5M inland) CH, Ⓑ, ✉, ⊙, Bar, R, V.

TRÉBEURDEN   10-16-16

Côte d'Armor 48°46'·35N 03°35'·06W   Rtg 3-2-2   *Continued overleaf*

TRÉBEURDEN *continued*

CHARTS
AC 3669; SHOM 7125, 7124, 7151; ECM 537, 538; Imray C34; Stanfords 17

TIDES
−0605 Dover; ML 5·5; Duration 0605; Zone −0100

Standard Port BREST (→)

Times				Height (metres)			
High Water		Low Water		MHWS	MHWN	MLWN	MLWS
0000	0600	0000	0600	6·9	5·4	2·6	1·0
1200	1800	1200	1800				
Differences TRÉBEURDEN							
+0100	+0110	+0120	+0100	+2·3	+1·9	+0·9	+0·4

SHELTER
Good in marina (3·5m). Access HW±3½ (±4¼ at sp) over moving sill (2m CD; 15m wide) at stbd side of ent; rest of sill is fixed 3·5m. Tide gauge floodlit, port side of sill. **Ⓥ** on pontoon F (2nd from ent). Do not manoeuvre within 10 mins of the sill dropping, due to strong underwater inrush. 15 deep-water waiting buoys outside, or ‡ off NE side of Ile Milliau, but exposed to W'lies.

NAVIGATION
WPT 48°45'·13N 03°40'·68W, 246°/066° from/to Lan Kerellec Dir lt, 4·1M. From W, appr is clear. From E and N, round Bar ar Gall and Le Crapaud WCM buoys; continue S for 1·5M, then alter 066° toward Ile Milliau (conspic CG bldg); thence as below to enter the marked chan to marina ent. From Ar Gouredec SCM buoy, VQ (6) + L Fl 10s, ✠ spire (conspic) brg 098° leads to ent via chan buoyed as shown.

LIGHTS AND MARKS
Le Crapaud WCM buoy, Q (9) 15s. Lan Kerellec Dir lt, Iso WRG 4s 8/5M, G058°-064°, W064°-069°, R069°-130°, leads 066° past Ile Milliau. IPTS (sigs 2 & 4) on bkwtr and on sill gateway; 4 Y SPM bns mark fixed sill.

RADIO TELEPHONE
Call *Port Trébeurden* VHF Ch 09 16.

TELEPHONE (Prefix ☎ Nos with zone code 02)
Hr Mr ☎ 96·23·64·00; Aff Mar 96.37.06.52; CROSS 98.89.31.31; SNSM 96·23·53·82; ⌗ 96·92·31·44; Police 96.23.51.96 (Jul/Aug); Ⓗ (Lannion) 96.05.71.11.

FACILITIES
Marina (400 + 160 visitors), ☎ as Hr Mr, ⚓ 96.47.40.87, FF105, FW, AC, P, D, BY, C (20 ton);
YC de Trébeurden ☎ 96·37·00·40 (open July-Aug);
Services: BY, ME, El, Sh, CH.
Town V, R, Bar, ✉, Ⓑ, ✈ (Lannion). Ferry: Roscoff/St.Malo.

LANNION (Léguer River)   10-16-17
Côte d'Armor 48°44'·00N 03°33'·50W   Rtg 3-4-2

CHARTS
AC 3669, *2668*; SHOM 7124, 7151; ECM 537, 538; Imray C34; Stanfords 17

TIDES
−0605 Dover; ML 5·4; Duration: no data; Zone −0100

Standard Port BREST (→)

Times				Height (metres)			
High Water		Low Water		MHWS	MHWN	MLWN	MLWS
0000	0600	0000	0600	6·9	5·4	2·6	1·0
1200	1800	1200	1800				
Differences LOCQUIREC							
+0058	+0108	+0120	+0100	+2·2	+1·8	+0·8	+0·3

SHELTER
Good, except in strong W/NW winds. ‡ in estuary or in non-drying pools off Le Yaudet and Le Beguen. It may be possible to dry out on the N bank just below Lannion town, but a recce by dinghy or on foot is advised.

NAVIGATION
WPT 48°44'·40N 03°36'·60W, 284°/104° from/to Pointe de Dourven 1·9M (also on Locquemeau ldg lts 122°). Beware drying sandbank extending approx 2ca N/NE from Pte de Dourven. No access at very LW, esp with strong NW/winds when seas break on the drying bar. Enter chan close to two G bn trs. Chan up river is easy, but narrow, steep-to and marked by trs/bns only as far as Le Yaudet.

LIGHTS AND MARKS
Large W radome conspic 3·5M NNE of ent. Pointe Beg-Léguer lt, Oc (4) WRG 12s 60m 13/10M; vis W084°-098°, R098°-129°, G007°-084°; lt is on a cottage gable end.

RADIO TELEPHONE
None.

TELEPHONE (Prefix ☎ Nos with zone code 02)
Hr Mr 96·37·06·52; Aff Mar 96·37·06·52; CROSS 98·89·31·31; SNSM 96·23·52·07; ⌗ 96·37·45·32; Auto 08.36.68.08.22; Police 96·37·03·78; Dr 96·37·42·52; Brit Consul 99·46·26·64.

FACILITIES
Quai de Loguivy AB in emergency, Slip, FW, C (1 ton).
Services: M, ME, El, Sh, SHOM, Ⓔ, CH.
Town M, CH, V, Gaz, R, Bar, ✉, Ⓑ, ⇌, ✈ (Morlaix, Lannion). Ferry: Roscoff.

ADJACENT HARBOURS IN BAIE DE LANNION

LOCQUEMEAU, Côte d'Armor, 48°43'·60N 03°34'·70W, AC 3669, 2668; SHOM 7124. HW −0600 on Dover (UT); +0110 on Brest; HW ht +1·5m on Brest; ML 5·3m. A small drying hbr by ent to Lannion River (10·16·17). There are two quays: the outer is accessible at LW, but open to W 'lies. Yachts can dry out at inner quay, on S side. Ldg lts 122° to outer quay: front FR 21m 6M, vis 068°-228°, W pylon + R top; rear, 484m from front, Oc (2+1) R 12s 39m 7M, W gable and R gallery. **Services:** ME, El, Sh; **Town** Bar.

LOCQUIREC, Côte d'Armor, 48°41'·50N 03°38'·68W. AC 3669, 2668; SHOM 7124. Tidal data as for Locquemeau, above. Small drying hbr at mouth of R Le Douron, with good shelter from W/SW winds. The whole estuary dries to shifting sandbanks (2·9m to 6·1m). Access HW±3. No lights, but a NCM buoy is 7ca N of Pte de Locqueric and a SHM bn tr (6ca S of the hbr) is conspic as the bay opens up. A pleasant temp ‡, or overnight if able to take the ground. Many moorings, inc 10 ⚓s. Land at slip.

MORLAIX   10-16-18
Finistere 48°35'.50N 03°50'.50W   Rtg 3-2-1

CHARTS
AC 2745, 3669; SHOM 7095, 7151; ECM 538; Imray C34, C35; Stanfords 17
TIDES
–0610 Dover; ML 5·3; Duration 0610; Zone –0100

Standard Port BREST (⟶)

Times				Height (metres)			
High Water		Low Water		MHWS	MHWN	MLWN	MLWS
0000	0600	0000	0600	6·9	5·4	2·6	1·0
1200	1800	1200	1800				

Differences MORLAIX (CHÂTEAU DU TAUREAU)

+0055	+0105	+0115	+0055	+2·0	+1·7	+0·8	+0·3

ANSE DE PRIMEL

+0100	+0110	+0120	+0100	+2·1	+1·7	+0·8	+0·3

SHELTER
Good in the bay and at Dourduff (dries), clear of extensive oyster beds marked by small orange buoys/stakes. Boats can go 5M up to Morlaix town and lock in to the Bassin à Flot; lock opens by day only, at HW –1½, HW and HW+1. Complete shelter at the marina; ❶'s pontoon on E bank, just N of slip and YC. A movable footbridge across the marina abeam the YC, is usually open during lock hours.
NAVIGATION
WPT 48°42'.71N 03°53'.44W, abeam Stolvezen PHM buoy, 356°/176° from/to Ile Louet lt, 2·25M (Grand Chenal). The three ent channels all have rky dangers:

(1) Chenal Ouest 188°, W of Ricard Is. Deepest chan, but unlit.
(2) Grand Chenal 176°, E of Ricard Is, shallower but lit.
(3) Chenal de Tréguier, 190°, best at night, but almost dries. Strong N'lies can raise a steep sea even in the estuary. The Penzé river lies W of Ile de Callot.
LIGHTS AND MARKS
Grand Chenal ldg lts 176°: front Ile Louet, Oc (3) WG 12s; rear La Lande, Fl 5s.
Chenal de Tréguier ldg lts 190°: Ile Noire, Oc (2) WRG 6s; rear La Lande, Fl 5s.
River up to Morlaix, 3M above Dourduff, is buoyed but unlit.
RADIO TELEPHONE
Port and marina VHF Ch 09 16.
TELEPHONE (Prefix ☎ Nos with zone code 02)
Hr Mr 98·62·13·14; Lock 98·88·54·92; Aff Mar 98·62·10·47; CROSS 98·89·31·31; SNSM 98·88·00·76; ⌗ 98·88·06·31; Auto 08.36.68.08.29; Police 98·88·58·13; Ⓗ 98·62·61·60; Brit Consul 99·46·26·64.
FACILITIES
Marina (180+30 visitors) ☎ 98·62·13·14, access as lock times, FF74, AC, FW, C (8 ton), P & D, Slip, ME, El, Sh, CH; **YC de Morlaix** ☎ 98·62·08·51;
Town P, D, SM, Ⓔ, SHOM, V, Gaz, R, Bar, ✉, Ⓑ, ▣, ⇒, ✈. Ferry: Roscoff.

OTHER HARBOURS AND ANCHORAGES N OF MORLAIX

PRIMEL-TRÉGASTEL, Finistere, 48°42'·80N 03°49'·30W, AC 2745, 3669; SHOM 7095, 7151. HW –0610 on Dover (UT); ML 5·3m; Duration 0600. See 10.16.18. Good ⌕, but open to N/NW'lies; seas break across ent in strong winds. All tides access. Beware drying rks off Pte de Primel to E, and off Ar Zammeguez (3m high, painted W/G) to W of ent. Enter exactly on daymarks 152°, both are W □ walls with R vert stripe, on hillside; or co-located ldg lts, both FR 35/56m 6M, front vis 134°-168°. Pass between a PHM and SHM bn, the former quite short. 15 (10 deep water) ❶s or ⌕ to SE or SW of bkwtr hd, Fl G 4s 6m 7M, in 2-9m. Le Diben on W side is FV port. Drying upper reaches are well sheltered. VHF Ch 09 16 (season). Hr Mr ☎ 02.98.62.28.40. Facilities: C (25 ton), FW, Slip, CH, El, ME, Sh, Ⓔ, R, Bar.

PENZÉ RIVER, Finistere, Ent 48°42'·00N 03°56'·40W, AC 2745; SHOM 7095. HW –0610 on Dover (UT), +0105 on Brest; HW ht +1·2m Brest; ML 5·0m; Duration 0605. Appr at mid-flood from NNW between Cordonnier and Guerhéon bn trs or, for deeper water, from ENE between Les Bizeyer and Le Paradis bn tr; thence pass W of Ile Callot. The Passe aux Moutons, between Carantec and Ile Callot, is a short cut from Morlaix estuary to the Penzé with adequate rise. Yachts can dry out inside Pempoul bkwtr on the W shore. The ⌕ off Carentec is exposed, especially to NW; landing stage dries about 4·6m. Further S the chan narrows and is scantily marked only by oyster withies and local moorings. SW of Pte de Lingos shelter is better; or moor off St Yves where the old ferry slips provide landing places. S of the bridge (11m) the river is buoyed and navigable on the tide for 3M to complete shelter at Penzé. Facilities at Carantec: El, ME, Sh, M, CH, P, D, Ⓔ. **Town** Ⓑ, Bar, ✉, R, V. **Penzé** AB (drying), limited V, R, Bar.

OTHER HARBOURS WEST OF ROSCOFF

MOGUÉRIEC, Finistere, 48°40'·40N 04°04'·40W, AC 3669, *2668*; SHOM 7151. Tides approx as for Ile de Batz (10.16.19). A small drying fishing hbr, 3M SSW of W ent to Canal de Batz, open to NW swell. Ldg lts 162°: both W trs/G tops, front on jetty, Iso WG 4s 9m, W158°-166°; rear FG 22m. Beware Méan Névez rk, dries 3·3m, to W of appr. ⌕ close SW of Ile de Siec, or 3ca WSW of Ar Skeul WCM bn tr in 4m, or 2ca NNE of Moguériec's drying jetty. Facilities: V, R, Bar, P.

PONTUSVAL, Finistere, 48°40'·65N 04°19'·08W, AC 3668, *2644*; SHOM 7150. HW +0605 on Dover (UT); ML 4·7m; Duration 0600; see 10.16.19 (BRIGNONAN). App from ECM buoy (48°41'·51N 04°19'·12W) via ldg marks 178° W bn on with ch spire 1M S. Ent between An Neudenn R bn tr to E and 3 white-topped rks to W. ⌕ here in approx 4m or dry out closer in. Hbr is open to N winds and often full of FVs. Entry at night prohib. Facilities: Bar, FW, R, V.

16

ROSCOFF   10-16-19

Finistere 48°43'.60N 03°58'.50W   Rtg 3-3-1

CHARTS

AC 2745, 3669; SHOM 7095, 7151; ECM 538; Imray C35; Stanfords 17

TIDES

−0605 Dover; ML 5·2; Duration 0600; Zone −0100

Standard Port BREST (→)

Times				Height (metres)			
High Water		Low Water		MHWS	MHWN	MLWN	MLWS
0000	0600	0000	0600	6·9	5·4	2·6	1·0
1200	1800	1200	1800				
Differences ROSCOFF							
+0055	+0105	+0115	+0055	+1·9	+1·6	+0·8	+0·3
ILE DE BATZ							
+0045	+0100	+0105	+0055	+2·0	+1·6	+0·9	+0·4
BRIGOGNAN							
+0040	+0045	+0055	+0040	+1·1	+0·9	+0·3	+0·1

SHELTER

Good in Roscoff (dries 4·9m) except in strong N/E winds. Access HW±2. AB on S side of jetty in Yacht Hbr, but FVs leave little room; or dry out against road wall or secure to ⚓ in SW corner. Close W of Ar Chaden are W ⚓s in 4-5m. Bloscon ferry hbr should only be entered with Hr Mr's approval, but ⚓s or ⚓ to the S, clear of ferries (good for crew change). Beware foul ground inshore and WIP.

NAVIGATION

WPT 48°46'·00N 03°55'·80W, 033°/213° from/to Men Guen Bras lt, 2·6M. The ent to Roscoff needs care due to many large rks in the area; best to enter near HW. See 10.16.5 for pilotage in the Canal de l'Ile de Batz. Chans are well marked and must be kept to. Appr to Bloscon is easier.

LIGHTS AND MARKS

Ile de Batz lt ho (conspic) Fl (4) 25s 69m 23M. Off Roscoff at E end of Canal de l'Ile de Batz are Ar Chaden Q (6)+L Fl WR 15s, SCM bn tr, and Men-Guen-Bras Q WRG, NCM. Ldg lts/marks 209° for the hbr: both Oc (2+1) G 12s, front 7m 7M, W col, G top, with B/W vert stripes on end of mole; rear conspic W lt ho 24m 15M. Bloscon jetty hd Fl WG 4s; appr in W sector 206°-216°; in fog, Fl W 2s.

RADIO TELEPHONE

Roscoff Ch 09. *Bloscon* Ch 12 16; 0830-1200, 1330-1800LT.

TELEPHONE (Prefix ☎ Nos with zone code 02)

Hr Mr (Port de Plaisance) 98·69·76·37; Hr Mr (Roscoff) 98·61·27·84; Aff Mar 98·69·70·15; CROSS 98·89·31·31; SNSM 98·61·27·84; ☩ (Roscoff) 98·69·19·67; ☩ (Bloscon) 98·61·27·86; Auto 08.36.68.08.29; Police 98·69·00·48; ⊞ 98·88·40·22; Dr 98·69·71·18; Brit Consul 99·46·26·64.

FACILITIES

Vieux Port (220+30 visitors) ☎ 98·69·76·37, AB (with fender board), FW, AC, M; **Quai Neuf** Reserved for FVs, C (5 ton); **Club Nautique de Roscoff** ☎ 98·69·72·79, Bar; **Bloscon** M, L, Slip.

Services: BY, ME, EI, Sh, CH. **Town** P, D, ME, EI, Sh, CH, Gaz, V, R, Bar, ⊠, Ⓑ, ⇌, ✈ (Morlaix). Ferry: Plymouth.

HARBOUR/ANCHORAGE CLOSE NORTH

ILE DE BATZ, Finistere, 48°44'·50N 04°00'·50W, AC 2745, 3669; SHOM 7095; HW +0610 Dover (UT); ML 5·2m. See 10·16·19. Porz-Kernoc'h gives good shelter but dries. E slip is reserved for ferries. ⚓ in E or W parts of the chan depending on wind, but holding ground poor. ⚓ prohib in area W of Roscoff landing slip. Ile de Batz lt ho Fl (4) 25s. Facilities: a few shops.

L'ABERWRAC'H   10-16-20

Finistere 48°36'·75N 04°35'·30W   Rtg 3-4-1

CHARTS
AC 1432, 2644; SHOM 7094, 7150; ECM 539; Imray C35; Stanfords 17

TIDES
+0547 Dover; ML 4·5; Duration 0600; Zone −0100

Standard Port BREST (→)

Times				Height (metres)			
High Water		Low Water		MHWS	MHWN	MLWN	MLWS
0000	0600	0000	0600	6·9	5·4	2·6	1·0
1200	1800	1200	1800				
Differences L'ABERWRAC'H, ILE CÉZON							
+0030	+0030	+0038	+0037	+0·8	+0·7	+0·2	0·0

SHELTER
Good, except in strong NW'lies. At La Palue either berth on the single pontoon (max LOA = 12m) or pick up one of 30 numbered W ⚓s. Free water taxi in summer every H, 0800-2200. Excellent shelter in all winds at Paluden, 1·5M up-river (off chartlet), on dumbell ⚓s; plus landing jetty, but ⚓ prohib.

NAVIGATION
WPT for Grand Chenal 48°37'·40N 04°38'·40W, 280°/100° from/to front ldg lt 2·6M. Keep clear of Le Libenter bank marked by WCM buoy, Q (9) 15s (Whis), brg 254° from Ile Vierge lt 3·0M; also Basse Trousquennou to S.
Two outer appr chans lead to the inner 128° appr line:
(1) Grand Chenal 100° (well lit and best for strangers) runs S of Libenter, Grand and Petit Pot de Beurre.
(2) Chenal de la Malouine, a narrow short cut from N/E, only by day and in good weather: 176° transit of Petit Pot de Beurre with Petite Ile de la Croix W bn; great precision is required. Caution: breakers and cross-tides.

LIGHTS AND MARKS
Ile-Vierge lt ho Fl 5s 77m 27M, Gy tr, Horn 60s, RC, vis 337°–325° (348°). For the Grand Chenal the 100° ldg lts/marks are: front QR, Ile Vrac' h, W □ tr orange top; and, 1·63M to the rear, Dir Q, Lanvaon, W □ tr orange △ on top. Then Dir Oc (2) WRG 6s, W127·2°-128·7°, leads 128° almost to the pontoon at La Palue. Unlit up river.

RADIO TELEPHONE
VHF Ch 09 16 (0700-2200LT in season).

TELEPHONE (Prefix ☎ Nos with zone code 02)
Hr Mr 98·04·91·62; Aff Mar 98·04·90·13; CROSS/SNSM 98·89·31·31; ⌗ 98·04·90·27; Météo 98·84·60·64; Auto 08.36.68.08.29; Police 98·04·00·18; Ⓗ 98·46·11·33; Dr 98·04·91·87; SAMU 15; Brit Consul 99·46·26·64.

FACILITIES
Pontoon (30, some visitors) ☎ 98·04·91·62, FF96, M, D, FW, ME, El, CH, BH (12 ton); **YC des Abers** ☎ 98·04·92·60, Bar, 🚿; **Services:** Sh, Ⓔ, Slip, C (3 ton mobile).
Town P, V, Gaz, R, 🅾, P, Bar, ✉, Ⓑ (Landeda, every a.m. except Mon), ⇌, ✈, (bus to Brest). Ferry: Roscoff.

L'ABERBENOIT   10-16-21

Finistere 48°34'·65N 04°36'·80W   Rtg 3-4-1

CHARTS
AC 1432, 2644; SHOM 7094, 7150; ECM 539, 540; Imray C35; Stanfords 17

TIDES
+0535 Dover; ML 4·7; Duration 0555; Zone −0100

Standard Port BREST (→)

Times				Height (metres)			
High Water		Low Water		MHWS	MHWN	MLWN	MLWS
0000	0600	0000	0600	6·9	5·4	2·6	1·0
1200	1800	1200	1800				
Differences L'ABERBENOIT							
+0022	+0025	+0035	+0020	+1·0	+0·9	+0·4	+0·2
PORTSALL							
+0015	+0020	+0025	+0015	+0·6	+0·5	+0·1	0·0

SHELTER
Excellent, but do not enter at night, in poor vis nor in strong WNW winds; best near LW when dangers can be seen. Six ⚓s and ⚓ as shown or further up-river. R navigable on the tide to Tréglonou bridge 3M upstream. Beware oyster beds.

NAVIGATION
WPT 48°37'·05N 04°38'·67W, Petite Fourche WCM, 337°/157° from/to Ile Guénioc, 1M. From WPT track 168° for 1M until abeam Ile Guénioc; thence 134° past Basse du Chenal and Karreg ar Poul Doun PHM bns to Men Renead SHM buoy. Alter stbd 160° to pass close to La Jument rk (PHM bn and R paint patch); thence 140°, passing 2 SHM buoys and leaving Le Chien IDM bn to port, leads to the fairway.

LIGHTS AND MARKS
Unlit. Chan bns and buoys must be carefully identified.

RADIO TELEPHONE
None.

TELEPHONE (Prefix ☎ Nos with zone code 02)
Hr Mr none; CROSS/SNSM 98·89·31·31; ⌗ 98·04·90·27; Météo 98·84·60·64; Auto 08.36.68.08.29; Police 98·48·10·10; Dr 98·89·75·67; Brit Consul 99·46·26·64.

FACILITIES
Le Passage Slip, M (free), L, FW; **Tréglonou** Slip; **Services:** Sh, ME, El. **Town** Gaz, ✉, Ⓑ (Ploudalmezeau), ⇌, ✈ (bus to Brest). Ferry: Roscoff.

16

LAMPAUL (ILE D'OUESSANT)

Finistere 48°26'·70N 05°07'·40W Rtg 4-5-2 **10-16-22**

CHARTS
AC 2694; SHOM 7123, 7149; ECM 540; Imray C36; Stan 17

TIDES
+0522 Dover; ML 3·9; Duration 0555; Zone –0100

Standard Port BREST (→)

Times				Height (metres)			
High Water		Low Water		MHWS	MHWN	MLWN	MLWS
0000	0600	0000	0600	6·9	5·4	2·6	1·0
1200	1800	1200	1800				
Differences BAIE DE LAMPAUL							
+0005	+0005	–0005	+0003	0·0	–0·1	–0·1	0·0
ILE DE MOLENE							
+0012	+0012	+0017	+0017	+0·4	+0·3	+0·2	+0·1

SHELTER
Bay is open to SW winds and swell; only usable in settled weather, prone to poor vis, esp in July. There are approx 24 ⚓s to S of the small drying hbr to E of pier, ent 15m wide, which normally has no room for visitors.

NAVIGATION
WPT 48°26'·30N 05°09'·00W, 250°/070° from/to Le Corce Rk, 1·4M. Bring Le Stiff lt ho 055° open N of Le Corce, which may be passed on either side. PHM/SHM bn trs mark Men-ar-Blank and Men-ar-Groas Rks closer inshore. Beware ferries using the T-shaped quay; they also use the Ch de la Fourche, but this is not advised for yachts. The ITZ extends 5M NW of Ushant to the NE-bound lane of the TSS (see Fig 10 (4) and 10.16.2).

LIGHTS AND MARKS
La Jument Fl (3) R 15s 36m **22**M; grey 8-sided tr, R top; obsc 199°-241°; Horn (3) 60s. An-Ividig (Nividic) VQ (9) 10s 28m 9M; W 8-sided tr, R bands; obsc 225°-290°; helicopter platform. Creac'h Fl (2) 10s 70m **34**M; W tr, B bands; obsc 247°-255°; Horn (2) 120s; RC; Racon. Le Stiff Fl (2) R 20s 85m **24**M; close to conspic radar tr 72m.

RADIO TELEPHONE
None. For Ouessant TSS/ITZ see under Brest 10.16.27.

TELEPHONE (Prefix ☎ Nos with zone code 02)
Hr Mr 98·89 20 05; Aff Mar 94·48·80·27; CROSS 98·89·31·31; Météo 98·84·60·64; Auto 08.36.68.08.29; SNSM 98·89·70·04; Police 98·68·10·39; Dr 98·89·92·70; Brit Consul 99·46·26·64.

FACILITIES
Few facilities: L, AB, FW, P & D (cans), Slip. **Town** Gaz, ✉, Ⓑ, ferry to Le Conquet and Brest ⇌, ✈. UK Ferry: Roscoff.

ADJACENT HARBOUR

BAIE DU STIFF, 48°28'·13N 05°03'·18W, is sheltered in S to NW winds. Appr is clear apart from Gorle Vihan with IDM bn. Dir lt 259°, Q WRG 11m 10/7M, vis W254°-264°, is on the mole. S of the lt ho, Porz Liboudou is for ferries, but 9 R ⚓s are available in 5m. Holding is poor; little room to ⚓.

L'ABERILDUT

Finistere 48°28'·30N 04°45'·72W Rtg 3-3-1 **10-16-23**

CHARTS
AC 3345, 2694, 2644; SHOM 7122, 7149; ECM 540; Imray C36; Stanfords 17

TIDES
+0520 on Dover (UT); ML 4·2m; Zone –0100

Standard Port BREST (→)

Times				Height (metres)			
High Water		Low Water		MHWS	MHWN	MLWN	MLWS
0000	0600	0000	0600	6·9	5·4	2·6	1·0
1200	1800	1200	1800				
Differences L'ABERILDUT							
+0010	+0010	+0023	+0010	+0·4	+0·3	0·0	0·0

SHELTER
Very good inside, but appr is open to W winds; access all tides and at night with care. Hbr partly dries, but a narrow chan at the ent has 2m, with pools to 6m inside. Beyond the FV quay (NW side) a pontoon provides landing and fuel. Some ⚓s; little room to ⚓, but ⚓s outside as chartlet. A useful passage hbr to await the tide in the Ch du Four.

NAVIGATION
WPT 48°28'·12N 04°48'·13W, 263°/083° from/to Dir lt, 1·6M. From N beware Les Liniou Rks 1·5M NNW of the WPT and Plateau des Fourches 1·2M SSW. Appr is fairly easy in good vis, but beware strong cross tides. At the ent leave both Men Tassin PHM bn and Roche du Crapaud, a large rounded rk, close to port to clear drying spit on S side of the narrow ent. For Chenal du Four see opposite and 10·16·5.

LIGHTS AND MARKS
Le Four tr, Fl (5) 15s 28m 18M, gy tr, siren (3+2) 60s, is 3·35M N of the WPT. Pointe de Corsen lt, Dir Q WRG 33m 12/8M, is 3·2M S of the WPT.
A stern transit 258° of Kéréon lt, gy tr, Oc (2+1) WR 24s 38m **17**M, with La Jument lt, Fl (3) R 15s 36m **22**M, gy tr + R top, (both off Ouessant) leads to the W sector of a powerful Dir lt 083°, Oc (2) WR 6s 12m **25/20**M, vis W081° -085°, R085°-087°, on W bldg at hbr ent; good daymark. Ldg marks (difficult to see from afar): front, Lanildut spire on with Brélès spire leads 079° into fairway. Drying rks are marked by Pierre de l'Aber SHM bn and Le Lieu PHM bn tr 5m; the latter is easier to see.

RADIO TELEPHONE
None.

TELEPHONE (Prefix ☎ Nos with zone code 02)
Hr Mr 98.04.41.31 (Jun-Sep); Aff Mar 98.48.66.54; Auto 08.36.68.08.29; ✠ 98.44.35.20; CROSS/SNSM 98.89.31.31; Police 98.48.10.10; Dr 98.04.33.08.

FACILITIES
Hbr, M (300, inc 12 ⚓s; FF52), FW, D, slips, AC at FV quay; **Services:** BY, Sh, ME, El, CH, M.
Village V, R, Bar, ✉. All needs at Brest 25km. Ferry: Roscoff.

CHENAL DU FOUR and CHENAL DE LA HELLE

See 10.16.5 for notes on these passages

10-16-24

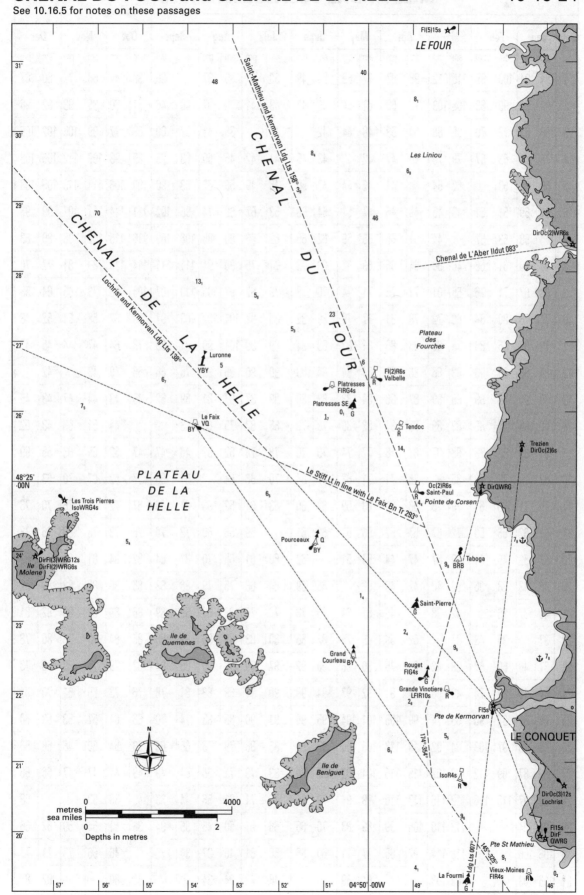

BREST TIDAL COEFFICIENTS 1998

Date	Jan am	Jan pm	Feb am	Feb pm	Mar am	Mar pm	Apr am	Apr pm	May am	May pm	June am	June pm	July am	July pm	Aug am	Aug pm	Sept am	Sept pm	Oct am	Oct pm	Nov am	Nov pm	Dec am	Dec pm
1	94	94	100	95	115	112	96	87	77	69	53	49	50	47	39	37		36	38	44	68	77	80	87
2	92	90	90	83	108	103	78	69	61	54	45	43	43	41		37	40	46	51	60	85	93	92	98
3	86	83	76	70	95	88	60	53	48	44	42		40		38	41	52	60	68	77	99	105	102	105
4	78	74	63	57	79	70	46	42	42		43	45	41	42	45	50	68	75	85	93	109	112	106	106
5	69	65	53		62	54		41	42	44	47	50	45	49	56	62	83	90	100	106	114	113	105	103
6	61	59	51	51	48	45	43	46	47	51	54	58	53	57	68	74	96	102	111	114	111	107	99	95
7		58	53	57		44	51	56	55	59	62	65	62	66	80	85	106	109	116	115	102	96	89	83
8	58	60	61	66	46	50	61	66	63	67	69	72	71	75	90	94	111	111	114	110	89	81	77	70
9	63	67	71	76	55	61	71	75	71	74	75	78	79	82	97	100	110	107	105	98	73	65	64	58
10	71	76	80	84	66	72	78	81	77	79	80	82	85	87	101	102	103	97	90	82	58	51	52	48
11	79	83	86	88	76	80	83	85	81	83	83	84	89	90	101	99	91	83	73	64	47	44	45	43
12	86	88	89	90	83	86	86	87	84	84	84	83	90	90	96	92	75	66	56	49	43		42	
13	89	90	89	89	88	89	87	86	84	83	82	80	89	87	87	81	59	52	45	43	44	47	43	45
14	90	89	87	85	89	89	85	84	82	80	78	75	85	82	75	68	48			44	51	55	48	52
15	87	85	82	78	88	87	81	78	77	74	73	70	78	74	62	57	46	47	47	52	59	63	55	59
16	82	79	75	70	85	83	75	71	71	67	67	64	70	66	54		51	55	57	62	67	70	63	67
17	75	71	66	61	79	76	66	61	63	59	62	60	63	61	52	53	61	66	67	72	74	76	70	73
18	67	62	56	50	72	67	57	52	56	53	60	61		59	56	60	72	76	76	79	78	80	76	78
19	57	52	46	41	62	57	47	44	51	51		62	60	61	65	70	81	84	82	84	81	82	80	81
20	48	43	38	36	52	46	42	43	53		65	69	64	68	75	79	86	88	85	86	82	82	82	82
21	40	37	36		42	38		46	57	61	73	78	72	76	83	86	89	89	86	86	81	80	82	81
22	37		39	43	37		52	59	68	74	82	86	80	83	88	90	89	88	85	84	78	76	80	78
23	37	40	50	57	38	42	67	75	80	86	90	92	87	89	90	90	86	84	82	79	73	69	75	73
24	44	49	66	74	49	56	84	91	92	97	94	95	90	91	89	88	81	78	76	73	65	61	70	67
25	56	62	82	90	65	74	99	105	101	104	95	95	91	90	85	83	74	70	68	64	57	53	63	60
26	69	75	97	103	84	92	110	113	105	105	93	91	88	86	79	75	65	60	59	54	50	48	58	56
27	82	87	109	112	100	107	115	115	104	102	87	84	83	79	71	66	54	49	49	44	47	47	56	56
28	93	97	115	116	112	116	113	110	98	94	79	75	75	71	61	56	44	39	40	38	50			58
29	101	104			118	118	105	99	89	83	70	65	66	61	50	45	35	34	38	41	54	60	62	66
30	106	106			118	114	92	85	77	71	60	55	56	51	40	37	34			46	66	73	71	77
31	105	103			109	103			64	59			46	42	34	34			52	60			82	87

TIDAL COEFFICIENTS   10-16-25

These indicate at a glance the magnitude of the tide on any particular day by assigning a non-dimensional coefficient to the twice-daily range of tide. The coefficient is based on a scale of 45 for mean neap (morte eau) and 95 for mean spring (vive eau) ranges. The coefficient is 70 for an average tide. A very small np tide may have a coefficient of only 20, whilst a very big sp tide might be as high as 120. The ratio of the coefficients of different tides equals the ratio of their ranges; the range, for example, of the largest sp tide (120) is six times that of the smallest np tide (20).

The table opposite is for Brest, but holds good elsewhere along the Channel and Atlantic coasts of France.

French tide tables, similar to Admiralty tide tables as in this Almanac, show for Secondary ports their time and height differences against the appropriate standard port for vive eau (springs) and for morte eau (neaps). The tidal coefficient for the day may be used to decide which correction(s) to apply. In general it is satisfactory to use the vive eau corrections for coefficients over 70 and the morte eau corrections for the others. Where it is necessary to obtain more accurate corrections (in estuaries for example) this can be done by interpolating or extrapolating.

Coefficients may also be used to determine rates of tidal streams on a given day, using a graph similar in principle to that shown in Table 9 (2). On the vertical axis plot tidal coefficients from 20 at the bottom to 120 at the top. The horizontal axis shows tidal stream rates from zero to (say) five knots. From the tidal stream atlas or chart, plot the np and sp rates against coefficient 45 and 95 respectively; join these two points. Entering with the tidal coefficient for the day in question, go horizontally to the sloping line, then vertically to read the required rate on the horizontal axis.

French translations of common tidal terms are as follows:

HW	Pleine mer (PM)
LW	Basse mer (BM)
Springs	Vive eau (VE)
Neaps	Morte eau (ME)
CD	Zero des cartes
MHWS	Pleine mer moyenne de VE
MHWN	Pleine mer moyenne de ME
MLWN	Basse mer moyenne de ME
MLWS	Basse mer moyenne de VE

ADJACENT HARBOURS

PORTSALL, Finistere, 48°33'·85N 04°42'·95W. AC 1432, 3688; SHOM 7094, 7150. HW +0535 on Dover (UT); ML 4·4m; Duration 0600. See 10.16.21. Small drying hbr at head of bay. Access HW±3. Good shelter except in strong N winds. Ldg marks: Le Yurc'h rk (7m) on with Ploudalmézeau spire leads 109°; thence 085° on W & RW marks. By night use W sector 084°-088° of lt Oc (4) WRG 12s 9m 13/10M, W col/R top. Appr marked by 5 bn trs. Beware many rks for about 2M off-shore. ‡ to W of ent, or go alongside quay in hbr. Facilities: Aff Mar ☎ 98·48·66·54; SNSM ☎ 02·98·48·77·44; Dr ☎ 02·98·48·10·46; **Quay** C (0·5 ton), D, FW, P, Slip; **Club Naut** ☎ 02·98·48·63·10; **Coop de Pêcheurs** ☎ 02·98·48·63·26, CH. **Town** Bar, ⊠, R, V.

ARGENTON, Finistere, 48°31'·32N 04°46'·25W. AC 3347, 2694; SHOM 7122. HW +0535 on Dover (UT); ML 4·6m; Duration 0600; use PORTSALL diffs 10.16.21. Small drying hbr; good shelter except in W winds when a swell comes up the bay into the hbr. Access HW±3. Appr 086° on 2 W bns & RW wall. Le Four lt Fl (5) 15s is 1·4M to W. Beware strong E-W tides. ‡ in deep water off hbr ent. 10 ⚓s. Facilities: FW, P on quay; **SC** ☎ 02·98·89·54·04. **Town** Bar, R, V.

ILE DE MOLENE, Finistere, 48°24'·13N 04°57'·26W. AC 2694; SHOM 7123, 7122, 7149. HW +0520 on Dover (UT); ML 4·6m; see 10.16.22. Hbr, part-drying, is easier at nps, good wx/vis. Beware strong tidal streams. Best appr is via Ch de la Helle, twixt Le Faix bn tr, VQ 16m, and Luronne WCM buoy. Track W to pick up ldg marks 215°: front, Trois Pierres bn, Iso WRG 4s, 15m; rear, RW N. Mill bn tr. Nearing front mark, alter stbd to align spire 199° between ECM bn tr and WCM buoy. ‡ S of N bkwtr hd in about 1·5m; 10 ⚓s in inner hbr, FF30. Dir lt 191°, Fl (3) WRG 12s, W190°-192°, is on old S pier; same lt, but Fl (2) WRG 6s, also covers Chenal des Las (W259·5°-262·5°). Facilities: FW, V, CH, R, Bar, ⊠.

LE CONQUET   10-16-26

Finistere 48°21'·60N 04°47'·15W   Rtg 3-4-2

CHARTS
AC 3345, 2694; SHOM 7122, 7149, 7148; ECM 540; Imray C36; Stanfords 17
TIDES
+0535 Dover; ML 3·9; Duration 0600; Zone −0100

Standard Port BREST (→)

Times				Height (metres)			
High Water		Low Water		MHWS	MHWN	MLWN	MLWS
0000	0600	0000	0600	6·9	5·4	2·6	1·0
1200	1800	1200	1800				
Differences LE CONQUET							
−0005	0000	+0007	+0007	−0·1	−0·1	−0·1	0·0

SHELTER
Good except in strong W winds. A busy fishing port with few yacht facilities. AB only briefly at quay for loading. ‡ prohib in Avant Port. Yachts can ‡ further up hbr but it dries and may be foul.
NAVIGATION
WPT 48°21'·50N 04°48'·50W, 263°/083° from/to Mole Ste Barbe lt, 1M. From the NW, beware the Grande Vinotière rks. Also note strong cross streams in the Chenal du Four.
LIGHTS AND MARKS
Ldg line 095° lt on Mole Ste Barbe, Oc G 4s in line with spire of Le Conquet church. La Louve R bn tr and end of Mole St Christophe in line at 079°.
RADIO TELEPHONE
Le Conquet Port (Hr Mr) VHF 11 16. Call: St Mathieu VHF Ch 16 for Chenal du Four and Chenal de la Helle (see 10.16.9).
TELEPHONE (Prefix ☎ Nos with zone code 02)
Hr Mr 98·89·08·07; Aff Mar 98·89·00·05; Météo 98·84·60·64; Auto 08.36.68.08.29; CROSS 98·89·31·31; SNSM 98·89·02·07; Police 98·89·00·13; Dr 98·89·01·86; Brit Consul 99·46·26·64.
FACILITIES
Hbr Slip, M, L, D; **Services:** ME, EI, P (cans), CH.
Town P, D, FW, ME, EI, V, Gaz, R, Bar, ⊠, ⑧, ⇌ (bus to Brest), ✈ (Brest). Ferry: Roscoff.

16

BREST   10-16-27

Finistere 48°21'·30N 04°25·70W (Moulin Blanc)   Rtg 1-1-2

CHARTS
AC 3428, 3427, 798; SHOM 7397, 7398, 7399, 7400, 7401, 7149, 7172; ECM 542; Imray C36; Stanfords 17

TIDES
+0520 Dover; ML 4·0; Duration 0605; Zone –0100
NOTE: Brest is a Standard Port. Tidal predictions for every day are given below; tidal coefficients are above.

SHELTER
Excellent in Brest, and at many ⚓s in the Rade de Brest (50 sq miles). Access at any tide H24. Yachts should use Moulin Blanc marina, not the Port du Commerce. Brest is a busy commercial, naval and fishing port. The Port Militaire and a zone round Ile Longue are prohib areas.

NAVIGATION
WPT 48°18'·30N 04°44'·00W, 248°/068° from/to front ldg lt (Pte du Petit Minou), 5·3M. Tidal streams run hard in the Goulet de Brest. In mid-chan beware rks, well marked; pass either side. As WPT to Marina, use Moulin Blanc PHM buoy, Fl (3) R 12s, 48°22'·85N 04°25'·90W, 207°/027° from/to MB1 and MB2 chan buoys, 0·55M.

LIGHTS AND MARKS
Apprs marked by lts at Pte St Mathieu, Pte du Petit Minou and Pte du Portzic. Oceanopolis bldg, W roof, is conspic. Marina, 2M E of the Port de Commerce, has buoyed chan; MB4 lt and the ECM lt By can be obsc'd by berthed craft.

RADIO TELEPHONE
Call: *Brest Port* (at Pte du Portzic) VHF Ch 08 16 (controls apprs to Brest). All vessels entering keep watch on Ch 16. Marina Ch 09 16 (H24).
Corsen-Ouessant, callsign *Ouessant Traffic* on Ch 13 79, operates a VTS reporting system which is mandatory for vessels > 300grt. It covers an area within a 35M radius arc centred on Le Stiff radar tr which includes the whole Ushant TSS/ITZ. It also provides CROSS Corsen (MRCC) with tfc info over a far larger area from Mont St Michel in the E and Pte de Penmarch in the S, thence out to 8°W. It broadcasts tfc info, urgent warnings and special weather bulletins in English & French, on Ch 79 at H+10 and +40. Routine weather bulletins are broadcast every 3hrs from 0150UT. It can give position and navigational help to any vessel, if necessary; monitor Ch 16 whilst in the area.

TELEPHONE (Prefix ☎ Nos with zone code 02)
Hr Mr Brest 98·44·13·44; Moulin Blanc 98·02·20·02; Aff Mar 98·80·62·25; CROSS 98·89·31·31; ⌗ 98·44·35·20; Auto 08.36.68.08.29; Météo 98·84·60·64; Police 98·22·83·90; Dr 98·44·38·70; Ⓗ 98·22·33·33; Brit Consul 99·46·26·64.

FACILITIES (MOULIN BLANC)
Marina (1225+100 visitors), ☎ 98·02·20·02, 🖂 98.41.67.91, FF89, P & D H24, FW, AC, Slip, ME, El, Ⓔ, SHOM, Sh, SM, CH, BH (14 & 35 ton), C (3 & 12 ton), Gaz, R, Ⓥ, V, Bar;
Sté des Régates de Brest ☎ 98·02·53·36, R.
BREST **Services:** CH, SM, ME, El, Sh, Ⓔ, SHOM.
City all facilities, Gaz, ⌧, Ⓑ, ⇌, ✈. Ferry: Roscoff.

ADJACENT ANCHORAGE TO THE WEST

ANSE DE BERTHAUME, 48°20'·50N 04°41'·75W. AC 3427. A useful passage ⚓ if awaiting the tide E into Goulet de Brest; N into Ch du Four, or S toward Raz de Sein. Good shelter in W'lies. ⚓ in 5m off slip N of Fort de Berthaume (conspic); 1ca NE, beware Le Chat rk, dries 6·8m. No lts.

RADE DE BREST   10-16-28

Finistere

TIDES
In most of the bays in the Rade de Brest tidal streams are weak, but in the main rivers they can exceed 2kn at sp.

SHELTER AND NAVIGATION
The Rade de Brest offers a sheltered cruising ground, useful in bad weather, with many attractive ⚓s.
To the NE, ½M beyond Pont Albert-Louppe (2 bridges: 29m and 25m clearance) is a good ⚓ at Le Passage. It is possible to explore R L'Elorn for about 6M to the drying port of Landerneau; keep well inboard of chan buoys.
On the S side of Rade de Brest are various naval sites with prohib ⚓ around Ile Longue. There are however ⚓s at Le Fret, on SE side of Ile Longue, and at Roscanvel on E side of the Quelern Peninsula.
To the SE, L'Aulne is a lovely river with steep wooded banks. Near the mouth of its estuary, on the N shore, is a good ⚓ and W ⚓s in 3m in Anse de l'Auberlach. Further E, 3 small drying rivers run into the Aulne from the north: R Daoulas, R de l'Hôpital and R du Faou and offer shelter for boats which can dry out.
Up the Aulne there are ⚓s near Landévennec, below Térénez bridge (27m), and also 1½M above that bridge. At Guily-Glaz, 14M above Landévennec, a lock (open HW Brest –2 to +1½) opens into the canalised river to Port Launay (AB on quay, FF20, AC, FW, R), and 3M further on to Chateaulin, AB on pontoons; most facilities.

H.W.Hts.m.

BREST

MEAN SPRING
AND NEAP CURVES

MEAN RANGES
Springs 5.9m
Neaps 2.8m

Springs occur 2 days
after
New and Full Moon.

CHART DATUM

M.H.W.N.   M.H.W.S.

Factor

M.L.W.S.   M.L.W.N.

L.W.Hts.m.

L.W. -5ʰ -4ʰ -3ʰ -2ʰ -1ʰ H.W. +1ʰ +2ʰ +3ʰ +4ʰ +5ʰ L.W.

RADE DE BREST *continued*

TIME ZONE –0100
(French Standard Time)
Subtract 1 hour for UT

For French Summer Time add ONE hour in non-shaded areas

FRANCE – BREST

LAT 48°23′N   LONG   4°30′W

TIMES AND HEIGHTS OF HIGH AND LOW WATERS

YEAR **1998**

JANUARY

Day	Time	m	Time	m	Time	m	Time	m
1 TH	0032	1.1	0633	7.1	1257	1.0	1855	6.8
2 F	0116	1.2	0718	7.0	1342	1.1	1940	6.6
3 SA	0202	1.3	0804	6.8	1429	1.3	2029	6.4
4 SU	0251	1.6	0855	6.5	1520	1.5	2122	6.1
5 M	0346	1.9	0951	6.2	1617	1.8	2223	5.9
6 TU	0448	2.1	1056	6.0	1722	2.0	2332	5.7
7 W	0558	2.2	1208	5.8	1833	2.1		
8 TH	0047	5.8	0711	2.1	1321	5.9	1944	2.0
9 F	0157	6.0	0820	1.9	1428	6.1	2048	1.8
10 SA	0257	6.2	0921	1.7	1525	6.3	2144	1.6
11 SU	0349	6.5	1013	1.4	1614	6.5	2232	1.4
12 M O	0435	6.7	1059	1.2	1658	6.6	2315	1.3
13 TU	0516	6.8	1141	1.1	1738	6.7	2355	1.2
14 W	0554	6.9	1219	1.2	1815	6.7		
15 TH	0032	1.3	0629	6.8	1256	1.3	1850	6.5
16 F	0107	1.4	0703	6.6	1330	1.5	1924	6.3
17 SA	0142	1.6	0737	6.4	1404	1.7	1958	6.1
18 SU	0217	1.9	0811	6.1	1441	2.0	2034	5.8
19 M	0254	2.2	0847	5.8	1519	2.3	2114	5.5
20 TU	0335	2.5	0930	5.5	1604	2.6	2204	5.3
21 W	0426	2.7	1025	5.2	1700	2.8	2309	5.1
22 TH	0528	2.9	1136	5.1	1809	2.8		
23 F	0024	5.2	0642	2.8	1255	5.2	1924	2.7
24 SA	0135	5.4	0753	2.6	1404	5.5	2026	2.4
25 SU	0234	5.8	0853	2.2	1500	5.8	2119	2.0
26 M	0324	6.2	0943	1.7	1548	6.2	2206	1.6
27 TU	0410	6.6	1030	1.3	1633	6.6	2251	1.2
28 W ●	0454	7.0	1115	0.9	1717	6.9	2335	0.9
29 TH	0538	7.2	1159	0.7	1800	7.1		
30 F	0020	0.8	0621	7.4	1243	0.6	1843	7.1
31 SA	0103	0.7	0705	7.4	1327	0.6	1926	7.0

FEBRUARY

Day	Time	m	Time	m	Time	m	Time	m
1 SU	0148	0.9	0749	7.2	1413	0.8	2011	6.8
2 M	0235	1.1	0836	6.8	1501	1.2	2059	6.4
3 TU	0326	1.5	0927	6.4	1553	1.7	2154	6.0
4 W	0422	1.9	1026	6.0	1653	2.1	2259	5.7
5 TH	0528	2.2	1137	5.6	1803	2.3		
6 F	0017	5.5	0646	2.4	1259	5.5	1922	2.4
7 SA	0139	5.6	0804	2.2	1415	5.7	2034	2.2
8 SU	0246	5.9	0909	1.9	1515	6.0	2132	1.9
9 M	0338	6.2	1001	1.6	1603	6.3	2219	1.6
10 TU	0422	6.5	1046	1.4	1644	6.5	2300	1.4
11 W O	0501	6.7	1124	1.2	1721	6.6	2337	1.3
12 TH	0536	6.8	1200	1.2	1754	6.7		
13 F	0011	1.2	0608	6.8	1232	1.2	1825	6.6
14 SA	0043	1.3	0638	6.7	1303	1.3	1856	6.5
15 SU	0114	1.4	0708	6.6	1334	1.5	1926	6.3
16 M	0145	1.6	0739	6.3	1406	1.7	1957	6.1
17 TU	0218	1.9	0810	6.1	1438	2.0	2031	5.8
18 W	0254	2.2	0845	5.7	1516	2.4	2111	5.5
19 TH	0337	2.5	0930	5.4	1604	2.6	2207	5.2
20 F	0433	2.7	1034	5.1	1707	2.8	2321	5.1
21 SA	0544	2.8	1157	5.0	1827	2.8		
22 SU	0047	5.2	0707	2.7	1324	5.3	1948	2.6
23 M	0201	5.6	0820	2.3	1432	5.7	2051	2.1
24 TU	0259	6.1	0918	1.7	1526	6.2	2143	1.6
25 W	0349	6.6	1008	1.2	1614	6.7	2231	1.1
26 TH ●	0435	7.1	1055	0.7	1659	7.1	2317	0.7
27 F	0520	7.5	1141	0.4	1742	7.3		
28 SA	0002	0.4	0604	7.7	1225	0.2	1825	7.4

MARCH

Day	Time	m	Time	m	Time	m	Time	m
1 SU	0046	0.4	0647	7.6	1309	0.3	1907	7.3
2 M	0130	0.5	0730	7.4	1354	0.4	1951	7.0
3 TU	0215	0.7	0815	7.0	1440	1.1	2036	6.6
4 W	0304	1.3	0903	6.4	1529	1.6	2127	6.1
5 TH	0357	1.9	0959	5.9	1626	2.2	2229	5.6
6 F	0502	2.5	1110	5.4	1736	2.5	2349	5.3
7 SA	0621	2.5	1238	5.3	1859	2.6		
8 SU	0118	5.4	0747	2.4	1401	5.4	2017	2.4
9 M	0230	5.8	0854	2.1	1501	5.8	2115	2.0
10 TU	0322	6.1	0945	1.8	1546	6.1	2201	1.7
11 W	0404	6.3	1027	1.5	1625	6.4	2240	1.5
12 TH	0440	6.6	1103	1.3	1659	6.6	2315	1.3
13 F O	0513	6.7	1135	1.2	1729	6.7	2346	1.2
14 SA	0543	6.8	1206	1.2	1759	6.7		
15 SU	0017	1.2	0612	6.7	1236	1.3	1828	6.6
16 M	0047	1.3	0641	6.6	1305	1.4	1857	6.5
17 TU	0117	1.5	0710	6.5	1334	1.6	1926	6.3
18 W	0148	1.7	0740	6.2	1405	1.9	1958	6.0
19 TH	0223	2.0	0814	5.9	1442	2.2	2036	5.7
20 F	0304	2.3	0856	5.5	1527	2.5	2126	5.4
21 SA	0357	2.6	0954	5.2	1625	2.8	2236	5.2
22 SU	0504	2.7	1115	5.1	1743	2.9		
23 M	0004	5.2	0627	2.6	1247	5.2	1915	2.6
24 TU	0127	5.5	0747	2.3	1403	5.7	2022	2.1
25 W	0231	6.1	0851	1.7	1501	6.2	2119	1.5
26 TH	0325	6.6	0944	1.1	1551	6.7	2209	1.0
27 F	0413	7.2	1033	0.6	1637	7.2	2256	0.6
28 SA ●	0459	7.5	1119	0.3	1709	7.5	2342	0.3
29 SU	0544	7.7	1205	0.2	1805	7.5		
30 M	0027	0.2	0627	7.7	1249	0.3	1847	7.4
31 TU	0111	0.4	0710	7.4	1333	0.6	1930	7.1

APRIL

Day	Time	m	Time	m	Time	m	Time	m
1 W	0154	0.8	0755	6.9	1418	1.1	2014	6.6
2 TH	0242	1.3	0842	6.3	1507	1.7	2104	6.1
3 F	0333	1.8	0936	5.8	1602	2.2	2203	5.6
4 SA	0439	2.3	1045	5.3	1708	2.6	2319	5.3
5 SU	0554	2.6	1210	5.1	1829	2.7		
6 M	0047	5.3	0718	2.5	1334	5.3	1949	2.5
7 TU	0201	5.5	0826	2.2	1434	5.6	2048	2.2
8 W	0255	5.9	0917	1.9	1519	6.0	2134	1.9
9 TH	0337	6.1	0958	1.7	1557	6.2	2213	1.6
10 F	0412	6.4	1034	1.5	1630	6.4	2247	1.5
11 SA O	0445	6.5	1107	1.3	1701	6.6	2319	1.3
12 SU	0515	6.6	1137	1.3	1731	6.7	2350	1.3
13 M	0545	6.6	1207	1.3	1800	6.7		
14 TU	0020	1.3	0615	6.6	1237	1.4	1830	6.6
15 W	0051	1.4	0645	6.5	1307	1.6	1901	6.4
16 TH	0124	1.6	0716	6.3	1340	1.8	1934	6.2
17 F	0200	1.8	0752	6.0	1417	2.1	2014	5.9
18 SA	0242	2.1	0836	5.7	1503	2.3	2104	5.6
19 SU	0334	2.3	0933	5.4	1600	2.6	2210	5.4
20 M	0438	2.5	1048	5.2	1713	2.7	2332	5.4
21 TU	0556	2.5	1215	5.3	1842	2.5		
22 W	0053	5.6	0715	2.1	1332	5.7	1951	2.1
23 TH	0201	6.1	0821	1.6	1433	6.2	2051	1.5
24 F	0257	6.6	0917	1.1	1525	6.7	2144	1.0
25 SA	0349	7.1	1008	0.7	1614	7.1	2234	0.6
26 SU ●	0437	7.4	1057	0.4	1700	7.4	2321	0.4
27 M	0523	7.5	1143	0.4	1744	7.5		
28 TU	0007	0.4	0607	7.5	1228	0.5	1827	7.3
29 W	0053	0.5	0651	7.2	1313	0.8	1911	7.0
30 TH	0138	0.9	0736	6.8	1358	1.3	1955	6.6

Chart Datum: 3 61 metres below Lallemand System (Mean Sea Level, Marseilles)

TIME ZONE –0100
(French Standard Time)
Subtract 1 hour for UT
For French Summer Time add
ONE hour in non-shaded areas

FRANCE – BREST

LAT 48°23′N   LONG 4°30′W

TIMES AND HEIGHTS OF HIGH AND LOW WATERS   YEAR **1998**

MAY

Day	Time	m	Time	m	Time	m	Time	m
1 F	0224	1.3	0823	6.3	1446	1.7	2043	6.2
2 SA	0314	1.8	0915	5.8	1538	2.2	2139	5.7
3 SU	0413	2.3	1017	5.4	1638	2.6	2245	5.4
4 M	0519	2.5	1131	5.2	1749	2.7		
5 TU	0002	5.3	0635	2.6	1249	5.2	1904	2.6
6 W	0116	5.4	0744	2.4	1353	5.5	2007	2.4
7 TH	0214	5.6	0838	2.1	1441	5.8	2057	2.1
8 F	0259	5.9	0922	1.9	1522	6.0	2138	1.9
9 SA	0338	6.1	1000	1.7	1557	6.3	2215	1.7
10 SU	0413	6.3	1035	1.5	1631	6.4	2249	1.5
11 M O	0446	6.4	1108	1.4	1703	6.6	2323	1.4
12 TU	0519	6.5	1140	1.4	1735	6.6	2357	1.4
13 W	0551	6.5	1213	1.4	1808	6.6		
14 TH	0030	1.4	0625	6.4	1246	1.5	1842	6.5
15 F	0106	1.5	0700	6.3	1321	1.7	1919	6.3
16 SA	0144	1.6	0739	6.1	1402	1.9	2002	6.1
17 SU	0228	1.8	0825	5.8	1448	2.1	2052	5.8
18 M	0319	2.1	0920	5.6	1544	2.4	2154	5.7
19 TU	0420	2.2	1029	5.4	1652	2.5	2307	5.6
20 W	0531	2.2	1146	5.5	1810	2.3		
21 TH	0022	5.8	0645	2.0	1300	5.8	1921	2.0
22 F	0130	6.1	0752	1.6	1404	6.2	2024	1.6
23 SA	0230	6.5	0851	1.3	1500	6.6	2120	1.2
24 SU	0325	6.9	0945	0.9	1551	6.9	2213	0.8
25 M ●	0416	7.1	1035	0.7	1639	7.1	2302	0.6
26 TU	0504	7.2	1123	0.7	1725	7.2	2350	0.6
27 W	0550	7.1	1209	0.8	1810	7.1		
28 TH	0036	0.7	0635	6.9	1254	1.0	1853	6.9
29 F	0121	1.0	0719	6.6	1339	1.3	1937	6.6
30 SA	0207	1.4	0804	6.2	1424	1.7	2022	6.2
31 SU	0253	1.7	0851	5.8	1511	2.1	2111	5.8

JUNE

Day	Time	m	Time	m	Time	m	Time	m
1 M	0343	2.1	0944	5.5	1603	2.4	2205	5.5
2 TU	0439	2.4	1044	5.2	1702	2.6	2308	5.3
3 W	0541	2.6	1151	5.2	1807	2.7		
4 TH	0016	5.3	0648	2.5	1257	5.3	1913	2.6
5 F	0120	5.4	0748	2.4	1354	5.5	2010	2.4
6 SA	0214	5.6	0839	2.2	1441	5.8	2058	2.1
7 SU	0300	5.8	0923	2.0	1522	6.0	2141	1.9
8 M	0341	6.0	1002	1.8	1601	6.2	2220	1.7
9 TU	0419	6.2	1039	1.6	1637	6.4	2258	1.5
10 W	0456	6.3	1116	1.5	1714	6.5	2335	1.4
11 TH	0532	6.4	1152	1.4	1750	6.6		
12 F	0013	1.3	0609	6.4	1229	1.5	1828	6.6
13 SA	0051	1.3	0648	6.4	1308	1.5	1909	6.5
14 SU	0133	1.4	0730	6.3	1351	1.6	1953	6.4
15 M	0217	1.5	0816	6.1	1438	1.8	2042	6.2
16 TU	0307	1.7	0908	5.9	1531	2.0	2138	6.0
17 W	0403	1.9	1009	5.7	1632	2.1	2242	5.9
18 TH	0506	2.0	1117	5.7	1742	2.1	2351	5.9
19 F	0615	1.9	1228	5.8	1852	2.0		
20 SA	0101	6.0	0724	1.8	1336	6.0	1959	1.7
21 SU	0206	6.3	0827	1.5	1437	6.3	2100	1.4
22 M	0305	6.5	0925	1.3	1532	6.6	2156	1.1
23 TU	0359	6.7	1018	1.1	1623	6.8	2247	1.0
24 W ●	0449	6.8	1107	1.0	1710	6.9	2335	0.9
25 TH	0535	6.8	1153	1.0	1755	6.9		
26 F	0020	0.9	0619	6.7	1236	1.1	1837	6.8
27 SA	0103	1.1	0700	6.5	1318	1.3	1917	6.6
28 SU	0145	1.3	0741	6.3	1359	1.6	1957	6.3
29 M	0226	1.6	0822	6.0	1441	1.9	2038	6.0
30 TU	0306	1.9	0905	5.7	1524	2.2	2122	5.7

JULY

Day	Time	m	Time	m	Time	m	Time	m
1 W	0352	2.3	0953	5.4	1613	2.5	2212	5.4
2 TH	0444	2.5	1050	5.2	1708	2.7	2312	5.2
3 F	0545	2.6	1154	5.2	1812	2.7		
4 SA	0019	5.2	0650	2.6	1259	5.3	1917	2.6
5 SU	0124	5.3	0751	2.5	1357	5.5	2016	2.4
6 M	0221	5.5	0844	2.2	1448	5.8	2107	2.1
7 TU	0310	5.8	0930	2.0	1532	6.1	2152	1.8
8 W	0354	6.0	1012	1.7	1614	6.3	2235	1.5
9 TH	0435	6.3	1053	1.5	1654	6.6	2316	1.3
10 F	0515	6.4	1134	1.4	1734	6.7	2356	1.1
11 SA	0555	6.6	1214	1.2	1815	6.8		
12 SU	0037	1.0	0636	6.6	1256	1.2	1857	6.8
13 M	0120	1.0	0718	6.6	1339	1.3	1941	6.7
14 TU	0204	1.1	0803	6.4	1425	1.4	2028	6.5
15 W	0251	1.3	0852	6.2	1515	1.6	2119	6.3
16 TH	0344	1.6	0946	6.0	1612	1.9	2217	6.1
17 F	0443	1.8	1050	5.8	1716	2.0	2324	5.9
18 SA	0549	2.0	1201	5.7	1827	2.1		
19 SU	0036	5.8	0700	2.0	1314	5.8	1939	2.0
20 M	0148	5.9	0810	1.9	1422	6.1	2046	1.7
21 TU	0253	6.1	0912	1.6	1520	6.3	2144	1.4
22 W	0349	6.4	1006	1.4	1612	6.6	2236	1.2
23 TH ●	0437	6.5	1054	1.3	1657	6.8	2322	1.1
24 F	0521	6.6	1138	1.2	1739	6.8		
25 SA	0004	1.0	0601	6.6	1218	1.2	1818	6.8
26 SU	0043	1.1	0639	6.6	1256	1.3	1853	6.7
27 M	0120	1.3	0714	6.4	1332	1.5	1928	6.5
28 TU	0155	1.5	0749	6.2	1408	1.7	2003	6.2
29 W	0231	1.8	0824	5.9	1445	2.0	2039	5.9
30 TH	0310	2.1	0903	5.6	1525	2.3	2119	5.6
31 F	0352	2.4	0950	5.3	1613	2.6	2210	5.3

AUGUST

Day	Time	m	Time	m	Time	m	Time	m
1 SA	0444	2.7	1049	5.1	1711	2.8	2315	5.1
2 SU	0548	2.8	1201	5.1	1821	2.8		
3 M	0031	5.1	0701	2.7	1313	5.3	1933	2.6
4 TU	0143	5.3	0806	2.5	1415	5.6	2035	2.3
5 W	0241	5.6	0900	2.2	1506	5.9	2126	1.9
6 TH	0330	6.0	0948	1.8	1552	6.3	2212	1.5
7 F	0415	6.3	1032	1.5	1635	6.7	2256	1.2
8 SA O	0457	6.6	1115	1.2	1717	7.0	2338	0.9
9 SU	0538	6.8	1158	1.0	1759	7.2		
10 M	0021	0.7	0620	6.9	1240	0.9	1841	7.2
11 TU	0104	0.7	0702	6.9	1324	0.9	1924	7.1
12 W	0147	0.8	0745	6.7	1409	1.1	2009	6.9
13 TH	0233	1.1	0831	6.5	1457	1.4	2058	6.5
14 F	0323	1.5	0923	6.1	1551	1.8	2153	6.1
15 SA	0419	1.9	1024	5.8	1652	2.1	2300	5.7
16 SU	0526	2.2	1137	5.6	1807	2.3		
17 M	0018	5.6	0641	2.3	1259	5.6	1926	2.2
18 TU	0139	5.6	0758	2.2	1413	5.9	2038	1.9
19 W	0246	5.9	0903	1.9	1512	6.2	2136	1.6
20 TH	0340	6.2	0955	1.6	1601	6.5	2224	1.3
21 F	0425	6.4	1040	1.4	1643	6.7	2307	1.2
22 SA ●	0505	6.6	1120	1.3	1721	6.8	2345	1.1
23 SU	0540	6.7	1156	1.2	1755	6.8		
24 M	0019	1.1	0613	6.6	1230	1.3	1826	6.7
25 TU	0052	1.3	0644	6.5	1302	1.4	1857	6.6
26 W	0122	1.5	0715	6.3	1334	1.6	1928	6.3
27 TH	0155	1.7	0746	6.1	1407	1.9	1959	6.0
28 F	0228	2.0	0819	5.8	1443	2.2	2033	5.7
29 SA	0304	2.4	0858	5.5	1524	2.5	2116	5.4
30 SU	0349	2.7	0950	5.2	1618	2.8	2216	5.1
31 M	0449	2.9	1103	5.0	1727	2.9	2338	5.0

16

Chart Datum: 3·64 metres below Lallemand System (Mean Sea Level, Marseilles)

TIME ZONE –0100
(French Standard Time)
Subtract 1 hour for UT
For French Summer Time add ONE hour in non-shaded areas

FRANCE – BREST

LAT 48°23′N   LONG 4°30′W

TIMES AND HEIGHTS OF HIGH AND LOW WATERS   YEAR 1998

SEPTEMBER

Day	Time	m		Day	Time	m
1 TU	0607 / 1228 / 1850	3.0 / 5.1 / 2.8		16 W	0131 / 0746 / 1402 / 2027	5.5 / 2.4 / 5.8 / 2.1
2 W	0105 / 0728 / 1343 / 2003	5.1 / 2.7 / 5.4 / 2.5		17 TH	0236 / 0850 / 1459 / 2122	5.8 / 2.1 / 6.1 / 1.7
3 TH	0213 / 0832 / 1440 / 2059	5.5 / 2.3 / 5.9 / 2.0		18 F	0325 / 0940 / 1544 / 2207	6.2 / 1.7 / 6.4 / 1.5
4 F	0306 / 0923 / 1529 / 2148	6.0 / 1.8 / 6.4 / 1.4		19 SA	0406 / 1022 / 1623 / 2246	6.4 / 1.5 / 6.6 / 1.3
5 SA	0352 / 1009 / 1614 / 2233	6.4 / 1.4 / 6.9 / 1.0		20 SU	0442 / 1059 / 1658 / 2321	6.6 / 1.3 / 6.6 / 1.2
6 SU	0436 / 1054 / 1657 / 2317	6.8 / 1.0 / 7.2 / 0.6		21 M	0515 / 1132 / 1729 / 2352	6.7 / 1.3 / 6.8 / 1.2
7 M	0518 / 1138 / 1739	7.1 / 0.7 / 7.5		22 TU	0545 / 1203 / 1758	6.7 / 1.3 / 6.8
8 TU	0000 / 0600 / 1221 / 1821	0.4 / 7.3 / 0.6 / 7.5		23 W	0022 / 0614 / 1233 / 1827	1.3 / 6.6 / 1.4 / 6.6
9 W	0044 / 0642 / 1304 / 1904	0.4 / 7.3 / 0.6 / 7.4		24 TH	0051 / 0643 / 1304 / 1856	1.5 / 6.5 / 1.6 / 6.4
10 TH	0127 / 0725 / 1350 / 1949	0.6 / 7.1 / 0.9 / 7.1		25 F	0122 / 0712 / 1335 / 1926	1.7 / 6.3 / 1.8 / 6.2
11 F	0213 / 0810 / 1438 / 2037	1.0 / 6.7 / 1.3 / 6.6		26 SA	0152 / 0743 / 1408 / 1958	2.0 / 6.0 / 2.1 / 5.8
12 SA	0302 / 0900 / 1531 / 2132	1.5 / 6.2 / 1.8 / 6.0		27 SU	0226 / 0819 / 1448 / 2038	2.3 / 5.7 / 2.4 / 5.5
13 SU	0358 / 1001 / 1630 / 2240	2.0 / 5.8 / 2.2 / 5.6		28 M	0309 / 0907 / 1538 / 2133	2.6 / 5.4 / 2.7 / 5.2
14 M	0505 / 1118 / 1750	2.4 / 5.5 / 2.5		29 TU	0405 / 1015 / 1644 / 2253	2.9 / 5.1 / 2.9 / 5.0
15 TU	0005 / 0625 / 1246 / 1915	5.4 / 2.6 / 5.5 / 2.4		30 W	0520 / 1144 / 1808	3.0 / 5.1 / 2.9

OCTOBER

Day	Time	m		Day	Time	m
1 TH	0028 / 0654 / 1308 / 1929	5.1 / 2.8 / 5.4 / 2.5		16 F	0214 / 0827 / 1435 / 2058	5.7 / 2.2 / 6.0 / 1.9
2 F	0143 / 0801 / 1411 / 2030	5.5 / 2.4 / 5.9 / 2.0		17 SA	0301 / 0916 / 1520 / 2142	6.1 / 1.9 / 6.3 / 1.6
3 SA	0239 / 0856 / 1502 / 2121	6.0 / 1.8 / 6.5 / 1.4		18 SU	0341 / 0957 / 1557 / 2219	6.4 / 1.7 / 6.5 / 1.4
4 SU	0328 / 0945 / 1549 / 2209	6.6 / 1.3 / 7.0 / 0.9		19 M	0416 / 1032 / 1631 / 2253	6.5 / 1.5 / 6.6 / 1.4
5 M	0413 / 1031 / 1634 / 2254	7.0 / 0.8 / 7.4 / 0.5		20 TU	0447 / 1105 / 1701 / 2324	6.7 / 1.4 / 6.7 / 1.4
6 TU	0456 / 1116 / 1718 / 2339	7.4 / 0.5 / 7.6 / 0.3		21 W	0517 / 1136 / 1731 / 2354	6.7 / 1.4 / 6.7 / 1.4
7 W	0539 / 1201 / 1801	7.5 / 0.4 / 7.7		22 TH	0546 / 1207 / 1800	6.7 / 1.5 / 6.6
8 TH	0023 / 0621 / 1245 / 1845	0.4 / 7.5 / 0.5 / 7.5		23 F	0023 / 0616 / 1237 / 1830	1.5 / 6.6 / 1.6 / 6.5
9 F	0107 / 0705 / 1330 / 1930	0.6 / 7.2 / 0.8 / 7.1		24 SA	0053 / 0645 / 1309 / 1900	1.7 / 6.4 / 1.8 / 6.4
10 SA	0153 / 0750 / 1418 / 2018	1.1 / 6.8 / 1.3 / 6.5		25 SU	0124 / 0717 / 1343 / 1933	2.0 / 6.2 / 2.0 / 5.9
11 SU	0242 / 0840 / 1510 / 2113	1.6 / 6.3 / 1.8 / 6.0		26 M	0159 / 0754 / 1423 / 2014	2.2 / 5.9 / 2.3 / 5.6
12 M	0338 / 0941 / 1616 / 2222	2.2 / 5.8 / 2.3 / 5.5		27 TU	0241 / 0840 / 1512 / 2107	2.5 / 5.6 / 2.6 / 5.3
13 TU	0444 / 1057 / 1730 / 2346	2.6 / 5.5 / 2.6 / 5.3		28 W	0335 / 0944 / 1613 / 2220	2.8 / 5.3 / 2.7 / 5.1
14 W	0603 / 1224 / 1854	2.7 / 5.4 / 2.5		29 TH	0445 / 1106 / 1730 / 2349	2.9 / 5.3 / 2.7 / 5.2
15 TH	0111 / 0724 / 1340 / 2005	5.4 / 2.6 / 5.7 / 2.2		30 F	0610 / 1229 / 1851	2.8 / 5.5 / 2.4
				31 SA	0108 / 0726 / 1337 / 1957	5.6 / 2.4 / 6.0 / 2.0

NOVEMBER

Day	Time	m		Day	Time	m
1 SU	0208 / 0826 / 1432 / 2052	6.1 / 1.9 / 6.5 / 1.4		16 M	0309 / 0925 / 1526 / 2148	6.1 / 1.9 / 6.2 / 1.8
2 M	0300 / 0918 / 1523 / 2143	6.6 / 1.3 / 7.0 / 0.7		17 TU	0345 / 1003 / 1602 / 2223	6.4 / 1.7 / 6.4 / 1.6
3 TU	0348 / 1007 / 1610 / 2230	7.1 / 0.9 / 7.4 / 0.6		18 W	0418 / 1038 / 1635 / 2256	6.5 / 1.6 / 6.5 / 1.5
4 W	0433 / 1055 / 1656 / 2317	7.4 / 0.6 / 7.6 / 0.5		19 TH	0450 / 1111 / 1706 / 2328	6.6 / 1.5 / 6.5 / 1.5
5 TH	0518 / 1141 / 1742	7.5 / 0.5 / 7.6		20 F	0522 / 1144 / 1738 / 2359	6.7 / 1.5 / 6.5 / 1.6
6 F	0003 / 0602 / 1228 / 1827	0.5 / 7.5 / 0.6 / 7.4		21 SA	0554 / 1216 / 1810	6.6 / 1.6 / 6.4
7 SA	0048 / 0647 / 1314 / 1913	0.8 / 7.2 / 0.8 / 7.0		22 SU	0031 / 0626 / 1250 / 1843	1.7 / 6.5 / 1.7 / 6.3
8 SU	0135 / 0733 / 1401 / 2002	1.2 / 6.9 / 1.3 / 6.5		23 M	0104 / 0701 / 1326 / 1919	1.8 / 6.4 / 1.8 / 6.1
9 M	0224 / 0823 / 1453 / 2055	1.7 / 6.4 / 1.8 / 6.0		24 TU	0141 / 0740 / 1407 / 2000	2.0 / 6.1 / 2.0 / 5.8
10 TU	0317 / 0919 / 1553 / 2158	2.2 / 5.9 / 2.2 / 5.5		25 W	0224 / 0826 / 1454 / 2051	2.3 / 5.9 / 2.2 / 5.6
11 W	0417 / 1026 / 1700 / 2312	2.5 / 5.6 / 2.5 / 5.3		26 TH	0315 / 0923 / 1550 / 2155	2.5 / 5.7 / 2.4 / 5.4
12 TH	0528 / 1143 / 1816	2.7 / 5.4 / 2.6		27 F	0418 / 1032 / 1657 / 2311	2.7 / 5.6 / 2.5 / 5.4
13 F	0030 / 0644 / 1259 / 1927	5.3 / 2.7 / 5.5 / 2.4		28 SA	0533 / 1149 / 1812	2.6 / 5.7 / 2.3
14 SA	0136 / 0750 / 1359 / 2024	5.6 / 2.5 / 5.7 / 2.2		29 SU	0028 / 0651 / 1300 / 1922	5.6 / 2.4 / 6.0 / 2.0
15 SU	0227 / 0842 / 1447 / 2109	5.9 / 2.2 / 6.0 / 1.9		30 M	0135 / 0755 / 1402 / 2023	6.0 / 1.9 / 6.4 / 1.5

DECEMBER

Day	Time	m		Day	Time	m
1 TU	0232 / 0852 / 1458 / 2118	6.5 / 1.4 / 6.8 / 1.1		16 W	0313 / 0932 / 1532 / 2153	6.0 / 2.0 / 6.0 / 1.9
2 W	0325 / 0945 / 1549 / 2209	6.9 / 1.0 / 7.1 / 0.9		17 TH	0351 / 1011 / 1610 / 2229	6.3 / 1.8 / 6.2 / 1.7
3 TH	0414 / 1036 / 1639 / 2258	7.2 / 0.8 / 7.3 / 0.7		18 F	0427 / 1048 / 1645 / 2305	6.5 / 1.6 / 6.4 / 1.6
4 F	0501 / 1125 / 1726 / 2346	7.4 / 0.6 / 7.3 / 0.7		19 SA	0502 / 1124 / 1720 / 2339	6.6 / 1.5 / 6.4 / 1.6
5 SA	0547 / 1213 / 1813	7.4 / 0.7 / 7.2		20 SU	0537 / 1159 / 1755	6.7 / 1.5 / 6.5
6 SU	0032 / 0633 / 1300 / 1859	0.9 / 7.2 / 0.9 / 6.9		21 M	0015 / 0612 / 1236 / 1831	1.6 / 6.7 / 1.5 / 6.4
7 M	0118 / 0718 / 1347 / 1945	1.2 / 6.9 / 1.2 / 6.5		22 TU	0051 / 0650 / 1313 / 1909	1.6 / 6.6 / 1.5 / 6.3
8 TU	0204 / 0804 / 1435 / 2033	1.6 / 6.5 / 1.6 / 6.1		23 W	0129 / 0730 / 1354 / 1950	1.7 / 6.5 / 1.6 / 6.2
9 W	0252 / 0853 / 1525 / 2125	2.0 / 6.1 / 2.0 / 5.7		24 TH	0212 / 0814 / 1439 / 2037	1.9 / 6.3 / 1.8 / 5.9
10 TH	0344 / 0947 / 1621 / 2225	2.4 / 5.7 / 2.4 / 5.4		25 F	0300 / 0904 / 1529 / 2131	2.1 / 6.1 / 2.0 / 5.7
11 F	0442 / 1049 / 1723 / 2332	2.6 / 5.5 / 2.6 / 5.3		26 SA	0355 / 1003 / 1628 / 2236	2.3 / 5.9 / 2.1 / 5.6
12 SA	0548 / 1158 / 1831	2.8 / 5.3 / 2.6		27 SU	0500 / 1110 / 1736 / 2348	2.3 / 5.8 / 2.2 / 5.7
13 SU	0041 / 0656 / 1307 / 1936	5.3 / 2.7 / 5.4 / 2.5		28 M	0613 / 1223 / 1847	2.3 / 5.9 / 2.1
14 M	0141 / 0758 / 1404 / 2029	5.5 / 2.5 / 5.6 / 2.3		29 TU	0101 / 0724 / 1333 / 1955	5.9 / 2.0 / 6.1 / 1.8
15 TU	0231 / 0848 / 1452 / 2113	5.8 / 2.3 / 5.8 / 2.1		30 W	0207 / 0829 / 1437 / 2057	6.2 / 1.7 / 6.4 / 1.5
				31 TH	0306 / 0928 / 1534 / 2153	6.6 / 1.3 / 6.7 / 1.2

Chart Datum: 3·04 metres below Lallemand System (Mean Sea Level, Marseilles)

CAMARET   10-16-29

Finistere 48°16'·80N 04°35'·19W Rtg 1-1-2

CHARTS
AC 3427, 798; SHOM 7401, 7148, 7149; Imray C36; ECM 540, 542; Stanfords 17

TIDES
+0500 Dover; ML 3·8; Duration 0610; Zone −0100

Standard Port BREST (←—)

Times				Height (metres)			
High Water		Low Water		MHWS	MHWN	MLWN	MLWS
0000	0600	0000	0600	6·9	5·4	2·6	1·0
1200	1800	1200	1800				
Differences CAMARET							
−0010	−0010	−0013	−0013	−0·3	−0·3	−0·1	0·0

SHELTER
Good, except in strong E winds. Plaisance La Pointe (5m) is mainly for visitors, but Styvel has some visitors berths for smaller craft (dredged 1·5m) and is nearer town. SW side of hbr mostly dries; FVs berth on SSE side.

NAVIGATION
WPT 48°18'·00N 04°36'·00W, 335°/155° from/to N mole lt, 1·2M. Beware rks W of Pte du Grand Gouin. ⚓ in hbr prohib.

LIGHTS AND MARKS
Lt ho at E end of N mole, Iso WG 4s, W135°-182°, G182°-027°; appr in W sector. The G SHM bn tr at the W end of the N mole is very conspic; also Tour Vauban and chapel close SW. Ldg line at 148°: front mark = top of the old fort; rear = Keraudren water tr on hill behind.

RADIO TELEPHONE
VHF Ch 09. For Ouessant Traffic see Fig 10 (4).

TELEPHONE (Prefix ☎ Nos with zone code 02)
Hr Mr 98·27·95·99; Aff Mar 98·27·93·28; SNSM 98·27·94·76; CROSS 98·89·31·31; ⊞ 98·27·93·02; Auto 08.36.68.08.29; Police 98·27·00·22;Dr 98·57·91·35; Brit Consul 40·63·16·02.

FACILITIES
Plaisance La Pointe (100+80 visitors) ☎ 98·27·95·99, FF93.50, FW, AC, C (8 ton), D, Access H24;
Plaisance 'Styvel' (200+30 visitors), FW, AC, Access H24, dredged 1·5m;
Services: M, ME, El, Ⓔ, Sh, CH, P, C (5 ton), SM, SHOM.
Town P, V, Gaz, R, Bar, ✉, Ⓑ, ⇌ (Brest), ✈ (Brest or Quimper). Ferry: Roscoff.

MORGAT   10-16-30

Finistere 48°13'·62N 04°29'·69W Rtg 2-3-1

CHARTS
AC 798; SHOM 6676, 6099; Imray C36; ECM 541, 542; Stanfords 17

TIDES
+0500 Dover; ML 3·8; Duration No data; Zone −0100

Standard Port BREST (←—)

Times				Height (metres)			
High Water		Low Water		MHWS	MHWN	MLWN	MLWS
0000	0600	0000	0600	6·9	5·4	2·6	1·0
1200	1800	1200	1800				
Differences MORGAT							
−0008	−0008	−0020	−0010	−0·4	−0·4	−0·2	0·0

SHELTER
The port is exposed to winds from the W and N, but the marina is protected by floating concrete wavebreaks. There are pleasant day ⚓s between Morgat and Cap de la Chèvre in the bays of St Hernot, St Norgard & St Nicolas; sheltered from the W. Also 2·5M to E in lee of Is de l'Aber.

NAVIGATION
WPT 48°12'·00N 04°28'·00W, 147°/327° from/to E bkwtr hd, 1·9M. There are rks close under the cliffs S of Pte de Morgat, and Les Verres 2M ESE of ent. Ent chan, dredged 1·5m, is marked by PHM buoy Fl R 4s, close SE of which is depth of 1m. Fl R/G 4s lts are at end of wavebreaks.

LIGHTS AND MARKS
Pte de Morgat lt, Oc (4) WRG 12s 77m 15/10M, is 4ca S of hbr; G sector covers Les Verres. Appr in W sector, 007°-257°, of inner Mole lt, Oc (2) WR 6s 8m 9/6M.

RADIO TELEPHONE
Marina VHF Ch 09 16.

TELEPHONE (Prefix ☎ Nos with zone code 02)
Hr Mr 98·27·01·97; Aff Mar 98·27·09·95; CROSS 98·89·31·31; Auto 08.36.68.08.29; SNSM 98·27·00 41; ⊞ 98·27·93·02; Police 98·27·00·22; Ⓗ 98·27·05·33; Brit Consul 40·63·16·02.

FACILITIES
Marina (450+50 visitors), ☎ 98·27·01·97, 🛥 98. 27.19.76, FF74, AC, FW, C (8 ton), Slip, CH, D, P, ME, Access H24;
YC du Crozon-Morgat ☎ 98·27·01·98;
Services: M, C (6 ton), El, Sh, Ⓔ.
Town (Crozon), V, Gaz, R, Bar, ✉, Ⓑ, ⇌, ✈ (Brest or Quimper). Ferry: Roscoff.

16

DOUARNENEZ   10-16-31
Finistere 48°06'·17N 04°20'·32W   Rtg 3-2-2

CHARTS
AC 798; SHOM 6677, 6099; Imray C36; ECM 542; Stanfords 17

TIDES
+0500 Dover; ML 3·7; Duration 0615; Zone –0100

Standard Port BREST (←)

Times				Height (metres)			
High Water		Low Water		MHWS	MHWN	MLWN	MLWS
0000	0600	0000	0600	6·9	5·4	2·6	1·0
1200	1800	1200	1800				
Differences DOUARNENEZ							
–0010	–0015	–0018	–0008	–0·5	–0·5	–0·3	–0·1

SHELTER
Very good; access H24, all weathers and tides to visitors'
berths in the marina (1·5m) at Tréboul, or in the river
outside (subject to wash from passing traffic). About 2ca
S of the marina the river has been dammed to form a
non-tidal basin (3·2m), Port Rhu, as a museum for classic
craft; limited access via a lock opening HW±1½ sp, HW±½
nps. The Fishing hbr is prohib to yachts and Port du
Rosmeur is full of moorings.

NAVIGATION
WPT 48°07'·00N 04°20'·30W, 353°/173° from/to Ile Tristan
lt, 0·81M. There are 3 rks, from 3 to 9ca NW of Ile Tristan
lt (in R sector), Basse Veur, Petite Basse Neuve and Basse
Neuve, least depth 1·8m.

LIGHTS AND MARKS
Approx 5M to W is Pte du Milier lt, Oc (2) WRG 6s 34m
16/11M, G080°-087°, W087°-113°, R113°-120°, W120°-
129°, G129°-148°, W148°-251°, R 251°-258°.
Ile Tristan Oc (3) WR 12s 33m 13/10M, vis R138°-153°, W
elsewhere; R sector covers Basse Veur and Basse Neuve,
least depth 1·8m.
On the high road bridge at S end of Port Rhu, Dir lt 157°,
Fl (5) WRG 20s 16m 5/4M, covers the Grande Passe and
river; vis G154°-156°, W156°-158°, R158°-160°.
Port Rhu lock ent is marked by a Fl R 5s and a Fl G 5s.

RADIO TELEPHONE
Marina VHF Ch 09 (0700-1200 and 1330-2100LT in season;
out of season 0830-1200, 1330-1730LT). Port Ch 12 16.

TELEPHONE (Prefix ☎ Nos with zone code 02)
Hr Mr (Plaisance) 98·74·02·56; Aff Mar 98·92·00·91;
CROSS 98·89·31·31; SNSM 98·89·63·16; ⌗ 98·92·01·45;
Météo 98·84·60·64; Auto 08.36.68.08.29; Police
98·92·01·22; Ⓗ 98·92·25·00; Brit Consul 01·40·63·16·02.

FACILITIES
Marina (380+30 Ⓥ) ☎ 98·74·02·56, ☎ 98.74.05.08, FF82,
Slip, FW, AC, P, D, C (6 ton), ME, El, Sh, Ⓔ;
Société des Regates de Douarnenez ☎ 98·92·02·03;
Services: M, CH, BH (12 ton), SM, Ⓔ.
Town Slip, P, D, Gaz, V, R, Bar, ✉, Ⓑ, ⇌ and ✈ (Quimper
22km). Ferry: Roscoff.

VOLVO PENTA SERVICE

Sales and service centres in area 17
Names and addresses of Volvo Penta dealers in
this area are available from:
France *Volvo Penta France* , 55 Avenue des Champs Pierreux, 92757 Cedex
Tel +33 1 55175457, Fax +33 1 55175261

Area 17

South Brittany
Raz de Sein to River Loire

VOLVO PENTA

17

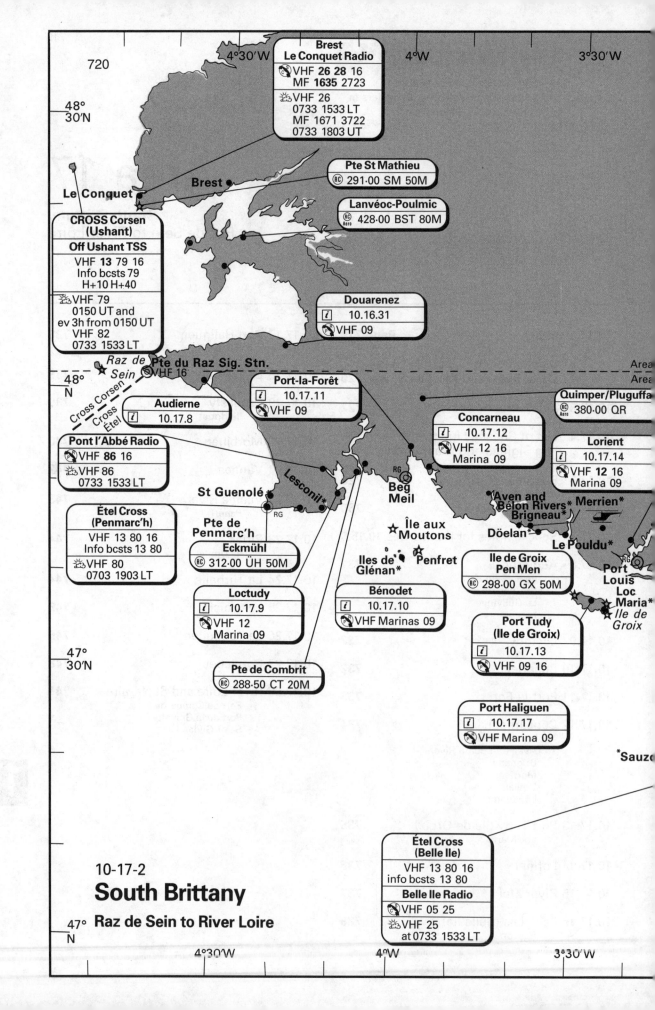

720

48°
30'N

**Brest
Le Conquet Radio**
📞 VHF **26 28** 16
MF **1635** 2723
☁ VHF 26
0733 1533 LT
MF 1671 3722
0733 1803 UT

Pte St Mathieu
Ⓡ 291·00 SM 50M

Lanvéoc-Poulmic
Ⓡ Aero 428·00 BST 80M

Brest •

Le Conquet ☆

**CROSS Corsen
(Ushant)**
Off Ushant TSS
VHF **13** 79 16
Info bcsts 79
H+10 H+40
☁ VHF 79
0150 UT and
ev 3h from 0150 UT
VHF 82
0733 1533 LT

Douarenez
ⓘ 10.16.31
📞 VHF 09

*Raz de
Sein* ☆ **Pte du Raz Sig. Stn.**
📞 VHF 16

48°
N

Cross Corsen
Cross
Étel

Audierne
ⓘ 10.17.8

Port-la-Forêt
ⓘ 10.17.11
📞 VHF 09

Concarneau
ⓘ 10.17.12
📞 VHF 12 16
Marina 09

Quimper/Pluguffa
Ⓡ Aero 380·00 QR

Lorient
ⓘ 10.17.14
📞 VHF **12** 16
Marina 09

Pont l'Abbé Radio
📞 VHF **86** 16
☁ VHF 86
0733 1533 LT

St Guenolé •

Lesconil*

RG

**Beg
Meil**

ⓇⒼ

**Aven and
Bélon Rivers*** **Merrien***
Brigneau*
Döelan*

Le Pouldu*

**Étel Cross
(Penmarc'h)**
VHF 13 80 16
Info bcsts 13 80
☁ VHF 80
0703 1903 LT

**Pte de
Penmarc'h**
Eckmühl
Ⓡ 312·00 ÜH 50M

RG

☆ **Île aux
Moutons**

**Iles de
Glénan*** ☆ **Penfret**

**Ile de Groix
Pen Men**
Ⓡ 298·00 GX 50M

ⓇⒼ
**Port
Louis
Loc
Maria***
*Ile de
Groix*

Loctudy
ⓘ 10.17.9
📞 VHF 12
Marina 09

Bénodet
ⓘ 10.17.10
📞 VHF Marinas 09

**Port Tudy
(Ile de Groix)**
ⓘ 10.17.13
📞 VHF 09 16

47°
30'N

Pte de Combrit
Ⓡ 288·50 CT 20M

Port Haliguen
ⓘ 10.17.17
📞 VHF Marina 09

*Sauz

10-17-2
South Brittany

47°
N
Raz de Sein to River Loire

**Étel Cross
(Belle Ile)**
VHF 13 80 16
info bcsts 13 80
Belle Ile Radio
📞 VHF 05 25
☁ VHF 25
at 0733 1533 LT

4°30'W   4°W   3°30'W

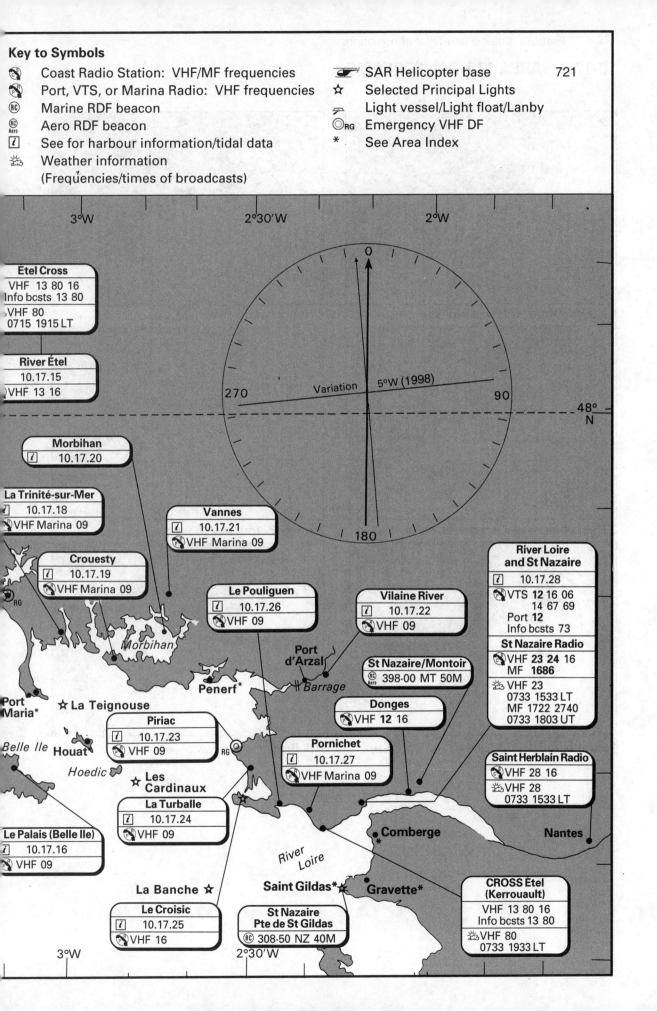

Key to Symbols

Coast Radio Station: VHF/MF frequencies
Port, VTS, or Marina Radio: VHF frequencies
Marine RDF beacon
Aero RDF beacon
See for harbour information/tidal data
Weather information
(Frequencies/times of broadcasts)

SAR Helicopter base
Selected Principal Lights
Light vessel/Light float/Lanby
Emergency VHF DF
See Area Index

Variation 5°W (1998)

48° N

Étel Cross
VHF 13 80 16
Info bcsts 13 80
VHF 80
0715 1915 LT

River Étel
10.17.15
VHF 13 16

Morbihan
10.17.20

La Trinité-sur-Mer
10.17.18
VHF Marina 09

Crouesty
10.17.19
VHF Marina 09

Vannes
10.17.21
VHF Marina 09

Le Pouliguen
10.17.26
VHF 09

Vilaine River
10.17.22
VHF 09

River Loire and St Nazaire
10.17.28
VTS **12** 16 06
14 67 69
Port **12**
Info bcsts 73

St Nazaire Radio
VHF **23 24** 16
MF **1686**
VHF 23
0733 1533 LT
MF 1722 2740
0733 1803 UT

Morbihan

Port d'Arzal

St Nazaire/Montoir
398·00 MT 50M

Barrage

Penerf*

Donges
VHF **12** 16

Saint Herblain Radio
VHF 28 16
VHF 28
0733 1533 LT

Port Maria*

☆ La Teignouse

Piriac
10.17.23
VHF 09

Pornichet
10.17.27
VHF Marina 09

Belle Ile   Houat
RG

Hoedic

☆ Les Cardinaux

La Turballe
10.17.24
VHF 09

Le Palais (Belle Ile)
10.17.16
VHF 09

Comberge
*

Nantes

La Banche ☆

Saint Gildas* ☆   ☆ Gravette*

Le Croisic
10.17.25
VHF 16

River Loire

St Nazaire Pte de St Gildas
308·50 NZ 40M

CROSS Étel (Kerrouault)
VHF 13 80 16
Info bcsts 13 80
VHF 80
0733 1933 LT

10-17-3   AREA 17 TIDAL STREAMS

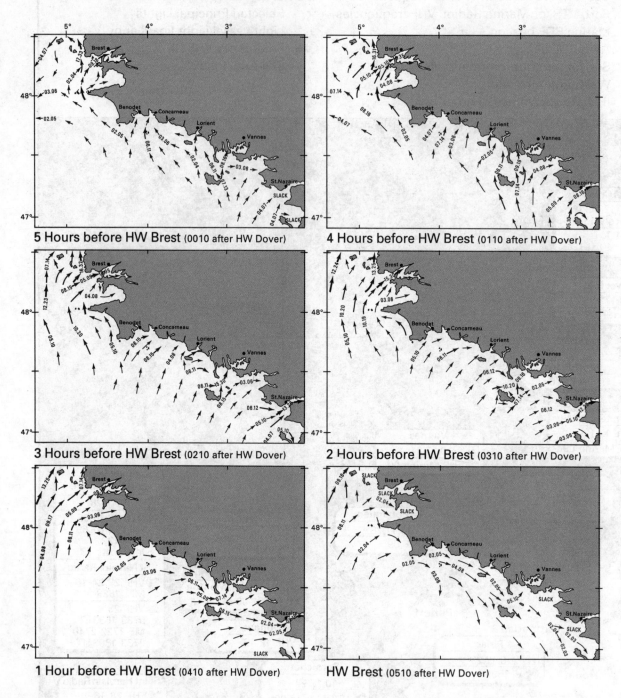

5 Hours before HW Brest (0010 after HW Dover)

4 Hours before HW Brest (0110 after HW Dover)

3 Hours before HW Brest (0210 after HW Dover)

2 Hours before HW Brest (0310 after HW Dover)

1 Hour before HW Brest (0410 after HW Dover)

HW Brest (0510 after HW Dover)

Northward 10.16.3   Southward 10.18.3

1 Hour after HW Brest (0610 after HW Dover)

2 Hours after HW Brest (0515 before HW Dover)

3 Hours after HW Brest (0415 before HW Dover)

4 Hours after HW Brest (0315 before HW Dover)

5 Hours after HW Brest (0215 before HW Dover)

6 Hours after HW Brest (0115 before HW Dover)

17

10.17.4 COASTAL LIGHTS, FOG SIGNALS AND WAYPOINTS

Abbreviations used below are given in 1.4.1. Principal lights are in **bold** print, places in CAPITALS, and light-vessels, light floats and Lanbys in *CAPITAL ITALICS*. Unless otherwise stated lights are white. m – elevation in metres; M – nominal range in miles. Fog signals are in *italics*. Useful waypoints are underlined – use those on land with care. All geographical positions should be assumed to be approximate. See 4.4.1. All positions are referenced to the ED 50 datum.

RAZ DE SEIN TO LESCONIL

CHAUSSÉE DE SEIN/ÎLE DE SEIN
Chaussée de Sein Lt By 48°03'·80N 05°07'·70W VQ (9) 10s 9m 8M; WCM HFP; Racon (O); *Whis*.
Ar-Men 48°03'·06N 04°59'·80W Fl (3) 20s 29m **23M**; W Tr, B top; *Horn (3) 60s*.
Île de Sein 48°02'·70N 04°51'·95W Fl (4) 25s 49m **29M**; W Tr, B top; RC.
Ar Guéveur 48°02'·00N 04°51'·32W 20m; W Tr; *Dia 60s*.
Men-Brial, 0·8M 115° from main Lt, Oc (2) WRG 6s 16m W12M, R9M, G7M; G&W Tr; vis G149°-186°, W186°-192°, R192°-221°, W221°-227°, G227°-254°.
Cornoc-An-Ar-Braden Lt By 48°03'·30N 04°50'·80W Iso G 4s; SHM; *Whis*.

RAZ DE SEIN
Tévennec 48°04'·33N 04°47'·64W Q WR 28m W10M R7M; W ■ Tr and dwelling; vis W090°-345°, R345°-090°; Dir Lt Fl 4s 24m 12M; same Tr; intens 324°-332°.
La Vieille 48°02'·49N 04°45'·31W Oc (2+1) WRG 12s 33m **W17M**, R14M, G13M; Gy ■ Tr; vis W290°-298°, R298°-325°, W325°-355°, G355°-017°, W017°-035°, G035°-105°, W105°-123°, R123°-158°, W158°-205°; R Lt on radio mast 3·4M ENE; *Horn (2+1) 60s*.
La Plate 48°02'·36N 04°45'·50W VQ (9) 10s 19m 8M; WCM.
Le Chat 48°01'·44N 04°48'·80W Fl (2) WRG 6s 27m W9M, R6M, G6M; SCM; vis G096°-215°, W215°-230°, R230°-271°, G271°-286°, R286°-096°; Ra refl.

AUDIERNE
Pointe de Lervily 48°00'·11N 04°33'·84W Fl (3) WR 12s 20m W14M, R11M; W Tr, R top; vis W211°-269°, R269°-294°, W294°-087°, R087°-121°.
Gamelle E By 47°59'·52N 04°31'·96W; SCM; *Bell*.
Gamelle W Lt By 47°59'·53N 04°32'·76W VQ (9) 10s; WCM; *Whis*.
Kergadec Dir Lt 006° 48°01'·01N 04°32'·80W Dir Q WRG 43m W12M, R9M, G9M; vis G000°-005·3°, W005·3°-006·7°, R006·7°-017°.
Jetée de Sainte-Évette 48°00'·38N 04°32'·98W Oc (2) R 6s 2m 7M; R lantern; vis 090°-270°.
Passe de l'Est Ldg Lts 331°. Front, Jetée de Raoulic 48°00'·60N 04°32'·37W Fl (3) WG 12s 11m W14M, G9M; W ● Tr; vis W shore-034°, G034°-shore, but may show W037°-055°. Rear, Kergadec, 0·5M from front, Dir FR 44m 9M ; W 8-sided Tr, R top; intens 321°-341°.

PORS POULHAN
W side of ent 47°59'·15N 04°27'·80W QR 14m 9M; W ■ Tr, R lantern.

SAINT GUÉNOLÉ
Chenal de Groumilli Ldg Lts 123°. Front, 47°48'·20N 04°22'·60W FG 9m 9M; Or ● on W Tr, B bands. Rear, 300m from front, FG 13m 9M ; Or ● on W Tr, B bands.
Basse Gaouac'h Lt By 47°48'·66N 04°24'·13W Fl (3) G 12s; SHM; *Whis*.
Scoedec 47°48'·46N 04°23'·10W Fl G 2·5s 6m 3M; G Tr.

Ldg Lts 055·4°. Front, 47°48'·75N 04°22'·65W VQ 5m 2M; G &W col. Rear, 320m from front, F Vi 12m 1M; G&W col; vis 040°-070°.
Ldg Lts 026·5°. Front 47°49'·05N 04°22'·60W QR 8m 4M; R mast. Rear, 51m from front, QR 12m 4M; mast, R&W bands; synch with front.

POINTE DE PENMARC'H
Eckmühl 47°47'·95N 04°22'·35W Fl 5s 60m **23M**; Gy 8-sided Tr; RC; *Horn 60s*.
Menhir 47°47'·80N 04°23'·90W Fl (2) WG 6s 19m W7M, G4M; W Tr, B band; vis G135°-315°, W315°-135°.

LE GUILVINEC
Cap Caval Lt By 47°46'·52N 04°22'·60W Q (9) 15s; WCM; *Whis*.
Locarec 47°47'·33N 04°20'·30W Iso WRG 4s 11m W9M, R6M, G6M; W tank on rk; vis G063°-068°, R068°-271°, W271°-285°, R285°-298°, G298°-340°, R340°-063°.
Kérity. Men Hir 47°47'·3N 04°20'·6W Fl R 2·5s 6m 2M; R ■ on Bn.
Detached Bkwtr Hd 47°47'·6N 04°20'·9W Fl (2) G 6s 5m 1M.
Névez Lt By 47°45'·90N 04°20'·00W Fl G 2·5s; SHM.
Spinec Lt By 47°45'·24N 04°18'·80W Q (6) + L Fl 15s; SCM; *Whis*.
Le Guilvinec Ldg Lts 053°. Môle de Léchiagat, spur, Front 47°47'·49N 04°17'·00W Q 7m 8M; W pylon; vis 233°-066°. Rocher Le Faoute's, Middle, 210m from front, Q WG 12m W14M, G11M; R ● on W pylon; vis W006°-293°, G293°-006°; synch with front. Rear, 0·58M from front, Dir Q 26m 8M; R ● on W pylon; vis 051·5°-054·5°; synch with front.
Capelan Lt By 47°47'·21N 04°17'·47W Fl (2) G 6s; SHM.
Môle de Léchiagat Hd 47°47'·51N 04°17'·09W Fl G 4s 5m 7M; W hut, G top.
Lost Moan 47°47'·07N 04°16'·69W Fl (3) WRG 12s 8m W9M, R6M, G6M; ■ on W Tr, R top; vis R327°-014°, G014°-065°, R065°-140°, W140°-160°, R160°-268°, W268°-273°, G273°-317°, W317°-327°.
Ar Guisty Bn 47°45'·69N 04°15'·50W; SCM.

LESCONIL
Reissant Bn 47°46'·45N 04°13'·43W; SCM.
Men-ar-Groas 47°47'·86N 04°12'·60W Fl (3) WRG 12s 14m W10M, R7M, G7M; W Tr, G top; vis G268°-313°, W313°-333°, R333°-050°.
E Bkwtr Hd 47°47'·77N 04°12'·56W QG 5m 5M; G Tr.
Karek Greis Lt By 47°46'·10N 04°11'·30W Q (3) 10s; ECM; *Whis*.

LOCTUDY TO CONCARNEAU

LOCTUDY
Rostolou By 47°46'·70N 04°07'·20W; ECM.
Roc'h Hélou By 47°47'·17N 04°08'·00W; WCM.
Bas Boulanger Lt By 47°47'·40N 04°09'·05W VQ (6) + L Fl 10s; SCM.
Bilien Lt By 47°49'·17N 04°08'·02W VQ (3) 5s; ECM; *Whis*.
Chenal de Bénodet By 47°48'·60N 04°06'·96W; ECM.
Basse Malvic By 47°48'·52N 04°06'·53W; WCM.
Pointe de Langoz, S side 47°49'·94N 04°09'·48W Fl (4) WRG 12s 12m **W15M**, R11M, G11M; W Tr, R top; vis W115°-257°, G257°-284°, W284°-295°, R295°-318°, W318°-328°, R328°-025°.
Men Audierne Bn 47°50'·37N 04°08'·98W; SHM.
Karek-Saoz 47°50'·08N 04°09'·30W QR 3m 2M; R Tr.
Les Perdrix 47°50'·31N 04°09'·88W Fl WRG 4s 15m W11M, R8M, G8M; ▲ on B&W Tr; vis G090°-285°, W285°-295°, R295°-090°.
Le Blas 47°50'·34N 04°10'·15W Fl (3) G 12s 5m 1M; G ▲ on truncated col.

BENODET
Ldg Lts 345·5°. Front, **Pte du Coq** 47°52'·38N 04°06'·61W, Dir Oc (2+1) G 12s 11m **17M**; W ● Tr, G stripe; intens 345°-347°. Common rear Pyramide, 336m from front, Oc (2+1) 12s 48m 11M; W Tr, G top; vis 338°-016°, synch with front.
Ldg Lts 000·5°. Front, Pte de Combrit 47°51'·92N 04°06'·70W, Oc (3+1) WR 12s 19m W12M , R9M; W ■ Tr, Gy corners; vis W325°-017°, R017°-325°; RC. Common rear, Pyramide, 0·63M from front.
Les Verrés Bn 47°51'·61N 04°06'·06W; SHM.
Le Four Bn 47°51'·85N 04°06'·32W; SHM.
Pte du Toulgoet Fl R 2s 2m 1M; R mast.
Le Taro Bn 47°50'·57N 04°04'·86W; WCM.
Men Déhou Bn 47°48'·18N 04°04'·63W; ECM.
Les Poulains Bn 47°47'·75N 04°03'·40W; NCM.
La Voleuse Lt By 47°48'·81N 04°02'·40W Q (6) + L Fl 15s; SCM; *Whis*.
La Vache Bn 47°49'·60N 04°02'·53W; SHM.
Men Vras Bn 47°49'·72N 04°01'·50W; ECM.

BEG-MEIL
Linuen Bn 47°50'·71N 03°57'·70W; SCM.
Chaussée de Beg'Meil Lt By 47°50'·82N 03°57'·23W Q (3) 10s; ECM.
Laouen Pod Bn 47°51'·29N 03°57'·91W; ECM.
Quay Hd 47°51'·72N 03°58'·85W Fl R 2s 6m 1M; R&W col.

PORT-LA-FORÊT
Le Scoré Bn 47°52'·81N 03°57'·48W; SCM.
Les Ormeaux Bn 47°53'·33N 03°58'·25W; PHM.
Channel Lt By 47°53'·46N 03°58'·05W Fl (2) G 6s; SHM.
Cap Coz Mole Hd 47°53'·55N 03°58'·20W Fl (2) R 6s 5m 6M.
Kerleven Mole Hd Fl G 4s 8m 6M.

CONCARNEAU
Ldg Lts 028·5°. Front, La Croix 47°52'·22N 03°55'·00W Oc (3) 12s 14m 13M; R&W Tr; vis 006·5°-093°. **Rear, Beuzec**, 1·34M from front, Dir Q 87m **23M**; Spire; intens 026·5°-030·5°.
Le Cochon 47°51'·53N 03°55'·47W Fl (3) WRG 12s 5m W9M, R6M, G6M; G Tr; vis G048°-205°, R205°-352°, W352°-048°; SHM.
Basse du Chenal Lt By 47°51'·58N 03°55'·60W QR, PHM.
Men Fall Lt By 47°51'·82N 03°55'·20W Fl G 4s; SHM.
Kersos Bn 47°51'·87N 03°54'·85W; SHM.
Lanriec 47°52'·07N 03°54'·56W QG 13m 8M; G Lt window on W gable; vis 063°-078°.
La Médée 47°52'·12N 03°54'·71W Fl R 2·5s 9m 4M; R Tr; PHM.
Marina Hd 47°52'·20N 03°54'·72W Fl (3) R 12s; R □ on post.

BAIE DE POULDOHAN
Petit Taro Bn 47°51'·17N 03°55'·21W; WCM.
Pouldohan 47°51'·03N 03°53'·61W Fl G 4s 7m 8M; W ■ Tr, G top; vis 053°-065°.
Roché Tudy Bn 47°50'·58N 03°54'·41W; SHM.

ÎLES DE GLENAN

ÎLES DE GLÉNAN/ÎLE AUX MOUTONS
Basse Pérennès Lt By 47°41'·15N 04°06'·05W Q (9) 15s 8m 5M; WCM; *Whis*; Ra refl.
Jument de Glénan Lt By 47°38'·80N 04°01'·32W Q (6) + L Fl 15s 10m 4M; SCM; *Whis*. Ra Refl.
Penfret 47°43'·32N 03°57'·10W Fl R 5s 36m **21M**; W ■ Tr, R top; auxiliary Lt Dir Q 34m 12M; same Tr; vis 295°-315°.
Île Cigogne 47°43'·10N 03°59'·59W Q (2) RG 5s 5m 2M; W Tr B top; vis G106°-108°, R108°-262°, G262°-268°, obsc 268°-106°; (shown 1May to 1Oct.)
Les Bluniers Bn 47°43'·42N 04°03'·73W; WCM.

Broc'h Bn 47°43'·22N 04°01'·31W; NCM.
La Pie Lt Bn 47°43'·81N 03°59'·67W; Fl (2) 6s 9m 3M; IDM.
Île de Bananec Bn 47°43'·32N 03°59'·11W; ECM.
Rouge de Glénan Lt By 47°45'·50N 04°03'·90W VQ (9) 10s 8m 8M; WCM; *Whis*; Ra refl.
Île-aux-Moutons 47°46'·55N 04°01'·62W Oc (2) WRG 6s 18m **W15M**, R11M, G11M; W ■ Tr and dwelling; vis W035°-050°, G050°-063°, W063°-081°, R081°-141°, W141°-292°, R292°-035°; **auxiliary Lt** Dir Oc (2) 6s 17m **24M**; same Tr; synch with main Lt, intens 278·5°-283·5°.
Grand Pourceaux Lt By 47°46'·05N 04°00'·75W Q; NCM.
Rochers Leuriou Bn 47°45'·20N 03°59'·90W; ECM.
Jaune de Glénan Lt By 47°42'·60N 03°49'·75W Q (3) 10s; ECM; *Whis*.
Cor-Loch By 47°42'·28N 03°52'·22W; IDM.
Basse an Ero By 47°40'·47N 03°55'·38W; SCM.
Laoennou By 47°39'·70N 03°54'·60W; IDM.

CONCARNEAU TO ÎLE DE GROIX

TRÉVIGNON TO PORT MANECH
Les Soldats Lt Bn 47°47'·91N 03°53'·32W VQ (9) 10s; WCM.
Môle Hd 47°47'·72N 03°51'·20W Fl G 4s 5m 8M; W col, G top.
Trévignon Bkwtr root 47°47'·65N 03°51'·22W Oc (3+1) WRG 12s 11m W14M, R11M, G11M; W ■ Tr, G top; vis W004°-051°, G051°-085°, W085°-092°, R092°-127°, R322°-351°.
Men Du Bn 47°46'·44N 03°50'·40W; IDM.
Corn Vas By 47°45'·92N 03°50'·18W; WCM.
Men ar Tréas By 47°45'·84N 03°49'·58W; SCM.
Île Verte Bn 47°46'·35N 03°47'·95W; ■ Tr.
Île de Raguénès 47°46'·95N 03°47'·65W; SCM.

PORT MANECH/AVEN AND BÉLON RIVERS
Pointe de Beg-ar-Vechen 47°48'·03N 03°44'·30W Oc (4) WRG 12s 38m W10M, R7M, G7M; W & R Tr; vis W (unintens) 050°-140°, W140°-296°, G296°-303°, W303°-311°, R311°-328° over Les Verrès, W328°-050°; obsc by Pte de Beg-Morg when brg less than 299°.
Les Verrès Bn 47°46'·70N 03°42'·60W; IDM.

BRIGNEAU/MERRIEN/DOËLAN
Brigneau Mole Hd 47°46'·95N 03°40'·10W Oc (2) WRG 6s 7m W12M, R9M, G9M; W col, R top; vis G280°-329°, W329°-339°, R339°-034°.
Brigneau By 47°46'·15N 03°39'·99W; SWM; *Whis*.
Merrien 47°47'·05N 03°38'·82W QR 26m 7M; W ■ Tr, R top; vis 004°-009°.
Port de la Merrien By 47°46'·52N 03°39'·09W; SCM.
Doëlan Ldg Lts 013·8°. Front, 47°46'·35N 03°36'·42W Oc (3) WG 12s 20m W13M, G10M; W Tr, G band and top; vis W shore-305°, G305°-314°, W314°-shore. Rear, 326m from front, QR 27m 9M; W Tr, R band and top.

LE POULDU TO LOMENER/RIVIÈRE DE QUIMPERLÉ
Le Pouldu Ent Bn 47°45'·76N 03°32'·11W; PHM.
Grand Cochon By 47°43'·09N 03°30'·73W; SCM.
Kerroc'h 47°42'·00N 03°27'·53W Oc (2) WRG 6s 22m W11M, R8M, G8M; W Tr, R top; vis R096·5°-112°·5, G112·5°-132°, R132°-302°, W302°-096·5°.
Anse de Stole Dir Lt 357·2° 47°42'·33N 03°25'·57W Dir Q WRG 13m W10M, R8M, G8M; W Tr, R top; vis G349·2°-355·2°, W355·2°-359·2°, R359·2°-005·2°.

ÎLE DE GROIX/PORT TUDY/LOCMARIA
Pen Men 47°38'·87N 03°30'·48W Fl (4) 25s 59m **29M**; W ■ Tr, B top; vis 309°-275°; RC.
Pointe des Chats 47°37'·30N 03°25'·25W Fl R 5s 16m **19M**; W ■ Tr and dwelling.
Port Tudy Môle N Hd 47°38'·78N 03°26'·62W Iso G 4s 12m 6M; W Tr, G top

17

Pointe de la Croix 47°38'·10N 03°25'·20W Oc WR 4s 16m W12M, R9M; W pedestal, R lantern; vis W169°-336°, R336°-345°, W345°-353°.

Edouard de Cougy By 47°37'·97N 03°23'·80W; ECM.

Les Chars Lt By 47°35'·74N 03°23'·50W Q (6) + L Fl 15s; SCM; *Whis.*

LORIENT

PASSE OUEST
Ldg Lts 057°. Front, Les Sœurs 47°42'·22N 03°21'·70W Dir Q 11m 13M, R Tr, W bands; vis intens 042·5°-058·5°, (4M) 058·5°-042·5°. Rear **Port Louis**, 740m from front, Dir Q 22m **18M**; W daymark, R bands on bldg. Lts intens 042·5°-058·5°, (4M) 058·5°-042·5°.

'L' Banc des Truics Lt By 47°40'·82N 03°24'·40W Q (9) 15s; WCM.

A2 Locqueltas Lt By 47°41'·00N 03°24'·90W Fl R 2·5s; PHM.

A5 Lt By 47°41'·56N 03°23'·02W Fl (2) G 6s; SHM.

A7 Lt By 47°41'·77N 03°22'·58W Fl G 2·5s; SHM.

Les Trois Pierres 47°41'·58N 03°22'·40W Q RG 11m R6M, G6M; B Tr, R bands; vis G060°-196°, R196°-002°.

Île aux Souris 47°42'·22N 03°21'·43W Dir Q WG 6m W3M, G2W; G Tr; vis W041·5°-043·5°, G043·5°-041·5°.

PASSE DU SUD
Ldg Lts 008·5°. **Front**, Fish Market 47°43'·82N 03°21'·67W Dir QR 16m **17M**; R ■ on Gy Tr; intens 006°-011°. **Rear**, Kergroise-La Perrière 515m from front Dir QR 34m **16M**; R ■, W stripe on Gy Tr; synch with front; intens 006°-011°.

Bastresse Sud Lt By 47°40'·83N 03°22'·01W QG; SHM; *Bell.*

Les Errants Lt By 47°41'·16N 03°22'·29W Fl (2) R 6s; PHM.

ENTRANCE CHANNEL
Île Saint Michel Passe de la Citadelle Ldg Lts 016·5°. **Front**, 47°43'·53N 03°21'·54W Dir Oc (3) G 12s 8m **16M**; W Tr, G top. **Rear**, 306m from front, Dir Oc (3) G 12s 14m **16M**; W Tr, G top; synch with front; both intens 014·5°-017·5°.

La Potée de Beurre Bn 47°42'·30N 03°21'·90W; SHM.

Chan W side, La Petite Jument 47°42'·63N 03°21'·98W Oc R 4s 5m 6M; R Tr; vis 182°-024°.

Chan E side, Tourelle de la Citadelle 47°42'·66N 03°21'·86W Oc G 4s 6m 6M; G Tr; vis 009°-193°.

Chan W side Le Cochon Fl R 4s 5m 5M; R Tr, G band.

KERNEVEL
Banc du Turc Lt By 47°43'·39N 03°21'·77W Fl (3) G 12s; SHM.

Port de Kernevel Marina ent Lt By 47°43'·47N 03°22'·01W Fl Y 2·5s 3m 2M; SPM with can topmark.

Ldg Lts 217° 47°43'·08N 03°22'·23W **Front**, Dir QR 10m **15M**; R ■ on R&W Tr; intens 215°-219°. **Rear**, 290m from front, Dir QR 18m **15M**; W■Tr, R top; synch with front; intens 215°-219°.

PORT-LOUIS
Jetty 47°42'·76N 03°21'·29W Iso G 4s 7m 6M; W Tr, G top.

KÉROMAN/FISHING HARBOUR/RADE DE PENMANÉ
Submarine base Ldg Lts 350°. **Front**, 47°43'·66N 03°21'·93W Dir Oc (2) R 6s 25m **15M**. **Rear**, 91m from front, Dir Oc (2) R 6s 31m **15M**; R&W topmark on Gy pylon, R top; Lts synch and intens 348°-353°.

E side of ent 47°43'·68N 03°21'·79W Fl RG 4s 7m 6M; W Tr, G top; vis G000°-235°, R235°-360°.

Pengarne 47°43'·94N 03°21'·13W Fl G 2·5s 3m 4M; G Tr.

Pointe de l'Espérance Dir Lt 037° 47°44'·57N 03°20'·58W Dir Q WRG 8m W10M, R8M, G8M; W Tr, G top; vis G034·2°-036·7°, W036·7°-037·2°, R037·2°-047·2°.

Ro-Ro Terminal 47°44'·48N 03°20'·88W Oc (2) R 6s 7m 6M.

Lorient Marina ent Lt By No. 8 47°44'·61N 03°20'·90W Fl R 2·5s; PHM.

LORIENT TO BELLE ÎLE

RIVIÈRE D'ÉTEL
Roheu Bn 47°38'·57N 03°14'·68W; SCM.

W side ent 47°38'·75N 03°12'·82W Oc (2) WRG 6s 13m W9M, R6M, G6M; R Tr; vis W022°-064°, R064°-123°, W123°-330°, G330°-022°; 2 FR on radio mast 2·3M NW; FR and F on radio masts 2·4M NW.

Les Pierres Noires Bn 47°35'·55N 03°13'·25W; IDM.

PORT MARIA
Le Pouilloux By 47°27'·97N 03°08'·93W; SCM.

Ldg Lts 006·5°. Front, 47°28'·65N 03°07'·15W Dir QG 5m 13M; W Tr, B band. Rear, 230m from front, Dir QG 13m 13M; W Tr, B band; both intens 005°-008°.

Main light 47°28'·85N 03°07'·42W Q WRG 28m W14M, R10M, G10M; W Tr; vis W246°-252°, W291°-297°, G297°-340°, W340°-017°, R017°-051°, W051°-081°, G081°-098°, W098°-143°.

Baz an Tréac'h By 47°27'·98N 03°07'·10W; IDM.

S Bkwtr Hd 47°28'·60N 03°07'·23W Oc (2) R 6s 9m 7M; W Tr, R top.

PLATEAU DES BIRVIDEAUX
Tower 47°29'·20N 03°17'·45W Fl (2) 6s 24m 10M; B Tr, R bands; IDM.

BELLE ÎLE/SAUZON/LE PALAIS
Pte des Poulains 47°23'·37N 03°15'·08W Fl 5s 34m **23M**; W ■ Tr and dwelling; vis 023°-291°.

Les Poulains By 47°23'·42N 03°16'·65W; WCM.

Goulphar 47°18'·67N 03°13'·67W Fl (2) 10s 87m **26M**; Gy Tr.

La Truie Bn 47°17'·10N 03°11'·62W; IDM.

N Poulains By 47°23'·70N 03°14'·86W; NCM.

Bas Gareau Bn 47°22'·85N 03°12'·97W; SHM.

Sauzon Jetée NW Hd 47°22'·58N 03°13'·00W Fl G 4s 8m 8M.

Jetée SE Hd Fl R 4s 8m 8M; W Tr, R top.

Le Palais Jetée Nord 47°20'·90N 03°09'·00W Fl (2+1) G 12s 11m 7M; W Tr; obsc 298°-170°.

La Truie du Bugul Bn 47°19'·60N 03°06'·50W; NCM.

Pointe de Kerdonis 47°18'·65N 03°03'·50W Fl (3) R 15s 35m **15M**; W ■ Tr and dwelling; obsc by Pointes d'Arzic and de Taillefer 025°-129°.

Les Galères By 47°18'·80N 03°02'·75W; ECM.

BAIE DE QUIBERON AND MORBIHAN

CHAUSSÉE AND PASSAGE DE LA TEIGNOUSE
Le Four Bn 47°27'·80N 03°06'·48W; SCM.

Bas Cariou By 47°27'·00N 03°06'·33W; WCM; *Bell.*

Bas du Chenal By 47°26'·70N 03°05'·70W; SCM.

Goué Vaz N By 47°26'·27N 03°05'·35W; NCM.

Goué Vaz S Lt By 47°25'·84N 03°04'·80W Q (6) + L Fl 15s; SCM; *Whis.*

Basse du Milieu Lt By 47°26'·00N 03°04'·10W Fl (2) G 6s 9m 2M; SHM HFP.

Goué Vaz E Lt By 47°26'·30N 03°04'·20W Fl (3) R 12s; PHM.

La Teignouse 47°27'·50N 03°02'·67W Fl WR 4s 19m **15**/11M; W ●Tr, R top vis W033°-039°, R039°-033°.

NE Teignouse Lt By 47°26'·62N 03°01'·80W Fl (3) G 12s; SHM.

Basse Nouvelle Lt By 47°27'·02N 03°01'·85W Fl R 2·5s; PHM.

Quiberon S Lt By 47°30'·10N 03°02'·30W Q (6) + L Fl 15s; SCM.

PORT HALIGUEN
New Bkwtr Hd 47°29'·36N 03°05'·90W Oc (2) WR 6s 10m W11M, R8M; W Tr, R top; vis W233°-240·5°, R240·5°-299°, W299°-306°, R306°-233°.

Quiberon N By 47°29'·68N 03°02'·52W; NCM.
Explosive Wk By 47°31'·25N 03°05'·36W; IDM.
Men er Roue Bn 47°32'·33N 03°06'·00W; IDM.

RIVIÈRE DE CRAC'H/LA TRINITÉ-SUR-MER
Ldg Lts 347°. Front, 47°34'·14N 03°00'·29W Q WRG 11m
W10M, R7M, G7M; W Tr, G top; vis G321°-345°, W345°-
013·5°, R013·5°-080°. **Rear**, 560m from front, Dir Q 21m **15M**;
W ● Tr, G top; synch with front, intens 337°-357°.
Le Rat By 47°32'·89N 03°01'·69W; IDM.
Souris By 47°32'·03N 03°01'·14W; IDM.
Petit Trého Lt By 47°33'·55N 03°00'·67W Fl (4) R 15s; PHM.
La Trinité-sur-Mer Dir Lt 347° 47°35'·09N 03°00'·90W Dir Oc
WRG 4s 9m W13M, R11M, G11M; W Tr; vis G345°-346°,
W346°-348°, R348°-349°.
S Pier Hd 47°35'·15N 03°01'·42W Oc (2) WR 6s 6m W10M,
R7M; W Tr, R top; vis R090°-293·5°, W293·5°-300·5°,
R300·5°-329°.

Buissons de Méaban By 47°31'·71N 02°58'·42W; SCM.
Méaban By 47°30'·83N 02°56'·14W; SCM.

MORBIHAN
Le Grand Mouton 47°33'·77N 02°54'·78W QG 4m 3M;
G tripod.
Le Grégan 47°33'·96N 02°54'·96W Q (6) + L Fl 15s 3m 8M;
SCM.
Auray No. 13 Bn 47°39'·53N 02°58'·57W; SHM.
Creizic S By 47°34'·68N 02°52'·75W; SCM.
Creizic N By 47°35'·00N 02°52'·12W; NCM.
Les Rechauds Bns 47°36'·25N 02°51'·20W; 2 x SHM.
Truie d'Arradon Bn 47°36'·63N 02°50'·18W; PHM.
Roguédas 47°37'·18N 02°47'·19W Fl G 2·5s 4m 4M; G Tr.

PLATEAU DU GRAND MONT
Basse de S Gildas By 47°29'·83N 02°52'·30W; WCM.
Roc de l' Epieu By 47°29'·55N 02°52'·86W; IDM.
Chimère By 47°28'·90N 02°53'·90W; SCM.
Basse du Grand Mont By 47°29'·05N 02°51'·08W; SCM.

CHAUSSÉE DU BÉNIGUET
Les Esclassiers W Bn 47°25'·72N 03°03'·00W; WCM.
Le Grand Coin Bn 47°24'·50N 03°00'·20W; ECM.

ÎLE DE HOUAT
Le Rouleau Bn 47°23'·74N 03°00'·20W; WCM.
Bonnenn Vraz Bn 47°24'·30N 02°59'·80W; WCM.
Port de Saint-Gildas Môle Nord 47°23'·63N 02°57'·26W
Fl (2) WG 6s 8m W9M, G6M; W Tr, G top; vis W168°-198°,
G198°-210°, W210°-240°, G240°-168°.
Men Grouiz Bn 47°22'·82N 02°54'·97W; ECM.
Er Rouzez By 47°22'·08N 02°54'·28W; ECM.

Pot de Feu By 47°21'·75N 02°59'·70W; IDM.

ÎLE DE HÖEDIC
Er Palaire Bn 47°20'·23N 02°54'·95W; WCM.
Les Sœurs Bn 47°21'·20N 02°54'·70W; WCM.
La Chèvre Bn 47°21'·16N 02°52'·50W; IDM.
Port de l'Argol Bkwtr Hd 47°20'·75N 02°52'·46W Fl WG 4s
10m W9M, G6M ; W Tr, G top; vis W143°-163°, G163°-183°,
W183°-203°, G203°-143°.
Le Chariot By 47°18'·94N 02°52'·90W; SCM.
Les Grands Cardinaux 47°19'·35N 02°50'·08W Fl (4) 15s 28m
13M; R and W Tr.
Cohfournik Bn 47°19'·48N 02°49'·72W; ECM.
Er Guéranic Bn 47°20'·58N 02°50'·43W; ECM.

CROUESTY TO LE CROISIC

PORT NAVALO/CROUESTY EN ARZON
Pte de Port-Navalo 47°32'·93N 02°55'·02W Oc (3) WRG 12s
32m **W15M**, R11M , G11M ; W Tr and dwelling; vis W155°-
220°, G317°-359°, W359°-015°, R015°-105°.
Ldg Lts 058°. **Front**, 47°32'·60N 02°53'·85W Dir Q 10m
19M; R panel with W vert stripe; intens 056·5°-059·5°. **Rear**,
315m from front, Dir Q 27m **19M**; Gy Tr; intens 056·5°-
059·5°.
N Jetty Hd Oc (2) R 6s 9m 7M; R and W ■ Tr, R top.
S Jetty Hd 47°32'·51N 02°54'·02W Fl G 4s 9m 7M; G&W
■ Tr.

PLATEAU DE S JACQUES/SAINT-JACQUES-EN-SARZEAU
Bas Rohaliguen S Jacques By 47°28'·25N 02°47'·45W; SCM.
Saint-Jacques-en-Sarzeau Lt Tr 47°29'·22N 02°47'·45W
Oc (2) R 6s 5m 6M; W 8-sided Tr, R top.

PLATEAU DE LA RECHERCHE
Recherche Lt By 47°25'·65N 02°50'·27W Q (9) 15s; WCM.
Locmariaquer By 47°25'·88N 02°47'·30W; IDM.

PÉNERF
Le Pignon 47°30'·10N 02°38'·85W Fl (3) WR 12s 6m W9M,
R6M; R ■ on Tr; vis R028·5°-167°, W167°-175°, R175°-
349·5°, W349·5°-028·5°.

VILAINE RIVER
Basse de Kervoyal 47°30'·43N 02°32'·55W Dir Q WR W8M,
R5M; vis W269°-271°, R271°-269°; SCM on B Tr.
Basse Bertrand 47°31'·10N 02°30'·63W Iso WG 4s 6m
W9M, G6M; G Tr; vis W040°-054°, G054°-227°, W227°-234°,
G234°-040°.
Penlan 47°31'·05N 02°30'·06W Oc (2) WRG 6s 26m **W15M**,
R11M, G11M; W Tr, R bands; vis R292·5°-025°, G025°-052°,
W052°-060°, R060°-138°, G138°-180°.
Pointe du Scal, 47°29'·72N 02°26'·78W QG 12s 8m 4M;
W ■ Tr, G top.

ÎLE DUMET
Fort 47°24'·80N 02°37'·10W Fl (2+1) WRG 15s 14m W7M,
R4M, G4M; W col, G top on fort; vis G090°-272°, W272°-
285°, R285°-325°, W325°-090°.
E Île Dumet Lt By 47°25'·20N 02°35'·00W Q (3) 10s; ECM.

MESQUER
Jetty Hd 47°25'·32N 02°27'·95W Oc (3+1) WRG 12s 7m
W10M, R7M, G7M; W col and bldg; vis W067°-072°, R072°-
102°, W102°-118°, R118°-293°, W293°-325°, G325°-067°.

PIRIAC-SUR-MER
Inner Mole Hd 47°23'·00N 02°32'·65W Oc (2) WRG 6s 8m
W10M, R7M, G7M; W col; vis R066°-148°, W149°-194°,
G201°-066°; Siren 120s.
Les Bayonelles Lt By 47°22'·58N 02°34'·90W Q (9) 15s;
WCM; Whis.
Oil Pipeline 47°22'·15N 02°32'·70W Oc (2+1) WRG 12s 14m
W12M, R9M, G9M; W ■, R stripe on R Tr; vis G300°-036°,
W036°-068°, R068°-120°.

LA TURBALLE/LE CROISIC
La Turballe Ldg Lts 006·5° both Dir F Vi 11/19m 3M, both intens
004°-009°.
Jetée de Garlahy 47°20'·77N 02°30'·83W Fl (4) WR 12s 13m
W10M, R7M; W pylon, R top; vis R060°-315°, W315°-060°.
Basse Hergo 47°18'·68N 02°31'·62W Fl G 2·5s 5m 3M; SHM.
Jetée de Tréhic Hd 47°18'·55N 02°31'·34W Iso WG 4s 12m
W13M, G10M; Gy Tr, G top; vis G042°-093°, W093°-137°,
G137°-345°; F Bu Fog Det Lt.
Le Grand Mabon 47°18'·11N 02°30'·94W Fl R 2·5s 6m 2M;
R pedestal.

17

LE CROISIC TO PTE DE ST GILDAS

PLATEAU DU FOUR/BANC DE GUÉRANDE
Bonen du Four Lt By 47°18'·60N 02°39'·20W Q; NCM; *Whis.*
Le Four 47°17'·94N 02°37'·96W Fl 5s 23m **19M**; W Tr, B stripes, G top.
W Basse Capella Lt By 47°15'·67N 02°44'·66W Q (9) 15s; WCM; *Whis.*
Goué-Vas-du-Four Lt By 47°14'·96N 02°38'·13W Q (6) + L Fl 15s; SCM.
S Banc Guérande Lt By 47°08'·87N 02°42'·74W VQ (6) + L Fl 10s; SCM; *Whis.*

PLATEAU DE LA BANCHE
W Banche Lt By 47°11'·65N 02°32'·34W VQ (9) 10s; WCM; *Whis.*
NW Banche Lt By 47°12'·90N 02°30'·95W Q 8m 4M; NCM HFP; *Bell.*
La Banche 47°10'·70N 02°28'·00W Fl (2+1) WR 15s 22m **W17M**, R11M; B Tr, W bands; vis R266°-280°, W280°-266°.
SE Banche By 47°10'·47N 02°26'·02W; ECM.

BAIE du POULIGUEN APPROACHES (Baie de la Baule)
Penchateau Lt By 47°15'·36N 02°24'·30W Fl R 2·5s; PHM.
Les Guérandaises Lt By 47°15'·06N 02°24'·23W Fl G 4s; SHM.
Les Evens By 47°14'·47N 02°22'·46W; PHM.
Les Troves By 47°14'·25N 02°22'·30W; SHM.
NNW Pierre Percée 47°13'·67N 02°20'·54W; NCM.
La Vieille Bn 47°14'·09N 02°19'·43W; SCM.
Sud de la Vieille By 47°13'·81N 02°19'·41W; IDM.
Le Caillou By 47°13'·71N 02°19'·11W; NCM.
Le Petit Charpentier Bn 47°13'·40N 02°18'·87W; SCM.

LE POULIGUEN.
Les Petits Impairs 47°16'·08N 02°24'·53W Fl (2) G 6s 6m 2M; G ▲, on Tr.
S Jetty 47°16'·48N 02°25'·30W QR 13m 9M; W col; vis 171°-081°.

PORT DE PORNICHET
La Baule S Bkwtr Hd 47°15'·55N 02°21'·07W Iso WG 4s 11m W10M, G7M; W Tr, G top; vis G084°-081°, W081°-084°.
South Ent QG 3m 1M.
North Ent QR 4m 1M.

Le Grand Charpentier 47°12'·90N 02°19'·05W Q WRG 22m W14M, R10M, G10M, Gy Tr, G lantern; vis G020°-049°, W049°-111°, R111°-310°, W310°-020°; Helicopter platform; Sig Stn 1·5M NE.

LOIRE APPROACHES
Loire Approach Lt By SN1 47°00'·15N 02°39'·75W L Fl 10s 8m 5M; SWM HFP; *Whis;* Racon (Z).
Loire Approach Lt By SN2 47°02'·15N 02°33'·45W Iso 4s 8m 5M; SWM HFP; Ra refl.
Thérésia Lt By 47°04'·92N 02°27'·20W Fl R 2·5s; PHM.
Les Chevaux Lt By 47°03'·58N 02°26'·29W Fl G 2·5s; SHM.
La Couronnée Lt By 47°07'·67N 02°20'·00W QG 8m 6M; SHM HFP; Racon.
Lancastria Lt By 47°08'·92N 02°20'·39W VQR 8m 2M; PHM HFP; Ra Refl.

PLATEAU DE LA LAMBARDE
SE Lambarde Lt By 47°10'·10N 02°20·72W Q (6) + L Fl 15s; SCM; *Bell.*
NW Lambard By 47°10'·88N 02°22'·78W; WCM.

PASSE DES CHARPENTIERS
Portcé Ldg Lts 025·5°. **Front**, 47°14'·62N 02°15'·36W Dir Q 6m **22M** ; W col; intens 024·7°-026·2°. **Rear**, 0·75M from front, Q 36m **27M**; W Tr; intens 024·7°-026·2° (H24).
No. 1 Lt By 47°10'·02N 02°18'·35W VQ G; SHM.
No. 7 Lt By 47°13'·37N 02°16'·02W VQ G; SHM.
Pointe d'Aiguillon 47°14'·60N 02°15'·70W Oc (4) WR 12s 27m **W15M**, R11M; W Tr; vis W233°-293°, W297°-300°, R300°-327°, W327°-023°, W027°-089°.

VILLE-ES-MARTIN
Jetty Hd 47°15'·40N 02°13'·58W Fl (2) 6s 10m 12M; W Tr, R top.
Les Morées 47°15'·05N 02°12'·95W Fl (3) WR 12s 11m W9M, R6M; G Tr; vis W058°-224°, R300°-058°.

SAINT-NAZAIRE
W Jetty Oc (4) R 12s 11m 10M; W Tr, R top.
East Jetty 47°16'·05N 02°12'·06W Oc (4) G 12s 11m 11M; W Tr, G top.
Old Môle Hd 47°16'·33N 02°11'·74W Oc (2+1) 12s 18m 11M; W Tr, R top; vis 153·5°-063·5°; weather signals.
Basse Nazaire S Lt By 47°16'·27N 02°11'·57W Q (6) + L Fl 15s; SCM.

POINTE DE MINDIN
W Môle 47°16'·27N 02°10'·04W Fl G 2·5s 6m 3M.

LE POINTEAU/PORT DE COMBERGE/PORT DE LA GRAVETTE
Le Pointeau Digue S Hd 47°14'·08N 02°10'·89W Fl WG 4s 4m W10M, G6M; G&W ● hut; vis G050°-074°, W074°-149°, G149°-345°, W345°-050°.
Port de Comberge S Jetty 47°10'·60N 02°09'·95W Oc WG 4s 7m W9M, G5M; W Tr, G top; vis W123°-140°, G140°-123°.
Port de la Gravette Jetty Hd 47°09'·80N 02°12'·60W Fl (3) WG 12s 7m W8M, G5M; W structure, G top; vis G224°-124°, W124°-224°.

SAINT GILDAS (Anse de Boucau)
Pte de Saint Gildas 47°08'·10N 02°14'·67W Q WRG 23m W11M, R6M, G6M; framework Tr on W house; vis R264°-308°, G308°-078°, W078°-088°, R088°-174°, W174°-180°, G180°-264°; RC.

RIVER LOIRE TO NANTES

Bridge (Chan centre) 47°17.16N 02°10'·16W Iso 4s 55m.

DONGES
SW dolphin 47°18'·12N 02°04'·90W Fl G 4s 12m 5M; Gy col.
NE dolphin (close ENE) Iso G 4s 12m 4M; G col.
Jetty Hd 47°18'·35N 02°04'·11W Fl (2) R 6s 9m 9M.

PAIMBŒUF
Môle Hd 47°17'·50N 02°01'·88W Oc (3) WG 12s 9m W10M, G7M; W ● Tr, G top; vis G shore-123°, W123°-shore.
Île du Petit Carnet 47°17'·29N 02°00'·29W Fl G 2·5s 8m 3M; W framework Tr, G top.
From Paimbœuf to Nantes Lts on S side are G, and N Red.

PORT DE TRENTE MOULT/NANTES
Trente Moult Bn off 47°11'·83N 01°34'·63W; SPM.
Quai du Président Wilson Hd 47°12'·02N 01°34'·37W Fl R 2·5s.

10.17.5   PASSAGE INFORMATION

SOUTH BRITTANY (charts 2643, 2646)

The *North Biscay Pilot* (Imray/RCC) or the Admiralty *Bay of Biscay Pilot* are recommended. The *French Pilot* (Vol 3) (Nautical/Robson), although out of print, contains many unique almost timeless sketches and transits. French charts (SHOM) are often larger scale than Admiralty charts, and hence more suitable for inshore waters. For French Glossary, see 1.4.2. The following Breton words have navigational significance: *Aber*: estuary. *Aven*: river, stream. *Bann*: hill. *Bian*: small. *Bras*: great. *Du*: black. *Enez, Inis*: island. *Garo*: rough, hard. *Glas*: green. *Goban*: shoal. *Gwenn*: white. *Karreg*: rock. *Ker*: house. *Men, mein*: rock, stone. *Morlenn*: creek. *Penn*: strait. *Porz*: harbour. *Raz*: tide race. *Ruz*: red. *Trez*: sand.

Mist and haze are quite common in the summer, fog less so. Winds are predominantly from SW to NW, often light and variable in summer, but in early and late season N or NE winds are common. Summer gales are infrequent, and are usually related to passing fronts. In summer the sea is often calm or slight, but swell, usually from W or NW, can severely affect exposed anchorages. When crossing B of Biscay, allow for a likely set to the E, particularly after strong W winds.

A particular feature of this coast during the summer is the sea and land breeze cycle, known locally as the *vent solaire*. After a quiet forenoon, a W'ly sea breeze sets in about midday, blowing onshore. It slowly veers to the NW, almost parallel to the coast, reaching Force 4 by late afternoon; it then veers further to the N, expiring at dusk. Around midnight a land breeze may pipe up from the NE and freshen sufficiently to kick up rough seas – with consequent disruption to moorings and anchs open to the NE. By morning the wind has abated.

Tidal streams are weak offshore, but can be strong in estuaries, channels and around headlands, especially nearer the English Chan. The tidal stream chartlets at 10.17.4 are based on NP 265 (Admiralty Tidal Stream Atlas for France, W Coast) which uses data from actual observations out to 15-25M offshore. The equivalent French Atlas gives more data, but based on computer predictions.

Inland waterways (10.15.18) can be entered from Lorient (10.17.14), Vilaine R (10.17.22) and the R. Loire (10.17.26).

RAZ DE SEIN TO BENODET (chart 2351)

Chaussée de Sein (chart 798) is a chain of islands, rks and shoals extending 15M W from the Pte du Raz. A WCM lt buoy marks the seaward end. For directions on Île de Sein (10.17.8) and Raz de Sein see *North Biscay Pilot* (RCC/Imray).

Raz de Sein (chart 798) is the chan between Le Chat bn tr (at E end of Chaussée de Sein) and the dangers extending 8ca off Pte du Raz, the extremity of which is marked by La Vieille lt ho and La Plate lt tr. The Plateau de Tévennec is 2M N of Raz de Sein; it consists of islets, rks and shoals which extend 5ca in all directions from the lt ho thereon. Other dangers on the N side of the Raz are rks and shoals extending nearly 1M W and WSW from Pte du Van, and Basse Jaune (dries) 1M to N. On the S side the main dangers, all 1·5M off La Vieille, are: to the SW, Kornog Bras, a rk with depth of 3m; to the S, Masklou Greiz, rky shoals on which sea can break heavily; and to the SE, Roche Moulleg.

In the middle of Raz de Sein the NE-going (flood) stream begins at HW Brest + 0550, sp rate 6·5kn; the SW-going (ebb) stream begins at HW Brest − 0030, sp rate 5·5kn. There are eddies near La Vieille on both streams. In good weather, near np, and with wind and tide together, the Raz presents no difficulty, but in moderately strong winds it should be taken at slack water, which lasts for about ½ hour at end of flood stream. In strong winds the chan must not be used with wind against tide, when there are overfalls with a steep breaking sea.

The B des Trépassés (1·5M ENE of La Vieille) is possible anch to await the S-going tide. Port Bestrée or Anse du Loc'h (1M and 4M E of Pte du Raz) may be suitable anchs if N-bound.

Audierne (10.17.8) lies between Raz de Sein and Pte de Penmarc'h (lt, fog sig, RC) off which dangers extend 1M to NW, W and S, and 3M to SE, and breaking seas occur in strong winds. The fishing hbrs of St Guénolé, Le Guilvinec (10.17.8) and Lesconil provide excellent shelter, but have difficult ents. Loctudy (10.17.9) is well sheltered from W/SW.

BENODET TO LORIENT (chart 2352)

Îles de Glénan (chart 3640, SHOM 6648, 10.17.12), lie to seaward of Loctudy and Concarneau. With offlying dangers they stretch 5M from W to E and 4M from N to S. The islands are interesting to explore, but anchs are rather exposed. Between Îles de Glénan and Bénodet lie Les Pourceaux, reefs which dry, and Île aux Moutons which has dangers extending SW and NW.

Along the coast the larger ports are Bénodet (10.17.10), Port-la-Forêt (10.17.11) and Concarneau (10.17.12). Anse de Bénodet has rky shoals on both sides but is clear in the middle. The coast from Pte de Mousterlin to Beg Meil is fringed by rks, many of which dry, extending 1M offshore. Chaussée de Beg Meil extends 8½ca SE, where Linuen rk (dries) is marked by bn. From Concarneau to Pte de Trévignon rks extend nearly 1·5M offshore in places.

Between Pte de Trévignon and Lorient are rky cliffs and several interesting lesser hbrs and anchs, delightful in fair weather; but most dry and are dangerous to approach in strong onshore winds. These include the Aven and Belon rivers, Brigneau, Merrien (mostly dries), Doëlan (but most of hbr dries) and Le Pouldu (Rivière de Quimperlé). All are described in 10.17.12 and the *North Biscay Pilot*.

Hazards SE and E of Pte de Trévignon include: Men Du, a rk 0·3m high, marked by IDM bn, about 1·25M SE of the same pt. Corn Vas, depth 1·8m, and Men ar Tréas, a rk which dries, are close S, both buoyed. Île Verte lies 6ca S of Ile de Raguénès, with foul ground another 2ca to S. The approaches to Aven and Bélon Rivers are clear, except for Le Cochon and Les Verrés (IDM bn) to the SE. Between Le Pouldu and Lorient, Grand Cochon (SCM buoy) and Petit Cochon lie about 1M offshore.

LORIENT TO QUIBERON (charts 2352, 2353)

The great seaport of Lorient (10.17.14) has sheltered apprs and 4 marinas. Île de Groix lies 4M SW. Its main offlying dangers are to the E and SE: shoals off Pte de la Croix; Les Chats which extend 1M SE from Pte des Chats; and shoals extending 7½ca S of Loc Maria. Port Tudy (10.17.13), on N coast, is the main hbr, and is easy of access and well sheltered except from NE.

7M SE of Lorient, River Étel (10.17.15) is an attractive hbr with a difficult ent which must only be approached in good weather and on the last of the flood. Further S do not appr the isthmus of the Quiberon peninsula closely due to rky shoals. 6M W of Quiberon lies Plateau des Birvideaux (lt), a rky bank (depth 4·6m) on which the sea breaks in bad weather.

Belle Île has no dangers more than 2½ca offshore, apart from buoyed rks which extend 7½ca W of Pte des Poulains, and La Truie rk marked by IDM bn tr 5ca off the S coast. The S coast is much indented and exposed to swell from W. In good settled weather (only) and in absence of swell there is an attractive anch in Port du Vieux Château (Ster Wenn), 1M S of Pte des Poulains; see *North Biscay Pilot*. On the NE coast lie Le Palais (10.17.16) and Sauzon, which partly dries but has good anch off and is sheltered from S and W. Off Le Palais the ESE-going (flood) stream begins at HW Brest − 0610, and the WNW-going at HW Brest + 0125, sp rates 1·5kn.

17

BAIE DE QUIBERON (chart 2353)

B de Quiberon is an important and attractive yachting area, with centres at Port Haliguen (10.17.17), La Trinité (10.17.18), Crouesty (10.17.19) and the Morbihan (10.17.20). The S side of the bay is enclosed by a long chain of islands, islets, rks and shoals from Presqu'île de Quiberon to Les Grands Cardinaux 13M SE. This chain includes the attractive islands of Houat (10.17.19) and Hoëdic, well worth visiting, preferably mid-week. The Bay is open to the E and SE.

From W or S, enter the B via Passage de la Teignouse in W sector (033°-039°) of La Teignouse lt ho; thence 068° between Basse Nouvelle lt buoy and NE Teignouse lt buoy. In this chan the NE-going (flood) stream begins at HW Brest – 0610, and the SW-going at HW Brest – 0005, sp rates 3·75 kn; in strong winds it is best to pass at slack water. Good alternative chans are Passage du Béniguet, NW of Houat, and Passage des Soeurs, NW of Hoëdic.

The Golfe du Morbihan, on the N side of B de Quiberon, is an inland sea containing innumerable islands and anchs. Port Navalo anch is on the E side of the ent with Port du Crouesty close SE. Inside, River Auray flows in from the NW and the city of Vannes (10.17.21) is on the N side. Sp stream rates in the vicinity of Grand Mouton achieve 8kn and elsewhere in the ent can exceed 4kn. Flood commences HW Brest – 0400 and turns at HW Brest + 0200.

CROUESTY TO LE CROISIC (chart 2353)

Eastwards from the Morbihan, dangers extend 1M seaward of Pte de St Jacques, and 3M offshore lies Plateau de la Recherche with depths of 1·8m. SE of Penerf (10.17.22), which provides good anch, Plateau des Mats is an extensive rky bank, drying in places, up to 1·75M offshore.

Approaching the R. Vilaine (10.17.22) beware La Grande Accroche, a large shoal with least depth 1m, astride the ent. The main lit chan keeps NW of La Grande Accroche, to the bar on N side thereof. Here the flood begins at HW Brest – 0515, and the ebb at HW Brest + 0035, sp rates 2·5kn. In SW winds against tide the sea breaks heavily; when the Passe de la Varlingue, 5ca W of Pte du Halguen, is better, but beware La Varlingue (dries). At Arzal/Camoël yachts can lock into the non-tidal river for canal to Dinan/St Malo (see 10.15.18).

S of Pte du Halguen other dangers, close inshore, are the rky shoals, depth 0·6m, of Basse de Loscolo and Basse du Bile. Off Pte du Castelli, the Plateau de Piriac extends about 1·75M NW with depths of 2·3m and drying rks closer inshore. The small hbr of Piriac (10.17.23) lies on the N side of Pointe du Castelli and Les Bayonelles (dry) extend 5ca W. A chan runs between Plateau de Piriac and Île Dumet (lt), which is fringed by drying rks and shoals particularly on N and E sides.

In the Rade du Croisic are the hbrs of La Turballe (10.17.24) and Le Croisic (10.17.25). Off Pte du Croisic dangers extend 1M to N and W. Plateau du Four, a dangerous drying bank of rks, lies about 4M W and WSW of Pte du Croisic, marked by buoys and lt ho near N end. Between Pte du Croisic and Pte de Penchâteau, Basse Lovre is a rky shoal with depths of 1m, 5ca offshore.

LE CROISIC TO R. LOIRE (chart 2353, 3216)

From Chenal du Nord, B du Pouliguen (10.17.26) is entered between Pte de Penchâteau and Pte du Bec, 3M to E. In SE corner of bay is the yacht hbr of Pornichet (10.17.27). The B is partly sheltered from S by rks and shoals extending SE from Pte de Penchâteau to Le Grand Charpentier, but a heavy sea develops in strong S-SW winds. The W chan through these rks runs between Penchâteau and Les Guérandaises lateral buoys; other chans lie further E.

The River Loire estuary (chart 3216), which carries much commercial tfc, is entered via either the Chenal du Nord or the Chenal du Sud. The former runs ESE between the mainland and two shoals, Plateau de la Banche and Plateau de la Lambarde; these lie about 4M S of B du Pouliguen. Chenal du Sud, the main DW chan, leads NE between Plateau de la Lambarde and Pte de St Gildas. Here the in-going stream begins at HW Brest – 0500, and the out-going at HW Brest + 0050, sp rates about 2·75kn.

In the near apprs to St Nazaire (10.17.28 and charts 2985, 2989) beware Le Vert, Les Jardinets and La Truie (all dry) which lie close E of the chan. The river is navigable as far as Nantes. On the E side of the estuary, between the Loire bridge and Pte de St Gildas, are the small drying hbrs of Comberge, La Gravette and St Gildas (10.17.28).

10.17.6   DISTANCE TABLE

Approximate distances in nautical miles are by the most direct route, whilst avoiding dangers and allowing for Traffic Separation Schemes. Places in *italics* are in adjoining areas; places in **bold** are in 10.0.5, Cross-Channel Distances.

1. *Le Conquet*	1																			
2. *Camaret*	13	2																		
3. *Morgat*	22	16	3																	
4. *Douarnenez*	29	21	11	4																
5. Audierne	30	28	27	30	5															
6. Loctudy	55	55	53	55	30	6														
7. Bénodet	58	58	57	60	33	4	7													
8. Port-la-Forêt	65	64	63	66	36	12	12	8												
9. Concarneau	63	62	61	64	37	12	11	4	9											
10. Lorient	84	86	85	88	61	38	36	33	32	10										
11. Le Palais (Belle Ile)	95	99	98	101	74	54	52	48	47	26	11									
12. Port Haliguen	100	105	104	107	80	59	57	55	53	32	11	12								
13. La Trinité	108	110	109	112	85	64	62	60	58	37	16	8	13							
14. Crouesty	108	110	109	112	85	64	62	60	58	37	16	9	8	14						
15. Vannes	120	121	120	123	96	75	73	71	69	48	27	20	19	12	15					
16. Arzal/Camoël	131	130	129	132	105	84	82	80	78	57	36	31	31	28	37	16				
17. Le Croisic	124	125	124	127	100	79	77	75	73	48	27	26	26	22	33	18	17			
18. La Baule/Pornichet	134	131	130	133	106	85	82	80	78	55	34	35	36	30	40	30	13	18		
19. St Nazaire	145	138	137	140	113	95	91	90	87	66	41	42	45	40	50	39	24	12	19	
20. *Pornic*	146	149	148	151	124	105	101	100	97	72	45	47	49	43	55	42	24	18	16	20

10.17.7   Special notes for France: See 10.15.8

AUDIERNE   10-17-8

Finistere 48°00'·61N 04°32'·33W   Rtg 3-3-1

CHARTS
AC 3640, 2351; SHOM 7147, 7148; Imray C36, C37; ECM 541

TIDES
+0440 Dover; ML 3·1; Duration 0605; Zone 0100

Standard Port BREST (◄—)

Times				Height (metres)			
High Water		Low Water		MHWS	MHWN	MLWN	MLWS
0000	0600	0000	0600	6·9	5·4	2·6	1·0
1200	1800	1200	1800				
Differences AUDIERNE							
−0035	−0030	−0035	−0030	−1·7	−1·3	−0·6	−0·2
ILE DE SEIN							
−0005	−0005	−0010	−0005	−0·7	−0·6	−0·2	−0·1
LE GUILVINEC							
−0010	−0025	−0025	−0015	−1·8	−1·4	−0·6	−0·1
LESCONIL							
−0008	−0028	−0028	−0018	−1·9	−1·4	−0·6	−0·1

SHELTER
Good in marina, 3 pontoons 2ca SW of the bridge. Access HW±3 in all but strong SE-SW winds when seas break at the ent. Chan is dredged about 1m; beware drying banks close to stbd. Quays reserved for FVs.
At Ste Evette a long bkwtr, Oc (2) R 6s, gives good shelter, except in SE-SW winds which cause swell. W 🅐s to the N are marked 'Payant-Visiteurs'. Keep clear of slip area as vedettes enter with much verve.

NAVIGATION
WPT 47°59'·54N 04°32'·91W, 186°/006° from/to Kergadec lt, 1·5M. Appr between La Gamelle, rks drying 0·9m in the middle of the bay, and Le Sillon de Galets rks to the W; see clearing brg 016°, W pyramid and bkwtr lt. Or from the SE, leave La Gamelle to port. Appr is difficult in strong SE-SW winds. Inside the ent, dredged chan initially favours the W bank with ldg marks, vert R/W chevrons, in line 359°. After 2ca chan turns NE, with astern transit 225° on 2nd set of R/W chevrons. Hold 045° for 0·5M till abeam fish market on stbd side, then alter 90° port to marina, keeping close to quays and pontoons; banks dry to stbd.

LIGHTS AND MARKS
By day from the WPT, Kergadec, W 8-sided lt tr, R top, on with old lt ho (hard to see) leads 006°. At night stay in the W sector (005°-007°) of Kergadec, Dir Q WRG 43m 12/9M. From SE, ldg marks/lts at 331°: Front Fl (3) WG 12s 11m 14/9M, W ○ tr on hbr bkwtr; rear FR 44m 9M (Kergadec).

RADIO TELEPHONE
None. Adjacent sig stn at Pte du Raz Ch 16.

TELEPHONE (Prefix ☎ Nos with zone code 02)
Hr Mr 98·70·07·91; Aff Mar 98·70·03·33; CROSS 98·89·31·31; SNSM 98·70·03·31; ⌗ 98·94·68·67; Auto 08.36.68.08.29; Police 98·70·04·38; Ⓗ 98·75·10·10; Brit Consul 40·63·16·02.

FACILITIES
Port de Plaisance (100+20 visitors) ☎ 98·75·04·93, FF99, AC, FW, CH, ME, EI, Ⓔ, Sh, Bar, R, V; **Poulgoazec** (E bank) C (15 ton), P & D (cans), Slip. **Town** V, Gaz, R, Bar, ✉, Ⓑ, bus to Quimper ⇌, ✈. Ferry: Roscoff. **Ste Evette**, Hr Mr ☎ 98.70.00.28, access H24, M, 🅾, Showers.

ADJACENT HARBOURS AND ANCHORAGES

ILE DE SEIN, Finistere, 48°02'·40N 04°50'·80W. AC 798, 2351; SHOM 5252, 7148. Tides, see above; ML 3·8m. Ile de Sein is the only inhabited Is in the Chaussée de Sein, a chain of islands, rks and shoals extending 15M W from the Pte du Raz. The outer end has a WCM lt buoy and 5M E is Ar-Men lt tr, Fl (3) 20s 29m, horn (3) 60s. The E end is separated from the mainland by the Raz de Sein; see 10.17.5 for passage details. Ile de Sein is worth visiting in fair weather, good vis and preferably near nps. Best appr is from the N, 187° via Chenal d'Ezaudi, with Men-Brial lt ho, Oc (2) WRG 6s, (W with B stripe) from left (on with third house (W with B stripe) from left (on with third house (W with B stripe) from left (on with third house) S of lt ho). Chan between drying rks is entered at Cornoc-An-Ar-Braden SHM By, Iso G 4s and tide sets across the chan, which is marked by bn trs. There are also chans from NE and E. ⚓ off or inside the mole, but open to N and E. Hbr partly dries. See *North Biscay Pilot* (RCC/Imray) for directions. Facilities: limited V, R, CH, Sh.

ST GUÉNOLÉ, Finistere, 47°48'·70N 04°22'·90W. AC 2351; SHOM 6645, 7146; ECM 543. Strictly a fishing port; yachts not welcomed. Access difficult in fresh W'lies, impossible in heavy weather. 3 sets of ldg marks/lts. Lts as 10.17.4. Pilot book & SHOM 6645 essential. Hr Mr ☎ 02.98.58.60.43.

LE GUILVINEC, Finistere, 47°47'·52N 04°17'·10W. AC 3640, 2351; SHOM 6646, 7146. HW + 0447 on Dover (UT); ML 3·0m. See 10.17.8. Good shelter and useful passage port; hbr (3m) accessible H24 for <2·5m draft, but total priority to FVs; no ent/exit 1600-1830. At NE end of hbr (amongst hosts of lesser buoys), secure to one large W 🅐; max stay 24hrs. Good ⚓ off ent in lee of reef but stay clear of fairway. Beware Lost Moan Rks SE of ent marked by RW bn tr, Fl (3) WRG 12s 8m 9/6M. Ent is easy if vis adequate to see ldg lts/marks. Three ldg lts, all synch, in line 053°: front, Mole de Lechiagat Q 7m 8m, W pylon, vis 233°-066°; middle, Rocher Le Faoutés, 210m from front, QWG 12m 14/11M, R □ on W pylon, vis W006°-293°, G293°-006°; rear, 0·58M from front, Dir Q 26m 8M, R □ on W pylon with R stripe, vis 051·5°-054·5°. VHF Ch 12. Facilities: Hr Mr ☎ 02.98.58.05.67; Aff Mar ☎ 02.98.58.13.13; ⌗, C, FW, D, P, EI, ME, Sh, CH, Ⓔ.

LESCONIL, Finistere, 47°47'·76N 04°12'·57W. AC 3640, 2351; SHOM 6646, 7146; ECM 543. Tides, see left column; ML 3m. Fishing port 3M SW of Loctudy; yachts tolerated at their own risk. Do not enter/leave 1630-1830LT due to FV inrush. Appr from Karek Greis ECM buoy, Q (3) 10s, on ldg line 325°, belfry just open W of Men ar Groas lt ho, Fl (3) WRG 12s 14m 10/7M; at night in W sector 313°-333°. Bkwtr lts are QG and Oc R 4s. Possible drying mooring inside S bkwtr; no 🅐s, no AB on quays. Hr Mr ☎ 02.98.82.22.97. Facilities of fishing port.

LOCTUDY   10-17-9

Finistere 47°50´.30N 04°10´.50W   Rtg 3-2-2

CHARTS
AC 3641, 2351/2; SHOM 6649, 6679, 7146; ECM 543; Imray C37, 38

TIDES
+0505 Dover (UT); ML 3·0; Duration 0615; Zone –0100

Standard Port BREST (←—)

Times				Height (metres)			
High Water		Low Water		MHWS	MHWN	MLWN	MLWS
0000	0600	0000	0600	6·9	5·4	2·6	1·0
1200	1800	1200	1800				
Differences LOCTUDY							
–0013	–0033	–0035	–0025	–1·9	–1·5	–0·7	–0·2

SHELTER
Excellent in marina and hbr, except in strong ESE winds. The many ⚓s and moorings in the river leave little space to ⚓. Keep clear of FVs, esp 17-1900LT daily when yachts are discouraged from entering/leaving hbr.

NAVIGATION
WPT 47°50´.12N 04°08´.86W, 105°/285° from/to Les Perdrix lt, 0·73M. From S and W, leave Bas Bilien ECM, VQ (3), to port, thence to WPT. From E/NE, give Men Audierne SHM bn a wide berth. Bar has least depth 0·9m, deeper to the N. Sp ebb runs at 3½kn; enter under power only. Appr 285° (to clear unmarked Karek Croisic rk) in W sector of Les Perdrix lt; when 300m short, alter port onto 274° as marina and Chateau Laubrière (conspic) come in transit. Beware rky ledges close S of Les Perdrix and SHM bn, Fl (3) G 12s. Pont l'Abbé (3M up-river) dries about 2m, but is accessible to shoal draft boats on the flood; chan marked by perches.

LIGHTS AND MARKS
Pte de Langoz Fl (4) WRG 12s 12m 15/11M (see 10.15.4). Karek-Saoz R bn tr QR 3m 1M. Les Perdrix B/W tr, Fl WRG 4s 15m 11/8M, G090°-285°, W285°-295°, R295°-090°. Le Blas Fl (3) G 12s 5m 1M.

RADIO TELEPHONE
Marina VHF Ch 09 (Office hrs); Port Ch 12.

TELEPHONE (Prefix ☎ Nos with zone code 02)
Hr Mr 98·87·51·36; Aff Mar 98·58·13·13; CROSS 97·55·35·35; SNSM 98·87·41·12; ⌗ 98·87·61·12; Auto 08·36·68·08·29; Dr 98·87·41·80; Ⓗ (6km) 98·82·40·40; Brit Consul 40.63.16.02.

FACILITIES
Marina (610+80 visitors;) ☎ 98·87·51·36, FF120, FW, AC, Slip, D & P, C (9 tons), CH, Sh, ME, El; new office/showers WC. **Town** Bar, V, R, Dr, Ⓞ, Ⓑ.

BÉNODET   10-17-10

Finistere 47°51´.80N 04°06´.40W   Rtg 2-1-1

CHARTS
AC 3641, 2352; SHOM 6679, 6649, 7313, 7146; ECM 543; Imray C37

TIDES
+0450 Dover; ML 3·1; Duration 0610; Zone –0100

Standard Port BREST (←—)

Times				Height (metres)			
High Water		Low Water		MHWS	MHWN	MLWN	MLWS
0000	0600	0000	0600	6·9	5·4	2·6	1·0
1200	1800	1200	1800				
Differences BÉNODET							
0000	–0020	–0023	–0013	–1·7	–1·3	–0·5	–0·1
CORNIGUEL							
+0015	+0010	–0015	–0010	–2·0	–1·6	–1·0	–0·7

SHELTER
Marinas at Ste Marine (W bank, town of Combrit) and at Anse de Penfoul (E bank, Bénodet), both accessible H24 at any tide. Caution: In both marinas, best to arr/dep near slack water to avoid the strong stream, esp 4kn ebb, through the pontoons with risk of damage. Some ⚓s available. ⚓ in Anse du Trez in offshore winds. Speed limit 3kn in hbr.
R Odet is navigable near HW to Quimper, but masted vessels must ⚓ at Poulguinan bridge (5·8m clearance), 1M beyond Corniguel and 0·5M below the city; pleasant ⚓s at Anse de Combrit, Anse de Kérautret, Porz Keraign, Porz Meilou, Anse de Toulven and SW of Lanroz. N of Lanroz the river shoals progressively to 0·5m in places. SHOM 6679 is recommended.

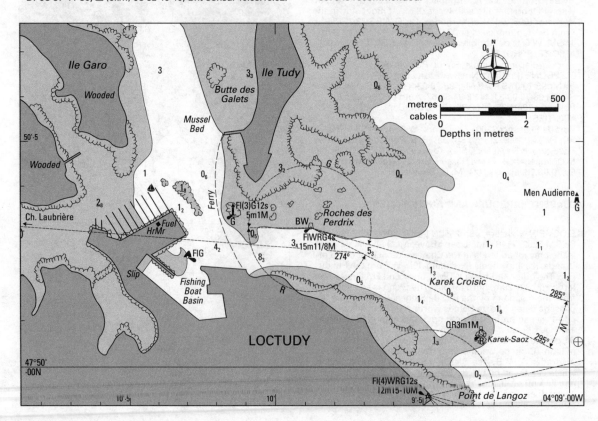

BÉNODET *continued*

NAVIGATION
WPT 47°51'·00N 04°06'·10W, 166°/346° from/to front ldg lt, 1·43M. The centre of the bay is clear for small craft, but beware Roches de Mousterlin at the SE end of the bay and various rks off Loctudy to the SW. There is a tanker chan past the Ile aux Moutons, 6M SSE of hbr.

LIGHTS AND MARKS
Ldg lts/daymarks 346°: Front, Oc (2+1) G 12s 11m 17M, intens 345°-347°, W ○ tr, G vert stripe, G top (hard to see until close); rear Oc (2+1) 12s 48m 11M, conspic W tr, G top, synch. Ile-aux-Moutons (6M SSE), Oc (2) WRG 6s 18m 15/11M + Dir Oc (2) 6s 17m 24M, intens 278°-283°.

RADIO TELEPHONE
Both marinas VHF Ch 09 (0800-2000LT in season).

TELEPHONE (Prefix ☎ Nos with zone code 02)
Hr Mr 98·56·38·72; Aff Mar 98·57·03·82; CROSS 97·55·35·35; SNSM 98·57·02·00; ⌗ 98·55·04·19; Météo 98·94·03·43; Police 17; Fire 18; Dr 98·57·22·21; Brit Consul 40·63·16·02.

FACILITIES
BENODET: **Anse de Penfoul Marina** (510+40 visitors AB; also 175 buoys +15 for visitors) ☎ 98·57·05·78, ⛽ 98.57.00.21, AC, FW, ▣, R, CH, ME, V, P, D, M, EI, Ⓔ, Sh, C, SM, Divers. **Quay** C (10 ton). **Town** All facilities, Gaz, ✉, Ⓑ, bus to Quimper ⇌, ✈.
COMBRIT: **Sainte Marine Marina** (350+70 visitors), FF118 or FF76 for ⚓, ☎ 98·56·38·72, ⛽ 98.51.95.17, AC, CH, FW. **Town** V, R, Bar, ▣, Ⓔ. Pedestrian ferry to Bénodet.

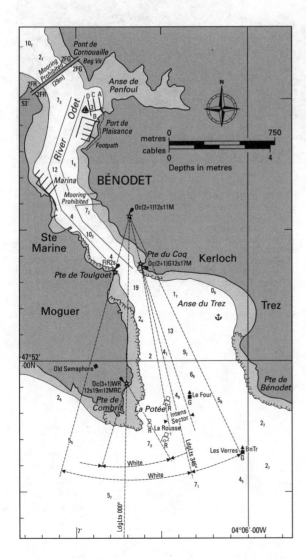

PORT-LA-FORÊT   10-17-11
Finistere 47°53'·55N 03°58'·17W   Rtg 2-1-2

CHARTS
AC 3641, 2352; SHOM 6650, 7146; ECM 543, 544; Imray C38

TIDES
+0450 Dover; ML 2·9; Duration 0615; Zone –0100
Use Differences CONCARNEAU 10.17.12

SHELTER
Very good in marina (2m); Ⓥ pontoon C-D. There is ⚓ inside Cap Coz and moorings to W of the inner chan, dredged 1·2m .

NAVIGATION
WPT 47°52'·77N 03°57'·62W, 154°/334° from/to Cap-Coz lt, 0·88M. Beware Basse Rouge 6·5ca S of Cap Coz, Le Scoré (unlit SCM bn) and buoyed oyster farms in apprs. At sp a shoal patch 0·9m just S of the ent denies access LW±1½; there are 3 W waiting buoys close WSW of the ent.

LIGHTS AND MARKS
Cap Coz, Fl (2) R 6s 5m 6M, and Kerleven bkwtr lt, Fl G 4s 8m 6M, lead 334° into chan marked with buoys and bns; the first pair of chan buoys are lit, Fl R 2·5s and Fl (2) G 6s.

RADIO TELEPHONE
VHF Ch 09.

TELEPHONE (Prefix ☎ Nos with zone code 02)
Hr Mr 98·56·98·45; Aff Mar 98·56·01·98; Rescue CROSS-Etel 97·55·35·35; Auto 08.36.68.08.29; SNSM 98·56·98·25; ⌗ (Concarneau) 98·97·01·73; Police 98·56·00·11; Ⓗ (Concarneau) 98·50·30·30; Brit Consul 40·63·16·02.

FACILITIES
Marina (900+100 visitors) ☎ 98·56·98·45, ⛽ 98.56.81.31, FF115, AC, D, P, FW, ME, EI, Sh, CH, Gaz, R, ▣, SM, V, Bar, BH (16 ton), C (4 ton), Slip (multi hull).
Town Gaz, ✉, Ⓑ, ⇌, ✈ Quimper. Ferry: Roscoff.

CONCARNEAU   10-17-12
Finistere 47°52'·10N 03°54'·68W   Rtg 2-1-1

CHARTS
AC 3641, 2352; SHOM 6650, 7146; ECM 543/4; Imray C38
TIDES
+0455 Dover; ML 3·0; Duration 0615; Zone −0100

Standard Port BREST (←—)

Times				Height (metres)			
High Water		Low Water		MHWS	MHWN	MLWN	MLWS
0000	0600	0000	0600	6·9	5·4	2·6	1·0
1200	1800	1200	1800				
Differences CONCARNEAU							
−0010	−0030	−0030	−0020	−1·9	−1·5	−0·7	−0·2
ILE DE PENFRET (Iles de Glénan)							
−0005	−0030	−0028	−0018	−1·9	−1·5	−0·7	−0·2

SHELTER
Good, except in strong S'lies. The marina (2m) has an
anti-wash barrier. The Arrière Port is solely for FVs; yacht
pontoon on NE corner of La Ville Close is only for locals.
NAVIGATION
WPT 47°50'·00N 03°56'·80W, 208°/028° from/to front ldg lt
028°, 2·52M. Beware rks around Men Cren and Le Cochon.
LIGHTS AND MARKS
Ldg lts 028°: front Oc (3) 12s 14m 13M, RW tr which is
hard to see against bldgs behind; rear, 1·35M from front,
Q 87m 23M, spire on skyline. Steer between Le Cochon G
bn tr, Fl WRG 12s, and Basse du Chenal PHM buoy, QR;
the former is easier to see than the ldg marks. Past Men
Fall SHM buoy Fl G 4s, steer 070° for Lanriec lt, QG 13m
8M, vis 063°-078°, G window on W gable, LANRIEC below.
RADIO TELEPHONE
Marina Ch 09 (0700-2100LT in season). FV hbr Ch 12 16 (H24).

TELEPHONE (Prefix ☎ Nos with zone code 02)
Marina Office 98·97·57·96; Hr Mr (FV hbr) 98·50·61·00;
Aff Mar 98·50·69·76; CROSS 97·55·35·35; 97·64·32·42;
Météo 98·94·03·43; Auto 08.36.68.08.29; ✚ 98·97·01·73;
Police 17; Fire 18; Ⓗ 98·50·30·30; Brit Consul 40·63·16·02.
FACILITIES
Marina (238 + 50 visitors; pontoon 'D'), FF125, P, D, FW,
M, AC, Slip, C (17 ton), Sh, ME, El, CH, SHOM, ACA, SM.
Town Ⓔ, Gaz, V, R, Bar, ✉, Ⓑ, bus to Quimper ⇌ and ✈.
Ferry: Roscoff.

OTHER HARBOURS AND ANCHORAGES BETWEEN CONCARNEAU AND LORIENT

ILES DE GLÉNAN, 47°43'·04N 03°59'·51W (twr on Île Cigogne). A good Pilot and large-scale chart are essential: AC 3640; SHOM 6648 (larger scale than AC 3640), 7146, 7313; ECM 243. Tides see 10.17.12. A low-lying archipelago, 10M SSW of Concarneau, with Ile aux Moutons and Les Pourceaux, both rky plateaux, to the N. Cardinal buoys mark Basse Jaune, a partly drying shoal to the E, and the SE, S and SW limits of the Islands. Visit in settled weather as ⚓s can be exposed. There is enough water HW±3 for most boats, but below half-tide careful pilotage is needed. **Conspic marks** are Penfret, highest island with lt Fl R 5s 36m 21M & Dir Q; and the tower (W with B top) on Ile Cigogne, HQ of Centre Nautique, Q (2) RG 5s 5m 2M. **Approaches.** Easiest is from the N, via WPT 47°44'·0N 03°57'·5W, to W side of Penfret, with bn on Ile Guéotec brg 192°. ⚓ there or proceed W to ⚓s and ⚓ in La Chambre, S of Ile de St Nicolas; at W end a wind turbine (5 FR) is conspic. Also from N, Cigogne tr in transit 181° with chy on Ile du Loc'h leads close E of La Pie IDM bn, Fl (2) 6s 9m 3M, to ⚓ NW of Ile de Bananec; or SE into the pool. From the W, Chenal des Bluiniers 095° dries 0·8m between Ile Drénec and St Nicolas. S apprs and night navigation are not advised. Other ⚓s: E side of Penfret; close E of Cigogne; and N of Ile du Loc'h. No facilities.

AVEN and BELON RIVERS, Finistère, 47°48'·05N 03°44'·20W, AC 2352, SHOM 7138, 7031. HW +0450 on Dover (UT), –0030 on Brest. HW ht –1·9m on Brest; ML 2·8m; Duration 0610. Both rivers are shallow in their upper reaches and have bars, shown on SHOM 7138 as dredged 0·6m. Seas rarely break on the Aven bar, but the Belon bar is impassable in bad weather. Beware Les Cochons de Rousbicout (drying 0·3m) to SW of ent and Les Verres to SE. Port Manech has ⚓s and a good ⚓ in 2·5m outside the bar which dries 0·9m. Very good shelter at Rosbras up the **Aven**; Pont-Aven, 3·6M up-river, only accessible for shoal craft. Moorings in 2·5m; or AB at the quay dries 2·5m. For the **Belon**, appr near HW from close to Pte de Kerhermen and hug the E shore to cross the bar (dries 0·3m); SHOM 7138/ pilot book is advisable. 1M up-river are 3 large ⚓s or ⚓ in deep water; ⚓s trots further up. Port Manech has only lt, Oc (4) WRG 12s 38m 10/7M, see 10.17.4 for sectors. Night entry not advised. Facilities (Aven): Aff Mar ☎ 02·98·06·00·73; **YC de l'Aven** (Port Manech). **Town** ME, Slip, C, FW, P&D, R, Bar.

BRIGNEAU, Finistère, 47°476'·82N 03°40'·00W. AC 2352; SHOM 7138, 7031; ECM 544. –0020 on Brest; ML 2·8m. Small drying, fair weather hbr. Strong onshore winds render the ent dangerous and the hbr untenable due to swell. Unlit RW buoy is 8ca S of hbr ent. By day bkwtr lt and rear W panel (hard to see) lead 331° to ent, close E of ruined factory. Dir lt on bkwtr, Oc (2) WRG 6s 7m 12/9M, W tr/R top, W329°-339°. Some ⚓s or AB on W quay, dries. Facilities: FW, AC, V.

MERRIEN, Finistère, 47°46'·51N 03°38'·98W. AC 2352; SHOM 7138, 7031; ECM 544. HW –0020 on Brest; ML 2·8m. Drying inlet with rky ledges either side of apprs. Ldg marks 005°: front W □ lt tr/R top; rear, house gable. Dir lt QR 26m 7M, vis 004°-009°. ⚓ outside ent or moor to ⚓ or AB on quay SE side. Avoid oyster beds beyond quay. Facilities: FW, AC, R.

DOËLAN, Finistère, 47°46'·20N 03°36'·45W. AC 2352; SHOM 7138, 7031; ECM 544. HW +0450 on Dover (UT), –0035 on Brest ; HW ht –2·2m on Brest; ML 3·1m; Duration 0607. Fair weather only, open to SW. Drying AB at quays; or afloat on W buoys just N and S of bkwtr. Conspic factory chy E of front ldg lt. Daymark, W bn/B stripe, (about 1km NNE of rear ldg lt) on with ldg lts 014°: front Oc (3) WG 12s 20m 13/10M, W tr/G band & top, W shore -305°, G305°- 314°, W314°-shore; rear QR 27m 9M, W tr/R band & top. Facilities: Aff Mar ☎ 02·98·96·62·38; **Services:** CH, El, Ⓔ, ME, Sh. **Town** D, P, FW, Dr, ✉, R, V, Bar.

LE POULDU (La Laïta or Quimperlé River), Finistère, 47°45'·70N 03°32'·20W. AC 2352; SHOM 7138, 7031; ECM 544. HW – 0020 on Brest; ML 2·8m. Strictly a fair weather hbr, but once inside a small marina on the E bank provides adequate shelter for small yachts. ⚓ in deeper pools upstream. At HW appr the estuary ent close E of a W ○ tr on low cliffs. The ent favours the W side, but chan shifts often and local advice is needed. In onshore winds the bar is dangerous on the ebb. Tides reach 6kn at sp. No lights. Facilities: FW, V, R, Bar.

PORT TUDY   10-17-13

Morbihan (Ile de Groix) 47°38'·74N 03°26'·63W   Rtg 2-4-2

CHARTS
AC 2352, 2646; SHOM 7139, 7031, 7032; ECM 544; Imray C38
TIDES
+0505 Dover; ML 3·1; Duration 0610; Zone –0100

Standard Port BREST (←—)

Times				Height (metres)			
High Water		Low Water		MHWS	MHWN	MLWN	MLWS
0000	0600	0000	0600	6·9	5·4	2·6	1·0
1200	1800	1200	1800				
Differences PORT TUDY (Ile de Groix)							
0000	–0025	–0025	–0015	–1·8	–1·4	–0·6	–0·1

SHELTER
Very good in marina or on pontoons outside, dredged 0·9-2·4m. Access via lock to marina HW –1½ to +2, (0630–2200) or less at small coefficients. Outer hbr is open to swell in strong N/NE winds, access H24. Moor fore and aft to buoys; max draft 3m. No ⚓ in hbr, often very crowded. Caution: ferries navigating with panache.
NAVIGATION
WPT 47°39'·14N 03°26'·28W, (100m E of Speerbrecker unlit ECM buoy), 039°/219° from/to N mole hd lt, 0·5M. Remain in R sector of E mole hd lt. Beware 3 large unlit mooring buoys 0·6M NW of ent and rks SE of appr.

PORT-TUDY

LIGHTS AND MARKS
Pen-Men lt ho (at NW end of island), Fl (4) 25s 59m 29M, W □ tr, B top. Pte de la Croix lt (at E end of island), Oc WR 4s 16m 12/9M. Ldg line at 220°, church spire in line with W end of N mole. By night, mole hd lts in transit 219° clears offlying rks to the NE. N mole hd, Iso G 4s 12m 6M. E mole hd, Fl (2) R 6s 11m 6M, vis 112°-226°.
RADIO TELEPHONE
VHF Ch 09 16 during lock opening times.
TELEPHONE (Prefix ☎ Nos with zone code 02)
Hr Mr 97·86·54·62; Aff Mar 97·37·16·22; CROSS 97·55·35·35; SNSM 97·86·82·87; ☷ 97·86·80·93; Auto 08·36·68·08·56; Police 97·86·81·17; Ⓗ (Lorient) 97·83·04·02.
FACILITIES
Marina (150), FF100, FF20 on buoy, FW, AC; **Quay** P & D (cans, 0800–1200 & 1400–1900, ☎ 97·86·80·96), ME, EI, Sh, C (3 ton), CH. **Town** V, R, ▣, ✉, Bar. Ferry to Lorient.

OTHER HARBOUR ON ILE DE GROIX

LOCMARIA, Morbihan, 47°37'·85N 03°26'·28W. AC 2352, SHOM 7139; –0020 Brest; ML 2·8m. Appr is open to the S, but tiny drying hbr gives shelter in offshore winds. Steer N for G bn tr initially; then ldg line 350°, W bn on with conspic Ho. Close in, 2 PHM bns and a SCM and NCM bn mark the unlit chan. Limited space inside to dry out; or ⚓ outside the hbr W of the ldg line. Few facilities in village, V, R.

17

LORIENT

Morbihan 47°42'·64N 03°21'·92W   Rtg 1-1-2

10-17-14

CHARTS

AC 304, 2352; SHOM 7140, 7139, 7031, 7032; ECM 544, 545; Imray C38

TIDES
+0455 Dover; ML 3·1; Duration 0620; Zone –0100

Standard Port BREST (←)

Times				Height (metres)			
High Water		Low Water		MHWS	MHWN	MLWN	MLWS
0000	0600	0000	0600	6·9	5·4	2·6	1·0
1200	1800	1200	1800				
Differences LORIENT							
+0003	–0022	–0020	–0010	–1·8	–1·4	–0·6	–0·2
PORT LOUIS							
+0004	–0021	–0022	–0012	–1·8	–1·4	–0·6	–0·1
PORT D'ETEL							
+0020	–0010	+0030	+0010	–2·0	–1·3	–0·4	+0·5

SHELTER
Very good. Ile de Groix shelters the ent from SW'lies. Hbr access all tides/weather. 4 marinas at: **Kernével**, W of main chan (enter between 2 Y buoys at N end of wavebreak, thence **Ⓥ** berths at S end); **Port Louis** (E of La Citadelle); **Locmiquélic** (E of Ile Ste Michel); and **Port du Lorient** in the city: berth in Avant Port or lock into the Bassin à Flot, HW±1 sp, ±15 mins nps; access HJ. No ⚓ in chans and hbr, but moorings ENE of La Citadelle and ⚓ for shoal draft in B de Locmalo. R Blavet is navigable on the flood for 6M to Hennebont where there are 🛟s and a pontoon in complete shelter; also moorings below first of 3 bridges, 21m least clearance. Caution: 0.3m patches beyond the first bridge. See 10.15.18 for canal access.

NAVIGATION
WPT Passe du Sud 47°40´·50N 03°22´·40W, 188°/008° from/to front ldg lt, 3·35M. WPT Passe de l'Ouest, 47°40´·80N 03°24´·92W, 237°/057° from/to front ldg lt, 3·0M. There are few navigational dangers if ldg lines are kept to, but yachts must keep clear of shipping in the main chan. Abeam La Citadelle a secondary yacht chan parallels the main chan to W of La Jument R bn tr, Oc R 4s and Le Cochon RGR bn tr, Fl R 4s.

LIGHTS AND MARKS
Conspic daymarks are Water Tr 8ca W of Kernevel, La Citadelle to stbd of ent, submarine pens at Pte de Keroman and 2 silos N of Ile St Michel.
Ldg and Dir lts as seen from seaward in sequence:
(1) Passe de l'Ouest: ldg lts 057°, both Dir Q; Front, Les Soeurs, 11m 13M; R tr, W bands. Rear, Port Louis 740m from front, 22m 18M; W daymark, R bands on bldg.
(2) Passe du Sud: ldg lts 008·5°, both Dir QR, intens 006°-011°, synch; Front, 16m 15M; R □, G bands on Gy tr. Rear, Kergroise, 515m from front, 28m 16M; R □, W stripe on Gy framework tr.
(3) Les Trois Pierres: QRG 11m 6M; conspic B tr, W bands, G 060°-196°, R196°-002°.
(4) Ile Saint-Michel: ldg lts 016·5°, both Dir Oc (3) G 12s 8/14m 16M, intens 015°-018°; W trs, G tops.
(5) Pte de Keroman: ldg lts 350°, both Dir Oc (2) R 6s 17M, synch, intens 349°-351°. Front, 25m; R ho, W bands; Rear, 31m; RW topmark on Gy pylon, R top.
(6) Kernével: ldg lts 217°, both Dir QR 14M, intens 215°-219°; Front, 10m. Rear, 18m; W □ tr, R top.
(7) Pte de l'Esperance: Dir lt 037°: Dir Q WRG 8m 10/7M; G034·2°-036·7°, W036·7°-037·2°, R037·2°-047·2°.
(8) Pont Gueydon: Dir lt 352°: Iso WRG 4s 6m 11/9M; G350°-351·5°, W351·5°-352·5°, R352·5°-355·5°.

RADIO TELEPHONE
Vigie Port Louis VHF Ch 11 16 (H24). Marinas Ch 09 (HO).

TELEPHONE (Prefix ☎ Nos with zone code 02)
Hr Mr Port de Plaisance 97·21·10·14; Aff Mar 97·37·16·22; CROSS 97·55·35·35; SNSM 97·64·32·42; ⌗ 97·37·29·57; Météo 97·64·34·86; Auto 08.36.68.08.56; Police 97·64·27·17; Ⓗ 97·37·51·33; Brit Consul 40·63·16·02.

FACILITIES (from seaward)
Kernével Marina (410+60 **Ⓥ**) ☎ 97·65·48·25; access H24, depth 3m; FW, AC, P & D (pontoon at S end of marina), ▣, Slip, BH (25 ton), C (100 ton), YC ☎ 97·47·47·25.
Port-Louis Marina (160+20 **Ⓥ**), ☎ 97·82·18·18, dredged 2m, FW, AC, C (150 ton).
Locmiquélic (S. Catherine) **Marina**, (217+10 ☎ 97·33·59·51, 🛟 97·33·89·25, depth 1·5-3m, FW, AC, C (40 ton), ▣.
Lorient Marina (320+50 **Ⓥ**) ☎ 97·21·10·14; FF110, Avant Port 2·5-3m depth, 2·3m in Bassin à Flot; P, D, FW, AC, ▣, Slip, BH (25 ton), C (100 ton), ME, EI, Ⓔ, Sh, CH, SHOM, ACA, Sh, SM; **Club Nautique de Lorient**, Bar, C (1½ ton), FW, Slip. **City** All facilities, ✉, Ⓑ, ⇌, ✈. Ferry: Roscoff.

RIVER ÉTEL   10-17-15
Morbihan 47°39´·60N 03°12´·38W   Rtg 4-4-2

CHARTS
AC 2352; SHOM 7138, 7032; ECM 545; Imray C38

TIDES
+0505 Dover (UT); ML 3·2m; Duration 0617. See 10.17.14

SHELTER
Excellent at marina (1·5-2m) on E bank 1M up-river from the ent, inside the town quay (FVs). Possible ⚓s S of conspic LB ho, off Le Magouër on the W bank or above town (beware strong streams). Pont Lorois (1·3M N) has 9·5m clearance.

NAVIGATION
WPT 47°38´·38N 03°12´·90W, 219°/039° from/to water tr (off chartlet), 1·47M. Appr only by day, in good visibility, at about HW –1½ on the last of the flood, with conspic water tr brg 039°. Bar dries approx 0·4m; buoyed/lit chan shifts. For directions in simple French, call *Semaphore d'Etel* Ch 13. If no VHF, pre-notify ETA by ☎; fly ensign at mast-head; expect visual sigs from Fenoux mast, close NW of ent:
Waggle of semaphore arrow = acknowledged; obey signals:
Arrow vert = maintain present course.
Arrow inclined = alter course in direction indicated.
Arrow horiz = no entry for all vessels; conditions dangerous.
● hoisted = no ent for undecked boats and craft <8m LOA.
R flag = insufficient depth over bar. Once inside, the chan is narrow, but well marked, up to Pte Saint-Germain.

LIGHTS AND MARKS
Lt W side of ent, Oc (2) WRG 6s 13m 9/6M, W022°-064°, R064°-123°, W123°-330°, G330°-022°; no ⚓ within 5ca of lt. Épi de Plouhinic bn, Fl R 2·5s 7m 2M, marks groyne at ent.

RADIO TELEPHONE
Call *Semaphore d'Etel* VHF Ch 13 16 (see above). Marina Ch 13 16 (HW–3 to +2). For CROSS Étel, see 10.15.8.

TELEPHONE (Prefix ☎ Nos with zone code 02)
Hr Mr 97·55·46·62, 🛟 97·55·34·14; Aff Mar 97·55·30·32; Auto 08·36·65·02·56; CROSS 97·55·35·35; Sig Tr 97·55·35·59; Police 97·55·32·11.

FACILITIES
Marina (180 + 20 visitors) FW, AC, C (6 ton), Slip; **Quay** P & D (cans), CH, EI, ME, Sh. **Town** Bar, Dr, R, V, ▣, Bus to ⇌ (Auray 15km) and ✈ (Lorient 32km).

LE PALAIS (BELLE ILE)   10-17-16

Morbihan 47°20'·89N 03°08'·98W   Rtg 2-3-1

CHARTS
AC 2353; Imray C39; SHOM 7142, 7032; ECM 545

TIDES
+0458 Dover; ML 3·1; Duration 0615; Zone –0100

Standard Port BREST (←)

Times				Height (metres)			
High Water		Low Water		MHWS	MHWN	MLWN	MLWS
0000	0600	0000	0600	6·9	5·4	2·6	1·0
1200	1800	1200	1800				
Differences LE PALAIS							
+0007	–0028	–0025	–0020	–1·8	–1·4	–0·7	–0·3
ILE DE HOUAT							
+0010	–0025	–0020	–0015	–1·7	–1·3	–0·6	–0·2
ILE DE HÖEDIC							
+0010	–0035	–0027	–0022	–1·8	–1·4	–0·7	–0·3

SHELTER
Good, except in strong E'lies which cause marked swell. Very crowded in season. Deep draft yachts moor on 3 trots of ⚓s inside Mole Bourdelle; shallow draft on ⚓s to port. Inner hbr mostly dries. Lock into the Bassin à Flot opens HW –1½ to +1 (0600-2200LT), for berths on S side in 2·5m; thence via lifting bridge into marina (1·7m).

NAVIGATION
WPT 47°21'·20N 03°08'·00W, 065°/245° from/to Jetée Nord lt, 0·80M. No navigational dangers, but beware fast ferries. ⚓ between Sauzon (see below) and Le Palais is prohib.

LIGHTS AND MARKS
Lts as chartlet. La Citadelle is conspic on N side of hbr.

RADIO TELEPHONE
VHF Ch 09.

TELEPHONE (Prefix ☎ Nos with zone code 02)
Hr Mr 97·31·42·90; Aff Mar 97·31·83·17; SNSM 97·47·48·49; CROSS 97·55·35·35; ⌗ 97·31·85·95; Auto 08.36.68.08.56; Police 97·31·80·22; Dr 97·31·40·90; H 97·31·48·48; Brit Consul 40·63·16·02.

FACILITIES
Marina ☎ 97·52·83·17, P, D, AC, FW, ME, El, Sh, Access HW–1½ to +1, HJ; **Avant Port** M, AB, P, D, Slip, FW, C (10 & 5 ton). **Town** V, Gaz, R, Bar, ⊠, Ⓑ, ⇌ (ferry to Quiberon), ✈. Ferry: Roscoff.

OTHER HARBOUR ON BELLE ILE

SAUZON, Belle Ile, 47°22'·53N 03°12'·93W. AC 2353; SHOM 7142, 7032; ECM 545; HW +0450 on Dover (UT); ML 3·0m; Duration 0615. Small attractive hbr, 4M WNW of Le Palais. Good shelter except in E winds. 12 ⚓s in about 1·5m on W side of Avant Port (FVs moor on E side), or dry out in inner hbr, or ⚓ N of the NW Jetée. Main lt QG 9m 6M. NW Jetée Fl G 4s. SE Jetée Fl R 4s. Facilities: FW on quay; V, R, Bar in village. Hr Mr only operates Jul/Aug.

PORT HALIGUEN   10-17-17

Morbihan 47°29'·40N 03°06'·00W   Rtg 1-2-2

CHARTS
AC 2353; Imray C38, 39; SHOM 7141, 7032, 7033; ECM 545

TIDES
+0500 Dover; ML 3·1; Duration 0615; Zone –0100

Standard Port BREST (←)

Times				Height (metres)			
High Water		Low Water		MHWS	MHWN	MLWN	MLWS
0000	0600	0000	0600	6·9	5·4	2·6	1·0
1200	1800	1200	1800				
Differences PORT HALIGUEN							
+0015	–0020	–0015	–0010	–1·7	–1·3	–0·6	–0·3
LA TRINITÉ							
+0020	–0020	–0015	–0005	–1·5	–1·1	–0·5	–0·2

SHELTER
Good, but uncomfortable in strong NW to NE winds. Access H24 at all tides. Marina boat will meet. Visitors usually berth alongside on pontoon 'V' to stbd of ent.

NAVIGATION
WPT 47°29'·80N 03°05'·00W, 060°/240° from/to bkwtr lt, 0·75M. From W or S, appr via Passage de la Teignouse. Banc de Quiberon, marked by NCM and SCM buoys, is shoal (1·5m) at S end. 500m ENE of bkwtr lt in R sector 240°-299°, beware 1·8m shoal, with unlit SCM buoy.

LIGHTS AND MARKS
W sector 246°-252° of Port-Maria Main lt, Q WRG 28m 14/10M, leads N of Banc de Quiberon; W sector 299°-306° of bkwtr lt, Oc (2) WR 6s 10m 12/9M, leads S of it.

RADIO TELEPHONE
VHF Ch 09.

TELEPHONE (Prefix ☎ Nos with zone code 02)
Hr Mr 97·50·20·56; Aff Mar 97·50·08·71; ⌗ 97·55·73·46; CROSS 97·55·35·35; SNSM 97·50·14·39; Météo 97·64·34·86; Auto 08.36.68.08.56; Police 97·50·07·39; Dr 97·50·13·94.

FACILITIES
Marina (760 + 100 visitors) ☎ 97·50·20·56, Slip, P, D, C (2 ton), BH (13 ton), ME, El, Sh, AC, CH, FW, ▣, SM, Bar, R, V. **Town** (Quiberon) V, Gaz, R, Ice, Bar, ⊠, Ⓑ, ⇌, ✈. Ferry: Roscoff.

PORT MARIA, Morbihan, 47°28'·65N 03°07'·25W. AC 2353; SHOM 5352, 7032. Tides as 10.17.17. Shelter good in all winds, but busy ferry/FV port; only suitable for yachts as a refuge or in emergency. Access dangerous in strong SE–SW winds. N half hbr dries. E mole reserved for ferries. ⚓ in SW of hbr in approx 2m. Hr Mr/Aff Mar ☎ 02·97·50·08·71; Facilities: ⌗, C (6 ton), FW at E quay, El, ME, Sh, SHOM.

LA TRINITÉ-SUR-MER   10-17-18

Morbihan 47°34'·06N 03°00'·60W   Rtg 2-1-2

CHARTS
AC 2358, 2353; Imray C39; SHOM 7141, 7033, 7034; ECM 545, 546

TIDES
+0455 Dover; ML 3·2; Duration 0610; Zone –0100

Standard Port BREST (←). Differences see 10.17.17.

SHELTER
Very good, except in strong SE/S winds near HW when La Vaneresse sandbank is covered. Access H24 at all tides. Marina boat will meet. No ‡/fishing in river. Speed limit 5kn.

NAVIGATION
WPT 47°31'·90N 02°59'·53W, 167°/347° from/to front ldg lt, 2·3M. No navigational dangers; the river is marked by buoys and perches. Best water close to E bank. Beware many oyster beds, marked with perches.

LIGHTS AND MARKS
Conspic daymarks include: Mousker rk, off-white top; caravan site 3ca NNE; and ⚓ spire at La Trinité. Ldg marks (below) are difficult to see by day. Pte de Kernevest ldg lts 347°: Front Q WRG 11m 10/7M (W345°-013°); rear Dir Q 21m 15M, synch, intens 337°-357°. 1M up-river: Dir lt 347°, Oc WRG 4s 9m 13/11M (W346°-348°). S Pier, Oc (2) WR 6s (W293°-300°). ♥ pontoon is first beyond ☆ Iso R 4s.

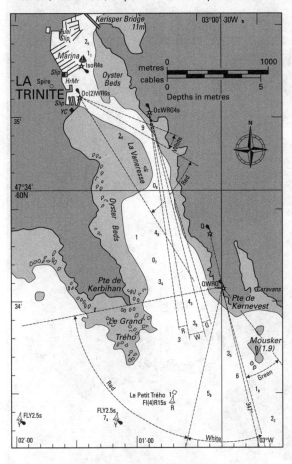

RADIO TELEPHONE
Marina VHF Ch 09.

TELEPHONE (Prefix ☎ Nos with zone code 02)
Hr Mr Port de Plaisance 97·55·71·49; Aff Mar 97·24·01·43 at Auray; CROSS 97·55·35·35; SNSM 97·55·02·30; ∰ 97·55·73·46; Météo 97·64·34·86; Auto 08.36.68.08.56; Police 97·55·71·62; Dr 97·55·74·03; Brit Consul 40·63·16·02.

FACILITIES
Marina (900+100 visitors) ☎ 97·55·71·27, AC, P, D, FW, BH (36 ton), Gridiron, M, ME, El, CH, SHOM, Ⓔ, SM, Sh;
Club Nautique ☎ 97·55·73·48.
Town V, Gaz, R, Bar, Ice, ✉, Ⓑ, ⇌ (Auray), ✈ (Lorient). Ferry: Roscoff or St Malo.

CROUESTY   10-17-19

Morbihan 47°32'·52N 02°54'·03W   Rtg 1-1-2

CHARTS
AC 2358, 2353; Imray C39; SHOM 6992, 7034, 7033; ECM 546

TIDES
+0505 Dover; ML 3·0; Duration 0555; Zone –0100

Standard Port BREST (←)

Times				Height (metres)			
High Water		Low Water		MHWS	MHWN	MLWN	MLWS
0000	0600	0000	0600	6·9	5·4	2·6	1·0
1200	1800	1200	1800				
Differences PORT NAVALO							
+0030	–0005	–0010	–0005	–2·0	–1·5	–0·8	–0·3

SHELTER
Good, protected from W'lies by Quiberon Peninsula; additional shelter in very large marina which contains 5 large separate basins. ♥ pontoons on S side of fairway.

NAVIGATION
WPT 47°32'·04N 02°55'·21W, 238°/058° from/to front ldg lt, 1·1M. There are no navigational dangers, the ent being well marked and dredged 1·8m. See also Morbihan 10.17.20.

LIGHTS AND MARKS
Ldg lts 058°: both Dir Q 10/27m 19M, intens 056·5°-059·5°. By day, front W vert stripe on R panel; rear grey lt ho. Bkwtr hds: N = Oc (2) R 6s, S = Fl G 4s, plus lead-in buoys.

RADIO TELEPHONE
VHF Ch 09.

TELEPHONE (Prefix ☎ Nos with zone code 02)
Hr Mr 97·53·73·33; Aff Mar 97·41·84·10; ∰ 97·63·18·71; CROSS 97·55·35·35; Auto 08.36.65.08.56; SNSM 97·41·35·35; Police 97·53·71·65; Dr 97·53·71·61; Brit Consul 40·63·16·02.

FACILITIES
Marina (1000+120 ♥) ☎ 97·53·73·33, ⌁ 97.53.90.22, P, D, AC, FW, ME, El, Sh, Slip, BH (45 ton), C (10 ton), CH, Bar, M, Ⓔ, SM. **Town** V, Gaz, R, Bar, ✉ & Ⓑ (Arzon), ⇌ (Vannes), ✈ (Vannes, Lorient, St Nazaire). Ferry: St Malo/Roscoff.

ISLAND HARBOUR IN THE BAIE DE QUIBERON

ÎLE HOUAT, 47°23'·60N 02°57'·25W. AC 2353; SHOM 7033. HW +0505 on Dover (UT); ML 3·1m; Duration 0605; See 10·17·16. Good shelter, except from N/NE'lies, at Port St Gildas, near E end of the N coast. Appr from N or NE passing abeam La Vieille rk (conspic 14m). Avoid rks 6m inboard of bkwtr and 15m off lt tr. Moor on double trots; no ‡ in hbr. S part of hbr dries. Keep clear of ferries and FVs on W and N quays. Lts as 10.17.4. Few facilities.

MORBIHAN   10-17-20
Morbihan 47°32'·92N 02°55'·26W   Rtg 3-3-1

CHARTS
AC 2358, 2353; Imray C39; SHOM 6992, 7034, 7033;
ECM 546

TIDES
−0515 Dover; ML 3·0; Zone −0100

Standard Port BREST (←—)

Times				Height (metres)			
High Water		Low Water		MHWS	MHWN	MLWN	MLWS
0000	0600	0000	0600	6·9	5·4	2·6	1·0
1200	1800	1200	1800				
Differences AURAY							
+0055	0000	+0020	+0005	−2·0	−1·4	−0·8	−0·2
VANNES							
+0220	+0200	+0200	+0125	−3·6	−2·7	−1·6	−0·5
ARRADON							
+0155	+0145	+0145	+0130	−3·7	−2·7	−1·6	−0·5
LE LOGEO							
+0155	+0145	+0145	+0125	−3·7	−2·7	−1·6	−0·5

The Golfe du Morbihan is an inland sea of about 50sq miles with deep apprs and ent. It is thick with islands, all but two privately owned. The many ⚓s (see chartlet and below) are increasingly restricted by extensive moorings. It is essential to use chain when ⚓ing, unless well out of the tide. Avoid oyster beds and, especially in SE, bird sanctuaries. Much of E & SE dries. Vannes, see 10.17.21.

NAVIGATION
WPT 47°32'·04N 02°55'·21W, 181°/001° from/to Petit Vezid front ldg mark, 2·2M. Beware very strong tides in the ent and some narrow chans, max 5¾kn sp ebb (8kn reported), but easing in the upper reaches. For a first visit springs should be avoided; it is likely to be impossible for an aux yacht to enter against a sp ebb. Abeam Port Navalo the flood and ebb begin 1¼hrs after LW and HW Port Navalo respectively; slack water lasts about 30mins at sp and 1hr at nps. HW times become later the further one goes into the Morbihan, ie HW Vannes is 2 hrs after HW Pt Navalo. At the ent the flood divides: a weaker flow into the River Auray; but the major stream buckets NE into the main chan, setting strongly toward Petit & Grand Mouton rks. To avoid these, keep up to the ldg line until safely past Grand Mouton, but beware shoals to port off Goëmorent R bn tr. Pilotage is not difficult, but due to higher than usual speeds over the ground, it helps to pre-plot the desired trks/distances within the channels; marks can then be more readily identified and track adjusted with ease, especially if beating.

LIGHTS AND MARKS
At the ent ldg daymarks on 001° are: front Petit Vezid W obelisk (looks like a yacht sail from afar), rear Baden ✠ spire (3·3M); maintain until abeam Port Navalo lt ho. Chans and dangers are well marked; the only lts are: Port Navalo Oc (3) WRG 12s 32m 15/11M at ent, W sector 359°-015°. Inside ent: Grand Mouton SHM bn, QG and Le Grégan SCM bn, Q (6) + L Fl 15s. Roguédas SHM bn, Fl G 2·5s, at W end of Ile de Boëdig marks appr to Vannes.

SHELTER AND FACILITIES (clockwise from ent)
PORT NAVALO: ⚓ in bay, but space limited by moorings, and exposed to W/NW winds. Convenient to await the tide. All facilities. ⌗ ☎ 02·97·41·21·53; Police 02·97·24·17·17.
LOCMARIAQUER: Drying ⚓ off village quay; ferries use the buoyed chan to jetty. V, R, ME.
SEPT ILES: Small, quiet ⚓; chan leads into Anse de Baden.
LE ROCHER: Good shelter, but almost full of moorings. Further N the river almost dries, but can be navigated on the tide.
BONO: Moor or ⚓ (rky bottom) off Banc de la Sarcelle. **Village**, ME, R, V, Gaz.
AURAY: Access at mid-flood via a bridge, 3ca S of town, with 14m clearance MHWS. Note: this clearance, coupled with little depth of water, may need careful calculations for safe passage by high-masted yachts. Moor in a pool S of the bridge; 12 ⚓s or drying AB at St Goustan beyond. Facilities: ME, El, Sh, SHOM, CH. **Town** R, V, Bar, ✉, ⇌.
ILE LONGUE: near SE tip ⚓ out of the stream. No landing.
LARMOR BADEN: good ⚓s to S, but many moorings; Aff Mar ☎ 02·97·57·05·66; V, R.
ILE BERDER: pleasant ⚓ E of the island; causeway to mainland.

PORT BLANC: Hr Mr ☎ 02·97·57·01·00. FW, P & D pontoon, but many moorings.
ILE AUX MOINES: a much-frequented, public island. The narrows between the mainland and Les Réchauds rks can be rough. ⚓ off N end, landing at Pte du Trec'h or pick up ⚓ (see Hr Mr) off Pte des Réchauds where there is a small marina. Water taxi available; call VHF Ch 09 or sound foghorn. Hr Mr ☎ 02·97·26·30·57, D, FW. Other quieter ⚓s off W side and S tip.
ARRADON: limited ⚓, exposed to S'ly. M, Slip, FW, ME. Hr Mr ☎ 02·97·26·01·23.
ILE PIRENN: exposed ⚓ in tidal stream.
ILE D'ARZ: a public island. ⚓ NE of Pte du Béluré; E of Le Bourg (good shelter), or to the W, depending on winds. Rudevent village: ME, El, Sh.
ILE DE BOEDIG: sheltered ⚓ in chan N of the E end of island.
ILE DE CONLEAU: ⚓ or moor in bight just S of village, as space permits. ME, El, Sh, R in village.
SÉNÉ: ME.
VANNES: see 10·17·21.
R NOYALO : ⚓ off Pte du Passage or in Anse de Truscat, 2M to SW of river ent. Depths further up-river are uncertain.
KERNERS: ⚓ off the Anse de Kerners in 3 to 6m.
ILE DE LA JUMENT (also known as Ar Gazek): good shelter to E of island out of the tide; convenient for leaving on the tide.

17

VANNES   10-17-21

Morbihan 47°38'·45N 02°45'·62W   Rtg 3-2-1

CHARTS

AC 2358, 2353; Imray C39; SHOM 7034; ECM 546

TIDES

See under MORBIHAN 10.17.20. ML 2·0m; Zone –0100

SHELTER

Very good, protected from all winds. Access by day only.
Waiting pontoons down/upstream of **swing bridge**,
which only opens whilst lock gate into wet basin is open,
as follows: Bridge opens at H and H+30 in season (15
Jun-15 Sep) and at weekends; but only at H out of
season. Outbound craft have priority over arrivals. Note:
during the first and final ½ hour periods when the lock is
open, the bridge may open at any time.

The narrow **lock gate**, remotely-controlled by the Hr Mr,
opens HW±2½ (0700-2200LT in season; 0900-1800 Mon-
Sat; and 0700-2100LT Sun out of season). Note: HW
Vannes –2½ just happens to be HW Port Tudy (10.17.13)
which is used by the Hr Mr to determine when the lock
opens. Or get the free annual schedule of lock hrs from:
Bureau du Port de Plaisance, La Rabine, 56000 Vannes.
Lock sill, 1·3m above CD, retains 2·4m inside wet basin.

Berthing: Marina boat may indicate a vacant finger
pontoon, but visitors usually berth N/S on pontoons D
and G just before movable inner foot-bridge (*passerelle*).

NAVIGATION

WPT: see 10·17·20. Beware very strong streams between
Pte de Toulindag and the mainland and in the Conleau
chan; also Les Réchauds rks marked by 2 SHM bns. Due
to an eddy around Ile d'Irus the stream runs mainly SW
between Les Réchauds and Pte d'Arradon. Thereafter
passage to Conleau is simple and well marked. Beacon'd
appr chan to Vannes is narrow, with min depth 0·7m;
only advised near HW.

LIGHTS AND MARKS

Bridge sigs (vert) on bridge's central pier are:
2 Ⓡ = no passage; 2 Oc Ⓡ = standby; 2 Ⓖ = proceed;
2 Oc Ⓖ = only transit if committed;
Ⓨ = unmasted boats may transit.
Lock sigs: Ⓖ and Ⓡ = Lock closed; No lts = Lock open.

RADIO TELEPHONE

VHF Ch 09. (Summer 0830-2100; winter HW±2½ and
0900-1200 and 1330-1800).

TELEPHONE (Prefix ☎ Nos with zone code 02)

Hr Mr 97·54·16·08; Aff Mar 97·63·40·95; ⌗ 97·63·18·71;
CROSS 97·55·35·35; SNSM 97·26·00·56; Météo 97·64·34·86;
Auto 08.36.68.08.56; Police 97·54·22·56; Dr 97·47·47·25;
Ⓗ 97·42·66·42; Brit Consul 40·63·16·02.

FACILITIES

Marina (240+60 visitors), ☎ 97·54·16·08, 📠 97.42.48.80,
FF99, Slip, 🅿, FW, AC, ME, C (12 ton); P & D @ HW±2½
from pontoon on E side of canal, just S of lock.
Town V, R, Sh, CH, El, Ⓔ, CH, SM, SHOM, ✉, Ⓑ, ⇌, ✈
(Vannes, Lorient or St Nazaire).

VILAINE RIVER   10-17-22
Morbihan 47°30'·40N02°28'·60W   Rtg 3-1-2

CHARTS
AC 2353; SHOM 2381, 5418, 7033; ECM 546; Imray C39
TIDES
+0500 Dover; ML (Penerf) 3·3; Duration 0610; Zone –0100

Standard Port BREST (←—)

Times				Height (metres)			
High Water		Low Water		MHWS	MHWN	MLWN	MLWS
0000	0600	0000	0600	6·9	5·4	2·6	1·0
1200	1800	1200	1800				
Differences PENERF							
+0020	–0025	–0015	–0015	–1·5	–1·1	–0·6	–0·3
TRÉHIGUIER							
+0035	–0020	–0005	–0010	–1·4	–1·0	–0·5	–0·3

SHELTER
Good shelter up-river: buoys at Tréhiguier; above Arzal dam in non-tidal waters, marinas at Arzal (N bank) and Camoël (S bank); and 5M upstream at La Roche Bernard on Ⓥ pontoon between old and new ports; also at Foleux marina, 4½M further up-river. Masted yachts can transit a swing bridge at Cran to reach Redon where there is a marina, crane and access to Brittany canals (10.15.18).
NAVIGATION
WPT Passe de la Grande Accroche 47°29'·00N 02°33'·90W, 232°/052° from/to Penlan lt, 3·3M. La Vilaine has a bar (min 0·5m), on which seas break in strong onshore winds esp at sp ebb. Best to enter/leave on last of the flood. River is well buoyed up to Tréhiguier and adequately so beyond; keep strictly to buoyed chan as silting occurs. Arzal dam lock opens at H, up to 9 times per day, 0700–2200 (LT) in Jul/ Aug; in other months 0800, 0900, 1200, 1400, 1600, 1700, 1900, 2000LT. But times vary daily; call Hr Mr VHF Ch 09 or recorded ☎ 97·45·01·15. Keep strictly to the buoyed chan to avoid the prohib area (Y buoys) below/above the dam. There is Ⓐ or room to ⚓ below the dam to await lock opening.
LIGHTS AND MARKS
There are three apprs and ldg lines to river ent:
(1) Passe de la Grande Accroche: Penlan lt ho on with Abbey de Prières at 052°. Marks are reportedly conspic by day.
(2) Penlan lt on with Billiers ch tr 023°, leaving Varlingue Rk (dries 0·3m) close to stbd.
(3) Passe de la Varlingue: W wall (not conspic) ≠ Abbey Tr 023°, keeping close to WCM bn and oyster poles off Le Logui.

Two principal lights are visible in the approaches:
(1) Basse Bertrand G tr, Iso WG 4s 6m 9/6M, W040°-054°, G054°-227°, W227°-234°, G234°-040°.
(2) Penlan, W tr, R bands Oc (2) WRG 6s 26m 15/11M, R292°-025°, G025°-052°, W052°-060°, R060°-138°, G138°-180°.
At the river mouth Petit Sécé W bn tr is easier to see than Nos 1 and 2 chan buoys.
RADIO TELEPHONE
Lock VHF Ch 18 (HX); Arzal-Camoël marina Ch 09 (French); no VHF at La Roche Bernard.
TELEPHONE (Prefix ☎ Nos with zone code 02)
Aff Mar 99·90·32·62; CROSS 97·55·35·35; ⌗ 97·63·18·71 at Vannes; Auto 08·36·68·08·56; Brit Consul 40·63·16·02. ARZAL/CAMOËL: Hr Mr 99·90·05·86; Dr 97.45.01.21; LA ROCHE BERNARD: Hr Mr 99·90·62·17; Ⓗ 99.90.61.20.
FACILITIES
ARZAL/CAMOËL: **Marina** (630 total, inc 25 visitors on each bank) ☎ 99·90·05·86, FF90, FW, AC, Ⓞ, C (15 ton), P, D, Gaz, SM, ME, EI, Sh, CH, Ⓔ, R, Bar. Note: these facilities are all at Arzal. Camoël has Hr Mr and showers.
Towns (both 3km) V, R, Bar, Ⓑ, ⊠.
LA ROCHE BERNARD: **Marina (New Port)** (110) ☎ 99·90·62·17, FF70, FW, AC, M, ME, EI, Ⓔ, Sh, CH; **Marina (Old Port)** (200), P, D, Ⓞ, C, AC, CH, FW, Slip. **Town** V, Gaz, R, Bar, Ice, ⊠, Ⓑ, ⇌ (Pontchateau), ✈ (Nantes or Rennes).
Foleux: ☎ 99.91.80.87. Marina on N bank; buoys off both banks. FW, AC, R.

ADJACENT HARBOUR

PENERF, Morbihan, 47°30'·10N 02°38'·80W, AC 2353; SHOM 5418, 7033. HW +0515 on Dover (UT); Duration 0610; ML 3·3m. See 10.17.22. Shelter good, except in fresh W'lies. SDs and SHOM 5418 are advised. Appr between Penvins PHM buoy and Borenis SHM buoy. Ldg marks: Le Pignon PHM lt bn on 359° with Le Tour du Parc spire. The 3 ents are not easy: **Passe de l'Ouest** is shoal and ill marked. **Passe du Centre** is the widest and easiest, ldg 150m W of a drying reef, marked by La Traverse SHM bn, N of which depth is 0·5m; thence 40m E of Le Pignon. **Passe de l'Est** has 4m, but is narrower and rks are close to stbd. It leads E of La Traverse and Le Pignon bns to join Passe du Centre. In the river, head ENE for 1M to Ⓐ off Penerf quay. Beware oyster beds. Le Pignon lt, Fl (3) WR 12s 6m 9/6M, W sector 349°-028° covers the appr, but night entry not advised. Facilities: P & D (on quay), Slip, CH, EI, ME, Sh. **Village** Bar, Dr, R, V.

17

PIRIAC   10-17-23

Loire Atlantique 47°23´·00N 02°32´·63W   Rtg 3-3-2

CHARTS
AC 2353; Imray C39, 40; SHOM 7033; ECM 546

TIDES
As for Le Croisic 10.17.25. Zone −0100. HW +0505 on Dover (UT); ML 3·1m; Duration 0605.

SHELTER
Good in new marina on the E side of the drying FV hbr in this small resort village. Access HW±3 over sill 2·4m above CD.

NAVIGATION
WPT 47°24´·30N 02°32´·10W, 017°/197° from/to hbr ent, 1·25M. From S and SW keep clear of Plateau de Piriac extending about 1M W and N from the hbr; to the W it is marked by a WCM buoy, Q (9) 15s, and to the NNW by 2 unlit NCM bns. Ile Dumet lies 3.5M WNW with lt, Fl (2+1) WRG 15s 14m 7/4M; at night its W sector (272° -285°) used in conjunction with the W sector (067°-072°) of Pte de Mesquer lt, Oc (3+1) WRG 12s 7m 10/7M, helps to position within the W sector of Piriac lt, see below; but night appr is not advised except in emergency.

LIGHTS AND MARKS
To the SE a 40m high metal pylon (rear ldg mark for Castelli oil pipeline) is a conspic daymark for Piriac. Inner mole head lt, Dir Oc (2) WRG 6s 8m 10/6M, R066°-148°, G148°-194°, W194°-201°, G201°-066°; W sector leads 197° through hbr ent. Bkwtr lts are Fl G 4s 5m 5M and Fl R 4s 4m 5M.

RADIO TELEPHONE
VHF Ch 09.

TELEPHONE
Hr Mr ☎ 02·40·23·52·32 (Jul-Aug only), ☎ 02·40·15·51·78. Aff Mar 02·40·23·33·35; ⌗ 02·40·23·32·51; CROSS 02·97·55·35·35; Auto 08·36·68·08·44; SNSM 02·40·23·55·74.

FACILITIES
Marina (480+20 visitors), FW, AC, D, P (cans) on quay, Slip, C (9 tons), CH, Ⓔ, El, ME, Sh; drying M, in FV hbr.

Ile Dumet, 3·5M WNW of Piriac, has pleasant ⚓ on NE side in 2m, clear of mussel beds. Appr with lt ho brg 215°.

PIRIAC-SUR-MER

LA TURBALLE   10-17-24

Loire Atlantique 47°20´·78N 02°30´·80W   Rtg 3-2-2

CHARTS
AC 2353; Imray C39, 40; SHOM 6826, 7033; ECM 546

TIDES
As for Le Croisic 10.17.25.

SHELTER
Good in all winds, but in strong SSW'lies heavy swell can enter. Access H24. Inside ent, turn smartly stbd into marina (1·5-2m) in SE corner.

NAVIGATION
WPT 47°20´·25N 02°32´·35W, 245°/065° from/to W bkwtr lt, 1·15M. Appr from S or W avoiding Plateau du Four, which is well marked/lit.

LIGHTS AND MARKS
Plateau du Four, Fl 5s 23m 19M, is 5M SW. Hbr is in G sector (136°-345°) of Le Croisic, Iso WG 4s, 2M to S. (Note: WPT is also on Le Croisic ldg line 156°). Appr in W sector (315°-060°) of W bkwtr lt, Fl (4) WR 12s, to pick up ldg lts 065°, both Dir F Vi 11/19m 3M, intens 004°-009°. By day Trescalan ✠ and water tr (conspic), 1M ENE of hbr, lead 070° to just S of ent. R bn tr is 80m off W bkwtr.

LA TURBALLE

RADIO TELEPHONE
VHF Ch 09.

TELEPHONE (Prefix ☎ Nos with zone code 02)
Hr Mr 40·62·80·40; Aff Mar 40·23·33·35; ⌗ 40·23·32·51; Auto 08·36·68·08·44; SNSM 40·23·42·67.

FACILITIES
Marina (290+20 visitors, pontoon B), ☎ 40·62·80·40, FF93, FW, AC, Slip, M, C (16 tons), BH (140 tons), D (H24), P at garage 500m, ME, El, Ⓔ, Sh, CH.

LE CROISIC   10-17-25

Loire Atlantique 47°18'·56N 02°31'·27W   Rtg 3-2-1

CHARTS
AC 2353, 2986, 2646; Imray C39; SHOM 6826, 7033, 7395; ECM 546, 547

TIDES
+0450 Dover; ML 3·3; Duration 0605; Zone –0100

Standard Port BREST (←—)

Times				Height (metres)			
High Water		Low Water		MHWS	MHWN	MLWN	MLWS
0000	0600	0000	0600	6·9	5·4	2·6	1·0
1200	1800	1200	1800				
Differences LE CROISIC							
+0015	–0040	–0020	–0015	–1·5	–1·1	–0·6	–0·3

SHELTER
Five drying (1·7m) basins, called *Chambres* are formed by islands *(Jonchères)*. Berth in the last *Chambre*, bows to pontoon or against the wall, access HW±1. See Hr Mr for mooring or ⚓ in Le Poul which is crowded; tripping line is advised. Safest ⚓ in Pen Bron Creek; streams run hard.

NAVIGATION
WPT 47°19'·00N 02°31'·80W, 336°/156° from/to front ldg lt, 1·2M. Sp tides reach 4kn. Safest ent is HW±1 sp, HW±2 np. Beware the rks at Hergo Tr, SHM, Fl G 2·5s. Note: the W sector (093°-137°) of Tréhic lt, Iso WG 4s, which leads clear of distant dangers, will lead onto close-in dangers. Keep to the ldg lines as appr and hbr dry extensively to the E.

LIGHTS AND MARKS
The sanatorium, hospital and ch belfry are conspic.
Outer ldg lts 156°: both Dir Oc (2+1) 12s 10/14m 18M; intens 154°-158°, synch; Y □s on W pylons, rear has G top.

Middle ldg lts 174°: both QG 5/8m 11M; vis 170°-177°; Y □s with G stripe on G & W pylons. Inner ldg lts 134°: both QR; R/W chequered □s on Fish market.

RADIO TELEPHONE
VHF Ch 09 (0800-1200; 1330-2000 in season).

TELEPHONE (Prefix ☎ Nos with zone code 02)
Hr Mr 40·23·10·95; Aff Mar 40·23·06·56; CROSS 97·55·35·35; SNSM 40·23·01·17; ⌘ 40·23·05·38; Météo 40·90·08·80; Auto 08.36.68.08.44; Police 40·23·00·19; Dr 40·23·01·70; Ⓗ 40·23·01·12; Brit Consul 40·63·16·02.

FACILITIES
Marina (5th Chambre; 220+15 Ⓥ), FF59, FW, ME, El, Sh; **Quai** Slip, C (10 & 180 ton), CH, Ⓔ, Divers. **Town** P & D (cans), V, Gaz, R, Bar, ✉, Ⓑ, ⇌, ✈ (St Nazaire).

LE POULIGUEN   10-17-26

Loire Atlantique 47°16'·40N 02°25'·40W   Rtg 3-2-2

CHARTS
AC 2989, 2986, 2353; Imray C39; SHOM 6797, 7395; ECM 547

TIDES
Sp +0435 Dover, Nps +0530 Dover; ML 3·3; Duration Sp 0530, Nps 0645; Zone –0100

Standard Port BREST (←—)

Times				Height (metres)			
High Water		Low Water		MHWS	MHWN	MLWN	MLWS
0000	0600	0000	0600	6·9	5·4	2·6	1·0
1200	1800	1200	1800				
Differences LE POULIGUEN							
+0020	–0025	–0020	–0025	–1·5	–1·1	–0·6	–0·3

SHELTER
Very good, except in SE winds. 30 Ⓥ berths to stbd at ent. Yachts up to 2m draft can stay afloat. Beware strong ebb tide. Fixed bridge up-river has 1m clearance MHWS. Le Pornichet, 3M to the E, is an easier approach and ent.

NAVIGATION
WPT 47°15'·20N 02°25'·00W, 250°/070° from/to Penchâteau PHM buoy, Fl R 2·5s, 0·58M. Best appr at HW –1 from W/SW between Pte de Penchateau and Les Evens (drying reef). The chan shifts, dries approx 1·5m and is marked by PHM and SHM poles. Beware swell and breakers in shallow water when wind in S. Reefs running 4M SE to Grand Charpentier lt ho, Q WRG, form a barrier across the Baie du Pouliguen which may be entered through any of 4 passes.

LIGHTS AND MARKS
From Penchâteau and Basse Martineau, leave La Vieille and Les Impairs to stbd, and three chan bns to port. S jetty QR 13m 9M, vis 171°-081°. Navigational lts are very hard to see against shore lts of La Baule and night appr is not advised.

RADIO TELEPHONE
Pouliguen VHF Ch 09, 0900-1230 & 1400-1900LT.

TELEPHONE (Prefix ☎ Nos with zone code 02)
Hr Mr 40·60·37·40, ⚓ 40.42.70.56; Aff Mar 40·42·32·55; SNSM 40·61·03·20; CROSS 97·55·35·35; Météo 40·90·00·80; Auto 08.36.68.08.44; ⌘ 40·61·32·04; Police 40·24·48·17; Dr 40·60·51·73.

FACILITIES (Le Pouliguen)
Quai (Pontoons 850+30 visitors) ☎ 40·60·03·50, Slip, P, D, AC, L, FW, C (18 ton), M, ME, Sh, CH, Ⓔ, El, Divers, SM; **La Baule YC** ☎ 40·60·20·90 (allocates berths for visitors). **Town** V, Gaz, R, Bar, ✉, Ⓑ, ⇌, ✈ (St Nazaire).

AGENTS WANTED
If you are interested in becoming our agent for any of the following ports, please write to: The Editor, Edington House, Trent, Sherborne, Dorset DT9 4SR, England – and get your free copy of the Almanac annually. You do not have to live in a port to be the agent, but at least a fairly regular visitor.

Great Yarmouth
Port Ellen (Islay)
Maryport
Workington
Holyhead
Lough Swilly
St Peter Port, Guernsey
Diélette
Portbail
Iles Chausey
St Malo/Dinard
Le Legue/St Brieuc
Tréguier
Lampaul
L'Aberildut
Le Palais (Belle Ile)
Morbihan/Vannes

St Gilles-Croix-de-Vie
Les Sables d'Olonne
Ile d'Oléron
River Seudre
Anglet/Bayonne
St Jean-de-Luz
Hendaye
Grandcamp-Maisy
Port-en-Bessin
Courseulles
Ouistreham/Caen
Emden
Dornumer-Accumersiel
Langeoog
Bremerhaven
Büsum

17

PORNICHET   10-17-27

Loire Atlantique 47°15'·55N 02°21'·05W   Rtg 1-1-2

CHARTS
AC 2989, 2986, 2353; Imray C39; SHOM 6797, 7395; ECM 547

TIDES
Sp +0435 Dover, Nps +0530 Dover; ML 3·3; Duration Sp 0530, Nps 0645; Zone –0100

Standard Port BREST (←—)

Times				Height (metres)			
High Water		Low Water		MHWS	MHWN	MLWN	MLWS
0000	0600	0000	0600	6·9	5·4	2·6	1·0
1200	1800	1200	1800				
Differences PORNICHET							
+0020	–0045	–0022	–0022	–1·4	–1·0	–0·5	–0·2

FACILITIES
Marina (1000+150 visitors) ☎ 40·61·03·20, FF115, AC, Slip, FW, P, D, BH (24 ton), V, R, Bar, ⊚, ME, EI, Ⓔ, Sh, CH, SHOM.
Town Bar, Dr, R, V, Ⓑ, ⊠, ⇌, ✈ (St Nazaire).

SHELTER
A very large artificial marina at the E end of the B de la Baule, with excellent shelter and facilities. Access at all tides for up to 2·5m draft, but engine required in narrow ent in W'ly >Force 8. Drying ⚓ as shown on chartlet inset.

NAVIGATION
Appr from the W, as for Le Pouliguen (3M), then direct via W sector (082°) of Iso WG 4s bkwtr lt; also from SW, track 035° between Les Evens PHM and Les Troves SHM unlit bns; or from SSE track 335° from Grand Charpentier lt.

LIGHTS AND MARKS
Navigational lts are very hard to see against shore lts of La Baule. S bkwtr Iso WG 4s 11m 10/7M, W081°-084° (3°), G084°-081° (357°). Inside ent, QR 4m 1M and QG 3m 1M on perches define the channel.

RADIO TELEPHONE
VHF Ch 09.

TELEPHONE (Prefix ☎ Nos with zone code 02)
Marina 40·61·03·20; ⌗ 40·61·32·04; Météo 40·90·08·80; Auto 08·36·68·08·44; Aff Mar 40·60·56·13; CROSS 97·55·35·35; Ⓗ (St Nazaire) 40·90·60·60; SNSM via CROSS; Dr La Baule 40·60·17·20; Brit Consul 40·63·16·02.

RIVER LOIRE/ST NAZAIRE

Loire Atlantique   Rtg (St Nazaire) 3-3-2   **10-17-28**

CHARTS
AC 2985, 2989, 2986; Imray C40; SHOM 6797, 7396, 7395;
ECM 248, 547

TIDES
St Nazaire: Sp +0445 Dover, Nps –0540 Dover; ML 3·6;
Duration Sp 0640, Nps 0445; Zone –0100

Standard Port BREST (←)

Times				Height (metres)			
High Water		Low Water		MHWS	MHWN	MLWN	MLWS
0000	0600	0000	0600	6·9	5·4	2·6	1·0
1200	1800	1200	1800				
Differences ST NAZAIRE							
+0030	–0040	–0010	–0010	–1·1	–0·8	–0·4	–0·2
LE GRAND CHARPENTIER							
+0015	–0045	–0025	–0020	–1·5	–1·1	–0·6	–0·3
DONGES							
+0040	–0030	0000	0000	–0·9	–0·7	–0·5	–0·4
CORDEMAIS							
+0055	–0005	+0105	+0030	–0·7	–0·5	–0·7	–0·4
LE PELLERIN							
+0110	+0010	+0145	+0100	–0·7	–0·5	–0·9	–0·4
NANTES (Chantenay)							
+0133	+0055	+0215	+0125	–0·6	–0·3	–0·8	–0·1

SHELTER
Hbr is mainly naval and commercial, but yachts can berth
at S end of Bassin Penhoet; ent via E lock and Bassin de St
Nazaire. ⚓ in Bonne Anse.

NAVIGATION
WPT 47°07'·95N 02°20'·00W, 205°/025° from/to front ldg lt,
7·3M, via S chan. Or appr from W, via N chan, to join dredged
chan (13·2m) SE of Grand Charpentier lt Q WRG. In strong W
winds the bar (outside chan) is only safe HW –3 to HW.
R Loire navigable 28M to Nantes and ent to canals (10.15.18).
Tolls may be due above Nantes; see 10.15.8.

LIGHTS AND MARKS
Appr ldg lts 025½°: both Q 6/36m 22/27M, intens 024°-027°.

RADIO TELEPHONE
St Nazaire Port VHF Ch 12 16 06 14 67 69 (H24). Other stns:
Donges Ch 12 16 (occas); Nantes Ch 12 16 06 67 69 (0700-
1100, 1300-1700, except Sun); water level reports (St Nazaire
to Nantes) broadcast on Ch 73 every 15min from H+00.

TELEPHONE (Prefix ☎ Nos with zone code 02)
ST NAZAIRE Hr Mr 40·00·45·20; Aff Mar 40·22·46·32;
CROSS 97·55·35·35; SNSM 40·61·03·20; ⌗ 40·66·82·65;
Météo 40·90·00·80; Auto 08.36.68.08.44; Police 40·70·55·00;
Dr 40·22·15·32; Ⓗ 40·90·60·60.
NANTES Hr Mr 40·44·20·54; Aff Mar 40·73·18·70;
⌗ 40·73·39·55; Météo 40·84·80·19; Auto 08.36.68.08.44;
Dr 40·47·03·19; Ⓗ 40·48·33·33; Brit Consul 40·63·16·02.

FACILITIES
ST NAZAIRE **Quai** P, D, L, FW, C, M, ME, El, Sh, CH, Ⓔ,
SHOM. **Town** V, Gaz, R, Bar, ✉, Ⓑ, ⇌, ✈.
NANTES **Quai** FW, C, CH, SHOM, ME, El, Ⓔ; **Trentemoult**
AB. **City** all facilities: ✉, Ⓑ, ⇌, ✈. Ferry: St Malo/Roscoff.

MINOR HARBOURS BETWEEN SAINT-NAZAIRE AND POINTE DE SAINT-GILDAS

The following three small hbrs lie NE of Pte de St-Gildas,
on the E side of the R Loire estuary; see chartlet above.
They are flanked by shellfish beds on rky ledges drying
to about 4ca offshore; they are sheltered from W'lies but
open to N'lies. Charts are AC 3216; SHOM 7395, 6797;
ECM 547. Tidal data may be interpolated from Le Grand
Charpentier, St-Nazaire (10.17.26) and Pornic (10.18.9).
The bay is shallow. Note: 4M N of Pte de St-Gildas is La
Truie rk, drying 2·6m and marked by unlit IDM bn; 1·3M
SSW of it is a shoal patch 0·7m.

PORT DE COMBERGE, Loire Atlantique, 47°10'·60N
02°09'·50W; this is position of S bkwtr lt, Oc WG 4s 7m 9/5M,
W tr with G top, W123°-140°, G elsewhere. Appr in the W
sector or by day on 136° with the bkwtr lt in transit with the
disused lt ho beyond. Beware Les Moutons, rk drying 0·4m,
7½ca NW of the bkwtr lt, close to the approach track. The ent
is narrow; tiny hbr dries about 2m, access from half-flood.
Hr Mr ☎ 02.40.27.82.85; Facilities: M, FW, YC, Slip, C (6 ton),
L. Other facilities at nearby town of St Michel-Chef-Chef.

PORT DE LA GRAVETTE, Loire Atlantique, 47°09'·71N
02°12'·60W; this is position of the lt on end of the bkwtr, Fl
(3) WG 12s 7m 8/5M, W sector 124°-224°, G elsewhere. The
hbr is 2·2M NE of Pte de St-Gildas. Daymarks are bkwtr lt
in transit 130° with La Treille water tr, 2M inland. Shellfish
beds to the W and E are marked by unlit NCM bns. On
rounding the 600m long bkwtr, turn stbd between lateral
buoys; there is about 1·2m water in the N part of the hbr
which dries closer in. Many local moorings, few facilities.

SAINT-GILDAS (Anse du Boucau), Loire Atlantique, 47°08'·45N
02°14'·65W. Make good L'Apcheu, SHM bn, 5ca N of Pte
de St Gildas lt ho, Q WRG 23m 11/6M (see 10.17.4). Two
SHM buoys, Fl G 2s, are laid May-Oct NW and N of the hbr
bkwtr which extends 3ca N and has a large automatic tide
gauge at its seaward end. Appr from about 1M N of Pte de
St-Gildas on a brg of 177° or at night in its W sector 174°-
180°. L'Ilot rky ledge is marked by a PHM bn. Pick up a
mooring in 1·5m in the N part of the hbr or dry out further
S. Hr Mr ☎ 02.40.21.60.07. VHF Ch 09. Facilities: Slips, YC,
FW, C (5 ton), V at Préfailles 1M to the E.

17

VOLVO PENTA SERVICE

**Sales and service centres in area 18
Names and addresses of Volvo Penta dealers in
this area are available from:**

France *Volvo Penta France* , 55 Avenue des Champs Pierreux, 92757 Cedex
Tel +33 1 55175457, Fax +33 1 55175261. **Spain** *Volvo Penta Espana SA*, Paeso
De La Castellana 130, 28046 Madrid Tel +34 1 5666100 Fax +34 1 5666200

Area 18

South Biscay
River Loire to Spanish Border

18

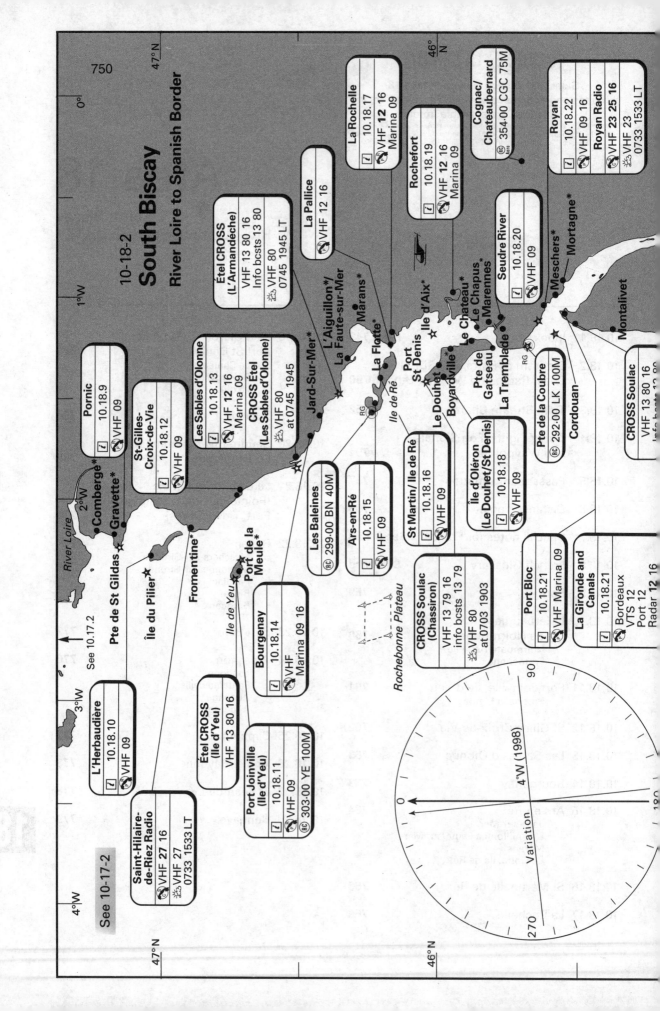

10-18-2
South Biscay
River Loire to Spanish Border

750

L'Herbaudière
☑ 10.18.10
⚓ VHF 09

Saint-Hilaire-de-Riez Radio
⚓ VHF 27 16
📻 VHF 27
0733 1533 LT

Étel CROSS (Ile d'Yeu)
VHF 13 80 16

Port Joinville (Ile d'Yeu)
☑ 10.18.11
⚓ VHF 09
Ⓡ 303·00 YE 100M

Bourgenay
☑ 10.18.14
⚓ VHF Marina 09 16

Pornic
☑ 10.18.9
⚓ VHF 09

St-Gilles-Croix-de-Vie
☑ 10.18.12
⚓ VHF 09

Les Sables d'Olonne
☑ 10.18.13
⚓ VHF 12 16 Marina 09

CROSS Étel (Les Sables d'Olonne)
📻 VHF 80 at 0745 1945

Étel CROSS (L'Armandèche)
VHF 13 80 16 Info bcsts 13 80
📻 VHF 80 0745 1945 LT

Les Baleines
Ⓡ 299·00 BN 40M

Ars-en-Ré
☑ 10.18.15
⚓ VHF 09

St Martin/ Ile de Ré
☑ 10.18.16
⚓ VHF 09

Île d'Oléron (Le Douhet/St Denis)
☑ 10.18.18
⚓ VHF 09

CROSS Soulac (Chassiron)
VHF 13 79 16 info bcsts 13 79
📻 VHF 80 at 0703 1903

Port Bloc
☑ 10.18.21
⚓ VHF Marina 09

La Gironde and Canals
☑ 10.18.21
⚓ Bordeaux VTS 12 Port 12 Radar **12** 16

La Pallice
⚓ VHF 12 16

La Rochelle
☑ 10.18.17
⚓ VHF **12** 16 Marina 09

Rochefort
☑ 10.18.19
⚓ VHF **12** 16 Marina 09

Cognac/ Chateaubernard
Ⓡ 354·00 CGC 75M

Royan
☑ 10.18.22
⚓ VHF 09 16

Royan Radio
⚓ VHF 23 25 16
📻 VHF 23 0733 1533 LT

Seudre River
☑ 10.18.20
⚓ VHF 09

Pte de la Coubre
Ⓡ 292·00 LK 100M

CROSS Soulac
VHF 13 80 16
info bcsts 13 80

River Loire

Pte de St Gildas ☆
Île du Pilier ☆
Comberge*
Gravette*

See 10.17.2

Fromentine*

Ile de Yeu
Port de la Meule*

See 10-17-2

Jard-Sur-Mer*
L'Aiguillon*/ La Faute-sur-Mer
Marans*
La Flotte*
Ile de Ré
RG
Le Douhet*
Port St Denis
Boyardville*
Ile d'Aix*
Le Chateau*
Le Chapus*
Pte de Gatseau*
Marennes*
La Tremblade*
Meschers*
Mortagne*
RG
Cordouan
Montalivet

Rochebonne Plateau

Variation 4°W (1998)
0
90
180
270

10.18.3 AREA 18 TIDAL STREAMS

5 Hours before HW Brest
(0010 after HW Dover)

4 Hours before HW Brest
(0110 after HW Dover)

3 Hours before HW Brest
(0210 after HW Dover)

2 Hours before HW Brest
(0310 after HW Dover)

1 Hour before HW Brest
(0410 after HW Dover)

HW Brest
(0510 after HW Dover)

CAUTION: Due to the very strong rates of the tidal streams in
some of the areas, many eddies may occur. Where possible
some indication of these eddies has been included. In many
areas there is either insufficient information or the eddies are
unstable. Generally tidal streams are weak offshore and
strong winds have a very great effect on the rate and direction
of the tidal streams.

1 Hour after HW Brest
(0610 after HW Dover)

2 Hours after HW Brest
(0515 before HW Dover)

3 Hours after HW Brest
(0415 before HW Dover)

4 Hours after HW Brest
(0315 before HW Dover)

5 Hours after HW Brest
(0215 before HW Dover)

6 Hours after HW Brest
(0115 before HW Dover)

CAUTION: Due to the very strong rates of the tidal streams in some of the areas, many eddies may occur. Where possible some indication of these eddies has been included. In many areas there is either insufficient information or the eddies are unstable. Generally tidal streams are weak offshore and strong winds have a very great effect on the rate and direction of the tidal streams.

18

10.18.4 COASTAL LIGHTS, FOG SIGNALS AND WAYPOINTS

Abbreviations used below are given in 1.4.1. Principal lights are in **bold** print, places in CAPITALS, and light-vessels, light floats and Lanbys in *CAPITAL ITALICS*. Unless otherwise stated lights are white. m – elevation in metres; M – nominal range in miles. Fog signals are in *italics*. Useful waypoints are underlined – use those on land with care. All geographical positions should be assumed to be approximate. See 4.4.1. All positions are referenced to the ED 50 datum.

Pte de Saint-Gildas 47°08'·10N 02°14'·67W Q WRG 23m W11M, R6M, G6M; framework Tr on W house; vis R264°-308°, G308°-078°, W078°-088°, R088°-174°, W174°-180°, G180°-264°; RC.

BAIE DE BOURGNEUF

PORNIC

Noëveillard Yacht Hbr Digue Ouest Hd 47°06'·53N 02°06'·61W Fl (2) R 6s 4m 3M; B col, T top.
Pte de Noëveillard 47°06'·68N 02°06'·84W Oc (3+1) WRG 12s 22m W13M, R9M, G9M; W ■ Tr, G top, W dwelling; vis G shore-051°, W051°-079°, R079°-shore.
Pte de Gourmalon Bkwtr Hd 47°06'·70N 02°06'·40W Fl (2) G 6s 4m 8M; W mast, G top.
La Bernerie-en-Retz Jetty Hd 47°04'·6N 02°02'·4W Fl R 2s 4m 5M; W structure, R top.
Le Collet 47°01'·80N 01°59'·00W Oc (2) WR 6s 7m W9M, R6M; vis Wshore-093°, R093°-shore.
Ldg Lts 118° both QG 4/12m 6M; W ■ G stripe, on W pylon.
Étier des Brochets 46°59'·90N 02°01'·90W Oc (2+1) WRG 12s 8m W10M, R7M, G7M; G Tr, W band; vis G071°-091°, W091°-102·5°, R102·5°-116·5°, W116·5°-119·5°, R119·5°-164·5°.
Bec de l'Époids 46°56'·40N 02°04'·50W Dir Iso WRG 4s 6m W12M, R9M, G9M; W n Tr, R top; vis G106°-113·5°, R113·5°-122°, G122°-157·5°, W157·5°-158·5°, R158·5°-171·5°, W171·5°-176°.

ÎLE DE NOIRMOUTIER
Île du Pilier 47°02'·62N 02°21'·53W Fl (3) 20s 33m **29M**; Gy ▲ Tr. Auxiliary Lt QR 10m 11M, same Tr; vis 321°-034°.
Passe de la Grise Lt By 47°01'·73N 02°19'·90W Q (6) + L Fl 15s; SCM.
P de l'Herbaudière Jetée Ouest Hd 47°01'·69N 02°17'·79W Oc (2+1) WG 12s 9m W10M, G7M; W col and hut, G top; vis W187·5°-190°, G190°-187·5°.
Ldg Lts 187·5°. Front, 47°01'·65N 02°17'·76W Q 10m 7M; Gy mast. Rear, 310m from front, Q 26m 7M; Gy mast.
Basse du Martroger 47°02'·65N 02°17'·05W Q WRG 11m W9M, R6M, G6M; NCM; vis G033°-055°, W055°-060°, R060°-095°, G095°-124°, W124°-153°, R153°-201°, W201°-240°, R240°-033°.
Pierre Moine 47°03'·43N 02°12'·30W Fl (2) 6s 14m 9M; IDM.
Pte des Dames 47°00'·73N 02°13'·18W Oc (3) WRG 12s 34m **W19M, R15M, G15M**; W ■ Tr; vis G016·5°-057°, R057°-124°, G124°-165°, W165°-191°, R191°-267°, W267°-357°, R357°-016·5°.
Noirmoutier Jetty Hd 46°59'·30N 02°12'·95W Oc (2) R 6s 6m 6M; W col, R top.
Pte de Devin 46°59'·20N 02°17'·40W Oc (4) WRG 12s 10m W11M, R8M, G8M; W col and hut, G top; vis G314°-028°, W028°-035°, R035°-134°.

FROMENTINE
Pte de Notre Dame-de-Monts 46°53'·30N 02°08'·50W Dir Oc (2) WRG 6s 21m W13M, R10M, G10M; W Tr, B top; vis G000°-043°, W043°-063°, R063°-073°, W073°-094°, G094°-113°, W113°-116°, R116°-175°, G175°-196°, R196°-230°.
Bridge, each side on centre span Iso 4s 32m **18M**; H24.
Tourelle Milieu 46°53'·60N 02°09'·00W Fl (4) R 12s 6m 5M; R ■ on Tr.

ROUTE DU GOIS CAUSEWAY
E shore Fl R 4s 6m 6M; R hut; vis 038°-218°.
E turning Pt Fl 2s 5m 5M; Gy pyramid structure.
W turning Pt Fl 2s 5m 3M; Gy pyramid structure.
Bassotière 46°56'·10N 02°08'·90W Fl G 2s 7m 2M; W tripod, G lantern; vis 180°-000°.
Les Boeufs Lt By 46°55'·10N 02°28'·00W VQ (9) 10s; WCM; *Bell.*

BAIE DE BOURGNEUF TO PERTUIS BRETON

ÎLE D'YEU/PORT JOINVILLE
Port Joinville Ldg Lts 219°. Front, Quai du Canada 46°43'·67N 02°20'·87W QR 11m 5M. Rear, Quai Georgette QR 16m 5M.
Jetty NW Hd 46°43'·83N 02°20'·73W Oc (3) WG 12s 9m W11M, G8M; W 8-sided Tr, G top; vis G shore-150°, W150°-232°, G232°-279°, W279°-285°, G285°-shore; *Horn (3) 30s.*
Les Chiens Perrins 46°43'·65N 02°24'·55W Q (9) WG 15s 16m W8M, G5M; WCM; vis G330°-350°, W350°-200°.
Petite Foule 46°43'·20N 02°22'·85W Fl 5s 56m **24M**; W ■ Tr, G lantern; RC.
P de la Meule 46°41'·75N 02°20'·60W Oc WRG 4s 9m W9M, R6M, G5M; Gy ■ Tr, R top; vis G007·5°-018°, W018°-027·5°, R027·5°-041·5°.
Pte des Corbeaux 46°41'·45N 02°17'·00W Fl (2+1) R 15s 25m **20M**; W ■ Tr, R top; obsc by Île de Yeu 083°-143°.

ST JEAN DE MONTS/ST GILLES-CROIX-DE-VIE
Pte de Grosse Terre 46°41'·60N 01°57'·84W Fl (4) WR 12s 25m **W17M**, R13M; W truncated conical Tr; vis W290°-125°, R125°-145°.
St Jean de Monts Jetty Hd 46°47'·15N 02°05'·05W Q (2) R 5s 10m 2M; W mast, R top.
Pilours Lt By 46°41'·04N 01°58'·01W VQ (6) + L Fl 15s; SCM; *Bell.*
Ldg Lts 043·5°. Front, 46°41'·92N 01°56'·67W Dir Oc (3+1) R 12s 7m 13M; W ■ Tr, R top; intens 033·5°-053·5°. Rear, 260m from front, Dir Oc (3+1) R 12s 28m 13M; W ■ Tr, R top; synch with front; intens 033·5°-053·5°.
Jetée de la Garenne Hd 46°41'·51N 01°57'·18W Q WG 8m, W8M, G6M; *Reed 20s.*

LES SABLES D'OLONNE
Les Barges 46°29'·76N 01°50'·42W Fl (2) R 10s 25m 13M; Gy Tr, helicopter platform; vis 265°-205°.
La Petite Barge Lt By 46°28'·96N 01°50'·53W Q (6) + L Fl 15s 8m 7M; SCM; *Whis.*
L'Armandèche 46°29'·47N 01°48'·21W Fl (2+1) 15s 42m **24M**; W 6-sided Tr, R top; vis 295°-130°.
Nouch Sud Lt By 46°28'·63N 01°47'·33W Q (6) + L Fl 15s; SCM.
Ldg Lts 033°. **Front**, 46°29'·48N 01°46'·28W Iso R 4s 14m **16M**; mast; H24. **Rear, La Potence,** 330m from front, Iso R 4s 33m **16M**; W ■ Tr; H24.
Ldg Lts 320°, Jetée des Sables Hd Front, 46°29'·49N 01°47'·43W QG 11m 8M; W Tr, G top. Rear, Tour de la Chaume, 465m from front, Oc (2+1) 12s 33m 13M; large Gy ■ Tr, W turret.
Ldg Lts 327°, Front, FR 6m 11M; R line on W hut. Rear, 65m from front, FR 9m 11M; R line on W Tr; intens 324°-330°.
Jetée St Nicolas Hd 46°29'·29N 01°47'·44W UQ (2) R 1s 16m 10M; W Tr, R top; vis 143°-094°.

BOURGENAY
Ldg Lts 040°. Front, 46°26'·40N 01°40'·50W QG 8M. Rear, QG 8M.
Roches du Joanne Lt By 46°25'·35N 01°41'·90W L Fl 10s; SWM.
Digue W Hd 46°26'·37N 01°40'·59W Fl R 4s 9M.

PLATEAU DE ROCHEBONNE (Offshore shoal)
NW Lt By 46°12'·90N 02°31'·60W Q (9) 15s; WCM; *Whis.*
NE Lt By 46°12'·80N 02°24'·80W Iso G 4s; SHM.

SW Lt By 46°10'·15N 02°26'·90W Fl (2) R 6s; PHM.
SE Lt By 46°09'·30N 02°21'·00W Q (3) 10s; ECM; *Bell*.

Les Baleines 46°14'·70N 01°33'·60W Fl (4) 15s 53m **27M**;
Gy 8-sided Tr, R lantern; RC.
Les Baleineaux 46°15'·87N 01°35'·12W Oc (2) 6s 23m 11M;
pink Tr, R top.

PERTUIS BRETON/ÎLE DE RÉ

JARD-SUR-MER/LA TRANCHE-SUR-MER
Jard-sur-Mer S Bkwtr Hd 46°24'·44N 01°34'·77W; PHM.
La Tranche Pier Hd 46°20'·62N 01°25'·50W Fl (2) R 6s 6m
6M; R col.
Pte du Grouin-du-Cou 46°20'·73N 01°27'·75W Fl WRG 5s
29m **W20M**, **R16M**, **G16M**; W 8-sided Tr, B top; vis R034°-
061°, W061°-117°, G117°-138°, W138°-034°.

L'AIGUILLON/LA FAUTE-SUR-MER
Le Lay Lt By 46°16'·17N 01°16'·41W Q (6) + L Fl 15s; SCM.
No. 1 By 46°16'·65N 01°16'·20W; SHM.

ANSE DE L'AIGUILLON/MARANS
Pte de L'Aiguillon Lt By 46°15'·40N 01°11'·42W L Fl 10s;
SWM.
Port du Pavé ent 46°18'·21N 01°07'·91W Fl G 4s 9m 7M; W
col, G top.

PORT DU PLOMB
W Môle 46°12'·18N 01°12'·13W Fl R 4s 9m 7M; W col, R top.

LA FLOTTE
La Flotte N Bkwtr Hd 46°11'·38N 01°19'·23W Fl WG 4s 10m
W12M, G9M; W ● Tr, G top; vis G130°-205°, W205°-220°,
G220°-257°; *Horn (3) 30s* (by day HW-2 to HW+2). Moiré
effect Dir Lt 212·5°.
Rivedoux-Plage Ldg Lts 200°. Front, N Pier Hd 46°09'·83N
01°16'·56W QG 6m 6M; W Tr, G top. Rear, 100m from front,
QG 9m 6M; W and G chequered col; synch with front.

St MARTIN DE RÉ
Bkwtr West Hd 46°12'·57N 01°21'·82W Fl R 2·5s 7m 4M;
W post, R top.
On ramparts, E of ent 46°12'·50N 01°21'·80W Oc (2) WR 6s
18m W10M, R7M; W Tr, R top; vis Wshore-245°, R245°-
281°, W281°-shore.
Mole Hd Iso G 4s 10m 6M; W tripod, G top; obsc by Pte de
Loix when brg less than 124°.

PORT D'ARS-EN-RÉ
Le Fier d'Ars Ldg Lts 265°. Front, 46°14'·12N 01°28'·65W Iso
4s 5m 11M; ■ on W hut; vis 141°-025°. **Rear**, 370m from
front, Dir Iso G 4s 13m **15M**; G ■ on dwelling; synch with
front, intens 263°-267°.
Ldg Lts 232°. Front, 46°12'·81N 01°30'·50W Q 5m 9M; W
hut, R lantern. Rear, 370m from front, Q 13m 11M; B stripe
on W framework Tr, G top; vis 142°-322°.

ÎLE DE RÉ SOUTH/PERTUIS D'ANTIOCHE/ÎLE D'OLÉRON

ÎLE DE RÉ (SOUTH)
Chanchardon 46°09'·78N 01°28'·33W Fl WR 4s 15m W11M,
R9M; B 8-sided Tr, W base; vis R118°-290°, W290°-118°.
Chauveau 46°08'·09N 01°16'·33W Oc (2+1) WR 12s 27m
W15M, R11M; W ● Tr, R top; vis W057°-094°, R094°-104°,
W104°-342°, R342°-057°.
Pte de Sablanceaux 46°09'·82N 01°15'·08W Q Vi 7m 1M; W
mast and hut, G top.

PERTUIS D'ANTIOCHE/LA ROCHELLE
Chauveau Lt By 46°06'·62N 01°15'·98W VQ (6) + L Fl 10s;
SCM; *Whis*.

Roche du Sud Lt By 46°06'·43N 01°15'·15W Q (9) 15s; WCM.
Le Lavardin 46°08'·15N 01°14'·45W Fl (2) WG 6s 14m
W11M, G8M; vis G160°-169°, W169°-160°; IDM.
La Pallice, Môle d'Escale 46°09'·42N 01°14'·43W Dir Lt 016°.
Dir Q WRG 33m W14M, R13M, G13M; Gy Tr; vis G009°-
014·7°, W014·7°-017·3°, R017·3°-031°. Sig Stn.
Tour Richelieu 46°08'·95N 01°10'·27W Fl (4) R 12s 10m 9M;
R Tr; RC; *Siren (4) 60s* (HW–1 to HW+1).
Les Minimes Lt By 46°08'·07N 01°11'·45W Q(9) 15s; WCM.
La Rochelle Ldg Lts 059°. Front, 46°09'·42N 01°09'·06W Dir Q
15m 13M; R ●Tr, W bands; intens 056°-062°; by day Fl 4s.
Rear, 235m from front, Q 25m 14M; W 8-sided Tr, G top; synch
with front, vis 044°-074°, obsc 061°-065° by St Nicolas Tr; by
day Fl 4s.
Lt By PA 46°05'·69N 01°42'·37W Iso 4s 8m 7M; SWM;
Whis; Ra refl.

ÎLE D'AIX/PASSAGE DE L'EST
Île d'Aix 46°00'·67N 01°10'·60W Fl WR 5s 24m **W24M**,
R20M; two W ● Trs, one for Lt, one to screen R sector;
vis R103°-118°, W118°-103°.
Fort Boyard Lt Tr 46°00'·03N 01°12'·78W Q (9) 15s.

FOURAS
Port Sud Bkwtr Hd 45°59'·03N 01°05'·63W Fl WR 4s 6m 9/6M.
Port Nord Pier Hd 45°59'·88N 01°05'·75W Oc (3+1) WG 12s
9m W11M, G8M; W&G Tr; vis G084°-127°, W127°-084°.

LA CHARENTE/ROCHEFORT
Ldg Lts 115°. Front, **Fort de la Pointe** 45°58'·02N 01°04'·29W
Dir QR 8m **19M**; W■Tr, R top. **Rear**, 600m from front, Dir QR
21m **20M**; W■Tr, R top; both intens 113°-117°. QR 21m 8M;
same Tr; vis 322°-067° over Port-des-Barques anchorage.
Port-des-Barques Ldg Lts 134·3°. Front, 45°57'·01N
01°04'·09W Iso G 4s 5m 9M. Rear, 490m from front, Iso G 4s
13m 11M; synch with front; intens 125°-145°.
Rochefort No. 1 Basin ent 45°56'·61N 00°57'·21W (unmarked).

ÎLE D'OLÉRON
Pte de Chassiron 46°02'·80N 01°24'·60W Fl 10s 50m, **28M**;
W ● Tr, B bands; part obsc 297°-351°; Sig Stn.
Rocher d'Antioche 46°04'·00N 01°23'·70W Q 20m 11M; NCM.

ST DENIS
E Jetty Hd 46°02'·16N 01°21'·97W Fl (2) WG 6s 6m W9M
G6M; □ hut; vis G205°-277°, W277°-292°, G292°-165°.
Dir Lt 205° 46°01'·67N 01°21'·84W Dir Iso WRG 4s 14m W11M,
R8M, G8M; vis G190°-204°, W204°-206°, R206°-220°.

PORT DU DOUHET/PASSAGE DE L'OUEST
N ent Bn 46°00'·18N 01°19'·10W; SHM.
Chan Lt By 46°00'·45N 01°17'·61W Q; NCM.
Chan Lt By 46°00'·29N 01°15'·26W Q; NCM.
Chan Lt By 45°59'·91N 01°14'·71W Q (3) 10s; ECM.

LE CHÂTEAU D'OLÉRON
Ldg Lts 319°. Front, 45°53'·05N 01°11'·45W QR 11m 7M; R
line on W Tr; vis 191°-087°. Rear, 240m from front, QR 24m
7M; W Tr, R top; synch with front.
Tourelle Juliar 45°54'·10N 01°09'·45W Q (3) WG 10s 12m
W11M; G8M; ECM; vis W147°-336°, G336°-147°.

BOYARDVILLE (LA PÉRROTINE)
La Pérrotine By 45°58'·37N 01°13'·20W; SHM.
Mole Hd 45°58'·30N 01°13'·76W Fl (2) R 6s 8m 5M; W Tr,
R top; obsc by Pte des Saumonards when brg less than 150°.

LA SEUDRE
Pont de la Seudre 45°48'·00N 01°08'·25W Q 20m 9M each
side, vis 054°-234° and 234°-054°.
Pte de Mus de Loup 45°47'·90N 01°08'·50W Oc G 4s 8m 6M;
vis 118° 147°.

18

LA COTINIÈRE
Dir Lt 048° 45°54'·45N 01°18'·50W Dir Oc WRG 4s 13m
W11M, R9M, G9M; W stripe with B border on W col; vis
G033°-046°, W046°-050°, R050°-063°.
Ent Ldg Lts 339°. 45°54'·80N 01°19'·70W Front, Dir Oc (2) 6s
6m 13M; W Tr, R top; vis 329°-349°. Rear, 425m from front,
Dir Oc (2) 6s 14m 12M; W Tr, R bands; synch with front;
intens 329°-349°.

ATT Maumusson Lt By 45°47'·00N 01°17'·80W; L Fl 10s;
SWM.

LA GIRONDE AND APPROACHES

LA GIRONDE, GRANDE PASSE DE L'OUEST
BXA Lt By 45°37'·60N 01°28'·60W Iso 4s 8m 7M; SWM;
Ra refl; Whis.
Pte de la Coubre 45°41'·87N 01°13'·93W Fl (2) 10s 64m
28M; W ● Tr, R top; RC; Sig Stn. F RG 42m R12M, G10M;
same Tr; vis R030°-043°, G043°-060°, R060°-110°.
Ldg Lts 081·5°. **Front**, 1·1M from rear, Dir Iso 4s 21m **20M**;
W mast on dolphin; intens 080·5°-082·5°; Q (2) 5s 10m 3M;
same structure. **La Palmyre, common rear**, 45°39'·77N
01°07'·15W Dir Q 57m **27M**; W radar Tr; intens 080·5°-
082·5°. Dir FR 57m **17M**; same Tr; intens 325·5°-328·5°.
Ldg Lts 327°. **Terre-Nègre**, Front, 1·1M from rear, Oc (3)
WRG 12s 39m **W18M**, R14M, G14M; W Tr, R top on W side;
vis R304°-319°, W319°-327°, G327°-000°, W000°-004°,
G004°-097°, W097°-104°, R104°-116°.
Pointe de Grave Jetée Nord Hd 45°34'·47N 01°03'·58W,
Q 6m 2M; NCM.
Spur 45°34'·38N 01°03'·57W Iso G 4s 5m 2M; vis 173°-020°.

LA GIRONDE, PASSE SUD
Cordouan 45°35'·25N 01°10'·34W Oc (2+1) WRG 12s 60m
22/18M; W ▲ Tr, dark Gy band and top; vis W014°-126°,
G126°-178·5°, W178·5°-250°, W(unintens)250°-267°,
R(unintens)267°-294·5°, R294·5°-014°; obsc in estuary when
brg more than 285°.
Ldg Lts 063°. **St Nicolas Front**, 45°33'·80N 01°04'·93W
Dir QG 22m **16M**; W ■ Tr; intens 061·5°-064·5°. **Rear, Pte de
Grave**, 0·84M from front, Oc WRG 4s 26m **W19M, R15M,
G15M**; W ■ Tr, B corners and top; vis W(unintens) 033°-054°,
W054°-233·5°, R233·5°-303°, W303°-312°, G312°-330°,
W330°- 341°, W(unintens) 341°-025°.
Ldg Lts 041°, **Le Chay Front**, 45°37'·35N 01°02'·30W Dir QR
33m **18M**; W Tr, R top; intens 039·5°-042·5°. **Rear, St Pierre**,
0·97M from front, Dir QR 61m **18M**; R water Tr; intens
039°-043°.

PORT BLOC/ROYAN/PAUILLAC/BLAYE
Port Bloc Ent N side 45°34'·20N 01°03'·66W Fl G 4s 9m 3M.
S Pier Hd Iso R 4s 8m 4M.
Royan Jetée Sud 45°37'·08N 01°01'·72W UQ (2) R 1s 11m
12M; Horn (2) 20s.
Royan Hbr Nouvelle Jetée Hd ent Oc (2) R 6s 8m 6M.
Pauillac NE Bkwtr 45°12'·02N 00°44'·50W Fl G 4s 7m 5M.
Ent E side 45°11'·89N 00°44'·52W QG 7m 4M.
Blaye Ent N side 45°07'·55N 00°39'·91W Q (3) R 5s 6m 3M.

LA GARONNE/BORDEAUX
Pont d'Aquitaine 44°52'·87N 00°32'·23W 4 F Vi.

LA GIRONDE TO L'ADOUR

Hourtin 45°08'·55N 01°09'·65W Fl 5s 55m **23M**; R ■ Tr.

BASSIN D'ARCACHON
Cap Ferret 44°38'·83N 01°14'·90W Fl R 5s 53m **27M**; W ●
Tr, R top; RC. Oc (3) 12s 46m 14M; same Tr; vis 045°-135°.
ATT-ARC Lt By 44°34'·89N 01°18'·61W L Fl 10s 8m 5M;
SWM; (frequently shifted); Whis.
Émissaire Lt By 44°30'·55N 01°17'·55W Fl (2) 6s 8m 5M;
IDM. Ra refl.
La Salie Wharf Hd 44°30'·90N 01°15'·60W Q (9) 15s 19m 10M; WCM.
Arcachon W Bkwtr Hd 44°39'·80N 01°09'·10W QG 6M.
La Vigne 44°40'·50N 01°14'·20W Iso R 4s 7m 5M; (occas.)
ZDS Lt By 44°28'·00N 01°19'·30W Fl (3) Y 12s 8m 4M; SPM.

ZDL Lt By 44°12'·90N 01°22'·00W Fl Y 4s; SPM.
Contis 44°05'·70N 01°18'·90W Fl (4) 25s 50m **23M**; W ● Tr,
B diagonal stripes.

CAPBRETON
Digue Nord Hd 43°39'·45N 01°26'·80W Fl (2) R 6s 13m 12M;
W ● Tr, R top; Horn 30s.

L'ADOUR TO BAIE DE FONTARABIE

ANGLET/BAYONNE
BA Lt By 43°32'·66N 01°32'·68W L Fl 10s 8m 8M; SWM.
Digue du large Hd 43°31'·96N 01°31'·92W QR 11m 8M;
W Tr, R top.
Digue extérieure Sud 43°31'·60N 01°31'·68W, Q (9) 15s 6M; WCM.
Jetée Sud Hd Iso G 4s 9m 10M; W ■ Tr, G top.
Jetée Nord Hd Oc (2) R 6s 12m 8M; W pylon, R top.
Boucau Ldg Lts 090°. Front, 43°31'·88N 01°31'·15W Dir
Q 9m **19M**. **Rear**, 250m from front, Dir Q 15m 19M; both
W Trs, R tops, both intens 086·5°-093·5°.
Ent Ldg Lts 111·5° (moved as necessary and lit when chan
practicable). Front, Dir FG 6m 14M. Rear, 149m from front,
Dir FG 10m 14M; W Tr, G bands; both intens 109°-114°.
Marina ent W side 43°31'·64N 01°30'·44W Fl G 2s 5m 2M;
W Tr, G top.

BIARRITZ
Pte Saint-Martin 43°29'·69N 01°33'·17W Fl (2) 10s 73m
29M; W Tr, B top.
Biarritz Ldg Lts 174° 43°29'·15N 01°33'·88W both Fl R 2s
7/19m 3M.
Guethary Ldg Lts 133°. Front, 43°25'·65N 01°36'·45W QR
11m 6M; W mast, R top. Rear, 66m from front, QR 33m 6M;
W Tr.
Aero Mo (L) 43°28'·45N 01°31'·90W 7·5s 80m.

ST JEAN DE LUZ
Socoa Ldg Lts 138·5°. Front, 43°23'·77N 01°41'·12W Q WR
36m W12M, R8M; W ■ Tr, B stripe; vis W shore-264°, R264°-
282°, W282°-shore. Rear, Bordagain, 115m from front, Oc 4s
43m 4M; W ○ Tr.
Ste Barbe Ldg Lts 101°. **Front**, 43°24'·03N 01°39'·79W
Dir Oc (3+1) R 12s 30m **18M**; W▲; intens 095°-107°. **Rear**,
340m from front, Dir Oc (3+1) R 12s 47m **18M**; B ▲ on W Tr;
synch with front; intens 095°-107°.
Digue des Criquas Hd 43°23'·92N 01°40'·59W Iso G 4s 11m
7M; G ■ Tr; Horn 15s.
Ldg Lts 150·7°, **Front**, 43°23'·32N 01°40'·07W Dir QG 18m
16M; W ■ Tr, R stripe. **Rear**, 410m from front, Dir QG 27m
16M; W ■ Tr, G stripe. Both intens 149·5°-152°.

HENDAYE
Cap Higuer 43°23'·59N 01°47'·44W Fl (2) 10s 63m **23M**.
Hendaye Epi Socoburu Hd 43°22'·90N 01°47'·28W L Fl R 10s
7m 5M.
Marina Digue Coude Fl (2) R 6s 6m 2M; vis 294°-114°.

10.18.5 PASSAGE INFORMATION

BAY OF BISCAY (charts 1104, 20, 2664, 1102)

The *North Biscay Pilot* (Imray/ICC), South to the Gironde, and *South Biscay Pilot* (Adlard Coles), Gironde to La Coruna, are recommended; as is the Admiralty *Bay of Biscay Pilot*. Larger scale French charts are more suitable for inshore waters. For French Glossary see 1.4.2. Some Breton words are in 10.17.5.

Despite its reputation, weather in the B of Biscay is better than in the English Chan, and the S part generally enjoys a warm and settled climate. The Atlantic swells are higher and longer. Although W winds mostly prevail, NE winds are often experienced with anticyclones over the continent. In summer the wind is seldom from SE or S. Often the wind varies in speed and direction from day to day. Sea and land breezes are well developed in summer months (see 10.17.5). Gales may be expected once a month in summer. Coastal rainfall is moderate, increasing in the SE corner, where thunder is more frequent. Sea fog may be met from May to October, but is less common in winter.

Tidal streams are weak offshore, but can be strong in estuaries and channels, and around headlands. The tidal stream chartlets at 10.18.4 are based on NP 265 (Admiralty Tidal Stream Atlas for France, W Coast) which uses data from actual observations out to 15-25M offshore. The equivalent French Atlas gives more data, but based on computer predictions.

The general direction and rate of the surface current much depends on wind: in summer it is SE, towards the SE corner of B of Biscay, where it swings W along N coast of Spain. In winter with W gales, the current runs E along N coast of Spain, sometimes at 3kn or more. When crossing B of Biscay, allow for a likely set to the E, particularly after strong W winds.

BAIE DE BOURGNEUF (charts 3216, 2646)

B de Bourgneuf is entered between Pte de St Gildas and Pte de l'Herbaudière, the NW tip of Île de Noirmoutier. Within the B the only yacht hbrs are Pornic (10.18.9) and L'Herbaudière (10.18.10). There are minor drying hbrs at La Bernerie-en-Retz, Le Collet, Port des Brochets and Bec de l'Epoids; with a good anch 5ca NE of Pte des Dames. The E and S sides of the B are encumbered with shoals, rks and oyster or mussel fisheries. The Bay is sheltered except in W winds, which can raise a heavy sea on the ebb stream.

From the NW (chart 3216) the approach is simple, but beware La Couronnée (dries 1·8m; buoyed) a rky bank about 2M WSW of Pte de St Gildas. Adjacent to it, Banc de Kerouars (least depth 1m; breaks) extends 3M further E. Approach Pornic in the W sector of Pte de Noveillard lt, ie S of Banc de Kerouars and NW of Notre Dame IDM bn tr, which lies 2M SW of Pornic and marks end of a line of rks extending ESE to La Bernerie. Pierre du Chenal is an isolated rk about 1M SSE of Notre Dame.

At the N end of Île de Noirmoutier, Chenal de la Grise, between Île du Pilier and Pte de l'Herbaudière and in the W sector of Martroger NCM bn lt, carries 3m, and gives access to L'Herbaudière marina. If heading E to Pornic, pass N of Martroger, and clear of Roches des Pères about 1M ENE. Extending 6M to seaward off the NW end of the island, beware Chaussée des Boeufs, buoyed rks, some drying on to which the tide sets. The S ent via Goulet de Fromentine (SHOM 5039; ECM 549) is difficult due to a shifting bar and 8 hrs of W-going stream; the conspic bridge has 24m clearance. Once inside, further progress to NNE is restricted to shoal draft at sp HW±1 by Route du Gois, causeway drying 3m.

ILE D'YEU TO PERTUIS BRETON (AC 2663)

Les Marguerites, rky shoals, lie SSW of Goulet de Fromentine, with the part-drying reef, Pont d'Yeu (SCM buoy), extending midway between the mainland and the Île d'Yeu; here anch is prohib due to underwater cables. The passage along the NE of the island carries 6-7m nearer to the island. The low-lying, wooded Côte de la Vendée continues 40M SE to Pte du Grouin Cou with few dangers more than 1·5M offshore, except near Les Sables-d'Olonne.

Île d'Yeu, 30m high, has the main lt ho near the NW end and on the NE coast a very conspic water tr close to Port Joinville (10.18.11), crowded in season . Pte des Courbeaux lt ho is at the low SE end of the island and a lesser lt is at the NW end. The SW coast is steep-to and rky, with a tiny drying hbr at Port de la Meule (best to anch outside) and, further E, anch at Anse des Vieilles, both only tenable in settled conditions.

14M to the E of Île d'Yeu lies St Gilles-Croix-de-Vie (10.18.12). Thence 14M further SE is Les Sables-d'Olonne (10.18.13), with Les Barges drying reef (lt) 2·5M W of the ent. Bourgenay (10.18.14) is 6M further SE. The approaches to these secure hbrs are exposed to onshore winds from SE to NW, and susceptible to swell. Jard-sur-Mer is a small drying hbr midway between Bourgenay and Pte du Grouin Cou.

PERTUIS BRETON (chart 2641)

Pertuis Breton is entered between Pte du Grouin du Cou and Pte des Baleines on Île de Ré, (both lit). Beware rky ledges (dry) extending 2·5M NW from Les Baleines. It gives access to the hbrs of Ars-en-Ré (10.18.15), St Martin (10.18.16) and La Flotte on the N shore of Île de Ré which is surrounded by shallows and drying areas. From St Martin to Pte de Sablanceaux there are extensive oyster beds.

On the mainland side, in fresh NW winds against tide a bad sea builds on the bank which extends 8M W of Pte du Grouin du Cou. 1M S of the Pte is Roche de l'Aunis (depth 0·8m). From the Pte sand dunes and mussel beds, with seaward limits marked by SPM buoys, run 8M ESE to the drying ent to Rivière Le Lay, which is fronted by a bar (dries 1m), dangerous in bad weather. The chan to L'Aiguillon/La Faute-sur-Mer (10.18.15) is marked by bns and buoys. 4M further E is entrance to Anse de l'Aiguillon, in which are extensive mussel beds. In NE corner is entrance to Sèvre Niortaise which, after 3·5M, gives access to the canal leading to the port of Marans. Further S is a sheltered route to La Rochelle and Pertuis d'Antioche via Coureau de la Pallice and the road bridge (30m clearance) from the mainland to Île de Ré.

PERTUIS D'ANTIOCHE (chart 2746)

A SWM buoy marks the W approach to Pertuis d'Antioche which runs between Île de Ré and Île d'Oléron, giving access to La Rochelle (10.18.17), Ile d'Aix, La Charente and Rochefort (10.18.19). Its shores are low-lying. Île de Ré forms the N side, fringed by rky ledges extending 2·5M SE from Pte de Chanchardon (lt) and nearly 1M from Pte de Chauveau (marked by lt tr and two bns). Off Pte de Chassiron (lt ho, Sig Stn), at the N tip of Île d'Oléron, reefs extend 5ca W, 1·5M N to Rocher d'Antioche (lit), and 1·5M E, and there is often a nasty sea.

Well offshore, 34-40M W of Île de Ré, Plateau de Rochebonne is a large rky plateau on which the sea breaks dangerously. It is steep-to on all sides, has least depth 3·3m and is buoyed.

18

ÎLE D'OLERON (charts 2746, 2663)

On the NE coast of Ile d'Oléron (10.18.18) there are marinas at Port St Denis and Le Douhet at the N end; further S are yacht and fishing hbrs at Boyardville and Le Château. All are sheltered from the prevailing W'lies.

From Pertuis d'Antioche, Grande Rade des Trousses is entered via either Passage de l'Est close to Île d'Aix (10.18.18) or Passage de l'Ouest, which run each side of La Longe le Boyard, an extensive sandbank on which stands Ft Boyard tr. From Grande Rade, where good anch is found except in fresh NW winds, the narrow and shallow Coureau d'Oléron winds between ledges, oyster beds and constantly changing shoals, with buoys moved to conform. About 2M SE of Le Chateau it is crossed by a bridge, clearance 15m; the bridge arch for the navigable chan is marked at road level by W □ boards, with G ▲ or R ■ superimposed, illuminated at night. Just N of bridge is Fort du Chapus, connected to mainland by causeway. SHOM 6335 is needed. S-going stream starts at HW Pte de Grave – 0230, N-going at HW Pte de Grave + 0500, sp rates 2kn. Up the Seudre River (10.18.20) there are anchs and yacht facilities at Marennes.

The W coast, from Pte de Chassiron 15M SSE to Pte de Gatseau, is bounded by drying rks and shoals. In bad weather the sea breaks 4 or 5M offshore. La Cotinière, the only hbr, is much used by fishing boats and is exposed to the Atlantic. Tidal streams are weak, sp rate 1kn, starting NW at HW Pte de Grave + 0300 and SE at HW Pte de Grave – 0505, but often overcome by current due to prevailing wind. The rate however increases towards Pte de Gatseau.

Here Pertuis de Maumusson separates the island from the mainland. Its ent is marked by a SWM buoy about 3M WSW of Pte de Gatseau. Banc de Gatseau and Banc des Mattes, both of which dry in places, lie N and S of the chan, and are joined by a sand bar which usually has a depth of about 1·5m. Depth and position vary, and buoys may not mark the best water. Any swell speedily forms breakers, and the chan is very dangerous then or in any onshore winds, especially on the ebb (sp rate 4kn). In calm weather with no swell, a stout craft and reliable engine, and having gained local advice, enter about HW – 1; ideally follow a local FV with deeper draught.

APPROACHES TO LA GIRONDE (chart 2910)

The Gironde (10.18.21) is formed from the Garonne and Dordogne, which join at Bec d'Ambès, 38M above Pte de Grave. BXA It buoy is moored off the mouth of the estuary, about 11M WSW of Pte de la Coubre. Banc de la Mauvaise, the S end of which dries extends 5M seaward. Cordouan lt ho is on a large sand spit in the middle of the estuary. Grande Passe de l'Ouest starts about 4M E of BXA buoy and is dredged through Grand Banc, the outer bar of La Gironde. Enter to seaward of buoys Nos. 1 and 2, and keep in buoyed chan with ldg lts. Off Terre-Nègre lt the SE-going stream begins at HW – 0500 (sp 1·5kn), and the NW-going at HW+0130 (sp 2·5kn).

Passe Sud, a lesser chan, is entered at the SWM lt buoy, 9M SW of Pte de Grave, and runs NE past Pte de Grave. There are two sets of ldg lts; the second lead over Platin de Grave, but it is better to pass NW of this shoal. Both entrance chans are dangerous in strong onshore winds, due to breakers and also the mascaret (bore) on the outgoing stream. Westerly swell breaks on La Mauvaise and around Cordouan, and sandbanks shift constantly. In places tidal streams run 4kn or more, and with wind against tide a dangerous sea can build.

LA GIRONDE TO CAPBRETON (charts 1102, 2664)

From Pte de la Négade to Capbreton, the coast is a featureless stretch of 107M broken only by the entrance to Arcachon (10.18.24). It is bordered by sand dunes and pine trees, and is often a lee shore with no shelter from W winds. 5M offshore a current usually sets N at about 0·5kn, particularly with a S wind; in winter this may be stronger after W winds. Within 1M of the coast there may be a S'ly counter-current.

A missile range lies offshore: its N boundary is from 45°27'·4N 01°13'·2W to 45°12'N 02°00'W, (245°/40M from Pte de la Négade); the S boundary is from 43°41'·5N 01°30'·2W to 44°N 02°25'W (295°/47M from Capbreton). The inshore limit is 3M off, but it joins the shore at Hourtin (45°08'·5N); S of Arcachon to ZDS SPM buoy (44°28'N); and in 2 small sectors off Biscarosse (44°20'N) and Lamanchs (44°15'N). The range is divided into blocks 31N and 31S, which are N and S of a clear chan (31B) 8M wide running 270° from Arcachon. 31N and 31S are sub-divided into N/S sectors delineated by distance off the coast. Thus, 31S 2745 means the S block, in a sector 27-45M offshore. Various sectors are activated from 0830LT Mon-Fri; never Sat/Sun. Navigation through active sectors is prohib from the coast to 12M offshore; beyond 12M it is strongly discouraged. *Centre d'Essais des Landes* broadcasts range activity on VHF Ch 06, after warning on Ch 06 and 16, at 0815 and 1615LT Mon-Thurs, and at 0815 and 1030LT Fri. For more info on request (Mon-Thurs 0800-1700LT; Fri 0800-1100) call *Landes* VHF Ch 06 or ☎ 05.58.78.18.00 (same hrs); also recorded data H24 on ☎ 05.58.82.22.42/43. Other sources of info include: Hr Mr, Aff Maritimes, CROSS Soulac and Sémaphores at La Coubre, Cap Ferret and Socoa; all on request Ch 16, which should be monitored on passage.

The Fosse (or Gouf) de Capbreton, a submarine canyon, runs at right angles to the coast. The 50m depth contour is 3ca W of Capbreton hbr bkwtr and the 100m line is 4ca further W. In strong W winds a dangerous sea breaks along the N and S edges of it. Strong N or W winds and swell make the ent to the large marina at Capbreton (10.18.25) impassable.

CAPBRETON TO SPANISH BORDER (charts 1343, 1102)

There is a marina at Anglet (10.18.26), but few facilities for yachts further up the R. Adour at Bayonne. At L'Adour ent the flood runs E and SE, sp rate 2-4kn; the ebb runs W, sp rate 3-5kn. S of Pte St Martin the coast has mostly sandy beaches and rky cliffs, with offlying rky shoals and Pyrenees mountains inland. In strong W winds the sea breaks over Loutrou shoal; and on Plateau de St Jean-de-Luz, a chain of rky shoals lying 1-4M offshore.

St Jean-de-Luz (chart 1343 and 10.18.27) is best approached first time or in bad weather through Passe d'Illarguita (between Illarguita and Belhara Perdun shoals): follow the 138° transit (Le Socoa lt on with Bordagain lt) until the Ste Barbe ldg lts (101°) are in transit; thence enter by Passe de l'Ouest on the 151° transit of the inner hbr ldg lts.

Baie de Fontarabie, in Spanish Rada de Higuer, lies on the border of France and Spain, and is entered between Pte Ste Anne and Cabo Higuer (a bare, rugged cape with lt ho) 1·75M WNW. Les Briquets (dry) lie 1M N of Pte Ste Anne. Keep to W of Banc Chicharvel and Bajo Iruarri in ent to B. Entry should not be attempted with strong onshore winds or heavy swell. R La Bidassoa is entered between breakwaters in SW corner of the B, giving access to marina at Hendaye-Plage (10.18.28). In the middle of the bay is a neutral area, marked by beacons and shown on chart 1181. To seaward of this area the boundary line (approximately 01°46'·2W) runs N from a white pyramid on the S shore, about 1M SW of Pte Ste Anne.

10.18.6   DISTANCE TABLE

Approximate distances in nautical miles are by the most direct route, whilst avoiding dangers and allowing for Traffic Separation Schemes. Places in *italics* are in adjoining areas; places in **bold** are in 10.0.5, Cross-Channel Distances.

1. *Le Conquet*	**1**																			
2. *St Nazaire*	145	**2**																		
3. Pornic	146	16	**3**																	
4. L'Herbaudière	144	16	10	**4**																
5. Port Joinville	147	35	30	20	**5**															
6. St Gilles-C-de-Vie	166	45	40	29	18	**6**														
7. Sables d'Olonne	181	65	55	40	31	16	**7**													
8. Bourgenay	190	74	64	49	40	25	9	**8**												
9. St Martin (I de Ré)	208	92	75	67	55	44	27	20	**9**											
10. La Rochelle	218	101	92	76	66	51	36	29	12	**10**										
11. Rochefort	242	126	116	102	84	75	61	54	36	26	**11**									
12. R La Seudre	242	125	116	100	89	71	58	52	33	24	30	**12**								
13. Port St Denis	220	103	94	78	59	48	33	30	21	13	26	22	**13**							
14. Port Bloc/Royan	234	122	115	107	97	85	71	60	56	52	68	27	42	**14**						
15. Bordeaux	289	177	170	162	152	140	126	115	111	107	123	82	97	55	**15**					
16. Cap Ferret	274	168	160	153	138	132	113	110	102	98	114	75	88	68	123	**16**				
17. Capbreton	316	220	215	211	192	186	169	166	165	156	172	131	145	124	179	58	**17**			
18. Anglet/Bayonne	328	232	223	223	200	195	181	178	177	168	184	143	157	132	187	70	12	**18**		
19. *Santander*	300	243	237	229	212	210	204	204	206	202	218	184	192	180	235	133	106	103	**19**	
20. *Cabo Finisterre*	382	404	399	390	377	395	393	394	406	407	423	399	397	401	456	376	370	373	274	**20**

10.18.7 Special Notes for France: see 10.15.8
10.18.8 French Glossary: see 1.4.2

PORNIC   10-18-9

Loire Atlantique 47°06'·55N 02°06'·59W   Rtg 3-2-1

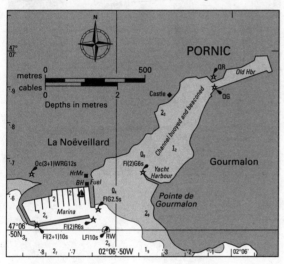

CHARTS
AC 2981, 2986, 2646; Imray C40; SHOM 7394, 7395, 7068; ECM 547, 549
TIDES
+0515 Dover; ML 3·6; Duration 0540; Zone –0100

Standard Port BREST (◀—)

Times				Height (metres)			
High Water		Low Water		MHWS	MHWN	MLWN	MLWS
0500	1100	0500	1100	6·9	5·4	2·6	1·0
1700	2300	1700	2300				
Differences PORNIC							
–0050	+0030	–0010	–0010.	–1·1	–0·8	–0·4	–0·2

SHELTER
Very good in large marina (2m); access HW±5. But no access LW±1 when Coeff >75, nor in winds >F7 from SE to W. Leave the SWM buoy to stbd, especially near LWS. Do not cut the corner round the S bkwtr head due to rky spur. Enter between the SHM pile and 2 PHM piles, on which the ☆s are mounted. A rky spur also extends SW from the head of the E jetty. Visitors berths are on P1 (for LOA >12m), P2 and P3 pontoons (first to stbd). Old hbr dries 1·8m; access HW±2½ via marked, lit drying chan.

NAVIGATION
WPT 47°06'·10N 02°08'·70W, 253°/073° from/to jetty hd, 1·5M. 4-6M WSW of hbr beware Banc de Kerouars, least depth 1m, on which seas break; it is unmarked, but the W sector of Pte de Noëveillard lt clears it by night. From the NW pass between this bank and the mainland. All other hazards are well marked. The S end of B de Bourgneuf is full of oyster beds, and many obstructions.
LIGHTS AND MARKS
Pte de Noëveillard Oc (3+1) WRG 12s 22m 13/9M; G shore-051°, W051°-079°, R079°-shore; the W sector lies between Notre-Dame rk, IDM bn tr, and the E end of Banc de Kerouars. Marina SW elbow Fl (2+1) 10s 4m 3M. Off the S jetty head Fl (2) R 6s 4m 2M; off E jetty head Fl G 2·5s 4m 2M. Entry sigs (simplified).
RADIO TELEPHONE
VHF Ch 09 (H24).
TELEPHONE (Prefix ☎ Nos with zone code 02)
Hr Mr 40·82·05·40; Aff Mar 40·82·01·69; ◫ 40·82·03·17; SNSM 40·82·00·47; Auto 08·36·68·08·44; CROSS 97·55·35·35; Police 40·82·00·29; Dr 40·82·01·80; Brit Consul 40·63·16·02.
FACILITIES
Port-la-Noëveillard Marina (754+90 visitors) ☎ 40·82·05·40, FF96, P, D (on pontoon), FW, ME, AC, El, Sh, BH (20 ton), C (6 ton) CH; **CN de Pornic** ☎ 40·82·34·72; **Services:** ME, El, Ⓔ, Sh, CH, SM. **Town** Market Sun am. V, Gaz, R, Bar, ✉, Ⓑ, ⇌, ✈ (Nantes). Ferry: Roscoff/St Malo.

18

L'HERBAUDIÈRE   10-18-10
Vendée 47°01'·70N 02°17'·77W (Ile de Noirmoutier)
Rtg 2-2-2

CHARTS
AC 2981, 2986, 2646; Imray C40; SHOM 7394, 7395; ECM 547, 549

TIDES
+0500 Dover; ML 3·4; Zone –0100

Standard Port BREST (←—)

Times				Height (metres)			
High Water		Low Water		MHWS	MHWN	MLWN	MLWS
0500	1100	0500	1100	6·9	5·4	2·6	1·0
1700	2300	1700	2300				
Differences L'HERBAUDIERE							
–0047	+0023	–0020	–0020	–1·4	–1·0	–0·5	–0·2
FROMENTINE							
–0045	+0020	–0015	+0005	–1·7	–1·3	–0·8	–0·1

SHELTER
Good in marina (E side), dredged 1·5m-2·5m; Ⓥs berth on pontoon F. FV hbr (W side); NB early morning departures. The ‡ off Pte des Dames lt, Oc (3) WRG 12s, is exposed to N and E winds.

NAVIGATION
WPT 47°03'·05N 02°17'·5W, 009°/189° from/to W jetty lt, 1·4M. There are rks and banks to the SW, NW and NE of Pte de l'Herbaudière. Ldg lts and white sector (187·5°-190°) of the W jetty lt both lead into ent chan, dredged to 1·3m and passing close W of two 0·8m patches; care needed at LWS. Two SHM buoys, Fl G 2s, and a PHM buoy, Fl (2) R 6s, mark the last 2ca of the chan. W bkwtr obscures vessels leaving.

LIGHTS AND MARKS
Visibility in summer is often poor. Conspic daymarks are R/W radio mast 500m W of hbr and water tr about 1M SE. Ile du Pilier, Fl (3) 20s 33m 29M, is 2·5M WNW of hbr. Appr in any of the 3 W sectors of Basse de Martroger, NCM bn, Dir Q WRG 11m 9/6M, G033°-055°, W055°-060°, R060°-095°, G095°-124°, W124°-153°, R153°-201°, W201°-240°, R240°-033°.
Ldg lts 188°, both grey masts, Q 10/26m 7M, vis 098°-278°, lead over Banc de la Blanche (1·8m) approx 2M N of hbr. L'Herbaudière W jetty, Oc (2+1) WG 12s 9m 10/7M, W187·5°-190° (2½°), G elsewhere. E jetty head Fl (2) R 6s 8m 4M; inner head Fl R 2·5s 3m 1M.

RADIO TELEPHONE
Hr Mr VHF Ch 09 (HO).

TELEPHONE (Prefix ☎ Nos with zone code 02)
Hr Mr 51·39·75·97; Aff Mar 51·39·01·64; SNSM 51·39·33·90; CROSS 97·55·35·35; Météo 40·84·80·19; Auto 08·36·68·08·85; ⌖ 51·39·06·80; Police 51·39·04·36 or 17; Dr 51·39·05·64; Brit Consul 40·63·16·02.

FACILITIES
Marina (442+50 visitors), ☎ / ☏ 51.39.75.97, FW, P, D, AC, C (25 ton), Slip, ME, SM, ◎, Gas, Gaz, V, R, Bar (July, Aug), Sh, SC; Quay Bar, R, ME, Sh, SM, V; Services: C, El, Ⓔ, Sh, CH.

Oc(2+1)WG12s
Horn30s
Vis W 187°·5-190°
G 190°-187.5°
Fl(2)R6s8m4M
FlR2.5s
Q10m7M
LB(conspic)
Fishing Harbour
Slip
Marina
Slip
Fuel
HrMr
Q26m7M
FlG2.5s
Q(2)R5s
Ldg Lts 188°
Rocks (dry)
Rocks (dry)
47° 01'·50N

PORT DE L'HERBAUDIERE

metres   0   200
cables   0   1
Depths in metres

ADJACENT HARBOUR ON ILE DE NOIRMOUTIER

NOIRMOUTIER-EN-L'ILE 46°59'·40N 02°13'·10W. AC 2981; SHOM 7394. Tides as above. Good shelter and AB, 4M SE of L'Herbaudiere, but FV hbr dries up to 3·0m on mud/gravel. Appr HW±1 across extensive drying rock ledges to the N and E of ent. The E'ly of 2 chans runs SSW from approx 47°00'·50N 02°11'·10W, then doglegs WNW to the ent. It is marked by 5 unlit PHM bns. An inshore chan runs S from off Pte des Dames lt ho, Oc (3) WRG12s 34m. It is more easily followed, keeping about 400m off 5 unlit SHM bns along the shore. Both chans meet at the ent where the flood tide sets S. S jetty hd has ☆ Oc (2) R 6s. Follow the jetty on N side for about 1M to hbr. A prior recce (3M overland from L'Herbaudiere) is advised. Hr Mr ☎ 02.51.39.08.39. Quay AB, FW, C (4 ton); Services: ME, El, Ⓔ, Sh, CH, SM. Town P, D, V, Gaz, R, Bar, ◎, ⊠, Ⓑ, ⇌ ✈ at Nantes, via ferry to Pornic and bus. Ferry: Roscoff or St Malo.

ADJACENT HARBOUR

FROMENTINE, Vendée, 46°53'·60N 02°08'·60W. AC 2981, SHOM 7394, 6853. HW +0550 on Dover (UT); ML 3·2m; Duration 0540. Tides above. Do not appr from Baie de Bourgneuf as there is a road causeway, dries 3m, from Ile de Noirmoutier to the mainland. Enter through Goulet de Fromentine, under the bridge (clearance 27m). The chan is buoyed, moved as necessary, but is very shallow, so dangerous in bad weather. At sp the ebb can reach 8kn, the flood 5kn. Do not attempt night entry. ‡ W of pier. Coming from N, beware Les Boeufs. Tourelle Milieu lies on the N side of Le Goulet de Fromentine, Fl (4) R 12s 6m 5M, R tr. Pte de Notre Dames-de-Monts Dir lt, Oc (2) WRG 6s 21m 13/10M, G000°-043°, W043°-063°, R063°-073°, W073°-094°, G094°-113°, W113°-116°, R116°-175°, G175°-196°, R196°-230°. Fromentine SWM lt buoy, L Fl 10s+bell, 46°53'·10N 02°11'·50W, is about 1·5M WSW of Pte du Notre Dames-de-Monts. Bridge, two x Iso 4s 32m 18M. Facilities: Aff Mar at Noirmoutier; ⌖ at Beauvois-sur-Mer; Quay Slip, C (3 ton), FW; Cercle Nautique de Fromentine-Barfatre (CNFB); Services: ME, El, Sh, CH.

PORT JOINVILLE, Ile d'Yeu

Vendée 46°43'·80N 02°20'·75W   Rtg 2-2-2   **10-18-11**

CHARTS
AC 3640, 2663; Imray C40; SHOM 6613, 6890, 6853; ECM 549, 1022

TIDES
+0550 Dover; ML 3·1; Duration 0600; Zone –0100

Standard Port BREST (←)

Times				Height (metres)			
High Water		Low Water		MHWS	MHWN	MLWN	MLWS
0500	1100	0500	1100	6·9	5·4	2·6	1·0
1700	2300	1700	2300				
Differences PORT JOINVILLE (Ile d'Yeu)							
–0025	+0010	–0030	–0030	–1·7	–1·3	–0·6	–0·2

SHELTER
Good in enlarged marina, but very crowded in season; best to pre-book as it is the only secure hbr on the island. The wet basin (3·7m) access HW±1½, is solely for FVs; no pontoons; tfc lts R & G, just S of lock. No ‡ in outer hbr; swell enters in N/NE winds. If the marina is full, yachts can moor between Gare Maritime and the ice factory, keeping clear of ferries to W. A grid to the W of the ice factory is marked by R paint lines on quay wall.

NAVIGATION
WPT Basse Mayence NCM, 46°44'·65N 02°19'·10W, 055°/235° from/to bkwtr lt, 1·3M. Chan dredged 2m, appr with care at LW. Beware Basse du Bouet (dries 0·6m) 3ca NW, La Sablaire shoal to the E and rks along the coast both sides of hbr ent.

LIGHTS AND MARKS
Very conspic high water tr brg 224° leads to hbr. Ldg lts 219°, both QR 11/16m 6M, vis 169°-269°; rear (mast) 85m from front.
NW jetty head Oc (3) WG 12s 9m 11/8M; G shore-150°, W150°-232°, G232°-279°, W279°-285°, G285°-shore; horn (3) 30s, tidal sigs. Quai du Canada hd Iso G 4s 7m 6M unintens 337°-067°. Galiote jetty root Fl R 2·5s 1M.

RADIO TELEPHONE
Marina VHF Ch 09 16 (HO).

TELEPHONE (Prefix ☎ Nos with zone code 02)
Hr Mr 51·58·38·11; Hbr Office 51·58·51·10; Aff Mar 51·58·35·39; ⌗ 51·55·10·58; CROSS 97·55·35·35; Météo 51·36·10·78; Auto 08·36·68·08·85; SNSM 51·58·35·39; Police 51·58·30·05; Dr 51·58·31·70; Ⓗ 51·68·30·23; Brit Consul 40·63·16·02. Note: There are phone-card telephones only.

FACILITIES
Marina (390+30 Ⓥ), ☎ 51·58·51·10, ⛽ 51.58.44.34, FF84.40 (142.40 in Jul/Aug); FW, AC, P, D, El, ME, Sh; **Wet Basin** Slip, FW, C (5 ton); **CN Ile d'Yeu** ☎ 51·58·31·50; **Services:** ME, El, Sh, CH, Ⓔ.
Town V, Gaz, R, Bar, ⊠, Ⓑ, ⇌ (St Gilles-Croix-de-Vie), ✈ (Nantes). Flights from airfield 2M west of Port Joinville to Nantes and (summers only) to Les Sables d'Olonne. Ferry: Roscoff or St Malo. Local ferries to Fromentine, St Gilles and Les Sables-d'Olonne.

ADJACENT HARBOUR ON ILE D'YEU

PORT DE LA MEULE, Ile d'Yeu, Vendée, 46°41'·75N 03°20'·60W. AC 2663; SHOM 6890, 6853. –0050 sp and – 0020 nps on Brest; ML 3·0m. A small, drying fishing hbr on the S side of Ile d'Yeu, only safe in settled offshore weather; untenable in S winds. Many FVs inside hbr; best to ‡ outside ent. Between Pte de la Père to the W and Pte de la Tranche to the SE, appr brg 034° on W chapel; then 022° towards W square patch on Gy □ lt tr, R top, Oc WRG 4s 9m 9/6/5M, vis G007°-018°, W018°-028°, R028°-042°. (Night ent not advised). Within 1ca of ent beware rks, first to port, then to stbd. Few facilities: Slips, R, Bar; V 1½ miles.

ST GILLES-CROIX-DE-VIE

Vendée 46°41'·60N 01°57'·05W   Rtg 2-1-2   **10-18-12**

CHARTS
AC 3640, 2663; Imray C40; SHOM 6613, 6853, 6523; ECM 1022, 549

TIDES
+0500 Dover; ML 3·2; Duration 0600; Zone –0100

Standard Port BREST (←)

Times				Height (metres)			
High Water		Low Water		MHWS	MHWN	MLWN	MLWS
0500	1100	0500	1100	6·9	5·4	2·6	1·0
1700	2300	1700	2300				
Differences ST GILLES-CROIX-DE-VIE							
–0032	+0013	–0033	–0033	–1·8	–1·3	–0·6	–0·3

SHELTER
Good shelter, and easy access except in strong SW'lies or swell when breakers form off ent. Chan (‡ prohib) is dredged 1·5m, but very shallow near bkwtr hds due to silting. Best arr/dep HW –2 to HW, to avoid strong ebb. On N bank are: small yacht basin inside Grand Môle; two tidal FV basins; beyond them the marina nominally dredged to 1·5m. If full, pick up ‡ or lie alongside quay (dries) on E bank below bridge. In good weather ‡ off ent, close SE of ldg line.

NAVIGATION
WPT Pill'Hours SCM, Q (6) +L Fl 15s, Bell, 46°41'·05N 01°58'·00W, 231°/051° from/to Jetée de la Garenne lt, 0·75M. Beware Rocher Pill'Hours (2·8m) and drying reefs extending 1ca (180m) SE. Tide runs very strongly in ent, particularly on ebb.

LIGHTS AND MARKS
Landmarks are Pte de Grosse-Terre (rky hdland) with lt ho, W truncated conical tr; the rear ldg lt structure; and two spires NE of the marina.
Pte de Grosse Terre Fl (4) WR 12s 25m 17/13M, vis W290°-125°, R125°-145°.
Ldg lts 043°: both Dir Oc (3+1) R 12s 7/28m 13M; both W □ trs, R top; intens 033·5°-053·5°, synch.
SE mole hd, QWG 8m 9/6M, vis G045°-335°, W335°-045°, Reed 20s.
NW mole hd, Fl (2) WR 6s 8m 10/7M, R045°-225°, W225°-045°.

RADIO TELEPHONE
VHF Ch 09 (season 0600-2200; out of season 0800-1200, 1400-1800LT).

TELEPHONE (Prefix ☎ Nos with zone code 02)
Hr Mr Port de Plaisance 51·55·30·83; Aff Mar 51·55·10·58; ⌗ 51·55·10·58; CROSS 97·55·35·35; SNSM 51·55·01·19; Météo 51·36·10·78; Auto 08·36·68·08·85; Police 51·55·01·19; Dr 51·55·11·93; Brit Consul 40·63·16·02.

FACILITIES
Port la Vie Marina (800+60 visitors) ☎ 51·55·30·83, ⛽ 51.55.31.43, Access H24, P, D, FW, AC, ME, EI, CH, Gaz, SM, BH (26 ton), Slip, R, V, Bar; **Quay** Slip, FW, C (6 ton); **CN de Havre de Vie** ☎ 51·55·87·91;
Services: ME, EI, Sh, CH, Ⓔ, C (15 ton), SM, SHOM.
Town V, Gaz, R, Bar, ✉, Ⓑ, ✈. A ferry runs to Ile d'Yeu.
Ferry: Roscoff or St Malo.

LES SABLES D'OLONNE 10-18-13

Vendée 46°29'·40N 01°47'·40W Rtg 3-2-2

CHARTS
AC 3640, 2663; Imray C40; SHOM 6551, 6522, 6523; ECM 1022

TIDES
+0530 Dover; ML 3·2; Duration 0640; Zone –0100

Standard Port BREST (←)

Times				Height (metres)			
High Water		Low Water		MHWS	MHWN	MLWN	MLWS
0500	1100	0500	1100	6·9	5·4	2·6	1·0
1700	2300	1700	2300				
Differences LES SABLES D'OLONNE							
–0030	+0015	–0035	–0035	–1·7	–1·3	–0·6	–0·3

SHELTER
Access at all tides; entry is easy except in winds from SE to SW when apprs get rough. Sailing is prohib in the entry chan to hbr. Commercial and FV Basins prohib to yachts. Access to marina (1·5 - 3·5m) H24. Visitors check in at pontoon port side, by Capitainerie. Pontoon L, at NE end, is for visitors and multihulls; or berth as directed.

NAVIGATION
WPT Nouch Sud SCM, Q (6)+L Fl 15s, 46°28'·63N 01°47'·35W, 220°/040° from/to front ldg lt 033°, 1·2M. To the W, beware Les Barges d'Olonne, extending 3M W of Pte de Aiguille. There are 2 appr chans: the SW chan with La Potence ldg lts 033°, which lead into SE chan on ldg line 320°. In bad weather use the SE chan. Le Noura and Le Nouch are two isolated rks on shallow patches S of Jetée St Nicolas. Further SE, Barre Marine breaks, even in moderate weather. A buoyed wk (dries) lies off hbr ent, to E of 320° ldg line. At hbr ent, dredged chan (2m) initially favours the E side, then mid-chan.

LIGHTS AND MARKS
Les Barges lt ho, Fl (2) R 10s 25m 13M, gy tr, 2M W of ent. L'Armandèche lt ho, Fl (2+1) 15s 42m 24M, 6ca W of ent. SW Chan ldg lts 033°: both Iso R 4s 14/33m 16M; rear, 330m from front (both H24). SE Chan ldg lts 320°: front QG 11m 8M; rear, 465m from front, Oc (2+1) 12s 33m 13M. St Nicolas jetty hd, UQ (2) R 1s 16m 10M vis 143°-094°; Horn (2) 30s. Inner ldg lts 327°, both FR 6/9m 11M; R/W vert stripes difficult to see by day.

RADIO TELEPHONE
Port VHF Ch 12 16 (0800-1800). Marina Ch 09 16 (0600-2400LT in season; 0800-2000LT out of season).

TELEPHONE (Prefix ☎ Nos with zone code 02)
Hr Mr Port de Plaisance 51·32·51·16; Aff Mar 51·21·01·80; CROSS 97·55·35·35; Météo 51·36·10·78; Auto 08·36·68·08·85; ⌗ 51·32·02·33; SNSM 51·21·20·55; Police 51·33·69·91; Dr 51·95·14·47; Ⓗ 51·21·06·33; Brit Consul 05·56·52·28·35.

FACILITIES
Port Olona Marina (1100+110 Ⓥ), ☎ 51·32·51·16, 🛥 51.32.37.13, FF90 (Jun/Sep), 130FF (Jul/Aug), Slip, P, D, FW, ME, El, AC, Sh, Ⓒ;
Services: El, Sh, CH, BH (27 ton), Ⓔ, SHOM, SM, Divers.
Town P, D, V, Gaz, R, Bar, ✉, Ⓑ, ⇌, ✈. Ferry: Roscoff or St Malo.

BOURGENAY 10-18-14

Vendée 46° 26'·38N 01° 40'·57W Rtg 4-2-2

CHARTS
AC 2663; Imray C41; SHOM 6522; ECM 1022

TIDES
+0600 Dover; ML 3·1; Duration 0640; Zone –0100. Use Differences LES SABLES D'OLONNE (10.18.13), 5·5M NW.

SHELTER
Good in the marina (2m). Caution: even in moderate weather, & especially with SW winds, a big swell can break at the ent.

NAVIGATION
WPT Fairway buoy SWM, L Fl 10s, 46°25'·35N 01°41'·90W, 220°/040° from/to pier head, 1·35M. 600m ENE of WPT, beware Roches de Joanne (2·9m; dangerous in bad wx) and shoal patch to E of ent, marked by unlit SHM buoy and bn. Ent chan, dredged 1·0m, has two 90° turns marked by luminous chevrons; 3kn speed limit.

LIGHTS AND MARKS
Ldg lts 040°: both QG 8M; front W hut with G □, vis 020°-060°; rear W pylon, W □ with G border, vis 010°-070°. The Iso G 4s 5M and Fl (2) R 6s 5M are not vis from seaward.

RADIO TELEPHONE
VHF Ch 09 16 (office hrs; in summer 0800-2100LT).

TELEPHONE (Prefix ☎ Nos with zone code 02)
Hr Mr/SNSM 51·22·20·36, 🛥 51.22.29.45; CROSS Etel 97·55·35·35; Auto 08·36·68·08·85; ⌗ 51·32·02·33; Aff Mar 51·21·81·71; Police 51·90·60·07; Dr 51·90·62·68; Ⓗ 51·96·00·41; Brit Consul 05·56·52·28·35.

FACILITIES
Marina (470+90 Ⓥ) ☎ 51·22·20·36, FF95, FW, AC, P, D, Slip;
Association Nautique de Bourgenay (ANB) ☎ 51·22·02·57;
Services: CH, C (15 ton), Gaz.
Town R, Ⓥ, V, Bar, ✉, Ⓑ, ⇌ (Les Sables d'Olonne), ✈ (La Lande, Chateau d'Olonne). Ferry: Roscoff or St Malo.

18

MINOR HARBOURS IN PERTUIS BRETON

JARD-SUR-MER, Vendée, 46°24'·45N 01°34'·75W. Rtg 4-5-3. AC 2641, 2663; SHOM 6522. HW +0600 on Dover (UT); HW−0010 & ht −2·0m on Brest; ML 3·1m; Duration 0640. Small drying hbr, access HW±2, 4·5m max at HW. Moorings inside bkwtr, inc 7 Y ⚓s. Hr Mr's office with blue roof and adjacent bldgs are conspic from afar. W daymarks 4ca (740m) E of hbr lead 038° via narrow ent between the drying Roches de l'Islatte and Roches de la Brunette, marked by buoys. Then pick up 293° transit of RW marks on W side of hbr, ldg to ent. There are no lights. Hr Mr (occas) ☎ 02·51·33·40·17; ⌗ ☎ 02·51·95·11·33; Facilities: **Jetty** FW, C (5 ton); **Services:** CH, Divers.

L'AIGUILLON/LA-FAUTE-SUR-MER, Vendée, 46°20'·00N 01°18'·60W. Rtg 4-3-2. AC 2641, 2663; SHOM 6521. HW +0535 on Dover (UT), HW −0030, ht +0·6m on Pte de Grave (Zone −0100); ML 3·4m. Shelter good in two yacht hbrs, but avoid in strong S or W winds; ent only safe in fine weather with off-shore winds. Access HW±2½. Beware mussel beds with steel piles which cover at HW; also oyster beds. The area is very flat and, being shallow, waves build up quickly in any wind. The bar to seaward dries and is dangerous in bad weather. Ent can best be identified by a conspic transformer on a hill, La Dive, opposite side of chan to Pointe d'Arcay. Enter at Le Lay SCM buoy, Q (6) + L Fl 15s, with transformer brg 033°. ⚓ in R Lay or berth at L'Aiguillon (NE bank); or in drying tidal basin at La Faute (SW bank). Hr Mrs (L'Aiguillon) ☎ 05.51.97.06.57; (La Faute) ☎ 05.51.56.45.02; Aff Mar ☎ 05.51.56.45.35; CROSS ☎ 05.56.09.82.00; Dr ☎ 05.51.56.46.17; Facilities: **Club Nautique Aiguillonais et Fautais** (CNAF) ☎ 05.51.97.04.60; **Services:** ME, CH.

MARANS, Vendée, 46°19'·00N 01°00'·00W. AC 2641, 2663; SHOM 6521; ECM 551. Tides: see L'Aiguillon above; HW at Brault lock = HW La Rochelle + 0020. Good shelter in non-tidal hbr approx 10M from SWM buoy, L Fl 10s, (46° 15'·40N 01°11'·42W) abeam Pte de l'Aiguillon with 10m high B bn. Buoyed chan, dries 1·0m, leads NE past Pavé jetty, Fl G 4s, thence 3½M up-river to Brault lifting bridge and 5ca to lock, open HW±2 sp, HW±1 np. Best arrival at HW. Waiting buoys before bridge; pontoon inside vast lock which has small swing bridge at far end. Straight 3M canal to stbd side pontoon. Brault lock ☎ 05.46.01.53.77; Facilities: **Quay** ☎ 05.46.01.10.36, AB (40+10 Ⓥ), FW, C (3 tons); P & D (cans); BY, ME, Sh, SM. **Town** V, R, Bar.

OTHER HARBOUR ON ILE DE RÉ

LA FLOTTE, Charente Maritime, 46°11'·35N 01°19'·25W. Rtg 3-4-2. AC 2641, 2746; SHOM 6668, 6521. HW +0535 on Dover (UT). La Flotte is 2M SE of St Martin (10·18·16). From NW keep clear of Le Couronneau; from E, keep N of bn off Pte des Barres. Appr on 215° in W sector of La Flotte lt ho, W tr with G top, Fl WG 4s 10m 12/9M; vis G130°-205°, W205°-220°, G220°-257°; horn (3) 30s by day HW±2. Moiré indicator shows vert B line when on course 215°, or chevrons to regain course. 5 waiting Bys outside; or ⚓ off in 3m, sheltered from S & W. Outer hbr sheltered by mole and dries 2·4m; access HW±3. 3 pontoons in outer hbr for 8 visitors; pre-booking advised. Inner hbr dries 2·7m. Hr Mr ☎ 46.09.67.66; ⌗ at St Martin; Facilities: **Quay** FF75, Slip, FW, Ⓥ berth on mole, Grid; **Cercle Nautique de la Flotte-en-Ré** (CNLF) (open Jul-15 Sep) ☎ 46.09.59.30, Bar; **Services:** P & D (cans), CH, ME, SM, ◪.

ARS-EN-RÉ,   10-18-15
Charente Maritime, 46°12'·70N 01°30'·62W   Rtg 4-3-1

CHARTS
AC 2641; Imray C41; SHOM 6521, 6333; ECM 551, 1022
TIDES
+0540 Dover; ML 3·7m; Zone −0100; See 10.18.16
SHELTER
Two sheltered marinas: (a) Bassin de la Criée (2m), is on NW side of chan approx 600m NE of town; access HW±2 over sill 2·5m CD, Ⓥ berths on pontoon H, to port.
(b) Bassin Prée, at head of chan, access HW ±2 over sill, dries 2·9m; Ⓥ berths to stbd. Or AB outside on NW quay drying to mud. Note: draught, tidal coefficient and wind/barometer dictate access times.
NAVIGATION
WPT 46°14'·62N 01°20'·66W (2ca S of Rocha NCM buoy), 085°/265° from/to first SHM chan buoy, 3·65M. Beware shoal ground close S of outer ldg line. The appr chan is restricted by rky ledges drying 0·4m and 1·5m; access HW±3. Chan is marked by 2 sets of ldg lts, buoys and bns. There is ⚓ in a pool (2m) close S of Pte du Fier. Port d'Ars is at the head of a chan in the SW corner of the bay, Le Fier d'Ars, which dries to salt pans & oyster beds.
LIGHTS AND MARKS
Conspic ✠ spire, white with black top, is in the town, about 1ca SE of the 232° ldg line. Outer ldg lts 265° (from near Le Rocha NCM buoy, Q): front, Iso 4s 5m 11M, W ☐ on hut, vis 141°-025°; rear, 370m from front, Dir Iso G 4s 13m 15M, G ☐ tr on house (synch, intens 264°-266°). Port d'Ars ldg lts, hard to see by day, lead 232° across Fiers d'Ars into hbr: front, Q 5m 9M, W ☐ with R lantern; rear, 370m from front, Q 13m 11M, B ☐ on W framework tr, G top, vis 142°-322°.
RADIO TELEPHONE
VHF Ch 09.
TELEPHONE (Prefix ☎ Nos with zone code 05)
Hr Mr (La Criée) 46·29.25·10, (La Prée) 46.29.08.52; SNSM 46.34.49.84; Aff Mar 46.09.68.89 (at La Flotte); CROSS 56.09.82.00; ⌗ 46.09.21.78; Auto 08.36.68.08.17; Police 46.29.41.48; Dr 46.29.44.19; Brit Consul 05.56.52.28.35.
FACILITIES
Marinas FF122, Slip, FW, C (6 ton); **Cercle Nautique d'Ars -en-Ré** ☎ 46.29.23.04 (Apl to Nov); **Services:** ME, El, Sh.

ST MARTIN, Ile de Ré   10-18-16

Charente Maritime 46°12'·56N 01°21'·84W   Rtg 3-3-1

CHARTS
AC 2641, 2746; Imray C41; SHOM 6668, 6521; ECM 551, 1022

TIDES
+0535 Dover; ML 3·7; Zone –0100

Standard Port POINTE DE GRAVE (→)

Times				Height (metres)			
High Water		Low Water		MHWS	MHWN	MLWN	MLWS
0000	0600	0500	1200	5·4	4·4	2·1	1·0
1200	1800	1700	2400				
Differences ST. MARTIN, Ile de Ré							
+0007	–0032	–0030	–0025	+0·5	+0·3	+0·2	–0·1

SHELTER
Complete shelter in non-tidal marina (depth 3m); often very crowded with queue to enter. 4 W waiting buoys off ent. Avant port is protected by bkwtr close to the NE and mole on NW side. Inside mole a waiting pontoon (season only) is dredged 2·3m; can be disturbed in fresh NW to NE winds. Access HW–3 to +2 via chan (dries 1·5m) to drying basin for FVs. Marina gates open about HW–2 and close HW+2½, depending on coefficient (sill is 0·8m above CD), 0630-2200LT May, Jun and Sept; 0500-2300 Jul and Aug. Berth as directed by Hr Mr.

NAVIGATION
WPT Rocha NCM Dy, Q, 46°14'·75N 01°20'·80W, 020°/200° from/to St Martin mole hd, 2·4M.
From the NW, pass N and E of Le Rocha, a rky bank

extending 2½M ENE from Pte du Grouin.
From SE, pass well N of unlit NCM bn, about ¾M NE of ent, marking Le Couronneau drying ledge in R sector (245°-281°) of St Martin lt ho Oc (2) WR 6s.
By day appr with lt ho and ⊞ ☐ tr in line 210°, or mole hd lt in transit 202° with ⊞ tr; the lt ho is easier to see.

LIGHTS AND MARKS
Citadelle is conspic 3ca E of hbr ent. Lt ho, Oc (2) WR 6s 18m 10/7M, vis W shore-245°, R245°-281°, W281°-shore, is on ramparts at SE side of ent. Mole hd, Iso G 4s 10m 6M, is obscured by Pte du Grouin when brg <124°.

RADIO TELEPHONE
VHF Ch 09 (0800-1900LT in summer).

TELEPHONE (Prefix ☎ Nos with zone code 05)
Hr Mr 46·09·26·69; Aff Mar 46·09·68·89 (in La Flotte); ⌗ 46·09·21·78; Météo 46·41·29·14; Auto 08·36·68·08·17; CROSS 56·09·82·00; Police 46·09·21·17; Dr 46·09·20·08; Ⓗ 46·09·20·01; Brit Consul 56·52·28·35.

FACILITIES
Marina (135+50 visitors), FF90, P, D, FW, AC, ME, El, Sh; **Quay** FW, C (4 ton); **YC St Martin** ☎ 46·09·22·07; **Services:** ME, El, Ⓔ, Sh, CH, SHOM.
Town P, D, V, Gaz, R, Bar, ⊠, Ⓑ, ≥, ✈ (La Rochelle).
Ferry: Roscoff or St Malo.

LA ROCHELLE   10-18-17

Charente Maritime 46°09'·40N 01° 09'·15W   Rtg 3-1-1

CHARTS
AC 2743, 2746, 2641; Imray C41; SHOM 6468, 6333/4; ECM 551, 1022

TIDES
+0515 Dover; ML 3·8; Zone –0100

Standard Port POINTE DE GRAVE (→)

Times				Height (metres)			
High Water		Low Water		MHWS	MHWN	MLWN	MLWS
0000	0600	0500	1200	5·4	4·4	2·1	1·0
1200	1800	1700	2400				
Differences LA ROCHELLE and LA PALLICE							
+0015	–0030	–0025	–0020	+0·6	+0·5	+0·3	–0·1

SHELTER
Excellent in **Port des Minimes**, a very large marina with 3·5m depth (max LOA 25m); in the Vieux Port, and in the Inner Basin. The large non-tidal **Bassin des Chalutiers** has pontoons on the N/NE sides for visitors >16m LOA. **Vieux Port**, in the old town, is entered beyond the two trs of St Nicolas and La Chaine. It has a tidal basin (dredged 1·3m) with 100+ berths for smaller yachts. On the E side a non-tidal **Inner Basin** (3m) is entered by a lock with sill 1·2m above CD, opens HW–2 to HW+½; night ent by prior arrangement ☎ 46.41.32.05. Note: La Pallice is strictly a commercial/FV port 3M W, with no yacht facilities.

NAVIGATION
WPT 46°06'·63N 01°15'·98W, Chauveau SCM By, VQ (6) + L Fl 10s, 240°/060° from/to Tour Richelieu, 4·6M. Appr from about 1M S of Le Lavardin lt tr on ldg line 059°. Off Pte des Minimes (SW of marina) drying rks extend ¼M offshore; further S there is a firing danger area marked by 5 SPM buoys. Shallow appr chan needs care at MLWS. Tour Richelieu (with tide gauge) marks a drying rky spit to the N of the chan; least depth in chan 0·2m. Ent to Port des Minimes is 1ca past Tour Richelieu, marked by WCM and 2 PHM buoys, all unlit; but mole heads are lit.

For Vieux Port stay on 059° ldg line in chan (35m wide), leaving 4 PHM buoys well to port.
Note: Passage under the bridge (30m clearance) between Ile de Ré and the mainland must be made N-bound between piers Nos 13 and 14, and S-bound between piers Nos 10 and 11. These passages are buoyed/lit.

LIGHTS AND MARKS
Ldg lts 059°: Front, Q 15m 14M (Fl 4s by day), R ○ tr, W bands; rear, Q 25m 14M (Fl 4s by day), W octagonal tr, G top; synch, obsc 061°-065° by St Nicolas tr.
Le Lavardin, rky shoal 3M WSW of Tr Richelieu, Fl (2) WG 6s 14m 11/8M, B tr, R band, vis G160°-169°, W169°-160°.
Tour Richelieu, Fl (4) R 12s 10m 9M, conspic R tr, RC, siren (4) 60s.
Port des Minimes: W mole hd Fl G 4s; E mole hd Fl (2) R 6s.

RADIO TELEPHONE
Port des Minimes Ch 09 (H24). Hbr Ch 06 11 12.

TELEPHONE (Prefix ☎ Nos with zone code 05)
Port des Minimes Hr Mr 46.41.68.73; Vieux Port Hr Mr 46.41.68.73; Aff Mar 46.41.43.91; CROSS 56.09.82.00; Météo 46.41.29.14; ⌗ 46.42.64.64; Auto 08.36.68.08.17; Dr 46.42.19.22; Police 46.34.67.55; Ⓗ 46.27.33.33; Brit Consul 56.52.28.35.

FACILITIES
PORT DES MINIMES
Marina (2,800+250 visitors on pontoons 14 and 15), FF95, ☎ 46.44.41.20, ⚓ 46.44.36.49, Gaz, AC, Slip, C (10 ton), P, D, FW, BH (50 ton), R. Hourly water bus to the town.
Société des Régates Rochellaises ☎ 46.44.62.44;
Services: ME, Sh, CH, Ⓔ, El, SHOM, SM.
VIEUX PORT
Quay FF95, Slip, FW, C (10 ton), BH (300 ton), SM, ME, Sh, CH, no toilets/showers, may be noisy.
Inner Basin (100) ☎ 46.41.32.05 (3m), FF95, Access HW –2 to HW+½. **Bassin des Chalutiers** FW, AC.
Town P, D, V, Gaz, R, Bar, ✉, Ⓑ, ⇌, ✈. Ferry to Ile de Ré; internal air services (and to London in season) from Laleu airport (2½km N of port). Ferry: Roscoff or St Malo.

ILE D'OLÉRON   10-18-18

Charente Maritime   Rtgs: see below

CHARTS
AC 2746, 2663; SHOM 6914, 6913, 6912, 6334, 6335; ECM 552

TIDES
+0545 Dover; ML 3·9; Duration 0540; Zone −0100

Standard Port POINTE DE GRAVE (→)

Times				Height (metres)			
High Water		Low Water		MHWS	MHWN	MLWN	MLWS
0000	0600	0500	1200	5·4	4·4	2·1	1·0
1200	1800	1700	2400				
Differences LE CHAPUS							
+0015	−0040	−0025	−0015	+0·6	+0·6	+0·4	+0·2
POINTE DE GATSEAU							
+0005	−0005	−0015	−0025	−0·1	−0·1	+0·2	+0·2

HARBOURS
Port St Denis and Le Douhet are in the N of the island, both with dedicated marinas. Boyardville and Le Chateau on the E coast are mainly for FVs, but have small marinas. La Cotinière, on the W coast, suffers from almost constant Atlantic swell and is much used by FVs. Beware fishing nets with very small floats especially near Port St Denis.

PORT ST DENIS   46°02'·16N 01°21'·97W   Rtg 3-4-2

SHELTER
Very good in large marina. Access HW±3½ for 2m draft over sill 1·5m CD. Max depth 2·5m. 3 W waiting buoys approx 700m E of ent in 0·7 - 1m.

NAVIGATION
WPT 46°03'·27N 01°20'·75W, 025°/205° from/to chan ent, 1·35M. Appr chan dries about 1·1m. Daymarks lead 258° to ent. By night 2 Dir lts lead 205° and 284° in sequence.

LIGHTS AND MARKS
Pte de Chassiron, Fl 10s 50m 28M, 1·9M WNW. Rocher d'Antioche bn, Q 20m 11M, 2·2M NNW. Daymarks: SHM perch on with church tr 258°. Dir lt, ½M S of hbr ent, Iso WRG 4s, W sector 204°-206°, leads 205° to pick up second Dir lt Fl (2) WG 6s on N pier; W sector 277°-292°, leads 284°.

RADIO TELEPHONE
VHF Ch 09.

TELEPHONE (Prefix ☎ Nos with zone code 05)
Hr Mr 46·47·97·97; Yacht Club Océan 46·47·80·50; Aff Mar 46·47·60·01; SNSM 46·47·06·33; Ⓗ (12km) 46·47·00·86; Auto 08·36·68·08·17.

FACILITIES
Marina (600+70 visitors) ☎ 46·47·97·97, 🕿 46.47.88.23, FF80, FW, AC, P, D, Slip, BH (10 ton); YCO ☎ 46·47·90·50.

LE DOUHET   46°00'·15N 01°19'·18W   Rtg 3-4-2

SHELTER
Very good in marina on SE side of hbr; FVs use NW part. Access HW −3½ to HW +3 for 1·5m draft, over sill 1·8m CD. Sill is marked by SHM bn, W of which a training wall protects pontoons. Ⓥ pontoon to port beyond sill.

NAVIGATION
WPT 46°00'·54N 01°17'·61W, NCM By Q, 068°/248° from/ to ent 1·1M. Unlit, buoyed appr chan dries about 1·5m to approx 0·35M offshore.

LIGHTS AND MARKS
No lts/ldg marks; bkwtrs marked by perches.

RADIO TELEPHONE
VHF Ch 09.

TELEPHONE (Prefix ☎ Nos with zone code 05).
Hr Mr 46·76·71·13, 🕿 46.76.78.26.

FACILITIES
Marina (305+45 visitors), FF70, FW, AC, Max LOA 15m; V at St Georges d'Oléron and La Brée.

OTHER HARBOURS ON ILE D'OLÉRON

BOYARDVILLE, Ile d'Oléron, Charente Maritime. Rtg 3-3-2. 45°58'·30N 01°13'·76W. AC 2746, 2663; SHOM 6913/4, 6334/5; ECM 552. HW +0545 on Dover (UT); tides as for Ile d'Aix (see 10.18.19). Fishing port, with good shelter in non-tidal marina (2m), but berths are usually taken and multiple rafting is the norm. Access HW±2 to drying appr chan and into marina to stbd via automatic lock, open approx HW±2. NB: Strong river current and awkward turn into marina. From La Perrotine SHM By steer 263° for 4ca to S bkwtr lt, Fl (2) R 6s 8m 5M. Six W waiting buoys ½M N of chan or ⚓ in 3m. VHF Ch 09. Hr Mr ☎ 05·46·47·23·71. **Marina** (165+45 visitors) FF70, AC, FW C (10 ton), Slip, P & D on quay; **YCB** ☎ 05·46·47·05·82. **Services:** ME, El, Sh, CH.

LE CHATEAU, Ile d'Oléron, Charente Maritime, 45°52'·95N 01°11'·30W. AC 2663; SHOM 6913, 6334, 6335; ECM 552. HW +0545 on Dover (UT); tides as for Ile d'Aix (10.18.19), ML 3·8m, duration 0540. Mainly occupied by FVs; yachts are tolerated, rather than welcomed. Possible drying berth on NE quay. Access HW±3. From N, appr via Chenal Est, to SCM bn marking Grand Montanne and ent to appr chan. From S, appr via Coureau d'Oléron, under mainland bridge (clnce 18m), thence 1M to ent chan. Ldg lts 319°, QR 11/24m 7M synch. Hr Mr ☎ 05·46·47·00·01. Facilities: Slip, L, FW, C (25 ton).

18

ROCHEFORT   10-18-19

Charente Maritime 45°56'·60N 00°57'·20W   Rtg 3-2-2

CHARTS
AC 2748, 2746; SHOM 4333, 6334; ECM 552
TIDES
+0610 Dover; Zone –0100

Standard Port POINTE DE GRAVE (→)

Times				Height (metres)			
High Water		Low Water		MHWS	MHWN	MLWN	MLWS
0000	0600	0500	1200	5·4	4·4	2·1	1·0
1200	1800	1700	2400				
Differences ROCHEFORT							
+0020	–0020	+0040	+0115	+1·0	+0·7	+0·1	+0·4
ILE D'AIX							
+0015	–0040	–0030	–0025	+0·7	+0·5	+0·3	–0·1

SHELTER
Rochefort is on N bank of La Charente, about 10M from Port-des-Barques. Entry advised on late flood, as bar breaks on ebb. ⚓ out of chan at Soubise or Martrou; or lock into Port de Plaisance on W bank. Bassin No 1 (access HW La Rochelle ±1; at nps access can be only HW±¼); waiting and fuel pontoon, just outside lock, dries to soft mud. Beware very strong currents here, other than at HW or LW. Bassin No 2 is entered from No 1, via lifting bridge. No 3 Bassin, 400m N, is for commercial craft only. The river is navigable 3·5M on to Tonnay-Charente.
NAVIGATION
WPT Les Palles NCM, Q, 45°59'·58N 01°09'·53W, 293°/ 113° from/to front ldg lt 115°, 4·0M. Stream in river runs about 2kn (4kn in narrows), and at sp there is a small bore. Beware wk just S of WPT. When WSW of Fouras pick up second (Port-des-Barques) ldg line (135°). The bar at Fouras carries about 0·5m. From Port-des-Barques follow the alignment of lettered pairs (RR to AA) of unlit ldg bns. Fixed bridge, 32m clearance, is 2M downriver of Basin No 1.
LIGHTS AND MARKS
Ile d'Aix Fl WR 5s 24m 24/20M; twin W trs with R tops; vis R103°-118°, W118°-103°. Ldg lts 115°, both QR, intens 113°-117°, W □ trs with R tops. Port Sud de Fouras, pier hd, Fl WR 4s 6m, 9/6M, vis R115°-177°, W177°-115°. Port-des-Barques ldg lts 135°, both Iso G 4s synch, intens 125°-145°, W □ trs; rear has B band on W side.
RADIO TELEPHONE
Port VHF Ch 12 16. Marina Ch 09 (HW±1).
TELEPHONE (Prefix ☎ Nos with zone code 05)
Hr Mr 46·83·99·96; Aff Mar 46·84·22·67; CROSS 56·09·82·00; ⌗ 46·99·03·90; Météo 46·41·11·11; Auto 08.36.68.08.17; Dr 46·99·61·11; Police 46·87·26·12; Brit Consul 56·52·28·35.
FACILITIES
Marina (380+20 visitors) in Basins 1 & 2 ☎ 46·83·99·96, 🔌 46·99·80·56, FF61, FW, ME, El, Sh, D & P (outside lock), AC, C (30 ton); **Port Neuf** Slip, FW; **Club Nautique Rochefortais** ☎ 46·87·34·61, Slip; **Services:** ME, El, Ⓔ, Sh, CH. **Town** P, D, V, Gaz, R, Bar, ✉, Ⓑ, ⇌, → (La Rochelle).
Ferry: Roscoff or St Malo.

ADJACENT ANCHORAGE AT MOUTH OF LA CHARENTE

ILE D'AIX, Charente Maritime, 46°01'·00N 01°10'·00W. AC 2746, 2748; SHOM 6914, 6334. HW +0545 on Dover (UT); ML 3·9m. Tides see 10.18.19. Only a fine weather ⚓ or pick up a buoy off the landing jetty at St Catherine's Pt, Fl WR 5s 24m 24/20M, the most southerly tip of the island. Moorings available E of St Catherine's Pt (shallow); four W buoys to west (deeper) and five SE of the pt. Facilities: C (1·5 ton), Slip, AB (SE jetty), V, R.

SEUDRE RIVER   10-18-20
Charente Maritime 45°48'·00N 01°08'·50W

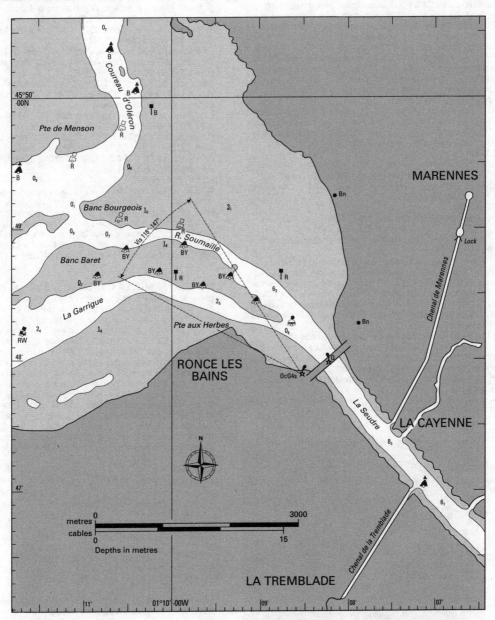

CHARTS
AC 2663; SHOM 6912, 6335; ECM 552

TIDES
+0545 Dover; ML 3·6; Duration Sp 0545, Np 0700

Standard Port POINTE DE GRAVE (⟶)

Times				Height (metres)			
High Water		Low Water		MHWS	MHWN	MLWN	MLWS
0000	0600	0500	1200	5·4	4·4	2·1	1·0
1200	1800	1700	2400				
Differences LA CAYENNE							
+0030	−0015	−0010	−0005	+0·2	+0·2	+0·3	0·0

SHELTER
Good in the yacht basin (2m) at Marennes. Lock opens about HW±2 sp, HW±1 np; or secure ⚓s at La Cayenne, La Grève (½M upstream), and at ent to Chenal de la Tremblade.

NAVIGATION
WPT 45°55'·88N 01°08'·65W, Chenal Est-Nord WCM buoy, for Chenal Est and Coureau d'Oléron. Best to appr La Seudre from N, through Coureau d'Oléron, and thence via Chenal de la Soumaille (dries about 0·7m). Chenal de la Garrigue carries slightly more water. Both are marked by bns and buoys.

Beware oyster beds. Pont de Seudre has clearance of 18m. Overhead power cables (24m) span Canal de Marennes. La Seudre is navigable to lock at Riberou. Beware: Pertuis de Maumusson is usable only in good weather, at about HW −1; see 8·18·5. In even moderate weather it is **extremely dangerous**, especially with out-going stream or any swell.

LIGHTS AND MARKS
There are no ldg lts/marks. Lights: Pte de Mus de Loup, Oc G 4s 8m 6M, vis 118°-147°. On bridge, between piers 6 and 7, Q 20m 10M, vis up/downstream. Chan marked by W boards.

RADIO TELEPHONE
VHF Ch 09.

TELEPHONE (Prefix ☎ Nos with zone code 05)
Marennes: Hr Mr 46·85·02·68; Aff Mar 46·85·14·33; Police 46·85·00·19; Dr 46·85·23·06. La Tremblade: Hr Mr 46·36·00·22; ⌗ 46·47·62·53; Dr 46·36·16·35; Auto 08.36.68.08.17; Brit Consul 56·36·16·35.

FACILITIES
MARENNES **Basin** ☎ 46·85·15·11, FW, AC, C (6 ton), ME, CH; **Services**: Sh, ME, CH. **Town** Slip, M, P, D, L, FW, V, R, Bar.
LA TREMBLADE **Quay** Slip, P, D, FW, C (5 ton); **Services**: ME, Sh, SM, CH. **Town** Slip, P, D, L, FW, Gaz, V, R, Bar, ⊠, Ⓑ, ⇌, ✈ (La Rochelle). Ferry: Roscoff or St Malo.

18

LA GIRONDE & CANALS   10-18-21

LA GIRONDE ESTUARY is a substantial waterway. The mouth of the estuary is 9M wide between Pointe de la Coubre and Pointe de Grave. From Royan to Bordeaux (55M) the river narrows from 6M wide to 2.5M at Pauillac. The outer apprs can be dangerous due to Atlantic swell, very strong tidal streams and currents, extensive shoals and shifting sandbanks, see 10·18·5. A combination of swell, strong W'lies and an ebb tide will raise dangerous, breaking seas some 5m high. Be alert for concentrations of shipping. In the Gironde and the R Dordogne the sp flood reaches 3kn and the ebb 4kn. In the R Garonne the sp flood starts with a small bore and then runs at about 3kn, while the ebb reaches 5kn. AC 2910 and 2916, or SHOM 7028 and 7029, are essential.

SHELTER
Yacht hbrs from Royan (10.18.22) to Bordeaux* include Port Bloc (10.18.23), St Georges-de-Didonne, Meschers, Mortagne, Pauillac*, Lamarque, Blaye* and Port de Bourg. For *hbrs, see 10·18·22.

NAVIGATION
WPT BXA SWM buoy, Iso 4s, Whis, Racon, 45°37'·60N 01°28'·60W, 261°/081° from/to Grande Passe de l'Ouest Nos 1 & 2 buoys, 4·8M. The estuary is entered via two approach channels:
(1) **Grande Passe de l'Ouest**. From BXA buoy 081° on La Palmyre ldg lts passes close S of Pte de la Coubre; thence 100° to pass abeam Pte de Terre-Nègre and enter the river on astern transit of 327° (see below). The chan is deep and well marked/lit. Give the Mauvaise bank, Banc de la Coubre and shoals around Cordouan a wide berth.
(2) **Passe du Sud**. From 'G' unlit SWM buoy track 063° on the ldg lts at St Nicolas/Pte de Grave until abeam Cordouan lt ho; thence 041° on Le Chay/St Pierre ldg lts to pick up the 327° astern transit (see below). The chan carries approx 5m through shoals; not advised in poor vis or heavy swell. Platin de Grave, between G4 and G7 Bys, has only 1·8m.
The astern transit 327° of Terre-Nègre lt with La Palmyre, FR 57m 17M, leads NE of Pte de Grave and up-river.

LIGHTS AND MARKS
(1) **Grande Passe de l'Ouest** ldg lts 081°, both intens 080·5°-082·5°: Front Dir Iso 4s 21m 22M, and Q (2) 5s 10m 3M same structure, W pylon on dolphin; rear, La Palmyre Dir Q 57m 27M, W radar tr. From No 9 SHM buoy, use W sector 097°- 104° of Pte de Terre-Nègre, Oc (3) WRG 12s 39m 18/14M.
(2) **Passe du Sud**, Outer ldg lts 063°: Front St Nicolas Dir QG 22m 16M, intens 061·5°-064·5°, W □ tr; rear, Pte de Grave Oc WRG 4s 26m 19/15M.
Inner ldg lts 041°, both QR 33/61m 18M, intens 039°-043°: Front, Le Chay; rear, Ste Pierre 0·97M from front.
Other major lts in estuary:
La Coubre lt ho, Fl (2) 10s 64m 28M RC, also FRG 42m 12/10M R030°-043°, G043°-060°, R060°-110°.
Courdouan lt Oc (2+1) WRG 12s 60m 22/18M, W014°-126°, G126°-178·5°, W178·5°-250°, W (unintens) 250°-267°, R (unintens) 267°-294·5°, R294·5°-014°; obscured in estuary when brg > 285°.

RADIO TELEPHONE
A VTS, which is compulsory for all vessels regardless of length, provides radar surveillance from BXA buoy to Bordeaux. Call *Bordeaux Traffic* or *Radar Verdon* on VHF Ch 12 16 (H24). In poor vis or on request *Radar Verdon* provides radar information between BXA and Verdon roads. Height of water is broadcast on Ch 17 every 5 mins, plus a weather bulletin and nav info on request.

CANAL LATÉRAL À LA GARONNE and CANAL DU MIDI
provide a popular route to the Mediterranean, despite over 130 locks. The transit can be done in about a week, but 12 days is more relaxed. Masts can be unstepped at Royan, Pauillac or Bordeaux. Leave Bordeaux at LW Pointe de Grave for the 30M passage up river to the first lock at Castets. Commercial traffic and W-bound boats have right of way. Most of the locks on the Canal Latéral à la Garonne are automatic. On the Canal du Midi there are many hire cruisers in the summer. Fuel is available by hose at Mas d'Agenais, Agen, Port Sud (Toulouse), Castelnaudary, Port la Robine, and by can elsewhere. V and FW are readily obtained. Further information from: Service de la Navigation de Toulouse, 8 Port St Etienne, 31079 Toulouse Cedex, ☎ 05·61·80·07·18. Tolls are listed in 10.15.8. *Guide Vagnon No 7* or *Navicarte No 11* are advised.

SUMMARY

Canal	From	To	Km/ Locks	Min Depth (m)	Min Height (m)
Latéral à la Garonne	Castets	Toulouse	193/ 53	2·2	3·5
Du Midi	Toulouse	Sete	240/ 65	1·6	3·0
De la Nouvelle	Salleles	Port la Nouvelle	37/ 14	1·5	3·1

Notes: Max LOA 30m; draft 1·5m (varies with season); max beam 5·5m. Headroom of 3·3m is to centre of arch; over a width of 4m, clearance is about 2·40m. Speed limit 8km/hr (about 4½kn), but 3km/hr under bridges/over aqueducts.

ROYAN   10-18-22

Charente Maritime 45°37'·20N 01°01'·54W   Rtg 3-1-1

CHARTS
AC 2910, 2916, 2664; Imray C41, 42; SHOM 7028, 7070; ECM 553, 554

TIDES
+0530 Dover; ML 3·2; Duration Sp 0615, Np 0655; Zone – 0100

Standard Port POINTE DE GRAVE (→)

Times				Height (metres)			
High Water		Low Water		MHWS	MHWN	MLWN	MLWS
0000	0600	0500	1200	5·4	4·4	2·1	1·0
1200	1800	1700	2400				
Differences ROYAN							
0000	–0005	–0005	–0005	–0·3	–0·2	0·0	0·0

SHELTER
Good. Easy access H24 except with strong W/NW winds. The ent chan is dredged 1·5m and basins approx 2·5m, but beware silting outside head of New Jetty. A good port of call for Canal du Midi with crane for masts.

NAVIGATION
WPT R1 SHM buoy, Iso G 4s, 45°36'·62N 01°01'·90W, 193°/013° from/to S Jetty lt, 0·47M. The Gironde apprs can be dangerous; see 10·18·5 and 10·18·21 for details; allow about 2 hrs from Pte de la Coubre to Royan. The banks off Royan shift and buoys are consequently altered. Off hbr ent, there is an eddy, running S at about 1kn on the flood and 3kn on the ebb. Beware fast ferries and FVs.

LIGHTS AND MARKS
See 10.14.21 for details of appr chans. Other lts as chartlet; the Iso 4s on end of Quai d'acceuil is a neon sign.

RADIO TELEPHONE
VHF Ch 09 16 (season 0800-2000; otherwise 0900-1800LT).

TELEPHONE (Prefix ☎ Nos with zone code 05)
Hr Mr 46·38·72·22; Aff Mar 46·39·26·30; CROSS 56·09·82·00; SNSM 46·38·75·79; ⌗ 46·38·51·27; Météo 56·34·20·11; Auto 08.36.68.08.17; Police 46·38·34·22; Dr 46·05·68·69; Ⓗ 46·38·01·77; Brit Consul 56·52·28·35.

FACILITIES
Marina (920 + 100 visitors) ☎ 46·38·72·22, ⚓ 46.39.42.47, FF132, Slip, P, D, FW, C (6 ton), BH (26 ton), ME, AC, El, Sh; **Les Régates de Royan** ☎ 46·05·44·§3; **Services:** CH, Ⓔ, SM, SHOM.
Town P, D, V, R, Bar, Gaz, ✉, Ⓑ, ⇌, ✈ (Bordeaux). Ferry: Roscoff or St Malo.

OTHER HARBOURS ON THE GIRONDE

MESCHERS-sur-GIRONDE, Charente Maritime, 45°33'·15N 00°56'·55W. AC 2910, 2916; SHOM 7028; ECM 554. Tides as for ROYAN, 5M down-river same bank. Good shelter in all weathers, but access via drying chan is HW–3 to HW. Appr close to Pte de Meschers between PHM and SHM unlit perches. Narrow chan has shore close to port and mudbank close to stbd. Ldg marks/lts 000° are 2 FW on W posts; entry to hbr is just before the front ldg mark. To stbd drying marina basin has access HW±3. Dead ahead an automatic lock gives access over sill 2m CD to a wet basin HW±2½ by day; waiting pontoons. Hr Mr ☎ 05.46.02.56.89; Auto 05.36.68.08.17. Facilities: **Marinas** (125 in drying basin, 123 in wet basin, 18 visitors), FW, AC. **Town** P & D (cans), R, Bar, V.

MORTAGNE-sur-GIRONDE (La Rive), Charente Maritime, 45°28'·25N 00°48'·75W. AC 2916; SHOM 7028, 7029. Tides, use RICHARD differences (10.18.21). Good shelter in marina on E bank of river, 14M from Royan/40M from Bordeaux (near the 75km mark). Leave the main Gironde chan at No 18 PHM buoy, Fl (2) R 6s, and head E for 4·5M to Mortagne appr chan. Ent is marked by large RW stone dolphin, with ☆ Oc R 2·5s 9m 4M; keep at least 20m clear SE of it due to concrete debris. Enter chan, 2·5m at mean tides, on 063°, between 2 unlit perches, for 0·9M across drying mudbanks to lock which opens HW–2 to HW. VHF Ch 09. Hr Mr ☎ 05.46.90.63.15. Facilities: **Marina** (130+20 visitors), 6m depth, FW, AC, Slip, ME, BY, BH (10 ton), V, Ice; Fuel, Aff Mar, ⌗, and SNSM at Royan; Auto 05.36.68.08.17.

PAUILLAC, Gironde, 45°11'·88N 00°44'·53W. Rtg 4-3-1. AC 2916, 2910; SHOM 7029; HW +0620 on Dover (UT); ML 3·0m. See 10.18.21. Excellent shelter in marina on W bank, 25M from Le Verdon, and at 47km post from Bordeaux. Access at all tides (depth 1·5m), but keep very close to NE side of ent at LW, due to silting. Visitors use pontoon A at ent. Beware current in the river on ent/dep. Lts: Fl G 4s 7m 5M on NE elbow of bkwtr. Ent at S end is marked by QG and QR. Hr Mr ☎ 05·56·59·12·16, ⚓ 05.56.59.25.82; VHF Ch 09 (0800–1800LT). Aff Mar 05·56·59·01·58; SNSM/CROSS 05·56·09·82·00; ⌗ 05·56 ·59·04·01; Météo 05·36·68·08·33. Facilities: **Marina** (200+ 50 Ⓥ), ☎ 05·56·59·12·16, FW, AC, Slip, ME, El, Sh; **Quay** FW, D, P (cans), C (14 ton); **CN de Pauillac** ☎ 05·56·59·12·58; **Services:** C for mast step/un-step, CH, Sh.

BLAYE, Charente Maritime, 45°07'·53N 00°39'·90W. AC 2916; SHOM 7029. HW +0715 on Dover (UT); HW +0145 and –0·3m on Pte de Grave; ML 2·4m. Good shelter; access good except in S to SW winds. Ent is abeam S end of of Ile Nouvelle at 37km post and close S of La Citadelle (conspic). N quay has Q (3) R 5s 6m 3M, on R mast. Max stay 24 hours. VHF Ch 12 (0800–1800LT). Hr Mr ☎ 05·57·42·13·63, ⚓ 05·57·42·28·19; Facilities: **Quay** Access HW±2½, FW, AC, P, D, C (25 ton), Slip, ME.

BORDEAUX, Gironde, 44°52'·80N 00°32'·30W. AC 2916; SHOM 7029, 7030. HW +0715 on Dover (UT); ML 2·4m. See 10.18.21. Bordeaux is about 55M up the Gironde estuary and R Garonne. Beware big ships, strong currents (up to 5kn when river in spate) and large bits of flotsam. The chan is well marked and lit. Pte du Jour marina is 2M from city centre, on W bank close S of Pont d'Aquitaine suspension bridge (clearance 51m), with 20 visitors berths and de-masting crane, (less handy than Royan's crane). Berths may also be available, by arrangement with Hr Mr, 1½M above bridge in No 2 Basin, access HW –1 to HW+½; crane available. Or berth on wharves between No 1 Basin and Pont de Pierre, but stream is strong. VHF Ch 12. Hr Mr ☎ 05·56·52·51·04; Aff Mar ☎ 05·56·52·26·23; ⌗ ☎ 05·56·44·47·10; Météo ☎ 05·56·90·91·21; Facilities: **Marina** ☎ 05·56·50·84·14 VHF Ch 09; **Sport Nautique de la Gironde** ☎ 05·56·50·84·14; **Services:** Slip, C (5 ton), ME, El, Sh, CH, Ⓔ, SHOM.

18

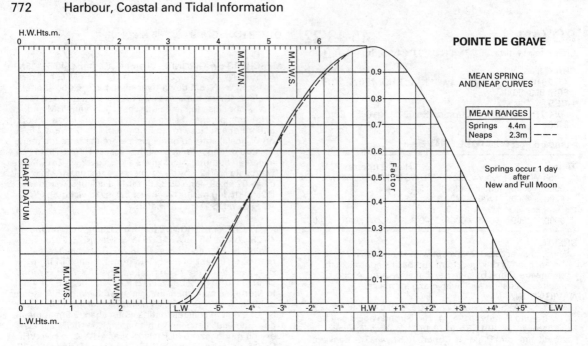

POINTE DE GRAVE

MEAN SPRING
AND NEAP CURVES

MEAN RANGES	
Springs	4.4m
Neaps	2.3m

Springs occur 1 day
after
New and Full Moon

PORT BLOC   10-18-23

Gironde 45°34'·18N 01°03'·64W   Rtg 3-4-2

CHARTS

AC 2910, 2664, 2916; Imray C42; ECM 553, 554; SHOM
7028, 6335. Note: 7029 & 7030 cover to Bordeaux/Libourne

TIDES

(Pauillac) +0720 Dover; ML 3·0; Duration: Sp 0615; Np
0655; Zone –0100
NOTE: Pte de Grave is a Standard Port; tidal predictions for
each day of the year are given below and apply to Port Bloc

Standard Port POINTE DE GRAVE (→)

Times				Height (metres)			
High Water		Low Water		MHWS	MHWN	MLWN	MLWS
0000	0600	0500	1200	5·4	4·4	2·1	1·0
1200	1800	1700	2400				
Differences RICHARD							
+0018	+0018	+0028	+0033	–0·1	–0·1	–0·4	–0·5
LAMENA							
+0035	+0045	+0100	+0125	+0·2	+0·1	–0·5	–0·3
PAUILLAC							
+0100	+0100	+0135	+0205	+0·1	0·0	–1·0	–0·5
LA REUILLE							
+0135	+0145	+0230	+0305	–0·2	–0·3	–1·3	–0·7
LE MARQUIS							
+0145	+0150	+0247	+0322	–0·3	–0·4	–1·5	–0·9
BORDEAUX							
+0200	+0225	+0330	+0405	–0·1	–0·2	–1·7	–1·0
LIBOURNE (La Dordogne)							
+0250	+0305	+0525	+0540	–0·7	–0·9	–2·0	–0·4

SHELTER

Good, but mainly a ferry hbr, dredged 3m and 4ca S of
Pte de Grave. Space for yachts is limited; possible AB on
pontoons on W side of the hbr. Royan is a better option.

NAVIGATION

WPT 13b SHM buoy, QG, 45°34'·66N 01°02'·90W, 047°/
227° from/to hbr ent, 7ca. Caution strong tidal streams. Ent
is 30m wide; ferries have priority.

LIGHTS AND MARKS

Pte de Grave lt ho, Oc WRG 4s 26m 19/15M, W □ tr, B
corners and top. Hbr ent: NW quay Fl G 4s 9m 3M, SE
bkwtr Iso R 4s 8m 4M. Le Verdon oil jetty is 1.5M SSE.

RADIO TELEPHONE

Radar Verdon Ch 11 12 (H24).

TELEPHONE (Prefix ☎ Nos with zone code 05)

Hr Mr 56·09·63·91; Aff Mar 56·09·60·23; CROSS 56·73·31·31;
⌗ 56·09·65·14; Météo 56·34·20·11; Auto 08·36·68·08·17;
Police 56·09·80·29; Dr 56·09·60·37; Brit Consul 56·52·28·35.

FACILITIES

Moto Yachting Club de la Pte de Grave ☎ 56·09·84·02, D,
FW, C (10 ton), ME, El, Sh, CH. **Town** P, Gaz, V, R, ✉ & ⑧
(Verdon), ⇌, ✈ (Bordeaux). Ferry: Local to Royan.

FRANCE – POINTE DE GRAVE

LAT 45°34′N   LONG 1°04′W

TIMES AND HEIGHTS OF HIGH AND LOW WATERS

YEAR 1998

JANUARY

Day	Time	m	Time	m	Time	m	Time	m
1 TH	0022	1.2	0641	5.5	1248	1.1	1906	5.3
2 F	0105	1.2	0727	5.5	1332	1.1	1952	5.2
3 SA	0150	1.3	0816	5.4	1417	1.2	2043	5.0
4 SU	0238	1.4	0909	5.2	1507	1.4	2142	4.8
5 M	0333	1.6	1011	5.0	1604	1.6	2251	4.7
6 TU	0436	1.7	1121	4.9	1708	1.7		
7 W	0007	4.7	0545	1.8	1234	4.8	1820	1.8
8 TH	0118	4.7	0658	1.8	1345	4.9	1932	1.7
9 F	0221	4.9	0807	1.6	1448	5.0	2036	1.6
10 SA	0316	5.1	0908	1.5	1542	5.1	2131	1.4
11 SU	0404	5.2	1000	1.3	1629	5.2	2219	1.3
12 M O	0447	5.4	1048	1.2	1711	5.3	2303	1.2
13 TU	0525	5.4	1130	1.1	1749	5.3	2342	1.2
14 W	0602	5.4	1209	1.2	1824	5.2		
15 TH	0019	1.2	0636	5.4	1245	1.2	1857	5.1
16 F	0054	1.3	0708	5.2	1320	1.3	1929	5.0
17 SA	0129	1.4	0740	5.1	1355	1.5	2002	4.8
18 SU	0205	1.6	0815	4.9	1431	1.7	2041	4.6
19 M	0244	1.8	0855	4.7	1510	1.9	2127	4.4
20 TU	0327	2.0	0944	4.5	1554	2.1	2227	4.3
21 W	0420	2.2	1049	4.3	1701	2.3	2341	4.2
22 TH	0526	2.3	1210	4.2	1813	2.3		
23 F	0054	4.3	0639	2.3	1326	4.3	1920	2.2
24 SA	0156	4.5	0744	2.1	1427	4.5	2017	1.9
25 SU	0248	4.8	0840	1.8	1517	4.8	2108	1.7
26 M	0334	5.1	0932	1.5	1602	5.1	2155	1.4
27 TU	0419	5.3	1020	1.3	1646	5.3	2241	1.2
28 W ●	0502	5.6	1107	1.0	1728	5.5	2326	1.0
29 TH	0546	5.7	1152	0.8	1811	5.6		
30 F	0011	0.9	0630	5.8	1236	0.8	1855	5.5
31 SA	0055	0.9	0715	5.8	1319	0.8	1939	5.4

FEBRUARY

Day	Time	m	Time	m	Time	m	Time	m
1 SU	0138	1.0	0801	5.6	1403	0.9	2025	5.2
2 M	0224	1.1	0850	5.4	1428	1.7	2116	5.0
3 TU	0313	1.3	0945	5.1	1540	1.4	2218	4.7
4 W	0411	1.6	1052	4.8	1640	1.7	2336	4.6
5 TH	0519	1.8	1211	4.6	1752	1.9		
6 F	0057	4.6	0636	1.9	1331	4.6	1911	1.9
7 SA	0208	4.7	0752	1.8	1440	4.7	2022	1.8
8 SU	0307	4.9	0856	1.6	1535	4.7	2118	1.6
9 M	0355	5.1	0948	1.4	1620	5.0	2206	1.4
10 TU	0434	5.2	1034	1.3	1657	5.2	2248	1.3
11 W O	0509	5.3	1114	1.2	1730	5.2	2325	1.2
12 TH	0541	5.4	1150	1.1	1801	5.2	2359	1.2
13 F	0612	5.4	1223	1.2	1830	5.2		
14 SA	0031	1.2	0641	5.3	1254	1.2	1859	5.1
15 SU	0102	1.3	0710	5.2	1325	1.3	1929	5.0
16 M	0134	1.4	0741	5.0	1356	1.5	2001	4.8
17 TU	0207	1.5	0815	4.8	1428	1.7	2038	4.6
18 W	0243	1.7	0854	4.6	1508	1.9	2124	4.4
19 TH	0327	2.0	0946	4.3	1556	2.1	2228	4.2
20 F	0424	2.2	1102	4.2	1703	2.3	2352	4.2
21 SA	0542	2.3	1235	4.2	1828	2.3		
22 SU	0114	4.4	0702	2.1	1352	4.4	1940	2.1
23 M	0218	4.7	0809	1.8	1451	4.7	2040	1.8
24 TU	0311	5.0	0907	1.5	1542	5.1	2133	1.4
25 W	0359	5.4	0959	1.2	1627	5.4	2222	1.1
26 TH ●	0445	5.7	1047	0.9	1711	5.6	2309	0.8
27 F	0529	5.9	1134	0.6	1754	5.7	2354	0.7
28 SA	0614	6.0	1218	0.6	1838	5.7		

MARCH

Day	Time	m	Time	m	Time	m	Time	m
1 SU	0038	0.6	0658	6.0	1301	0.6	1921	5.6
2 M	0121	0.7	0743	5.8	1343	0.8	2005	5.4
3 TU	0205	0.9	0829	5.5	1427	1.1	2051	5.1
4 W	0252	1.2	0921	5.1	1515	1.4	2147	4.8
5 TH	0346	1.5	1025	4.7	1612	1.8	2303	4.5
6 F	0452	1.8	1150	4.5	1724	2.1		
7 SA	0033	4.5	0613	2.0	1316	4.4	1849	2.1
8 SU	0151	4.6	0735	1.9	1428	4.6	2003	2.0
9 M	0252	4.8	0839	1.7	1522	4.8	2101	1.7
10 TU	0339	5.0	0930	1.5	1603	5.0	2147	1.5
11 W	0416	5.1	1013	1.3	1636	5.1	2227	1.3
12 TH	0448	5.2	1051	1.2	1706	5.2	2303	1.2
13 F O	0518	5.3	1125	1.1	1735	5.2	2335	1.2
14 SA	0547	5.3	1157	1.1	1803	5.3		
15 SU	0006	1.1	0615	5.3	1226	1.2	1831	5.2
16 M	0036	1.2	0643	5.2	1255	1.3	1859	5.1
17 TU	0105	1.2	0712	5.1	1323	1.4	1929	5.0
18 W	0136	1.4	0744	4.9	1355	1.5	2003	4.8
19 TH	0210	1.5	0820	4.7	1430	1.7	2043	4.6
20 F	0250	1.8	0907	4.4	1514	2.0	2140	4.4
21 SA	0342	2.0	1017	4.2	1614	2.2	2259	4.2
22 SU	0455	2.1	1150	4.2	1740	2.2		
23 M	0031	4.3	0622	2.1	1318	4.4	1902	2.1
24 TU	0145	4.6	0737	1.8	1423	4.7	2010	1.8
25 W	0245	5.0	0839	1.4	1517	5.1	2107	1.4
26 TH	0336	5.4	0934	1.1	1605	5.4	2159	1.0
27 F	0423	5.7	1024	0.8	1650	5.7	2248	0.8
28 SA ●	0509	5.9	1111	0.6	1734	5.8	2334	0.6
29 SU	0554	6.0	1156	0.5	1817	5.8		
30 M	0019	0.5	0638	6.0	1240	0.6	1901	5.7
31 TU	0102	0.6	0723	5.8	1322	0.8	1944	5.5

APRIL

Day	Time	m	Time	m	Time	m	Time	m
1 W	0145	0.8	0809	5.4	1405	1.1	2029	5.2
2 TH	0231	1.1	0858	5.0	1451	1.5	2120	4.8
3 F	0323	1.5	1000	4.6	1546	1.8	2229	4.6
4 SA	0426	1.8	1124	4.4	1655	2.1	2359	4.4
5 SU	0544	2.0	1252	4.3	1818	2.2		
6 M	0121	4.5	0707	2.0	1402	4.5	1934	2.1
7 TU	0225	4.6	0813	1.8	1455	4.7	2033	1.8
8 W	0312	4.8	0903	1.6	1534	4.9	2119	1.6
9 TH	0349	5.0	0945	1.4	1606	5.0	2159	1.4
10 F	0421	5.1	1022	1.3	1636	5.1	2235	1.3
11 SA O	0451	5.2	1056	1.2	1705	5.2	2308	1.2
12 SU	0520	5.2	1127	1.2	1735	5.3	2339	1.2
13 M	0549	5.2	1157	1.2	1804	5.2		
14 TU	0009	1.2	0618	5.2	1226	1.2	1833	5.2
15 W	0040	1.2	0648	5.1	1255	1.3	1904	5.1
16 TH	0111	1.3	0721	4.9	1328	1.5	1938	4.9
17 F	0146	1.4	0758	4.7	1404	1.6	2020	4.7
18 SA	0226	1.6	0846	4.5	1447	1.8	2115	4.5
19 SU	0317	1.8	0952	4.3	1545	2.1	2228	4.4
20 M	0424	2.0	1117	4.3	1705	2.1	2353	4.5
21 TU	0547	1.9	1244	4.5	1826	2.0		
22 W	0111	4.7	0703	1.7	1352	4.8	1937	1.7
23 TH	0214	5.0	0809	1.4	1449	5.1	2038	1.4
24 F	0310	5.4	0906	1.1	1540	5.4	2133	1.0
25 SA	0400	5.7	0958	0.8	1627	5.6	2224	0.8
26 SU ●	0447	5.9	1047	0.6	1712	5.8	2312	0.6
27 M	0533	5.9	1133	0.6	1757	5.8	2358	0.6
28 TU	0619	5.8	1217	0.7	1841	5.7		
29 W	0042	0.7	0705	5.6	1300	0.9	1925	5.5
30 TH	0126	0.9	0750	5.3	1343	1.2	2009	5.2

18

Chart Datum: 2·83 metres below Lallemand System (Mean Sea Level, Marseilles)

TIME ZONE –0100
(French Standard Time)
Subtract 1 hour for UT
For French Summer Time add ONE hour in non-shaded areas

FRANCE – POINTE DE GRAVE

LAT 45°34′N   LONG 1°04′W

TIMES AND HEIGHTS OF HIGH AND LOW WATERS

YEAR **1998**

MAY

Day	Time	m	Time	m
1 F	0211 / 0838 / 1429 / 2057	1.2 / 5.0 / 1.5 / 4.9	16 SA: 0130 / 0746 / 1346 / 2008	1.3 / 4.8 / 1.5 / 4.9
2 SA	0300 / 0933 / 1521 / 2154	1.5 / 4.6 / 1.8 / 4.6	17 SU: 0211 / 0835 / 1431 / 2102	1.5 / 4.6 / 1.7 / 4.7
3 SU	0357 / 1046 / 1623 / 2310	1.8 / 4.4 / 2.1 / 4.4	18 M: 0302 / 0936 / 1528 / 2209	1.6 / 4.5 / 1.9 / 4.6
4 M	0508 / 1208 / 1737	2.0 / 4.3 / 2.2	19 TU: 0404 / 1052 / 1640 / 2324	1.7 / 4.4 / 1.9 / 4.6
5 TU	0031 / 0625 / 1319 / 1851	4.4 / 2.1 / 4.4 / 2.1	20 W: 0518 / 1212 / 1755	1.7 / 4.5 / 1.9
6 W	0139 / 0733 / 1413 / 1953	4.5 / 1.9 / 4.6 / 2.0	21 TH: 0038 / 0631 / 1322 / 1906	4.8 / 1.6 / 4.8 / 1.6
7 TH	0232 / 0826 / 1455 / 2042	4.6 / 1.8 / 4.7 / 1.8	22 F: 0145 / 0738 / 1422 / 2010	5.0 / 1.4 / 5.0 / 1.4
8 F	0313 / 0910 / 1531 / 2124	4.8 / 1.6 / 4.9 / 1.6	23 SA: 0243 / 0838 / 1515 / 2108	5.3 / 1.1 / 5.1 / 1.1
9 SA	0349 / 0948 / 1604 / 2202	4.9 / 1.4 / 5.0 / 1.5	24 SU: 0337 / 0933 / 1605 / 2202	5.3 / 0.9 / 5.5 / 0.9
10 SU	0422 / 1023 / 1636 / 2238	5.0 / 1.3 / 5.1 / 1.3	25 M: 0427 / 1024 / 1652 / ●2252	5.6 / 0.8 / 5.6 / 0.7
11 M O	0454 / 1056 / 1707 / 2312	5.1 / 1.3 / 5.2 / 1.3	26 TU: 0516 / 1112 / 1738 / 2339	5.6 / 0.8 / 5.6 / 0.7
12 TU	0526 / 1129 / 1739 / 2345	5.1 / 1.2 / 5.2 / 1.2	27 W: 0602 / 1157 / 1823	5.6 / 0.9 / 5.6
13 W	0557 / 1201 / 1812	5.1 / 1.3 / 5.2	28 TH: 0024 / 0648 / 1240 / 1907	0.8 / 5.4 / 1.0 / 5.4
14 TH	0019 / 0630 / 1233 / 1846	1.2 / 5.0 / 1.3 / 5.1	29 F: 0108 / 0732 / 1323 / 1949	1.0 / 5.2 / 1.2 / 5.2
15 F	0053 / 0705 / 1307 / 1924	1.3 / 4.9 / 1.4 / 5.0	30 SA: 0151 / 0816 / 1407 / 2032	1.2 / 5.0 / 1.5 / 5.0
			31 SU: 0237 / 0903 / 1454 / 2119	1.4 / 4.6 / 1.7 / 4.7

JUNE

Day	Time	m	Time	m
1 M	0327 / 0958 / 1548 / 2215	1.7 / 4.4 / 1.9 / 4.5	16 TU: 0251 / 0922 / 1515 / 2151	1.4 / 4.7 / 1.6 / 4.8
2 TU	0426 / 1106 / 1650 / 2324	1.9 / 4.3 / 2.1 / 4.4	17 W: 0347 / 1028 / 1618 / 2258	1.5 / 4.6 / 1.7 / 4.8
3 W	0533 / 1216 / 1758	2.0 / 4.3 / 2.1	18 TH: 0451 / 1141 / 1727	1.5 / 4.6 / 1.7
4 TH	0036 / 0641 / 1318 / 1902	4.3 / 2.0 / 4.4 / 2.1	19 F: 0009 / 0600 / 1253 / 1837	4.8 / 1.5 / 4.7 / 1.6
5 F	0139 / 0740 / 1409 / 1958	4.4 / 1.9 / 4.5 / 1.9	20 SA: 0117 / 0709 / 1357 / 1944	4.9 / 1.4 / 4.9 / 1.4
6 SA	0231 / 0829 / 1452 / 2045	4.6 / 1.7 / 4.7 / 1.8	21 SU: 0221 / 0814 / 1455 / 2047	5.0 / 1.3 / 5.1 / 1.2
7 SU	0314 / 0911 / 1531 / 2128	4.7 / 1.6 / 4.9 / 1.6	22 M: 0319 / 0913 / 1547 / 2143	5.2 / 1.2 / 5.2 / 1.1
8 M	0353 / 0950 / 1607 / 2208	4.8 / 1.5 / 5.0 / 1.5	23 TU: 0412 / 1006 / 1636 / 2235	5.3 / 1.0 / 5.4 / 0.9
9 TU	0429 / 1027 / 1643 / 2246	4.8 / 1.4 / 5.1 / 1.3	24 W: 0502 / 1055 / 1722 / ●2324	5.3 / 1.0 / 5.4 / 0.9
10 W O	0505 / 1104 / 1718 / 2324	5.0 / 1.3 / 5.2 / 1.2	25 TH: 0548 / 1140 / 1806	5.3 / 1.0 / 5.4
11 TH	0540 / 1140 / 1755	5.1 / 1.3 / 5.2	26 F: 0009 / 0631 / 1223 / 1847	0.9 / 5.2 / 1.1 / 5.3
12 F	0002 / 0616 / 1217 / 1833	1.2 / 5.0 / 1.3 / 5.2	27 SA: 0051 / 0712 / 1303 / 1926	1.0 / 5.1 / 1.2 / 5.2
13 SA	0040 / 0655 / 1254 / 1915	1.2 / 5.0 / 1.4 / 5.1	28 SU: 0131 / 0750 / 1344 / 2004	1.2 / 4.9 / 1.4 / 5.0
14 SU	0119 / 0738 / 1334 / 2000	1.2 / 4.9 / 1.4 / 5.0	29 M: 0212 / 0829 / 1425 / 2042	1.4 / 4.7 / 1.6 / 4.7
15 M	0202 / 0826 / 1421 / 2052	1.3 / 4.8 / 1.5 / 4.9	30 TU: 0254 / 0911 / 1510 / 2127	1.6 / 4.5 / 1.8 / 4.6

JULY

Day	Time	m	Time	m
1 W	0342 / 1003 / 1601 / 2221	1.8 / 4.3 / 2.0 / 4.4	16 TH: 0328 / 1003 / 1557 / 2234	1.3 / 4.7 / 1.5 / 4.8
2 TH	0437 / 1107 / 1700 / 2328	2.0 / 4.2 / 2.1 / 4.2	17 F: 0426 / 1113 / 1703 / 2344	1.5 / 4.6 / 1.6 / 4.7
3 F	0540 / 1216 / 1805	2.1 / 4.2 / 2.1	18 SA: 0533 / 1229 / 1814	1.6 / 4.6 / 1.6
4 SA	0040 / 0645 / 1320 / 1908	4.2 / 2.0 / 4.3 / 2.1	19 SU: 0057 / 0645 / 1340 / 1926	4.7 / 1.6 / 4.7 / 1.6
5 SU	0145 / 0743 / 1413 / 2004	4.3 / 1.9 / 4.5 / 1.9	20 M: 0207 / 0756 / 1442 / 2033	4.8 / 1.5 / 4.9 / 1.4
6 M	0238 / 0833 / 1459 / 2054	4.5 / 1.8 / 4.7 / 1.7	21 TU: 0309 / 0859 / 1537 / 2132	4.9 / 1.4 / 5.1 / 1.2
7 TU	0324 / 0918 / 1541 / 2139	4.6 / 1.6 / 4.9 / 1.5	22 W: 0404 / 0953 / 1625 / 2224	5.0 / 1.2 / 5.2 / 1.1
8 W	0406 / 1001 / 1621 / 2223	4.8 / 1.4 / 5.0 / 1.4	23 TH: 0451 / 1041 / 1708 / ●2311	5.1 / 1.1 / 5.3 / 1.0
9 TH	0445 / 1042 / 1700 / O 2305	4.9 / 1.3 / 5.2 / 1.2	24 F: 0534 / 1125 / 1748 / 2353	5.1 / 1.1 / 5.3 / 1.0
10 F	0524 / 1123 / 1740 / 2347	5.1 / 1.2 / 5.3* / 1.1	25 SA: 0612 / 1205 / 1825	5.1 / 1.1 / 5.3
11 SA	0604 / 1203 / 1821	5.1 / 1.1 / 5.3	26 SU: 0032 / 0648 / 1242 / 1859	1.1 / 5.1 / 1.2 / 5.2
12 SU	0028 / 0645 / 1244 / 1904	1.0 / 5.1 / 1.1 / 5.3	27 M: 0109 / 0720 / 1318 / 1931	1.2 / 4.9 / 1.3 / 5.0
13 M	0110 / 0727 / 1326 / 1949	1.0 / 5.1 / 1.2 / 5.3	28 TU: 0144 / 0752 / 1354 / 2005	1.3 / 4.8 / 1.4 / 4.8
14 TU	0152 / 0813 / 1411 / 2038	1.1 / 5.0 / 1.3 / 5.1	29 W: 0220 / 0828 / 1432 / 2042	1.5 / 4.6 / 1.6 / 4.6
15 W	0237 / 0904 / 1500 / 2132	1.2 / 4.8 / 1.4 / 5.0	30 TH: 0259 / 0904 / 1513 / 2128	1.7 / 4.4 / 1.8 / 4.4
			31 F: 0343 / 1003 / 1603 / 2226	1.9 / 4.2 / 2.0 / 4.2

AUGUST

Day	Time	m	Time	m
1 SA	0438 / 1110 / 1705 / 2339	2.1 / 4.1 / 2.2 / 4.1	16 SU: 0509 / 1211 / 1755	1.8 / 4.5 / 1.8
2 SU	0546 / 1226 / 1817	2.2 / 4.1 / 2.2	17 M: 0046 / 0626 / 1329 / 1914	4.5 / 1.9 / 4.6 / 1.7
3 M	0057 / 0655 / 1334 / 1924	4.1 / 2.1 / 4.3 / 2.1	18 TU: 0201 / 0744 / 1435 / 2025	4.6 / 1.8 / 4.8 / 1.6
4 TU	0203 / 0756 / 1429 / 2022	4.3 / 2.0 / 4.5 / 1.9	19 W: 0305 / 0849 / 1529 / 2122	4.7 / 1.6 / 5.0 / 1.4
5 W	0256 / 0848 / 1516 / 2113	4.5 / 1.7 / 4.8 / 1.6	20 TH: 0356 / 0942 / 1614 / 2211	4.9 / 1.4 / 5.1 / 1.2
6 TH	0342 / 0936 / 1559 / 2200	4.7 / 1.5 / 5.0 / 1.3	21 F: 0438 / 1027 / 1653 / 2255	5.0 / 1.2 / 5.2 / 1.1
7 F	0425 / 1021 / 1641 / 2246	5.0 / 1.3 / 5.3 / 1.1	22 SA: 0515 / 1108 / 1727 / ●2334	5.1 / 1.1 / 5.3 / 1.1
8 SA	0506 / 1105 / 1723 / O 2330	5.1 / 1.1 / 5.4 / 0.9	23 SU: 0547 / 1145 / 1759	5.1 / 1.1 / 5.3
9 SU	0548 / 1148 / 1806	5.3 / 1.0 / 5.5	24 M: 0009 / 0618 / 1218 / 1829	1.1 / 5.1 / 1.2 / 5.2
10 M	0013 / 0630 / 1231 / 1849	0.8 / 5.3 / 0.9 / 5.6	25 TU: 0042 / 0647 / 1250 / 1858	1.2 / 5.0 / 1.2 / 5.1
11 TU	0055 / 0712 / 1313 / 1934	0.8 / 5.3 / 0.9 / 5.5	26 W: 0113 / 0716 / 1321 / 1928	1.3 / 4.9 / 1.4 / 4.9
12 W	0137 / 0757 / 1357 / 2021	0.9 / 5.2 / 1.0 / 5.3	27 TH: 0144 / 0747 / 1354 / 2000	1.4 / 4.7 / 1.5 / 4.7
13 TH	0220 / 0844 / 1443 / 2112	1.0 / 5.0 / 1.2 / 5.1	28 F: 0214 / 0823 / 1429 / 2039	1.6 / 4.5 / 1.7 / 4.5
14 F	0308 / 0940 / 1537 / 2212	1.3 / 4.7 / 1.4 / 4.8	29 SA: 0253 / 0906 / 1510 / 2128	1.8 / 4.3 / 2.0 / 4.2
15 SA	0403 / 1049 / 1640 / 2326	1.5 / 4.5 / 1.7 / 4.6	30 SU: 0338 / 1006 / 1604 / 2239	2.1 / 4.1 / 2.2 / 4.0
			31 M: 0438 / 1127 / 1722	2.3 / 4.1 / 2.3

Chart Datum: 2·83 metres below Lallemand System (Mean Sea Level, Marseilles)

TIME ZONE –0100
(French Standard Time)
Subtract 1 hour for UT
For French Summer Time add ONE hour in non-shaded areas

FRANCE – POINTE DE GRAVE

LAT 45°34′N   LONG 1°04′W

TIMES AND HEIGHTS OF HIGH AND LOW WATERS

YEAR **1998**

SEPTEMBER

Day	Time	m	Time	m	Time	m	Time	m
1 TU	0008	4.0	0603	2.3	1252	4.2	1844	2.2
2 W	0127	4.2	0718	2.1	1358	4.5	1950	2.0
3 TH	0227	4.5	0818	1.9	1450	4.8	2046	1.6
4 F	0317	4.8	0910	1.5	1536	5.1	2136	1.3
5 SA	0402	5.1	0958	1.3	1620	5.4	2223	1.0
6 SU	0445	5.3	1044	1.0	1703	5.6	O 2308	0.8
7 M	0528	5.5	1129	0.8	1746	5.8	2352	0.7
8 TU	0610	5.5	1213	0.7	1830	5.8		
9 W	0035	0.7	0653	5.5	1256	0.8	1915	5.7
10 TH	0117	0.8	0737	5.3	1339	0.9	2001	5.4
11 F	0200	1.0	0824	5.1	1424	1.2	2052	5.1
12 SA	0246	1.3	0918	4.8	1516	1.5	2154	4.7
13 SU	0340	1.7	1029	4.6	1619	1.8	2314	4.5
14 M	0448	2.0	1157	4.4	1738	2.0		
15 TU	0041	4.4	0610	2.1	1320	4.5	1903	1.9
16 W	0156	4.5	0731	2.0	1426	4.7	2014	1.7
17 TH	0256	4.7	0834	1.7	1519	4.9	2108	1.5
18 F	0342	4.9	0925	1.5	1559	5.1	2153	1.3
19 SA	0419	5.0	0933	1.3	1632	5.2	2233	1.2
20 SU	0449	5.1	1046	1.2	1702	5.3	● 2309	1.2
21 M	0518	5.1	1120	1.2	1731	5.3	2342	1.2
22 TU	0547	5.1	1152	1.2	1759	5.2		
23 W	0012	1.2	0615	5.1	1222	1.3	1827	5.1
24 TH	0041	1.3	0643	5.0	1251	1.4	1855	5.0
25 F	0110	1.5	0712	4.9	1321	1.5	1925	4.8
26 SA	0139	1.6	0744	4.7	1354	1.7	1959	4.5
27 SU	0213	1.8	0822	4.5	1431	1.9	2043	4.3
28 M	0253	2.1	0916	4.3	1519	2.1	2151	4.1
29 TU	0348	2.3	1035	4.1	1629	2.3	2324	4.0
30 W	0511	2.4	1208	4.2	1801	2.3		

OCTOBER

Day	Time	m	Time	m	Time	m	Time	m
1 TH	0053	4.2	0637	2.3	1323	4.5	1916	2.0
2 F	0158	4.5	0745	2.0	1421	4.9	2016	1.7
3 SA	0250	4.9	0841	1.6	1511	5.2	2108	1.3
4 SU	0337	5.2	0933	1.3	1556	5.5	2157	1.0
5 M	0422	5.5	1021	1.0	1641	5.8	O 2244	0.8
6 TU	0505	5.6	1107	0.8	1725	5.9	2329	0.7
7 W	0549	5.7	1152	0.7	1810	5.9		
8 TH	0013	0.7	0633	5.6	1236	0.7	1856	5.7
9 F	0056	0.9	0718	5.5	1320	0.9	1943	5.4
10 SA	0140	1.1	0806	5.2	1406	1.2	2036	5.1
11 SU	0226	1.5	0900	4.9	1457	1.5	2139	4.7
12 M	0320	1.8	1010	4.6	1559	1.9	2302	4.4
13 TU	0426	2.1	1138	4.5	1717	2.1		
14 W	0028	4.4	0548	2.2	1300	4.5	1843	2.1
15 TH	0140	4.5	0708	2.1	1407	4.7	1953	1.9
16 F	0236	4.7	0811	1.9	1458	4.9	2045	1.7
17 SA	0318	4.9	0900	1.7	1537	5.0	2128	1.5
18 SU	0351	5.0	0942	1.5	1608	5.1	2206	1.4
19 M	0420	5.1	0933	1.3	1636	5.2	2241	1.3
20 TU	0448	5.2	1053	1.3	1704	5.2	● 2312	1.3
21 W	0517	5.2	1124	1.3	1733	5.2	2342	1.3
22 TH	0546	5.2	1155	1.3	1801	5.1		
23 F	0011	1.4	0615	5.1	1225	1.4	1830	5.0
24 SA	0040	1.5	0645	5.0	1255	1.5	1900	4.8
25 SU	0110	1.6	0717	4.8	1328	1.6	1933	4.6
26 M	0145	1.8	0755	4.7	1406	1.8	2017	4.4
27 TU	0225	2.0	0847	4.5	1452	2.0	2121	4.2
28 W	0317	2.2	1000	4.5	1555	2.2	2249	4.2
29 TH	0430	2.3	1127	4.4	1719	2.2		
30 F	0017	4.3	0556	2.2	1246	4.6	1838	2.0
31 SA	0125	4.6	0708	2.0	1349	4.9	1942	1.7

NOVEMBER

Day	Time	m	Time	m	Time	m	Time	m
1 SU	0221	5.0	0809	1.6	1443	5.3	2038	1.3
2 M	0311	5.3	0904	1.3	1532	5.6	2130	1.0
3 TU	0358	5.5	0956	1.0	1619	5.8	2219	0.8
4 W	0443	5.7	1045	0.8	1706	5.9	O 2306	0.8
5 TH	0529	5.8	1132	0.7	1752	5.9	2352	0.8
6 F	0615	5.7	1218	0.8	1840	5.7		
7 SA	0036	1.0	0702	5.6	1303	1.0	1928	5.4
8 SU	0121	1.2	0750	5.3	1349	1.2	2021	5.1
9 M	0207	1.5	0842	5.0	1439	1.6	2121	4.7
10 TU	0259	1.8	0944	4.8	1537	1.9	2235	4.5
11 W	0400	2.1	1101	4.6	1646	2.1	2355	4.4
12 TH	0513	2.3	1222	4.5	1806	2.2		
13 F	0105	4.5	0629	2.2	1330	4.6	1916	2.0
14 SA	0200	4.6	0734	2.1	1424	4.7	2011	1.9
15 SU	0244	4.8	0827	1.9	1505	4.9	2056	1.7
16 M	0318	4.9	0911	1.7	1539	5.0	2135	1.6
17 TU	0350	5.1	0949	1.6	1610	5.1	2210	1.5
18 W	0421	5.2	1025	1.5	1641	5.1	2243	1.4
19 TH	0452	5.2	1058	1.4	1712	5.2	● 2315	1.4
20 F	0523	5.2	1131	1.4	1742	5.1	2346	1.4
21 SA	0554	5.2	1204	1.4	1813	5.0		
22 SU	0018	1.5	0627	5.1	1237	1.5	1845	4.9
23 M	0049	1.6	0703	5.0	1312	1.6	1922	4.8
24 TU	0127	1.7	0743	4.9	1351	1.7	2006	4.6
25 W	0208	1.9	0834	4.7	1437	1.8	2104	4.4
26 TH	0259	2.0	0937	4.6	1533	2.0	2218	4.4
27 F	0404	2.1	1052	4.6	1644	2.0	2340	4.4
28 SA	0520	2.1	1208	4.7	1759	1.9		
29 SU	0052	4.7	0633	1.9	1316	5.0	1907	1.7
30 M	0153	4.9	0738	1.7	1416	5.2	2009	1.4

DECEMBER

Day	Time	m	Time	m	Time	m	Time	m
1 TU	0247	5.2	0838	1.4	1510	5.5	2105	1.2
2 W	0337	5.5	0949	1.1	1601	5.6	2157	1.0
3 TH	0425	5.6	1025	0.9	1650	5.7	O 2246	0.9
4 F	0513	5.7	1115	0.8	1739	5.7	2334	0.9
5 SA	0600	5.7	1202	0.9	1827	5.6		
6 SU	0019	1.0	0647	5.6	1248	1.0	1914	5.4
7 M	0104	1.2	0733	5.4	1334	1.2	2003	5.1
8 TU	0149	1.5	0820	5.2	1420	1.5	2053	4.8
9 W	0237	1.7	0909	4.9	1510	1.8	2150	4.6
10 TH	0329	2.0	1007	4.7	1608	2.0	2256	4.4
11 F	0429	2.2	1117	4.5	1714	2.2		
12 SA	0006	4.4	0537	2.3	1230	4.5	1825	2.2
13 SU	0109	4.4	0645	2.2	1334	4.5	1927	2.1
14 M	0200	4.6	0744	2.1	1425	4.6	2018	1.9
15 TU	0243	4.7	0835	2.0	1508	4.8	2102	1.8
16 W	0321	4.9	0918	1.8	1545	4.9	2140	1.6
17 TH	0357	5.1	0958	1.6	1620	5.0	2217	1.5
18 F	0431	5.2	1035	1.5	1654	5.1	● 2252	1.5
19 SA	0506	5.2	1112	1.4	1727	5.1	2327	1.4
20 SU	0540	5.3	1148	1.4	1801	5.1		
21 M	0002	1.4	0616	5.3	1225	1.4	1836	5.0
22 TU	0038	1.5	0654	5.2	1302	1.4	1914	5.0
23 W	0114	1.5	0735	5.1	1341	1.5	1957	4.8
24 TH	0157	1.6	0822	5.0	1425	1.6	2048	4.7
25 F	0245	1.8	0917	4.9	1515	1.7	2150	4.6
26 SA	0342	1.9	1021	4.8	1615	1.8	2303	4.6
27 SU	0448	1.9	1133	4.8	1723	1.8		
28 M	0018	4.6	0559	1.9	1245	4.9	1834	1.7
29 TU	0127	4.8	0709	1.7	1352	5.0	1942	1.6
30 W	0227	5.1	0815	1.5	1453	5.2	2044	1.4
31 TH	0322	5.3	0916	1.3	1549	5.4	2140	1.2

18

Chart Datum: 2·83 metres below Lallemand System (Mean Sea Level, Marseilles)

ARCACHON   10-18-24
Gironde 44°39'·83N 01°09'·04W   Rtg 5-1-1

MINOR HARBOURS IN THE ARCACHON BASIN

FONTAINEVIEILLE, Gironde, 44°43'·36N 01°04'·51W. AC 2664; SHOM 6766 (essential); ECM 255. Tides as 10.18.24. Drying marina on NE side of Bassin d'Arcachon, access HW±3 via Chenal de Mouchtalette. Proceed from E0 pile to E8, where fork left onto NNE for 7ca to hbr ent. No lts. Boats dry out on pontoons. Hr Mr ☎ 05.56.82.17.31; Auto 05.36.65 .08.33. Facilities: **Marina** (178+ 2), FW, Fuel, Slip, ME.

AUDENGE, Gironde, 44°40'·65N01°01'·50W. AC 2664; SHOM 6766 (essential); ECM 255. Tides as 10.18.24. Drying marina and oyster port 5·5M E of Arcachon, access sp HW–2 to HW, nps HW–1 to HW. Appr from G0 pile via drying Chenal d'Audenge to G8 pile, 5ca short of the ent. Hr Mr ☎ 05.56.26.88.97. The Old Port (84 berths) is to the N; the New Port has 130 pontoon berths, FW, AC, Fuel, Slip, YC.

ARCACHON *continued*

CAPBRETON 10-18-25

Landes 43°39'·42N 01°26'·82W   Rtg 4-2-1

CHARTS
 AC 2664; Imray C42; SHOM 6766, 7070; ECM 255, 1024
TIDES
 +0620 Dover; ML 2·5; Zone –0100

Standard Port POINTE DE GRAVE (←—)

Times				Height (metres)			
High Water		Low Water		MHWS	MHWN	MLWN	MLWS
0000	0600	0500	1200	5·4	4·4	2·1	1·0
1200	1800	1700	2400				
Differences ARCACHON							
+0010	+0025	0000	+0020	–1·1	–1·0	–0·8	–0·6
CAP FERRET							
–0015	+0005	–0005	+0015	–1·4	–1·2	–0·8	–0·5

SHELTER
 Good in marina (max LOA 15m), but it is impossible to ent Bassin d'Arcachon in strong SW-N winds or at night. If marina full, good ↓ N of it, except in strong N'lies. Around the Bassin are many small drying hbrs worth exploring: on the W, La Vigne*, Le Canon, Piquey and Claouey; on the NE, Port de Lège, Ares, Andernos, Fontainevieille*, Lanton (Cassy) and Audenge*; and on the S, La Teste and Gujan. *see below.
NAVIGATION
 WPT 44°34'·89N 01°18'·61W, ATT ARC (SWM) buoy, 270°/090° from/to N Passe first chan buoys, 0·7M. Only appr is the shorter, buoyed N Passe which runs E & NE between Banc d'Arguin and Banc du Toulinguet toward Cap Ferret where it meets the S Passe. The latter, although used by a few local FVs, is now closed to navigation. The dunes (103m high) are very conspic. Between the two ent chans beware shifting sand banks on which seas break in any wind, but the chan can be seen through the breakers. Buoys are adjusted frequently.
 Best time to start appr is HW–1 and no later than HW+1. The chan bar (mean depth 4·5m) is impassable from HW+1 until LW, due to the ebb (6kn sp) and it is best to wait until LW+3. When swell is higher than 1m, bar may be dangerous. Best to leave on the last of the flood; wait in a convenient "lagoon" ↓ near No 10 PHM buoy in the Banc d'Arguin. For navigation update call *Cap Ferret Semaphore* Ch 16 10 (HJ); or Service de la Marine Gironde ☎ 05·56·82·32·97. Beware firing ranges between Arcachon and Capbreton, out to 40M offshore; see 8.18.5.
LIGHTS AND MARKS
 Cap Ferret Fl R 5s 53m 27M and Oc (3) 12s 46m 14M, vis 045°-135°. ATT-ARC (landfall/SWM buoy, L Fl 10s) is moved as necessary to indicate approach to N Passe. La Salie IDM buoy Fl (2) 6s is off chartlet, about 1M WSW of the S Passe ent and Wharf de Salie WCM bn, Q (9) 15s 19m 10M. Marina: W bkwtr QG, E bkwtr QR. Secondary chans in the Bassin d'Arcachon are marked by piles lettered A to K, plus pile number, clockwise from the N.
RADIO TELEPHONE
 VHF Ch 09 16 (H24).
TELEPHONE (Prefix ☎ Nos with zone code 05)
 Hr Mr 56·22·36·75, ⚓ 56.83.26.19; Aff Mar 57·52·57·07; ✕ 56·83·05·89; SNSM 56·83·22·44; CROSS 56·73·31·31; Auto 08·36·68·08·33; Police 56·83·04·63; Dr 56·83·04·72; Ⓗ 56·83·39·50; Brit Consul 56·52·28·35.
FACILITIES
 Marina (2192+ 57 visitors), FF150 (2nd night free), Access HW±3, FW, AC, D, Slip, C (10/20 ton), BH (45 ton); **YC du Bassin d'Arcachon** ☎ 56·83·22·11, P, D, FW, Slip, R, Bar; **Services:** P, D, ME, El, Ⓔ, SHOM, Sh, CH, SM, ▣. **Town** V, R, Gaz, ✉, Ⓑ, ⇌, ✈ (Bordeaux). Ferry: Roscoff or St Malo.

CHARTS
 AC 1102; SHOM 6586, 6557, 6786; ECM 555, 1024
TIDES
 +0450 Dover; ML 2·3; Zone –0100

Standard Port POINTE DE GRAVE (←—)

Times				Height (metres)			
High Water		Low Water		MHWS	MHWN	MLWN	MLWS
0000	0600	0500	1200	5·4	4·4	2·1	1·0
1200	1800	1700	2400				
Differences CAPBRETON							
–0030	–0020	0000	0000	–1·4	–0·8	–0·7	–0·5

SHELTER
 Good. Appr advised HW–3 to +1; not before LW+2½. Narrow canalised ent dangerous in strong winds from W to N. Do not enter if swell or seas break in mid-chan; they often break on either side. Hbr and chan dredged 1·5m. Visitors' pontoon 'B' (first to stbd of marina ent). There are 3 basins.
NAVIGATION
 WPT 49°39'·69N 01°27'·41W, 303°/123° from/to N pier lt, ½M. Bkwtr lts in line 123° lead to hbr ent. Depths shoal rapidly in last 3ca from 50m to 3m; see 8.18.5 for Gouf de Capbreton. No ↓ off ent. Marina is entered through gap in training wall on SE side of Boucarot Chan, abeam conspic Capitainerie bldg.

LIGHTS AND MARKS
 N pier hd, Fl (2) R 6s 13m 12M, Horn 30s. S bkwtr hd, Fl (2) G 6s 7m 12M. Fl R 4s and Fl G 4s lts at marina ent. Casino is conspic S of ent.
RADIO TELEPHONE
 VHF Ch 09 (0800-1900 in season).
TELEPHONE (Prefix ☎ Nos with zone code 05)
 Hr Mr 58·72·21·23; Aff Mar 58·72·10·43; ✕ 59·46·68·80; SNSM 58·72·47·44; CROSS 56·73·31·31; Auto 08.36.68.08.40; Ⓗ (Bayonne) 59·44·35·35; Police 58·72·01·18.
FACILITIES
 Marina (950+58 visitors), ☎ 58·72·21·23, ⚓ 58.72.40.35, FF124, Slip, BH (28 ton), AC, P, D, FW, ME, El, C (1·5 ton), Sh, ▣; **Club Nautique Capbreton-Hossegor-Seignone** ☎ 58·72·03·39; **Services:** Sh, CH, SM, Ⓔ; ⇌ Bayonne (17km); ✈ Biarritz (25km).

18

MINOR HARBOURS IN THE ARCACHON BASIN (cont)

LA VIGNE, Gironde, 44°40'·50N 01°14'·20W. AC 2664; SHOM 6766; ECM 255. HW time & ht approx as Cap Ferret above; ML 2·4m. Access HW±2. See 8.18.24. Good shelter, but crowded; beware strong currents across hbr ent. 2 perches mark the ent and on the SW point, a lt Iso R 4s 7m 4M. A small bkwtr (unlit) protrudes into the ent from the NE side. Aff Mar ☎ 05·56·60·52·76. Facilities: **Marina** (268 + 2) Max LOA 8·5m, ☎ 05·56·60·54·36, AC, Slip, CH, C (2 ton), P, D.

ANDERNOS, Gironde, 44°44'·32N 01°06'·05W. AC 2664; SHOM 6766; ECM 255. HW time & ht approx as Arcachon 10.18.24; ML 2·4m; access about HW±2. Dredged channel to Bétey, with side chan to Andernos, is very well marked by lateral poles D0 to D14. Jetty was rebuilt (1995) with drying 'Halte Nautique' (pontoon) at outer end; only for yachts able to take the ground, max LOA 12m. Also ↓ on flat drying fore-shore. Hr Mr ☎ 56.82.00.12. Few facilities.

ANGLET/BAYONNE Pyrénées Atlantique 49°31'·95N 01°31'·92W Rtg 3-2-3   10-18-26

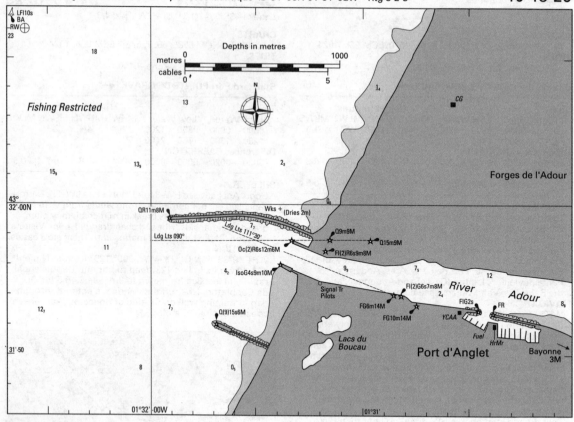

CHARTS
AC 1343, 1102; SHOM 6536, 6557, 6786; ECM 555
TIDES
+0450 Dover (UT); ML 2·5; Zone −0100

Standard Port POINTE DE GRAVE (←)

Times				Height (metres)			
High Water		Low Water		MHWS	MHWN	MLWN	MLWS
0000	0600	0500	1200	5·4	4·4	2·1	1·0
1200	1800	1700	2400				
Differences L'ADOUR (BOUCAU)							
−0030	−0035	−0025	−0040	−1·2	−1·1	−0·4	−0·3

SHELTER
Very good in Anglet marina, 0·70M from ent, on S bank of
R Adour. (New marina planned to W of existing marina).
Possible berths at Bayonne, 3M up river, on S bank below
bridge. ⚓ prohib in river which is well marked.
NAVIGATION
WPT 43°32'·66N 01°32'·68W, BA SWM buoy, 322°/142°
from/to N bkwtr lt, 0·9M. Access good except in strong W
winds. Strong tidal stream, max 5kn at sp ebb.
LIGHTS AND MARKS
BA HFP buoy, L Fl 10s (WPT), is NW of ent. Pte St Martin Fl (2)
10s 73m 29M is 2·45M SSW of hbr. Ldg lts 090°, both Q 9/
15m 14M, intens 087°-093°. Inside ent, further ldg lts 111°,
both QG, moved as required. 3 more sets of ldg lts upriver to
Bayonne. IPTS (full code) from sig tr on S side of ent.
RADIO TELEPHONE
Marina Ch 09. Port/pilots 12 16 (0800-1200; 1400-1800LT).
TELEPHONE (Prefix ☎ Nos with zone code 05)
Marina 59·63·05·45; Hr Mr Bayonne 59·63·11·57; CROSS
56·09·82·00; ⌗ 59·59·08·29; Aff Mar 59·55·06·68; SNSM
59·83·40·50; Ⓗ 59·44·35·35; Météo 59·23·84·15; Auto
08·36·65·08·64.
FACILITIES
Marina (367+58 visitors), ☎ 59·63·05·45; P, D, FW, ME, El,
AC, C (1·3 ton), Ⓓ, BH (13 ton), Slip, Sh; **Port** C (30 ton),
Slip, FW, P, D; **YC Adour Atlantique** ☎ 59·63·16·22;
Services: CH, Ⓔ, SHOM.
Town ⚓, ✈ (Biarritz). Ferry: Bilboa-Portsmouth.

ST JEAN-DE-LUZ   10-18-27
Pyrénées Atlantique, 43°23'·92N 01°40'·53W   Rtg 3-3-1

CHARTS
AC 1343, 1102; SHOM 6526, 6558, 6786; ECM 555
TIDES
HW +0435 on Dover (UT); ML 2·5m; Zone −0100

Standard Port POINTE DE GRAVE (←)

Times				Height (metres)			
High Water		Low Water		MHWS	MHWN	MLWN	MLWS
0000	0600	0500	1200	5·4	4·4	2·1	1·0
1200	1800	1700	2400				
Differences ST JEAN DE LUZ (SOCOA)							
−0040	−0045	−0030	−0045	−1·1	−1·1	−0·6	−0·4

SHELTER
Except in strong NW winds, the bay can be entered at all
times and good ⚓s found in approx 4m on the W and SE
sides. Beware antipollution booms off the beaches and a
submerged jetty in SE corner of bay. There are 2 hbrs:
St Jean-de-Luz in S of bay with a small marina (2·5m) at
Ciboure, close to rear QG ldg lt. Sailing is prohib in the
port. Unmasted craft may ⚓ in La Nivelle River via fixed
bridge 1·9m clearance.
Socoa hbr (dries about 0·5m) on the NW side of the bay,
close S of conspic fort. Tide gauge at ent.
NAVIGATION
WPT 43°24'·16N 01°40'·71W, 331°/151° from/to W ent,
2½ca. Yachts can approach within the N quadrant direct to
hbr ent, but in heavy W'ly weather seas break on various
shoals on the Plateau de St Jean-de-Luz. 3M W of hbr ent
beware Les Briquets rks, drying 0·4m, 2M NE of Hendaye.
The 3 appr chans are defined by ldg lts: The main outer
chan leads 138° between Illarguita and Belhara Perdun
banks. Thence, or if coming from the W, the middle chan
leads 101° past the hbr breakwaters. The inner chan leads
151° through the W ent into the bay and to St Jean de Luz
hbr. The E ent to the bay is not recommended. There are
other chans but these are unlit and not advised without
local knowledge. Speed limit in the bay is 7kn.

ST JEAN-DE-LUZ continued

LIGHTS AND MARKS

Outer 138° ldg lts: Front, Socoa lt, QWR 36m 12/8M, W □ tr, B stripe, vis W shore-264°, R264°-282°, W282°-shore; R sector covers Socoa hbr ent. Rear Q 67m 20M, hard to see by day, but nearby Bordagain tr, 100m, is more conspic. Ste Barbe ldg lts 101°, both Oc (3+1) R 12s 30/47m 18M; front, W bldg with △ gable; rear B ▲ on W tr. Inner 151° ldg lts, both Dir QG 18/27m 16M intens 149·5°-152°; front, W tr, R stripe; rear, W tr, G stripe. Digue des Criquas hd, Iso G 4s 11m 7M. Digue d'Artha is a detached unlit bkwtr across the middle of the bay. La Rhune, an 898m high conical mountain, is conspic in good vis 5·5M SSE of hbr.

RADIO TELEPHONE

Marina VHF Ch 09 16.

TELEPHONE (Prefix ☎ Nos with zone code 05)

ST JEAN-DE-LUZ: Hr Mr 59·47·26·81; Aff Mar 59·47·14·55; ≢ 59.47.18.61; CROSS 56.73.31.31; Météo 59·22·03·30; Auto 08.36.68.08.64; SNSM 59.47.22.98; Police 59.26.01.55;-SOCOA: As for St Jean de Luz.

FACILITIES

ST JEAN-DE-LUZ **Quay** FW, AC, P, C (6 ton), Slip; **Services:** Ⓔ, ME, El, Sh, CH.
SOCOA **Jetty** C (1 ton), FW, P, D, AC, Slip, BY; **YC Basque** ☎ 59·47·18·31; **Services:** ME, CH, El, Sh.
Town V, R, Bar, Ⓞ, ✉, Ⓑ, ⇌.

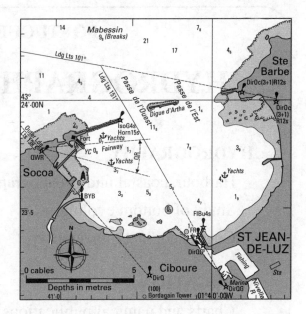

HENDAYE   10-18-28

Pyrénées Atlantique, 43°22'·91N 01°47'·25W   Rtg 2-2-1

CHARTS

AC 1181, 1102; SHOM 6556, 6558, 6786; ECM 555

TIDES

HW +0450 on Dover (UT); ML 2·3m; Zone –0100
Use differences **ST JEAN DE LUZ (SOCOA)** 10-18-27

SHELTER

Excellent in marina (3m); access H24. Or in Port of Refuge (S of C Higuer) in 2-3m. Good ⚓ in river off Fuenterrabia. Moorings in the B de Chingoudy are exposed to N/NE and S/SW gales. NB: Hendaye is on the French bank of the Rio Bidassoa; Fuenterrabia on the Spanish side. A neutral area lies in the Baie de Fontarabie.

NAVIGATION

WPT 43°24'·00N 01°46'·50W, 025°/205° from/to W bkwtr hd 1·25M. Beware Les Briquets 8ca N of Pte Ste Anne at E end of the Baie and, near centre of B, keep clear of Bajo Iruarri. River ent is easy except in heavy N'ly swell; sp ebb is very strong. Inshore of Pte des Dunes lt, Fl R 2·5s, hug the E training wall for best water. A spit drying 1·3m (SHM bn, VQ (3) G 5s) off Fuenterrabia narrows the chan to about 100m before marina ent opens up.

LIGHTS AND MARKS

On W end of bay, Cabo Higuer lt ho , Fl (2) 10s 63m 23M. River ent bkwtrs: East L Fl R 10s 7m 5M; West Fl (3) G 9s 9m 5M. River dredged to 2m. Marina ent between Fl (2) R 6s 6m 2M on elbow of W bkwtr (hd marked by FR strip lt) and Fl Y 4s 5m 3M at E side; near the latter is a conspic RW TV relay mast (40m).

RADIO TELEPHONE

Marina VHF Ch 09 (H24).

TELEPHONE (Prefix ☎ Nos with zone code 05)

Hr Mr 59·48·06·10; ≢ 59.20.70.82; Aff Mar 59·20·77·67; CROSS 59.09.82.00; Météo 59.24.58.80; Auto 08.36.68.08.64; SNSM 59.20.60.33; Police 59.20.65.52; Ⓗ 59.20.08.22.

FACILITIES

Marina (600 + 120) ☎ 59.48.06.10, FF135, AC, FW, P, D, BH (30 ton), Slip; Boats > 17m LOA should moor in Baie de Chingoudy; **Club Maritime Hendayais** ☎ 59·20·03·02, Bar; **Services:** CH, Sh, El, Ⓔ, ME.
Town V, R, Bar, Gaz, ✉, Ⓑ, ⇌, ✈ (Fuenterrabia or Biarritz). Local ferry from marina to Fuenterrabia. UK ferry from Bilbao/Santander.

For continuation westward along the coasts of Spain and Portugal to Gibraltar, consult the 1998 IBERIAN GUIDE, published separately. It can be obtained by completing the card in this Almanac and forwarding it with your remittance.

18

PORTUGUESE NAVY

HYDROGRAPHIC INSTITUTE

HYDROGRAPHY

Harbour, coastal and oceanographic surveys

Study of bottom evolution

Coastal engineering support

NAVIGATION

Charts and nautical publications

Notices to Mariners

Buoyage studies

Manoeuvering trials

Certification of magnetic compasses and navigational lights

OCEANOGRAPHY

Tidal propagation studies

Wave data acquisition and processing

Coastal and inshore dynamic circulation studies

Sedimentological and fishery charts

Geophysical surveys

Pollution of the marine environment

Evaluation of the impact of oil spills on the marine and coastal environment

SCHOOL OF HYDROGRAPHY AND OCEANOGRAPHY

Specialist courses in Hydrography, Oceanography and Navigation.

⚓ ⚓ ⚓ ⚓ ⚓ ⚓ ⚓ ⚓

Rua das Trinas 49, 1296 LISBOA CODEX, PORTUGAL
☎ (01) 395 51 19. 📠 (01) 396 05 15

VOLVO PENTA SERVICE

Sales and service centres in area 19
Names and addresses of Volvo Penta dealers in
this area are available from:

France *Volvo Penta France* , 55 Avenue des Champs Pierreux, 92757 Cedex
Tel +33 1 55175457, Fax +33 1 55175261
Netherlands *Volvo Penta Benelux B.V.*, Nijverheidsweg 1, Postbus 195,
3640 Ad Mijdrecht Tel +31 2972 80111, Fax +31 2972 87364.

**VOLVO
PENTA**

Area 19

North-East France
Barfleur to Dunkerque

19

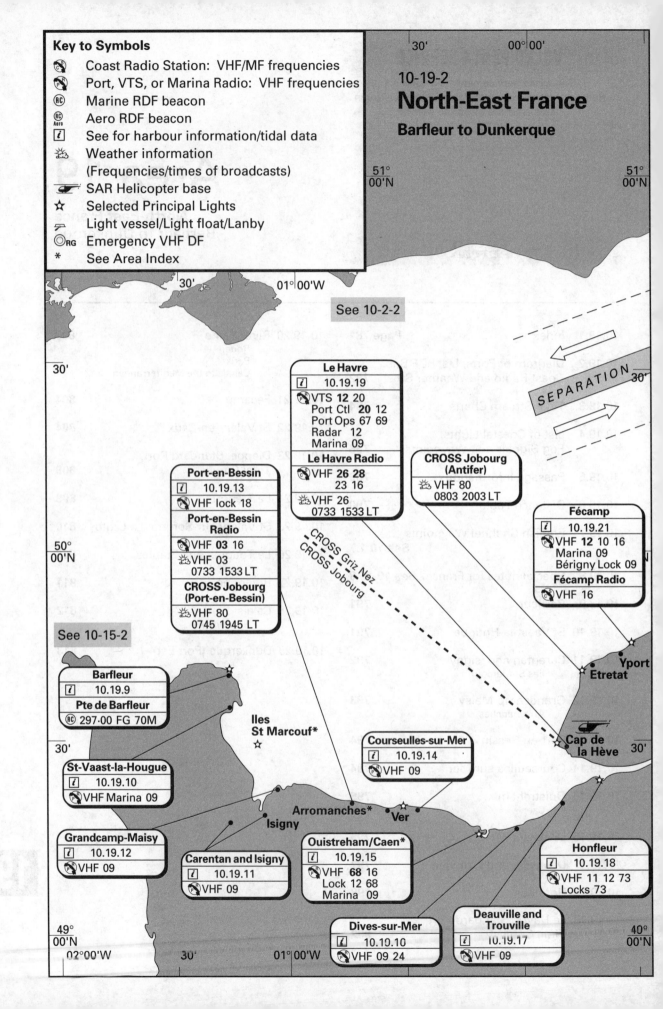

Key to Symbols

🕿	Coast Radio Station: VHF/MF frequencies
🕿	Port, VTS, or Marina Radio: VHF frequencies
ⓇⒸ	Marine RDF beacon
ⓇⒸ Aero	Aero RDF beacon
ⓘ	See for harbour information/tidal data
☲	Weather information (Frequencies/times of broadcasts)
🚁	SAR Helicopter base
☆	Selected Principal Lights
⌐	Light vessel/Light float/Lanby
◎RG	Emergency VHF DF
*	See Area Index

10-19-2
North-East France
Barfleur to Dunkerque

See 10-2-2

SEPARATION

Le Havre
ⓘ 10.19.19
🕿 VTS **12** 20
　 Port Ctl **20** 12
　 Port Ops 67 69
　 Radar 12
　 Marina 09
Le Havre Radio
🕿 VHF **26 28**
　　 23 16
☲ VHF 26
　 0733 1533 LT

CROSS Jobourg (Antifer)
☲ VHF 80
　 0803 2003 LT

Fécamp
ⓘ 10.19.21
🕿 VHF **12** 10 16
　 Marina 09
　 Bérigny Lock 09
Fécamp Radio
🕿 VHF 16

Port-en-Bessin
ⓘ 10.19.13
🕿 VHF lock 18
Port-en-Bessin Radio
🕿 VHF **03** 16
☲ VHF 03
　 0733 1533 LT
CROSS Jobourg (Port-en-Bessin)
☲ VHF 80
　 0745 1945 LT

CROSS Griz Nez
CROSS Jobourg

See 10-15-2

Barfleur
ⓘ 10.19.9
Pte de Barfleur
ⓇⒸ 297·00 FG 70M

Iles
St Marcouf*
☆

Courseulles-sur-Mer
ⓘ 10.19.14
🕿 VHF 09

Yport
● Etretat

St-Vaast-la-Hougue
ⓘ 10.19.10
🕿 VHF Marina 09

Arromanches*　Ver
Isigny

🚁 Cap de
la Hève

Grandcamp-Maisy
ⓘ 10.19.12
🕿 VHF 09

Carentan and Isigny
ⓘ 10.19.11
🕿 VHF 09

Ouistreham/Caen*
ⓘ 10.19.15
🕿 VHF **68** 16
　 Lock 12 68
　 Marina 09

Honfleur
ⓘ 10.19.18
🕿 VHF 11 12 73
　 Locks 73

Dives-sur-Mer
ⓘ 10.10.10
🕿 VHF 09 24

Deauville and Trouville
ⓘ 10.19.17
🕿 VHF 09

ENGLAND

01° 00'E 30' 02° 00'E 30' 03° 00'E

See 10-3-2

CROSS Gris Nez
(Dover Strait TSS)
VHF **13** 79 16
Info b'casts
VHF 79 at H+10
and 0710 1910 LT

Dunkerque
Lanby

51° 00'N

ITZ

For details
see Fig. 10(5)

ZONE

RG

ITZ

St Inglevert
387·50 ING 50M

Dunkerque
ⓘ 10.19.29
VHF **73** 12 16
Marinas 09
Lock 73
Dunkerque Radio
VHF **24 61** 16
VHF 61
0733 1533 LT
CROSS Gris Nez
(Dunkerque)
VHF 79
0720 1920 LT

Gravelines*

51° 00'N

Calais/Dunkerque
418·00 MK 15M

Calais
ⓘ 10.19.28
VHF **12** 16
Marina 12
Lock 12
Calais Radio
VHF **01 87** 16
VHF 87
0733 1533 LT

30'

Pte du
Haut Blanc ☆ **Berck**

Cap d'Alprech
294·00 PH 20M

Le Touquet
and Étaples
10.19.26
VHF 09

Boulogne
10.19.27
VHF **12**
Marina 09
Boulogne Radio
VHF **23 25** 16
MF **1770** 2744
2747 3722 3792
VHF 23
0733 1533 LT
MF 1692
0703 1833 UT

Cayeux

Ault

50° 00'N

Le Tréport
ⓘ 10.19.24
VHF 12 72 16
Marina 12

St Valéry-sur-
Somme/Le Crotoy
ⓘ 10.19.25
VHF 09

50° 00'N

St Valéry-en-Caux
ⓘ 10.19.22
VHF 09

Pte d'Ailly
305·50 AL 50M
CROSS Gris Nez
(Ailly)
VHF 79
0703 1903 LT

Dieppe
ⓘ 10.19.23
VHF **12** 16
Dieppe Radio
VHF **02 24** 16
VHF 02
0733 1533 LT

30'

0

270 Variation 3°W (1998) 90

180

River Seine
ⓘ 10.19.20
VHF 68 **73** 15
Radar 73 or 13

Rouen*
VHF 73 68
Locks 18 or 22
Rouen Radio
VHF 25 27 16

19

49° 00'N

49° 00'N

01° 00'E 30' 02° 00'E 30' **Paris*** 03° 00'E

10-19-3 AREA 19 TIDAL STREAMS

5 Hours before HW Dover (0345 before HW Le Havre)

4 Hours before HW Dover (0245 before HW Le Havre)

3 Hours before HW Dover (0145 before HW Le Havre)

2 Hours before HW Dover (0045 before HW Le Havre)

1 Hour before HW Dover (0015 after HW Le Havre)

HW Dover (0115 after HW Le Havre)

Westward 10.15.3   Northward 10.2.3   North-eastward 10.3.3   Eastward 10.20.3

1 Hour after HW Dover (0215 after HW Le Havre)

2 Hours after HW Dover (0315 after HW Le Havre)

3 Hours after HW Dover (0415 after HW Le Havre)

4 Hours after HW Dover (0515 after HW Le Havre)

5 Hours after HW Dover (0615 after HW Le Havre)

6 Hours after HW Dover (0510 before HW Le Havre)

19

10.19.4 COASTAL LIGHTS, FOG SIGNALS AND WAYPOINTS

Abbreviations used below are given in 1.4.1. Principal lights are in **bold** print, places in CAPITALS, and light-vessels, light floats and Lanbys in *CAPITAL ITALICS*. Unless otherwise stated lights are white. m – elevation in metres; M – nominal range in miles. Fog signals are in *italics*. Useful waypoints are underlined – use those on land with care. All geographical positions should be assumed to be approximate. See 4.4.1. All positions are referenced to the ED 50 datum.

NOTE:　For English Channel Waypoints see 10.1.7.

POINTE DE BARFLEUR TO DEAUVILLE

Pte de Barfleur-Gatteville 49°41'·83N 01°15'·87W Fl (2) 10s 72m **29M**; Gy Tr, B top; obsc when brg less than 088°; RC; *Horn (2) 60s.*
La Jamette Bn 49°41'·92N 01°15'·51W; ECM.
La Grotte By 49°41'·12N 01°14'·78W; SHM.
Roche-à-l'Anglais By 49°40'·84N 01°14'·85W; SHM.
Le Hintar By 49°40'·75N 01°14'·76W; PHM.

BARFLEUR

Ldg Lts 219·5°. Front, 49°40'·24N 01°15'·53W Oc (3) 12s 7m 10M; W ■ Tr. Rear, 288m from front, Oc (3) 12s 13m 10M; Gy and W ■ Tr, G top; vis 085°-355°; synch with front.
Jetée Est Hd 49°40'·39N 01°15'·38W Oc R 4s 5m 6M; W hut, R top.
Jetée Ouest Hd Fl G 4s 8m 6M; W pylon, G top.

Pte de Saire Lt Tr 49°36'·44N 01°13'·71W Oc (2+1) 12s 11m 10M; W Tr, G top.

Moulard Bn 49°39'·42N 01°13'·87W; ECM.
Dranguet Bn 49°36'·82N 01°12'·92W; ECM.
Le Vitéquet Bn 49°36'·15N 01°13'·29W; SCM.
Le Gavendest By 49°34'·67N 01°13'·74W; SCM; *Whis.*
La Dent By 49°34'·63N 01°14'·12W; SCM.

ST VAAST-LA-HOUGUE

Jetty Hd 49°35'·25N 01°15'·35W Oc (2) WRG 6s 12m W10M, R7M, G7M; W 8-sided Tr, R top; vis R219°-237°, G237°-310°, W310°-350°, R350°-040°; *Siren Mo(N) 30s.*
NE side Bkwtr Hd Iso G 4s 6m 3M; W tank, G top.
SW side, Groyne Hd Oc (4) R 12s 6m 6M; W hut, R top.
Ldg Lts 267°. Front, La Hougue 49°34'·31N 01°16'·30W Oc 4s 9m 10M; W pylon, G top. Rear, Morsalines 1·8M from front, 49°34'·25N 01°18'·95W Oc (3+1) WRG 12s 90m W11M, R8M, G8M; W 8-sided Tr, G top; vis W171°-316°, G316°-321°, R321°-342°, W342°-355°.

Quineville Lt By 49°31'·85N 01°12'·40W Q (9) 10s; WCM.
S Floxel By 49°30'·75N 01°13'·70W; ECM.
SW Marcouf Lt By 49°29'·80N 01°11'·92W Q (9) 15s; WCM.

ÎLES SAINT-MARCOUF

Île du Large Lt Tr 49°29'·90N 01°08'·70W VQ (3) 5s 18m 8M; ■ Gy Tr, G top.

CARENTAN

CI Lt By 49°25'·50N 01°07'·00W Iso 4s; SWM.
Ldg Lts 209·5°. **Front**, 49°20'·55N 01°11'·05W Dir Oc (3) R 12s 6m **18M**; W mast, R top; intens 208·2°-210·7°. Rear, 723m from front, Oc (3) 12s 14m 10M; W gantry, G top; vis 120°-005°; synch with front.
W Channel Ent Bn 49°22'·00N 01°09'·90W Fl (3) G 12s; G △, on G Bn.

ISIGNY-SUR-MER

IS By 49°24'·30N 01°06'·30W; NCM.
Ldg Lts 172·5°. **Front**, 49°19'·50N 01°06·70W Dir Oc (2+1) 12s 7m **18M**; intens 170·5°-174·5°. **Rear**, 625m from front, Dir Oc (2+1) 12s 19m **18M**; W pylon, B top; synch with front; intens 170·5°-174·5°.

GRANDCAMP-MAISY

La Maresquerie 49°23'·20N 01°02'·65W Oc 4s 28m 12M; vis 090°-270°.
Jetée Est Hd 49°23'·54N 01°02'·88W Oc (2) R 6s 9m 9M; *Horn Mo(N) 30s.*
Perré 49°23'·40N 01°02'·40W Oc 4s 8m 12M; G pylon on W hut; vis 083°-263°.
Ldg Lts 146°. Front, 49°23'·41N 01°02'·93W Dir Q 9m **15M**. Rear,102m from front, Dir Q 12m **15M**. Both vis:144·5°-147·5°.

Norfalk Lt By 49°28'·83N 01°03'·40W Q (3) 10s; ECM.
Est du Cardonnet Lt By 49°26'·97N 01°01'·00W VQ (3) 5s; ECM.
Broadsword Lt By 49°25'·39N 00°52'·90W Q (3) 10s; ECM.
Cussy Lt By 49°29'·50N 00°43'·25W VQ (9) 10s; WCM.

PORT-EN-BESSIN/ARROMANCHES

Ldg Lts 204°. Front, 49°21'·00N 00°45'·56W Oc (3) 12s 25m 10M; W pylon, G top; vis 069°-339°; *Siren 20s* – sounded over a sector of 90° each side of Ldg line, continuous in the W sector, interrupted in the E (TD 1997). Rear, 93m from front, Oc (3) 12s 42m 11M; W and Gy Ho; synch with front; vis 114°-294° RC.
Môle Est Hd Oc R 4s 14m 7M; R pylon.
Môle Ouest Hd 49°21'·21N 00°45'·42W Fl WG 4s 13m W10M, G7M; G pylon; vis G065°-114·5°, W114·5°-065°.
Oc (2) R 6s and Fl (2) G 6s mark the pier Hds.
Bombardons By 49°21'·70N 00°39'·15W; WCM.
Roseberry By 49°23'·15N 00°36'·15W; ECM.

Ver 49°20'·47N 00°31'·15W Fl (3) 15s 42m **26M**; W Tr, Gy top; obsc by cliffs of St Aubin when brg more than 275°; RC.
Fosse de Courseulles Lt By 49°21'·33N 00°27'·61W Iso 4s; SWM.

COURSEULLES-SUR-MER

Jetée Ouest Hd 49°20'·47N 00°27'·28W Iso WG 4s 7m W9M, G6M; brown pylon on Dn, G top; vis W135°-235°, G235°-135°; *Horn 30s* sounded from HW±2 hours.

Essarts de Langrune By 49°22'·65N 00°21'·25W; NCM.
Luc By 49°20'·85N 00°18'·20W; NCM.
Lion By 49°20'·80N 00°15'·92W; NCM.

OUISTREHAM/CAEN

Ouistreham Lt By 49°20'·48N 00°14'·73W VQ (3) 5s; ECM.
Merville Lt By 49°19'·71N 00°13'·30W VQ; NCM.
Ouistreham Main Lt 49°16'·85N 00°14'·80W Oc WR 4s 37m **W17M**, R13M; W Tr, R top; vis W151°-115°, R115°-151°.
Ldg Lts 185°. **Front**, 49°17'·16N 00°14'·72W Jetée Est Hd Dir Oc (3+1) R 12s 10m **17M**; W pylon, R top; Ra refl. **Rear**, 610m from front, Dir Oc (3+1) R 12s 30m **17M**; Tripod, R top; synch with front; intens 183·5°-186·5°.
Enrochements Est Hd (St-Médard) 49°18'·08N 00°14'·54W Oc (2) R 6s 7m 8M; W pylon, R top; Ra refl.
Enrochements Ouest Hd 49°17'·50N 04°14'·74W Iso G 4s 11m 7M; W pylon, G top; Ra refl; *Horn 10s,* (TD 1992).

Viaduc de Calix, Caen 49°11'·23N 00°19'·70W Iso 4s on E and W sides; FG on N side, FR on S side.

DIVES
D1 Lt By 49°18'·78N 00°05'·67W L Fl 10s; SWM.
Dives-sur-Mer 49°17'·85N 00°05'·20W Oc (2+1) WRG 12s
6m W12M, R9M, G9M, R hut; vis G125°-157°, W157°-162°,
R162°-194°.

DEAUVILLE/TROUVILLE
Semoy Lt By 49°24'·20N 00°02'·45E VQ (3) 5s; ECM.
Trouville SW Lt By 49°22'·60N 00°02'·64E VQ (9) 10s; WCM.
W Jetty 49°22'·44N 00°04'·17E Fl WG 4s 10m W9M, G6M;
B pylon, G top; vis W005°-176°, G176°-005°.
Trouville East 49°22'·28N 00°04'·41E Fl (4) WR 12s 8m W7M,
R4M; W pylon, R top; vis W131°-175°, R175°-131°.
Ldg Lts 148°. Front, 49°22'·09N 00°04'·57E Oc R 4s 11m
12M; W Tr, R top; vis 330°-150°; *Horn (2) 30s*. Rear, 217m
from front, Oc R 4s 17m 10M; W pylon, R top; synch with
front; vis 120°-170°.

ESTUAIRE DE LA SEINE/LE HAVRE
Ratelets Lt By 49°25'·35N 00°01'·80E Q (9) 15s; WCM.
Ratier S Lt By 49°25'·21N 00°07'·22E VQ (6) + L Fl 10s; SCM.
Ratier NW Lt By 49°26'·85N 00°02'·55E VQ G; SHM.
Ducan-L-Clinch Lt By 49°27'·23N 00°02'·58E VQ (9) 10s;
WCM.

CHENAL DE ROUEN
No. 4 Lt By 49°27'·05N 00°02'·64E QR; PHM.
No. 7 Lt By 49°26'·24N 00°04'·82E QG; SHM.
Digue du Ratier Hd 'A' 49°25'·97N 00°06'·66E VQ 10m 4M;
NCM; Ra refl; tide gauge.
Spillway Lt Bn 49°25'·80N 00°12'·80E VQ (9) 10s 15m 7M;
WCM.

HONFLEUR
Falaise des Fonds 49°25'·53N 00°12'·93E Fl (3) WRG 12s
15m **W17M**, R13M, G13M; W ■ Tr, G top; vis G040°-080°,
R080°-084°, G084°-100°, W100°-109°, R109°-162°, G162°-
260°.
Digue Est Hd 49°25'·73N 00°14'·04E Q 9m 8M; NCM;
Horn (5) 40s. (Km 356 from Paris.)

LA SEINE MARITIME
La Risle, Digue Sud 49°26'·37N 00°22'·07E Iso G 4s 11m 6M;
W pylon, G top; Ra refl; (Km 346 from Paris).
Marais-Vernier 49°27'·78N 00°26'·89E Fl G 4s 8m 5M; W Col,
R top (Km 340).
Digue Nord, Tancarville 49°28'·81N 00°28'·30E QR 9m 6M;
W col, R top; (Km 337).
Quillebeuf 49°28'50N 00°31'·63E QG 12m 8M (Km 332·4).
Caudebec-en-Caux 49°31'·52N 00°43'·78E VQ R (Km 310).
Duclair 49°28'·80N 00°52'·32E QR (Km 278).

ROUEN
Feu de Rouen 49°26'·42N 01°02'·62E Oc (2) R 6s 10m (Km
245·5).

APPROACHES TO LE HAVRE
Spoil Gnd Lt By 49°27'·84N 00°02'·38E Q (9) 15s; WCM.
N du Mouillage Lt By 49°28'·65N 00°01'·36E Fl (4) Y 15s;
SPM.
RN Lt By 49°28'·68N 00°01'·10W Fl (2) 6s; IDM.
RNA Lt By 49°28'·70N 00°05'·45W Iso 4s; SWM.
HP Lt By 49°29'·61N 00°03'·70W Fl Y 4s; SPM; *Whis*.

LHA Lanby 49°31'·44N 00°09'·78W Mo (A) 12s 10m 7M; W
By, R stripes; Racon.
Ldg Lts 106·8°. Front, **Quai Roger Meunier** 49°28'·97N
00°06'·58E Dir F 36m **25M**; Gy Tr, G top; intens 106°-108°;
(H24). Rear, 0·73M from front, **Quai Joannes Couvert**
Dir F 78m **25M**; Gy Tr, G top; intens 106°-108° (H24); Ra refl.

Cap de la Hève 49°30'·79N 00°04'·24E Fl 5s 123m **24M**;
W 8-sided Tr, R top; vis 225°-196°.

LE HAVRE
Digue Sud Hd 49°29'·11N 00°05'·46E VQ (3) G 2s 15m 11M;
W Tr, G top.
Digue Nord Hd 49°29'·25N 00°05'·52E Fl R 5s 15m **21M**; W
Tr, R top; *Horn 15s*.
Yacht Hbr, Digue Augustin Normand 49°29'·32N 00°05'·63E
Q (2) G 5s 5m 2M.

LE HAVRE TO CAP D'ANTIFER
Octeville W Lt By 49°31'·67N 00°01'·90E VQ (6) + L Fl 10s;
SCM.
Port du Havre-Antifer 49°39'·59N 00°09'·28E Dir Oc WRG 4s
24m **W15M**, R13M, G13M; W pylon, B top; vis G068·5°-
078·5°, W078·5°-088·5°, R088·5°-098·5°.
A17 Lt By 49°41'·60N 00°01'·75E Iso G 4s; SHM.
A18 Lt By 49°42'·07N 00°02'·21E QR; PHM.
Port d'Antifer Ldg Lts 127·5°. **Front**, 49°38'·36N 00°09'·20E
Dir Oc 4s 105m **22M**; W pylon, G top vis 127°-128°. **Rear**,
430m from front, Dir Oc 4s 124m **22M**; W mast, G top. By day
both show FW Lts **33M**; vis 126·5°-128·5°; (occas.)

CAP D'ANTIFER TO POINTE DU HAUT BLANC
Cap d'Antifer 49°41'·07N 00°10'·00E Fl 20s 128m **29M**;
Gy 8-sided Tr, G top; vis 021°-222°.
Yport Ldg Lts 166°. Front, 49°44'·40N 00°18'·70E Oc 4s 10m,
W mast, G top. Rear, 30m from front, Oc 4s 14m, W pylon,
G top on house.

FÉCAMP
Jetée Nord 49°45'·99N 00°21'·87E Fl (2) 10s 15m **16M**;
Gy Tr, R top; *Horn (2) 30s*.
Jetée Sud Hd, 49°45'·95N 00°21'·89E QG 14m 9M; Gy Tr, G
top; vis 072°-217°.
Jetée root QR 10m 4M.

Paluel Lt By 49°52'·20N 00°38'·10E Q; NCM.

SAINT VALÉRY-EN-CAUX
Jetée Ouest 49°52'·47N 00°42'·62E Fl (2) G 6s 13m 14M; W
Tr, G top.
Jetée Est Hd 49°52'·35N 00°42'·75E Fl (2) R 6s 8m 4M;
W mast.

Roches d'Ailly Lt By 49°56'·58N 00°56'·90E VQ; NCM; *Whis*.
Pointe d'Ailly 49°55'·13N 00°57'·56E Fl (3) 20s 95m **31M**;
W ■ Tr, G top; RC; *Horn (3) 60s*. (TD 1997.)
D1 Lt By 49°57'·11N 01°01'·35E VQ (3) 5s; ECM; *Bell*.
Daffodils Wk Lt By 50°02'·52N 01°04'·10E VQ (9) 10s; WCM.
Berneval Wk By 50°03'·46N 01°06'·62E; WCM.

DIEPPE
Jetée Est Hd 49°56'·22N 01°05'·15E Iso R 4s 12m 8M; R col.
Jetée Ouest 49°56'·32N 01°05'·04E Iso G 4s 11m 8M, W Tr,
G top; *Horn 30s*.
Falaise du Pollet 49°55'·98N 01°05'·37E Q R 35m 12M; R &
W structure; vis 105·5°-170·5°.

Penly No. 1 Lt By 49°59'·10N 01°11'·47E Fl (3) Y 12s; SPM.
Penly No. 2 Lt By 49°59'·50N 01°12'10E Fl Y 4s; SPM.

LE TRÉPORT
Jetée Ouest Hd 50°03'·94N 01°22'·22E Fl (2) G 10s 15m
20M; W Tr, G top; *Horn Mo(N) 30s*.
Jetée Est 50°03'·93N 01°22'·30E Oc R 4s 8m 6M; W col,
R top. Port signals Fl (5) G 500m SE.
Ault 50°06'·32N 01°27'·31E Oc (3) WR 12s 95m **W18M**,
R14M, W Tr, R top; vis W040°-175°, R175°-220°.

19

BAIE DE SOMME/LE CROTOY/ST VALÉRY-SUR-SOMME.
Cayeux-sur-Mer 50°11'·60N 01°30'·80E Fl R 5s 32m **22M**; W Tr, R top.
AT-SO Lt By 50°14'·29N 01°28'·65E VQ; NCM.
Pte du Hourdel Lt Tr 50°12'·85N 01°34'·10E Oc (3) WG 12s 19m W12M, G9M; W Tr, G top; vis W053°-248°, G248°-323°; *Reed (3) 30s.*
Le Crotoy 50°12'·93N 01°37'·45E Oc (2) R 6s 19m 9M; W pylon; vis 285°-135°.
Yacht Hbr, E side 50°13'·02N 01°38'·10E Fl G 2s 4m 2M.
St Valéry-sur-Somme, Embankment Hd 50°12'·29N 01°35'·92E Q (3) G 6s 2m 2M; G pylon; Ra refl.
W Hd of embankment 50°11'·40N 01°37'·60E Iso G 4s 9m 9M; W pylon, G top; vis 347°-222°.
La Ferté Môle Hd 50°11'·20N 01°38'·70E Fl R 4s 9m 9M; W pylon, R top; vis 000°-250°.

SOMME TO LE TOUQUET
FM By 50°20'·40N 01°31'·00E; WCM.
Pointe de Haut-Blanc (Berck-Plage) 50°23'·90N 01°33'·75E Fl 5s 44m **23M**; W Tr, R bands, G top.
Vergoyer SW Lt By 50°26'·90N 01°00'·10E VQ (9) 10s; WCM.
Bassurelle Lt By 50°32'·70N 00°57'·80E Fl (4) R 15s 6M; Racon (B); R refl; *Whis.*
Écovouga Wk By 50°33'·70N 00°59'·20E; ECM.
Vergoyer W Lt By 50°34'·65N 01°13'·70E Fl G 4s; SHM.
Vergoyer E Lt By 50°35'·75N 01°19'·80E VQ (3) 5s; ECM.
Vergoyer NW Lt By 50°37'·10N 01°18'·00E Fl (2) G 6s; SHM.
Vergoyer N Lt By 50°39'·65N 01°22'·30E VQ; NCM; Racon (C).

LE TOUQUET TO DUNKERQUE

LE TOUQUET
Le Touquet (La Canche) 50°31'·40N 01°35'·60E Fl (2) 10s 54m **25M**; Or Tr, brown band; W and G top.
Mérida Wk By 50°32'·80N 01°33'·30E; WCM.
Camiers, Rivière Canche ent, N side 50°32'·80N 01°36'·40E Oc (2) WRG 6s 17m W10M, R7M, G7M; R pylon; vis G015°-090°, W090°-105°, R105°-141°.

Cap d'Alprech 50°41'·96N 01°33'·83E Fl (3) 15s 62m **23M**; W Tr, B top; RC; FR Lts on radio mast 600m ENE.
Ophélie Lt By 50°43'·91N 01°30'·92E Fl G 4s; SHM.

BOULOGNE
Approaches Lt By 50°45'·36N 01°31'·15E VQ (6) + L Fl 10s 8m 6M; SCM; Ra refl; *Whis.*
Digue (Carnot) 50°44'·48N 01°34'·13E Fl (2+1) 15s 25m **19M**; W Tr, G top; *Horn (2+1) 60s.*
Digue Nord Hd 50°44'·76N 01°34'·27E Fl (2) R 6s 10m 7M; R Tr.
Jetée SW 50°43'·95N 01°35'·19E FG 17m 5M; W col, G top; *Horn 30s.*

ZC1 Lt By 50°44'·94N 01°27'·30E Fl (4) Y 15s; SPM.
Bassure de Baas Lt By 50°48'·50N 01°33'·15E VQ; NCM; *Bell.*
ZC2 Lt By 50°53'·50N 01°31'·00E Fl (2+1) Y 15s; SPM.
Cap Gris-Nez 50°52'·05N 01°35'·07E Fl 5s 72m **29M**; W Tr, B top; vis 005°-232°; RG; *Horn 60s.*
Lt By 50°54'·11N 01°32'·03E Fl (2) 6s; IDM.
Abbeville Lt By 50°56'·05N 01°37'·70E VQ (9) 10s; WCM.
CA3 Lt By 50°56'·80N 01°41'·25E Fl G 4s; SHM; *Whis.*
Sangatte 50°57'·23N 01°46'·57E Oc WG 4s 12m W8M, G6M; W pylon, B top; vis G065°-089°, W089°-152°, G152°-245°.
RCW Lt By 51°01'·20N 01°45'·45E VQ; NCM.
CA2 Lt By 51°00'·91N 01°48'·86E Q; NCM.
CA4 Lt By 50°58'·94N 01°45'·18E VQ (9) 10s 8m 8M; WCM; R refl; *Whis.*

CA6 Lt By 50°58'·30N 01°45'·70E VQ R; PHM.
CA5 Lt By 50°57'·70N 01°46'·20E QG; SHM.
CA8 Lt By 50°58'·43N 01°48'·72E QR; PHM; *Bell.*
CA10 Lt By 50°58'·68N 01°50'·00E Fl (2) R 6s; PHM.

CALAIS
Jetée Ouest Hd 50°58'·30N 01°50'·48E Iso G 3s 12m 9M; (in fog Iso 3s); W Tr, G top; *Bell (1) 5s.*
Jetée Est Hd 50°58'·45N 01°50'·54E Fl (2) R 6s 12m **17M**; Gy Tr, R top; *Horn (2) 40s;* Ra refl (in fog 2 Fl (2) 6s (vert) on request).
Calais 50°57'·73N 01°51'·28E Fl (4) 15s 59m **22M**; W 8-sided Tr, B top; vis 073°-260°.

MPC Lt By 51°06'·09N 01°38'·36E Fl Y 2·5s 10m 6M; SPM.
SANDETTIÉ Lt F 51°09'·40N 01°47'·20E Fl 5s 12m **24M**; R hull; *Horn 30s;* Racon (T).
Ruytingen SW Lt By 51°04'·99N 01°46'·90E Fl (3) G 12s; SHM; *Whis.*
Ruytingen W Lt By 51°06'·90N 01°50'·60E VQ; NCM.
Ruytingen NW Lt By 51°09'·05N 01°57'·40E Fl G 4s; SHM.
Ruytingen N Lt By 51°13'·12N 02°10'·42E VQ; NCM.
Ruytingen SE Lt By 51°09'·20N 02°09'·00E VQ (3) 15s; ECM.
DUNKERQUE LANBY 51°03'·00N 01°51'·83E Fl 3s 10m **25M**; R tubular structure on circular By; Racon.
RCE Lt By 51°02'·40N 01°53'·20E Iso G 4s; SHM.
Walde 50°59'·57N 01°55'·00E Fl (3) 12s 13m 4M; B pylon on hut.
DKA Lt By 51°02'·59N 01°57'·06E L Fl 10s; SWM.
Dyck E Lt By 51°05'·70N 02°05'·70E Q (3) 10s; ECM.
Haut-fond de Gravelines Lt By 51°04'·10N 02°05'·10E VQ (9) 10s; WCM.
DW5 Lt By 51°02'·20N 02°01'·00E QG; SHM.

GRAVELINES
Jetée Ouest 51°00'·98N 02°05'·55E Fl (2) WG 6s 9m W8M, G8M; Y ● Tr, G top; vis W317°-327°, G078°-085°, W085°-244°.
Jetée Est 51°00'·98N 02°05'·69E Fl (3) R 12s 5m 4M.

DUNKERQUE APPROACHES
DKB Lt By 51°03'·00N 02°09'·34E VQ (9) 10s; WCM.
Port Ouest Ldg Lts 120°. **Front**, 51°01'·72N 02°11'·99E Dir FG 16m **21M**; W col, G top; intens 119°-121°. **Rear**, 600m from front, Dir FG 30m **21M**; W col, G top; intens 119°-121°. By day both show F 28M.
Jetée Clipon Hd 51°02'·69N 02°09'·86E Fl (4) 12s 24m 13M; W ● col, R top; vis 278°-243°; *Siren (4) 60s.*
DY1 Lt By 51°09'·00N 02°15'·00E Fl G 4s; SHM.
DY2 Lt By 51°09'·50N 02°19'·50E Fl (2) R 6s; PHM.
DY3 Lt By 51°11'·50N 02°22'·50E Q; NCM.
DW23 Lt By 51°03'·60N 02°15'·25E QG; SHM; *Bell.*
DW29 Lt By 51°03'·88N 02°20'·32E Fl (3) G 12s; SHM.
E1 Lt By 51°04'·12N 02°23'·18E Fl (2) G 6s; SHM.
E2 Lt By 51°04'·38N 02°22'·40E VQ (6) + L Fl 10s; SCM.
E4 Lt By 51°04'·62N 02°24'·60E Fl R 4s; PHM.
E6 Lt By 51°04'·86N 02°27'·27E QR; PHM.
E7 Lt By 51°05'·20N 02°28'·60E Fl R, *Whis;* SWM.
E8 Lt By 51°05'·50N 02°28'·62E Fl (3) G, SHM.
E11 Lt By 51°07'·30N 02°30'·71E Fl G; SHM.
E12 Lt By 51°07'·95N 02°30'·78E VQ (6) + L Fl 10s; SCM.

DUNKERQUE PORT EST
Dunkerque 51°02'·98N 02°21'·94E Fl (2) 10s 59m **26M**; W Tr, B top.
Jetée Ouest Hd 51°03'·68N 02°21'·04E Oc (2+1) WG 12s 35m **W15M**, G12M; W Tr, brown top; vis G252°-310°, W310°-252°; Sig Stn; *Dia (2+1) 60s.*
Jetée Est Hd 51°03'·63N 02°21'·28E Fl (2) R 10s 12m **16M**; R □ on W pylon, R top. *Horn (2) 20s;* Fl (2) 10s (in fog).

10.19.5   PASSAGE INFORMATION

For detailed sailing directions refer to: *Normandy and Channel Islands Pilot* (Adlard Coles/Brackenbury), The *Shell Channel Pilot* (Imray/Cunliffe) and *North France Pilot* (Imray/Thompson). Also the Admiralty *Channel Pilot* and *Dover Strait Pilot.*

The coasts of Normandy and Picardy are convenient to hbrs along the S Coast of England – the distance from (say) Brighton to Fécamp being hardly more than an overnight passage. It should be noted however that many of the hbrs dry, so that a boat which can take the ground is an advantage. For details of TSS in the Dover Strait, see Fig. 10 (4). Notes on the English Channel and on cross-Channel passages appear in 10.3.5 and 10.15.5; see 10.0.5 for cross-Channel distances. For French glossary, see 1.4.2. The coast and ports westward from Pte de Barfleur are covered in Area 15.

The inland waterways system can be entered via the Seine (10.19.20), St Valéry-sur-Somme (10.19.25), Calais, Gravelines (10.19.28), and Dunkerque (10.19.29). See 10.15.8 for tolls.

PTE DE BARFLEUR TO GRANDCAMP (chart 2135, *2613*)

Raz de Barfleur (10.15.5) must be avoided in bad weather. In calm weather it can be taken at slack water (HW Cherbourg –4½ and +2) or the inshore passage used, passing 5ca E of La Jamette ECM bn. Pte de Barfleur marks the W end of B de Seine, which stretches 55M east to C d'Antifer, 12M N of Le Havre. There are no obstructions on a direct course across the Bay, but a transhipment area for large tankers is centred about 10M ESE of Pte de Barfleur. A feature of the Baie de Seine is the stand of tide at HW. Caution: The W end of the Baie de Seine is affected by floating Sargassum weed; in hbrs from St Vaast to Grandcamp propeller fouling is commonplace.

S from Barfleur (10.19.9) the coast runs SSE 4M to Pte de Saire, with rks and shoals up to 1M offshore. 2M S of Pte de Saire is St Vaast-la-Hougue (10.19.10): approach S of Île de Tatihou, but beware drying rks: La Tourelle, Le Gavendest and La Dent, which lie near the approaches and are buoyed.

Îles St Marcouf (10.19.11) lie 7M SE of St Vaast-la-Hougue, about 4M offshore, and consist of Île du Large (lt) and Île de Terre about ¼M apart. Banc de St Marcouf, with depths of 2·4m and many wks, extends 2·5M NW from the islands, and the sea breaks on this in strong N or NE winds. The Banc du Cardonnet, with depths of 5·2m and many wks, extends for about 5M ESE from the islands.

At the head of B du Grand Vey, about 10M S of Îles St Marcouf, are the (very) tidal hbrs of Carentan and Isigny (10.19.11); entry is only possible near HW. The Carentan chan is well buoyed and adequately lit. It trends SSW across sandbanks for about 4M, beyond which it runs between two breakwaters leading to a lock gate, and thence into canal to Carentan. The Isigny chan is deeper, but the hbr dries. Neither chan should be attempted in strong onshore winds.

On E side of B du Grand Vey, Roches de Grandcamp (dry) extend more than 1M offshore, N and W of Grandcamp (10.19.12), but they are flat and can be crossed from the N in normal conditions HW±1½. Three NCM buoys mark the N edge of the shoal. Heavy kelp can give false echo soundings.

GRANDCAMP TO DEAUVILLE (chart 2136, *2613*)

Between Pte de la Percée and Port-en-Bessin (10.19.13) a bank lies offshore, with drying ledges extending 3ca. A race forms over this bank with wind against tide. Off Port-en-Bessin the E-going stream begins about HW Le Havre – 0500, and the W-going at about HW Le Havre + 0050, sp rates 1·25kn.

From Port-en-Bessin the coast runs east 4M to C Manvieux, beyond which lie remnants of the wartime hbr of Arromanches, where there is occas anch. Between C Manvieux and Langrune, 10M E, Plateau du Calvados lies offshore. Rocher du Calvados (dries 1·6m) lies on the W part of this bank. There are numerous wrecks and obstructions in the area.

Roches de Ver (dry) lie near centre of Plateau du Calvados, extending 8ca offshore about 1M W of Courseulles-sur-Mer (10.19.14). The approach to this hbr is dangerous in strong onshore winds. Les Essarts de Langrune (dry) lie E of Courseulles-sur-Mer, and extend up to 2·25M seaward of Langrune. At their E end lie Roches de Lion (dry), which reach up to 1·5M offshore in places and extend to a point 2·5M W of Ouistreham ferry hbr and marina (10.19.15). Here a canal leads 7M inland to a marina in the centre of Caen.

6M E of Ouistreham is R. Dives (10.19.16) with marina. The banks dry for 1M to seaward, and entry is only possible from HW ± 2½, and not in fresh onshore wind conditions.

Deauville/Trouville (10.19.17), 8M ENE of Dives, is an important yachting hbr. The sands dry more than 5ca offshore; in strong W or N winds the entrance is dangerous and the sea breaks between the jetties. In such conditions it is best attempted within 15 mins of HW, when the stream is slack. To the NE beware Banc de Trouville (dries 2m), and shoal water to the N where Les Ratelets dries at the mouth of the Seine.

ESTUAIRE DE LA SEINE/LE HAVRE (charts 2146, 2990)

The Seine est is entered between Deauville and Le Havre, and is encumbered by shallow and shifting banks which extend seawards to Banc de Seine, 15M W of Le Havre. With wind against tide there is a heavy sea on this bank. Here the SW-going stream begins at HW Le Havre + 0400, and the NE-going at HW Le Havre – 0300, sp rates 1·5kn. Between Deauville and Le Havre the sea can be rough in W winds.

Chenal du Rouen is the main chan into R. Seine, and carries much commercial tfc. The S side of the chan is contained by Digue du Ratier, a training wall which extends E to Honfleur (10.19.18). With almost 24 hours access/exit, Honfleur is a useful starting port when bound up-river. See 10.19.20 for notes on R. Seine, Rouen and Paris; and canals to the Med.

Le Havre (10.19.19) is a large commercial port, as well as a yachting centre. From the NW, the most useful mark is the Le Havre Lanby 9M W of C de la Hève (lt). The appr chan, which runs 6M WNW from the hbr ent, is well buoyed and lit. Strong W winds cause rough water over shoal patches either side of the chan. Coming from the N or NE, there is deep water close off C de la Hève, but from here steer S to join the main ent chan. Beware Banc de l'Éclat (depth 0·1m), which lies on N side of main chan and about 1·5M from harbour ent.

9M N of C de la Hève is Port d'Antifer, a VLCC harbour. A huge breakwater extends about 1·5M seaward, and should be given a berth of about 1·5M, or more in heavy weather when there may be a race with wind against tide. Commercial vessels in the buoyed app chan have priority. Yachts should cross the app chan to the NW of A17/A18 lt buoys; at 90° to its axis; as quickly as possible, and well clear of ships in the chan. Crossing vessels should contact *Vigie Port d'Antifer* and any priority vessel on VHF Ch 16. Off Cap d'Antifer the NE-going stream begins about HW Le Havre – 0430, and the SW-going at about HW Le Havre + 0140. There are eddies close inshore E of Cap d'Antifer on both streams.

CAP D'ANTIFER TO DIEPPE (chart *2451*)

From C d'Antifer to Fécamp (10.19.21) drying rks extend up to 2½ca offshore. At Fécamp pierheads the E-going stream begins about HW Le Havre – 0500, and the W-going at about HW Le Havre + 0025, sp rates 2·75kn. Off Pte Fagnet, close NE of Fécamp, lie Les Charpentiers (rks which dry, to almost 2ca offshore).

From Fécamp to St Valéry-en-Caux (10.19.22), 15M ENE, (and beyond to Le Treport and Ault) the coast consists of chalk cliffs broken by valleys. There are rky ledges, extending 4ca offshore in places. The nuclear power station at Paluel 3M W of St Valéry-en-Caux (prohibited area marked by lt buoy) is conspic. Immediately E of St Valéry-en-Caux shallow sandbanks, Les Ridens, with a least depth of 0·6m, extend about 6ca offshore. At St Valéry-en-Caux ent the E-going

19

stream begins about HW Dieppe – 0550, and the W-going stream begins about HW Dieppe – 0015, sp rates 2·75kn. E of the ent a small eddy runs W on the E-going stream.

Between St Valéry-en-Caux and Pte d'Ailly (lt, fog sig, RC) there are drying rks 4ca offshore in places. About 1·5M E of Pte de Sotteville a rky bank (depth 4·2m) extends about 1M NNW; a strong eddy causes a race over this bank.

Drying rks extend 5ca off Pte d'Ailly, including La Galère, a rk which dries 6·8m, about 3ca N of the Pte. Dangerous wks lie between about 1·2M WNW and 1·5M NNW of the lt ho. About 6M N of Pte d'Ailly, Les Ecamias are banks with depths of 11m, dangerous in a heavy sea.

From Pte d'Ailly to Dieppe (10.19.23) the coast is fringed by a bank, drying in places, up to 4ca offshore. E of Pte d'Ailly an eddy runs W close inshore on first half of E-going stream. Off Dieppe the ENE-going stream begins about HW Dieppe – 0505, and the WSW-going at about HW Dieppe + 0030, sp rates 2kn.

DIEPPE TO BOULOGNE

Between Dieppe and Le Tréport (10.19.24), 14M NE, rky banks, drying in places, extend 5ca offshore. A prohib area extends 6ca off Penly nuclear power station and is marked by lt Bys. About 3M NW of Le Tréport, Ridens du Tréport (depth 5·1m) should be avoided in bad weather. Banc Franc-Marqué (depth 3·6m) lies 2M offshore, and about 3M N of Le Tréport.

N of Ault (lt) the coast changes from medium cliffs to low sand dunes. Offshore there are two shoals, Bassurelle de la Somme and Quémer, on parts of which the sea breaks in bad weather. 4·5M NW of Cayeux-sur-Mer the stream is rotatory anti-clockwise. The E-going stream begins about HW Dieppe –0200, and sets 070° 2·5kn at sp : the W-going stream begins about HW Dieppe + 0600, and sets 240° 1·5kn at sp.

B de Somme, between Pte du Hourdel and Pte de St Quentin, is a shallow, drying area of shifting sands. The chan, which runs close to Pte du Hourdel, is buoyed, but the whole est dries out 3M to seaward, and should not be approached in strong W or NW winds. For St Valéry-sur-Somme and Le Crotoy, see 10.19.25.

From Pte de St Quentin the coast runs 17M N to Pte du Touquet, with a shallow coastal bank which dries to about 5ca offshore, except in the approaches to the dangerous and constantly changing Embouchure de l'Authies (about 7M north), where it dries up to 2M offshore.

Le Touquet/Étaples (10.19.26) lies in the Embouchure de la Canche, entered between Pte du Touquet and Pte de Lornel, and with a drying bank which extends 1M seaward of a line joining these two points. Le Touquet-Paris-Plage lt is shown from a conspic tr, 1M S of Pte du Touquet. Off the entrance the N-going stream begins about HW Dieppe – 0335, sp rate 1·75kn; and the S-going stream begins about HW Dieppe + 0240, sp rate 1·75kn.

In the approaches to Pas de Calais a number of shoals lie offshore: La Bassurelle, Le Vergoyer, Bassure de Baas, Le Battur, Les Ridens, and The Ridge (or Le Colbart). In bad weather, and particularly with wind against tide in most cases, the sea breaks heavily on all these shoals. From Pte de Lornel to Boulogne (10.19.27; chart 438) the coast dries up to 5ca offshore. Off Digue Carnot the N-going stream begins HW Dieppe – 0130, and the S-going at HW Dieppe + 0350, sp rates 1·75kn.

BOULOGNE TO DUNKERQUE (charts 2451, 1892, 323)

Between Boulogne and C Gris Nez (lt, fog sig) the coastal bank dries about 4ca offshore. The NE-bound traffic lane of the TSS Fig. 10 (4) lies only 3M off C Gris Nez. Keep a sharp lookout not only for coastal traffic in the ITZ, but also cross-Channel traffic, particularly very fast hovercraft, jetfoils and catamarans. 1M NW of C Gris Nez the NE-going stream begins at HW Dieppe – 0150, and the SW-going at HW Dieppe + 0355, sp rates 4kn.

In bad weather the sea breaks heavily on Ridens de Calais, 3M N of Calais (10.19.28 and chart 1352), and also on Ridens de la Rade about 1·5M NE of the hbr. The drying hbr of Gravelines (10.19.28), which should not be used in strong onshore winds, is about 3M SW of Dunkerque Port Ouest; this is a commercial/ferry port which yachts should not enter. The old port, Dunkerque Port Est (10.19.29), has good yacht facilities and is 7·5M further E.

Offshore a series of banks lie roughly parallel with the coast: Sandettié bank (about 14M to N), Outer Ruytingen midway between Sandettié and the coast, and the Dyck banks which extend NE'wards for 30M from a point 5M NE of Calais. There are well-buoyed channels between some of these banks, but great care is needed in poor visibility. In general the banks are steep-to on the inshore side, and slope seaward. In bad weather the sea breaks on the shallower parts.

10.19.6   DISTANCE TABLE

Approximate distances in nautical miles are by the most direct route, whilst avoiding dangers and allowing for Traffic Separation Schemes. Places in *italics* are in adjoining areas; places in **bold** are in 10.0.5, Cross-Channel Distances; places underlined are in 10.0.7, Distances across the North Sea.

1. *Cherbourg*	1																			
2. Barfleur	20	2																		
3. St Vaast	26	10	3																	
4. Carentan	41	26	20	4																
5. Grandcamp-Maisy	39	21	16	13	5															
6. Courseulles	54	39	35	37	25	6														
7. Ouistreham	66	46	46	46	35	11	7													
8. Dives-sur-Mer	69	53	49	51	38	17	8	8												
9. Deauville/Trouville	76	56	53	56	43	21	14	7	9											
10. Honfleur	82	62	69	62	50	28	24	17	10	10										
11. Le Havre	70	56	53	56	45	23	19	13	8	9	11									
12. Fécamp	80	64	63	72	64	40	39	39	32	34	25	12								
13. St Valéry-en-Caux	82	77	78	88	80	55	58	55	44	45	38	15	13							
14. Dieppe	108	94	95	105	94	75	68	67	61	63	54	29	16	14						
15. St Valéry-sur-Somme	130	120	120	132	125	103	103	97	95	95	85	62	45	35	15					
16. Étaples	134	124	130	140	130	110	110	117	100	100	90	70	58	50	19	16				
17. Boulogne	142	138	133	145	135	118	115	108	108	110	101	76	61	54	30	12	17			
18. Calais	160	148	157	170	168	140	138	129	128	130	121	96	81	74	50	32	20	18		
19. Dunkerque	182	170	179	192	190	162	160	151	150	152	143	118	103	96	69	51	42	22	19	
20. *Nieuwpoort*	197	185	194	207	205	177	175	166	165	167	158	133	118	111	84	66	57	37	15	20

10.19.7   English Channel Waypoints.   See 10.1.7.

10.19.8   Special Notes for France: See 10.15.8.

BARFLEUR   10-19-9

Manche 49°40'·40N 01°15'·40W   Rtg 3-4-1

CHARTS
AC 1349, 2135, 1106, *2613*; SHOM 7090, 5609, 6864; ECM 528; Imray C32; Stanfords 1, 7

TIDES
−0208 Dover; ML 3·9; Duration 0550; Zone −0100

Standard Port CHERBOURG (←—)

Times				Height (metres)			
High Water		Low Water		MHWS	MHWN	MLWN	MLWS
0300	1000	0400	1000	6·4	5·0	2·5	1·1
1500	2200	1600	2200				
Differences BARFLEUR							
+0110	+0055	+0052	+0052	+0·1	+0·3	0·0	0·0

SHELTER
Excellent, but ent difficult in fresh E/NE winds. Hbr dries; access HW ±2½. Yachts berth at SW end of quay, clear of FVs; limited space. Beware rks/shoals in SE of hbr. Safe to ⚓ outside hbr in off-shore winds. See Hr Mr for moorings.

NAVIGATION
WPT 49°41'·30N 01°14'·21W, 039°/219° from/to front ldg lt, 1·35M. In rough weather, esp wind against tide, keep 5M off Pte de Barfleur to clear the Race; see 10.19.5. From the N, identify La Jamette ECM bn and La Grotte SHM buoy. From the S, keep seaward of Pte Dranguet and Le Moulard, both ECM bns. Beware cross currents and Le Hintar rks (buoyed) and La Raie (bn) to E of ldg line. The chan may not be clearly identified until close in. A new spur bkwtr (55m long) is still planned from the ☆ Fl G 4s, halfway across the ent, toward the ☆ Oc R 4s.

LIGHTS AND MARKS
Pte de Barfleur lt ho is conspic 1½M NNW of hbr, Fl (2) 10s 72m 29M, grey tr, B top, Reed (2) 60s. The church tr is a conspic daymark.
Ldg lts 219°: both Oc (3) 12s 7/13m 10M, W ☐ trs, synch; not easy to see by day. Buoys are small. Jetée Est Oc R 4s 5m 6M. Jetée Ouest Fl G 4s 8m 6M.

RADIO TELEPHONE
None.

TELEPHONE (Prefix ☎ Nos with zone code 02)
Hr Mr 33.54.08.29; Aff Mar 33.23.36.12; CROSS 33.52.72.13; SNSM 33.23.10.10; ♯ 33.53.79.65; Météo 33.53.53.44; Auto 08.36.68.08.50; Police 17; SAMU 15; Dr 33.54.00.02; Brit Consul 33.44.20.13.

FACILITIES
NW Quay (125 + 20 visitors), AB 38FF, M, Slip, L, D, FW, AC (long cable needed); **SC** ☎ 02.33.54.07.30.
Town Gaz, ME (Montfarville: 1km S), V, R, Bar, ✉, Ⓑ, bus to Cherbourg for ₤, ✈, Ferry.

ST VAAST-LA-HOUGUE   10-19-10

Manche 49°35'·25N 01°15'·35W   Rtg 3-2-1

CHARTS
AC 1349, 2135, *2613*; SHOM 7090, 6864, 7056; ECM 527, 528; Imray C32; Stanfords 1, 7

TIDES
−0240 Dover; ML 3·9; Duration 0530; Zone −0100

Standard Port CHERBOURG (←—)

Times				Height (metres)			
High Water		Low Water		MHWS	MHWN	MLWN	MLWS
0300	1000	0400	1000	6·4	5·0	2·5	1·1
1500	2200	1600	2200				
Differences ST VAAST-LA-HOUGUE							
+0110	+0045	+0050	+0100	+0·2	+0·2	0·0	−0·1

SHELTER
Excellent in marina, 2·3m; lock open HW−2¼ to HW+3. Crowded in season. If full, or awaiting lock, ⚓ off in White sector of jetty lt between brgs of 330° and 350°, but this ⚓ becomes untenable in strong E-S winds.

NAVIGATION
WPT 49°34'·40N 01°13'·78W, 130°/310° from/to main jetty lt (Oc 6s) 1·3M. Appr in W sector, leaving La Dent SCM By to stbd and Le Bout du Roc ECM By and Le Creux de Bas ECM bn to port. The ent is wide and well marked. Beware boats at ⚓, cross currents and oyster beds. "Le Run" appr is not advised and should not be attempted >1·2m draft.

LIGHTS AND MARKS
Do not confuse similar towers (conspic) on Ile de Tatihou and La Hougue Pte. From N, Pte de Saire Oc (2+1) 12s 11m 10M. From E, ldg lts 267°: front La Hougue Oc 4s 9m 10M; rear Morsalines Oc (3+1) WRG 12s 90m 11/8M in W sector. Main jetty hd lt, Oc (2) WRG 6s 12m 10/7M, W tr + R top, vis W310°-350°. R/G tfc sigs at lock ent.

RADIO TELEPHONE
VHF Ch 09.

TELEPHONE (Prefix ☎ Nos with zone code 02)
Hr Mr 33.54.48.81, ☎ 33.54.09.55; Aff Mar 33.54.43.61; ♯ 33.44.16.00; CROSS 33.52.72.13; SNSM 33.54.42.52; Météo 02.36.65.08.50; Police 33.54.12.11; Dr 33.54.43.42; Brit Consul 33.44.20.13.

FACILITIES
Marina (655 + 150 Ⓥ) ☎ 02.33.54.48.81, FF100, Access HW −2¼ to +3, FW, C (25 ton), AC, D, P, BY, ME, El, Sh, Gaz, CH, Bar, R, ☐, V, Slip; **Cercle Nautique de la Hougue** ☎ 02.33.54.55.73, Bar, R, C (3 ton), P, D, CH, FW, V.
Town P, D, V, Gaz, R, Bar, ☐, ✉, Ⓑ, ₤ (bus to Valognes), Cherbourg: ✈, Ferry.

CARENTAN/ISIGNY   10-19-11

Manche Rtg 4-2-1   Calvados Rtg 4-4-3

CHARTS
AC 2135, *2613*; SHOM 7056; ECM 527; Imray C32; Stan'd 1
TIDES
–0225 Dover; ML Rade de la Capelle 4·3; Duration 0510; Zone –0100

Standard Port CHERBOURG (←)

Use differences RADE DE LA CAPELLE 10.19.12
HW Carentan is HW Cherbourg +0100. See tidal graph for Carentan appr chan (facing page).

SHELTER
Temp ⚓ N of buoyed chans in winds <F5. Entry protected from prevailing S to W winds, but is not to be attempted in onshore winds >F5. Drying out on the hard sands of the estuary is not advised; nor is an early approach, as a bore (*mascaret*) may occur in the river channels between LW and HW –2½ particularly at springs.
At **Carentan** complete shelter in the canal/river and in the locked marina (max/min depths 3·5/2·9m).
At **Isigny** drying pontoons on SW bank ¼M N of town.
In emergency the Iles St Marcouf, conspic 5M N, provide some shelter from NNE, N and W winds (see next col).
NAVIGATION
WPT Cl SWM buoy, Iso 4s, 49°25'·30N 01°07'·10W. For **Carentan**: leave WPT at HW–2 to –1½, tracking 214° to ent to drying chan, 1·6M. Chan is liable to vary in both depth and direction. Graph on facing page gives approx access times, using draft and tidal range at Cherbourg. Least water (drying 3·4m) reported between No 5b and 7 buoys. All buoys have R or G reflective panels; 5 are lit, Fl (3) 12s R/G. After about 4M the chan enters between 2 bkwtrs, marked by bns. 3·5M further on the chan divides into three, forming a small pool. Enter the lock ahead (opens HW –2 to HW +3, tfc sigs); waiting pontoons are on E side above and below lock. Lock-keeper will assign ▼ berth.
Isigny: leave WPT at HW –2½ heading about 150°/1·1M for IS unlit NCM buoy and ent to buoyed chan which is deeper than Carentan's, but unlit. From IS buoy track about 212° for 1·25M to first chan buoys. Pairs of buoys

are spaced at approx 3ca intervals, but between Nos 9/10 and 11/12 the interval is 6ca, with a SHM perch midway.
LIGHTS AND MARKS
Carentan: Bkwtr outer bns are lit, Fl (3)R 12s and Fl (3)G 12s. Ldg lts: Front Oc (3)R 12s 6m 17M and rear Oc (3) 12s 14m 11M, lead 209°30' for 1·6M from the ends of the bkwtrs and immediately outside (not valid within the buoyed chan). From front ldg lt, lock is approx 3M.
Lock sigs: FG = lock open, FR = lock closed.
Isigny: Ldg lts, both Oc (2+1) 12s 7/19m 18M synch & intens 171°-175°, lead 173° for 1·9M between bkwtrs to front ldg lt. Here turn port into R l'Aure for ½M to town.
RADIO TELEPHONE
VHF Carentan Ch 09 (0800-1800LT & in lock opening hrs). Ch 09 also at Isigny (0900-1800LT).
TELEPHONE (Prefix ☎ Nos with zone code 02)
Hr Mr Carentan 33.42.24.44; Lockmaster 33.71.10.85; Hr Mr Isigny 31.22.10.67; Aff Mar 33.44.00.13; ⌗ 33.44.16.00; CROSS 33.52.72.13; Auto 08.36.68.08.50; Police 33.42.00.17; ⊞ 33.42.14.12; Dr 33.42.33.21; Brit Consul 33.44.20.13.
FACILITIES
CARENTAN:
Marina (220 + 50 visitors) ☎ 33.42.24.44, FF79, Access HW –2 to HW +3, FW, AC, P & D (0900-1000), Slip, C (50 ton), BH (16 ton);
YC Croiseurs Côtiers de Carentan ☎ 33.42.40.42, Bar;
Services: ME, El, Sh, CH, BY. **Town** Bar, ⑧, D, P, ✉, ⇌, R, V, ✈ (Cherbourg). Ferry: Cherbourg.
ISIGNY
Quay AB (55+5), FW, AC, P, D, C (8 ton), Slip; **Club Nautique** AB, C, R, Bar; **Services**: ME, El, Sh. **Town** R, V, Bar, ⑧, ✉.

ADJACENT ANCHORAGE

ILES ST MARCOUF, Manche, 49°29'·70N 01°08'·70W. AC 2135, *2613*; SHOM 7056. Tides, 10.19.12. The 2 islands, Ile de Terre and to the N, Ile du Large, look from afar like ships at ⚓. The former is a bird sanctuary and is closed to the public; the latter has a small dinghy hbr on the W side. ⚓ SW or SE of Ile du Large or SE or NE of the Ile de Terre. Holding is poor on pebbles and kelp; no shelter in S'lies. Ile du Large lt, VQ (3) 5s 18m 9M. Both islands are surrounded by drying rks, uninhabited and lack facilities.

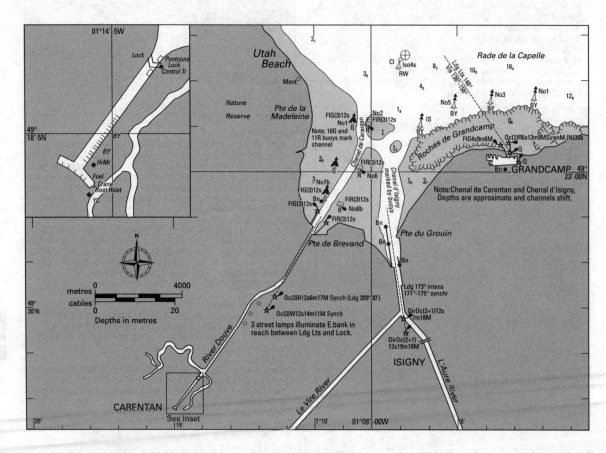

CARENTAN *continued*

CARENTAN TIDAL GRAPH

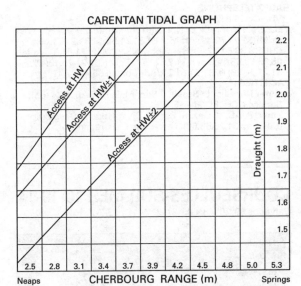

Caution: This graph, based on data from Port-Carentan, includes a safety clearance of 0·5m. Skippers may wish to add an additional margin to cater for depth variations due to shifting of the channel and/or Météorological conditions.

GRANDCAMP

GRANDCAMP-MAISY   10-19-12

Calvados 49°23'·50N 01°02'·87W

CHARTS
AC 2135, *2613*; SHOM 7056; ECM 527; Imray C32; Stan'd 1
TIDES
–0220 Dover; ML Rade de la Capelle 4·4; Duration 0510; Zone –0100

Standard Port CHERBOURG (←)

Times				Height (metres)			
High Water		Low Water		MHWS	MHWN	MLWN	MLWS
0300	1000	0400	1000	6·4	5·0	2·5	1·1
1500	2200	1600	2200				
Differences RADE DE LA CAPELLE (3M to NW)							
+0115	+0050	+0130	+0117	+0·8	+0·9	+0·1	+0·1
ILES SAINT MARCOUF							
+0118	+0052	+0125	+0110	+0·6	+0·7	+0·1	+0·1

SHELTER
Access day & night, but difficult in NW to NE winds > F6. Safe appr sp HW ±2, nps HW ±1.5. Gate into wet basin, with marina to the W, opens at LW Dunkerque (10.19.29) and closes at HW Dunkerque, ie approx local HW ±2½. ⓥ on N pontoon at E end. SW corner of basin is very dirty.
NAVIGATION
WPT 49°25'·00N 01°04'·60W, 326°/146° from/to front ldg lt 2·0M. Large flat rks, Les Roches de Grandcamp, extend about 1½M out from the hbr and dry approx 1·5m; heavy kelp cover can cause echosounders to under-read.
LIGHTS AND MARKS
3 NCM Bys, numbered 1, 3 and 5, mark the seaward limit of Les Roches de Grandcamp. Appr between Nos 3 & 5. E pier hd lt, Oc (2) R 6s, on a RW col. Ldg lts 146°: both Dir Q 9/12m 15M (vis 144·5°-147·5°). Two other ldg lts: Oc 4s 8/28m 12M, to E and S of hbr, lead 221°.

RADIO TELEPHONE
VHF Ch 09.
TELEPHONE (Prefix ☎ Nos with zone code 02)
Hr Mr 31.22.63.16; Aff Mar 31.22.60.65; CROSS 33.52.72.13; SNSM 31.22.67.12; Météo 21.33.25.26; Auto 08.36.68.08.14; Police 31.22.00.18; Dr 31.22.60.44; Ⓗ Bayeux 31.51.51.51; Brit Consul 35.42.27.47.
FACILITIES
Marina (268 + 25 visitors) ☎ 31.22.63.16, FF55, EI, FW, BH (5 ton), Bar, V, AC; **Services:** ME, EI, ✉, Sh, CH, Gaz, C. **Town** P & D (cans), Gaz, ✉, Ⓑ, ⇌ (Carentan), ✈ (Caen). Ferry: Cherbourg, Ouistreham.

ANCHORAGE BETWEEN PORT-EN-BESSIN AND COURSEULLES-SUR-MER

ARROMANCHES, Manche, 49°21'·80N 00°37'·20W. AC 2135, *2613*; SHOM 6927. HW is –0040 on Le Havre; see Port-en-Bessin (10.19.13). Strictly a fair weather ⚓, with little shelter from the WW II Mulberry caissons which are conspic esp at LW. Rocher du Calvados dries 1·6m, 7ca ENE of ent. There are many wrecks offshore; 3 to the W and N are marked by a WCM and two ECM buoys. The most N'ly ECM buoy (Roseberry, 49°23'·2N 00°36'·1W) bears approx 025°/1·5M from the ent (lat/long as line 1) which is marked by a small unlit PHM and SHM buoy. Enter on about 245° for ⚓ in 3m to S of the caissons, or sound closer inshore. Caution rky plateau off the beach and obstructions to SE of ent, marked by four W buoys. Facilities: **YC Port Winston** ☎ 31.22.31.01, 2 slips (dinghies).

19

PORT-EN-BESSIN   10-19-13
Calvados 49°21'·22N 00°45'·40W

CHARTS
AC 2136, *2613*; SHOM 7056; ECM 527; Imray C32; Stan'd 1
TIDES
−0215 Dover; ML 4·4; Duration 0520; Zone −0100

Standard Port LE HAVRE (→)

Times				Height (metres)			
High Water		Low Water		MHWS	MHWN	MLWN	MLWS
0000	0500	0000	0700	7·9	6·6	2·8	1·2
1200	1700	1200	1900				
Differences PORT-EN-BESSIN							
−0055	−0030	−0030	−0055	−0·7	−0·7	−0·2	−0·1
ARROMANCHES							
−0055	−0025	−0027	−0035	−0·6	−0·6	−0·2	−0·2

SHELTER
Good in 2nd basin; outer hbr dries completely. There is little room for yachts. Basins accessible HW ±2. Contact Hr Mr on arrival. Waiting berths on Quai de L'Epi.
NAVIGATION
WPT 49°22'·00N 00°44'·90W, 024°/204° from/to front ldg lt 204°, 1·1M. ‡ prohib in outer hbr and 1ca either side of 204° transit. Busy fishing port. Yachts may stay for up to 24 hrs. Ent is difficult with strong N/NE winds and >F8 it is dangerous. Beware submerged jetty (marked by R bn) to port of ent chan. Keep out of G sector of Mole Ouest lt.
LIGHTS AND MARKS
Ldg lts 204°: Front Oc (3) 12s 25m 10M, W pylon, G top, vis 069°-339°; Siren 20s (sounded over 90° each side of ldg line, continuous in W sector, interrupted in E sector); rear, Oc (3) 12s 42m 11M, W and grey house; vis 114°-294°, synch with front; RC. Other lts as chartlet; inner pier hds are Oc (2) R 6s and Fl (2) G 6s.
Entry sigs: Ⓡ over Ⓖ, or R over G flags = basins closed. Bridge has FR lt each side, and FR in the middle when shut. Lock opens HW ±2. When lock open, bridge opens whenever possible to suit yachts and FVs.

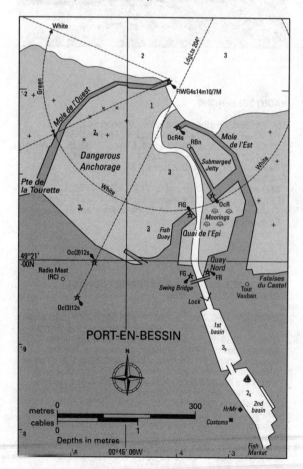

PORT-EN-BESSIN

RADIO TELEPHONE
VHF Ch 18 (HW ±2) for lock opening.
TELEPHONE (Prefix ☎ Nos with zone code 02)
Hr Mr 31.21.70.49; Aff Mar 31.21.71.52; ⌗ 31.21.71.09; CROSS 33.52.72.13; Semaphore/SNSM 31.21.81.51; Auto 08.36.68.08.14; Lock 31.21.71.77; Police 31.21.70.10; Dr 31.21.74.26; Ⓗ 31.51.51.51; Brit Consul 35.42.27.47.
FACILITIES
Outer Hbr Slip, L; **Bassin II** Slip, M, L, FW, AB, C (4 ton);
Services: CH, El, Ⓔ, ME, Sh.
Town P, AB, V, Gaz, R, Bar, ✉, Ⓑ, ⇌ (bus to Bayeux), ✈ (Caen, ☎ 31.26.58.00). Ferry: See Ouistreham.

COURSEULLES-SUR-MER 10-19-14
Calvados 49°20'·48N 00°27'·27W   Rtg 3-2-2

CHARTS
AC 1349, 2136, *2613*; SHOM 5598, 6927; ECM 526, 527; Imray C32; Stanfords 1
TIDES
−0300 Dover; ML 4·6; Duration No data; Zone −0100

Standard Port LE HAVRE (→)

Times				Height (metres)			
High Water		Low Water		MHWS	MHWN	MLWN	MLWS
0000	0500	0000	0700	7·9	6·6	2·8	1·2
1200	1700	1200	1900				
Differences COURSEULLES-SUR-MER							
−0045	−0015	−0020	−0025	−0·5	−0·5	−0·1	−0·1

SHELTER
Good except in strong W to NE winds. Avant Port dries 2·5m; best entry at HW −1. The lock into Bassin Joinville (3m) opens HW ±2. New Basin marina (2m) is usually full and only suited to small shoal draft; cross sill (dries 3m) HW ±3. Swing bridges to both marinas open on request.
NAVIGATION
WPT 49° 22'.00N 00° 28'.70W, 314°/134° from/to landfall By SWM Iso 4s, 1.0M. Plateau du Calvados extends 2M seaward and banks dry for 0.6M. Outer ldg marks: front Bernières-sur-mer church tr on with La Delivrande church twin spires (partly obscd by trees), lead 134° close to landfall buoy. Beware rks awash at CD either side of ldg line. Maintain 134° for 0.55M until ent bears 198°.

COURSEULLES *continued*

LIGHTS AND MARKS
W bkwtr lt, Iso WG 4s 7m 9/6M (stay in W sector); also marked by SHM bns and conspic crucifix at root. E bkwtr marked by PHM bns and Oc (2) R 6s 9m 7M at root. This lt in transit with Chateau (conspic) leads 194° to hbr ent.

RADIO TELEPHONE
VHF Ch 09, 0900-1200LT and HW±3.

TELEPHONE (Prefix ☎ Nos with zone code 02)
Hr Mr 31.37.51.69; Control tr 31.37.46.03; Aff Mar 31.37.46.19; CROSS 33.52.72.13; SNSM 31.37.45.47; ⌗ West Quai, no ☎; Météo 31.26.28.11; Auto 08.36.68.08.14; Police 31.37.07.13; Dr 31.37.45.24; Brit Consul 35.42.27.47

FACILITIES
Joinville Basin ☎ 31.37.51.69, FF100, Slip, P & D (cans), FW, AC, Sh, C (10 ton), CH; **New Basin** ☎ 31.37.46.03, P, D, FW, ME, EI, Sh; **Société des Régates de Courseulles** ☎ 31.37.47.42, Bar. **Services:** BY, ME, EI, Ⓔ, Sh, CH, SM. **Town** P, D, V, Gaz, R, Bar, ⊠, Ⓑ, ⇌ (bus to Caen), ✈ (Caen). Ferry: See Ouistreham.

OUISTREHAM   10-19-15
Calvados 49°16'·88N 00°14'·81W (E lock)   Rtg 3-1-2

CHARTS
AC 1349, 2136, *2613*; SHOM 7055, 6927, 6928; ECM 526; Imray C32; Stanfords 1

TIDES
−0118 Dover; ML 4·6; Duration 0525; Zone −0100

Standard Port LE HAVRE (⟶)

Times				Height (metres)			
High Water		Low Water		MHWS	MHWN	MLWN	MLWS
0000	0500	0000	0700	7·9	6·6	2·8	1·2
1200	1700	1200	1900				

Differences OUISTREHAM

−0045	−0010	−0005	0000	−0·3	−0·3	−0·2	−0·3

Note: There is a double HW at Ouistreham (also at Dives and Trouville). The HW differences, when referred to the start of the stand at Le Havre, give the time of the first HW.

SHELTER
Very good in marina (depth 3·5m and access HW±3), 1ca S of locks on E side. Waiting pontoon on E of Avant Port.

NAVIGATION
WPT ECM buoy, VQ (3) 5s, 49° 20'·48N 00° 14'·73W, 352°/172° from/to No 1 & 2 buoys, 1·26M. Ent chan is marked by training walls, with bns. Yachts normally enter canal by smaller E lock. Beware turbulence in locks. Lock opens for arrivals at HW−2½*, −1½, +2¼ and +3¾*; and for departures at HW−3, −2, +1¾ and +2¾*. * denotes extra openings (0700-2000LT) mid Jun-mid Sep; also at w/ends and public hols only, from 1 Apr-mid Jun and mid Sep-31 Oct. Detailed timings, which may vary, posted at SRCO.

LIGHTS AND MARKS
From WPT, pick up ldg lts 185°, both Dir Oc (3+1) R 12s 10/30m 17M, synch, intens 183·5°−186·5°. Chan has lt bys. Main lt ho, W + R top, conspic, Oc WR 4s 37m 17/13M. IPTS (full code) shown from control tr. Yachts may only enter when Ⓦ shows to port or stbd of lowest main tfc lt, indicating E or W lock. Waiting pontoon is no longer lit.

RADIO TELEPHONE
Call *Ouistreham Port* VHF Ch **68** 16; Lock Ch 12 68 (HW −2 to HW +3). Sté des Régates Ch 09 (office hours).

TELEPHONE (Prefix ☎ Nos with zone code 02)
Hr Mr/Lock 31.97.14.43; Port de Plaisance 31.97.13.05; Aff Mar 31.97.18.65; CROSS 33.52.72.13; SNSM 31.97.14.43; Ferry terminal 31.96.80.80; ⌗ 31.86.61.50; Météo 31.26.68.11; Auto 08.36.68.08.14; Police 31.97.13.15; Dr 31.97.18.45; Brit Consul 35.42.27.47; Taxi 31.97.35.67.

FACILITIES
Marina (600 + 65 visitors) ☎ 31.97.13.05, FF130, Slip, FW, ME, EI, Sh, CH, AC, BH (8 ton), Gas, Gaz, Kos, SM, Bar, P, D, (Fuel pumps open ½hr before outbound lock opening); **Société des Régates de Caen-Ouistreham** (SRCO) ☎ 31.97.13.05, FW, ME, EI, Sh, CH, V, Bar; **Services:** BY, Sh, EI, Ⓔ, ME, CH, SM, SHOM. **Town** V, Gaz, R, Bar, ⊠, Ⓑ, ⇌ (bus to Caen), ✈ (Caen). Ferry: to Portsmouth. (May-Sept, also to Poole).

CAEN 49°11'·03N 00°21'·13W. Charts: AC 1349, SHOM 7055.

Passage and Facilities:
The 8M canal passage is simple and takes approx 1¾hrs. Bridges will open free for yachts which transit at the posted times; at other times fees (at least FF81) are due. Daily transit times are posted at the SRCO YC: S-bound is usually pm and N-bound am. It is important to be *at the first bridge* (Pegasus) at/before the posted transit time; allow ½hr from Ouistreham to Pegasus bridge. Depths 2·5m to 10m; max speed 7kn; transit only permitted by day; no overtaking. Outbound vessels have right of way. Keep listening watch on Ch 68. There are 3 moving bridges, at: Bénouville (Pegasus) (2½M from locks), Colombelles (5M) and La Fonderie (8M). Tfc lts no longer used. Calix (6½M) is now a fixed 33m high viaduct. Turn stbd after La Fonderie bridge for marina at Bassin St Pierre in city centre. VHF *Caen Port* Ch 12 68. Hr Mr ☎ 02.31.52.12.88; Aff Mar ☎ 02.31.85.40.55; ⌗ ☎ 02.31.86.61.50; **Marina** (64 visitors) ☎ 02.31.95.24.47, FF80, P & D (cans), ME, Sh, EI, AB, FW; **Services:** ME, EI, Sh, SM, CH. **City** Ⓑ, Bar, Ⓗ, ⊠, R, V, ⇌, ✈ (Carpiquet).

19

DIVES-SUR-MER   10-19-16

Calvados 49°17'·86N 00°05'·13W   Rtg 3-2-2

CHARTS
AC 2146; SHOM 6928; ECM 526; Imray C32; Stanfords 1
TIDES
−0135 Dover; ML 5·1m; Duration; Zone −0100

Standard Port LE HAVRE (→)

Times				Height (metres)			
High Water		Low Water		MHWS	MHWN	MLWN	MLWS
0000	0500	0000	0700	7·9	6·6	2·8	1·2
1200	1700	1200	1900				

Differences DIVES-SUR-MER

−0100	−0010	0000	0000	+0·3	+0·2	+0·2	+0·1

Note: There is a double HW at Dives (also at Ouistreham and Trouville). The HW differences, when referred to the start of the stand at Le Havre, give the time of the first HW.

SHELTER
Good, but appr dries to 1M offshore and can be difficult in NW/NE > F5. Marina ent 400m W of Dir It, off shallow R La Dives. Access HW±3 (HW±2½ for draft >1·5m) via single gate. Sill below gate is 2·5m above CD; gate opens when tide 4·5m above CD. Or follow river chan to berth on YC pontoon (2 ⊘) below footbridge (max draft 1·5m).
NAVIGATION
WPT 49°18'·78N 00°05'·67W, Landfall buoy "DI", L Fl 10s, 339°/159° from/to No 1 and 2 Bys, 4ca. (Note: buoy "DI" is off chartlet). Two waiting Bys (untenable in WNW F4) are reported close to WPT in 3m. Beware sandbanks (drying 4·2m) each side of buoyed chan; keep well clear of two large SHM bns on W side. After last chan buoys, hug the shore to G (R horiz band) Division buoy and 4 G perches marking submerged training wall leading to marina ent.
LIGHTS AND MARKS
By day ent is seen at W end of densely wooded hills behind Houlgate.
Dir It 159° Oc (2+1) WRG 12s 7m 12/9M, R hut opposite Pte de Cabourg, vis G125°-157°, W157°-162°, R162°-194°. W sector covers chan only up to Nos 3/4 marks; thence follow the chan buoys/bns. 4 PHM and 2 SHM buoys, all unlit, are moved to suit shifting chan; Nos 3 and 5 SHMs are bns, lit QG 12m 4M and Fl G 4s 13m 4M respectively. Close E of marina ent a Division buoy, IQG (2+1), indicates preferred chan to port and marks shoals to N. Caution: Buoys/bns may not be numbered; positions are approximate due to the lack of large-scale charts.
RADIO TELEPHONE
VHF Ch 09, H24.
TELEPHONE (Prefix ☎ Nos with zone code 02)
Hr Mr 31.24.48.00; CROSS 35.52.72.13; Météo = via Hr Mr; Auto 08.36.68.08.14; Police 31.24.85.00; Dr 31.91.05.44.

FACILITIES
Marina (Port Guillaume) (545+55 visitors) ☎ 31.24.48.00, ⛴ 31.24.73.02, AC, FW, P, D, ⬜, Slip, BH (30 ton), C (1·5 ton); **Cabourg YC** ☎ 31.91.23.55, Bar; **Services:** BY, ME, EI, CH, Sh.
Town V, R, Bar, ⑧, ✉, ✈ (Deauville). Ferry: Ouistreham.

DEAUVILLE/TROUVILLE 10-19-17
Calvados 49°22'·44N 00°04'·23E   Rtg 3-1-1

CHARTS
AC 1349, 2146, *2613*; SHOM 6928, 6736; ECM 526, 1012; Imray C32; Stanfords 1

TIDES
−0130 Dover; ML 5·1; Duration 0510; Zone −0100

Standard Port LE HAVRE (⟶)

Times				Height (metres)			
High Water		Low Water		MHWS	MHWN	MLWN	MLWS
0000	0500	0000	0700	7·9	6·6	2·8	1·2
1200	1700	1200	1900				
Differences TROUVILLE							
−0100	−0010	0000	+0005	+0·4	+0·3	+0·3	+0·1

Note: There is a double HW at Trouville (also at Ouistreham and Dives). The HW differences, when referred to the start of the stand at Le Havre, give the time of the first HW.

SHELTER
Good in marina and Yacht Hbr, but ent to chan difficult in NW/N winds > force 6. Chan and river dry 2·4m; no access LW±2½, for 2m draft. Marina lock opens H24, if enough water outside. Yacht Hbr gate open HW −2 to HW +2½.

NAVIGATION
WPT 49°23'·00N 00°03'·70E, 328°/148° from/to W bkwtr lt Fl WG 4s, 0·65M. Semoy ECM, VQ (3) 5s, marks wreck 2·2M from ent, on ldg line. Do not appr from E of N due to Les Ratelets and Banc de Trouville. Trouville SW buoy, WCM, VQ (9) 10s, is 1M WNW of ent.

LIGHTS AND MARKS
Casino is conspic on Trouville side. Ldg lts 148°, both Oc R 4s synch. Yacht Hbr ent sigs (vert): 3 Ⓡ = closed; 3 Ⓖ = passage one way; 2 Ⓖ over Ⓦ = passage both ways.

RADIO TELEPHONE
Marina and Yacht Hbr VHF Ch 09.

TELEPHONE (Prefix ☎ Nos with zone code 02)
Hr Mr Marina 31.98.30.01; Marina lock 31.8895.96; Hr Mr Yacht Hbr 31.98.50.40; Yacht Hbr lock 31.88.36.21; Aff Mar 31.88.36.21; SNSM 31.88.31.70; CROSS 33.52.72.13; ⌗ 31.88.35.29; Auto (local) 08.36.68.08.14; Auto (regional) 08.36.68.08.76; Police 31.88.13.07; Dr 31.88.23.57; Ⓗ 31.14.33.33; Brit Consul 35.42.27.47.

FACILITIES
Port Deauville (Marina) (800 + 100 visitors) ☎ 31.98.30.01, 🕾 31.88.70.55, FF111, D, AC, FW, ME, El, Sh, C (6 ton), BH (45 ton), Slip, CH, SM, R, Bar; **Deauville Marina Club**.
Yacht Hbr (320+80 visitors) ☎ 31.98.50.40, FF97, FW, AC, Slip, D (pump S end of Bassin Morny), P (cans, 20m); **Deauville YC** ☎ 31.88.38.19, L, FW, C (8 ton), AB, CH, Bar; **Services:** CH, ME, El, Sh.
Both towns P (cans), V, Gaz, R, Bar, ✉, Ⓑ, BY, CH, Slip, Sh, ME, El, Ⓔ, ⇌, ✈ Deauville. Ferry: See Le Havre and Ouistreham.

22'·5

Ldg Lts 148°

White ★FlWG4s12/9M Green

G

G

G

2

G

Fl(4)WR12s8m7/4M Red

G

IsoG4s5M

R

R

Dredged 1m above CD

G

G

Recommended Course

R

R

Obsc

OcR4s12MHorn(2)30s

QG

Red

YC(CNTH)

N

metres   0   200
cables   0   1
Depths in metres

49°22'·00N

Visitors

3

Boat Lift 45T

Diesel

Lock

YC

HrMr

Wooden Piers

OcR4s vis 120°–170°

Casino (conspic)

TROUVILLE

Fish Quay

Slip

Slip

Gate

HrMr

Yacht Harbour

La Touques

Slip

C

PORT DEAUVILLE (MARINA)

DEAUVILLE

Bassin Morny

Club House DYC

00°04'·50E

0°05'

19

HONFLEUR   10-19-18

Calvados 49° 25'·75N 00° 13'·93E   Rtg 1-2-1

CHARTS

AC 2994, 2146, *2613*; SHOM 6796, 6683; ECM 1012; Imray C31; Stanfords 1

TIDES

−0135 Dover; ML 5·0; Duration 0540; Zone −0100

Standard Port LE HAVRE (→)

Times				Height (metres)			
High Water		Low Water		MHWS	MHWN	MLWN	MLW
0000	0500	0000	0700	7·9	6·6	2·8	1·2
1200	1700	1200	1900				
Differences HONFLEUR							
−0135	−0135	+0015	+0040	+0·1	+0·1	+0·1	+0·3
ANTIFER							
+0025	+0015	+0005	−0007	+0·1	0·0	0·0	0·0

In the Seine there is a HW stand of about 2hrs 50 mins. The HW time differences refer to the beginning of the stand.

SHELTER

Excellent in the Vieux Bassin. Visitors raft on pontoon at NW quay. Ask YC if hoping to berth on YC finger pontoons. Larger yachts can enter Bassin de l'Est; see Hr Mr.

NAVIGATION

WPT Ratier NW SHM buoy, VQG, 49°26'·63N, 00°03'·41E, at ent to well buoyed Chenal de Rouen. Appr at HW ±3, keeping between the Digue Nord, marked by posts, and the PHM chan buoys to avoid shipping. Ent between No 19 SHM buoy and very conspic radar tr. Beware strong currents across ent.

The **outer lock** (fitted with recessed bollards and ladders, but no pontoons) operates H24 and is open at H, every hour for arrivals; and every H+30 for departures. Access H24 for 1·5m draft; but for 2m draft no access LW±1. At the Vieux Bassin the old lock gate is permanently open.

The **road bridge** lifts as shown below (LT). Yachts leaving have priority over arrivals.

Mid season (1 Mar-31 May; 16 Sept-31 Oct)
Weekdays: 0730, 1030, 1530, 1830.
Sat/Sun/Hols: 0730, 0830, 0930, 1030, 1730, 1830, 1930, 2030.

High Season (1 Jun-15 Sept)
Every day: same as Sat/Sun/National holidays in mid-season.

Low season (1 Nov-28 Feb)
Weekdays: as mid season.
Sat/Sun/Hols: 0730, 0830, 0930, 1030, 1530, 1630, 1730, 1830.

LIGHTS AND MARKS

Falaise des Fonds lt, 0·75M W of ent Fl (3) WRG 12s 15m, 17/13M, W □ tr, vis G040°-080°, R080°-084°, G0084°-100°, W100°-109°, R109°-162°, G162°-260°. E mole Q 9m 9M, Y metal framework tr with B top, Reed (5) 40s. W mole QG 10m 6M, G framework tr.

Traffic signals (all vert, from the top) at lock:

3 ®	=	Closed; no passage
3 Ⓖ	=	One way passage
ⒼⒼⓌ	=	Two way passage
ⒼⓌⒼ	=	Passage only allowed with special instructions.

Note: The Pont de Normandie, 1·7M E of Honfleur ent, has 52m clearance and a pile lt, Fl Y 2·5s 3m, on N side of chan.

RADIO TELEPHONE

Hr Mr VHF Ch 09 16; Lock 09 16 (H24); Radar Tower Ch **73** 16 (H24).

TELEPHONE (Prefix ☎ Nos with zone code 02)

Hr Mr 31.89.20.02, ⚓ 31.89.42.10; Lock Mr 31.98.72.82; CROSS 33.52.72.13; Aff Mar 31.89.20.67; ⌗ 31.89.12.13; SNSM 31.88.11.13; Auto (regional) 08.36.68.08.76; Auto (offshore) 08.36.68.08.08; Police 31.89.21.24; Dr 31.89.34.05; Ⓗ 31.89.04.74; Cercle Nautique 31.98.87.13; Brit Consul 35.42.27.47.

FACILITIES

Vieux Bassin Yacht Hbr (120 + 30 Ⓥ, max LOA 20m), FF95 AB, FW, AC; **Cercle Nautique d'Honfleur** ☎ 31.89.87.13, M; **Services:** BY, Sh, Ⓔ, C (10 ton), Slip.
Town P & D (cans), V, R, Bar, Ⓞ Gaz, ✉, Ⓓ, ⇌, ✈
Deauville. Ferry: Le Havre.

TIME ZONE –0100
(French Standard Time)
Subtract 1 hour for UT

For French Summer Time add
ONE hour in non-shaded areas

FRANCE – LE HAVRE

LAT 49°29′N   LONG   0°07′E

TIMES AND HEIGHTS OF HIGH AND LOW WATERS

YEAR **1998**

JANUARY

Time	m		Time	m
1 0008	7.8	**16** 0046	7.6
0715	1.3	0744	1.7
TH 1223	7.9	F 1255	7.6
1939	1.1	2004	1.5
2 0052	7.8	**17** 0121	7.5
0758	1.4	0815	1.9
F 1308	7.8	SA 1328	7.5
2022	1.2	2034	1.8
3 0137	7.7	**18** 0155	7.3
0841	1.6	0846	2.1
SA 1355	7.7	SU 1401	7.2
2104	1.4	2102	2.1
4 0223	7.5	**19** 0228	7.0
0925	1.8	0916	2.4
SU 1444	7.5	M 1434	7.0
2148	1.7	2132	2.4
5 0315	7.3	**20** 0303	6.8
1013	2.1	0950	2.7
M 1540	7.3	TU 1514	6.7
2238	2.0	2211	2.8
6 0420	7.1	**21** 0349	6.6
1110	2.3	1036	3.0
TU 1647	7.1	W 1607	6.4
2338	2.3	2303	3.0
7 0530	7.0	**22** 0452	6.4
1219	2.5	1136	3.2
W 1801	7.0	TH 1721	6.3
8 0052	2.4	**23** 0010	3.2
0641	7.1	0616	6.4
TH 1339	2.4	F 1250	3.2
1914	7.0	1852	6.3
9 0212	2.3	**24** 0131	3.1
0750	7.2	0729	6.6
F 1452	2.2	SA 1413	2.9
2023	7.2	2001	6.6
10 0320	2.1	**25** 0249	2.7
0850	7.4	0826	6.9
SA 1555	1.9	SU 1522	2.4
2121	7.4	2055	7.0
11 0419	1.9	**26** 0349	2.2
0941	7.6	0915	7.3
SU 1652	1.6	M 1619	1.9
2210	7.6	2142	7.3
12 0511	1.7	**27** 0443	1.8
1026	7.7	1000	7.6
M 1740	1.4	TU 1711	1.4
O 2253	7.7	2227	7.6
13 0555	1.6	**28** 0534	1.4
1106	7.8	1043	7.8
TU 1821	1.3	W 1800	1.1
2333	7.7	● 2311	7.8
14 0634	1.5	**29** 0622	1.1
1144	7.8	1127	8.0
W 1857	1.3	TH 1848	0.8
		2355	8.0
15 0010	7.7	**30** 0708	1.0
0710	1.5	1212	8.1
TH 1220	7.8	F 1932	0.7
1931	1.4		
		31 0040	8.0
		0752	0.9
		SA 1257	8.1
		2014	0.7

FEBRUARY

Time	m		Time	m
1 0124	8.0	**16** 0123	7.4
0833	1.0	0817	1.8
SU 1342	8.0	M 1331	7.4
2055	1.0	2032	1.8
2 0209	7.8	**17** 0152	7.2
0914	1.3	0843	2.0
M 1427	7.7	TU 1400	7.2
2134	1.3	2058	2.1
3 0253	7.5	**18** 0222	7.0
0955	1.7	0913	2.3
TU 1517	7.4	W 1435	6.9
2216	1.8	2129	2.5
4 0345	7.2	**19** 0300	6.8
1043	2.1	0947	2.7
W 1616	7.1	TH 1519	6.6
2308	2.3	2212	2.9
5 0453	6.9	**20** 0350	6.5
1145	2.5	1041	3.0
TH 1731	6.8	F 1620	6.3
		2313	3.2
6 0017	2.6	**21** 0503	6.3
0611	6.8	1152	3.2
F 1307	2.7	SA 1754	6.2
1855	6.7		
7 0144	2.7	**22** 0036	3.2
0732	6.8	0640	6.4
SA 1430	2.5	SU 1323	3.0
2013	6.9	1924	6.4
8 0302	2.5	**23** 0209	2.9
0839	7.1	0753	6.7
SU 1542	2.2	M 1448	2.5
2112	7.1	2028	6.8
9 0409	2.1	**24** 0321	2.3
0930	7.3	0850	7.1
M 1643	1.8	TU 1553	1.9
2159	7.4	2121	7.3
10 0502	1.9	**25** 0421	1.7
1012	7.5	0939	7.5
TU 1729	1.5	W 1651	1.3
2239	7.5	2208	7.6
11 0543	1.7	**26** 0518	1.3
1050	7.7	1025	7.9
W 1806	1.4	TH 1745	0.9
O 2315	7.6	● 2253	7.9
12 0618	1.5	**27** 0609	0.9
1124	7.8	1111	8.1
TH 1839	1.3	F 1834	0.5
2348	7.7	2338	8.1
13 0651	1.4	**28** 0655	0.6
1157	7.8	1156	8.3
F 1911	1.2	SA 1918	0.4
14 0020	7.7		
0722	1.5		
SA 1229	7.7		
1940	1.3		
15 0052	7.6		
0751	1.6		
SU 1301	7.7		
2007	1.5		

MARCH

Time	m		Time	m
1 0022	8.2	**16** 0023	7.6
0738	0.5	0725	1.4
SU 1240	8.3	M 1234	7.6
2000	0.4	1940	1.4
2 0106	8.2	**17** 0053	7.5
0819	0.7	0751	1.6
M 1325	8.2	TU 1304	7.5
2039	0.7	2005	1.6
3 0148	7.9	**18** 0121	7.4
0857	1.0	0818	1.8
TU 1409	7.9	W 1334	7.3
2116	1.2	2032	1.9
4 0230	7.6	**19** 0152	7.1
0936	1.5	0846	2.1
W 1455	7.4	TH 1409	7.0
2154	1.8	2101	2.3
5 0312	7.2	**20** 0228	6.9
1019	2.0	0920	2.4
TH 1550	7.0	F 1451	6.7
2241	2.4	2139	2.7
6 0419	6.8	**21** 0314	6.6
1116	2.5	1005	2.8
F 1704	6.6	SA 1546	6.4
2346	2.8	2233	3.0
7 0541	6.5	**22** 0419	6.3
1236	2.8	1110	3.0
SA 1837	6.5	SU 1707	6.2
		2355	3.2
8 0116	3.0	**23** 0555	6.3
0713	6.5	1243	3.0
SU 1406	2.7	M 1850	6.4
1959	6.6		
9 0243	2.7	**24** 0134	2.9
0823	6.8	0720	6.6
M 1527	2.3	TU 1414	2.5
2057	6.9	2000	6.8
10 0356	2.3	**25** 0252	2.3
0913	7.0	0822	7.1
TU 1627	1.8	W 1525	1.8
2141	7.2	2056	7.3
11 0447	2.0	**26** 0357	1.7
0954	7.3	0915	7.5
W 1710	1.6	TH 1627	1.3
2218	7.4	2145	7.7
12 0524	1.7	**27** 0456	1.1
1028	7.5	1004	7.9
TH 1744	1.4	F 1723	0.8
2251	7.6	2231	8.0
13 0557	1.5	**28** 0549	0.7
1100	7.7	1050	8.2
F 1816	1.3	SA 1813	0.5
O 2321	7.6	● 2317	8.2
14 0628	1.4	**29** 0636	0.5
1131	7.7	1136	8.3
SA 1846	1.2	SU 1859	0.3
2352	7.7		
15 0658	1.3	**30** 0001	8.3
1203	7.7	0720	0.4
SU 1914	1.3	M 1221	8.3
		1940	0.4
		31 0044	8.2
		0801	0.5
		TU 1306	8.2
		2019	0.7

APRIL

Time	m		Time	m
1 0127	8.0	**16** 0056	7.4
0839	0.9	0756	1.6
W 1350	7.8	TH 1314	7.3
2056	1.2	2010	1.9
2 0209	7.6	**17** 0130	7.2
0917	1.4	0827	1.9
TH 1435	7.4	F 1352	7.1
2134	1.8	2042	2.1
3 0248	7.2	**18** 0208	7.0
0958	2.0	0902	2.2
F 1528	6.9	SA 1435	6.8
2217	2.4	2119	2.5
4 0350	6.8	**19** 0254	6.7
1050	2.5	0944	2.5
SA 1639	6.5	SU 1529	6.5
2319	2.9	2211	2.9
5 0508	6.4	**20** 0354	6.5
1205	2.8	1045	2.7
SU 1809	6.4	M 1643	6.4
		2329	3.0
6 0043	3.1	**21** 0521	6.4
0640	6.4	1213	2.7
M 1329	2.8	TU 1819	6.6
1933	6.5		
7 0207	2.9	**22** 0104	2.8
0755	6.6	0647	6.7
TU 1446	2.5	W 1341	2.3
2031	6.8	1929	6.9
8 0319	2.5	**23** 0222	2.2
0847	6.9	0752	7.1
W 1549	2.1	TH 1453	1.8
2114	7.1	2027	7.4
9 0412	2.1	**24** 0328	1.6
0927	7.1	0848	7.5
TH 1634	1.8	F 1557	1.3
2150	7.3	2119	7.7
10 0452	1.8	**25** 0429	1.2
1001	7.4	0940	7.9
F 1712	1.5	SA 1656	0.9
2221	7.5	2207	8.0
11 0528	1.5	**26** 0525	0.8
1033	7.5	1029	8.1
SA 1746	1.4	SU 1749	0.6
O 2252	7.6	● 2254	8.2
12 0601	1.4	**27** 0614	0.5
1105	7.6	1116	8.2
SU 1818	1.3	M 1836	0.5
2323	7.6	2339	8.2
13 0631	1.4	**28** 0659	0.5
1137	7.6	1202	8.2
M 1846	1.4	TU 1919	0.6
2354	7.6		
14 0659	1.4	**29** 0023	8.1
1209	7.6	0741	0.6
TU 1913	1.4	W 1248	8.0
		1959	0.9
15 0025	7.6	**30** 0106	7.9
0727	1.4	0820	0.9
W 1241	7.5	TH 1332	7.7
1941	1.6	2037	1.4

19

Chart Datum: 4·38 metres below Lallemand System (Mean Sea Level, Marseilles)

TIME ZONE –0100
(French Standard Time)
Subtract 1 hour for UT
For French Summer Time add
ONE hour in non-shaded areas

FRANCE – LE HAVRE

LAT 49°29′N   LONG   0°07′E

TIMES AND HEIGHTS OF HIGH AND LOW WATERS

YEAR **1998**

MAY

	Time	m		Time	m
1 F	0148 / 0859 / 1418 / 2114	7.6 / 1.4 / 7.3 / 1.9	**16** SA	0113 / 0815 / 1340 / 2030	7.4 / 1.7 / 7.2 / 2.1
2 SA	0232 / 0939 / 1508 / 2157	7.2 / 1.9 / 6.9 / 2.4	**17** SU	0155 / 0852 / 1425 / 2110	7.2 / 1.9 / 7.1 / 2.3
3 SU	0324 / 1027 / 1611 / 2254	6.8 / 2.4 / 6.6 / 2.9	**18** M	0242 / 0935 / 1517 / 2202	6.9 / 2.2 / 6.8 / 2.6
4 M	0432 / 1131 / 1727	6.4 / 2.7 / 6.4	**19** TU	0339 / 1033 / 1625 / 2313	6.7 / 2.4 / 6.7 / 2.7
5 TU	0005 / 0551 / 1243 / 1846	3.0 / 6.3 / 2.8 / 6.5	**20** W	0455 / 1149 / 1748	6.7 / 2.4 / 6.8
6 W	0118 / 0708 / 1351 / 1950	2.9 / 6.5 / 2.6 / 6.7	**21** TH	0034 / 0616 / 1309 / 1858	2.6 / 6.8 / 2.2 / 7.1
7 TH	0224 / 0808 / 1452 / 2037	2.6 / 6.7 / 2.3 / 7.0	**22** F	0151 / 0722 / 1421 / 1958	2.2 / 7.1 / 1.8 / 7.4
8 F	0321 / 0852 / 1546 / 2114	2.3 / 6.9 / 2.0 / 7.2	**23** SA	0258 / 0822 / 1527 / 2053	1.7 / 7.5 / 1.4 / 7.7
9 SA	0411 / 0929 / 1632 / 2148	2.0 / 7.2 / 1.8 / 7.4	**24** SU	0401 / 0917 / 1628 / 2144	1.3 / 7.7 / 1.1 / 7.9
10 SU	0453 / 1003 / 1712 / 2221	1.7 / 7.3 / 1.6 / 7.5	**25** M ●	0459 / 1009 / 1723 / 2232	1.0 / 7.9 / 0.9 / 8.0
11 M O	0530 / 1038 / 1746 / 2255	1.6 / 7.4 / 1.5 / 7.6	**26** TU	0551 / 1058 / 1813 / 2319	0.8 / 8.0 / 0.9 / 8.1
12 TU	0603 / 1112 / 1817 / 2328	1.5 / 7.5 / 1.5 / 7.6	**27** W	0639 / 1145 / 1857	0.7 / 8.0 / 0.9
13 W	0634 / 1147 / 1848	1.4 / 7.5 / 1.5	**28** TH	0003 / 0722 / 1231 / 1938	8.0 / 0.8 / 7.9 / 1.2
14 TH	0001 / 0706 / 1222 / 1921	7.6 / 1.4 / 7.5 / 1.6	**29** F	0047 / 0802 / 1316 / 2017	7.8 / 1.1 / 7.7 / 1.5
15 F	0036 / 0740 / 1259 / 1955	7.5 / 1.5 / 7.4 / 1.8	**30** SA	0129 / 0840 / 1400 / 2055	7.6 / 1.4 / 7.4 / 1.9
			31 SU	0212 / 0919 / 1446 / 2136	7.3 / 1.8 / 7.0 / 2.3

JUNE

	Time	m		Time	m
1 M	0258 / 1001 / 1538 / 2223	6.9 / 2.2 / 6.7 / 2.7	**16** TU	0232 / 0932 / 1506 / 2157	7.2 / 1.8 / 7.1 / 2.2
2 TU	0353 / 1052 / 1639 / 2321	6.6 / 2.6 / 6.5 / 2.9	**17** W	0326 / 1023 / 1605 / 2256	7.1 / 2.0 / 7.0 / 2.3
3 W	0458 / 1152 / 1746	6.4 / 2.8 / 6.5	**18** TH	0431 / 1126 / 1717	6.9 / 2.1 / 7.0
4 TH	0025 / 0608 / 1256 / 1851	3.0 / 6.4 / 2.8 / 6.6	**19** F	0005 / 0545 / 1237 / 1826	2.3 / 7.0 / 2.1 / 7.1
5 F	0130 / 0714 / 1359 / 1948	2.8 / 6.5 / 2.6 / 6.8	**20** SA	0119 / 0654 / 1351 / 1931	2.2 / 7.1 / 2.0 / 7.3
6 SA	0231 / 0809 / 1458 / 2034	2.5 / 6.7 / 2.4 / 7.0	**21** SU	0231 / 0759 / 1500 / 2031	1.9 / 7.3 / 1.7 / 7.5
7 SU	0327 / 0854 / 1550 / 2114	2.2 / 6.9 / 2.1 / 7.2	**22** M	0336 / 0900 / 1602 / 2126	1.6 / 7.5 / 1.5 / 7.7
8 M	0415 / 0934 / 1635 / 2152	2.0 / 7.1 / 1.9 / 7.4	**23** TU	0435 / 0954 / 1659 / 2216	1.3 / 7.7 / 1.3 / 7.8
9 TU	0457 / 1013 / 1714 / 2229	1.8 / 7.3 / 1.8 / 7.5	**24** W ●	0530 / 1044 / 1751 / 2302	1.1 / 7.8 / 1.3 / 7.9
10 W O	0535 / 1050 / 1751 / 2305	1.6 / 7.4 / 1.7 / 7.6	**25** TH	0620 / 1131 / 1838 / 2346	1.0 / 7.8 / 1.3 / 7.9
11 TH	0611 / 1128 / 1828 / 2341	1.5 / 7.5 / 1.6 / 7.6	**26** F	0704 / 1216 / 1919	1.0 / 7.8 / 1.4
12 F	0649 / 1206 / 1906	1.4 / 7.5 / 1.6	**27** SA	0028 / 0743 / 1258 / 1958	7.8 / 1.1 / 7.7 / 1.5
13 SA	0020 / 0728 / 1246 / 1945	7.6 / 1.4 / 7.5 / 1.6	**28** SU	0109 / 0820 / 1339 / 2034	7.6 / 1.4 / 7.5 / 1.8
14 SU	0101 / 0807 / 1329 / 2025	7.5 / 1.4 / 7.4 / 1.8	**29** M	0148 / 0855 / 1419 / 2110	7.4 / 1.7 / 7.2 / 2.1
15 M	0145 / 0848 / 1415 / 2108	7.4 / 1.6 / 7.2 / 2.0	**30** TU	0228 / 0931 / 1501 / 2147	7.1 / 2.1 / 7.0 / 2.4

JULY

	Time	m		Time	m
1 W	0306 / 1009 / 1547 / 2231	6.8 / 2.4 / 6.7 / 2.7	**16** TH	0309 / 1009 / 1540 / 2237	7.3 / 1.7 / 7.2 / 2.1
2 TH	0355 / 1055 / 1643 / 2323	6.5 / 2.7 / 6.5 / 2.9	**17** F	0407 / 1102 / 1646 / 2338	7.1 / 2.0 / 7.1 / 2.3
3 F	0504 / 1151 / 1748	6.3 / 2.9 / 6.5	**18** SA	0517 / 1207 / 1757	7.0 / 2.2 / 7.0
4 SA	0025 / 0614 / 1257 / 1853	3.0 / 6.3 / 2.9 / 6.6	**19** SU	0051 / 0632 / 1324 / 1908	2.3 / 7.0 / 2.3 / 7.1
5 SU	0134 / 0722 / 1406 / 1951	2.9 / 6.4 / 2.7 / 6.8	**20** M	0208 / 0744 / 1438 / 2016	2.1 / 7.1 / 2.1 / 7.3
6 M	0240 / 0819 / 1507 / 2041	2.6 / 6.7 / 2.5 / 7.0	**21** TU	0316 / 0850 / 1543 / 2114	1.9 / 7.3 / 1.9 / 7.5
7 TU	0336 / 0907 / 1559 / 2125	2.3 / 6.9 / 2.1 / 7.2	**22** W	0418 / 0946 / 1642 / 2204	1.6 / 7.5 / 1.7 / 7.7
8 W	0425 / 0950 / 1646 / 2205	1.9 / 7.2 / 1.9 / 7.4	**23** TH ●	0516 / 1034 / 1736 / 2249	1.4 / 7.6 / 1.6 / 7.8
9 TH O	0510 / 1031 / 1729 / 2245	1.7 / 7.4 / 1.7 / 7.6	**24** F	0605 / 1118 / 1821 / 2330	1.2 / 7.7 / 1.5 / 7.8
10 F	0553 / 1111 / 1813 / 2325	1.4 / 7.5 / 1.5 / 7.7	**25** SA	0647 / 1158 / 1901	1.2 / 7.7 / 1.4
11 SA	0637 / 1152 / 1856	1.2 / 7.6 / 1.4	**26** SU	0008 / 0723 / 1236 / 1936	7.8 / 1.2 / 7.7 / 1.5
12 SU	0006 / 0720 / 1234 / 1939	7.8 / 1.1 / 7.7 / 1.4	**27** M	0045 / 0757 / 1312 / 2009	7.7 / 1.3 / 7.6 / 1.7
13 M	0049 / 0802 / 1317 / 2021	7.8 / 1.1 / 7.6 / 1.4	**28** TU	0121 / 0828 / 1348 / 2040	7.5 / 1.6 / 7.4 / 1.9
14 TU	0133 / 0843 / 1401 / 2103	7.7 / 1.2 / 7.5 / 1.6	**29** W	0155 / 0857 / 1423 / 2110	7.3 / 1.9 / 7.1 / 2.2
15 W	0219 / 0924 / 1448 / 2147	7.5 / 1.5 / 7.4 / 1.8	**30** TH	0230 / 0926 / 1458 / 2142	7.0 / 2.2 / 6.9 / 2.5
			31 F	0307 / 1000 / 1538 / 2222	6.8 / 2.6 / 6.7 / 2.8

AUGUST

	Time	m		Time	m
1 SA	0354 / 1046 / 1633 / 2317	6.5 / 2.9 / 6.5 / 3.1	**16** SU	0453 / 1140 / 1731	6.9 / 2.5 / 6.9
2 SU	0500 / 1149 / 1750	6.3 / 3.1 / 6.4	**17** M	0027 / 0615 / 1303 / 1852	2.5 / 6.8 / 2.6 / 6.9
3 M	0028 / 0630 / 1308 / 1907	3.2 / 6.2 / 3.1 / 6.5	**18** TU	0151 / 0738 / 1424 / 2007	2.4 / 6.6 / 2.5 / 7.1
4 TU	0151 / 0743 / 1426 / 2009	2.9 / 6.4 / 2.8 / 6.8	**19** W	0304 / 0845 / 1533 / 2105	2.1 / 7.1 / 2.2 / 7.3
5 W	0300 / 0840 / 1528 / 2059	2.5 / 6.8 / 2.4 / 7.1	**20** TH	0411 / 0937 / 1635 / 2152	1.8 / 7.4 / 1.9 / 7.5
6 TH	0356 / 0928 / 1621 / 2144	2.0 / 7.1 / 2.0 / 7.4	**21** F	0507 / 1021 / 1726 / 2233	1.5 / 7.6 / 1.7 / 7.7
7 F	0448 / 1011 / 1711 / 2226	1.6 / 7.4 / 1.7 / 7.7	**22** SA ●	0551 / 1100 / 1805 / 2310	1.3 / 7.7 / 1.5 / 7.8
8 SA O	0537 / 1053 / 1800 / 2308	1.3 / 7.6 / 1.4 / 7.8	**23** SU	0626 / 1135 / 1839 / 2345	1.3 / 7.7 / 1.5 / 7.8
9 SU	0625 / 1136 / 1845 / 2351	1.0 / 7.8 / 1.1 / 8.0	**24** M	0659 / 1209 / 1911	1.2 / 7.7 / 1.5
10 M	0709 / 1219 / 1929	0.8 / 7.9 / 1.0	**25** TU	0018 / 0730 / 1242 / 1941	7.7 / 1.3 / 7.6 / 1.6
11 TU	0034 / 0752 / 1302 / 2011	8.0 / 0.8 / 7.9 / 1.1	**26** W	0051 / 0758 / 1314 / 2009	7.5 / 1.5 / 7.5 / 1.8
12 W	0118 / 0832 / 1346 / 2051	8.0 / 0.9 / 7.8 / 1.2	**27** TH	0122 / 0832 / 1345 / 2035	7.4 / 1.8 / 7.3 / 2.1
13 TH	0203 / 0911 / 1429 / 2131	7.8 / 1.2 / 7.6 / 1.6	**28** F	0153 / 0848 / 1414 / 2102	7.2 / 2.1 / 7.1 / 2.4
14 F	0250 / 0952 / 1515 / 2216	7.5 / 1.6 / 7.3 / 1.9	**29** SA	0224 / 0917 / 1448 / 2136	6.9 / 2.5 / 6.8 / 2.7
15 SA	0344 / 1039 / 1615 / 2312	7.2 / 2.1 / 7.1 / 2.3	**30** SU	0305 / 0956 / 1534 / 2223	6.6 / 2.9 / 6.5 / 3.1
			31 M	0402 / 1051 / 1641 / 2330	6.3 / 3.2 / 6.3 / 3.3

Chart Datum: 4·38 metres below Lallemand System (Mean Sea Level, Marseilles)

TIME ZONE –0100
(French Standard Time)
Subtract 1 hour for UT

For French Summer Time add
ONE hour in non-shaded areas

FRANCE – LE HAVRE

LAT 49°29′N   LONG 0°07′E

TIMES AND HEIGHTS OF HIGH AND LOW WATERS

YEAR **1998**

Chart Datum: 4·30 metres below Lallemand System (Mean Sea Level, Marseilles)

SEPTEMBER

Day	Time / m	Day	Time / m
1 TU	0529 6.1 / 1212 3.4 / 1818 6.3	**16** W	0138 2.7 / 0730 6.7 / 1413 2.7 / 1956 6.9
2 W	0102 3.2 / 0708 6.3 / 1348 3.1 / 1936 6.6	**17** TH	0255 2.3 / 0834 7.1 / 1525 2.3 / 2052 7.2
3 TH	0227 2.7 / 0813 6.7 / 1500 2.6 / 2032 7.0	**18** F	0400 1.9 / 0922 7.3 / 1624 2.0 / 2136 7.4
4 F	0330 2.1 / 0904 7.2 / 1557 2.0 / 2120 7.4	**19** SA	0450 1.6 / 1001 7.5 / 1707 1.7 / 2213 7.6
5 SA	0425 1.6 / 0949 7.5 / 1651 1.5 / 2205 7.8	**20** SU	0528 1.4 / 1036 7.7 / 1742 1.6 / 2246 7.8
6 SU	0518 1.1 / 1032 7.8 / 1742 1.2 / 2248 8.0	**21** M	0600 1.3 / 1108 7.7 / 1813 1.5 / 2318 7.8
7 M	0607 0.8 / 1115 8.0 / 1829 0.9 / 2332 8.2	**22** TU	0631 1.3 / 1139 7.7 / 1844 1.5 / 2350 7.7
8 TU	0652 0.6 / 1158 8.1 / 1913 0.7	**23** W	0701 1.4 / 1210 7.7 / 1913 1.6
9 W	0016 8.3 / 0735 0.6 / 1242 8.1 / 1955 0.8	**24** TH	0021 7.6 / 0728 1.6 / 1241 7.6 / 1939 1.7
10 TH	0100 8.2 / 0815 0.8 / 1325 8.0 / 2034 1.0	**25** F	0051 7.5 / 0752 1.8 / 1310 7.4 / 2005 2.0
11 F	0145 7.9 / 0853 1.1 / 1407 7.7 / 2114 1.4	**26** SA	0121 7.3 / 0818 2.1 / 1338 7.2 / 2032 2.2
12 SA	0231 7.6 / 0932 1.7 / 1449 7.4 / 2156 1.9	**27** SU	0152 7.0 / 0846 2.5 / 1411 6.9 / 2104 2.6
13 SU	0323 7.1 / 1017 2.2 / 1548 7.0 / 2250 2.4	**28** M	0232 6.6 / 0921 2.9 / 1456 6.6 / 2145 2.9
14 M	0433 6.7 / 1118 2.7 / 1708 6.7	**29** TU	0326 6.4 / 1011 3.2 / 1557 6.3 / 2245 3.2
15 TU	0008 2.8 / 0603 6.6 / 1246 2.9 / 1838 6.7	**30** W	0443 6.2 / 1126 3.5 / 1728 6.3

OCTOBER

Day	Time / m	Day	Time / m
1 TH	0017 3.2 / 0631 6.3 / 1311 3.2 / 1901 6.5	**16** F	0229 2.5 / 0812 7.0 / 1500 2.5 / 2030 7.0
2 F	0153 2.8 / 0742 6.7 / 1431 2.6 / 2003 7.0	**17** SA	0330 2.1 / 0858 7.3 / 1554 2.1 / 2112 7.3
3 SA	0301 2.1 / 0836 7.2 / 1531 2.0 / 2054 7.5	**18** SU	0417 1.8 / 0936 7.5 / 1636 1.8 / 2148 7.5
4 SU	0359 1.5 / 0923 7.7 / 1627 1.4 / 2140 7.9	**19** M	0455 1.6 / 1008 7.6 / 1712 1.6 / 2220 7.6
5 M	0453 1.1 / 1007 8.0 / 1720 1.0 / 2225 8.1	**20** TU	0529 1.5 / 1038 7.7 / 1745 1.5 / 2251 7.7
6 TU	0544 0.7 / 1052 8.2 / 1809 0.7 / 2311 8.3	**21** W	0601 1.5 / 1109 7.7 / 1816 1.5 / 2323 7.7
7 W	0631 0.6 / 1136 8.3 / 1853 0.6 / 2356 8.4	**22** TH	0631 1.5 / 1140 7.7 / 1845 1.6 / 2354 7.6
8 TH	0715 0.6 / 1220 8.3 / 1936 0.7	**23** F	0659 1.7 / 1210 7.6 / 1913 1.7
9 F	0041 8.2 / 0755 0.8 / 1303 8.1 / 2017 1.0	**24** SA	0024 7.5 / 0726 1.8 / 1239 7.5 / 1941 1.9
10 SA	0126 8.0 / 0835 1.2 / 1347 7.8 / 2056 1.4	**25** SU	0056 7.3 / 0754 2.1 / 1310 7.3 / 2010 2.1
11 SU	0213 7.6 / 0914 1.8 / 1430 7.4 / 2138 2.0	**26** M	0131 7.1 / 0824 2.4 / 1347 7.0 / 2042 2.4
12 M	0306 7.1 / 0958 2.4 / 1528 6.9 / 2230 2.5	**27** TU	0213 6.8 / 0858 2.8 / 1431 6.7 / 2122 2.7
13 TU	0415 6.7 / 1058 2.9 / 1644 6.6 / 2346 2.9	**28** W	0304 6.5 / 0946 3.1 / 1528 6.5 / 2217 3.0
14 W	0544 6.5 / 1226 3.1 / 1814 6.5	**29** TH	0413 6.4 / 1055 3.3 / 1648 6.4 / 2339 3.1
15 TH	0115 2.8 / 0709 6.7 / 1351 2.9 / 1934 6.7	**30** F	0551 6.4 / 1233 3.2 / 1821 6.6
		31 SA	0114 2.7 / 0706 6.8 / 1356 2.6 / 1928 7.0

NOVEMBER

Day	Time / m	Day	Time / m
1 SU	0227 2.2 / 0803 7.3 / 1501 2.0 / 2024 7.4	**16** M	0333 2.2 / 0903 7.3 / 1557 2.1 / 2119 7.3
2 M	0329 1.6 / 0854 7.7 / 1600 1.5 / 2114 7.8	**17** TU	0417 1.9 / 0937 7.5 / 1638 1.9 / 2152 7.4
3 TU	0426 1.1 / 0941 8.0 / 1654 1.1 / 2202 8.1	**18** W	0456 1.7 / 1009 7.6 / 1716 1.7 / 2225 7.5
4 W	0519 0.8 / 1027 8.2 / 1745 0.8 / 2249 8.3	**19** TH	0532 1.7 / 1040 7.7 / 1749 1.6 / 2258 7.6
5 TH	0608 0.7 / 1113 8.3 / 1833 0.7 / 2336 8.3	**20** F	0604 1.7 / 1113 7.7 / 1821 1.6 / 2331 7.5
6 F	0653 0.7 / 1158 8.3 / 1917 0.7	**21** SA	0634 1.7 / 1145 7.6 / 1851 1.6
7 SA	0023 8.2 / 0736 1.0 / 1243 8.1 / 1959 1.0	**22** SU	0004 7.5 / 0704 1.8 / 1217 7.6 / 1922 1.7
8 SU	0110 7.9 / 0817 1.4 / 1327 7.8 / 2040 1.4	**23** M	0039 7.4 / 0737 2.0 / 1252 7.4 / 1956 1.9
9 M	0157 7.6 / 0857 1.9 / 1413 7.4 / 2122 1.9	**24** TU	0117 7.2 / 0811 2.3 / 1331 7.2 / 2031 2.1
10 TU	0249 7.1 / 0941 2.4 / 1505 7.0 / 2211 2.4	**25** W	0200 7.0 / 0848 2.6 / 1416 7.0 / 2110 2.4
11 W	0351 6.8 / 1037 2.9 / 1612 6.6 / 2315 2.9	**26** TH	0249 6.8 / 0934 2.8 / 1508 6.8 / 2201 2.7
12 TH	0507 6.6 / 1150 3.1 / 1731 6.5	**27** F	0349 6.7 / 1036 3.0 / 1616 6.6 / 2310 2.8
13 F	0030 2.9 / 0626 6.6 / 1306 3.0 / 1850 6.4	**28** SA	0512 6.7 / 1155 2.9 / 1740 6.7
14 SA	0141 2.7 / 0734 6.8 / 1413 2.7 / 1954 6.8	**29** SU	0032 2.6 / 0628 6.9 / 1316 2.6 / 1852 7.0
15 SU	0242 2.4 / 0824 7.1 / 1509 2.4 / 2041 7.0	**30** M	0149 2.2 / 0730 7.3 / 1428 2.1 / 1953 7.3

DECEMBER

Day	Time / m	Day	Time / m
1 TU	0257 1.8 / 0825 7.6 / 1532 1.6 / 2049 7.7	**16** W	0339 2.3 / 0904 7.2 / 1604 2.2 / 2125 7.2
2 W	0358 1.4 / 0917 7.9 / 1630 1.2 / 2142 8.0	**17** TH	0424 2.1 / 0941 7.4 / 1647 1.9 / 2202 7.3
3 TH	0454 1.1 / 1006 8.1 / 1724 1.0 / 2232 8.1	**18** F	0504 1.9 / 1016 7.5 / 1725 1.8 / 2238 7.4
4 F	0546 1.0 / 1054 8.2 / 1813 0.8 / 2321 8.2	**19** SA	0540 1.8 / 1051 7.5 / 1759 1.6 / 2313 7.5
5 SA	0633 1.0 / 1140 8.2 / 1900 0.8	**20** SU	0614 1.8 / 1125 7.7 / 1834 1.6 / 2349 7.5
6 SU	0009 8.1 / 0718 1.1 / 1225 8.0 / 1943 1.0	**21** M	0649 1.8 / 1201 7.7 / 1910 1.5
7 M	0055 7.9 / 0800 1.4 / 1310 7.8 / 2025 1.3	**22** TU	0025 7.5 / 0726 1.8 / 1239 7.6 / 1947 1.6
8 TU	0141 7.6 / 0840 1.8 / 1354 7.5 / 2105 1.8	**23** W	0106 7.4 / 0804 1.9 / 1320 7.5 / 2025 1.8
9 W	0228 7.3 / 0922 2.3 / 1440 7.1 / 2147 2.2	**24** TH	0148 7.3 / 0844 2.1 / 1404 7.3 / 2106 2.0
10 TH	0319 6.9 / 1008 2.7 / 1533 6.8 / 2236 2.6	**25** F	0235 7.1 / 0927 2.4 / 1452 7.1 / 2151 2.2
11 F	0418 6.7 / 1102 3.0 / 1637 6.5 / 2333 2.9	**26** SA	0327 7.0 / 1019 2.5 / 1549 7.0 / 2246 2.4
12 SA	0525 6.6 / 1205 3.1 / 1747 6.4	**27** SU	0432 6.9 / 1122 2.6 / 1700 6.9 / 2353 2.4
13 SU	0038 3.0 / 0634 6.6 / 1313 3.0 / 1859 6.5	**28** M	0548 7.0 / 1235 2.6 / 1817 7.0
14 M	0145 2.8 / 0735 6.8 / 1419 2.8 / 1959 6.7	**29** TU	0109 2.3 / 0657 7.2 / 1354 2.3 / 1926 7.2
15 TU	0246 2.6 / 0824 7.0 / 1516 2.5 / 2046 6.9	**30** W	0226 2.1 / 0800 7.4 / 1505 1.9 / 2030 7.4
		31 TH	0333 1.7 / 0858 7.7 / 1608 1.5 / 2128 7.7

19

H.W.Hts.m.

LE HAVRE

MEAN SPRING
AND NEAP CURVES

MEAN RANGES
Springs 6.7m
Neaps 3.8m

Springs occur 2 days
after
New and Full Moon.

LE HAVRE   10-19-19

Seine Maritime 49°29'·18N 00°05·51E   Rtg 1-1-2

CHARTS
AC 2990, 2146, *2613*; SHOM 6683, 6796, 6736; ECM 526,
1012; Imray C31; Stanfords 1

TIDES
–0103 Dover; ML 4·9; Duration 0543; Zone –0100.
Le Havre is a Standard Port; tidal predictions are given
above. There is a stand at HW of about 3 hours.

SHELTER
Excellent in the marina, access H24. ♥ berth pontoon O.
Or request Hr Mr for long stay in Bassin du Commerce.

NAVIGATION
WPT 49°31'·05N 00°04'·00W, 287°/107° from/to bkwtrs,
6·4M. ⚓ prohib in and to the N of the fairway; it is also
prohib to cross the fairway E of buoys LH7 and LH8. Banc
de l'Éclat, awash at LW, lies N of appr chan and lobster
pots close each side. Obey IPTS at end of Digue Nord.

LIGHTS AND MARKS
Ldg lts 107° both Dir FW 36/78m 25M; grey trs, G tops;
intens 106°-108° (H24). 2 chys, RW conspic, on ldg line.

RADIO TELEPHONE
Call: *Havre Port* Control tr VHF Ch 12 20 (or 2182 kHz).
Port Ops Ch 67 69 (H24). Radar Ch 12. Marina Ch 09.

TELEPHONE (Prefix ☎ Nos with zone code 02)
Hr Mr 32.74.74.00; Hr Mr Port de Plaisance 35.21.23.95;
Aff Mar 35.22.41.03; CROSS 33.52.72.23; ⌗ 35.41.33.51;
SNSM 35.22.41.03; Météo 35.42.21.06; Auto 08.36.68.08.76;
Dr 35.41.23.61; Ⓗ 35.73.32.32; Brit Consul 35.42.27.47.

FACILITIES
Marina (973 + 41 visitors) ☎ 35.21.23.95, 🖂 35.22.72.72,
FF103, AC, BH (16 ton), C (6 ton), CH, Slip, P & D (cash in
working hrs; credit card at other times), El, FW, Gas, Gaz,
R, Ⓖ, V; **YC Sport Nautique (SNH)** ☎ 35.21.01.41, Bar;
Sté des Régates du Havre (SRH) ☎ 35.42.41.21, R, Bar;
Services: Ⓔ, ME, El, Sh, CH, SHOM, ACA.
City All needs. Ferry: Portsmouth.

RIVER SEINE   10-19-20

CHARTS
AC 2880, 2994, 2146, *2613*; SHOM 6796, 6117; Imray C31

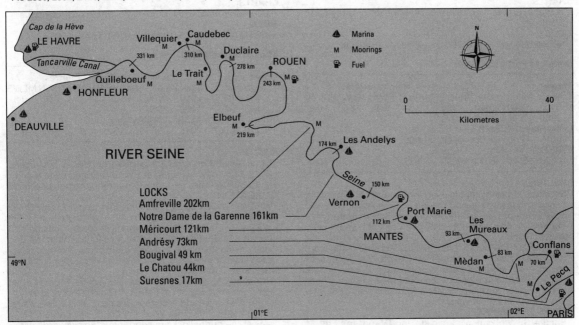

TIDES

Standard Port LE HAVRE (⟵) Zone –0100

Times				Height (metres)			
High Water		Low Water		MHWS	MHWN	MLWN	MLWS
0000	0500	0000	0700	7·9	6·6	2·8	1·2
1200	1700	1200	1900				

Differences TANCARVILLE*							
–01057	–0100	+0105	+0140	–0·1	–0·1	0·0	+1·0
QUILLEBOEUF*							
–0045	–0050	+0120	+0200	0·0	0·0	+0·0	+1·4
VATTEVILLE*							
+0005	–0020	+0225	+0250	0·0	–0·1	+0·8	+2·3
CAUDEBEC*							
+0020	–0015	+0230	+0300	–0·3	–0·2	+0·9	+2·4
ROUEN							
+0440	+0415	+0525	+0525	–0·2	–0·1	+1·6	+3·6

*HW differences refer to the start of the stand, which lasts about 2¾ hrs up to Vatteville and about 1¾hrs at Duclair.

It is important to study the tides. The flood stream starts progressively later as a boat proceeds upriver. So even a 4kn boat leaving the estuary at LW can carry the flood for the 78M (123km) to Rouen. But going down river on the ebb a boat will meet the flood. Rather than ⚓ for about 4 hrs, in a fast boat it is worth continuing, because the ebb starts sooner the further downstream one gets. Between Quilleboeuf (335km) and La Mailleraye (303km) the Seine bore (*mascaret*) still runs at HWS if the river is in flood.
NAVIGATION: The Seine gives access to Paris and central France, and to the Mediterranean via the canals (below). But there is a constant traffic of barges (*péniches*), and in the tidal section (below Amfreville) the strong stream and ships' wash make it dangerous to moor alongside and uncomfortable to ⚓. Masts can be lowered at Deauville, Le Havre (marina) and Rouen. Yacht navigation is prohib at night, and ⚓s are scarce. A good ⚓ ⓦ light is needed, and it is useful to have a radar reflector and a VHF aerial, even with the mast lowered. Listen on Ch 73.
ENTRY is usually via the dredged/buoyed Chenal de Rouen, which can be rough in a strong W'ly wind and ebb tide. Care is needed, especially near the mouth where there are shifting banks and often morning fog.
ENTRY VIA THE CANAL DE TANCARVILLE may be preferred if sea conditions are bad, but with 3 locks and 9 bridges delays must be expected. To enter the Canal at Le Havre transit the lock Quinette de Rochemont (E of the front ldg lt) into Bassin Bellot. At the E end transit the

Vétillart lock; thence via 3 bridges through Garage de Graville, Bassin de Despujols, and across the N end of Bassin de Lancement, which leads into the canal proper with 3 more bridges. Exit into the Seine (at 338km) via locks close E of Tancarville suspension bridge (50m).
LOCKS: Locks are as shown above. Call VHF Ch 18[t] or 22. Above Amfreville the current is about 1kn in summer, but more in winter.
FACILITIES: The most likely places for mooring and fuel are shown above. For Rouen and Paris see below.
REFERENCE: For detailed information see *A Cruising Guide to the Lower Seine* (Imray).

ROUEN, Seine Maritime, 49°26'·63N 01°03'·00E. AC 2880, 2994; SHOM 6117. HW +0330 on Dover (UT); ML 6·2m; Duration 0400. Yacht navigation prohib SS+½ to SR–½. Use pontoon SE side Bassin St Gervais (N bank) for mast unstep/restep (max stay 48 hrs); or mast step at Darse des Docks 250km. Berth in La Halte de Plaisance NE side of Ile Lacroix. VHF call *Rouen Port* Ch 73 68; 82 for height of water. Hr Mr 02.35.52.54.56; Aff Mar 02.35.98.53.98; ⌗ 02.35.98.27.60; Météo 02.35.80.11.44; Facilities: **Bassin St Gervais** C (3 to 25 ton), FW; **La Halte de Plaisance** (50) ☎ 02.35.88.00.00, FW, AC, Slip, C (30 ton), BH (4 ton); **Rouen YC** ☎ 02.35.66.52.52; **Services:** ME, El, Sh, P, D, CH, Ⓔ.

PARIS. The Touring Club de France ☎ 01.42.65.90.70, 🚢 01.42.65.11.31, has AB, AC, FW on the N bank near Place de la Concorde, but noise and wash intrude. The **Port de Paris-Arsenal**, the first basin of the Canal St Martin, has complete shelter for 112 + 65 visitors; depth 1·9m. Ent is on the NE bank 170m before Pont d'Austerlitz at lock 9, which, with air clearance of 5·2m, is remotely controlled by Hr Mr (0800-2345LT); waiting pontoon (with intercom to Hr Mr) upstream. VHF Ch 09. Caution strong current if river in flood. Hr Mr ☎ 01.43.41.39.32, 🚢 01.44.74.02.66; AC, FW, C (7 ton), D & P (cans), Ⓞ, plus city amenities; Aff Mar ☎ 01.42.73.55.05; River Police 01.47.07.17.17; Metro stns: Quai de la Rapée and Bastille (lines 1, 5), RER, ⇌, ✈.

CANALS TO THE MEDITERRANEAN
The quickest route is Le Havre/Paris/St Mammes/canal du Loing/canal du Briare/canal Latéral à la Loire/canal du Centre/Saône/Rhône, approx 1318km (824M), 182 locks. Max dimensions: LOA 38·5m, beam 5m, draft 1·8m, air draft 3·5m. Further info and dates of closures (*chomages*) are available every March from the French Tourist Office, 178 Piccadilly, London, W1V OAL, ☎ 0171 629-2869, 🚢 0171 493-6594. Tolls are due; see 10.15.8.

19

FÉCAMP   10-19-21

Seine Maritime 49°45'·97N 00°21'·85E   Rtg 3-1-2

CHARTS
AC 1352; SHOM 7207, 6765, 6824; ECM 1012; Imray C31;
Stanfords 1

TIDES
−0044 Dover; ML 4·9; Duration 0550; Zone −0100

Standard Port DIEPPE (⟶)

Times				Height (metres)			
High Water		Low Water		MHWS	MHWN	MLWN	MLWS
0100	0600	0100	0700	9·3	7·4	2·5	0·8
1300	1800	1300	1900				
Differences FÉCAMP							
−0015	−0010	−0030	−0040	−1·0	−0·6	+0·3	+0·4
ETRETAT							
−0020	−0020	−0045	−0050	−1·2	−0·8	+0·3	+0·4

SHELTER
Excellent in basins, but in even moderate W/NW winds a
considerable surf runs off the ent and the Avant Port (Ⓥ
at 'V' pontoon) can be uncomfortable. Bassin Bérigny is
entered via lock, HW −2 to HW; pontoons at E end.

NAVIGATION
WPT 49°46'·10N 00°21'·12E, 282°/102° from/to Jetée Nord
lt, 0·50M. Beware the Charpentier Rks off Pte Fagnet and
strong cross currents, depending on tides. Access best at
HW +1. Ent chan dredged 1·5m, but prone to silting; best
water is close to N jetty. Boats < 1·2m draft can enter at
any tide and in most weathers.

LIGHTS AND MARKS
Ent lies SSW of conspic ⊕, sig stn and TV mast on Pte
Fagnet cliff. N jetty Fl (2) 10s 15m 16M, grey tr, R top;
horn (2) 30s sounded HW −2½ to HW +2; root QR 10m
4M. Jetée Sud hd, QG 14m 9M; obscd by cliff when brg
more than 217°. QR and QG in transit 082° lead towards
hbr ent. IPTS on tr by Avant Port show when Bassin
Bérigny lock is open.

RADIO TELEPHONE
VHF Ch **12** 10 16 (HW −3 to HW + 1). Ch 09 Marina and
Écluse Bérigny (0800-1200; 1400-2000LT).

TELEPHONE (Prefix ☎ Nos with zone code 02)
Hr Mr 35.28.25.53; Aff Mar 35.28.16.35; ⌗ 35.28.19.40;
SNSM 35.28.00.91; CROSS 21.87.21.87; Auto 08.36.68.08.76;
Police 35.28.16.69; Ⓗ 35.28.05.13; Brit Consul 35.42.27.47.

FACILITIES
Marina (580 + 30 visitors) ☎ 35.28.13.58, FF113, FW, AC,
D, C (Mobile 36 ton);
Bassin Bérigny lock ☎ 35.28.23.76, AB, M, D, FW, Slip;
Sté des Régates de Fécamp ☎ 35.28.08.44, AB, FW;
Services: Slip, M, ME, El, Ⓔ, Sh, CH, Gaz, C (30 ton).
Town EC Mon; P, D, V, Gaz, R, Bar, ⊠, Ⓑ, ⇌, ✈ (Le Havre).

ST VALÉRY-EN-CAUX   10-19-22

Seine Maritime 49°52'·44N 00°42'·54E   Rtg 3-2-2

CHARTS
AC *2451*; SHOM 6794; ECM 1012; Imray C31; Stanfords 1

TIDES
−0044 Dover; ML 4·6; Duration 0530; Zone −0100

Standard Port DIEPPE (⟶)

Times				Height (metres)			
High Water		Low Water		MHWS	MHWN	MLWN	MLWS
0100	0600	0100	0700	9·3	7·4	2·5	0·8
1300	1800	1300	1900				
Differences ST VALÉRY-EN-CAUX							
−0007	−0007	−0015	−0025	−0·8	−0·6	−0·2	−0·1

SHELTER
Good. Avant Port dries 3m; access from HW −3. Lock opens
HW ±2¼ by day; by night, at HW±½ (bridge opens H and
H+30 during these periods). Ⓥ pontoon to stbd, past lock.

NAVIGATION
WPT 49°53'·00N 00°42'·50E, 000°/180° from/to Jetée Ouest
lt, 0·50M. Coast dries to approx 150m off the pier hds. Ent
is easy, but in fresh W to NE winds confused seas break
across ent. Shingle builds up against W wall; hug the E
side. Inside the pier hds, wave-breaks (marked by posts
each side) dampen the swell. 6 W waiting buoys N of lock.

LIGHTS AND MARKS
Hbr is hard to see between high chalk cliffs. From N or W
the nuclear power stn at Paluel is conspic 3M W of ent.
From E a white bldg is conspic E of ent, as is a vert white
stripe in the cliffs close W of ent. Lts as on chartlet. Tfc
sigs at the bridge/lock are coordinated to seaward/inland:
Ⓖ = ent/exit; Ⓡ = no ent/ exit; Ⓡ + Ⓖ = no movements.

RADIO TELEPHONE
VHF Ch 09 (French only).

TELEPHONE (Prefix ☎ Nos with zone code 02)
Hr Mr 35.97.01.30; Aff Mar 35.28.16.35; ⌗ 35.28.19.40;
CROSS 21.87.21.87; SNSM 35.97.09.03; Météo
21.31.52.23; Auto 08.36.68.08.76; Police 35.97.05.27;
Dr 35.97.20.13; Ⓗ 35.97.06.21; Brit Consul 35.42.27.47.

FACILITIES
Marina (580 + 20 visitors) ☎ 35.97.01.30, ⚓ 35.97.90.73,
FF102, AC, FW, C (6 ton), CH, El, Gaz, ME, Sh, SM, V, Bar;
Club Nautique Valeriquais ☎ 35.97.10.88, C (8 ton), Bar;
Services: M, Ⓔ, **Town** EC Mon (all day); P, D, CH, V, Gaz,
R, Bar, ⊠, Ⓑ, ⇌, ✈ (Dieppe). Ferry: Dieppe,

TIME ZONE –0100
(French Standard Time)
Subtract 1 hour for UT

For French Summer Time add
ONE hour in non-shaded areas

FRANCE – DIEPPE

LAT 49°56′N LONG 1°05′E

TIMES AND HEIGHTS OF HIGH AND LOW WATERS

YEAR **1998**

JANUARY

Day	Time	m	Day	Time	m
1 TH	0106 / 0803 / 1325 / 2028	9.3 / 1.0 / 9.3 / 0.7	**16** F	0142 / 0834 / 1356 / 2054	9.0 / 1.3 / 8.9 / 1.2
2 F	0149 / 0846 / 1409 / 2110	9.2 / 1.0 / 9.2 / 0.8	**17** SA	0217 / 0905 / 1430 / 2122	8.8 / 1.5 / 8.7 / 1.5
3 SA	0234 / 0929 / 1454 / 2153	9.1 / 1.2 / 9.0 / 1.0	**18** SU	0251 / 0934 / 1503 / 2150	8.5 / 1.7 / 8.3 / 1.8
4 SU	0321 / 1014 / 1543 / 2239	8.8 / 1.4 / 8.7 / 1.3	**19** M	0323 / 1005 / 1537 / 2223	8.1 / 2.1 / 7.9 / 2.1
5 M	0411 / 1104 / 1637 / 2330	8.5 / 1.7 / 8.3 / 1.7	**20** TU	0359 / 1043 / 1616 / 2305	7.8 / 2.4 / 7.5 / 2.5
6 TU	0510 / 1203 / 1741	8.2 / 2.0 / 8.0	**21** W	0443 / 1132 / 1708 / 2357	7.4 / 2.7 / 7.1 / 2.8
7 W	0032 / 0618 / 1313 / 1855	1.9 / 7.9 / 2.1 / 7.8	**22** TH	0543 / 1233 / 1820	7.1 / 2.9 / 6.8
8 TH	0146 / 0733 / 1431 / 2010	2.1 / 7.9 / 2.0 / 7.9	**23** F	0105 / 0705 / 1348 / 1946	2.9 / 7.0 / 2.9 / 7.0
9 F	0302 / 0844 / 1542 / 2118	2.0 / 8.2 / 1.7 / 8.2	**24** SA	0226 / 0823 / 1508 / 2055	2.8 / 7.3 / 2.5 / 7.4
10 SA	0410 / 0946 / 1645 / 2216	1.7 / 8.5 / 1.4 / 8.5	**25** SU	0339 / 0923 / 1613 / 2151	2.3 / 7.9 / 2.0 / 8.0
11 SU	0508 / 1039 / 1740 / 2306	1.5 / 8.8 / 1.2 / 8.8	**26** M	0438 / 1013 / 1708 / 2239	1.8 / 8.4 / 1.5 / 8.5
12 M	0559 / 1125 / 1827 / O 2350	1.3 / 9.0 / 1.0 / 9.0	**27** TU	0531 / 1100 / 1759 / 2325	1.4 / 8.9 / 1.0 / 8.9
13 TU	0643 / 1207 / 1908	1.2 / 9.1 / 0.9	**28** W	0621 / 1145 / 1848 ●	1.0 / 9.2 / 0.7
14 W	0030 / 0722 / 1244 / 1946	9.1 / 1.1 / 9.2 / 0.9	**29** TH	0010 / 0709 / 1229 / 1936	9.3 / 0.8 / 9.5 / 0.4
15 TH	0107 / 0800 / 1321 / 2022	9.1 / 1.1 / 9.1 / 1.0	**30** F	0054 / 0756 / 1314 / 2021	9.5 / 0.6 / 9.7 / 0.3
			31 SA	0138 / 0840 / 1358 / 2103	9.6 / 0.6 / 9.7 / 0.3

FEBRUARY

Day	Time	m	Day	Time	m
1 SU	0221 / 0922 / 1442 / 2144	9.5 / 0.7 / 9.5 / 0.6	**16** M	0220 / 0906 / 1433 / 2121	8.8 / 1.4 / 8.6 / 1.4
2 M	0305 / 1003 / 1527 / 2224	9.3 / 0.9 / 9.1 / 0.9	**17** TU	0249 / 0933 / 1502 / 2149	8.5 / 1.6 / 8.3 / 1.8
3 TU	0351 / 1047 / 1616 / 2308	8.9 / 1.3 / 8.6 / 1.4	**18** W	0319 / 1006 / 1533 / 2224	8.1 / 2.0 / 7.8 / 2.2
4 W	0441 / 1137 / 1713	8.3 / 1.7 / 8.0	**19** TH	0355 / 1047 / 1613 / 2308	7.7 / 2.4 / 7.4 / 2.6
5 TH	0002 / 0544 / 1241 / 1824	1.9 / 7.8 / 2.1 / 7.6	**20** F	0443 / 1140 / 1712	7.3 / 2.7 / 6.9
6 F	0111 / 0703 / 1401 / 1947	2.3 / 7.6 / 2.3 / 7.5	**21** SA	0009 / 0553 / 1249 / 1844	2.9 / 6.9 / 2.9 / 6.8
7 SA	0234 / 0825 / 1522 / 2105	2.4 / 7.7 / 2.1 / 7.7	**22** SU	0128 / 0731 / 1417 / 2016	2.9 / 7.0 / 2.7 / 7.2
8 SU	0352 / 0935 / 1632 / 2207	2.1 / 8.0 / 1.7 / 8.2	**23** M	0257 / 0849 / 1538 / 2122	2.6 / 7.5 / 2.1 / 7.8
9 M	0456 / 1029 / 1728 / 2256	1.7 / 8.5 / 1.4 / 8.6	**24** TU	0408 / 0948 / 1642 / 2217	2.0 / 8.2 / 1.5 / 8.5
10 TU	0548 / 1114 / 1814 / 2337	1.4 / 8.8 / 1.1 / 8.8	**25** W	0508 / 1039 / 1739 / 2306	1.4 / 8.8 / 0.9 / 9.0
11 W	0629 / 1152 / 1853 O	1.2 / 9.0 / 1.0	**26** TH	0603 / 1127 / 1832 / ● 2352	0.9 / 9.3 / 0.5 / 9.5
12 TH	0013 / 0706 / 1227 / 1927	9.0 / 1.1 / 9.1 / 0.9	**27** F	0655 / 1213 / 1921	0.5 / 9.7 / 0.2
13 F	0047 / 0739 / 1300 / 2000	9.1 / 1.0 / 9.1 / 1.0	**28** SA	0037 / 0743 / 1258 / 2007	9.8 / 0.3 / 9.9 / 0.0
14 SA	0119 / 0811 / 1332 / 2029	9.1 / 1.1 / 9.1 / 1.0			
15 SU	0150 / 0840 / 1403 / 2056	9.0 / 1.2 / 8.9 / 1.2			

MARCH

Day	Time	m	Day	Time	m
1 SU	0120 / 0827 / 1342 / 2049	9.9 / 0.2 / 10.0 / 0.0	**16** M	0122 / 0814 / 1336 / 2029	9.0 / 1.0 / 9.0 / 1.0
2 M	0203 / 0908 / 1425 / 2128	9.8 / 0.3 / 9.8 / 0.3	**17** TU	0151 / 0841 / 1405 / 2055	8.9 / 1.2 / 8.8 / 1.3
3 TU	0245 / 0947 / 1508 / 2205	9.5 / 0.6 / 9.3 / 0.8	**18** W	0219 / 0907 / 1434 / 2122	8.7 / 1.4 / 8.5 / 1.6
4 W	0328 / 1027 / 1553 / 2245	9.0 / 1.1 / 8.7 / 1.3	**19** TH	0248 / 0938 / 1504 / 2153	8.4 / 1.7 / 8.1 / 2.0
5 TH	0415 / 1113 / 1646 / 2334	8.4 / 1.7 / 8.0 / 2.0	**20** F	0323 / 1015 / 1543 / 2234	8.0 / 2.1 / 7.7 / 2.4
6 F	0513 / 1212 / 1755	7.7 / 2.2 / 7.4	**21** SA	0406 / 1104 / 1635 / 2331	7.5 / 2.5 / 7.2 / 2.8
7 SA	0041 / 0632 / 1332 / 1924	2.5 / 7.3 / 2.5 / 7.2	**22** SU	0508 / 1209 / 1758	7.0 / 2.7 / 6.9
8 SU	0207 / 0805 / 1459 / 2050	2.6 / 7.3 / 2.3 / 7.4	**23** M	0047 / 0642 / 1336 / 1938	2.9 / 6.9 / 2.7 / 7.1
9 M	0333 / 0920 / 1615 / 2152	2.4 / 7.7 / 1.9 / 8.0	**24** TU	0220 / 0814 / 1504 / 2053	2.6 / 7.4 / 2.1 / 7.8
10 TU	0441 / 1014 / 1711 / 2238	1.9 / 8.2 / 1.5 / 8.4	**25** W	0338 / 0920 / 1614 / 2151	1.9 / 8.1 / 1.4 / 8.5
11 W	0530 / 1056 / 1755 / 2317	1.5 / 8.6 / 1.2 / 8.7	**26** TH	0442 / 1016 / 1715 / 2243	1.3 / 8.8 / 0.8 / 9.1
12 TH	0610 / 1132 / 1831 / 2351	1.3 / 8.8 / 1.0 / 8.9	**27** F	0541 / 1106 / 1810 / 2331	0.8 / 9.4 / 0.4 / 9.6
13 F	0644 / 1205 / 1904 O	1.1 / 9.0 / 0.9	**28** SA	0635 / 1153 / 1901 ●	0.4 / 9.8 / 0.1
14 SA	0022 / 0716 / 1236 / 1934	9.0 / 1.0 / 9.1 / 0.9	**29** SU	0016 / 0724 / 1238 / 1947	9.9 / 0.2 / 10.0 / 0.0
15 SU	0052 / 0746 / 1306 / 2003	9.1 / 1.0 / 9.1 / 0.9	**30** M	0100 / 0809 / 1322 / 2029	10.0 / 0.1 / 10.0 / 0.0
			31 TU	0142 / 0850 / 1405 / 2108	9.9 / 0.2 / 9.8 / 0.3

APRIL

Day	Time	m	Day	Time	m
1 W	0224 / 0928 / 1448 / 2145	9.6 / 0.5 / 9.4 / 0.8	**16** TH	0153 / 0846 / 1412 / 2100	8.8 / 1.3 / 8.6 / 1.5
2 TH	0306 / 1007 / 1532 / 2223	9.0 / 1.0 / 8.7 / 1.4	**17** F	0225 / 0918 / 1446 / 2133	8.5 / 1.5 / 8.3 / 1.8
3 F	0351 / 1050 / 1623 / 2310	8.4 / 1.6 / 8.0 / 2.1	**18** SA	0301 / 0955 / 1522 / 2214	8.1 / 1.9 / 7.8 / 2.2
4 SA	0446 / 1146 / 1728	7.7 / 2.2 / 7.3	**19** SU	0345 / 1042 / 1613 / 2308	7.7 / 2.2 / 7.4 / 2.5
5 SU	0013 / 0600 / 1300 / 1854	2.6 / 7.1 / 2.5 / 7.0	**20** M	0444 / 1144 / 1732	7.3 / 2.5 / 7.1
6 M	0136 / 0734 / 1425 / 2022	2.8 / 7.0 / 2.5 / 7.3	**21** TU	0021 / 0610 / 1305 / 1904	2.7 / 7.1 / 2.4 / 7.3
7 TU	0300 / 0853 / 1541 / 2124	2.5 / 7.4 / 2.1 / 7.8	**22** W	0148 / 0740 / 1432 / 2021	2.4 / 7.5 / 2.0 / 7.9
8 W	0408 / 0947 / 1639 / 2210	2.0 / 7.9 / 1.7 / 8.2	**23** TH	0308 / 0850 / 1544 / 2123	1.9 / 8.2 / 1.4 / 8.6
9 TH	0459 / 1029 / 1723 / 2249	1.6 / 8.4 / 1.4 / 8.6	**24** F	0414 / 0949 / 1647 / 2217	1.3 / 8.8 / 0.9 / 9.1
10 F	0539 / 1105 / 1800 / 2322	1.4 / 8.6 / 1.1 / 8.8	**25** SA	0515 / 1042 / 1744 / 2306	0.8 / 9.3 / 0.5 / 9.5
11 SA	0614 / 1137 / 1834 / O 2353	1.2 / 8.8 / 1.0 / 8.9	**26** SU	0611 / 1130 / 1837 / ● 2353	0.5 / 9.7 / 0.2 / 9.8
12 SU	0647 / 1209 / 1905	1.1 / 8.9 / 1.0	**27** M	0702 / 1217 / 1924	0.3 / 9.9 / 0.2
13 M	0024 / 0719 / 1240 / 1935	9.0 / 1.0 / 9.0 / 1.0	**28** TU	0037 / 0747 / 1302 / 2007	9.9 / 0.2 / 9.9 / 0.3
14 TU	0054 / 0748 / 1310 / 2003	9.0 / 1.0 / 8.9 / 1.1	**29** W	0120 / 0830 / 1345 / 2047	9.8 / 0.3 / 9.7 / 0.5
15 W	0124 / 0817 / 1340 / 2031	8.9 / 1.1 / 8.8 / 1.2	**30** TH	0203 / 0909 / 1429 / 2125	9.5 / 0.6 / 9.3 / 1.0

Chart Datum: 4·43 metres below Lallemand System (Mean Sea Level, Marseilles)

19

TIME ZONE –0100
(French Standard Time)
Subtract 1 hour for UT

For French Summer Time add ONE hour in non-shaded areas

FRANCE – DIEPPE

LAT 49°56′N   LONG   1°05′E

TIMES AND HEIGHTS OF HIGH AND LOW WATERS

YEAR **1998**

MAY

Day	Time	m	Time	m	Time	m	Time	m
1 F	0245	9.0	0948	1.1	1513	8.7	2203	1.5
2 SA	0330	8.4	1030	1.6	1602	8.1	2248	2.1
3 SU	0421	7.7	1121	2.1	1700	7.5	2345	2.5
4 M	0525	7.2	1225	2.5	1812	7.1		
5 TU	0057	2.7	0644	7.0	1338	2.5	1933	7.2
6 W	0211	2.6	0805	7.2	1448	2.3	2041	7.5
7 TH	0318	2.3	0906	7.6	1549	2.0	2131	8.0
8 F	0413	1.9	0952	8.0	1639	1.6	2212	8.3
9 SA	0459	1.6	1031	8.3	1722	1.4	2248	8.6
10 SU	0539	1.4	1107	8.6	1800	1.2	2323	8.8
11 M O	0616	1.2	1141	8.7	1835	1.2	2356	8.9
12 TU	0651	1.1	1214	8.8	1908	1.1		
13 W	0028	8.9	0724	1.1	1247	8.9	1940	1.1
14 TH	0100	8.9	0757	1.1	1320	8.8	2012	1.2
15 F	0133	8.8	0830	1.2	1355	8.7	2045	1.4
16 SA	0209	8.6	0906	1.4	1433	8.4	2121	1.7
17 SU	0248	8.3	0945	1.6	1516	8.1	2204	2.0
18 M	0334	7.9	1032	1.9	1608	7.7	2256	2.2
19 TU	0432	7.6	1129	2.1	1715	7.5		
20 W	0002	2.3	0547	7.5	1241	2.1	1834	7.6
21 TH	0121	2.3	0708	7.7	1401	1.8	1948	8.0
22 F	0238	1.8	0819	8.2	1513	1.4	2053	8.5
23 SA	0346	1.3	0922	8.7	1618	1.0	2150	9.0
24 SU	0448	0.9	1018	9.1	1717	0.7	2242	9.3
25 M ●	0546	0.7	1109	9.4	1811	0.6	2331	9.5
26 TU	0638	0.5	1157	9.5	1900	0.5		
27 W	0017	9.6	0726	0.4	1243	9.6	1945	0.6
28 TH	0101	9.5	0810	0.5	1328	9.4	2026	0.8
29 F	0144	9.3	0851	0.7	1411	9.1	2106	1.1
30 SA	0226	8.9	0930	1.1	1455	8.7	2144	1.5
31 SU	0310	8.5	1010	1.5	1540	8.2	2226	1.9

JUNE

Day	Time	m	Time	m	Time	m	Time	m
1 M	0356	7.9	1053	2.0	1629	7.7	2313	2.3
2 TU	0448	7.4	1145	2.3	1726	7.4		
3 W	0011	2.6	0550	7.1	1245	2.5	1831	7.2
4 TH	0116	2.6	0701	7.0	1351	2.5	1940	7.3
5 F	0221	2.5	0810	7.3	1454	2.3	2041	7.6
6 SA	0322	2.2	0907	7.6	1551	2.0	2130	8.0
7 SU	0415	1.9	0953	8.0	1641	1.7	2213	8.3
8 M	0502	1.6	1035	8.3	1725	1.5	2252	8.5
9 TU	0545	1.4	1113	8.5	1805	1.4	2329	8.7
10 W O	0624	1.2	1151	8.7	1842	1.3		
11 TH	0005	8.8	0702	1.1	1227	8.8	1919	1.2
12 F	0041	8.9	0740	1.0	1304	8.9	1956	1.2
13 SA	0119	8.9	0819	1.0	1343	8.8	2035	1.3
14 SU	0158	8.8	0858	1.1	1425	8.7	2115	1.4
15 M	0241	8.6	0940	1.3	1509	8.4	2158	1.6
16 TU	0328	8.3	1025	1.5	1559	8.2	2247	1.8
17 W	0421	8.1	1117	1.7	1657	8.0	2346	2.0
18 TH	0525	7.9	1219	1.8	1805	7.9		
19 F	0054	2.0	0638	7.9	1330	1.8	1917	8.1
20 SA	0209	1.8	0750	8.1	1443	1.6	2025	8.4
21 SU	0319	1.5	0857	8.4	1551	1.3	2127	8.7
22 M	0424	1.2	0958	8.7	1652	1.1	2223	9.0
23 TU	0523	1.0	1052	9.0	1748	1.0	2313	9.2
24 W ●	0618	0.8	1142	9.2	1838	0.9		
25 TH O	0000	9.3	0707	0.7	1228	9.3	1925	0.9
26 F	0044	9.3	0752	0.7	1312	9.2	2007	1.0
27 SA	0127	9.2	0833	0.8	1354	9.1	2047	1.1
28 SU	0207	8.9	0911	1.0	1434	8.8	2124	1.4
29 M	0247	8.6	0947	1.4	1514	8.5	2159	1.7
30 TU	0327	8.2	1021	1.7	1555	8.1	2237	2.1

JULY

Day	Time	m	Time	m	Time	m	Time	m
1 W	0409	7.8	1101	2.1	1639	7.7	2321	2.4
2 TH	0457	7.4	1148	2.4	1731	7.3		
3 F	0014	2.6	0556	7.1	1246	2.6	1834	7.2
4 SA	0118	2.7	0706	7.0	1353	2.6	1944	7.3
5 SU	0226	2.6	0816	7.2	1501	2.4	2046	7.6
6 M	0330	2.2	0915	7.6	1600	2.1	2138	7.9
7 TU	0426	1.9	1004	8.0	1651	1.8	2223	8.3
8 W	0514	1.6	1048	8.3	1737	1.5	2305	8.6
9 TH O	0600	1.3	1130	8.6	1820	1.3	2345	8.8
10 F	0644	1.1	1210	8.8	1903	1.1		
11 SA	0026	9.0	0727	0.9	1251	9.0	1945	1.0
12 SU	0107	9.1	0810	0.8	1333	9.1	2027	1.0
13 M	0149	9.1	0852	0.8	1415	9.1	2109	1.1
14 TU	0232	9.0	0934	0.9	1459	8.9	2151	1.2
15 W	0317	8.8	1016	1.1	1545	8.7	2236	1.4
16 TH	0406	8.5	1102	1.4	1636	8.4	2327	1.7
17 F	0502	8.2	1156	1.6	1737	8.1		
18 SA	0029	1.9	0610	7.9	1302	1.9	1848	8.0
19 SU	0142	1.9	0725	7.9	1417	1.9	2001	8.0
20 M	0258	1.8	0839	8.0	1530	1.7	2110	8.3
21 TU	0406	1.5	0945	8.4	1634	1.5	2210	8.6
22 W	0508	1.2	1042	8.7	1732	1.3	2303	8.9
23 TH ●	0604	1.0	1132	8.9	1823	1.1	2348	9.1
24 F	0652	0.9	1216	9.1	1909	1.0		
25 SA	0030	9.1	0735	0.8	1256	9.1	1949	1.0
26 SU	0109	9.1	0813	0.9	1333	9.1	2026	1.1
27 M	0146	9.0	0848	1.0	1410	8.9	2059	1.3
28 TU	0221	8.8	0919	1.3	1445	8.7	2129	1.5
29 W	0256	8.5	0947	1.6	1519	8.3	2159	1.9
30 TH	0330	8.1	1018	1.9	1553	7.9	2233	2.2
31 F	0407	7.6	1055	2.3	1633	7.5	2317	2.5

AUGUST

Day	Time	m	Time	m	Time	m	Time	m
1 SA	0452	7.2	1144	2.7	1725	7.2		
2 SU	0013	2.8	0556	6.9	1247	2.9	1838	7.0
3 M	0124	2.9	0721	6.9	1405	2.9	1959	7.1
4 TU	0243	2.6	0837	7.2	1519	2.5	2104	7.6
5 W	0351	2.2	0935	7.7	1619	2.0	2156	8.1
6 TH	0446	1.7	1024	8.2	1711	1.6	2243	8.5
7 F	0537	1.3	1109	8.7	1800	1.3	2327	8.9
8 SA O	0626	1.0	1153	9.0	1848	1.0		
9 SU	0010	9.2	0714	0.7	1235	9.3	1933	0.8
10 M	0052	9.4	0759	0.5	1318	9.5	2017	0.7
11 TU	0135	9.5	0842	0.5	1400	9.5	2059	0.7
12 W	0218	9.4	0922	0.6	1443	9.3	2140	0.9
13 TH	0302	9.2	1002	0.8	1526	9.0	2221	1.2
14 F	0348	8.8	1044	1.2	1613	8.6	2308	1.5
15 SA	0440	8.3	1133	1.7	1710	8.1		
16 SU	0005	1.9	0545	7.8	1236	2.1	1821	7.7
17 M	0120	2.2	0706	7.6	1356	2.3	1944	7.7
18 TU	0242	2.1	0828	7.7	1516	2.1	2101	8.0
19 W	0356	1.8	0939	8.1	1625	1.8	2203	8.4
20 TH	0500	1.4	1034	8.6	1724	1.4	2253	8.8
21 F	0553	1.1	1120	8.9	1811	1.2	2336	9.0
22 SA ●	0637	1.0	1200	9.1	1852	1.1		
23 SU	0013	9.1	0715	0.9	1236	9.2	1927	1.1
24 M	0048	9.1	0749	0.9	1309	9.1	2001	1.1
25 TU	0120	9.1	0820	1.0	1341	9.0	2031	1.2
26 W	0152	8.9	0848	1.2	1412	8.8	2058	1.4
27 TH	0223	8.6	0913	1.5	1442	8.5	2124	1.7
28 F	0252	8.3	0939	1.8	1511	8.2	2153	2.0
29 SA	0323	7.9	1011	2.2	1544	7.7	2231	2.4
30 SU	0357	7.4	1054	2.7	1628	7.3	2320	2.8
31 M	0455	6.9	1150	3.0	1731	6.9		

Chart Datum: 4·43 metres below Lallemand System (Mean Sea Level, Marseilles)

TIME ZONE –0100
(French Standard Time)
Subtract 1 hour for UT

For French Summer Time add
ONE hour in non-shaded areas

FRANCE – DIEPPE

LAT 49°56′N   LONG 1°05′E

TIMES AND HEIGHTS OF HIGH AND LOW WATERS   YEAR **1998**

SEPTEMBER

Date	Time	m	Date	Time	m
1 TU	0026	3.0	16 W	0227	2.4
	0618	6.7		0818	7.5
	1308	3.2		1504	2.4
	1906	6.8		2051	7.7
2 W	0153	2.9	17 TH	0345	1.9
	0757	7.0		0927	8.0
	1439	2.8		1615	1.9
	2029	7.3		2150	8.3
3 TH	0316	2.4	18 F	0447	1.5
	0905	7.6		1019	8.5
	1549	2.2		1710	1.5
	2129	8.0		2237	8.7
4 F	0419	1.8	19 SA	0536	1.2
	0959	8.3		1101	8.9
	1646	1.6		1753	1.3
	2219	8.6		2316	8.9
5 SA	0514	1.2	20 SU	0616	1.1
	1047	8.8		1138	9.1
	1739	1.1		1830	1.1
	2306	9.1		● 2351	9.1
6 SU	0606	0.8	21 M	0650	1.0
	1132	9.3		1210	9.2
	1830	0.8		1902	1.1
	O 2350	9.5			
7 M	0656	0.5	22 TU	0022	9.1
	1215	9.6		0721	1.0
	1917	0.6		1241	9.2
				1933	1.1
8 TU	0034	9.7	23 W	0053	9.1
	0742	0.3		0750	1.1
	1258	9.8		1311	9.1
	2002	0.4		2002	1.2
9 W	0117	9.8	24 TH	0123	9.0
	0825	0.3		0818	1.2
	1340	9.8		1340	8.9
	2044	0.5		2029	1.4
10 TH	0200	9.7	25 F	0152	8.8
	0905	0.4		0843	1.5
	1422	9.6		1408	8.7
	2123	0.7		2054	1.6
11 F	0243	9.4	26 SA	0220	8.4
	0944	0.8		0908	1.8
	1504	9.2		1436	8.3
	2203	1.1		2122	1.9
12 SA	0327	8.9	27 SU	0250	8.1
	1024	1.3		0937	2.2
	1550	8.6		1508	7.9
	2248	1.6		2156	2.3
13 SU	0418	8.3	28 M	0323	7.6
	1111	1.9		1016	2.6
	1645	8.0		1548	7.4
	2343	2.1		2241	2.7
14 M	0523	7.6	29 TU	0412	7.1
	1214	2.4		1109	3.0
	1759	7.5		1646	7.0
				2344	3.0
15 TU	0059	2.4	30 W	0529	6.8
	0649	7.3		1224	3.2
	1338	2.6		1815	6.8
	1928	7.4			

OCTOBER

Date	Time	m	Date	Time	m
1 TH	0108	3.0	16 F	0320	2.2
	0714	6.9		0903	7.9
	1358	3.0		1550	2.1
	1952	7.2		2126	8.0
2 F	0240	2.5	17 SA	0420	1.7
	0832	7.6		0953	8.4
	1518	2.3		1643	1.6
	2058	7.9		2212	8.5
3 SA	0349	1.8	18 SU	0507	1.4
	0930	8.3		1034	8.8
	1619	1.6		1725	1.4
	2152	8.6		2250	8.8
4 SU	0448	1.2	19 M	0546	1.2
	1020	9.0		1109	9.0
	1715	1.0		1801	1.2
	2241	9.2		2324	8.9
5 M	0542	0.7	20 TU	0619	1.2
	1107	9.5		1141	9.1
	1807	0.7		1833	1.2
	O 2327	9.7		● 2355	9.0
6 TU	0633	0.4	21 W	0650	1.1
	1152	9.8		1211	9.1
	1857	0.4		1904	1.2
7 W	0012	9.9	22 TH	0025	9.0
	0721	0.2		0721	1.2
	1235	10.0		1241	9.1
	1942	0.3		1934	1.2
8 TH	0056	10.0	23 F	0055	8.9
	0804	0.3		0749	1.3
	1318	9.9		1310	9.0
	2025	0.4		2003	1.3
9 F	0140	9.8	24 SA	0125	8.8
	0845	0.5		0816	1.5
	1401	9.7		1339	8.8
	2105	0.6		2030	1.5
10 SA	0223	9.5	25 SU	0154	8.6
	0924	0.9		0843	1.8
	1443	9.2		1409	8.5
	2145	1.1		2059	1.8
11 SU	0308	8.9	26 M	0227	8.2
	1004	1.4		0913	2.1
	1529	8.6		1443	8.1
	2229	1.6		2133	2.1
12 M	0359	8.2	27 TU	0259	7.8
	1051	2.0		0951	2.5
	1623	7.9		1523	7.7
	2323	2.2		2216	2.5
13 TU	0503	7.6	28 W	0347	7.4
	1153	2.6		1042	2.9
	1735	7.4		1618	7.2
				2314	2.8
14 W	0037	2.6	29 TH	0459	7.0
	0626	7.2		1152	3.1
	1316	2.8		1737	7.0
	1904	7.2			
15 TH	0203	2.5	30 F	0031	2.9
	0755	7.1		0632	7.1
	1440	2.5		1319	2.9
	2027	7.5		1911	7.3
			31 SA	0201	2.5
				0754	7.7
				1443	2.3
				2023	7.9

NOVEMBER

Date	Time	m	Date	Time	m
1 SU	0316	1.8	16 M	0426	1.8
	0857	8.4		1000	8.4
	1549	1.6		1647	1.7
	2122	8.6		2218	8.4
2 M	0418	1.2	17 TU	0508	1.5
	0951	9.0		1037	8.7
	1647	1.1		1727	1.5
	2214	9.2		2253	8.6
3 TU	0514	0.8	18 W	0546	1.4
	1040	9.5		1110	8.9
	1742	0.7		1803	1.3
	2303	9.6		2327	8.8
4 W	0607	0.5	19 TH	0620	1.3
	1127	9.8		1143	9.0
	1833	0.4		1837	1.3
	O 2350	9.9		● 2359	8.9
5 TH	0656	0.4	20 F	0653	1.3
	1212	9.9		1215	9.0
	1921	0.4		1910	1.3
6 F	0036	9.9	21 SA	0031	8.9
	0742	0.4		0724	1.4
	1257	9.9		1246	8.9
	2005	0.4		1941	1.3
7 SA	0121	9.8	22 SU	0103	8.8
	0824	0.6		0755	1.5
	1340	9.7		1317	8.8
	2047	0.7		2013	1.4
8 SU	0205	9.4	23 M	0136	8.7
	0905	1.0		0826	1.7
	1425	9.2		1351	8.6
	2128	1.1		2045	1.6
9 M	0251	8.9	24 TU	0212	8.4
	0946	1.5		0900	1.9
	1511	8.7		1428	8.3
	2211	1.6		2122	1.9
10 TU	0341	8.3	25 W	0251	8.1
	1032	2.1		0939	2.2
	1603	8.0		1510	8.0
	2302	2.1		2204	2.1
11 W	0439	7.7	26 TH	0338	7.8
	1129	2.6		1027	2.5
	1706	7.5		1601	7.6
	2356	2.4		2256	2.4
12 TH	0005	2.6	27 F	0437	7.5
	0549	7.3		1124	2.5
	1240	2.8		1709	7.4
	1821	7.2			
13 F	0120	2.7	28 SA	0002	2.5
	0709	7.3		0554	7.4
	1356	2.7		1244	2.6
	1942	7.3		1831	7.5
14 SA	0233	2.5	29 SU	0121	2.3
	0822	7.6		0714	7.8
	1505	2.4		1405	2.3
	2048	7.7		1946	7.9
15 SU	0335	2.1	30 M	0239	1.9
	0916	8.0		0822	8.3
	1601	2.0		1517	1.7
	2137	8.1		2051	8.5

DECEMBER

Date	Time	m	Date	Time	m
1 TU	0346	1.4	16 W	0428	2.0
	0921	8.9		1002	8.3
	1619	1.2		1653	1.8
	2148	9.0		2223	8.2
2 W	0446	1.0	17 TH	0513	1.7
	1015	9.3		1041	8.5
	1717	0.8		1735	1.5
	2241	9.4		2301	8.5
3 TH	0542	0.7	18 F	0552	1.5
	1105	9.6		1117	8.7
	1811	0.6		1813	1.4
	O 2331	9.6		● 2337	8.7
4 F	0633	0.6	19 SA	0629	1.4
	1153	9.7		1153	8.9
	1901	0.5		1849	1.3
5 SA	0018	9.7	20 SU	0012	8.8
	0721	0.6		0704	1.4
	1239	9.7		1227	8.9
	1947	0.5		1925	1.2
6 SU	0105	9.6	21 M	0047	8.9
	0806	0.8		0739	1.4
	1324	9.6		1302	8.9
	2031	0.7		2000	1.2
7 M	0150	9.4	22 TU	0124	8.8
	0848	1.1		0815	1.4
	1408	9.2		1339	8.9
	2113	1.0		2037	1.3
8 TU	0235	9.0	23 W	0202	8.7
	0929	1.4		0853	1.6
	1453	8.8		1419	8.7
	2154	1.5		2116	1.4
9 W	0321	8.5	24 TH	0243	8.5
	1012	1.9		0932	1.8
	1540	8.2		1501	8.4
	2237	1.9		2156	1.6
10 TH	0410	8.0	25 F	0327	8.2
	1058	2.3		1017	2.0
	1631	7.7		1549	8.1
	2326	2.4		2242	1.9
11 F	0505	7.5	26 SA	0418	8.0
	1154	2.7		1109	2.2
	1731	7.3		1645	7.9
				2337	2.0
12 SA	0024	2.6	27 SU	0521	7.8
	0609	7.3		1212	2.3
	1258	2.8		1754	7.7
	1839	7.1			
13 SU	0130	2.7	28 M	0043	2.1
	0720	7.3		0634	7.9
	1405	2.7		1327	2.2
	1951	7.2		1910	7.8
14 M	0237	2.6	29 TU	0200	2.0
	0826	7.5		0748	8.1
	1509	2.4		1444	1.9
	2052	7.5		2022	8.2
15 TU	0337	2.3	30 W	0316	1.7
	0918	7.9		0855	8.5
	1605	2.1		1554	1.5
	2141	7.9		2126	8.6
			31 TH	0421	1.3
				0954	8.9
				1656	1.1
				2224	9.0

19

Chart Datum: 4·43 metres below Lallemand System (Mean Sea Level, Marseilles)

H.W.Hts.m.

MEAN SPRING
AND NEAP CURVES

MEAN RANGES	
Springs 8.5m	——
Neaps 4.9m	- - -

Springs occur 2 days
after
New and Full Moon.

CHART DATUM

Factor

L.W.Hts.m.

DIEPPE   10-19-23

Seine Maritime 49°56'·36N 01°05'·08E   Rtg 1-1-1

DIEPPE

Depths in metres

CHARTS
AC 2147, *2451*; SHOM 7317, 7083, 6824; ECM 1011, 1012;
Imray C31; Stanfords 1

TIDES
–0011 Dover; ML 4·9; Duration 0535; Zone –0100
NOTE: Dieppe is a Standard Port. Tidal predictions for
each day of the year are given above.

SHELTER
Very good. Access at all tides, but entrance is exposed to
winds from NW to NE, causing a heavy scend. A fixed
wavebreak across the narrowest part of the chan protects
and gives access (15m wide) at its E end to the marina
Jehan Ango (9 pontoons) in the Avant Port at Quai Henri
IV. Or yachts can lock into the Bassin Duquesne HW –2 to
+1; bridge opens H and H+30 during each period; berth in
NW corner. The new ferry terminal is at the E side of port
ent. Yachts prohib in Arrière Port.

NAVIGATION
WPT 49°56'·48N 01°04'·60E, 298°/118° from/to W jetty
extension, 0·35M. Ent to hbr is simple, but beware strong
stream across ent. ⌀ is prohib in a zone 5ca off pierhead.
Ent chan and Avant Port are dredged 5m. Entry/exit are
controlled during ferry movements. Due to restricted
visibility, yachts **must** request entry on Ch 12, 2M before
hbr ent; also 10 mins before leaving.

LIGHTS AND MARKS
Dieppe lies in a gap between high chalk cliffs, identified
by a castle with pinnacle roofs on the W side of the gap
and the conspic ch spire on the E cliff. ECM buoy (DI), VQ
(3) 5s, bell, is 2·5M WNW of hbr ent. W jetty head, Iso G
4s 11m 8M, Horn 30s. E jetty head, Iso R 4s 12m 8M. QR
12m 3M at SW corner of ferry berths.

IPTS (full code) shown from stns at root of W jetty and on
W side of hbr; repeated (simplified code) where shown
on chartlet.

DIEPPE *continued*

Extra sigs combined with IPTS:
Ⓖ to right = Ferry entering; Ⓡ to right = Ferry leaving.
Ⓦ to left = Bassin Duquesne lock gates open.
ⓇⓇ (hor) to right = Dredger in chan.
Lock sigs at Bassin Duquesne: 2 Ⓖ (vert) = closed.
Request bridge & lock to open = Sound 2 blasts; request
will not be met unil H or H+30 within period HW−2 to +1.
Ⓖ = Enter, no exit; Ⓡ = No exit (shown only into Bassin
Duquesne).

RADIO TELEPHONE
Dieppe Port VHF Ch **12** (HO) 16 (H24) for entry/depart; see
NAVIGATION. Ch 09 for marina which also monitors Ch 12.

TELEPHONE (Prefix ☎ Nos with zone code 02)
Hr Mr 35.84.10.55; Hr Mr (Port de Plaisance) 35.40.19.79;
Aff Mar 35.06.96.70; CROSS 21.87.21.87; ⌗ 35.82.24.47;
SNSM 35.84.10.55; Météo 21.31.52.23; Auto 08.36.68.08.76;
Police 35.06.96.74; Ⓗ 35.06.76.76; Brit Consul 35.42.27.47.

FACILITIES
Port de Plaisance (Jehan Ango) ☎ 35.40.19.79 (380 inc 50
Ⓥ) FF130, FW, AC, D by credit card-operated pumps H24
(P by cans), C (12 ton); **Bassin Duquesne** (80 inc 50 Ⓥ, but
mostly now used by locals) ☎ 35.84.22.99, FW, AC, C (30
& 3 ton); **Cercle de la Voile de Dieppe** ☎ 35.84.22.99, FW,
R, Bar; **Services:** ME, EI, Ⓔ, Sh, CH, Sh. **Town** P, D, FW, V,
Gaz, R, Bar, ✉, ▣, Ⓑ, ⇆, ✈. Ferry: Dieppe - Newhaven.

LE TRÉPORT   10-19-24

Seine Maritime 50°03'·95N 01°22'·24E   Rtg 3-2-2

CHARTS
AC 1352, 2147, 2612, *2451*; SHOM 7207, 7083, 6824; ECM
1011; Imray C31; Stanfords 1

TIDES
−0025 Dover; ML 5·0; Duration 0530; Zone −0100

Standard Port DIEPPE (←—)

Times				Height (metres)			
High Water		Low Water		MHWS	MHWN	MLWN	MLWS
0100	0600	0100	0700	9·3	7·4	2·5	0·8
1300	1800	1300	1900				
Differences LE TRÉPORT							
+0005	0000	+0007	+0007	+0·1	+0·1	0·0	+0·1
CAYEUX							
0000	+0005	+0015	+0010	+0·5	+0·6	+0·4	+0·4

SHELTER
Good in marina at S side of first S Basin (3·7m), E of FVs.
But ent chan and most of Avant Port dry; S side is dredged
1·5m, but prone to silting. Lock opens HW±4 May-Nov;
out of season HW ±3. Port de Commerce is only used by
yachts as an overflow.

NAVIGATION
WPT 50°04'·30N 01°21'·70E, 315°/135° from/to ent, 0·52M.
Coast dries to approx 300m off the pier hds. Shingle spit
extends NW from E pier hd; keep well to the W. Entry
difficult in strong on-shore winds which cause scend in
Avant Port.

LIGHTS AND MARKS
Le Tréport is identified between high chalk cliffs, with
crucifix (lit) above town and conspic church S of hbr. No
ldg lts/marks. IPTS were installed 1996, as shown. W jetty
Fl (2) G 10s 15m 20M. E jetty Oc R 4s 8m 6M.
Lock sigs shown from head of dredged/piled chan to S
Basin: Ⓖ = enter lock; Ⓡ = no entry.

RADIO TELEPHONE
Call: *Capitainerie Le Tréport* VHF Ch 12 16 (HW ±3).

TELEPHONE (Prefix ☎ Nos with zone code 02)
Hr Mr 35.86.17.91, ⚓ 35.86.60.11; Lock (into marina)
35.50.63.06; Aff Mar 35.06.96.70; SNSM 35.86.10.91; Auto
08.36.68.08.76; CROSS 03.21.87.21.87; ⌗ 35.86.15.34;
Police 35.86.12.11; Dr 35.86.16.23; Brit Consul 03.21.96.33.76.

FACILITIES
Marina (130+10) FF105.48, AC, FW; **Avant Port** M;
Port de Commerce C (10 ton);
YC de la Bresle ☎ 35.86.19.93, C, Bar; **Services:** ME, CH,
EI, Ⓔ, P, D, Gaz.
Town P, D, V, Gaz, R, Bar, ✉, Ⓑ, ⇆, ✈ (Dieppe). Ferry:
Dieppe.

19

ST VALÉRY-SUR-SOMME/
LE CROTOY   10-19-25

Somme   Rtg 3-3-2

CHARTS
AC *2451*; SHOM 7084; ECM 1011; Imray C31; Stanfords 1
TIDES
LE HOURDEL –0010 Dover; ML —; Zone –0100

Standard Port DIEPPE (←)

Times				Height (metres)			
High Water		Low Water		MHWS	MHWN	MLWN	MLWS
0100	0600	0100	0700	9·3	7·4	2·5	0·8
1300	1800	1300	1900				
Differences ST VALÉRY-SUR-SOMME							
+0035	+0035	No data		+0·9	+0·7	No data	
LE HOURDEL							
+0020	+0020	No data		+0·8	+0·6	No data	

SHELTER
The B de Somme is open to W and can be dangerous in onshore winds >F6. All 3 very well sheltered hbrs (ie Le Hourdel, Le Crotoy and St Valéry-sur-Somme) are FV ports; small cargo vessels very occasionally berth at St Valéry town quay. Yachts can:
(1) dry out on hard sand at Le Hourdel; access HW±1½.
(2) enter Le Crotoy marina when tidal range at Dover >4·4m (approx Coefficient 85) with max. draft 1·5m.
(3) enter (HW ±1) St Valéry marina (max. draft 2·5m).
(4) enter Abbeville Canal at St Valéry (max. draft 3m up to Abbeville) by prior arrangement and daylight only.
NAVIGATION
WPT 'ATSO' NCM By, VQ, 50°14'·29N 01°28'·65E, about 1M W of buoyed chan (shifts). From N, beware being set by the flood onto shoals off Pte St Quentin. The whole estuary dries up to 3M seaward of Le Hourdel. The sands build up in ridges offshore, but inside Pte du Hourdel are generally flat, except where R Somme and minor streams scour their way to the sea. If Dover tidal range >4·4m, at HW ±1 there is sufficient water over the sands inside Pte du Hourdel for vessels <1·5m draft.
Start appr from 'ATSO' at HW St Valéry –2. Buoys are moved to suit ever-shifting chans. Follow chan with lateral buoys numbered S1 to S50 (some lit), in strict order (no corner-cutting!) to small unlit WCM Division buoy, in variable position E of Pte du Hourdel; then see below. Departure from Le Hourdel/Le Crotoy is not possible before HW –2; St Valéry HW–1.
LIGHTS AND MARKS
Only landmark is Cayeux-sur-Mer lt ho (W with R top) Fl R 5s 32m 22M (off chartlet to SSW). Pte du Hourdel lt ho Oc (3) WG 12s 19m 12/9M. Le Crotoy Oc (2) R 6s 19m 9M.

LE HOURDEL: Chan unmarked; follow 'S' buoys, then head SW toward end of shingle spit; hug the shingle.
LE CROTOY: From Division By chan runs N & E with lateral Bys C1 to C10. Enter hbr very close to FV stages (port-side). Secure at last FV stage and ask YC for berth. Tidal hbr badly silted (1995), with 2 drying pontoons.
ST VALÉRY-SUR-SOMME: From Division buoy, buoyed chan continues with SHMs becoming bns on submerged training wall, the seaward end of which is lit, Q (3) G 6s 2m 2M; then four bns on end of groynes. Iso G 4s 9m 9M marks beginning of tree-lined promenade; submerged dyke opposite marked with PHM bns. W tr on head of Digue du Large, Fl R 4s 9m 9M, leads into marina, dredged 2m, and town quay.
RADIO TELEPHONE
VHF Ch 09 (St Valéry HW ±2; Le Crotoy YC Jul/Aug only).
TELEPHONE (Prefix ☎ Nos with zone code 03)
St Valéry Hr Mr 22.26.91.64; Le Crotoy 22.27.83.11 (Port de plaisance); Aff Mar 22.27.81.44; ⌗ 22.24.04.75; Lock (canal) 22.60.80.23; CROSS 21.87.21.87; Auto 08.36.68.08.80; Police 22.60.82.08; Dr 22.26.92.25; Brit Consul 21.96.33.76.
FACILITIES
ST VALÉRY
Marina and YC Sport Nautique Valéricain (250 + 30) ☎ 22.26.91.64, FW, AC, C (6 ton), Slip, R, ▣, Bar; Access HW ±1; **Services:** ME, EI, CH, Ⓔ, charts.
Town EC Mon; P, D, CH, V, Gaz, R, Bar, ✉, Ⓑ, ⇌ and ✈ (Abbeville). Ferry: See Boulogne.
LE CROTOY
Marina (280) ☎ 22.27.83.11, FW, C (6 ton), Slip; **YC Nautique de la Baie de Somme** ☎ 22.27.83.11, Bar.
Town EC Mon; Ⓑ, Bar, D, P, ✉, R, ⇌, V.

LE TOUQUET/ÉTAPLES
10-19-26

Pas de Calais   Rtg 4-3-2

CHARTS
AC *2451*; SHOM 7085; ECM 1011; Imray C31; Stanfords 1, 9
TIDES
–0010 Dover; ML 5·3; Duration 0520; Zone –0100

Standard Port DIEPPE (←)

Times				Height (metres)			
High Water		Low Water		MHWS	MHWN	MLWN	MLWS
0100	0600	0100	0700	9·3	7·4	2·5	0·8
1300	1800	1300	1900				
Differences LE TOUQUET (ÉTAPLES)							
+0007	+0017	+0032	+0032	+0·2	+0·3	+0·4	+0·4
BERCK							
+0007	+0017	+0028	+0028	+0·5	+0·5	+0·4	+0·4

SHELTER
Good, except in strong W'lies. Drying moorings to stbd off Le Touquet YC. At Étaples, access HW±2 to small marina (1.2m) close downstream of low bridge; beware strong 5kn current.

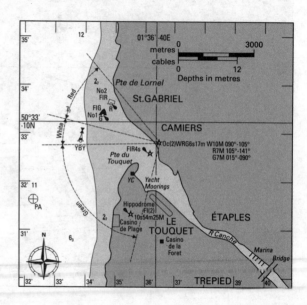

LE TOUQUET/ETAPLES *continued*

NAVIGATION

WPT 50°35'·00N 01°31'·80E, 308°/128° from/to Camiers lt, 3·8M. Appr & ent are not easy; estuary dries 2M offshore. In even moderate SW/W winds seas break heavily a long way out and entry should not be attempted. Best app is at HW −1 to reach Étaples marina at slack water. The chan is always shifting and buoys, some lit, are moved accordingly; prior info advised. Drying wreck 2M NW of Le Touquet lt ho, is marked by unlit WCM Mérida buoy.

LIGHTS AND MARKS

Le Touquet is at the S end of the Terres de Tourmont, a conspic range 175m high, visible for 25M.
Appr between Pte de Lornel and Pte du Touquet, where La Canche lt ho is conspic Or tr, brown band, W & G top, Fl (2) 10s 54m 25M.
Camiers lt Oc (2) WRG 6s 17m 9/6M (R pylon hard to see by day) is on NE side of estuary. Chan ent usually lies in It's R sector (105°-141°), but may lie in G sector, (015°-090°) ie S of the WCM wreck buoy, which is itself within the W sector (090°-105°).
Canche No 2 PHM buoy, Fl (2) R 6s, is first lateral chan buoy; essential to follow the buoys; do not cut corners.

Bn, Fl R 4s 8m 2M, approx 4ca SW of Camiers Lt, marks the seaward end of sunken training wall defining NE side of River Canche to marina; wall also marked by posts.

RADIO TELEPHONE

VHF Ch 09 (both hbrs), 77 (Le Touquet only).

TELEPHONE (Prefix ☎ Nos with zone code 03)

Hr Mr Le Touquet 21.05.12.77; Hr Mr Étaples 21.84.54.33, ⚓ 21.09.76.96; Aff Mar Étaples 21.94.61.50; Auto 08.36.68.08.62; ⌗ 21.05.01.72; CROSS 21.87.21.87; Police 21.94.60.17; Dr 21.05.14.42; Brit Consul 21.96.33.76.

FACILITIES

LE TOUQUET
Cercle Nautique du Touquet ☎ 21.05.12.77, M, P, Slip, ME, D, FW, C, CH, R, Bar; **Services:** BY, Sh, SM.
Town P, D, V, Gaz, R, Bar, ✉, Ⓑ, ⇌, ✈.
ÉTAPLES
Marina (115 + 15 visitors), FF85, FW, C (8 ton), AC, P, D; **Quay** BH (130 ton), FW, Slip; **Centre Nautique de la Canche** ☎ 21.94.74.26, Bar, Slip;
Services: CH, El, Ⓔ, M, ME, Sh, D.
Town Ⓑ, Bar, D, P, ✉, R, ⇌, V. ✈ Le Touquet. Ferry: Boulogne-Folkestone.

BOULOGNE-SUR-MER   10-19-27

Pas de Calais 50°44'·56N 01°34'·13E   Rtg 2-2-2

CHARTS

AC 438, *1892, 2451*; SHOM 7247,7323, 7085; ECM 1010, 1011; Imray C31, C8; Stanfords 1, 9, 20

TIDES

0000 Dover; ML 4·9; Duration 0515; Zone −0100

Standard Port DIEPPE (◀—)

Times				Height (metres)			
High Water		Low Water		MHWS	MHWN	MLWN	MLWS
0100	0600	0100	0700	9·3	7·4	2·5	0·8
1300	1800	1300	1900				
Differences BOULOGNE							
+0015	+0026	+0037	+0036	−0·4	0·0	+0·2	+0·4

SHELTER

Good, except in strong NW'lies. Ent possible at all tides and in most weather. Very busy ferry and FV port; beware wash from FVs. Marina pontoons (2·9m) are on SW side of tidal basin alongside Quai Chanzy; max LOA 10m. If >10m, pre-arrange. No yacht berths on Quai Gambetta; FVs only. When R Liane in spate beware turbulent water.

NAVIGATION

WPT 50°44'·50N 01°33'·00E, 270°/090° from/to S bkwtr (Digue Carnot) lt, 0·72M. Fairway buoy SCM, VQ (6) + L Fl 10s, is 295°/2·1M from S bkwtr lt. Cap d'Alprech lt ho, Fl (3) 15s 62m 23M, is 2·5M S of hbr ent. E side of hbr dries. Obey IPTS from SW jetty (see below). No navigational dangers and ent is easily identified and well marked, but keep W and S of Digue Nord lt tr, Fl (2) R 6s, as outer half of bkwtr covers at HW.

LIGHTS AND MARKS

Monument tr is conspic 2M E of hbr ent. Cathedral dome is conspic, 0·62M E of marina. St Nicolas Ch spire leads 123° through Avant Port. Ldg lts 123°: front 3 FG in ▽; rear Dir FR, intens 113°-133°, lead towards marina. 2 Bu lts (hor) upriver of marina = sluicing from R Liane.
IPTS are shown from SW jetty hd (FG ☆), and from Quai Gambetta, opposite ☆ 3FG ▽ (chartlet), visible from marina. One Ⓡ (below IPTS) = dredger working (this does not prohibit movements).

RADIO TELEPHONE

VHF Ch **12** (H24). Marina Ch 09. Forecasts by CROSS Gris Nez Ch 79 at H+10 (0710-1910LT).

TELEPHONE (Prefix ☎ Nos with zone code 03)

Hr Mr 21.80.72.00; Hr Mr Plaisance 21.31.70.01; Control Tr 21.31.52.43; Aff Mar 21.30.53.23; CROSS 21.87.21.87; Météo 21.83.53.71; Auto 08.36.65.08.08; Police 21.31.75.17; Emergency 17; Ⓗ 21.99.33.33; Brit Consul 03.21.96.33.76.

FACILITIES

Marina (114 + 17 visitors, at least) ☎ 21.31.70.01, FF100, FW, AC, D, Slip, C (20 ton); **Quai Gambetta** FVs only; **YC Boulonnais** ☎ 21.31.80.67, C, R, Bar;
Services: Ⓔ, ME, El, Sh, M, Divers, SHOM;
Town P (cans), V, Gas, Gaz, R, Bar, ✉, Ⓑ, ⇌, ✈ (Le Touquet). SeaCat to Folkestone.

CALAIS   10-19-28

Pas de Calais 50°58'·34N 01°50'·50E   Rtg 3-3-2

CHARTS
AC 1352, *1892, 323*; SHOM 6474, 6651; ECM 1010; Imray C8; Stanfords 1, 20

TIDES
+0048 Dover; ML 4·0; Duration 0525; Zone –0100

Standard Port DIEPPE (←)

Times				Height (metres)			
High Water		Low Water		MHWS	MHWN	MLWN	MLWS
0100	0600	0100	0700	9·3	7·4	2·5	0·8
1300	1800	1300	1900				
Differences CALAIS							
+0043	+0057	+0105	+0054	–2·2	–1·3	–0·5	+0·2

SHELTER
Very good, especially in the marina at Bassin de l'Ouest (3-6m). R waiting buoys outside lock (times below). Ent is rough with heavy swell in strong NW to NE winds; access H24. Enter Bassin Carnot only if bound for the canals.

NAVIGATION
WPT 50°58'·50N 01°49'·90E, 298°/118° from/to Jetée Ouest lt, 0·43M. Beware the Ridens de la Rade, about 4ca N of ent, a partly drying (0·6m) sandbank on which seas break. From the E it may be best to keep seaward of this bank until able to round CA8 PHM lt buoy and appr from 1M W of hbr. Byelaws require yachts to have engine running (even if sailing) and not to impede commercial vessels/ferries. Ent is relatively easy and well marked but there is much shipping. Keep a good lookout.

LIGHTS AND MARKS
Cap Blanc-Nez and Dover Patrol monument are conspic 5·5M WSW of hbr ent. Several churches and bldgs in the town are conspic. From a position ¼M SE of CA 10 PHM buoy, Fl (2) R 6s, the main lt ho (conspic), Fl (4) 15s, leads 141° through ent. The intens sector (115·5°-121·5°) of Dir FR 14m 14M at Gare Maritime leads close past the W jetty Iso G 3s. Hbr Control is conspic, pyramidal bldg on port-side as Arrière Port is entered.
IPTS (full code), shown from Hbr Control, to be obeyed. If no sigs are shown (ie no ferries under way), yachts may enter/leave. Or they may follow a ferry entering/leaving, keeping to the stbd side of the fairway. Supplementary traffic sigs, shown alongside the top IPTS lt, are:
Ⓡ = ferry leaving; no movements.
Ⓖ = ferry entering; no movements.
One Ⓡ (alongside lower IPTS lt) = dredger working, (this does not prohibit movements).
Bassin de l'Ouest: Lock gates and bridge open HW –1½, HW and HW +½. (Sat and Sun HW –2, HW and HW +1).
Ⓨ = 10 mins before lock opens.
Ⓡ = All movements prohib.
Ⓖ = Movement authorised.
4 blasts = Request permission to enter.
Prior to leaving, best to tell bridge operator your ETD.
Bassin Carnot: Gates open HW –1½ to HW +¾. Lock sigs:
ⓋⓋ (hor) = Enter.
ⓇⓇ (hor) = Do not enter.
Ⓖ = Exit from basin permitted.
Ⓡ = Do not exit from basin.
2 blasts = Request permission to enter.

RADIO TELEPHONE
Whilst underway in appr's and hbr, keep a close listening watch on Ch **12** 16 (H24) *Calais Port Traffic* and marina. Carnot lock Ch 12 (occas). Hoverport Ch 20 (occas).
Cap Gris Nez, Channel Navigation Info Service (CNIS), call: *Gris Nez Traffic* Ch **13** 79 16 (H24). Info broadcasts in English and French on Ch 79, at H + 10, and also at H + 25 when vis is < 2M. *CROSS Gris Nez* Ch 15, 67, **68**, 73.

TELEPHONE (Prefix ☎ Nos with zone code 03)
Hr Mr (Marina) 21.34.55.23; Hr Mr (Port) 21.96.31.20; Aff Mar 21.34.52.70; CROSS 21.87.21.87; SNSM 21.96.31.20; ☷ 21.34.75.40; Météo 21.33.24.25; Auto 08.36.68.08.62; Police 21.96.74.17; Ⓗ 21.46.33.33; Brit Consul 21.96.33.76.

FACILITIES
Marina (350 + 400 visitors) ☎ 21.34.55.23, ➷ 21.96.10.78. AB pontoon: 51FF summer, 42FF winter; AB quay: 25FF summer, 21FF winter. D, P (cans), FW, C (6 ton), BH (3 ton), AC, CH, Gaz, R, Ⓞ, Sh, SM, V, Bar; Access HW –1½ to HW +½; **YC de Calais** ☎ 21.97.02.34, M, P, Bar; **Town** CH, SM, ME, V, Gaz, R, Bar, ⊠, Ⓑ, ⇌, ✈. Ferry: Dover.

ADJACENT HARBOUR

GRAVELINES, Nord, 51°00'·90N 02°05'·75E, AC 1350, *323*; SHOM 7057, 6651. HW +0045 on Dover (UT); HW +0100 and –2·8m on Dieppe; ML 3·3m; Duration 0520. Good shelter, but chan dries 1·5m. Safest entry HW –1; do not attempt it in strong onshore winds. Appr to bkwtrs, with old lt ho (unlit, conspic B/W spiral) in transit with wtr tr 142°. Nuclear power stn 1M NE. Beware strong E-going stream across ent at HW. Keep to W on entry and to E when inside. Hbr dries (soft mud). Yachts may take the ground or enter Bassin Vauban via lock open HW ±1½; waiting pontoon outside. Lts: W bkwtr, Fl (2) WG 6s 9m 8M, vis G078°-085° (very close inshore from W), W085°-244° (seaward arc), W317°-327° (within ent chan); E bkwtr, Fl (3) R 12s 5m 6M; 130m N of this lt is a NCM bn, VQ 6m 4M. Aff Mar ☎ 03.28.23.06.12. VHF Ch 09 (HO). Facilities: **Bassin Vauban** (410+40) ☎ 03.28.23.13.42, FW, AC, BH (12 ton), C (3 ton); **YC Gravelines** ☎ 03.28.23.14.68, M, C (10 ton); **Services:** CH, El, M, ME, Sh. **Town** Ⓑ, Bar, D, P, ⊠, R, ⇌, V, Ⓞ.

CALAIS

DUNKERQUE (Port Est) 10-19-29

Nord 51°03'·67N 02°21'·10E

CHARTS
AC 1350, *323*, 1872; SHOM 7057, 6651; ECM 1010; Imray C30; Stanfords 1, 20

TIDES
+0050 Dover; ML 3·2; Duration 0530; Zone –0100

Standard Port DIEPPE (←)

Times				Height (metres)			
High Water		Low Water		MHWS	MHWN	MLWN	MLWS
0100	0600	0100	0700	9·3	7·4	2·5	0·8
1300	1800	1300	1900				
Differences DUNKERQUE							
+0050	+0122	+0121	+0108	–3·5	–2·4	–1·1	–0·1

SHELTER
Good; hbr accessible at all tides/weather, but fresh NW–NE winds cause heavy seas at ent and scend in hbr. Yachts must use E Port (a busy commercial port), **not** the W Port (ferry). Choice of 2 tidal marinas, either side of Port d'Echouage, ¾M down E side of hbr; or enter non-tidal marinas in Bassin du Commerce and Bassin de la Marine via Ecluse Trystram or Watier and three swing bridges.

NAVIGATION
WPT (E Port) 51°03'·90N 02°21'·00E, 355°/175° from/to Jetée Ouest lt, 0·20M. From the W, fetch the Dunkerque Lanby (Fl 3s), 5M N of Calais, thence to DKA SWM buoy (L Fl 10s), and then via series of DW lt buoys past W Port to DW 29 SHM buoy, ½M WNW of ent. From the E, via Nieuwpoort Bank WCM buoy, Q (9) 15s, the E1-12 buoys (10.19.4) lead S of Banc Hills. Streams reach about 3½kn.

LIGHTS AND MARKS
Main lt ho Fl (2) 10s 59m 28M, W tr with B top. Ldg lts: Outer (both F Vi) lead 179° through ent. A second pair, with common rear, lead 185°. (Both pairs are "Big Ship"). Inner, both Oc (2) 6s, lead 137° toward marinas. The East jetty is also illuminated by 6 bright sodium lights.
IPTS (full) shown from head of Jetée Ouest.
Lock sigs (H24), shown at Ecluse Watier, consist of three horiz pairs disposed vertically. Middle pair refer to Ecluse Watier and lowest pair to Ecluse Trystram:

Ⓖ Ⓖ	=	lock open.
Ⓡ Ⓡ	=	lock closed.

Lock sigs at each lock:

Ⓖ Ⓖ	=	lock ready.
Ⓖ+ Fl Ⓖ	=	enter and secure on side of Fl Ⓖ.
Ⓦ Ⓦ	=	enter lock; slack water, both gates open.
Ⓡ Ⓡ	=	lock in use, no entry.

RADIO TELEPHONE
Call *Dunkerque Port* VHF Ch 12 16 **73** (H24) for traffic info (English spoken). Locks Ch 73. Marinas Ch 09.

TELEPHONE (Prefix ☎ Nos with zone code 03)
Hr Mr 28.29.72.61, 🕾 28.29.72.75; Port Control 28.29.72.87; Aff Mar 28.26.73.00; CROSS 21.87.21.87; SNSM 28.66.86.14; ⧈ 28.64.78.16; Météo 28.66.45.25; Auto 08.36.68.08.59; Police 28.59.13.22; Ⓗ 28.66.70.01; Brit Consul 28.66.33.33.

FACILITIES
Port du Grand Large (185+25 visitors) ☎ 28.63.23.00, 🕾 28.66.66.62, FF65, H24 access (3m), FW, AC, BH (30 ton), YC, Bar, Ⓓ;
YC Mer du Nord Marina (180+40 visitors) ☎ 28.66.79.90, 🕾 28.66.36.62, FF95, approx 2m, Slip, D, P, FW, C (7½ ton), AC, ME, SM, R, Bar;
Access H24 via Ecluse Trystram, or Watier (unlikely) to:
Bassin du Commerce (120+13 Ⓥ) YC de Dunkerque (YCD) marina (4m) ☎/🕾 28.21.13.77, M, D, L, FW, CH; and to:
Port du Bassin de la Marine (250) , FW, AC, YC.
Services: SHOM, P, D, M, ME, El, Ⓔ, Sh, CH. **Town** P, D, V, Gaz, R, Bar, ✉, Ⓑ, ⇌, ✈ (Lille). Ferry: Ramsgate.

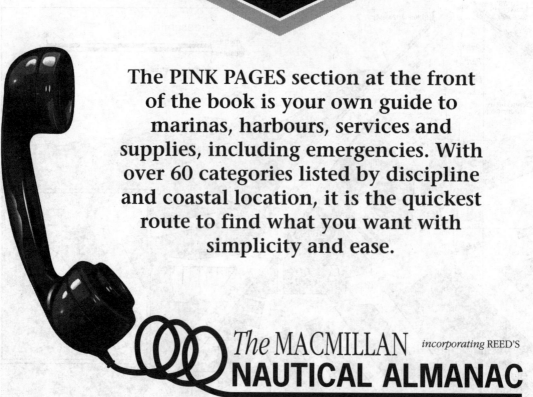

VOLVO PENTA SERVICE

Sales and service centres in area 20
Names and addresses of Volvo Penta dealers in
this area are available from:

Netherlands *Volvo Penta Benelux B.V.*, Nijverheidsweg 1, Postbus 195,
3640 Ad Mijdrecht Tel +31 2972 80111, Fax +31 2972 87364.

**VOLVO
PENTA**

Area 20

Belgium and the Netherlands
Nieuwpoort to Delfzijl

20

Key to Symbols

Coast Radio Station: VHF/MF frequencies
Port, VTS, or Marina Radio: VHF frequencies
Marine RDF beacon
Aero RDF beacon
See for harbour information/tidal data
Weather information
(Frequencies/times of broadcasts)
SAR Helicopter base
Selected Principal Lights
Light vessel/Light float/Lanby
Emergency VHF DF
See Area Index

816

Nes* (Ameland)
Scheveningen VHF **23** 16
Scheveningen VHF 23
0805 1305
1905 0005 LT

Emshörn
Eemshaven

Lauwersoog
10.20.32
VHF 09
Locks 22
Firing Practice 71

Termunterzijl

Delfzijl
10.20.33
VHF 14
Radar 66
Sea Locks 11
Bridge 11 14

53°
N

Borkumriff Lt.By
Borkum
Rottum

see Fig. 10 (6)

Ameland
299·00 AD 50M

Oostmahörn
Zoutkamp

Leeuwarden CG
Schiermonnikoog*
Radar 05 67 73

Harlingen
10.20.28
VHF **11**
Locks 22

IJsselmeer
10.20.25
VHF
Locks 18 22 20

10-20-2

Belgium and the Netherlands

Nieuwpoort to Delfzijl

Amsterdam
10.20.24
VHF 14
Info 04

6°E

ZONE

SEPARATION

Brandaris

Waddenzee

Markermeer

5°E

West Terschelling
10.20.30
VTS 02
VHF 78
0805 1305
1905 0005 LT

Zeegat van Terschelling
10.20.31

Vlieland
10.20.29
VHF 09
303·50 VL 20M

54°
N

Grote Kaap

Egmond
aan Zee

Noordzee
Kanaal

4°E

Eierland
301·00 ER 20M

Oudeschild
10.20.27
VHF 09

For traffic Scheme
see Fig.10(6)

3°E

Den Helder
10.20.26
VTS 12
Port 14
Bridge 18
Lock 22

IJmuiden
10.20.23
VTS **09** 22 11 68
W of IJmuiden Lt By
VHF 12
IJmuiden Lt By to
N Sea Locks
VHF 09
Locks 22

53°
N

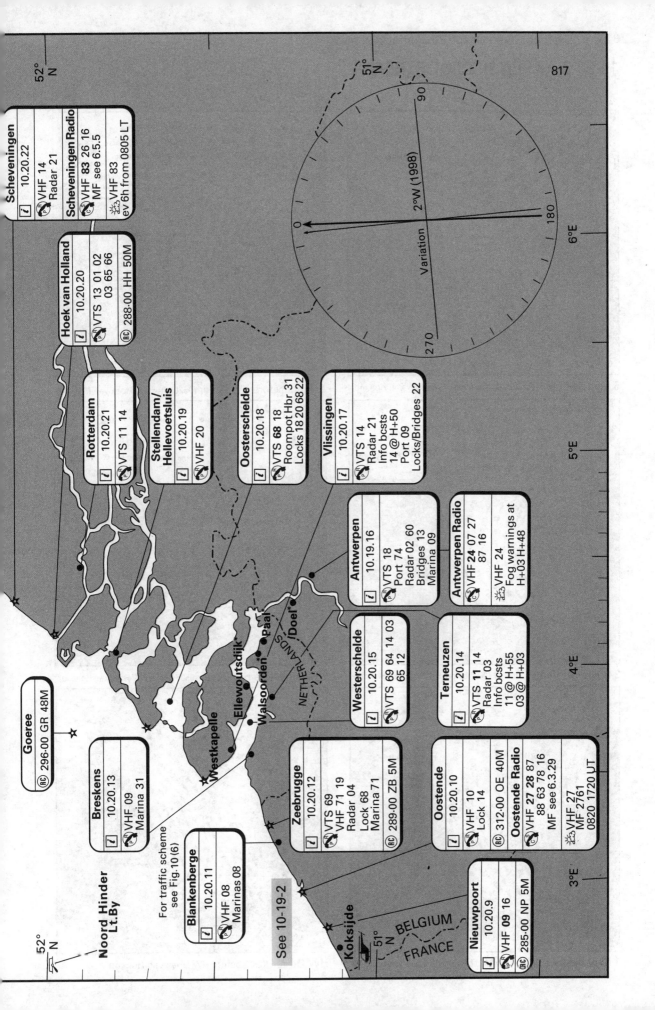

Scheveningen
10.20.22
- ℹ️
- 📻 VHF 14
  Radar 21

Scheveningen Radio
- 📻 VHF **83** 26 16
  MF see 6.5.5
- 🌬️ VHF 83
  ev 6h from 0805 LT

Hoek van Holland
10.20.20
- ℹ️
- 📻 VTS **13** 01 02
  03 65 66
- Ⓡ 288·00 HH 50M

Rotterdam
10.20.21
- ℹ️
- 📻 VTS 11 14

Stellendam/ Hellevoetsluis
10.20.19
- ℹ️
- 📻 VHF 20

Oosterschelde
10.20.18
- ℹ️
- 📻 VTS **68** 18
  Roompot Hbr 31
  Locks 18 20 68 22

Vlissingen
10.20.17
- ℹ️
- 📻 VTS 14
  Radar 21
  Info bcsts
  14 @ H+50
  Port 09
  Locks/Bridges 22

Antwerpen
10.19.16
- ℹ️
- 📻 VTS 18
  Port 74
  Radar 02 60
  Bridges 13
  Marina 09

Antwerpen Radio
- 📻 VHF **24** 07 27
  87 16
- 🌬️ VHF 24
  Fog warnings at
  H+03 H+48

Westerschelde
10.20.15
- ℹ️
- 📻 VTS **69** 64 14 03
  65 12

Terneuzen
10.20.14
- ℹ️
- 📻 VTS **11** 14
  Radar 03
  Info bcsts
  11 @ H+55
  03 @ H+03

Goeree
Ⓡ 296·00 GR 48M ☆

Noord Hinder
Lt.By

For traffic scheme
see Fig.10(6)

Breskens
10.20.13
- ℹ️
- 📻 VHF 09
  Marina 31

Blankenberge
10.20.11
- ℹ️
- 📻 VHF 08
  Marinas 08

Zeebrugge
10.20.12
- ℹ️
- 📻 VTS 69
  VHF 71 19
  Radar 04
  Lock 68
  Marina 71
- Ⓡ 289·00 ZB 5M

Oostende
10.20.10
- ℹ️
- 📻 VHF 10
  Lock 14
- Ⓡ 312·00 OE 40M

Oostende Radio
- 📻 VHF **27** 28 87
  88 63 78 16
  MF see 6.3.29
- 🌬️ VHF 27
  MF 2761
  0820 1720 UT

Nieuwpoort
10.20.9
- ℹ️
- 📻 VHF 09 16
- Ⓡ 285·00 NP 5M

See 10-19-2

Westkapelle

Ellewoutsdijk*
Paal*

Walsoorden* Doel*

NETHERLANDS

BELGIUM

Koksijde

FRANCE

817

52°
N

51°
N

51°
N

2°W (1998)

Variation

0

90

180

270

6°E

5°E

4°E

3°E

52°
N

52°
N

10-20-3　AREA 20 TIDAL STREAMS

5 Hours before HW Dover (0420 after HW Hoek van Holland)

4 Hours before HW Dover (0520 after HW Hoek van Holland)

3 Hours before HW Dover (0605 before HW Hoek van Holland)

2 Hours before HW Dover (0505 before HW Hoek van Holland)

1 Hour before HW Dover (0405 before HW Hoek van Holland)

HW Dover (0305 before HW Hoek van Holland)

South-westward 10.19.3   North-westward 10.4.3   North-eastward 10.21.3

1 Hour after HW Dover (0205 before HW Hoek van Holland)

2 Hours after HW Dover (0105 before HW Hoek van Holland)

3 Hours after HW Dover (0005 before HW Hoek van Holland)

4 Hours after HW Dover (0055 after HW Hoek van Holland)

5 Hours after HW Dover (0155 after HW Hoek van Holland)

6 Hours after HW Dover (0255 after HW Hoek van Holland)

20

10.20.4 COASTAL LIGHTS, FOG SIGNALS AND WAYPOINTS

Abbreviations used below are given in 1.4.1. Principal lights are in **bold** print, places in CAPITALS, and light-vessels, light floats and Lanbys in *CAPITAL ITALICS*. Unless otherwise stated lights are white. m – elevation in metres; M – nominal range in miles. Fog signals are in *italics*. Useful waypoints are underlined – use those on land with care. All geographical positions should be assumed to be approximate. See 4.4.1. All positions are generally referenced to the largest scale Admiralty chart and are mainly based on the ED 50 datum. Some offshore positions are referenced to the OSGB 36 datum depending on which Admiralty chart is used.

CROSSING THE NORTH SEA

Garden City Lt By 51°29'·20N 02°17'·90E Q (9) 15s; WCM.
Twin Lt By 51°32'·10N 02°22'·62E Fl (3) Y 9s; SPM.
Birkenfels Lt By 51°39'·05N 02°32'·05E Q (9) 15s; WCM.
Track Ferry Lt By 51°33'·80N 02°36'·50E Fl Y 5s; SPM.
NHR-SE Lt By 51°45'·50N 02°40'·00E Fl G 5s; SHM; Racon (N).
NHR-S Lt By 51°51'·40N 02°28'·75E Fl Y 10s; SPM; *Bell*.
Noordhinder Lt By 52°00'·20N 02°51'·50E Fl (2) 10s; Racon (T); SWM
NHR-N Lt By 52°10'·90N 03°05'·00E L Fl 8s; Racon (K); SWM.

BELGIUM

WEST HINDER TO SCHEUR CHANNEL

West Hinder Lt 51°23'·36N 02°26'·36E Fl (4) 30s 23m 13M; *Horn Mo(U) 30s*; Racon (W).
WH Zuid Lt By 51°22'·75N 02°26'·36E Q (6) + L Fl 15s; SCM.
Oost-Dyck Lt By 51°21'·57N 02°31'·23E QG; SHM.
A-Z Lt By 51°21'·50N 02°37'·00E Fl (3) G 10s; SHM.
A-N Lt By 51°23'·50N 02°37'·00E Fl (4) R 20s; PHM.
KB Lt By 51°21'·75N 02°43'·00E Q; NCM.
Middelkerke Bk Lt By 51°18'·25N 02°42'·80E Fl G 5s; SHM.
MBN Lt By 51°20'·87N 02°46'·40E Q; NCM.
SW Akkaert Lt By 51°22'·33N 02°46'·42E Q (9) 15s; WCM.
Mid Akkaert Lt By 51°24'·23N 02°53'·50E VQ (3) 5s; ECM.
Scheur 1 Lt By 51°23'·18N 03°02'·00E Fl G 5s; SHM.
Goote Bank Lt By 51°26'·98N 02°52'·72E Q (3)10s; ECM.
BT Ratel Lt By 51°11'·62N 02°28'·00E Fl (4) R 15s; PHM.

NIEUWPOORT AND APPROACHES

Trapegeer Lt By 51°08'·46N 02°34'·45E Fl G 10s; SHM.
Den Oever Wreck Lt By 51°09'·20N 02°39'·50E Q; NCM.
Nieuwpoort Bk Lt By 51°10'·21N 02°36'·16E Q (9) 15s; WCM.
Weststroombank Lt By 51°11'·39N 02°43'·15E Fl (4) R 20s; PHM.
E Pier, near root 51°09'·32N 02°43'·89E Fl (2) R 14s 26m **16M**; R Tr, W bands.
E Pier Hd 51°09'·46N 02°43'·17E FR 11m 10M; W Tr; vis 025°-250°, 307°-347°; *Horn Mo (K) 30s*.
W Pier Hd 51°09'·40N 02°43'·09E FG 11m 9M; W Tr; vis 025°-250°, 284°-324°; RC; *Bell (2) 10s*.

OOSTENDE AND APPROACHES

D1 Wk Lt By 51°14'·00N 02°38'·65E Q (3) 10s; ECM.
LST 420 Lt By 51°15'·50N 02°40'·70E Q (9) 15s; WCM.
Zuidstroombank Lt By 51°12'·33N 02°47'·50E Fl R 5s; PHM.
Middelkerkebank S Lt By 51°14'·78N 02°42'·00E Q (9) R 15s; PHM.
Oostendebank W Lt By 51°16'·25N 02°44'·85E Q (9) 15s; WCM.
Oostendebank E Lt By 51°17'·36N 02°52'·00E Fl (4) R 20s; PHM.
Nautica Ena Wk Lt By 51°18'·12N 02°52'·85E Q; NCM.
Wenduinebank W Lt By 51°17'·28N 02°52'·87E Q (9) 15s; WCM.
Buitenstroombank Lt By 51°15'·20N 02°51'·80E Q; NCM.

Binnenstroombank Lt By 51°14'·50N 02°53'·73E Q (3) 10s; ECM.
Oostende 51°14'·23N 02°55'·91E Fl (3) 10s 65m **27M**; W Tr; obsc 069·5°-071°.
W Pier Hd 51°14'·36N 02°55'·12E FG 14m 10M; W ○ Tr; vis 057°-327°; *Bell (1) 4s*.
E Pier Hd FR 15m 12M; W ○ Tr; vis 333°-243°; *Horn Mo(OE) 30s*.
Ldg Lts 128°, Front, 51°14'·18N 02°55'·62E. Both FR 4M on W framework Trs, R bands; vis 051°-201°.
A1 Lt By 51°22'·42N 02°53'·42E Iso 8s; SWM.
Oostendebank N Lt By 51°21'·25N 02°53'·00E Q; NCM.
A1 bis Lt By 51°21'·70N 02°58'·10E L Fl 10s; SWM.
SWW Lt By 51°22'·00N 03°01'·00E Fl (4) R 20s; PHM.
WBN Lt By 51°21'·50N 03°02'·71E QG; SHM.
Wenduine Bk E Lt By 51°18'·85N 03°01'·70E QR; PHM.
A2 Lt By 51°22'·50N 03°07'·05E Iso 8s; SWM.

BLANKENBERGE

Comte Jean Jetty 51°18'·78N 03°06'·95E Fl (2) 8s 30m **20M**; W Tr, B top; vis 065°-245°.
W Mole Hd FG 14m 11M; W Tr; intens 065°-290°, unintens 290°-335°.
E Pier Hd FR 12m 11M; W Tr; vis 290°-245°; *Bell (2) 15s*.

SCHEUR CHANNEL

S2 Lt By 51°23'·40N 02°58'·17E QR; PHM.
S3 Lt By 51°24'·35N 03°03'·00E Q; NCM.
S4 Lt By 51°25'·07N 03°02'·93E Fl (4) R 10s; PHM.
S5 Lt By 51°23'·73N 03°05'·90E Fl G 5s; SHM.
S6 Lt By 51°24'·25N 03°06'·00E Fl R 5s; PHM.
Droogte van Schooneveld (MOW 5) 51°25'·50N 03°09'·00E Fl (5) Y 20s 12m 2M; measuring Bn with platform; Ra refl.
S7 Lt By 51°24'·02N 03°10'·40E Fl G 5s; SHM.
S8 Lt By 51°24'·48N 03°10'·50E Fl (4) R 10s; PHM.
S9 Lt By 51°24'·47N 03°15'·06E QG; SHM.
S10 Lt By 51°24'·92N 03°15'·07E Fl R 5s; PHM.
S12 Lt By 51°24'·67N 03°18'·30E Fl (4) R 10s; PHM.
Scheur-Wiel Lt By 51°24'·26N 03°18'·00E Q; NCM.

ZEEBRUGGE AND APPROACHES

S-Z Lt By 51°23'·72N 03°07'·67E Q (3) 10s; ECM.
Zand Lt By 51°22'·56N 03°10'·16E QG; SHM.
W Outer Bkwtr Hd 51°21'·79N 03°11'·25E Oc G 7s 31m 7M; vis 057°-267°; *Horn (3) 30s*.
E Bkwtr Oc R 7s 31m 7M; vis 087°-281°.
Heist, Mole Hd 51°20'·90N 03°12'·25E Oc WR 15s 22m, **W20M**, **R18M**; vis W068°-145°, R145°-201°, W201°-296°; Tfc sigs.

NETHERLANDS

APPROACHES TO WESTERSCHELDE

WIELINGEN CHANNEL

Z Lt By 51°22'·60N 03°10'·80E Q (9) 15s; WCM.
BVH Lt By 51°23'·15N 03°12'·05E Q (6) + L Fl R 15s; PHM.
MOW3 Tide Gauge 51°23'·45N 03°12'·00E Fl (5) Y 20s; Racon (H); SPM; *Whis*.
Wielingen Lt By 51°23'·30N 03°15'·00E Fl (3) G 15s; SHM.
W1 Lt By 51°23'·50N 03°18'·00E Fl G 5s; SHM.
W2 Lt By 51°24'·64N 03°21'·58E Iso R 8s; PHM.
W3 Lt By 51°24'·03N 03°21'·58E Iso G 8s; SHM.
W4 Lt By 51°24'·92N 03°24'·48E L Fl R 5s; PHM.
W5 Lt By 51°24'·33N 03°24'·48E L Fl G 5s; SHM.
W6 Lt By 51°25'·15N 03°27'·25E L Fl R 8s; PHM.
W7 Lt By 51°24'·65N 03°27'·30E L Fl G 8s; SHM.
W8 Lt By 51°25'·48N 03°30'·15E L Fl R 5s; PHM.
W9 Lt By 51°24'·97N 03°30'·13E L Fl G 5s; SHM.
W10 Lt By 51°25'·80N 03°33'·00E QR; PHM.

Wave observation post 51°22'·84N 03°22'·82E Fl (5) Y 20s.
Kruishoofd 51°23'·73N 03°28'·36E Iso WRG 8s 14m W8M, R6M, G5M; W ■ Tr, B post; vis R074°-091°, W091°-100°, G100°-118°, W118°-153°, R153°-179°, W179°-198°, G198°-205°, W205°-074°.
Nieuwe Sluis 51°24'·48N 03°31'·38E Oc WRG 10s 27m W14M, R11M, G10M; B 8-sided Tr, W bands; vis R055°-086°, W086°-091·5°, G091·5°-134°, W134-140·5°, G140·5°-144·5°, W144·5°-236·5°, G236·5°-243°, R243°-260°, G260°-263·5, R263·5-292°, W292°-055°; Horn (3) 30s.

APPROACHES TO BRESKENS
Songa Lt By 51°25'·34N 03°33'·78E QG; SHM.
SS-VH Lt By 51°24'·75N 03°34'·00E Q; NCM.

BRESKENS FERRY HARBOUR
W Mole Hd 51°24'·40N 03°33'·23E FG 8m 4M; B & W mast; in fog FY; Ra refl; Fog Det Lt.

BRESKENS
W Mole Hd 51°24'·09N 03°34'·12E F WRG 6m; Gy mast; vis R090°-128°, W128°-157°, G157°-169·5°, W169·5°-173°, R173°-194°, G194°-296°, W296°-300°, R300°-320°, G320°-090°; in fog FY; Horn Mo (U) 30s.

WESTKAPELLE TO VLISSINGEN
Noorderhoofd Ldg Lts 149·5°, NW Hd of dyke. Front, 0·73M from rear, Oc WRG 10s 20m W13M, R10M, G10M; R Tr, W band; vis R353°-008°, G008°-029°, W029°-169°.
Westkapelle, Common rear, 51°31'·80N 03°26'·90E Fl 3s 50m **28M**; Tr, R top; obsc on certain brgs.
Zoutelande Ldg Lts 326°, Front, 1·8M from rear, FR 21m 12M; R ■ Tr; vis 321°-352°.
Molenhoofd 51°31'·61N 03°26'·07E Oc WRG 6s 9m; W mast R bands; vis R306°-329°, W329°-349°, R349°-008°, G008°-034·5°, W034·5°-036·5°, G036·5°-144°, W144°-169°, R169°-198°.
Kaapduinen, Ldg Lts 130°. Front, 51°28'·52N 03°31'·05E Oc 5s 26m 13M; Y ■ Tr, R bands; vis 115°-145°. Rear, 220m from front, Oc 5s 35m 13M; Y ■ Tr, R bands; synch with front; vis 107·5°-152·5°.
Fort de Nolle 51°27'·00N 03°33'·20E Fl WRG 2·5s 11m W6M, R4M, G4M; W col, R bands; vis R293°-309°, W309°-324·5°, G324·5°-336·5°, R336·5°-027°, G027°-044°, R044°-090°, G090°-110·5°, W110·5°-114·5°, G114·5°-119°, R119-130°.

VLISSINGEN (FOR KANAAL DOOR WALCHEREN)
Ldg Lts 117°. Leugenaar causeway, Front, 51°26'·47N 03°34'·22E Oc R 5s 5m 7M; W&R pile; intens 108°-126°.
Sardijngeul rear, 550m from front, Oc WRG 5s 8m W12M, R9M, G8M; R △ with W bands on R & W mast; synch; vis R245°-271°, G271°-285°, W285°-123°, R123°-147°.
Koopmanshaven, W Mole root 51°26'·42N 03°34'·61E Iso WRG 3s 15m W12M, R10M, G9M; R pylon; vis R253°-270°, G270°-059°, W270°-059°, G059°-071°, W071°-077°, R077°-101°, G101°-110°, W110°-114°.
Buitenhaven E Mole Hd 51°26'·37N 03°34'·75E FG 4M.
Buitenhaven W Mole Hd 51°26'·44N 03°36'·12E FR 10m 5M; also Iso WRG 4s; B mast; vis W072°-021°, G021°-042°, W042°-056°, R056°-072°; Tfc sigs; Horn 15s.
Schone Waardin 51°26'·60N 03°37'·95E Oc WRG 9s 10m W13M, R10M, G9M; R mast, W bands; vis: R248°-260·5°, G260·5°-269°, W269°-287·5°, G287·5°-326°, R326°-341°, G341°-023°, W023°-024°, G024°-054°, R054°-065°, W065°-075·5°, G075·5°-079°5°, R079·5°-083°.

VLISSINGEN OOST
W Mole Hd 51°26'·94N 03°40'·17E FR 8m 5M; W col; in fog FY; Horn (2) 20s.

Ldg Lts 023°. Front, 51°27'·91N 03°04'·07E Oc R 8s 7m 8M; G post. Rear, 100m from front, Oc R 8s 12m 8M; G mast; synch with front, both vis 015°-031°.
Flushing E Hbr Dir Lt 305° 51°27'·93N 03°40'·62E Dir F WRG; vis 303·5°-304·9°; W304·9°-305·1°, G305·1°-306·5°.

WESTERSCHELDE

BORSSELE-NOORDNOL
Pier Hd 51°25'·55N 03°42'·80E Oc WRG 5s; 9m; R mast, W bands; vis R305°-331°, W331°-341°, G341°-000°, W000°-007°, R007°-023°, G023°-054°, W054°-057°, G057°-113°, W113°-128°, R128°-155°, W155°-305°.
Borssele, Total Jetty, NW end 51°24'·85N 03°43'·61E Iso WR 10s; vis R133°-141·5°, W141·5°-133°.
Borssele-Everingen 51°24'·73N 03°44'·20E Iso WRG 4s 9m; W structure, R band; vis R021°-026°, G026°-080°, W080°-100°, R100°-137°, W137°-293°, R293°-308°, W308°-344°, G344°-357°, W357°-021°.

ELLEWOUTSDIJK
W Pier Hd (unlit) 51°23'·14N 03°49'·12E.

TERNEUZEN (FOR GENT)
Nieuw Neuzenpolder Ldg Lts 125°. Front, 51°21'·10N 03°47'·23E Oc 5s 18m 13M; W col, B bands; intens 117°-133°. Rear, 365m from front, Oc 5s 18m 13M; B&W Tr; synch with front; intens 117°-133°.
Dow Chemical Jetty, 4 dolphins showing Fl 3s and Fl R 3s; Horn 15s.
West Buitenhaven E Mole Hd (for Westsluis and Middensluis) 51°20'·61N 03°48'·93E FR 5M; tfc sigs.
Oost Buitenhaven E Mole Hd (Oostsluis) 51°20'·60N 03°49'·81E FR 5M; Tfc sigs.
Jacht Haven W Jetty 51°20'·59N 03°49'·68E Oc WRG 5s 14m W9M, R7M, G6M; B&W Tr; vis R090°-115°, W115°-238·5°, G238·5°-248°, W248°-279°, R279°-004°.
W Mole Hd 51°20'·62N 03°49'·72E FG 6m; Gy mast; in fog FY.

HOEDEKENSKERKE
De Val 51°25'·20N 03°55'·08E Iso WRG 2s 6m W8M, R5M, G4M; R Tr, W band; vis R008°-034°, W034°-201°, R201°-206°, W206°-209°, G209°-328. W328°-008°.

HANSWEERT (FOR KANAAL DOOR ZUID BEVELAND)
W Mole Hd 51°26'·45N 04°00'·50E Oc WRG 10s 9m W9M, R7M, G6M; R Tr, W band; vis R288°-310°, W310°-334°, G334°-356·5°, W356·5°-042·5°, R042·5°-061·5°, W061·5°-082·5°, G082·5°-102·5°, W102·5°-114·5°, R114·5°-127·5°, W127·5°-288°; in fog FY.

WALSOORDEN
S Mole Hd Ent 51°22'·96N 04°02'·18E FR 5m; Gy col.

PAAL APPROACHES
Speelmansgat Lt Bn 51°22'·03N 04°06'·26E Fl (5) Y 20s.

ZANDVLIET
Ldg Lts 118°. Front, 51°20'·70N 04°16'·40E Oc WRG 5s 11m W9M, R7M, G6M; vis R shore-350°, W350°-017°, G017°-019°, W019°-088°, G088°-109°, W109°-125°, R125°-shore. Rear, 200m from front, Oc 5s 18m 9M.

DOEL/LILLO/ANTWERPEN (Belgium)
Ldg Lts 185·5°. Front, 51°18'·51N 04°16'·25E Fl WRG 3s 5m W9M, R7M, G6M; vis Rshore-175°, W175°-202°, G202°-306·5°, W306·5°-330·9°, R330·9°-shore. Rear, 260m from front, Fl 3s 14m 9M; synch with front. By day vis 183°-185°.
Doel Jetty Hd 51°18'·72N 04°16'·18E Oc WR 5s 9m W9M, R7M; Y □, B stripes on Tr; vis R downstream-185°, W185°-334°, R334°-upstream shore.

Lillo Pier SE end 51°18'·20N 04°17'·28E Oc WRG 10s 5m W9M, R7M, G6M; R ☐ W band on B Bn; vis Rshore-303·1°, W303·1°-308·2°, G308·2°-096·5°, W096·5°-148°, R148°-shore.
No. 109 Lt By 51°14'·04N 04°23'·80E Iso G 8s; SHM.
Antwerp Nic Marina 51°14'·15N 04°23'·77E F WR 9m 3M; vis Wshore-283°-R283°-shore.

OOSTERSCHELDE AND APPROACHES

OUTER APPROACHES
Wave observation post VR 51°30'·35N 03°14'·53E Fl Y 5s.
SW Thornton Lt By 51°31'·01N 02°51'·00E Iso 8s; SWM.
TB Lt By 51°34'·45N 02°59'·15E Q; NCM.
ZSB Lt By 51·36'·64N 03°15'·77E VQ (9) 10s; WCM.
Westpit Lt By 51°33'·70N 03°10'·00E Iso 8s; SWM.
Rabsbank Lt By 51°38'·30N 03°10'·00E Iso 4s; SWM.
Middelbank Lt By 51°40'·90N 03°18'·30E Iso 8s; SWM.
MD 3 Lt By 51°42'·75N 03°27'·06E Fl G5s; SHM/.
Schouwenbank Lt By 51°45'·00N 03°14'·40E Mo (A) 8s; SWM; Racon (O).

WESTGAT/OUDE ROOMPOT (selected marks)
OG-WG Lt By 51°37'·23N 03°23'·87E VQ (9) 10s; WCM.
WG1 Lt By 51°38'·05N 03°26'·30E L Fl G 5s; SHM.
WG4 Lt Bn 51°38'·60N 03°28'·80E L Fl R 8s; PHM.
WG7 Lt By 51°39'·45N 03°32'·75E L Fl G 5s; SHM.
WG-GB Lt By 51°39'·75N 03°32'·75E VQ (6) + L Fl 10s; SCM.
OR2 By 51°39'·53N 03°33'·78E; PHM.
OR5 Lt By 51°38'·60N 03°35'·45E L Fl G 8s; SHM.
OR 6 Lt By 51°38'·78N 03°36'·39E L Fl R 8s; PHM.
OR8 By 51°38'·28N 03°37'·40E; PHM.
OR11 Lt By 51°37'·03N 03°38'·48E L Fl G 5s; SHM.
OR12 Lt By 51°37'·35N 03°39'·30E L Fl R 5s; PHM.
Roompotsluis Ldg Lts 073·5°. Front, 51°37'·38N 03°40'·80E Oc G 5s. Rear, 280m from front, Oc G 5s; synch.
N Bkwtr Hd 51°37'·34N 03°40'·17E FR 6m; *Horn(2) 30s*.

SOPHIAHAVEN/COLIJNSPLAAT
Roompot Marina N Mole Hd 51°35'·78N 03°43'·27E FR.
Colijnsplaat E Jetty Hd 51°36'·28N 03°51'·15E FR 3m 3M; *Horn*.
Zeeland Bridge. N and S passages marked by FY Lts, 14m.

KATS/GOESSCHE SAS (GOES)/WEMELDINGE
Kats S Jetty Hd 51°34'·44N 03°53'·72E Oc WRG 8s 5m 5M; vis W344°-153°, R153°-165°, G165°-200°, W200°-214°, G214°-258°, W258°-260°, G260°-313°, W313°-331°.
Goessche Sas S Mole Hd 51°32'·28N 03°55'·92E FR.
Wemeldinge W Jetty Hd 51°31'·34N 04°00'·25E FG.
W Hd new ent 51°31'·20N 04°00'·90E Oc WRG 5s 7m W9M, R7M, G7M; vis R105·5°-114°, W114°-124°, G124°-140·5°, W140·5°-144°, G144°-192°, W192°-205°, R205°-233·5°, W233·5°-258·5°, R258·5°-296·5°. R & G Lts mark canal.

YERSEKE/THOLENSCHE GAT/GORISHOEK
O25/Sv 12 Lt By 51°31'·40N 04°02'·42E QG; SHM.
Ldg Lts 155° (through Schaar van Yerseke). Front, 51°30'·07N 04°03'·46E Iso 4s 8m; in fog FY. Rear, 180m from front, Iso 4s 13m; synch; in fog 2 FY. FG and FR mark mole Hds.
Tholensche Gat. Strijenham 51°31'·40N 04°08'·91E Oc WRG 5s 9m W8M, R5M, G5M; R ☐, W bands, on mast; vis Wshore-268°, R268°-281·5°, W281·5°-297°, G297°-310°, R310°-060·5°, G060·5°-068°, W068°-082°, R082°-115°, W 115°-shore.

Werkhaven (Bergsediepsluis) W Mole Hd 51°30'·93N 04°09'·75W FG.
Gorishoek 51°31'·57N 04°04'·68E Iso WRG 8s 7m W6M, R4M, G4M; R pedestal, W bands; vis R260°-278°, W278°-021°, G021°-025°, W025°-071°, G071°-085°, W085°-103°, R103°-120°, W120°-260°.
Galgeplaat Lt By 51°32'·67N 03°59'·04E Q (6) + L Fl 15s; SCM.

STAVENISSE/ST ANNALAND
Hoek Van Ouwerkerk Ldg Lts 009·2° Front, 51°36'·92N 03°58'·27E Iso WRG 6s; viz R267°-306°, W306°-314°, G314°-007·5°, W007·5°-011·5°, G011·5°-067°, W067°-068·5°, G068·5°-085°, W085°-102·°5, G102·5°-112·5°, R112·5°-121·5°. Rear, 300m from front, Iso 6s.
Keeten B Lt By 51°36'·41N 03°58'·15E Mo (A) 8s; SWM; Racon (K).
Stavenisse E Mole Hd 51°35'·73N 04°00'·35E Oc WRG 5s 10m W12M, R9M, G8M; B pylon; W075°-090°, R090°-105·5°, W105·5°-108°, G108°-118·5°, W118·5°-124°, G124°-155°, W155°-158°, G158°-231°, W231°-238·5°, R238·5°-253°, W253°-350°.
St Annaland Entrance W side 51°36'·32N 04°06'·60E FG.

ZIJPE/ANNA JACOBAPOLDER
Veerhaven N Mole Hd 51°38'·63N 04°06'·02E Iso G 4s.
St Philipsland, on dyke 51°39'·17N 04°07'·16E Oc WRG 4s 9m W8M, R5M, G4M; pylon on B ● col; vis W051°-100°, R100°-144°, W144°-146°, G146°-173°.
Zijpsche Bout 51°38'·83N 04°05'·78E Oc WRG 10s 9m W12M, R9M, G8M; mast on R col; vis R208°-211°, W211°-025°, G025°-030°, W030°-040°, R040°-066°.
Tramweghaven S Mole 51°38'·90N 04°05'·87E Iso R 4s 7m.

KRAMMER/BRUINISSE/KRAMMERSLUIZEN
Stoofpolder 51°39'·52N 04°06'·39E Iso WRG 4s 10m W12M, R9M, G8M; B Tr, W bands; vis W147°-154°, R154°-226·5°, G226·5°-243°, W243°-253°, G253°-259°, W259°-263°, G263°-270°, R270°-283°, W283°-008°.
Bruinisse N Mole Hd 51°39'·94N 04°06'·03E FR 4M; Gy Bn.
Krammersluizen N Bkwtr Hd 51°39'·78N 04°08'·35E FR.

DE VAL/ZIERIKZEE
Engelsche Vaarwater Ldg Lts 019°. Front, 51°37'·75N 03°55'·60E Iso WRG 3s 7m W6M, R4M, G4M; R pedestal, W band; vis R290°-306°, W306°-317·5°, G317·5°-334°, W334°-336·5°, G336·5°-017·5°, W017·5°-026°, G026°-090°, R090°-108°, W108°-290°. Rear, 300m from front, Iso 3s 15m 6M; R ■ on W mast, R bands.
Zierikzee W Jetty Hd 51°37'·95N 03°53'·45E Oc WRG 6s 10m W6M, R4M, G4M; R pedestal, W band; vis G063°-100°, W100°-133°, R133°-156°, W156°-278°, R278°-306°, G306°-314°, W314°-333°, R333°-350°, W350°-063°.

FLAUWERSPOLDER/SCHELPHOEK/BURGHSLUIS
Flauwerspolder W Mole Hd 51°40'·70N 03°50'·86E Iso WRG 4s 7m W6M, R4M, G4M; W daymark, B band on pylon; vis R303°-344°, W344°-347°, G347°-083°, W083°-086°, G086°-103°, W103°-110°, R110°-128°, W128°-303°.
Schelphoek E Bkwtr Hd 51°41'·28N 03°48'·79E Fl (2) 10s 8m.
Hammen. Burghsluis S Mole Hd 51°40'·59N 03°45'·56E F WRG 9m W8M, R5M, G4M; mast on R col; vis W218°-230°, R230°-245°, W245°-253·5°, G253·5°-293°, W293°-000°, G000°-025·5°, W025·5°-032°, G032°-041°, R041°-070°, W070°-095°.

HARINGVLIET AND APPROACHES
Buitenbank Lt By 51°51'·20N 03°25'·80E Iso 4s; SWM.
Bollen Lt By 51°50'·00N 03°33'·00E VQ (9) 10s; WCM.
MW Lt By 51°44'·30N 03°23'·75E Q (9) 15s; WCM.
MN Lt By 51°47'·70N 03°30'·00E Q; NCM.
BG2 51°46'·10N 03°37'·20E Fl Y 5s; Y pile.
West Schouwen 51°42'·58N 03°41'·60E Fl (2+1)15s 58m **30M**; Gy Tr, R diagonal stripes on upper part.
Ooster Lt By 51°47'·97N 03°41'·32E Q (9) 15s; WCM.
SH Lt By 51°49'·50N 03°45'·90E VQ (9) 10s; WCM.
Ha10 51°51'·80N 03°51'·80E Fl Y 5s; Y pile.
SG Lt By 51°52'·00N 03°51'·50E Iso 4s; SWM.
SG 2 Lt By 51°51'·80N 03°53'·50E Iso R 2s; PHM.

SG 5 Lt By 51°50'·97N 03°55'·45E L Fl G 8s; SHM.
SG 9 Lt By 51°50'·81N 03°57'·41E L Fl G 8s; SHM.
SG 19 By 51°51'·24N 04°00'·20E; SHM.
G1 Lt By 51°50'·23N 04°02'48E L Fl G 8s; SHM.

STELLENDAM
N Mole Hd 51°49'·93N 04°02'·09E FG; *Horn (2) 15s.*

HELLEVOETSLUIS/HELIUSHAVEN
Haven W side 51°49'·23N 04°07'·74E Iso WRG 10s 16m
W11M, R8M, G7M; W Tr, R cupola; vis G shore-275°, W275°-
294°, R294°-316°, W316°-036°, G036°-058°, W058°-095°,
R095°-shore.
Tramhaven E Mole Hd 51°49'·23N 04°08'·00E FG 6m.
Heliushaven W Jetty 51°49'·29N 04°07'·23E FR 7m 4M.
Hoornsche Hoofden, watchhouse on dyke 51°48'·32N
04°11'·05E Oc WRG 5s 7m W7M, R5M, G4M; vis W288°-
297°, G297°-313°, W313°-325°, R325°-335°, G335°-344·5°,
W344·5°-045°, G045°-055°, W055°-131°, R131°-shore.

MIDDELHARNIS/NIEUWENDIJK
Middelharnis W Pier Hd 51°46'·65N 04°11'·81E F WRG 5m
W8M, R5M, G4M; vis W144°-164·5°, R164·5°-176·5°,
G176·5°-144°.
Nieuwendijk Ldg Lts 303·5°. Front, 51°45'·10N 04°19'·48E
Iso WRG 6s 8m W9M, R7M, G6M; B framework Tr;
vis G093°-100°, W100°-103·5°, R103·5°-113°, W113°-093°.
Rear, 450m from front, F 11m 9M; B framework Tr.

VOLKERAKSLUIZEN/WILLEMSTAD
Jachtensluis W side, S ent 51°41'·50N 04°23'·20E FG (sport).
Jachtensluis E side, E ent 51°41'·97N 04°25'·52E FR.
Noorder Voorhaven, W Mole Hd 51°42'·08N 04°25'·88E
FG 6m 4M; R lantern on pedestal; in fog FY.
Willemstad HD 9A Lt By 51°41'·84N 04°26'·75E Iso G 4s; SHM.

HOEK VAN HOLLAND AND APPROACHES
. Noord Hinder Lt By 52°00'·15N 02° 51'·50E Fl (2) 10s: Racon
(T); *Horn (2) 30s*; SWM.
Euro Platform 51°59'·99N 03°16'·55E Mo (U) 15s; W structure,
R bands; helicopter platform; *Horn Mo(U) 30s.*
Goeree 51°55'·53N 03°40'·18E Fl (4) 20s 32m **28M**; R and W
chequered Tr on platform; RC; helicopter platform; Racon (T);
Horn (4) 30s.

Westhoofd 51°48'·83N 03°51'·90E Fl (3) 15s 56m **30M**;
R ■ Tr.
Kwade Hoek 51°50'·25N 03°59'·07E Iso WRG 4s 10m W12M,
R9M, G8M; B mast, W bands; vis W 235°-068°, R068°-088°,
G088°-107°, W107°-113°, R113°-142°, W142°-228°, R228°-
235°; FR on radio mast 4·2M NE.
Adriana Lt By 51°56'·13N 03°50'·63E VQ (9)10s; WCM.
MC Lt By 52°01'·18N 03°53'·57E Iso 4s; SWM; Racon (M).
Hinder Lt By 51°54'·60N 03°55'·50E Q (9) 15s; WCM.
MV Lt By 51°57'·50N 03°58'·50E Q (9) 15s; WCM.
MVN Lt By 51°59'·66N 04°00'·29E VQ; NCM.
Indusbank N Lt By 52°02'·92N 04°03'·73E Q; NCM.

HOEK VAN HOLLAND/ROTTERDAM
Maasvlakte 51°58'·25N 04°00'·94E Fl (5) 20s 67m **28M**;
B 8-sided Tr, Y bands; vis 340°-267°.
Nieuwe Noorderdam Hd 51°59'·71N 04°02'·92E FR 25m
10M; Or Tr, B bands; helicopter platform; in fog Al Fl WR 6s;
vis 278°-255°.
Nieuwe Zuiderdam Hd 51°59'·19N 04°02'·58E FG 25m 10M;
Y Tr, B bands; helicopter platform; in fog Al Fl WG 6s; vis
330°-307°; *Horn 10s.*
Maasmond Ldg Lts 107° **Front**, 51°58'·60N 04°07'·58E Iso
4s 30m **21M**; R Tr, W bands. **Rear**, 0·6M from front, Iso 4s
47m **21M**: both vis 101°-123°, synch.

Maassluis Buitenhaven E Ent 51°54'·99N 04°14'·89E FG.
Viaardingen Buitenhaven E Ent 51°54'·04N 04°21'·02E FG.
Spuihaven W Ent 51°54'·03N 04°24'·06E FR.
Veerhaven E Ent 51°54'·45N 04°28'·82E FG.

HOEK VAN HOLLAND TO DEN HELDER
SCHEVENINGEN
SCH Lt By 52°07'·80N 04°14'·20E Iso 4s; SWM.
Scheveningen 52°06'·30N 04°16'·17E Fl (2) 10s 49m **29M**;
brown Tr; vis 014°-244°.
Ldg Lts 156°. Front, 52°05'·82N 04°15'·68E Iso 4s 17m 14M.
Rear, 100m from front, Iso 4s 21m 14M; synch with front.
SW Mole Hd 52°06'·28N 04°15'·22E FG 11m 9M; G 6-sided
Tr, W bands, R lantern; *Horn (3) 30s.*

Noordwijk-aan-Zee 52°15'·00N 04°26'·10E Oc (3) 20s 32m
18M; W ■ Tr.
Survey platform 52°16'·40N 04°17'·90E FR and Mo (U) 15s;
Horn Mo (U) 20s.
Eveline Lt By 52°25'·55N 04°25'·15E VQ (9) 10s; WCM.

IJMUIDEN
A-NE Lt By 52°27'·95N 03°48'·70E L Fl Y 10s; SPM.
IJ 3 Lt By 52°29'·80N 04°12'·10E Fl (3) Y 10s; SPM.
IJmuiden Lt By (IJM) 52°28'·50N 04°23'·87E Mo (A) 8s;
SWM; Racon (Y); (also known as Verkenningston.)
Ldg Lts 100·5°. **Front**, F WR 30m **W16M**, R13M; dark R Tr;
vis W050°-122°, R122°-145°, W145°-160°; RC. By day F 4m
vis 090·5°-110·5°. **Rear**, 570m from front, Fl 5s 52m **29M**;
dark R Tr; vis 019°-199°.
S Bkwtr Hd 52°27'·86N 04°32'·00E FG 14m 10M; in fog Fl 3s;
Horn (2) 30s.

NOORDZEE KANAAL/AMSTERDAM/IJSSELMEER
Ø Km mark 52°27'·86N 04°35'·64E.
20 Km mark 52°25'·21N 04°51'·94E.
Sixhaven Yacht Hbr 52°23'·02N 04°53'·77E F & FR.
Oranjesluizen (to IJsselmeer) 52°22'·98N 04°57'·70E.

IJMUIDEN TO TEXEL
BSP Lt By 52°30'·80N 04°30'·00E Fl (4) Y 12s; SPM.
CP-Q8-A Platform 52°35'·75N 04°31'·80E Mo (U) 15s.
Egmond-aan-Zee 52°37'·20N 04°37'·40E Iso WR 10s 36m
W18M, R14M; W Tr; vis W010°-175°, R175°-188°.
Petten Lt By 52°47'·38N 04°36'·80E VQ (9) 10s; WCM.

ZEEGAT VAN TEXEL
Vinca G Lt By 52°46'·10N 04°12'·00E Q (9) 15s; WCM; Racon (D).
TX1 Lt By 52°48'·17N 04°15'·60E Fl G 5s; SHM.
ZH Lt By 52°54'·70N 04°34'·84E VQ (6) + L Fl 10s; SCM.
MR Lt By 52°56'·80N 04°33'·90E Q (9) 15s; WCM.
NH Lt By 53°00'·30N 04°35'·45E VQ; NCM.
Grote Kaap 52°52'·90N 04°42'·98E Oc WRG 10s 31m W11M,
R8M, G8M; vis G041°-088°, W088°-094°, R094°-131°.

SCHULPENGAT
Schulpengat. Ldg Lts 026·5°. **Front**, 53°00'·88N 04°44'·52E
Iso 4s **18M**; vis 024·5°-028·5°. Rear, **Den Hoorn** 0·83M from
front, Oc 8s **18M**; church spire; vis 024°-028°.
Huisduinen 52°57'·20N 04°43'·37E F WR 27m W14M, R11M;
■ Tr; vis W070°-113°, R113°-158°, W158°-208°.
Kijkduin, Rear, 52°57'·35N 04°43'·60E Fl (4) 20s 56m **30M**;
brown Tr; vis except where obsc by dunes on Texel.

SG Lt By 52°52'·95N 04°38'·00E *Mo (A) 8s*; Racon (Z); SWM.
S1 Lt By 52°53'·57N 04°38'·88E Iso G 4s; SHM.
S2 Lt By 52°53'·87N 04°38'·02E Iso R 4s; PHM.
S3 Lt By 52°54'·48N 04°39'·62E Iso G 8s; SHM.
S4 Lt By 52°54'·65N 04°39'·53E Iso R 8s; PHM.
S5 Lt By 52°55'·40N 04°40'·30E Iso G 4s; SHM.

20

S6 Lt By 52°55'·55N 04°39'·78E Iso R 4s; PHM.
S7 Lt By 52°56'·30N 04°40'·99E Iso G 8s; SHM.
S6A Lt By 52°56'·57N 04°40'·60E QR; PHM.
S8 By 52°57'·12N 04°41'·10E; PHM.
S9 By 52°56'·90N 04°42'·15E; SHM.
S10 Lt By 52°57'·65N 04°41'·65E Iso R 8s; PHM.
S11 Lt By 52°57'·60N 04°43'·35E Iso G 4s; SHM.
S14/MG17 Lt By 52°58'·42N 04°43'·40E VQ (6) + L Fl 10s; SCM.

MOLENGAT
Verkenningston MG Lt By 53°03'·95N 04°39'·45E Mo (A) 8s; SWM.

MG1 Lt By 53°02'·05N 04°41'·46E Iso G 4s; SHM.
MG2 Lt By 53°02'·18N 04°41'·87E Iso R 4s; PHM.
MG6 Lt By 53°01'·08N 04°41'·83E Iso R 4s; PHM.
MG5 Lt By 53°01'·08N 04°41'·52E Iso G 4s; SHM.
MG9 Lt By 53°00'·07N 04°41'·50E QG; SHM.
MG10 Lt By 53°00'·13N 04°41'·83E Iso R 8s; PHM.
MG13 Lt By 52°59'·17N 04°42'·30E Iso G 8s; SHM.
MG16 Lt By 52°59'·10N 04°42'·86E QR; PHM.
MG 18 By 52°58'·67N 04°43'·70E; PHM.
MG20 Lt By 52°58'·77N 04°44'·40E Iso R 8s; PHM.

MARSDIEP/DEN HELDER
T3 Lt By 52°58'·12N 04°46'·49E Iso G 8s; SHM.
Marinehaven, W Bkwtr Hd (Harssens I) 52°58'·00N 04°46'·84E QG 12m 8M; *Horn 20s.*
MH6, E side of ent 52°57'·97N 04°47'·51E Iso R 4s 9m 4M; R pile; Ra refl.
Ent W side, Fl G 5s 9m 4M; vis 180°-067° (H24).
Ent E side, QR 9m 4M; (H24.)
Ldg Lts 191°. Front, 52°57'·42N 04°47'·17E Oc G 5s 16m 14M; B △ on bldg; vis 161°-221°. Rear, 275m from front, Oc G 5s 25m 14M; B ▽ on bldg; vis 161°-247°, synch.

Schilbolsnol 53°00'·56N 04°45'·78E F WRG 27m **W15M**, R12M, G11M; G Tr; vis W338°-002°, G002°-035°, W035°-038° (leading sector for Schulpengat), R038°-051°, W051°-068°.
Mok 53°00'·25N 04°46'·85E Oc WRG 10s 10m W10M, R7M, G6M; vis R229°-317°, W317°-337°, G337°-112°.

WADDENZEE

DEN OEVER/STEVINSLUIZEN
M13 Lt By 52°59'·36N 04°52'·62E Iso G 8s; SHM.
LW Lt By 52°59'55N 04°56'·00E L Fl 10s; SWM.
W1 Lt By 52°59'·01N 04°56'·82E Iso G 4s; SHM.
W9 Lt By 52°57'·30N 04°57'·61E Iso G 8s; SHM.
O5 Lt By 52°56'·89N 05°01'·98E Iso G 4s; SHM.
Ldg Lts 131° 52°56'·37N 05°03'·04E Front and Rear both Oc 10s 7M; vis 127°-137°.
Detached Bkwtr N Hd 52°56'·80N 05°02'·38E L Fl R 10s.
Stevinsluizen W wall, 80m from Hd 52°56'·27N 05°02'·23E Iso WRG 2s; vis G195°-213°, W213°-227°, R227°-245°.

TEXELSTROOM/OUDESCHILD
T17 Lt By 53°01'·20N 04°51'·50E Iso G 8s; SHM.
T14 Lt By 53°02·28N 04°51'·56E Iso R 8s; PHM.
Oudeschild S Mole Hd 53°02'·37N 04°51'·26E FR 7m; *Horn (2) 30s* (sounded 0600-2300).
Oc 6s 7m Lt seen between FR and FG leads into hbr.
T23 Lt By 53°03'·55N 04°55'·70E QG; SHM.
T27 Lt By 53°03'·52N 04°59'·25E Iso G 8s; SHM.

DOOVE BALG/KORNWERDERZAND/LORENTZ-SLUIZEN
D4 Lt By 53°02'·61N 05°03'·74E Iso R 8s; PHM.
D3A/J2 Lt By 53°01'·98N 05°07'·84E Fl (2+1) G 10s; G post, R band.
D10 Lt By 53°02'·84N 05°10'·79E Iso R 8s; PHM.

D24 Lt By 53°03'·83N 05°15'·65E Iso R 8s; PHM.
Kornwerderzand Buitenhaven, W Mole Hd 53°04'·82N 05°20'·13E FG 9m 7M; *Horn Mo(N) 30s.*
Spuihaven Noord, W Mole Hd 53°04'·81N 05°19'·69E L Fl G 10s 7m 7M.

BOONTJES/APPROACHES TO HARLINGEN
BO11/KZ/2 53°05'·00N 05°20'·31E Q; NCM.
BO15 Lt By 53°05'·75N 05°22'·14E Fl G 2s; SHM.
BO28 Lt By 53°07'·85N 05°22'·65E Iso R 8s; PHM.
BO34 Lt By 53°08'·90N 05°23'·05E Iso R 2s; PHM.
BO40 Lt By 53°09'·90N 05°23'·40E Iso R 4s; PHM.

VLIESTROOM (selected marks)
VL1 Lt By 53°18'·97N 05°08'·80E QG; SHM.
VL2/SG1 Lt By 53°19'·67N 05°09'·23E VQ (9) 10s; WCM.
VL 8 Lt By 53°18'·57N 05°10'·95E L Fl R 8s; PHM.
VL9 Lt By 53°17'·85N 05°10'·00E Iso G 4s; SHM.
VL12/WM1 Lt By 53°17'·15N 05°11'·24E VQ (9) 10s; WCM.
VL16 Lt By 53°16'·90N 05°10'·72E L Fl R 8s; PHM.
VL15 Lt By 53°15'·95N 05°09'·80E L Fl G 8s; SHM.

APPROACH TO HARLINGEN/BLAUWE SLENK/POLLENDAM (selected marks)
BS1/IN2 Lt By 53°15'·22N 05°10'·00E VQ; NCM.
BS3 Lt By 53°14'·82N 05°10'·43E L Fl G 5s; SHM.
BS7 Lt By 53°14'·14N 05°11'·25E L Fl G 8s; SHM.
BS11 Lt By 53°13'·68N 05°13'·08E Iso G 4s; SHM.
BS19 Lt By 53°13'·35N 05°17'·20E QG; SHM.
BS27 Lt By 53°11'·95N 05°18'·40E QG; SHM.
BS31 Lt By 53°11'·62N 05°19'·77E L Fl G 8s; SHM.
BS 33 Lt By 53°10'·73N 05°23'·51E VQ G; SHM.

HARLINGEN
Ldg Lts 112°. Front, 53°10'·56N 05°24'·42E Iso 6s 8m 13M; vis 097°-127°; and FG 9m 7. Rear, 500m from front, Iso 6s 19m 13M; both on B masts, W bands; vis 104·5°-119·5° (H24).

N Mole Hd 53°10'·57N 05°24'·42E Iso R 5s 8m 4M; R pedestal.

TEXEL TO AMELAND
APPROACHES TO EIERLANDSE GAT
Eierland, N Pt of Texel 53°10'·97N 04°51'·40E Fl (2) 10s 52m **29M**; R Tr; RC.
TX 3 Lt By 52°58'·61N 04°22'·50E Fl (3) G 10s; SHM.
VL South Lt By 53°08'·95N 04°26'·63E L Fl Y 10s; SPM.
VL1 Lt By 53°11'·00N 04°35'·40E Fl (2) G 10s; SHM.
Baden Lt By 53°13'·62N 04°41'·35E Q (9) 15s; WCM.
EG Lt By 53°13'·39N 04°47'·15E VQ (9) 10s; WCM.

ZEEGAT VAN TERSCHELLING AND APPROACHES
VL CENTER LANBY 53°27'·00N 04°40'·00E Fl 5s 12M; Racon (C); *Horn (2) 30s.*
Vlieland 53°17'·79N 05°03'·58E Iso 4s 53m **20M**; RC.
VL3 Lt By 53°16'·98N 04°39'·68E Fl (3) G 9s; SHM.
VL5 Lt By 53°22'·90N 04°44'·00E QG; SHM.
VL7 Lt By 53°25'·53N 04°54'·01E Fl (3) G 9s; SHM.
SM Lt By 53°19'·29N 04°55'·71E Iso 4s; SWM.

ZUIDER STORTEMELK (selected marks)
ZS-Bank Lt By 53°18'·98N 04°57'·98E VQ; NCM.
ZS1 Lt By 53°18'·85N 04°59'·62E Fl G 5s; SHM.
ZS13/VS2 Lt By 53°18'·80N 05°05'·93E Fl (2+1) G 12s; leave to port for Vlieland and to stbd for Terschelling and Harlingen.

VLIELAND
VS3 Lt By 53°18'·37N 05°06'·25E QG; SHM.
VS5 Lt By 53°18'·08N 05°06'·20E L Fl G 5s; SHM.
VS14 Lt By 53°17'·62N 05°05'70E L Fl R 8s; PHM.

E Mole Hd 53°17'·73N 05°05'·59E FG.
W Mole Hd 53°17'·72N 05°05'·57E FR.

WEST TERSCHELLING
Ent via Schuitengat (Bys changed frequently).
VL 2/SG 1 Lt By 53°19'·67N 05°09'·30E VQ (9) 10s; WCM.
SG 17 Lt By 53°21'·20N 05°13'·37E L Fl G 8s; SHM.
Brandaris Tr 53°21'·67N 05°12'·99E Fl 5s 55m **29M**; Y ■ Tr;
vis except where obsc by dunes on Vlieland and Terschelling.
Ldg Lts 053·5°, W Hbr Mole Hd, Front, 53°21'·30N 05°13'·18E
FR 5m 5M; R post, W bands; *Horn 15s*. **Rear**, on dyke, 1·1M
from front Iso 5s 14m **19M**; vis 045°-061°.
W Terschelling E Pier Hd 53°21'·31N 05°13'·27E FG 5m 4M.

ZEEGAT VAN AMELAND AND APPROACHES
TG Lt By 53°24'·22N 05°02'·40E Q (9) 15s; WCM.
Otto Lt By 53°24'·70N 05°06'·60E VQ (3) 5s; ECM.
VL 11 Lt By 53°28'·13N 05°04'·03E L Fl G 10s; SHM.
TE 1 Lt By 53°30'·02N 05°13'·60E Fl (3) G 9s; SHM.
TE 3 Lt By 53°31'·86N 05°23'·00E L Fl G 10s; SHM.
TE 5 Lt By 53°33'·70N 05°32'·63E Fl (3) G 10s; SHM.
TS Lt By 53°28'·20N 05°21'·60E VQ; NCM.

Ameland, W end 53°27'·02N 05°37'·60E Fl (3) 15s 57m **30M**;
brown Tr, W bands; RC.
BR Lt By 53°30'·70N 05°33'·62E Q; NCM.
Ballumerbocht 53°25'·90N 05°44'·2E Iso R 4s 5m 4M.

NES
Nieuwe Veerdam Mole Hd 53°26'·02N 05°46'·53E Iso 6s 2m 8M.
Reegeul R3 53°28'·80N 05°46'·0E Iso G 4s

AMELAND TO DELFZIJL

AMELAND TO SCHIERMONNIKOOG
TE9 Lt By 53°37'·45N 05°51'·85E Fl (3) G 9s; SHM.
TE13 Lt By 53°41'·15N 06°11'·15E QG; SHM.
AM Lt By 53°31'·00N 05°44'·80E VQ; NCM.
NAM21 Lt By 53°31'·20N 05°55'·50E Fl Y; SPM.
WRG Lt By 53°32'·90N 06°03'·30E Q; NCM.
WG Lt By 53°32'·25N 06°06'·11E Iso 8s; SWM.
Schiermonnikoog 53°29'·20N 06°08'·90E Fl (4) 20s 43m
28M; ● Tr, dark R Tr. F WR 29m **W15M**, R12M; (same Tr); vis
W210°-221°, R221°-230°.
Ferry Pier Hd 53°28'·17N 06°12'·21E 2 F.

LAUWERSOOG/OOSTMAHORN/ZOUTKAMP
Lauwersoog E Mole Hd 53°24'·72N 06°12'·14E FR 4M.
Lauwersoog W Mole Hd 53°24'·73N 06°12'·09E FG 3M; in
fog FY; *Horn (2) 30s*.
Oostmahorn Ent 53°23'·01N 06°09'·72E FG.
Zoutkamp Ent (unlit) 53°20'·42N 06°17'·66E.

DELFZIJL ENTRANCE
W Mole Hd E Ent 53°19'·05N 07°00'·38E FG; Ra refl.
Ldg Lts 203°. Front, 53°18'·56N 07°00'·25E Iso 4s. Rear,
310m from front; Iso 4s.
Zeehavenkanaal, N side (odd numbered posts Fl G. S side
(even numbered posts Fl R).
E side Ent No. 21 (Marina ent) 53°19'·83N 06°56'·12E QG; W
post on dolphin.

TERMUNTERZIJL
BW 13 By 53°18'·70N 07°02'·37E; SHM.

For Die Ems see also 10.21.4.

10.20.5   PASSAGE INFORMATION

North Sea Passage Pilot (Imray/Navin) covers the North Sea and Belgian/Dutch coasts to Den Helder. *Cruising Guide to the Netherlands* (Imray/Navin) continues to the Ems. Refer also to *Havengids Nederland* (Vetus) in Dutch, well illustrated.

BELGIUM (chart 1872)

Features of this coast are the long shoals lying roughly parallel to it. Mostly the deeper, buoyed chans run within 3M of shore, where the outer shoals can give some protection from strong W or SW winds. Strong W to NE winds can equally create dangerous conditions especially in wind against tide situations. Approaching from seaward it is essential to fix position from one of the many marks, so that the required chan is correctly identified before shoal water is reached. Shipping is a hazard, but it helps to identify the main routes.

From the SW/W, the natural entry to the buoyed chans is at Dunkerque Lanby. From the Thames, bound for Oostende (10.20.10) or the Westerchelde (10.20.15), identify W Hinder lt. From the N, route via NHR-S and NHR-SE buoys or the N Hinder lt buoy. For TSS see Fig 10 (6).

Off the Belgian coast the E-going stream begins at HW Vlissingen – 0320 (HW Dover – 0120), and the W-going at HW Vlissingen + 0240 (HW Dover + 0440), sp rates 2kn. Mostly the streams run parallel with the coast. Nieuwpoort lies 8M from the French border. From the W (Dunkerque), approach through Passe de Zuydcoote (buoyed with least depth 3·3m) and West Diep. From ENE app through Kleine Rede, the inner road off Oostende which carries a depth of 6m. There are other apprs through the chans and over the banks offshore, but they need care in bad weather.

Sailing E from Oostende, leave about HW Vlissingen – 0300 to carry the E-going stream. If bound for Blankenberge (10.20.11) it is only necessary to keep a mile or two offshore, but if heading E of Zeebrugge (10.20.12) it is advisable to clear the hbr extension by 1M or more. The main route to Zeebrugge for commercial shipping is through Scheur (the deep water chan of the Westerschelde) as far as Scheur-Zand lt buoy, about 3M NW of hbr ent. There is much commercial traffic, and yachts should keep clear (S of) the buoyed chan so far as possible. Beware strong tidal stream and possibly dangerous seas in approaches to Zeebrugge.

NETHERLANDS (charts 325, 110, 2322)

While British Admiralty charts are adequate for through passages, coastal navigation, and entry to the main ports, larger scale Dutch charts are essential for any yacht exploring the cruising grounds along this coast or using any of the smaller hbrs. For Dutch Glossary, see 1.4.2.

Numerous wrecks and obstructions lie offshore and in coastal areas; those that could be hazardous are marked. The Off Texel TSS extends NNE from the TX 1 lt buoy, see Fig.10 (6): the separation zone incorporates the Helder gas field. Some 20–30M N lie the Placid and Petroland fields with production platforms. For general notes on N Sea oil and gas installations, see 10.5.5. The shoals of the N Sea coast and Waddenzee are liable to change due to gales and tidal streams. Sea level may also be affected by barometic pressure; wise to take advice from the Coastguard.

WESTERSCHELDE TO DEN HELDER

The main approach chans to Westerschelde are Scheur/ Wielingen and Oostgat, but yachts are required to keep clear of these. From Zeebrugge keep close to S side of estuary until past Breskens (10.20.13) when, if proceeding to Vlissingen (10.20.17), cross close W of By H-SS. From N, use Deurloo/ Spleet chans to S side of estuary. The tide runs hard in the estuary, causing a bad sea in chans and overfalls on some banks in strong winds. Vessels under 20m must give way to larger craft; and yachts under 12m are requested to stay just outside the main buoyed chans, including those between Walsoorden and Antwerpen (10.20.16) if navigation permits.

The Oosterschelde (10.20.18 and chart 192) is entered via the Roompotsluis, in the South half of the barrage. Coming from the S, Oostgat runs close to the Walcheren shore. Westkapelle l t ho is conspic near the W end of Walcheren. There are two lesser lts nearby: Molenhoofd 5ca WSW and Noorderhoofd 7ca NNW. Having passed the latter the coast runs NE past Domburg but becomes shallower as the Roompot is approached, so it is necessary to keep near the Roompot chan which here is marked by unlit buoys. It is important to have updated information on the buoyage and the chans.

The Schaar, Schouwenbank, Middelbank and Steenbanken lie off the W approaches to Oosterschelde. Westgat and Oude Roompot are the main channels, both well marked. From the north, Geul van de Banjaard (unlit) leads to Oude Roompot. Further north, the Slijkgat (lit) is the approach chan to Stellendam (10.20.19) and entry to the Haringvliet.

Shipping is very concentrated off Hoek van Holland (10.20.20) at the ent to Europoort and Rotterdam (10.20.21). Maas TSS must be noted and regulations for yachts obeyed, see 10.20.20.

The coast N to Den Helder is low, and not easily visible from seaward, like most of the Dutch coast. Conspic landmarks include: Scheveningen light house and big hotels, Noordwijk aan Zee light, big hotels and breakwaters at Zandvoort, and two l t ho's at IJmuiden, chys of steelworks N of IJmuiden, Egmond aan Zee lt, and chys of nuclear power station 1·5M NNE of Petten. For TSS see Figs 10 (5) & 10 (6). 3M W of IJmuiden (10.20.23) the N-going stream begins at HW Hoek van Holland – 0120, and the S-going at HW Hoek van Holland + 0430, sp rates about 1·5kn. Off ent to IJmuiden the stream turns about 1h earlier and is stronger, and in heavy weather there may be a dangerous sea. At IJmuiden the Noordzeekanaal leads to Amsterdam and the IJsselmeer.

THE WEST FRISIAN ISLANDS (charts 2593)

N from Den Helder (10.20.26), thence E for nearly 150M along the Dutch and German coasts, lies the chain of Frisian Is. They have similar characteristics – being low, long and narrow, with the major axis parallel to the coast. Texel is the largest and, with Vlieland and Terschelling, lies further offshore.

Between the islands, narrow chans (*zeegat* in Dutch, *Seegat* in German) give access to/from the North Sea. Most of these chans are shallow for at least part of their length, and in these shoal areas a dangerous sea builds up in a strong onshore wind against the outgoing (ebb) tide. The zeegaten between Den Helder and Texel, between Vlieland and Terschelling and the zeegat of the Ems are safe for yachts up to force 8 winds between SW and NE. All the others are unsafe in strong onshore*winds.

The flood stream along this coast is E-going, so it starts to run in through the zeegaten progressively from W to E. Where the tide meets behind each island, as it flows in first at the W end and a little later at the E end, is formed a bank called a *wad* (Dutch) or *Watt* (German). These banks between the islands and the coast are major obstacles to E/W progress inside the islands. The chans are narrow and winding, marked by buoys and/or withies (⚲ ⚱) in the shallower parts, and they mostly dry; so that it is essential to time the tide correctly.

This is an area most suited to shallow-draft yachts, particularly flat bottomed or with bilge keels, centreboards or legs, that can take the ground easily. Whilst the zeegaten are described briefly below, the many chans inside the islands and across the Waddenzee are mentioned only for orientation.

TEXEL TO TERSCHELLING

Zeegat van Texel (chart 191) lies between Den Helder and the Is of Texel, and gives access to the Waddenzee, the tidal part of the former Zuider Zee. Haaksgronden shoals extend 5M seaward, with three chans: Schulpengat on S side, leading into Breewijd; Westgat through centre of shoals, where the stream sets across the chan, is only suitable for passage in good weather and in daylight; and Molengat near the Texel shore. Schulpengat is the well marked main chan, buoys being prefixed with lettor 'S'; but strong SW winds cause rough sea against the SW-going (ebb) stream which begins at HW Helgoland – 0330, while the NE-going (flood) stream begins at HW Helgoland + 0325, sp rates 1·5kn. Molengat is marked by buoys prefixed by letters 'MG', but strong winds between W and N cause a bad sea. When coming from the NW or NE the Molengat is always the best route unless the weather is exceptionally bad. Routeing via the Schulpengat involves a southerly deviation of approx 15M and leads W of the very dangerous Zuider Haaks which should be avoided in bad weather. In Molengat the N-going (ebb) stream begins at HW Helgoland – 0145, and the S-going (flood) stream at HW Helgoland + 0425, sp rates 1·25kn. For Oudeschild, see 10.20.27.

E of Den Helder and the **Marsdiep**, the flood makes in three main directions through the SW Waddenzee:
(a) to E and SE through Malzwin and Wierbalg to Den Oever (where the lock into IJsselmeer is only available during daylight hours on working days); thence NE along the Afsluitdijk, and then N towards Harlingen (10.20.28);
(b) to NE and E through Texelstroom and Doove Balg towards the Pollen flats; and (c) from Texelstroom, NE and N through Scheurrak, Omdraai and Oude Vlie, where it meets the flood stream from Zeegat van Terschelling. The ebb runs in reverse. The Kornwerderzand locks (available H24), near NE end of Afsluitdijk, also give access to the IJsselmeer (10.20.25).
Eierlandsche Gat, between Texel and Vlieland, consists of dangerous shoals between which run very shallow and unmarked chans, only used by fishermen.

Zeegat van Terschelling (chart 112 and 10.20.31), between Vlieland (10.20.29) and Terschelling, gives access to the hbrs of Vlieland, West Terschelling (10.20.30) and Harlingen (10.20.28); also to the locks at Kornwerderzand. Shallow banks extend more than 5M seaward; the main chan (buoyed) through them is Zuider Stortemelk passing close N of Vlieland. In this chan the buoys are prefixed by letters 'ZS', and the E-going (flood) stream begins at HW Helgoland + 0325, while the W-going (ebb) stream begins at HW Helgoland – 0230, sp rates 2·5kn. Vliesloot leads to Oost Vlieland hbr. Approach West Terschelling via West Meep and Slenk. From Zuider Stortemelk the Vliestroom, a deep well buoyed chan (buoys prefixed by letters 'VL'), runs S about 4M until its junction with Blauwe Slenk and Inschot. Blauwe Slenk runs ESE to Harlingen; and Inschot SE to Kornwerderzand.

AMELAND TO DELFZIJL (charts 2593, 3509, 3510)

Zeegat van Ameland, between Terschelling and Ameland, is fronted by the sandbank of Bornrif extending 3M seaward. Westgat is the main entrance, with buoys prefixed by letters 'WG'. The chan runs close N of Terschelling, and divides into Boschgat and Borndiep. For Nes (Ameland), see 10.20.28. In Westgat the flood stream begins at HW Helgoland + 0425, and the ebb stream at HW Helgoland – 0150, sp rates 2kn. A dangerous sea develops in strong onshore winds.

Friesche Zeegat, between Ameland and Schiermonnikoog (10.20.33), has a main chan also called Westgat and buoys marked 'WG'. In strong winds the sea breaks across the whole passage. Westgat leads S through Wierumer Gronden, past Engelsmanplaat (a prominent sandbank) and into Zoutkamperlaag which is the main chan (marked by buoys prefixed 'Z') to Lauwersoog (10.20.32), where locks give access to the Lauwersmeer and inland waterways.

Further E, the estuary of R Ems (chart 3509) runs seaward past the SW side of the German island of Borkum (10.21.11). It leads to Delfzijl and Termunterzijl (10.20.33), or Emden (10.21.9), see 10.21.5. Hubertgat, which runs parallel to and S of the main Westerems chan, is slightly more direct when bound to/from the W, but in both these well lit chans there is a dangerous sea in strong NW winds over the ebb. The E-going (flood) stream begins at HW Helgoland + 0530, and the W-going (ebb) stream begins at HW Helgoland –0030, sp rates 1·5kn.

CROSSING NORTH SEA FROM BELGIUM AND SCHELDE (charts 1406, 323)

Avoid major traffic areas and cross TSS (Fig. 10(5)) at 90° to take departure from either Dunkerque Lanby or W Hinder lt depending on destination. From Dunkerque Lanby make good Ruytingen SW buoy, thence CS4 buoy and S Goodwin lt F (on W-going stream) or E Goodwin lt F (on N-going stream). From W Hinder lt for N Thames Estuary, make good Garden City buoy (on E-going stream) or Twin buoy (on W-going stream) in order to make N or S Galloper buoys and thence Long Sand Head buoy. Avoid shallower patches over W Hinder, Fairy, N Falls and Galloper Banks, particularly in rough weather when under-keel clearance may be reduced. For distances across the North Sea, see 10.0.7.

CROSSING NORTH SEA FROM THE NETHERLANDS Charts 1406, 1408, 1872, 2449, 3371)

From ports S of Hoek van Holland proceed westward across banks avoiding shallow patches to pick up Birkenfels buoy, across N Hinder W TSS (Fig 10 (5)) and thence to N Galloper buoy (for N Thames estuary) or Outer Gabbard buoy (for Lowestoft and North). For ports N of Hoek van Holland passages can be made from coast to coast avoiding TSS areas and crossing DW routes (Figs 10 (5) and (6)) with care.

10.20.6   DISTANCE TABLE

Approximate distances in nautical miles are by the most direct route, whilst avoiding dangers and allowing for Traffic Separation Schemes. Places in *italics* are in adjoining areas; places in **bold** are in 10.0.6, Distances across the North Sea.

	1	2	3	4	5	6	7	8	9	10	11	12	13	14	15	16	17	18	19	20
1. *Dunkerque*	1																			
2. **Nieuwpoort**	15	2																		
3. **Oostende**	26	9	3																	
4. Blankenberge	35	18	9	4																
5. **Zeebrugge**	40	23	13	5	5															
6. **Vlissingen**	55	39	29	21	16	6														
7. **Roompotsluis**	68	51	40	33	28	24	7													
8. Stellendam	90	83	72	55	50	45	32	8												
9. Hook of Holland	92	77	67	59	54	47	48	16	9											
10. Rotterdam	112	97	87	79	74	67	68	36	20	10										
11. **Scheveningen**	106	91	81	73	68	61	50	30	14	34	11									
12. IJmuiden	131	116	106	98	93	86	87	55	39	59	25	12								
13. Amsterdam	144	129	110	111	106	99	100	68	52	72	38	13	13							
14. **Den Helder**	169	154	131	136	131	120	125	93	77	97	63	38	51	14						
15. Den Oever	180	165	142	147	142	131	136	104	88	108	74	49	*62	11	15					
16. Harlingen	199	184	161	166	161	150	155	123	107	127	93	68	81	30	21	16				
17. Vlieland	202	187	164	169	164	153	158	126	110	130	96	71	84	33	33	18	17			
18. Terschelling	201	186	163	168	163	152	157	125	109	129	95	70	83	39	34	19	7	18		
19. **Delfzijl**	277	262	239	244	239	228	233	201	185	205	171	146	159	115	110	102	92	85	19	
20. *Borkum*	257	242	219	224	219	208	213	181	165	185	151	126	139	95	90	80	72	65	22	20

*Amsterdam to Den Oever via IJmuiden and Den Helder = 62M; but via the IJsselmeer = 45M.

SPECIAL NOTES FOR BELGIUM AND THE NETHERLANDS   10-20-7

BELGIUM

PROVINCES are given for ports in lieu of UK 'counties'.

CHARTS Those most widely used are the '*Vlaamse Banken*' issued by the Hydrografische Dienst der Kust. Imray C30 is also popular amongst Belgian yachtsmen.

TIME ZONE is –0100, which is allowed for in tidal predictions but no provision is made for daylight saving schemes shown by the non-shaded areas on the tide tables (see 9.1.2).

HARBOURS: Although the Hr Mr ☎ is given for Belgian hbrs, he is not the key figure for yachtsmen that he is in UK hbrs. Berths and moorings are administered by the local YCs. The prefix VVW = *Vlaamse Vereniging voor Watersport* ≅ Association of Flemish Watersports.

SIGNALS IPTS (see colour plate 9) are used at Nieuwpoort, Oostende and Zeebrugge, which are the Ports of entry. In season (early April to late Sept) Blankenberge is also a Port of entry with Customs.
Small craft wind warnings (onshore wind >F3; offshore wind >F4) apply to craft <6m LOA and are shown at these 3 ports and Blankenberge as follows:
Day: 2 black ▼s, points together. By night: Lt Fl Bu.

TELEPHONE To call UK from Belgium, dial 00-44 then the UK area code minus the prefix 0, followed by the number required. To call Belgium from UK, dial 00-32 then the code and number. Dialling codes are 3 digits, followed by a 6 digit subscriber No.

Emergencies: Police 101; Fire, Ambulance and Marine 100. 112 (EC emergency number) is not yet available in Belgium.

MARINE RESCUE CO-ORDINATION CENTRE Oostende, ☎ (059) 70.10.00, 70.11.00, 70.77.01 or 70.77.02. In emergency ☎ 100, or call *Oostende Radio* VHF Ch 16 (☎ 70.24.38). For medical advice call *Radiomédical Oostende* on Ch 16.

PUBLIC HOLIDAYS New Year's Day, Easter Mon, Labour Day (1 May), Ascension Day, Whit Mon, National Day (21 July), Feast of the Assumption (15 Aug), All Saints' Day (1 Nov), Armistice Day (11 Nov), King's Birthday or Fete de la Dynastie (15 Nov), Christmas Day.

RULES: Hbr police are strict about yachts using their engines entering hbr. If sails are used as well, hoist a ▼. Yachts may not navigate within 200m of shore (MLWS).

INLAND WATERWAYS: *Immatriculatieplaat* (licence plates) are required for all yachts on the Flemish waterways. These plates cost 1000Bef (1996) and are obtainable from: 2000 ANTWERPEN, Markgravestraat 16. ☎ 03/232.98.05; or from offices in Brussels and other cities. Boats should fly the 'drapeau de navigation', a R flag with W □ in centre. Belgian Competence requirements for helmsmen are the same as the Dutch (RH col).
Note: More info from Belgian Tourist Office, 29 Princes St, London W1R 7RG, ☎ 0171-6290230, 🖷 6290454; or Federation Royale Belge du Yachting, FRYB/KBJV, PB 241 Bouchoutlaan, 1020 Brussels, Belgium.

NETHERLANDS

PROVINCES are given in lieu of 'counties' in the UK.

CHARTS The following Dutch charts are quoted:
a. Zeekaarten (equivalent to AC); issued by the Royal Netherlands Navy Hydrographer, and updated by Dutch Notices to Mariners; available from chart agents.
b. Dutch Yacht Charts (DYC) "Kaarten voor Kust-en Binnenwateren"; issued every March by the Hydrographer in 8 sets, booklet format (54 x 38cm), covering coastal and inland waters.
c. ANWB Waterkaarten (ANWB); 18 charts of inland waterways (lettered A to S, excluding Q) .

TIME ZONE is –0100, which is allowed for in tidal predictions, but no provision is made for daylight saving schemes as indicated by the non-shaded areas (see 9.1.2).

HARBOURS The term marina is little used; most yacht hbrs are private clubs or Watersport Associations (WSV or WV): *Gem (Gemeentelijke)* = municipal. Sometimes (in Belgium also) berth-holders show a green tally if a berth is free, or a red tally if returning same day; but best to check with Hr Mr. Duty-free fuel (coloured red) is not available for pleasure craft. A tourist tax of f1.00/person/night is often levied.

CUSTOMS Main customs/ports of entry are Breskens, Vlissingen, Roompotsluis*, Hoek van Holland, Maassluis, Vlaardingen, Schiedam, Rotterdam, Scheveningen, IJmuiden, Den Helder, Harlingen, Vlieland*, West Terschelling, Lauwersoog and Delfzijl. No entry/customs at Stellendam, Den Oever or Kornwerderzand. *Summer only.

BUOYAGE Buoys are often named by the abbreviations of the banks or chans which they mark (e.g. VL = Vliestroom). A division buoy has the abbreviations of both chans meeting there, eg VL2-SG2 = as above, plus Schuitengat. Some chans are marked by withies: SHM bound ⟰; PHM unbound ⟱. On tidal flats (e.g. Friesland) where the direction of main flood stream is uncertain, bound withies are on the S side of a chan and unbound on the N side. In minor chans the buoyage may be moved without notice to accommodate changes.
The SIGNI buoyage system is used on some inland waters, including the IJsselmeer (see 10.20.25), but not on the Westerschelde, Waddenzee, Eems and Dollard.

SIGNALS Traffic signals The standard French/Belgian system is not used in the Netherlands. Where possible the local system is given.

Sluicing signals The following signals may be shown:
By day: A blue board, with the word 'SPUIEN' on it; often in addition to the night signal of 3 ®in a △.

Visual storm signals Lt sigs only are shown day and night, as per the International System (see 10.15.8), at Vlissingen, Hoek van Holland, Amsterdam, IJmuiden, Den Helder, West Terschelling, Harlingen, Eierland, Ameland, Oostmahorn, Schiermonnikoog, Zoutkamp and Delfzijl.

Inland waterways
Bridge signals (shown on each side):
To request bridges to open sound 'K' (—·—).
Ⓖ = Bridge open.   Ⓨ = You may pass under this arch.
Ⓡ = Bridge closed (opens on request).
Ⓡ over Ⓖ = Bridge about to open.
2 Ⓡ (vert) = Bridge out of use.
2 Ⓖ (vert) = Bridge open but not in use (you may pass).

Railway bridges
Opening times of railway bridges are in a free annual leaflet '*Openingstijden Spoorwegbruggen*' available from ANWB, L & A/Wat, Postbus 93200, 2509 BA, Den Haag; (send A5 sae with international reply coupon).

RADIO TELEPHONE Use low power setting (1 watt), except for emergencies and public correspondence. Monitor TSS info broadcasts and make contact on VTS sector channels. Note: Do not use Ch M in Dutch waters, where it is a salvage frequency; Ch 31 is for Dutch marinas (little used).

TELEPHONE To call UK from the Netherlands, dial 00-44; then the UK area code minus the prefix 0, followed by the number required. To call the Netherlands from the UK dial 00-31 then the area code minus the prefix 0, plus number.
Emergencies: Fire, Police, Ambulance, dial 112.

MARINE RESCUE CO-ORDINATION is the task of the Coast Guard Centre at IJmuiden which keeps watch H24 on VHF Ch 16, 2182Khz and 500Khz; ☎ (0255) 534344; 🖷 523496.

PUBLIC HOLIDAYS New Year's Day, Easter Mon, Queen's Birthday (30 April), Liberation Day (5 May), Ascension Day, Whit Mon, Christmas and Boxing Days.

INLAND WATERWAYS: All craft must carry a copy of the waterway regulations, *Binnenvaart Politiereglement (BPR)*, as given in the current ANWB publication *Almanak voor Watertoerisme, Vol 1* (written in Dutch). At present craft >15m LOA or capable of more than 20kph (11kn) must be commanded by the holder of a Certificate of Competence. On lakes, rivers and canals this may be the International or Helmsman's Overseas Certificate of Competence, but the RYA Coastal Skipper (or higher) Certificate of Competence is required for navigation on the Schelde, Waddensee and IJsselmeer.
Note: Further information, including a useful publication 'Watersports Paradise', can be obtained from the Dutch Tourism Board, 25 Buckingham Gate, London, SW1E 6LD, ☎ 0171-931 0707; or the Royal Netherland Embassy, 12a Kensington Palace Gdns, London W8 4QU ☎ 0171-229 1594.

10.20.8 DUTCH GLOSSARY   **See 1.4.2**

NIEUWPOORT
(NIEUPORT)

10-20-9

Belgium, West Flanders 51°09'·40N 02°43'·23E   Rtg 2-1-2

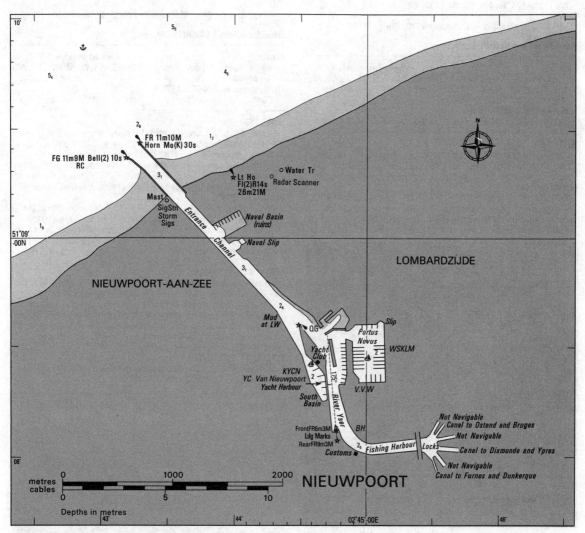

CHARTS
AC 125, 1872, *2449*; Belgian 101, D11; DYC 1801; SHOM 7214; ECM 1010; Imray C30; Stanfords 1, 19, 20

TIDES
+0105 Dover; ML 2·7; Duration 0515; Zone −0100

Standard Port VLISSINGEN (→)

Times				Height (metres)			
High Water		Low Water		MHWS	MHWN	MLWN	MLWS
0300	0900	0400	1000	4·7	3·9	0·8	0·3
1500	2100	1600	2200				
Differences NIEUWPOORT							
−0110	−0050	−0035	−0045	+0·6	+0·5	+0·4	+0·1

SHELTER
Good except in strong NW'lies. There are two yacht hbrs, access H24, run by three YCs: Royal YC of Nieuwpoort (**KYCN**) to the SW gets very full; but there is always room in the Portus Novus, run by the Air Force YC (**WSKLM**) at the N and E side; and **VVW-N**ieuwpoort to the S and centre.

NAVIGATION
WPT 51°10'·00N 02°42'·00E, 308°/128° from/to ent, 0·90M. The bar (1·5m) is liable to silt up but there is usually sufficient water for yachts. At sp the stream reaches 2kn across the ent. The 1M long ent chan to both yacht hbrs is dredged, although levels can drop to about 2m. Note: For activity at firing range E of Nieuwpoort, call range officer on Ch 67; range is not used mid-June to end Sept.

LIGHTS AND MARKS
Lt ho Fl (2) R 14s 26m 21M; conspic R tr, W bands. E pier head FR 11m 10M, W tr, vis 025°-250°, 307°-347°, Horn Mo (K) 30s. W pier head, FG 11m 9M, W tr, vis 025°-250°, 284°-324°, Bell (2) 10s, RC.
IPTS from root of W pier, plus: 2 cones, points together or Fl Bu lt = No departure for craft < 6m LOA. Watch out for other tfc sigs, especially STOP sign near exit from Novus Portus, shown in conjunction with IPTS.

RADIO TELEPHONE
VHF Ch 09 16 (H24).

TELEPHONE (Dial code 058)
Hr Mr/Pilots 233000, 🕾 231575; Lock 233050; CG/Marine Police 233045; Marine Rescue Helicopter 311714; ⌗ 233451; Duty Free Store 233433; Ⓗ (Oostende) 707631; Dr 233089; Brit Consul (02) 2179000; Police 234246.

FACILITIES
KYCN (420 + 80 Ⓥ) ☎ 234413, 600BeF, M, FW, C (10 ton), Slip, CH, Gas, ME, El, Sh, V, D, Ⓓ, R, Bar;
WSKLM (500 + Ⓥ) ☎ 233641, 🕾 239845, 300BeF, M, L, FW, C (2 ton mobile), CH, R, Bar;
VVW-N (950 + Ⓥ) ☎ 235232, 🕾 234058, 400BeF, Slip, FW, BH (45 ton), C (15 ton), AC (meters), CH, D, R, Bar, Free bicycles for shopping;
Services: D, L, ME, El, Sh, C (15 ton), Gaz, CH, SM.
Town P, D, V, R, Bar, ⊠, Ⓑ, ⇌, ✈ (Ostend). Ferry: See Ostend. (Fuel can be bought at the hbr by arrangement).

20

OOSTENDE (OSTEND)   10-20-10

Belgium, West Flanders 51°14'·30N 02°55'·18E   Rtg 1-1-1

CHARTS

AC 125, 325, 1872, *2449*; SHOM 7214; ECM 1010; DYC 1801; Imray C30; Stanfords 1, 19, 20

TIDES

+0120 Dover; ML 2·6; Duration 0530; Zone –0100

Standard Port VLISSINGEN (⟶)

Times				Height (metres)			
High Water		Low Water		MHWS	MHWN	MLWN	MLWS
0300	0900	0400	1000	4·7	3·9	0·8	0·3
1500	2100	1600	2200				
Differences OOSTENDE							
–0055	–0040	–0030	–0045	+0·4	+0·4	+0·3	+0·1

SHELTER

Very good, esp in the Mercator Yacht Hbr (1·2m); ent via Montgomery Dock and lock. NSYC (2·7m) and ROYC may be uncomfortable due ferries and/or strong W/NW winds.

NAVIGATION

WPT 51°15'·00N 02°53'·97E, 308°/128° from/to ent, 0·98M. Avoid the offshore banks esp in bad weather; appr via West Diep inside Stroombank or from the NW via Kwintebank and buoyed chan. Busy ferry/commercial hbr.

LIGHTS AND MARKS

Europa Centrum bldg (105m) is conspic 3ca SSW of ent. Lt ho Fl (3) 10s 63m 27M, conspic W tr with 2 sinusoidal blue bands, RC. Ldg lts 128°, both FR 12/18m 4M, both X on W pylons, R bands, vis 051°-201°. W pier, FG 12m 10M, W tr, vis 057°-327°, Bell 4s.
E pier FR 13m 12M, W tr, vis 333°-243°, horn Mo (OE) 30s. IPTS shown from E pier, plus QY lts = keep clear of ent and chan, ferry arr/dep; repeated at Montgomery Dock. 2 ▼, points together or Fl Bu lt = No departure for craft < 6m LOA; (shown at ent to Montgomery dock).

RADIO TELEPHONE

Port VHF Ch 10 16 (H24). All vessels inc yachts, call *Signal Post* Ch 09 to ent/dep. Mercator lock/yacht hbr Ch 14 (H24).

TELEPHONE (Dial code 059)

Hr Mr 330905, ⚓ 330387; Life Saving 701100; ⌗ 322009; Police 500925; Ⓗ 707637; Weather (no code needed): 1603 (Dutch), 1703 (French); Brit Consul (02) 2179000.

FACILITIES

Berthing fees: See 10.20.9. **Montgomery Dock** (70 + 50 Ⓥ) YC, Bar, R, FW, Slip; **North Sea YC** (N end of Montgomery Dock) ☎ 702754, FW, AB, R, Bar; **Mercator Yacht Hbr** (450+50 Ⓥ) ☎ 705762, FW, D, AC, C, Slip; **Royal Oostende YC** (1M SE up Voorhaven, 160 + 40 Ⓥ) ☎ 321452, Slip, M, FW, AB, C (½ ton), R, Bar; Access via Achterhaven to the Belgian, Dutch and French canals. **Services:** ME, CH, Sh, El, SM, D at FV hbr or by tanker ☎ 500874. **Town** All amenities, ⇌, ✈. Ferry: Ramsgate.

BLANKENBERGE   10-20-11

Belgium, West Flanders 51°18'·95N 03°06'·60E   Rtg 3-1-2

CHARTS

AC 325, 1872, *2449*; DYC 1801; Imray C30; Stanfords 1, 19

TIDES

+0130 Dover; ML 2·5; Duration 0535; Zone –0100

Standard Port VLISSINGEN (⟶)

Times		Height (metres)			
High Water	Low Water	MHWS	MHWN	MLWN	MLWS
All times	All times	4·7	3·9	0·8	0·3
Differences BLANKENBERGE					
–0040	–0040	–0·3	–0·1	+0·3	+0·1

SHELTER

Good. Keep to port, past the FV hbr, to the old Yacht Hbr (2·4m); VNZ pontoons are on N side and SYCB to the E. Or turn stbd into new Hbr and marina (2·4m) with 15 pontoons, numbered clockwise I - XV from the N; these are controlled by VNZ, SYCB and VVW. From early Apr to late Sept Blankenberge is a Port of Entry, with Customs.

NAVIGATION

WPT 51°19'·60N 03°05'·40E, 314°/134° from/to piers, 1M. Do not attempt entry in strong NW'lies. Beware strong tides (& fishing lines) across ent. Access HW ±2; ent chan between piers silts, only dredged 1·5m in season. Do not try to enter/depart LW±1½, especially at sp. Oct-end May, only ent/leave HW±1, unless depth is pre-checked.

LIGHTS AND MARKS

Conspic high-rise blocks E of lt ho, Fl (2) 8s 30m 20M, W tr B top. Ldg lts 134°, both FR 5/8m 3M, (Red X on mast) show the best water. A Water tr is conspic on E side of new Hbr. FS by lt ho shows 2 ▼, points inward, or Fl Bu lt = No departure for craft < 6m LOA (small craft warning). Caution: 3 unlit Y SPM buoys and one Fl (4) Y 20s lie about 400m off hbr ent and to E and W.

RADIO TELEPHONE

Marinas VHF Ch 08. *Blankenberge Rescue* Ch 08; or relay Zeebrugge Traffic Centre Ch 69.

TELEPHONE (Dial code 050)

Hr Mr: use VNZ, SYCB or VVW Tel Nos; ⌗ 544223; Police 429842; Dr 333668; Ⓗ 413701; Brit Consul (02) 2179000.

FACILITIES

Fees: Based on beam, ie 3m = 400BeF; 3.5m = 500 BeF; plus 100BeF for every additional 0·25m.
Old Yacht Hbr (mainly locals): **YC Vrije Noordzeezeilers (VNZ)** ☎ 429150, AC, M, FW, Bar, R; **Scarphout YC (SYCB)** ☎ 411420, C (10/2½ ton), CH, FW, AC, Slip, Bar, R; **New Hbr** (best for visitors): **Marina (VVW)** ☎ 417536, AC, FW, Bar, Ⓓ, Slip, P, D (hoco, duty free), ME, Ch, Ⓒ, El, CM, CH, C (20 ton). **Town** Gaz, R, Bar, ⊠, Ⓑ, ⇌, ✈ Ostend.

ZEEBRUGGE 10-20-12

Belgium, West Flanders 51°21'·80N 03°11'·60E   Rtg 1-1-2

CHARTS

AC 97, 325, 1872, *2449*; Zeekaart 1441; DYC 1801, 1803; Imray C30; Stanfords 1, 19

TIDES

+0110 Dover; ML 2·4; Duration 0535; Zone –0100

Standard Port VLISSINGEN (→)

Times				Height (metres)			
High Water		Low Water		MHWS	MHWN	MLWN	MLWS
0300	0900	0400	1000	4·7	3·9	0·8	0·3
1500	2100	1600	2200				
Differences ZEEBRUGGE							
–0035	–0015	–0020	–0035	+0·1	+0·1	+0·3	+0·1

SHELTER

Very good in the Yacht Hbr, access H24. Caution on ent/dep due to limited vis and fast FVs; give all jetties a wide berth. Brugge is 6M inland by canal.

NAVIGATION

WPT Scheur-Zand ECM By, Q (3) 10s, 51°23'·70N 03°07'·68E, 309°/129° from/to ent, 3·1M. Beware strong currents in hbr apprs (up to 4kn at HW –1) and major WIP on container terminal in outer hbr N of Leopold Dam. Zeebrugge is the main Belgian fishing port and a ferry terminal, so keep clear of FVs and ferries. When LNG-Gas Tanker is under way all movements prohib in hbr/apprs .

LIGHTS AND MARKS

Heist (W inner bkwtr hd) Oc WR 15s 22m 20/18M, Gy ○ tr. Ldg lts toward Vissershaven for marina at W end:
(1) 136°: Oc 5s 22/45m 8M, vis 131°-141° synch (H24).
(2) 154°: Front Oc WR 6s 20m 3M, R △, W bands; rear Oc 6s 34m 3M, R ▽, W bands, synch (H24).
(3) 220°: Front 2FW neon (vert) 30/22m; rear FW neon 30m. Both W concrete columns, B bands.
(4) 193°: Front 2FR (vert) 30/22; rear FR 29m. Both W concrete columns, R bands.

IPTS are shown at NE end of Leopold Dam. A QY lt at S side of Visserhaven prohibits ent/dep Visserhaven.

RADIO TELEPHONE

Port Control VHF Ch 71 (H24). Marina Ch 71. Locks Ch 68.

TELEPHONE (Dial code 050)

Hr Mr 543241; Port Control 546867; Lock Mr 543231; CG 545072; Sea Saving Service 544007; ⌗ 54.54.55; Police 544148; Dr 544590; Ⓗ 320832; Brit Consul (02) 2179000.

FACILITIES

Berthing fees: See 10.20.9.
Yacht Hbr (100 + 70) ☎ 544903, AB, FW, Slip, Sh, CH, D;
Royal Belgian SC ☎ 544903, M, AB; **Alberta** (R, Bar of RBSC) ☎ 544197; **Services:** ME, El, CH.
Town P, D, FW, ME, El, Sh, CH, Gaz, V, R, Bar, ⊠, Ⓑ, ≋ 15 mins to Brugge, tram to Oostende, ✈ (Ostend).
Ferry: Zeebrugge-Felixstowe/Hull.

BRESKENS 10-20-13

Zeeland 51°24'·02N 03°34'·15E   Rtg 1-1-1

CHARTS

AC 325, 120; Zeekaart 120, 101; DYC 1801, 1803; Imray C30; Stanfords 1, 19

TIDES

+0210 Dover; ML no data; Duration 0600; Zone –0100

Standard Port VLISSINGEN (→)

Times				Height (metres)			
High Water		Low Water		MHWS	MHWN	MLWN	MLWS
0300	0900	0400	1000	4·7	3·9	0·8	0·3
1500	2100	1600	2200				
Differences BRESKENS: Use VLISSINGEN figures							
CADZAND (7M WSW)							
–0030	–0025	–0020	–0025	–0·2	–0·2	–0·2	–0·1

SHELTER

Good in all winds; access H24, 5m at ent. Ⓥ berth on the N finger (4m). ⌕ off Plaat van Breskens, in fine weather, not in commercial/fishing hbr. Beware fast ferries.

NAVIGATION

WPT SS-VH NCM By, Q, 51°24'·75N 03°34'·00E, 353°/173° from/to W mole lt (within W sector), 0·69M. Beware strong tides across the ent. Do not confuse the ent with the ferry port ent, 0·7M WNW, where yachts are prohib.

LIGHTS AND MARKS

Large bldg/silo on centre pier in hbr and two apartment blocks (30m) SE of marina are conspic. W mole hd F WRG 6m; vis R090°-128°, W128°-157°, G157°-169·5°, W169·5°-173°, R173°-194°, G194°-296°, W296°-300°, R300°-320°, G320°-090°; Horn Mo (U) 30s. E mole hd FR 5m.
Nieuwe Sluis lt, Oc WRG 10s 28m 14/10M, B 8-sided tr, W bands, is 1·2M W of ferry hbr.

RADIO TELEPHONE

Marina VHF Ch 31.

TELEPHONE (Dial code 0117)

Hr Mr 381902; ⌗ 382610; Police (0117) 453156; Dr 381566/381956; Ⓗ (0117) 459000; Brit Embassy (070) 3645800.

FACILITIES

Marina (Jachthaven Breskens) ☎ 381902, f30, FW, ▣, AC;
YC Breskens ☎ 383278, R, Bar;
Services: SM, CH, D & P (fuel pontoon is in FV hbr), Gaz, chart agent, BY, C (15 ton), El, Ⓔ, ME, Sh, Slip.
Town V, R, Bar, ⊠, Ⓑ, Gas, ≋ (Flushing), ✈ (Ostend or Brussels). Ferry: See Vlissingen.

20

TERNEUZEN   10-20-14

Zeeland 51°20'·62N 03°49'·75E   Rtg 1-1-2

CHARTS
AC 120; Zeekaart 1443; DYC 1803.2; Imray C30
TIDES
+0230 Dover; ML 2·5; Duration 0555; Zone –0100

Standard Port VLISSINGEN (→)

Times				Height (metres)			
High Water		Low Water		MHWS	MHWN	MLWN	MLWS
0300	0900	0400	1000	4·7	3·9	0·8	0·3
1500	2100	1600	220				
Differences TERNEUZEN							
+0020	+0020	+0020	+0030	+0·4	+0·3	+0·1	0·0

SHELTER
Very good except in strong NW winds. Marina in the Veerhaven is tidal and exposed to NE. Or enter the E lock (Oostsluis) and see Lockmaster for berth as on chartlet. Yachts are prohib in W Hbr and lock (Westsluis).
NAVIGATION
WPT No 18 PHM Buoy, Iso R 8s, 51°20'·95N 03°48'·83E, 299°/119° from/to Veerhaven ent, 0·65M. The Terneuzen-Gent canal is 17M long with 3 bridges, min clearance 6·5m when closed.
LIGHTS AND MARKS
The Dow Chemical works and storage tanks are conspic 2M W of hbr. For the Veerhaven, the water tr to SE and the Oc WRG lt on W mole are conspic. When entry prohib, a second R lt is shown below FR on E mole. Sigs for Oostsluis: R lts = entry prohib; G lts = entry permitted.
RADIO TELEPHONE
Call: *Havendienst Terneuzen* VHF Ch 11 (H24); also info broadcasts every H+00 for vessels in the basins & canal. East lock Ch 18. For Terneuzen-Gent canal call on Ch 11 and keep watch during transit. Contact Zelzate Bridge (call: *Uitkijk Zelzate*) direct on Ch 11, other bridges through Terneuzen or, at the S end, *Havendienst Gent* Ch 05 11 (H24). See also 10.20.15.
TELEPHONE (Dial code 0115)
Hr Mr 612161; CG (0255) 534344 (H24); ⌗ 612377; Police 613017; Ⓗ 688000; Dr 112; Brit Consul (020) 6764343.

FACILITIES
Yacht Hbr (120) ☎ 697089, Slip, ME, El, Sh, BH (15 ton), FW; **WSV de Honte YC** ☎ 617633, AB f21.84, L, FW, ▣; **Neuzen YC** ☎ 614411, AB f16.70, M, L, FW; **Services:** ME, El, BY, P, D, L, FW, C (40 ton), AB, Sh, Gaz. **Town** P, D, CH, V, R, Bar, ⌧, Ⓑ, ✈ (Ghent) Ferry: See Vlissingen.

WESTERSCHELDE   10-20-15

Zeeland

CHARTS
AC 120, 139, 325; Zeekaart 1443; DYC 1803; Imray C30
TIDES
+0200 Dover; ML Hansweert 2·6, Westkapelle 2·0, Bath 2·8; Duration 0555; Zone –0100

Standard Port VLISSINGEN (→)

Times				Height (metres)			
High Water		Low Water		MHWS	MHWN	MLWN	MLWS
0300	0900	0400	1000	4·7	3·9	0·8	0·3
1500	2100	1600	2200				
Differences WESTKAPELLE							
–0025	–0015	–0010	–0025	–0·5	–0·5	0·0	0·0
HANSWEERT							
+0100	+0050	+0040	+0100	+0·7	+0·6	+0·1	0·0
BATH							
+0125	+0115	+0115	+0140	+1·1	+0·9	+0·1	0·0

SHELTER AND FACILITIES
Some hbrs for yachts between Terneuzen and Antwerpen (38M) are listed below in sequence from seaward:
ELLEWOUTSDIJK, 51°23'·00N 03°49'·00E. DYC 1803.2. HW +0200 and +0·3m on Vlissingen; ML 2·6m. Small, safe hbr; unlit. Dries, easy access HW ±3; 1·5m at MLWS. Hr Mr ☎ (0113) 548248 FW, D, Gaz; **YC Ellewoutsdijk** ☎ 548446.
HOEDEKENSKERKE, 51°25'·25N 03·55'·00E. DYC 1803.3. Disused ferry hbr (dries) on N bank, abeam ☆ Iso WRG 2s R ☐ tr, W band. Access HW–2½ to +3 for 1m draft. **YC WV Hoedekenskerke** ☎ (0113) 63x259; Ⓥ berths, P, D, Gaz, FW, ME. **Town** ⌧, Ⓑ, ⇌ (Goes).
HANSWEERT, 51°26'·40N 04°00'·75E. DYC 1803.3. Tidal differences above. Can be used temporarily, but it is the busy ent to Zuid Beveland canal. Lt Oc WRG 10s, R lattice tr, W band, at ent. Waiting berths outside lock on E side. Ⓥ berths in inner hbr, W side; **Services:** ME, BY, P, D, C (17 ton), CH, R. **Town** ⌧, Ⓑ, ⇌ (Kruiningen-Yerseke).
WALSOORDEN, 51°23'·00N 04°02'·00E. DYC 1803.3. HW is +0110 and +0·7m on Vlissingen; ML 2·6m. Prone to swell. SHM buoy 57A, L Fl G 8s, is 1ca N of ent. Ldg lts 220° both Oc 3s. Hbr ent marked with FG and FR. Yacht basin dead ahead on ent to hbr, depths 2 to 2·8m. *Zandvliet Radio* VHF Ch 12. Hr Mr ☎ (0114) 681235, FW, Slip; **Services:** Gas, P, D, BY, ME, El. **Town** R, Bar, ⌧.
PAAL, 51°21'·30N 04°06'·70E. DYC 1803.3. HW +0120 and +0·8m on Vlissingen; ML 2·7m. Unlit, drying yacht hbr on W side at river mouth, ent marked by withy. Appr from No. 63 SHM buoy, L Fl G 8s, and Tide gauge, Fl (5) Y 20s across drying Speelmansgat. *Zandvliet Radio* VHF Ch 12. Hr Mr ☎ (0114) 315548; **Jachthaven** AC, FW; **Services:** V, P, D, Gaz, ME, El, R.

DOEL, Antwerpen, 51°18'·70N 04°16'·15E. DYC 1803.5. HW +0100 and +0·7m on Vlissingen. Small drying hbr on W bank. Ldg lts 185·5°: front Fl WRG 3s; rear Fl 3s, synch. N pier hd lt, Oc WR 5s. Hr Mr ☎ (03) 7733072; **YC de Noord** ☎ 7733669, R, Bar, FW.
LILLO, Antwerpen, 51°18'·24N 04°17'·40E. DYC 1803.5. 1M SE of Doel on opp bank; small drying hbr for shoal-draft only; HW±3. Landing stage in river has Oc WRG 10s. Hr Mr (035) 686456; **YC Scaldis.**

WESTERSCHELDE *continued*

NAVIGATION
WPTs: See Breskens (10.20.13), Terneuzen (10.20.14) and Vlissingen (10.20.17). The approaches into the estuary from seaward are described in detail under 10.20.17; also the busy junction area between Vlissingen and Breskens. The Westerschelde chan winds through a mass of well marked sand-banks. It is the waterway to Antwerpen and Gent (via canal), very full of shipping and barges (which may not always conform to the rules; beware unpredict-able actions). It is necessary to work the tides, which average 2½kn, more at springs. Yachts should keep to the edge of main chan. Alternative chans must be used with caution, particular going downstream on the ebb.

LIGHTS AND MARKS
The apprs to Westerschelde are well lit by lt ho's: on the S shore at Kruishoofd and Nieuwe Sluis, and on the N shore at Westkapelle. See 10.20.4. The main fairways are, for the most part, defined by ldg lts and by the W sectors of the many Dir lts.

RADIO TELEPHONE
Commercial traffic in the Westerschelde must comply with a comprehensive VTS which covers from the N Sea Outer Apprs up-river to Antwerp. Yachts should listen at all times on the VHF Ch for the area in which they are (see next column). Do not transmit, unless called; if you have a problem and need help, state vessel's name, position and the nature of the problem. Dutch is the primary language, English secondary.
If you have an **emergency**, call initially on the working/channel in use; you may then be switched to *Schelde Cordination Centre* (SCC at Vlissingen) Ch 67.

Seven Traffic Centres control the following areas; see also Fig 10 (6) for diagram:
In offshore approaches:
(1) *Wandelaar* Ch 65 (NW of Oostende);
(2) *Zeebrugge* Ch 69 (W, N and E of Zeebrugge);
(3) *Steenbank* Ch 64 (NW of Vlissingen).
Within the Westerschelde:
(4) *Vlissingen* Ch 14 (Vlissingen to E2A/PvN SPR buoys at approx 51°24'N 03°44'E);
(5) *Terneuzen* Ch 03 (thence to Nos 32/35 buoys at approx 51°23'N 03°57'E);
(6) *Hansweert* Ch 65 (thence to Nos 46/55 buoys at approx 51°24'N 04°02'E);
(7) *Zandvliet* Ch 12 (thence to Antwerpen).
Also *Terneuzen* Ch 11 covers the Terneuzen-Gent Canal. In addition, 16 unmanned Radar stns within the 7 Traffic areas provide radar and hbr info on separate VHF Ch's.
Broadcast reports of visibility, met, tidal data and ship movements are made in Dutch and English at:
Every H+55 on Ch 14 by *Vlissingen*;
Every H+00 on Ch 11 by *Terneuzen*;
Every H+35 on Ch 12 by *Zandvliet*.

ANTWERPEN (ANTWERP)   10-20-16

Antwerpen 51°13'·85N 04°23'·77E   Rtg 3-1-1

CHARTS
AC 139; Zeekaart 1443; DYC 1803.5

TIDES
+0342 Dover; ML 2·9; Duration 0605; Zone –0100

Standard Port VLISSINGEN (→)

Times				Height (metres)			
High Water		Low Water		MHWS	MHWN	MLWN	MLWS
0300	0900	0400	1000	4·7	3·9	0·8	0·3
1500	2100	1600	2200				
Differences ANTWERPEN							
+0128	+0116	+0121	+0144	+1·1	+0·9	0·0	0·0

SHELTER
Excellent in Jachthaven Antwerpen (marina) on W bank, 4ca SW of Kattendijksluis and ½M from city centre (via two tunnels). Access by lock HW ±1 (H24, 1 Apr-31 Oct)). In winter lock opens only by arrangement. A T-shaped ferry pontoon is 2½ca N of ent, with waiting berths on the inshore side; also a waiting buoy (IMALSO) is off the ent.

NAVIGATION
For Westerschelde see 10.20.13/14/15/17. It is advised to check off the buoys coming up-river. After No 116 PHM buoy, Iso R 8s, there is a gap of 1.5M before reaching No. 107 SHM buoy, Iso G 8s, which marks a 90° bend in the river onto S and is close to the pontoon (see SHELTER). No 109 SHM buoy, Iso G 8s, is 250m NE of marina ent.

LIGHTS AND MARKS
The marina is marked by a concrete pile, black topmark and lt, F WR 9m 3M, (W shore-283°, R 283°-shore). Lock entry and depth signals are no longer used

RADIO TELEPHONE
Call *Jachthaven Antwerpen* VHF Ch 09 (HW±1). Call Port Operations *Antwerpen Havendienst* Ch 74 (H24) and for Safety; VTS Ch 18; Radar Ch 02 60; Bridges Ch 13.

TELEPHONE (Dial code 03)
Hr Mr 2190895, ☎ 2196748; ⌗ 2340840; Police 321840; Ⓗ 2177111.

FACILITIES
Jachthaven Antwerpen Marina ☎ 2190895, FW, D, R, V, Gaz, El, Sh, AC, C (1·5 ton), Slip; **Royal YC van België** ☎ 2192682, Bar, R, M, C (5 ton), D, P, CH; FW, L, Slip; **Kon. Liberty YC** ☎ 2191147; **Services:** BY, ME, BH, ACA, DYC Agent.
City All facilities, ⊠, Ⓑ, ⇌, ✈. Ferry: Ostend-Ramsgate.

VLISSINGEN (FLUSHING) 10-20-17

Zeeland 51°26'·36N 03°34'·70E (Koopmanshaven). Rtg 1-3-1

CHARTS
AC 120, 1872, 1874; Zeekaart 1442, 1443, 1533; DYC 1801.3, 1803.8; Imray C30; Stanfords 1, 19

TIDES
+0215 Dover; ML 2·3; Duration 0555; Zone –0100
NOTE: Vlissingen is a Standard Port. Tidal predictions for each day of the year are given opposite.

SHELTER
Very good in both yacht hbrs:
1. **Michiel de Ruyter** marina (2·9m) in the Vissershaven has 6m wide ent, approached from the Koopmanshaven. Storm barrier is open 1 Apr-1 Nov. Sill with 1·0m water at MLWS; check depth gauge on barrier wall. Small swing bridge (pedestrian) is operated by Hr Mr 0800-2000LT, with R/G tfc lts. The bridge is open 2000-0800LT, but only for yachts to leave; ®® (vert) tfc lts prohibit arrival from sea, because the marina is not lit.
2. **VVW Schelde** (3m) is near the ent to the Walcheren Canal. Entering the Buitenhaven beware ferries. Keep to port and S of ferry terminal for the locks, which operate H24; yachts use smallest, most N'ly lock. Waiting possible on piles to SE. Marina is to NW, past both Binnenhaven.

NAVIGATION
WPT H-SS NCM buoy, Q, 51°25'·97N 03°37'·54E, 125°/ 305° from/to Buitenhaven ent, 0·95M.
Commercial Shipping: Yachts should keep clear of the busy shipping chans, ie Wielingen from the SW, Scheur from the W, and Oostgat from the NW. To the E of where Wielingen and Scheur merge (NCM buoy S-W), be aware of the major ship anchorages: Wielingen Noord and Zuid either side of the fairway as defined by buoys W6, 7, 9, 10 and Songa. Close to the E, Vlissingen Roads are also a major anchorage (N of buoys SS-VH to SS7, and SW of H-SS). There is a precautionary TSS area between this anch and Vlissingen itself. Yachts are forbidden to sail in the TSS fairways. Ocean-going ships often manoeuvre off the town to transfer pilots. Fast ferries frequently enter/leave the Buitenhaven terminal.
Recommended Yacht routes: From the SW there are few dangers. After Zeebrugge, keep S of the Wielingen chan buoys (W1-9). Off Breskens be aware of the fast ferries to/from Vlissingen; continue E to SS3 buoy, then cross to Vlissingen on a N'ly track, keeping W of H-SS buoy.

From the W, keep clear of the Scheur chan by crossing to the S of Wielingen as soon as practicable.
From N, by day, in vicinity of Kaloo or DR1 buoys, follow the Geul van de Rassen, Deurloo and Spleet chans to SP4 buoy. Turn S to cross Wielingen at 90° between buoys W6 and W8; thence via W9 as per the SW approach.
A variation after Deurloo is to use the Nollegeul channel (NG1-15), crossing quickly to the Vlissingen shore as and when traffic in Oostgat permits.
Another route, slightly further offshore, is to skirt the NW side of Kaloo bank to Botkil-W buoy, thence SE via Geul van de Walvischstaart to SP5 and 4 buoys.
None of these N'ly routes is lit. By night the Oostgat can be used with caution keeping outside the SW edge of the buoyed chan.

LIGHTS AND MARKS
From NW, Oostgat ldg lts 117°: Front Leugenaar, Oc R 5s 5m 7M; rear Sardijngeul, 550m from front, Oc WRG 5s 10m 12/8M, R △, W bands on R and W mast.
Note: Conspic Radar Tr (close NW of Koopmanshaven) shows a Fl Y lt to warn if ships are approaching from the NW, ie around the blind arc from Oostgat/Sardijngeul.
The lt ho at the root of the W bkwtr of Koopmanshaven is brown metal framework tr, Iso WRG 3s 15m 12/9M. On S side of de Ruyter marina is a conspic W metal framework tr (50m), floodlit.
Buitenhaven tfc sigs from mole W side of ent:
R flag or extra ® near FR on W mole hd = Entry prohib.

RADIO TELEPHONE
Havenschap Vlissingen Ch 09. Lock & bridge info Ch 22. See also Westerschelde (10.20.15) for VTS.

TELEPHONE (Dial code 0118)
Hr Mr 468080; East Hbr Port Authority 478741; Schelde Tfc Coordination Centre 424790; Buitenhaven Lock 412372; ⌗ 484600; Police 415050; Ⓗ 425000; Dr 412233; Brit Consul (020) 6764343.

FACILITIES
Michiel de Ruyter (100 + 40 visitors) ☎ 414498, f27.42, D, FW, AC, Bar, R, YC, ▣;
Jachthaven 'VVW Schelde' (90 + 50 visitors) ☎ 465912, f13.50, AC, Bar, C (10 ton), CH, D, FW, R, ▣, M, Slip, (Access H24 via lock), approx 1km by road from ferry terminal; **Services**: BY, Sh, ME, Sh, SM, bikes for hire..
Town P, D, CH, V, R, Bar, ✉, Ⓑ, ⇌, ✈ (Antwerpen).
Ferry: Vlissingen-Sheerness; local to Breskens.

TIME ZONE –0100
(Dutch Standard Time)
Subtract 1 hour for UT
For Dutch Summer Time add ONE hour in non-shaded areas

NETHERLANDS – VLISSINGEN (FLUSHING)

LAT 51°27′N   LONG 3°36′E

TIMES AND HEIGHTS OF HIGH AND LOW WATERS

YEAR **1998**

JANUARY

Day	Time	m	Day	Time	m
1 TH	0329 / 1000 / 1546 / 2216	4.8 / 0.2 / 4.9 / 0.5	**16** F	0416 / 1035 / 1631 / 2240	4.6 / 0.3 / 4.6 / 0.6
2 F	0410 / 1048 / 1630 / 2300	4.7 / 0.2 / 4.8 / 0.5	**17** SA	0447 / 1109 / 1707 / 2316	4.5 / 0.4 / 4.5 / 0.7
3 SA	0455 / 1136 / 1717 / 2348	4.6 / 0.2 / 4.7 / 0.6	**18** SU	0526 / 1145 / 1747 / 2345	4.4 / 0.5 / 4.4 / 0.8
4 SU	0546 / 1226 / 1811	4.5 / 0.2 / 4.6	**19** M	0606 / 1215 / 1826	4.3 / 0.6 / 4.2
5 M	0036 / 0639 / 1316 / 1912	0.7 / 4.3 / 0.3 / 4.4	**20** TU	0025 / 0646 / 1244 / 1915	0.8 / 4.1 / 0.7 / 4.0
6 TU	0130 / 0745 / 1410 / 2022	0.8 / 4.2 / 0.4 / 4.2	**21** W	0106 / 0736 / 1339 / 2011	0.9 / 3.9 / 0.8 / 3.9
7 W	0236 / 0850 / 1516 / 2129	0.9 / 4.1 / 0.6 / 4.2	**22** TH	0205 / 0836 / 1455 / 2109	1.0 / 3.8 / 0.9 / 3.8
8 TH	0346 / 1001 / 1637 / 2242	0.9 / 4.1 / 0.6 / 4.2	**23** F	0340 / 0946 / 1616 / 2225	1.1 / 3.7 / 0.9 / 3.8
9 F	0506 / 1107 / 1746 / 2346	0.9 / 4.2 / 0.6 / 4.3	**24** SA	0445 / 1055 / 1715 / 2325	1.0 / 3.9 / 0.8 / 4.0
10 SA	0609 / 1208 / 1841	0.7 / 4.4 / 0.5	**25** SU	0546 / 1155 / 1816	0.8 / 4.1 / 0.7
11 SU	0042 / 0706 / 1259 / 1928	4.4 / 0.5 / 4.5 / 0.4	**26** M	0021 / 0640 / 1246 / 1859	4.3 / 0.6 / 4.4 / 0.6
12 M ○	0128 / 0751 / 1347 / 2010	4.5 / 0.4 / 4.7 / 0.4	**27** TU	0106 / 0726 / 1326 / 1945	4.5 / 0.5 / 4.6 / 0.5
13 TU	0216 / 0838 / 1432 / 2050	4.6 / 0.3 / 4.7 / 0.5	**28** W ●	0149 / 0816 / 1406 / 2030	4.6 / 0.3 / 4.8 / 0.4
14 W	0255 / 0920 / 1515 / 2128	4.6 / 0.3 / 4.8 / 0.5	**29** TH	0233 / 0900 / 1449 / 2117	4.8 / 0.1 / 5.0 / 0.3
15 TH	0337 / 0958 / 1552 / 2206	4.6 / 0.3 / 4.7 / 0.6	**30** F	0313 / 0945 / 1531 / 2159	4.8 / 0.2 / 5.0 / 0.3
			31 SA	0355 / 1033 / 1615 / 2247	4.8 / 0.0 / 5.0 / 0.4

FEBRUARY

Day	Time	m	Day	Time	m
1 SU	0439 / 1118 / 1702 / 2329	4.8 / 0.0 / 4.9 / 0.4	**16** M	0455 / 1116 / 1711 / 2315	4.5 / 0.4 / 4.5 / 0.6
2 M	0525 / 1205 / 1752	4.7 / 0.0 / 4.7	**17** TU	0525 / 1139 / 1745 / 2345	4.4 / 0.4 / 4.3 / 0.6
3 TU	0016 / 0615 / 1256 / 1847	0.5 / 4.5 / 0.2 / 4.5	**18** W	0600 / 1210 / 1818	4.3 / 0.5 / 4.2
4 W	0105 / 0715 / 1342 / 1956	0.6 / 4.3 / 0.3 / 4.2	**19** TH	0019 / 0635 / 1256 / 1908	0.7 / 4.1 / 0.6 / 4.0
5 TH	0206 / 0819 / 1445 / 2059	0.8 / 4.1 / 0.5 / 4.0	**20** F	0116 / 0735 / 1345 / 2016	0.8 / 3.9 / 0.8 / 3.8
6 F	0316 / 0936 / 1553 / 2215	0.9 / 4.0 / 0.7 / 3.9	**21** SA	0215 / 0858 / 1504 / 2132	0.9 / 3.8 / 0.9 / 3.7
7 SA	0440 / 1050 / 1725 / 2336	0.9 / 4.0 / 0.7 / 4.0	**22** SU	0400 / 1016 / 1640 / 2249	1.0 / 3.8 / 0.9 / 3.8
8 SU	0556 / 1156 / 1825	0.7 / 4.2 / 0.6	**23** M	0509 / 1125 / 1746 / 2355	0.8 / 4.0 / 0.8 / 4.1
9 M	0035 / 0656 / 1255 / 1915	4.2 / 0.5 / 4.4 / 0.6	**24** TU	0616 / 1222 / 1835	0.6 / 4.3 / 0.6
10 TU	0126 / 0741 / 1341 / 1955	4.4 / 0.4 / 4.6 / 0.5	**25** W	0045 / 0711 / 1307 / 1928	4.4 / 0.4 / 4.6 / 0.5
11 W ○	0205 / 0826 / 1421 / 2031	4.5 / 0.3 / 4.7 / 0.5	**26** TH ●	0129 / 0758 / 1348 / 2015	4.6 / 0.2 / 4.9 / 0.3
12 TH	0242 / 0901 / 1457 / 2106	4.6 / 0.2 / 4.7 / 0.5	**27** F	0210 / 0843 / 1430 / 2058	4.8 / 0.0 / 5.0 / 0.3
13 F	0317 / 0938 / 1532 / 2145	4.6 / 0.2 / 4.7 / 0.5	**28** SA	0253 / 0927 / 1513 / 2143	4.9 / -0.1 / 5.1 / 0.2
14 SA	0352 / 1016 / 1607 / 2216	4.6 / 0.2 / 4.7 / 0.5			
15 SU	0422 / 1046 / 1639 / 2251	4.6 / 0.3 / 4.6 / 0.5			

MARCH

Day	Time	m	Day	Time	m
1 SU	0335 / 1013 / 1556 / 2228	4.9 / -0.2 / 5.1 / 0.2	**16** M	0356 / 1020 / 1608 / 2222	4.6 / 0.3 / 4.6 / 0.4
2 M	0418 / 1058 / 1642 / 2312	4.9 / -0.1 / 4.9 / 0.3	**17** TU	0426 / 1048 / 1639 / 2249	4.6 / 0.3 / 4.5 / 0.5
3 TU	0505 / 1142 / 1729 / 2356	4.8 / 0.0 / 4.7 / 0.4	**18** W	0452 / 1116 / 1710 / 2321	4.5 / 0.4 / 4.4 / 0.5
4 W	0552 / 1225 / 1822	4.7 / 0.1 / 4.5	**19** TH	0522 / 1146 / 1741 / 2349	4.4 / 0.5 / 4.3 / 0.5
5 TH	0042 / 0645 / 1315 / 1925	0.5 / 4.4 / 0.3 / 4.2	**20** F	0559 / 1220 / 1826	4.3 / 0.5 / 4.1
6 F	0140 / 0756 / 1416 / 2036	0.6 / 4.2 / 0.6 / 3.9	**21** SA	0041 / 0648 / 1310 / 1926	0.6 / 4.1 / 0.7 / 3.9
7 SA	0250 / 0915 / 1524 / 2200	0.9 / 3.9 / 0.8 / 3.7	**22** SU	0140 / 0810 / 1414 / 2050	0.8 / 3.8 / 0.9 / 3.7
8 SU	0414 / 1036 / 1705 / 2320	0.8 / 3.9 / 0.8 / 3.9	**23** M	0304 / 0941 / 1606 / 2217	0.9 / 3.8 / 0.9 / 3.7
9 M	0545 / 1150 / 1815	0.7 / 4.1 / 0.7	**24** M	0440 / 1055 / 1721 / 2325	0.7 / 4.0 / 0.8 / 4.0
10 TU	0019 / 0646 / 1245 / 1906	4.1 / 0.5 / 4.4 / 0.6	**25** W	0556 / 1157 / 1815	0.5 / 4.3 / 0.6
11 W	0107 / 0730 / 1329 / 1946	4.3 / 0.3 / 4.5 / 0.4	**26** TH	0019 / 0648 / 1242 / 1908	4.3 / 0.3 / 4.7 / 0.4
12 TH	0147 / 0805 / 1402 / 2016	4.4 / 0.3 / 4.6 / 0.5	**27** F	0106 / 0735 / 1326 / 1953	4.6 / 0.1 / 4.9 / 0.3
13 F	0221 / 0839 / 1437 / 2045	4.5 / 0.2 / 4.6 / 0.5	**28** SA ●	0146 / 0823 / 1407 / 2037	4.8 / -0.1 / 5.0 / 0.2
14 SA	0252 / 0912 / 1507 / 2120	4.6 / 0.2 / 4.7 / 0.4	**29** SU	0229 / 0907 / 1453 / 2126	4.9 / -0.2 / 5.1 / 0.2
15 SU	0322 / 0946 / 1538 / 2155	4.6 / 0.2 / 4.7 / 0.4	**30** M	0312 / 0952 / 1536 / 2207	5.0 / -0.2 / 5.0 / 0.2
			31 TU	0356 / 1036 / 1620 / 2252	5.0 / -0.1 / 4.9 / 0.2

APRIL

Day	Time	m	Day	Time	m
1 W	0440 / 1117 / 1707 / 2335	4.9 / 0.0 / 4.7 / 0.3	**16** TH	0426 / 1056 / 1646 / 2254	4.5 / 0.4 / 4.5 / 0.4
2 TH	0529 / 1159 / 1758 / 2339	4.7 / 0.2 / 4.4 / 0.4	**17** F	0500 / 1120 / 1717 / 2339	4.5 / 0.5 / 4.4 / 0.4
3 F	0026 / 0625 / 1245 / 1855	0.4 / 4.4 / 0.4 / 4.1	**18** SA	0537 / 1201 / 1757	4.4 / 0.6 / 4.2
4 SA	0115 / 0729 / 1350 / 2010	0.5 / 4.2 / 0.7 / 3.8	**19** SU	0026 / 0625 / 1250 / 1855	0.5 / 4.2 / 0.7 / 3.9
5 SU	0230 / 0850 / 1505 / 2136	0.7 / 3.9 / 0.9 / 3.6	**20** M	0119 / 0746 / 1400 / 2020	0.6 / 3.9 / 0.8 / 3.8
6 M	0349 / 1016 / 1634 / 2255	0.7 / 3.9 / 0.9 / 3.8	**21** TU	0246 / 0906 / 1525 / 2145	0.7 / 3.9 / 0.9 / 3.8
7 TU	0514 / 1125 / 1755 / 2358	0.6 / 4.1 / 0.8 / 4.0	**22** W	0416 / 1021 / 1646 / 2255	0.6 / 4.1 / 0.8 / 4.0
8 W	0620 / 1218 / 1835	0.5 / 4.3 / 0.6	**23** TH	0520 / 1126 / 1744 / 2351	0.4 / 4.4 / 0.6 / 4.3
9 TH	0045 / 0706 / 1306 / 1915	4.2 / 0.4 / 4.5 / 0.6	**24** F	0626 / 1217 / 1846	0.2 / 4.7 / 0.4
10 F	0126 / 0745 / 1339 / 1945	4.4 / 0.3 / 4.5 / 0.5	**25** SA	0038 / 0716 / 1303 / 1932	4.6 / 0.1 / 4.9 / 0.3
11 SA ○	0155 / 0815 / 1411 / 2022	4.5 / 0.3 / 4.6 / 0.4	**26** SU ●	0123 / 0759 / 1346 / 2017	4.8 / -0.1 / 5.0 / 0.2
12 SU	0226 / 0848 / 1441 / 2056	4.5 / 0.2 / 4.6 / 0.4	**27** M	0205 / 0846 / 1431 / 2103	4.9 / -0.1 / 5.0 / 0.1
13 M	0256 / 0921 / 1511 / 2131	4.6 / 0.2 / 4.7 / 0.4	**28** TU	0251 / 0927 / 1516 / 2147	5.0 / -0.1 / 4.9 / 0.1
14 TU	0325 / 0949 / 1541 / 2202	4.7 / 0.3 / 4.6 / 0.3	**29** W	0335 / 1012 / 1602 / 2236	5.0 / 0.0 / 4.8 / 0.1
15 W	0356 / 1026 / 1612 / 2230	4.6 / 0.3 / 4.6 / 0.4	**30** TH	0422 / 1056 / 1646 / 2315	4.9 / 0.1 / 4.6 / 0.2

Chart Datum: 2·32 metres below Normaal Amsterdams Peil

20

TIME ZONE –0100
(Dutch Standard Time)
Subtract 1 hour for UT

For Dutch Summer Time add
ONE hour in non-shaded areas

NETHERLANDS – VLISSINGEN (FLUSHING)

LAT 51°27′N   LONG 3°36′E

TIMES AND HEIGHTS OF HIGH AND LOW WATERS

YEAR **1998**

MAY

	Time	m		Time	m
1 F	0509 1138 1738	4.7 0.3 4.4	**16** SA	0442 1106 1701 2330	4.5 0.3 4.4 0.4
2 SA	0002 0608 1226 1836	0.3 4.5 0.5 4.1	**17** SU	0521 1151 1746	4.4 0.6 4.2
3 SU	0100 0705 1314 1939	0.4 4.2 0.7 3.8	**18** M	0016 0608 1235 1845	0.4 4.3 0.7 4.0
4 M	0206 0820 1436 2100	0.6 4.0 0.9 3.7	**19** TU	0116 0719 1345 1956	0.5 4.1 0.8 3.9
5 TU	0315 0946 1555 2226	0.7 3.9 0.9 3.7	**20** W	0226 0840 1455 2112	0.5 4.1 0.8 3.9
6 W	0434 1056 1716 2322	0.6 4.0 0.8 3.9	**21** TH	0346 0956 1610 2219	0.5 4.2 0.8 4.0
7 TH	0546 1145 1806	0.5 4.2 0.7	**22** F	0450 1056 1720 2322	0.4 4.4 0.6 4.3
8 F	0009 0636 1231 1846	4.1 0.4 4.3 0.6	**23** SA	0556 1152 1821	0.2 4.6 0.5
9 SA	0050 0705 1306 1926	4.2 0.4 4.4 0.5	**24** SU	0016 0652 1240 1912	4.5 0.1 4.8 0.3
10 SU	0125 0746 1342 1955	4.4 0.4 4.5 0.4	**25** M ●	0101 0738 1326 1958	4.7 0.0 4.9 0.2
11 M O	0152 0816 1415 2026	4.5 0.3 4.6 0.3	**26** TU	0147 0826 1415 2046	4.8 0.0 4.9 0.1
12 TU	0227 0851 1446 2106	4.6 0.3 4.6 0.3	**27** W	0233 0907 1458 2130	4.9 0.1 4.8 0.1
13 W	0257 0922 1515 2141	4.6 0.3 4.6 0.3	**28** TH	0319 0952 1546 2215	4.9 0.2 4.7 0.1
14 TH	0330 0955 1548 2216	4.6 0.4 4.6 0.3	**29** F	0406 1033 1636 2259	4.8 0.3 4.6 0.2
15 F	0405 1030 1626 2244	4.6 0.4 4.5 0.3	**30** SA	0456 1116 1725 2346	4.7 0.4 4.4 0.3
			31 SU	0548 1155 1811	4.5 0.6 4.2

JUNE

	Time	m		Time	m
1 M	0035 0641 1244 1906	0.4 4.3 0.8 4.0	**16** TU	0016 0558 1231 1829	0.3 4.4 0.7 4.2
2 TU	0129 0746 1344 2010	0.5 4.0 0.9 3.8	**17** W	0105 0701 1326 1936	0.3 4.3 0.8 4.1
3 W	0236 0850 1459 2126	0.6 3.9 0.9 3.7	**18** TH	0211 0811 1430 2045	0.3 4.2 0.8 4.0
4 TH	0340 1006 1605 2235	0.6 3.9 0.9 3.8	**19** F	0310 0918 1535 2149	0.4 4.2 0.8 4.1
5 F	0445 1105 1704 2326	0.6 4.0 0.8 3.9	**20** SA	0426 1026 1650 2256	0.4 4.3 0.7 4.2
6 SA	0546 1155 1754	0.6 4.2 0.7	**21** SU	0530 1127 1756 2351	0.3 4.5 0.6 4.4
7 SU	0016 0625 1236 1846	4.1 0.5 4.3 0.6	**22** M	0631 1222 1852	0.2 4.6 0.4
8 M	0049 0708 1309 1926	4.2 0.5 4.4 0.5	**23** TU	0046 0721 1313 1946	4.6 0.2 4.7 0.3
9 TU	0126 0746 1346 2000	4.4 0.4 4.5 0.4	**24** W ●	0133 0805 1402 2032	4.7 0.2 4.7 0.2
10 W O	0157 0815 1417 2041	4.5 0.4 4.6 0.3	**25** TH	0220 0847 1447 2115	4.8 0.2 4.7 0.1
11 TH	0236 0856 1456 2118	4.6 0.4 4.6 0.3	**26** F	0306 0929 1531 2202	4.8 0.3 4.7 0.1
12 F	0309 1011 1531 2155	4.7 0.4 4.6 0.2	**27** SA	0352 1011 1617 2246	4.8 0.4 4.6 0.2
13 SA	0347 1015 1609 2239	4.6 0.5 4.5 0.2	**28** SU	0438 1052 1701 2328	4.7 0.5 4.5 0.2
14 SU	0426 1056 1648 2326	4.6 0.5 4.4 0.3	**29** M	0525 1131 1745	4.5 0.6 4.3
15 M	0509 1140 1735	4.5 0.6 4.3	**30** TU	0010 0609 1216 1829	0.3 4.4 0.8 4.2

JULY

	Time	m		Time	m
1 W	0055 0655 1316 1921	0.5 4.1 0.9 4.0	**16** TH	0049 0641 1306 1909	0.2 4.5 0.7 4.3
2 TH	0145 0749 1410 2016	0.6 4.0 0.9 3.8	**17** F	0146 0748 1401 2016	0.3 4.3 0.8 4.2
3 F	0251 0845 1516 2114	0.7 3.8 1.0 3.7	**18** SA	0239 0855 1510 2122	0.4 4.2 0.8 4.1
4 SA	0356 1006 1615 2236	0.7 3.8 0.9 3.8	**19** SU	0350 1002 1614 2229	0.5 4.2 0.8 4.2
5 SU	0444 1111 1718 2331	0.7 3.9 0.8 3.9	**20** M	0506 1109 1735 2337	0.5 4.3 0.7 4.3
6 M	0545 1156 1816	0.7 4.1 0.7	**21** TU	0611 1216 1840	0.4 4.4 0.5
7 TU	0015 0636 1239 1855	4.1 0.6 4.3 0.6	**22** W	0035 0706 1305 1932	4.5 0.4 4.5 0.3
8 W	0056 0716 1317 1938	4.3 0.6 4.5 0.5	**23** TH ●	0125 0750 1356 2018	4.7 0.4 4.6 0.2
9 TH O	0135 0752 1358 2018	4.5 0.5 4.6 0.2	**24** F	0212 0831 1437 2106	4.8 0.4 4.7 0.2
10 F	0213 0836 1435 2100	4.6 0.5 4.7 0.2	**25** SA	0257 0911 1519 2145	4.8 0.5 4.7 0.2
11 SA	0252 0915 1513 2141	4.7 0.4 4.7 0.2	**26** SU	0337 0952 1557 2226	4.8 0.5 4.7 0.2
12 SU	0332 0958 1555 2230	4.8 0.4 4.7 0.1	**27** M	0417 1025 1637 2306	4.7 0.6 4.6 0.3
13 M	0413 1042 1635 2315	4.8 0.4 4.6 0.1	**28** TU	0456 1106 1716 2335	4.6 0.7 4.5 0.4
14 TU	0456 1126 1721	4.7 0.5 4.5	**29** W	0536 1146 1751	4.5 0.7 4.3
15 W	0006 0546 1216 1811	0.1 4.6 0.6 4.4	**30** TH	0016 0615 1220 1836	0.5 4.3 0.8 4.2
			31 F	0044 0700 1253 1920	0.6 4.1 0.9 4.0

AUGUST

	Time	m		Time	m
1 SA	0134 0756 1354 2020	0.8 3.9 1.0 3.8	**16** SU	0216 0828 1439 2058	0.5 4.2 0.8 4.1
2 SU	0250 0856 1531 2126	0.9 3.8 1.0 3.7	**17** M	0314 0939 1605 2216	0.7 4.0 0.9 4.1
3 M	0407 0959 1635 2240	0.9 3.8 1.0 3.8	**18** TU	0446 1055 1719 2325	0.7 4.1 0.7 4.2
4 TU	0506 1116 1729 2346	0.9 3.9 0.8 4.0	**19** W	0555 1206 1831	0.7 4.3 0.5
5 W	0600 1216 1828	0.8 4.2 0.7	**20** TH	0029 0649 1256 1922	4.5 0.6 4.5 0.4
6 TH	0036 0648 1255 1916	4.3 0.7 4.4 0.5	**21** F	0119 0738 1342 2005	4.7 0.5 4.6 0.3
7 F	0116 0728 1336 1956	4.5 0.6 4.6 0.3	**22** SA ●	0205 0818 1422 2045	4.8 0.5 4.7 0.2
8 SA O	0156 0812 1416 2042	4.7 0.5 4.7 0.2	**23** SU	0241 0855 1459 2121	4.8 0.5 4.7 0.2
9 SU	0233 0855 1455 2127	4.9 0.4 4.8 0.1	**24** M	0317 0930 1535 2200	4.8 0.6 4.7 0.3
10 M	0315 0940 1536 2212	5.0 0.4 4.8 0.0	**25** TU	0356 1006 1607 2236	4.8 0.6 4.7 0.3
11 TU	0356 1026 1616 2258	5.0 0.4 4.8 0.0	**26** W	0427 1038 1646 2308	4.7 0.6 4.6 0.4
12 W	0438 1110 1701 2342	4.9 0.5 4.7 0.1	**27** TH	0502 1104 1716 2336	4.5 0.7 4.5 0.5
13 TH	0526 1156 1747	4.7 0.6 4.6	**28** F	0535 1135 1747 2359	4.4 0.7 4.3 0.6
14 F	0028 0617 1246 1841	0.2 4.6 0.6 4.4	**29** SA	0610 1205 1828	4.2 0.8 4.1
15 SA	0118 0720 1335 1948	0.3 4.3 0.7 4.3	**30** SU	0035 0656 1256 1926	0.8 4.0 0.9 3.9
			31 M	0125 0756 1355 2029	0.9 3.8 1.1 3.8

Chart Datum: 2·32 metres below Normaal Amsterdams Peil

TIME ZONE –0100
(Dutch Standard Time)
Subtract 1 hour for UT
For Dutch Summer Time add ONE hour in non-shaded areas

NETHERLANDS – VLISSINGEN (FLUSHING)

LAT 51°27′N LONG 3°36′E

TIMES AND HEIGHTS OF HIGH AND LOW WATERS   YEAR **1998**

SEPTEMBER

Day	Time	m	Day	Time	m
1 TU	0245 / 0911 / 1550 / 2144	1.1 / 3.7 / 1.1 / 3.7	16 W	0424 / 1041 / 1704 / 2315	0.9 / 3.9 / 0.8 / 4.2
2 W	0426 / 1036 / 1655 / 2305	1.0 / 3.8 / 0.9 / 3.9	17 TH	0551 / 1156 / 1820	0.8 / 4.2 / 0.6
3 TH	0536 / 1140 / 1755	0.9 / 4.0 / 0.7	18 F	0019 / 0646 / 1240 / 1905	4.5 / 0.7 / 4.4 / 0.4
4 F	0006 / 0620 / 1229 / 1850	4.3 / 0.7 / 4.3 / 0.5	19 SA	0105 / 0722 / 1328 / 1945	4.7 / 0.6 / 4.6 / 0.3
5 SA	0055 / 0706 / 1311 / 1938	4.6 / 0.6 / 4.6 / 0.3	20 SU ●	0148 / 0755 / 1402 / 2026	4.8 / 0.6 / 4.7 / 0.2
6 SU O	0130 / 0752 / 1350 / 2019	4.9 / 0.5 / 4.8 / 0.1	21 M	0218 / 0829 / 1436 / 2058	4.8 / 0.6 / 4.7 / 0.3
7 M	0210 / 0836 / 1433 / 2105	5.0 / 0.4 / 4.9 / 0.0	22 TU	0252 / 0905 / 1507 / 2132	4.8 / 0.5 / 4.8 / 0.3
8 TU	0251 / 0921 / 1512 / 2150	5.1 / 0.4 / 5.0 / 0.0	23 W	0325 / 0941 / 1539 / 2205	4.8 / 0.5 / 4.8 / 0.4
9 W	0333 / 1006 / 1556 / 2233	5.1 / 0.4 / 5.0 / 0.0	24 TH	0355 / 1010 / 1611 / 2236	4.7 / 0.6 / 4.7 / 0.5
10 TH	0415 / 1045 / 1636 / 2315	5.0 / 0.4 / 4.9 / 0.1	25 F	0427 / 1040 / 1641 / 2300	4.6 / 0.6 / 4.6 / 0.6
11 F	0502 / 1132 / 1723	4.8 / 0.5 / 4.8	26 SA	0458 / 1106 / 1711 / 2326	4.5 / 0.7 / 4.5 / 0.7
12 SA	0002 / 0552 / 1220 / 1815	0.2 / 4.6 / 0.6 / 4.6	27 SU	0528 / 1135 / 1745	4.4 / 0.7 / 4.3
13 SU	0048 / 0656 / 1316 / 1922	0.4 / 4.3 / 0.7 / 4.3	28 M	0000 / 0601 / 1216 / 1825	0.8 / 4.2 / 0.8 / 4.1
14 M	0145 / 0805 / 1420 / 2036	0.6 / 4.1 / 0.8 / 4.1	29 TU	0046 / 0656 / 1310 / 1925	0.9 / 4.0 / 0.9 / 3.9
15 TU	0255 / 0914 / 1534 / 2155	0.8 / 3.9 / 0.9 / 4.0	30 W	0156 / 0820 / 1434 / 2110	1.1 / 3.8 / 1.1 / 3.8

OCTOBER

Day	Time	m	Day	Time	m
1 TH	0346 / 0946 / 1620 / 2224	1.1 / 3.8 / 0.9 / 4.0	16 F	0524 / 1129 / 1800 / 2358	0.9 / 4.1 / 0.6 / 4.4
2 F	0456 / 1102 / 1726 / 2336	1.0 / 4.0 / 0.7 / 4.3	17 SA	0625 / 1222 / 1846	0.8 / 4.3 / 0.5
3 SA	0556 / 1200 / 1819	0.8 / 4.3 / 0.5	18 SU	0046 / 0706 / 1306 / 1925	4.6 / 0.7 / 4.5 / 0.4
4 SU	0026 / 0642 / 1246 / 1909	4.7 / 0.6 / 4.6 / 0.3	19 M	0121 / 0737 / 1337 / 1958	4.7 / 0.6 / 4.6 / 0.4
5 M O	0105 / 0728 / 1325 / 1958	5.0 / 0.5 / 4.9 / 0.1	20 TU ●	0156 / 0805 / 1408 / 2032	4.7 / 0.6 / 4.7 / 0.4
6 TU	0146 / 0813 / 1405 / 2042	5.1 / 0.4 / 5.0 / 0.0	21 W	0226 / 0838 / 1438 / 2106	4.8 / 0.5 / 4.7 / 0.4
7 W	0228 / 0857 / 1447 / 2127	5.2 / 0.3 / 5.1 / 0.0	22 TH	0255 / 0912 / 1511 / 2136	4.8 / 0.5 / 4.8 / 0.4
8 TH	0311 / 0943 / 1531 / 2210	5.2 / 0.3 / 5.1 / 0.0	23 F	0327 / 0945 / 1541 / 2206	4.7 / 0.5 / 4.7 / 0.5
9 F	0356 / 1027 / 1615 / 2253	5.1 / 0.3 / 5.0 / 0.2	24 SA	0359 / 1015 / 1613 / 2229	4.7 / 0.6 / 4.6 / 0.6
10 SA	0440 / 1109 / 1701 / 2336	4.9 / 0.4 / 4.9 / 0.3	25 SU	0430 / 1046 / 1645 / 2300	4.6 / 0.6 / 4.5 / 0.7
11 SU	0530 / 1155 / 1756	4.6 / 0.5 / 4.6	26 M	0502 / 1116 / 1716 / 2332	4.4 / 0.6 / 4.4 / 0.8
12 M	0022 / 0552 / 1249 / 1900	0.5 / 4.3 / 0.6 / 4.3	27 TU	0538 / 1156 / 1757	4.3 / 0.7 / 4.3
13 TU	0118 / 0738 / 1355 / 2011	0.8 / 4.0 / 0.8 / 4.1	28 W	0021 / 0625 / 1245 / 1856	0.9 / 4.1 / 0.8 / 4.1
14 W	0224 / 0856 / 1520 / 2134	1.0 / 3.8 / 0.9 / 4.0	29 TH	0115 / 0740 / 1406 / 2036	1.0 / 3.9 / 0.9 / 3.9
15 TH	0416 / 1019 / 1655 / 2300	1.1 / 3.9 / 0.8 / 4.2	30 F	0245 / 0905 / 1536 / 2150	1.1 / 3.8 / 0.8 / 4.1
			31 SA	0410 / 1019 / 1645 / 2258	1.0 / 4.0 / 0.7 / 4.3

NOVEMBER

Day	Time	m	Day	Time	m
1 SU	0520 / 1126 / 1750 / 2351	0.9 / 4.3 / 0.5 / 4.7	16 M	0011 / 0630 / 1228 / 1852	4.4 / 0.8 / 4.3 / 0.5
2 M	0616 / 1213 / 1846	0.7 / 4.6 / 0.3	17 TU	0055 / 0706 / 1310 / 1931	4.5 / 0.7 / 4.5 / 0.5
3 TU	0039 / 0706 / 1258 / 1935	4.9 / 0.5 / 4.9 / 0.1	18 W	0126 / 0740 / 1341 / 2000	4.6 / 0.6 / 4.6 / 0.5
4 W O	0126 / 0750 / 1342 / 2018	5.1 / 0.4 / 5.0 / 0.1	19 TH ●	0159 / 0816 / 1412 / 2036	4.7 / 0.5 / 4.6 / 0.5
5 TH	0208 / 0837 / 1425 / 2105	5.2 / 0.3 / 5.1 / 0.1	20 F	0232 / 0848 / 1446 / 2106	4.7 / 0.5 / 4.7 / 0.5
6 F	0251 / 0922 / 1510 / 2146	5.1 / 0.3 / 5.1 / 0.1	21 SA	0303 / 0922 / 1515 / 2136	4.7 / 0.5 / 4.7 / 0.5
7 SA	0336 / 1007 / 1556 / 2227	5.0 / 0.3 / 5.1 / 0.3	22 SU	0336 / 0955 / 1548 / 2210	4.7 / 0.5 / 4.7 / 0.6
8 SU	0423 / 1052 / 1646 / 2315	4.8 / 0.3 / 4.9 / 0.4	23 M	0407 / 1025 / 1622 / 2240	4.6 / 0.5 / 4.6 / 0.7
9 M	0512 / 1138 / 1736 / 2356	4.6 / 0.4 / 4.7 / 0.6	24 TU	0446 / 1105 / 1659 / 2321	4.5 / 0.5 / 4.5 / 0.7
10 TU	0606 / 1229 / 1835	4.3 / 0.6 / 4.4	25 W	0521 / 1146 / 1742	4.4 / 0.6 / 4.4
11 W	0044 / 0710 / 1329 / 1948	0.9 / 4.1 / 0.7 / 4.1	26 TH	0002 / 0609 / 1238 / 1836	0.8 / 4.2 / 0.6 / 4.2
12 TH	0155 / 0819 / 1456 / 2106	1.0 / 3.9 / 0.8 / 4.1	27 F	0106 / 0711 / 1340 / 1956	1.0 / 4.0 / 0.7 / 4.1
13 F	0314 / 0945 / 1604 / 2221	1.1 / 3.8 / 0.8 / 4.1	28 SA	0205 / 0830 / 1455 / 2112	1.0 / 4.0 / 0.7 / 4.2
14 SA	0450 / 1056 / 1726 / 2326	1.1 / 4.0 / 0.7 / 4.3	29 SU	0325 / 0942 / 1616 / 2219	1.0 / 4.0 / 0.6 / 4.3
15 SU	0544 / 1148 / 1815	0.9 / 4.2 / 0.6	30 M	0440 / 1048 / 1726 / 2321	0.9 / 4.3 / 0.5 / 4.6

DECEMBER

Day	Time	m	Day	Time	m
1 TU	0542 / 1146 / 1815	0.7 / 4.5 / 0.4	16 W	0019 / 0630 / 1236 / 1856	4.2 / 0.8 / 4.2 / 0.7
2 W	0015 / 0640 / 1236 / 1910	4.8 / 0.6 / 4.8 / 0.2	17 TH	0059 / 0710 / 1316 / 1930	4.4 / 0.7 / 4.4 / 0.6
3 TH O	0102 / 0733 / 1321 / 1958	4.9 / 0.4 / 4.9 / 0.2	18 F ●	0132 / 0748 / 1347 / 2006	4.5 / 0.6 / 4.5 / 0.6
4 F	0149 / 0818 / 1408 / 2042	5.0 / 0.3 / 5.0 / 0.2	19 SA	0207 / 0821 / 1420 / 2041	4.6 / 0.5 / 4.6 / 0.5
5 SA	0236 / 0905 / 1456 / 2126	5.0 / 0.2 / 5.1 / 0.2	20 SU	0243 / 0900 / 1456 / 2115	4.7 / 0.4 / 4.7 / 0.5
6 SU	0321 / 0952 / 1543 / 2210	4.9 / 0.2 / 5.0 / 0.4	21 M	0317 / 0935 / 1531 / 2152	4.7 / 0.4 / 4.7 / 0.6
7 M	0406 / 1038 / 1626 / 2252	4.8 / 0.3 / 4.9 / 0.5	22 TU	0350 / 1015 / 1608 / 2230	4.6 / 0.4 / 4.7 / 0.6
8 TU	0455 / 1122 / 1718 / 2336	4.6 / 0.3 / 4.7 / 0.7	23 W	0428 / 1101 / 1646 / 2311	4.6 / 0.4 / 4.7 / 0.7
9 W	0546 / 1209 / 1816	4.4 / 0.4 / 4.5	24 TH	0509 / 1140 / 1732 / 2349	4.5 / 0.4 / 4.6 / 0.7
10 TH	0019 / 0639 / 1255 / 1916	0.8 / 4.2 / 0.6 / 4.2	25 F	0556 / 1230 / 1821	4.3 / 0.4 / 4.4
11 F	0120 / 0735 / 1359 / 2015	1.0 / 4.0 / 0.7 / 4.0	26 SA	0039 / 0652 / 1326 / 1928	0.8 / 4.2 / 0.5 / 4.3
12 SA	0226 / 0846 / 1503 / 2135	1.1 / 3.8 / 0.8 / 3.9	27 SU	0146 / 0800 / 1426 / 2035	0.9 / 4.1 / 0.5 / 4.2
13 SU	0336 / 1006 / 1614 / 2242	1.1 / 3.8 / 0.8 / 4.0	28 M	0245 / 0906 / 1530 / 2148	0.9 / 4.1 / 0.6 / 4.2
14 M	0445 / 1105 / 1731 / 2338	1.1 / 3.9 / 0.8 / 4.1	29 TU	0400 / 1017 / 1645 / 2252	0.9 / 4.2 / 0.6 / 4.3
15 TU	0534 / 1156 / 1815	0.9 / 4.1 / 0.7	30 W	0516 / 1120 / 1756 / 2352	0.8 / 4.4 / 0.5 / 4.5
			31 TH	0620 / 1216 / 1850	0.6 / 4.6 / 0.4

Chart Datum: 2·32 metres below Normaal Amsterdams Peil

20

VLISSINGEN (FLUSHING)

MEAN SPRING
AND NEAP CURVES

MEAN RANGES
Springs 4·4m
Neaps 3·1m

Springs occur 2 days
after
New and Full Moon.

OOSTERSCHELDE   10-20-18

Zeeland 51°37'·30N 03°40'·20E (Roompotsluis)

CHARTS
AC 192, 120, 110; Zeekaart 1448; DYCs 1805, 1801; Imray C30; Stanfords 19

TIDES
+0230 Dover Zone –0100; ML Sas van Goes 2·0, Zierikzee 1·8; Duration Sas van Goes 0615, Zierikzee 0640

Standard Port VLISSINGEN (←)

Times				Height (metres)			
High Water		Low Water		MHWS	MHWN	MLWN	MLWS
0300	0900	0400	1000	4·7	3·9	0·8	0·3
1500	2100	1600	2200				
Differences ROOMPOTSLUIS (outside)							
–0005	+0015	+0020	–0005	–1·1	–1·0	–0·2	0·0
ROOMPOTSLUIS (inside)							
+0115	+0105	+0045	+0105	–1·4	–1·1	–0·1	+0·1
WEMELDINGE							
+0150	+0120	+0055	+0115	–0·9	–0·6	–0·3	–0·1
KRAMMER LOCKS							
+0215	+0125	+0100	+0110	–1·0	–0·9	–0·3	–0·1
BERGSEDIEP LOCK							
+0145	+0125	+0105	+0115	–0·6	–0·4	–0·2	0·0

SHELTER
Good shelter in many hbrs at any tide; see facing page. Veerse Meer is a non-tidal waterway with moorings; enter from Oosterschelde via Zandkreekdam lock. The Schelde-Rijn Canal can be entered at Bergsediepsluis near Tholen; and the S Beveland Canal at Wemeldinge.

NAVIGATION
WPT WG1 SHM buoy, QG, 51°38'·05N 03°26'·30E at ent to Westgat/Oude Roompot buoyed chan. There are several offshore banks, see 10.20.5. Not advised to enter in strong W/NW'lies, and only from HW –6 to HW +1½ Zierikzee. All vessels must use the Roompotsluis (lock). The areas each side of the barrier are very dangerous due to strong tidal streams and many obstructions. Passage is prohib W of Roggenplaat. Zeelandbrug has 12·2m clearance at centre of arch in buoyed chans. Clearance (m) is indicated on some of bridge supports. If wind < F 7, bascule bridge near N end lifts at H & H+30, Mon-Fri 0700-2130; Sat/Sun from 0900.

LIGHTS AND MARKS
See 10.20.4. Roompotsluis ldg lts 073·5° both Oc G 5s; Ent: N side FR, S side FG; depth 5m.

RADIO TELEPHONE
VHF-fitted craft must monitor Ch 68 in the Oosterschelde. Ch 68 broadcast local forecasts at H+15. *Verkeerspost Wemeldinge* Ch 68 MUST be called if entering canal; also for radar guidance in poor vis. Call *Zeelandbrug* Ch 18 for opening times and clearance. Locks: *Roompotsluis* Ch 18. *Krammersluizen* Ch 22 (H24). Zandreek *Sluis Kats* Ch 18; *Sluis Grevelingen* Ch 20; Bergse Diepsluis Ch 18.

HARBOURS AND FACILITIES

The following are some of the more important of the many hbrs (anti-clockwise from the Roompotsluis):

ROOMPOT MARINA: (150 + 80 visitors) ☎ (0113) 374125, f22.00, Rtg 1-2-3, AC, D, P, Slip, FW, Gas, Gaz, Ⓞ, R, V, Bar, Ⓑ, Dr ☎ 372565.

COLIJNSPLAAT: Hr Mr ☎ (0113) 695762; Rtg 1-2-2, **YC WV Noord Beveland** f21.700, AC, Slip, FW, Ⓞ; secure at first floating jetty and report arrival by loudspeaker or at hbr office; beware strong current across hbr ent; **Services:** P, D, BH (40 ton), ME, SM, Sh. **Town** Dr ☎ 695304, V, R, Bar, Gaz, ✉, Ⓑ, ⇌ (Goes), ✈ (Rotterdam).

KATS: Hr Mr ☎ (0113) 600270; Rtg 2-3-3, **Rest Nautic BV** f20.00, AC, ME, BH (35 ton), FW, SM, Ⓞ; uncomfortable in strong E winds.

SAS VAN GOES: Lock ☎ (0113) 216744, VHF Ch 18; opens Mon-Fri 0600-2200, Sat/Sun 0800-2000. **Jachthaven Het Goese Sas** ☎ 223944, f19.50, Rtg 1-3-2, AC, FW, D, ME, Slip, BH (12 ton), Ⓞ.

GOES: The canal to Goes starts at Sas van Goes (lock); no facilities at Wilhelminadorp; bridge operates same hrs as lock. Town bridges open every H 0800-2000 in season, but not 1200. Rtg 1-4-1. Outskirts of Goes: **YC WV De Werf** ☎ (0113) 216372, f19.50, AC, FW, C (3½ ton), P, D; **Marina Stadshaven** in centre: ☎ 216136, f19.50, AC, FW; **Services:** ME, El, Sh, Ⓞ, Gaz, Dr ☎ 227451, Ⓗ ☎ 227000. **Town** V, R, ✉, Ⓑ, ⇌, ✈ (Antwerpen).

WEMELDINGE: Hr Mr ☎ (0113) 622093. Rtg 1-4-3. Yachts transit the Kanaal door Zuid Beveland via a section 1km E of the town. Use the former ent (via R/G tfc lts) to berth at the yacht hbrs in the Voorhaven or Binnenhaven; in the former a larger marina is planned. SHM buoy O21 to N of the E mole marks a shoal. **Services:** f26.60, ME, SM, AC, C (6·5 ton) ME, FW, P, D, Dr ☎ 6227451, Ⓗ ☎ 6227000. **Town** V, R, ✉, Ⓑ, ⇌ (Goes), ✈ (Antwerpen).

YERSEKE: Leave to port the preferred chan buoy at hbr ent. Rtg 1-4-2. Hr Mr VHF Ch 09. Both marinas are S of the outer FV hbr: **Prinses Beatrix Haven** ☎ (0113) 571726, f23.00, 1·6m, FW, D, BH (10 ton); **Services:** SM, Sh, El, Dr ☎ 571444. **Town** V, R, ✉, Ⓑ, ⇌ (Kruiningen-Yerseke), ✈ .

STAVENISSE: Hr Mr ☎ (0166) 692815. Rtg 3-4-3. **Marina** at end of hbr canal (access HW±3 for 1·8m draft), f12.10, Slip, FW, P & D (cans), Sh, C (4·5 ton), V, Gaz.

ST ANNALAND: **WV St Annaland** Hr Mr ☎ (0166) 652783, Rtg 1-2-2, f16.50, AC, FW; **YC** ☎ 652634, Ⓞ, Bar, R; Dr ☎ 652400. **Services:** ME, P, D, Sh, El, CH, BH (25 ton), Gaz, BY. **Town** V, R, Ⓑ, ✉, ⇌ (Bergen op Zoom), ✈ (Antwerpen).

BRUINISSE: via lock (Ch 20) to Grevelingenmeer. Rtg 1-1-2. **WV 'Bru'** Hr Mr ☎ (0111) 481506, f18.40, FW; **Jachthaven Bruinisse** Hr Mr ☎ 481485, f21.00, FW, AC, P, D, Slip, Ⓞ, Gaz, Bar, V; **Services:** ME, Sh, C (16 ton). MHW = NAP + 1.53m; Dr ☎ 481280. **Town** ✉, Ⓑ, ✈ (Rotterdam).

ZIJPE: Rtg 1-5-3. **Vluchthaven**, berth in SW corner; free for 3 days, but yacht must not be left unattended.

ZIERIKZEE: Rtg 1-2-1. Hr Mr ☎ (0111) 413174; **Haven 't Luitje** and **Nieuwe Haven: WV Zierikzee** Hr Mr ☎ 414877, f21.10, FW, AC; Note: For yachts >15m LOA pre-arrange berth with Hr Mr, Jun-Aug; **Services:** ME, Sh, SM, CH. **Town** Dr 412080, Ⓗ 416900, Ⓞ, V, R, ✉, Ⓑ, ✈ (Rotterdam).

BURGHSLUIS: Rtg 1-5-3. Hr Mr ☎ (0111) 653114; **Jachthaven** f15.40, FW, AC, C (6 ton), ME. Facilities at Burg-Haamstede P, D, Gaz, ✉, Ⓑ, ✈ (Rotterdam).

NEELTJE JANS: Rtg 1-5-1. Hr Mr ☎ (0113) 374225. Ⓥ jetty in Beton Haven, f14.00. **Delta Expo** worth visiting.

TOWNS ON THE VEERSE MEER (non-tidal). Formerly free moorings at many of the islands are no longer. You **must** buy a Zeeland (smart) Card for f100 at a VVV (tourist office) or PO; pay for a night, f7.50, using the card in an *automaat*. Normal dues apply at towns below:

KORTGENE: Rtg 1-1-2. Hr Mr and **Delta Marina** ☎ (0113) 301315, f26.80, P, D, FW, AC, CH, El, Ⓞ, ME, R, Sh, SM, V, C (16 ton). **Town** Dr ☎ 301319, V, R, Bar, ✉, Ⓑ, ⇌ (Goes), ✈ (Rotterdam).

WOLPHAARTSDIJK: **WV Wolphaartsdijk (WVW)** Rtg 1-2-2. Hr Mr ☎ (0113) 581565, f13.90, P & D, C (20 ton), Ⓞ; **Royal YC Belgique (RYCB)** ☎ 581496, f11.40, P & D, Sh.

DE PIET: Rtg 1-5-1. There are 72m of pontoons for small craft; 4 other little havens around De Omloop. Use card.

ARNEMUIDEN: Rtg 1-5-2. **Jachthaven Oranjeplaat** Hr Mr ☎ (0118) 501248, f14.70, Slip, P & D, C (12 ton), ⇌.

VEERE: Rtg 1-2-1. Yacht berths at: **Jachtclub Veere** in the Stadshaven, very busy, ☎ (0118) 501246, f19.50, FW, AC; **Marina Veere** on canal side, ☎ 501553, f22.00, FW, AC; **Jachtwerf Oostwatering** ☎ 501665, f18.50, FW, AC, Ⓞ; **WV Arne**, at Oostwatering – report at Ⓥ jetty, ☎ 501484/501929, f12.50, FW, AC. **Town** Dr ☎ 501271, V, R, Bar, ✉, Ⓑ, ⇌ (Middelburg), ✈ (Rotterdam).

MIDDELBURG: (This town is about 3M S of Veere on the Walcheren canal to Vlissingen). Rtg 1-4-1. No mooring in Kanaal door Walcheren. All bridges & Veere lock: Ch 22. **WV Arne** in the Dockhaven, ☎ (0118) 627180, f16.20, FW, AC, ME, El, Sh, SM, Ⓞ; **Services:** D, Gaz, CH, BY, AC, Sh, Slip. **Town** Dr ☎ 612637; Ⓗ 625555; V, R, Bar, ✉, Ⓑ, ⇌, ✈ (Rotterdam).

STELLENDAM & HELLEVOETSLUIS

Zuid Holland 51°49'·88N 04°02'·10E   Rtgs: (Stellendam) 4-5-3; (Hellevoetsluis) 1-2-1.

CHARTS

AC 2322; Zeekaart 1447, 1448; DYC 1801.6, 1807.6; Imray C30; Stanfords 19

TIDES

+0300 Dover; ML 1·2; Duration 0510; Zone –0100

Standard Port VLISSINGEN (←—)

Times				Height (metres)			
High Water		Low Water		MHWS	MHWN	MLWN	MLWS
0300	0900	0400	1000	4·7	3·9	0·8	0·3
1500	2100	1600	2200				

Differences HARINGVLIETSLUIZEN

| +0015 | +0015 | +0015 | –0020 | –1·7 | –1·6 | –0·4 | 0·0 |

NOTE: Double LWs occur. The rise after the 1st LW is called the Agger. Water levels on this coast are much affected by weather. Prolonged NW gales can raise levels by up to 3m.

SHELTER

Good in Stellendam marina, beyond the lock and the Inner hbr; or go 3M to Hellevoetsluis for one of the 3 yacht hbrs: Heliushaven (1·9-5m); via swing bridge into Het Groote Dok (2-4m); and via lock into the Voorne canal (2·8-4·8m).
In the Haringvliet there are about 6 large pontoons (*vlot* on the DYC) equipped for barbecue picnics; but they are prone to wash and only useable in calm conditions.
Within 10M upstream of Hellevoetsluis there are good yacht facilities on the S bank at Middelharnis, Stad aan't Haringvliet and Den Bommel; on the N bank at YC De Put (Vuile Gat) and Hitsertse Kade. If bound for Rotterdam, proceed via Spui or Dordrecht.

NAVIGATION

WPT Slijkgat SG SWM buoy, Iso 4s, 51°52'·00N 03°51'·50E, 290°/110° from/to Kwade Hoek lt, 5·0M. From the N, the Gat van de Hawk chan to Stellendam lock is no longer buoyed and is dangerous due to long-term WIP south of Maasvlakte. It is therefore best to take the well buoyed/lit Slijkgat chan along the Goeree shore, but it is dangerous to enter Slijkgat in strong W/NW winds.
Beware a shoal about 5ca from the lock, marked by SHM buoys. Keep clear of dam during sluicing.
Lock and lifting bridge operate H24 throughout the year.

Within the Haringvliet the 3M leg to Hellevoetsluis is well marked by 10 PHM buoys (DG2 to DG18 and HV2); only DG16 is lit as on chartlet. The SW side of the Haringvliet has 6 SHM buoys (DG1-11) leading to the well buoyed, but unlit Aardappelengat chan (S of Slijkplaat) and the ent to Middelharnis.

LIGHTS AND MARKS

Haringvlietsluizen sluicing sigs: 3 ® in △, shown from pier heads on dam; danger area marked by small Y buoys. Hellevoetsluis lt Iso WRG 8s 16m 11/7M, W stone tr, R cupola. G shore-275°, W275°-294°, R294°-316°, W316°-036°, G036°-058°, W058°-095°, R096°-shore.

RADIO TELEPHONE

For lock call: *Goereese Sluis* VHF Ch 20. Hellevoetsluis Hr Mr Ch 74.

TELEPHONE (Dial codes: 0187 Stellendam; 0181 Hellevoetsluis)

Hr Mr Stellendam 491000, Hellevoetsluis 330911; ⌗ Rotterdam (010) 4298088 or Vlissingen (0118) 484600; Police, Fire, Ambulance 112; Brit Consul (020) 6764343.

FACILITIES

STELLENDAM (0187)
Stellendam Marina ☎ 493769, ⚓ 493807 (70/175 berths inc ⓥ, eventually 400). FW, AC, Fuel, Slip, C, Bar, R, V.
Town V, R, Bar, ✉ (2½ km), ✈ (Rotterdam).
HELLEVOETSLUIS (0181)
Marina, Het Groote Dok ☎ 312166, f18.75, swing bridge opens every H in daylight from 0800 in summer; waiting pontoons are downstream. El, Gaz, FW, ME, CH;
Helius Haven YC ☎ 315868, AB f16, P, D, FW;
Voorne Canal YC ☎ 315476, AB f16, P, D, FW;
Services: CH, El, ME.
Town P, D, V, R, Bar, ✉, Ⓑ, ✈ (Rotterdam).
Ferry: Hook of Holland-Harwich; or Rotterdam-Hull.

TIME ZONE –0100
(Dutch Standard Time)
Subtract 1 hour for UT
For Dutch Summer Time add
ONE hour in non-shaded areas

NETHERLANDS – HOEK VAN HOLLAND

LAT 51°59′N   LONG 4°07′E

TIMES AND HEIGHTS OF HIGH AND LOW WATERS

YEAR **1998**

JANUARY

Day	Times (m)
1 TH	0416 (2.1), 0926 (0.1), 1630 (2.3)
2 F	0014 (0.4), 0455 (2.0), 1005 (0.1), 1715 (2.2)
3 SA	0055 (0.4), 0541 (2.0), 1055 (0.1), 1806 (2.2)
4 SU	0155 (0.4), 0629 (1.9), 1145 (0.0), 1851 (2.1)
5 M	0227 (0.4), 0726 (1.8), 1245 (0.1), 1956 (2.0)
6 TU	0250 (0.5), 0825 (1.8), 1354 (0.1), 2105 (2.0)
7 W	0310 (0.5), 0940 (1.8), 1516 (0.1), 2216 (1.9)
8 TH	0354 (0.5), 1045 (1.8), 1616 (0.2), 2326 (1.9)
9 F	0724 (0.4), 1156 (1.8), 1714 (0.2)
10 SA	0025 (1.9), 0825 (0.4), 1249 (1.9), 2040 (0.3)
11 SU	0125 (2.0), 0935 (0.3), 1341 (2.0), 1905 (0.3)
12 M O	0216 (2.0), 1015 (0.3), 1425 (2.1), 1954 (0.4)
13 TU	0258 (2.0), 0805 (0.2), 1515 (2.2), 2315 (0.4)
14 W	0345 (2.0), 0846 (0.2), 1555 (2.2)
15 TH	0006 (0.4), 0426 (2.0), 0914 (0.2), 1635 (2.2)
16 F	0045 (0.4), 0458 (2.0), 0954 (0.1), 1715 (2.1)
17 SA	0136 (0.4), 0535 (2.0), 1046 (0.1), 1755 (2.1)
18 SU	0130 (0.4), 0616 (1.9), 1125 (0.1), 1836 (2.0)
19 M	0050 (0.4), 0644 (1.9), 1215 (0.1), 1915 (1.9)
20 TU	0115 (0.4), 0736 (1.8), 1310 (0.1), 2005 (1.8)
21 W	0210 (0.3), 0836 (1.7), 1405 (0.2), 2054 (1.8)
22 TH	0255 (0.3), 0930 (1.7), 1455 (0.2), 2159 (1.8)
23 F	0450 (0.3), 1035 (1.7), 1734 (0.3), 2310 (1.8)
24 SA	0545 (0.3), 1145 (1.7), 1840 (0.3)
25 SU	0015 (1.8), 0627 (0.3), 1245 (1.8), 2010 (0.3)
26 M	0110 (1.9), 0649 (0.3), 1329 (2.0), 2145 (0.3)
27 TU	0148 (2.0), 0713 (0.2), 1411 (2.1), 1935 (0.4)
28 W ●	0235 (2.0), 0749 (0.2), 1450 (2.2), 2009 (0.4)
29 TH	0318 (2.1), 0825 (0.1), 1536 (2.3), 2315 (0.4)
30 F	0355 (2.1), 0901 (0.0), 1617 (2.3)
31 SA	0016 (0.4), 0441 (2.1), 0945 (0.0), 1659 (2.3)

FEBRUARY

Day	Times (m)
1 SU	0050 (0.3), 0525 (2.0), 1031 (0.0), 1745 (2.2)
2 M	0146 (0.3), 0608 (2.0), 1125 (0.0), 1836 (2.1)
3 TU	0214 (0.4), 0701 (1.9), 1224 (0.0), 1929 (2.0)
4 W	0205 (0.4), 0754 (1.9), 1335 (0.0), 2035 (1.9)
5 TH	0235 (0.4), 0906 (1.8), 1444 (0.1), 2145 (1.8)
6 F	0335 (0.4), 1014 (1.8), 1555 (0.2), 2316 (1.7)
7 SA	0445 (0.4), 1136 (1.8), 1704 (0.3)
8 SU	0020 (1.8), 0825 (0.3), 1235 (1.9), 2100 (0.3)
9 M	0119 (1.8), 0935 (0.2), 1335 (2.0), 2154 (0.3)
10 TU	0209 (1.9), 1016 (0.2), 1418 (2.1), 2235 (0.3)
11 W	0255 (2.0), 1056 (0.2), 1458 (2.1), 2300 (0.4)
12 TH	0334 (2.0), 0824 (0.2), 1539 (2.1), 2346 (0.4)
13 F	0409 (2.0), 0854 (0.1), 1615 (2.1)
14 SA	0026 (0.3), 0434 (2.0), 0935 (0.1), 1651 (2.1)
15 SU	0047 (0.3), 0508 (2.0), 1009 (0.1), 1726 (2.1)
16 M	0107 (0.3), 0538 (2.0), 1049 (0.1), 1754 (2.0)
17 TU	0117 (0.3), 0616 (1.9), 1135 (0.1), 1835 (1.9)
18 W	0100 (0.3), 0645 (1.9), 1224 (0.1), 1905 (1.9)
19 TH	0115 (0.2), 0723 (1.8), 1325 (0.1), 1944 (1.8)
20 F	0205 (0.2), 0824 (1.7), 1444 (0.2), 2116 (1.7)
21 SA	0305 (0.3), 0955 (1.7), 1524 (0.3), 2220 (1.7)
22 SU	0535 (0.2), 0955 (1.7), 1800 (0.3), 2346 (1.7)
23 M	0607 (0.2), 1209 (1.8), 1950 (0.3)
24 TU	0045 (1.8), 0624 (0.2), 1306 (1.9), 2120 (0.3)
25 W	0136 (1.9), 0644 (0.2), 1351 (2.1), 2215 (0.3)
26 TH ●	0215 (2.0), 0725 (0.1), 1430 (2.2), 2245 (0.3)
27 F	0256 (2.0), 0802 (0.0), 1512 (2.3), 2025 (0.3)
28 SA	0336 (2.1), 0839 (−0.1), 1555 (2.3), 2355 (0.3)

MARCH

Day	Times (m)
1 SU	0417 (2.1), 0921 (−0.1), 1639 (2.3)
2 M	0034 (0.3), 0502 (2.1), 1009 (−0.1), 1725 (2.2)
3 TU	0114 (0.3), 0545 (2.1), 1059 (0.0), 1811 (2.1)
4 W	0204 (0.3), 0635 (2.0), 1209 (0.0), 1905 (2.0)
5 TH	0134 (0.3), 0729 (1.9), 1334 (0.0), 2005 (1.8)
6 F	0215 (0.2), 0835 (1.8), 1446 (0.1), 2115 (1.7)
7 SA	0304 (0.3), 0955 (1.7), 1544 (0.2), 2245 (1.6)
8 SU	0436 (0.3), 1114 (1.7), 1900 (0.3)
9 M	0005 (1.7), 0524 (0.2), 1229 (1.9), 2035 (0.2)
10 TU	0110 (1.8), 0910 (0.2), 1325 (2.0), 2145 (0.2)
11 W	0159 (1.9), 1005 (0.1), 1409 (2.0), 2204 (0.2)
12 TH	0234 (1.9), 1034 (0.1), 1446 (2.1), 2235 (0.3)
13 F O	0315 (1.9), 0809 (0.1), 1515 (2.1), 2305 (0.3)
14 SA	0345 (2.0), 0846 (0.1), 1551 (2.1), 2350 (0.3)
15 SU	0415 (2.0), 0904 (0.1), 1626 (2.1)
16 M	0007 (0.2), 0441 (2.0), 1225 (0.1), 1655 (2.0)
17 TU	0037 (0.2), 0515 (2.0), 1255 (0.1), 1725 (2.1)
18 W	0115 (0.2), 0538 (2.0), 1100 (0.1), 1755 (2.0)
19 TH	0144 (0.2), 0616 (1.9), 1134 (0.1), 1825 (1.9)
20 F	0020 (0.2), 0645 (1.9), 1244 (0.1), 1904 (1.9)
21 SA	0134 (0.1), 0736 (1.8), 1404 (0.2), 2005 (1.7)
22 SU	0224 (0.2), 0845 (1.7), 1510 (0.2), 2134 (1.6)
23 M	0340 (0.2), 1036 (1.7), 1630 (0.3), 2254 (1.6)
24 TU	0530 (0.2), 1146 (1.8), 1920 (0.3)
25 W	0005 (1.7), 0544 (0.2), 1239 (2.0), 2105 (0.2)
26 TH	0105 (1.8), 0614 (0.1), 1325 (2.1), 2134 (0.2)
27 F	0149 (1.9), 0655 (0.0), 1408 (2.2), 2215 (0.3)
28 SA ●	0230 (2.0), 0738 (−0.1), 1450 (2.3), 1959 (0.3)
29 SU	0315 (2.1), 0818 (−0.1), 1536 (2.3), 2038 (0.3)
30 M	0355 (2.1), 0859 (−0.1), 1616 (2.2)
31 TU	0024 (0.3), 0439 (2.1), 0946 (0.0), 1702 (2.1)

APRIL

Day	Times (m)
1 W	0105 (0.2), 0526 (2.1), 1039 (0.0), 1748 (2.0)
2 TH	0206 (0.2), 0611 (2.1), 1220 (0.1), 1846 (1.9)
3 F	0040 (0.2), 0705 (2.0), 1314 (0.1), 1946 (1.7)
4 SA	0134 (0.1), 0804 (1.9), 1425 (0.1), 2054 (1.6)
5 SU	0250 (0.1), 0935 (1.7), 1524 (0.2), 2235 (1.5)
6 M	0355 (0.1), 1105 (1.7), 1815 (0.2), 2345 (1.6)
7 TU	0504 (0.1), 1216 (1.8), 2004 (0.2)
8 W	0045 (1.7), 0554 (0.1), 1306 (1.9), 2104 (0.2)
9 TH	0136 (1.8), 0935 (0.1), 1346 (2.0), 2144 (0.2)
10 F	0216 (1.9), 1026 (0.1), 1419 (2.0), 2215 (0.2)
11 SA O	0250 (1.9), 0754 (0.1), 1456 (2.0), 2250 (0.2)
12 SU	0316 (1.9), 0825 (0.1), 1525 (2.1), 2320 (0.2)
13 M	0345 (2.0), 1110 (0.2), 1556 (2.1), 2330 (0.2)
14 TU	0416 (2.0), 1145 (0.1), 1626 (2.0)
15 W	0005 (0.1), 0445 (2.0), 1224 (0.1), 1700 (2.0)
16 TH	0055 (0.1), 0516 (2.0), 1304 (0.2), 1730 (1.9)
17 F	0130 (0.1), 0545 (2.0), 1340 (0.2), 1805 (1.9)
18 SA	0203 (0.1), 0621 (2.0), 1200 (0.2), 1845 (1.8)
19 SU	0019 (0.1), 0709 (1.9), 1357 (0.2), 1946 (1.7)
20 M	0200 (0.1), 0826 (1.8), 1444 (0.2), 2116 (1.6)
21 TU	0300 (0.1), 0955 (1.8), 1555 (0.3), 2224 (1.6)
22 W	0405 (0.1), 1110 (1.8), 1900 (0.3), 2345 (1.6)
23 TH	0454 (0.1), 1216 (2.0), 2036 (0.2)
24 F	0035 (1.8), 0550 (0.0), 1258 (2.1), 2126 (0.2)
25 SA	0125 (1.9), 0629 (0.0), 1345 (2.2), 2205 (0.2)
26 SU ●	0207 (2.0), 0711 (−0.1), 1429 (2.2), 1938 (0.2)
27 M	0250 (2.1), 0756 (0.0), 1513 (2.2), 2015 (0.2)
28 TU	0335 (2.1), 0839 (0.0), 1557 (2.1)
29 W	0005 (0.2), 0417 (2.2), 0928 (0.1), 1645 (2.0)
30 TH	0105 (0.1), 0502 (2.1), 1324 (0.1), 1731 (1.9)

20

Chart Datum: 0·84 metres below Normaal Amsterdams Peil

TIME ZONE –0100
(Dutch Standard Time)
Subtract 1 hour for UT
For Dutch Summer Time add ONE hour in non-shaded areas

NETHERLANDS – HOEK VAN HOLLAND

LAT 51°59′N   LONG 4°07′E

TIMES AND HEIGHTS OF HIGH AND LOW WATERS   YEAR **1998**

MAY

Day	Time m	Time m	Time m	Time m
1 F	0156 0.1	0551 2.1	1426 0.1	1825 1.8
2 SA	0235 0.1	0646 2.0	1305 0.2	1925 1.7
3 SU	0104	0750 1.9	1405 0.2	2024 1.6
4 M	0214 0.0	0854 1.8	1504 0.2	2200 1.5
5 TU	0334 0.1	1025 1.7	1755 0.3	2316 1.5
6 W	0435 0.1	1134 1.8	1900 0.2	
7 TH	0016 1.6	0525 0.1	1236 1.9	2020 0.2
8 F	0055 1.7	0614 0.1	1316 1.9	2105 0.2
9 SA	0139 1.8	0705 0.1	1349 2.0	2145 0.2
10 SU	0215 1.8	0740 0.2	1425 2.0	2230 0.2
11 M ○	0245 1.9	0850 0.2	1455 2.0	2250 0.2
12 TU	0315 2.0	1030 0.2	1526 2.0	2310 0.1
13 W	0345 2.0	1126 0.2	1601 2.0	2350 0.1
14 TH	0419 2.0	1205 0.2	1635 2.0	
15 F	0035 0.1	0456 2.0	1245 0.2	1705 1.9
16 SA	0125 0.1	0525 2.0	1325 0.2	1748 1.9
17 SU	0205 0.1	0605 2.0	1355 0.2	1835 1.8
18 M	0005 0.0	0651 2.0	1440 0.2	1925 1.7
19 TU	0120 0.0	0754 1.9	1520 0.3	2046 1.6
20 W	0225 0.0	0925 1.8	1715 0.3	2200 1.6
21 TH	0330 0.0	1035 1.9	1845 0.3	2310 1.6
22 F	0424 0.0	1146 2.0	1950 0.2	
23 SA	0010 1.8	0520 0.0	1235 2.1	2055 0.2
24 SU	0057 1.9	0605 0.0	1325 2.1	2135 0.2
25 M ●	0147 2.0	0656 0.0	1408 2.1	1915 0.2
26 TU	0231 2.1	0735 0.1	1455 2.1	1959 0.2
27 W	0317 2.1	0825 0.1	1541 2.0	
28 TH	0001 0.1	0401 2.2	1220 0.2	1625 2.0
29 F	0046 0.1	0447 2.1	1304 0.2	1718 1.9
30 SA	0136 0.0	0535 2.1	1354 0.2	1805 1.8
31 SU	0221 0.0	0625 2.0	1456 0.2	1853 1.7

JUNE

Day	Time m	Time m	Time m	Time m
1 M	0024 0.0	0715 1.9	1344 0.3	1944 1.6
2 TU	0124 0.0	0825 1.8	1435 0.3	2054 1.5
3 W	0300	0925 1.7	1545 0.3	2236 1.5
4 TH	0404 0.1	1100 1.7	1645 0.3	2335 1.6
5 F	0504 0.1	1156 1.8	1735 0.2	
6 SA	0014 1.6	0554 0.1	1240 1.9	1824 0.2
7 SU	0106 1.7	0645 0.2	1315 1.9	2125 0.2
8 M	0134 1.8	0740 0.2	1351 1.9	1935 0.2
9 TU	0215 1.9	0820 0.3	1425 2.0	1954 0.2
10 W ○	0246 2.0	0804 0.3	1506 2.0	2024 0.1
11 TH	0318 2.0	1050 0.3	1536 2.0	2100 0.1
12 F	0358 2.1	1205 0.3	1615 2.0	
13 SA	0021 0.1	0432 2.1	1214 0.3	1650 1.9
14 SU	0106 0.1	0511 2.1	1316 0.2	1735 1.8
15 M	0145 0.0	0555 2.0	1355 0.2	1815 1.8
16 TU	0232 0.0	0641 2.0	1445 0.3	1908 1.7
17 W	0039 0.0	0746 1.9	1530 0.3	2026 1.7
18 TH	0145 0.0	0855 1.9	1640 0.3	2130 1.7
19 F	0255 0.0	1005 1.9	1800 0.3	2240 1.7
20 SA	0355 0.0	1112 2.0	1915 0.3	2339 1.8
21 SU	0453 0.1	1211 2.0	2005 0.3	
22 M	0038 1.9	0555 0.1	1305 2.0	2110 0.3
23 TU	0128 2.0	0639 0.1	1355 2.0	1905 0.2
24 W ●	0215 2.1	0729 0.2	1442 2.0	1949 0.1
25 TH	0300 2.1	0815 0.3	1531 2.0	2035 0.1
26 F	0347 2.2	1200 0.3	1616 1.9	
27 SA	0025 0.1	0825 2.1	1255 0.3	1658 1.9
28 SU	0116 0.0	0517 2.1	1346 0.3	1745 1.8
29 M	0205 0.0	0606 2.0	1430 0.3	1829 1.8
30 TU	0000 0.0	0655 2.0	1457 0.3	1926 1.7

JULY

Day	Time m	Time m	Time m	Time m
1 W	0035 0.0	0746 1.9	1410 0.3	2005 1.7
2 TH	0134 0.1	0840 1.8	1510 0.3	2055 1.6
3 F	0330 0.1	0934 1.7	1605 0.3	2155 1.6
4 SA	0446 0.2	1035 1.7	1716 0.3	2320 1.6
5 SU	0534 0.2	1156 1.8	1806 0.2	
6 M	0020 1.7	0625 0.2	1245 1.8	1840 0.2
7 TU	0106 1.8	0720 0.3	1325 1.9	1920 0.2
8 W	0146 1.9	0750 0.3	1359 1.9	1934 0.2
9 TH ○	0219 2.0	0744 0.3	1439 2.0	2005 0.1
10 F	0259 2.1	0813 0.4	1531 2.0	2036 0.1
11 SA	0337 2.1	1120 0.4	1557 2.0	2110 0.1
12 SU	0417 2.2	1200 0.3	1637 2.0	2145 0.0
13 M	0455 2.2	1250 0.3	1718 1.9	2225 0.0
14 TU	0539 2.1	1346 0.3	1805 1.8	2320 0.1
15 W	0628 2.1	1425 0.3	1855 1.8	
16 TH	0015 0.0	0721 2.0	1500 0.4	1955 1.8
17 F	0124 0.0	0825 2.0	1510 0.4	2100 1.8
18 SA	0235 0.0	0936 1.9	1534 0.4	2210 1.8
19 SU	0346 0.1	1045 1.9	1635 0.4	2318 1.8
20 M	0445 0.2	1155 1.9	1725 0.3	
21 TU	0019 1.9	0544 0.2	1255 1.9	1814 0.3
22 W	0116 2.0	0634 0.3	1349 1.9	1906 0.2
23 TH ●	0205 2.1	0723 0.3	1435 2.0	1945 0.2
24 F	0248 2.1	1050 0.4	1521 2.0	2019 0.1
25 SA	0336 2.2	1146 0.4	1606 2.0	2059 0.1
26 SU	0416 2.2	1236 0.4	1641 2.0	2139 0.1
27 M	0457 2.1	1315 0.4	1718 1.9	2214 0.0
28 TU	0539 2.1	1354 0.4	1759 1.9	2305 0.1
29 W	0615 2.0	1434 0.4	1835 1.8	2353 0.1
30 TH	0705 1.9	1330 0.4	1925 1.8	
31 F	0045 0.1	0750 1.9	1410 0.3	2015 1.7

AUGUST

Day	Time m	Time m	Time m	Time m
1 SA	0144 0.2	0840 1.8	1510 0.3	2110 1.7
2 SU	0235 0.2	0934 1.7	1640 0.3	2215 1.6
3 M	0507 0.3	1044 1.7	1735 0.3	2325 1.7
4 TU	0610 0.3	1154 1.7	1825 0.2	
5 W	0037 1.8	0700 0.3	1256 1.8	1906 0.2
6 TH	0120 1.9	0800 0.4	1340 1.9	1905 0.2
7 F	0159 2.0	0724 0.4	1415 2.0	1935 0.2
8 SA ○	0237 2.1	0755 0.4	1457 2.0	2010 0.1
9 SU	0315 2.2	0825 0.4	1537 2.1	2045 0.0
10 M	0355 2.3	1145 0.4	1617 2.0	2121 0.0
11 TU	0437 2.3	1224 0.4	1701 2.0	2206 0.0
12 W	0519 2.2	1315 0.4	1745 2.0	2256 0.0
13 TH	0605 2.2	1406 0.4	1831 1.9	2345 0.0
14 F	0659 2.1	1430 0.4	1921 1.9	
15 SA	0054 0.1	0759 2.0	1430 0.4	2030 1.9
16 SU	0214 0.1	0903 1.9	1516 0.4	2140 1.8
17 M	0330 0.2	1026 1.8	1609 0.4	2255 1.8
18 TU	0435 0.2	1146 1.8	1726 0.3	
19 W	0010 1.9	0814 0.3	1249 1.8	2055 0.3
20 TH	0109 2.0	0917 0.3	1346 1.9	2134 0.2
21 F	0154 2.1	1010 0.4	1429 2.0	1930 0.2
22 SA ●	0238 2.2	0724 0.4	1509 2.0	2006 0.2
23 SU	0315 2.2	1126 0.5	1545 2.0	2039 0.1
24 M	0355 2.2	1205 0.4	1618 2.0	2116 0.1
25 TU	0436 2.2	1256 0.4	1655 2.0	2155 0.2
26 W	0512 2.1	1315 0.4	1725 2.0	2236 0.2
27 TH	0546 2.0	1315 0.4	1805 1.9	2314 0.2
28 F	0614 2.0	1154 0.4	1836 1.9	
29 SA	0005 0.2	0656 1.9	1300 0.3	1909 1.9
30 SU	0100 0.2	0735 1.9	1356 0.3	2004 1.8
31 M	0154 0.3	0834 1.8	1435 0.3	2135 1.7

Chart Datum: 0·84 metres below Normaal Amsterdams Peil

TIME ZONE –0100
(Dutch Standard Time)
Subtract 1 hour for UT

For Dutch Summer Time add
ONE hour in non-shaded areas

NETHERLANDS – HOEK VAN HOLLAND

LAT 51°59′N   LONG   4°07′E

TIMES AND HEIGHTS OF HIGH AND LOW WATERS

YEAR **1998**

SEPTEMBER

Time	m	Time	m
1 0305 0.4 / 0955 1.7 / TU 1710 0.3 / 2245 1.7		**16** 0425 0.4 / 1124 1.7 / W 1655 0.3 / 2354 1.9	
2 0540 0.4 / 1103 1.7 / W 1757 0.3 / 2356 1.8		**17** 0816 0.3 / 1233 1.8 / TH 2046 0.3	
3 0644 0.4 / 1220 1.8 / TH 1827 0.3		**18** 0059 2.0 / 0905 0.3 / F 1324 1.9 / 2124 0.2	
4 0049 1.9 / 0840 0.4 / F 1315 1.9 / 1834 0.2		**19** 0145 2.1 / 1006 0.4 / SA 1415 2.0 / 1909 0.2	
5 0135 2.1 / 0935 0.4 / SA 1355 2.0 / 1905 0.2		**20** 0225 2.2 / 1024 0.4 / SU 1455 2.0 / ● 1950 0.2	
6 0212 2.2 / 0729 0.4 / SU 1436 2.1 / O 1941 0.1		**21** 0259 2.2 / 1045 0.5 / M 1525 2.1 / 2019 0.2	
7 0252 2.3 / 0805 0.4 / M 1515 2.1 / 2020 0.0		**22** 0335 2.2 / 1136 0.5 / TU 1555 2.1 / 2055 0.2	
8 0335 2.4 / 0839 0.4 / TU 1555 2.2 / 2100 0.0		**23** 0409 2.2 / 1210 0.4 / W 1625 2.1 / 2126 0.2	
9 0415 2.4 / 0918 0.5 / W 1636 2.2 / 2142 0.0		**24** 0441 2.2 / 1237 0.4 / TH 1655 2.1 / 2154 0.3	
10 0459 2.3 / 1306 0.4 / TH 1719 2.1 / 2230 0.1		**25** 0515 2.1 / 1310 0.4 / F 1725 2.0 / 2235 0.3	
11 0546 2.2 / 1335 0.4 / F 1808 2.1 / 2325 0.1		**26** 0542 2.0 / 1054 0.4 / SA 1755 2.0 / 2314 0.3	
12 0632 2.1 / 1400 0.4 / SA 1858 2.0		**27** 0609 2.0 / 1139 0.3 / SU 1830 2.0	
13 0100 0.2 / 0735 1.9 / SU 1350 0.4 / 1954 1.9		**28** 0010 0.3 / 0645 2.0 / M 1250 0.3 / 1905 1.9	
14 0216 0.2 / 0846 1.8 / M 1445 0.4 / 2121 1.8		**29** 0125 0.4 / 0733 1.8 / TU 1355 0.3 / 2004 1.8	
15 0315 0.3 / 1016 1.7 / TU 1550 0.4 / 2246 1.8		**30** 0235 0.4 / 0916 1.7 / W 1505 0.3 / 2206 1.7	

OCTOBER

Time	m	Time	m
1 0440 0.5 / 1036 1.7 / TH 1746 0.3 / 2313 1.8		**16** 0746 0.4 / 1215 1.8 / F 2000 0.3	
2 0630 0.5 / 1146 1.7 / F 1750 0.3		**17** 0039 2.1 / 0850 0.3 / SA 1304 1.9 / 2104 0.2	
3 0014 2.0 / 0817 0.4 / SA 1245 1.9 / 1805 0.2		**18** 0126 2.1 / 0925 0.4 / SU 1355 2.0 / 2145 0.3	
4 0106 2.2 / 0915 0.4 / SU 1325 2.0 / 1835 0.2		**19** 0158 2.2 / 1021 0.4 / M 1424 2.0 / 1935 0.3	
5 0147 2.3 / 0706 0.4 / M 1410 2.1 / O 1916 0.1		**20** 0235 2.2 / 1027 0.4 / TU 1455 2.1 / ● 2004 0.3	
6 0227 2.4 / 0735 0.4 / TU 1449 2.2 / 1955 0.0		**21** 0309 2.2 / 0815 0.4 / W 1525 2.1 / 2024 0.3	
7 0310 2.4 / 0816 0.4 / W 1532 2.3 / 2036 0.0		**22** 0341 2.2 / 0849 0.4 / TH 1555 2.1 / 2105 0.3	
8 0353 2.4 / 0856 0.4 / TH 1615 2.3 / 2118 0.1		**23** 0415 2.2 / 1200 0.4 / F 1629 2.1 / 2136 0.4	
9 0436 2.3 / 0939 0.4 / F 1657 2.3 / 2208 0.2		**24** 0445 2.1 / 0956 0.3 / SA 1659 2.1 / 2204 0.4	
10 0522 2.2 / 1029 0.4 / SA 1742 2.2 / 2303 0.2		**25** 0515 2.1 / 1030 0.3 / SU 1742 2.1 / 2245 0.4	
11 0611 2.0 / 1135 0.4 / SU 1836 2.1		**26** 0545 2.0 / 1104 0.3 / M 1801 2.1 / 2324 0.4	
12 0050 0.3 / 0704 1.9 / M 1306 0.3 / 1935 2.0		**27** 0626 2.0 / 1145 0.2 / TU 1845 2.0	
13 0155 0.3 / 0820 1.7 / TU 1410 0.3 / 2049 1.9		**28** 0100 0.4 / 0709 1.9 / W 1307 0.3 / 1934 1.9	
14 0255 0.4 / 0944 1.6 / W 1514 0.3 / 2225 1.8		**29** 0215 0.5 / 0815 1.7 / TH 1425 0.3 / 2126 1.8	
15 0610 0.4 / 1115 1.7 / TH 1634 0.3 / 2350 1.9		**30** 0330 0.5 / 0806 0.4 / F 1524 0.3 / 2233 1.9	
		31 0607 0.5 / 1116 1.7 / SA 1625 0.3 / 2346 2.0	

NOVEMBER

Time	m	Time	m
1 0747 0.4 / 1210 1.9 / SU 1726 0.2		**16** 0055 2.1 / 0900 0.4 / M 1325 1.9 / 1834 0.3	
2 0038 2.2 / 0906 0.4 / M 1259 2.0 / 1810 0.2		**17** 0136 2.1 / 0946 0.4 / TU 1400 2.0 / 1924 0.3	
3 0118 2.3 / 0945 0.4 / TU 1345 2.1 / 1849 0.1		**18** 0209 2.1 / 1005 0.4 / W 1429 2.0 / 1955 0.3	
4 0205 2.4 / 0716 0.4 / W 1427 2.2 / O 1936 0.1		**19** 0241 2.1 / 0804 0.4 / TH 1454 2.1 / ● 2014 0.4	
5 0246 2.4 / 0755 0.4 / TH 1509 2.3 / 2015 0.1		**20** 0316 2.1 / 0835 0.3 / F 1536 2.2 / 2240 0.4	
6 0336 2.3 / 0835 0.3 / F 1556 2.3 / 2059 0.2		**21** 0349 2.1 / 0905 0.3 / SA 1605 2.2 / 2336 0.3	
7 0417 2.2 / 0926 0.3 / SA 1637 2.3 / 2149 0.3		**22** 0418 2.1 / 0935 0.4 / SU 1636 2.3	
8 0506 2.1 / 1009 0.3 / SU 1725 2.3 / 2250 0.3		**23** 0015 0.4 / 0455 2.1 / M 1009 0.4 / 1709 2.1	
9 0555 2.0 / 1104 0.3 / M 1815 2.2		**24** 0045 0.4 / 0528 2.0 / TU 1045 0.2 / 1748 2.1	
10 0030 0.4 / 0645 1.9 / TU 1219 0.2 / 1915 2.1		**25** 0127 0.4 / 0605 2.0 / W 1129 0.2 / 1826 2.1	
11 0136 0.4 / 0755 1.8 / W 1324 0.2 / 2030 2.0		**26** 0200 0.5 / 0656 1.9 / TH 1224 0.2 / 1925 2.0	
12 0224 0.4 / 0904 1.7 / TH 1445 0.3 / 2155 1.9		**27** 0214 0.5 / 0753 1.8 / F 1345 0.2 / 2035 1.9	
13 0546 0.5 / 1046 1.7 / F 1604 0.3 / 2316 1.9		**28** 0255 0.5 / 0920 1.7 / SA 1450 0.2 / 2200 2.0	
14 0656 0.4 / 1145 1.8 / SA 1716 0.3		**29** 0354 0.5 / 1024 1.8 / SU 1556 0.2 / 2316 2.0	
15 0009 2.0 / 0806 0.4 / SU 1235 1.9 / 1800 0.3		**30** 0720 0.5 / 1135 1.9 / M 1655 0.2	

DECEMBER

Time	m	Time	m
1 0006 2.1 / 0815 0.4 / TU 1232 2.0 / 1745 0.2		**16** 0105 2.0 / 0855 0.4 / W 1325 1.9 / 1920 0.3	
2 0055 2.2 / 0905 0.4 / W 1319 2.1 / 1829 0.2		**17** 0145 2.0 / 0955 0.3 / TH 1359 2.0 / 2010 0.4	
3 0145 2.3 / 0658 0.4 / TH 1406 2.2 / O 1915 0.2		**18** 0214 2.0 / 0755 0.4 / F 1435 2.0 / ● 2050 0.4	
4 0230 2.3 / 0740 0.4 / F 1450 2.3 / 1959 0.2		**19** 0255 2.1 / 0815 0.3 / SA 1509 2.1 / 2210 0.4	
5 0315 2.2 / 0826 0.3 / SA 1537 2.3 / 2045 0.3		**20** 0325 2.1 / 0844 0.2 / SU 1540 2.2 / 2304 0.4	
6 0405 2.2 / 0908 0.2 / SU 1622 2.3 / 2135 0.4		**21** 0401 2.1 / 0915 0.2 / M 1617 2.2 / 2355 0.4	
7 0448 2.1 / 0955 0.2 / M 1708 2.3		**22** 0439 2.1 / 0949 0.2 / TU 1655 2.2	
8 0124 0.4 / 0539 2.0 / TU 1049 0.2 / 1755 2.2		**23** 0046 0.4 / 0516 2.0 / W 1029 0.1 / 1732 2.2	
9 0225 0.4 / 0629 1.9 / W 1145 0.1 / 1848 2.1		**24** 0125 0.4 / 0555 1.9 / TH 1116 0.1 / 1817 2.1	
10 0055 0.4 / 0725 1.8 / TH 1255 0.1 / 1956 2.0		**25** 0210 0.4 / 0639 1.9 / F 1205 0.1 / 1905 2.1	
11 0206 0.5 / 0814 1.7 / F 1355 0.2 / 2100 1.9		**26** 0240 0.5 / 0735 1.8 / SA 1305 0.1 / 2009 2.0	
12 0255 0.5 / 0935 1.6 / SA 1515 0.2 / 2220 1.8		**27** 0250 0.5 / 0846 1.8 / SU 1425 0.1 / 2126 2.0	
13 0410 0.5 / 1105 1.7 / SU 1625 0.3 / 2325 1.9		**28** 0314 0.5 / 0955 1.8 / M 1525 0.1 / 2236 2.0	
14 0504 0.4 / 1155 1.7 / M 1725 0.3		**29** 0405 0.5 / 1105 1.8 / TU 1626 0.2 / 2340 2.0	
15 0019 1.9 / 0757 0.4 / TU 1245 1.8 / 1825 0.3		**30** 0510 0.4 / 1205 1.9 / W 1725 0.2	
		31 0040 2.1 / 0856 0.4 / TH 1302 2.0 / 1820 0.2	

20

Chart Datum: 0·84 metres below Normaal Amsterdams Peil

HOEK VAN HOLLAND
MEAN SPRING AND NEAP CURVES

MEAN RANGES	
Springs	1·9m ————
Neaps	1·5m – – – –

Springs occur 3 days
after
New and Full Moon.

HOEK VAN HOLLAND 10-20-20
(HOOK OF HOLLAND)

Zuid Holland 51°59'·50N 04°02'·78E (Ent)

CHARTS
AC 132, 122; Zeekaart 1540, 1349, 1350, 1449; DYC 1809, 1801; Imray C30, Y5; Stanfords 19

TIDES
+0251 Dover; ML 0·9; Duration 0505; Zone –0100.
HOEK VAN HOLLAND is a Standard Port; predictions for every day of the year are given above. Double LWs occur, more obviously at sp; in effect a LW stand. Predictions are for the *lower* LW. The 1st LW is about 5½ hrs after HW and the 2nd LW about 4¼ hrs before the next HW. The slight rise after the first LW is called the Agger. Water levels on this coast are much affected by the weather. Prolonged NW gales can raise the levels by up to 3m.

SHELTER
Ent safe except in strong on-shore winds when heavy seas/swell develop. Berghaven hbr is closed to yachts; better shelter at Maassluis (3m), 6M up river (km 1019).

NAVIGATION
WPTs From S: MV-N NCM lt By, Q, 51°59'·65N 04°00'·30E, 288°/108° from/to Nieuwe Zuiderdam lt, 1·5M. From N: Indusbank NCM lt By, Q, 52°02'·93N 04°03'·72E, 010°/190° from/to Nieuwe Noorderdam lt, 3·2M. There are no real navigational dangers but it is a very busy waterway with a constant stream of ocean-going and local ships. Keep clear of ships manoeuvering whilst transferring pilots.
Crossing the Entrance: To cross the Maasgeul (seaward of the bkwtrs), yachts should call *Maas Ent* Ch 03, with position and course, and keep watch on Ch 03. Cross under power on a track, 030°/210°, close W of line joining buoys MV (51°57'·50N 03°58'·50E), MV-N (51°59'·65N 04°00'·30E) and Indusbank N (52°02'·93N 04°03'·72E). Beware the strong tidal set across the ent.
Rules for Yachts (in Nieuwe Waterweg): Comply with VTS (see R/T). Keep to stbd bank, not too close due to sunken debris. No tacking/beating; no ⚓. Eng ready for instant start. Able to motor at 3.24kn (6km/hr). Hoist a radar

reflector, esp in poor vis or at night. Cross chan quickly at 90°. Docks, inc the Calandkanaal/Beerkanaal (Europoort), are prohib to yachts, except for access to a marina.
Note: An anti-flood barrier is being constructed across the Nieuwe Waterweg approx 2M up-stream from the conspic ldg lt trs (Iso R 6s) at Berghaven, near Km 1027.

LIGHTS AND MARKS
Maasvlakte Fl (5) 20s 66m 28M; B 8-sided tr, W bands; vis 340°-267° (H24).
Nieuwe Noorderdam, hd FR 24m 10M; Or tr, B bands, helipad; in fog Al Fl WR 6s.
Nieuwe Zuiderdam, hd FG 24m 10M; Or tr, B bands, helipad; in fog Al Fl WG 6s; Horn 10s.
Ldg lts 107° (for Nieuwe Waterweg): Both Iso R 6s 29/43m 18M; R trs, W bands; vis 100°-114° (H24); synch.
Traffic Sigs from Pilot/Sig Stn, which has RDF bn HH 288, (N side of Nieuwe Waterweg, close W of Berghaven):

Ⓡ Ⓡ Ⓡ
Ⓦ   =   No entry to, or exit from, Maas Estuary
Ⓡ Ⓡ Ⓡ

Nieuwe Waterweg:

Ⓡ Ⓡ   Ⓡ Ⓡ
Ⓦ   =   No entry.   Ⓦ   =   No exit
Ⓡ Ⓡ   Ⓡ Ⓡ

Patrol vessels show a Fl Bu lt. If such vessels show a Fl R lt, it means 'Stop'.

RADIO TELEPHONE
The Maas-Rotterdam VTS (H24) covers from approx 38M W of the Hook up to central Rotterdam; see Fig 10 (5) and the schematic diagram following 10.20.21.
3 main **Traffic Centres**, each on Ch 13, with their radar stn sub-sectors *(italics)* on a dedicated VHF Ch, are as follows:
(1)   **Traffic Centre Hoek van Holland (VCH)**
Maas Approach Ch 01, (Outer apps, from 38M W of Hook);
Pilot Maas Ch 02, (from approx 11M in to 4M W of Hook);
Maas Ent (Maasmond) Ch 03, (from 4M in to km 1031);
Rozenburg Ch 65, (Nieuwe Waterweg to km 1023);
(2)   **Traffic Centre Botlek (VCB)**
Maassluis Ch 80, (km 1023 to km 1017);
Botlek Ch 61, (km 1017 to km 1011);
(3)   **Traffic Centre Stad (VCS)**
Eemhaven Ch 63, (km 1011 to km 1007);
Waalhaven Ch 60, (km 1007 to km 1003);
Note: Hartel and Maasboulevard Tfc Centres, and their radar sectors, have been omitted because yachts would not often enter their areas. The Hbr Coordination Centre (HCC) administers Rotterdam port on Ch 11 14.
Yachts should **first report** to *Maas Approach* or *Pilot Maas* (or to *Maas Ent* if using the ITZ), stating name/type of vessel, position & destination; then obey instructions, listening on the appropriate VHF Ch's as shown by W □ signboards on the river banks. (Km signs are similar).
Info broadcasts (weather, vis, tfc and tidal) by Traffic Centres and radar stns on request.
Other stations: Oude Maas Ch 62; Spijkenisserbrug and Botlekbrug Ch 18; Brienenoordbrug Ch 20; Bridge at Alblasserdam Ch 22; Dordrecht Ch 19 04 71 (H24).

TELEPHONE (Dial code 010)
Port Authority (HCC) 4251400; Pilot (Hook) 4251422; Police 4141414; Ⓗ 4112800; Brit Consul (020) 6764343.

FACILITIES
Maassluis ☎ 5912277, AB, CH, El, FW. **Services:** BY, ME, Sh.
Town P, D, V, R, Bar, ⊠ Ⓑ ⇌ ✈ (Rotterdam)
Ferry: Hook-Harwich (HSS); Rotterdam Europoort-Hull.

ROTTERDAM   10-20-21
Zuid Holland 51°54'·00N 04°28'·00E   Rtg 1-1-2

CHARTS
AC 133, 132, 122; Zeekaart 1540/1/2; DYC 1809; Stanfords 19
TIDES
+0414 Dover; ML 0·9; Duration 0440; Zone –0100

Standard Port VLISSINGEN (←)

Times				Height (metres)			
High Water		Low Water		MHWS	MHWN	MLWN	MLWS
0300	0900	0400	1000	4·7	3·9	0·8	0·3
1500	2100	1600	2200				
Differences MAASSLUIS							
+0125	+0100	+0110	+0255	–2·7	–2·2	–0·5	0·0
VLAARDINGEN							
+0150	+0125	+0135	+0320	–2·7	–2·2	–0·5	0·0

NOTE 1: Maasluis and Vlaardingen are both referenced to Vlissingen, as shown above, in British Admiralty Tables. The Dutch *Guide to the Netherlands and Belgian coasts* (HP11) shows the following time differences relative to HW and the first LW at Hoek van Holland:

	HW	LW
Maasluis	+0113	+0038
Vlaardingen and Schiedam	+0114	+0112
Rotterdam	+0123	+0352

These figures, plus the tidal curves, take account of local river conditions. The Dutch Tables (HP33) do not include Secondary Port differences; in effect all the major ports, including Rotterdam, are regarded as Standard Ports and full daily predictions are published.
NOTE 2: Double LWs occur. The rise after the first LW is called the Agger. See 10.20.20.

SHELTER
Good in the yacht hbrs (see FACILITIES), but in the river there is always a considerable sea and swell due to constant heavy traffic; Europoort/Rotterdam is the world's largest port complex. All but local yachts are discouraged from using the Nieuwe Maas.
NAVIGATION
See 10.20.20. There are no navigational dangers other than the amount of heavy sea-going traffic. Berghaven to Rotterdam is about 19M. 7M before the centre of Rotterdam, the Oude Maas joins (km 1013); same rules apply as in 10.20.20. Min speed 3.24kn (6km/hr).
Note: Special regulations apply to yachts in the Rhine. These are given in a French booklet *Service de la Navigation du Rhin* obtainable from 25 Rue de la Nuée Bleu, 6700 Strasbourg.

LIGHTS AND MARKS
Marks to locate Yacht Havens:
(1) Ent to Vlaardingen YC (2·7m) is on N bank by Delta Hotel, between km posts 1010-1011.
(2) 2M on, just above the ent to Wilhelmina Haven is the Spuihaven (1·8-2·3m); N bank by km 1007.
(3) Parkhaven and the lock into Coolhaven Yacht Hbr are clearly identified on the N bank by the huge Euromast in the park (km 1002·5).
(4) The Royal Maas YC at the Veerhaven (3·3m), a centre for traditional yachts, is on the N bank (km 1001·5).
(5) City Marina (4·0m) is between Noordereiland and S bank; km post 1000 is on NW bank. Enter beyond the eye-catching Erasmus bridge (lifting section at SE end); then 2nd ent to stbd, via lifting bridge.
RADIO TELEPHONE
The VTS Ch's for central Rotterdam are 63, 60, 81 and 21; see 10.20.20 and the diagram overleaf. The Hbr Coordination Centre (HCC) administers Rotterdam port on Ch 11 14. Call HCC Ch 11 for emergencies. English is official second language. Erasmus bridge Ch 18.
TELEPHONE (Dial code 010)
Hbr Coordination Centre (HCC) 4251400, also Emergency; ⌗ 4298088; Police 4141414; Ⓗ 4112800; Brit Consul (020) 6764343.
FACILITIES
Vlaardingen YC (Oude Haven via lock/bridge), M, BY, ME, SM, FW, P, D, Gaz, ≠; **Hr Mr** ☎ 4346786.
Schiedam YC (Spuihaven) ☎ 4267765, D, L, FW, ME, EI, Sh, CH, AB, ≠;
Coolhaven Yacht Hbr ☎ 4738614, Slip, M, P, D, L, FW, ME, EI, Sh, C, CH, AB, V, R, Bar;
Royal Maas YC ☎ 4137681, D, L, FW, ME, EI, SH, CH, AB; home of the "Brown Fleet", traditional Dutch barges.
City Marina (51°54'·68N 04°29'·82E, S bank close to Noordereiland). ☎ via (0187) 493769, ☎ 493807, 110 AB in 4m, FW, AC, YC, Water taxi.
YC IJsselmonde ☎ 482833, AB (1·2-1·8m), AC, FW; on S bank at km 994, opposite the Hollandsche IJssel fork (off chartlet).
Services: P, D, ME; Gaz, ACA, DYC Agent.
City all facilities, ✉, Ⓑ, ≠, ✈, Ferry: Rotterdam - Hull, also Hook-Harwich (HSS).

20

TS IN MAAS PRECAUTIONARY AREA AND TSS

See descriptive text under 10.20.20 RADIO TELEPHONE

SCHEVENINGEN 10-20-22

Zuid Holland 52°06'·28N 04°15'·35E   Rtg 2-1-1

CHARTS
AC 122, 2322; Zeekaart 1035, 1349, 1350, 1449; DYC 1801; ANWB H/J; Imray Y5; Stanfords 19

TIDES
+0320 Dover; ML 0·9; Duration 0445; Zone −0100

Standard Port VLISSINGEN (←)

Times				Height (metres)			
High Water		Low Water		MHWS	MHWN	MLWN	MLWS
0300	0900	0400	1000	4·7	3·9	0·8	0·3
1500	2100	1600	2200				
Differences SCHEVENINGEN							
+0105	+0100	+0220	+0245	−2·5	−2·1	−0·5	−0·1

NOTE: Double LWs occur. The rise after the 1st LW is called the Agger. Water levels on this coast can be much affected by the weather. Prolonged NW gales can raise levels by up to 3m, whilst strong E winds can lower levels by 1m.

SHELTER
Good, but ent can be difficult in on-shore NW winds >F6. The yacht marina in the Second Hbr gives very good shelter. Access H24.

NAVIGATION
WPT SCH (SWM) buoy, Iso 4s, 52°07'·80N 04°14'·20E, 336°/156° from/to ent, 1·6M. Strong tidal streams running NE/SW across the ent can cause problems. Strong winds from SW to N cause a scend in the outer hbr. Beware large ships entering and leaving.

LIGHTS AND MARKS
Outer ldg lts, Iso 4s, 156°; Inner Oc G 5s 131°.

Tfc signals (from Semaphore Mast):
Ⓡ over Ⓦ = Entry prohib. Ⓦ over Ⓡ = Exit prohib.
Fl Ⓨ = entry difficult due to vessels leaving.
Q Ⓨ is shown by ent to First Hbr (W side) when vessels are entering or leaving port.

Tide signals:
Ⓖ over Ⓦ = tide rising. Ⓦ over Ⓖ = tide falling.
Ⓡ = less than 5m in entry chan.

RADIO TELEPHONE
Call: *Scheveningen Haven* VHF Ch 14 (H24) prior to entry/dep to de-conflict from ferries. Radar Ch 21.

TELEPHONE (Dial code 070)
Marina Hr Mr 3520017, mobile 06-52727153; Port Hr Mr 3527701; Traffic Centre 3527721; ⌗ 3514481; Police 3104911; Dr 3455300; Ambulance 3222111; Brit Consul (020) 6764343.

FACILITIES
YC Scheveningen (223 + 100 visitors) ☎ 3520017, f27.00, AC, Bar, C (15 ton), CH, D, El, FW, ME, R, 🅾, Sh, SM; **Clubhouse** ☎ 3520308; **Hbr** Slip, FW, ME, Sh, C (60 ton), CH, R, Bar; **Services:** ME, El, Sh, CH, SM, DYC Agent. **Town** P, D, V, R, Bar, ✉, Ⓑ, ⇌, ✈ Rotterdam/Amsterdam. Ferry: See Rotterdam or Hoek van Holland.

IJMUIDEN   10-20-23
Noord Holland 52°28'.03N 04°32'.00E   Rtgs: see Facilities

CHARTS
AC 2322, 124; Zeekaart 1450, 1543, 1035, 1350; DYC 1801;
Imray Y5; Stanfords 19

TIDES
+0400 Dover; ML 1·0; Zone –0100

Standard Port VLISSINGEN (←—)

Times				Height (metres)			
High Water		Low Water		MHWS	MHWN	MLWN	MLWS
0300	0900	0400	1000	4·7	3·9	0·8	0·3
1500	2100	1600	2200				
Differences IJMUIDEN							
+0145	+0140	+0305	+0325	–2·6	–2·2	–0·5	–0·1

SHELTER
Very good at SPM marina (5·5m - 3m depths) on S side of
Buitenhaven, close E of S bkwtr QG (see chartlet). There
are also temp (24hrs) berths at canal locks. There are
small marinas at IJmond (under lift-bridge in Zijkanaal C,
km 10) and Nauwerna (Zijkanaal D, km 12).

NAVIGATION
WPT IJM (SWM) buoy, Mo (A) 8s, Racon, 52°28'.70N
04°23'.93E, 275°/095° from/to ent, 5·0M. Beware strong
tidal streams across hbr ent, scend inside Buitenhaven
and heavy merchant tfc. The 4 locks into Noordzeekanaal
are: North, Middle, South and Small; yachts normally use
the Small (Kleine) lock, adjacent to the South. One in/out
cycle per hour, 0600-2100 daily, is scheduled. Note: the
canal level may be above or below sea level.

LIGHTS AND MARKS
Ldg lts 100° into Buitenhaven and Zuider Buitenkanaal:
Front lt ho FWR 30m 16/13M, W050°-122°, R122°-145°,
W145°-160°, RC; rear lt ho, Fl 5s 52m 29M. Both are dark
R trs and show a Ⓦ lt by day.
Marina ent marked by SPM buoy, VQ, "IJM3-SPM", 1ca to
N. Ent sigs: Ⓡ = no entry; Ⓡ+Ⓖ = get ready; Ⓖ = go.
Traffic, tidal, sluicing & storm sigs are shown at/near the
conspic Hbr Ops Centre (HOC) bldg, next to front ldg lt.
Traffic sigs (large frame adjacent to the front ldg lt):
There are 9 lts in a 3 x 3 frame, of which, for **inbound**
yachts, only the 3 right-hand lts normally apply:
Top RH lt (for S Lock) Fl Ⓖ   = wait for lock entry.
            Ⓖ   = clear to enter.
          Fl Ⓡ   = vessels exiting.
            Ⓡ   = lock not in use.
Centre RH lt (for Zuider Buiten Kanaal)
          Fl Ⓡ   = vessels exiting.
            Ⓡ   = traffic prohib.
Bottom RH lt   Ⓡ   = entry prohib, all vessels.
For **outbound yachts** only the top LH lt applies (for
Zuider Buitenkanaal) Fl Ⓡ   = vessels entering.
            Ⓡ   = traffic prohib.
Tidal sigs, from radar tr on HOC bldg:
Ⓖ over Ⓦ = rising tide; Ⓦ over Ⓖ = falling tide.

RADIO TELEPHONE
Call the following VTS stns (H24) in sequence for entry:
Traffic Centre IJmuiden   Ch 88 (W of IJM buoy).
IJmuiden Hbr Control (HOC)   Ch 61 (IJM buoy to locks).
(Seaport Marina)   Ch 74; call *SPM*.
IJmuiden Locks   Ch 22.
Traffic Centre Noordzeekanaal Ch 03 (Lock to km 11·2).
Amsterdam Port Control   Ch 14 (Km 11·2 to A'dam).
Yachts should monitor the appropriate Ch for tfc info.
Radar assistance is available on request Ch 88 and 61.
Visibility reports are broadcast on all Chans every H+00
when vis <1000m.

TELEPHONE (Dial code 0255)
Traffic Centre IJmuiden 534542; Hbr Ops (HOC) 519027;
Pilot 564503; ⌗ 560800; CG 537644; Police 535035; Ⓗ
565100; Brit Consul (020) 6764343; Emergencies 112.

FACILITIES
Seaport Marina (SPM) ☎ 560300/📠 560301. Rtg 3-1-1.
(600 inc Ⓥ), f34.80, AC, FW, D & P, BH (70 ton), El, Ⓔ, CH,
Gas, Slip, SM, Sh, ME, R, Bar, ◻, in summer, bus/≋ to
Amsterdam and Haarlem; **WV IJmond** Rtg 1-4-1. Hr Mr ☎
(023) 5375003, AB f10.80 inc AC, D, BY, C (20 ton), ◻, Bar,
V, R. **Town** P, D, Gaz, V, R, Bar, ✉, Ⓑ, ≋ (bus to
Beverwijk), ✈ Amsterdam. Ferry: IJmuiden-Newcastle.

20

AMSTERDAM   10-20-24

Noord Holland 52°23'·00N 04°54'·00E   Rtgs: see Facilities

CHARTS
AC 124; Zeekaart 1543; DYC 1801, 1810; ANWB G, I
TIDES
Amsterdam is between the Noordzeekanaal and the IJsselmeer, both of which are non-tidal; Zone –0100.
SHELTER
Complete in any of 5 yacht hbrs/marinas (see chartlet & Facilities). The main one is Sixhaven, on the N bank, NE of the ⇌ (conspic); it is small, pleasant and well located, so mostly full by 1800. WV Aeolus is a good alternative. Twellega is more for the larger yacht; bus to city centre. Gem. Haven on the S bank, close NW of the Hbr bldg (conspic), is prone to wash from passing ships and not recommended. There is a small marina, WV Zuiderzee, on N bank immediately E of Oranjesluizen.
NAVIGATION
See 10.20.23. The 13·5M transit of the Noordzeekanaal is simple, apart from the volume of commercial traffic. The speed limit is 9kn. Schellingwoude bridge (9m), at 500m E of Oranjesluizen, opens: all year Mon-Fri 0600-0700, 0900-1600, 1800-2200. Sat 0600-2200. Sun & Public hols from 1 Apr to 1 Nov: 0900-2100; 1 Nov to 1 Apr: closed. There are waiting pontoons both sides of Oranjesluizen. Amsterdam gives access to canals running to N & S and also, via the Oranjesluizen (H24), into the IJsselmeer.
LIGHTS AND MARKS
Both banks of the canal and the ents to branch canals and basins are lit. The chan E towards the Oranjesluizen and the Amsterdam-Rijn canal is lit/buoyed.
RADIO TELEPHONE
VHF Ch 14. See also 10.20.23. Oranjesluizen Ch 18.
TELEPHONE (Dial code 020)
Port Control 6221201; ⌗ 5867511; Emergency 112; Police 5599111; Dr 5555555; Brit Consul: 6764343.
FACILITIES
Marinas: Sixhaven (60 + some Ⓥ) ☎ 6370892, Rtg 1-4-1, f12.00 inc AC, FW, Bar (weekends);
ZV Aeolus ☎ 6360791, Rtg 1-4-1, f10.00 inc AC, YC, FW;
Gem. Haven ☎ 5503636, Rtg 1-5-1, f15.00, no facilities;
Twellega ☎ 6320616, Rtg 1-2-2, f18.00, AC, FW, Sh, P, C (30 ton); **WV Zuiderzee** No ☎, Rtg 1-5-2, f10, YC, AC, FW;
Gem. Haven Amsterdam (min 3 days), f34.50.
City: All facilities, Gaz, Ⓔ, ACA, DYC Agent, Ⓑ, ⊠, ⇌, ✈.
Ferries: IJmuiden-Newcastle. See also Hoek van Holland.

IJSSELMEER   10-20-25

CHARTS
AC *1408*, 2593; Zeekaart 1351, 1454; DYC 1810: up to date copy is essential to avoid live firing ranges, fishing areas and other hazards; it also has many hbr chartlets.
TIDES
The IJsselmeer is non-tidal. Tides at locks at Den Oever and Kornwerderzand: –0230 Dover; ML 1·2; Zone –0100

Standard Port HELGOLAND (⟶)

Times				Height (metres)			
High Water		Low Water		MHWS	MHWN	MLWN	MLWS
0200	0700	0200	0800	2·7	2·3	0·4	0·0
1400	1900	1400	2000				
Differences KORNWERDERZAND							
–0210	–0315	–0300	–0215	–0·5	–0·4	–0·1	+0·2
DEN OEVER							
–0245	–0410	–0400	–0305	–0·8	–0·6	0·0	+0·2

SHELTER
Excellent in the many marinas, some of which are listed below. Most berths are bows on to a pontoon, stern lines to piles; there are few ⌕s.
NAVIGATION
The IJsselmeer is the un-reclaimed part of the former Zuiderzee; it is separated from the Waddenzee by the 20M long Afsluitdijk, completed in 1932. It is divided into two parts by the Houtribdijk, with locks at Enkhuizen to the NW and Lelystad in the SE. The SW part is the Markermeer (20M x 15M, 2-4·5m deep); the rest of the IJsselmeer is 30M x 20M, 7m max. Three ents via locks:
(1)   IJmuiden, Noordzeekanaal to Oranjesluizen (10.20.24).
(2)   Den Oever (SW end of the Afsluitdijk): Appr from Waddenzee via well marked/lit chan; ldg lts 132°, both Oc 10s to ent, thence follow Dir Iso WRG 2s, 220° to wait in Buitenhaven. 2 bridges and locks operate in unison HO. From IJsselmeer, wait in Binnenhaven; FR/G at ent.
(3)   Kornwerderzand lock (NE end of the Afsluitdijk) H24. From Waddenzee, via W, NW or NE chans. Ent has FR/G and Iso G 6s. Wait in Buitenhaven; yachts use the smaller E lock. From IJsselmeer, ldg lts Iso 4s 348° to FR/G at ent; wait in Binnenhaven (3·8m).
Standard lock sigs (vert): Ⓡ Ⓡ Ⓡ = not in service; Ⓡ = no entry; Ⓡ Ⓖ = stand by; Ⓖ = enter.

IJSSELMEER continued

Speed limits: in buoyed chans and <250m from shore 10·5kn. Hbr limits vary; see ANWB Almanak Vol 2. Strong winds get up very quickly and often cause short seas; they can also raise the water level on a lee shore, or lower it on a weather shore, by 1m or more. Most hbrs have water level gauges which should be checked in bad weather. In non-tidal waters CD usually refers to the level at which the water is kept. In the Netherlands, this may be Kanaalpeil, which is related to Normaal Amsterdams Peil (NAP), which in turn is approx Mean Sea Level.

A firing range, operational Tues to Thurs 1000 - 1900LT, extends S from Breezanddijk (53°01'·0N 05°12'·5E) to 3M N of Medemblik then NNW to Den Oever (DYC 1810.3). Call the range control on Ch 71 *Schietterrein Breezanddijk*. Scheveningen Radio broadcasts firing times on the day of firing after Dutch forecasts, at even hours; also at 1900 the previous day in English Ch 25, 27, 83 after the weather.

BUOYAGE The SIGNI buoyage system is used in the whole of the IJsselmeer. The main features are:
(1) Lateral buoyage as for IALA (Region A).
(2) Supplementary PHM & SHM buoys may be R/W or G/W respectively; they also indicate a least depth of 2m.
(3) At division of chan, a spherical buoy as follows:
a. Chans of equal importance = R & G bands; topmark R and G sphere;
b. Main chan to port = G above R bands; topmark G △ or G △ above a G ○;
c. Main chan to stbd = R above G bands; topmark R □ or R □ above a R ○.

RADIO TELEPHONE
VHF Ch's at locks are: Oranjesluizen 18; Enkhuizen 22; Den Oever 20; Kornwerderzand 18; Lelystad 20.

HARBOURS AND FACILITIES
A useful guide, one of the few in English, is *IJsselmeer Harbours* by Hilary Keatinge (Barnacle Marine 1988). It is essential to have the *Almanac voor Watertoerisme*, Vol I onboard; it contains the BPR (Waterway Code). Some of the many hbrs are listed below (clockwise from the NW):

DEN OEVER: Jachthaven (3m) to port of ent; Hr Mr ☎ (0227) 511789, f14.75, D, P, FW, ⬚.
MAKKUM: Approx 1M SE of Kornwerderzand, a SHM buoy MA5, Iso G4s, marks the 4·1M buoyed chan. FR/FG lts lead 092° into Makkum, Hr Mr ☎ (0515) 231450. To stbd, **Marina Makkum** (2·5m) ☎ (0515) 232828, f19.25, P, D, AC, FW, SM, Gaz, V, Bar, R, ⬚. 4 other marinas/YCs are further E; BY, ME, C (30 ton), BH (30 ton). **Town** Ⓑ, Dr, V, R.
WORKUM: 2·5M N of Hindeloopen; FW ldg lts 081° along buoyed chan to **It Soal Marina** ☎ (0515) 542937, f19.25, BY, ME, C, FW, P (cans), Gaz, BH; **Jachthaven Anne Wever** ☎ (0515) 542361, f14.50, C (40 ton).
HINDELOOPEN: has 2 marinas, one in town and one 180m to N. **Jachthaven Hindeloopen** (500) Hr Mr ☎ (0514) 521866, f22.50, P, D, FW, AC, ⬚, BH (30 ton), CH, R, Bar; **Old Hbr** f9.00, D, P, FW, ME, EI, Sh; **W.V Hylper Haven** Hr Mr ☎ (0514) 522019, f9.00, P, D, FW, ME, EI, Sh.
STAVOREN: Ent Buitenhaven 048° on Dir lt Iso 4s between FR/G. Marina, f12.00, E of ent in Oudehaven; ☎ (0514) 681216, VHF Ch 74. Or, 1km S, ent Nieuwe Voorhaven (FR/G & Fl 5s Dir lt) then via lock to **Stavoren Marina** (3m) ☎ 681566, f18.25, BY, ME, C, FW, P, D, SM, Gaz, BH (20 ton); **Outer Marina** (3·5m) close S of Nieuwe Voorhaven, f22.50. 3 other marinas. **Town** Ⓑ, Dr, V, R, ⇌.
LEMMER: Appr on ldg lts 038°, Iso 8s, to KL5/VL2 By; then ldg lts 083°, Iso 8s, through Lemstergeul. Lastly FG and Iso G 4s lead 065° into town and some 14 marinas. **Gem. Jachthaven** Hr Mr ☎ (0514) 561331, f14.00; **Services:** BY, ME, C, FW, P, D, Gaz, SM. **Town** Ⓑ, Dr, V, R, ✉.
URK: Hbr ent ½M SE of lt ho, Fl 5s 27m 18M. Dir lt Iso G 4s to hbr ent, FR/G. Hbr has 4 basins; keep NNW to berth in Nieuwe Haven, Westhaven or Oosthaven (3·3m), f11.75. Hr Mr ☎ (0527) 689970. **Westhaven** P & D (cans); SM; **Oosthaven** ME, EI, Sh, Ⓔ, CH. **Town** EC Tues; Ⓑ, ✉, Dr.
KETELHAVEN: Ent Ketelmeer via bridge (12·9m) which lifts at S end; after 4M to By WK1 Iso G 4s, ldg lts Iso 8s 101°/0·7M in buoyed chan. Turn S for unlit marina ent (2·2m). **Marina** (200) f14.75, FW, AC, R. Hr Mr ☎ (0321) 312271. W ent has FG/R lts to Ketelsluis: Hr Mr ☎ 318237 D, P (cans).
LELYSTAD: has 2 marinas: 2M NNE of lock is **Flevo** (550) ☎ (0320) 279803, f22.50, BY, ME, C, FW, AC, D, P (cans), ⬚, BH (50 ton), R, Bar, V. Close N of the lock is **Houtribhaven** (560) Hr Mr ☎ 260198, f14.75, D, CH, V, R, Bar, C (12 ton). Radio mast, R lts, (140m) is conspic; marinas are lit.

MARKERMEER

MUIDERZAND: Ent 1M N of Hollandsebrug at buoys IJM5-JH2/IJM3. **Marina** ☎ (036) 5365151, f22.00, FW, AC, D, P.
NAARDEN: 1M SE of Hollandsebrug (12·9m), ent at GM54 buoy. **Gem Jachthaven** (1000) ☎ (035) 6942106, f15.75, D, P, AC, FW, EI, BH, C, CH, V, R, Bar, ⇌ (Naarden-Bussum).
MUIDEN: Ldg lts Q 181° into **KNZ & RV Marina** (2·6m), W of ent; home of Royal Netherlands YC (150 berths). Hr Mr ☎ (0294) 261450, f26.20, D, P (cans), CH, FW, Bar, R. On E bank **Stichting Jachthaven** (70) ☎ 261223, f19.00, D, P.
DURGERDAM: Convenient for Oranjesluizen. Ldg lts 337°, both FR. Keep strictly to chan which is ½M E of overhead power lines. Berth to stbd of ent (1·8m), f13.00. ☎ (020) 4904717.
MARKEN (picturesque show piece): Ent Gouwzee from N, abeam Volendam, thence via buoyed chan; Dir FW lt 116° between FR/G at hbr (2·2m). Lt ho, conspic, Oc 8s 16m 9M, on E end of island. Hr Mr ☎ (0299) 603231, f12.50, FW, AC, V, R, Ⓑ, P & D (cans).
MONNICKENDAM: Appr as for Marken, then W to MO10 Iso R 8s and ldg lts FR at 236°. Hr Mr ☎ (0299) 658585. 4 marinas & facilities: f13.50, ME, C, FW, P (cans), D, Gaz, AC, CH.
VOLENDAM: Berth to stbd (2·4m). Dir lt Fl 5s 313°. FR/FG at ent. ☎ (0299) 369620, f10.20, ME, FW, C, P, D, Gaz, SM.
EDAM: Appr via unlit chan keeping Iso W 8s between FG /R at narrow ent; beware commercial traffic. **Jachthaven Galgenveld** (2·5m) S side of outer hbr, f13.75. Or lock into the Oorgat and via S canal to Nieuwe Haven. Hr Mr ☎ (0299) 371092, f8.25, ME, EI, Sh. **Town** Bar, ⬚, ✉, Gaz, Ⓑ.
HOORN: Radio tr (80m) 1·5M ENE of hbr. Iso 4s 15M 10M and FR/G at W Hbr ent. Four options: to port **Stichting Jachthaven Hoorn** (700) Hr Mr ☎ (0299) 215208, f14.75, FW, AC, ⬚, CH, V, ME, EI, Sh, C; to stbd ⚓ in **Buitenhaven** (2m); ahead & to stbd **Vluchthaven Marina** f15.75, (100) ☎ 213540 FW; ahead to **Binnenhaven** (2·7m) via narrow lock (open H24) AB f14.75, P, FW.
Town V, CH, ✉, R, Dr, P & D (cans), Ⓑ, Gaz, ⇌.
ENKHUIZEN: From SW, appr via buoyed chan and ldg lts Iso 4s at 039°; from NE, ldg lts Iso 8s at 230° and FR /G at bkwtrs lead to Krabbersgat lock and hbr. Call lock Ch 22. The 2 marinas and Buitenhaven are NE of the lock: **Compagnieshaven** (500) Hr Mr ☎ (0228) 313353 f20.00, P, D, FW, AC, CH, BH (12), Gaz, ⬚; **Buyshaven** (195) ☎ 315660, f16.25, FW, AC; **Buitenhaven** ☎ 312444 f11.50, FW. **Town** EC Mon; Market Wed; C, Slip, CH, SM, ME, EI, Sh, Ⓑ, Bar, P & D (cans), Dr, ✉, ⇌.

Continued

20

IJSSELMEER (WEST)   *Continued*

ANDIJK: Visitors use **Stichting Jachthaven Andijk,** the first of 2 marinas; (600) ☎ (0228) 593085, f14.75, narrow ent with tight turn between FR/G lts. ME, C (20), SM, Gaz, ◻, D, CH.

MEDEMBLIK: Ent on Dir lt Oc 4s 232° between FR/G. Go via Oosterhaven (P & D) into Middenhaven (short stay), then via bridge to Westerhaven. **Pekelharinghaven** (120) Hr Mr ☎ (0227) 542175, f14.00; ent is to port by Castle, CH, Bar, R; **Middenhaven** Hr Mr ☎ 541686, f11.25, FW; **Stichting Jachthaven** Hr Mr ☎ 541861 in Westerhaven, f14.00, FW, AC, ◻, C. **Town** Ⓑ, CH, ME, El, SM, Sh, ✉, Dr, Bar, ◻, R, V.

INLAND ROUTE TO RIVER EMS (DELFZIJL)

As an alternative to the shallow tidal route inshore of the Frisian Islands, or as a bad weather option, masted yachts can transit the canals/lakes from the IJsselmeer to Delfzijl without lowering masts. From Lemmer to Delfzijl is about 100M/180km, via Prinses Margrietkanaal, Leeuwarden, Dokkumer Ee, Dokkum, Lauwersmeer, Zoutkamp, Reit Diep, Groningen and Eemskanaal. Leeuwarden can also be reached from Harlingen via the Van Harinxma Kanaal or from Stavoren via the Johan Frisco Kanaal. Minimum depths approx 1·8m. ANWB charts A and B are needed.

DEN HELDER   10-20-26

Noord Holland 52°58'·00N 04°47'·35E

CHARTS

AC 191, 2322, 2593; Zeekaart 1454, 1546; DYC 1811.2, 1801; ANWB F; Imray Y5; Stanfords 19

TIDES

−0430 Dover; ML 1·1; Duration No data; Zone −0100

Standard Port HELGOLAND(→)

Times				Height (metres)			
High Water		Low Water		MHWS	MHWN	MLWN	MLWS
0200	0700	0200	0800	2·7	2·3	0·4	0·0
1400	1900	1400	2000				
Differences DEN HELDER							
−0410	−0520	−0520	−0430	−0·9	−0·7	0·0	+0·2

SHELTER

Good in the Naval Hbr, the yacht hbr (KMYC) being hard to stbd on entering. Den Helder is the main base of the Royal Netherlands Navy which owns and runs the KMYC and the Marinehaven Willemsoord. Caution: many FVs, ferries and off-shore service vessels. 2 other YCs/marinas both of which can only be reached via the Rijkszeehaven, Moorman bridge, Nieuwe Diep and lock, offer AB in or near the Binnenhaven: MWV and YC Den Helder; see below under FACILITIES for details.

NAVIGATION

WPT Schulpengat SG (SWM) buoy, Mo (A) 8s, 52°52'·95N 04°38'·00E, 206·5°/026·5° from/to Kaap Hoofd, 6·0M. Two chans lead via the Marsdiep to the hbr ent:
(1) From N, the Molengat is good except in strong NW winds when seas break heavily.
(2) From S, the Schulpengat is well marked and lit. Beware fast ferries to/from Texel and strong tidal streams across the hbr ent.

LIGHTS AND MARKS

Schulpengat: Ldg lts 026·5° on Texel; front Iso 4s 18M; rear Oc 8s 18M, Ch spire, both vis 025°-028°. Kijkduin lt ho Fl (4) 20s 56m 30M, R tr, is conspic 2·3M WSW of hbr. Molengat: Ldg lts 141·5°; front Iso 5s 13m 8M; rear, 650m from front, FW 22m 8M; tr on Ⓗ; both vis 124°-157°. Hbr ldg lts 191°. Both Oc G 5s 16/25m 14M (synch); front B ▲ on bldg; rear B ▼ on B framework tr.
A 60m radar tower is conspic on the E side of hbr ent.
Entry sigs, from Harssens hbr office on W side of ent: ℟℟ (vert) = No entry/exit; no traffic allowed within hbr.
Bridges: Moorman bridge operates 7 days a week H24. Access to the North Holland Canal via the Nieuwe Diep and Koopvaardersschutsluis.Van Kinsbergen bridge operated by Hr Mr, 0500-2300 Mon-Fri; 0700-1400 Sat. All bridges remain closed 0715-0810, 1200-1215, 1245-1300, Mon-Fri. Also 0830-0910 Mon and 1545-1645 Fri. All LT.

RADIO TELEPHONE

Monitor VTS Ch 12 *Den Helder Traffic* in the Schulpengat, Molengat and Marsdiep; weather forecast available on request. Port Ch 14 (H24); also Ch 14 for van Kinsbergen bridge (remote control). Koopvaardersschutsluis Ch 22 (H24), which also operates Burgemeester Vissersbrug by remote control. Moormanbridge Ch 18 (H24).

TELEPHONE (Dial code 0223)
Municipal Hr Mr 613955, ☎ 627780, mobile ☎ 0652 97 94 80; Hr Mr (Yacht Haven) 637444; Pilot 617424; Vessel Traffic Centre 652770; Naval Base Commander 656822; ⌗ 615182; Emergency 112; Police 655700; Ⓗ 611414; Water Police 616767; Immigration 657515; Brit Consul (020) 6764343.

FACILITIES

In naval hbr: **KMYC** ☎ 652645, f13.80, FW, D, Bar, R; In or near Binnenhaven:
MWV YC ☎ 617076, f11.50, P (at garage), D, L, FW, AB; **Yacht Haven Den Helder** ☎ 637444, f15.65, ME, El, Sh, C, CH, Slip, FW, R, Bar; **YC WSOV** ☎ 652173; **YC HWN** ☎ 624422;
Services: CH, SM, Floating dock, Gaz.
Town P, CH, V, R, Bar, ✉, Ⓑ, ⇌, ✈ (Amsterdam).
Ferry: Hook of Holland-Harwich; Rotterdam-Hull.

OUDESCHILD   10-20-27

Texel, 53°02'·39N 04°51'·26E   Rtg 1-2-2

CHARTS
AC 191, 2593; Zeekaart 1546, 1454; DYC 1811·3

TIDES
−0355 Dover; ML 1·1m; Duration 0625; Zone −0100

Standard Port HELGOLAND (→)

Times				Height (metres)			
High Water		Low Water		MHWS	MHWN	MLWN	MLWS
0200	0700	0200	0800	2·7	2·3	0·4	0·0
1400	1900	1400	2000				
Differences OUDESCHILD							
−0310	−0420	−0445	−0400	−0·9	−0·7	0·0	+0·2

SHELTER
Good in marina (2·1m) in NE basin. Beware strong cross tides at ent. A Port of Entry in summer. Yachts are advised not to ent/dep Mon a.m & Fri a.m when all FVs sail/return.

NAVIGATION
WPT 53°02'·28N 04°51'·72E, 111°/291° from/to hbr ent, 3ca. From seaward, app via Schulpengat or Molengat into Marsdiep (see 10.20.26). Thence from abeam ferry hbr of 't Horntje (Texel) steer NE via Texelstroom for 3·5M to hbr ent, marked by PHM buoy (T14), Iso R 8s. Enter on course 291° with dir lt, Oc 6s, midway between S mole hd FR and N mole hd FG. Speed limit 5kn (9kph).

LIGHTS AND MARKS
Dir lt Oc 6s 14m on G mast. Mole hd lts FR 7m and FG 7m are on R/W and G/W banded poles. Horn (2) 30s on S mole hd, sounded 0600-2300.

RADIO TELEPHONE
No marina VHF. Hr Mr Ch 09, 08000-2000LT. See 10.20.26 for VTS and radar assistance/info on request.

TELEPHONE (Dial code 0222)
Hr Mr (marina) ☎ 313608 (1100-1130; 1800-1930LT); Port Hr Mr 312710/home 313538; CG 316270; Police 322188 (in season); Ambulance 312323 (H24) or 06-11; Taxi 312323.

FACILITIES
Marina (Schoeiershoek; 200 berths) ☎ 313608, f22.50, FW, AC, Slip, D, Slip, ☑, Gaz, Bar, R; **YC WV Texel;**
Services: CH, ME, BY, Sh, Dry dock, C, SM, V by mobile shop in season.
Village (walking distance), P, V (supermarket), ⒷB, ✉, R. Ferry from 't Horntje to Den Helder. UK ferries from Hook/ Rotterdam. ✈ Amsterdam.

HARLINGEN   10-20-28

Friesland 53°10'·63N 05°24'·22E

CHARTS
AC 112, 2593; Zeekaart 1454, 1456; DYC 1811·5; ANWB B; Imray Y5

TIDES
−0210 Dover; ML 1·2; Duration 0520; Zone −0100

Standard Port Helgoland (→)

Times				Height (metres)			
High Water		Low Water		MHWS	MHWN	MLWN	MLWS
0200	0700	0200	0800	2·7	2·3	0·4	0·0
1400	1900	1400	2000				
Differences HARLINGEN							
−0155	−0245	−0210	−0130	−0·4	−0·3	−0·1	+0·2
NES (AMELAND)							
−0135	−0150	−0245	−0225	+0·1	+0·2	+0·2	+0·2

SHELTER
Very good in Noorderhaven, but ent can be rough at HW with W/NW winds. Entering on the flood, beware strong stream across ent. Note: Access to/from Noorderhaven is restricted by the two N/S bridges either end of the Oude Buitenhaven; these open in unison 2 x per hr 0600-2200 in season (on request in winter) and are shut at times of boat trains/ferries. Some berths at Van Harinxma yacht hbr; but only advised if going via the canal on to the lakes.

NAVIGATION
WPT SM buoy from seaward (see 10.20.29). Then follow the buoyed Vliestroom and Blauwe Slenk chans which narrow for the last 2½M. Pleasure craft should use the Hanerak, a buoyed (Nos HR1-23) chan, parallel about 600m S of the Pollendam which is used by ferries. Caution: When training wall is covered, tidal stream sweeps across the Pollendam, marked by lateral lt bns.

LIGHTS AND MARKS
Ldg lts 112°, both Iso 6s. Dir lt F WR 20m 13/10M, R113°-116°, W152°-068°. R 3° sector covers the Pollendam.

RADIO TELEPHONE
VHF Ch 11 (Mon 0000 to Sat 2200LT). Harinxma Canal locks Ch 22.

TELEPHONE (Dial code 0517)
Hr Mr 413041; CG (Brandaris) (0562) 442341; ⌗ 418750; Police 413333; Ⓗ 499999; Brit Consul (020) 6764343.

FACILITIES
Noorderhaven Yacht Hbr ☎ 415666, FW, El, CH, V, R, Bar, ☑; **Yacht Hbr Van Harinxma Canal** ☎ 416898, FW, ☑, C (6 ton); **Services:** CH, El, E, Gaz, Diving/salvage, El, ME (by arrangement), D, P. **Town** EC Mon; LB, D, P, V, R, Bar, SM, ✉, ⒷB, ⇌, ✈ (Amsterdam). Ferry: See Hook.

NES, AMELAND, Friesland, 53°26'·28N 05°46'·62E. AC 2593, Zeekaart 1458, DYC 1811.6, 1812.2. HW −0055 on Dover; ML 1·6m; Duration 0625. See 10.20.28. Shelter from all but E/S winds. Yacht pontoons at N end of hbr (0·8m) beyond ferry terminal; W side dries to soft mud. Beware sandbanks in the Zeegat van Ameland. Enter from Molengat at MG28-R1 SCM By, VQ(6) + L Fl 10s. Lts: Ameland (W end), Fl (3) 15s 57m 30M, RC. Ferry pier hd Iso 6s 2m 8M. L Fl R 8s and L Fl G 8s piles at ent to yacht hbr ('t Leye Gat, 140 berths), f15.00. Facilities: Gaz, YC. Hr Mr ☎ (0515) 32159.

20

VLIELAND   10-20-29

WEST FRISIAN ISLANDS
Friesland 53°17'·73N 05°05'·57E   Rtg 2-3-2

CHARTS
AC 112, 2593; Zeekaart 1456; DYC 1811.4/.5; Imray Y5

TIDES
−0300 Dover; ML 1·4; Duration 0610; Zone −0100

Standard Port HELGOLAND (→)

Times				Height (metres)			
High Water		Low Water		MHWS	MHWN	MLWN	MLWS
0200	0700	0200	0800	2·7	2·3	0·4	0·0
1400	1900	1400	2000				
Differences VLIELAND-HAVEN							
−0250	−0320	−0355	−0330	−0·3	−0·2	+0·1	+0·2

SHELTER
Good; yacht hbr (2m) is very/over-crowded in season. ‡ in 4-9m, about 0·5M W of the hbr (and nearer the village), except in SE/SW winds; but do not ‡ in buoyed chan between hbr and ferry pier (no berthing). From the S a safe ‡ is in Fransche Gaatje, SE of Richel, 6M from hbr.

NAVIGATION
WPT SM (SWM) By, Iso 4s, 53°19'·05N 04°55'·73E, 274°/094° from/to ZS1 and ZS2 Bys, 2·3M (via ZS Bank NCM). See 10.20.31. In fresh W/NW winds a heavy ground swell can raise dangerous seas from the WPT to ZS1/2 Bys. The Zuider Stortemelk is deep, well marked/lit and leads to the Vliestroom. Vliesloot, which forks off to the S, is narrow and in places has only 2·5m at LW sp; keep in mid-chan.

LIGHTS AND MARKS
Main It ho Iso 4s 53m 20M; R tr, W lantern, R top; RC. Tfc sigs: R Flag or ®® at ent = hbr closed (full).

RADIO TELEPHONE
Hr Mr Ch 09; CG Ch 02 (Brandaris, W. Terschelling). All vessels in the Zeegat van Terschelling and N Waddenzee must monitor Ch 02 for the *Brandaris Traffic Centre VTS*.

TELEPHONE (Dial code 0562)
Hr Mr 451729; CG (0562) 442341; ⌗ 451522; Police 451312; Dr 451307; Brit Consul (020) 6764343.

FACILITIES
Yacht Hbr (250) ☎ 451729, f19.50, FW, dinghy slip, Ⓘ; **Hbr** C (10 ton), P & D (cans, 10 mins); D by hose at Harlingen. **Village** El, CH, Ⓔ, Gaz, V, R, ⊠, Ⓑ, ⇌ (ferry to Harlingen), ✈ (Amsterdam). Ferry: Hook of Holland-Harwich.

WEST TERSCHELLING   10-20-30

WEST FRISIAN ISLANDS
Friesland 53°21'·40N 05°13'·23E

CHARTS
AC 112, 2593; Zeekaart 1456; DYC 1811.4/.5; Imray Y5

TIDES
−0300 Dover; ML 1·4; Duration No data; Zone −0100

Standard Port HELGOLAND (→)

Times				Height (metres)			
High Water		Low Water		MHWS	MHWN	MLWN	MLWS
0200	0700	0200	0800	2·7	2·3	0·4	0·0
1400	1900	1400	2000				
Differences WEST TERSCHELLING							
−0220	−0250	−0335	−0310	−0·4	−0·2	+0·1	+0·2

SHELTER
Good, especially in marina in NE corner of hbr beyond ferry and FV quays. Very crowded in season; considerable commercial traffic and ferries in confined waters.

NAVIGATION
WPT: SM buoy from all directions (see 10.20.29 and .31). Thence through Stortemelk and Vliestroom into West Meep. At NOM4-S13 ECM buoy, VQ (3) 5s, 53°19'·15N 05°15'·65E, enter Slenk chan leading WNW into the Schuitengat. Follow the chan buoys and ldg lts 053° to hbr ent. Note: this longer route is necessary because the ent to Schuitengat has become too shallow/narrow. Do not attempt Boomkensdiep which is no longer buoyed.

LIGHTS AND MARKS
Brandaris tr (conspic Y □ tr), Fl 5s 55m 29M, storm sigs. Ldg lts 053°: front (W mole) FR 5m 5M; R post, W bands; Horn 15s; rear (on dyke 1·1M from front, off chartlet) Iso 5s 14m 19M; vis 045°-061° (intens 045°-052°).

RADIO TELEPHONE
Hr Mr Ch 09. CG Ch 02 04 16 67. *Brandaris* (VTS) Ch 02 broadcasts wx, vis, tfc, tidal info at odd H+30 in Dutch and English on request. Yachts in the area must monitor Ch 02 (see 10.20.29); visitors can get update on nav/chans.

TELEPHONE (Dial code 0562)
Hr Mr 442910/442919; CG 442341; ⌗ 442884.

FACILITIES
Marina: Stichting Passantenhaven (500) ☎ 443337, f24.00 (f2.15/metre + f1.00 per head + f1.00) max 3 nights, C, FW; **Hbr** Slip; **Services:** Gaz, ME, SM, Chart agent. **Village** EC Wed; CH, V, R, Bar, ⊠, P & D (cans, see Hr Mr; nearest D by hose is at Harlingen), Ⓑ, ⇌ (ferry to Harlingen), ✈ (Amsterdam). Ferry: Hook-Harwich; Europoort-Hull.

ZEEGAT VAN TERSCHELLING (Het Vlie)   10-20-31

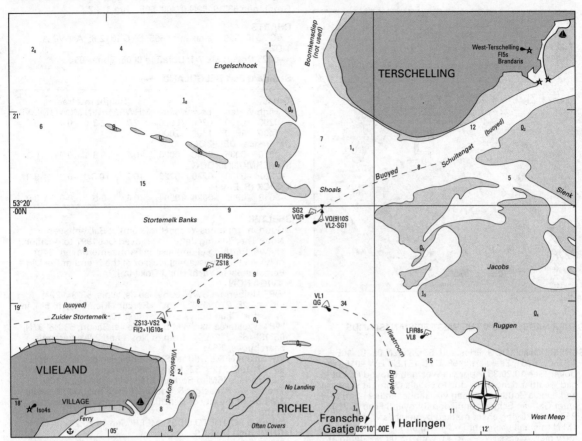

LAUWERSOOG   10-20-32

Friesland, 53°24'·72N 06°12'·10E

CHARTS
AC 3509, 3761, Zeekaart 1458, DYC 1812.3

TIDES
HW –0150 on Dover; ML 1·7m; Zone –0100

Standard Port HELGOLAND (→)

Times				Height (metres)			
High Water		Low Water		MHWS	MHWN	MLWN	MLWS
0200	0700	0200	0800	2·7	2·3	0·4	0·0
1400	1900	1400	2000				
Differences LAUWERSOOG							
–0130	–0145	–0235	–0220	+0·2	+0·3	+0·3	+0·3

SHELTER
Outer hbr has swell in bad weather. Pontoons in inner FV hbr to await lock. Complete shelter in Noordergat marina (2·4m-2·8m) 3ca SE of lock; ♥s berth on first pontoon.

NAVIGATION
Lock hrs (LT) May-Sept: 0700-2000 Mon-Fri; 0700-1900 Sat; 0800-1200 & 1400-1800 Sun. Oct-Apr: 0700-1800 Mon -Fri; 0700-1700 Sat. Enter the Lauwersmeer for canals from Harlingen to Delfzijl; no need to lower mast.

LIGHTS AND MARKS
W mole FG 3M. E mole FR 4M. Visserhaven mole FR. Lock lead-in jetty Iso 4s. Firing range 1·5m ENE of hbr ent is marked by Fl Y 10s beacons, which alternate W/R when the range is active; info is broadcast on Ch 71.

RADIO TELEPHONE
Hbr VHF Ch 09; Lock Ch 22; Range broadcast Ch 71.

TELEPHONE (Dial code 0519)
Hr Mr 349023; Lock 349043; Marina 349040.

FACILITIES
Noordergat marina, ☎ 349040, f15.00, Gaz, BY, D (E end of hbr), FW; P (ferry terminal, W end of hbr), Bar, R, V, YC.

OTHER HARBOURS IN THE LAUWERSMEER

OOSTMAHORN, Friesland, 53°22'·90N 06°09'·71E. AC 3509, Zeekaarten 1458, DYC 1812·3. Non-tidal hbr on W side of Lauwersmeer; lock in as for Lauwersoog. Floating bns with Y flags mark fishing areas. Main hbr with FR and FG lts at ent has marina (2·2-3·0m). Approx 450m to the SSE the Voorm Veerhaven marina has 1·5-2m. Hr Mr ☎ (0519) 321445/321880; f13.50, most facilities in the marinas.

ZOUTKAMP, Groningen, 53°20'·43N 06°17'·63E. AC 3509, Zeekaarten 1458, DYC 1812·3; non-tidal. Appr down the Zoutkamperril (2·6-4·5m); approx 2ca before lock/bridge, Hunzegat marina (1·5-2·1m) is to port. Beyond the lock and close to port is Oude Binnenhaven marina (2m), f10. FR lts at lock. Facilities: **Hunzegat** ☎ (0595) 402875, AC, FW, SC, Slip. **Oude-Binnenhaven** AC, C, FW, ME, El, Sh, C (20 ton), BH. **Town** D, P, SM, Gaz, ✉, R, V, Dr.

20

DELFZIJL continued

⚓ See Yacht Hr Mr

OTHER HARBOUR ON THE WEST FRISIAN ISLANDS

SCHIERMONNIKOOG, Friesland, 53°28'·12N 06°10'·10E. AC3509, 3761, Zeekaart 1458, DYC 1812.3. HW –0150 on Dover. See 10.20.33. Appr via Westgat, buoyed/lit, but in bad weather dangerous due to shoals (3·8m) at seaward end. Leave Zoutkamperlaag via Glinder chan (1·5m) to enter Gat van Schiermonnikoog (buoyed). From GVS16-R1 buoy a drying chan, marked by perches/withies, runs 1M N to small yacht hbr (1·3-1·5m) about 1M W of the ferry pier. Access HW –2 to +1, with 1·5m max depth at HW in apprs. Picturesque, but very full in high season; not cheap, ie f27.00. Lts: at W end of island, lt ho Fl (4) 20s 43m 28M, R tr; Ferry pier hd lt FW and Fl (5) Y 20s tide gauge. Hr Mr ☎ (0519) 51544 (May-Sept); Facilities: FW, AC. Note: The CG station at the lt ho provides radar surveillance of the Terschelling/German Bight TSS out to 48M radius and coordinates local SAR operations. It keeps watch on VHF Ch 00, 05, 16, 67 and 73 (all H24); ☎ 0519 531247, 📠 0519 531000.

AGENTS WANTED

If you are interested in becoming our agent for any of the following ports, please write to: The Editor, Edington House, Trent, Sherborne, Dorset DT9 4SR, England – and get your free copy of the Almanac annually. You do not have to live in a port to be the agent, but at least a fairly regular visitor.

Great Yarmouth	St Gilles-Croix-de-Vie
Port Ellen (Islay)	Les Sables d'Olonne
Maryport	Ile d'Oléron
Workington	River Seudre
Holyhead	Anglet/Bayonne
Lough Swilly	St Jean-de-Luz
St Peter Port, Guernsey	Hendaye
Diélette	Grandcamp-Maisy
Portbail	Port-en-Bessin
Iles Chausey	Courseulles
St Malo/Dinard	Ouistreham/Caen
Le Legue/St Brieuc	Emden
Tréguier	Dornumer-Accumersiel
Lampaul	Langeoog
L'Aberildut	Bremerhaven
Le Palais (Belle Ile)	Büsum
Morbihan/Vannes	

DELFZIJL   10-20-33
Groningen 53°19'·00N 07°00'·50E   Rtg 1-3-2

CHARTS
AC 3510, 3509; Zeekaart 1555; DYC 1812.6; ANWB A
TIDES
–0025 Dover; ML 2·1; Duration 0605; Zone –0100

Standard Port HELGOLAND (→)

Times				Height (metres)			
High Water		Low Water		MHWS	MHWN	MLWN	MLWS
0200	0700	0200	0800	2·7	2·3	0·4	0·0
1400	1900	1400	2000				
Differences DELFZIJL							
+0020	–0005	–0040	0000	+0·9	+0·9	+0·3	+0·3
SCHIERMONNIKOOG							
–0120	–0130	–0240	–0220	+0·2	+0·3	+0·3	+0·3
KNOCK (R. Ems)							
+0018	+0005	–0028	+0004	+0·6	+0·6	0·0	0·0

SHELTER
Good in Neptunus Yacht Hbr (3·5m) at Balkenhaven. Note: The Floating Jetty was moved Oct 1997 to position shown. Berthing (4·5m) also in Farmsumerhaven (24hr only) via the Eemskanaal lock; or at the N end of the Old Eemskanaal in Yacht Hbr 't Dok (4m).
NAVIGATION
WPT Huibertgat SWM buoy, Iso 8s, Whis, 53°34'·90N 06°14'·32E, 270°/090° from/to Borkum Kleiner lt, 15·5M, in W sector. Chan buoys unlit for first 10M.
WPT Westereems SWM buoy, Iso 4s, Racon, 53°36'·97N, 06°19'·48E, 272°/092° from/to Nos 1 and 2 Westereems chan buoys, 1·6M.
WPT from N & E: Riffgat SWM buoy, Iso 8s, 53° 38'·90N 06° 27'·10E, 312°/132° from/to Westereems chan buoys, 3·2M; and 8·75M to Borkum Kleiner lt (See 10.21.10). Thence via Ranselgat & Doekegat (well buoyed/lit) to ent 3M ESE of the city of Delfzijl. Beware strong cross tides at the ent.
INLAND ROUTE TO IJSSELMEER: See 10.20.25.
LIGHTS AND MARKS
From the river, appr ldg lts 203°, both Iso 4s. Hbr ent, FG on W arm and FR on E arm (in fog, Horn 15s and FY). Zeehavenkanaal has Fl G lts to N and Fl R to S.
Entry sigs: 2 R Flags or 2 Ⓡ = No movements, unless over Ⓖ directed by Hr Mr.
RADIO TELEPHONE
All vessels, except recreational craft, must call *Delfzijl Radar* VHF Ch 66 (H24) for VTS, co-ordinated with Ems Traffic. *Port Control* is Ch 14; Sea Locks Ch 11. Traffic, wx and tidal info is broadcast every even H+10 on Ch 14 in Dutch and English on request. *Ems Traffic* Ch 15 18 20 21 (H24) broadcasts every H + 50 weather and tidal info in German, including gale warnings for coastal waters between Die Ems and Die Weser.
TELEPHONE (Dial code 0596)
Hr Mr (Delfzijl Port Authority) 640400, 📠 630424; Neptunus Hr Mr 615004; Hr Mr 't Dok 616560; Sea locks 613293; CG (Police) 613831; ⊞ 615060; Police 112; Ⓗ 644444; Brit Consul (020) 6764343.
FACILITIES
Neptunus Yacht Hbr ☎ 615004, f15.00, D, Bar, M, L, FW; **Yacht Hbr 't Dok** AB f10.00, D, FW; **Ems Canal** L, FW, AB; **Motor Boat Club Abel Tasman** ☎ 616560 Bar, M, D, FW, L, 🅿, V. **Services:** CH, ACA, DYC Agent, ME, El, Gaz. **Town** P, D, V, R, Bar, ✉, Ⓑ, ⇥, ✈ (Groningen/Eelde). Ferry: See Hook of Holland.

ADJACENT HARBOURS

TERMUNTERZIJL Groningen, 53°18'·21N 07°02'·30E. AC 3510; Zeekaart 1555; DYC 1812. HW –0025 on Dover (UT); use Differences Delfzijl. Ent (1·3M ESE of Delfzijl ent) is close to BW13 SHM buoy Fl G 5s (53°18'·70N 07°02'·40E); thence chan marked by 7 R and 7 G unlit bns. Yachts berth in Vissershaven (0·9m), stbd of ent, or on pontoons (1m) to port of ent, f10.00. Hr Mr ☎ (0596) 601891 (Apr-Sept), VHF Ch 09, FW, AC, Bar, R.

EMDEN see 10.21.9

SOUTHERN NORTH SEA WAYPOINTS 10-20-34

Southern North Sea waypoint and major light positions south of 54°N are listed alphabetically. They are mainly referenced to the ED 50 European Datum, or to the datum shown on the largest scale Admiralty chart.

AREAS 20 and 21

A1 bis Lt By	51°21'·70N 02°58'·10E
A2 Lt By	51°22'·50N 03°07'·05E
Adriana Lt By	51°56'·13N 03°50'·63E
Akkaert NE Lt By	51°27'·31N 02°59'·38E
Akkaert Mid Lt By	51°24'·23N 02°53'·50E
Akkaert SW Lt By	51°22'·33N 02°46'·42E
Ameland Lt	53°27'·02N 05°37'·60E
A-Noord Lt By	51°23'·50N 02°37'·00E
A-Zuid Lt By	51°21'·50N 02°37'·00E
Bergues N Lt By	51°20'·00N 02°24'·62E
BG 2 Lt By	53°58'·42N 03°17'·50E
Binnenstroombank Lt By	51°14'·50N 02°53'·73E
Birkenfels Lt By	51°39'·05N 02°32'·05E
Bol van Heist Lt By	51°23'·15N 03°12'·05E
Bollen Lt By	51°50'·00N 03°33'·00E
Borkumriff Lt By	53°47'·50N 06°22'·13E
BR Lt By	53°30'·70N 05°33'·62E
BSP Lt By	53°30'·80N 04°30'·00E
BT Ratel Lt By	51°11'·62N 02°28'·00E
Buitenbank Lt By	51°51'·20N 03°25'·80E
Buitenstroombank Lt By	51°15'·20N 02°51'·80E
Dovetief Lt By	53°45'·38N 07°09'·80E
Eierland Lt	53°10'·97N 04°51'·40E
Elbe 1 Lt F	54°00'·00N 08°06'·58E
Eveline Lt By	52°25'·55N 04°25'·15E
Fairy W Lt By	51°23'·90N 02°09'·44E
Garden City Lt By	51°29'·20N 02°17'·90E
Goeree Lt	51°55'·53N 03°40'·18E
Goote Bank Lt By	51°26'·98N 02°52'·72E
GW/Ems Lt F	54°10'·00N 06°20'·80E
Harle Lt By	53°49'·28N 07°49'·00E
Hinder Lt By	51°54'·60N 03°55'·50E
Hubert Gat Lt By	53°34'·90N 06°14'·32E
IJmuiden Lt By (IJM)	52°28'·50N 04°23'·87E
Juist-N Lt By	53°43'·90N 06°55'·40E
Juisterriff-N Lt By	53°42'·90N 06°45'·82E
JW 5/Jade 1 Lt By	53°52'·47N 07°44'·10E
Kaloo Lt By	51°35'·60N 03°23'·30E
KB Lt By	51°21'·75N 02°43'·00E
Kijkduin Lt	52°57'·35N 04°43'·60E
LST '420' Lt By	51°15'·50N 02°40'·70E
Maas Centre Lt By	52°01'·18N 03°53'·57E
Magne Lt By	51°39'·15N 03°19'·60E
MBN Lt By	51°20'·87N 02°46'·40E
MD 3 Lt By	51°42'·75N 03°27'·06E
Middelbank Lt By	51°40'·90N 03°18'·30E
Middelkerk S Lt By	51°14'·78N 02°42'·00E
Middelkerk Bk Lt By	51°18'·25N 02°42'·80E
MV Lt By	51°57'·50N 03°58'·50E
MW 1 Lt By	51°51'·25N 03°09'·40E

Nautica Ena Lt By	51°18'·12N 02°52'·85E
NHR-N	52°10'·90N 03°05'·00E
Nieuwpoort E Pier Lt	51°09'·32N 02°43'·89E
Nieuwpoort Bk Lt By	51°10'·21N 02°36'·16E
Noordhinder Lt By	52°00'·20N 02°51'·50E
Norderney N Lt By	53°46'·10N 07°17'·22E
Oost Dyck Lt By	51°21'·57N 02°31'·23E
Oost Dyck W Lt By	51°17'·18N 02°26'·42E
Oostendebank N Lt By	51°21'·25N 02°53'·00E
Oostendebank Oost Lt By	51°17'·36N 02°52'·00E
Oostendebank W Lt By	51°16'·25N 02°44'·85E
Ooster Lt By	51°47'·97N 03°41'·32E
Osterems Lt By	53°41'·94N 06°36'·20E
Petten Lt By	52°47'·38N 04°36'·80E
Rabsbank Lt By	51°38'·30N 03°10'·00E
Riffgat Lt By	53°38'·90N 06°27'·10E
SBZ Lt By	51°42'·50N 03°16'·70E
SCH Lt By	52°07'·80N 04°14'·20E
Scheur 3 Lt By	51°24'·35N 03°03'·00E
Scheur 4 Lt By	51°25'·07N 03°02'·93E
Scheur-Wielingen Lt By	51°24'·26N 03°18'·00E
Scheur-Zand Lt By	51°23'·68N 03°07'·68E
Schlucter Lt By	53°44'·70N 07°04'·22E
Schlusseltone Lt By	53°56'·30N 07°54'·87E
Schouwenbank Lt By	51°45'·00N 03°14'·40E
SG (Haringvliet) Lt By	51°52'·00N 03°51'·50E
SG (Schulpengat) Lt By	52°52'·95N 04°38'·00E
SM Lt By	53°19'·29N 04°55'·71E
Schiermonnikoog Lt	53°29'·20N 06°08'·90E
TB Lt By	51°34'·45N 02°59'·15E
TG1/Ems Lt By	53°43'·38N 06°22'·40E
TG3 Lt By	53°44'·65N 06°31'·20E
TG5 Lt By	53°45'·90N 06°40'·10E
TG7 Lt By	53°47'·35N 06°49'·78E
TG9 Lt By	53°48'·45N 06°57'·80E
TG11 Lt By	53°49'·64N 07°06'·60E
TG13 Lt By	53°51'·00N 07°15'·50E
TG15 Lt By	53°52'·20N 07°24'·35E
TG17/JW1 Lt By	53°53'·47N 07°33'·22E
TG19/JW2 Lt By	53°55'·10N 07°44'·60E
Thornton SW Lt By	51°31'·01N 02°51'·00E
Track Ferry Lt By	51°33'·80N 02°36'·50E
Trapegeer Lt By	51°08'·46N 02°34'·45E
Twin Lt By	51°32'·10N 02°22'·62E
TX 1 Lt By	52°48'·17N 04°15'·60E
TX 3 Lt By	52°58'·61N 04°22'·50E
VL 1 (Eierland) Lt By	53°11'·00N 04°35'·40E
VL 11 (Ameland)	53°28'·13N 05°04'·03E
Vlieland Lt	53°17'·79N 05°03'·58E
W Hinder Lt	51°23'·36N 02°26'·36E
Wandelaar SW Lt By	51°22'·00N 03°01'·00E
Wenduinebank E Lt By	51°18'·85N 03°01'·70E
Wenduinebank N Lt By	51°21'·50N 03°02'·71E
Wenduinebank W Lt By	51°17'·28N 02°52'·87E
Weser Lt By	53°54'·25N 07°50'·00E
Weser 1/Jade 2 Lt By	53°52'·13N 07°47'·36E
Westerems Lt By	53°36'·98N 06°19'·50E
Westpit Lt By	51°33'·70N 03°10'·00E
Weststroombank Lt By	51°11'·39N 02°43'·15E
WG (Schiermonnikoog) Lt By	53°32'·25N 06°06'·11E
WG-OG (Westgat) Lt By	51°37'·23N 03°28'·87E
Wielingen Zand Lt By	51°22'·60N 03°10'·80E
Zand Lt By	51°22'·56N 03°10'·16E
ZSB Lt By	51°36'·64N 03°15'·77E
Zuidstroombank Lt Buoy	51°12'·33N 02°47'·50E

VOLVO PENTA SERVICE

Sales and service centres in area 21
Names and addresses of Volvo Penta dealers in
this area are available from:
Germany *Volvo Penta Central Europe GmbH,* Redderkoppel 5, Postfach 9013,
D-24151 Kiel Tel +49 431 39940, Fax +49 431 396774

Area 21

Germany
Emden to Danish border

VOLVO PENTA

21

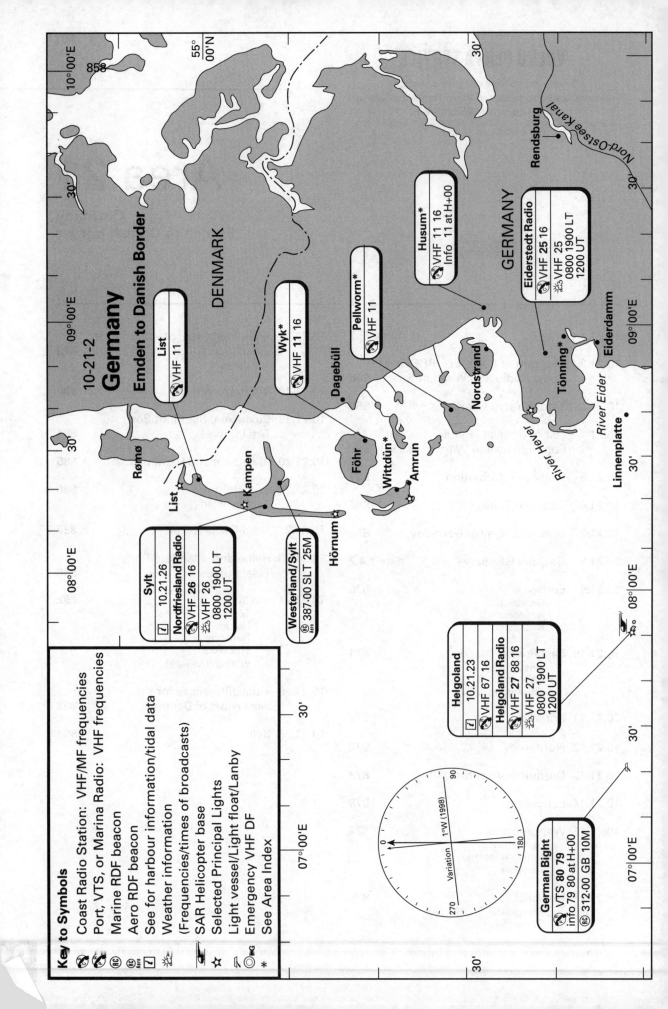

Key to Symbols

Coast Radio Station: VHF/MF frequencies
Port, VTS, or Marina Radio: VHF frequencies
Marine RDF beacon
Aero RDF beacon
See for harbour information/tidal data
Weather information
(Frequencies/times of broadcasts)
SAR Helicopter base
Selected Principal Lights
Light vessel/Light float/Lanby
Emergency VHF DF
See Area Index

10-21-2
Germany
Emden to Danish Border

10°00'E
09°00'E
08°00'E
07°00'E

55°
00'N

30'

DENMARK

GERMANY

Rømø
List
Kampen
Sylt
Hörnum
Föhr
Wittdün*
Amrun
Dagebüll
Nordstrand
Rendsburg
Nord-Ostsee Kanal
Tönning*
River Eider
Eiderdamm
Linnenplatte
River Hever

List
VHF 11

Wyk*
VHF 11 16

Pellworm*
VHF 11

Husum*
VHF 11 16
Info 11 at H+00

Eiderstedt Radio
VHF 25 16
VHF 25
0800 1900 LT
1200 UT

Sylt
10.21.26
Nordfriesland Radio
VHF 26 16
VHF 26
0800 1900 LT
1200 UT

Westerland/Sylt
387.00 SLT 25M

Helgoland
10.21.23
VHF 67 16
Helgoland Radio
VHF 27 88 16
VHF 27
0800 1900 LT
1200 UT

German Bight
VTS 80 79
info 79 80 at H+00
312.00 GB 10M

Variation 1°W (1998)
0
90
180
270

859

Brunsbüttel
10.21.21
ⓘ 🕭 VHF **12** 16

Nord-Ostee Kanal
10.21.22
ⓘ 🕭 VHF 13 02
Radar 67
Kanal 13 02 03 12
Ports 73

River Elbe and Hamburg
10.21.20
ⓘ 🕭 VTS 74
Port **74** 14 13 16
Elbe Port **12** 16
Oste Bridge 69
Stör Lock 09

Hamburg Radio
🕭 VHF 27 83 16

GERMANY

Nord-Ostee Kanal

Elbe-Weser Radio
🕭 VHF **24** 01 16
📠 VHF 24
0800 1900 LT
1200 UT

Otterndorf*

River Elbe

River Weser/ Bremerhaven
10.21.18
ⓘ 🕭 VTS 22 02 04
07 05 82 21
Info 22 at H+20,19 at
H+30, 63 at H+30
Ports VHF 12 14 16

Bremen Radio
🕭 VHF 28 25 16

Büsum
10.21.24
ⓘ 🕭 VHF **11** 16

Scharnhörn

Cuxhaven
10.21.19
ⓘ 🕭 VHF 69
Lock 69

Alte Weser
🔘 309·00 AR 20M

Grosser
Vogelsand ☆

River
Weser

Nordenham

Dangastersiel*

Brake •

Elbe Lt F
🔘 298·00 EL 10M

River Jade/ Wilhelmshaven
10.21.17
ⓘ 🕭 VTS 20 63 16
Info 63 20 at H+10
VHF 11
Locks 13
Bridges 11

River Jade

Hooksiel
10.21.16
ⓘ 🕭 VTS 63
Info 80 79

River Ems/Emden
10.21.9
ⓘ 🕭 VTS **18** 20 21
Info 18 20 at H+50
VHF 13
Lock 13

Rüstersiel*
Wangersiel*

Jever

Ems-Jade-Kanal

Wangerooge
10.21.15
ⓘ 🕭 VHF 17
🔘 309·50 WE 20M

Spiekeroog*

Neuharlingersiel*
Bensersiel*

Dornumer-Accumersiel
10.21.13
ⓘ

Norddeich*
10.21.?
🕭 VHF 28 61 16
📠 VHF 28
0800 1900 LT
1200 UT

Harlesiel*
🕭 VHF Lock 17

Baltrum*

Neessmersiel*

• Leer

Langeoog
10.21.14
ⓘ 🕭 VHF 17

For Traffic Separation
Schemes see Fig. 10(6)

Norderney
10.21.12
ⓘ 🕭 VHF 14

Juist*

Greetsiel*

River Ems

Borkum
10.21.11
ⓘ 🕭 VHF 14
🔘 302·00 BE 20M

Emshörn •

See 10-20-2

NETHERLANDS

21

10-21-3   AREA 21 TIDAL STREAMS

5 Hours before HW Dover (0440 before HW Helgoland)

4 Hours before HW Dover (0340 before HW Helgoland)

3 Hours before HW Dover (0240 before HW Helgoland)

2 Hours before HW Dover (0140 before HW Helgoland)

1 Hour before HW Dover (0040 before HW Helgoland)

HW Dover (0020 after HW Helgoland)

South-westward 10.20.3

1 Hour after HW Dover (0120 after HW Helgoland)

2 Hours after HW Dover (0220 after HW Helgoland)

3 Hours after HW Dover (0320 after HW Helgoland)

4 Hours after HW Dover (0420 after HW Helgoland)

5 Hours after HW Dover (0520 after HW Helgoland)

6 Hours after HW Dover (0620 after HW Helgoland)

21

10.21.4 COASTAL LIGHTS, FOG SIGNALS AND WAYPOINTS

Abbreviations used below are given in 1.4.1. Principal lights are in **bold** print, places in CAPITALS, and light vessels, light floats and Lanbys in *CAPITAL ITALICS*. Unless otherwise stated lights are white. m – elevation in metres; M – nominal range in miles. Fog signals are in *italics*. Useful waypoints are underlined – use those on land with care. All geographical positions should be assumed to be approximate. See 4.4.1. All positions are referenced to the ED 50 datum.

CROSSING THE NORTH SEA

GW12 Lt By 54°13'·30N 07°22'·40E QR; PHM.
GW8 Lt By 54°12'·90N 06°51'·20E Fl (2) R 9s; PHM.
GW4 Lt By 54°12'·50N 06°20'·60E QR; PHM.
BG2 Lt By 53°58'·42N 03°17'·50E L Fl R 10s; PHM.

RIVER EMS AND APPROACHES

Westerems Lt By 53°36'·98N 06°19'·50E Iso 4s; SWM; Racon (T).
Hubert Gat Lt By 53°34'·90N 06°14'·32E Iso 8s; *Whis*; SWM.
Borkum Grosser 53°35'·38N 06°39'·82E Fl (2) 12s 63m **24M**; Brown Tr. F WRG 46m **W19M, R15M, G15M**; vis G107·4°-109°, W109°-111·2°, R111·2°-112·6°.
Borkum Kleiner 53°34'·78N 06°40'·08E FW 32m **30M**; R Tr, W bands; FW (intens) 089·9°-090·9° (Ldg sector for Hubertgat); RC; Fl 3s **16M**; vis 088°-089·9°; Q (4) 10s **16M**; vis 090·9°-093°; RC; Iso Y 4s on tide gauge 420m SW.

BORKUM

Fischerbalje 53°33'·21N 06°43'·00E Oc (2) WRG 16s 15m **W16M**, R12M, G11M; W I Tr, R top and lantern, on tripod; vis R260°-313°, G313°-014°, W014°-068°, (Ldg sector to Fischerbalje); R068°-123°. Fog Det Lt.
Schutzhafen Ent 53°33'·52N 06°45'·11E FG 10m 4M, and FR 8m 4M.

Campen 53°24'·39N 07°01'·00E F 62m **30M**; R framework Tr, 2 galleries, W central col, G cupola; vis 127°-127·3°. Fl 5s (same Tr); vis 126·5°-127°. Fl (4) 15s (same Tr) vis 127·3°-127·8°.

ALTE EMS

H11 By 53°34'·65N 06°33'·62E; SHM.
A2a By 53°32'·93N 06°39'·53E; PHM.
A3 By 53°32'·85N 06°39'·25E; SHM.
A5 By 53°31'·81N 06°39'·95E; SHM.
33/ Alte Ems II By 53°27'·80N 06°51'·38E; SHM.

EEMSHAVEN (Netherlands)

W Pier 53°27'·80N 06°50·15E FG 8m 3M.

DUKE GAT

No. 35 Lt By 53°27'·08N 06°52'·88E Fl G 4s; SHM.
No. 37 Lt By 53°26'·00N 06°55'·00E QG; SHM.
No. 41 Lt By 53°24'·32N 06°56'·80E Fl (2) G 9s; SHM.
No. 45 By 53°22'·05N 06°58'·57E; SHM.
No. 49 Lt By 53°20'·02N 06°59'·75E Oc (2) G 9s; SHM.

KNOCK

K4 Lt Buoy 53°19'·87N 07°00'·82E QR; PHM.
Knock 53°20'·37N 07°01'·50E F WRG 28m W12M, R9M, G8M; Gy Tr, four galleries, broad top, radar antenna; vis W270°-299°, R299-008·3°, G008·3°-023°, W023°-026·8°, R026·8°-039°, W039°-073°, R073°-119°, W119°-154°; Fog Det Lt.

DELFZIJL ENTRANCE (Netherlands)

W Mole Hd, E ent 53°19'·10N 07°00'·38E FG; Ra refl.

E Mole Hd FR In fog FY; *Horn 15s*.
Ldg Lts 203°. Front, 53°18'·68N 07°00'·26E Iso 4s. Rear, 310m from front, Iso 4s.
Zeehavenkannaal, N side (odd numbered posts); 3 QG; 4 Fl G 2s, 6 Fl G 5s; R Refl.
Zeehavenkannaal, S side (even numbered posts); 1 Fl (2) R 6s; 1 Fl R 2s, 5 Fl R 5s, 1 QR; R Refl.
E side, ent No. 21 (Marina ent) Fl G 5s; W post on dolphin.

TERMUNTERZIJL (Netherlands)

BW13 By 53°18'·70N 07°03'·37E; SHM.
Wybelsum 53°20'·20N 07°06'·57E F WR 16m W6M, R5M; W framework Tr, R bands; radar antenna; vis W295°-320°, R320°-024°, W024°-049°; Fog Det Lt.

EMDEN

Logum Ldg Lts 075·2°. Front, 53°20'·17N 07°08'·05E Oc (2) 12s 16m 12M; W mast, R bands. Rear, 630m from front, Oc (2) 12s 28m 12M; W mast, R bands; synch with front.
Ldg Lts 087·6°. Front, 53°20'·07N 07°12'·15E Oc 5s 14m 14M; intens on Ldg line. Rear, 0·8M from front, Oc 5s 30m 14M; synch with front, intens on Ldg line.
Outer Hbr E pier Hd FG 7m 5M; R ○ Tr, B band.
W Pier Hd 53°20'·10N 07°10'·57E FR 10m 4M; R 8-sided Tr; *Horn Mo (ED) 30s*.

RIVER EMS TO RIVER JADE, INCLUDING EAST FRISIAN ISLANDS.

OUTER LIMIT OF INSHORE TRAFFIC ZONE

TG1/Ems Lt By 53°43'·38N 06°22'·40E IQ. G 13s; SHM.
TG3 Lt By 53°44'·65N 06°31'·20E Fl (2) G 9s; SHM.
TG5 Lt By 53°45'·90N 06°40'·10E Oc (3) G 12s; SHM.
TG7 Lt By 53°47'·35N 06°49'·78E Fl (2) G 9s; SHM.
TG9 Lt By 53°48'·45N 06°57'·80E Oc (3) G 12s; SHM.
TG11Lt By 53°49'·64N 07°06'·60E Fl (2) G 9s; SHM.
TG13 Lt By 53°51'·00N 07°15'·50E Oc (3) G 12s; SHM.
TG15 Lt By 53°52'·20N 07°24'·35E Fl (2) G 9s; SHM.
TG17/JW 1 Lt By 53°53'·47N 07°33'·22E IQ 13s; SHM.
TG19/JW 2 Lt By 53°55'·10N 07°44'·60E Oc (3) G 12s; SHM.

BORKUMRIFF Lt By 53°47'·50N 06°22'·13E Oc 4s; SWM; Racon (T).
GW/EMS Lt F 54°10'·00N 06°20'·80E Iso 8s 12m **17M**; *Horn Mo (R) 30s (H24)*; Racon (T).

INSHORE ROUTE EMS TO JADE

Riffgat Lt By 53°38'·90N 06°27'·10E Iso 8s; SWM.
Oosterems Lt By 53°41'·94N 06°36'·20E Iso 4s; SWM.
Juisterriff -N Lt By 53°42'·90N 06°45'·82E Q; NCM.
Juist - N Lt By 53°43'·90N 06°55'·40E VQ; NCM.
53°40'·95N 07°03'·50E Aero Fl 5s 14m (occas).
Schluchter Lt By 53°44'·70N 07°04'·22E Iso 8s; SWM.
Dovetief Lt By 53°45'·38N 07°09'·80E Iso 4s; SWM.
Platform 54°42'·1N 07°10'·0E; Mo (U) 15s 24m 9M; R platform, Y stripes; *Horn Mo (U) 30s*.
Norderney N Lt By 53°46'·10N 07°17'·22E Q; NCM.
Accumer Ee Lt By 53°47·27N 07°28·37E Iso 8s; SWM; (frequently moved.)
Otzumer Balje Lt By 53°48'·01N 07°37'·38E Iso 4s; SWM; (frequently moved.)
Harle Lt By 53°49'·28N 07°49'·00E Iso 8s; SWM.

GREETSIEL

Meßstation Lt Bn 53°32'·97N 07°02'·22E Fl Y 4s 15m 3M.

JUIST

Training Wall, S end 53°39'·70N 06°59'·92E; pile; SCM.
Juist 53°41'·9N 07°03'·5E Aero Fl 5s 14m.

Schluchter Lt By 53°44'·70N 07°04'·22E Iso 8s; SWM.

NORDDEICH
W Training Wall, Hd 53°38'·7N 07°09'·0E FG 8m 4M;
G framework Tr, W lantern; vis 021°-327°.
E Training Wall Hd FR 8m 4M; R & W s on R Tr; vis 327°-237°;
Fog Lt.
Ldg Lts 144°. Front, Iso WR 6s 6m W6M, R4M; B mast;
vis R078°-122°, W122°-150°. Rear, 140m from front, Iso 6s
9m 6M; B mast; synch with front.

NORDERNEY
Norderney 53°42'·6N 07°13'·8E Fl (3) 12s 59m **23M**;
R 8 sided Tr; unintens 067°-077° and 270°-280°.
Fish Hbr W Mole Hd 53°41'·9N 07°09'·9E Oc (2) R 9s 13m 4M;
R&W Tr.
Norderney N Lt By 53°46'·10N 07°17'·22E Q; NCM.

BALTRUM
Baltrum Groyne Hd 53°43'·3N 07°21'·7E Oc WRG 6s 7m
W6M, R4M, G3M; vis G074·5°-090°, W090°-095°, R095°-
074·5°.

NESSMERSIEL
Mole N Hd 53°41'·9N 07°21'·7E Oc 4s 6m 5M; G mast.
Accumer Ee Lt By 53°47·27N 07°28'·37E Iso 8s; SWM;
(frequently moved.)

LANGEOOG
W Mole Hd 53°43'·42N 07°30'·13E Oc WRG 6s 8m W7M,
R5M, G4M; R basket on R mast; vis G064°-070°, W070°-
074°, R074°-326°, W326°-330°, G330°-335°, R335°-064°;
Horn Mo (L) 30s (0730-1800LT).

DORNUMER-ACCUMERSIEL
W Bkwtr Hd 53°41'·25N 07°29'·40E.

BENSERSIEL
E Training Wall Hd 53° 41'·84N 07°32'·90E Oc WRG 6s 6m
W5M, R3M, G2M; vis G110°-119°, W119°-121°, R121°-
110°.
Ldg Lts 138°. Front, Iso 6s 7m 9M. Rear, 167m from front,
Iso 6s 11m 9M. Both intens on Ldg line.

Otzumer Balje Lt By 53°48'·01N 07°37'·38E Iso 4s SWM;
(frequently moved.)

SPIEKEROOG
Spiekeroog 53°45'·0N 07°41'·3E FR 6m 4M; R mast;
vis 197°-114°.

NEUHARLINGERSIEL
Training Wall Hd 53°43'·22N 07°42'·30E Oc 6s 6m 5M;
G mast.

HARLESIEL
Harle Lt By 53°49'·28N 07°49'·00E Iso 8s; SWM.
Carolinensieler Balje, Leitdamm 53°44'·13N 07°50'·10E L Fl
8s 7m 6M; G mast.
N Mole Hd 53°42'·63N 07°48'·70E Iso R 4s 6m 7M.

WANGEROOGE
Wangerooge, W end 53°47'·45N 07°51'·52E Fl R 5s 60m
23M; R ○ Tr, 2 W bands; same Tr; F WRG 24m **W22M**,
W15M, **R17M**, R11M, **G18M**, G10M; vis R358·5°-008°,
W008°-018·5°, G018·5°-055°, W055°-060·5°, R060·5°-065·5°,
W065·5°–071°, G(18M) 119·4°-138·8°, W(22M) 138·8°-152·2°,
Ldg sector, R(17M) 152·2°-159·9°; RC.
E Mole Hd 53°46'·50N 07°52'·17E FG 3m 5M.

RIVER JADE AND APPROACHES
JW5/Jade 1 Lt By 53°52'·47N 07°44'·10E Oc G 4s; SHM.
Weser 1/Jade 2 Lt By 53°52'·13N 07°47'·36E Fl (2+1) G 15s;
Racon (T); SHM.
Mellumplate 53°46'·35N 08°05'·60E F 27m **24M**; R□Tr, W
band; vis 116·1°-116·4°; Ldg sector for outer part of
Wangerooger Fahrwasser. The following Lts are shown from
the same Tr over sectors indicated. Fl 4s **23M**; vis 114°-
115·2°. Fl (4) 15s; vis 117·2°-118·4°. Oc WRG 29m W14M,
R11M, G10M; vis R000°-006°, W006°-037·6°, G037·6°-114°,
R118·4°-168°, W168°-183·5°, R183·5°-212°, W212°-266°,
R266°-280°, W280°-000°. Mo (A) 7·5s; vis 115·2°-116·1°.
Ldg sector. Mo (N) 7·5s; vis116·4°-117·2°; Ldg sector.
Helicopter platform.
No. 7/Lt By 53°50'·30N 07°51'·24E Oc (3) G 12s; SHM.
No.11/Lt By 53°49'·23N 07°55'·08E Fl G 4s; SHM.
No.15/Blaue Balje Lt By 53°48'·13N 07°58'·88E IQ. G 13s;
SHM.
No.19 Lt By 53°47'·02N 08°01'·97E QG; SHM.
No.23 Lt By 53°45'·21N 08°02'·81E Oc (3) G 12s; SHM.
Minsener Oog, Buhne A N end 53°47'·30N 08°00'·45E
F WRG 16m W13M, R10M, G9M; □ Tr; vis R050°-055°,
W055°-134·8°, G134·8°-146·7°, W146·7°-156·6°, R156·6°-
211·3°, W211·3°-255·2°, G255·2°-290·2°, W290·2°-050°.
Oldoog, Buhne C 53°45'·40N 08°01'·35E Oc WRG 4s 25m
W13M, R10M, G9M; B col, W bands, Radar Tr (55m);
vis W176·5°-184·2°, G184·2°-200·3°, W200·3°-210, R210°-
274°, W274°-033°; Fog Det Lt.
Schillig 53°41'·85N 08°01'·78E Oc WR 6s 15m **W15M**,
R12M; B pylon, W band; vis W195·8°-221°, R221°-254·5°,
W254·5°-278·3°.
Hooksielplate Cross Lt 53°40'·20N 08°09'·00E Oc WRG 3s
25m W7M, R5M, G4M, Radar Tr (55m), R bands; vis R345°-
359·3°, W359·3°-002·1°, G002·1°-011·8°, W011·8°-018·5°,
R018·5°-098·7°, W098·7°-104·6°, G104·6°-115·3°, W115·3°-
119·8°, R119·8°-129·2°; Fog Det Lt.
No. 31/Reede/W Siel 1 Lt By 53°41'·59N 08°04'·50E Oc (3) G
12s; SHM.

WANGERSIEL
No.37/Hooksiel Lt By 53°39'·38N 08°06'·63E IQ G 13s; SHM.

HOOKSIEL
H3 By 53°38'·68N 08°05'·42E; SHM.
Voslapp Ldg Lts 164·5°. **Front**, 53°37'·19N 08°06'·88E Iso
6s 15m **24M**; R Tr, W bands, R lantern; R Refl; intens on Ldg
line. **Rear**, 2·35M from front Iso 6s 60m **27M**; W Tr, R bands.
Same structure, Cross light F RWG 20m W9M, R6M, G5M;
vis W200°-228°, G228°-248°, W248°-269°, R269°-310°.
Tossens. Ldg Lts 146°. **Front**, 53°34'·56N 08°12'·42E Oc 6s
15m **20M**; W Tr, R band, R lantern. **Rear**, 2M from front, Oc
6s 51m **20M**; R ○ Tr, W stripes, 3 galleries.

WILHELMSHAVEN
Eckwarden Ldg Lts 154°. **Front, Solthörner Watt** 53°32'·45N
08°13'·09E Iso WRG 3s 15m **W19M**, W12M, R9M, G8M;
R Tr, W bands; vis R346°-348°, W348°-028°, R028°-052°,
W (intens) 052°-054° Ldg sector, G054°-067·5°, W067·5°-
110°, G110°-152·6°; W (intens) 152·6° across fairway, with
undefined limit on E side of Ldg line. **Rear**, 1·27M from front,
Iso 3s 41m **21M**; R Tr & lantern; synch with front.
Neuer Vorhaven Ldg Lts 207·8°. Front, Iso 4s 17m 11M; B
mast, R lantern. Rear, 180m from front, Iso 4s 23m 11M; Y
bldg; intens on Ldg line.
W Mole Hd Oc G 6s 15m 4M.
E Mole Hd Oc R 6s 5M.
Fluthaffen N Mole Hd 53°30'·91N 08°09'·40E F WG 9m
W6M, G3M; G Tr; vis W216°-280°, G280°-010°, W010°-020°,
G020°-130°.
Flutmole Hd FR 6m 5M.

21

Arngast Dir Lt 53°28'·91N 08°10'·97E F WRG 30m **W21M**, W10, **R16M, G17M**, G7M; R I Tr, W bands; vis: W135°-142°, G142°-150°, W150°-152°, G152°-174·6°, R180·5°-191°, W191°-213°, R213°-225°, W(10M) 286°-303°, G(7M) 303°-314°. Same structure Fl WG 3s **W20M**, vis: G174·6°-175·5°, W175·5°-176·4°. Same structure Fl (2) W 9s; vis: 177·4°-180·5°. Same structure Oc 6s **20M**; vis: 176·4°-177·4°.

DANGAST
Lock 53°26'·85N 08°06'·60E.

VARELER SIEL
Lock 53°24'·65N 08°11'·40E.

RIVER WESER AND APPROACHES

Weser Lt By 53°54'·25N 07°50'·00E Iso 5s 12m **17M**; SWM; Racon.
Schlüsseltonne Lt By 53°56'·30N 07°54'·87E Iso 8s; SWM.
Alte Weser 53°51'·85N 08°07'·72E F WRG 33m **W22M, R19M, G17M**; R O Tr, 2 W bands, B base, floodlit; vis W288°-352°, R352°-003°, W003°-017°, Ldg sector for Alte Weser, G017°-045°, W045°-074°, G074°-118°, W118°-123°; Ldg sector for Alte Weser, R123°-140°, G140°-175°, W175°-183°, R183°-196°, W196°-238°; Fog Det Lt; RC; *Horn Mo (AL) 60s.*
Tegeler Plate, N end 53°47'·90N 08°11'·50E Oc (3) WRG 21m **W21M, R17M, G16M**; R Tr, gallery, W lantern, R roof; vis W329°-340°, R340°-014°, W014°-100°, G100°-116°, W116°-119°; Ldg sector for Neue Weser, R119°-123°, G123°-144°, W144°-147°; Ldg sector for Neue Weser R147°-264°; Fog Det Lt.
Hohe Weg, NE part 53°42'·80N 08°14'·65E F WRG 29m **W19M, R16M, G15M**; R 8-sided Tr, 2 galleries, G lantern; vis W102°-138·5°, G138·5°-142·5°, W142·5°-145·5°, R145·5°-184°, W184°-278·5°; Fog Det Lt.
Robbennordsteert 53°42'·20N 08°20'·45E F WR 11m W10M, R7M; R col; vis W324°-004°, R004°-090°, W090°-121°.
Robbenplate Ldg Lts 122·3°. **Front**, 53°40'·92N 08°23'·06E Oc 6s 15m **17M**; R tripod; intens on Ldg line. **Rear**, 0·54M from front, Oc 6s 37m **18M**; R Tr, 3 galleries, G lantern; vis 116°-125·5°; synch with front; Fog Det Lt.
Wremerloch Ldg Lts 140·1°. Front, 53°38'·41N 08°25'·10E Iso 6s 15m13M. Rear, 0·57M from front, Iso 6s 31m 14M; synch with front; Ra Refl.
Dwarsgat Ldg Lts 320·1°. Front, 53°43'·15N 08°18'·55E Iso 6s 16m **15M**. Rear, 0·75M from front, Iso 6s 31m **17M**; synch with front (same Ldg Line as Wremer Loch).
Langlütjen Ldg Lts 305·2°. Front, 53°39'·50N 08°23'·07E Oc 6s 15m 13M; B mast, B & W gallery; vis 288°-310°; Ra Refl. Rear, 0·5M from front, Oc 6s 31m 14M; synch with front.
Imsum Ldg Lts 125·2°. Front 53°36'·42N 08°30'·59E Oc 6s 15m 13M; R tripod with gallery; **Rear**, 1·02M from front, Oc 6s 39m **16M**; synch with front.
Solthorn Ldg Lts 320·6°. Front 53°38'·34N 08°27'·39E Iso 4s 15m 13M; R&W mast. **Rear**, 700m from front, Iso 4s 31m **17M**; synch with front.
Fischeriehafen Ldg Lts 150·8°. **Common front**, 53°31'·93N 08°34'·60E Oc 6s 17m **18M**, R ▽ on W mast. **Rear**, 0·68M from front, Oc 6s 45m **18M** 2 R ▽s on W mast, R bands; synch with front.
No. 61 Lt By 53°32'·28N 08°34'·04E QG; SHM; Km 66·0.

BREMERHAVEN
Vorhafen N Pier Hd 53°32'·19N 08°34'·57E FR 15m 5M.
S Pier Hd 53°32'·14N 08°34'·57E FG 15m 5M.
Nordenham Hafen N ent 53°28'·10N 08°29'·14E FG; Km 56·0.
Hafen von Brake Dir Lt 53°18'·88N 08°29'·27E Dir Iso WRG 4s 15m W9M, R7M, G7M; vis R345°-352·5°, W(intens) 352·5°-356°, G356°-360°; Km 40·5.
Hunte 1 Lt By 53°15'·50N 08°28'·95E IQG; SHM; Km 32·7.

BREMEN
Hasenbüren Sporthafen 53°07'·51N 08°40'·02E 2 FY (vert); Km 11·6.

GERMAN BIGHT

GERMAN BIGHT Lt F 54°10'·70N 07°26'·01E Iso 8s 12m **17M**; R hull marked D-B; RC; Racon; *Horn Mo (DB) 30s.*
D-B Weser Lt By 54°02'·42N 07°43'·05E Oc (3) R 12s; PHM; Racon.

HELGOLAND
Restricted area Helgoland-W By 54°10'·65N 07°48'·29E; WCM.
Helgoland-O Lt By 54°09'·00N 07°53'·57E Q (3) 10s; ECM; *Whis.*
Helgoland 54°10'·96N 07°53'·01E Fl 5s 82m **28M**; Brown ■ Tr, B lantern, W balcony. FR on radio masts 180m SSE and 740m NNW.
Cable Area Oc (3) WG 8s 18m W6M, G4M; W mast, R bands; vis W239°-244°, G244°-280°, W280°-285°.

Vorhafen. Ostmole, S elbow Oc WG 6s 5m W7M, G4M; G post; vis W203°-250°, G250°-109°; Fog Det Lt.
Ostmole Hd FG 7m 4M; vis 289°-180°; *Horn (3) 30s.*
Sudmole Hd Oc (2) R 12s 7m 4M; G post, R lantern; vis 101°-334°.
Binnenhafen Ldg Lts 302·2° W Pier, Front, Oc R 6s 8m 7M. Rear, 50m from front, Oc R 6s 10m 7M; synch with front.

DÜNE
Düne -S Lt By 54°09'·57N 07°56'·04E Q (6) + L Fl 15s; SCM.
Ldg Lts 020°. Front, Iso 4s 11m 8M; intens on Ldg line. Rear, 120m from front, Iso WRG 17m W11M, R10M, G10M; synch with front; vis G010°-018·5°, W018·5°-021°, R201°-030°, G106°-125°, W125°-130°, R130°-144°.
Sellebrunn W Lt By 54°14'·43N 07°49'·83E Q (9) 15s; WCM; *Whis.*
Nathurn-N By 54°13'·40N 07°49'·05E; NCM.

RIVER WESER TO RIVER ELBE

Nordergründe N Lt By 53°57'·08N 08°00'·17W VQ; NCM.
Westertill N Lt By 53°58'·18N 08°06'·82E Q; NCM.
Scharnhörnriff W Lt By 53°58'·53N 08°08'·80E Q (9) 15s; WCM.
Scharnhörnriff N Lt By 53°58'·99N 08°11'·25E Q; NCM.

RIVER ELBE AND APPROACHES

ELBE 1 Lt F 54°00'·00N 08°06'·58E Iso 10s 12m **17M**; R hull and Lt Tr; RC; Racon (T); *Horn Mo (R) 30s* (H24).
Grosser Vogelsand 53°59'·78N 08°28'·68E Fl (3) 12s 39m **25M**; helicopter platform on R ● Tr, W bands; vis 085·1°-087·1°; Fog Det Lt, Same Tr, Iso 3s **26M**; vis 087·1°-091·1°. Oc 6s **26M**; vis 091·1°-095·1°. Fl (4) 15s **19M**; vis 095·1°-101·9°. Fl (4) R 15s 12M; vis 101·9°-105·1°. Fl R 3s **15M**; vis 113°-270°. Oc (4) R 18s 9M; vis 322·5°-012°; Fog Det Lt; *Horn Mo (VS) 30s.*
Neuwerk, S side 53°54'·95N 08°29'·85E L Fl (3) WRG 20s 39m **W16M**, R12M, G11M; vis G165·3°-215·3°, W215·3°-238·8°, R238·8°-321°, R343°-100°.
No.1 Lt By 53°59'·27N 08°13'·30E QG; SHM.
No.5 Lt By 53°59'·35N 08°19'·08E QG; SHM.
No.19 Lt By 53°57'·83N 08°34'·48E QG; SHM.
No.25 Lt By 53°56'·67N 08°38'·32E QG; SHM.

CUXHAVEN
Ldg Lts 151·2°. **Baumrönne**, front, 53°51'·25N 08°44'·24E 1·55M from rear, Fl 3s 25m **17M**; W Tr, B band on gallery; vis 143·8°-149·2°. Same Tr, Iso 4s **17M**; vis 149·2°-154·2°. Fl (2) 9s **17M**; vis 154·2°-156·7°. **Altenbruch, common rear**, 53°49'·83N 08°45'·50E Iso 4s 58m **21M**; intens on Ldg line; synch with front. Same structure, Iso 8s 51m **22M**; synch with front.

Altenbruch Ldg Lts 261°. **Common front**, 53°50'·08N 08°47'·75E Iso 8s 19m **19M**; W Tr, B bands. Same structure, Iso WRG 8s W8M, R9M, G8M; vis G117·5°-124°, W124°-135°, R135°-140°. Rear, Wehldorf Iso 8s 31m 11M; W Tr, B bands; synch with front.
No. 35 Lt By 53°50'·73N 08°45'·86E Oc (2) G 9s; SHM.
No. 43 Lt By 53°50'·27N 08°52'·30E Oc (2) G 9s; SHM.

OTTERNDORF
Medem, Hadelner Kanal ent 53°50'·20N 08°53'·93E Fl (3) 12s 6m 5M; B △, on B col.

Balje Ldg Lts 130·8°. **Front**, 53°51'·33N 09°02'·70E Iso 8s 24m **17M**; W Tr, R bands. **Rear**, 1·35M from front, Iso 8s 54m **21M**; W Tr, R bands; intens on Ldg line; synch with front. Zweidorf 53°53'·42N 09°05'·69E Oc R 5s 9m 3M; R □ on W pylon; vis 287°-107°.
No. 51 Lt By 53°51'·07N 09°00'·22E QG; SHM.
No. 57 Lt By 53°52'·55N 09°06'·38E QG SHM.

BRUNSBÜTTEL
Ldg Lts 065·5°. Front, **Schleuseninsel** Iso 3s 24m **16M**; R Tr, W bands; vis North of 063·3°. Rear, **Industriegebiet**, 0·9M from front, Iso 3s 46m **21M**; R Tr, W bands; synch with front.
Alterhaven N Mole (Mole 4) Hd 53°53'·29N 09°07'·59E F WR (vert) 15m W10M, R8M; vis R275·5°-079°, W079°-084°.

NORD-OSTSEE KANAL (KIEL CANAL),
RENDSBURG/KIEL-HOLTENAU
No. 2/Obereider 1 Lt By 54°18'·95N 09°42'·71E Fl (2+1) R 15s; PHM.
Kiel Nordmole 54°21'·83N 10°09'·18E Oc (2) WR 9s 23m.
Tiessenkal Oc (3) WG 12s 22m.

FRIEBURG
Entrance Bn (unlit) 53°50'·25N 09°18'·90E; SHM.
Rhinplatte Nord 53°48'·09N 09°23'·36E Oc WRG 6s 11m W6M, R4M, G3M; vis: G122°-144°, W144°-150°, R150°-177°, W177°-122°; Ra refl.

STÖRLOCH/BORSFLETH, STÖR/BEIDENFLETH
Stör Ldg Lts 093·8°. Front, 53°49'·29N 09°23'·91E Fl 3s 7m 6M; △ on R ● Tr. Rear, 200m from front, Fl 3s 12m 6M; synch with front.

GLÜCKSTADT
Glückstadt Ldg Lts 131·8° **Front**, Iso 8s 15m **19M**; W Tr, R bands; intens on Ldg line. **Rear**, 0·68M from front, Iso 8s 30m **21M**; W Tr, R bands; intens on Ldg line.
N Mole Oc WRG 6s 9m W9M R6M, G6M; W Tr with gallery; vis R330°-343°, W343°-346°, G346°008°, G123°-145°, W145°-150°, R150°-170°.
N Pier Hd 53°47'·15N 09°24'·58E FR 5m 4M. (FG on South Mole Hd.)
Pagensand Ldg Lts 135° 53°42'·15N 09°30'·30E. Front, Iso 4s 20m 13M; W Tr, R bands. Rear, 880m from front, Iso 4s 32m 13M.

STADE
Stadersand 53°37'·74N 09°31'·72E Iso 8s 20m 14M.

HAMBURG

HAMBURGER YACHT HAFEN, WEDEL
No. 122 Lt By 53°34'·20N 09°40'·68E Oc (2) R 9s; PHM.
E Ent E Pier Hd 53°34'·30N 09°40'·87E FG 3M.
(Both ent show FR & FG May to Oct.)

SCHULAU
No. 123 Lt By 53°33'·90N 09°42'·05E Fl G 4s; SHM.
E Ent E Pier Hd 53°34'·14N 09°42'·05E FG.

NEUENSCHLEUSE
119/HN1 LT By 53°34'·08N 09°39'·49E QG; SHM.

MÜHLENBERG
Ent E Pier Hd 53°33'·22N 09°49'·48E (unmarked).

TEUFELSBRÜCK
Ent Bkwtr Hd 53°32'·88N 09°52'·12E (unmarked).

RÜSCHKANAL
East Ent 53°32'·63N 09°51'·10E FR 8m 5M.

CITY SPORTHAFEN
Brandenburger Hafen Ent 53°32'·56N 09°58'·88E Iso Or 2s.

RIVER ELBE TO DANISH BORDER

INSHORE ROUTE RIVER ELBE TO SYLT

Süderpiep Lt By 54°06'·00N 08°21'·90E Iso 8s; SWM; *Whis*.
Ausseneider Lt By 54°14'·04N 08°18'·21E Iso 4s; SWM.
Hever Lt By 54°20'·45N 08°18'·80E Oc 4s; SWM; *Whis*.
Rütergat Lt By 54°31'·02N 08°12'·00E Iso 8s; SWM.
Amrum Bank S Lt By 54°32'·00N 08°04'·95E Q (6) + L Fl 15s; SCM.
Vortrapptief Lt By 54°35'·00N 08°12'·20E Oc 4s; SWM.
Amrum Bank W Lt By 54°38'·00N 07°55'·40E Q (9) 15s; WCM.
Theeknobs W Lt By 54°43'·52N 08°09'·95E Q (9) 15s; WCM.
Amrum Bank N Lt By 54°45'·00N 08°07'·00E Q; NCM.
Lister Tief Lt By 55°05'·38N 08°16'·88E Iso 8s; SWM *Whis*.

BÜSUM
Süderpiep Lt By 54°06'·00N 08°21'·90E Iso 8s; SWM; *Whis*.
Büsum 54°07'·65N 08°51'·55E Iso WRG 16s 22m **W17M**, R14M, G13M; vis W248°-317°, R317°-024°, W024°-084°, G084°-092·5°, W092·5°-094·5° Ldg sector for Süder Piep, R094·5°-097°, W097°-148°.
W Mole Hd Oc (3) R 12s 10m 4M; R Tr; FW Fog Det Lt.
E Mole Hd 54°07'·21N 08°51'·70E Oc (3) G 12s 10m 4M; G Tr; vis 260°-168°.
Ldg Lts 355·1°. Front, 54°07'·53N 08°51'·58E Iso 4s 9m 13M; B mast, W bands. Rear, 110m from front, Iso 4s 12m 13M; synch with front.

RIVER EIDER
St Peter 54°17'·30N 08°39'·15E L Fl (2) WRG 15s 23m **W15M**, R13M, G11M; R Tr, B lantern; vis R271°-294°, W294°-325°, R325°-344°, W344°-035°, G035°-055°, W055°-068°, R068°-091°, W091°-113°, G113°-115°, W115°-116°, Ldg sector for Mittelhever; R116°-130°.

Eiderdamm Lock, N Mole, W end Oc (2) R 12s 8m 5M; W Tr.
S Mole, W end Oc G 6s 8m 5M: W Tr, Gy top.

TÖNNING
W Mole Hd 54°16'·01N 08°57·12E FR 5m 4M; R col.
Quay 54°18'·95N 08°57'·12E FG 5m 4M; G col.

RIVER HEVER
Hever Lt By 54°20'·45N 08°18'·80E Oc 4s; SWM; *Whis*.
No. 3 Lt By 54°20'·69N 08°23'·12E Fl G 4s; SHM.
No. 8 Lt By 54°21'·39N 08°27'·11E Fl R 4s; PHM.
Norderhever Lt By 54°22'·52N 08°30'·80E Fl (2+1) R 15s; PHM.
Westerheversand 54°22'·45N 08°38'·50E Oc (3) WRG 15s 41m **W21M, R17M, G16M**; R Tr, W bands; vis W012·2°-069°, G069°-079·5°°, W079·5°-080·5°; Ldg sector for Hever, R080·5°-107°, W107°-157°, R157°-169°, W169°-206·5°, R206·5°-218·5°, W218·5°-233°, R233°-248°.

HUSUM

Husumer Au Outer Ldg Lts 106·5°. Front, 54°28'·57N 09°00'·78E Iso R 8s 8m 5M; R mast, W bands; intens on Ldg line. Rear, 0·52M from front, Iso R 8s 17m 6M; Y mast; synch with front.
Inner Ldg Lts 090°. Front, 54°28'·79N 09°00'·32E Iso G 8s 7m 3M; R mast, W bands; intens on Ldg line. Rear, 40m from front, Iso G 8s 9m 3M; intens on Ldg line; synch with front.

NORDSTRAND

Strucklahnungshörn, W Mole Hd 54°30'·00N 08°48'·5E Oc G 6s 8m 2M.

PELLWORM

Pellworm S side Ldg Lts 041°. **Front**, 54°29'·82N 08°40'·05E Oc WR 5s 14m **W20M**, W11M, R8M. Intens on Ldg line; vis W303·5°-313·5°, R313.5°-316·5°. **Rear**, 0·8M from front, Oc 5s 38m **20M**; R Tr, W band; synch with front. Same Tr as rear Lt, Cross Light Oc WR 5s 38m W14M, W9M, R11M, R6M; vis R11M 122·6°-140°, W14M 140°-161·5°, R11M 161·5°-179·5°, W14M 179·5°-210·2°, R6M 255°-265·5°, W9M 265·5°-276°, R6M 276°-297°, W9M 297°-307°.

WITTDÜN, AMRUM

Rütergat Lt By 54°31'·02N 08°12'·00E Iso 8s; SWM.
Amrum Hafen Ldg Lts 272°. Front, 54°37'·88N 08°22'·92E Iso R 4s 11m 10M; W mast, R stripe; intens on Ldg Line. **Rear**, 0·9M from front, Iso R 4s 33m **15M**.
Amrum 54°37'·90N 08°21'·36E Fl 7·5s 63m **23M**; R Tr, W bands.
Wriakhorn Cross Lt 54°37'·62N 08°21'·22E L Fl (2) WR 15s 26m W9M, R7M; vis W297·5°-319·5°, R319·5°-330°, W330°-005·5°, R055·5°-034°.
Nebel 54°38'·75N 08°21'·75E Oc WRG 5s 16m **W20M**, **R15M, G15M**; R Tr, W band; vis R255·5°-258·5°, W258·5°-260·5°, G260·5°-263·5°.
Norddorf 54°40'·19N 08°18'·60E Oc WRG 6s 22m **W15M**, R12M, G11M; W Tr, R lantern; vis W009-032°, G032-034°, W034°-036·8°; Ldg sector, R036·8°-099°, W099°-146°, R146°-176·5°, W176·5-178·5°, G178·5°-188°, G(unintens) 188°-202°, W(partially obscd) 202°-230°.

LANGENESS

Nordmarsch 54°37'·58N 08°31'·85E L Fl (3) WR 20s 13m W14M, R11M; Dark Brown Tr; vis W268°-279°, R279°-306°, W306°-045°, R045°-070°, W070°-218°.

OLAND

Near W Pt 54°40'·51N 08°41'·28E F WRG 7m W13M, R10M, G9M; R Tr; G086°-093°, W093°-160°, R160°-172°.

SCHLÜTTSIEL

Schl No. 20 By 54°40'·83N 08°44'·60E; PHM.
Harbour ent, S side 54°40'·89N 08°45'·10E; SHM.

WYK, FÖHR

Nieblum 54°41'·10N 08°29'·20E Oc (2) WRG 10s 11m **W19M, R15M, G15M**; R Tr, W band; vis G028°-031°, W031°-032·5°, R032·5°-035·5°.

DAGEBÜLL

Dagebüllhaven 53°43'·82N 08°41'·43E Iso WRG 8s 23m **W18M, R15M, G15M**; G mast; vis G042°-043°, W043°-044·5°, R044·5°-047°.
FW Lts shown on N and S Mole Hd.

SYLT

Threeknobs-W Lt By 54°43'·52N 08°09'·95E Q (9) 15s; WCM.
Hörnum Odde Lt By 54°44'·20N 08°18'·00E QR; PHM.
Hörnum Ldg Lts 012·5°. Front, 54°44'·82N 08°17'·45E Iso 8s 20m 14M; R Tr, W band; intens on Ldg line. **Rear**, **Hörnum** 54°45'·29N 08°17'·60E Iso 8s 45m **15M**; R Tr, W band; synch with front; intens on Ldg line. Same Tr Fl (2) 9s 48m **20M**. N Pier Hd FG 6m 3M; vis 024°-260°.
South Mole Hd 54°45'·57N 08°17'·97E FR 7m 4M; R mast.
Kampen, Rote Kliff 54°56'·87N 08°20'·50E Oc (4) WR 15s 62m **W20M**, R16M; W Tr, B band; vis W193°-260°, W(unintens) 260°-339°, W339°-165°, R165°-193°.
Lister Tief Lt By 55°05'·38N 08°16'·88E Iso 8s; SWM; *Whis*.

Ellenbogen N end, List West 55°03'·25N 08°24'·19E Oc WRG 6s 19m W14M, R11M, G10M; W Tr, R lantern; vis R040°-133°, W133°-196°, R196°-210°, W210°-227°, R227°-266·4°, W266·4°-268°, G268°-285°, W285°-310°, W(unintens) 310°-040°.
N side, List Ost 55°03'·00N 08°26'·70E Iso WRG 6s 22m W14M, R11M, G10M; W Tr, R band; vis W(unintens) 010·5°-098°, W098°-262°, R262°-278°, W278°-296°, R296°-323·3°, W323·3°-324·5°, G324·5°-350°, W350°-010·5°, Q 4M on Tr 9·4M NNE, shown when firing takes place.

List Land 55°01'·07N 08°26'·47E Oc WRG 3s 13m W12M, R9M, G8M; W mast, R band; vis W170°-203°, G203°-212°, W212°-215·5°, R215·5°-232·5°, W232·5°-234°, G234°-243°, W243°-050°.
List Hafen N Mole Hd 55°01'·03N 08°26'·52E FG 5m 3M; G mast; vis 218°-038°.
S Mole Hd 55°01'·01N 08°26'·51E FR 5m 4M; R mast; vis 218°-353°.

10.21.5 PASSAGE INFORMATION

Refer to: Admiralty Pilot *North Sea (East)*; *Cruising Guide to Germany and Denmark* (Imray/Navin) and *Frisian Pilot* (Adlard Coles/Brackenbury). For German Glossary, see 1.4.2.

RIVER EMS (charts 3509, 3510)

The River Ems forms the boundary between Netherlands and Germany, and is a major waterway leading to Eemshaven, Delfzijl (10.20.33), Emden (10.21.9), Leer and Papenburg. Approach through Hubertgat or Westerems, which join W of Borkum; the latter is advised at night. Both are well buoyed but can be dangerous with an ebb stream and a strong W or NW wind. The flood begins at HW Helgoland + 0530, and the ebb at HW Helgoland – 0030, sp rates 1·5kn.

From close SW of Borkum the chan divides: Randzel Gat to the N and Alte Ems running parallel to it to the S – as far as Eemshaven on the S bank. About 3M further on the chan again divides. Bocht van Watum is always varying so keep in main chan, Ostfriesisches Gatje, for Delfzijl and beyond. Off Eemshaven the stream runs 2-3kn.

Osterems is the E branch of the estuary of R. Ems, passing between Borkum and Memmert. It is poorly marked, unlit and much shallower than Westerems. It also gives access to the Ley chan, leading to the hbr of Greetsiel (10.21.9). But it is not advised except with local knowledge and in ideal weather.

RIVER EMS TO RIVER JADE (chart 3761)

The route to seaward of the Frisian Is from abeam Borkum to the E end of Wangerooge is about 50 miles. This is via the ITZ, S of the Terschellinger-German Bight TSS, Fig. 10 (6), the E-going lane of which is marked on its S side by SHM buoys lettered DB1, DB3, DB5 etc. About 4M S of this line of buoys the landward side of the ITZ is marked by landfall buoys showing the apprs to the eight main seegaten between the East Frisian Is. There are major lts on Borkum, Norderney and Wangerooge. Near the TSS the E-going stream begins at HW Helgoland – 0500, and the W-going at HW Helgoland + 0100, sp rates 1·2kn. Inshore the stream is influenced by the flow through the seegaten.

THE EAST FRISIAN ISLANDS (chart 3761)

The East Frisian Islands have fewer facilities for yachtsmen than the Dutch Islands to the W, and most of them are closer to the mainland. For general notes, see 10.20.5 and 10.21.10. For navigating inside the islands, in the so-called watt chans, it is essential to have the large scale pleasure craft charts and to understand the system of channel marking. Withies, unbound (⚲ with twigs pointing up) are used as PHMs, and withies which are bound (⚱ with twigs pointing down) as SHMs. Inshore the islands the *conventional direction of buoyage is always from West to East*, even though this may conflict with the actual direction of the flood stream in places.

Borkum (10.21.11 and chart 3509) lies between Westerems and Osterems, with high dunes each end so that at a distance it looks like two separate islands. Round the W end of Borkum are unmarked groynes, some extending 2¾ca offshore. Conspic landmarks include Grosse bn and Neue bn, a water tr, Borkum Grosser lt ho, Borkum Kleiner lt ho, and a disused lt ho; all of which are near the W end of the island.

Memmert on the E side of Osterems is a bird sanctuary, and landing is prohibited. There are Nature Reserves (entry prohibited) inshore of Baltrum, Langeoog and the W end of Spiekeroog (chart 1875). **Juist** (10.21.10) is the first of the chain of similar, long, narrow and low-lying islands. Most have groynes and sea defences on their W and NW sides. Their bare sand dunes are not easy to identify, so the few conspic landmarks must be carefully selected. Shoals extend seaward for 2M or more in places. The seegaten between the islands vary in position and depth, and all of them are dangerous on the ebb tide, even in a moderate onshore wind. Norderneyer Seegat is a deep chan close W of **Norderney**,

but it is approached across dangerous offshore shoals, through which lead two shallow buoyed channels, Dovetief and Schluchter. Dovetief is the main chan, but Schluchter is more protected from the NE. Depths vary considerably and at times the chans silt up. Neither should be used in strong winds. Further inshore, Norderneyer Seegat leads round the W end of the island to the harbour of Norderney (10.21.12). Beware groynes and other obstructions along the shore.

SW of Norderney, Busetief leads in a general S direction to the tidal hbr of Norddeich (10.21.9), which can also be approached with sufficient rise of tide from Osterems through the Norddeich Wattfahrwasser with a depth of about 2m at HW. Busetief is deeper than Dovetief and Schluchter, and is buoyed. The flood begins at HW Helgoland – 0605, and the ebb at HW Helgoland – 0040, sp rates 1kn.

Baltrum (10.21.10) is about 2·5M long, very low in the E and rising in the W to dunes only about 15m high. With local knowledge and only in good weather it could be approached through Wichter Ee, a narrow unmarked channel between Norderney and Baltrum; but it is obstructed by drying shoals and a bar and is not advised. A small pier and groyne extend about 2ca from the SW corner of Baltrum. The little hbr dries, and is exposed to the S and SW. Southwards from Wichter Ee, the Nessmersiel Balje, with buoys on its W side prefixed by 'N', leads to the sheltered hbr of Nessmersiel (10.21.9).

Proceeding E, the next major chan through the islands is Acummer Ee between Baltrum and **Langeoog**. Shoals extend 2M offshore, depths in chan vary considerably and it is prone to silting; it is marked by buoys prefixed with 'A', moved as necessary. In onshore winds the sea breaks on the bar and the chan should not be used. Apart from Langeoog (10.21.14), Accumer Ee gives access to the mainland hbrs of Dornumer-Accumersiel (10.21.13) and Bensersiel (10.21.15).

Between Langeoog and **Spiekeroog**, the buoyed Westerbalje and Otzumer Balje chans lead inward. The latter is normally the deeper (0·7m–2·0m) but both chans may silt up and should be used only in good weather and on a rising tide.

Harle chan (buoys prefixed by 'H') leads W of **Wangerooge** (10.21.15), but beware Buhne H groyne which extends 7½ca WSW from end of island to edge of fairway. Dove Harle (buoys prefixed by 'D') leads to the hbr. In bad weather Harlesiel, 4M S on the mainland, is a more comfortable berth.

Blau Balje leads between the E end of Wangerooge and **Minsener Oog**. Although marked by buoys (prefixed 'B' and moved as necessary) this chan is dangerous in N winds and there is a prohib area (15 May–31 Aug) S of the E end of Wangerooge for the protection of seals.

RIVER JADE (charts 3368, 3369)

To the E of Wangerooge and Minsener Oog lie the estuaries of R. Jade and R. Weser. Although not so hazardous as R. Elbe, the outer parts of both rivers can become very rough with wind against tide, and are dangerous on the ebb in strong NW winds. The Jade is entered from Jade 1 buoy via the Wangerooger Fahrwasser (buoyed) which leads SSE past Wangersiel and the yachting centre of Hooksiel (10.21.16) to Wilhelmshaven (10.21.17). To the S of Wilhelmshaven, the Jadebusen is a large, shallow area of water, through which chans run to the small hbrs of Dangastersiel and Vareler Siel.

RIVER WESER (charts 3368, 3405, 3406, 3407)

The River Weser is an important waterway leading to the ports of Bremerhaven, Nordenham, Brake and Bremen which in turn connect with the inland waterways. The upper reaches, *Unterweser*, run from Bremen to Bremerhaven (10.21.17) and below Bremerhaven the *Aussenweser* flows into a wide estuary split by two main chans, Neue Weser and Alte Weser. The position and extent of sandbanks vary: on the W side they tend to be steep-to, but on the E side there are extensive shoals (e.g. Tegeler Plate).

Weser lt buoy marks the approach from NW to Neue Weser (the main fairway) and Alte Weser which are separated by Roter Sand and Roter Grund, marked by the disused Roter

21

Sand lt tr (conspic). Both chans are well marked and they join about 3M S of Alte Weser lt tr (conspic). From this junction Hohewegrinne (buoyed) leads inward in a SE direction past Tegeler Plate lt tr (conspic) on the NE side and Hohe Weg lt tr (conspic) to the SW; here it is constrained by training walls. In the Aussenweser the stream, which runs over 3kn at sp, often sets towards the banks and the branch chans which traverse them.

The Weser-Elbe Wattfahrwasser is a demanding, but useful inshore passage between R. Weser and R. Elbe. It leads NNE from the Wurster Arm (E of Hohe Weg), keeping about 3M offshore; SE of Neuwerk and around Cuxhaven training wall. It normally requires two tides, but there are suitable anchs.

RIVER ELBE (charts 3261, 3262, 3266, 3268)

Yachts entering the Elbe are probably bound for the Nord-Ostsee Kanal ent at Brunsbüttel (10.21.21). See 10.21.19 for Cuxhaven and 10.21.20 for up-river to Hamburg. From E end of TSS the chan is well marked by buoys and beacon trs. Commercial traffic is very heavy. At Elbe 1 lt Float the E-going (flood) stream begins at HW Helgoland – 0500, and the W-going (ebb) stream at HW Helgoland + 0500, sp rates 2kn. The stream runs harder N of Scharnhörn, up to 3·5kn on the ebb, when the Elbe estuary is dangerous in strong W or NW winds.

ELBE TO NORTH FRISIAN ISLANDS (charts 1875, 3767)

The W coast of Schleswig-Holstein is flat and marshy, with partly-drying banks extending 5-10M offshore. Between the banks and islands, the chans change frequently. Süderpiep and Norderpiep lead to Büsum (10.21.24) and Meldorfer Hafen, joining S of Blauort. Norderpiep has a bar (depth 3m) and is unlit; Süderpiep is deeper and preferable in W'lies. Landmarks from seaward are Tertius bn and Blauortsand bn, and a conspic silo at Büsum.

Approaching R. Eider from seaward, find the Ausseneider lt buoy, about 6M W of the buoyed ent chan. The ent can be rough in W winds, and dangerous in onshore gales. St Peter lt ho is conspic on N shore. Here the estuary winds up to the Eiderdamm, a storm barrage with a lock (H24) and sluices. Tönning is about 5M up-river. The upper Eider parallels the Nord-Ostsee Kanal which it joins at Gieselau.

The R. Hever consists of several chans on the N side of Eiderstedt Peninsula, and S of the North Frisian Islands of **Süderoogsand** and **Pellworm**. Mittelhever is the most important of the three buoyed chans through the outer grounds, all of which meet SE of Süderoogsand before they separate once more into Heverstrom leading to Husum (10.21.24), and Norderhever which runs NE between Pellworm and Nordstrand into a number of watt channels. Schmaltief and Rütergat give access to **Amrum** (hbr on SE side), to Wyk on the E side of **Fohr** and to Dagebüll.

Sylt (10.21.26) is the largest of the N Frisian Islands, almost 20M long from S to N. It has a straight seaward coast, and a peninsula on its E side connects by Hindenburgdamm to the mainland. Vortrapptief is the chan inward between Amrum and Sylt, leading to Hörnum Hafen. It has a depth of about 4m (subject to frequent change) and is buoyed and lit. The area should not be approached in strong W winds. The flood (ESE-going) stream begins at HW Helgoland – 0350, and the ebb (WNW-going) at HW Helgoland + 0110, sp rates 2·5kn.

Lister Tief is the chan between the N end of Sylt and the Danish island of **Rømø**; it gives access to List Roads and hbr as well as to Danish hbrs. Lister Tief is well buoyed, with a least depth over the bar of about 4m. In relative terms it is the safest chan on this coast (after Süderpiep), available for yachts seeking anch under the lee of Sylt in strong W winds (when however there would be a big swell over the bar on the ebb). Beware buoyed obstructions (ODAS), 18M WSW of List West lt ho.

FROM GERMAN BIGHT TO UK (charts 2182A, 1405, 3761, 2593, 1505)

From the Elbe, Weser and Jade estuaries, skirt the E ends of TSS to take departure from Helgoland (10.21.23). Thence parallel the N side of TSS, Fig 10 (6), towards Botney Ground (BG2 buoy) if heading to ports north of the Humber. If bound for the Thames Estuary or down Channel, it is advisable to follow the ITZ westwards until well S of Texel (TX 1 lt buoy); thence take departure westward from the Netherlands (see 10.20.5). The edges of the TSS are well marked by lt buoys. Avoid areas of offshore industrial activity (10.5.5). West of German Bight streams run approx E/W, spring rates under 1kn. For distances across the North Sea, see 10.0.7.

10.21.6   DISTANCE TABLE

Approximate distances in nautical miles are by the most direct route, whilst avoiding dangers and allowing for Traffic Separation Schemes. Places in *italics* are in adjoining areas; places in **bold** are in 10.0.7, Distances across the North Sea.

		1	2	3	4	5	6	7	8	9	10	11	12	13	14	15	16	17	18	19	20
1.	*Den Helder*	**1**																			
2.	*Delfzijl*	115	**2**																		
3.	Borkum	95	22	**3**																	
4.	Emden	125	10	32	**4**																
5.	Norderney	115	41	31	47	**5**															
6.	Langeoog	130	56	46	63	18	**6**														
7.	Wangerooge	148	65	55	80	29	21	**7**													
8.	**Helgoland**	153	81	67	85	44	35	24	**8**												
9.	Hooksiel	150	83	71	97	44	34	19	35	**9**											
10.	**Wilhelmshaven**	159	89	80	106	53	43	27	43	9	**10**										
11.	**Bremerhaven**	180	100	88	115	62	47	38	44	36	45	**11**									
12.	Cuxhaven	175	105	95	120	69	60	42	38	47	56	58	**12**								
13.	**Brunsbüttel**	192	120	110	137	84	77	55	51	64	70	78	17	**13**							
14.	Kiel/Holtenau	245	173	163	190	137	130	108	104	117	123	131	70	53	**14**						
15.	Hamburg	229	159	104	174	81	114	61	88	101	101	81	54	37	90	**15**					
16.	Husum	198	127	105	137	85	77	52	47	73	82	82	66	76	129	113	**16**				
17.	*Hörnum Lt (Sylt)*	192	119	97	129	77	72	60	38	69	78	80	63	75	128	112	48	**17**			
18.	*Esbjerg*	187	155	133	165	123	119	109	83	116	125	127	110	126	179	163	95	47	**18**		
19.	*Thyboron*	322	222	200	232	186	204	178	154	301	310	201	200	196	249	233	163	120	90	**19**	
20.	*Skagen*	378	327	305	337	291	308	283	259	405	414	306	304	301	231	338	268	225	195	104	**20**

SPECIAL NOTES FOR GERMANY
10-21-7

LANDS are given in place of the 'counties' in the UK.

CHARTS: German charts are issued by the Bundesamt für Seeschiffahrt und Hydrographie (BSH), Hamburg. In this Almanac those prefixed 'D' are standard German nautical charts. The BSH prefix refers to the 3000 Series of charts for pleasure craft. These are a convenient size (42 x 59cm) and are stowed in a clear polythene envelope; each set has up to 16 sheets at medium/large scale. All charts are corrected by Nachrichten für Seefahrer (NfS) = Notices to Mariners. Where possible the AC, Imray and Dutch chart numbers are also quoted.

TIME ZONE is –0100, which is allowed for in the tidal predictions, but no provision is made for daylight saving schemes which are indicated by the non-shaded areas on the tide tables (see 9.1.2).

LIGHTS: In coastal waters particular use is made of light sectors. A ldg or Dir sector (usually W, and often intens) may be flanked by warning sectors to show the side on which the vessel has deviated: If to port, a FR lt or a Gp Fl W lt with an even number of flashes; if to stbd, a FG lt or a Gp Fl W lt with an odd number of flashes. Crossing lts with R, W and G sectors may indicate the limits of roadsteads, turning points in chans etc.

SIGNALS: Local port, tidal, distress and traffic signals are given where possible:

Traffic signals

ⓇⓇ	= Passage/entry prohib.
Ⓡ	= Be prepared to pass or enter.
Ⓦ ⓇⓇ	= Bridge closed or down; vessels which can pass under the available clearance may proceed, but beware of oncoming tfc which has right of way.
ⓌⓌ ⓇⓇ	= Lift bridge will remain at first step; vessels which can pass under the available vertical clearance may proceed.
ⒼⒼ	= Passage/entry permitted; oncoming tfc stopped.
Ⓦ ⒼⒼ	= Passage permitted, but beware of oncoming traffic which may have right of way.
Ⓡ Ⓡ	= Bridge, lock or barrage closed to navigation.
Ⓡ	= Exit from lock prohib.
Ⓖ	= Exit from lock permitted.

Visual storm signals in accordance with the International System (see 10.15.8) are shown at: Borkum, Norderney, Norddeich, Accumersiel, Bensersiel, Bremerhaven, Brunsbüttel, Die Oste, Glückstadt, Stadersand, Hamburg, Büsum, Tönning, Husum, Wyk, List and Helgoland.

Signals hoisted at masts

By day	By night	Meaning
R cylinder	Ⓦ Ⓡ	= Reduce speed to minimize wash.
● ● ▼	Ⓦ Ⓡ Ⓦ Ⓡ Ⓡ Ⓡ Ⓖ	= Fairway obstructed.
● ▼ ▲ (or R board with W band)	Ⓡ Ⓖ Ⓦ	= Chan permanently closed.

When motoring under sail, always display a motoring ▼. Rule 25e is strictly enforced and non-compliance will incur a fine.

HARBOURS: There are no commercially run marinas. Most yacht hbrs are owned by the state or community and run by a local Yacht Club (as in Belgium and the Netherlands).

BROADCASTS: Information broadcasts by VTS centres and associated communications, see Fig 10 (7).

TELEPHONES: To call UK from Germany, dial 00 44; then the UK area code, but omitting the prefix 0, followed by the number required. To call Germany from UK, dial 00-49, and area code minus initial zero, then desired number.

EMERGENCIES: Police: dial 110. Fire, Ambulance: dial 112.

MARINE RESCUE CO-ORDINATION CENTRES: Coast station, Elbe-Weser Radio ☎ (04721) 22066. Kiel Radio, ☎ (0431) 39011. Norddeich Radio, ☎ (04931) 1831.

WEATHER FORECASTS: Similar to the British Marinecall; from 1 April –30 Sept, forecast and outlook are available by dialling 0190 1160 plus two digits for the following areas:

-40 = Inland pleasure craft;
-45 = North Frisian Islands and Helgoland;
-46 = R Elbe from Elbe 1/Cuxhaven to Hamburg;
-47 = Weser Estuary and Jade Bay;
-48 = East Frisian Islands and Ems Estuary;
-53 = For foreign pleasure craft;
-54 = Denmark;
-55 = Netherlands.

For year round weather synopsis, forecast and outlook, dial 0190 1169 plus two digits as follows:
-20 = General information;
-21 = North Sea and Baltic;
-22 = German Bight and SW North Sea;
-31 = 5 day bulletin for North Sea and Baltic, containing an outlook and forecasts of wind, sea state, air and water temperature, plus warnings of fog, thunderstorms etc.

Strong wind (>F6) and storm warnings for the German North Sea coast may be obtained from ☎ 040 3 196628 (H24); if no warnings are in force, a wind forecast is given.

PUBLIC HOLIDAYS: New Year's Day, Good Friday, Easter Monday, Labour Day (1 May), Ascension Day, Whit Monday, Day of German Unity (3 Oct), Christmas Day and Boxing Day.

NATIONAL WATER PARKS exist in the Wadden Sea areas (tidal mud flats) of Lower Saxony, (excluding the Jade and Weser rivers and the Ems-Dollart estuary), and along the west coast of Schleswig-Holstein. Conservation of the ecology is the prime aim. The Parks (shown on AC & BSH charts) are divided into 3 zones with certain rules:
Zone 1 comprises the most sensitive areas (about 30%) where yachts must keep to buoyed chans, except HW±3. Speed limit 8kn.
Zone 2 is a buffer zone.
Zone 3 is the remainder. No special constraints exist in Zones 2 and 3.

CUSTOMS: Entry hbrs are Borkum, Norderney, Norddeich, Wilhelmshaven, Bremerhaven, Cuxhaven. Not Helgoland.

GAS: Sometimes Calor gas bottles can be re-filled. German 'Flussig' gas can be used with Calor regulators.

CURRENCY: 1 Deutsche Mark = 100 Pfennig.

USEFUL ADDRESSES: German National Tourist Office, 65 Curzon St, London W1Y 7PE; ☎ 0891 600100 (recorded info); ✆ 0171-495 6129. German Embassy, 23 Belgrave Sq, Chesham Place, London SW1X 8PX (☎ 0171-235 5033).

10.21.8 GERMAN GLOSSARY: See 1.4.2.

EMDEN   10-21-9

Niedersachsen, Ostfriesland, 53°20'·10N 07°10'·80E

CHARTS
AC 3510; BSH 90, 91, 3012 sheets 5 & 6

TIDES
HW +0022 on Dover (UT); ML 1·9m; Zone – 0100

Standard Port HELGOLAND (→)

Times				Height (metres)			
High Water		Low Water		MHWS	MHWN	MLWN	MLWS
0200	0700	0200	0800	2·7	2·3	0·4	0·0
1400	1900	1400	2000				
Differences EMDEN							
+0041	+0028	–0011	+0022	+0·8	+0·8	0·0	0·0
EMSHÖRN							
–0037	–0041	–0108	–0047	+0·1	+0·2	0·0	0·0
KNOCK (R. Ems)							
+0018	+0005	–0028	+0004	+0·6	+0·6	0·0	0·0

SHELTER
Good shelter, except in SW winds, in Außenhafen (3m) at yacht hbr on E side just before Nesserlander Lock. If full, lock into Binnenhafen, sheltered in all winds; Jarßumer Hafen (5m) in SE corner is mainly for locals and far from city. Possible AB at Alter Binnenhafen (4·5m), Ratsdelft (3m) and Falderndelft (3m) in city centre, if requested to lock-keeper. Lock hrs 0700-1900LT (0700-1530 Sun). For opening sound M (– –). Exceptionally, Binnenhafen can be entered via Vorhafen and Grosse Seeschleuse (H24).

NAVIGATION
See Delfzijl (10.20.33) and Borkum (10.21.11) for outer approaches via well buoyed/lit R Ems to abeam Knock lt ho. Thence 6M via Emder Fahrwasser which has drying banks and training walls close outboard of chan buoys. 3 conspic HT pylons (101m) help identify Außenhafen.

LIGHTS AND MARKS
Fahrwasser ldg lts 075°, both Oc (2) 12s 16/28m 12M (off chartlet). Ldg lts 088°, both Oc 5s 14/30m 12M, lead to hbr ent, marked by FR and FG lts. City centre bears 030°/2M.

RADIO TELEPHONE
Radar cover of the Ems is as follows:
Borkum Radar   Ch 18   Buoys 1 - 35;
Knock Radar   Ch 20   Buoys 35 - 57;
Wybelsum Radar   Ch 21   Buoys 57 - Emden Hbr ent;
Ems Traffic broadcasts info H+50 Ch 15, 18, 20 & 21.
Emden locks Ch 13 (H24).

TELEPHONE (Dial code 04921)
Hr Mr ☎ 897260/897265 (H24); Nesserlander lock ☎ 897-270; Weather ☎ 21458; Tourist Info 20094; Police 110; Fire/Ambulance 112.

FACILITIES
Yacht Club ☎ 26020 FW, AC, AB 11DM; all amenities in city (1M). Ferry to Borkum.
Note: The Ems-Jade canal, 39M to Wilhelmshaven, can be used by yachts with lowering masts & max draft 1·7m. Min bridge clearance 3·75m. It has 6 locks. Speed limit 4kn.

OTHER MAINLAND HARBOURS BETWEEN RIVERS EMS AND JADE

GREETSIEL, Niedersachsen, 53°32'·90N 07°02'·15E. AC 3509, 3761; BSH 89, 3012, 3015.5 & .2. HW –0400 on Dover (UT), –0010 on Helgoland (zone –0100); ML 2·6m. Buoyed chan leads from Osterems 3M SE, then NE to Ley bn, Fl Y 4s, tide gauge. Dir lt 165°, F WRG 10m 8M, leads between 1M long bkwtrs to lock; access HW–4 to +3. Yachts berth on marina pontoons (3m). A canal connects Greetsiel to Emden. There are a few facilities: Hr Mr ☎ (04926) 760; ☷ ☎ (04931) 2764. **Village** R, V, ⇌.

NORDDEICH, Niedersachsen, 53°38'·75N 07°08'·98E. AC 3761, BSH 3012.1, 3015.5. HW –0030 on Dover (UT); See 10.21.11. Very good shelter in hbr, reached by chan 50m wide, 2m deep and over 1M long between two training walls which cover at HW and are marked by stakes. Hr divided by central mole; yachts berth in W hbr. Lts on W training wall hd FG 8m 4M, vis 021°-327°. On E training wall hd FR 8m 4M, vis 327°-237°. Ldg lts 144°: front, Iso WR 6s 6m 6/4M; rear, 140m from front, Iso W 6s 9m 6M synch. Ldg lts 350°: front Iso WR 3s 5m 6/4M; rear, 95m from front, Iso W 3s 8m 6M. Ldg lts 170°: front Iso W 3s 12m 10M; rear, 420m from front, Iso W 3s 23m 10M, synch. Hr Mr VHF Ch 14, ☎ 8060; ☷ ☎ 2735; YC ☎ 3560; Facilities: AB, C (5 ton), D ☎ 2721, FW, Slip, CH, BSH agent. **Town** ⓑ, Bar, Dr, ✉, R, ⇌, V, Gaz. Ferry to Juist and Norderney.

NESSMERSIEL, Niedersachsen, 53°41'·80N 07°21'·73E. AC 1875, 3761; BSH 3015.6, D89; HW –0040 on Dover (UT); –0020 on Helgoland (zone –0100); HW ht –0·2m on Helgoland. Good shelter in all weathers. Appr down the Nessmersieler Balje, chan marked by SHM buoys and bns leading to end of Leitdamm. There a lt bn, Oc 4s 5M, together with unlit bns mark the course of the Leitdamm on W; ‡ mark the E side of chan. Leitdamm covers at HW. Beyond ferry berth is a Yachthafen (1½M); secure to pontoons S of Ferry Quay. Hbr dries (2m at HW). Hr Mr ☎ 2981; ☷ ☎ 2735. Facilities: **Nordsee YC Nessmersiel**; no supplies except FW. **Village** (1M to S) has limited facilities. Ferry to Baltrum.

EAST FRISIAN ISLANDS   10-21-10

THE EAST FRISIAN ISLANDS off the North Sea coast of Germany and the North Frisian Islands off Schleswig-Holstein and Denmark together comprise the German Frisian Islands. The East Frisian Islands run from the Ems estuary to the Jade Bay with two small islands in the Elbe estuary. They lie between 3 and 20M off-shore and were, at one time, the north coast. The area between the low-lying islands and the present coastline which is now flooded by the sea is called the Watten. The islands are known locally as the Ostfriesischen and the inhabitants speak a patois known as Fries, a language with a close resemblance to English.

TIDES: The gaps between the islands are known as *Seegats* and the watersheds (where the tide meets having swept both ways round the island, usually about ⅓ of the way from the E end of the S side) are known as *Watts*. Tidal streams are very slack over the watts but very strong in the Seegats, especially on the sp ebb. Persistent strong W/NW winds may raise the sea level by over 0.25m (exceptionally by 3m); against the ebb they cause steep dangerous seas over the bars near the entrance to the Seegats. Strong E/SE winds can lower sea level by more than 0.25m, dangerously reducing clearances. All the Seegats are dangerous in winds >F4 with any N in them.

BUOYAGE: Deep water chans are buoyed, but shoal chans are marked by withies (*pricken* in German). Withies the natural way up ⳁ are to be taken as PHMs and withies bound or inverted thus ⳁ are to be taken as SHMs. As stated in 10.21.5, the conventional direction of buoyage is always from West to East inside the islands, so leave PHMs to the N whichever way the stream is flowing.

BRIEF NOTES:
BORKUM (14 sq miles): The largest island, see 10.21.11.
LUTJEHORN: Bird sanctuary; landing prohib.
MEMMERT: Bird sanctuary; landing prohib. Lt on stone tr with G cupola, Oc (2) WRG 14s 15m 17/12M.
JUIST (6½ sq miles): No yacht hbr. See next column.
NORDERNEY (10 sq miles): Lt on R octagonal tr, Fl (3) W 12s 59m 23M. See 10.21.12.
BALTRUM (3 sq miles): Pretty island with small town and hbr at W end. See next column.
LANGEOOG (7 sq miles): See 10.21.14.
SPIEKEROOG (5 sq miles): See next column.
WANGEROOGE (2 sq miles): See 10.21.15.
MINSENER OOG: Large bn. Beware groynes and overfalls in strong NW winds.
ALTE MELLUM: Bird sanctuary; landing prohib.
SCHARHÖRN: Between Alte Mellum and Neuwerk; (off chartlet, in Elbe estuary). Uninhabited.
GROSSES KNECHTSAND: Between Alte Mellum and Neu Werk; Bird sanctuary; landing prohib; (off chartlet).
NEUWERK (off chartlet, in Elbe estuary): Island only inhabited by LB crew and lt ho men. Lt in ☐ brick tr with B cupola, L Fl (3) WRG 20s 38m 16/12M. On W side there is a conspic W radar tr and landing stage. Ferry to Cuxhaven.

OTHER HARBOURS IN THE EAST FRISIAN ISLANDS

JUIST, Niedersachsen, 53°39'·70N 07°00'·00E. AC 3509; BSH 90, 3015.4. HW –0105 on Dover (UT); –0035 on Helgoland (zone –0100); HW ht +0·1 on Helgoland (both differences valid at Memmert). Ent through narrow chan running N in the centre of the S side of island, marked by withies to port. To the W of these is the long (5ca) landing pier. Conspic marks are: West bn, on Haakdünen at W end of island, Juist water tr in centre and East bn, 1M from E end of island. Aero lt Fl W 5s 14m (occas) at the airfield. There is no yacht hbr, but yachts can dry out on soft mud alongside quay in ferry hbr. ⚓ 1ca S of W part of town ½M E of steamer pier or at E end of island. Hr Mr ☎ 724; ⌗ ☎ 351. Facilities: FW, Slip, C; villages of Oosdorp, Westdorp and Loog in centre of island have limited facilities, V, R, Bar, Gaz. Ferry to Norddeich.

BALTRUM, Niedersachsen, 53°43'·30N 07°21'·80E. AC 1875, 3761; BSH 3015.6/7. HW –0040 on Dover (UT); Use differences Langeoog 10.21.14. Shelter is good except in SW winds. Without detailed local knowledge and ideal conditions, the appr via the unmarked, drying Wichter Ee Seegat is not recommended. Better appr is at HW via the Norderneyer Wattfahrwasser running S of Norderney (which also gives access to Neßmersiel). Hbr partly dries. Yacht moorings in the Bootshafen at the E end of hbr. Lt at the groyne head Oc WRG 6s 7m 6/3M G082·5°-098°, W098°-103°, R103°-082·5°. Hr Mr ☎ (04939) 448. Facilities: Hbr AB, FW; **Baltrumer Bootsclub YC. Village** (¼M NNE) V, R, Bar. No fuel. Ferry from Neßmersiel.

SPIEKEROOG, Niedersachsen, 53°45'·00N 07°40'·40E. AC 3368, 1875, 3761; BSH 89, 3015.8. HW –0008 on Dover (UT); ML 1·3m; Duration 0555. See differences 10.21.14. Good shelter except in S/SW winds which cause heavy swell. Small ferry hbr (1.6m) on S side of Spiekeroog with yacht pontoons is reached by marked chan, dredged 1·2m. Lt on R mast, FR 6m 4M, vis 197°-114°. Hr Mr ☎ (04976) 235. Facilities: 60+40 visitors, 14DM, C (15 ton), town is ½M from hbr. Ferry from Nieuharlingersiel.

21

BORKUM   10-21-11

EAST FRISIAN ISLANDS
Niedersachsen 53°33'·50N 06°45'·10E

CHARTS
AC 3509, 3761; BSH 3015/2, D90; DYC 1812; ANWB A

TIDES
–0105 Dover; ML 1·4; Duration 0610; Zone –0100

Standard Port HELGOLAND (→)

Times				Height (metres)			
High Water		Low Water		MHWS	MHWN	MLWN	MLWS
0200	0700	0200	0800	2·7	2·3	0·4	0·0
1400	1900	1400	2000				
Differences BORKUM (FISCHERBALJE)							
–0048	–0052	–0124	–0105	0·0	0·0	0·0	0·0
EMSHÖRN							
–0037	–0041	–0108	–0047	+0·1	+0·2	0·0	0·0

SHELTER
Good in the yacht hbr (1·8 - 2·5m), which is preferred to the Schutzhafen (5 - 7·5m) close to the E; access to both H24 with good facilities. To the NE is the tiny triangular Kleinbahnhafen (ferry hbr) prohib to yachts. Note: The S part of the island is a Nature Reserve. Borkum town is 7km NW.

NAVIGATION
WPT Riffgat (SWM) buoy, Iso 8s, 53°38'·90N 06°27'·10E, 302°/122° from/to Fischerbalje lt, 11M. See also 10.20.33. There are many groynes extending up to 2¾ca (500m) off shore. From any direction, pick up the Fischerbalje lt at the end of the Leitdamm. Beware strong currents across the buoyed Fischerbalje chan. Speed limit in hbrs 5kn.

LIGHTS AND MARKS
Landmarks: Water tr, Grosse and Kleine lt ho's at Borkum town; 2 wind turbines 3ca NNE of yacht hbr ent. From the Fischerbalje lt the chan up to the hbr is well buoyed/lit. Yacht hbr ent is abeam F7 SHM buoy, Oc (3) G 12s. Schutzhafen ent shows FR on W and FG on E moles. Fischerbalje lt, Oc (2) WRG 16s 15m 16/11M, W tr with R top and lamp on tripod; R260°-313°, G313°-014°, W014°-068°. Initial app in sector R068°-123° until abm. Fog det lt.

RADIO TELEPHONE
Hr Mr VHF Ch 14 (In season Mon-Fri 0700-2200; Sat 0800-2100; Sun 0700-2000). See also Delfzijl, 10.20.30.

TELEPHONE (Dial code 04922)
Hr Mr 2420; CG Borkum Kleiner Lt Tr; ⌖ 2287; Police 3950; Ⓗ 813; Brit Consul (040) 446071.

FACILITIES
Yacht Hbr (50 + 200 visitors) ☎ 7333, AB, FW, Slip, D, R, Bar, AC, C (6 ton), V, R; **Kleinbahnhof** C (hand), AB.
Town P, ME, El, Gaz, V, R, Bar, ⊠, Ⓑ, ⇌ (ferry to Emden), ✈ (to Emden and Bremen). Ferry: Hamburg-Harwich.

NORDERNEY   10-21-12

EAST FRISIAN ISLANDS
Niedersachsen 53°41'·94N 07°09'·93E

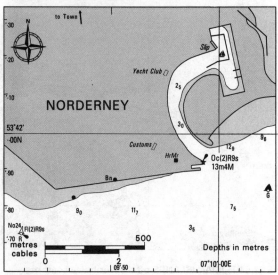

CHARTS
AC 3761; DYC 1812; Zeekarten 1353; BSH 3015, 3012, D89

TIDES
–0042 Dover; ML 1·4; Duration 0605; Zone –0100

Standard Port HELGOLAND (→)

Times				Height (metres)			
High Water		Low Water		MHWS	MHWN	MLWN	MLWS
0200	0700	0200	0800	2·7	2·3	0·4	0·0
1400	1900	1400	2000				
Differences NORDERNEY (RIFFGAT)							
–0024	–0030	–0056	–0045	+0·1	+0·1	0.0	0·0
NORDDEICH HAFEN							
–0018	–0017	–0029	–0012	+0·2	+0·2	0·0	0·0
MEMMERT							
No data		No data		+0·1	+0·1	0·0	0·0

SHELTER
Good; the hbr is accessible H24. Yacht hbr is at the NE of the hbr, where yachts lie bow to pontoon, stern to posts; or AB on W wall of hbr, as crowded in Jul/Aug. Hbr speed limit 3kn.

NAVIGATION
WPT Dovetief SWM buoy, Iso 4s, 53°45'·35N 07°09'·83E, 013°/193° from/to D8 PHM buoy, Oc (2) R 9s, 1·63M. Ent through the Dovetief (see 10.21.5) is well buoyed but the bar can be dangerous in on-shore winds and following seas which break on it, especially on an ebb tide. Follow the buoyed chan closely around W tip of island. Ent via the Schlucter is no longer advised as it has less water (1997). Ent at night is dangerous. Note: Tidal streams run across the Schlucter and Dovetief, not along it. Beware merchant shipping.

LIGHTS AND MARKS
Land marks: in centre of island Norderney lt ho, 8-sided R brick tr, Fl (3) 12s 59m 23M. Water tr in town (conspic). W mole head Oc (2) R 9s 13m 4M, RW ○ tr.

RADIO TELEPHONE
VHF Ch 14 (Mon 0700-1200, 1230-1730; Tues 0900-1200, 1230-1900; Wed – Sun 0700-1200, 1230-1900).

TELEPHONE (Dial code 04932)
Hr Mr 2850; CG 2293; ⌖ 2386; Weather 549; Police 788; Ⓗ 477 and 416; Brit Consul (040) 446071.

FACILITIES
M, L, FW, C (10 ton), V, R, CH, SM, Slip, ME, El, Sh, P, D, Gaz; **Yacht Club** Bar.
Town V, R, Bar, ⊠, Ⓑ, ⇌ (ferry to Norddeich), ✈ (to Bremen). Ferry: Hamburg-Harwich.

DORNUMER-ACCUMERSIEL
10-21-13

Niedersachsen 53°41'·40N 07°29'·40E

CHARTS
AC 1875, 3761; BSH 3015, Sheet 7, D89
TIDES
−0040 Dover; ML 1·4; Duration 0600; Zone −0100

Standard Port HELGOLAND (→)

Use Differences LANGEOOG (10.21.14)

SHELTER
The marina provides complete shelter in all winds; depth 3m, access HW ±4. Ent is narrow; keep to W of chan on entering. Marina is fenced so obtain a key before leaving.
NAVIGATION
Appr through Accumer Ee (see 10.21.5 and 10.21.14) leading into Accumersieler Balje and to AB3 SHM buoy, IQ G 13s. From here keep four withies ‡ to stbd, clear of the Leitdamm. Note warnings on German chart D89.

LIGHTS AND MARKS
None.
RADIO TELEPHONE
None.
TELEPHONE (Dial code 04933)
Hr Mr 1732; Deputy Hr Mr 441; ‡ (04971) 7184; Lifeboat (04972) 247; Weather 0190 116048; Police 2218; Ⓗ 04941-940; Brit Consul (040) 446071.
FACILITIES
Dornumer Yacht Haven (250) YC ☎ 2240; All facilities; FW, R, Slip, Gaz, D, ME, El, Sh; pontoons are lifted out of season.
Town V, R, Bar, ✉, Ⓑ, ⇌ (Harlesiel), ✈ (Bremen or Hamburg). Ferry: Hamburg-Harwich.

LANGEOOG
10-21-14

EAST FRISIAN ISLANDS
Niedersachsen 53°43'·42N 07°30'·20E

CHARTS
AC 1875, 3761; ANWB A; BSH 3015, Sheet 7, D89
TIDES
−0010 Dover; ML No data; Duration 0600; Zone −0100

Standard Port HELGOLAND (→)

Times				Height (metres)			
High Water		Low Water		MHWS	MHWN	MLWN	MLWS
0200	0700	0200	0800	2·7	2·3	0·4	0·0
1400	1900	1400	2000				
Differences LANGEOOG							
+0003	−0001	−0034	−0018	+0·3	+0·3	0·0	0·0
SPIEKEROOG							
+0003	−0003	−0031	−0012	+0·4	+0·4	+0·1	+0·1
NEUHARLINGERSIEL							
No data		No data		+0·5	+0·5	0·0	0·0

SHELTER
Hbr is well sheltered by 20m high sand dunes, but it is open to the S. The E side of hbr dries; chan to yacht pontoons is marked by ‡ withies.
NAVIGATION
WPT Accumer Ee (see 10.21.5) SWM buoy, Iso 8s, 53°47'·27N 07°28'·37E, 045°/225° from/to A1 chan buoy, SHM, Oc (2) G 9s, 1·40M; thence via buoyed chan to A9/B26 SHM lt buoy. W sector of W mole lt leads 072° to ent.

Ice protectors extend about 40m E of E mole, awash at HW, marked by withies.
LIGHTS AND MARKS
Lt bn on W mole, Oc WRG 6s 8m 7/4M; G064°-070°, W070°-074°, R074°-326°, W326°-330°, G330°-335°, R335°-064°, Horn Mo (L) 30s (sounded 0730-1800LT). Daymarks: Langeoog ch and water tr 1·5M to NNW.
RADIO TELEPHONE
Hr Mr VHF Ch 17, 0700-1700.
TELEPHONE (Dial code 04972)
Hr Mr 502; Lifeboat CG 247; ‡ 275; Weather Emden 21458; Police 810; Dr 589; Brit Consul (040) 446071.
FACILITIES
Langeoog Marina (70 + 130 visitors) ☎ 552, Slip, FW, C, (12 ton), El, Bar, R; **Segelverein Langeoog YC**.
Village (1½ M) P, D, V, R, Gaz, Bar, ✉, Ⓑ, ⇌ (ferry to Norddeich), ✈ (to Bremen). Ferry: Hamburg-Harwich. NOTE: Motor vehicles are prohib on the island. Village is 1½M away; go by foot, pony and trap or train. Train connects with ferries to Bensersiel.

21

OTHER MAINLAND HARBOURS BETWEEN RIVERS EMS AND JADE

BENSERSIEL, Niedersachsen, 53°41'·80N 07°32'·90E. AC 1875, 3761; BSH 3015.7. HW –0024 on Dover (UT); +0005 on Helgoland (zone –0100); HW ht +0·4m on Helgoland. Very good shelter in the yacht hbr (dries). Ent chan from Rute 1·5M between training walls with depth of 1·5m. Walls cover at HW. Yacht hbr to SW just before hbr ent (2m); also berths on the SW side of main hbr.
Lights: E training wall hd Oc WRG 6s 6m 5/2M, G110°-119°, W119°-121°, R121°-110°. W mole hd FG; E mole hd FR. Ldg lts 138°, both Iso W 6s 7/11m 9M (intens on line), synch. Hr Mr VHF Ch 14, ☎ (04971) 2502; ⌗ ☎ (04421) 42031; Facilities: FW, C (8 ton), D (on E pier), P (cans), El, Slip, ME, Sh.
Town Ⓑ, Bar, ✉, R, ⇌, V, Gaz. Ferry to Langeoog.

NEUHARLINGERSIEL, Niedersachsen, 53°43'·20N 07°42'·40E. AC 3368, 1875, 3761; BSH 3015.8. HW 0000 on Dover (UT); see differences under 10.21.14. Appr chan well marked from Bakledge N end of Leitdamm, Oc 6s. Beware strong tidal streams across the ent. Chan runs close E of Leitdamm which is marked by stakes with ⚓. It covers at HW. Yachts lie in NE corner of hbr; where there are many poles. Visitors berths very limited. Hr Mr ☎ (04974) 289.
Facilities: **Quay** FW, D.
Village (picturesque) V, R, Bar. Ferry to Spiekeroog (35 mins).

HARLESIEL, Niedersachsen, 53°44'·10N 07°50'·10E. AC 3369, 3368; BSH 3015.8. HW –0100 on Dover (UT); HW (zone –0100) –0005 and ht +0·5m on Helgoland. Excellent shelter S of lock which opens approx HW ±1. 120 yacht berths on pontoons to W by village or at BY to E after passing through lock on W side of dyke. River navigable up to Carolinensiel. Lock, VHF Ch 17, 0700-2100. Hr Mr ☎ (04464) 1472, berthing fees similar to Wangerooge; ⌗ ☎ 249; YC ☎ 1473; Facilities: BY, C, V, R, Slip, P, D, FW.
Town El, ME, Gaz, ✉, V, ✈ and ferry to Wangerooge.

WANGEROOGE   10-21-15

EAST FRISIAN ISLANDS
Niedersachsen 53° 46'·50N 07° 52'·18E

CHARTS
AC 3368, 1875; BSH D2, 3015 Sheet 8
TIDES
E Wangerooge, –0009 Dover; ML 1·9. Duration 0600
W Wangerooge, –0014 Dover; ML 1·5. Zone –0100

Standard Port WILHELMSHAVEN (→)

Times				Height (metres)			
High Water		Low Water		MHWS	MHWN	MLWN	MLWS
0200	0800	0200	0900	4·3	3·7	0·6	0·0
1400	2000	1400	2100				
Differences WEST WANGEROOGE							
–0101	–0058	–0035	–0045	–1·1	–0·9	–0·2	0·0
EAST WANGEROOGE							
–0058	–0053	–0024	–0034	–1·0	–0·8	–0·1	0·0
ALTE WESER LIGHT HOUSE							
–0055	–0048	–0015	–0029	–1·0	–0·9	–0·2	0·0

SHELTER
Good in all winds, but SW gales, and S'lies at HW, cause heavy swell and difficult conditions in hbr. Best access HW±2. Yachts on marina pontoons at E side of hbr have 1·3 to 1·8m depth; rafting no more than two deep. The W jetty is for ferries only.
NAVIGATION
WPT Harle (SWM) By, Iso 8s, 53°49'·28N 07°49'·00E, 351°/171° from/to Buhne H WCM buoy, VQ (9) 10s, 2·4M. From seaward the Harle chan (see 10.21.5) leads inward between Spiekeroog and Wangerooge; it varies in depth and position, and care is needed. Beware Buhne H groyne, extending 7½ca, buoyed.
LIGHTS AND MARKS
Wangerooge lt ho Fl R 5s 60m 23M; R ○ tr with two W bands; same structure: Dir lt, F WRG 24m 22/10M, R358·5°-008°, W008°-018·5°, G018·5°-055°, W055°-060·5°, R060·5°-065·5°, W065·5°-071°, G (18M) 119·4°-138·8°, W (22M) 138·8°-152·2° (ldg sector), R152·2°-159·9°, RC. Note: the last 3 GWR sectors above lead in from seaward; they are not shown on the chartlet.
RADIO TELEPHONE
Hr Mr VHF Ch 17, 0700-1700.
TELEPHONE (Dial code 04469)
Hr Mr 630; ⌗ 223; Weather Bremerhaven 72220; Police 205; Ambulance 588; Brit Consul (040) 446071.
FACILITIES
Wangerooge YC ☎ 364, 11.10DM, FW, L, El, M, Gaz.
Village El, V, P and D (cans), CH, ▣, Ⓑ, ⇌ (ferry to Harlesiel), ✈ (to Harle and Helgoland). Ferry: Hamburg-Harwich.

HOOKSIEL   10-21-16

Niedersachsen 53°38'·85N 08°05'40E

CHARTS
AC 3369; BSH 3015 Sheet 10, D7

TIDES
+0034 Dover; ML no data; Duration 0605; Zone –0100

Standard Port WILHELMSHAVEN (⟶)

Times				Height (metres)			
High Water		Low Water		MHWS	MHWN	MLWN	MLWS
0200	0800	0200	0900	4·3	3·7	0·6	0·0
1400	2000	1400	2100				
Differences HOOKSIEL							
–0023	–0022	–0008	–0012	–0·5	–0·4	–0·1	0·0
SCHILLIG							
–0031	–0025	–0006	–0014	–0·7	–0·6	–0·1	0·0

SHELTER
Temp AB in the Vorhafen (approx 1m at MLWS) but it is very commercial and uncomfortable in E winds. Beyond the lock there is complete shelter in the Binnentief, 2M long and approx 2·8m deep. Best berths for visitors in Alter Hafen Yacht Hbr in the town. Max draught 2m; bigger yachts go to YCs; see Lockmaster.

NAVIGATION
WPT No 37/Hooksiel 1 SHM buoy, IQ G 13s, 53°39'·38N 08°06'·63E 227°/047° from/to ent 1·1M. See also 10.21.17 for outer appr's. Ent is marked by H3 SHM buoy, approx 1M W of main Innenjade chan. Caution: strong cross tide, tanker pier and restricted area to SE of ent. Appr to lock through Vorhafen, enclosed by two moles. Depth in chan 2·5m. Lock opens Mon - Fri 0800-1900, Sat/Sun 0900-2000 (LT); actual times on board at lock. Secure well in lock.

LIGHTS AND MARKS
Ldg lts 164·5°, both Iso 6s 15/24m 24/27M, synch/intens, lead W of the WPT. Conspic chys of oil refinery 1·7M S of lock, which is in the W047°-062° sector of Hooksielplate Cross lt, Oc WRG 3s. There is a street lamp on the N mole and L Fl R 6s on dayglo R pile on S mole. Usual R/G tfc sigs at lock.

RADIO TELEPHONE
Port VHF Ch 63. VTS Centre, *German Bight Traffic* Ch 80 79 broadcasts info every H in German/English; *Jade Traffic* broadcasts info in German every H+10 Ch 20 63. Radar cover of the Jade is as follows:

Jade Radar I	Ch 63	Buoys 1 - 33;
Jade Radar II	Ch 20	Buoys 33 - 58.

TELEPHONE (Dial code 04425)
Hr Admin 958012; Lockmaster 430; ⌗ 1302; CG (0421) 5550555; Weather (0190) 116047; Police 269; Ⓗ (04421) 2080; Dr 1080; Brit Consul (040) 446071.

FACILITIES
Visitors Yacht Hr (50) AB, 9DM (at 1DM/metre LOA). AC, FW, Bar; **Whf** (Werft BY) ☎ 95850, BH (25 ton), Slip; **Alter Hafen** AB, FW, V, R, Bar; **Wilhelmshaven YC** ☎ 285. **Town** BY, SM, ME, El, CH, P, D, Gaz, V, R, Bar, Ⓑ, ✉, ⇌ (Wilhelmshaven), ✈ (Wilhelmshaven or Bremen).

ADJACENT HARBOURS ON THE RIVER JADE

WANGERSIEL, Niedersachsen, 53°41'·00N 08°01'·60E. AC 3369; BSH 3015.9/10. HW –0100 on Dover (UT); use SCHILLIG differences 10.21.16; ML 3·3m. From spar buoy W2 (PHM) besom perches mark the N side of the chan to the hbr. Best water 10 to 20m from perches. Depth at ent, 1·3m. Chan keeps shifting especially at E end. Boats drawing 1·5m can cross the bar HW ±2½. Most of hbr dries. Berth on N quay. YC and FW are in the NW corner. Hr Mr ☎ 238. Facilities: No fuel. At Horumersiel (¼M) V, R, Bar.

RÜSTERSIEL, Niedersachsen, 53°33'·74N 08°09'·33E. AC 3369; BSH 3015.12. Tides approx as Wilhelmshaven, 3M to the S. Appr from No 47 SHM buoy, IQ G 13s; SW for 9ca to Maadesiel, close N of NWO oil pier and tanks. A conspic factory chy (275m) is 4ca N of ent. The outer hbr dries; access HW±2 via sluice gate. The small marina (3m) is 8ca up the Maade river; or continue 1M, via opening bridge (0700-1700 Mon-Fri), to berth on N quay at Rüstersiel.

TIME ZONE –0100
(German Standard Time)
Subtract 1 hour for UT
For German Summer Time add ONE hour in non-shaded areas

GERMANY – WILHELMSHAVEN

LAT 53°31′N   LONG   8°09′E

TIMES AND HEIGHTS OF HIGH AND LOW WATERS

YEAR **1998**

JANUARY

Time	m	Time	m
1 TH 0217 0840 1449 2055	4.3 0.1 4.1 0.2	**16** F 0255 0917 1520 2124	4.4 0.2 4.0 0.2
2 F 0258 0922 1531 2133	4.4 0.0 4.1 0.2	**17** SA 0331 0949 1554 2153	4.3 0.2 3.9 0.2
3 SA 0340 1001 1613 2212	4.3 0.2 4.0 0.2	**18** SU 0404 1019 1625 2222	4.2 0.2 3.8 0.2
4 SU 0425 1045 1700 2257	4.3 0.1 4.0 0.3	**19** M 0437 1049 1658 2254	4.1 0.2 3.8 0.3
5 M 0515 1135 1751 2347	4.3 0.2 3.9 0.4	**20** TU 0510 1118 1731 2327	4.0 0.3 3.7 0.4
6 TU 0608 1228 1845	4.2 0.3 3.8	**21** W 0547 1152 1812	3.9 0.4 3.6
7 W 0043 0706 1327 1946	0.5 4.1 0.4 3.8	**22** TH 0009 0634 1240 1909	0.6 3.8 0.6 3.6
8 TH 0149 0815 1435 2057	0.6 4.1 0.5 3.8	**23** F 0110 0739 1348 2022	0.7 3.7 0.6 3.6
9 F 0304 0932 1548 2211	0.5 4.0 0.4 3.9	**24** SA 0227 0857 1507 2139	0.7 3.7 0.6 3.7
10 SA 0422 1046 1659 2318	0.4 4.0 0.4 4.0	**25** SU 0346 1012 1622 2245	0.6 3.8 0.5 3.9
11 SU 0533 1150 1801	0.3 4.1 0.3	**26** M 0457 1117 1726 2342	0.4 4.0 0.3 4.1
12 M 0014 0632 1243 1853 O	4.2 0.3 4.2 0.4	**27** TU 0557 1212 1821	0.2 4.0 0.2
13 TU 0100 0720 1327 1936	4.3 0.2 4.2 0.4	**28** W 0031 0650 1302 1911	4.2 0.1 4.1 0.1
14 W 0139 0801 1406 2014	4.4 0.2 4.2 0.3	**29** TH 0117 0739 1351 1959	4.3 0.0 4.2 0.1
15 TH 0217 0840 1444 2051	4.4 0.2 4.1 0.3	**30** F 0202 0827 1438 2045	4.4 -0.1 4.1 0.0
		31 SA 0246 0912 1521 2126	4.4 -0.2 4.1 0.0

FEBRUARY

Time	m	Time	m
1 SU 0331 0954 1604 2206	4.4 -0.2 4.1 0.0	**16** M 0339 0950 1556 2156	4.1 0.1 3.9 0.0
2 M 0416 1037 1648 2249	4.4 -0.1 4.0 0.1	**17** TU 0411 1021 1628 2227	4.1 0.1 3.9 0.1
3 TU 0504 1122 1733 2334	4.3 0.1 4.0 0.2	**18** W 0442 1047 1657 2255	4.0 0.1 3.8 0.2
4 W 0551 1207 1819	4.3 0.2 3.9	**19** TH 0510 1110 1726 2323	3.9 0.2 3.7 0.3
5 TH 0019 0642 1255 1913	0.3 4.1 0.4 3.8	**20** F 0544 1141 1811	3.8 0.4 3.6
6 F 0115 0747 1358 2024	0.5 3.9 0.5 3.8	**21** SA 0010 0641 1240 1921	0.5 3.6 0.5 3.5
7 SA 0232 0909 1518 2146	0.5 3.8 0.6 3.8	**22** SU 0125 0802 1406 2047	0.6 3.6 0.6 3.6
8 SU 0359 1032 1638 2303	0.4 3.8 0.4 4.0	**23** M 0255 0931 1537 2208	0.5 3.7 0.5 3.8
9 M 0518 1141 1745	0.3 3.9 0.4	**24** TU 0420 1048 1655 2315	0.3 3.8 0.3 4.0
10 TU 0002 0619 1232 1837	4.1 0.2 4.0 0.3	**25** W 0530 1152 1759	0.1 4.0 0.2
11 W 0047 0705 1313 1919 O	4.3 0.2 4.1 0.3	**26** TH 0009 0629 1246 1853 ●	4.2 0.0 4.1 0.1
12 TH 0124 0743 1350 1956	4.3 0.1 4.1 0.2	**27** F 0058 0720 1335 1942	4.3 -0.2 4.1 -0.1
13 F 0200 0819 1423 2030	4.4 0.1 4.1 0.1	**28** SA 0145 0808 1422 2028	4.4 -0.3 4.1 -0.2
14 SA 0234 0852 1454 2100	4.3 0.1 4.0 0.1		
15 SU 0307 0921 1525 2128	4.2 0.1 4.0 0.0		

MARCH

Time	m	Time	m
1 SU 0231 0855 1506 2111	4.4 -0.3 4.1 -0.2	**16** M 0244 0852 1459 2103	4.2 0.0 4.0 -0.1
2 M 0318 0940 1549 2154	4.4 -0.3 4.1 -0.2	**17** TU 0316 0922 1530 2133	4.1 -0.1 4.0 -0.1
3 TU 0404 1022 1631 2236	4.4 -0.1 4.1 -0.1	**18** W 0348 0952 1602 2203	4.0 -0.1 3.9 -0.1
4 W 0449 1103 1712 2316	4.3 0.0 4.1 0.0	**19** TH 0418 1019 1630 2229	4.0 0.0 3.9 0.0
5 TH 0533 1141 1753 2354	4.2 0.0 4.0 0.1	**20** F 0444 1038 1655 2252	3.9 0.0 3.8 0.1
6 F 0621 1223 1843	4.0 0.3 3.9	**21** SA 0512 1102 1733 2330	3.7 0.4 3.6 0.3
7 SA 0045 0724 1324 1955	0.3 3.8 0.5 3.8	**22** SU 0603 1154 1837	3.6 0.4 3.5
8 SU 0202 0848 1448 2124	0.4 3.7 0.5 3.8	**23** M 0040 0723 1320 2006	0.4 3.5 0.5 3.6
9 M 0336 1017 1616 2247	0.3 3.7 0.5 3.9	**24** TU 0214 0857 1458 2135	0.4 3.6 0.5 3.8
10 TU 0502 1129 1727 2348	0.2 3.8 0.3 4.1	**25** W 0347 1022 1624 2248	0.2 3.7 0.3 4.0
11 W 0601 1217 1816	0.1 3.9 0.2	**26** TH 0502 1130 1732 2346	0.0 3.9 0.1 4.2
12 TH 0029 0642 1253 1854	4.2 0.1 4.0 0.2	**27** F 0603 1216 1829	-0.2 4.0 -0.1
13 F 0103 0717 1327 1930 O	4.2 0.0 4.0 -0.2	**28** SA 0038 0657 1317 1920 ●	4.3 -0.4 4.1 -0.2
14 SA 0138 0751 1359 2004	4.2 0.0 4.0 0.0	**29** SU 0127 0746 1403 2007	4.3 -0.4 4.1 -0.3
15 SU 0212 0823 1430 2034	4.2 0.0 4.0 -0.1	**30** M 0215 0833 1447 2052	4.4 -0.4 4.1 -0.3
		31 TU 0303 0919 1530 2136	4.4 -0.3 4.2 -0.3

APRIL

Time	m	Time	m
1 W 0349 1001 1611 2217	4.3 -0.1 4.2 -0.2	**16** TH 0326 0925 1538 2140	4.0 -0.1 4.0 -0.2
2 TH 0433 1039 1650 2256	4.2 0.0 4.2 -0.1	**17** F 0357 0953 1608 2208	4.0 -0.1 4.0 -0.1
3 F 0516 1114 1730 2333	4.1 0.2 4.1 0.0	**18** SA 0427 1016 1638 2237	3.9 0.0 3.9 0.0
4 SA 0603 1155 1820	3.9 0.3 3.9	**19** SU 0459 1044 1716 2315	3.7 0.1 3.8 0.1
5 SU 0022 0704 1254 1930	0.2 3.7 0.4 3.8	**20** M 0548 1134 1816	3.6 0.3 3.7
6 M 0135 0824 1415 2057	0.3 3.5 0.5 3.8	**21** TU 0019 0702 1253 1937	0.2 3.6 0.4 3.7
7 TU 0307 0952 1544 2220	0.3 3.6 0.5 3.9	**22** W 0147 0830 1427 2104	0.2 3.6 0.4 3.9
8 W 0432 1104 1656 2321	0.2 3.7 0.3 4.0	**23** TH 0317 0954 1551 2219	0.0 3.7 0.2 4.0
9 TH 0531 1150 1743	0.1 3.9 0.2	**24** F 0432 1104 1700 2320	-0.1 3.9 0.0 4.2
10 F 0001 0608 1232 1820	4.1 0.0 4.0 0.0	**25** SA 0535 1203 1801	-0.3 4.0 -0.1
11 SA 0035 0643 1258 1858 O	4.1 0.0 4.0 0.0	**26** SU 0016 0632 1256 1857 ●	4.3 -0.4 4.0 -0.3
12 SU 0112 0719 1334 1936	4.1 -0.1 4.0 -0.1	**27** M 0110 0724 1343 1947	4.3 -0.4 4.1 -0.3
13 M 0148 0753 1406 2009	4.1 -0.1 4.1 -0.1	**28** TU 0159 0810 1426 2032	4.4 -0.3 4.2 -0.3
14 TU 0221 0824 1436 2039	4.1 -0.1 4.1 -0.2	**29** W 0245 0854 1508 2116	4.4 -0.2 4.3 -0.3
15 W 0253 0853 1507 2110	4.1 -0.1 4.0 -0.2	**30** TH 0332 0936 1549 2158	4.3 -0.1 4.3 -0.2

Chart Datum: 2·26 metres below Normal Null (German reference level)

TIME ZONE –0100
(German Standard Time)
Subtract 1 hour for UT

For German Summer Time add
ONE hour in non-shaded areas

GERMANY – WILHELMSHAVEN

LAT 53°31′N   LONG   8°09′E

TIMES AND HEIGHTS OF HIGH AND LOW WATERS   YEAR **1998**

MAY

	Time	m		Time	m
1 F	0417 / 1015 / 1629 / 2237	4.1 / 0.0 / 4.2 / -0.1	**16** SA	0341 / 0933 / 1551 / 2156	4.0 / -0.1 / 4.1 / -0.1
2 SA	0502 / 1052 / 1711 / 2318	4.0 / 0.1 / 4.1 / 0.0	**17** SU	0417 / 1005 / 1628 / 2232	3.9 / 0.0 / 4.0 / -0.1
3 SU	0548 / 1134 / 1759	3.8 / 0.3 / 4.0	**18** M	0457 / 1042 / 1713 / 2317	3.8 / 0.1 / 4.0 / 0.0
4 M	0005 / 0643 / 1227 / 1902	0.1 / 3.6 / 0.4 / 3.9	**19** TU	0547 / 1132 / 1809	3.7 / 0.2 / 3.9
5 TU	0108 / 0751 / 1336 / 2019	0.3 / 3.5 / 0.5 / 3.9	**20** W	0015 / 0652 / 1241 / 1919	0.1 / 3.7 / 0.3 / 3.9
6 W	0226 / 0908 / 1456 / 2136	0.3 / 3.5 / 0.5 / 3.9	**21** TH	0130 / 0808 / 1402 / 2036	0.1 / 3.7 / 0.3 / 4.0
7 TH	0345 / 1018 / 1608 / 2238	0.2 / 3.7 / 0.3 / 4.0	**22** F	0250 / 0925 / 1520 / 2149	0.0 / 3.8 / 0.2 / 4.1
8 F	0444 / 1110 / 1700 / 2323	0.1 / 3.8 / 0.2 / 4.0	**23** SA	0403 / 1035 / 1629 / 2254	-0.1 / 3.9 / 0.0 / 4.2
9 SA	0527 / 1148 / 1742	0.0 / 3.9 / 0.1	**24** SU	0508 / 1137 / 1733 / 2355	-0.2 / 4.0 / -0.1 / 4.2
10 SU	0002 / 0606 / 1226 / 1825	4.1 / 0.0 / 4.0 / 0.0	**25** M ●	0609 / 1233 / 1835	-0.3 / 4.1 / -0.2
11 M O	0043 / 0646 / 1306 / 1906	4.1 / -0.1 / 4.1 / -0.1	**26** TU	0052 / 0703 / 1321 / 1928	4.3 / -0.2 / 4.2 / -0.2
12 TU	0123 / 0724 / 1342 / 1943	4.1 / -0.1 / 4.1 / -0.1	**27** W	0143 / 0749 / 1404 / 2013	4.3 / -0.2 / 4.3 / -0.2
13 W	0158 / 0757 / 1414 / 2016	4.1 / -0.1 / 4.1 / -0.1	**28** TH	0229 / 0831 / 1446 / 2057	4.3 / -0.1 / 4.4 / -0.2
14 TH	0232 / 0830 / 1445 / 2050	4.1 / -0.1 / 4.1 / -0.2	**29** F	0315 / 0914 / 1529 / 2141	4.2 / 0.0 / 4.3 / -0.2
15 F	0306 / 0902 / 1518 / 2123	4.0 / -0.1 / 4.1 / -0.2	**30** SA	0401 / 0956 / 1611 / 2223	4.1 / 0.0 / 4.3 / -0.1
			31 SU	0446 / 1034 / 1652 / 2304	3.9 / 0.1 / 4.2 / 0.0

JUNE

	Time	m		Time	m
1 M	0529 / 1113 / 1737 / 2346	3.8 / 0.2 / 4.1 / 0.1	**16** TU	0455 / 1044 / 1710 / 2320	3.9 / 0.1 / 4.2 / -0.1
2 TU	0615 / 1158 / 1829	3.7 / 0.3 / 4.0	**17** W	0546 / 1135 / 1803	3.8 / 0.1 / 4.1
3 W	0035 / 0708 / 1252 / 1929	0.2 / 3.6 / 0.4 / 3.9	**18** TH	0014 / 0643 / 1234 / 1903	0.0 / 3.8 / 0.2 / 4.1
4 TH	0135 / 0810 / 1357 / 2036	0.3 / 3.6 / 0.5 / 3.9	**19** F	0116 / 0746 / 1340 / 2010	0.0 / 3.8 / 0.3 / 4.1
5 F	0243 / 0916 / 1506 / 2140	0.3 / 3.7 / 0.4 / 3.9	**20** SA	0225 / 0854 / 1452 / 2122	0.1 / 3.8 / 0.2 / 4.1
6 SA	0346 / 1017 / 1609 / 2236	0.2 / 3.8 / 0.3 / 4.0	**21** SU	0336 / 1004 / 1603 / 2231	0.1 / 3.9 / 0.1 / 4.2
7 SU	0440 / 1107 / 1702 / 2325	0.1 / 3.9 / 0.2 / 4.0	**22** M	0444 / 1110 / 1712 / 2336	0.1 / 4.0 / 0.1 / 4.2
8 M	0528 / 1151 / 1751	0.1 / 4.0 / 0.1	**23** TU	0547 / 1210 / 1816	-0.1 / 4.1 / -0.1
9 TU	0011 / 0613 / 1235 / 1837	4.1 / 0.0 / 4.1 / 0.0	**24** W ●	0036 / 0644 / 1301 / 1912	4.3 / 0.0 / 4.3 / -0.1
10 W O	0054 / 0655 / 1315 / 1917	4.1 / -0.1 / 4.1 / -0.1	**25** TH	0128 / 0732 / 1345 / 1959	4.3 / 0.0 / 4.4 / -0.1
11 TH	0134 / 0733 / 1351 / 1956	4.1 / -0.1 / 4.2 / -0.1	**26** F	0214 / 0814 / 1427 / 2043	4.3 / 0.1 / 4.5 / -0.1
12 F	0213 / 0811 / 1427 / 2035	4.1 / -0.1 / 4.2 / -0.1	**27** SA	0258 / 0857 / 1510 / 2127	4.2 / 0.1 / 4.4 / 0.0
13 SA	0251 / 0848 / 1502 / 2113	4.1 / -0.1 / 4.3 / -0.1	**28** SU	0343 / 0938 / 1552 / 2207	4.1 / 0.1 / 4.4 / 0.0
14 SU	0330 / 0923 / 1539 / 2150	4.0 / 0.0 / 4.2 / -0.1	**29** M	0423 / 1015 / 1630 / 2244	3.9 / 0.1 / 4.3 / 0.1
15 M	0410 / 1000 / 1621 / 2231	4.0 / 0.0 / 4.2 / -0.1	**30** TU	0501 / 1049 / 1709 / 2320	3.8 / 0.2 / 4.2 / 0.1

JULY

	Time	m		Time	m
1 W	0539 / 1126 / 1750 / 2359	3.8 / 0.3 / 4.1 / 0.2	**16** TH	0535 / 1130 / 1752	3.9 / 0.1 / 4.3
2 TH	0619 / 1207 / 1836	3.7 / 0.4 / 4.0	**17** F	0007 / 0626 / 1222 / 1844	0.0 / 3.9 / 0.2 / 4.2
3 F	0042 / 0707 / 1257 / 1930	0.3 / 3.7 / 0.5 / 3.9	**18** SA	0059 / 0719 / 1319 / 1945	0.2 / 3.9 / 0.3 / 4.2
4 SA	0136 / 0806 / 1401 / 2034	0.4 / 3.7 / 0.5 / 3.9	**19** SU	0200 / 0822 / 1427 / 2057	0.3 / 3.9 / 0.3 / 4.1
5 SU	0241 / 0914 / 1512 / 2141	0.4 / 3.8 / 0.5 / 3.9	**20** M	0311 / 0936 / 1543 / 2214	0.3 / 3.9 / 0.3 / 4.1
6 M	0348 / 1018 / 1618 / 2243	0.3 / 3.9 / 0.4 / 4.0	**21** TU	0425 / 1048 / 1658 / 2324	0.2 / 4.1 / 0.2 / 4.1
7 TU	0448 / 1113 / 1716 / 2337	0.2 / 4.0 / 0.2 / 4.0	**22** W	0533 / 1152 / 1804	0.2 / 4.2 / 0.1
8 W	0541 / 1202 / 1807	0.1 / 4.1 / 0.1	**23** TH ●	0023 / 0630 / 1244 / 1900	4.2 / 0.2 / 4.3 / 0.0
9 TH O	0026 / 0629 / 1247 / 1854	4.1 / 0.0 / 4.2 / 0.0	**24** F	0114 / 0719 / 1328 / 1947	4.2 / 0.2 / 4.4 / 0.0
10 F	0111 / 0714 / 1329 / 1938	4.1 / 0.0 / 4.3 / 0.0	**25** SA	0159 / 0801 / 1409 / 2030	4.2 / 0.2 / 4.5 / 0.0
11 SA	0155 / 0757 / 1409 / 2023	4.2 / 0.0 / 4.3 / 0.0	**26** SU	0240 / 0841 / 1450 / 2110	4.2 / 0.2 / 4.5 / 0.1
12 SU	0238 / 0839 / 1448 / 2105	4.2 / 0.0 / 4.4 / -0.1	**27** M	0318 / 0919 / 1527 / 2146	4.1 / 0.1 / 4.4 / 0.1
13 M	0319 / 0917 / 1527 / 2144	4.1 / 0.0 / 4.4 / -0.2	**28** TU	0353 / 0951 / 1602 / 2217	4.0 / 0.1 / 4.3 / 0.1
14 TU	0359 / 0955 / 1611 / 2226	4.1 / 0.0 / 4.4 / -0.1	**29** W	0426 / 1021 / 1636 / 2249	3.9 / 0.1 / 4.2 / 0.1
15 W	0445 / 1040 / 1700 / 2315	4.0 / 0.1 / 4.3 / 0.0	**30** TH	0459 / 1053 / 1711 / 2321	3.9 / 0.2 / 4.1 / 0.2
			31 F	0532 / 1127 / 1747 / 2353	3.8 / 0.3 / 4.0 / 0.3

AUGUST

	Time	m		Time	m
1 SA	0609 / 1205 / 1829	3.8 / 0.5 / 3.9	**16** SU	0034 / 0648 / 1253 / 1919	0.3 / 4.0 / 0.4 / 4.1
2 SU	0033 / 0658 / 1258 / 1927	0.5 / 3.7 / 0.6 / 3.8	**17** M	0131 / 0751 / 1402 / 2036	0.5 / 3.9 / 0.5 / 4.0
3 M	0133 / 0805 / 1409 / 2041	0.6 / 3.7 / 0.6 / 3.8	**18** TU	0246 / 0911 / 1528 / 2201	0.5 / 3.9 / 0.4 / 4.0
4 TU	0249 / 0922 / 1529 / 2157	0.5 / 3.8 / 0.5 / 3.9	**19** W	0410 / 1033 / 1651 / 2317	0.5 / 4.1 / 0.3 / 4.0
5 W	0404 / 1031 / 1640 / 2303	0.4 / 3.9 / 0.3 / 4.0	**20** TH	0523 / 1140 / 1758	0.4 / 4.2 / 0.2
6 TH	0510 / 1129 / 1740 / 2359	0.3 / 4.1 / 0.2 / 4.1	**21** F	0014 / 0620 / 1229 / 1848	4.1 / 0.3 / 4.3 / 0.1
7 F	0606 / 1219 / 1833	0.2 / 4.2 / 0.1	**22** SA ●	0058 / 0705 / 1310 / 1931	4.2 / 0.3 / 4.4 / 0.1
8 SA O	0048 / 0656 / 1305 / 1921	4.1 / 0.1 / 4.3 / 0.0	**23** SU	0138 / 0745 / 1348 / 2010	4.2 / 0.2 / 4.5 / 0.1
9 SU	0136 / 0744 / 1348 / 2007	4.2 / 0.1 / 4.4 / -0.1	**24** M	0215 / 0821 / 1425 / 2046	4.2 / 0.2 / 4.5 / 0.2
10 M	0221 / 0827 / 1430 / 2052	4.2 / 0.0 / 4.5 / -0.2	**25** TU	0248 / 0854 / 1459 / 2117	4.2 / 0.1 / 4.4 / 0.1
11 TU	0303 / 0907 / 1512 / 2134	4.2 / 0.0 / 4.5 / -0.2	**26** W	0319 / 0923 / 1531 / 2146	4.1 / 0.1 / 4.3 / 0.1
12 W	0344 / 0946 / 1556 / 2216	4.1 / 0.0 / 4.5 / -0.1	**27** TH	0350 / 0951 / 1603 / 2215	4.0 / 0.1 / 4.2 / 0.2
13 TH	0428 / 1029 / 1644 / 2302	4.1 / 0.1 / 4.4 / 0.1	**28** F	0421 / 1022 / 1635 / 2244	4.0 / 0.2 / 4.1 / 0.2
14 F	0514 / 1116 / 1732 / 2348	4.1 / 0.2 / 4.4 / 0.1	**29** SA	0451 / 1052 / 1704 / 2309	3.9 / 0.2 / 4.0 / 0.3
15 SA	0559 / 1202 / 1821	4.0 / 0.3 / 4.2	**30** SU	0519 / 1121 / 1736 / 2337	3.9 / 0.4 / 3.9 / 0.5
			31 M	0558 / 1202 / 1827	3.7 / 0.6 / 3.8

Chart Datum: 2·26 metres below Normal Null (German reference level)

21

TIME ZONE –0100
(German Standard Time)
Subtract 1 hour for UT

For German Summer Time add
ONE hour in non-shaded areas

GERMANY – WILHELMSHAVEN

LAT 53°31′N   LONG   8°09′E

TIMES AND HEIGHTS OF HIGH AND LOW WATERS

YEAR **1998**

SEPTEMBER

	Time	m		Time	m
1 TU	0029 0701 1309 1942	0.7 3.7 0.6 3.7	**16** W	0220 0849 1511 2147	0.8 3.9 0.6 3.8
2 W	0149 0825 1437 2110	0.7 3.7 0.6 3.7	**17** TH	0352 1017 1642 2306	0.7 4.0 0.4 3.9
3 TH	0320 0949 1603 2229	0.7 3.9 0.5 3.9	**18** F	0510 1125 1747	0.6 4.2 0.3
4 F	0439 1057 1713 2332	0.5 4.1 0.3 4.0	**19** SA	0000 0604 1211 1830	4.0 0.4 4.3 0.2
5 SA	0542 1151 1810	0.4 4.2 0.1	**20** SU ●	0036 0643 1246 1905	4.1 0.3 4.3 0.2
6 SU O	0025 0635 1239 1900	4.1 0.2 4.3 0.0	**21** M	0110 0720 1322 1941	4.2 0.1 4.3 0.2
7 M	0114 0724 1325 1947	4.2 0.1 4.4 –0.1	**22** TU	0145 0755 1357 2016	4.2 0.1 4.4 0.2
8 TU	0159 0809 1409 2033	4.2 0.0 4.5 –0.2	**23** W	0218 0827 1430 2047	4.2 0.1 4.3 0.2
9 W	0242 0852 1454 2117	4.2 0.0 4.5 –0.1	**24** TH	0247 0855 1501 2114	4.2 0.1 4.2 0.2
10 TH	0324 0932 1539 2200	4.2 0.0 4.5 0.0	**25** F	0316 0923 1532 2142	4.1 0.1 4.2 0.2
11 F	0406 1014 1624 2241	4.2 0.0 4.4 0.2	**26** SA	0346 0951 1601 2208	4.0 0.2 4.1 0.3
12 SA	0448 1056 1710 2322	4.2 0.2 4.3 0.3	**27** SU	0414 1019 1628 2230	4.0 0.3 4.0 0.3
13 SU	0529 1138 1757	4.1 0.3 4.2	**28** M	0440 1045 1657 2254	3.9 0.4 3.8 0.5
14 M	0005 0617 1227 1856	0.5 4.0 0.4 3.9	**29** TU	0515 1120 1743 2340	3.8 0.6 3.7 0.7
15 TU	0101 0723 1338 2016	0.7 3.9 0.6 3.8	**30** W	0612 1223 1856	3.7 0.7 3.6

OCTOBER

	Time	m		Time	m
1 TH	0059 0736 1352 2027	0.9 3.7 0.7 3.6	**16** F	0321 0949 1615 2239	0.9 4.0 0.6 3.8
2 F	0237 0907 1525 2154	0.8 3.9 0.5 3.8	**17** SA	0440 1058 1720 2333	0.8 4.2 0.4 4.0
3 SA	0405 1022 1642 2303	0.6 4.1 0.3 4.0	**18** SU	0534 1142 1800	0.5 4.3 0.3
4 SU	0513 1121 1743 2359	0.4 4.2 0.2 4.1	**19** M	0007 0611 1216 1832	4.1 0.4 4.3 0.3
5 M O	0608 1211 1835	0.3 4.3 0.0	**20** TU ●	0039 0648 1252 1908	4.2 0.3 4.2 0.3
6 TU	0049 0659 1300 1924	4.2 0.1 4.4 –0.1	**21** W	0114 0726 1329 1944	4.2 0.2 4.2 0.3
7 W	0135 0746 1347 2010	4.2 0.0 4.5 –0.1	**22** TH	0148 0800 1403 2016	4.2 0.2 4.2 0.2
8 TH	0219 0831 1433 2056	4.3 0.0 4.5 0.0	**23** F	0218 0829 1434 2044	4.2 0.2 4.2 0.2
9 F	0301 0915 1520 2139	4.3 0.0 4.5 0.1	**24** SA	0247 0857 1504 2111	4.2 0.1 4.1 0.2
10 SA	0342 0956 1605 2218	4.3 0.1 4.4 0.2	**25** SU	0316 0924 1534 2137	4.1 0.2 4.1 0.3
11 SU	0422 1035 1649 2255	4.3 0.2 4.2 0.4	**26** M	0344 0952 1602 2200	4.1 0.3 4.0 0.4
12 M	0503 1115 1737 2337	4.2 0.4 4.1 0.6	**27** TU	0413 1022 1634 2227	4.0 0.4 3.9 0.5
13 TU	0551 1204 1836	4.1 0.5 3.8	**28** W	0449 1058 1719 2312	3.9 0.5 3.7 0.7
14 W	0033 0657 1314 1952	0.7 4.0 0.6 3.6	**29** TH	0542 1155 1825	3.8 0.6 3.6
15 TH	0150 0821 1444 2121	0.9 3.9 0.7 3.6	**30** F	0024 0659 1316 1951	0.9 3.8 0.6 3.6
			31 SA	0156 0826 1446 2117	0.9 3.9 0.5 3.7

NOVEMBER

	Time	m		Time	m
1 SU	0325 0944 1606 2230	0.7 4.1 0.3 3.9	**16** M	0448 1103 1719 2330	0.6 4.1 0.4 4.0
2 M	0437 1048 1711 2330	0.5 4.2 0.1 4.0	**17** TU	0533 1143 1757	0.5 4.2 0.4
3 TU	0537 1143 1808	0.3 4.3 0.1	**18** W	0006 0615 1223 1836	4.1 0.4 4.2 0.4
4 W O	0023 0632 1236 1901	4.1 0.2 4.4 0.0	**19** TH ●	0044 0657 1302 1913	4.2 0.3 4.2 0.3
5 TH	0111 0723 1326 1947	4.2 0.1 4.5 0.0	**20** F	0120 0732 1337 1946	4.2 0.2 4.2 0.2
6 F	0154 0809 1413 2031	4.3 0.0 4.5 0.1	**21** SA	0152 0804 1410 2017	4.2 0.2 4.2 0.2
7 SA	0237 0854 1500 2114	4.4 0.1 4.4 0.2	**22** SU	0223 0835 1442 2048	4.2 0.2 4.1 0.2
8 SU	0320 0937 1548 2156	4.4 0.1 4.3 0.3	**23** M	0253 0906 1515 2116	4.2 0.2 4.1 0.3
9 M	0402 1019 1634 2234	4.4 0.2 4.1 0.4	**24** TU	0324 0936 1547 2144	4.1 0.2 4.0 0.4
10 TU	0443 1059 1721 2315	4.3 0.3 3.9 0.6	**25** W	0358 1010 1624 2217	4.1 0.3 3.9 0.4
11 W	0530 1146 1815	4.1 0.4 3.7	**26** TH	0437 1050 1709 2300	4.0 0.4 3.8 0.6
12 TH	0006 0630 1246 1920	0.7 4.0 0.6 3.6	**27** F	0528 1142 1808	3.9 0.4 3.7
13 F	0112 0743 1402 2035	0.7 3.9 0.7 3.6	**28** SA	0002 0632 1249 1920	0.7 3.9 0.5 3.7
14 SA	0230 0902 1523 2150	0.9 3.9 0.7 3.7	**29** SU	0120 0748 1409 2038	0.8 3.9 0.4 3.7
15 SU	0347 1011 1631 2248	0.8 4.0 0.5 3.9	**30** M	0242 0905 1527 2152	0.7 4.1 0.3 3.8

DECEMBER

	Time	m		Time	m
1 TU	0357 1015 1637 2258	0.5 4.2 0.2 4.0	**16** W	0449 1106 1718 2331	0.6 4.1 0.5 4.1
2 W	0504 1117 1740 2356	0.4 4.3 0.1 4.1	**17** TH	0540 1152 1803	0.5 4.1 0.4
3 TH O	0606 1215 1837	0.2 4.3 0.1	**18** F ●	0013 0626 1235 1843	4.2 0.3 4.1 0.3
4 F	0047 0701 1307 1925	4.2 0.1 4.4 0.1	**19** SA	0052 0705 1313 1920	4.2 0.2 4.1 0.2
5 SA	0131 0749 1355 2008	4.3 0.1 4.4 0.2	**20** SU	0129 0742 1350 1956	4.2 0.1 4.1 0.2
6 SU	0215 0835 1444 2053	4.4 0.1 4.3 0.3	**21** M	0203 0818 1428 2033	4.2 0.1 4.1 0.2
7 M	0300 0922 1533 2138	4.4 0.1 4.2 0.3	**22** TU	0238 0855 1504 2106	4.2 0.1 4.1 0.2
8 TU	0345 1007 1620 2219	4.2 0.1 4.0 0.4	**23** W	0312 0929 1539 2137	4.2 0.1 4.0 0.3
9 W	0427 1049 1704 2257	4.3 0.2 3.9 0.5	**24** TH	0348 1004 1619 2213	4.2 0.2 3.9 0.3
10 TH	0510 1128 1748 2338	4.2 0.4 3.7 0.6	**25** F	0431 1047 1704 2257	4.2 0.2 3.8 0.4
11 F	0559 1214 1838	4.1 0.5 3.6	**26** SA	0519 1135 1755 2348	4.1 0.3 3.8 0.5
12 SA	0028 0656 1309 1936	0.7 4.0 0.6 3.6	**27** SU	0613 1230 1853	4.1 0.3 3.8
13 SU	0128 0801 1415 2043	0.8 3.9 0.7 3.6	**28** M	0050 0715 1335 2000	0.6 4.1 0.4 3.7
14 M	0239 0909 1525 2149	0.8 3.9 0.6 3.7	**29** TU	0202 0828 1449 2114	0.6 4.1 0.4 3.8
15 TU	0349 1012 1627 2245	0.7 4.0 0.5 3.9	**30** W	0319 0944 1604 2227	0.5 4.1 0.3 3.9
			31 TH	0435 1055 1714 2332	0.4 4.2 0.2 4.1

Chart Datum: 2·26 metres below Normal Null (German reference level)

WILHELMSHAVEN
MEAN SPRING AND NEAP CURVES

MEAN RANGES
Springs 4·3m ———
Neaps   3·1m – – –

Springs occur 3 days after
New and Full Moon.

WILHELMSHAVEN   10-21-17

Niedersachsen 53°31'·00N 08°09'·00E

CHARTS
AC 3369; BSH 3015 Sheet 12, D7

TIDES
+0050 Dover; ML 2·3; Duration 0615; Zone –0100
WILHELMSHAVEN is a Standard Port. Predictions above.

SHELTER
Good in the yacht hbrs at Großer Hafen and Nordhafen, inside the sea lock, the latter rather remote. Sea lock operates Mon-Thur: 0600-1830; Fri: 0600-1700; Sat, Sun and hols: 0800-1600 (all LT). The tidal yacht hbr in Nassauhafen is better for a short stay.

NAVIGATION
WPT 1b/Jade 1 SHM buoy, Oc G 4s, 53°52'·42N 07°44'·10E, 296°/116° from/to Mellumplate lt, 14·2M. From abeam this lt, it is approx 15M to Wilhelmshaven, a busy commercial port, via the deep, wide and well marked fairway.
Note: The Ems-Jade canal, 39M to Emden, is usable by yachts with lowering masts and max draft 1·7m. Min bridge clearance 3·75m. It has 6 locks. Speed limit 4kn.

LIGHTS AND MARKS
R Jade is well marked/lit; for principal lts see 10.21.4. Ldg lts 208° into Neuer Vorhafen both Iso 4s. Fluthafen N mole FWG 9m 6/3M (sectors on chartlet); S arm, hd FR.

RADIO TELEPHONE
Port Ch 11 16 (H24). Sea lock Ch 13. Bridge opening Ch 11. See 10.21.16 for VTS, broadcast info and radar assistance.

TELEPHONE (Dial code 04421)
Hr Mr 291256; Port Authority 4800-20; Naval base/Port Captain 306 71 (operator); Sea Lock 186480; VTS 489381; ☷ 480723; Weather Bremerhaven 72220; Water Police 942358; Ⓗ 8011; Brit Consul (040) 446071.

FACILITIES
Nassauhafen Marina (28 + 100 Ⓥ) ☎ 41439, 11DM, AC, P, D, BY, Slip, ME, Bar, FW, SM, R; **Wiking Sportsboothafen** (30) ☎ 41301 AC, Bar, CH, EI, FW, Gaz, ME, R, SM, V, Sh; **Hochsee YC Germania** ☎ 44121.
Town BY, 3M, ME, CH, EI, P, D, Gaz, V, ✉, Ⓑ, ⇌, ✈.
Ferry: Hamburg-Harwich.

ADJACENT HARBOUR IN JADEBUSEN

DANGAST, Niedersachsen, 53°27'·00N 08°07'·00E. AC 3369; BSH 3015.13. HW +0055 on Dover (UT); –0007 on Helgoland (zone –0100). 4M S of Wilhelmshaven, drying hbr in the wide bay of Jadebusen, which mostly dries. Appr via Stenkentief, marked on NW side by stakes, thence SW into Dangaster Aussentief (0·5m at LWS). Unlit, other than Arngast lt, F WRG (not visible from SW), R tr, W bands, in the middle of Jadebusen. Yacht hbr (dries) on W side just before lock into Dangaster Tief, access HW ±2. Facilities usual amenities can be found in the seaside town of Dangast.

21

BREMERHAVEN   10-21-18

Federal State of Bremen 53°32'·16N 08°34'·57E

CHARTS
AC 3406, 3405; BSH 3011 Sheets 7, 8 & 10, D4

TIDES
+0051 Dover; ML 2·0; Duration 0600; Zone –0100

Standard Port WILHELMSHAVEN (←)

Times				Height (metres)			
High Water		Low Water		MHWS	MHWN	MLWN	MLWS
0200	0800	0200	0900	4·3	3·7	0·6	0·0
1400	2000	1400	2100				
Differences BREMERHAVEN							
+0029	+0046	+0033	+0038	–0·3	–0·1	–0·1	0·0
NORDENHAM							
+0051	+0109	+0055	+0058	–0·2	–0·1	–0·3	–0·1
BRAKE							
+0118	+0119	+0140	+0151	–0·2	–0·2	–0·4	–0·2
ELSFLETH							
+0130	+0131	+0200	+0210	–0·1	–0·1	–0·3	0·0
VEGESACK							
+0200	+0156	+0245	+0249	–0·2	–0·2	–0·6	–0·2
BREMEN							
+0207	+0204	+0307	+0307	–0·1	–0·1	–0·6	–0·2

SHELTER
Yachts may berth in R Geeste, but exposed to SW/W winds. Or, via Vorhafen, lock into the Fischereihafen II; sound Q (— — · —) and ent on Ⓖ. There are 3 YC/marinas: The Weser YC Yacht Haven to E of Handelshafen; the Nordseeyachting Marina (NYC or Bremerhaven Marina), 1·3M S of locks on W side (3m); and the WVW Wulstorf Marina 0·5M beyond. Further up the R Weser there are yacht hbrs at Nordenham, Rodenkirchen and Brake; and on the R Hunte at Elsfleth and Oldenburg.

NAVIGATION
WPT Alte Weser: Schlüsseltonne (SWM) buoy, Iso 8s, 53°56'·30N 07°54'·87E, 300°/120° from/to Alte Weser lt, 9M. For R Weser (very well marked) see 10.21.5. Leave R Weser at SHM lt buoy 61. Beware much commercial shipping; also ferries using R Geeste.
Note: The Geeste and Hadelner Kanals (1·5m depth; air draft 2·7m) link Bremerhaven to Otterndorf (32M).

LIGHTS AND MARKS
Ldg lts, both Oc 6s 17/45m 18M, synch, lead 151° down main chan (R Weser). Vorhafen ent, FR & FG 15m 5M, is close SW of conspic 112m radar tr.

RADIO TELEPHONE
Radar cover and info in the outer Weser is as follows:
Alte Weser Radar	Ch 22	Neue Weser: buoys 3 - 19H;
ditto	ditto	Alte Weser: buoys A1 - 16a;
Hohe Weg Radar I & II	Ch 02	Buoys 21 - 37;
Robbenplate Rdr I & II	Ch 04	Buoys 37 - 53;
Blexen Radar	Ch 07	Buoys 53 - 63;
Luneplate Radar I	Ch 05	Buoys 63 - 58;

Bremerhaven Weser Traffic broadcasts info in German at H+20 on all the above chans. *Bremerhaven Port* & locks Ch 12 16 (H24). *Brake Lock* Ch 10 (H24). *Bremen-Weser Traffic* broadcasts at H+30 on Ch 19 78 81; *Oslebshausen Lock Radio* Ch 12. *Bremen Port Radio* Ch.03 14 16 (H24). *Hunte Traffic* broadcasts at H+30 on Ch 63. *Hunte Bridge Radio* Ch 73 (HJ).

TELEPHONE (Dial code 0471)
Hr Mr 481260; Weser YC Hafen 23531; NYC Marina 77555 WVW Marina 73268; Fischereihafen Lock 4811; Weather 72220; Police 47011; Ⓗ 42028; Brit Consul (040) 446071.

FACILITIES
Weser YC ☎ 23531 C, AC, FW, R, Bar; **NYC Marina** ☎ 77555 P, D, C, Slip, AC, FW; **WVW Marina** ☎ 73268, FW, Slip, C, El, P, D; **City** all facilities: ACA, Gaz, ⇌, ✈.

The yacht lay with a very slight heel (thanks to a pair of small bilge-keels on her bottom) in a sort of trough she had dug for herself, so that she was still ringed with a few inches of water, as it were with a moat.
   For miles in every direction lay a desert of sand. To the north it touched the horizon, and was only broken by the blue dot of Neuwerk Island and its lighthouse. To the east it seemed also to stretch to infinity, but the smoke of a steamer showed where it was pierced by the stream of the Elbe. To the south it ran up to the pencil-line of the Hanover shore. Only to the west was it broken by any vestiges of the sea it had arisen from.

Riddle of the Sands: Erskine Childers

CUXHAVEN
MEAN SPRING AND NEAP CURVES

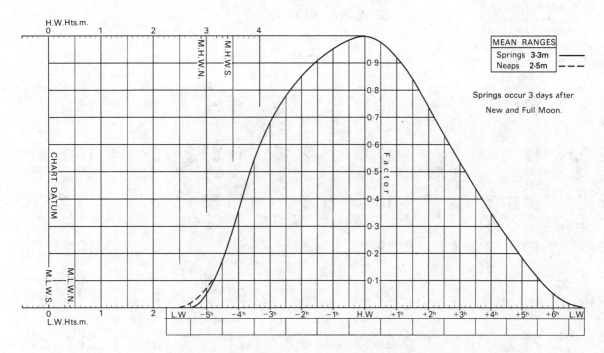

MEAN RANGES
Springs 3·3m ———
Neaps 2·5m - - - -

Springs occur 3 days after
New and Full Moon.

CUXHAVEN   10-21-19

Niedersachsen 53°52'·48N 08°42'·56E (Marina ent). Rtg 1-1-1

CHARTS
AC 3261; BSH 3010 Sheet 1

TIDES
+0103 Dover; ML 1·7; Duration 0535; Zone −0100
CUXHAVEN is a Standard Port; predictions are below

Standard Port CUXHAVEN (→)

Times				Height (metres)			
High Water		Low Water		MHWS	MHWN	MLWN	MLWS
0200	0800	0200	0900	3·3	2·9	0·4	0·0
1400	2000	1400	2100				
Differences SCHARHÖRN (11M to NW)							
−0045	−0047	−0057	−0059	0·0	0·0	0·0	0·0

SHELTER
Good in the YC marina (4m; closed in winter). Marina Cuxhaven, close S of radio mast, is entered from Alter Hafen via bridge which opens H and H+30, requested by 2 long blasts. Yachts > 20m LOA may berth in the Alter Hafen or Alter Fischereihafen. See 10.21.22 for Otterndorf.

NAVIGATION
WPT No 31 SHM buoy, Fl G 4s, 53°53'·97N 08°41'·27E, 332°/152° from/to marina ent, 1·7M. From No 23 SHM buoy, appr is in W sector (144°-149°) of Baumrönne ldg lt Fl 3s. Chan well marked/lit, see 10.21.4, and .20. Ebb runs up to 5kn off Cuxhaven. Much commercial shipping.

LIGHTS AND MARKS
Ent to YC Marina is close NW of conspic radar tr, and N of main lt ho (dark R with copper cupola) FWR, Fl (4) 12s, Oc 6s and Fl (5) 12s (for sectors see chartlet). YC marina ent, N side FWG; S side FWR, shown 1 Apr-31 Oct.

RADIO TELEPHONE
Radar cover of the outer Elbe is as follows:

Elbe West Radar	Ch 65	G. Bight lt float - buoy 1;
Elbe East Radar	Ch 19	Elbe lt float - buoy 5;
Scharhörn Radar	Ch 18	Buoys 3 - 15;
Neuwerk Radar	Ch 05	Buoys 13 - 29;
Cuxhaven Radar	Ch 21	Buoys 27 - 41;
Belum Radar	Ch 03	Buoys 39 - 53.

Cuxhaven Elbe Traffic on Ch 71 broadcasts nav/weather info in German & English every H + 55. CG & LD: Ch 10.
Cuxhaven Elbe Port Ch 12 16 (H24). Port/lock work Ch 69.

TELEPHONE (Dial code 04721)
Hr Mr 34111 (Apr-Oct); CG 38011; LB 34622 and Ch 16; Weather 36400; Port Authority 501450; ⌗ 21085; British Cruising Ass'n and Little Ship Club 57270; ☎ 572757; Police 110; Dr & Fire 112; Brit Consul (040) 446071.

FACILITIES
Cuxhaven YC Marina (Segler-Vereinigung) ☎ 34111 (summer only), 20DM, Slip, FW, P & D (cans), C (10 ton), AC, BY, ME, El, Sh, CH, SM, Gaz, chart agent, Ⓔ, R, Bar, ⊙, ⌗; **Cuxhaven Marina** ☎ 37363, open all year, 90 berths inc approx 45 for Ⓥ, 20DM, usual facilities. Swing bridge opens every H and H+30 during daytime.
City All facilities, ⇌, ✈ (Bremen, Hamburg, Hanover).
Ferry: Hamburg -Harwich.

TIME ZONE –0100
(German Standard Time)
Subtract 1 hour for UT
For German Summer Time add ONE hour in non-shaded areas

GERMANY – CUXHAVEN

LAT 53°52'N LONG 8°43'E

TIMES AND HEIGHTS OF HIGH AND LOW WATERS

YEAR **1998**

JANUARY

Day	Time	m	Time	m	Time	m	Time	m
1 TH	0226	3.4	0932	0.1	1458	3.3	2149	0.2
16 F	0302	3.5	1007	0.2	1531	3.2	2215	0.2
2 F	0308	3.5	1014	0.1	1540	3.2	2227	0.2
17 SA	0337	3.4	1039	0.2	1605	3.0	2245	0.2
3 SA	0349	3.4	1054	0.0	1623	3.2	2306	0.2
18 SU	0412	3.3	1108	0.2	1638	3.0	2315	0.2
4 SU	0434	3.4	1139	0.1	1711	3.1	2351	0.3
19 M	0447	3.2	1139	0.2	1713	2.9	2348	0.3
5 M	0525	3.4	1229	0.2	1804	3.1		
20 TU	0523	3.1	1211	0.3	1750	2.9		
6 TU	0043	0.4	0621	3.3	1323	0.3	1900	3.0
21 W	0021	0.4	0601	3.0	1246	0.4	1833	2.8
7 W	0141	0.4	0721	3.3	1422	0.4	2003	3.0
22 TH	0104	0.5	0651	2.9	1335	0.4	1930	2.8
8 TH	0249	0.5	0831	3.2	1533	0.4	2113	3.0
23 F	0207	0.5	0758	2.9	1446	0.5	2042	2.8
9 F	0406	0.4	0946	3.2	1647	0.3	2225	3.0
24 SA	0327	0.5	0915	2.9	1606	0.4	2155	2.9
10 SA	0522	0.3	1058	3.2	1757	0.3	2332	3.2
25 SU	0448	0.4	1029	3.0	1721	0.3	2300	3.1
11 SU	0629	0.3	1201	3.2	1857	0.3		
26 M	0558	0.3	1131	3.1	1823	0.3	2354	3.2
12 M (○)	0027	3.3	0725	0.2	1255	3.3	1947	0.3
27 TU	0656	0.2	1223	3.2	1916	0.2		
13 TU	0111	3.4	0812	0.2	1339	3.3	2029	0.4
28 W (●)	0041	3.3	0745	0.1	1311	3.2	2005	0.1
14 W	0149	3.5	0853	0.3	1417	3.3	2106	0.4
29 TH	0126	3.4	0832	0.0	1359	3.3	2052	0.1
15 TH	0226	3.6	0931	0.3	1455	3.3	2142	0.3
30 F	0209	3.5	0918	-0.1	1444	3.2	2136	0.0
31 SA	0253	3.5	1003	-0.1	1527	3.2	2217	0.0

FEBRUARY

Day	Time	m	Time	m	Time	m	Time	m
1 SU	0336	3.5	1045	-0.1	1609	3.2	2257	0.0
16 M	0345	3.2	1040	0.0	1606	3.0	2250	0.0
2 M	0421	3.5	1128	0.0	1656	3.2	2341	0.1
17 TU	0419	3.2	1111	0.1	1640	3.0	2321	0.0
3 TU	0511	3.5	1214	0.1	1744	3.1		
18 W	0452	3.1	1139	0.1	1711	2.9	2348	0.1
4 W	0028	0.2	0601	3.4	1300	0.2	1832	3.1
19 TH	0522	3.0	1202	0.2	1743	2.8		
5 TH	0115	0.3	0655	3.2	1349	0.3	1927	3.0
20 F	0016	0.2	0558	2.9	1235	0.3	1829	2.7
6 F	0214	0.3	0800	3.1	1455	0.4	2038	2.9
21 SA	0106	0.4	0657	2.8	1338	0.4	1938	2.7
7 SA	0331	0.3	0921	3.0	1616	0.4	2159	2.9
22 SU	0225	0.4	0819	2.7	1507	0.4	2103	2.8
8 SU	0458	0.3	1044	3.0	1737	0.3	2315	3.1
23 M	0358	0.3	0946	2.8	1638	0.3	2222	2.9
9 M	0614	0.2	1153	3.1	1842	0.3		
24 TU	0523	0.2	1102	3.0	1755	0.2	2326	3.1
10 TU	0014	3.3	0713	0.2	1244	3.2	1932	0.3
25 W	0630	0.1	1201	3.1	1855	0.1		
11 W (○)	0056	3.4	0757	0.1	1325	3.2	2012	0.3
26 TH (●)	0019	3.3	0724	-0.1	1252	3.2	1946	0.0
12 TH	0132	3.5	0835	0.1	1359	3.2	2047	0.2
27 F	0105	3.4	0812	-0.2	1340	3.2	2033	-0.1
13 F	0206	3.5	0909	0.1	1432	3.2	2120	0.1
28 SA	0149	3.4	0859	-0.3	1425	3.2	2118	-0.2
14 SA	0240	3.4	0942	0.1	1503	3.2	2151	0.0
15 SU	0312	3.3	1011	0.1	1534	3.1	2219	0.0

MARCH

Day	Time	m	Time	m	Time	m	Time	m
1 SU	0234	3.5	0945	-0.3	1508	3.1	2202	-0.2
16 M	0247	3.3	0944	0.0	1505	3.1	2156	-0.2
2 M	0320	3.5	1029	-0.2	1552	3.2	2244	-0.2
17 TU	0319	3.2	1014	-0.1	1536	3.1	2226	-0.2
3 TU	0406	3.5	1108	-0.1	1636	3.2	2327	-0.1
18 W	0353	3.1	1044	-0.1	1609	3.0	2257	-0.1
4 W	0454	3.4	1153	0.1	1720	3.2		
19 TH	0426	3.1	1111	0.0	1640	3.0	2323	-0.1
5 TH	0008	0.1	0541	3.3	1233	0.2	1803	3.1
20 F	0454	3.0	1131	0.0	1708	2.9	2346	0.1
6 F	0049	0.2	0630	3.1	1316	0.3	1855	3.0
21 SA	0524	2.9	1157	0.2	1747	2.8		
7 SA	0142	0.2	0734	2.9	1419	0.4	2007	2.9
22 SU	0027	0.2	0616	2.7	1252	0.3	1852	2.7
8 SU	0300	0.2	0859	2.8	1546	0.4	2135	2.9
23 M	0141	0.3	0737	2.7	1421	0.4	2020	2.8
9 M	0435	0.2	1028	2.8	1715	0.4	2258	3.0
24 TU	0317	0.2	0910	2.7	1601	0.4	2147	2.9
10 TU	0559	0.1	1140	2.9	1824	0.3	2357	3.2
25 W	0449	0.1	1033	2.9	1724	0.2	2257	3.1
11 W	0656	0.1	1228	3.1	1911	0.2		
26 TH	0601	-0.1	1138	3.0	1829	0.0	2352	3.3
12 TH	0036	3.3	0740	-0.1	1303	3.1	1948	0.1
27 F	0659	-0.2	1230	3.1	1923	-0.1		
13 F (○)	0109	3.3	0809	0.0	1334	3.2	2023	0.1
28 SA (●)	0041	3.4	0750	-0.4	1318	3.1	2012	-0.3
14 SA	0142	3.3	0842	0.0	1406	3.2	2056	0.0
29 SU	0128	3.4	0837	-0.4	1403	3.2	2057	-0.3
15 SU	0216	3.3	0914	0.0	1435	3.2	2126	-0.1
30 M	0214	3.5	0922	-0.3	1447	3.2	2142	-0.3
31 TU	0302	3.5	1007	-0.2	1531	3.3	2227	-0.2

APRIL

Day	Time	m	Time	m	Time	m	Time	m
1 W	0349	3.4	1050	-0.1	1614	3.3	2309	-0.1
16 TH	0329	3.1	1017	-0.1	1542	3.1	2234	-0.2
2 TH	0436	3.3	1130	0.0	1655	3.3	2348	0.0
17 F	0403	3.1	1045	-0.1	1614	3.1	2303	-0.1
3 F	0521	3.2	1207	0.2	1737	3.2		
18 SA	0435	3.0	1111	0.0	1647	3.0	2332	-0.1
4 SA	0027	0.1	0611	3.0	1249	0.2	1829	3.0
19 SU	0509	2.9	1141	0.1	1727	2.9		
5 SU	0117	0.1	0713	2.8	1349	0.3	1939	2.9
20 M	0012	0.0	0559	2.8	1233	0.2	1827	2.8
6 M	0232	0.2	0834	2.7	1513	0.4	2106	2.9
21 TU	0119	0.1	0713	2.7	1354	0.3	1949	2.9
7 TU	0405	0.2	1002	2.7	1643	0.4	2229	3.0
22 W	0248	0.1	0841	2.7	1528	0.2	2114	3.0
8 W	0530	0.1	1113	2.9	1754	0.2	2328	3.2
23 TH	0417	0.0	1004	2.8	1651	0.1	2225	3.1
9 TH	0627	0.0	1159	3.0	1840	0.1		
24 F	0530	-0.2	1110	3.0	1758	-0.1	2324	3.2
10 F	0007	3.2	0702	0.0	1231	3.1	1916	0.0
25 SA	0631	-0.3	1206	3.1	1856	-0.2		
11 SA (○)	0040	3.2	0735	-0.1	1304	3.1	1953	0.0
26 SU (●)	0017	3.3	0725	-0.4	1256	3.1	1949	-0.3
12 SU	0116	3.2	0812	-0.1	1338	3.1	2029	-0.1
27 M	0108	3.4	0814	-0.4	1342	3.2	2037	-0.3
13 M	0151	3.2	0846	-0.1	1409	3.2	2102	-0.1
28 TU	0156	3.4	0859	-0.3	1426	3.3	2121	-0.2
14 TU	0224	3.2	0917	-0.1	1439	3.2	2133	-0.2
29 W	0243	3.4	0943	-0.2	1508	3.4	2205	-0.2
15 W	0255	3.2	0947	-0.1	1509	3.2	2204	-0.2
30 TH	0331	3.4	1027	-0.1	1551	3.4	2249	-0.2

Chart Datum: 1·66 metres below Normal Null (German reference level)

TIME ZONE –0100
(German Standard Time)
Subtract 1 hour for UT

For German Summer Time add
ONE hour in non-shaded areas

GERMANY – CUXHAVEN

LAT 53°52′N   LONG 8°43′E

TIMES AND HEIGHTS OF HIGH AND LOW WATERS   YEAR **1998**

MAY

Day	Time	m	Time	m	Time	m	Time	m
1 F	0418	3.3	1107	0.0	1633	3.3	2329	-0.1
2 SA	0505	3.1	1145	0.2	1716	3.2		
3 SU	0010	0.0	0555	2.9	1227	0.3	1807	3.1
4 M	0058	0.1	0652	2.8	1321	0.3	1910	3.0
5 TU	0202	0.2	0802	2.7	1433	0.4	2027	3.0
6 W	0322	0.2	0919	2.7	1554	0.4	2143	3.0
7 TH	0441	0.1	1028	2.8	1706	0.3	2244	3.1
8 F	0540	0.0	1117	3.0	1757	0.1	2328	3.1
9 SA	0621	0.0	1155	3.1	1838	0.1		
10 SU	0007	3.2	0659	-0.1	1232	3.1	1920	0.0
11 M O	0047	3.2	0740	-0.1	1309	3.2	2001	-0.1
12 TU	0126	3.2	0818	-0.1	1343	3.2	2037	-0.1
13 W	0201	3.2	0851	-0.1	1414	3.3	2110	-0.1
14 TH	0234	3.2	0923	-0.1	1446	3.3	2143	-0.2
15 F	0309	3.2	0955	-0.1	1520	3.2	2215	-0.2
16 SA	0346	3.1	1027	-0.1	1556	3.2	2249	-0.1
17 SU	0424	3.0	1100	0.0	1635	3.2	2327	-0.1
18 M	0505	2.9	1139	0.1	1720	3.1		
19 TU	0012	0.0	0556	2.8	1257	0.2	1817	3.0
20 W	0112	0.0	0702	2.8	1339	0.2	1928	3.0
21 TH	0227	0.0	0819	2.8	1500	0.2	2045	3.1
22 F	0347	-0.1	0934	2.9	1619	0.1	2155	3.2
23 SA	0459	-0.2	1041	3.0	1727	0.0	2257	3.3
24 SU	0602	-0.3	1140	3.1	1829	-0.1	2355	3.3
25 M ●	0700	-0.3	1234	3.2	1927	-0.2		
26 TU	0051	3.4	0753	-0.2	1322	3.3	2017	-0.2
27 W	0141	3.4	0838	-0.1	1405	3.4	2101	-0.1
28 TH	0228	3.4	0921	0.0	1448	3.5	2146	-0.1
29 F	0315	3.4	1005	0.0	1530	3.5	2231	-0.1
30 SA	0403	3.2	1047	0.1	1613	3.4	2314	0.0
31 SU	0450	3.1	1126	0.2	1657	3.4	2354	0.0

JUNE

Day	Time	m	Time	m	Time	m	Time	m
1 M	0536	2.9	1205	0.3	1744	3.2		
2 TU	0037	0.1	0625	2.8	1250	0.3	1837	3.2
3 W	0127	0.2	0720	2.8	1346	0.4	1938	3.1
4 TH	0228	0.3	0822	2.8	1453	0.4	2045	3.0
5 F	0337	0.2	0927	2.8	1603	0.3	2148	3.0
6 SA	0441	0.1	1026	2.9	1705	0.2	2244	3.1
7 SU	0535	0.1	1114	3.0	1758	0.1	2333	3.1
8 M	0622	0.0	1158	3.1	1847	0.0		
9 TU	0018	3.2	0706	0.0	1239	3.2	1932	0.0
10 W O	0059	3.2	0748	-0.1	1317	3.3	2011	-0.1
11 TH	0138	3.2	0825	-0.1	1352	3.3	2048	-0.1
12 F	0217	3.3	0903	-0.1	1428	3.4	2126	-0.1
13 SA	0255	3.2	0940	0.0	1505	3.4	2203	-0.1
14 SU	0335	3.2	1016	0.0	1543	3.3	2241	-0.1
15 M	0416	3.1	1054	0.0	1625	3.3	2323	-0.1
16 TU	0502	3.0	1138	0.1	1715	3.3		
17 W	0013	0.0	0555	3.0	1229	0.2	1810	3.2
18 TH	0108	0.0	0653	3.0	1328	0.2	1912	3.2
19 F	0210	0.1	0757	3.0	1437	0.3	2020	3.2
20 SA	0320	0.1	0905	3.0	1550	0.2	2129	3.3
21 SU	0431	0.0	1013	3.0	1701	0.1	2236	3.3
22 M	0537	-0.1	1116	3.1	1807	0.0	2339	3.3
23 TU	0639	-0.1	1214	3.3	1908	-0.1		
24 W ●	0037	3.4	0734	0.0	1304	3.4	2001	-0.1
25 TH	0129	3.4	0821	0.1	1348	3.5	2046	0.0
26 F	0216	3.4	0904	0.1	1430	3.6	2131	0.0
27 SA	0302	3.3	0947	0.2	1512	3.6	2215	0.1
28 SU	0347	3.2	1028	0.1	1554	3.5	2256	0.1
29 M	0429	3.1	1104	0.2	1634	3.4	2332	0.1
30 TU	0509	3.0	1139	0.2	1716	3.3		

JULY

Day	Time	m	Time	m	Time	m	Time	m
1 W	0009	0.2	0549	2.9	1217	0.2	1759	3.2
2 TH	0048	0.3	0633	2.9	1259	0.4	1847	3.1
3 F	0133	0.3	0722	2.9	1350	0.4	1942	3.1
4 SA	0228	0.3	0821	2.9	1455	0.4	2047	3.0
5 SU	0334	0.3	0927	2.9	1606	0.4	2154	3.0
6 M	0441	0.2	1028	3.0	1713	0.3	2255	3.1
7 TU	0541	0.2	1121	3.1	1812	0.2	2347	3.2
8 W	0634	0.0	1208	3.2	1902	0.1		
9 TH O	0033	3.2	0721	0.1	1251	3.3	1947	0.0
10 F	0117	3.3	0804	0.0	1332	3.4	2029	0.0
11 SA	0201	3.3	0848	0.0	1412	3.5	2112	0.0
12 SU	0244	3.3	0931	0.0	1452	3.5	2153	0.0
13 M	0324	3.3	1008	0.0	1531	3.5	2232	-0.1
14 TU	0405	3.2	1046	0.0	1614	3.5	2316	0.0
15 W	0452	3.1	1131	0.1	1704	3.4		
16 TH	0006	0.0	0544	3.1	1222	0.2	1759	3.4
17 F	0058	0.1	0637	3.1	1315	0.3	1855	3.4
18 SA	0151	0.2	0733	3.1	1414	0.3	1956	3.3
19 SU	0253	0.3	0836	3.1	1524	0.3	2108	3.2
20 M	0405	0.3	0948	3.1	1640	0.3	2222	3.2
21 TU	0519	0.2	1059	3.2	1752	0.1	2331	3.3
22 W	0625	0.2	1201	3.3	1855	0.1		
23 TH ●	0030	3.3	0720	0.1	1251	3.4	1949	0.1
24 F O	0120	3.3	0808	0.2	1334	3.6	2035	0.1
25 SA	0205	3.3	0849	0.3	1414	3.6	2117	0.1
26 SU	0246	3.3	0929	0.3	1454	3.6	2156	0.1
27 M	0325	3.3	1006	0.2	1531	3.5	2231	0.1
28 TU	0400	3.3	1038	0.1	1607	3.4	2303	0.1
29 W	0435	3.1	1110	0.2	1644	3.3	2336	0.0
30 TH	0511	3.0	1144	0.3	1723	3.3		
31 F	0010	0.3	0548	3.0	1218	0.3	1801	3.2

AUGUST

Day	Time	m	Time	m	Time	m	Time	m
1 SA	0043	0.4	0627	2.9	1256	0.4	1845	3.1
2 SU	0124	0.4	0717	2.9	1349	0.5	1944	3.0
3 M	0225	0.4	0823	2.9	1504	0.5	2058	2.9
4 TU	0343	0.4	0937	3.0	1625	0.4	2213	3.0
5 W	0459	0.4	1044	3.1	1737	0.3	2317	3.1
6 TH	0604	0.3	1140	3.2	1836	0.2		
7 F	0010	3.2	0658	0.2	1228	3.3	1926	0.1
8 SA O	0058	3.3	0747	0.1	1312	3.4	2011	0.1
9 SU	0144	3.3	0833	0.1	1354	3.5	2056	0.0
10 M	0228	3.4	0916	0.1	1435	3.6	2139	0.0
11 TU	0309	3.3	0956	0.0	1516	3.6	2220	-0.1
12 W	0349	3.3	1035	0.0	1600	3.6	2303	0.0
13 TH	0435	3.3	1119	0.1	1649	3.5	2350	0.1
14 F	0524	3.2	1208	0.2	1741	3.5		
15 SA	0038	0.3	0613	3.2	1256	0.3	1834	3.4
16 SU	0125	0.4	0704	3.1	1349	0.4	1934	3.2
17 M	0224	0.5	0808	3.1	1459	0.4	2050	3.1
18 TU	0342	0.5	0927	3.1	1624	0.4	2214	3.1
19 W	0506	0.4	1047	3.2	1746	0.3	2329	3.2
20 TH	0617	0.4	1152	3.4	1850	0.2		
21 F	0025	3.3	0711	0.2	1240	3.5	1938	0.2
22 SA ●	0109	3.3	0754	0.3	1319	3.5	2019	0.2
23 SU	0148	3.3	0832	0.3	1355	3.6	2057	0.2
24 M	0224	3.3	0908	0.3	1432	3.6	2132	0.2
25 TU	0257	3.3	0941	0.2	1506	3.5	2204	0.2
26 W	0329	3.2	1011	0.1	1538	3.4	2233	0.2
27 TH	0400	3.2	1042	0.1	1613	3.3	2304	0.2
28 F	0433	3.1	1113	0.2	1648	3.2	2334	0.3
29 SA	0507	3.1	1143	0.3	1720	3.2		
30 SU	0000	0.4	0539	3.0	1211	0.3	1755	3.1
31 M	0030	0.5	0620	2.9	1254	0.6	1847	2.9

Chart Datum: 1·66 metres below Normal Null (German reference level)

21

TIME ZONE –0100
(German Standard Time)
Subtract 1 hour for UT

For German Summer Time add
ONE hour in non-shaded areas

GERMANY – CUXHAVEN

LAT 53°52′N   LONG 8°43′E

TIMES AND HEIGHTS OF HIGH AND LOW WATERS

YEAR **1998**

SEPTEMBER

Day	Time	m	Day	Time	m
1 TU	0123 / 0723 / 1406 / 2003	0.6 / 2.9 / 0.6 / 2.9	**16** W	0318 / 0908 / 1609 / 2204	0.7 / 3.1 / 0.5 / 3.0
2 W	0246 / 0846 / 1537 / 2130	0.6 / 2.9 / 0.5 / 2.9	**17** TH	0451 / 1035 / 1739 / 2323	0.6 / 3.2 / 0.4 / 3.1
3 TH	0418 / 1007 / 1703 / 2247	0.6 / 3.0 / 0.4 / 3.0	**18** F	0607 / 1141 / 1842	0.6 / 3.4 / 0.3
4 F	0536 / 1112 / 1810 / 2347	0.4 / 3.2 / 0.3 / 3.2	**19** SA	0015 / 0657 / 1224 / 1922	3.2 / 0.5 / 3.5 / 0.3
5 SA	0637 / 1204 / 1904	0.3 / 3.4 / 0.2	**20** SU ●	0050 / 0733 / 1257 / 1956	3.3 / 0.4 / 3.5 / 0.3
6 SU O	0037 / 0728 / 1249 / 1951	3.3 / 0.2 / 3.5 / 0.1	**21** M	0123 / 0809 / 1331 / 2031	3.3 / 0.3 / 3.5 / 0.3
7 M	0123 / 0814 / 1332 / 2036	3.3 / 0.1 / 3.5 / 0.0	**22** TU	0156 / 0844 / 1407 / 2105	3.3 / 0.3 / 3.5 / 0.3
8 TU	0208 / 0858 / 1415 / 2121	3.4 / 0.1 / 3.6 / 0.0	**23** W	0229 / 0917 / 1440 / 2136	3.3 / 0.2 / 3.4 / 0.3
9 W	0250 / 0941 / 1459 / 2204	3.4 / 0.0 / 3.6 / 0.0	**24** TH	0258 / 0947 / 1510 / 2205	3.3 / 0.2 / 3.4 / 0.3
10 TH	0331 / 1022 / 1544 / 2246	3.4 / 0.1 / 3.6 / 0.1	**25** F	0328 / 1016 / 1542 / 2233	3.3 / 0.1 / 3.3 / 0.3
11 F	0414 / 1105 / 1631 / 2329	3.4 / 0.1 / 3.5 / 0.2	**26** SA	0359 / 1045 / 1615 / 2300	3.2 / 0.2 / 3.2 / 0.3
12 SA	0459 / 1148 / 1720	3.4 / 0.3 / 3.5	**27** SU	0429 / 1113 / 1646 / 2323	3.2 / 0.3 / 3.1 / 0.4
13 SU	0012 / 0544 / 1232 / 1811	0.4 / 3.3 / 0.4 / 3.3	**28** M	0459 / 1138 / 1717 / 2350	3.1 / 0.4 / 3.0 / 0.5
14 M	0056 / 0634 / 1323 / 1913	0.5 / 3.2 / 0.4 / 3.1	**29** TU	0536 / 1215 / 1805	3.0 / 0.5 / 2.9
15 TU	0155 / 0742 / 1435 / 2033	0.6 / 3.1 / 0.6 / 3.0	**30** W	0038 / 0636 / 1321 / 1919	0.7 / 2.9 / 0.6 / 2.8

OCTOBER

Day	Time	m	Day	Time	m
1 TH	0200 / 0759 / 1454 / 2049	0.7 / 2.9 / 0.6 / 2.8	**16** F	0422 / 1008 / 1714 / 2259	0.8 / 3.2 / 0.5 / 3.0
2 F	0339 / 0928 / 1627 / 2214	0.7 / 3.0 / 0.4 / 3.0	**17** SA	0540 / 1115 / 1818 / 2350	0.7 / 3.3 / 0.4 / 3.1
3 SA	0505 / 1040 / 1741 / 2320	0.6 / 3.2 / 0.3 / 3.1	**18** SU	0631 / 1158 / 1855	0.5 / 3.4 / 0.3
4 SU	0610 / 1135 / 1838	0.4 / 3.4 / 0.1	**19** M	0023 / 0706 / 1230 / 1926	3.3 / 0.4 / 3.4 / 0.3
5 M O	0013 / 0703 / 1222 / 1928	3.2 / 0.3 / 3.5 / 0.0	**20** TU ●	0053 / 0741 / 1304 / 2002	3.3 / 0.4 / 3.4 / 0.3
6 TU	0059 / 0752 / 1308 / 2015	3.3 / 0.1 / 3.5 / 0.0	**21** W	0127 / 0819 / 1341 / 2038	3.3 / 0.3 / 3.4 / 0.3
7 W	0144 / 0838 / 1353 / 2059	3.3 / 0.1 / 3.6 / 0.0	**22** TH	0200 / 0853 / 1414 / 2109	3.3 / 0.2 / 3.4 / 0.3
8 TH	0227 / 0922 / 1439 / 2144	3.4 / 0.1 / 3.6 / 0.1	**23** F	0230 / 0923 / 1444 / 2137	3.4 / 0.2 / 3.3 / 0.3
9 F	0309 / 1005 / 1526 / 2227	3.4 / 0.1 / 3.6 / 0.2	**24** SA	0258 / 0947 / 1515 / 2204	3.3 / 0.2 / 3.3 / 0.3
10 SA	0351 / 1047 / 1613 / 2307	3.5 / 0.2 / 3.5 / 0.3	**25** SU	0328 / 1020 / 1547 / 2231	3.3 / 0.2 / 3.2 / 0.3
11 SU	0433 / 1128 / 1701 / 2347	3.5 / 0.3 / 3.4 / 0.5	**26** M	0359 / 1048 / 1620 / 2257	3.2 / 0.3 / 3.1 / 0.4
12 M	0517 / 1210 / 1752	3.4 / 0.4 / 3.2	**27** TU	0431 / 1118 / 1654 / 2327	3.2 / 0.4 / 3.0 / 0.5
13 TU	0031 / 0608 / 1301 / 1854	0.6 / 3.2 / 0.5 / 3.1	**28** W	0509 / 1155 / 1740	3.1 / 0.5 / 2.9
14 W	0129 / 0716 / 1412 / 2012	0.7 / 3.1 / 0.5 / 3.0	**29** TH	0014 / 0604 / 1255 / 1847	0.6 / 3.0 / 0.5 / 2.8
15 TH	0249 / 0841 / 1543 / 2141	0.8 / 3.1 / 0.6 / 2.8	**30** F	0127 / 0721 / 1418 / 2013	0.7 / 3.0 / 0.5 / 2.8
			31 SA	0300 / 0847 / 1548 / 2138	0.7 / 3.1 / 0.4 / 2.9

NOVEMBER

Day	Time	m	Day	Time	m
1 SU	0427 / 1003 / 1706 / 2248	0.6 / 3.2 / 0.3 / 3.1	**16** M	0549 / 1119 / 1817 / 2347	0.6 / 3.3 / 0.4 / 3.2
2 M	0537 / 1103 / 1808 / 2345	0.4 / 3.4 / 0.1 / 3.2	**17** TU	0632 / 1159 / 1854	0.5 / 3.3 / 0.4
3 TU	0635 / 1155 / 1903	0.3 / 3.5 / 0.0	**18** W	0022 / 0712 / 1237 / 1932	3.3 / 0.4 / 3.3 / 0.3
4 W O	0034 / 0728 / 1245 / 1953	3.3 / 0.2 / 3.5 / 0.0	**19** TH ●	0058 / 0752 / 1314 / 2009	3.3 / 0.3 / 3.3 / 0.3
5 TH	0120 / 0817 / 1332 / 2037	3.3 / 0.1 / 3.5 / 0.1	**20** F	0132 / 0828 / 1349 / 2041	3.4 / 0.2 / 3.3 / 0.3
6 F	0203 / 0901 / 1419 / 2121	3.4 / 0.1 / 3.6 / 0.1	**21** SA	0203 / 0859 / 1421 / 2112	3.4 / 0.2 / 3.3 / 0.3
7 SA	0246 / 0945 / 1508 / 2206	3.5 / 0.2 / 3.5 / 0.3	**22** SU	0233 / 0930 / 1454 / 2142	3.4 / 0.2 / 3.3 / 0.3
8 SU	0329 / 1030 / 1557 / 2248	3.5 / 0.2 / 3.4 / 0.3	**23** M	0305 / 1001 / 1528 / 2212	3.3 / 0.2 / 3.2 / 0.3
9 M	0412 / 1113 / 1646 / 2328	3.5 / 0.2 / 3.3 / 0.4	**24** TU	0338 / 1032 / 1603 / 2242	3.3 / 0.3 / 3.1 / 0.4
10 TU	0456 / 1155 / 1736	3.4 / 0.3 / 3.1	**25** W	0413 / 1107 / 1641 / 2317	3.2 / 0.3 / 3.0 / 0.4
11 W	0011 / 0545 / 1243 / 1833	0.6 / 3.3 / 0.4 / 2.9	**26** TH	0454 / 1148 / 1727	3.2 / 0.4 / 2.9
12 TH	0103 / 0646 / 1344 / 1940	0.7 / 3.1 / 0.5 / 2.8	**27** F	0002 / 0545 / 1241 / 1827	0.5 / 3.1 / 0.4 / 2.9
13 F	0211 / 0802 / 1501 / 2057	0.8 / 3.1 / 0.6 / 2.8	**28** SA	0104 / 0651 / 1350 / 1940	0.6 / 3.1 / 0.4 / 2.9
14 SA	0332 / 0921 / 1623 / 2210	0.8 / 3.1 / 0.6 / 2.9	**29** SU	0223 / 0807 / 1510 / 2058	0.6 / 3.1 / 0.4 / 2.9
15 SU	0450 / 1029 / 1731 / 2307	0.7 / 3.2 / 0.5 / 3.0	**30** M	0346 / 0923 / 1627 / 2210	0.6 / 3.2 / 0.4 / 3.0

DECEMBER

Day	Time	m	Day	Time	m
1 TU	0500 / 1030 / 1736 / 2313	0.4 / 3.3 / 0.2 / 3.1	**16** W	0550 / 1123 / 1816 / 2348	0.5 / 3.2 / 0.4 / 3.2
2 W	0605 / 1129 / 1837	0.3 / 3.4 / 0.1	**17** TH	0640 / 1208 / 1900	0.4 / 3.2 / 0.4
3 TH O	0008 / 0704 / 1225 / 1931	3.2 / 0.2 / 3.5 / 0.1	**18** F ●	0028 / 0724 / 1248 / 1939	3.3 / 0.3 / 3.2 / 0.3
4 F	0056 / 0756 / 1315 / 2017	3.4 / 0.1 / 3.5 / 0.2	**19** SA	0105 / 0802 / 1324 / 2015	3.3 / 0.2 / 3.2 / 0.2
5 SA	0141 / 0841 / 1403 / 2101	3.5 / 0.1 / 3.5 / 0.3	**20** SU	0139 / 0837 / 1401 / 2051	3.4 / 0.2 / 3.3 / 0.2
6 SU	0225 / 0927 / 1452 / 2147	3.6 / 0.2 / 3.4 / 0.3	**21** M	0213 / 0913 / 1438 / 2127	3.4 / 0.2 / 3.2 / 0.2
7 M	0310 / 1015 / 1543 / 2232	3.6 / 0.2 / 3.3 / 0.4	**22** TU	0248 / 0948 / 1515 / 2201	3.4 / 0.2 / 3.2 / 0.2
8 TU	0354 / 1100 / 1632 / 2313	3.5 / 0.2 / 3.2 / 0.4	**23** W	0323 / 1022 / 1552 / 2233	3.3 / 0.2 / 3.1 / 0.3
9 W	0437 / 1141 / 1718 / 2351	3.5 / 0.3 / 3.0 / 0.5	**24** TH	0400 / 1100 / 1632 / 2311	3.3 / 0.2 / 3.1 / 0.3
10 TH	0522 / 1222 / 1805	3.4 / 0.4 / 2.9	**25** F	0442 / 1143 / 1719 / 2355	3.3 / 0.2 / 3.0 / 0.3
11 F	0034 / 0612 / 1309 / 1857	0.6 / 3.2 / 0.4 / 2.8	**26** SA	0532 / 1232 / 1811	3.3 / 0.2 / 2.9
12 SA	0125 / 0711 / 1406 / 1957	0.6 / 3.1 / 0.4 / 2.8	**27** SU	0048 / 0628 / 1327 / 1911	0.4 / 3.2 / 0.3 / 2.9
13 SU	0229 / 0818 / 1514 / 2104	0.7 / 3.1 / 0.6 / 2.8	**28** M	0151 / 0732 / 1433 / 2018	0.5 / 3.2 / 0.3 / 2.9
14 M	0341 / 0927 / 1624 / 2208	0.7 / 3.0 / 0.5 / 2.9	**29** TU	0305 / 0845 / 1548 / 2131	0.5 / 3.2 / 0.3 / 3.0
15 TU	0451 / 1029 / 1726 / 2303	0.6 / 3.1 / 0.5 / 3.1	**30** W	0423 / 0959 / 1703 / 2241	0.4 / 3.2 / 0.2 / 3.1
			31 TH	0536 / 1108 / 1812 / 2344	0.3 / 3.3 / 0.2 / 3.2

Chart Datum: 1·66 metres below Normal Null (German reference level)

RIVER ELBE/HAMBURG   10-21-20
Niedersachsen/Schleswig-Holstein   Rtg 1-1-2

CHARTS
AC 3262, 3266, 3268; BSH 3010 Sheets 1 to 12 (as shown below), D46, D47, D48

TIDES

Glückstadt	ML 1·2	Duration 0515	Zone -0100
Brunshausen	ML 1·1	Duration 0510	
Hamburg	ML 1·3	Duration 0435	

Standard Port CUXHAVEN (←)

Times				Height (metres)			
High Water		Low Water		MHWS	MHWN	MLWN	MLWS
0200	0800	0200	0900	3·3	2·9	0·4	0·0
1400	2000	1400	2100				
Differences GLÜCKSTADT							
+0205	+0214	+0220	+0213	−0·2	−0·2	−0·1	+0·1
STADERSAND							
+0241	+0245	+0300	+0254	−0·1	0·0	−0·2	+0·1
SCHULAU							
+0304	+0315	+0337	+0321	+0·1	+0·1	−0·2	+0·1
HAMBURG							
+0338	+0346	+0421	+0406	+0·3	+0·3	−0·3	0·0

NAVIGATION
Distances: Elbe It float to Cuxhaven = 24M; Cuxhaven to Wedel Yacht Haven = 45M; Wedel to City Sport Hafen = 11·5M. The river has 13m up to Hamburg and is tidal to Geesthacht, 24M above Hamburg. Strong W winds can raise the level by as much as 4m. Entry should not be attempted with strong W/NW winds against the ebb. It is a very busy waterway and at night the many lights can be confusing. Yachts should keep to stbd, preferably just outside the marked chan. Elbe VTS (not mandatory for yachts) offers radar guidance and broadcasts met, nav & tidal info; see 10.21.19 & .21 and R/TELEPHONE below.

SHELTER AND FACILITIES
Some of the better hbrs are listed below, but it is not a particularly salubrious yachting area:

FREIBURG: 7M above Brunsbüttel on the SW bank. Small vessels can enter at HW and there is excellent shelter at Freiburg Reede. ML 2·2m. Hr Mr ☎ (04779) 8314. Facilities: ME, El, Sh, C, FW, Slip, YC; **Jugendheim & YC Klubheim** V, R, Bar. (Sheet 4).

STÖRLOCH/BORSFLETH: Ent approx 600m above locks on E bank. ML 2·8m. Hr Mr ☎ (04124) 71437. Facilities: FW, YC. Stör Bridge VHF Ch 09, 16. (Sheet 4).

STÖR/BEIDENFLETH: ML 2·8m (Sheet 4). **Langes Rack YC**.

GLÜCKSTADT: on the NE bank, 2½M above mouth of R Stör. Good shelter; inner and outer hbrs have 2m depth. Lock into inner hbr opens HW −2 to +½. VHF Ch 11. Hr Mr ☎ (04124) 2087; ⌗ ☎ 2171. YC, FW, C, D, V, R, ⌾, Bar. (Sheet 5).

WISCHHAFEN: Hr Mr ☎ (04770) 334; ⌗ 3014 FW, M, Slip, P, D, ML 2·7m. (Sheet 5).

RUTHENSTROM: Ldg marks into hbr, two bns with △ topmarks on 197°. ML 2·6m. Hr Mr ☎ (04143) 5282; C, Slip, FW, ME, El, Sh. (Sheet 6).

KRÜCKAUMÜNDUNG JACHTHAFEN: ☎ (04125) 1521 Slip, FW. ML 2·7m. ⌗ ☎ 20551. (Sheet 6).

PINNAUMÜNDUNG JACHTHAFEN: Ent via lock gate on N bank after passing through main locks. ML 2·5m. Hr Mr ☎ (04101) 22447 Slip, M, FW, YC, C. (Sheet 6).

PINNAU-NEUENDEICH: Marina 1½M up the Pinnau from main locks and another at approx 2M. (Sheet 6).

ABBENFLETH: Ent marked by two bns in line 221° with △ topmarks. (Sheets 6/7).

HASELDORF Hafen: Hr Mr ☎ (04129) 268 Slip, FW, V, YC.

R.SCHWINGE on SW bank, 12M up-river from Glückstadt:
> BRUNSHAUSEN (04141) 3085
> HÖRNE/WÖHRDEN ML 2·8m
> STADE (04141) 101275 C, YC, V; Access HW ±2.
> Very good shelter in scenic town. ⌗ ☎ 3014. (Sheets 7/8).

LÜHE: Hafen in town of Lühe. (Sheet 8).

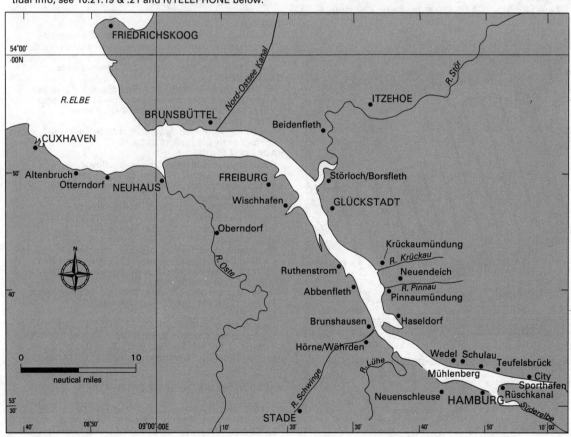

HAMBURG

A busy commercial port with several marinas. Visitors berth at Wedel in Hamburger Yachthafen or in the City Sporthafen, in city centre esp for visitors (see below).

WEDEL: on N bank, 12M downstream from Hamburg, very good shelter H24; **Hamburger Yachthafen**, 11DM, (1800 berths + 300 being added) with 2 ents marked by FR and FG lts. A conspic 20m tall radar tr is at W corner of hbr. Hr Mr ☎ (04103) 4438 (office), 5632 (Hr Mr east), 88608 (Hr Mr west); ⌗ ☎ 2688; D & P, Bar, BH (16 ton), BY, C, CH, EI, Ⓔ, FW, ME, SC, Sh, Slip, SM. (Sheets 8/9).

SCHULAU: Good shelter, 7ca E of Wedel. Beware strong tidal streams across ent, marked by FR and FG lts. Hr Mr ☎ 2422, Slip, C, P, D, ME, Ⓗ, CH, SC. (Sheet 8/9).

NEUENSCHLEUSE: opposite Wedel. (Sheet 9).

MÜHLENBERG: N bank, (250), Slip, FW, SC. Small boats only; 0·6m above CD. (Sheets 9/10).

TEUFELSBRÜCK: small hbr on N bank. Good shelter, sandbar at ent. Bar, FW, SC. (Sheets 9/10).

RÜSCHKANAL: on S bank in Finkenwerder, C, CH, EI, FW, ME, Slip, Sh, with 4 SCs and nearby resort area.

CITY SPORTHAFEN: (80+50) ☎ 364297, 20DM, D, P, FW, AC; Ent on N bank beyond St Pauli-Landungsbrücken.

RADIO TELEPHONE

Elbe VTS: see 10.21.19 for radar cover up to buoy No 53. See 10.21.21 for buoys 51 - 125. Then *Hamburg Radar*:
Ch 19 Buoys 123 - 129;
Ch 03 Buoys 129 - Seemanshöft;
Ch 63 Seemanshöft - Vorhafen (outer hbr);
Ch 07 Parkhafen - Kuhwerder Vorhafen;
Ch 05 Kuhwerder Vorhafen - Norderelbbrücke;
Ch 80 Köhlbrand - Hamburger Häfen.
Hamburg Port Traffic and Hbr Control vessel Ch 13 14 **73** (H24). Süderelbe: Rethe and Kattwyk bridges and Harburg lock Ch 13 (H24). All stns monitor Ch 16.

TELEPHONE (Dial code 040)

Met 3190 8826/7; Auto 0190 116456; Brit Consul 446071.

FACILITIES

City all facilities, ACA, ✉, Ⓑ, ⇌, ✈. Ferry: Hamburg-Harwich.

HAMBURGER YACHTHAFEN, WEDEL

BRUNSBÜTTEL   10-21-21

Schleswig-Holstein 53°53'·28N 09°07'·85E Rtg 1*-3-2

CHARTS

AC 2469, 3262; BSH 3010 Sheet 3

TIDES

+0203 Dover; ML 1·4; Duration 0520; Zone –0100

Standard Port CUXHAVEN (←)

Times				Height (metres)			
High Water		Low Water		MHWS	MHWN	MLWN	MLWS
0200	0800	0200	0900	3·3	2·9	0·4	0·0
1400	2000	1400	2100				
Differences BRUNSBÜTTEL							
+0057	+0105	+0121	+0112	–0·2	–0·2	–0·1	0·0

SHELTER

Good in drying yacht hbr, access HW ±3, outside the locks to the W in the Alter Hafen. Waiting posts are close E of FWG ☆ at ent to Alter Vorhafen. Very good shelter in yacht hbr inside, immediately NW of Neue locks.

NAVIGATION

No navigational dangers in the near apprs, but commercial traffic is heavy. The stream sets strongly across ents to locks. Yachts usually use the smaller SE locks.

LIGHTS AND MARKS

Ldg lts 065°, both Iso 3s 24/46m 16/21M, synch, for locks. For lock entry sigs see 10.21.22.

RADIO TELEPHONE

Radar cover of the inner Elbe is as follows:
Brunsbüttel Radar I	Ch 04	Buoys 51 - 59;
S. Margarethen Radar	Ch 18	Buoys 57a - 65;
Freiburg Radar	Ch 22	Buoys 63 - 77;
Rhinplatte Radar	Ch 05	Buoys 75 - 89;
Pagensand Radar	Ch 66	Buoys 87 - 103;
Hetlingen Radar	Ch 21	Buoys 101 - 115;
Wedel Radar	Ch 60	Buoys 113 - 125.

Brunsbüttel Elbe Traffic broadcasts info every H + 05 on Ch 68 in English and German for the inner Elbe. See 10.21.22 for Kanal entry. *Brunsbüttel Elbe Port* Ch 12 16.

TELEPHONE (Dial code 04852)

Hr Mr 8011 ext 360; CG 8444; ⌗ 87241; Weather 36400; Police 112; Ⓗ 601; Brit Consul (040) 446071.

FACILITIES

Alter hafen ☎ 3107, Rtg 3-3-2, AC, FW, Slip, C (20 ton), R, SC; **Kanal-Yachthafen*** ☎ 8011, DM12.00, FW, AC, ⌗, Bar. **Town** P, D, EI, ME, Sh, Gaz, V, R, LB, Ⓗ, Bar, ✉, Ⓑ, ⇌, ✈ (Hamburg). KIEL: **Nautischer Dienst** (0431) 331772 ACA.

HARBOUR ON SOUTH BANK OF THE ELBE

OTTERNDORF, Niedersachsen, 53°50'·20N 08°54'·00E. AC 3261, 3262; BSH 3014.11. HW +0100 on Dover (UT); HW +0120 and +0·5m on Helgoland; ML 2·9m; Duration 0525. Ent marked by Medem lt bn Fl (3) 12s 6m 5M & perches. Chan (0·6m) from Elbe divides and yachts can take the W branch to Kutterhafen (0·9m) or the canal to E, through lock then turn sharp stbd to yacht hbr. Lockmaster ☎ (04751) 3190; Yacht hbr ☎ 13131 C, AC, FW, Bar. **Town** (3km) ME, Gaz, V, ✉.

NORD-OSTSEE KANAL
(Kiel Canal)   10-21-22
Schleswig-Holstein

CHARTS
AC 2469, 696 (Kieler Förde); BSH 3009, Sheets 1-4
NAVIGATION
The Canal runs from Brunsbüttel (10.21.21) to Kiel-Holtenau, 53·3M (98·7 km). Km posts start from Brunsbüttel. Width is 103 to 162m on the surface, and depth 11m. Yachts may only use the Canal and its ents by day and good vis. (This does not apply to craft going to the Inner or Old Hbrs at Brunsbüttel, or to the yacht berths at Holtenau). Speed limit is 8kn. All 6 bridges have 40m clearance. Fly flag 'N' (no pilot). Sailing, except motor sailing is prohib; yachts must then display a B ▼, or a B pennant. Canal dues are paid at the Holtenau locks at the 'Dues Office' (N bank). Yachts purely in transit are not usually troubled by the Customs Authority; they should fly the third substitute of the International Code.
SHELTER
The principal port along the canal is Rensburg, between km posts 60 and 67, with all facilities including 3 yacht hbrs in the Obereidersee. Rensburg is linked to Tönning (see under 10.21.24) by the R Eider and Gieselau Canal. There are 9 passing places (sidings or *weichen*). Yachts are to regulate their passage so as to reach their planned berthing places during daylight. These may be at:
1) Brunsbüttel (km 0);
2) Kudensee siding (km 9·5);
3) Dückerswisch siding (km 20·7);
4) Fischerhütte siding (km 35);
5) Oldenbüttel siding (km 40), at ent to Gieselau Canal;
6) Breiholz siding (km 48);
7) Schülp siding (km 57);
8) The Obereidersee (Rendsburg), ent at km 66;
9) The Borgstedter See, ent at km 70;
10) Königsförde siding (km 80);
11) Grossnordsee siding (km 85), or ⚓ in Flemhuder See;
12) Schwartenbek siding (km 92);
13) Kiel-Holtenau (km 98·7).
Kiel-Holtenau, at the Baltic end of the canal, is a major port with a Yacht Hbr on the N bank (E of locks); all usual facilities. Two pairs of locks (yachts usually use the N pair) lead into the Kieler Förde which is practically tideless and at almost the same level as the canal.

SIGNALS
Lock signals (shown at signal tr and centre pier of lock):

®̇	= no entry.
Ẇ over ®̇	= prepare to enter.
Ẇ	= yachts may enter (berth on pontoons).
Ẇ over Ġ	= enter without pilot (yachts follow ships flying Flag N); secure to middle wall.
Ġ	= enter with pilot; secure to middle wall.
Ẇ over Ẇ and Ġ	= enter with pilot and secure by Ẇ lt.

In the canal, the only traffic sig applicable to yachts is :

3 ®̇ (vert)	= STOP. Keep to stbd; give way to large vessel approaching.

RADIO TELEPHONE
Before entering, yachts should report as follows (all H24):
at Brunsbüttel to *Kiel Kanal I* on Ch 13;
or at Holtenau to *Kiel Kanal IV* on Ch 12.
If out-bound to the W, call *Brunsbüttel Elbe Traffic* Ch 68.
Ports: Ostermoor (Brunsbüttel to Burg) Ch 73;
Breiholz (Breiholz to Audorf) Ch 73.
Canal. Maintain listening watch as follows:
Kiel Kanal I   Ch 13   Brunsbüttel ent and locks;
Kiel Kanal II   Ch 02   Brunsbüttel to Breiholz;
Kiel Kanal III Ch 03   Breiholz to Holtenau;
Kiel Kanal IV   Ch 12   Holtenau ent and locks.
Info broadcasts by *Kiel Kanal II* on Ch 02 at H+15, H+45; and by *Kiel Kanal III* on Ch 03 at H+20, H+50. Vessels should monitor these broadcasts and not call the station if this can be avoided.
FACILITIES
A BP fuel barge is on the N bank, close E of the Holtenau locks. At Wik (S side of locks) **Nautischer Dienst** (Kapt Stegmann & Co) ☎ 0431 331772 are ACA & BSH Agents. The **British Kiel YC** is 5ca NNW of Stickenhörn ECM buoy, Q (3) 10s, 1M NNE of the locks. It is part of a military centre with no commercial facilities; but AB (about 18DM) may well be available for visitors to whom a friendly welcome is extended. Call *Sailtrain* VHF Ch 67 or ☎ (0431) 398833.

21

HELGOLAND
MEAN SPRING
AND NEAP CURVES

MEAN RANGES
Springs 2·7m
Neaps 1·9m

Springs occur 3 days
after
New and Full Moon.

HELGOLAND   10-21-23

Schleswig-Holstein 54°10'·30N 07°54'·00E   Rtg 1-2-1

CHARTS
AC 1875, 3761; D3, 88; BSH 3013, 3014.2 & .3, 3015
TIDES
−0030 Dover; ML 1·4; Duration 0540; Zone −0100
Helgoland is a Standard Port and tidal predictions for each
day of the year are given below.
SHELTER
Good in safe artificial hbr (5m); yachts should berth on
pontoons on the NE side of the Südhafen which gets very
crowded, rafting 10 deep. Or ⌕ in the SW part of the
Vorhafen, sheltered except in SE'lies; get permission from
Port Control VHF Ch 67. Due to pier construction no yacht
berths in Binnenhafen until 1999, except for refuelling.
Yachts are prohib from the Nordost hbr, the Dünen hbr
and from landing on Düne Island.
NOTE: Helgoland is not a port of entry into Germany.
Customs in Helgoland are for passport control. Duty free
goods are obtainable; hence many day-trippers by ferry.
NAVIGATION
WPT Helgoland ECM buoy, Q (3) 10s, Whis, 55°09'·00N
07°53'·57E, 202°/022° from/to Düne front ldg lt, 2·1M.
Beware the Hogstean shoal, 4ca S of Sudmole head lt, and
other rky shoals either side of chan. The S chan and ent
are used by ferries. Beware lobster pots around Düne Is.
Caution: Entry is prohib at all times into Nature Reserves
close either side of the appr chans from SSW and NW.
These Reserves extend about 2M NE and SW of Helgoland;
their limits are marked by Cardinal buoys. Marine police
are active in this respect. A smaller Reserve, lying to the
N, E and S of Düne, is a prohib ⌕, with other restrictions.
See BSH 3014.2 and AC 126, 3761 and 1875 for limits.
LIGHTS AND MARKS
Helgoland lt ho, Fl 5s 82m 28M; brown □ tr, B lantern, W
balcony.
Düne ldg lts 020°: front Iso 4s 11m 8M; rear Dir Iso WRG
4s 17m 11/10M synch, W sector 018·5°-021°.
Binnenhafen ldg lts 302°: both Oc R 6s, synch.
RADIO TELEPHONE
Helgoland Port Radio Ch 67 16 (Mon-Fri: 0700-1800; Sat
0800-1700; Sun 0800-1000LT). Coast Radio Ch 03 16 27 88
(H24). Info broadcasts in English and German every H on
Ch 79 80 by *German Bight Traffic* (at Helgoland lt ho) for
26M radius of Helgoland.
TELEPHONE (Dial code 04725)
Hr Mr 504; CG 210; ▦ 304; Met 606; Police 607; Dr 7345; Ⓗ
8030; LB 210; SAR 524; Brit Consul (040) 446071.
FACILITIES
Vorhafen L, AB; **Südhafen** ☎ 504, AB 13DM, D, FW, ME,
CH, C (mobile 12 ton), V, R, Bar; **Binnenhafen** ☎ 504, P, D,
FW, ME, CH, AB, V, R, Bar; **Wasser Sport Club** ☎ 585 Bar,
R, M, C (12 ton), D, P, CH, ME, El, Sh, FW, Ⓢ, V.
Town Gaz, V, R, Bar, ✉, Ⓑ, ⇌ (ferry Cuxhaven), ✈ (to
Bremen, Hamburg and Cuxhaven). Ferry: Hamburg-
Harwich.

AGENTS WANTED

If you are interested in becoming our agent for any of the
following ports, please write to: The Editor, Edington House,
Trent, Sherborne, Dorset DT9 4SR, England – and get your
free copy of the Almanac annually. You do not have to live in
a port to be the agent, but at least a fairly regular visitor.

Great Yarmouth
Port Ellen (Islay)
Maryport
Workington
Holyhead
Lough Swilly
St Peter Port, Guernsey
Diélette
Portbail
Iles Chausey
St Malo/Dinard
Le Legue/St Brieuc
Tréguier
Lampaul
L'Aberildut
Le Palais (Belle Ile)
Morbihan/Vannes

St Gilles-Croix-de-Vie
Les Sables d'Olonne
Ile d'Oléron
River Seudre
Anglet/Bayonne
St Jean-de-Luz
Hendaye
Grandcamp-Maisy
Port-en-Bessin
Courseulles
Ouistreham/Caen
Emden
Dornumer-Accumersiel
Langeoog
Bremerhaven
Büsum

TIME ZONE –0100
(German Standard Time)
Subtract 1 hour for UT

For German Summer Time add
ONE hour in non-shaded areas

GERMANY – HELGOLAND

LAT 54°11′N   LONG   7°53′E

TIMES AND HEIGHTS OF HIGH AND LOW WATERS

YEAR **1998**

JANUARY

Day	Time	m	Time	m	Time	m	Time	m
1 TH	0115	2.8	0805	0.0	1343	2.7	2020	0.1
16 F	0155	2.9	0839	0.2	1417	2.6	2048	0.2
2 F	0156	2.8	0847	0.0	1424	2.6	2058	0.1
17 SA	0230	2.8	0913	0.2	1452	2.5	2120	0.2
3 SA	0237	2.8	0928	0.0	1507	2.6	2140	0.2
18 SU	0303	2.7	0944	0.2	1526	2.4	2152	0.2
4 SU	0322	2.8	1015	0.0	1555	2.5	2228	0.2
19 M	0336	2.6	1017	0.2	1601	2.4	2227	0.2
5 M	0414	2.8	1107	0.1	1649	2.5	2321	0.3
20 TU	0412	2.6	1050	0.2	1639	2.3	2303	0.3
6 TU	0510	2.7	1200	0.2	1746	2.4		
21 W	0450	2.5	1128	0.3	1722	2.3	2348	0.4
7 W	0019	0.3	0610	2.7	1301	0.2	1849	2.4
22 TH	0540	2.4	1222	0.4	1818	2.2		
8 TH	0129	0.4	0718	2.6	1413	0.3	1958	2.4
23 F	0054	0.5	0648	2.3	1334	0.4	1928	2.2
9 F	0246	0.3	0831	2.6	1527	0.3	2110	2.4
24 SA	0213	0.5	0805	2.3	1451	0.4	2041	2.3
10 SA	0400	0.2	0943	2.6	1633	0.2	2216	2.6
25 SU	0330	0.4	0917	2.4	1600	0.3	2145	2.5
11 SU	0505	0.2	1047	2.6	1730	0.2	2312	2.7
26 M	0436	0.3	1018	2.5	1659	0.2	2241	2.6
12 M O	0559	0.2	1140	2.7	1818	0.3	2358	2.8
27 TU	0533	0.1	1108	2.6	1751	0.1	2330	2.7
13 TU	0644	0.2	1225	2.7	1858	0.3		
28 W ●	0622	0.0	1155	2.6	1838	0.1		
14 W	0038	2.9	0724	0.2	1304	2.7	1936	0.3
29 TH	0015	2.8	0707	0.0	1242	2.7	1924	0.0
15 TH	0116	2.9	0802	0.2	1341	2.7	2013	0.2
30 F	0058	2.8	0752	-0.1	1329	2.6	2008	0.0
31 SA	0141	2.8	0837	-0.2	1412	2.6	2049	-0.1

FEBRUARY

Day	Time	m	Time	m	Time	m	Time	m
1 SU	0225	2.8	0919	-0.1	1454	2.6	2130	0.0
16 M	0236	2.6	0915	0.0	1454	2.4	2127	0.0
2 M	0310	2.8	1004	0.0	1540	2.6	2216	0.0
17 TU	0308	2.6	0946	0.0	1527	2.4	2200	0.0
3 TU	0359	2.8	1050	0.1	1628	2.5	2304	0.1
18 W	0340	2.5	1015	0.1	1558	2.4	2228	0.1
4 W	0450	2.7	1136	0.2	1718	2.5	2354	0.2
19 TH	0409	2.4	1042	0.1	1630	2.3	2300	0.2
5 TH	0543	2.6	1228	0.3	1813	2.4		
20 F	0446	2.3	1121	0.3	1715	2.2	2354	0.3
6 F	0058	0.3	0648	2.5	1338	0.4	1924	2.4
21 SA	0546	2.3	1227	0.4	1824	2.2		
7 SA	0219	0.3	0807	2.4	1501	0.3	2045	2.4
22 SU	0116	0.4	0708	2.3	1355	0.4	1948	2.2
8 SU	0344	0.2	0929	2.4	1618	0.3	2200	2.5
23 M	0246	0.3	0835	2.2	1521	0.4	2108	2.4
9 M	0455	0.1	1038	2.5	1718	0.3	2300	2.7
24 TU	0405	0.2	0949	2.4	1633	0.2	2214	2.5
10 TU	0549	0.1	1130	2.6	1805	0.2	2346	2.8
25 W	0509	0.0	1047	2.6	1732	0.1	2308	2.7
11 W	0631	0.1	1211	2.6	1844	0.2		
26 TH ●	0603	-0.1	1136	2.6	1822	0.0	2354	2.7
12 TH	0023	2.8	0708	0.1	1247	2.6	1920	0.2
27 F	0649	-0.2	1223	2.6	1908	-0.1		
13 F	0059	2.8	0743	0.1	1319	2.6	1953	0.1
28 SA	0038	2.8	0735	-0.3	1309	2.6	1951	-0.2
14 SA	0133	2.8	0816	0.1	1351	2.5	2025	0.0
15 SU	0205	2.7	0846	0.0	1422	2.5	2056	0.0

MARCH

Day	Time	m	Time	m	Time	m	Time	m
1 SU	0122	2.8	0820	-0.3	1353	2.6	2035	-0.2
16 M	0140	2.6	0819	-0.1	1354	2.5	2033	-0.2
2 M	0208	2.8	0904	-0.2	1437	2.6	2118	-0.2
17 TU	0210	2.5	0849	-0.1	1424	2.4	2104	-0.2
3 TU	0255	2.8	0946	-0.1	1520	2.6	2202	-0.1
18 W	0242	2.5	0919	-0.1	1455	2.4	2135	-0.1
4 W	0341	2.7	1028	0.0	1604	2.6	2245	0.0
19 TH	0312	2.5	0946	-0.1	1524	2.4	2203	-0.1
5 TH	0427	2.7	1109	0.1	1649	2.5	2331	0.1
20 F	0339	2.4	1009	0.0	1553	2.3	2230	0.0
6 F	0517	2.5	1157	0.2	1741	2.4		
21 SA	0410	2.3	1041	0.1	1632	2.2	2315	0.2
7 SA	0031	0.2	0621	2.3	1306	0.3	1853	2.3
22 SU	0503	2.2	1141	0.3	1737	2.2		
8 SU	0154	0.2	0744	2.2	1435	0.4	2021	2.3
23 M	0032	0.2	0625	2.1	1311	0.3	1904	2.2
9 M	0327	0.1	0912	2.2	1601	0.3	2144	2.4
24 TU	0208	0.2	0758	2.1	1447	0.3	2032	2.2
10 TU	0443	0.1	1024	2.3	1704	0.2	2245	2.6
25 W	0335	0.0	0920	2.3	1606	0.1	2145	2.5
11 W	0535	0.0	1113	2.4	1747	0.2	2326	2.7
26 TH	0443	-0.1	1024	2.4	1709	0.0	2242	2.6
12 TH	0611	0.0	1150	2.5	1823	0.1		
27 F	0539	-0.3	1115	2.5	1801	-0.2	2331	2.7
13 F O	0001	2.7	0645	0.0	1223	2.5	1859	0.0
28 SA ●	0629	-0.4	1201	2.5	1848	-0.3		
14 SA	0035	2.7	0719	0.0	1254	2.5	1931	0.0
29 SU	0016	2.7	0714	-0.4	1246	2.6	1933	-0.3
15 SU	0109	2.7	0750	0.0	1324	2.5	2003	-0.1
30 M	0101	2.8	0759	-0.3	1331	2.6	2017	-0.3
31 TU	0148	2.8	0844	-0.2	1415	2.6	2102	-0.3

APRIL

Day	Time	m	Time	m	Time	m	Time	m
1 W	0236	2.7	0925	-0.1	1458	2.6	2145	-0.2
16 TH	0216	2.5	0853	-0.2	1428	2.5	2113	-0.2
2 TH	0321	2.7	1004	0.0	1540	2.6	2227	-0.1
17 F	0248	2.4	0922	-0.1	1458	2.4	2143	-0.1
3 F	0405	2.5	1044	0.1	1623	2.5	2312	0.0
18 SA	0319	2.4	0949	-0.1	1530	2.4	2215	-0.1
4 SA	0455	2.4	1132	0.2	1715	2.4		
19 SU	0354	2.3	1024	0.1	1611	2.3	2259	0.0
5 SU	0010	0.1	0559	2.2	1238	0.3	1826	2.3
20 M	0445	2.2	1120	0.2	1712	2.2		
6 M	0128	0.2	0719	2.1	1404	0.4	1953	2.3
21 TU	0008	0.1	0559	2.1	1244	0.3	1834	2.3
7 TU	0259	0.1	0846	2.1	1531	0.3	2116	2.4
22 W	0138	0.0	0728	2.2	1416	0.2	1959	2.4
8 W	0417	0.1	0957	2.3	1637	0.2	2217	2.5
23 TH	0305	-0.1	0849	2.2	1536	0.1	2112	2.5
9 TH	0508	0.0	1045	2.4	1718	0.1	2257	2.6
24 F	0414	-0.2	0955	2.3	1640	-0.1	2212	2.6
10 F	0542	0.0	1119	2.4	1754	0.0	2331	2.6
25 SA	0512	-0.3	1049	2.4	1736	-0.2	2306	2.7
11 SA O	0615	-0.1	1152	2.5	1831	-0.1		
26 SU ●	0605	-0.4	1138	2.5	1827	-0.3	2356	2.7
12 SU	0007	2.6	0650	-0.1	1226	2.5	1907	-0.1
27 M	0653	-0.4	1224	2.6	1913	-0.3		
13 M	0043	2.6	0723	-0.1	1257	2.5	1939	-0.2
28 TU	0042	2.8	0736	-0.3	1308	2.7	1958	-0.3
14 TU	0115	2.6	0754	-0.1	1327	2.5	2010	-0.2
29 W	0128	2.8	0820	-0.2	1352	2.7	2042	-0.2
15 W	0145	2.5	0824	-0.2	1357	2.5	2042	-0.2
30 TH	0215	2.7	0902	-0.1	1436	2.7	2126	-0.2

Chart Datum: 1·68 metres below Normal Null (German reference level)

21

TIME ZONE –0100
(German Standard Time)
Subtract 1 hour for UT

For German Summer Time add
ONE hour in non-shaded areas

GERMANY – HELGOLAND

LAT 54°11′N   LONG 7°53′E

TIMES AND HEIGHTS OF HIGH AND LOW WATERS

YEAR **1998**

MAY

Day	Time	m	Time	m	Time	m	Time	m
1 F	0302	2.6	0942	0.0	1519	2.7	2210	-0.1
2 SA	0348	2.4	1024	0.1	1603	2.6	2256	0.0
3 SU	0438	2.3	1111	0.2	1654	2.5	2350	0.1
4 M	0536	2.2	1209	0.3	1758	2.4		
5 TU	0057	0.1	0646	2.1	1323	0.3	1914	2.4
6 W	0216	0.2	0803	2.1	1443	0.3	2031	2.4
7 TH	0330	0.1	0912	2.2	1551	0.2	2133	2.5
8 F	0425	0.0	1004	2.3	1639	0.1	2218	2.5
9 SA	0504	0.0	1042	2.4	1718	0.0	2257	2.5
10 SU	0541	-0.1	1118	2.5	1800	0.0	2337	2.5
11 M O	0620	-0.1	1155	2.5	1840	-0.1		
12 TU	0014	2.5	0656	-0.2	1230	2.5	1915	-0.2
13 W	0048	2.6	0728	-0.2	1302	2.6	1948	-0.2
14 TH	0120	2.5	0800	-0.2	1334	2.6	2022	-0.2
15 F	0154	2.5	0832	-0.1	1407	2.6	2055	-0.2
16 SA	0229	2.5	0904	-0.1	1440	2.5	2130	-0.1
17 SU	0307	2.4	0939	0.0	1518	2.5	2210	-0.1
18 M	0349	2.3	1021	0.0	1604	2.4	2257	-0.1
19 TU	0441	2.2	1115	0.1	1702	2.4	2358	0.0
20 W	0546	2.2	1226	0.2	1813	2.4		
21 TH	0115	0.0	0702	2.2	1347	0.2	1929	2.5
22 F	0234	-0.1	0817	2.3	1503	0.1	2040	2.6
23 SA	0343	-0.2	0923	2.3	1609	-0.1	2143	2.6
24 SU	0443	-0.3	1022	2.4	1709	-0.2	2242	2.6
25 M	0540	-0.3	1116	2.5	1806	-0.2	● 2337	2.7
26 TU	0631	-0.2	1204	2.6	1855	-0.2		
27 W	0026	2.7	0715	-0.2	1247	2.7	1939	-0.2
28 TH	0111	2.7	0757	-0.1	1331	2.8	2023	-0.2
29 F	0157	2.7	0841	0.0	1416	2.7	2109	-0.1
30 SA	0245	2.5	0923	0.0	1501	2.7	2154	-0.1
31 SU	0332	2.4	1004	0.1	1545	2.7	2238	0.0

JUNE

Day	Time	m	Time	m	Time	m	Time	m
1 M	0418	2.3	1048	0.2	1632	2.6	2325	0.1
2 TU	0508	2.2	1136	0.3	1724	2.5		
3 W	0018	0.2	0604	2.2	1234	0.3	1825	2.5
4 TH	0119	0.2	0707	2.2	1341	0.3	1931	2.4
5 F	0226	0.2	0813	2.2	1450	0.3	2036	2.4
6 SA	0328	0.1	0912	2.3	1550	0.2	2132	2.5
7 SU	0420	0.0	1000	2.4	1639	0.1	2220	2.5
8 M	0505	0.0	1042	2.5	1726	0.0	2304	2.5
9 TU	0547	0.0	1122	2.5	1811	-0.1	2344	2.5
10 W O	0627	-0.1	1201	2.6	1850	-0.1		
11 TH	0021	2.6	0703	-0.1	1238	2.6	1927	-0.1
12 F	0059	2.6	0740	-0.1	1315	2.7	2005	-0.1
13 SA	0137	2.6	0817	-0.1	1351	2.7	2042	-0.1
14 SU	0216	2.5	0853	0.0	1428	2.7	2121	-0.1
15 M	0257	2.5	0932	0.0	1509	2.6	2206	-0.1
16 TU	0344	2.4	1018	0.0	1558	2.6	2256	-0.1
17 W	0437	2.3	1111	0.1	1654	2.6	2351	0.0
18 TH	0535	2.3	1211	0.2	1756	2.6		
19 F	0054	0.0	0639	2.3	1320	0.2	1903	2.6
20 SA	0204	0.0	0746	2.3	1433	0.1	2012	2.6
21 SU	0314	0.1	0853	2.4	1542	0.0	2119	2.6
22 M	0418	-0.1	0957	2.5	1647	-0.1	2223	2.6
23 TU	0517	-0.1	1056	2.6	1746	-0.1	2321	2.7
24 W	0611	-0.1	1147	2.7	1838	-0.1 ●		
25 TH	0013	2.7	0657	0.0	1231	2.8	1923	-0.1
26 F	0058	2.7	0738	0.1	1314	2.9	2007	0.0
27 SA	0142	2.7	0805	0.0	1358	2.8	2052	0.0
28 SU	0228	2.6	0903	0.1	1441	2.8	2134	0.0
29 M	0310	2.5	0941	0.1	1522	2.7	2213	0.1
30 TU	0351	2.4	1019	0.2	1603	2.7	2252	0.1

JULY

Day	Time	m	Time	m	Time	m	Time	m
1 W	0433	2.3	1100	0.2	1646	2.6	2333	0.2
2 TH	0517	2.3	1144	0.3	1733	2.5		
3 F	0018	0.2	0607	2.3	1237	0.3	1828	2.4
4 SA	0116	0.3	0706	2.3	1343	0.4	1932	2.4
5 SU	0223	0.3	0810	2.3	1453	0.3	2039	2.4
6 M	0328	0.2	0911	2.4	1556	0.2	2139	2.5
7 TU	0424	0.1	1003	2.5	1652	0.1	2231	2.5
8 W	0514	0.1	1050	2.6	1742	0.0	2316	2.6
9 TH	0559	0.0	1135	2.6	1827	0.0	2358 O	2.6
10 F	0642	0.0	1217	2.7	1908	0.0		
11 SA	0040	2.6	0724	0.0	1258	2.7	1949	-0.1
12 SU	0123	2.7	0805	0.0	1337	2.8	2030	-0.1
13 M	0204	2.6	0843	0.0	1416	2.8	2111	-0.1
14 TU	0245	2.5	0922	0.0	1458	2.8	2156	-0.1
15 W	0332	2.5	1009	0.0	1548	2.8	2247	0.0
16 TH	0425	2.5	1101	0.1	1642	2.7	2337	0.1
17 F	0518	2.5	1153	0.2	1738	2.7		
18 SA	0029	0.2	0613	2.5	1254	0.2	1838	2.7
19 SU	0133	0.2	0716	2.4	1406	0.2	1948	2.6
20 M	0247	0.2	0827	2.5	1523	0.2	2103	2.6
21 TU	0359	0.1	0938	2.6	1633	0.1	2212	2.6
22 W	0501	0.1	1041	2.7	1733	0.0	2312	2.6
23 TH	0555	0.1	1134	2.8	1825	0.0 ●		
24 F	0003	2.7	0642	0.1	1218	2.8	1909	0.0
25 SA	0046	2.7	0723	0.2	1259	2.9	1951	0.1
26 SU	0126	2.7	0803	0.2	1340	2.9	2032	0.1
27 M	0205	2.6	0841	0.2	1418	2.8	2108	0.1
28 TU	0243	2.5	0915	0.1	1454	2.8	2141	0.1
29 W	0318	2.5	0948	0.1	1530	2.7	2215	0.1
30 TH	0354	2.4	1024	0.2	1608	2.6	2249	0.2
31 F	0432	2.4	1059	0.3	1646	2.5	2323	0.3

AUGUST

Day	Time	m	Time	m	Time	m	Time	m
1 SA	0511	2.4	1139	0.4	1729	2.5		
2 SU	0008	0.4	0600	2.3	1236	0.4	1828	2.4
3 M	0113	0.4	0705	2.3	1352	0.4	1941	2.4
4 TU	0229	0.4	0817	2.4	1510	0.4	2055	2.4
5 W	0342	0.3	0924	2.5	1618	0.2	2159	2.5
6 TH	0442	0.2	1021	2.6	1715	0.1	2251	2.6
7 F	0535	0.2	1111	2.7	1804	0.0	2337	2.6
8 SA	0623	0.1	1156	2.8	1849	0.0 O		
9 SU	0022	2.7	0707	0.0	1239	2.8	1931	-0.1
10 M	0106	2.7	0749	0.0	1320	2.9	2014	-0.1
11 TU	0148	2.7	0829	0.0	1402	2.9	2057	-0.1
12 W	0229	2.6	0909	0.0	1445	2.9	2140	0.0
13 TH	0314	2.6	0954	0.1	1533	2.9	2227	0.1
14 F	0403	2.6	1043	0.1	1624	2.8	2314	0.2
15 SA	0453	2.6	1132	0.2	1716	2.7		
16 SU	0001	0.3	0545	2.5	1229	0.3	1815	2.6
17 M	0102	0.4	0649	2.5	1343	0.3	1930	2.5
18 TU	0223	0.4	0807	2.5	1510	0.3	2053	2.5
19 W	0346	0.4	0926	2.6	1628	0.2	2208	2.6
20 TH	0453	0.3	1033	2.7	1726	0.2	2305	2.6
21 F	0543	0.3	1123	2.8	1812	0.1	2350	2.7
22 SA	0626	0.3	1204	2.9	1852	0.1 ●		
23 SU	0029	2.7	0705	0.2	1242	2.9	1930	0.2
24 M	0105	2.7	0741	0.2	1318	2.9	2006	0.2
25 TU	0139	2.7	0815	0.1	1352	2.8	2038	0.2
26 W	0212	2.6	0847	0.1	1424	2.7	2107	0.1
27 TH	0244	2.6	0917	0.1	1457	2.7	2138	0.2
28 F	0317	2.5	0950	0.1	1532	2.6	2208	0.2
29 SA	0349	2.5	1021	0.2	1604	2.6	2236	0.3
30 SU	0422	2.5	1052	0.4	1639	2.5	2310	0.4
31 M	0503	2.4	1139	0.5	1731	2.4		

Chart Datum: 1·68 metres below Normal Null (German reference level)

TIME ZONE –0100
(German Standard Time)
Subtract 1 hour for UT
For German Summer Time add ONE hour in non-shaded areas

GERMANY – HELGOLAND

LAT 54°11′N   LONG 7°53′E

TIMES AND HEIGHTS OF HIGH AND LOW WATERS   YEAR **1998**

SEPTEMBER

Day	Time	m	Day	Time	m
1 TU	0008 / 0604 / 1253 / 1847	0.5 / 2.3 / 0.5 / 2.3	**16** W	0201 / 0749 / 1456 / 2044	0.6 / 2.5 / 0.4 / 2.4
2 W	0132 / 0725 / 1423 / 2013	0.6 / 2.4 / 0.5 / 2.3	**17** TH	0332 / 0916 / 1620 / 2201	0.6 / 2.6 / 0.3 / 2.5
3 TH	0259 / 0846 / 1544 / 2128	0.5 / 2.5 / 0.3 / 2.5	**18** F	0442 / 1023 / 1717 / 2255	0.5 / 2.8 / 0.2 / 2.6
4 F	0413 / 0952 / 1648 / 2227	0.4 / 2.6 / 0.2 / 2.6	**19** SA	0528 / 1108 / 1754 / 2332	0.4 / 2.8 / 0.2 / 2.7
5 SA	0512 / 1046 / 1740 / 2316	0.3 / 2.7 / 0.1 / 2.6	**20** SU ●	0604 / 1143 / 1828	0.3 / 2.9 / 0.2
6 SU O	0602 / 1133 / 1827	0.2 / 2.8 / 0.0	**21** M	0006 / 0641 / 1219 / 1903	2.7 / 0.3 / 2.8 / 0.2
7 M	0001 / 0647 / 1216 / 1910	2.7 / 0.1 / 2.9 / –0.1	**22** TU	0040 / 0717 / 1254 / 1937	2.7 / 0.2 / 2.8 / 0.2
8 TU	0045 / 0729 / 1300 / 1954	2.7 / 0.0 / 2.9 / –0.1	**23** W	0112 / 0749 / 1327 / 2007	2.7 / 0.2 / 2.8 / 0.2
9 W	0128 / 0811 / 1344 / 2037	2.7 / 0.0 / 2.9 / –0.1	**24** TH	0142 / 0819 / 1357 / 2036	2.7 / 0.1 / 2.7 / 0.2
10 TH	0210 / 0853 / 1429 / 2120	2.7 / 0.0 / 2.9 / 0.0	**25** F	0213 / 0849 / 1427 / 2104	2.6 / 0.1 / 2.7 / 0.2
11 F	0253 / 0937 / 1515 / 2202	2.7 / 0.1 / 2.9 / 0.2	**26** SA	0243 / 0919 / 1458 / 2132	2.6 / 0.1 / 2.6 / 0.3
12 SA	0338 / 1022 / 1602 / 2245	2.7 / 0.2 / 2.8 / 0.3	**27** SU	0312 / 0948 / 1528 / 2157	2.6 / 0.2 / 2.6 / 0.3
13 SU	0424 / 1109 / 1653 / 2333	2.7 / 0.3 / 2.7 / 0.4	**28** M	0342 / 1017 / 1601 / 2227	2.5 / 0.3 / 2.4 / 0.5
14 M	0516 / 1206 / 1755	2.6 / 0.4 / 2.5	**29** TU	0420 / 1058 / 1649 / 2321	2.5 / 0.5 / 2.3 / 0.6
15 TU	0035 / 0624 / 1323 / 1914	0.6 / 2.5 / 0.4 / 2.4	**30** W	0519 / 1207 / 1803	2.4 / 0.6 / 2.3

OCTOBER

Day	Time	m	Day	Time	m
1 TH	0044 / 0640 / 1339 / 1933	0.7 / 2.4 / 0.5 / 2.3	**16** F	0303 / 0853 / 1555 / 2139	0.7 / 2.6 / 0.4 / 2.4
2 F	0219 / 0808 / 1508 / 2057	0.6 / 2.5 / 0.4 / 2.4	**17** SA	0416 / 1000 / 1652 / 2232	0.5 / 2.7 / 0.3 / 2.5
3 SA	0342 / 0921 / 1618 / 2201	0.5 / 2.6 / 0.2 / 2.5	**18** SU	0503 / 1043 / 1727 / 2307	0.4 / 2.8 / 0.3 / 2.6
4 SU	0444 / 1019 / 1713 / 2252	0.3 / 2.8 / 0.1 / 2.6	**19** M	0537 / 1117 / 1758 / 2338	0.4 / 2.8 / 0.3 / 2.7
5 M O	0536 / 1107 / 1802 / 2338	0.2 / 2.8 / –0.1 / 2.7	**20** TU ●	0613 / 1153 / 1833	0.3 / 2.8 / 0.2
6 TU	0623 / 1153 / 1847	0.1 / 2.9 / –0.1	**21** W	0012 / 0651 / 1229 / 1908	2.7 / 0.2 / 2.8 / 0.2
7 W	0022 / 0708 / 1238 / 1930	2.7 / 0.0 / 2.9 / –0.1	**22** TH	0045 / 0724 / 1302 / 1939	2.7 / 0.2 / 2.7 / 0.2
8 TH	0106 / 0751 / 1324 / 2015	2.8 / 0.0 / 2.9 / 0.0	**23** F	0115 / 0754 / 1331 / 2007	2.7 / 0.1 / 2.7 / 0.2
9 F	0149 / 0835 / 1411 / 2057	2.8 / 0.0 / 2.9 / 0.1	**24** SA	0144 / 0823 / 1400 / 2034	2.7 / 0.1 / 2.6 / 0.2
10 SA	0232 / 0918 / 1457 / 2138	2.8 / 0.1 / 2.8 / 0.2	**25** SU	0214 / 0852 / 1430 / 2102	2.7 / 0.1 / 2.6 / 0.2
11 SU	0314 / 1002 / 1543 / 2220	2.8 / 0.2 / 2.7 / 0.4	**26** M	0243 / 0922 / 1502 / 2129	2.6 / 0.2 / 2.5 / 0.3
12 M	0359 / 1049 / 1633 / 2308	2.7 / 0.3 / 2.6 / 0.5	**27** TU	0315 / 0955 / 1537 / 2203	2.6 / 0.3 / 2.4 / 0.4
13 TU	0452 / 1146 / 1736	2.6 / 0.4 / 2.4	**28** W	0355 / 1036 / 1625 / 2254	2.5 / 0.4 / 2.3 / 0.6
14 W	0011 / 0601 / 1301 / 1854	0.6 / 2.5 / 0.5 / 2.3	**29** TH	0450 / 1138 / 1733	2.4 / 0.5 / 2.3
15 TH	0133 / 0726 / 1432 / 2021	0.7 / 2.5 / 0.5 / 2.3	**30** F	0009 / 0605 / 1302 / 1858	0.7 / 2.4 / 0.5 / 2.3
			31 SA	0140 / 0729 / 1431 / 2021	0.6 / 2.5 / 0.3 / 2.4

NOVEMBER

Day	Time	m	Day	Time	m
1 SU	0304 / 0846 / 1544 / 2129	0.5 / 2.6 / 0.2 / 2.5	**16** M	0423 / 1007 / 1651 / 2234	0.5 / 2.7 / 0.3 / 2.6
2 M	0411 / 0948 / 1643 / 2225	0.4 / 2.8 / 0.1 / 2.6	**17** TU	0504 / 1047 / 1727 / 2309	0.4 / 2.7 / 0.3 / 2.7
3 TU	0507 / 1041 / 1736 / 2314	0.3 / 2.8 / 0.0 / 2.7	**18** W	0544 / 1126 / 1804 / 2344	0.3 / 2.7 / 0.3 / 2.7
4 W O	0559 / 1131 / 1824	0.1 / 2.9 / 0.0	**19** TH ●	0624 / 1203 / 1840	0.2 / 2.7 / 0.2
5 TH	0000 / 0646 / 1218 / 1907	2.7 / 0.1 / 2.9 / 0.0	**20** F	0018 / 0659 / 1236 / 1911	2.7 / 0.2 / 2.7 / 0.2
6 F	0044 / 0730 / 1304 / 1950	2.8 / 0.1 / 2.9 / 0.1	**21** SA	0049 / 0731 / 1307 / 1942	2.7 / 0.1 / 2.7 / 0.2
7 SA	0128 / 0816 / 1352 / 2035	2.9 / 0.1 / 2.9 / 0.2	**22** SU	0120 / 0802 / 1338 / 2012	2.7 / 0.1 / 2.6 / 0.2
8 SU	0212 / 0901 / 1441 / 2118	2.9 / 0.1 / 2.8 / 0.3	**23** M	0152 / 0834 / 1411 / 2042	2.7 / 0.1 / 2.6 / 0.2
9 M	0256 / 0946 / 1528 / 2200	2.8 / 0.2 / 2.6 / 0.4	**24** TU	0224 / 0906 / 1445 / 2114	2.7 / 0.2 / 2.6 / 0.3
10 TU	0340 / 1033 / 1618 / 2247	2.8 / 0.3 / 2.5 / 0.5	**25** W	0258 / 0943 / 1525 / 2152	2.7 / 0.2 / 2.5 / 0.4
11 W	0431 / 1127 / 1716 / 2344	2.7 / 0.4 / 2.4 / 0.6	**26** TH	0340 / 1027 / 1612 / 2241	2.6 / 0.3 / 2.4 / 0.5
12 TH	0534 / 1232 / 1824	2.6 / 0.4 / 2.3	**27** F	0433 / 1122 / 1713 / 2345	2.6 / 0.3 / 2.3 / 0.5
13 F	0054 / 0649 / 1348 / 1940	0.7 / 2.5 / 0.5 / 2.3	**28** SA	0538 / 1232 / 1826	2.5 / 0.4 / 2.3
14 SA	0214 / 0808 / 1506 / 2054	0.7 / 2.5 / 0.5 / 2.3	**29** SU	0103 / 0653 / 1352 / 1942	0.6 / 2.6 / 0.3 / 2.3
15 SU	0329 / 0917 / 1608 / 2153	0.6 / 2.6 / 0.4 / 2.5	**30** M	0223 / 0808 / 1507 / 2053	0.5 / 2.7 / 0.2 / 2.4

DECEMBER

Day	Time	m	Day	Time	m
1 TU	0335 / 0916 / 1612 / 2155	0.3 / 2.7 / 0.1 / 2.5	**16** W	0425 / 1012 / 1652 / 2236	0.5 / 2.6 / 0.3 / 2.6
2 W	0438 / 1016 / 1709 / 2250	0.2 / 2.8 / 0.1 / 2.6	**17** TH	0513 / 1056 / 1734 / 2315	0.4 / 2.7 / 0.3 / 2.7
3 TH	0535 / 1111 / 1802 / O 2339	0.1 / 2.8 / 0.1 / 2.7	**18** F	0557 / 1135 / 1812 / ● 2351	0.2 / 2.7 / 0.2 / 2.7
4 F	0626 / 1202 / 1847	0.1 / 2.9 / 0.1	**19** SA	0636 / 1210 / 1847	0.2 / 2.7 / 0.3
5 SA	0024 / 0712 / 1248 / 1930	2.8 / 0.1 / 2.9 / 0.2	**20** SU	0026 / 0711 / 1246 / 1922	2.7 / 0.1 / 2.7 / 0.1
6 SU	0109 / 0758 / 1336 / 2016	2.9 / 0.1 / 2.8 / 0.2	**21** M	0101 / 0747 / 1323 / 1958	2.7 / 0.1 / 2.6 / 0.1
7 M	0156 / 0846 / 1426 / 2101	2.9 / 0.1 / 2.7 / 0.3	**22** TU	0137 / 0822 / 1359 / 2031	2.7 / 0.1 / 2.6 / 0.2
8 TU	0241 / 0933 / 1515 / 2144	2.9 / 0.1 / 2.6 / 0.3	**23** W	0211 / 0857 / 1435 / 2106	2.7 / 0.1 / 2.6 / 0.3
9 W	0325 / 1017 / 1601 / 2227	2.8 / 0.2 / 2.5 / 0.4	**24** TH	0247 / 0936 / 1515 / 2146	2.7 / 0.1 / 2.5 / 0.3
10 TH	0410 / 1103 / 1649 / 2314	2.8 / 0.3 / 2.4 / 0.5	**25** F	0330 / 1021 / 1603 / 2233	2.7 / 0.1 / 2.4 / 0.3
11 F	0501 / 1153 / 1743	2.7 / 0.4 / 2.3	**26** SA	0421 / 1111 / 1656 / 2326	2.7 / 0.2 / 2.4 / 0.3
12 SA	0008 / 0600 / 1251 / 1844	0.5 / 2.6 / 0.5 / 2.3	**27** SU	0517 / 1207 / 1756	2.6 / 0.2 / 2.4
13 SU	0112 / 0708 / 1358 / 1951	0.6 / 2.5 / 0.5 / 2.3	**28** M	0029 / 0620 / 1314 / 1903	0.4 / 2.6 / 0.3 / 2.4
14 M	0224 / 0817 / 1506 / 2057	0.6 / 2.5 / 0.5 / 2.4	**29** TU	0144 / 0731 / 1429 / 2015	0.4 / 2.6 / 0.3 / 2.4
15 TU	0330 / 0919 / 1605 / 2152	0.5 / 2.5 / 0.4 / 2.5	**30** W	0301 / 0845 / 1541 / 2124	0.3 / 2.7 / 0.2 / 2.5
			31 TH	0412 / 0954 / 1646 / 2228	0.2 / 2.7 / 0.1 / 2.6

Chart Datum: 1·68 metres below Normal Null (German reference level)

21

BÜSUM   10-21-24

Schleswig-Holstein, 54°07'·20N 08°51'·60E   Rtg 2-2-2

CHARTS
AC 1875, 3767; BSH105, 3014.4

TIDES
HW +0036 on Dover (UT); ML 1·8m; Duration 0625

Standard Port HELGOLAND (←)

Times				Height (metres)			
High Water		Low Water		MHWS	MHWN	MLWN	MLWS
0100	0600	0100	0800	2·7	2·3	0·4	0·0
1300	1800	1300	2000				
Differences BÜSUM							
+0054	+0049	−0001	+0027	+0·9	+0·9	+0·1	0·0
LINNENPLATE							
+0047	+0046	+0034	+0046	+0·7	+0·6	+0·1	0·0
SÜDERHÖFT							
+0103	+0056	+0051	+0112	+0·8	+0·7	+0·1	0·0

SHELTER
Very good; after lock turn 90° stbd into yacht hbr (2·5m) in Basin IV. Lock manned H24; for opening, call on VHF or sound 1 long blast in appr chan; 2 long blasts on reaching lock if not already open; comply with R/G lts.

NAVIGATION
WPT 54°06'·50N 08°19'·10E, SWM buoy Iso 8s, 270°/090° from/to Süderpiep No 2 PHM buoy, 5M. Appr by 2 well-buoyed chans, Süderpiep and Norderpiep (unlit), each approx 15M long; night appr not advised. Beware strong tidal streams across ent and sudden winds over the moles.

LIGHTS AND MARKS
Lt ho Iso WRG 6s 22m 17/14/13M; W092·5°-094·5° leads 093·5° for last 4M of Süderpiep. Hbr lts as chartlet. A high bldg is conspic 9ca NW of hbr; silo is conspic in hbr.

RADIO TELEPHONE
VHF call Büsum Port Ch 11 16.

TELEPHONE (Dial code 04834)
Hr Mr 2183; CG 2025; ## 2376; Dr 2088; YC 2997.

FACILITIES
Yacht hbr AB 13.50DM, AC, FW, M, BY, EI, ME, C, P, D, ⊡.
Town CH, V, R, Bar, ✉, Ⓑ, ⇌, Ⓗ, ✈ (Hamburg).
Note: Meldorf yacht hbr is 4M ESE; full yacht facilities.

OTHER HBRS ON W COAST OF SCHLESWIG-HOLSTEIN

TÖNNING, Schleswig-Holstein, 54°18'·92N 08°57'·11E. AC 3767; BSH104, 3014.8. HW +0246 and +0·5m on Helgoland; ML 2·7m. Eiderdamm lock, 5·5M seawards, operates H24. VHF Ch 14 16. Lock N mole Oc (2) R 12s; S mole Oc G 6s. R Eider with the Gieselau Kanal links Tönning with the Kiel Canal (see 10.21.22). Above the dam, R Eider is tidal, depending on operation of sluices HW +3 to HW+½, (beware strong currents). Berth in middle of S quay, 3m at MHW. If heading E up river, bridge (clnce 5·6m) opens on request Mon-Sat 0600-SS. Hr Mr ☎ (04861) 1400; Dr ☎ 389; Ⓗ ☎ 706; Facilities: Quay 13,50DM, FW, P, D, BY, C (5 ton), Slip; YC ☎ 754 (all welcome). Town Ⓑ, ✉, ⇌,

Gaz.

HUSUM, Schleswig-Holstein, 54°28'·78N 09°00'·00E. AC 3767; BSH 105, 3013.12. HW + 0036 on Dover (UT); ML 1·9m; Duration 0555. See 10.21.26. A sluice/lock, 7ca W of rly bridge, is shut when level > 0·3m over MHW, as shown by Ⓡ. Beware the canal effect when passing big ships in the narrow appr chan. In the outer hbr yachts should turn stbd just before rly bridge for pontoons on S bank, or pass through bridge (clnce 5m when shut) to inner hbr by SC Nordsee; both dry. VHF call Husum Port Ch 11. Tfc reports broadcast on Ch 11 every H +00 from HW −4 to HW +2. Outer ldg lts 106° both Iso R 8s, synch & intens on ldg line. Inner ldg lts 090° both Iso G 8s, synch & intens on ldg line. Night entry not advised. Hr Mr ☎ (04841) 667217; Sluice ☎ 2565; Husum YC ☎ 65670; SC Nordsee ☎ 3436; ## ☎ 61759. AB 13.50DM, P, D, at hbr.

HARBOURS IN THE NORTH FRISIAN ISLANDS

PELLWORM, 54°31'·31N 08°41'·24E. AC 3767; BSH 3013.11. Tides: see Suderoogsand/Husum, opposite. Outer appr via Norderhever; ldg lts 041° Oc 5s. Ent chan from NH18 PHM buoy, Fl (2+1) R 15s, has 0·2m; access near HW. VHF Ch 11. Small yacht hbr 2·8m at MHW; drying on soft mud.

WYK, Island of Föhr, 54°41'·70N 08°34'·80E. AC 3767; BSH107, 3013.6. HW +0107 on Dover (UT); +0137 on Helgoland (zone −0100); ML 2·8. Good yacht hbr (1·5m) to N of ent, sheltered in all winds; visitors berth W side of pontoon 1. Access H24. Also berths on E quay of inner hbr. Ferry hbr (4m). Lts: Oldenhorn (SE point of Föhr), R tr, Oc (4) WR 15s 10m 13/10M; W208°-245°, R245°-298°, W298°-333°, R333°-080°. S mole Oc (2) WR 12s 12m 7/4M; W220°-322°, R322°-220°. Port VHF Ch 11 16. Yacht hbr Hr Mr ☎ (04681) 3030; Commercial Hr Mr ☎ 2852; YC ☎ 1280; Dr ☎ 8998; ## ☎ 2594; Facilities: Hbr road (500m), CH, ⊡, P & D (cans); Yacht Hbr 18DM, R, V; W Quay D.

WITTDÜN, Amrum, 54°37'·85N 08°24'·65E. AC 3767; BSH107, 3013.6. HW +0107 on Dover (UT); +0137 on Helgoland (zone −0100); ML 2·7m; Duration 0540. See 10.21.26. Wittdün is the main hbr of Amrum. Yachts berth S of stone quay, lying bows to pontoon, stern to posts. Good shelter except in E winds. The quay 800m to the E is reserved for ferries only. Chan has 2m and is marked by PHM withies ⌇. Ldg lts 272°: Both Iso R 4s 11/33m 10/15M; W masts, R bands; intens on ldg line. Lt ho Fl 7·5s 63m 23M; R tr, W bands; same location as rear ldg lt. It is not advisable to enter at night. Wriakhörn, Cross lt, is 1M WSW of hbr, L Fl (2) WR 15s 26m 9/7M; W297·5°-319·5°, R319·5°-330°, W330°-005·5°, R005·5°-034°. Hr Mr ☎ (04682) 2294; ## ☎ 2026; Dr ☎ 2612; Facilities: AB 18DM, P & D (cans) at Nebel; Amrum YC ☎ 2054.

TIDAL DIFFERENCES FOR WEST COAST OF DENMARK   10-21-25

These figures are mean values, to be used with caution.

Standard Port HELGOLAND (←)

Times				Height (metres)			
High Water		Low Water		MHWS	MHWN	MLWN	MLWS
0300	0700	0100	0800	2·7	2·3	0·4	0·0
1500	1900	1300	2000				
Differences HØJER							
+0247	+0322	No data		−0·3	−0·2	0·0	0·0
RØMØ HAVN							
+0227	+0302	+0221	+0201	−0·8	−0·7	−0·1	0·0
GRADYB BAR							
+0137	+0152	No data		−1·2	−1·1	−0·1	0·0
ESBJERG							
+0307	+0307	+0221	+0221	−1·1	−0·9	−0·2	−0·1
BLAVANDSHUK							
+0147	+0157	+0131	+0121	−0·9	−0·9	−0·1	0·0
TORSMINDE							
+0337	+0357	+0301	+0231	−1·8	−1·6	−0·1	0·0
THYBORON							
+0427	+0537	+0631	+0431	−2·3	−2·0	−0·3	0·0
HANSTHOLM							
+0407	+0647	+0601	+0351	−2·4	−2·0	−0·3	0·0
HIRTSHALS							
+0402	+0627	+0601	+0321	−2·4	−2·0	−0·3	0·0

SYLT 10-21-26

Schleswig-Holstein 54°45'·54N 08°17'·86E (Hörnum)
Rtgs: Hörnum 3-3-1; List 3-3-1

CHARTS
AC 3767/8; BSH D107, D108, 3013.3 List, 3013.5 Hörnum

TIDES
+0110 Dover; ML 1·8; Duration 0540; Zone –0100

Standard Port HELGOLAND (◄──)

Times				Height (metres)			
High Water		Low Water		MHWS	MHWN	MLWN	MLWS
0100	0600	0100	0800	2·7	2·3	0·4	0·0
1300	1800	1300	2000				
Differences LIST							
+0252	+0240	+0201	+0210	–0·7	–0·6	–0·2	0·0
HÖRNUM							
+0223	+0218	+0131	+0137	–0·5	–0·3	–0·2	0·0
AMRUM-HAFEN							
+0138	+0137	+0128	+0134	+0·2	+0·2	+0·1	0·0
DAGEBÜLL							
+0226	+0217	+0211	+0225	+0·6	+0·6	–0·1	0·0
SUDEROOGSAND							
+0116	+0102	+0038	+0122	+0·3	+0·4	+0·1	0·0
HUSUM							
+0205	+0152	+0118	+0200	+1·2	+1·1	+0·1	0·0

SHELTER
The island of Sylt, about 20M long, has Westerland (the capital) in the centre, List in the N and Hörnum in the S. The Hindenburgdamm connects it to the mainland.
LIST: The small hbr is sheltered except in NE/E winds. Ent is 25m wide and hbr 3m deep.

HÖRNUM: Good in the small hbr, approx 370m x 90m, protected by outer mole on SE side and by 2 inner moles. Yacht haven at the N end. Good ⚓ in Hörnum Reede in W and N winds and in Hörnumtief in E and S winds. There are two other hbrs; Rantum (9DM) and Munkmarsch (13.50DM) which both dry; access HW ±3. Large areas of Sylt are nature reserves; landing prohib.

NAVIGATION
LIST WPT: Lister Tief SWM buoy, Iso 8s, 55°05'·37N 08°16'·87E, 292°/112° from/to List Ost lt, 6·1M. Lister Tief (see 10.21.5) is well marked. In strong W/NW winds expect a big swell on the bar (depth 4m) on the ebb, which sets on to Salzsand. NE quay is open construction and not suitable for yachts. Chan buoys through roadstead lead to hbr. Access at all tides, but beware strong tidal streams across ent.
HÖRNUM WPT: Vortrapptief (SWM) buoy, Oc 4s, 54°35'·00N 08°12'·20E, 215°/035° from/to Norddorf lt (Amrum), 6·35M. Appr through Vortrapptief buoyed chan (see below) inside drying banks. In strong W winds the sea breaks on off-lying banks and in the chan. Final appr from NE, keeping mid-chan in hbr ent. Access at all tides.

LIGHTS AND MARKS
LIST: See 10.21.4 for List West lt Oc WRG 6s, List Ost Iso WRG 6s, List Land Oc WRG 3s and Kampen L Fl WR 10s. Rømø church is conspic. N mole hd FG, vis 218°-038°. S mole hd FR, vis 218°-353°.
HÖRNUM: Conspic radio mast (5 Fl R lts) 3M N of hbr. Follow W034°-036·8° leading sector of Norddorf lt (Oc WRG 6s) until Hörnum lt, Fl (2) 9s, bears 012°. N pier hd FG, vis 024°-260°. Outer mole hd FR (mole floodlit).

RADIO TELEPHONE
List VHF Ch 11.

TELEPHONE (Dial code 04651)
LIST: Hr Mr 870374; Police 870510; Ⓗ 870841; ∰ 870413, CG 870365; Dr 870350.
HÖRNUM: Hr Mr 881027; Dr 881016; Police 881510; CG 881256.

FACILITIES
LIST: **Hbr** AB 14DM, FW, ∰, C (35 ton), Slip, SC. **Village** V, R, Bar, P & D (cans), Ferry to Römö (Denmark).
WESTERLAND: CG 85199; Police 7047. **Town** V, R, Bar, P & D (cans), Gaz, ∰, ✉, Ⓑ, ⇌, ✈.
HÖRNUM: Sylter YC ☎ 880274, AB 18DM, Bar, AC, FW, ▢. **Town** V, R, Bar, ME, ✉, Ⓑ.

Late Corrections

Up to and including *Admiralty Notices to Mariners,* Weekly Edition No. 24/97.

Navigational information in the main body of this Almanac is corrected to *Admiralty Notices to Mariners,* Weekly Edition No. 16/1997. For ease of reference each correction is sequentially numbered, followed by the Almanac page number.

AREA 1 – South-West England

1.193   PLYMOUTH, FACILITIES, Sutton Hbr Marina, line 2, after C delete (masts only).

AREA 2 – Central Southern England

2.237   POOLE HARBOUR, NAVIGATION, lines 9-10, Note: No 16a East Looe PHM buoy has been moved 300m NE to 50°41'·14N 01°55'·85W. It now indicates best water through the Looe Channel which is gradually deepening as a result of Coastal Protection work on the adjacent shoreline. FACILITIES, Dorset Yacht Co, add: Ent is marked by 2FR (vert) and two 2FG (vert).

3.239   CHARTLET, move No 16a East Looe PHM buoy 300m NE to 50°41'·14N 01°55'·85W.

4.256   SOUTHAMPTON, FACILITIES, Itchen Marina, add ☎ 335606; VHF Ch 12.

5.266   PORTSMOUTH, TELEPHONE, after AQHM amend ☎ to 722831.

6.267   PORTSMOUTH, CHARTLET, delete No 66 PHM lt pile at approx 50°49'·50N 01°06'·20W (Portchester Lake).

7.268   PORTSMOUTH, TABLE OF LOCAL VISUAL SIGNALS. SIGNALS 1, 2 and 3: delete the Day signals (consisting of flags and black balls). SIGNAL 5: add night signal of ⓇⓌⓇ vertically disposed.

AREA 4 – Thames Estuary

8.313   HERNE BAY, penultimate line, after 2FG (vert) insert: R bn on B dolphin, Fl Y 5s, is approx 1M ENE of bkwtr hd.

9.323   RIVER THAMES, BRIDGES, after list of bridges, amend next sentence: Tower Bridge sounds horn for 10s, every 20s when bascules are open for shipping.

10.344   RIVER DEBEN, NAVIGATION, lines 1/2, amend position of Woodbridge Haven SWM buoy to 51°58'·15N 01°23'·90E, as at May 1997. Updated position will be published after the Spring 1998 survey.

AREA 5 – East England

11.363   KING'S LYNN, CHARTLET, delete ☆ Fl Y 2s (on ebb) at approx 52°45'·35N 00°23'·45E (W side of river, adjacent to ☆ 2FG (vert)).

12.368   RIVER HUMBER, CHARTLET, at Bull Sand Fort, 53°33'·70N 00°04'·16E, delete ☆ Fl (2) 5s 20m 4M, Horn 30s and topmark. Insert North Fort NCM buoy, Q, 1ca NE of the Fort; and South Fort SCM buoy, Q (6) + L Fl 15s, 1ca SW of the Fort.

13.371 RIVER TEES/MIDDLES-
BROUGH, lines 16-17, amend Hr
Mr details to:☎ (01642) 452541,
📠 467855.

AREA 8 – North-West Scotland

14.458 LOCH NEVIS, lines 3/4, delete: or
1M further ... holding poor. Substitute: or 6 R ⚓s off Inverie, £5, 10m
max LOA. Call *Old Forge* VHF Ch
16, 12; FW, Bar, R, showers, 🚿.

15.459 LOCH SUNART, SHELTER, line
6, after ⚓s add: and jetty. FACILI-
TIES, SALEN, line 2, after El,
add: jetty ☎ 01967 431333.

16.468 LOCH MELFORT, CHARTLET,
amend 2FR (vert) on Melfort Pier
to Dir FR 6m 3M (1/4-31/10). Add
Dir FG at approx 56°16'·20N
05°30'·10W (close NE of the Dir
FR). LIGHTS & MARKS, amend
2FR (vert) to Dir FR. Add a Dir
FG is close NE. Note: These two
lights are not leading lights and
should not be used as a transit line.
An approaching yacht should make
good a N'ly track keeping the FR
and FG lights an equal angle off
the port and starboard bow respectively.

AREA 10 – North-West England,
Isle of Man and North Wales

17.522 MENAI STRAIT, CAERNAR-
FON, R/T, add: Marina VHF Ch
80.

AREA 13 – North Ireland

18.613 CARLINGFORD LOUGH,
LIGHTS & MARKS, amend range

(19M) of Haulbowline light to
17M.

19.614 ARDGLASS, LIGHTS &
MARKS, line 3, delete: On NE
side of ent, SHM beacon Fl G 5s
10m 4M. CHARTLET, delete SHM
beacon, Fl G 5s, at approx
54°15'·67N 05°35'·94W.

AREA 16 – North Brittany

20.706 ROSCOFF, LIGHTS & MARKS,
last line, amend W sector to 200°-
210° (Light on pier head at
Bloscon ferry terminal.

AREA 17 – South Brittany

21.735 ILES DE GLÉNAN, line 13, delete
lt on Ile Cigogne, Q (2) RG 5s 5m
2M.

AREA 19 – North-East France

22.812 CALAIS, CHARTLET, insert
beacon, FY, at approx 50°58'·12N
01°50'·72E, on W side of ent to
Arrière Port.

AREA 20 – Belgium and the
Netherlands

23.845 ROTTERDAM, LIGHTS &
MARKS, (5) line 4, after SE end
insert: 11m clearance under fixed
span.

Index

Explanation

Abbreviations are entered under the full word and not the abbreviation.
> For example St Abb's comes under Saint not St.

The prefix C before a page number indicates a Coast Radio Station.
The prefix L before a page number indicates an entry in the lists of Coastal Lights, Fog Signals and Waylights.
The prefix R before a page number indicates a Radio Navigational Aid.
<u>Page numbers shown in bold type indicate</u> ports/harbours with chartlet.

A

A1/A2 Lt By, 820
A17/A18 Lt By, L 787, L 855
Abandon ship, 134
Abbenfleth, 885
Abbeville, Canal, 810
Abbeville Lt By, L 787
Abbreviations and symbols, 4-7
Aberaeron, 542
Aberbenoit, L', L 694, **707**
Aberdaron, 540
Aberdeen, R 56, L 390, 392, **405**
Aberdeen tides, 406-408
Aberdour, 396
Aberdovey, L 534, **542**
Aberildut, L', L 694, **708**
Abermenai Point, 508
Aberporth, R 49, 542
Abersoch, **540**
Abertay, R 56, L 390, 392
Aberwrac'h, L', L 693, 696, **707**
Aberystwyth, L 534, **542**
A'Bhraige, Loch, L 445, 456
Accumer Ee, 873
Achilbeg Island, L 610
Achill Sound, L 608, L 610, 611
Adjusting compass, 24
Admiralty Chart symbols, 66-67
Admiralty Notices to Mariners, 3
Admiralty tidal stream atlases, 145
Adour, L' (Boucau), L 756, 758, 778
Adrigole, 596
Aero radiobeacons, 48
Agger, The, 844
Aground, vessels, 16, 68
Aigle, Pointe a l', L 663, 685
Aiguillon, L', L 728, 757, 764
Ailly, Pointe d', R 54, L 787, 790
Ailsa Craig, L 478, L 489
Aircraft directing signals/procedures,
> 133
Airds Pt, L 446
Air traffic control centres, SAR, 130
Aix, Ile d', L 755, 768
Alarm signal, radiotelephone, 128
Albert Bridge, 323
Alde/Ore, River, **344**
Aldeburgh, L 307, 345
Alderney, R 50, 178, L 638, 642
> anchorages around, 642
Alderney Race, 664
Aline, Loch, L 446, **460**
Alligande, L 638
Allington Lock, 317
Almanak voor Watertoerisme (ANWB),
849
Alprech, Cap d', R 54, L 797, 911

Alsh, Kyle of Loch, L 445, 448, 456
Alt, River, 515
Alte Ems, L 862
Alte Mellum, 871
Altenbruch, L 865
Alterhaven, L 865
Alte Weser, R 54, L 864, 874
Althorne, 332
Alum Bay, 241
Amble, L 358, 360, **379**
Ameland, R 54, L 825, 827, 851
Amendments, record of, 3
Amlwch, L 506, 525
Amplitudes, 30
Amrum, L 865, L 866, 868, 892, 893
Amsterdam, **848**
Anchor lights, 16, 68
Ancresse Bay, L', 649
Andernos, 777
Andijk, 850
Anglesey, 508, 522
Anglesey Radio, C 88
Anglet, L 756, **778**
Anglia Field Platform A48/19, R 56
Annalong Harbour, L 606, 613
Annan Waterfoot, 509
Annat Lt By, L 390
Anstruther, L 390, **401**
Antifer, Cap, 804
Antifer, Cap d', R 54, 179, L 787, 789
Antwerpen (Antwerp), L 822, 826, **833**
Antwerpen (Antwerp) Radio, C 96
Anvil Point, L 216, 219
Appin, Port, 461
Appingedam, C 97, C 97
Appledore, 560
Approaches to St Helier, 655
Aran Islands, 611, 628
Aranmore, L 608
Arbroath, L 390, **403**
Arcachon, L 756, 758, **776**
Arcachon Radio, C 95
Ardfern, 469
Ardglass, L 606, **614**
Ardgowan Pt, L 489
Ardgroom Harbour, 597
Ardinamar, 468
Ardminish Bay, 481
Ardmore Pt, L 446, L 489
Ardnakinna Point, L 569
Ardnamurchan Point, L 446, 447, 448
Ardnave Point, 481
Ardrishaig, L 476, 480, **483**
Ardrossan, L 478, **495**
Ardyne Lt By, L 489
Area indexes
> Area 1, 167
> Area 2, 211
> Area 3, 273
> Area 4, 297
> Area 5, 351

Area 6, 381
Area 7, 411
Area 8, 439
Area 9, 471
Area 10, 499
Area 11, 529
Area 12, 563
Area 13, 599
Area 14, 633
Area 15, 657
Area 16, 687
Area 17, 719
Area 18, 749
Area 19, 781
Area 20, 815
Area 21, 857
Area of Concern, Solent, 243
Areas, Map of (Ch 10), 150
Areas, shipping forecasts, 110
Argenton, 711
Arinagour, L 446, 459
Arisaig, L 446, 458
Arklow, L 568, **581**
Armadale Bay, 458, L 446
Armandèche, L', L 754
Arnemuiden, 839
Arngast, L 864
Arnish Point, L 444
Arnside, 512
Arradon, 741
Arran, Isle of, L 478, 480, 485
Arrivals from non-EC countries, 19
Arrochar, 490
Arromanches, L 786, 793, 794
Ars-en-Ré, L 755, **764**
Arundel, 282
Arzal, 683, 743
Ashlett Creek, 257
Ashton, L 489
Askaig, Port (Islay), 481
ATT-ARC Lt By, L 756
ATT Maumusson Lt By, L 756
Audenge, 776
Audierne, L 724, 729, **731**
August Rock By, L 172, 183
Aulne, L' River, 683, 712-713
Ault, L 787
Auray, 741
Auskerry, L 417, 431
Autolink R/T, 81
Automatic telephone weather services
> (Marinecall), 105
Aven, River, L 725, 729, 735
Avoch, 425
Avonmouth, L 536, 539, 558
Avonmouth tides, 555-557
Avon River (Devon), 199
Axmouth/Beer, 209
Ayr, L 478, L 489, 496
Ayr, Point of (N Wales), 507
Ayre, Point of (IoM), R 57, L 505, 507

B

C

Q

R

S

Y

Z